tools you need to
reater math success.

PRENTICE HALL

REACHING
TODAY'S
STUDENTS

Achieve grea
by connecting with t

To achieve success in today's middle grades classroom, you need to connect to the way students think. And only one program—**Prentice Hall Middle Grades Math**—helps you meet this need head-on. This new program draws on students' prior knowledge and relates math to their everyday lives.

Building MATH SKILLS **&** **Checking** UNDERSTANDING

But connecting is only the first part of the process. Next, **Middle Grades Math** helps students build stronger skills. It achieves this through an exclusive and continuous process of *building* math skills and *checking* understanding. Then students *immediately apply* these skills to real-world, problem-solving situations.

This emphasis on connecting with the way students think, on building skills, and then continuously checking understanding is what makes **Prentice Hall Middle Grades Math** stand apart.

Relating to their world

Building on prior knowledge

math success
way students think.

Building stronger skills

Asking the right questions at the right time

Checking for immediate understanding

Listening to student feedback

Encouraging different approaches

Building MATH SKILLS & Checking UNDERSTANDING

Ongoing opportunities to bu… ensure greater

- Building on prior knowledge

- Pacing content in manageable parts

- Building stronger skills through student-friendly step-by-step instruction

DATA ANALYSIS Connection

1-3 Mean, Median, and Mode

What You'll Learn

1. To find the mean
2. To find the median or mode

...And Why

You can find the median length of comedy movies or discover which hobby is most popular.

Here's How

Look for questions that
- build understanding
- ✔ check understanding

Work Together

Finding Averages

Is your name longer than average? Let's find out!

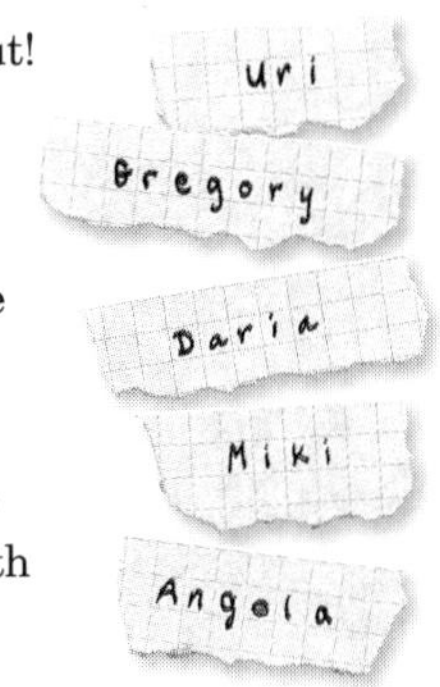

1. Write the names of the students in your class on strips of graph paper as shown.
2. Find the average length of the names of the students in your group. Describe how your group found this number.
3. *Analyze* Compare your work with other groups. Did everyone find the average length of the names the same way? Explain.

THINK AND DISCUSS

1 *Finding the Mean*

You are probably familiar with the word *average*. In mathematics, an average is called a mean. The **mean** is the sum of the data divided by the number of data items.

Wingspan of Jet Airliners

Type	Wingspan (meters)
Airbus A330	60
McDonnell Douglas DCB Super 63	45
Boeing 707	44
Ilyushin IL-96-300	58
Ilyushin IL-62	43

Source: *The Cambridge Factfinder*

■ **EXAMPLE 1** *Real-World Problem Solving*

Airplanes Use the data table at the left. Find the mean wingspan of the jet airliners.

Step 1: Find the sum of the data.

Step 2: Divide the sum by the number of data items.

Method 1: Paper and Pencil

① 60 + 45 + 44 + 58 + 43 = 250

② 250 ÷ 5 = 50 (5)250, − 25, 000)

Method 2: Calculator

① 60 [+] 45 [+] 44 [+] 58 [+] 43 [=] 250

② 250 [÷] 5 [=] 50

The mean wingspan of the jet airliners is 50 meters.

kills and check understanding

sessment success.

EXCLUSIVE FEATURE

✔ Try It Out

provides students with immediate skill check.

4. The wingspan of the Concorde is 26 meters. Suppose you include this value with the set of data in Example 1.
   a. *Estimation* Estimate the mean. Do you think the mean will be greater than or less than 50?
   b. ✔ *Try It Out* Find the mean.

5. ✔ *Try It Out* Find the mean of each data set.
   a. 23, 25, 19, 20, 21, 23, 23 b. 6, 3, 4, 6, 4, 5, 6, 4,

- Asking the right questions at the right time to immediately assess understanding

2 *Finding the Median or Mode*

If the data set has an extreme high or low value, the median is a better measure to use. The **median** is the middle number in a set of ordered data.

Order the data.

18 3 20 17 22 20 19 ⟶ 3 17 18 19 20 20 22

↑ median

6. *Temperature* The daily temperatures (°F) at noon for one week are 86, 78, 92, 79, 87, 91, and 77.
   a. Order the data values.
   b. ✔ *Try It Out* Find the median.

When there is an even number of data items, you can find the median by adding the two middle numbers and dividing by 2.

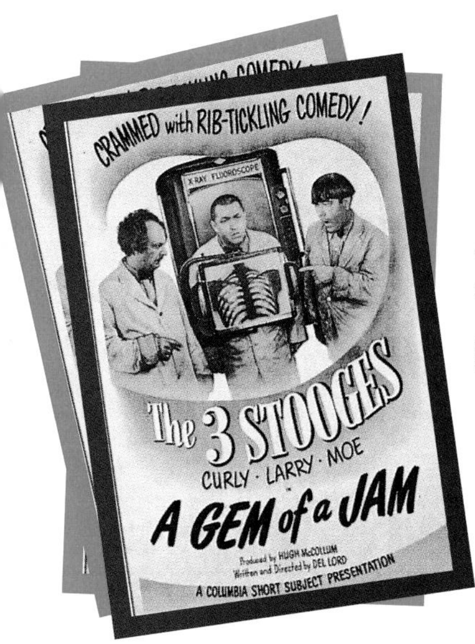

In the 1930s and early 1940s, the Three Stooges became popular in short films that played for 15–20 minutes before each feature film.

EXAMPLE 2 *Real-World Problem Solving*

Entertainment Find the median length of the comedy movies at the right.

Lengths of 10 Comedy Movies (min)

111	105	100	101	101
92	87	96	92	95

111 105 100 101 101 92 87 96 92 95 ⟵ List the data.

87 92 92 95 96 100 101 101 105 111 ⟵ Order the data.

↑ ↑ ⟵ Identify the middle numbers.

$\frac{96 + 100}{2} = 98$ ⟵ Add and divide by 2.

The median is 98.

- Applying skills right away in a problem-solving context

7. ✔ *Try It Out* Find the median of each data set.
   a. 78, 90, 88, 76, 102, 79, 80 b. 10, 5, 7, 13, 14, 12, 12, 10

Building MATH SKILLS **& Checking** UNDERSTANDING

Solid preparation for future algebra and geometry study.

- **Middle Grades Math** provides a solid foundation in fundamental middle grades topics, including fractions, decimals, ratios, proportions, and percents.

- Readying students for future math study, **Middle Grades Math** integrates key algebra, geometry, and data analysis topics throughout the three-book series.

ALGEBRA Connection

6-10 Using Proportions with Percents

What You'll Learn

1. To find what percent one number is of another
2. To find a number when you know a percent and a part

...And Why

Business people use percents to advertise sales.

Here's How

Look for questions that
- build understanding
- ✓ check understanding

THINK AND DISCUSS

1 *Finding a Percent*

You can use models to understand the relationship of one number to another. You can use your model to write a proportion to express the relationship as a percent.

■ **EXAMPLE 1** *Real-World Problem Solving*

Hiking Eighteen students in a class of 25 students plan to go on a class hiking trip. What percent of the students plan to go on the trip?

Model the relationship.

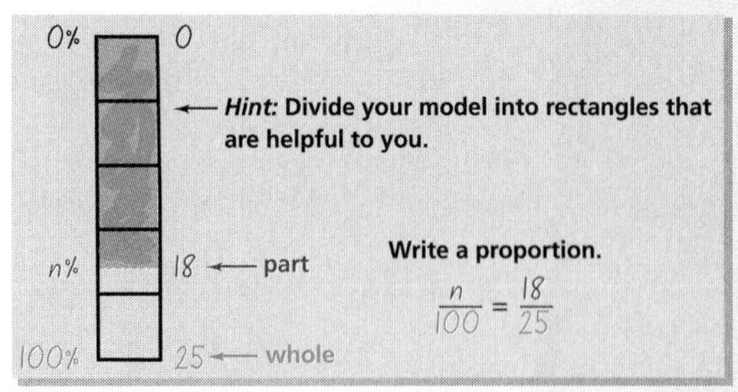

Solve the proportion.

$\frac{n}{100} = \frac{18}{25}$ ← Simplify by multiplying each side by 100.

$n = \frac{1800}{25}$ ← Divide.

$n = 72$

72% of the class plan to go on the trip.

1. *Look Back* The model in Example 1 has five equal rectangles. What percent does each rectangle represent?
2. ✓*Try It Out* Draw a model for each problem. Then solve.
   a. What percent of 90 is 36?
   b. What percent of 60 is 15?

Comprehensive approach to assessment leads to greater success on standardized tests.

The **Interactive Student Tutorial** CD-ROM has been developed to help students perform better on tests. It uses innovative self tests and provides helpful hints, lesson tutorials, and instant scoring.

Assessment Success Kits give you the most comprehensive collection of assessment preparation resources available for middle grades math.
Each kit contains:

- Assessment Success Booklet
- Interactive Student Tutorial CD-ROM
- Resource Pro® CD-ROM with Planning Express® –an exclusive lesson planning tool containing all teaching resources

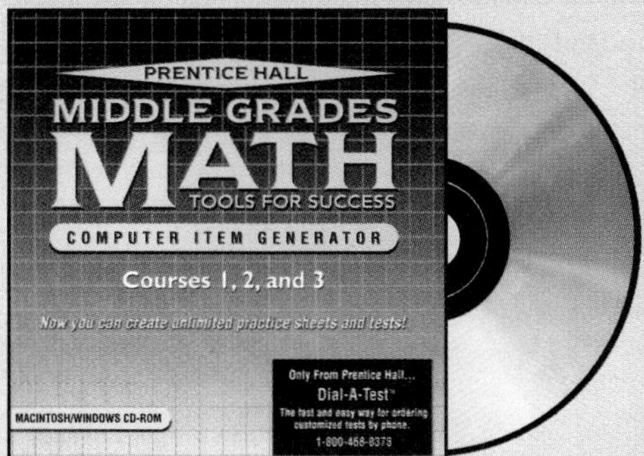

Includes Dial-A-Test™

Computer Item Generator with Standardized Test Prep on CD-ROM allows you to easily customize practice sheets and tests to meet local, state, and national assessment objectives.

More opportunities than ever to assess progress throughout the course.

PRENTICE HALL EXCLUSIVES

- **Think & Discuss questions** within the lesson build understanding as concepts are presented.
- **Try It Out questions** within the lesson provide an immediate skill check after each worked-out example.

ADDITIONAL ASSESSMENT OPTIONS

- Checkpoint quizzes
- Wrap Up chapter review
- On Your Own exercises
- Mixed Review
- Chapter Assessments
- Cumulative Reviews
- Journal
- Portfolio
- Chapter Projects with rubrics
- Problem Solving Practice pages
- Pre-Course Skills Assessment
- Mid-Course Assessment
- End-of-Course Assessment
- Student Self-Assessment Survey
- Skills Handbook

Resources to better connect with your students and more effectively manage your time.

PLUS...Resource Pro® CD-ROM with Planning Express®

Exclusive lesson planning tool containing all teaching resources

For connecting with your students

- **Student Edition with Practice Workbook**
- **Teaching Transparencies**
- **Interdisciplinary Units**
- **Manipulatives Kits**
- **Calculator Packages**
- ✔ **Multimedia Math Hot Pages® CD-ROM**
- ✔ **Math Tools Software**
- ✔ **Interactive Student Tutorial CD-ROM**

✔ = **PRENTICE HALL EXCLUSIVES**

For managing your time

- **Teacher's Edition**
- **Solution Key**
- **Teaching Resources**
  - ✔ **Chapter Support Files organized by chapter**
  - **Multiple-Use Classroom Resources**
  - **Spanish Resources**
  - ✔ **Computer Item Generator with with Standardized Test Practice CD-ROM**
  - **Cumulative Assessment**
  - **Tools for Studying Smarter**
  - **Computational Practice Skills Review**
- ✔ **Resource Pro® CD-ROM with Planning Express®**
- ✔ **Assessment Success Kits**
- **Professional Development book**

PRENTICE HALL

For more information call:
1-800-848-9500

See us on the Internet http://www.phschool.com

Teacher's Edition

PRENTICE HALL

MIDDLE GRADES MATH
TOOLS FOR SUCCESS

Course 2

AUTHORS

Suzanne H. Chapin

Mark Illingworth

Marsha S. Landau

Joanna O. Masingila

Leah McCracken

CONSULTING AUTHORS

Sadie Chavis Bragg

Bridget A. Hadley

Vincent O'Connor

Anne C. Patterson

PRENTICE HALL
Needham, Massachusetts
Upper Saddle River, New Jersey

We are grateful to our reviewers, who advised us in the development stages and provided invaluable feedback, ideas, and constructive criticism to help make this program one that meets the needs of middle grades teachers and students.

REVIEWERS

All Levels

Ann Bouie, Ph.D., Multicultural Reviewer, Oakland, California

Dorothy S. Strong, Ph.D., Chicago Public Schools, Chicago, Illinois

Course 1

Darla Agajanian, Sierra Vista School, Canyon Country, California

Rhonda Bird, Grand Haven Area Schools, Grand Haven, Michigan

Gary Critselous, Whittle Springs Middle School, Knoxville, Tennessee

Rhonda W. Davis, Durant Road Middle School, Raleigh, North Carolina

Leroy Dupee, Bridgeport Public Schools, Bridgeport, Connecticut

Jose Lalas, Ph.D., California State University, Dominguez Hills, California

Richard Lavers, Fitchburg High School, Fitchburg, Massachusetts

Lavaille Metoyer, Houston Independent School District, Houston, Texas

Course 2

Raylene Bryson, Alexander Middle School, Huntersville, North Carolina

Susan R. Buckley, Dallas Public Schools, Dallas, Texas

Sheila Cunningham, Klein Independent School District, Klein, Texas

Natarsha Mathis, Hart Junior High School, Washington, D.C.

Jean Patton, Clements Middle School, Covington, Georgia

Judy Trowell, Arkansas Department of Higher Education, Little Rock, Arkansas

Course 3

Michaele F. Chappell, Ph.D., University of South Florida, Tampa, Florida

Bettye Hall, Math Consultant, Houston, Texas

Joaquin Hernandez, Barbara Goleman Senior High, Miami, Florida

Steven H. Lapinski, Henrico County Public Schools, Richmond, Virginia

Dana Luterman, Lincoln Middle School, Kansas City, Missouri

Loretta Rector, Leonardo da Vinci School, Sacramento, California

Elias P. Rodriguez, Leander Middle School, Leander, Texas

Anthony C. Terceira, Providence School Department, Providence, Rhode Island

STAFF CREDITS

The people who made up the *Middle Grades Math* team—representing editorial, design, marketing, page production, editorial services, production, manufacturing, technology, electronic publishing, and advertising and promotion—and their managers are listed below. Bold type denotes core team members.

Barbara A. Bertell, Bruce Bond, Therese Bräuer, Christopher Brown, **Judith D. Buice**, Kathy Carter, Linda M. Coffey, Noralie V. Cox, Sheila DeFazio, Edward de Leon, Christine Deliee, Gabriella Della Corte, Jo DiGiustini, Robert G. Dunn, Audra Floyd, David B. Graham, Maria Green, Kristen Guevara, Jeff Ikler, Mimi Jigarjian, Elizabeth A. Jordan, Russell Lappa, Joan McCulley, Paul W. Murphy, Cindy A. Noftle, Caroline M. Power, Olena Serbyn, Dennis Slattery, Martha G. Smith, Kira Thaler Marbit, Robin Tiano, **Christina Trinchero**, **Stuart Wallace**, **Cynthia A. Weedel, Jeff Weidenaar, Mary Jane Wolfe,** Stewart Wood

We would like to give special thanks to National Math Consultants Ann F. Bell and Brenda Underwood for all their help in developing this program.

PRENTICE HALL

Printed in the United States of America.

ISBN: 0-13-434687-4

6 7 8 9 10 04 03 02 01 00

AUTHORS

Suzanne H. Chapin, Ed.D., is Professor of Mathematics Education at Boston University. Dr. Chapin also directs all mathematics professional development in a landmark Boston University/Chelsea Public Schools Partnership program, working closely with teachers, administrators, and parents to provide opportunities for all students to learn mathematics. *Proportional Reasoning and Probability strands and Tools for Problem Solving*

Mark Illingworth is a classroom teacher in the Hollis Public Schools, Hollis, New Hampshire. He was awarded the New Hampshire Presidential Award for Excellence in Science and Mathematics Teaching. Mr. Illingworth's original formal training was as a mechanical engineer, a profession that by definition applies mathematics and science to solving real-world problems. One of his greatest interests is in making math meaningful and interesting to young learners. *Graphing strand and projects*

Marsha S. Landau, Ph.D., formerly of National Louis University in Evanston, Illinois, is an active workshop leader in city and suburban school districts on such topics as preparing middle school students for success on standardized tests. Dr. Landau also is a leader in the Center for Talent Development at the School of Education and Social Policy at Northwestern University in programs for academically talented urban and suburban students. *Algebra, Functions, and Computation strands*

Joanna O. Masingila, Ph.D., is an Associate Professor of Mathematics and Mathematics Education at Syracuse University and a Fulbright Scholar in the department of Education Communication and Technology at Kenyatta University in Nairobi, Kenya. Dr. Masingila is also a coach and member of the Inquiry Leadership Team, working with teachers in two schools in the Syracuse City School District. *Geometry strand*

Leah McCracken is a teacher at Lockwood School District in Billings, Montana, and an educational technologies instructor at Montana State University in Billings. Ms. McCracken is a very active member of and speaker for the Montana Council of Teachers of Mathematics and a recipient of numerous teaching awards, including the Montana Teacher of the Year. *Data Analysis strand*

Content Overview

Course 1 chapter titles

1 Using Statistics to Analyze Data
2 Patterns and Algebraic Thinking
3 Adding and Subtracting Decimals
4 Multiplying and Dividing Whole Numbers and Decimals
5 Investigating Fractions
6 Using Fractions
7 Ratios, Proportions, and Percents
8 Tools of Geometry
9 Geometry and Measurement
10 Algebra: Integers and Graphing
11 Exploring Probability

Course 2 chapter titles

1 Interpreting Data and Statistics
2 Applications of Decimals
3 Algebra: Integers and Equations
4 Fractions and Number Theory
5 Applications of Fractions
6 Using Proportions and Percents
7 Investigating Geometry
8 Geometry and Measurement
9 Using Probability
10 Algebra: Patterns and Functions
11 Graphing in the Coordinate Plane

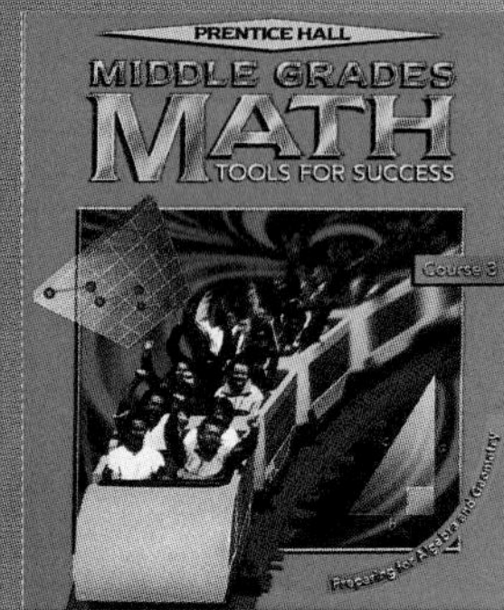

Course 3 chapter titles

1 Drawing Conclusions from Statistical Data
2 Integers and Variable Expressions
3 Equations and Inequalities
4 Graphing in the Coordinate Plane
5 Rational Numbers and Irrational Numbers
6 Applications of Proportions
7 Applications of Percent
8 Patterns in Geometry
9 Geometry and Measurement
10 Functions and Polynomials
11 Probability

Algebra Strand

Course 1 provides a solid foundation in fundamental middle grades topics such as decimals and fractions, with an age-appropriate introduction to key algebraic topics. Course 2 handles algebraic topics in more depth, and Course 3 is a complete Pre-Algebra course. Algebraic connections are highlighted in every chapter of the series.

Geometry & Measurement Strand

Geometry readiness topics are integrated throughout the three-book series, providing a solid preparation for future math study. The topics grow in depth and complexity as students build their measurement skills, increase their understanding of geometric relationships, and develop visualization skills.

Data Analysis Strand

Chapter 1 of each course focuses on real-world data—a unique and motivating topic with which to start the school year—while reviewing key topics in the context of the data. The level of thought required of students increases with each course—from *analysis* to *interpretation* to *drawing conclusions.*

Problem Solving Strand

Before the first chapter of each text, four course-specific "mini-lessons" in the Problem Solving Overview help students focus on the "big picture" of problem solving. Building on past experiences, the Overview and the Problem Solving lessons in each chapter encourage students to approach problems in a variety of course-appropriate ways.

Teacher's Edition

PRENTICE HALL

MIDDLE GRADES MATH

TOOLS FOR SUCCESS

CONTENTS

COURSE 2

Contents

The "Tools for Problem Solving" section, which appears before Chapter 1, helps students review their problem solving skills and can be used before or with Chapter 1. At the end of the book, there are a number of useful resources. Extra Practice pages for each chapter contain additional exercises correlated to each lesson. The Skills Handbook provides an in-text tutorial of math skills that students may need to review. The skills covered in this section are the same as the skills tested in the Precourse test. The Glossary/Study Guide provides not only a definition with a page reference but also an example of most vocabulary terms.

CHAPTER 1 Interpreting Data and Statistics

Problem Solving and Connections

While reviewing whole number skills, students explore visual representations of relationships by interpreting and creating data displays, including double line graphs, double bar graphs, stem-and-leaf plots, and box-and-whisker plots. Studying data analysis in the first chapter allows students to use these concepts with real-world data throughout the year.

CHAPTER 2

Applications of Decimals

Problem Solving and Connections

After reviewing whole numbers in Chapter 1, students practice and extend their computational skills with decimals. Students estimate answers to develop the ability to know when calculated answers are reasonable.

CHAPTER 3

Algebra: Integers and Equations

Problem Solving and Connections

...and More!

CHAPTER PROJECT

Theme: Recreation
Board Walk

Using manipulatives, students build a basic understanding of integers and computation with integers. After collecting data, they see how variables are used in the real world. Finally, they apply their knowledge of integers and variables to solve equations. By studying integers, variables, and equations early in the year, students practice these concepts all year long!

CHAPTER 4

Fractions and Number Theory

Problem Solving and Connections

Through models and real-world applications, students review and extend their knowledge of number theory and fractions by using geometric models and looking at patterns. Using real-world situations, students relate fractions to decimals.

CHAPTER

5 Applications of Fractions

Problem Solving and Connections

While using their estimation skills, students develop a sense of the relative size of fractions. Students continue using estimates to determine when calculated answers are reasonable. Students further their understanding of algebra by solving equations containing fractions.

CHAPTER

6 Using Proportions and Percents

Problem Solving and Connections

ASSESSMENT

CHAPTER PROJECT

Theme: Art and Drafting
Chills and Thrills

Students develop proportional reasoning and extend their algebra skills by applying proportions in geometric situations and to maps and scale drawings. They also use proportional reasoning to understand percents and find percent of change.

CHAPTER 7

Investigating Geometry

Problem Solving and Connections

Students further their reasoning skills by exploring visual patterns to develop the properties of triangles and quadrilaterals. They further their data analysis skills by using proportional reasoning and algebra to create circle graphs.

CHAPTER

8 Geometry and Measurement

Problem Solving and Connections

Students use their knowledge of rectangles to understand the formulas for the areas of triangles and parallelograms. They investigate the circumference of a circle to understand the ratio for Pi. Then they apply their reasoning skills and algebra skills to find the surface area and volume of prisms and cylinders.

CHAPTER

9 Using Probability

Problem Solving and Connections

Using proportional reasoning, students explore experimental probability through simulations, and they compare experimental results with theoretical results. They further their understanding of data analysis in situations requiring probability.

CHAPTER 10

Algebra: Patterns and Functions

Problem Solving and Connections

Now that students have a firm grasp of using algebra to solve equations, they extend their algebra skills by identifying mathematical patterns and representing patterns using rules. Based on an understanding of patterns, students look at functions using tables, rules, and graphs.

CHAPTER 11

Graphing in the Coordinate Plane

Problem Solving and Connections

After graphing data throughout the text, students extend their graphing skills to include all four quadrants of the coordinate plane. They graph linear and nonlinear equations. Students use their algebra and geometric skills together by graphing translations, reflections, and rotations.

Of Special Interest

Real-World Problem Solving

A variety of applications that pique the interests of middle grades students provides settings for students to apply problem solving skills

Problem Solving Strategies

Real-World Applications

Math Integration

Woven throughout: strands of algebra, geometry, data analysis, measurement, statistics, probability, patterns, and number sense

Algebra

Chapter 3: Integers and Equations
Chapter 10: Patterns and Functions

Algebra Connection Lessons:

- **1–9** Exploring Scatter Plots
- **2–3** Adding and Subtracting Decimals
- **2–5** Multiplying Decimals
- **2–8** Order of Operations and the Distributive Property
- **5–4** Solving Equations with Fractions by Adding and Subtracting
- **5–9** Solving Equations with Fractions by Multiplying and Dividing
- **6–3** Proportions
- **6–10** Using Proportions with Percents
- **6–11** Finding Percent of Change
- **7–2** Classifying and Measuring Angles
- **7–3** Triangles
- **8–4** Circumference and Area of Circles
- **8–5** Exploring Square Roots
- **8–6** Exploring the Pythagorean Theorem

Geometry

Chapter 7: Investigating Geometry
Chapter 8: Geometry and Measurement

Geometry Connection Lessons:

- **4–1** Relating Fractions to Models
- **4–5** Prime Factorization
- **5–5** Multiplying Fractions and Mixed Numbers
- **6–4** Using Similar Figures
- **6–5** Exploring Maps and Scale Drawings
- **11–6** Translations
- **11–7** Symmetry and Reflections
- **11–8** Rotations

Data Analysis/Statistics

Chapter 1: Interpreting Data and Statistics

Data Analysis Connection Lessons:

- **2–1** Comparing and Rounding Decimals
- **3–1** Evaluating and Writing Variable Expressions
- **4–6** Simplifying Fractions
- **6–1** Exploring Ratios Using Data
- **6–9** Finding the Percent of a Number
- **7–8** Circle Graphs
- **9–1** Experimental Probability
- **9–8** Estimating Population Size
- **10–7** Interpreting Graphs
- **11–3** Finding the Slope of a Line

Math at Work

Introducing students to a wide range of career possibilities that highlight how mathematics is applied in these careers

- Amusement Park Designer, 254
- Architect, 290
- Artist, 445
- Automotive Engineer, 476
- Detective, 58
- Farm Operator, 357
- Pediatrician, 151
- Pollster, 25
- Software Developer, 116
- Songwriter, 204
- Teacher, 422

Technology

To provide students with meaningful experiences to utilize technology.

Calculator

Lesson Integration *(optional)*:17, 76, 77, 131, 132, 156–158, 177–180, 196, 199, 212, 207, 238, 242, 346, 349, 350, 351, 352, 353, 364, 365, 378, 424, 492, 508

Math Toolbox *(optional)*:

- **213** Using a Fraction Calculator
- **458** Three Views of a Function
- **485** Exploring Slope

Computer

Lesson Integration *(optional)*: 12, 14, 133, 447, 448

Math Toolbox *(optional)*:

- **111** Using Spreadsheets
- **250** Creating Similar Figures
- **313** Sum of the Measures of the Angles of a Polygon
- **397** Using Random Numbers

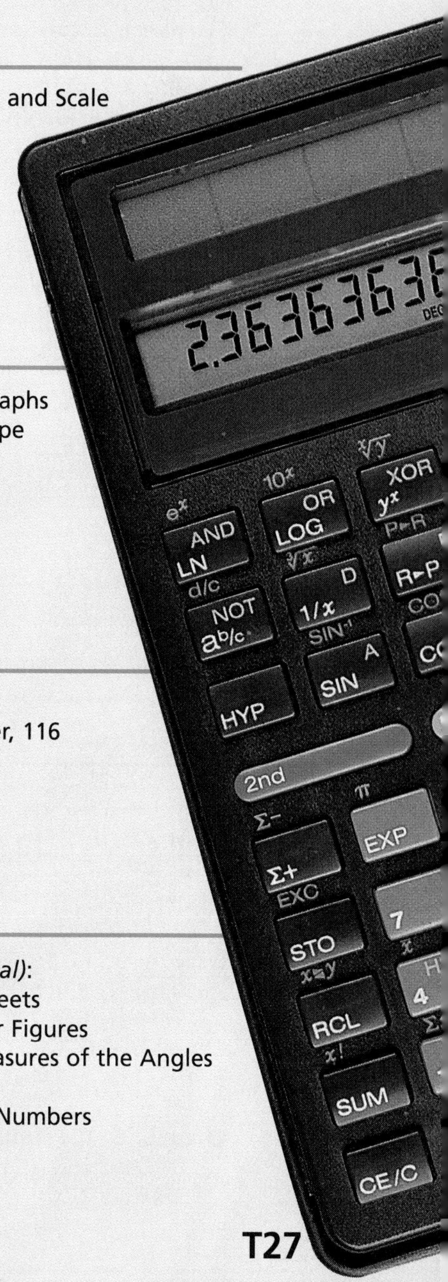

Building Student Success Every Step of the Way

Opportunities to build on students' experiences and check their skills, ensuring that students thoroughly grasp a concept before moving on

Building Skills through Student Experiences

Helping students build the skills they need to succeed by providing just the right mixture of experiences and probing questions to guide their thinking

Work Together

Activities that provide students with hands–on learning opportunities, working cooperatively

Activities to Begin Lesson

Discovery Activities, 160, 193, 200, 305, 344, 412, 416
Finding a Pattern, 67, 155, 288, 359, 434
Activating Prior Knowledge, 30, 34, 176, 454, 482
Data Gathering, 92, 237, 336
Hands–on Activity, 80, 144, 205, 297, 323, 349, 354

Activities to Complete Lesson

Reinforcing Skills, 6, 41, 127, 474
Extending Skills, 234, 247, 278, 310, 316, 341, 448, 451, 496, 500
Applying Skills, 14, 19, 23, 56, 98, 104, 219, 252, 394, 403, 425

Building Understanding

Analyze, 5, 30, 34, 41, 98, 118, 237, 247, 252, 292, 323, 369, 377, 413, 454
Calculator, 76, 349, 350, 364
Data Collection, 234, 336, 451
Draw a Conclusion, 67, 245, 299, 349, 368, 473
Error Alert, 119, 148, 232, 408
Estimation, 292, 341, 350
Explain, 9, 82, 131, 160, 176, 340, 351, 438
Go a Step Further, 97, 118, 161, 233, 237, 256, 257, 267, 345, 350, 416, 460, 473
Look Back, 4, 54, 172, 189, 201, 206, 271, 272, 345, 451, 478, 483, 495, 500
Mental Math, 60, 450, 477
Modeling, 51, 102, 107, 193, 200, 205, 299, 345, 359, 373
Number Sense, 51, 80, 241, 318, 341, 355
Open–ended, 14, 23, 59, 148, 402, 413
Patterns, 107, 112, 113, 173, 355, 438, 494
Predict, 318, 393, 451
Reasoning, 5, 8, 9, 30, 35, 39, 50, 54, 55, 56, 59, 68, 73, 92, 98, 131, 147, 155, 160, 177, 189, 252, 267, 291, 323, 355, 359, 361, 364, 393, 394, 409, 413, 416, 420, 425, 435, 446, 450, 477, 482, 487
Spatial Reasoning/Visual Thinking, 245, 340, 369
Technology, 448
Think About It, 12, 13, 68, 69, 97, 102, 156, 165, 177, 189, 232, 278, 291, 292, 309, 315, 324, 369, 407, 409, 419, 472, 486, 495, 506

Assessing Student Understanding

Traditional and alternative assessment opportunities to evaluate student understanding

Ongoing Assessment within Instruction

✔ *Try It Out*

To check understanding or provide immediate practice and reinforcement

Chapter 1, 5, 8, 17, 18, 22, 23, 31, 35, 39, 40
Chapter 2, 51, 52, 54, 55, 59, 60, 68, 69, 72, 73, 77, 81, 82
Chapter 3, 93, 94, 97, 98, 102, 103, 104, 106, 107, 113, 114, 118, 119, 122, 123, 126, 127, 130, 131
Chapter 4, 145, 147, 148, 149, 152, 153, 155, 156, 157, 161, 162, 165, 173, 177, 178
Chapter 5, 188, 189, 193, 194, 197, 198, 200, 201, 205, 206, 207, 210, 211, 218, 219, 222, 223
Chapter 6, 232, 233, 234, 237, 238, 241, 242, 246, 247, 251, 252, 256, 257, 260, 261, 267, 268, 271, 272, 277
Chapter 7, 289, 292, 293, 298, 299, 306, 309, 315, 316, 318, 319, 324, 325
Chapter 8, 336, 338, 341, 346, 351, 355, 360, 361, 362, 365, 369, 370, 374, 375, 378
Chapter 9, 392, 393, 401, 402, 407, 408, 409, 413, 416, 417, 419, 424
Chapter 10, 435, 438, 439, 446, 447, 448, 451, 455, 456, 459, 460
Chapter 11, 473, 474, 478, 479, 483, 486, 487, 494, 495, 496, 499, 500, 506

Informal Assessment

CHAPTER PROJECT

Chapter Projects (with rubrics)

Marketing: Estimate the Size of a Crowd, 2–3
Science: Use Specific Gravity, 48–49
Recreation: Design a Board Game, 90–91
Measurement: Invent Your Own Ruler, 142–143
Cooking: Write Your Own Recipe, 186–187
Art and Drafting: Design an Amusement Park, 230–231
Construction: Build a Tower, 286–287
Packaging: Design Boxes for Shipping Cylinders, 334–335
Logic: Make Three Number Cubes, 390–391
Graphing: Graphing Data, 432–433
Business: Find a Sample Size, 470–471

Formal Assessment

Standardized Test Prep

Within Lessons, 11, 20, 24, 42, 56, 70, 83, 93, 96, 108, 125, 132, 150, 166, 175, 179, 191, 202, 208, 234, 262, 269, 273, 276, 300, 307, 311, 317, 320, 347, 352, 356, 373, 375, 379, 396, 405, 414, 421, 436, 449, 475, 478, 480, 497

In Problem Solving Practice 33, 71, 117, 171, 217, 255, 328, 358, 423, 464, 504
In Chapter Wrap Ups 44–45, 86–87, 138–139, 182–183, 226–227, 282–283, 330–331, 386–387, 428–429, 466–467, 510–511
In Chapter Assessments 46, 88, 140, 184, 228, 284, 332, 388, 430, 468, 512
In Cumulative Reviews 47, 89, 141, 185, 229, 285, 333, 389, 431, 469, 513
In Checkpoints, 38, 62, 129, 163, 244, 322, 380, 411, 445, 489

Chapter Assessment

Journal 11, 37, 53, 58, 100, 128, 154, 163, 175, 191, 203, 240, 270, 294, 312, 342, 356, 405, 410, 449, 457, 481, 489

Portfolio 42, 84, 136, 180, 224, 280, 326, 383, 426, 463, 508

✔ **Checkpoints** 21, 38, 62, 79, 110, 129, 163, 175, 204, 221, 244, 270, 301, 322, 353, 380, 411, 422, 445, 457, 489, 503
Chapter Wrap Ups 44–45, 86–87, 138–139, 182–183, 226–227, 282–283, 330–331, 386–387, 428–429, 466–467, 510–511
Chapter Assessments 46, 88, 140, 184, 228, 284, 332, 388, 430, 468, 512
Cumulative Reviews 47, 89, 141, 185, 229, 285, 333, 389, 431, 469, 513
Mixed Reviews 7, 11, 15, 21, 25, 29, 32, 38, 42, 53, 58, 62, 66, 70, 74, 79, 84, 96, 100, 105, 110, 116, 121, 125, 129, 133, 136, 146, 151, 154, 158, 163, 167, 170, 175, 180, 191, 196, 199, 203, 209, 212, 216, 221, 224, 236, 240, 249, 254, 259, 263, 266, 270, 274, 280, 290, 295, 301, 304, 307, 312, 317, 322, 326, 339, 343, 348, 353, 357, 363, 367, 371, 376, 380, 383, 396, 400, 405, 411, 415, 418, 421, 426, 437, 440, 444, 449, 453, 457, 463, 476, 481, 484, 489, 492, 498, 503, 508

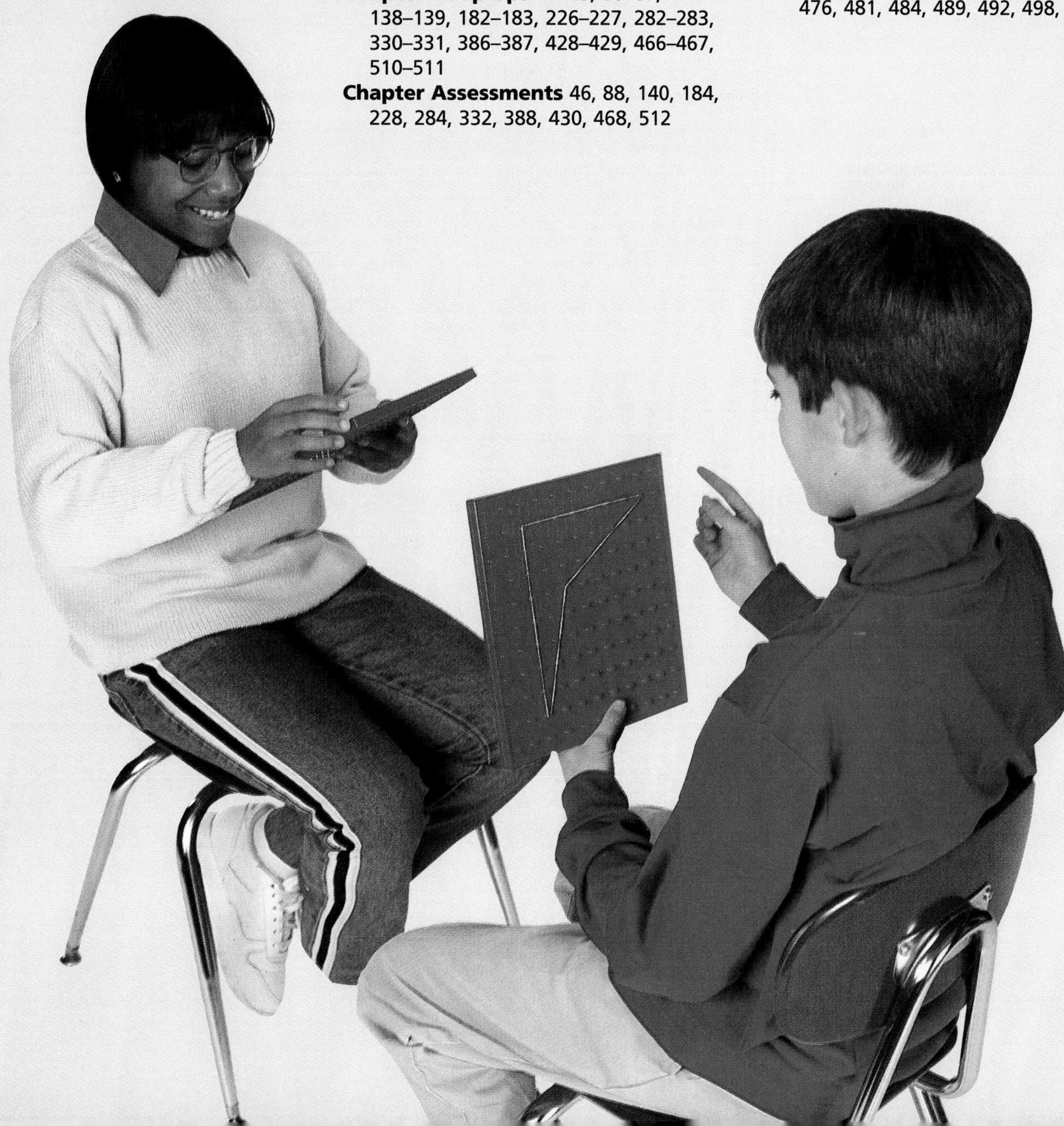

Pacing Guide for Prentice Hall Middle Grades Math

This chart is provided merely as a guide to help you customize your course. To accommodate flexible scheduling, many lessons are subdivided into parts. In your Teacher's Edition, these parts are indicated in red by the symbol ▼. The Assignment Options in each lesson indicate which practice exercises in the Student Edition correspond to the parts of each lesson.

	Chapter 1 (9 lessons)	Chapter 2 (8 lessons)	Chapter 3 (10 lessons)	Chapter 4 (9 lessons)	Chapter 5 (9 lessons)	Chapter 6 (11 lessons)
Traditional Class Periods (40–45 minutes)	16	12	15	14	16	18
Block Scheduling Class Periods (90 minutes)	8	6	7	7	8	9

	Chapter 7 (9 lessons)	Chapter 8 (11 lessons)	Chapter 9 (8 lessons)	Chapter 10 (7 lessons)	Chapter 11 (8 lessons)	TOTALS
Traditional Class Periods (40–45 minutes)	14	16	15	11	13	**160**
Block Scheduling Class Periods (90 minutes)	7	8	7	6	7	**80**

Detailed Chapter Pacing Options precede each chapter and give you lesson-by-lesson pacing suggestions for that specific chapter.

Teaming—Working with Teachers in Other Disciplines

Making Connections

Have you ever heard the following questions from your students? "Does the math I use in math class have anything to do with science? With social studies?" Students don't always make connections. Forming a multidisciplinary team of teachers can help students see these connections.

Teaming . . . Getting Started

- Form a team of core subject teachers with a common planning period.
- Display all the content area courses of study on a common school year calendar. Look for overlapping topics or common themes to use as a starting point. Choose one of these topics or themes for a possible unit.
- Look for links to other disciplines. What math skills will your students use in the study of this topic? Can you connect this to a language arts skill? How does this topic relate to science? to social studies?
- Organize your brainstorming in a web. Use lines to connect the topic to each discipline. Continue the webbing by adding skills and topics from the curriculum of each discipline.
- Use your web and your curriculum calendar to plan an interdisciplinary unit. Don't be too ambitious at first. Start with two disciplines and add others later. An example of a two-discipline web is shown
- By becoming involved in all subject areas, you and your students will see how math relates to the real world. You will have a better understanding of your students, since you will see a more complete picture of everything they are studying.

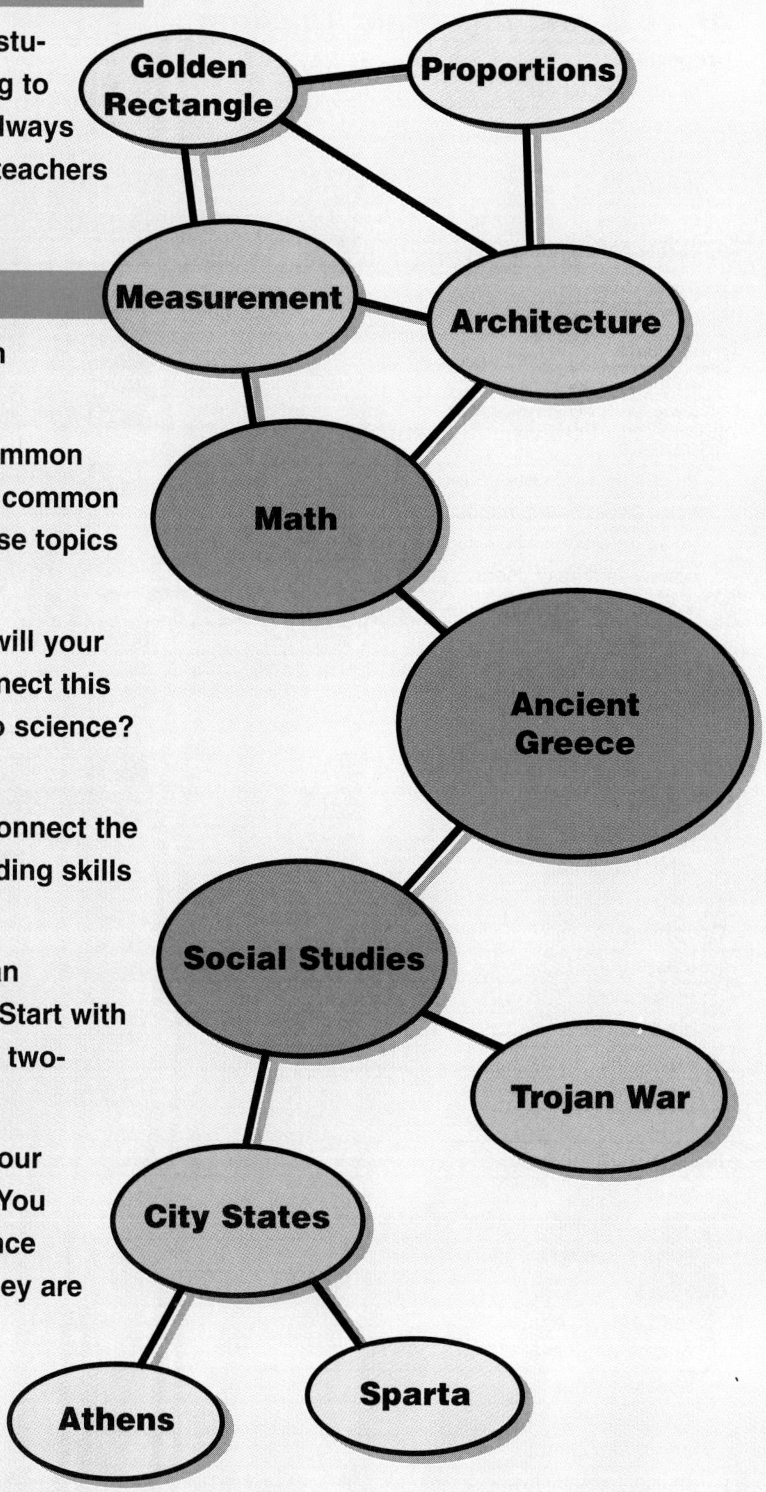

Scope and Sequence for Prentice Hall Middle Grades Math

Course	1	2	3
Algebra and Algebraic Thinking			
Properties			
of whole numbers	Maintain and Apply	Maintain and Apply	Maintain and Apply
commutative	Introduce	Develop	Maintain and Apply
associative	Introduce	Develop	Maintain and Apply
distributive	Introduce	Develop	Maintain and Apply
of integers	Introduce	Develop	Maintain and Apply
of rational numbers			Introduce/Develop
Expressions			
order of operations	Introduce/Develop	Develop	Develop
evaluate	Develop	Develop	Develop
simplify	Develop	Develop	Develop
write from word phrases	Introduce/Develop	Develop	Maintain and Apply
Equations			
solve one-step equations	Introduce/Develop	Develop	Develop
solve two-step equations		Introduce/Develop	Develop
solve equations with integer solutions		Introduce/Develop	Develop
solve systems of linear equations		Introduce	Develop
write from word sentences	Introduce	Introduce/Develop	Maintain and Apply
formulas	Develop	Develop	Develop
Functions			
write a rule	Introduce/Develop	Develop	Develop
look for a pattern strategy	Introduce	Develop	Maintain and Apply
input-output tables	Develop	Develop	Develop
linear	Introduce	Develop	Develop
quadratic		Introduce/Develop	Develop
other nonlinear		Introduce	Develop
step			Introduce
Graphing			
integers	Introduce	Develop	Maintain and Apply
inequalities		Introduce	Develop
ordered pairs	Develop	Develop	Maintain and Apply
equations	Introduce	Develop	Develop
functions	Develop	Develop	Develop
slope		Introduce	Develop
Inequalities			
write			Introduce/Develop
solve one-step inequalities			Introduce/Develop
solve two-step inequalities			Introduce/Develop
Integers			
read and write	Introduce	Develop	Maintain and Apply
on a number line	Introduce	Develop	Maintain and Apply
absolute value		Introduce/Develop	Maintain and Apply
compare and order	Introduce/Develop	Maintain and Apply	Maintain and Apply
add and subtract	Introduce	Develop	Develop
multiply and divide		Introduce/Develop	Develop

Course	1	2	3
Algebra and Algebraic Thinking (cont.)			
equations		Introduce/Develop	Develop
Polynomials			
simplify			Introduce
add and subtract			Introduce
multiply			Introduce
Rational numbers			Introduce/Develop
simplify			Introduce/Develop
compare and order			Introduce/Develop
add and subtract			Introduce/Develop
multiply and divide			Introduce/Develop
equations			Introduce/Develop
Irrational numbers			Introduce/Develop
Real numbers			Introduce/Develop
Communication			
Create written and oral problems	Develop	Develop	Develop
Evaluate effectiveness of different representations	Develop	Develop	Develop
Interpret mathematical ideas through discussing, listening, modeling, questioning, reading, viewing, and writing	Develop	Develop	Develop
Make convincing arguments using mathematical ideas	Develop	Develop	Develop
Relate mathematical language to everyday language	Develop	Develop	Develop
Relate topics to the history of mathematics	Develop	Develop	Develop
Use writing to clarify ideas	Develop	Develop	Develop
Verbalize and define concepts	Develop	Develop	Develop
Work in groups	Develop	Develop	Develop
Decimals			
Read and write	Develop	Develop	Maintain and Apply
Place value	Develop	Develop	Maintain and Apply
Compare and order	Develop	Maintain and Apply	Maintain and Apply
Equivalent decimals	Develop	Maintain and Apply	Maintain and Apply
Add and subtract	Develop	Develop	Maintain and Apply
Multiply and divide			
decimals by whole numbers	Develop	Maintain and Apply	Maintain and Apply
two decimals	Develop	Develop	Maintain and Apply
decimals by powers of 10	Develop	Develop	Maintain and Apply
Estimate			
rounding	Develop	Develop	Maintain and Apply
operations	Develop	Develop	Maintain and Apply
Convert decimals to fractions	Develop	Develop	Develop

Introduce — *Develop* — *Maintain and Apply*

Course	1	2	3
Decimals (cont.)			
Convert decimals to percents			
Terminating and repeating			
Scientific notation			
Estimation			
Decimals			
value			
operations			
Dimensional analysis			
Fractions			
proper, improper, and mixed numbers			
operations			
Geometry			
angle measure			
length			
area			
volume			
Integers			
sums and differences			
products and quotients			
Number lines			
Percents			
Precision			
Proportions			
Reasonableness of estimates			
Significant digits			
Solutions of equations			
Square roots			
Strategies			
choose the computation method			
clustering			
compatible numbers			
front-end			
rounding			
Whole numbers			
whole number values			
operations			
Fractions			
Equivalent fractions			
Simplest form			
Mixed numbers and improper fractions			
Compare and order			
Add and subtract			
like denominators			
unlike denominators			
mixed numbers			
Reciprocal			
Multiply and divide			
whole numbers and fractions			
fractions and fractions			
whole numbers and mixed numbers			

Course	1	2	3
Fractions (cont.)			
fractions and mixed numbers			
mixed numbers			
Estimate			
rounding			
operations			
Convert fractions to decimals			
Convert fractions to percents			
Geometry and Spatial Reasoning			
Angles			
classify			
measure			
estimate measure			
Constructions			
congruent segments			
parallel lines			
perpendicular lines			
perpendicular bisectors			
angle bisectors			
congruent angles			
Polygons			
identify			
classify triangles			
different viewpoints			
Pythagorean theorem			
classify quadrilaterals			
Congruence			
Nets			
Similarity			
Symmetry			
Tessellations			
Transformations			
translations			
reflections			
rotations			
dilations			
Three-dimensional figures			
Coordinate geometry			
Spatial visualization			
Measurement			
Customary system			
use customary units of length, area, volume, weight, and capacity			
choose appropriate units			
convert within customary system			
Metric system			
use metric units of length, area, volume, weight, and capacity			
choose appropriate units			
convert within metric system			
Length			
estimate			

Course	1	2	3
Measurement (cont.)			
perimeter	D	M	M
radius, diameter, and circumference	D	D	M
Area			
estimate area of irregular figures	D	D	D
of squares and rectangles	D	D	M
of parallelograms and rhombuses	D	D	M
of triangles	D	D	M
of trapezoids	I	I/D	M
of circles	D	D	M
of composite figures	I/D	I/D	D
Surface area			
of prisms	I	D	D
of cylinders		I	D
Volume			
estimate	I	D	D
of prisms	D	D	D
of cylinders		I/D	D
of cones and pyramids			I/D
of spheres			I
Indirect measurement			
scale drawing	I	D	M
Pythagorean theorem		I	D
using similar triangles	I	D	M
ratios in right triangles	I	D	M
trigonometric ratios			I/D
Relate perimeter and area	M	M	M
Relate perimeter, area, and volume		I	D
Temperature	M	M	M
Time			
convert units of time	M	M	M
estimate	D	D	M
elapsed time	D	D	M
time zones	M	M	M
Mental Math			
Divisibility	D	D	M
Solving equations	D	D	M
Strategies			
choose the computation method	D	D	M
compatible numbers	D	D	M
patterns	D	D	M
use properties	D	D	D
Modeling and Manipulatives			
Decimals	D	M	M
Distributive property	D	D	M
Equations			
one-step	D	D	D
two-step		I/D	D
Exponents	I/D	M	M
Factors	D	D	D
Fractions	D	D	D

Course	1	2	3
Modeling and Manipulatives (cont.)			
Geometry			
area	D	D	D
squares and square roots	I	I	D
surface area	D	D	D
volume	D	D	D
Integers			
absolute value	I	I/D	D
add and subtract	D	D	D
opposites	D	D	D
zero	D	D	D
Manipulatives			
algebra tiles	I/D	M	M
area models	I	D	M
centimeter cubes/counters	M	M	M
compasses	I	D	M
decimal models	I/D	M	M
fraction models	I/D	M	M
graph paper	M	M	M
paper folding	M	M	M
pattern blocks	M	M	M
percent models	I	D	M
protractors	M	M	M
rulers (metric and customary)	M	M	M
spinners	M	M	M
tangrams	M	M	M
Number line models	D	M	M
Number patterns	D	D	M
Percent	D	D	M
Probability			
outcomes	D	D	D
simulations	D	D	D
Problem Solving	D	M	M
Pythagorean theorem		I/D	D
Ratios	I/D	D	D
Rational numbers			I
Tree diagrams	I	D	M
Variable expressions	I/D	D	D
Venn diagrams	I	D	D
Number Sense and Quantitative Reasoning			
Read and write numbers	D	M	M
Place value			
whole number	M	M	M
decimal	D	D	M
Compare and order			
whole numbers	M	M	M
decimals	D	M	M
fractions	D	D	D
integers	I/D	M	M
rationals			I/D

I = *Introduce* D = *Develop* M = *Maintain and Apply*

Course	1	2	3
Number Sense and Quantitative Reasoning (cont.)			
irrationals			
Number theory			
divisibility rules			
factors			
prime and composite numbers			
prime factorization			
greatest common factor			
multiples			
least common multiple			
Exponents			
positive			
negative			
Scientific notation			
Square numbers and square roots			
Patterns and Functions			
Geometric patterns			
Pascal's triangle			
Sequences			
recognize and complete			
arithmetic			
geometric			
Fibonacci sequence			
Strategy: look for a pattern			
Tessellations			
Functions			
linear			
quadratic			
other nonlinear			
absolute value			
step			
graph			
interpret graphs			
multiple representations			
write a rule			
input-output tables			
Probability			
Simple probability			
Counting principle			
Tree diagrams/sample spaces			
Odds			
Independent and dependent events			
Experimental probability			
Theoretical probability			
Probability of complements			
Conduct experiments			
use samples to predict			
random samples			
random numbers			
simulate a problem			

Course	1	2	3
Probability (cont.)			
conduct a survey			
fair and unfair games			
use a computer			
Factorial notation			
Permuations			
Combinations			
Pascal's triangle			
Problem Solving			
Analyze and make decisions			
find and classify data			
interpret data			
determine trends from data			
make predictions from data			
decide how to present data			
Strategies			
draw a diagram			
guess and test			
look for a pattern			
make a model			
make a table			
simulate the problem			
solve a simpler problem			
too much or too little information			
use logical reasoning			
use multiple strategies			
use a proportion			
work backward			
write an equation			
Use a calculator			
Use a computer			
Use estimation			
Use formulas			
Use graphs			
Proportional Reasoning			
Ratios			
read and write			
equal ratios			
Rate			
unit rate			
unit price			
distance, rate, time problems			
dimensional analysis			
Proportions			
solve proportions			
estimate solutions to proportions			
reason with proportions			
Proportionals in similar figures			
find missing parts			
scale drawings			
scale factors			

Course	1	2	3
Proportional Reasoning (cont.)			
ratio of sides and areas		Introduce/Develop	Develop
ratio of sides and volumes		Introduce	Develop
indirect measurement			Introduce/Develop
Sine, cosine, and tangent			Introduce/Develop
Percents			
understand concept	Develop	Develop	Maintain and Apply
write as ratio and decimal	Develop	Develop	Develop
greater than 100		Introduce/Develop	Develop
less than 1		Introduce/Develop	Develop
estimate	Develop	Develop	Develop
modeling	Introduce	Develop	Maintain and Apply
find using a proportion	Introduce/Develop	Develop	Develop
find using an equation			Introduce/Develop
find percent of a number	Introduce/Develop	Develop	Develop
find percent one number is of another		Introduce/Develop	Develop
find number when percent is known		Introduce/Develop	Develop
percent of change		Introduce/Develop	Develop
Applications of percents			
markup		Introduce	Develop
discount	Introduce	Develop	Maintain and Apply
commission			Introduce/Develop
sales tax	Introduce	Develop	Develop
simple interest	Introduce	Develop	Develop
compound interest		Introduce	Develop
Reasoning			
Construct Venn diagrams	Introduce/Develop	Develop	Maintain and Apply
Justify answers	Develop	Develop	Develop
Make and test conjectures	Develop	Develop	Develop
Make generalizations	Develop	Develop	Develop
Reason from graphs	Introduce/Develop	Develop	Develop
Reason with proportions		Introduce/Develop	Develop
Recognize patterns	Develop	Develop	Develop
Use logical reasoning	Introduce/Develop	Develop	Maintain and Apply
Use spatial visualization	Introduce/Develop	Develop	Develop
Statistics			
Analyze data			
mean, median, and mode	Develop	Develop	Develop
range	Introduce/Develop	Develop	Develop
quartile		Introduce	Introduce/Develop
outlier		Introduce/Develop	Develop
Collect data from a variety of sources	Develop	Develop	Develop
Conduct surveys			
analyze questions		Introduce	Develop
population	Introduce/Develop	Develop	Develop
sample	Develop	Develop	Develop
random sample	Introduce/Develop	Develop	Develop
Organize and display data			
tables and charts	Develop	Develop	Develop
frequency tables	Introduce/Develop	Develop	Develop
line plots	Introduce/Develop	Develop	Develop

Course	1	2	3
Statistics (cont.)			
histograms		Introduce/Develop	Develop
bar graphs	Develop	Maintain and Apply	Maintain and Apply
double bar graphs		Introduce/Develop	Develop
stacked bar graphs			Introduce/Develop
sliding bar graphs			Introduce/Develop
line graphs	Develop	Maintain and Apply	Maintain and Apply
multiple line graphs		Introduce/Develop	Develop
circle graphs	Introduce	Introduce/Develop	Develop
scatter plots		Introduce/Develop	Develop
stem-and-leaf plots	Introduce	Develop	Develop
back-to-back stem-and-leaf plots			Introduce
box-and-whisker plots	Introduce	Develop	Develop
draw and compare different representations	Introduce	Develop	Develop
Choose an appropriate graph or statistic	Develop	Develop	Develop
Identify misleading graphs and statistics	Introduce/Develop	Develop	Develop
Reason from graphs	Introduce/Develop	Develop	Develop
Make predictions from graphs	Introduce/Develop	Develop	Develop
Technology			
Use a calculator			
for computation	Develop	Develop	Develop
for problem solving	Develop	Develop	Develop
for algebra	Develop	Develop	Develop
for fractions	Introduce	Develop	Maintain and Apply
from geometry and measurement	Develop	Develop	Develop
for graphing functions	Introduce	Introduce	Develop
for statistics	Develop	Develop	Develop
to evaluate square roots		Introduce/Develop	Develop
to evaluate trigonometric functions			Introduce/Develop
special keys	Develop	Develop	Develop
Use a computer			
to create a spreadsheet	Introduce/Develop	Develop	Develop
to display data in graphs	Introduce/Develop	Develop	Develop
to draw and measure geometric figures	Introduce/Develop	Develop	Develop
to graph equations	Introduce/Develop	Develop	Develop
to generate random numbers	Introduce	Introduce	Develop
to simulate problems	Introduce	Introduce	Develop
Whole Numbers			
Place value	Maintain and Apply	Maintain and Apply	Maintain and Apply
Number lines	Maintain and Apply	Maintain and Apply	Maintain and Apply
Add, subtract, multiply, and divide	Maintain and Apply	Maintain and Apply	Maintain and Apply
Determine reasonableness of answers	Introduce/Develop	Develop	Maintain and Apply
Rounding	Maintain and Apply	Maintain and Apply	Maintain and Apply
Multiplying and dividing by powers of 10	Introduce	Develop	Maintain and Apply

Introduce *Develop* *Maintain and Apply*

PRENTICE HALL

MIDDLE GRADES MATH

TOOLS FOR SUCCESS

Course 2

Prentice Hall dedicates this mathematics program to all mathematics educators and their students.

AUTHORS

Suzanne H. Chapin

Mark Illingworth

Marsha S. Landau

Joanna O. Masingila

Leah McCracken

CONSULTING AUTHORS

Sadie Chavis Bragg

Bridget A. Hadley

Vincent O'Connor

Anne C. Patterson

PRENTICE HALL

MIDDLE GRADES MATH

TOOLS FOR SUCCESS

Course 2

PRENTICE HALL
Needham, Massachusetts
Upper Saddle River, New Jersey

AUTHORS

Suzanne H. Chapin, Ed.D., Boston University, Boston, Massachusetts
Proportional Reasoning and Probability strands, and Tools for Problem Solving

Mark Illingworth, Hollis Public Schools, Hollis, New Hampshire
Graphing strand

Marsha S. Landau, Ph.D., Formerly, National Louis University, Evanston, Illinois
Algebra, Functions, and Computation strands

Joanna O. Masingila, Ph.D., Syracuse University, Syracuse, New York
Geometry strand

Leah McCracken, Lockwood School District, Billings, Montana
Data Analysis strand

CONSULTING AUTHORS

Sadie Chavis Bragg, Ed.D., Borough of Manhattan Community College, The City University of New York, New York, New York

Bridget A. Hadley, Mathematics Curriculum Specialist, Hopkinton, Massachusetts

Vincent O'Connor, Formerly, Milwaukee Public Schools, Milwaukee, Wisconsin

Anne C. Patterson, Volusia County Schools, Daytona Beach, Florida

PRENTICE HALL

Printed in the United States of America.

ISBN: 0-13-434683-1

5 6 7 8 9 10 04 03 02 01 00 99 98

We are grateful to our reviewers, who advised us in the development stages and provided invaluable feedback, ideas, and constructive criticism to help make this program one that meets the needs of middle grades teachers and students.

REVIEWERS

All Levels

Ann Bouie, Ph.D., Multicultural Reviewer, Oakland, California

Dorothy S. Strong, Ph.D., Chicago Public Schools, Chicago, Illinois

Course 1

Darla Agajanian, Sierra Vista School, Canyon Country, California

Rhonda Bird, Grand Haven Area Schools, Grand Haven, Michigan

Gary Critselous, Whittle Springs Middle School, Knoxville, Tennessee

Rhonda W. Davis, Durant Road Middle School, Raleigh, North Carolina

Leroy Dupee, Bridgeport Public Schools, Bridgeport, Connecticut

Jose Lalas, Ph.D., California State University, Dominguez Hills, California

Richard Lavers, Fitchburg High School, Fitchburg, Massachusetts

Lavaille Metoyer, Houston Independent School District, Houston, Texas

Course 2

Raylene Bryson, Alexander Middle School, Huntersville, North Carolina

Susan R. Buckley, Dallas Public Schools, Dallas, Texas

Sheila Cunningham, Klein Independent School District, Klein, Texas

Natarsha Mathis, Hart Junior High School, Washington, D.C.

Jean Patton, Clements Middle School, Covington, Georgia

Judy Trowell, Arkansas Department of Higher Education, Little Rock, Arkansas

Course 3

Michaele F. Chappell, Ph.D., University of South Florida, Tampa, Florida

Bettye Hall, Math Consultant, Houston, Texas

Joaquin Hernandez, Barbara Goleman Senior High, Miami, Florida

Steven H. Lapinski, Henrico County Public Schools, Richmond, Virginia

Dana Luterman, Lincoln Middle School, Kansas City, Missouri

Loretta Rector, Leonardo da Vinci School, Sacramento, California

Elias P. Rodriguez, Leander Middle School, Leander, Texas

Anthony C. Terceira, Providence School Department, Providence, Rhode Island

STAFF CREDITS

The people who made up the *Middle Grades Math* team—representing editorial, design, marketing, page production, editorial services, production, manufacturing, technology, electronic publishing, and advertising and promotion—and their managers are listed below. Bold type denotes core team members.

Barbara A. Bertell, Bruce Bond, Therese Bräuer, Christopher Brown, **Judith D. Buice**, Kathy Carter, Linda M. Coffey, Noralie V. Cox, Sheila DeFazio, Edward de Leon, Christine Deliee, Gabriella Della Corte, Jo DiGiustini, Robert G. Dunn, Barbara Flockhart, Audra Floyd, David B. Graham, Maria Green, Kristen Guevara, Jeff Ikler, Mimi Jigarjian, Elizabeth A. Jordan, Russell Lappa, Joan McCulley, Paul W. Murphy, Cindy A. Noftle, Caroline M. Power, Olena Serbyn, Dennis Slattery, Martha G. Smith, Kira Thaler Marbit, Robin Tiano, **Christina Trinchero**, **Stuart Wallace**, **Cynthia A. Weedel**, **Jeff Weidenaar**, **Mary Jane Wolfe**, Stewart Wood

We would like to give special thanks to National Math Consultants Ann F. Bell and Brenda Underwood for all their help in developing this program.

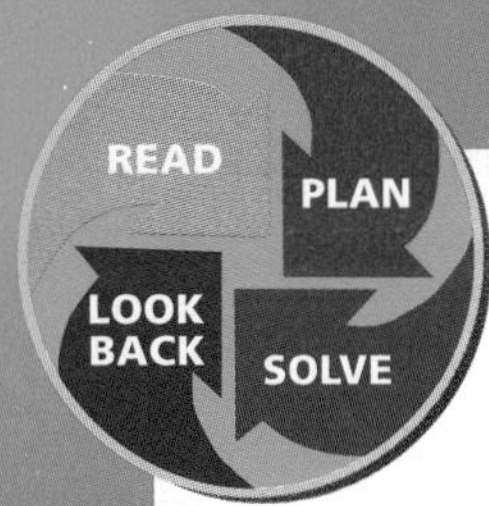

Tools for Problem Solving... An Overview

CONTENTS

page

The four "mini-lessons" in this Overview focus on the big picture of problem solving. They introduce students to the four-step problem solving plan, problem solving strategies, cooperative learning, and standardized tests.

To the Student:

The key to your success in math is your ability to use math in the real world—both now and in the future. To succeed you need math skill and some problem solving tools too. In this Problem Solving Overview, you'll learn how to use a four-step plan for problem solving, how to choose strategies for solving problems, how to best work in groups, and how to apply strategies to standardized tests.

As you work through the book, you'll find plenty of opportunities to improve your problem solving skills. The more you build on a skill, the better you'll get. And the better you get, the more confident you'll become. So keep at it!

Problem Solving Strategies

- Draw a Diagram
- Guess and Test
- Look for a Pattern
- Make a Model
- Make a Table
- Simulate a Problem
- Solve a Simpler Problem
- Too Much or Too Little Information
- Use Logical Reasoning
- Use Multiple Strategies
- Work Backward
- Write an Equation

The "mini-lessons" can be covered in any order and at any time throughout the year, but they're especially well suited for use at the beginning of the course. You could spend from a couple of days to a week on the Overview. Each "mini-lesson" contains a portion to be discussed in class followed by Exercises that students can work on individually or in groups.

PROBLEM SOLVING

The Four-Step Approach

Problem solving is a skill — a skill that you may use without even knowing it. Problem solving involves logical reasoning, wise decision making, and reflecting on solutions.

How you approach a problem is one skill that can make a difference in whether or not you solve the problem. George Polya, a mathematician, devised a four-step method for solving problems.

POLYA'S FOUR-STEP APPROACH

1. Read and understand the problem.
2. Plan how to solve the problem.
3. Solve the problem.
4. Look back.

As you follow each step of Polya's approach, ask yourself questions about the problem.

SAMPLE PROBLEM

A gardener has 32 feet of fencing. He wants to fence a rectangular area to have the largest garden possible. If he uses all of the fence material, what dimensions give him the greatest area?

READ

Read for understanding. Summarize the problem.

Read the problem again. What information is given? What information is missing? Most importantly, what are you being asked to find or to do?

The four-step approach gives students a simple yet effective path to problem solving success. Most students have used this approach (or a similar one) in earlier courses. By reviewing it at the beginning of the year, they can get into the "problem solving" mode as they approach word problems, which they will find in every lesson in this book.

Organize your information.

✓ 32 ft fencing

✓ fence must be rectangle

✓ perimeter must be 32 ft

* find greatest area

PLAN
Decide a strategy.

Consider the strategies you know. Could you use one of them? Have you ever solved a similar problem? If so, try the same approach.

To get a clear idea of the problem, the first thing you might do is draw a diagram.

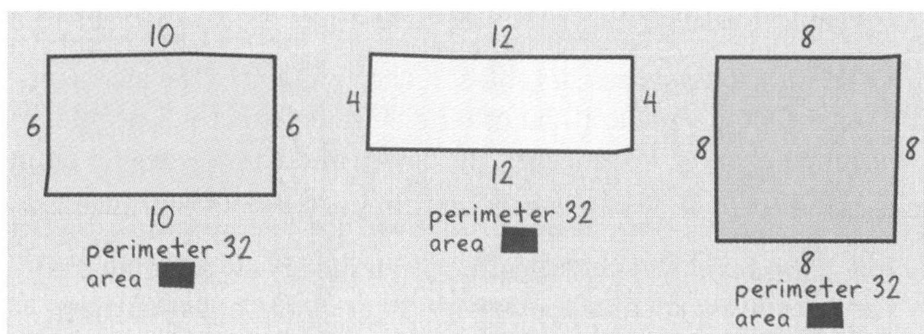

SOLVE
Try the strategy.

Making a table will help you organize your information. Start with length 1 ft.

Length ℓ	Width w	Perimeter $P = 2\ell + 2w$	Area $A = \ell w$
1 ft	15 ft	32 ft	15 ft^2
2 ft	14 ft	32 ft	28 ft^2
3 ft	13 ft	32 ft	39 ft^2
4 ft	12 ft	32 ft	48 ft^2
5 ft	11 ft	32 ft	55 ft^2
6 ft	10 ft	32 ft	60 ft^2
7 ft	9 ft	32 ft	63 ft^2
8 ft	8 ft	32 ft	64 ft^2
9 ft	7 ft	32 ft	63 ft^2

Students should remember the key words "Read," "Plan," "Solve," and "Look Back." You may want to discuss each step of the Sample Problem as a class or in small groups.

You do not need to continue the table because a 9 ft × 7 ft rectangle is the same as a 7 ft × 9 ft rectangle. The table shows that the area is greatest when the length and width are each 8 ft.

LOOK BACK
Think about how you solved the problem.

This is the most important step in solving problems. Check that you answered the original question. Ask yourself some questions.

- Is your answer reasonable?
- Does your answer make sense?
- Could you have solved the problem another way?

EXERCISES *On Your Own*

Use Polya's four-step method to solve each problem. Remember that there are many ways to solve problems.

1. There are two sizes of tables in the cafeteria. One size seats exactly 5 people and the other size seats exactly 8 people. At lunch exactly 79 students sat down, and there were no empty seats. How many tables of each size are in the cafeteria?
   3 small and 8 large tables or 11 small and 3 large tables
2. *Languages* In one school 65 students speak Spanish and 49 students speak Japanese. If 80 students speak either Spanish or Japanese, how many students speak *both* Spanish and Japanese? **34 students**
3. *Geometry* How many triangles are in the diagram at the right? **16 triangles**

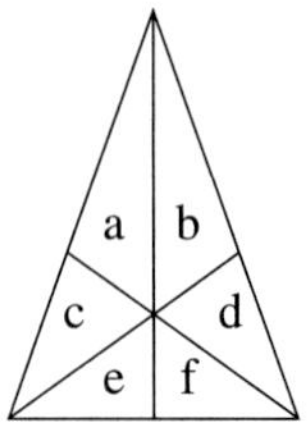

4. *Carpentry* A lumberyard worker cuts a board in half. Then he cuts each piece in half. Then he cuts each of those pieces in half again.
   a. How many cuts did the worker make? **7 cuts**
   b. How many pieces of wood are there? **8 pieces**
5. *Physical Science* Earth's atmosphere is divided into four regions: the mesosphere, the stratosphere, the thermosphere, and the troposphere. The stratosphere is higher in altitude than the troposphere, but not as high as the thermosphere. The mesosphere is just below the thermosphere. Arrange the regions in order from lowest altitude to highest altitude.
   troposphere, stratosphere, mesosphere, thermosphere

As suggested earlier, you might want to assign the Exercises for homework or have students work on them in groups in class. Encourage students to use the four-step approach to solve each Exercise.

PROBLEM SOLVING

Using Strategies

There are many ways to solve problems. Some of the strategies you have learned in previous math courses are Draw a Diagram, Look for a Pattern, Guess and Test, and Make a Table.

Different students solve problems in different ways. Remember that any method that works is a good method!

SAMPLE PROBLEM

The town of Lewiston celebrates Founder's Day with a parade of antique vehicles. One kind of vehicle in the parade is the cycle. Some antique cycles have 2 wheels and some antique cycles have 3 wheels.

During the parade, 24 different antique cycles were counted. There were a total of 54 wheels on these 24 cycles.

How many of the cycles in the parade had 3 wheels?

The solutions shown here and on the next page use three strategies to solve the problem. As you examine the solutions, ask yourself, "Which strategy would I use?"

Solution 1

STRATEGIES: ***Guess and Test*** **and** ***Make a Table***

Use the Make a Table strategy when you use Guess and Test to keep your guesses organized.

2 wheels	3 wheels	Number of Cycles (24)	Number of Wheels (54)	
12	12	24	$(12 \cdot 2) + (12 \cdot 3) = 60$	high
15	9	24	$(15 \cdot 2) + (9 \cdot 3) = 57$	high
17	7	24	$(17 \cdot 2) + (7 \cdot 3) = 55$	high
20	4	24	$(20 \cdot 2) + (4 \cdot 3) = 52$	low
18	6	24	$(18 \cdot 2) + (6 \cdot 3) = 54$	✓

Six antique cycles in the Founder's Day parade had three wheels.

This section shows students that there is often more than one way to succeed at solving a problem and reviews familiar problem solving techniques. Not all the strategies are included here, but students will add to their repertoire of problem solving techniques as the year progresses.

Solution 2

STRATEGY: ***Draw a Diagram***

The Draw a Diagram strategy helps you see the relationships in a problem.

All 24 cycles in the parade have *at least* 2 wheels.

You have accounted for 48 wheels.

Now add wheels until you have 54.

54 wheels in all.

So, 6 cycles have three wheels.

WHAT? A steel penny-farthing bicycle, like the one shown on page xxiii, could weigh as much as 50 or 60 lb. A modern racing bicycle can be a combination of titanium and aluminum and can weigh as little as 19 lb.

Encourage students to solve the Sample Problem before looking at the strategies used in the book. Then they can compare their solutions to those presented. You could ask students to give solutions that differ from those in the book.

EXERCISES *On Your Own*

1. **Money** Petra and Kim are sisters who baby-sit after school and on weekends. Petra charges $4 per hour and Kim charges $5 per hour. On Saturday they baby-sat a total of 11 hours and together made $47. How much money did each girl earn on Saturday? **Kim made $15; Petra made $32.**

2. **Geometry** The diagrams show the diagonals in several figures. How many diagonals are in a figure with 9 sides? **27 diagonals**

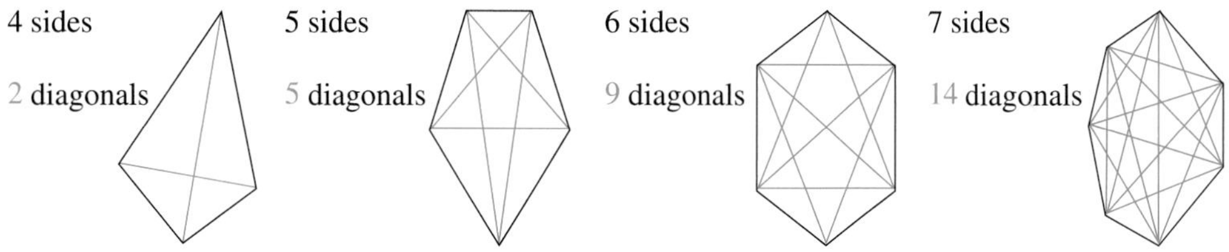

3. **Sports** Students at Maxfield Middle School can choose between two sports in the fall: soccer and track. In the winter the sports are basketball, volleyball, gymnastics, and swimming. In the spring there are two choices: tennis and cross-country. How many different combinations of sports are available to a student who wishes to play one sport each season? **16 combinations**

4. A commuter train leaves for the city every 40 min. The first train leaves at 5:20 A.M. What is the departure time closest to 12:55 P.M.? **12:40 P.M.**

5. Yesterday, Sam walked from his house to the grocery store. At 3:35 P.M., he passed a mailbox that is three blocks from his house. He passed the town fire station at 3:39 P.M. At that point he was four blocks from the grocery store and half the way there. Suppose Sam walked at the same speed all the way to the grocery store. At what time did Sam arrive at the grocery store? Explain your answer. **3:55 P.M.**

6. **Money** Zachary sells juice drinks at sports events. After last weekend's game, he had some $1 bills, some $5 bills, and some $10 bills. He had a total of 17 bills worth a total of $87. How many of each type of bill did he have? **2 $1 bills, 13 $5 bills, 2 $10 bills or 7 $1 bills, 4 $5 bills, 6 $10 bills**

7. **Number Sense** Find the sum of the numbers.

$$1 + 3 + 5 + 7 + \ldots + 295 + 297 + 299$$

22,500

You might want to assign the Exercises for homework or have students work on them in groups in class. Encourage students to use one strategy. You could ask some students or groups to solve one or more of the Exercises using as many different strategies as possible. Students should not be limited to the strategies used in the lesson.

PROBLEM SOLVING

Working Together

Have you ever heard the saying "Two heads are better than one"? You may be asked to work in a cooperative group during math class this year. You will have an opportunity to learn new methods and share your ideas as you solve problems with other students.

Solving problems in a group involves responsibility and cooperation. Usually classrooms have individual and group rules.

Individual rules can include the following.

- You are responsible for your own work.
- You are responsible for your own behavior.

Group rules can include the following.

- You must be willing to help other group members.
- Group members should try to answer questions themselves before asking a teacher.

In a cooperative learning group, members work together to solve problems, but some members of the group may also have specific responsibilities.

People know that working together and valuing others is paramount, especially in today's workplace. There are many opportunities throughout the program where students will be asked to work together to solve a problem, to gather data, or to make conclusions. This lesson provides the framework for working together.

- The **recorder** takes notes and records information.
- The **researcher** tracks down information that is not immediately available.
- Each member of the group should have general supplies such as paper and pencil, a calculator, and a ruler. The **organizer** makes sure any unusual items, like a stopwatch or masking tape, are available.
- The **presenter** explains the group's solution process to the rest of the class.

Remember that even though members of a group have different jobs, each one must help solve the problem.

EXERCISES *On Your Own*

Solve the following problems with your small group. Assign a job to each member of your group. Switch roles for each problem.

1. *Money* Ahmed has 3 pennies, 2 nickels, 3 dimes, and 2 quarters. How many different amounts of money can Ahmed make by using all the possible combinations of coins? **75 different amounts**

2. Annie, Ben, Clarisse, and David each sit in one of the four desks in the third row. Each day they sit in a different order. How many days can they do this before they must repeat a previous pattern? **24 ways**

3. *Sports* José can run 5 km in 30 min. In the same amount of time, Juan can run 3 km. How much of a head start does Juan need for both runners to finish an 8-km course at the same time? **32 min**

4. *Patterns* A marching-band director wanted to arrange the band members in pairs for a parade, but she was one person short. She then tried to arrange the band members by fives and by sevens and was one person short each time. What is the least number of people that are in the band? **69 people**

5. The clock in the old town hall loses 8 minutes every 3 days. The town residents have decided that eventually it will get back to the correct time on its own. Suppose that the clock is correct at noon on June 10. When will the clock show the correct time again? **at noon on March 7, if there is no leap year**

These Exercises can provide students with the opportunity to practice working in groups successfully, especially if you plan to have students work in groups throughout the year.

PROBLEM SOLVING

Preparing for Standardized Tests

You can use problem-solving skills to answer multiple-choice questions. Understanding the relationships in multiple-choice problems can help you choose the correct answer.

SAMPLE PROBLEM 1

Cooking Cassandra's recipe for salad dressing calls for 3 tablespoons (tbsp) olive oil and 1 tbsp lemon juice. By mistake, she used 3 tbsp lemon juice and 1 tbsp olive oil. How many more tablespoons of olive oil must she add to have the correct mix?

A. 2 **B.** 8 **C.** 9 **D.** 15 **E.** Not Here

Read and Understand You are asked to find how many more tablespoons of olive oil Cassandra needs.

Keep in mind that Cassandra put in 3 tbsp lemon juice. She only needed 1 tbsp.

Plan an Approach Thinking about the problem logically is a good way to solve it.

Since Cassandra put in three times as much lemon juice as the recipe states, she needs three times as much olive oil.

Solve the Problem

$$3 \times \text{original amount of olive oil} = \text{new amount of olive oil}$$

$$3 \times 3 \text{ tbsp} = 9 \text{ tbsp}$$

Cassandra needs a total of 9 tbsp olive oil. Since she already put in 1 tbsp olive oil, she only needs 8 more tablespoons.

Choice B is the correct answer.

Look Back When Not Here is an answer choice, you need to check each of the other possible choices before choosing Not Here. For this problem, choice E is not correct. Thinking about the problem logically helps you eliminate choices A, C, and D as possible answers.

This section boosts students' preparation for standardized tests. Throughout the text— in lessons, Mixed Reviews, Problem Solving Practice pages, and Cumulative Reviews— students will continue to practice standardized test-type problems. Encourage students to add other helpful hints they might be able to apply when taking mathematics tests.

Another strategy for answering multiple-choice questions is to Work Backward. You can check each choice to see which results in a correct answer by substituting the values into the problem.

SAMPLE PROBLEM 2

Money In a pile of dimes and quarters, there are twice as many dimes as quarters. The total value of the coins is $9.45. How many quarters are in the pile?

A. 11 **B.** 18 **C.** 21 **D.** 24

Work Backward Check each answer to see if it works.

A: 11 quarters = 2.75 22 dimes = 2.20 2.75 + 2.20 = 4.95 ✗

B: 18 quarters = 4.50 36 dimes = 3.60 4.50 + 3.60 = 8.10 ✗

C: 21 quarters = 5.25 42 dimes = 4.20 5.25 + 4.20 = 9.45 ✔

Choice C is the correct answer.

EXERCISES *On Your Own*

Use problem-solving strategies to choose the best answer.

1. *Money* In an antique desk Lia found some stamps worth 4¢ and 5¢. The value of the stamps was $1.00. There were 22 stamps in all. How many 5¢ stamps were in the desk? D

A. 3 **B.** 6 **C.** 9 **D.** 12

2. *Number Sense* Find the missing number.

1 4 16 64 ■ 1,024 4,096 C

A. 96 **B.** 192 **C.** 256 **D.** 342 **E.** Not Here

3. *Money* Kate bought some CDs for $80, sold them for $95, bought them back for $120, and sold them again for $130. How much money did she make? E

A. $0 **B.** $15 **C.** $30 **D.** $50 **E.** Not Here

4. Given the numbers 0 and 5, it is *not* reasonable to conclude — B

A. that the sum is greater than the product
B. that the product is greater than the sum
C. that the difference equals the sum
D. that the difference is greater than the product

You might want to assign the Exercises for homework or have students work on them in groups. Have students discuss which answers they eliminated first, and why, or any other helpful test-taking hints they wish to share with their classmates.

Pre-Course Skills Assessment

A broad range of assessment tools are available to reach a variety of learners. Options for Formal and Informal Assessment appear on the **Assessing Progress** pages that precede each chapter.

Computer Item Generator

With the Computer Item Generator, you can customize assessment and create customized practice worksheets.

Standardized Test Preparation

You may wish to take advantage of the Standardized Test Preparation component that is available on the Computer Item Generator and the Resource Pro™ CD-ROM. With this component, you can generate tests to help students prepare for these standardized tests:

CAT5 California Achievement Test, 5th Edition
ITBS Iowa Test of Basic Skills, Form M
MAT7 Metropolitan Achievement Test, 7th Edition
SAT9 Stanford Achievement Test, 9th Edition
Terra Nova Comprehensive Test of Basic Skills, 5th Edition

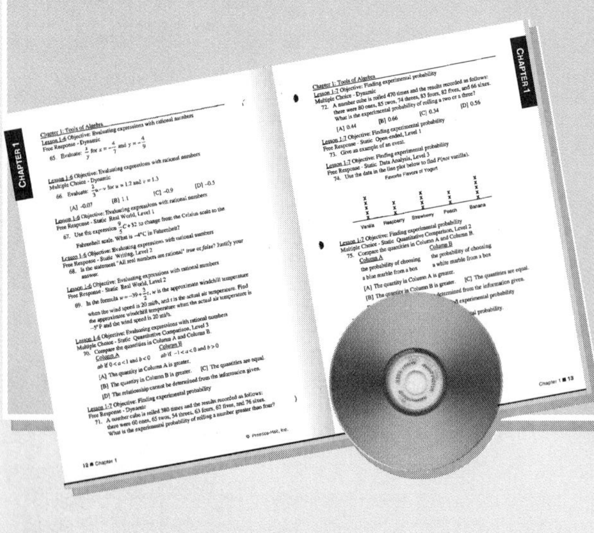

Pre-Course Skills Assessment

The Pre-Course Skills Assessment, available in the *Cumulative Assessment* booklet in the Teaching Resources, covers the 16 skills addressed in the **Skills Handbook** at the back of the Student Edition.

Structure The Pre-Course Skills Assessment is a four-page test. There are four, free-response test items for each of the 16 skills covered in the Skills Handbook at the back of the Student Edition.

Scoring Usually, three out of four responses correct (75%) should demonstrate that the student has sufficient mastery of the skill to be able to succeed in this program. However, you may wish to set your own criteria.

Progress and Remediation Chart To assist you in assessing the skill level of your students, a Progress and Remediation Chart appears with the Pre-Course Skills Assessment. This chart identifies the skills assessed, student achievement on the assessment, and suggests where remediation, if necessary, will be found within the *Prentice Hall Middle Grades Math* program.

Pre-Course Skills Assessment

To the Teacher:
The Pre-Course Skills Assessment contains 4 test items for each of the 16 skills listed below. Usually, 3 out of 4 correct should demonstrate skill; however, you may want to set your own criteria.

Progress and Remediation Chart

Student Name ____________ Date ________

Skill	Test Items	Number of Items Correct	Demonstrates Skill? (yes or no)	Suggested Remediation
1. Comparing and Ordering Whole Numbers	1–4			Student Edition p. 528
2. Rounding Whole Numbers	5–8			Student Edition p. 529
3. Multiplying Whole Numbers	9–12			Student Edition p. 530
4. Dividing Whole Numbers	13–16			Student Edition p. 531
5. Place Value and Decimals	17–20			Student Edition p. 532
6. Reading and Writing Decimals	21–24			Student Edition p. 533
7. Rounding Decimals	25–28			Student Edition p. 534
8. Multiplying Decimals	29–32			Student Edition p. 535
9. Zeros in the Product	33–36			Student Edition p. 536
10. Dividing a Decimal by a Whole Number	37–40			Student Edition p. 537
11. Powers of Ten	41–44			Student Edition p. 538
12. Zeros in Decimal Division	45–48			Student Edition p. 539
13. Adding and Subtracting Fractions with Like Denominators	49–52			Student Edition p. 540
14. Metric Units of Length	53–56			Student Edition p. 541
15. Metric Units of Capacity	57–60			Student Edition p. 542
16. Metric Units of Mass	61–64			Student Edition p. 543

Pre-Course Skills Assessment

Skill 1: Comparing and Ordering Whole Numbers

Use > or < to compare the numbers.

1. 65,432 ■ 65,342 2. 586,563 ■ 586,653

Write the numbers from least to greatest.

3. 2,875; 2,457; 2,886; 2,268; 2,826
4. 40,609; 40,906; 45,606; 45,060

1. >
2. <
3. 2,268; 2,457; 2,826; 2,875; 2,886
4. 40,609; 40,906; 45,060; 45,606

Skill 2: Rounding Whole Numbers

5. Round 542 to the nearest ten.
6. Round 8,742 to the nearest thousand.
7. Round $\underline{3}$52,709 to the place of the underlined digit.
8. Round 62,5$\underline{2}$4,017 to the place of the underlined digit.

5. 540
6. 9,000
7. 400,000
8. 62,520,000

Skill 3: Multiplying Whole Numbers

Find each product.

9. 67 × 8 10. 49 × 53
11. 4 × 396 12. 70 × 82

9. 536
10. 2,597
11. 1,584
12. 5,740

Skill 4: Dividing Whole Numbers

Divide.

13. $9\overline{)759}$ 14. $38\overline{)1,761}$
15. 854 ÷ 6 16. 857 ÷ 46

13. 84 R3
14. 46 R13
15. 142 R2
16. 18 R29

Pre-Course Skills Assessment (continued)

Skill 5: Place Value and Decimals

17. Write the value of the digit 4 in 0.354. 17. 4 thousandths
18. Write the value of the digit 4 in 374.89. 18. 4 ones
19. Write the value of the underlined digit in 52.7$\underline{8}$1. 19. 8 hundredths
20. Write the value of the underlined digit in 9.$\underline{6}$321. 20. 6 tenths

Skill 6: Reading and Writing Decimals

21. Write a decimal for seven and fourteen hundredths. 21. 7.14
22. Write a number for sixty thousand forty-eight. 22. 60,048
23. Write 4,000,000.006 in words. 23. four million and six thousandths
24. Write 37.0009 in words. 24. thirty-seven and nine ten-thousandths

Skill 7: Rounding Decimals

25. Round 589.284 to the nearest tenth. 25. 589.3
26. Round 1.6543 to the nearest hundredth. 26. 1.65
27. Round 0.5005 to the nearest thousandth. 27. 0.501
28. Round 49.63 to the nearest whole number. 28. 50

Skill 8: Multiplying Decimals

Multiply.

29. 3.2 × 0.9 30. 0.9 × 612
31. 3.7 × 24.8 32. 0.03 × 15.6

29. 2.88
30. 550.8
31. 91.76
32. 0.468

Pre-Course Skills Assessment (continued)

Skill 9: Zeros in the Product

Multiply.

33. 0.9 × 0.03 34. 0.08 × 0.08
35. 0.6 × 0.13 36. 0.27 × 0.04

33. 0.027
34. 0.0064
35. 0.078
36. 0.0108

Skill 10: Dividing a Decimal by a Whole Number

Divide.

37. $4\overline{)54.1}$ 38. $67\overline{)30.552}$
39. 46.886 ÷ 17 40. 69.836 ÷ 26

37. 13.525
38. 0.456
39. 2.758
40. 2.686

Skill 11: Powers of Ten

Multiply.

41. 0.06 × 1,000 42. 273.9 × 0.01

Divide.

43. 0.8 ÷ 1,000 44. 3.05 ÷ 0.01

41. 60
42. 2.739
43. 0.0008
44. 305

Skill 12: Zeros in Decimal Division

Divide.

45. $0.14\overline{)0.091}$ 46. $0.06\overline{)0.288}$
47. 0.00054 ÷ 0.18 48. 0.009 ÷ 0.45

45. 0.65
46. 4.8
47. 0.003
48. 0.02

Pre-Course Skills Assessment (continued)

Skill 13: Adding and Subtracting Fractions with Like Denominators

Add or subtract. Write the answers in simplest form.

49. $\frac{4}{9} + \frac{2}{9}$ 50. $6\frac{1}{4} - 2\frac{1}{4}$
51. $2\frac{4}{8} + 3\frac{6}{8}$ 52. $5\frac{5}{12} - 2\frac{1}{12}$

49. $\frac{2}{3}$
50. 4
51. $6\frac{1}{4}$
52. $3\frac{1}{3}$

Skill 14: Metric Units of Length

Complete each equation.

53. 3.9 cm = ■ km 53. 0.000039
54. 0.4 mm = ■ cm 54. 0.04
55. ■ m = 90 km 55. 90,000
56. 2,500 mm = ■ m 56. 2.5

Skill 15: Metric Units of Capacity

Complete each equation.

57. ■ kL = 4.6 L 57. 0.0046
58. 1.6 L = ■ mL 58. 1,600
59. 23,000,000 mL = ■ L 59. 23,000
60. ■ L = 80 kL 60. 80,000

Skill 16: Metric Units of Mass

Complete each equation.

61. 2,300 mg = ■ kg 61. 0.0023
62. 500 g = ■ mg 62. 500,000
63. ■ kg = 3,004,000 mg 63. 3.004
64. 7.3 kg = ■ g 64. 7,300

1 Interpreting Data and Statistics

Chapter Overview

To accommodate flexible scheduling, most lessons are divided into parts. Assignment Options are given in the Teacher's Edition for each lesson.

Lesson 1-1 Reporting Frequency

Pages 4–7

NCTM 1, 2, 3, 4, 7

Part 1 Frequency Tables and Line Plots
Part 2 Using Histograms
Key terms: line plot, frequency table, histogram, intervals

▼ **Project Link**

Lesson 1-2 Making Bar and Line Graphs

Pages 8–11

NCTM 1, 2, 3, 4, 5

Part 1 Making a Bar Graph
Part 2 Making a Line Graph
Key terms: bar graph, line graph

Alternative Activity 1-2

Journal

Lesson 1-3 Technology: Spreadsheets and Data Displays

Pages 12–15

NCTM 1, 2, 3, 4

Part 1 Understanding Spreadsheets
Part 2 Double Bar and Double Line Graphs
Key terms: spreadsheet, cell, double bar graph, double line graph, legend

Alternative Activity 1-3

Lesson 1-7 Random Samples and Surveys

Pages 30–32

NCTM 1, 2, 3, 4

Part 1 Identifying a Sample
Part 2 Writing Survey Questions
Key terms: population, random sample, biased questions

▼ **Project Link**

Lesson 1-8 Using Data to Persuade

Pages 34–38

NCTM 1, 3, 4

Journal

▼ **Project Link**

☑ **Checkpoint 2**

Lesson 1-9 Algebra: Exploring Scatter Plots

Pages 39–42

NCTM 1, 2, 3, 4, 13

Part 1 Reading and Drawing Scatter Plots
Part 2 Interpreting Scatter Plots
Key terms: scatter plot, positive trend, negative trend, no trend

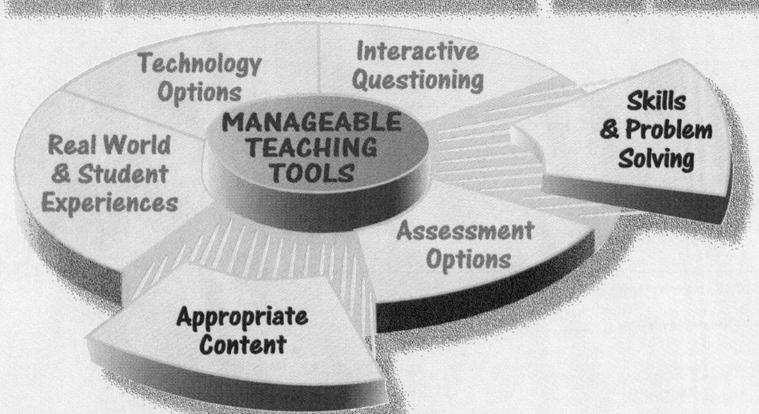

Pacing Options

This chart suggests pacing only for the core lessons and their parts. It is provided merely as a possible guide. It will help you determine how much time you have in your schedule to cover other features, such as the Chapter Project, Math Toolboxes, Wrap Up, and Assessment.

	1 Class Period	1 Class Period	1 Class Period	1 C Pe
Traditional (40–45 min class periods)	1–1 ▼1, 1–1 ▼2	1–2 ▼1, 1–2 ▼2	1–3 ▼1, 1–3 ▼2	1 ▼
Block Scheduling (90 min class periods)	1–1 ▼1, 1–1 ▼2, 1–2 ▼1, 1–2 ▼2	1–3 ▼1, 1–3 ▼2, 1–4 ▼1	1–4 ▼2, 1–5 ▼1, 1–5 ▼2	1–6 ▼, 1

CHAPTER PROJECT

THEME: MARKETING

TOO MANY TO COUNT

Goal: Collect, analyze, and make predictions from a random sample

NCTM STANDARDS

1 Problem Solving	6 Number Systems and Number Theory	10 Statistics
2 Communication	7 Computation and Estimation	11 Probability
3 Reasoning	8 Patterns and Functions	12 Geometry
4 Mathematical Connections	9 Algebra	13 Measurement
5 Number and Number Relationships		

Pages	Lesson
Pages 17–21	**Lesson 1-4 Mean, Median, and Mode**
NCTM 1, 2, 3, 5, 7	Part 1 Finding Mean, Median, and Mode Part 2 Describing Data with Mean, Median, or Mode **Key terms:** mean, average, median, mode, outlier ✓ **Checkpoint 1**
Pages 22–25	**Lesson 1-5 Stem-and-Leaf Plots**
NCTM 1, 2, 4, 5	Part 1 Displaying Data Using Stem-and-Leaf Plots Part 2 Finding Range **Key terms:** stem-and-leaf plot, range **Alternative Activity** 1-5 **Math at Work**
Pages 27–29	**Lesson 1-6 Problem Solving Strategy**
NCTM 1, 3, 4, 5	**Use Logical Reasoning** **Project Link**

Optional Materials and Manipulatives

graph paper (1-1, 1-2, 1-3, 1-7, 1-8, 1-9)
nursery rhyme or poem (1-1)
population chart (1-2)
movie section of paper (1-2)
spreadsheet program (1-3)
computer (1-3)
calculator (1-4)
number cube (1-4)
metric ruler (1-5)
newspaper or magazine (1-8)
Optional calculator use is integrated throughout the course.

lass riod	1 Class Period	1 Class Period	1 Class Period	1 Class Period	1 Class Period	1 Class Period	1 Class Period	1 Class Period	1 Class Period	1 Class Period
–4 2	1–5 1	1–5 2	1–6	1–7 1, 1–7 2	1–8	1–8, 1–9 1	1–9 2			
–8	1–9 1, 1–9 2									

Meeting Individual Needs

Accommodating Diverse Learning Styles

In your Teacher's Edition, you will find suggestions as to how you can help students complete mathematical tasks in Chapter 1 by meeting individual needs and supporting various learning styles. Here are some examples:

VISUAL LEARNING
sketching stem and leaf plots *(p. 22)*

TACTILE LEARNING
tracing across spreadsheets using fingers to find cells *(p. 12)*

AUDITORY LEARNING
creating mnemonics for mean, median, and mode *(p. 17)*

KINESTHETIC LEARNING
forming a human histogram by standing in lines *(p. 6)*

GIFTED AND TALENTED
describing situations that would use modes, medians, and means *(p. 18)*

DIVERSITY collaborating with partners to find good problem-solving strategies *(p. 28)*

ACQUIRING ENGLISH PROFICIENCY (AEP)
drawing diagrams to follow logic problems *(p. 27)*

EARLY FINISHERS
Performance-Based Project, MathBlaster® Mystery, Interdisciplinary Units

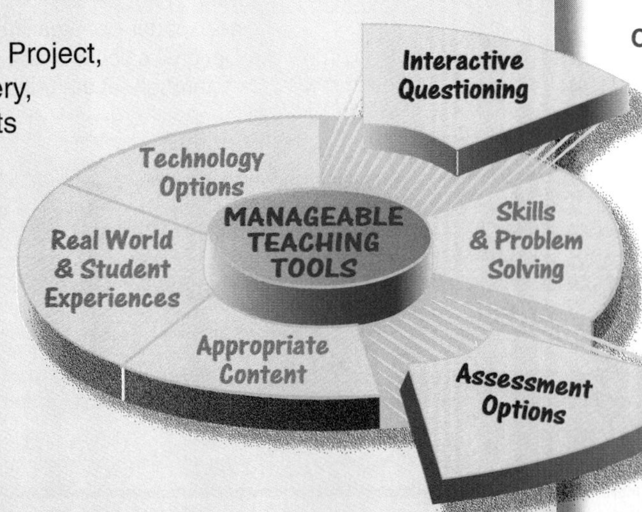

Assessing Progress

A broad range of assessment tools are available to reach a variety of learners.

INFORMAL ASSESSMENT

Informal assessments provide day-to-day feedback to help give you a picture of conceptual understanding and skill development.

ONGOING ASSESSMENT is built into lesson instruction and the Teaching Notes of the Teacher's Edition.

In the Teacher's Edition
Lesson Quiz for every lesson

In the Student Edition
On Your Own, Mixed Review, Journal, Portfolio, Project Link, Chapter Wrap Up

Look for **Interactive Questions** within lessons that

- **BUILD UNDERSTANDING** with labels such as **Analyze, Reasoning, Estimation, Writing, and Summarize**
- ✔ **CHECK UNDERSTANDING** with the **Try It Out** label.

FORMAL ASSESSMENT

Formal assessment can occur before and after the chapter, as well as at natural breaking points in the chapter.

Checkpoints
Two forms of each self-assessment Checkpoints are available: one in the Student Edition and another in the Chapter Support File in the Teaching Resources box.

- Mid-Chapter Checkpoint 1, page 21
- End-of-Chapter Checkpoint 2, page 38

Chapter 1 Assessment, page 46.
Two alternative forms are available in the Chapter Support File. They may be used after a chapter has been completed, or as a pre-test and post-test comparison.

Cumulative Review, page 47.
Assesses skills and concepts in Chapters 1.
An alternative form is available in Chapter Support File.

Computer Item Generator for Chapter 1
Customized tests can be generated for each lesson and for mid-chapter and end-of-chapter assessments, and for pre- and post-test comparisons of achievement.

PERFORMANCE-BASED ASSESSMENT

CHAPTER PROJECT The Chapter Project in the student edition provides a real-world connection to the math context of the chapter. The Teacher's Edition contains a scoring rubric.

A Performance Assessment with a scoring rubric can be found in the Chapter Support File in the Teaching Resources box.

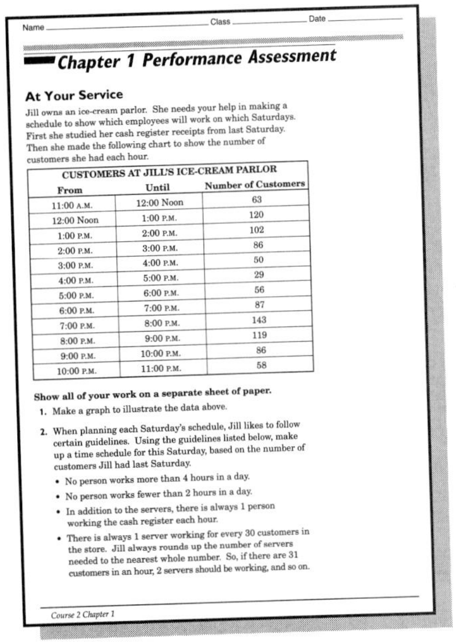
Name ____ Class ____ Date ____

Chapter 1 Performance Assessment

At Your Service

Jill owns an ice-cream parlor. She needs your help in making a schedule to show which employees will work on which Saturdays. First she studied her cash register receipts from last Saturday. Then she made the following chart to show the number of customers she had each hour.

CUSTOMERS AT JILL'S ICE-CREAM PARLOR		
From	**Until**	**Number of Customers**
11:00 A.M.	12:00 Noon	63
12:00 Noon	1:00 P.M.	120
1:00 P.M.	2:00 P.M.	102
2:00 P.M.	3:00 P.M.	86
3:00 P.M.	4:00 P.M.	50
4:00 P.M.	5:00 P.M.	29
5:00 P.M.	6:00 P.M.	56
6:00 P.M.	7:00 P.M.	87
7:00 P.M.	8:00 P.M.	143
8:00 P.M.	9:00 P.M.	119
9:00 P.M.	10:00 P.M.	86
10:00 P.M.	11:00 P.M.	58

Show all of your work on a separate sheet of paper.

1. Make a graph to illustrate the data above.
2. When planning each Saturday's schedule, Jill likes to follow certain guidelines. Using the guidelines listed below, make up a time schedule for this Saturday, based on the number of customers Jill had last Saturday.
   - No person works more than 4 hours in a day.
   - No person works fewer than 2 hours in a day.
   - In addition to the servers, there is always 1 person working the cash register each hour.
   - There is always 1 server working for every 30 customers in the store. Jill always rounds up the number of servers needed to the nearest whole number. So, if there are 31 customers in an hour, 2 servers should be working, and so on.

Course 2 Chapter 1

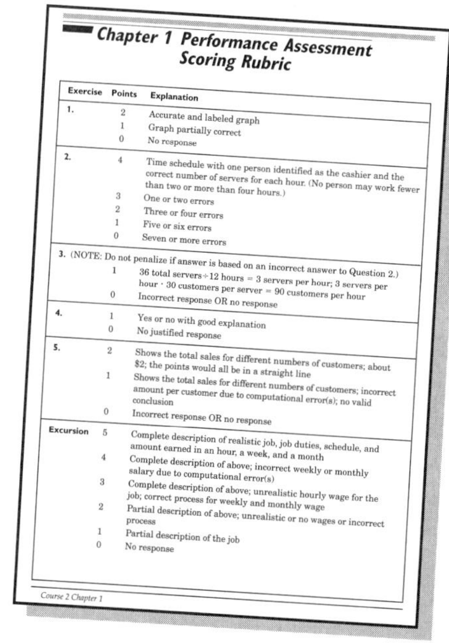
Chapter 1 Performance Assessment Scoring Rubric

Exercise	Points	Explanation
1.	2	Accurate and labeled graph
	1	Graph partially correct
	0	No response
2.	4	Time schedule with one person identified as the cashier and the correct number of servers for each hour. (No person may work fewer than two or more than four hours.)
	3	One or two errors
	2	Three or four errors
	1	Five or six errors
	0	Seven or more errors
3. (NOTE: Do not penalize if answer is based on an incorrect answer to Question 2.)		
	1	36 total servers ÷ 12 hours = 3 servers per hour; 3 servers per hour · 30 customers per server = 90 customers per hour
	0	Incorrect response OR no response
4.	1	Yes or no with good explanation
	0	No justified response
5.	2	Shows the total sales for different numbers of customers; about \$2; the points would all be in a straight line
	1	Shows the total sales for different numbers of customers; incorrect amount per customer due to computational error(s); no valid conclusion
	0	Incorrect response OR no response
Excursion	5	Complete description of realistic job, job duties, schedule, and amount earned in an hour, a week, and a month
	4	Complete description of above; incorrect weekly or monthly salary due to computational error(s)
	3	Complete description of above; unrealistic hourly wage for the job; correct process for weekly and monthly wage
	2	Partial description of above; unrealistic or no wages or incorrect process
	1	Partial description of the job
	0	No response

Course 2 Chapter 1

Correlation to Standardized Tests

Lesson		CAT5	Terra Nova	ITBS, Form M	MAT7	SAT9	Local Test
		STANDARDIZED TEST ITEMS					
1-1	Reporting Frequency					PS24	
1-2	Making Bar and Line Graphs	CA9–11	24, 26, 50, 51, 52		CP34–36	PS25	
1-3	Technology: Spreadsheets and Data Displays		25	PD20–31	CP37–38	PS21–23	
1-4	Mean, Median, and Mode	CA47	40	CE18	CP40	PS26	
1-5	Stem-and-Leaf Plots			CE23			
1-6	Problem Solving Strategy: Use Logical Reasoning	CA13, 17, 44	41, 45, 53	PD2–3, 5–8, 10–11, 18		PS18, 45, 47	
1-7	Random Samples and Surveys	CA48					
1-8	Using Data to Persuade						
1-9	Algebra: Exploring Scatter Plots						

CAT5 California Achievement Test, 5th Edition, Level 17
Terra Nova Comprehensive Test of Basic Skills, Level 17
ITBS Iowa Test of Basic Skills, Form M, Level 13
MAT7 Metropolitan Achievement Test, 7th Edition, Intermediate 2
SAT9 Stanford Achievement Test, 9th Edition, Intermediate 3

CA: Concepts and Applications
PS: Problem Solving
PR: Math Procedures
CP: Concepts and Problem Solving
MC: Math Computation
PD: Problem Solving and Data Interpretation
CE: Concepts and Estimation

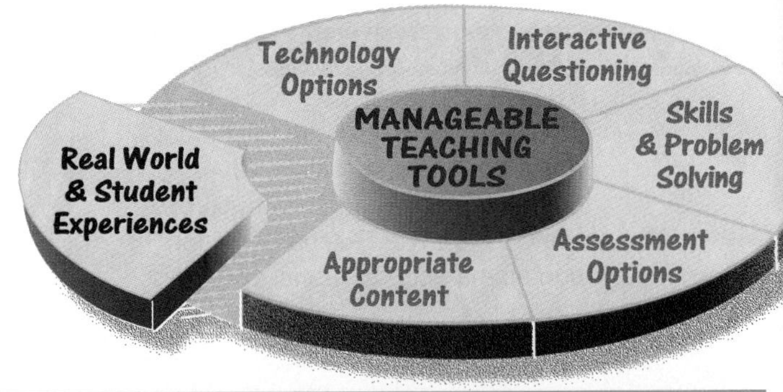

MAKING CONNECTIONS

TEAM TEACHING WITH PRENTICE HALL MATERIALS

MIDDLE GRADES MATH INTERDISCIPLINARY UNITS

- **Agriculture: Activities 2, 4, & 9**
- **Health, Exercise, and Fitness: Activities 1, 3, & 12**
- **The Arts: Activity 10**

INTERDISCIPLINARY EXPLORATIONS

- ***Where River Meets Sea* pp. 22, 23, 39, & 40**
- ***Mill Life in the 1840s* pp. 30 & 31**

PRENTICE HALL SCIENCE

L Life Science **E** Earth Science **P** Physical Science

L Lab p. 528 (graphing data)

E Sec. 1-2 Recording and Analyzing Data
Lab p. 202 (change in temperature)
Lab p. 550 (graphing climate info.)

Lesson	Interdisciplinary Connections	Real World Connections	Math Integration
1-1	Health	Hobbies Business Entertainment	Data Analysis
1-2	Social Studies	Entertainment Data Collection Music	Data Analysis
1-3	Social Studies	Television Business Library Circulations	Data Analysis
1-4	Sports Science	Data Collection Environment Education	Data Analysis
1-5	Nutrition Earth Science Social Studies Sports	Data Collection Gardening Food Pollster	Data Analysis
1-6	Foreign Languages Sports	Fundraising Pets	Data Analysis
1-7	History	Shopping Public Transportation Polling	Data Analysis
1-8	Marketing Sports Nutrition	Business Advertising Television Medicine Environment	Data Analysis
1-9	Science Biology Social Studies	Books Trees Movies	Statistics

School to Home

MATERIALS:
food packages or cans of food
newspaper
trash can
paper
pencil

English version is in the Chapter Support File. Spanish version is in the Spanish Resources.

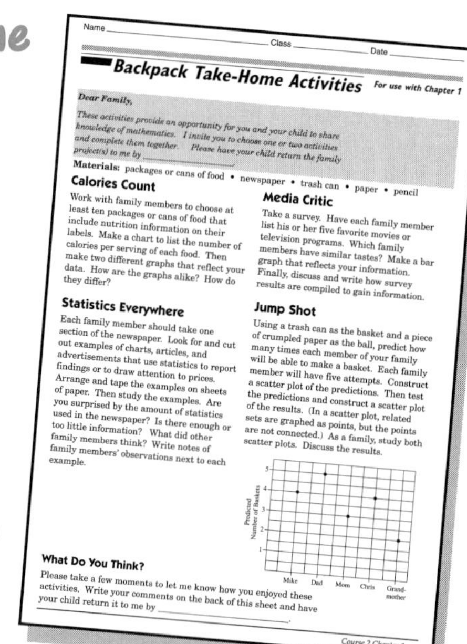

Name ______ Class ______ Date ______

Backpack Take-Home Activities *For use with Chapter 1*

Dear Family,

These activities provide an opportunity for you and your child to share knowledge of mathematics. I invite you to choose one or two activities and complete them together. Please have your child return the family project(s) to me by ______.

Materials: packages or cans of food • newspaper • trash can • paper • pencil

Calories Count

Work with family members to choose at least ten packages or cans of food that include nutrition information on their labels. Make a chart to list the number of calories per serving of each food. Then make two different graphs that reflect your data. How are the graphs alike? How do they differ?

Media Critic

Take a survey. Have each family member list his or her five favorite movies or television programs. Which family members have similar tastes? Make a bar graph that reflects your information. Finally, discuss and write how survey results are compiled to gain information.

Statistics Everywhere

Each family member should take one section of the newspaper. Look for and cut out examples of charts, articles, and advertisements that use statistics to report findings or to draw attention to prices. Arrange and tape the examples on sheets of paper. Then study the examples. Are you surprised by the amount of statistics used in the newspaper? Is there enough or too little information? What did other family members think? Write notes of family members' observations next to each example.

Jump Shot

Using a trash can as the basket and a piece of crumpled paper as the ball, predict how many times each member of your family will be able to make a basket. Each family member will have five attempts. Construct a scatter plot of the predictions. Then test the predictions and construct a scatter plot of the results. (In a scatter plot, related sets are graphed as points, but the points are not connected.) As a family, study both scatter plots. Discuss the results.

Predicted Number of Baskets
1 2 3 4 5
Mike Dad Mom Chris Grand-mother

What Do You Think?

Please take a few moments to let me know how you enjoyed these activities. Write your comments on the back of this sheet and have your child return it to me by ______.

Course 2 Chapter 1

Using Technology to Enhance Instruction

For the Student

Multimedia Math Hot Pages™

This interactive software and video package on CD-ROM integrates solid math content through a variety of media.

- Hot Page™ 1-4
- Hot Page™ 1-5
- Hot Page™ 1-9

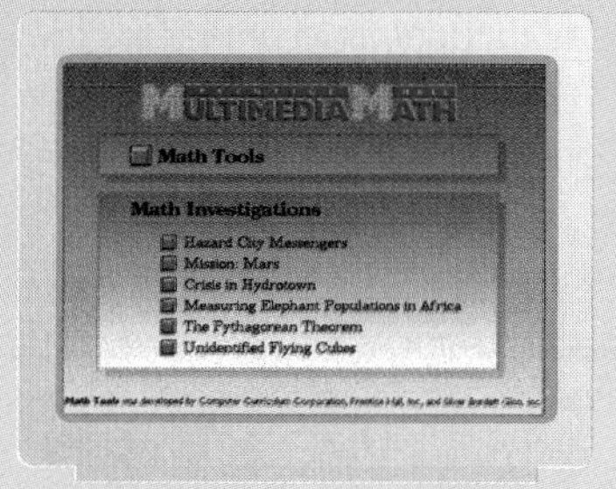

Multimedia Math Investigations

These in-depth interactive activities on CD-ROM develop real-world applications of mathematics. They allow students the opportunity to reinforce key concepts.

- Measuring Elephant Populations in Africa
- Hazard City Messengers

MathBlaster® Mystery

This award-winning, interactive software program on CD-ROM can be used to maintain skills or to accommodate early finishers.

- Level: Earn 4 coins; Pay 4 coins
- Mission Mode (all lessons)
- Kitchen Comparisons (1-2, 1-3, 1-9)
- Number Guesser (1-1, 1-5, 1-7)
- Equation Maker (1-4)
- Word Problems (1-6, 1-8, Problem Solving Practice)

Math Tools/Math Labs

This software, available on CD-ROM, includes on-screen Math Lab activities. Students use linkable, interactive tools to explore math concepts.

- Math Lab: Double Line Graphs (1-3)

Interactive Student Tutorial

Available on CD-ROM, this test preparation program contains self-tests with questions in standardized test format. Software includes electronic versions of the text lessons and an on-line glossary.

Internet Connection

For Students

Support for the Chapter Project
A career-oriented link for Math at Work feature

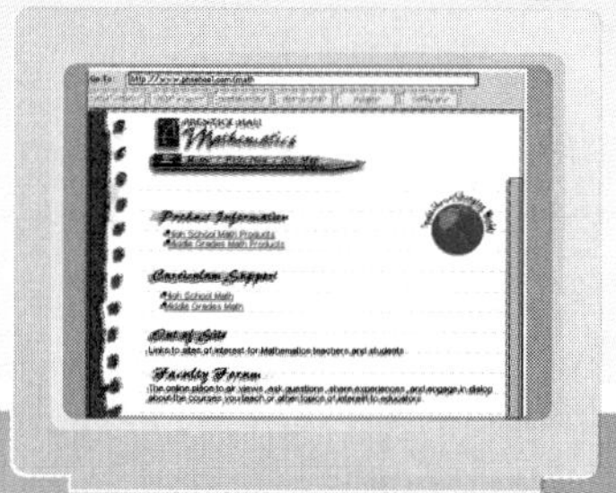

www.phschool.com/math

For teachers

Curriculum Support
Product Information
Regional Support Information

For the Teacher

Computer Item Generator with Standardized Test Practice

This software generates customized practice sheets and tests. It also generates unlimited practice sheets for the standardized tests listed on page 2D.

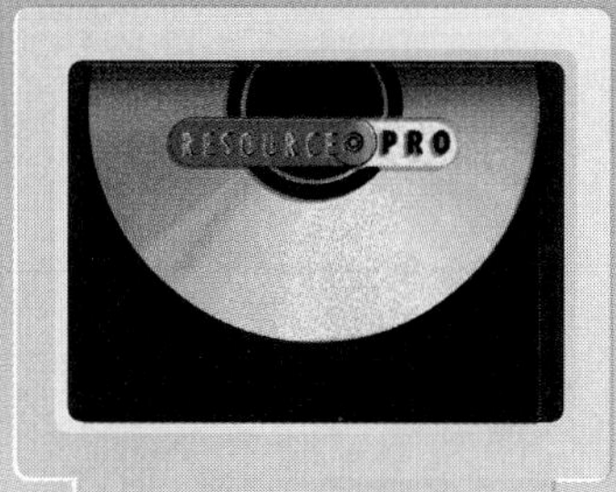

Resource Pro™ with Planning Express™

Available on CD-ROM, this software can be used to customize and plan lessons. It contains over 1,700 resource pages.

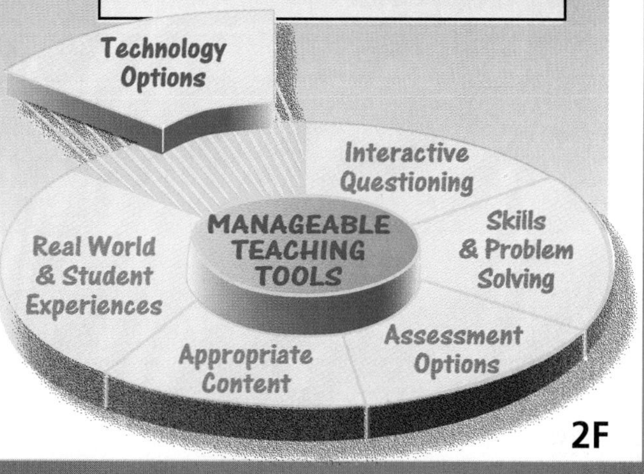

CHAPTER 1

INTERPRETING DATA AND STATISTICS

CONNECTING TO PRIOR LEARNING Have students bring newspapers and magazines to the classroom. Each student can choose a graph or other display of data from one of the periodicals. Ask students to describe how the display makes the data easy to read and understand. Students can compare displays.

CULTURAL CONNECTIONS Not every culture celebrates a birthday in the same way, but the song "Happy Birthday to You" is surprisingly widespread. Ask students to research and discuss how other cultures celebrate birthdays and to look for common practices.

INTERDISCIPLINARY CONNECTIONS Social scientists often study large groups of people. These scientists frequently use surveys and graphs. Discuss how a social scientist could use a survey and graph to study exercise habits in the United States.

ABOUT THE PROJECT The Chapter Project gives students an opportunity to explore the connection between math and marketing. The Project Link questions help students take a survey, display the results in a graph, and use the results to plan a market strategy.

Internet • For information and activities related to the Chapter Project, visit the Prientice Hall site at www.phschool.com/mgm2/ch1

1 Interpreting Data and Statistics

WHAT YOU WILL LEARN IN THIS CHAPTER

- How to collect, record, and interpret data
- How to construct, read, and interpret tables, charts, and graphs
- How to use technology to graph data

LAUNCHING THE CHAPTER PROJECT

Have students estimate the student attendance at their school. Ask:

- *About how many students are in each classroom?*
- *About how many classrooms are there in the school?*

PROJECT NOTEBOOK Encourage students to keep all project-related materials in a separate folder or notebook.

TRACKING THE PROJECT You may wish to have students read Finishing the Chapter Project on page 43 to help them get an overview of the project. Set benchmark deadlines for students to show you their work in progress.

CHAPTER PROJECT

THEME: MARKETING

TOO MANY TO COUNT

Chances are there's at least one person in a crowd like this one that has the same birthday as you! How many people do you think have the same favorite food? How many like the same television show? What kinds of cars do the people in the crowd have? Pollsters face questions like these all of the time, and they take surveys to help answer them.

Estimate the Size of a Crowd and Take a Survey For the chapter project you will use averages to estimate the size of a crowd. You will also take a survey and present your results in a graph.

- How to use logical reasoning to solve problems

PROBLEM SOLVING

Steps to help you complete the project:

p. 7 **Project Link:** *Collecting Data*
p. 29 **Project Link:** *Analyzing*
p. 32 **Project Link:** *Surveying*
p. 38 **Project Link:** *Calculating*
p. 43 ***Finishing the Chapter Project***

SCORING RUBRIC

3 You correctly used three different display methods to show the data you collected. Your displays are attractive and self-explanatory. You identified both the best display method and the best averaging method. You gave reasons to support your choices.

2 You created three displays of your data and calculated the mean, median, and mode. Either your displays or your explanations are not as complete or neat as they could be.

1 Your survey data is complete, but you only completed two displays of the data. Either your displays are not self-explanatory, or you neglected to compare display methods or averaging techniques.

0 Either your survey was not thorough or complete, or you left out important parts of your presentation.

1-1 Teaching Notes

1 Focus

CONNECTING TO PRIOR KNOWLEDGE Ask students to define *frequency*. **Answers may vary. Sample: number of times something occurs** Then have students list where frequencies are used, such as weather reports or when counting medals in the Olympics.

2 Teach

THINK AND DISCUSS

ERROR ALERT! Example 2 Students may be confused about how a histogram displays data. **Remediation:** Have students compare a section of the histogram with a line plot of the same data.

ASSESSMENT Have students compare a frequency table with a line plot and a histogram. Then have students discuss the purpose, characteristics, advantages, and disadvantages of each.

ADDITIONAL EXAMPLES

FOR EXAMPLE 1

Maria surveyed friends to find how many pets each has. The responses were 0 1 1 2 3 0 1 1 3 2 1 2 1 0 1 0 0.

Lesson Planning Options

Prerequisite Skills

- reading graphs (precourse)
- recognizing basic graph vocabulary (precourse)

Vocabulary/Symbols

line plot, frequency table, histogram, intervals

Materials/Manipulatives

- graph paper
- nursery rhyme or poem

Resources

Student Edition

Skills Handbook, p. 528
Extra Practice, p. 514
Glossary/Study Guide

Teaching Resources

Chapter Support File, Ch. 1
- Lesson Planner 1-1
- Practice 1-1, Reteaching 1-1
- Answer Masters 1-1

Teaching Aids Masters 1, 2
Glossary, Spanish Resources

Transparencies

1, 32–36, 78, Minds on Math 1-1

Warm Up

Mari packaged 14 seashells in a box. If she had 360 seashells, how many full boxes did she have? How many shells were left over after the boxes were filled? **25; 10**

1-1 Reporting Frequency

What You'll Learn

1. To display data in a frequency table or a line plot
2. To make a histogram

...And Why

Knowing how to display the frequency of data can help you analyze information.

Here's How

Look for questions that
- build understanding
- ✔ check understanding

THINK AND DISCUSS

1 *Frequency Tables and Line Plots*

Below are the number of letters in each of the words of The Pledge of Allegiance.

1 6 10 2 3 4 2 3 6 6 2 7 3 2 3
8 3 5 2 6 3 6 5 3 11 4 7 3 7 3 3

You can organize and display the data in a line plot or in a frequency table. A **line plot** uses a number line with × marks to represent each data item. A **frequency table** lists each data item together with the number of times it occurs.

EXAMPLE 1

a. Display the data above in a line plot.

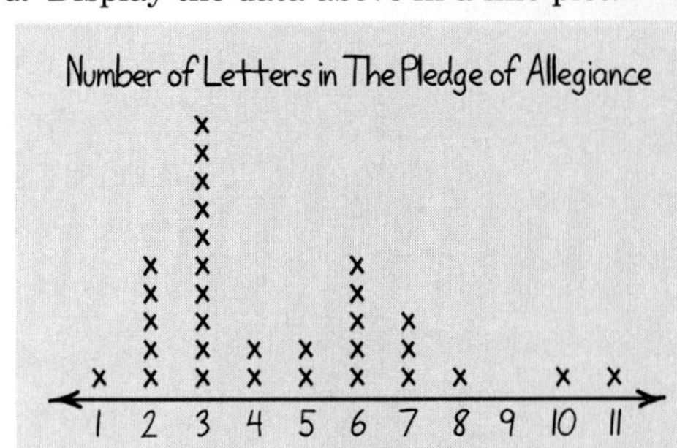

b. Display the data above in a frequency table.

Number of Letters in The Pledge of Allegiance

Number of Letters	1	2	3	4	5	6	7	8	9	10	11
Tally	|	𝍸	𝍸 𝍸	||	||	𝍸	|||	|		|	|
Frequency	1	5	10	2	2	5	3	1	0	1	1

1. **Look Back** Which display do you prefer for the data? Why? **Check students' work.**

Now you may assign Exercises 1–8.

a. Display the data in a line plot.

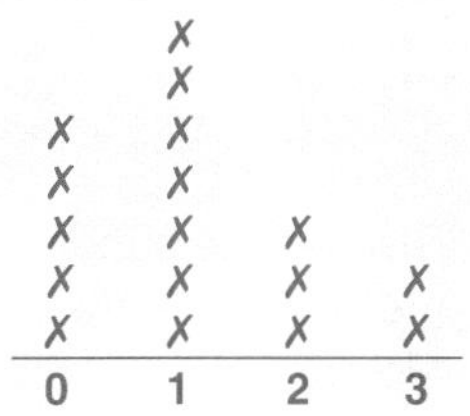

b. Display the data in a frequency table.

Pets	Tally	Frequency
0	𝍸	5
1	𝍸 II	7
2	III	3
3	II	2

FOR EXAMPLE 2

Use the following data to draw a histogram. Use intervals of two.

Children in Family

Children	Tally	Frequency
1	II	2
2	𝍸 I	6
3	IIII	4
4	II	2
5	II	2
6	I	1

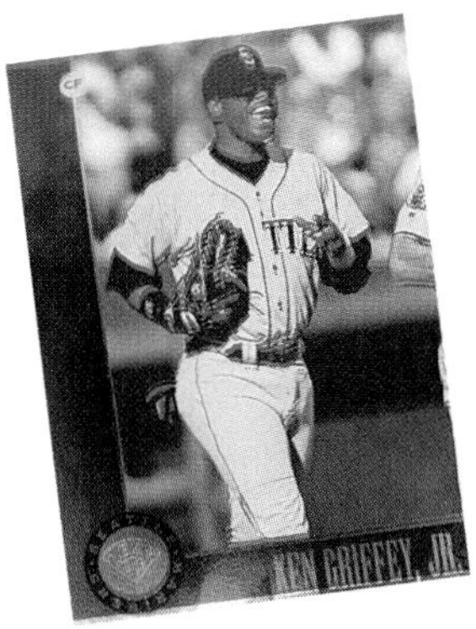

How Many Baseball Cards Do You Have?

Number	Tally	Number	Tally
11	I	21	I
12	𝍸	22	IIII
13	II	23	
14	I	24	III
15	IIII	25	I
16	I	26	
17	II	27	III
18		28	I
19		29	
20	IIII	30	𝍸 II

2 *Using Histograms*

You can use a **histogram** to show frequency. The height of each bar gives the frequency of the data. There are no spaces between consecutive bars.

The information on the horizontal axis of a histogram is grouped into *intervals* of equal size. Intervals must not overlap.

EXAMPLE 2 *Real-World Problem Solving*

Hobbies Use the data at the left to draw a histogram.

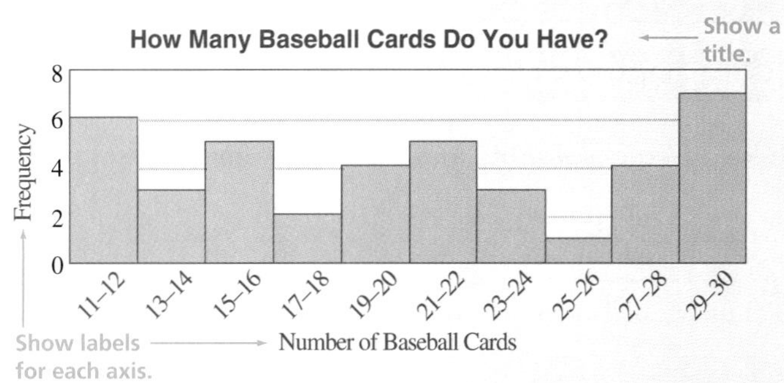

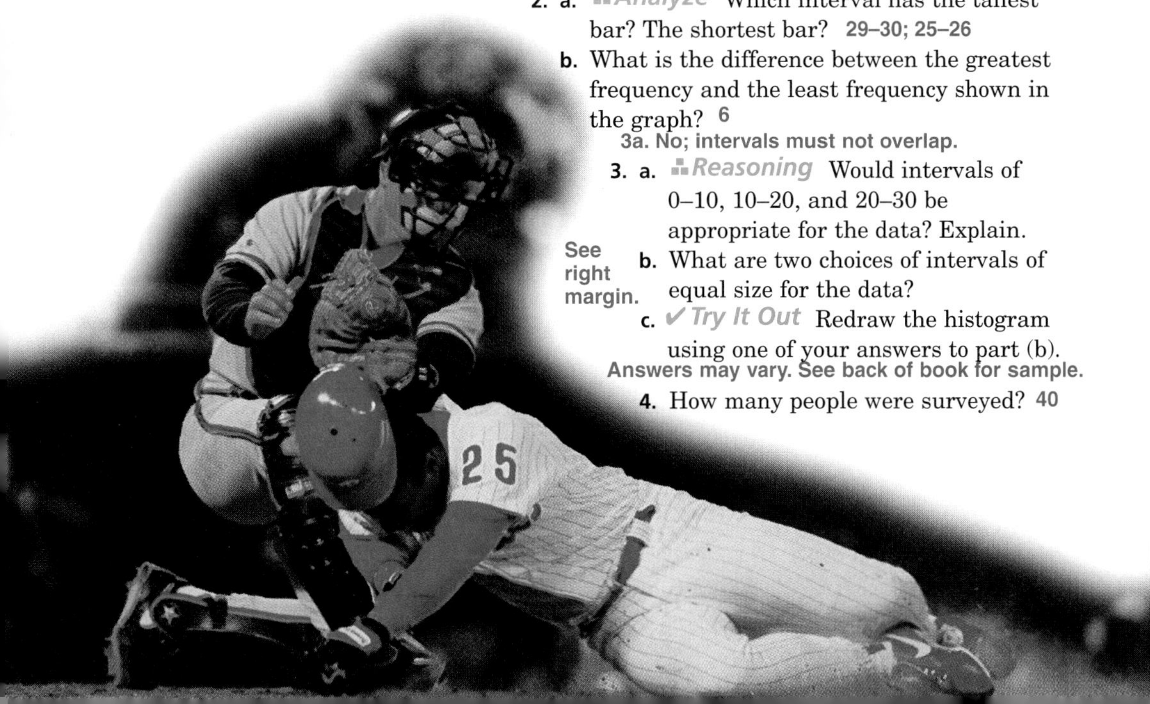

2. a. *Analyze* Which interval has the tallest bar? The shortest bar? **29–30; 25–26**

   b. What is the difference between the greatest frequency and the least frequency shown in the graph? **6**

3a. No; intervals must not overlap.

3. a. *Reasoning* Would intervals of 0–10, 10–20, and 20–30 be appropriate for the data? Explain.

   b. What are two choices of intervals of equal size for the data? **See right margin.**

   c. *✔ Try It Out* Redraw the histogram using one of your answers to part (b). **Answers may vary. See back of book for sample.**

4. How many people were surveyed? **40**

Technology Options

Prentice Hall Technology

Software for Learners

- Math Blaster® Mystery*
- Interactive Student Tutorial, Chapter 1*

Teaching Resource Software

- Computer Item Generator 1-1
- Resource Pro™ Chapter 1*

Internet • For related mathematics activities, visit the Prentice Hall site at www.phschool.com/math

**Available on CD-ROM only*

3b. Sample: 11–15, 16–20, 21–25, 26–30 and 11–13, 14–16, 17–19, 20–22, 23–25, 26–28, 29–31

Assignment Options for Exercises On Your Own

To provide flexible scheduling, this lesson can be subdivided into parts.

1 **Core** 1–7
Extension 8

2 **Core** 9, 11–13
Extension 10

Use Mixed Review to maintain skills.

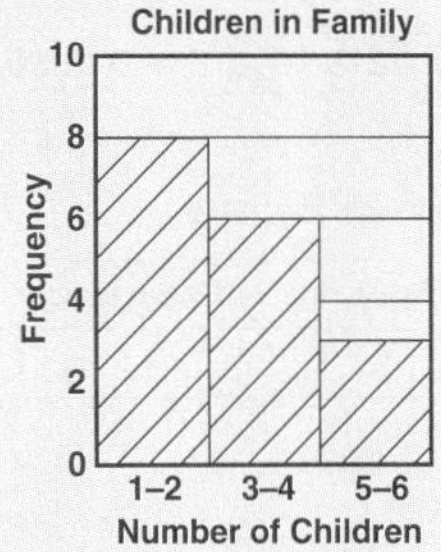

Work Together

KINESTHETIC LEARNING Ask students to stand in 12 rows based on the month they were born. The rows resemble a histogram or line plot.

AEP Ask students to relate the new vocabulary with familiar words. A *histogram* tells a story, or history, visually. The French word for story is *histoire* and the Spanish is *historia*.

3 Practice/Assess

EXERCISES *On Your Own*

Exercise 13 Discuss the suggested intervals of 6:00–6:29 and 6:30–6:59. Ask students why the intervals are not 6:00–6:30 and 6:30–7:00. **The last time in an interval cannot be the first time in the next interval.** Discuss other possible intervals, such as 6:01–6:30 and 6:31–7:00.

pages 6–7 On Your Own

1. Tickets Sold

Number of Tickets	Frequency
45	2
46	4
47	0
48	2
49	1
50	3
51	2
52	0
53	1

Tickets Sold

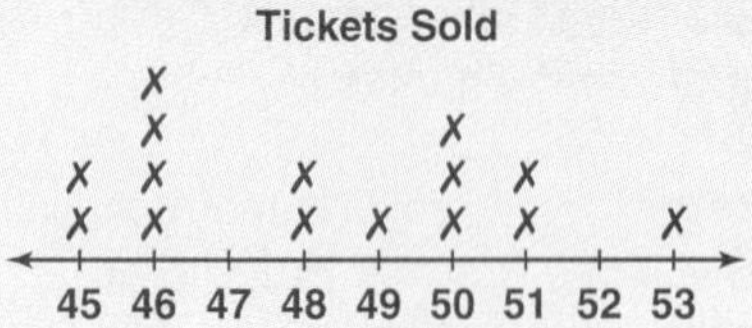

2. Age of Students

Age	Frequency
11	4
12	5
13	5
14	3

Age of Students

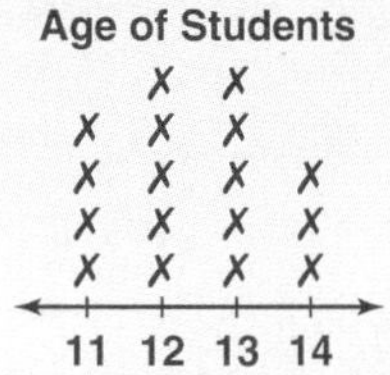

10. The advantage of a histogram is that it gives you a visual picture of a set of data; its disadvantage is that you cannot tell the frequency of each part of the data in an interval.

Work Together

Making Data Displays

Work in groups to collect data and make a display. Ask twelve people one of the questions at the left.

5–8. Check students' work.

5. Record the responses in a frequency table.
6. Create a histogram for your data.
7. Explain why you chose the interval you used.
8. What response was most frequent? Least frequent?

Now you may assign Exercises 9–13.

EXERCISES *On Your Own*

Make a frequency table and a line plot for each set of data. **1–2. See margin.**

1. tickets sold per day: 45 48 51 53 50 46 46 50 51 48 46 45 50 49 46
2. ages of students: 13 12 14 12 11 12 13 14 13 13 14 11 12 12 13 11 11
3. number of TVs per household: 1 3 2 2 1 4 1 2 2 1 3 1 3 3 2 2 3 1
4. miles from home to shopping center: 2 4 10 5 4 6 7 9 5 5 3 1 10 8 6 4 3

3–4. See back of book.

5. *Business* Estelle works at a book store. She made the line plot at the right to show the number of books each customer bought one morning.
   a. How many customers did Estelle have? **16 people**
   b. How many customers bought more than three books? **4 people**

Number of Books Purchased

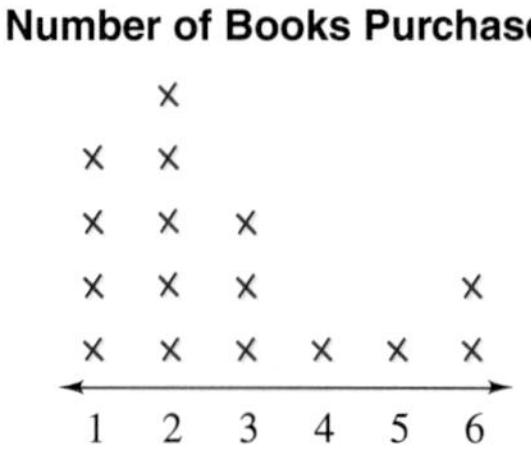

6. the number of times each person has flown in an airplane

The line plot at the right shows responses to a survey.

6. What do the numbers in the line plot represent?
7. How many people answered the survey? **16 people**

How Many Times Have You Flown in an Airplane?

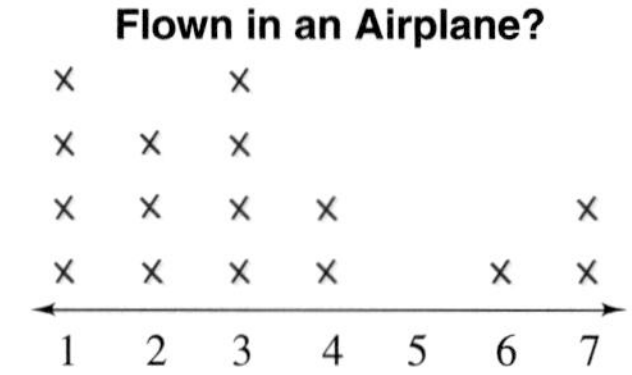

8. *Open-ended* Choose a nursery rhyme or poem. Write the number of letters in each word. Make a line plot of the data. **Check students' work.**

WRAP UP

IDENTIFYING THE BIG IDEA Ask students to explain how to use *frequency tables*, *line plots*, and *histograms* to display data.

PROJECT LINK Be sure students choose a picture of a large crowd. Discuss strategies students can use to guess how many people are in their pictures.

LESSON QUIZ

1. Make a frequency table and a line plot for the set of data. **Check students' work.**

   Students per class: 25 24 25 23 24 23 24 24 23

2. Explain why a histogram is not a good way to display this data. **Answers may vary. Sample: There are not enough different items to create intervals.**

PRACTICE

Practice 1-1 *Reporting Frequency*

Make a line plot for the data.

1. boxes of juice sold per day:
   26 21 26 24 27 23 24 22
   26 21 23 26 24 26 23

Ms. Makita made a line plot to show the scores her students got on a test. At the right is Ms. Makita's line plot.

2. What does each data item or ✗ represent? a student
3. How many more students scored 75 than scored 95? 3 students
4. How many students scored over 85? 13 students
5. What scores did the same number of students get? 80 and 85, 75 and 90

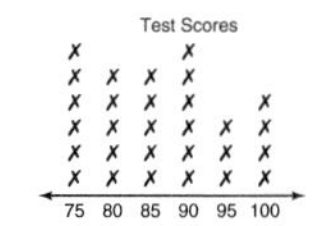

Nathan asked 24 classmates to estimate the total number of hours (to the nearest quarter hour) they spend doing homework Monday through Thursday. The frequency table below shows their responses.

6. Can you tell from the table how many students do homework for two hours or less? Explain. No; the interval includes 2–2.75 h.
7. How many more students do homework for at least 5 h than do homework for less than 4 h? 10 students
8. Make a histogram for the data. Use the intervals in the table.

Hours Spent Doing Homework

Number of Hours	Frequency
1 – 1.75	1
2 – 2.75	1
3 – 3.75	2
4 – 4.75	6
5 – 5.75	8
6 – 6.75	3
7 – 7.75	2
8 – 8.75	1

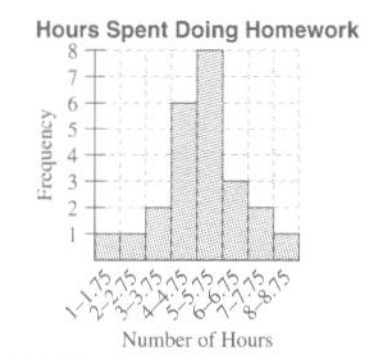

Practice

In copymaster and workbook formats

9. *Entertainment* Use the histogram at the right.
   a. About how many of the people surveyed saw fewer than two movies last summer? **a. 12 people** **b. 4–5; 15 people**
   b. Which interval shows the greatest number of responses? What is the number of responses for this interval?
   c. About how many more people saw 4–5 movies than 10–11 movies? **14 people**
   d. About how many people answered the survey? **50 people**

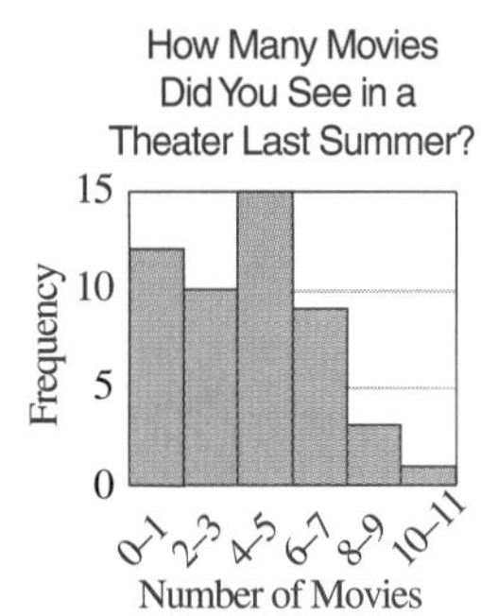

10. *Writing* What is an advantage and a disadvantage of displaying information in a histogram? **Answers may vary. See margin p. 6 for sample.**

Use each table of data to make a histogram. 11–12. See back of book.

11. How Many Hours Do You Sleep Each Night?

Number of Hours	5–6	7–8	9–10	11–12
Frequency	4	12	9	1

12. How Many Meals Did You Eat Out Last Month?

Number of Meals	0–3	4–7	8–11	12–15
Frequency	8	12	3	7

13. *Health* Gabriel asked 16 people what time they get up in the morning. The data at the right show their answers.
    a. Make a frequency table and a histogram for the data. Use half-hour intervals such as 6:00–6:29 and 6:30–6:59.
    b. Which half-hour interval is the most common? **6:00–6:29**

    a. See back of book.

5:30	6:45	5:45	6:15
6:25	6:20	7:15	7:45
8:00	7:00	8:00	7:30
6:00	7:10	7:50	6:10

Mixed Review

Compare. Use < (is less than), > (is greater than), or = (is equal to). *(Previous Course)*

14. 10 + 2 ■ 15 − 3 **=**
15. 7 × 2 ■ 5 × 3 **<**
16. 9 × 4 ■ 24 + 8 **>**
17. 56 ÷ 8 ■ 13 − 8 **>**

Use mental math. *(Previous Course)*

18. 58 + 12 **70**
19. 638 − 328 **310**
20. 594 + 406 **1,000**
21. 702 − 212 **490**

CHAPTER PROJECT

PROJECT LINK: COLLECTING DATA

In a magazine or newspaper, find a picture of a large crowd. Use a sporting event or concert. Guess how many people are in the picture. Save the picture to use later in your project.

Check students' work.

RETEACHING

Reteaching 1-1 *Reporting Frequency*

Aimee asked students in her grade how many CDs they own. She displayed her data in a **frequency table.** Each tally stands for 1 CD.

Students' CD Collections

Number of CDs	17	18	19	20	21	22	23	24
Tally	卌 I	I	卌	III	I	IIII	II	IIII
Frequency	6	1	5	3	1	4	2	4

She displayed the same data in a **line plot.** Each ✗ stands for 1 CD.

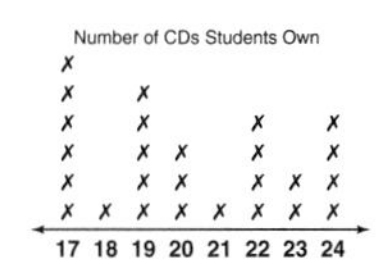

She also made a **histogram** to show the frequencies. The bars represent intervals of equal size. The height of each bar gives the frequency of the data.

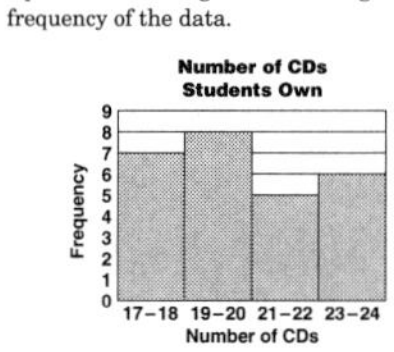

Use the frequency table for Exercises 1–3.

1. Ms. Ortiz's class is planning a school garden. She asked her students how many rose bushes they want in the garden. She recorded the data in a frequency table. Complete the table.

Number of Rose Bushes	1	2	3	4	5	6
Tally	I	IIII	III	卌 I	I	I
Frequency	1	4	3	6	1	1

2. Use the frequency table to make a line plot for the data.

3. Draw a histogram of the students' data.

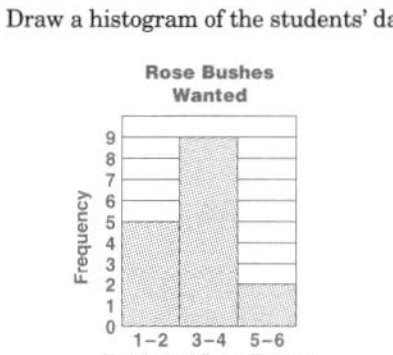

ENRICHMENT

Minds on Math Transparency

1-1

Place the digits 2, 4, 5, 6, and 9 in the boxes to make the smallest possible difference.

□□□
− □□

245
− 96
149

See *Solution Key* for worked-out answers.

1-2 Teaching Notes

1 Focus

CONNECTING TO PRIOR KNOWLEDGE Ask students to name kinds of graphs they have seen. Discuss the places students have seen the graphs and the ways students would use them.

2 Teach

THINK AND DISCUSS

Example 1 Identify the parts of the graph: *title*, *labels*, *scale*, *bars*. Ask students why we estimate the heights of the bars.

ERROR ALERT! Example 2 Students may use a line graph to find the values for years not shown. **Remediation:** Explain that line graphs may predict future values and estimate past values. You do not know actual values for years not shown.

REASONING Question 5 Ask students to consider other possible scenarios, such as a decrease in the number of screens.

TACTILE LEARNING Have students trace with their finger from the point on the top of the bar to the vertical axis.

DIVERSITY Some students may have never seen one or all of the movies listed. Ask volunteers to give a brief synopsis of each movie.

Lesson Planning Options

Prerequisite Skills

- reading graphs (precourse)

Vocabulary/Symbols

bar graph, line graph

Materials/Manipulatives

- graph paper
- population chart
- movie section of paper

Resources

Student Edition

Skills Handbook, p. 528
Extra Practice, p. 514
Glossary/Study Guide

Teaching Resources

Chapter Support File, Ch. 1
- Lesson Planner 1-2
- Practice 1-2, Reteaching 1-2
- Alternative Activity 1-2
- Answer Masters 1-2

Teaching Aids Masters 1, 2
Glossary, Spanish Resources

Transparencies

1, Minds on Math 1-2

Warm Up

Evaluate each of the following operations for $n = 6$.
Multiply n by 4 and add 6. 30
Multiply n by 9 and add 12. 66

1-2 Making Bar and Line Graphs

What You'll Learn

1. To make a bar graph
2. To make a line graph and use a line graph to make predictions

...And Why

You can analyze graphs to compare amounts and to see changes over time.

Here's How

Look for questions that
- build understanding
- ✔ check understanding

THINK AND DISCUSS

1 Making a Bar Graph

You can use a **bar graph** to compare amounts. To make a bar graph, choose an appropriate scale for the vertical axis. Be sure to give your graph a title and to label each axis.

EXAMPLE 1 *Real-World Problem Solving*

Entertainment Make a bar graph. Use the table at the left.

Popular Movies

Movie	Income (in millions)
Apollo 13	$172.1
Batman	$251.2
E.T.	$399.8
Jurassic Park	$357.1
Toy Story	$182.4

Source: *Variety*

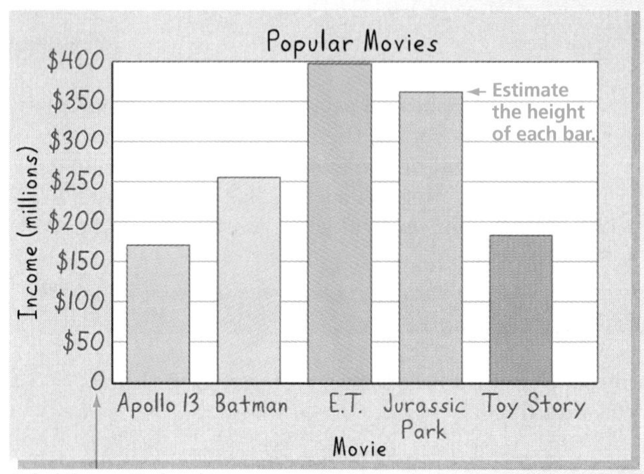

Label the vertical scale using equally spaced intervals.

1. ✔ *Try It Out* Suppose the income for a movie was $340 million. Explain how to estimate the bar height for a graph with the same scale as the one shown in Example 1.

1. Each line marks $50 million. Find the line for $350 million. The top of the bar should be $10 million or $\frac{1}{5}$ of the line space below the $350 million line.

2. Answer may vary. See margin p. 10 for sample.

2. *Reasoning* The year each movie came out is listed below.

Apollo 13	*Batman*	*E.T.*	*Jurassic Park*	*Toy Story*
1995	1989	1982	1993	1995

Do you expect any movie in this list to overtake E.T. in income? Explain.

Now you may assign Exercises 1–5.

■ ADDITIONAL EXAMPLES

FOR EXAMPLE 1

Make a bar graph. Use the following table.

Longest Broadway Runs

Play	No. of Performances*
A Chorus Line	6,137
Cats	5,748
Les Miserables	3,845
The Phantom of the Opera	3,542

***through July 1996**

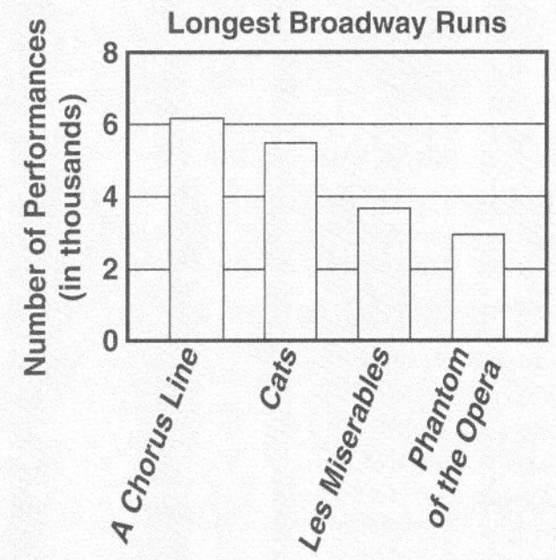

FOR EXAMPLE 2

Make a line graph. Use the following data.
Check students' work.

U. S. Radio Stations Playing Primarily Rock Music

Year	Number
1991	529
1992	592
1993	643
1994	721
1995	808

4. The number of screens has been increasing at about 1,000 screens per year.

Indoor Movie Screens in the United States
(in thousands)

Year	Number
1980	14.9
1984	17.4
1988	21.7
1992	24.2
1996	28.9

Source: Motion Picture Association of America

2 *Making a Line Graph*

To show how an amount changes over time, make a **line graph.** You can use a line graph to look for trends and make predictions.

■ **EXAMPLE 2** *Real-World Problem Solving*

Entertainment Use the data at the left. Make a line graph.

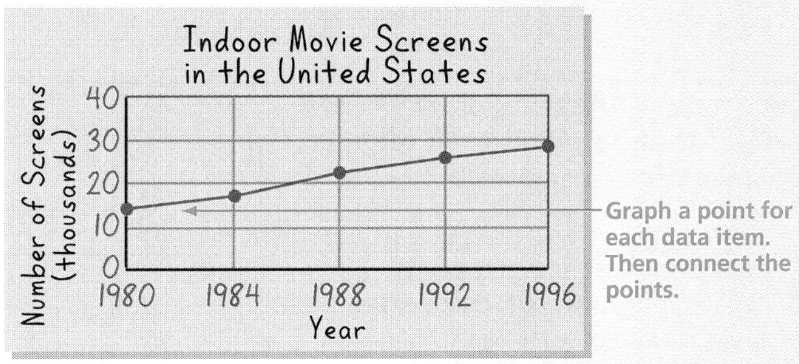

3. *Explain* In Example 2, how do you estimate the position of the point for 1980?
14.9 is almost 15, so place it halfway between 10 and 20.
4. What trend do you see in the graph in Example 2?
See above left.

■ **EXAMPLE 3** *Real-World Problem Solving*

Suppose the trend for the number of screens continues. Use the line graph to predict the number of screens in 2000 and 2004.

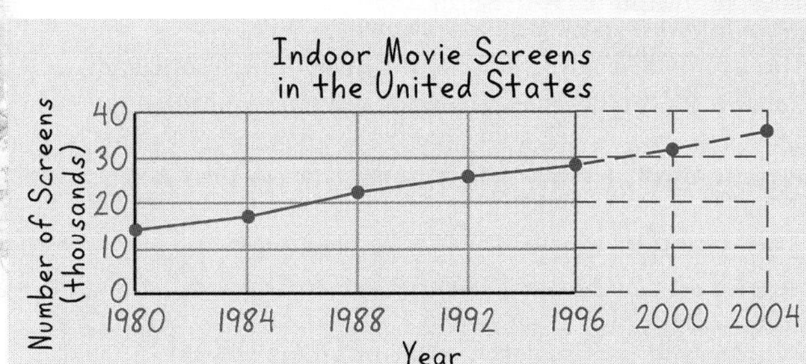

There will be about 32,500 indoor movie screens in 2000.
There will be about 37,000 screens in 2004.

5. *Reasoning* Is it likely that the number of indoor movie screens in 2000 and 2004 will be exactly what is predicted in Example 3? Explain. **No; the prediction is an estimate.**

Diorama by Gerard Fritch

Now you may assign Exercises 6–14.

Technology Options

Prentice Hall Technology

Software for Learners

- Math Blaster® Mystery*
- Interactive Student Tutorial, Chapter 1*

Teaching Resource Software

- Computer Item Generator 1-2
- Resource Pro™ Chapter 1*

Internet • For related mathematics activities, visit the Prentice Hall site at www.phschool.com/math

**Available on CD-ROM only*

Assignment Options for Exercises On Your Own

To provide flexible scheduling, this lesson can be subdivided into parts.

1 **Core** 1–3, 5
Extension 4

2 **Core** 6–10, 12–14
Extension 11

Use Mixed Review to maintain skills.

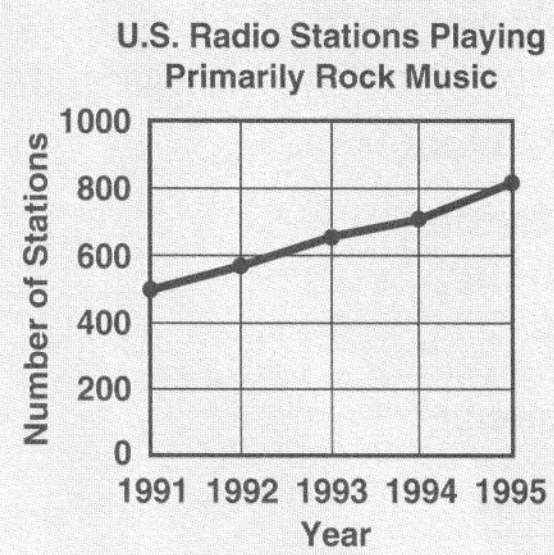

FOR EXAMPLE 3

Suppose the trend for the number of U. S. radio stations playing primarily rock music continues. Use the line graph to predict the number of stations in 2000 and 2004. **There will be about 1,160 stations in 2000. There will be about 1,440 stations in 2004.**

ASSESSMENT Ask students: *What type of graph should you use to show monthly average rain fall for a year?* **bar graph** *to show the change in temperatures at each hour in a day?* **line graph**

3 Practice/Assess

EXERCISES *On Your Own*

RESEARCH Exercise 10 Call your local Chamber of Commerce to find the population for your city.

WRAP UP

IDENTIFYING THE BIG IDEA Ask: *Which graphs are best suited for which purposes?*

pages 8–9 Think and Discuss

2. ***Jurassic Park*'s income is almost the same as *E.T.*'s. It had been released 11 years later than *E.T.*, so it might overtake *E.T.***

pages 10–11 On Your Own

1.

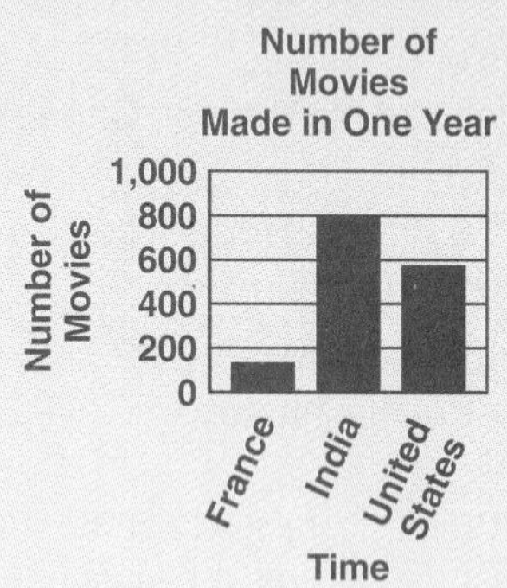

11a.

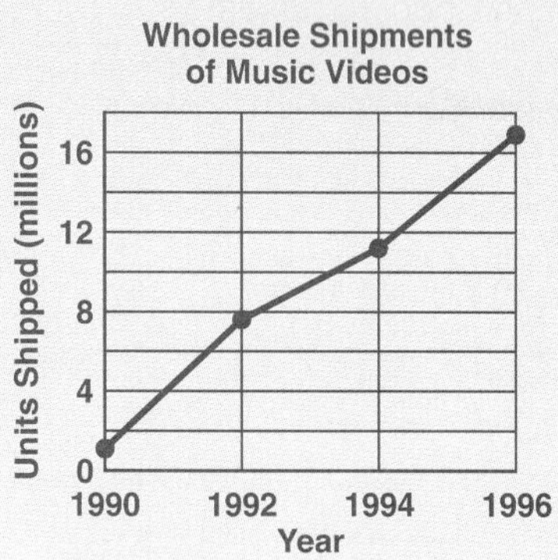

b. **The number of music videos is increasing by about 5 million units every 2 years.**

c. **Check students' work. The extended graph should show a shipment of about 22 million in 1998 and 27 million in 2000.**

EXERCISES *On Your Own*

1. *Entertainment* The data below show the number of movies made in one year in three countries. Make a bar graph using the data. Be sure your graph has a title and labels on the axes.

Country	France	India	United States
Number of movies	133	806	578

See margin.

The graph at the right shows cargo traffic for one year at each airport. Use the graph for Exercises 2–5.

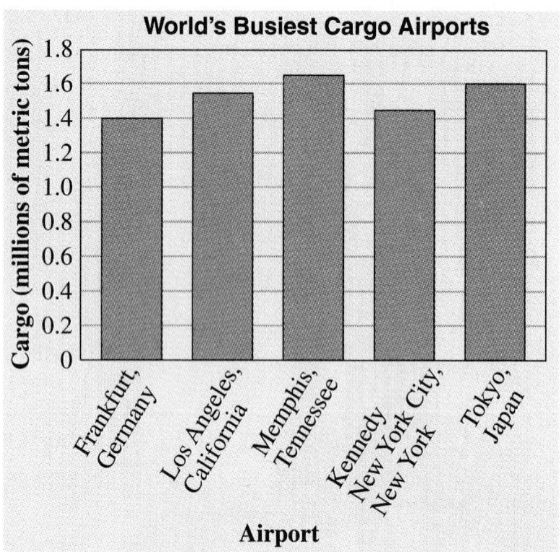

2. Which airport has the least cargo traffic? **Frankfurt, Germany**
3. Which airports have more cargo traffic than Kennedy airport in New York City? **Los Angeles, Memphis, and Tokyo**
4. Estimate the number of metric tons of cargo traffic at the Memphis airport. **about 1.65 million metric tons**
5. Rank the airports from most to least busiest. **Memphis, Tokyo, Los Angeles, Kennedy, Frankfurt**

Would you use a line or a bar graph to display each of the following? Why?

6. the population in Alaska in 1950, 1960, 1970, 1980, and 1990 **Line graph; the population changes over time.**
7. the number of boys and the number of girls by grade at your school **Bar graph; two quantities are being compared.**

Use the graph at the right for Exercises 8 and 9.

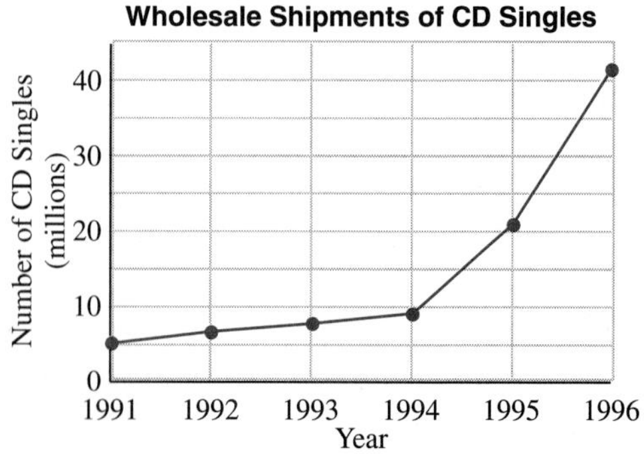

8. Estimate the change in the number of CD singles shipped from 1994 to 1995. **about 12 million CD singles**
9. What trend do you see in the shipment of CD singles? **The number of CD singles is rapidly increasing.**
10. *Research* Find the population of your state or your city for 1960, 1970, 1980, and 1990. Make the appropriate graph of your data. Describe any trends that you see. **Check students' work.**

JOURNAL Ask students to share some ways of using bar and/or line graphs in business, manufacturing, or sales.

LESSON QUIZ

Students enrolled at West High School

Year	Number
1992	478
1993	532
1994	520
1995	545
1996	588

1. Draw a bar graph or a line graph of the data.

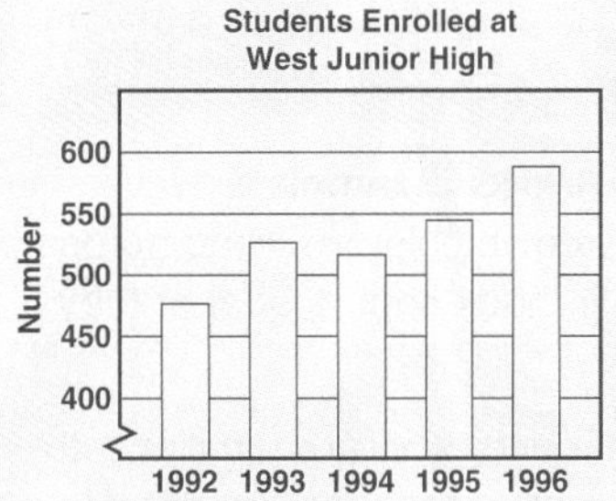

2. Describe any trends. The enrollment is increasing.

11. a. Use the data at the right. Draw a line graph.
    b. Describe the trends you see in your graph.
    c. Extend your graph to predict the shipments of music videos in 1998 and 2000. a–c. See margin p. 10.

12a. Check students' work.

12. a. *Data Collection* Choose five movies that are showing at movie theaters now. Interview 20 people. Find how many people have seen each movie. Graph your results.
    b. Explain why you chose the graph you used. You use a bar graph to compare quantities.

13. **Choose A, B, or C.** Suppose you collected data on the number of students attending your school for the past ten years. Which type of graph would be best for your data? B

    A. histogram B. line graph C. bar graph

14. *Writing* Is the graph below appropriate for the data? Justify your answer. No; use bar graph to compare quantities.

Wholesale Shipments of Music Videos

Year	Units shipped (in millions)
1990	1.1
1992	7.6
1994	11.2
1996	16.9

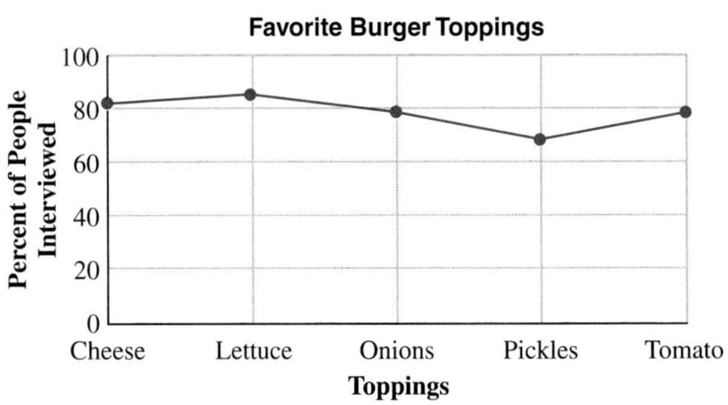

JOURNAL
Use examples to explain when you would use a bar graph and a line graph.

16. 4 students are 12 years old, 16 students are 13, 12 students are 14.

Mixed Review

Use the data at the right for Exercises 15–17. *(Lesson 1-1)*

15. How many students are in the class? 32 students

16. What is the frequency of each response? See above.

17. Which response is the most common? 13

Ages of Students in Mr. Harris's Class

Age	Number of Students
12	||||
13	𝍸 𝍸 𝍸 |
14	𝍸 𝍸 ||

Calculate. *(Previous Course)*

18. 4×27 108 19. $18 \div 3$ 6 20. $84 - 23$ 61 21. $37 + 19$ 56 22. $63 \div 21$ 3

PRACTICE

Practice 1-2 *Making Bar and Line Graphs*

Would you use a line graph or a bar graph to display each of the following? Explain.

1. the number of Sandburg Middle School graduates in 1990, 1991, 1992, and 1993
   line graph because the data change as time goes by
2. the number of students who are the oldest child in their family in each grade at the Emerson Middle School
   bar graph because the numbers of oldest siblings can be compared from grade to grade
3. Make a line graph of the number of teachers in the school district using the data below.

Teachers in School District

Year	Number of Teachers
1990	425
1991	430
1992	420
1993	410

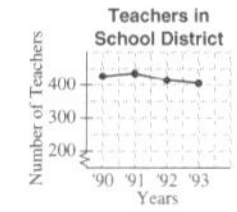

4. Estimate the number of teachers in 1994.
   400 teachers
5. Make a bar graph that shows the numbers of seventh-grade students with given numbers of siblings (brothers and sisters).

How Many Siblings Do You Have?

Number of Siblings	Number of Students
0	4
1	6
2	5
3	3
4	1
5 or more	1

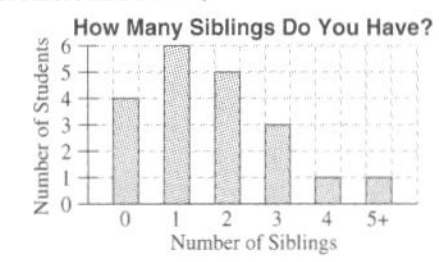

Survey your classmates about one of the following topics: time spent watching TV last weekend, number of books read last month, color of hair, distance from home to school, or some other topic. Show all your work on a separate sheet of paper. Answers may vary.

6. Show the results in a table.
   See students' tables.
7. Show the results in a graph.
   See students' graphs.

In copymaster and workbook formats

RETEACHING

Reteaching 1-2 *Making Bar and Line Graphs*

Samantha surveyed her classmates about a color for the new school flag.

Favorite Color for School Flag

Color	Number of Students
Blue	8
Green	2
Yellow	5
Red	7

She displayed her data in a **bar graph.** Colors are along the horizontal axis.

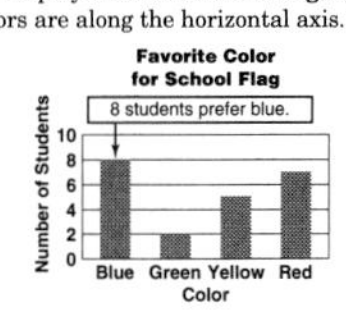

Kemar measured the temperature each day at noon for one week.

Noon Temperatures

Day	Temperature
Monday	1°C
Tuesday	5°C
Wednesday	12°C
Thursday	6°C
Friday	10°C

He displayed his data in a **line graph.** Days are along the horizontal axis.

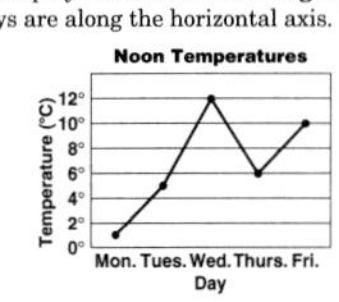

1. Andrea surveyed her friends about their favorite types of sandwich. Make a bar graph to display her data.

Sandwiches Preferred by Students

Type of Sandwich	Number of Students
Tuna	10
Peanut Butter	4
Cheese	5
Bologna	2

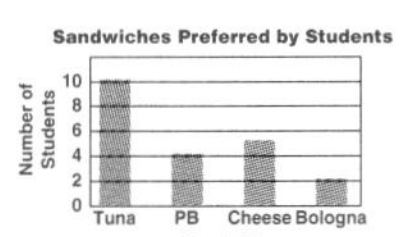

2. Tito recorded the number of students who used a computer lab after school. Make a line graph from his data.

Computer Lab Use After School

Day of the Week	Number of Students
Monday	5
Tuesday	15
Wednesday	25
Thursday	10
Friday	5

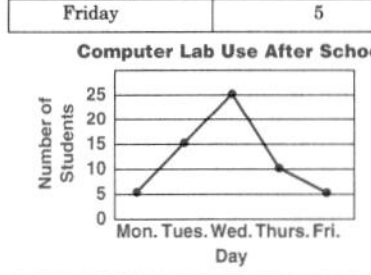

Reteaching

ENRICHMENT

Minds on Math Transparency

1-2

Place one X in as many small squares as possible without forming a line of three Xs in a row either vertically, horizontally, or diagonally. What is the greatest number of Xs for which you can do this?

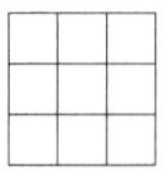

6

See *Solution Key* for worked-out answers.

1-3 Teaching Notes

1 Focus

CONNECTING TO PRIOR KNOWLEDGE
Have students review differences in the use of line graphs and bar graphs. **Line graphs show changes over time. Bar graphs show comparisons of amounts.** Challenge students to think of situations in which combining line graphs would be useful. **comparing temperatures in two cities**

2 Teach

THINK AND DISCUSS

TACTILE LEARNING **Example 1** Have students trace down column C and across row 3 with their index fingers so that they intersect at C3.

AEP Pair students who are familiar with spreadsheets with those who are not. Have pairs review and analyze the basic structure of a spreadsheet.

Example 1 Stress the following points.

- Columns are named with letters. Rows are named with numbers. These letters and numbers are not data.
- The name for each cell in column C includes a C. The name for each cell in row 1 includes a 1.

Lesson Planning Options

Prerequisite Skills

- making and using graphs (1-1 and 1-2)

Vocabulary/Symbols

spreadsheet, cell, double bar graph, double line graph, legend

Materials/Manipulatives

- graph paper
- computer
- spreadsheet program

Resources

Student Edition

Skills Handbook, p. 528
Extra Practice, p. 514
Glossary/Study Guide

Teaching Resources

Chapter Support File, Ch. 1
- Lesson Planner 1-3
- Practice 1-3, Reteaching 1-3
- Alternative Activity 1-3
- Answer Masters 1-3

Teaching Aids Master 3
Glossary, Spanish Resources

Transparencies
3, 26–31, Minds on Math 1-3

Warm Up

Complete the pattern 2.4, 2, 1.6, 1.2, ■, ■. **0.8, 0.4**

TECHNOLOGY Connection

1-3 Spreadsheets and Data Displays

What You'll Learn

1. To use a spreadsheet to make graphs
2. To interpret and make double bar and double line graphs

...And Why

By analyzing graphs, you can understand information presented in books, magazines, and newspapers.

Here's How

Look for questions that
- build understanding
- ✔ check understanding

THINK AND DISCUSS

1 Understanding Spreadsheets

A **spreadsheet** is a tool for organizing and analyzing data. A **cell** is a box where a row and a column meet.

■ EXAMPLE 1 *Real-World Problem Solving*

Television What is the value in cell C3?

Households with VCR and Households with Cable TV
(in millions)

	A	B	C
1	Year	VCR	Cable TV
2	1986	32.5	42.0
3	1988	56.2	48.6
4	1990	65.4	54.9
5	1992	70.3	57.2
6	1994	72.8	59.7
7	1996	78.8	64.0

column ↓ ← cell C3 ← row

Source: The Motion Picture Association of America and Nielsen

The value in cell C3 is 48.6, which represents 48.6 million households.

1. ✔ *Think About It* What is the value in cell B6? **72.8**

2. Which cell tells the number of households with VCRs in 1990? **B4**
Now you may assign Exercises 1–4.

2 Double Bar and Double Line Graphs

You can use a spreadsheet program to create a graph of data. The graphs on the next page show the data above.

A **double bar graph** compares two sets of data. A **double line graph** compares changes over time of two sets of data. The **legend,** or key, identifies the data compared in a graph.

ERROR ALERT! Examples 2 and 3 Students may confuse the use of bar graphs and line graphs. **Remediation:** Stress that a bar graph compares data, and a line graph shows changes over time. A double bar graph compares two sets of data. A double line graph compares two sets of changes.

ADDITIONAL EXAMPLES

FOR EXAMPLE 1

What is the value in cell C6? **72**

Record Highs in Juneau and Record Lows in Key West (°F)

	A	B	C
1	Date	Key West	Juneau
2	9/1	71	70
3	9/2	69	69
4	9/3	70	69
5	9/4	70	71
6	9/5	71	72

FOR EXAMPLE 2

When did the record high in Juneau rise above 70°F? **9/4 and 9/5**

Record Highs in Juneau and Record Lows in Key West

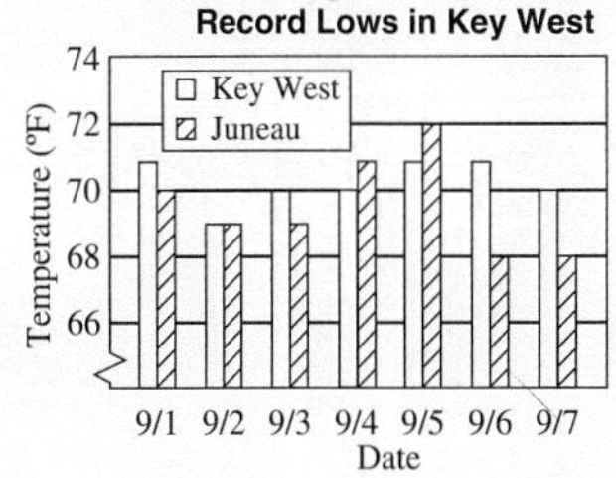

EXAMPLE 2

When did the number of households with VCRs exceed 60 million? When did the number with cable TV exceed 60 million?

The first United States space shuttle was named *Enterprise* after NASA received 400,000 requests from *Star Trek* fans.

Households with VCR and Households with Cable TV

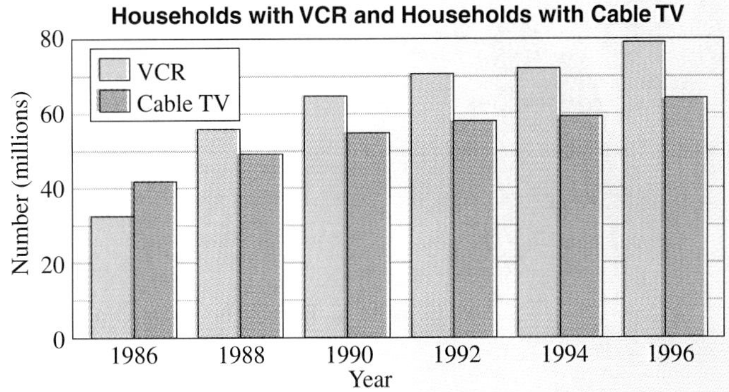

The number of households with VCRs exceeded 60 million in 1990. The number with cable TV exceeded 60 million in 1996.

EXAMPLE 3

Compare the VCR and cable TV data shown in the graph.

Households with VCR and Households with Cable TV

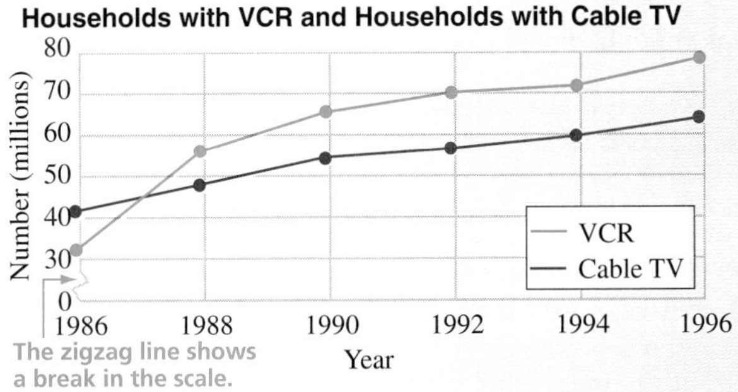

The number of households with VCRs exceeded the number with cable TV between 1986 and 1988. After 1988, the number with VCRs continued to be greater than the number with cable TV.

3. ✔*Think About It* Why would it be confusing if the two graphs above did not have a legend?
You would have to guess which line or color corresponds to each set of data.

Technology Options

Prentice Hall Technology

Software for Learners

- Math Lab: Double Line Graphs*
- Math Blaster® Mystery*
- Interactive Student Tutorial, Chapter 1*

Teaching Resource Software

- Computer Item Generator 1-3
- Resource Pro™ Chapter 1*

Internet • For related mathematics activities, visit the Prentice Hall site at www.phschool.com/math.

**Available on CD-ROM only*

Assignment Options for Exercises On Your Own

To provide flexible scheduling, this lesson can be subdivided into parts.

1. **Core** 1–3
   Extension 4
2. **Core** 5–7, 9, 10
   Extension 8

Use Mixed Review to maintain skills.

FOR EXAMPLE 3

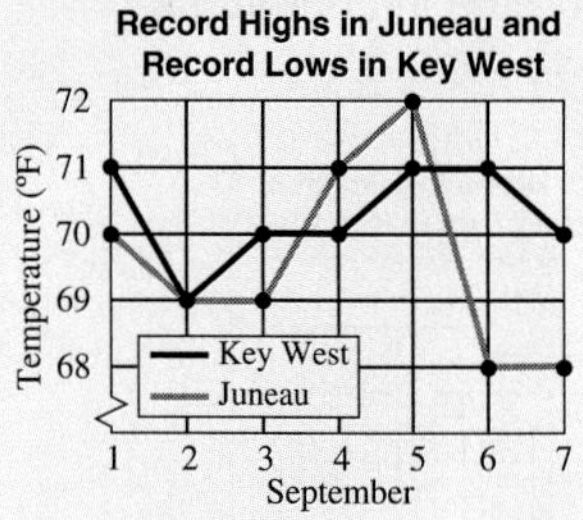

Compare the high and low temperature data shown in the graph. **The greatest difference occurred on 9/6. The least difference occurred on 9/2.**

Work Together

OPEN-ENDED Question 4b Refer students to the questions asked in the examples. Suggest they write similar types of questions about their graph.

3 Practice/Assess

EXERCISES *On Your Own*

ASSESSMENT Have students bring a double bar or a double line graph from a newspaper or magazine to class. Have students work backward with a partner and enter the data in a spreadsheet. Encourage students to share their graphs and spreadsheets with the class.

page 14 Work Together

4a.

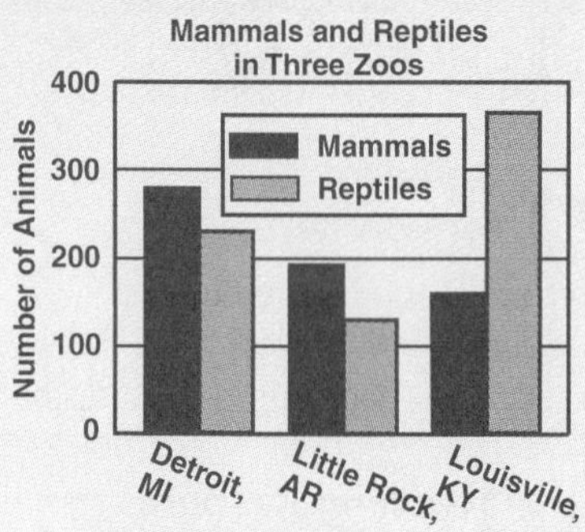

Use a bar graph because you are comparing two quantities which do not represent change over time.

b. Sample: Which zoo has more reptiles than mammals?

pages 14–15 On Your Own

4. Humans get many more calories from carbohydrates than cats and dogs. Cats and dogs get more calories than humans from fat and many more calories from protein.

5b. Answers may vary. Sample: People have been buying more bicycles because they want to exercise more or because they are concerned about the environment.

page 15 Mixed Review

11b. The table tells how many people had between 16 and 20 pennies in their pockets. You cannot tell how many people had 16, 17, 18, 19, or 20 pennies.

Work Together *Using a Spreadsheet*

Work in a group. Use the data below.

Mammals and Reptiles in Three Zoos

	A	B	C
1	Location of Zoo	Number of Mammals	Number of Reptiles
2	Detroit, MI	284	228
3	Little Rock, AR	195	139
4	Louisville, KY	168	365

4. a. Enter the data in a spreadsheet program if possible. Then graph the data. Explain why you chose the graph you made.
   b. *Open-ended* Write a question that could be answered using your graph. **a–b. See margin.**

Now you may assign Exercises 5–10.

EXERCISES *On Your Own*

Use the spreadsheet at the right for Exercises 1–4.

Recommended Nutrition in Dog and Cat Foods
(out of 100 calories)

	A	B	C	D
1	animal	fat	protein	carbohydrates
2	dog	37	26	37
3	cat	46	28	26

1. What value is in cell C3? **28**
2. In which cell is the value 46? **B3**
3. How many more calories from fat are in cat food than in dog food? **9 calories**
4. *Writing* Recommended nutrition for humans in 100 calories of food is 30 calories of fat, 10 calories of protein, and 60 calories of carbohydrates. Compare this with the recommended nutrition for cats and dogs. **See margin.**
5. *Business* The double line graph at the right shows bicycle and automobile production over several years.
   a. In which year are the two lines closest together? **1965**
   b. *Reasoning* The two graphs begin to separate widely after the year you identified in part (a). What do you think could account for this? **See margin.**

Worldwide Bicycle and Automobile Production

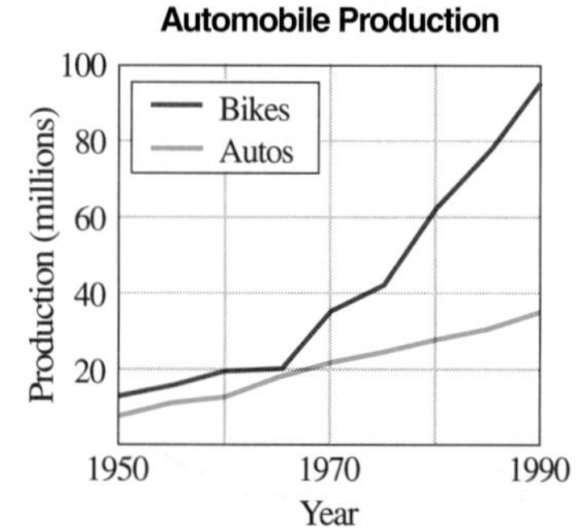

Source: Watchman Institute

WRAP UP

IDENTIFYING THE BIG IDEA Ask students to describe how to make and how to interpret *double line* and *double bar graphs.*

LESSON QUIZ

1996 Presidential Election Results (in thousands of popular votes)

	A	B	C
1	State	Clinton	Dole
2	AK	67	101
3	MT	167	179
4	TN	906	861
5	NH	245	197

1. What value is in cell B4? **906**
2. In which cell is the value 179? **C3**
3. Draw a double line or double bar graph to display the data. **Check students' work.**

Use the graph at the right for Exercises 6–8.

6. Which library circulated the most children's books? The most adults' books?
   Corpus Christi, TX; Albany, NY
7. Which library had the greatest total circulation? **Corpus Christi, TX**
8. a. Which library had the greatest difference between the number of adults' books and children's books circulated? **Albany, NY**
   b. *Reasoning* Suppose you were the librarian in that community. About how many adults' books would you buy for each children's book?
   3 books

Public Libraries Book Circulation

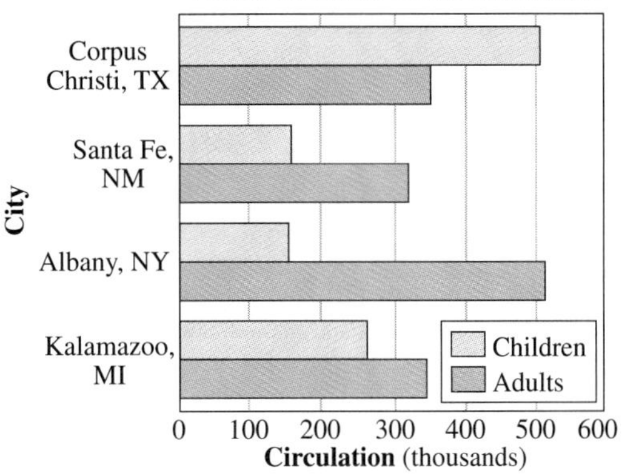

Draw a graph for each set of data. **9–10. See back of book.**

9. population of four western states

Population

	A	B	C
1	State	1980	1990
2	ID	943,935	1,006,749
3	NV	800,493	1,201,833
4	OR	2,633,105	2,842,321
5	WA	4,132,156	4,866,692

Source: *The Information Please Almanac*

10. spending on movie and theater/opera tickets

Total Spent on Tickets (in billions)

	A	B	C
1	Year	Movies	Theater/Opera
2	1991	4.7	4.5
3	1992	5.3	6.0
4	1993	5.0	6.8
5	1994	5.5	8.7
6	1995	5.6	9.0

Source: *The World Almanac*

Mixed Review

Money **Use the frequency table at the right for Exercises 11 and 12.** *(Lesson 1-1)*

11. a. Can you tell from the table how many people had exactly 17 pennies in their pockets? **no**
    b. Why or why not? **See margin p. 14.**
12. Make a histogram of the data.
    See back of book.

Pennies in Pocket

Number	Frequency	Number	Frequency
1–5	12	21–25	5
6–10	6	26–30	6
11–15	10	31–35	0
16–20	7	36–40	4

Extra Practice, Lesson 1-3, page 514

PRACTICE

Practice 1-3 *Spreadsheets and Data Displays*

Use the spreadsheet at the right for Exercises 1–4.

Tickets Sold to Concert Performances

	A	B	C
1	Performance	Adult Tickets	Student Tickets
2	Thursday	47	65
3	Friday	125	133
4	Saturday	143	92

1. What is the value in cell B3? 125
2. Which cell shows 65 tickets sold? C2
3. How many more adult tickets than student tickets were sold on Saturday? 51 tickets
4. The concert producer thought she would have the greatest attendance on Saturday. Compare the data with her expectation. Friday had the greatest overall attendance, but Saturday had the greatest number of adults in attendance.

Decide whether a double bar graph or a double line graph is more appropriate for the given data. Draw the graph.

5. students taking foreign language classes

Year	Boys	Girls
1990	45	60
1991	50	55
1992	70	60
1993	55	75

Students Taking a Foreign Language

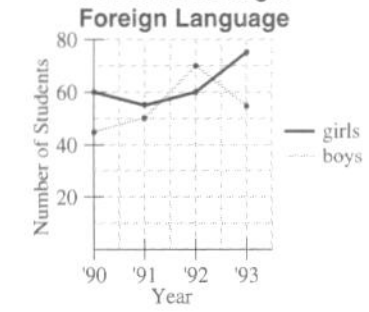

6. extracurricular sport activities

Sport	Boys	Girls
basketball	40	30
volleyball	30	40
soccer	40	25

Extracurricular Sports

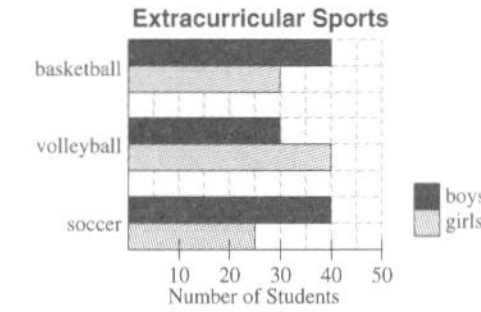

Practice

In copymaster and workbook formats

RETEACHING

Reteaching 1-3 *Spreadsheets and Data Displays*

A **spreadsheet** is one way to organize data.

Columns are labeled A, B, C, and so on. Rows are numbered 1, 2, 3, and so on. The box where column B and row 3 meet is called **cell** B3. The *value* in cell B3 is 10.

Butter and Margarine Sales at Crep's Grocery

	A	B	C
1	Day	Butter	Margarine
2	Monday	9	7
3	Tuesday	10	9
4	Wednesday	7	6
5	Thursday	9	6
6	Friday	10	8
7	Saturday	11	9

You can use the data from this spreadsheet to make a **double bar graph.** A double bar graph compares two sets of data.

- Spreadsheet column A gives the labels for the bars.
- Spreadsheet column B gives the heights for one set of bars.
- Spreadsheet column C gives the heights for another set of bars.
- The **legend,** or key, tells what kinds of data the graph is comparing.

Butter and Margarine Sales at Crep's Grocery

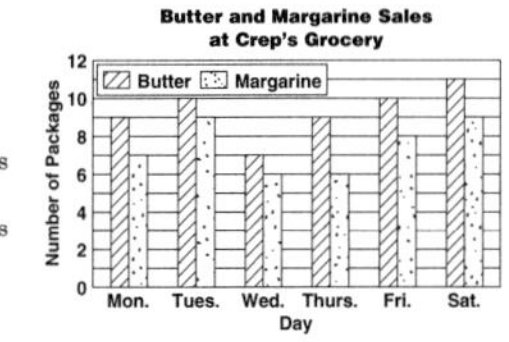

Use the data in the spreadsheet to complete Exercises 1–3.

Percents of Families Who Prefer Frozen Vegetables and Fresh Vegetables

	A	B	C
1	Year	Frozen	Fresh
2	1994	61	39
3	1995	70	30
4	1996	78	22
5	1997	84	16

1. What is the value in cell B4? cell C2? 78, 39
2. In which cell is the year 1997? 1994? A5; A2
3. Make a double bar graph from the spreadsheet. Include a legend.

Percents of Families Who Prefer Frozen Vegetables and Fresh Vegetables

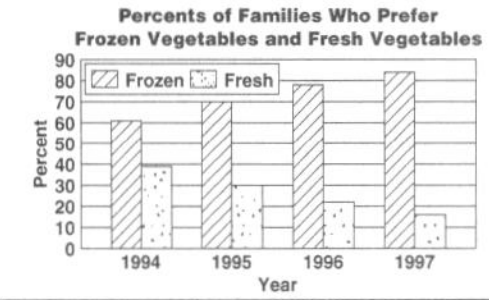

ENRICHMENT

Minds on Math Transparency

1-3

Holland Middle School is in a ten-team conference. During basketball season, each basketball team plays each other team at home. How many conference basketball games are played in a season?

90 games

See *Solution Key* for worked-out answers.

MATH TOOLBOX

In this toolbox, students review dividing whole numbers. Students will use dividing whole numbers to find *mean* in Lesson 1-4.

COOPERATIVE GROUPS **Exercises 1–5** Have students work on these exercises with a partner. Partners can check each other's work as they complete each exercise.

ERROR ALERT! **Exercise 10** Students may forget to use zero as a place holder. **Remediation:** Have students draw a grid to ensure the proper place value of the digits in the quotient. Students can check their work by multiplying the quotient by the divisor and adding a remainder.

ASSESSMENT **Exercises 20 and 21** Have students share techniques for keeping the quotient properly aligned and for dividing by a two-digit number.

Materials/Manipulatives

- calculator

MATH TOOLBOX — SKILLS REVIEW

Dividing Whole Numbers

Before Lesson 1-4

The calculation below indicates the vocabulary associated with division.

$$\begin{array}{r} 7 \\ 6\overline{)45} \\ -\,42 \\ \hline 3 \end{array}$$

divisor → 6; 7 ← quotient; 45 ← dividend; 3 ← remainder

You can write the answer as 7 R3.

To divide, first estimate the quotient by rounding the divisor, the dividend, or both. Then use these steps:

Step 1 Find each digit of the quotient by dividing from left to right.

Step 2 Multiply and subtract.

Step 3 Repeat Steps 1 and 2 until the remainder is less than the divisor.

EXAMPLE

Find each quotient.

a. $741 \div 8$

Estimate: $720 \div 8 = 90$

$$\begin{array}{r} 93 \\ 8\overline{)744} \\ -\,72 \\ \hline 24 \\ -\,24 \\ \hline 0 \end{array}$$

b. $838 \div 43$

Estimate: $800 \div 40 = 20$

$$\begin{array}{r} 19\ R21 \\ 43\overline{)838} \\ -\,43 \\ \hline 408 \\ -\,387 \\ \hline 21 \end{array}$$

21 ← remainder

Find each quotient.

1. $4\overline{)60}$ 15
2. $8\overline{)72}$ 9
3. $7\overline{)92}$ 13 R1
4. $3\overline{)845}$ 281 R2
5. $6\overline{)78}$ 13
6. $6\overline{)469}$ 78 R1
7. $3\overline{)653}$ 217 R2
8. $8\overline{)648}$ 81
9. $9\overline{)231}$ 25 R6
10. $4\overline{)415}$ 103 R3
11. $43\overline{)273}$ 6 R15
12. $52\overline{)281}$ 5 R21
13. $69\overline{)207}$ 3
14. $38\overline{)121}$ 3 R7
15. $81\overline{)433}$ 5 R28
16. $94 \div 4$ 23 R2
17. $66 \div 9$ 7 R3
18. $90 \div 5$ 18
19. $68 \div 6$ 11 R2
20. $58 \div 8$ 7 R2
21. $382 \div 72$ 5 R22
22. $580 \div 68$ 8 R36
23. $279 \div 43$ 6 R21
24. $232 \div 27$ 8 R16
25. $331 \div 93$ 3 R52

1-4 Teaching Notes

1 Focus

CONNECTING TO PRIOR KNOWLEDGE
Have students recall situations where they have used an average. **Answers may vary. Sample: finding grade point averages, calculating batting averages**

2 Teach

THINK AND DISCUSS

AUDITORY LEARNING Suggest students create a poem or mnemonic to help them remember the definitions for *mean*, *median*, and *mode*. Have volunteers read their works aloud.

Example 1 Be sure students understand that *the sum of the responses* means the sum of the data items.

Example 2 Emphasize that for an odd number of items, the median is the middle number in a set of data that has been ordered. If there is an even number of items in a set of ordered data, students must average the two middle numbers to find the median.

Example 3 Ask students if a set of data always has a mode. Why or why not? **No; there may not be any repetition in data items.**

1-4 Mean, Median, and Mode

What You'll Learn

1. To find mean, median, and mode
2. To choose mean, median, or mode to describe data

...And Why

You can analyze data from surveys using mean, median, and mode.

Here's How

Look for questions that
- build understanding
- ✔ check understanding

20 Responses to "How Many Times a Day Do You Drink from the Water Fountain?"		
0	1	1
5	2	10
2	3	5
1	5	2
2	3	4
3	5	5
2	2	

THINK AND DISCUSS

1 *Finding Mean, Median, and Mode*

To make a general statement about a set of data, you can find the *mean, median,* or *mode* of the data. The **mean** is the sum of the data divided by the number of items in the set of data. The mean is often referred to as the *average*.

■ **EXAMPLE 1** *Real-World Problem Solving*

Survey Data Find the mean of the data at the left below.

First find the sum of the responses.

63 ÷ 20 = 3.15 ← Divide the sum by the number of responses.

The mean is 3.15. These students drink from the water fountain about three times a day.

1. ✔ *Try It Out* Earl conducted the survey. Suppose he forgot to include his own data. He does not drink from the fountain. What is the mean when you include this data? **3 times a day**

The **median** is the middle number in a set of data that is written in order. The median of an even number of data items is the mean of the two middle items.

■ **EXAMPLE 2**

Find the median of the water fountain data in the chart.

First write the data in order from least to greatest.

0 1 1 1 2 2 2 2 2 2 3 3 3 4 5 5 5 5 5 10

The two middle items are 2 and 3.

$2 + 3 = 5$
$5 \div 2 = 2.5$ ← Find the mean of the two middle items.

The median is 2.5.

2. ✔ *Try It Out* Find the median of the data below. **42**
71 23 54 65 22 23 71 59 34 37 42

Lesson Planning Options

Prerequisite Skills
- adding and dividing to compute averages (precourse)
- recognizing what an average is and how to find it (precourse)

Vocabulary/Symbols
mean, average, median, mode, outlier

Materials/Manipulatives
- calculator
- number cube

Resources

Student Edition
Skills Handbook, p. 531
Extra Practice, p. 514
Glossary/Study Guide

Teaching Resources
Chapter Support File, Ch. 1
- Lesson Planner 1-4
- Practice 1-4, Reteaching 1-4
- Answer Masters 1-4

Glossary, Spanish Resources

Transparencies
15, 32, 78, Minds on Math 1-4

Warm Up
What fraction of 2 dollars is 2 quarters? $\frac{1}{4}$

Question 4 Elicit the fact that the outlier in the set of data in Examples 1 and 2 is 10. The set of data in Example 3 has no outliers. Point out that a set of data can have more than one outlier.

ADDITIONAL EXAMPLES

Use this data set for Additional Examples 1–3.
11 6 8 12 4 1 7 3 9 8

FOR EXAMPLE 1

Find the mean of the data. 6.9

FOR EXAMPLE 2

Find the median of the data. 7.5

FOR EXAMPLE 3

Find the mode of the data. 8

FOR EXAMPLE 4

Explain whether the mean, the median, or the mode best describes each of the following situations.

a. the favorite movie of students in one class mode

b. the number of chairs in each classroom in a school **mean**

c. the cost of CDs in a music store **mean or median**

EXTENSION Example 4 Have students work with a partner and describe a situation in which knowing a mode would be of value. **Answers may vary. Sample: finding a group of students' favorite school subject** A median **finding the pay most students get for babysitting** A mean. **knowing your average in a certain class**

Technology Options

Prentice Hall Technology

Software for Learners

- Hot Page™ 1–4*
- Math Blaster® Mystery*
- Interactive Student Tutorial, Chapter 1*

Teaching Resource Software

- Computer Item Generator 1-4
- Resource Pro™ Chapter 1*

Internet • For related mathematics activities, visit the Prentice Hall site at www.phschool.com/math

**Available on CD-ROM only*

Assignment Options for Exercises On Your Own

To provide flexible scheduling, this lesson can be subdivided into parts.

1 **Core** 1–6, 8, 9
Extension 7

2 **Core** 10–14
Extension 15

Use Mixed Review to maintain skills.

The data item that occurs most often is the **mode.** A set of data may have more than one mode. There is no mode when all the data items occur the same number of times.

EXAMPLE 3

Find the mode of the data at the left.

Make a frequency table to organize the data.

rose	pansy	peony	daisy	orchid
|||	||	|	|||	|

There are two modes, rose and daisy.

3. ✔ *Try It Out* Find the mode(s) of the following data.
17 15 23 22 12 17 22 25 36 22 17 17 and 22
Now you may assign Exercises 1–9.

2 *Describing Data with Mean, Median, or Mode*

A data item that is far apart from the rest of the data is called an **outlier.** The outlier usually affects the mean of a set of data more than it affects the median or the mode.

4. ✔ *Try It Out* What is the outlier of the following data?
5 10 12 13 8 9 5 6 26 11 5 **26 is the outlier; 10; 8.4.**
   a. Find the mean with and without the outlier.
   b. How did the outlier affect the mean?
   The outlier increased the mean by 1.6.

EXAMPLE 4

Which best describes each situation, the mean, the median, or the mode? Explain.

a. the favorite book of students in the third grade

Mode; use the mode when the data are not numerical or when choosing the most popular item.

b. the number of students in each class at school

Mean; use the mean when there are no outliers to distort the data.

c. the number of pets your classmates have

Mean or median; use the median when there are outliers that may distort the data or use the median to describe the middle value.

CONNECTING TO THE STUDENTS' WORLD
Example 4 If you have extended class periods or block-scheduling, have students work as a class to record when someone makes informal use of mean, median, or mode. *We always have chicken for dinner* could indicate a mode. *I've received about 4 calls each day this week* could indicate a mean. Have students keep a class chart for a week and discuss why mean, median, or mode was used.

Work Together

Before students begin the assignment, encourage them to decide how they will collect the data (verbally, written) and how they will record it (tally, data sheets).

DIVERSITY Help students be aware that some topics may be embarrassing to some people. Have students keep this in mind if choosing a topic of their own.

ERROR ALERT! Question 5 Students may remember *mean* as average but might confuse *median* and *mode*. **Remediation:** Encourage students to use mnemonic devices to help them remember. Suggest students think of *median* as the median, or *central divider*, of a highway. *Mode* can be remembered as the *most* frequent.

ASSESSMENT Have students find the mean, median, and mode for the following list of test scores: 98 81 77 92 84 87 81 80
mean: 85; median: 82.5; mode: 81
Ask students how they could use each measure. **Answers may vary.**

Work Together *Finding Mean, Median, and Mode*

Work with a partner to collect data on one of the topics at the right or a topic of your own. Collect at least 10 pieces of data.
5–6. Check students' work.

5. Find the mean, median, and mode of the data.

6. Does the mean, median, or mode best describe the data you collected?

DATA CHOICES

- Number of buttons on people's clothing
- Number of pages in a book
- Number of times the letter "e" appears in a paragraph

Now you may assign Exercises 10–15.

EXERCISES *On Your Own*

Find the mean, median, and mode of each set.

1. hours of practice before a concert
 2 1 0 1 5 3 4 2 0 3 1 2
 2; 2; 1 and 2

2. one team's hockey scores **2; 2; 3**
 3 2 1 3 0 3 1 1 2 3 3

3. daily low temperatures (°F) for a week **63; 62; 62**
 55 58 62 62 65 67 72

4. number of grocery purchases of the first nine people in an express check-out lane
 3 6 2 5 3 4 8 3 2 **4; 3; 3**

5. number of seconds for a 200-m run
 27 30 25 28 29 33 32 25 25 35
 28.9; 28.5; 25

6. number of hours of homework per night
 1 2 3 2 3 3 2 3 1 4
 2.4; 2.5; 3

7. *Environment* Fifty people live in a state where there is a deposit on aluminum cans. They were asked whether they returned their cans. Their responses are at the right.
 a. What is the mode? **Always**
 b. *Reasoning* From the data at the right, is it reasonable to conclude that only one out of fifty people gives to charity? **No; people may give to charity in other ways than contributing their aluminum cans.**

Do You Return Aluminum Cans?

Response	Frequency
Give them to a charity	1
Never	4
Sometimes	12
Always	33

8. *Data Collection* Roll one number cube 20 times. Make a frequency table to record the number you roll each time. Find the mean, median, and mode of your data.
 Check students' work.

9. a. The total weight of all the students on a football team is 2,730 lb. The mean is 130 lb. How many students are on the team? **21 students**
 b. The median weight is 125 lb. Only one student weighs 125 lb. How many students weigh more than 125 lb?
 10 students

3 Practice/Assess

EXERCISES *On Your Own*

REASONING Exercise 7b You may wish to have volunteers collect data about which states require a deposit for aluminum cans.

OPEN-ENDED Exercise 14 Some students may not have access to ten people who are readers and may need to make up data.

CONNECTION TO SCIENCE Exercise 15a Students may want to discuss the life expectancy of more familiar animals such as cats and dogs.

Wrap Up

IDENTIFYING THE BIG IDEA Have students suggest examples of situations where they would use *mean*, *median*, or *mode*.

LESSON QUIZ

1. Surveyors asked some students how many times per week they ate fruit. The students answered:

   12 9 10 8 8 9 10 6 7 10 6 1

   a. What is the sum of the responses? 96

   b. Find the mean. 8

   c. Find the median. 8.5

   d. Find the mode. 10

CHECKPOINT 1

Checkpoint 1 *Lessons 1-1 through 1-4*

1. **Circle A, B, C, or D.** Which rows of the spreadsheet below most likely generated the double bar graph below?

Normal Maximum/Minimum Temperatures (°F) in January

	A	B	C
1	State	Max	Min
2	CO	43	16
3	CA	55	42
4	AK	50	30
5	NY	37	26

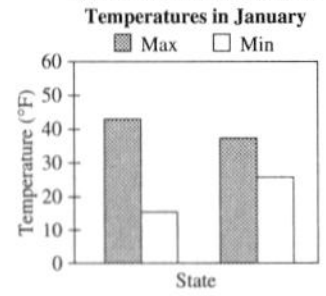

A. rows 4 and 5
(B.) rows 2 and 5 (circled)
C. rows 3 and 4
D. rows 2 and 4

2. a. Make a frequency table and a histogram of the data below.

   10 7 7 9 10 8 11 12 10 8 10

   b. Find the mean, median, and mode.

   9.27; 10; 10

Number	Tally	Frequency
7	ǀǀ	2
8	ǀǀ	2
9	ǀ	1
10	ǀǀǀǀ	4
11	ǀ	1
12	ǀ	1

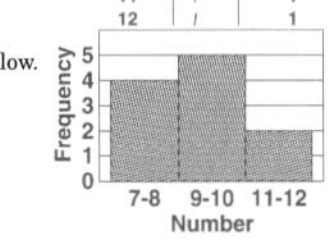

page 21 Checkpoint 1

1.

Number	Frequency
1	2
2	2
3	2
4	2
5	3
6	1
7	2
8	2
9	1

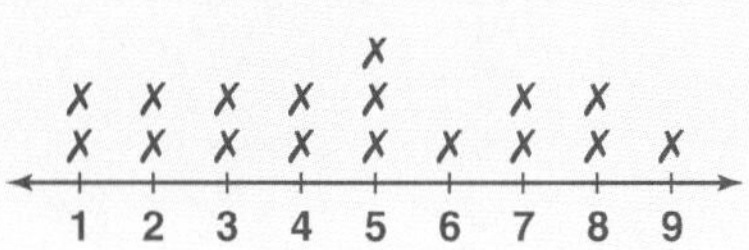

4.

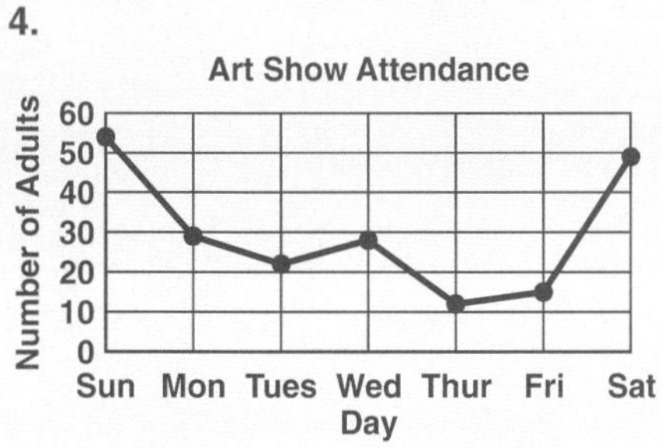

10. *Education* A Jonesburg Middle School seventh-grade social studies class took a test recently. The class scores are shown in the tally at the right.
    a. Find the mean, median, and mode of the data.
    b. What is the outlier in this set of data? 60
    c. Does the outlier raise or lower the mean? lower
    d. Which measure—the mean, the median, or the mode—most accurately reflects how the class did as a whole? Justify your answer.

Grade	Tally	Grade	Tally
60	ǀ	85	𝍸 ǀǀǀǀ
78	ǀǀǀ	87	ǀǀ
80	𝍸 ǀǀǀ	91	ǀ
81	ǀǀ	94	ǀ

a. 82.2; 81; 85

d. Answers may vary. Sample: Median; the mean is affected by outliers, and the mode represents only a few students.

Birthday Bash

The Rose Hill Retirement Home celebrated seven birthdays last Sunday. Mrs. Ullsca turned 102, while the "baby" of the group, Mrs. Hansen, turned a mere 78. Family members and friends gathered for the party. Other birthdays celebrated were Mr. Harlem, 79; Mr. Joyla, 84; Mr. Ajayi, 85; Miss Rugas, 81; and Mrs. Greene, 79.

11. a. Find the mean, median, and mode of the data found in the article above. Round the mean to the nearest whole number.
    b. Is there an outlier? If there is, identify it. a. 84; 81; 79
    c. Does the mean, the median, or the mode most accurately reflect the age of those celebrating a birthday? Explain.

    11b. Yes; 102; the outlier increases the mean.

c. Answers may vary. Sample: Median; all the ages other than the outlier are close together.

12. *Writing* Ten people were surveyed about the number of times a person's teeth should be brushed each day. Their responses are shown in the table at the right. Explain why the mean is not a good representation of this data. See below right.

How Many Times a Day Should You Brush Your Teeth?

Response	Frequency
3 times	9
10 times	1

12. The outlier represents only one person but significantly increases the mean.

13. **Choose A, B, C, or D.** Dominic's test grades in his Spanish class are 89, 94, 82, 84, 98. What score must Dominic make on his next exam to average 90 points? C

    A. 100 B. 97 C. 93 D. 90

14. *Open-ended* Find the number of books ten people read last summer. Find the mean, median, and mode of the data.

    Check students' work.

2. Does mean, mode, or median best describe each of the following situations? Explain.
   a. the number of CDs each of your classmates owns Mean or median; use the median when there are outliers that may distort the data.
   b. the most popular brand of athletic shoes mode
   c. a student's test average mean

15. a. *Science* Calculate the mean life expectancy for the animals in the table. 12.7 years
   b. What is the median of the data? What is the mode? 12 years; 12 and 15 years
   c. *Reasoning* Does the mean, median, or mode describe the data the best? Explain. Answers may vary. Sample: Mean; the mean is the only measure that takes all the data into account.

Average Life Expectancy of Some Hoofed Animals

Animal	Years	Animal	Years
Bison	15	Goat	8
Cow	15	Horse	20
Deer	8	Moose	12
Donkey	12	Pig	10
Elk	15	Sheep	12

Mixed Review

Would you use a double bar graph or a double line graph to display each of the following. Why? *(Lesson 1-3)*

17. Double bar graph; the graph compares two sets of quantities at one time.

16. the change in taxes for the average household for two cities over the last ten years

17. the cost of seven different items at two different grocery stores

16. Double line graph; the graph shows two quantities that change over time.

Estimate. *(Previous Course)*

18. 197×3 600
19. 42×19 800
20. $359 \div 60$ 6
21. $88 - 32$ 60
22. $128 + 98$ 230
23. *Choose a Strategy* Find two numbers that have a sum of 30 and a product of 81. 27 and 3

✓ CHECKPOINT 1

Lessons 1-1 through 1-4

1. Make a frequency table and a line plot of the data below.
   5 7 8 3 5 4 6 7 8 9 1 2 5 4 2 1 3
   See margin p. 20.

Find the mean, median, and mode of the data below.

2. *Sports* golf scores for 18-hole games
   120 112 130 128 124
   117 118 117 121 113
   120; 119; 117

3. *Cars* average miles per gallon
   25 28 23 27 21 22 25
   24 25 27 28 29 22 24
   25; 25; 25

4. Graph the data below. Explain why you chose the graph you drew. See margin p. 20 for graph; use a line graph to show change over time.

Art Show Attendance

Day	Sun.	Mon.	Tues.	Wed.	Thur.	Fri.	Sat.
Number of Adults	54	29	22	28	12	15	49

PRACTICE

Practice 1-4 Mean, Median, and Mode

The sum of the heights of all the students in Mrs. Maloney's class is 1,472 in.

1. The mean height is 5 ft 4 in. How many students are in the class? (1 ft = 12 in.) 23 students
2. The median height is 5 ft 2 in. How many students in Mrs. Maloney's class are 5 ft 2 in. or taller? at least 12 students
   How many are shorter? up to 11 students

The number of pages read (to the nearest multiple of 50) by the students in Mr. Sullivan's class last week are shown in the tally table at the right.

Pages	Tally
50	I
100	
150	II
200	~~IIII~~ I
250	I
300	~~IIII~~
350	III
400	IIII
450	I
500	I

3. Find the mean, the median, and the mode of the data.
   mean: 287.5, median: 300, mode: 200
4. What is the outlier in this set of data? 50
5. Does the outlier raise or lower the mean? lower
6. Would you use the mean, median, or mode to most accurately reflect the typical number of pages read by a student? Explain. The median, because there is an outlier.

Kenny hopes to have a 9-point average on his math quizzes. His quiz scores are 7, 6, 10, 8, and 9. Each quiz is worth 12 points.

7. What is Kenny's average quiz score? 8 points
8. There are two more quizzes. How many more points does Kenny need to have a 9-point quiz average? 23 points
9. Write the numbers from 1 to 6 on slips of paper. Place the numbers in a paper bag or an envelope. Draw out a number 20 times, each time replacing the number before drawing again. Complete the tally table. Find the mean, median, and mode.
   Answers will vary.

Number	Tally
1	
2	
3	
4	
5	
6	

In copymaster and workbook formats

RETEACHING

Reteaching 1-4 Mean, Median, and Mode

Alexis, Rita, Ming, Mario, and Jewel are in the Library Club. During the summer they read the following numbers of books.
11, 6, 11, 8, 3

To find the **mean,** or average, number of books read by the Library Club members:
① Find the sum of the numbers of books read. $11 + 6 + 11 + 8 + 3 = 39$
② Divide the sum by the number of readers, 5. $39 \div 5 = 7.8$

The mean is 7.8 books.

To find the **median,** or middle value, of the data set:
① Arrange the numbers in order. 3, 6, **8**, 11, 11
② Find the middle number. ↑ 8 is the middle number.

The median is 8 books.

The **mode** is the number that occurs most often. In this data set, 11 occurs twice. The mode is 11. 3, 6, 8, **11**, **11**

Use the table to complete Exercises 1–4.

Game Points Scored by Jerry		
10	11	15
18	9	16
10	12	10

1. Jerry plays basketball. What number would you divide by to find the mean number of points Jerry scored per game? 9
2. What is the mean number of points Jerry scored? 12.3 points
3. Write the data in order. Then find the median number of points Jerry scored.
   9, 10, 10, 10, 11, 12, 15, 16, 18; 11 points
4. What is the mode of the data? 10 points
5. Here are the miniature golf scores for 7 friends.
   23, 30, 39, 32, 35, 14, 23
   Find the mean, median, and mode of the data.
   mean 28 median 30 mode 23
6. The scores for a geography quiz are listed below. Find the mean, median, and mode of the scores.
   7 8 6 9 9 8 10 6 9 8 9 7
   mean 8 median 8 mode 9

Reteaching

ENRICHMENT

Minds on Math Transparency

1-4

Of 100 students asked if they like rock-and-roll or country music, 7 said they like neither, 90 said they like rock-and-roll music, and 57 said they like country music. How many students like both?

54 students

See *Solution Key* for worked-out answers.

1-5 Teaching Notes

1 Focus

CONNECTING TO PRIOR KNOWLEDGE Ask students to name the characteristics of a useful graph. **informative labels, easy to read, visually clear** Tell students another method of displaying data is a stem-and-leaf plot. Ask students to imagine how the plot appears based on its name.

2 Teach

THINK AND DISCUSS

VISUAL LEARNING Drawing a sketch similar to this one may help students with a visual learning style remember the name of the stem and leaf plot.

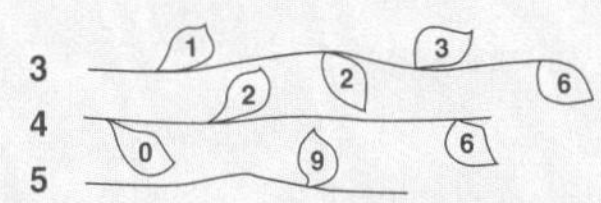

ERROR ALERT! Example 1 The organization of the stem-and-leaf plot may confuse students if they expect the smallest number at the bottom of the stem column instead of at the top. **Remediation:** Point out that a stem-and-leaf plot starts where reading a page of text starts: at the top left corner. Mention also that the smallest stems of a tree are at the outer edges, just as the smallest numbers of a stem-and-leaf plot are at the top of the stem column.

Lesson Planning Options

Prerequisite Skills

- subtracting whole numbers and decimals (precourse)
- finding mean, median, and mode (1-4)

Vocabulary/Symbols

stem-and-leaf plot, range

Materials/Manipulatives

- metric unit ruler

Resources

Student Edition

Skills Handbook, p. 532
Extra Practice, p. 514
Glossary/Study Guide

Teaching Resources

Chapter Support File, Ch. 1
- Lesson Planner 1-5
- Practice 1-5, Reteaching 1-5
- Alternative Activity 1-5
- Answer Masters 1-5

Glossary, Spanish Resources

Transparencies
40–42, Minds on Math 1-5

Warm Up

Find the average of the following set of numbers to the nearest whole number: 54, 38, 49, and 44. **46**

1-5 Stem-and-Leaf Plots

What You'll Learn

1. To organize and display data using stem-and-leaf plots
2. To find range using stem-and-leaf plots

...And Why

Stem-and-leaf plots give you a visual picture of data while displaying the data values.

Here's How

Look for questions that
- build understanding
- ✔ check understanding

THINK AND DISCUSS

1 Displaying Data Using Stem-and-Leaf Plots

A **stem-and-leaf plot** is a display that organizes your data by showing each item in order. The leaf is the last digit to the right. The stem is the remaining digit or digits.

10.6 (leaf → 6; stem → 10.)　　27 (leaf → 7; stem → 2)

EXAMPLE 1 *Real-World Problem Solving*

Nutrition Use the table at the left below. Draw a stem-and-leaf plot of the data.

Choose the stems. For this data, the stems are made using the values in the ones place. Draw a line to the right of the stems.

```
        0 |
stems → 1 |
        2 |
```

For this data, the leaves are the values in the tenths place.

```
0 | 7 7 9
1 | 1 6 4 5   ← leaves
2 | 6 1 6
```

Arrange the leaves from least to greatest. Include a key to explain what your stems and leaves represent.

```
0 | 7 7 9
1 | 1 4 5 6
2 | 1 6 6
   0 | 7 means 0.7  ← key
```

Iron in Three Ounces of High-Protein Foods

Food	Iron (in milligrams)
Clams	2.6
Crab meat	1.1
Salmon	0.7
Tuna	1.6
Ground beef	2.1
Steak	2.6
Lamb	1.4
Ham	0.7
Chicken	0.9
Turkey	1.5

Source: *Home and Garden Bulletin, No. 72*

1. ✔ *Try It Out* Make a stem-and-leaf plot of the data below. See margin p. 24.

Wind Speeds Recorded During a Storm
(in miles per hour)

9 14 30 16 18 25 29 25 38 34 33

Now you may assign Exercises 1–8.

ADDITIONAL EXAMPLES

FOR EXAMPLE 1

Use the data to draw a stem-and-leaf plot.

High Temperatures for Central City (°F) October 13–26

Week 1	81	73	67	81	77	79	73
Week 2	80	74	61	66	70	67	73

6 | 1 6 7 7
7 | 0 3 3 3 4 7 9
8 | 0 1 1

8 | 0 means 80

FOR EXAMPLE 2

Find the range of the data in the stem-and-leaf plot. 29

1 | 6
2 | 4 8
3 | 2 5 5 9
4 | 3 5

1 | 6 means 16

Work Together

Ask students the following questions to get them started.

- *What key will you use for your stem-and-leaf plot?* **Answers may vary. Sample: 1 | 5 means 15.**
- *How will your stem-and-leaf plot help you quickly find the median, mode, and range?* **Since you ordered the data from least to greatest, look for the middle value to find the median, look for the**

2 *Finding Range*

The **range** of a set of data is the difference between the greatest and least data items.

8. Sample: How many western states have more counties than Idaho?

■ EXAMPLE 2

Find the range of the data in the stem-and-leaf plot.

12 | 4 4 8 ←least data item
13 | 3 7 8 8
14 |
15 | 2 7 9 ←greatest data item

12 | 4 means 12.4

$15.9 - 12.4 = 3.5$

The range of the data is 3.5.

2. ✔ *Try It Out* What is the range of the data in Example 1? 1.9

You can also find the range of data in a list.

3. ✔ *Try It Out* What is the range of the data given below?
Alaska mountain heights (ft): 16,390 14,573 20,320 16,550 15,885 14,163 14,831 16,237 17,400 16,286
6,157 ft

Work Together — *Using Stem-and-Leaf Plots*

Social Studies Work with a partner.

4. Make a stem-and-leaf plot.
See margin p. 24.
5. Find the mean, median, and mode of the data. Round the mean to the nearest whole number.
37; 36; no mode
6. Does the mean, the median, or the mode best describe the data?
Answers may vary. Sample: mean
7. What is the range of the data? 48
8. *Open-Ended* Write a question that you could answer using your stem-and-leaf plot.
See above for sample.

Now you may assign Exercises 9–15.

Counties in Western States

State	Number of Counties
Arizona	15
California	58
Colorado	63
Idaho	44
Montana	56
Nevada	16
New Mexico	33
Oregon	36
Utah	29
Washington	39
Wyoming	23

Source: *The World Almanac*

Technology Options

Prentice Hall Technology

Software for Learners

- Math Blaster® Mystery*
- Interactive Student Tutorial, Chapter 1*

Teaching Resource Software

- Computer Item Generator 1-5
- Resource Pro™ Chapter 1*

Internet • For related mathematics activities, visit the Prentice Hall site at www.phschool.com/math

**Available on CD-ROM only*

Assignment Options for Exercises On Your Own

To provide flexible scheduling, this lesson can be subdivided into parts.

1 **Core** 1–7
Extension 8

2 **Core** 9–13, 15
Extension 14

Use Mixed Review to maintain skills.

repeated values to find the mode, and subtract the first number from the last number to find the range.

After completing the activity, have each pair of students join another pair to compare their stem-and-leaf plots and their answers to Questions 5–7. Have them answer each other's questions for Question 8.

ASSESSMENT Ask students to write a description of a stem-and-leaf plot to instruct someone how to make and use such a plot. Encourage students to write their descriptions for a friend in another class. Have volunteers share their work with the class.

3 Practice/Assess

EXERCISES *On Your Own*

Exercises 1 and 4 Make sure students understand that the key to these stem-and-leaf plots should include a decimal point.

WRAP UP

IDENTIFYING THE BIG IDEA Ask students to explain how to organize and display data in a stem-and-leaf plot.

pages 22–23 Think and Discuss

1.

0	9
1	4 6 8
2	5 5 9
3	0 3 4 8

2 | 5 means 25

page 23 Work Together

4.

1	5 6
2	3 9
3	3 6 9
4	4
5	6 8
6	3

6 | 3 means 63

pages 24–25 On Your Own

4.

9	6 7 7
10	2
11	5 5 5 6
12	3
13	7
14	1 4

14 | 1 means 14.1

15a.

3	5 8
4	2 2 7
5	0 5 7
6	
7	
8	2 8

8 | 2 means 82

EXERCISES *On Your Own*

Create a stem-and-leaf plot for each set of data. 1–3. See below.

1. sales of twelve companies (millions of dollars)
   1.3 1.4 2.3 1.4 2.4 2.5
   3.9 1.4 1.3 2.5 3.6 1.4
2. heights of giant sunflowers (in inches)
   98 99 94 87 83 74
   69 88 78 99 100 87 77
3. high temperatures (°F) in the desert
   99 113 112 98 100 103 101
   111 104 108 109 112 113 118
4. heights of ceilings in older homes (in feet)
   9.7 12.3 10.2 11.5 14.1 9.6
   13.7 14.4 11.5 9.7 11.6 11.5
   See margin.

Use the stem-and-leaf plot at the right for Exercises 5–8.

4	3 6 7
5	1 2
6	1 7
7	1 8
8	2 6 8

8 | 2 means 82

5. How many data items are there? 12
6. What is the least value given? The greatest value given? 43; 88
7. How many values are greater than 65? 6
8. **Choose A, B, C, or D.** Which of the following is most likely the source of the data in the stem-and-leaf plot? B
   - A. test scores for a class
   - B. average monthly temperatures in Dallas (in °F)
   - C. depth of 12 swimming pools (in feet)
   - D. numbers of books in New York City libraries

1.

1	3 3 4 4 4 4
2	3 4 5 5
3	6 9

2 | 3 means 2.3

3.

9	8 9
10	0 1 3 4 8 9
11	1 2 2 3 3 8

11 | 1 means 111

The stem-and-leaf plot at the right shows kilometers walked during a benefit walk. Use it for Exercises 9–13.

16	1 1 2 3 5 5
17	0 2 2
18	4 5 8 9
19	3 6 7 9 9 9

19 | 3 means 19.3

9. What place values are the leaves? tenths
10. How many data items are there? 19
11. How many people walked more than 19 km? 6
12. Find the range. 3.8
13. *Writing* How would you find the median? See below.
14. *Data Collection* Measure the width of the hands of at least ten people. Measure using metric units. Make a stem-and-leaf plot of the data you collect. Check students' work.

2.

6	9
7	4 7 8
8	3 7 7 8
9	4 8 9 9
10	0

9 | 4 means 94

13. Count up from 16 | 1 or down from 19 | 9. The median, 18.4, is the tenth leaf.

Math at Work

If you have block scheduling or extended class periods, consider having each member of the class bring in a poll from a newspaper or magazine. Organize students in small groups. Have each group choose one poll from among its members. Then the group determines the type of graph that will best display the data from the poll. The group makes a display that shows both the data from the poll and the graph of the data to present to the class.

LESSON QUIZ

1. Create a stem-and-leaf plot for the following set of data.
   46 42 40 68 53 64 62 59 63

4 | 0 2 6
5 | 3 9
6 | 2 3 4 8   4 | 0 means 40

2. Find the range of the same data. 28

15. *Sports* The table at the right shows the career wins for ten women who had won the most golf tournaments during their careers as of 1996.
    a. Make a stem-and-leaf plot of the data. See margin p. 24.
    b. Find the range of the data. 53

Career Wins for Top Women Golfers

Name	Wins	Name	Wins
Kathy Whitworth	88	Nancy Lopez	47
Mickey Wright	82	JoAnne Carner	42
Patty Berg	57	Sandra Haynie	42
Betsy Rawls	55	Carol Mann	38
Louise Suggs	50	Patty Sheehan	35

Source: *Sports Illustrated Sports Almanac*

Mixed Review

Estimate. *(Previous Course)*

16. 122 + 237 — 360
17. 393 − 27 — 360
18. 48 × 47 — 2,500
19. 9 × 119 — 1,200
20. 5,250 − 4,798 — 20. Answers may vary. Sample: 450

Compare. Use <, >, or =. *(Previous Course)*

21. 12 × 3 ■ 45 − 9 =
22. 24 ÷ 2 ■ 3 × 6 <
23. 9 × 6 ■ 8 × 7 <
24. 81 ÷ 3 ■ 9 × 4 <

25. *Choose a Strategy* A student is standing in the middle of a line of students. There are 23 students ahead of him. How many students are in the line? 47

Math at Work

POLLSTER

Pollsters interview people to find out their opinions and their preferences. Pollsters use math to analyze data, finding the mean, median, mode, and range to get an overall look at the data they collect. They often graph data to display their findings.

Internet Connection: Visit this Gallup Web site for more information: www.gallup.com

PRACTICE

Practice 1-5 Stem-and-Leaf Plots

The stem-and-leaf plot at the right shows the number of baskets scored by one of ten intramural teams last season. Use the stem-and-leaf plot for Exercises 1–5.

5 | 2 6 9
6 | 0 4 6
7 | 1 5
8 | 4 8

8 | 4 means 84

1. How many data items are there? 10
2. What is the least measurement given? 52
3. What is the greatest measurement given? 88
4. In how many games did the team score less than 70 baskets? 6 games
5. Find the mean, median, mode, and range. mean: 67.5 median: 65, mode: none, range: 36

The stem-and-leaf plot at the right shows the number of pages read for book reports by a 7th grade literature class. Use the stem-and-leaf plot for Exercises 6–9.

19 | 0 5 5
20 | 0 5 9 9
21 | 6
22 | 5 6 8
23 | 2 5 8 8 8
24 | 0 0 4 6
25 | 0 5 5 7 9

25 | 0 means 250

6. What numbers make up the stems? 19, 20, 21, 22, 23, 24, 25
7. What numbers make up the leaves for the first stem? 0, 5, 5
8. How many students read at least 200 pages? 22 students
9. Find the mean, median, mode, and range. mean: 229 median: 235, mode: 238, range: 69
10. Use the data below to create a stem-and-leaf plot. Find the mean, median, mode, and range of the data.

science test scores: 83 73 78 60 85
92 95 85 99 68

6 | 0 8
7 | 3 8
8 | 3 5 5
9 | 2 5 9

9 | 2 means 92

mean: 81.8, median: 84, mode: 85, range: 39

Practice

In copymaster and workbook formats

RETEACHING

Reteaching 1-5 Stem-and-Leaf Plots

Make a **stem-and-leaf plot** of the summer earnings data.

① Make a column of the tens digits of the data in order from least to greatest. These are the stems.
② Record the ones digits for each tens digit in order from least to greatest. These are the leaves.
③ Make a *key* to explain what the stems and leaves represent.

Summer Earnings					
\$35	\$35	\$38	\$15	\$52	\$40
\$20	\$23	\$56	\$12	\$14	\$58

① stems: 1, 2, 3, 4, 5

② leaves:
1 | 2 4 5
2 | 0 3
3 | 5 5 8
4 | 0
5 | 2 6 8

1 | 2 means 12

The **range** of a set of data is the difference between the greatest value (58) and the least value (12).

The range of the summer earnings is 58 − 12 = 46, or \$46.

1. Complete the stem-and-leaf plot of this set of data.
   24 36 64 42 59
   61 16 63 54 39
   36 45 15 27 51

1 | 5 6
2 | 4 7
3 | 6 6 9
4 | 2 5
5 | 1 4 9
6 | 1 3 4

1 | 5 means 15

2. Use the stem-and-leaf plot you made to find the greatest value, least value, and range of the data. 64; 15; 49

3. Brandy recorded these high temperatures for two weeks in July. Make a stem-and-leaf plot of her data. Find the range.
   92 86 91 90 85
   82 84 78 79 83
   84 89 86 87

7 | 8 9
8 | 2 3 4 4 5 6 6 7 9
9 | 0 1 2

7 | 8 means 78

The range is 14.

4. Mr. Wang recorded these test scores. Make a stem-and-leaf plot of the data. Find the range.
   66 83 58 65 66
   66 82 55 57 71
   40 43 41 56 71
   74 81 85 63 62

4 | 0 1 3
5 | 5 6 7 8
6 | 2 3 5 6 6 6
7 | 1 1 4
8 | 1 2 3 5

8 | 1 means 81

The range is 45.

ENRICHMENT

Minds on Math Transparency

1-5

Nine copies of a newsletter cost less than \$10. Ten copies of the same newsletter at the same price cost more than \$11. What is the cost of one newsletter?

S1.11

See *Solution Key* for worked-out answers.

Extra Practice, Lesson 1-5, page 514

MATH TOOLBOX

This toolbox provides students with an opportunity to explore quartiles using a box-and-whisker plot. Students may want to use box-and-whisker plots to display the results of their Chapter Project surveys.

REASONING Exercise 1 Make sure students understand the meaning of the word *quartile.* Have students share their answers to the question with the class. To expand the discussion, ask: *What would be different about the set of data if the middle quartile was in the middle of the box-and-whisker plot?* **Answers may vary. Sample: There would be an odd number of data.**

AEP You may wish to relate *quartile* to *quarter.*

ERROR ALERT! Students may have trouble finding the quartile of a set of data that contains an even number of items. **Remediation:** Refer back to Lesson 1-4 where students found the median of an even set of data. Remind them to find the mean of the two middle items. It may help some students to write an evenly spaced, ordered list on a piece of paper. Students can fold the paper in half to find the middle quartile, and then in half again to divide the data into four sections.

Resources

Teaching Resources

Teaching Aids Master 26

Transparencies

11

page 26 Math Toolbox

2. 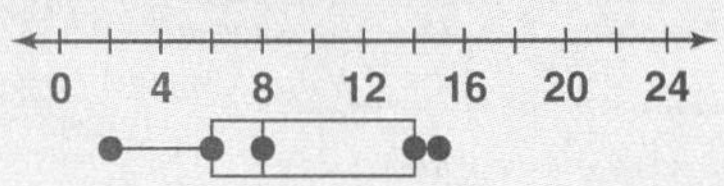

3. 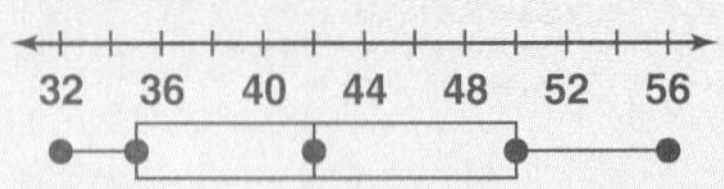

4. 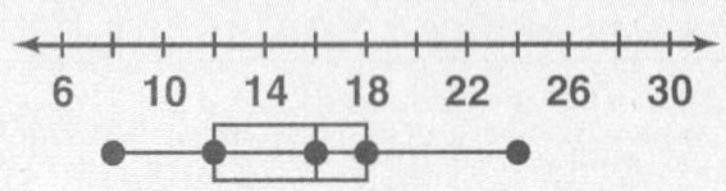

5. 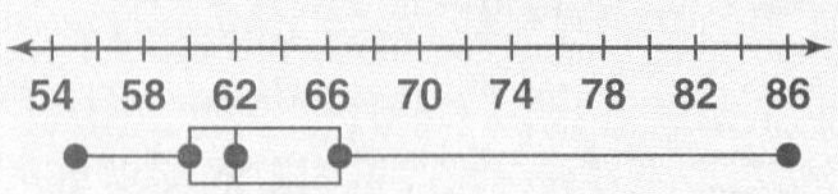

pages 27–28 Think and Discuss

1. **Five people, Keesha, Frieda, Pascal, Jered, and Mika, each study one foreign language, French, German, Italian, Spanish, or Mandarin Chinese. No two people study the same language. Keesha, Frieda, and Jered each study either German or Spanish or Italian. Keesha does not study Italian and German. Freida and Pascal do not study Mandarin Chinese. Either Frieda or Pascal studies French. A woman studies Italian.**
2. **What language does each person, other than Mr. Sanchez, study?**

MATH TOOLBOX EXPLORATION

Box-and-Whisker Plots

After Lesson 1-5

A box-and-whisker plot is another way to display data. A **box-and-whisker plot** shows you how the data are distributed. The diagram at the right identifies the important features of a box-and-whisker plot.

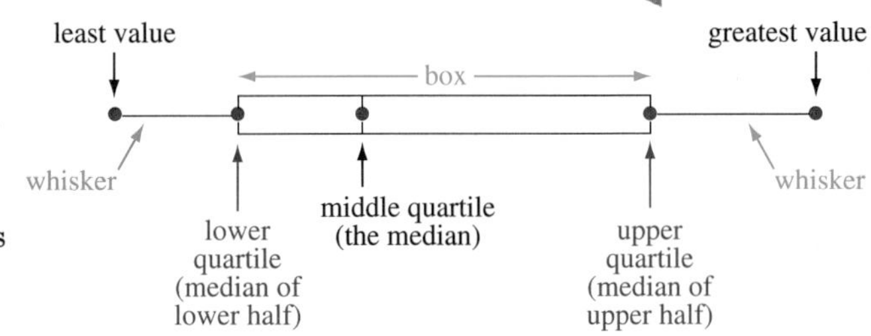

■ EXAMPLE

The director of a computer center recorded the number of users each hour for one day. The results were 13, 14, 22, 25, 30, 29, 27, 18, 19, 14, 18, 19. Draw a box-and-whisker plot of the data.

least value → 13 14 14 18 18 19 19 22 25 27 29 30 ← greatest value — **List the data in order.**

The lower quartile is 16. The middle quartile is 19. The upper quartile is 26. — **Find the quartiles.**

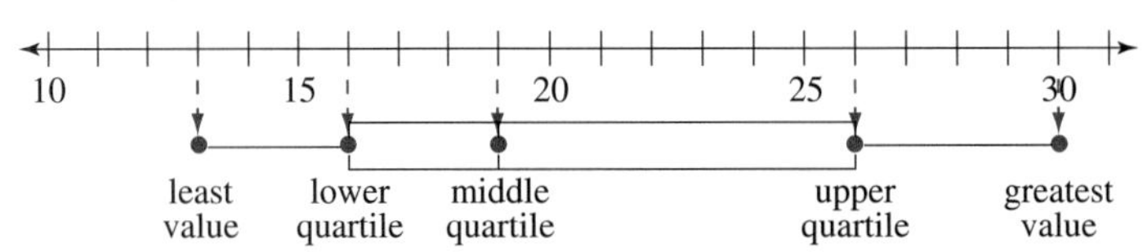

Use a number line to draw the box-and-whisker plot.

1. *Reasoning* In the Example, why is the middle quartile not in the middle of the box? **The data in the second quartile are closer together than in the third.**

Create a box-and-whisker plot for each data set. **2–5. See margin.**

2. 2 3 5 7 7 8 8 10 14 14 15 15
3. 32 34 34 36 40 42 42 42 46 54 54 56
4. 8 11 11 13 14 14 16 16 16 17 19 22 24
5. 62 55 60 86 62 65 68 70 55 60 65 62 58 60 62 68 65

6. a. In Exercise 5, what is the outlier? **86**
   b. *Reasoning* How does the outlier affect the way the box-and-whisker plot looks? **An outlier makes a very long whisker.**

1-6 Teaching Notes

1 Focus

CONNECTING TO PRIOR KNOWLEDGE Ask students to describe what logic is. Then challenge students to name logic games or puzzles they have played, such as Twenty Questions.

2 Teach

THINK AND DISCUSS

ERROR ALERT! and AUDITORY LEARNING Students may at first be overwhelmed by a logic problem like the one in the example and not know where to start to solve it.
Remediation: Break the problem into parts. Read one bit of information and talk about what it means to the problem. Use the information to begin eliminating possibilities.

Point out that a logic table helps keep track of information so it is easier to solve a problem. Emphasize that if students are ever unsure how to find an answer, they should read the problem carefully, break the problem into parts, and try fitting information into a table.

AEP Following logic problems may be especially difficult for students who already have difficulty with the language. Encourage these students to work with another student to Draw a Diagram or Make a Model or Table.

PROBLEM SOLVING STRATEGY

1-6 Use Logical Reasoning

READ PLAN SOLVE LOOK BACK

Problem Solving Strategies

- Draw a Diagram
- Guess and Test
- Look for a Pattern
- Make a Model
- Make a Table
- Simulate a Problem
- Solve a Simpler Problem
- Too Much or Too Little Information
- ✔ Use Logical Reasoning
- Use Multiple Strategies
- Work Backward
- Write an Equation

THINK AND DISCUSS

Have you ever solved a logic puzzle? They can be fun — if you know a good strategy!

Sample Problem

Keesha, Frieda, Pascal, Jered, and Mika are each studying different foreign languages. Mika gave Mr. Sanchez, his neighbor, the following information.

- The woman studying Italian is not Keesha. Also, Keesha is not studying German.
- Frieda and Pascal do not study Mandarin Chinese, but one of them does study French.
- Keesha, Frieda, and Jered drive to their classes together. One of them studies German, one studies Spanish, and one studies Italian.

Mr. Sanchez thought for a while, used paper and pencil to organize the information, and told Mika exactly what language each person was studying. Who is studying which language?

READ
Read for understanding. Summarize the problem.

Think about what you are being asked.

1. What information are you given? **1–2. See margin p. 26.**
2. What information do you need to find?

PLAN
Decide on a strategy.

Logical reasoning can help you eliminate impossibilities, organize alternatives, and find a solution. Consider the first clue.

3. a. Is Keesha studying Italian? German? **no; no**
   b. Is she studying French? What information gives you the answer? **No; Keesha must study German, Italian, or Spanish.**
   c. What language is Keesha studying? Which clues did you use? **See above.**

3c. Spanish; Keesha is studying either German, Italian, or Spanish, but she cannot be studying German or Italian.

Lesson Planning Options

Prerequisite Skills

- grouping numbers and objects by their characteristics (precourse)
- making tables (precourse)

Resources

Student Edition

Skills Handbook, p. 531
Extra Practice, p. 514
Glossary/Study Guide

Teaching Resources

Chapter Support File, Ch. 1
- Lesson Planner 1-6
- Practice 1-6, Reteaching 1-6
- Answer Masters 1-6

Glossary, Spanish Resources

Transparencies
5, 79, Minds on Math 1-6

Warm Up

Find the two pairs of numbers that have a greatest common factor (GCF) of 7. **Answers may vary. Sample: 21 and 28; 14 and 21**

DIVERSITY Some students perform better on logic problems if they work with a partner and approach the problems cooperatively rather than competitively. The goal of solving the problem is not to *win* by saying the answer first. The goal is to develop a plan that can be used to solve other problems.

■ ADDITIONAL PROBLEM

A farmer has a fox, a chicken, and a bag of corn. He must carry all three across a river in a boat that will hold only himself and one other item. He cannot leave the chicken alone with either the fox or the corn. How will the farmer take all three across the river? **Take the chicken across first, either the fox or the corn second, bring the chicken back, leave the chicken and take either the fox or corn, and then come back to get the chicken.**

ASSESSMENT Think of a three-digit number. Let students, one at a time, guess what your number is. Reply to each student with *higher*, *lower*, or got it until one student finds the correct number. Repeat several times using a new number each time.

3 Practice/Assess

EXERCISES *On Your Own*

Exercises 1 and 2 Suggest that students start these exercises by drawing a diagram.

Technology Options

Prentice Hall Technology

Software for Learners

- Math Blaster® Mystery*
- Interactive Student Tutorial, Chapter 1*

Teaching Resource Software

- Computer Item Generator 1-6
- Resource Pro™ Chapter 1*

Internet • For related mathematics activities, visit the Prentice Hall site at www.phschool.com/math

**Available on CD-ROM only*

Assignment Options for Exercises On Your Own

Core 1, 2, 4–6
Extension 3

Use Mixed Review to maintain skills.

SOLVE
Try the strategy.

A table can help you organize your thoughts. Consider each piece of information separately. Write an X for choices you eliminate, and a dot when you know what language a person is studying.

	French	German	Italian	Mandarin Chinese	Spanish
Keesha	X	X	X	X	●
Frieda	■ ×	■ ×	■ ●	■ ×	X
Mika	■ ×	■ ×	■ ×	■ ●	X
Pascal	■ ●	■ ×	■ ×	■ ×	X
Jered	■ ×	■ ●	■ ×	■ ×	X

4. In the row for Keesha, there is an X in every box but one. Why? **4–5. See left.**
5. In the column for Spanish, there is an X in every box but one. Why?
6. Copy and complete the table. Find the language each person is taking. **See table above.**

4. Keesha must be studying one language, but she cannot be studying German, Italian, French, or Mandarin Chinese because of the information in the clues.

5. If Keesha is studying Spanish, none of the other four people is studying Spanish.

LOOK BACK
Think about how you solved the problem.

7. How did the table help you solve this problem? **When one question is answered, you can cross out the rest of the row and the rest of the column.**

Now you may assign Exercises 1–6.

EXERCISES *On Your Own*

Use logical reasoning to solve.

1. *Sports* Three lockers contain the school's basketballs, footballs, and soccer balls. Each locker contains only one type of ball, but the labels on them are incorrect. The locker marked "footballs" has basketballs. Which balls are in the locker labeled "basketballs," and which are in the locker labeled "soccer balls"? **See below.**

2. Skye's class sold calendars to raise money for a field trip. The top four sellers were Skye, Amalie, Mandela, and Scott. Skye sold more calendars than Amalie, but fewer than Mandela. Scott also sold more than Amalie, but fewer than Skye. Who sold the most calendars in the class? **Mandela**

1. The locker marked "basketballs" has soccer balls. The locker marked "soccer balls" has footballs.

WRAP UP

IDENTIFYING THE BIG IDEA Ask students to describe how to solve problems using logical reasoning.

PROJECT LINK Review the definition of mean, or average, with students.

LESSON QUIZ

Use logical reasoning to solve.

1. Val has the same number of sisters and brothers. Her brother has twice as many sisters as he has brothers. How many children are in Val's family? 7
2. An even two-digit number is a multiple of 7 and has digits whose sum is 10. What is the number? 28

Use any strategy to solve each problem. Show your work.

3. Use a diagram like the one at the right and the information below to determine how many students had no pets. 7 students
   - Of 50 students surveyed, 30 had cats and 25 had dogs.
   - Sixteen students had both cats and dogs, but no gerbils.
   - Five reported that they had only gerbils. Four noted they had both dogs and gerbils. Two had both cats and gerbils.
   - Only one student had all three pets mentioned.

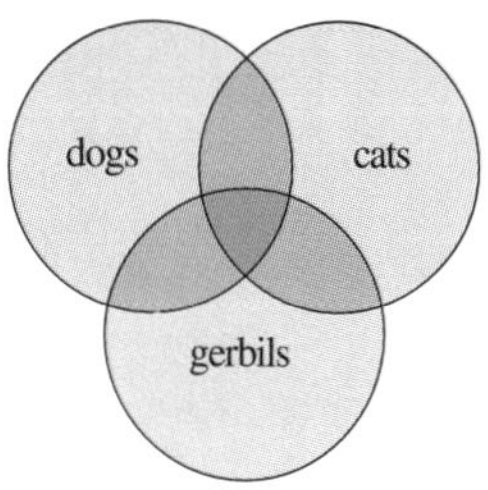

4. Mato has 10 loose identical red socks and 10 loose identical blue socks in his sock drawer. What is the least number of socks he would have to choose to be sure to find a matched pair? 3 socks
5. The African pavilion at the zoo has ostriches and zebras. The number of legs is 14 more than twice the number of heads. Find the number of zebras. 7 zebras
6. Popsville is 20 mi from Topsville. Mopsville is 5 mi from Popsville along the same road. How far could Mopsville be from Topsville? 15 mi or 25 mi

Mixed Review

Use the stem-and-leaf plot at the right for Exercises 7–9. *(Lesson 1-5)*

7. What number has stem 1 and leaf 0? 10
8. Find the mean, median, and mode. 5; 10.5; 10
9. Which measure in Exercise 8 could Trinh use to convince her parents that she has plenty of time left for homework? mode

Miles Trinh Biked per Day

Stem	Leaves
0	5 5 7 8 8 9 9
1	0 0 0 1 2 7 8
2	2 5 8 8 9 9

2 | 5 means 25

Find the value of each expression. *(Previous Course)*

10. $123 - 75$ 48
11. 24×8 192
12. $60 \div 4$ 15
13. $292 + 41$ 333
14. 57×3 171

CHAPTER PROJECT

PROJECT LINK: ANALYZING

Use the picture you found for the Project Link on page 7. To estimate the number of people in the crowd, first divide the picture into equal rectangular sections. Count the number of people in several sections. Be careful! The people in the front of the picture appear larger than those in the back. Find the mean (average) number of people in a rectangle. Use your average to estimate the number of people in the picture.

Check students' work.

PRACTICE

Practice 1-6 Problem-Solving Strategy: Use Logical Reasoning

Use logical reasoning to solve each problem. Show your work.

1. Alicia, Barb, Cathy, Dahlia, and Ellen each arrive at school in a different way. One rides in a car pool, one rides her bike, one walks every day, one rides in her family car, and one rides the school bus. Cathy does not ride in a motor vehicle. Barb enjoys the bus ride along the country road. Ellen is last to be picked up on the car pool route. Alicia lives across the street from school. How does each of the girls arrive at school?
   Alicia walks, Barb takes the school bus, Cathy rides her bike, Dahlia rides in a car, and Ellen rides in a car pool.
2. The top four cross-country runners crossed the finish line as follows. Susan came in after Mary. Donna came in before Susan but did not win the race. Genevieve was last to finish. What was the order of the winners?
   Mary, Donna, Susan, Genevieve

Use any strategy to solve each problem. Show your work.

3. Nick took some money from his piggy bank. He bought a book for \$3.50 and he earned \$3.00 for raking leaves. Now he has \$4.50. How much did Nick take from his bank? \$5.00
4. Find the median of all positive odd multiples of 3 that are less than 50. 24
5. How many different ways can you have \$1 in change using nickels, dimes, quarters, and half-dollars? 40 ways
6. Which number shown at the right is described below?
   The difference of the digits is 3.
   It is a multiple of 3.
   It is greater than the average of 84 and 41.
   It is less than the product of 9 and 11.
   It is even. 96

   85 41 52 74 69 30 96

Theodore works for Mr. Jonas. Mr. Jonas agreed to start Theodore at \$.01 the first day, \$.02 the second day, \$.04 the third day, \$.08 the fourth day, and so on.

7. How much does Theodore earn on the fifteenth day? \$163.84
8. How much did Theodore earn in fifteen days? \$327.67
9. Markie, Bernard, Lyssa, and Hermann entered a race. How many different ways can they finish the race? 24 ways

In copymaster and workbook formats

RETEACHING

Reteaching 1-6 Problem-Solving Strategy: Use Logical Reasoning

Travis, Seritta, Ariel, and Tess are going hiking, boating, biking, and surfing.

① Tess does not know how to surf.
② Ariel asked the hiker to show her a map.
③ Tess and Ariel talked with the biker and the boater.
④ Travis doesn't like water.

Tell who will do each activity.

Read What do you need to find out? *The problem asks you to tell who will do each activity.*

	Hiker	Boater	Biker	Surfer
Travis				
Seritta				
Ariel				
Tess				no

Plan Make a logic table. Use the clues from the problem. Write *yes* or *no* in each box.

Solve Fact ① tells you Tess is not the surfer. Write *no* in the box where Tess and Surfer meet.

Fact ② says that Ariel is not the hiker. Write *no* for this.

	Hiker	Boater	Biker	Surfer
Travis				
Seritta				
Ariel	no	no	no	yes
Tess		no	no	no

Fact ③ says that Tess and Ariel are not the boater nor the biker. Write *no* in four boxes, leaving Ariel to be the surfer. Write *yes* in the box where Ariel and Surfer meet.

Complete the logic table. *Travis is the biker, Seritta is the boater, Ariel is the surfer, and Tess is the hiker.*

	Hiker	Boater	Biker	Surfer
Travis	no	no	yes	no
Seritta	no	yes	no	no
Ariel	no	no	no	yes
Tess	yes	no	no	no

Reteaching

Complete the logic table to solve the problem.

1. Iona, Sara, Pete, and Tim went to the Northwest Coast Indian Conference. They are from the Noottka, Salish, Haida, and Tlingit families. Pete and Sara had not seen a Haida for a year. The Tlingit gave Iona and Tim a wood carving. Iona is not the Noottka. Sara joined the Noottka at the evening ceremonies. The Tlingit is not a woman. Who is the Noottka? the Salish? the Haida? the Tlingit? Tim; Sara; Iona; Pete

	Iona	Sara	Pete	Tim
Noottka	no	no	no	yes
Salish	no	yes	no	no
Haida	yes	no	no	no
Tlingit	no	no	yes	no

ENRICHMENT

Minds on Math Transparency

1-6

I am the part of the set of whole numbers between 100 and 400 that contain the digit 2. How many whole numbers are in my set?

138

See *Solution Key* for worked-out answers.

1-7 Teaching Notes

1 Focus

CONNECTING TO PRIOR KNOWLEDGE Ask students to describe surveys they have seen or taken part in. Encourage students to discuss the possible uses of those surveys. A magazine survey, for example, can give the editors a good idea of the readers' interests.

2 Teach

Work Together

CONNECTION TO HISTORY Have students analyze the survey and find out more about the election from the library. Do their opinions change?

THINK AND DISCUSS

ERROR ALERT! Students may have difficulty determining biased questions. **Remediation:** Tell students to look for words that limit the answers, such as *all* or *never*. Also check for double negatives since they can be very confusing. If a statement has double negatives, say the statement without them.

AUDITORY LEARNING Group students in pairs. One student states aloud a biased question. The partner restates it as a fair question. Next the first student states aloud a fair question. The partner restates it as a biased question. The pairs change roles and repeat the activity.

Lesson Planning Options

Prerequisite Skills

- identifying biased statements (precourse)

Vocabulary/Symbols

population, random sample, biased questions

Materials/Manipulatives

- graph paper

Resources

Student Edition

Skills Handbook, p. 528
Extra Practice, p. 514
Glossary/Study Guide

Teaching Resources

Chapter Support File, Ch. 1
- Lesson Planner 1-7
- Practice 1-7, Reteaching 1-7
- Answer Masters 1-7

Glossary, Spanish Resources

Transparencies

Minds on Math 1-7

Warm Up

Find the number halfway between 0.784 and 0.76 **0.772**

1-7 Random Samples and Surveys

What You'll Learn

1. To identify a random sample
2. To write survey questions

...And Why

Candidates for public office use samples and surveys to measure public opinion.

Here's How

Look for questions that
- build understanding
- check understanding

Work Together

Analyzing a Survey

Work with a partner to analyze the situation below.

1. *Analyze* In the presidential election of 1948, Thomas Dewey and Harry Truman were candidates for president. On the day of the election, the people taking election polls said that Mr. Dewey had won. The polling was done by telephone. Why do you think the pollsters were wrong?
See back of book.

THINK AND DISCUSS

1 *Identifying a Sample*

In the presidential election of 1948, the people taking polls could not survey all 50 million voters. To collect data from a whole group, or **population**, is usually impractical. A sample of the population can often provide enough information.

WHO? President Truman celebrated his victory by showing a headline written before the vote was counted.

2. *Reasoning* Suppose you are studying the eating habits of college students. What question could you ask to decide if Joe Smith is a member of the population you are studying? **See below.**

You can use a **random sample** to predict the responses of a population. A sample is random if the members of the population have an equal chance of being selected.

2. Answers may vary. Sample: Do you currently attend college?

■ **EXAMPLE 1**

Suppose you are surveying customers at a mall to find which stores they shop at the most. Would you get a random sample of customers if you stood at one entrance to the mall?

Customers entering at one entrance may be shopping at only the stores that are near that entrance. So this would not be a random sample.

3. For Example 1, how could you get a random sample?
Survey people at each entrance during the same time interval.

Now you may assign Exercises 1–6.

AEP This lesson may be difficult for some students because of the specific meaning of words such as *population.* You may wish to pair these students with those who have strong language skills. Suggest students record the terms and their meanings in their math notebooks.

ADDITIONAL EXAMPLES

FOR EXAMPLE 1

Suppose you survey students in your school about their snacking habits. Would you get a random sample if you questioned different English classes? **yes**

FOR EXAMPLE 2

Which of the following questions is biased? Which is fair? Why?

a. *Which is a brighter color, pink or green?* **Fair; the question represents the colors equally.**

b. *Is an electric pink shirt brighter than a green shirt?* **Biased; it makes pink sound brighter, influencing responses.**

ASSESSMENT Have students work together to make a checklist for evaluating surveys. Their checklists should assess accuracy, sample randomness, and possible bias.

3 Practice/Assess

EXERCISES *On Your Own*

Exercises 7–10 Have students rewrite as fair questions the questions they consider biased.

2 *Writing Survey Questions*

Biased questions are unfair questions. They can make assumptions that may or may not be true or make one answer seem better than another.

EXAMPLE 2 *Real-World Problem Solving*

Television Which of the following questions is biased? Which is fair? Why?

a. "Do you think the extreme violence of Saturday morning cartoons affects young, impressionable children?"

This question is biased. It assumes cartoons are violent. Also the words "extreme" and "young, impressionable" may influence responses.

b. "Is there violence in some Saturday morning cartoons?"

This question is fair. It does not make any assumptions about cartoons or the people watching them.

4. *✔Try It Out* Write a fair survey question about the time of day your school starts. Then write a biased question.

4. Sample: Fair: What time do you believe the school should start?
Biased: When should the school start so you don't need to wake up so early?

Now you may assign Exercises 7–11.

EXERCISES *On Your Own*

1. *Public Transportation* Jeremy is an urban planner. He wants to know how the city's bus drivers are affected by work crews in the streets. How can he survey a random sample? **Survey bus drivers at the end of each shift.**

You want to survey teenagers in Idaho about their snacking habits. Tell whether each of the following will give you a random sample. Justify each of your answers.

2. You ask five teenagers in a group to name their favorite snack. **No; only teenagers in groups of five or more have a chance of being surveyed.**
3. For three mornings you stand at the same place on Broadway Avenue in Boise, Idaho. You survey all the teenagers who pass you. **3. No; only teenagers from the nearby school are likely to be surveyed, and some of them you might ask more than once.**
4. You select teenagers from lists of middle school and high school students in each Idaho county. You survey them by telephone. **Yes; each teenager has an equal chance of being surveyed.**

Technology Options

Prentice Hall Technology

Software for Learners

- Math Blaster® Mystery*
- Interactive Student Tutorial, Chapter 1*

Teaching Resource Software

- Computer Item Generator 1-7
- Resource Pro™ Chapter 1*

Internet • For related mathematics activities, visit the Prentice Hall site at www.phschool.com/math

Available on CD-ROM only

Assignment Options for Exercises On Your Own

To provide flexible scheduling, this lesson can be subdivided into parts.

1 **Core** 1–5
Extension 6

2 **Core** 7–10
Extension 11

Use Mixed Review to maintain skills.

PRACTICE

Practice 1-7 *Random Samples and Surveys*

You want to survey students in your school about their exercise habits. Tell whether the following will give you a random sample. Justify your answer. Answers may vary. Samples are shown.

1. You select every tenth student on an alphabetical list of the students in your school. You survey the selected students in their first-period classes. random sample
2. At lunchtime you stand by a vending machine. You survey every student who buys something from the vending machine. Not a random sample; students that use the vending machine may not represent all types of students.

Tell whether the following questions are biased or fair. Rewrite biased questions as fair questions. Answers may vary. Samples are shown.

3. Do you think bike helmets should be mandatory for all bike riders? Fair
4. Do you prefer the natural beauty of hardwood floors in your home? Biased; Do you prefer hardwood floors in your home?
5. Do you exercise regularly? Fair
6. Do you eat at least the recommended number of servings of fruits and vegetables to ensure a healthy and long life? Biased; How many servings of fruits and vegetables do you eat?
7. Do you prefer the look and feel of thick lush carpeting in your living room? Biased; Do you prefer thick carpeting?
8. Do you take a daily multiple vitamin to supplement your diet? Fair
9. Do you read the newspaper to be informed about world events? Fair
10. Do you feel that the TV news is a sensational portrayal of life's problems? Biased; Does TV news portray life accurately?

Practice

In copymaster and workbook formats

RETEACHING

Reteaching 1-7 *Random Samples and Surveys*

Carlos is curious about sports that students in his school like best. He cannot interview every student in the school. But he could interview a sample of the school **population.**

Carlos wants a **random sample.** A sample is random if everyone has an equal chance of being selected. How will Carlos get a random sample? He considers two possibilities:
① He can interview 30 students at a soccer game.
② He can interview 5 students in each of 6 class changes.

Carlos realizes that students at a soccer game probably like soccer better than other sports. That would not be a random sample. He decides on the interviews during class changes.

What question will he ask? He considers two possibilities:
① "Which sport do you prefer, football, soccer, baseball, or tennis?"
② "Which do you enjoy most, the slow sport of baseball or one of the more exciting sports like football, soccer, or tennis?"

The second question is **biased.** It makes one answer seem better than another. Carlos decides to ask the first question.

Circle the letter of the best answer for Exercises 1 and 2.

1. You want to find how many people in your community are vegetarian. Where would be the best place to take a survey?
   A. a health food store **B.** a steak house **(C.)** a shopping mall
2. Which of these is an unbiased question?
   A. Will you vote for the young inexperienced candidate, Mr. Soong, or the experienced candidate, Ms. Lopez?
   (B.) Will you vote for Mr. Soong or Ms. Lopez?

You plan to survey people to see what percent own their home and what percent rent. Tell whether the following will give a random sample. Justify your answer.

3. You interview people outside a pool supply store in the suburbs. No; you are more likely to interview homeowners.
4. You interview people in the street near an apartment complex. No; you are more likely to interview renters.
5. You mail a survey to every 20th person in the telephone book. Yes; you can't tell if people own or rent.

ENRICHMENT

Minds on Math Transparency

1-7

When you multiply 2,178 by four, the product is 8,712. Notice that the digits in the product are the reverse of the digits in 2,178. Find the four-digit number whose digits are reversed when multiplied by nine.

1,089

See *Solution Key* for worked-out answers.

WRAP UP

IDENTIFYING THE BIG IDEA Have students explain how they could fairly survey a random sample of students about favorite music groups.

PROJECT LINK Student survey questions should be interesting and unbiased.

LESSON QUIZ

1. If you ask members of the swimming club what their favorite exercise is, would you get a random sample of the students in your school? Explain. **No, all the students in the school do not have an equal chance of being chosen.**
2. Is the question *Do you prefer sweet chocolate or sour candy?* fair or biased? Why? **Biased; the words sweet and sour may influence responses.**

5. Suppose you are gathering information about visitors to Yosemite National Park. You survey every tenth person entering the park. Would you get a random sample of visitors? Why or why not? Yes; each visitor has an equal chance of being surveyed.
6. *Writing* Tell how you would find a random sample of the students in your school. Answers may vary. Sample: ask every tenth student entering school in the morning.

Tell whether the following questions are biased or fair. Explain.

7. Do you prefer getting invigorating exercise or being a couch potato? Biased; the terms "invigorating" and "couch potato" may influence responses.
8. Do you prefer to exercise or watch television? Fair; the question does not give preference to one answer or the other.
9. Do you prefer rock music or jazz? Fair; the question does not give preference to one answer or the other.
10. Do you prefer, harsh rock music or soothing jazz? Biased; the question assumes rock music is harsh and jazz is soothing.
11. Explain how you can tell if a survey question is biased. Words are used to make one choice seem better than the other.

Mixed Review

Find the mean, median, and mode of each set of data. Identify any outliers and tell how they affect the mean. (Lesson 1-4)

12. 122 114 113 116 120
    123 119 117 123 111
    117.8; 118; 123; no outliers
13. 54 99 50 49 55 50
    49 50 58 47 55
    56; 50; 50; 99; the outlier significantly increases the mean.
14. Inez surveyed a group of students at Midtown Middle School about the number of books they read over the summer. Her results are at the right. (Lesson 1-1)
    a. What should be the title of the histogram? Summer Book Reading at Midtown Middle School
    b. What should be the label of each axis?
    c. How many people answered Inez's survey? 23 people
    b. horizontal: Number of Books Read; vertical: Number of Students

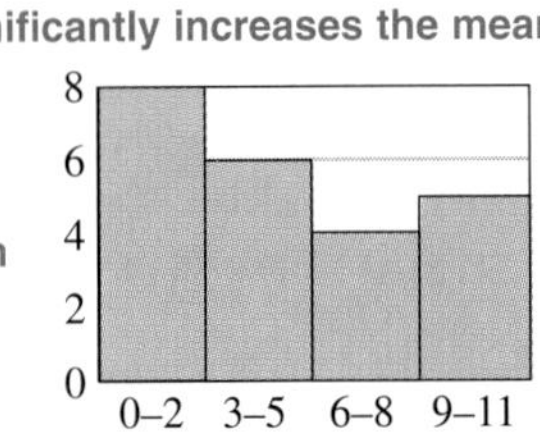

CHAPTER PROJECT

PROJECT LINK: SURVEYING

Suppose you want to know what kinds of foods people might buy during a sporting event or a concert. Write a fair survey question. Survey a random sample of the students in your grade. Use a graph to display your results.

Check students' work.

Extra Practice, Lesson 1-7, page 514

PROBLEM SOLVING PRACTICE ★★

This page provides a variety of problems that can be used to reinforce and enhance the students' problem solving skills. Encourage students to read each problem carefully. Then have them decide on the best strategy to solve the problems.

COOPERATIVE GROUPS Exercise 4
Students can work on this exercise in pairs. Students can discuss strategies for finding an estimate of the number of hours Jim worked.

PROBLEM SOLVING PRACTICE ★★★★★

Choose the best answer.

1. A sports reporter rounded the attendance at a professional basketball game to the nearest thousand. How did he report the attendance of 14,538 people? D

   A. 10,000 B. 14,000
   C. 14,500 D. 15,000

2. Danzell went on a five-day fishing trip with his family. The number of fish that he caught each day was 6, 4, 7, 2, and 6. What was the mean (average) number of fish that he caught each day? J

   F. 2 G. 3
   H. 4 J. 5

3. Mario's Sandwich Shop received orders from people at three different addresses on the same street: 2525, 2432, and 2784. In which of the following ways should the orders be delivered to take the least time? A

   A. 2432 2525 2784
   B. 2525 2432 2784
   C. 2784 2432 2525
   D. 2432 2784 2525

Please note that items 4–8 have *five* answer choices.

4. Jim has a part-time job. He works 8 to 12 hours each week. Is it reasonable to assume that during four weeks he will work – H

   F. less than 30 hours
   G. exactly 30 hours
   H. more than 30 hours
   J. exactly 50 hours
   K. more than 50 hours

Favorite Juice Drink

Juice	Number of Students
Orange	11
Apple	8
Pineapple	3
Grapefruit	2
Tomato	5

5. The table above shows the results of a survey on students' favorite juice drinks. How many flavors of juice were chosen by more than 5 students? B

   A. 1 B. 2 C. 3
   D. 4 E. 5

6. Use the table above. Which type of juice is the mode? F

   F. Orange
   G. Apple
   H. Pineapple
   J. Grapefruit
   K. Tomato

7. Maria was reading a novel for a book report. After four days, she had read 340 pages. On the fifth day, Maria read 88 pages. A reasonable conclusion would be that Maria read — C

   A. less than 55 pages each day
   B. between 55 and 79 pages each day
   C. between 80 and 95 pages each day
   D. more than 96 pages each day
   E. Not Here

8. Which set of data has 24 for the median?

   G F. 24, 24, 22, 23 G. 23, 27, 25, 22
   H. 22, 24, 27, 20 J. 23, 27, 20, 28
   K. Not Here

1-8 Teaching Notes

1 Focus

CONNECTING TO PRIOR KNOWLEDGE
Have students recall some biased questions. Ask students to explain why someone might purposely create a question that is inaccurate or biased. **Answers may vary. Sample: to convince people to buy a product**

2 Teach

Work Together

DIVERSITY Ask students who have knowledge of farming to share what they know about economic realities such as seed costs, yields, and profit. Some may know about farming in other countries.

THINK AND DISCUSS

REASONING **Question 5** You may wish to brainstorm ideas and have a volunteer record suggestions on the board.

Example 2 Have students find the mean, median, and mode to determine how the data about Harry's Hamburger Heaven can be displayed more accurately.

Lesson Planning Options

Prerequisite Skills

- making graphs (1-1, 1-2, and 1-3)
- reading and interpreting graphs (1-1, 1-2, and 1-3)

Materials/Manipulatives

- graph paper
- newspaper or magazine

Resources

Student Edition
Skills Handbook, p. 528
Extra Practice, p. 514
Glossary/Study Guide

Teaching Resources
Chapter Support File, Ch. 1
- Lesson Planner 1-8
- Practice 1-8, Reteaching 1-8
- Answer Masters 1-8

Teaching Aids Masters 1, 2
Glossary, Spanish Resources

Transparencies
1, Minds on Math 1-8

Warm Up

What operations would you use to convert 9 ft 7 in. to inches?
multiplication and addition

1-8 Using Data to Persuade

What You'll Learn

1. To recognize how presentation of data can influence opinion

...And Why

You can evaluate displays of data for their accuracy and determine if the displays are trying to influence you.

Here's How

Look for questions that
- build understanding
- ✔ check understanding

Work Together

Analyzing Data

Business You and your partner are struggling to make ends meet on a peanut farm. You decide to look for outside investors. You compile the data below. Decide how you will go about convincing people to invest in your peanut farm.

Peanut Facts

Average size of farm: 100 acres Peanut seeds planted: 100 pounds/acre Cost of seed: $.70/pound Average yield: 2,705 pounds/acre Average profit: $63/acre	548 peanuts make one 12-ounce jar of peanut butter. 30,000 peanut butter sandwiches can be made from one acre of peanuts. 800 million pounds of peanut butter are expected to be eaten each year.	In two tablespoons of peanut butter • there are 210 calories. • there are 0 mg of cholesterol. • there are 16 g of fat. • there are 7 g of protein.

Source: Peanut Advisory Board

1. *Analyze* Which data would convince investors to invest in your farm? **See below.**
2. Which data would you not present to possible investors? **Answers may vary. Sample: cost of seed, calories, fat content**
3. One investor heard that peanut butter is high in cholesterol. How would you respond to this? **The data show that there is no cholesterol in peanut butter.**

THINK AND DISCUSS

Data is often presented to influence you. As you look at data displays, consider these questions: Is the information shown accurately? Is the presentation trying to influence you?

1. Answers may vary. Sample: average yield, average profit; number of sandwiches per acre, pounds of peanut butter expected to be eaten each year

REASONING Question 6 Ask students to share their changes with the class. Have them explain why they recommend those changes.

■ ADDITIONAL EXAMPLES

FOR EXAMPLE 1

Which graph is more likely to convince someone that the price of gold increased greatly from January to July in 1993? Why? **The second graph is more persuasive. The vertical scale makes the price of gold seem to increase at a faster rate.**

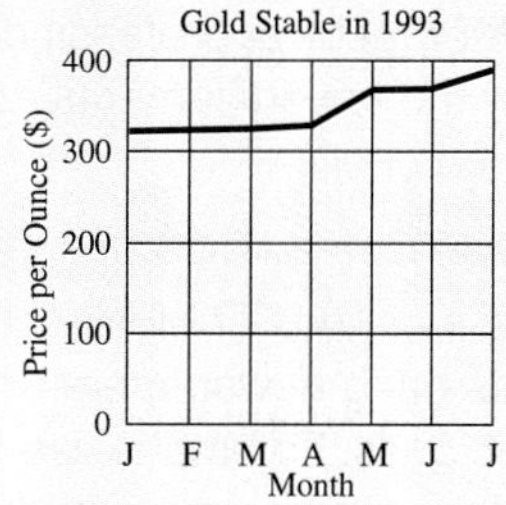

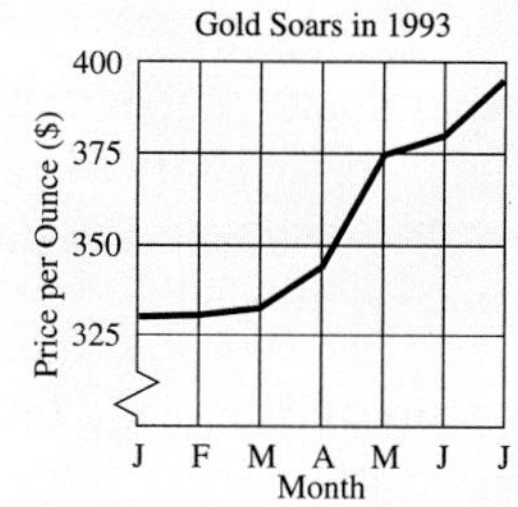

■ EXAMPLE 1 *Real-World Problem Solving*

Business Which graph is more likely to convince someone to invest in a peanut farm? Why?

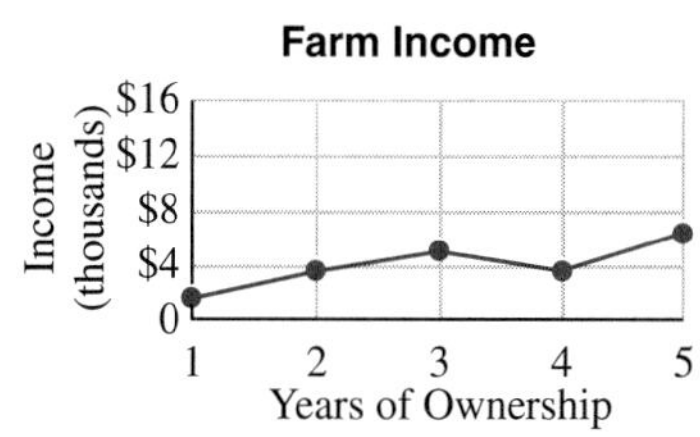

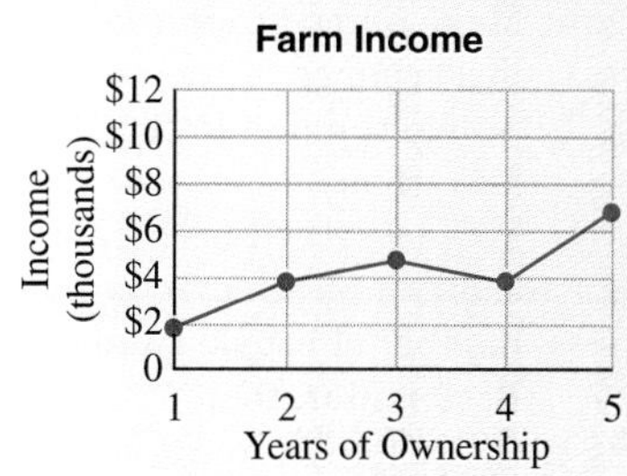

The second graph is more persuasive. The vertical scale makes the farm income seem greater, which makes the farm look like a good investment.

4. First graph; the vertical scale on the first graph is smaller, so small changes are not as noticeable as in the second graph.

5. Answers may vary. Sample: scale break; excessive color and graphics, inappropriate scale

4. *✔Try It Out* Suppose you do not want to emphasize that the income decreased one year. Which graph from Example 1 would you use? Why?
4–5. See left.

5. *Reasoning* What can you look for to tell if a graph was made to influence you?

■ EXAMPLE 2 *Real-World Problem Solving*

Business The poster at the left is part of an ad campaign at Harry's Hamburger Heaven. Below are data about Harry's hamburgers. Is the ad misleading?

Item	Calories	Fat (g)	Average Number Sold Daily
Kiddie Burger	480	35	80
Hamburger Plus	575	42	68
Health Burger	580	40	65
Golden Fried Hamburger	660	57	43
Burger Deluxe	700	55	75

Most of the types of hamburgers made and most of the ones sold have more than 500 calories. So, the ad is misleading.

Answers may vary. Sample: "Home of the under-500-calorie Kiddie Burger"

6. *Reasoning* How would you change the ad to better reflect the data?

Now you may assign Exercises 1–10.

Technology Options

Prentice Hall Technology

Software for Learners

- Hot Page™ 1–9*
- Math Blaster® Mystery*
- Interactive Student Tutorial, Chapter 1*

Teaching Resource Software

- Computer Item Generator 1-8
- Resource Pro™ Chapter 1*

Internet • For related mathematics activities, visit the Prentice Hall site at www.phschool.com/math

**Available on CD-ROM only*

Assignment Options for Exercises On Your Own

Core 1, 3–10
Extension 2

Use Mixed Review to maintain skills.

FOR EXAMPLE 2

Suppose another poster that is part of the advertising campaign at Harry's Hamburger Heaven states that they sell over 2,000 hamburgers each week. Is this advertisement misleading? **No; the average number of hamburgers sold daily is 331, which is an average of 2,317 per week.**

CONNECTION TO HEALTH To show how data can be used to persuade, have students look for advertisements promoting products based on claims, testimonials, or surveys of doctors or other medical professionals. Ask students how the advertisements are intended to influence the public.

CONNECTION TO POLITICS If you have extended class periods or block scheduling, have students bring newspapers and news magazines to class. To emphasize how persuasive data can be, have students look for advertisements that put a *spin* on polls to place a candidate in a favorable light or to influence voters on important issues.

VISUAL LEARNING Display articles or advertisements that could be misleading in the classroom.

ERROR ALERT! Students may not understand how to manipulate data without being untruthful. **Remediation:** Point out that by emphasizing one detail, and ignoring or de-emphasizing other details, you can use statistics to mislead.

pages 36–37 On Your Own

1a.

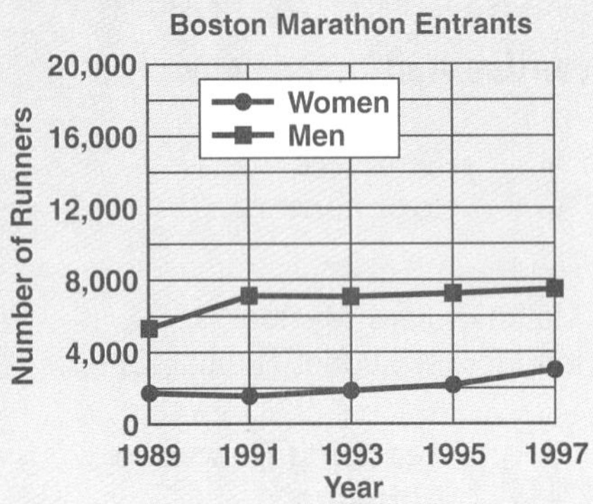

b.

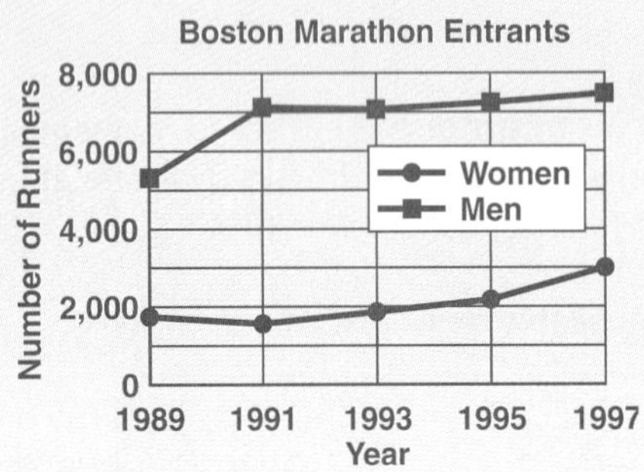

c. Second; the sponsors want to see increasing number of participants.

EXERCISES *On Your Own*

1. *Sports* Use the data at the right.

a. Make a line graph that shows little change in the number of people running in the Boston Marathon.

b. Make a second line graph that shows great change in the number of people running the Boston Marathon.

c. *Advertising* You want the sponsors of the Boston Marathon to increase their contributions. Which of your graphs would you use? Explain. **a–c. See margin.**

Boston Marathon Entrants

Year	Women	Men
1989	1,743	5,320
1991	1,562	7,124
1993	1,861	7,069
1995	2,175	7,241
1997	2,998	7,473

2. a. *Open-ended* Find a graph in a newspaper or magazine. Describe the data presented. **a–b. Check students' work.**

b. Is the graph trying to influence you? Explain.

3. *Television* Use the data at the right to make two different histograms. One will show that there is little relationship between income and hours of television watched. The other will show that there is a strong relationship between income and hours of television watched. **See back of book for samples.**

Television Viewing and Income

Annual Income	Hours of TV per Week
Under $30,000	53
$30,000 to $39,999	49
$40,000 to $49,999	48
$50,000 to $59,999	47
$60,000 and more	46

4. *Nutrition* Farnaz asked students at her school, "What's your favorite pizza topping?" She drew the double bar graph below. Explain why the graph is misleading.

4. The graph makes it appear that there is much greater preference for pepperoni than there really is.

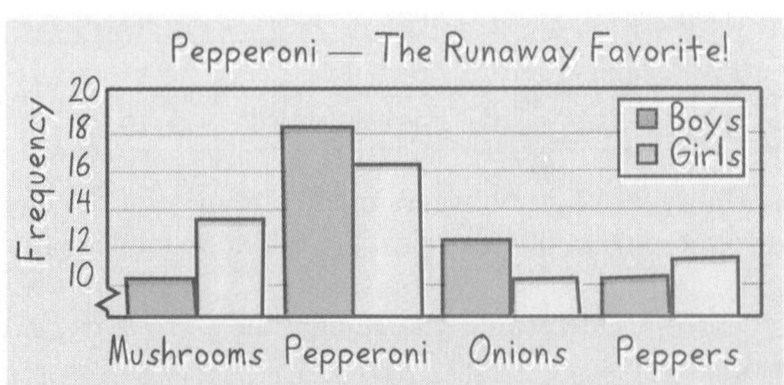

If you have block scheduling or extended class periods, have students vote on several advertisements to determine how many students trust or mistrust the advertisements.

Work Together

ASSESSMENT Encourage students to compile checklists based on their experience in using data to persuade. These checklists should list ways data may be used to persuade, and ways to determine if statistics are misleading.

3 Practice/Assess

EXERCISES *On Your Own*

WRITING Exercise 10 Ask students:

- *How are the two graphs different?* **The first graph has more space between its vertical labels and does not start at zero.**
- *What is misleading about these graphs?* **The first graph indicates greater increase.**

WRAP UP

IDENTIFYING THE BIG IDEA Ask students to explain how to evaluate claims based on data.

JOURNAL Have students discuss ways in which a set of data maybe misleading.

PROJECT LINK Ask students to justify their predictions.

---

5. Chantay has a 93, 83, 76, 92, and 76 on her social studies exams.
   a. Chantay wants to show her parents how well she is doing in her class. Does the mean, the median, or the mode make her grades look the best? **mean**
   b. Should her teacher use the mean, the median, or the mode to encourage Chantay to study harder? **mode**

6. *Medicine* The graph below and the data at the right show measles cases in the United States over several years.

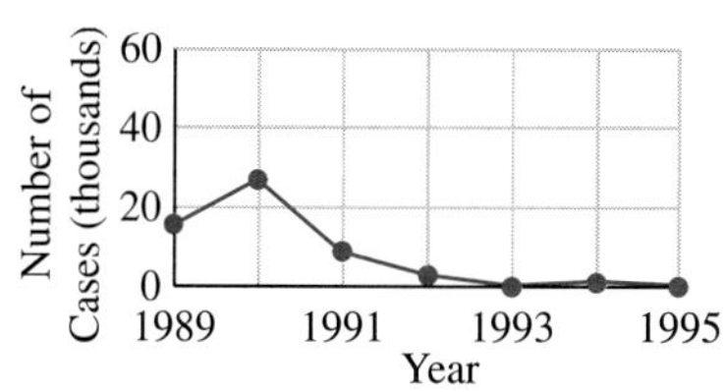

6a. Large scale and extra space at the top of the graph make the 1990 outbreak appear less significant.

Measles Cases Reported in the United States

Year	Number of Cases (in thousands)
1989	18.2
1990	27.8
1991	9.6
1992	2.2
1993	0.3
1994	1.0
1995	0.3

Source: *Statistical Abstract*

   a. *Reasoning* What does this graph seem to say about the outbreak of measles in 1990?
   b. Draw a better graph. Give your graph a title. **Answers may vary. See back of book for sample graph; Measles Cases Decline after 1990 Outbreak.**

Environment **Use the graphs below.**

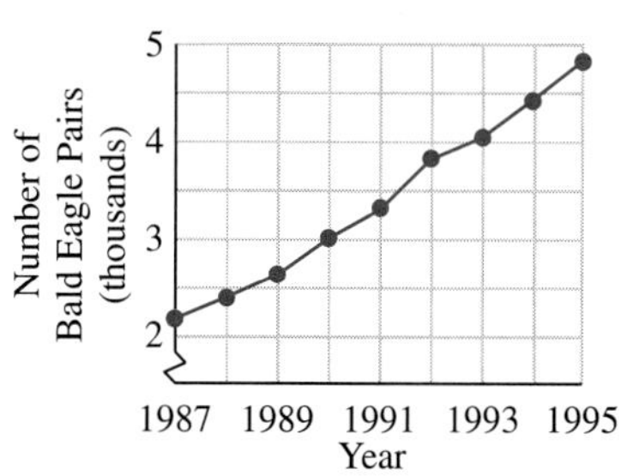

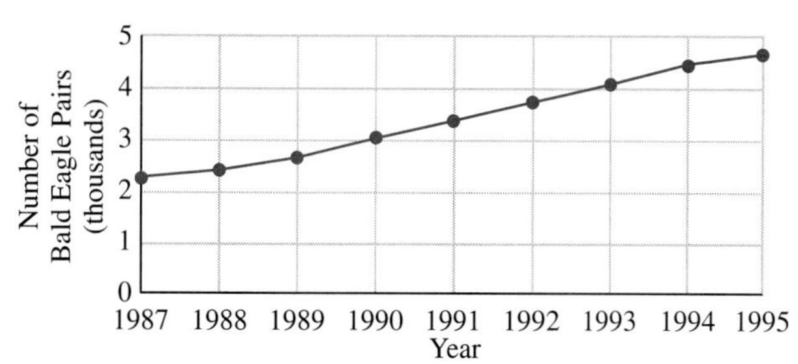

7. What is the first graph trying to tell you about the change in the number of bald eagle pairs? Write a title for the graph. **7–8. See margin.**
8. What is the second graph trying to tell you about the change in the number of bald eagle pairs? Write a title for the graph.
9. Estimate the range of the data. **about 2,500 pairs**
10. *Writing* Does either graph accurately show the change in the number of bald eagle pairs without being misleading? Explain. **Answers may vary. Sample: Both graphs are misleading; see margin for reasoning.**

JOURNAL
Describe some ways you can analyze data to determine if it is influencing your opinion.

CHECKPOINT 2

Checkpoint 2

Lessons 1-5 through 1-8

1. Create a stem-and-leaf plot for this set of data.
   Daily low temperatures (°F)
   23 35 25 32 23 18 26
   16 21 31 17 18 22

1	6 7 8 8
2	1 2 3 3 5 6
3	1 2 5

1 | 6 means 16

2. Alvin, Betina, and Chang each play tennis, soccer, and racquetball. Alvin plays a sport that does not require a racquet. Chang does not play racquetball. Who plays which sport?
   Alvin plays soccer; Betina plays racquetball; Chang plays tennis.
3. Choose a survey topic. Write a survey question. How could you get a random sample?
   Answers may vary. Check students' answers.

pages 36–37 On Your Own

7. **The number of bald eagle pairs increased a lot from 1987 to 1995; Sample title: "Bald Eagle Population Increases Rapidly."**
8. **The number of bald eagle pairs had grown steadily; Sample title: "Bald Eagle Population Shows Slow but Steady Rise."**
10. **The first graph makes the relative increase appear greater than it is; the second graph suggests that the number had been increasing over a long period of time.**

page 38 Checkpoint

1. **Elsa carried the pink towel and a beach ball; Anna carried the blue towel and sandwiches; LaTonya carried the striped towel and iced tea.**

PRACTICE

Practice 1-8 *Using Data to Persuade*

The table at the right shows the number of students enrolled in swimming classes for 1991 to 1993.

Swim Class Enrollment	Boys	Girls
1991	375	360
1992	400	395
1993	410	420

1. Use the data to create a double line graph that emphasizes the increase in the number of students enrolled in summer swim classes.

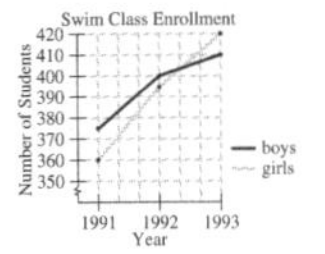

2. Use the data again to create a second double line graph that does not emphasize the increase in the number of students enrolled in the summer swim classes.

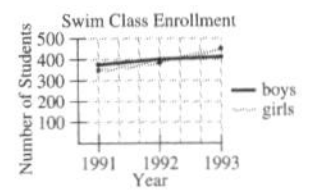

3. Which graph could be used to request additional reserved times for swim classes at the pool? The first graph because it reinforces the need for additional time for swim classes.

Vince has the following scores on chapter tests in his math class. Use this data in Exercises 4–6.

95 89 83 90 83

4. Find the mean, median, and mode of his test scores. mean: 88; median: 89; mode: 83
5. Should Vince describe his tests using the mean, median, or mode to show his ability to do well in math? The median is the highest measure of his score.
6. Should his teacher use the mean, the median, or the mode to encourage Vince to check his work carefully on the next test? The mode is the lowest measure of his scores.

In copymaster and workbook formats

RETEACHING

Reteaching 1-8 *Using Data to Persuade*

The graphs show the same information but give different impressions.

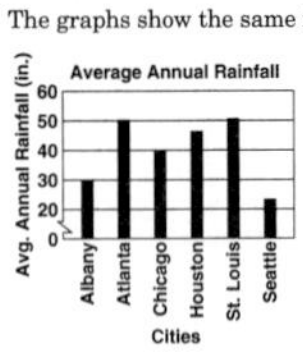

The values from 0 to 10 are not on the vertical axis. This makes the differences in the data appear greater.

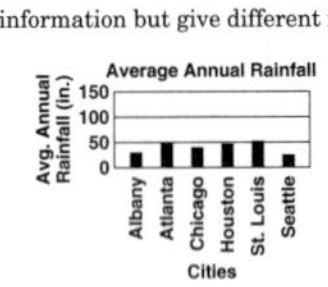

Numbers used on the vertical scale are too large. This makes the differences look less significant.

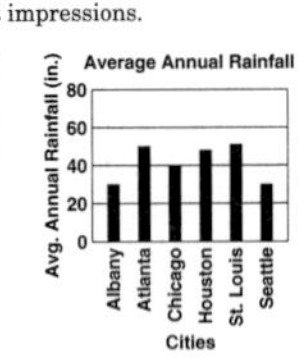

This graph is the most accurate. The vertical scale begins at 0. The scale shows the differences fairly.

Use the table to complete Exercises 1–4.

Average Number of Clear Days per Year	
Albany	62
Atlanta	114
Boise	116
Houston	85
St. Louis	80
Seattle	66

1. Suppose a bar graph was made using intervals of 100 on the vertical axis. Would the scale show differences in the data fairly? no
2. Which scale range on the vertical axis would present the data more accurately, 60 to 120 or 0 to 120? 0 to 120
3. Draw a graph to make the differences in the data appear unfairly small. Answers may vary. Sample given

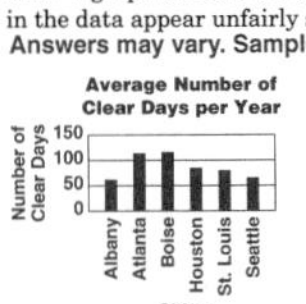

4. Draw a graph that accurately represents the data in the table. Answers may vary. Sample given

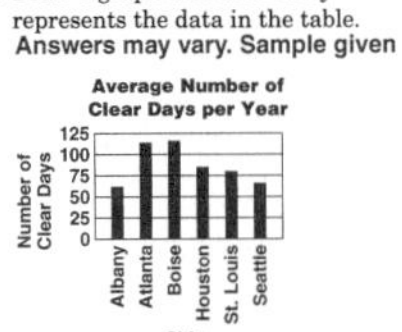

Reteaching

ENRICHMENT

Minds on Math Transparency

1-8

During a twelve-hour period, the digit 1 shows up most often on a digital clock. Which digit shows up next to most often?

2

See *Solution Key* for worked-out answers.

LESSON QUIZ

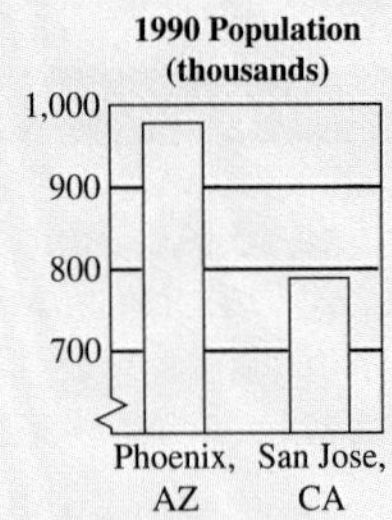

1. What impression is given by this graph? **The population of Phoenix is twice that of San Jose.**
2. How would you change the graph to better reflect the data? **Change the vertical scale.**
3. Redraw the graph accurately. **Check students' work.**

Mixed Review

Is each question biased or fair? If biased, rewrite it as a fair question. *(Lesson 1-7)*

11. Would you prefer a vacation in sunny Florida or wintry Maine? **Biased; would you prefer to vacation in Florida or Maine?**

12. Do you prefer a cat or a dog for a pet? **fair**

Mental Math **Estimate each answer.** *(Previous Course)*

13. 12×33 **300** **14.** $154 \div 16$ **10** **15.** $89 - 21$ **70** **16.** $72 + 27$ **100** **17.** 51×38 **2,000**

CHAPTER PROJECT

PROJECT LINK: CALCULATING

Use your Project Links from pages 29 and 32. Suppose the students you surveyed are a representative sample of the people in the crowd picture. Use your results to make predictions about the food preferences of the people in your crowd picture. **Check students' work.**

✓ CHECKPOINT 2

Lessons 1-5 through 1-8

1. Elsa, Anna, and LaTonya went to the beach. Each girl carried a towel and a second item. One girl carried a pink towel and a beach ball. Another carried iced tea and a striped towel. Anna carried the sandwiches. Elsa did not carry the iced tea nor a blue towel. Identify the items each girl carried. **See margin p. 37.**
2. *Entertainment* For the data at the right, would the mean, the median, or the mode be best to impress movie makers? Explain. **Mode; although the mode does not represent the data well, it is greater than the mean and the median.**
3. Make a stem-and-leaf plot of the data at the right. **See above right.**
4. *Open-ended* Choose a survey topic. Write two survey questions, one biased and one fair. **Check students' work.**
5. **Choose A, B, or C.** Which is the best way to survey a random sample of students from your school about which radio station is their favorite? **A**
   - **A.** Survey five students in each first-period class.
   - **B.** Survey twelve band students.
   - **C.** Call 25 friends.

3.

0	9
1	0 3 7
2	1 1 7

2 | 1 means 21

Movies Filmed in Georgia

Year	Number
1990	27
1991	21
1992	21
1993	17
1994	13
1995	9
1996	10

Source: Georgia Film Commission

Extra Practice, Lesson 1-8, p. 514

1-9 Teaching Notes

1 Focus

CONNECTING TO PRIOR KNOWLEDGE Have students recall how to plot points for ordered pairs.

2 Teach

THINK AND DISCUSS

CONNECTION TO SCIENCE **Example 1** This example focuses on graphing and analyzing scientific data on the growth of red maple trees. Encourage students to find the same data about a type of tree they are familiar with.

KINESTHETIC LEARNING Students can do experiments to create their own data. For example, they can find the melting time for a piece of ice and plot it against the size or weight. For a negative trend, students can explore how many of the same textbook an individual can lift. Have a volunteer begin by lifting as many heavy textbooks as possible. Next, have the volunteer lift as many lighter textbooks as possible, and so on. The trend will show fewer textbooks for greater weight.

ALGEBRA Connection

1-9 Exploring Scatter Plots

What You'll Learn

1. To read and draw scatter plots
2. To interpret scatter plots

...And Why

Scientists use scatter plots to look for the relationship between two sets of data, such as the ages of trees and their diameters.

Here's How

Look for questions that
- build understanding
- ✔ check understanding

THINK AND DISCUSS

1 *Reading and Drawing Scatter Plots*

You can investigate the relationship between two sets of data using a **scatter plot.** The two sets of data are graphed as points, but the points are not connected.

The table below shows the number of books in bookbags and the bookbag weights. The scatter plot graphs the data.

Bookbag Weights

Number of Books	Weight (lb)
3	6
3	8
4	6.5
4	7
4	9
5	7
5	10
6	7.5
6	8
6	12
7	9.5
7	11
7	16
8	12
8	16.5

Bookbag Weights

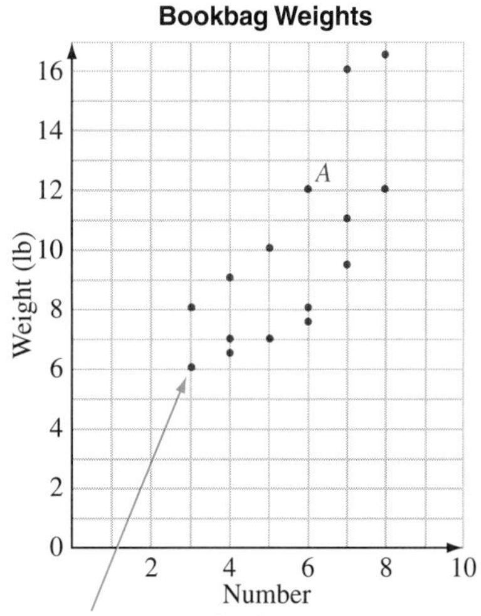

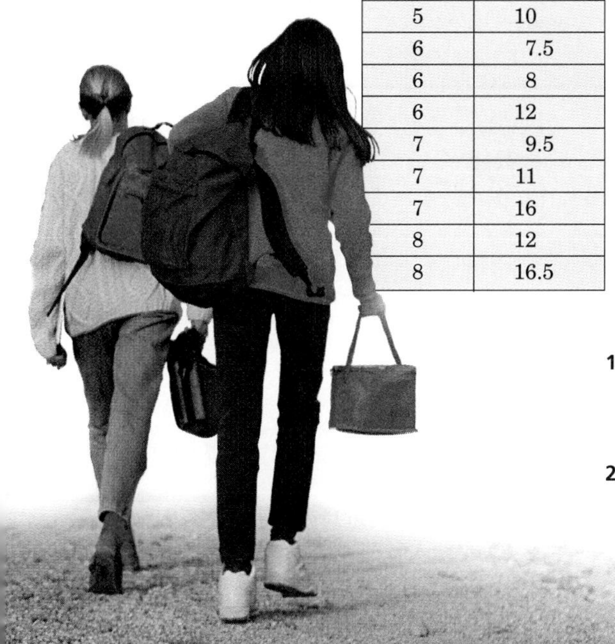

1. a. ✔ *Try It Out* For point A, how many books are in the bookbag? **6 books**
   b. How much does this bookbag weigh? **12 lb**
2. *Reasoning* Suppose a bookbag contains 10 books. How much do you think it might weigh? Explain. **See back of book.**

Lesson Planning Options

Prerequisite Skills

- interpreting graphs (1-1, 1-2, 1-3, and 1-8)

Vocabulary/Symbols

scatter plot, positive trend, negative trend, no trend

Materials/Manipulatives

- graph paper

Resources

Student Edition

Skills Handbook, p. 532
Extra Practice, p. 514
Glossary/Study Guide

Teaching Resources

Chapter Support File, Ch. 1
- Lesson Planner 1-9
- Practice 1-9, Reteaching 1-9
- Answer Masters 1-9

Teaching Aids Masters 1, 2
Glossary, Spanish Resources

Transparencies

1, 37–39, Minds on Math 1-9

Warm Up

Use numbers to write the following word expression: eight and one-third minus five and two sevenths.
$8\frac{1}{3} - 5\frac{2}{7}$

ADDITIONAL EXAMPLE

FOR EXAMPLE

Describe the trend in the scatter plot.

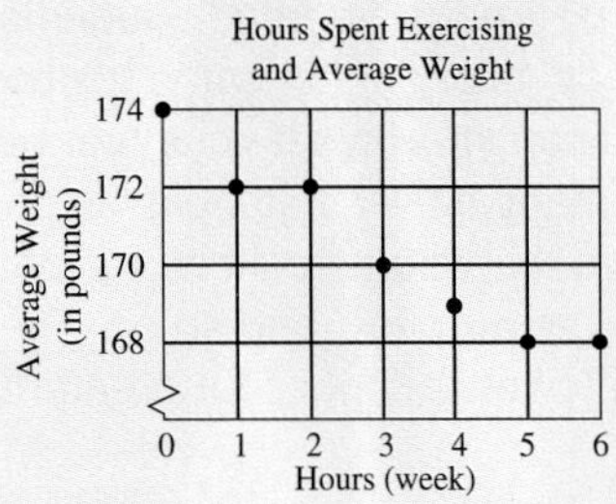

There is a negative trend between the number of hours and weight.

AEP The information in scatter plots is relatively independent of language, but make sure all students understand the terms used to describe the trend.

EXTENSION If you have extended class periods or block shceduling, introduce students to lines of best fit. Ask students to try to fit lines to several of the scatter plots in the lesson. Have students speculate as to how the lines can be used to make predictions.

Work Together

ASSESSMENT Group students in pairs and have each student in a pair interview the other about scatter plots. Ask students to decide what distinguishes a scatter plot from another type of graph, how to read a scatter plot, and how to describe a trend. Have students share their results with the class.

Technology Options

Prentice Hall Technology

Software for Learners

- Hot Page™ 1–5*
- Math Blaster® Mystery*
- Interactive Student Tutorial, Chapter 1*

Teaching Resource Software

- Computer Item Generator 1-9
- Resource Pro™ Chapter 1*

Internet • For related mathematics activities, visit the Prentice Hall site at www.phschool.com/math

**Available on CD-ROM only*

Assignment Options for Exercises On Your Own

To provide flexible scheduling, this lesson can be subdivided into parts.

1 **Core** 1, 2

2 **Core** 3–7
Extension 8

Use Mixed Review to maintain skills.

Now you may assign Exercises 1–2.

2 *Interpreting Scatter Plots*

You can use scatter plots to look for *trends*, or relationships. In the bookbag graph there is a relationship between the number of books in a bag and the weight of the bag. As the number of books increases, the weight of the bag generally increases.

You can examine a scatter plot to see whether there is a trend and what kind of trend is shown.

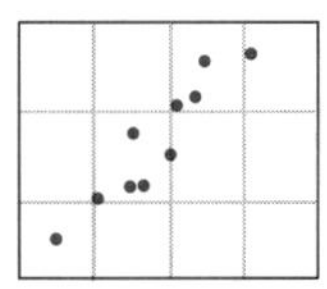

Positive trend

As one set of values increases, the other set tends to increase.

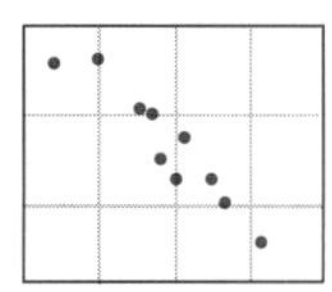

Negative trend

As one set of values increases, the other set tends to decrease.

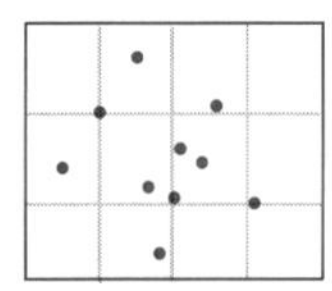

No trend

The points show no relationship.

WHAT? HISTORY The largest red maple tree in the United States is located in St. Clair County, Michigan. At a height about 4.5 ft from the ground, this giant tree has a diameter of 70.5 in.

Source: *The Guinness Book of Records*

EXAMPLE *Real-World Problem Solving*

Describe the trend in the scatter plot.

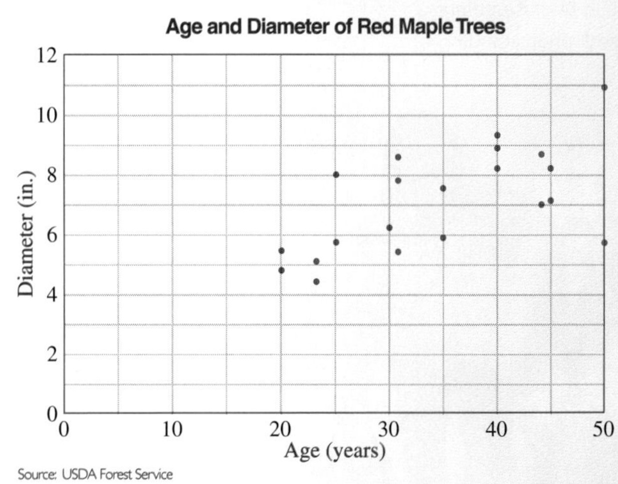

Source: USDA Forest Service

There is a positive trend between the age of a red maple tree and its diameter.

3. ✔ *Try It Out* What kind of trend do you see in the bookbag scatter plot on page 39? **positive**

3 Practice/Assess

EXERCISES *On Your Own*

REASONING Exercise 2b Ask students if they can easily determine the relationship by just studying the data in the table. **no** Then have them look at the scatter plot they drew in Exercise 2a to determine the relationship and answer the question.

CONNECTION TO SOCIAL STUDIES
Exercise 6 Ask students to speculate about how they might use the trend observed in part (b).

WRAP UP

IDENTIFYING THE BIG IDEA Ask students to explain how to read and construct scatter plots.

PORTFOLIO Share with students the criteria you will use to assess their work in portfolios, as well as how you plan to use the results. Students should understand how the rubrics are used to assess their work, how each piece in the portfolio counts, and how the scores they get in their portfolios will affect their overall evaluation.

Work Together

Making a Scatter Plot

Work with a partner. Use the data at the right.

Movie Attendance

Year	Average Ticket Cost (dollars)	Admissions (millions)
1982	2.94	1,175
1984	3.36	1,199
1986	3.71	1,017
1988	4.11	1,085
1990	4.23	1,189
1992	4.15	1,173
1994	4.18	1,292
1996	4.42	1,339

Source: Motion Picture Association of America

4. Make a scatter plot using the average cost of a ticket and the number of people attending movies. **See back of book.**

5. a. What labels did you choose for the axes?
b. What intervals did you choose for the axes?

5a. Average Ticket Cost (dollars); Movie Admissions (millions)

b. Check students' work.

6. *Analyze* What sort of trend do you see? **weak positive**

Now you may assign Exercises 3–8.

EXERCISES *On Your Own*

Biology **Use the data at the right.**

1–5. See back of book.

1. Can you see any pattern in the wolf population? In the moose population?

2. a. Make a scatter plot to compare the moose population and wolf population.
b. *Reasoning* Do you see any relationship between the two populations? Explain.

Tell what trend you would expect to see in scatter plots comparing the following sets of data. Explain your reasoning.

3. the number of children in a family and the number of pets

4. hours spent watching television and hours spent studying

5. area of a state and the number of governors the state has had

Moose and Wolf Populations on Isle Royale, Michigan

Year	Wolf	Moose	Year	Wolf	Moose
1980	50	664	1989	11	1,397
1981	30	650	1990	15	1,216
1982	14	700	1991	12	1,313
1983	23	900	1992	12	1,600
1984	24	811	1993	13	1,879
1985	22	1,062	1994	15	1,770
1986	20	1,025	1995	16	2,422
1987	16	1,380	1996	22	1,178
1988	12	1,653			

Source: National Park Service, Isle Royale, Michigan

PRACTICE

Practice 1-9 Exploring Scatter Plots

Tell what trend you would expect to see in scatter plots comparing the following sets of data. Explain your reasoning. Answers may vary. Samples given.

1. a person's height and the person's shoe size Positive trend; as a person grows taller, his or her foot gets larger.
2. the age of a child and amount of weekly allowance that the child receives Positive trend; generally, as a child gets older, his or her allowance increases.
3. the distance one lives from school and the length of the school day No trend; the distance one lives from school is not related to the length of the day.
4. the average number of hours a child sleeps and the age of the child Negative trend; as a child grows older, he or she needs less sleep.
5. Make a scatter plot of the following data. Does the scatter plot show any trend? If so, what? yes; positive trend

Number of Hours of Practice	Number of Successful Free Throws out of 10
6	3
7	5
8	6
9	6
10	7
11	7
12	6
13	7

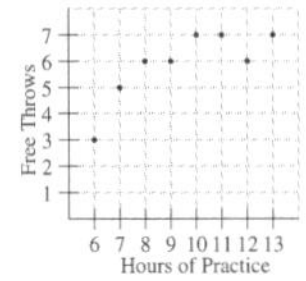

6. **Circle A, B, or C.** Which of the following scatter plots below probably compares the temperature and the number of people at the toboggan slide?

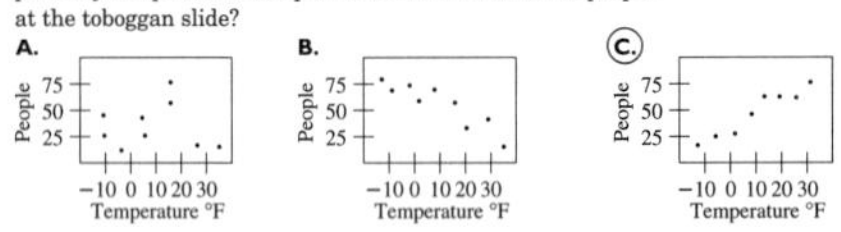

Practice

In copymaster and workbook formats

RETEACHING

Reteaching 1-9 Exploring Scatter Plots

Gilbert is investigating the relationship between the number of credit cards a person has and the amount of credit card debt.

First, he made a table from his data. Then he plotted the data in a scatter plot.

Credit Cards and Credit Card Debt

Number of Cards	Amount of Debt
1	$0
1	$1,000
1	$5,000
2	$3,000
2	$5,000
3	$10,000
3	$5,000
3	$8,000
4	$10,000
5	$19,000

Gilbert's scatter plot shows a **positive trend** in the data. That means as the number of credit cards goes up so does the amount of debt. As one value goes up, so does the other.

In a **negative trend,** one value goes up while the other goes down.

1. Dana surveyed her friends about how much TV they watch and their average test scores. Her results are shown below. Complete the scatter plot for the data.

Test Scores and TV

TV Hours Per Day	Average Test Score	TV Hours Per Day	Average Test Score
1	98	3	79
1	86	3	73
2	90	3	75
2	82	4	62
2	85	5	68

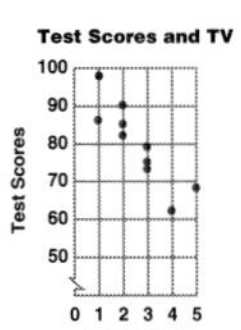

2. Is the trend in the data negative or positive? Explain. Negative; as one value goes up, the other goes down.
3. Describe the relationship Dana likely found between test scores and TV time. The more TV students watch, the lower their test scores.

ENRICHMENT

Minds on Math Transparency

1-9

A store owner bought several boxes of denim shirts to sell at her store. The shirts cost her $6 each and come one dozen to a box. The third digit on the total on her receipt was missing. If the receipt read $12D84, where D is the missing digit, how many shirts did she buy?

2,064

See *Solution Key* for worked-out answers.

LESSON QUIZ

1. Make a scatter plot of the following data.

Time	Temperature (°F)
6 A.M.	12
7 A.M.	13
8 A.M.	18
9 A.M.	25
10 A.M.	32

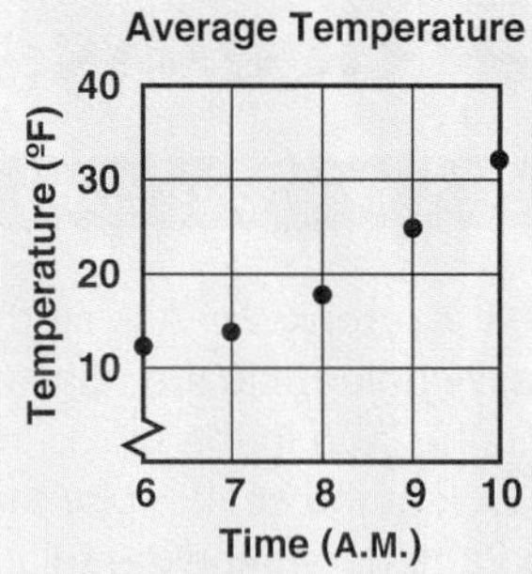

2. What is the relationship between the time and temperature? **There is a positive trend.**

6. *Social Studies* Use the data at the right.
   a. Make a scatter plot showing the relationship between the number of households and number of people per household. **a–b. See margin p. 43.**
   b. *Writing* Do you see a trend in your scatter plot? Support your answer.

Households in the United States

Year	Number of Households (in millions)	Number of People per Household
1950	43.6	3.37
1960	52.8	3.33
1970	63.4	3.14
1980	80.8	2.76
1990	93.3	2.63

Source: *Statistical Abstract of the United States*

7. **Choose A, B, or C.** Carmella made a scatter plot comparing the daily temperature and the number of people at a beach. Which of the three scatter plots below most likely represents the data? Explain your choice.

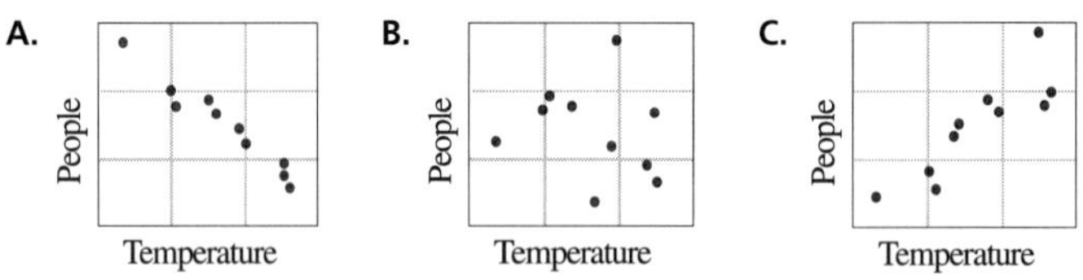

7. C; as temperature rises, more people go to the beach.

8. Make a scatter plot of the data below. Describe any trends you see in the data. **See margin p. 43 for graph.**

Average Temperature in Northern Latitudes

Latitude (°)	0	10	20	30	40	50	60	70	80
Temp. (°F)	79.2	80.1	77.5	68.7	57.4	42.4	30.0	12.7	1.0

As the latitude increases, the average temperature decreases. There is a negative trend.

PORTFOLIO

For your portfolio, choose one or two items from your work for this chapter. Here are some possibilities:
- corrected work
- work you found challenging
- part of your project

Explain why you have included each selection.

Mixed Review

Make a stem-and-leaf plot for each set of data. *(Lesson 1-5)*

9. number of students per teacher
   27 29 34 24 29 19
   30 19 25 22 27 15
   See right.
10. depths at different points in pond (in feet)
    3.7 9.6 9.4 8.4 8.6 7.5 6.8
    8.8 7.9 9.2 10.3 10.1 7.8

9.

1	5 9 9
2	2 4 5 7 7 9 9
3	0 4

1 | 5 means 15 students

10.

3	7
4	
5	
6	8
7	5 8 9
8	4 6 8
9	2 4 6
10	1 3

10 | 1 means 10.1 ft

11. Is the question "Do you prefer summer or fall?" biased? Explain. *(Lesson 1-7)*
    No; the question shows no preference to either choice.
12. *Choose a Strategy* Valerie had three bags of fruit. The first was labeled "peaches," the second "plums," and the third "pears." No bag had a correct label. Valerie reached into the bag marked "plums" and picked out a peach. Match each bag's label with the fruit in the bag.
    "Plums" had peaches, "peaches" had pears, and "pears" had plums.

Extra Practice, Lesson 1-9, page 514

FINISHING THE CHAPTER PROJECT

PROJECT DAY You may wish to plan a project day on which students share their completed projects. Encourage students to explain their process as well as their product.

PROJECT NOTEBOOK Ask students to review their project work and bring their notebooks up to date.

Have students review their methods for conducting market research, making graphs, and calculating summary statistics for the project.

SCORING RUBRIC

3 You correctly used three different display methods to show the data you collected. Your displays are attractive and self-explanatory. You identified both the best display method and the best averaging method. You gave reasons to support your choices.

2 You created three displays of your data and calculated the mean, median, and mode. Either your displays or your explanations are not as complete or neat as they could be.

1 Your survey data is complete, but you only completed two displays of the data. Either your displays are not self-explanatory, or you neglected to compare display methods or averaging techniques.

0 Either your survey was not thorough or complete, or you left out important parts of your presentation.

FINISHING THE CHAPTER PROJECT

CHAPTER PROJECT

Estimate the Size of a Crowd and Take a Survey The Project Link questions on pages 7, 29, 32, and 38 should help you to complete your project. Here is a checklist to help you gather together the parts of your project.

- ✔ a crowd picture with your estimate of its size
- ✔ your survey question and a graph that displays the results of your survey
- ✔ an estimate of survey results using the size of the crowd in your picture

Use your estimate of the crowd size and your survey results to plan what type of concessions you would have at a new stadium or arena.

Be sure all of your work is neat and clear. You want to impress the city planners!

Reflect and Revise

Review your project with a friend or someone at home. Is your method for finding the estimate of the size of the crowd clear? Do you explain how you chose your random sample? If necessary, make changes to improve your project.

Web Extension

Prentice Hall's Internet site contains information you might find helpful as you complete your project. Visit www.phschool.com/mgm2/ch1 for some links and ideas related to taking surveys.

pages 41–42 On Your Own

6a.

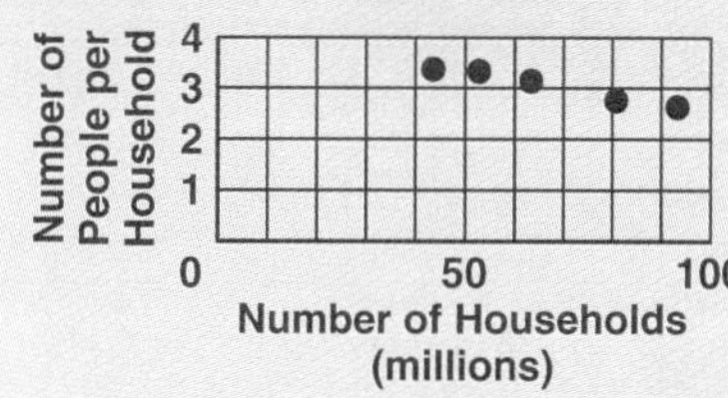

b. There is a negative trend. As the number of households has increased, the number of people per household has declined.

8.

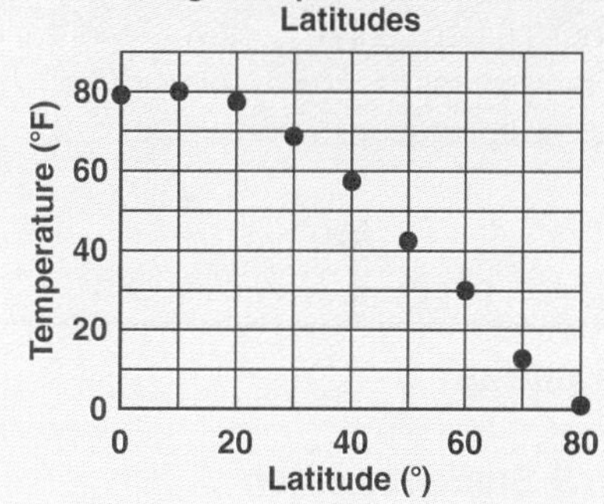

STUDENT SELF-ASSESSMENT SURVEY

Chapter 1 Student Self-Assessment Survey

1. Now that you have finished this chapter, think about what you have learned about interpreting data. Check each topic that you feel confident you understand.
   - ______ organize data in frequency tables, line plots, and histograms (1-1)
   - ______ make bar and line graphs (1-2)
   - ______ use a line graph to make predictions (1-2)
   - ______ use a spreadsheet to make graphs (1-3)
   - ______ make double line and double bar graphs (1-3)
   - ______ find and use mean, median, and mode (1-4)
   - ______ make stem-and-leaf plots (1-5)
   - ______ find range using stem-and-leaf plots (1-5)
   - ______ use logical reasoning to solve problems (1-6)
   - ______ identify a random sample (1-7)
   - ______ write survey questions (1-7)
   - ______ recognize how presentation of data can influence opinion (1-8)
   - ______ read and draw scatter plots (1-9)
2. Before the Chapter Assessment, I need to review ______
3. a. Check one. In general, I thought this chapter was
   ___ a snap ___ easy ___ average ___ hard ___ a monster
   b. Why do you feel this way? ______
4. In this chapter, I did my best work on ______
5. In this chapter, I had trouble with ______
6. List three situations where you might find data used in a misleading way. ______
7. The math in this chapter dealt with interpreting data. Do you like doing this kind of math? ______ Explain. ______
8. Did you make graphs on the computer? ______ If so, describe how making graphs on the computer compares with making graphs by hand. ______

Assessment

Vocabulary/Symbols

average, bar graph, biased questions, cell, double bar graph, double line graph, frequency table, histogram, intervals, legend, line graph, line plot, mean, median, mode, negative trend, no trend, outlier, population, positive trend, random sample, range, scatter plot, spreadsheet, stem-and-leaf plot

Materials / Manipulatives

- graph paper
- calculator

Resources

Student Edition

Extra Practice, p. 514
Glossary/Study Guide

Teaching Resources

Chapter Support File, Ch. 1
- Student Self-Assessment Survey

Glossary, Spanish Resources
Tools for Studying Smarter

WRAP UP

Exercise 1 Before doing this exercise, ask students for the range of the data. Have the class offer suggestions for intervals to use in graphing the data.

Exercise 6 Some students may have trouble beginning. Encourage students to write down the data and use a table to organize it.

WRITING **Exercise 7** Have students brainstorm in groups for ideas.

ASSESSMENT **Exercise 9** Have students work with partners. Encourage partners to plan their graphs together before beginning to draw them and to check their graphs for accuracy. After the graphs are drawn, have the class as a whole discuss conclusions.

Remind students that the new mathematical terms in this chapter are defined in the Student Study Guide/Glossary in the back of the textbook.

1 WRAP UP

Collecting and Reporting Data 1-1

To organize data, you can make a frequency table and use it to create a line plot or a histogram.

Cooked	Frequency
0–2	11
3–5	8
6–8	4
9–11	2

1. Frances surveyed her classmates to see how many times a month each cooked dinner at home. The frequency table at the right shows their responses. Make a line plot or a histogram of the data. See back of book.

Displaying Data 1-2, 1-3, 1-4, 1-5

Spreadsheets can be useful tools for organizing data. You can create graphs from a spreadsheet. A **bar graph** compares amounts and a **line graph** shows changes in data over time.

	A	B	C
1	year	0–19 yr	20–39 yr
2	1980	72.5	72.4
3	1985	70.3	80.6
4	1990	71.7	82.1
5	1995	75.8	81.0

2. The spreadsheet shows the population (in millions) for two age groups in the United States.
   a. What is the value in cell B3? 70.3
   b. Which cell has the value 82.1? C4

3a. See back of book.

3. a. Make a graph of the data at the right.
   b. Estimate the population in 2000 for people ages 0–19 years old. Answers may vary. Sample: 78 million people

The **mean, median** and **mode** of a set of data, along with any **outliers,** reflect the characteristics of the data.

You can use a **stem-and-leaf** plot to organize a set of data.

Week 1	Week 2
25	0
15	10
35	20
15	25
15	30
40	40
75	40

4. Meredith plays the French horn. At the right is a record of her practice time in minutes for two weeks. 27.5; 25; 40 and 15
   a. Find the mean, median, and modes of the data.
   b. What is the outlier? How does it affect the mean?
   c. Meredith wishes to impress her teacher with how much she has practiced. Will Meredith show her teacher the mean, median, or one of the modes of her daily practice time? the mode 40

   b. 75 is an outlier; it increases the mean.
5. Make a stem-and-leaf plot of the data in the table. See back of book.

Problem Solving Strategies 1-6

6. Sam, Katie, and Martin went to a costume party as a spider, a fox, and a fish. Each brought a treat to the party. The fish did not bring oatmeal cookies. The spider brought apples. Martin was the fox, and Katie made popcorn. Which costume did each person wear and what treat did each person bring?

6. Sam was the spider and brought apples; Katie was the fish and brought popcorn; Martin was the fox and brought cookies.

Samples and Surveys and Using Data to Persuade 1-7, 1-8

A **random sample** is selected if the members of the population have an equal chance of being selected.

Biased questions are unfair questions. They make assumptions that may or may not be true or make one answer seem better than another.

7. *Writing* The editor of the school newspaper has asked you to write an article on what improvements students would like to see in the school bus service.
   a. Write a fair question for your survey.
   b. How would you choose your random sample?

7a. Sample: How many minutes before the first period should the school bus arrive?
b. Sample: Survey every fifth person on each bus.

8. *Open-ended* Describe an advertisement you have seen in which data were used to persuade. Check students' work.

Scatter Plots 1-9

Scatter plots show the relationship between two sets of data.

a. See back of book.

9. a. Make a scatter plot of the data at the right.
   b. Is there a relationship between the weight of an animal and its pulse? Explain.
   No; there is no clear trend in the data.

10. **Choose A, B, or C.** Which of the scatter plots below shows a positive trend? B

A. 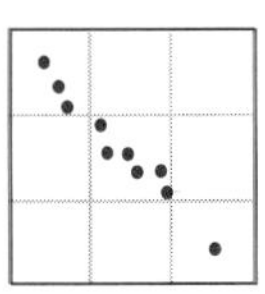
B. 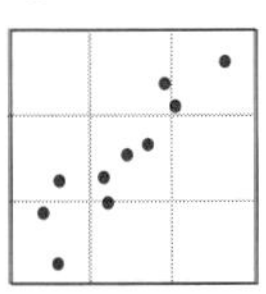
C. 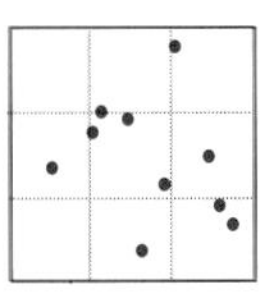

Average Weights and Pulse Rates of 9 Animals

Animal	Weight (in pounds)	Pulse (in beats/min)
Carp	17	59
Cat	9	130
Cod	11	48
Fox	10	240
Mink	2	340
Porcupine	15	300
Rabbit	3	150
Salmon	6	38
Squirrel	1	390

CHAPTER ASSESSMENT • FORM A

Chapter 1 Assessment • Form A

Answers

1. One hundred students were asked, "How many hours of TV did you watch last night?" The responses were recorded in a frequency table as shown. Create a histogram for the data.

Hours	Frequency
0–1	15
1.1–2	25
2.1–3	31
3.1–4	20
over 4	9

1. 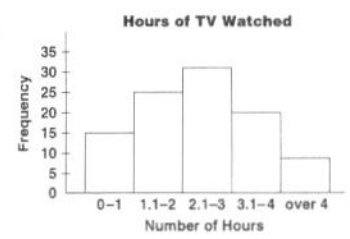

Use the spreadsheet below for Exercises 2–3.

	A	B	C	D
1	Type of Store	Pens Sold	Pencils Sold	Markers Sold
2	Supermarket	14	11	3
3	Book Store	27	22	9

2. What value is in cell B3? — 2. 27
3. In which cell is the value 3? — 3. D2

The double line graph below shows how much money Andreas and John spent for lunch each week during the month of October. Use the graph to answer Exercises 4–6.

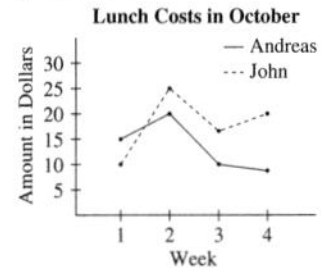

4. During which week did Andreas spend more than John? — 4. week 1
5. During which week was the difference between the amount each spent the greatest? — 5. week 4
6. How much more did Andreas spend than John in week 1? — 6. $5

CHAPTER ASSESSMENT • FORM A

Chapter 1 Assessment • Form A (continued)

Sandy recorded the number of pets owned by 15 friends. Use the data to answer Exercises 7–9.
0 0 1 1 1 1 2 2 2 2 2 3 3 6 10

7. Find the mean, median, and mode. — 7. mean: 2.4; median: 2; mode: 2
8. Does the mean or the median best represent the data? Explain. — 8. median because there is an outlier
9. **Choose A, B, C, or D.** What is the range of the data? — 9. D
   A. 0 **B.** 2
   C. 8 **D.** 10
10. Make a stem-and-leaf plot to show the number of used cars sold each month at a car lot during the year.
    1 7 19 12 26 29 10 9 21 22 30 33

10.

0	1 7 9
1	0 2 9
2	1 2 6 9
3	0 3

0 | 1 means 1

11. Tell whether this question is biased or fair. Explain.
    Would you prefer a vacation in pleasant, sunny Florida or in the barren wasteland of the Arctic?

11. biased because of the words *pleasant, sunny, barren,* and *wasteland*

Choose a Strategy

12. Ten friends went to a carnival. Five rode the roller coaster and the Ferris wheel. Two rode the Ferris wheel but not the roller coaster. Each friend rode at least one of the two rides. How many rode only the roller coaster? — 12. 3 friends

Writing

13. Explain how the graph below could be redrawn to be less misleading.

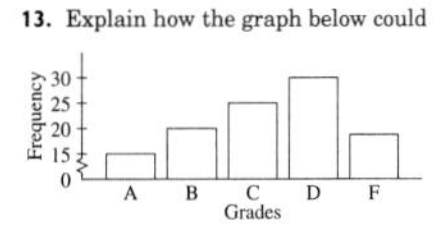

Redraw the graph with frequencies beginning at zero.

CHAPTER ASSESSMENT • FORM B

Chapter 1 Assessment • Form B

Choose the best answer. Circle A, B, C, or D.

1. One hundred students responded to the question, "How many hours of studying did you do last night?" The responses were recorded in a frequency table. What would the vertical axis on a bar graph show?
   A. intervals (B.) frequencies C. bars D. areas

The double line graph at the right shows how much money Sundi and Melissa spent for entertainment each month. Use the graph to answer Exercises 2–5.

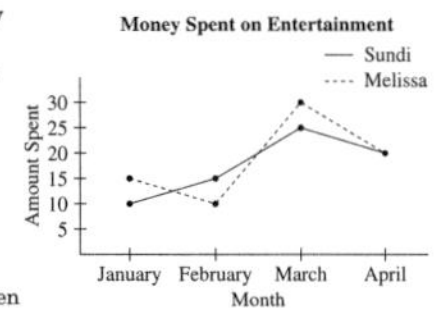

2. During which month did Melissa spend less than Sundi?
   A. January (B.) February
   C. March D. April
3. During which month was the difference between the amount each spent the least?
   A. January B. February C. March (D.) April
4. Estimate Sundi's total during the four months.
   A. $50 B. $60 (C.) $70 D. $75
5. About how much more did Melissa spend on entertainment in March than in February?
   A. $10 (B.) $20 C. $30 D. $40

Alex recorded the number of CDs owned by a group of 15 friends. Use the data to answer Exercises 6–9.

2, 3, 3, 4, 4, 4, 4, 6, 7, 7, 7, 8, 8, 9, 16

6. Which statement is *not* correct?
   A. The mode is less than the median. B. The median is less than the mean.
   (C.) The mean is less than the mode. D. The median is 6.
7. Which best represents the data?
   A. mean (B.) median C. mode D. range
8. What is the outlier, if any, in the data?
   A. none B. 2 C. 9 (D.) 16
9. What is the range of the data?
   A. 2 (B.) 14 C. 15 D. 16

Assessment

CHAPTER ASSESSMENT • FORM B

Chapter 1 Assessment • Form B (continued)

10. The scatter plot at the right shows the relationship between two sets of data. Which of the following is true?

   A. As the values of one set of data increase, the values of the other set tend to increase.
   B. The points show a positive trend between the two sets of data.
   (C.) As the values of one set of data decrease, the values of the other set tend to increase.
   D. The points show no trend between the two sets of data.
11. The data list shows the number of computers sold each month at AES Computers during its first year in business.
    12 17 29 22 36 39 20 9 21 32 30 43
    A stem-and-leaf plot of the data would have which values for the stems?
    (A.) 0, 1, 2, 3, 4 B. 9, 12, 21, 30, 43
    C. 0, 1, 2, 3, 6, 7, 9 D. 10, 20, 30, 40
12. Which would be a better way to ask this survey question?
    Do you think student freedom is unfairly denied by not allowing students the right to go off campus for lunch?
    (A.) Do you think students should be allowed off campus during lunch?
    B. Do you think that unfair restriction of students at lunchtime should be tolerated by the community?
    C. Do you think that punishing students by not allowing them to go off campus during lunch is fair?
    D. Do you think that well-behaved students should be rewarded by being allowed to go off campus at lunch?
13. Use the spreadsheet. In which cell is the value 4?

	A	B	C	D
1	Family	Boys	Girls	Adults
2	Smythe	2	2	3
3	Lee	1	4	1

    A. A1 B. B3 (C.) C3 D. D2

Choose a Strategy

14. Four students ran a race. Thomas placed before Terry but after Troy. Terry placed before Ted. How did the runners place from first to last?
    A. Thomas, Troy, Ted, Terry (B.) Troy, Thomas, Terry, Ted
    C. Ted, Troy, Thomas, Terry D. Terry, Thomas, Troy, Ted

Teaching Resources

Chapter Support File, Ch. 1, and Spanish Resources

Teacher's Edition

See pp. 2C–D for Assessment Options.

Teaching Resource Software

- Computer Item Generator, Ch. 1

ASSESSMENT

ENHANCED MULTIPLE CHOICE QUESTIONS are more complex than traditional multiple choice questions, which assess only one skill. Enhanced multiple choice questions assess the processes that students use, as well as the end results. They are written so that students can use more than one strategy to solve the problem. Using multiple strategies is encouraged by the National Council of Teachers of Mathematics (NCTM). **Exercise 5** is an enhanced multiple choice question.

Exercise 8 If students have trouble beginning, suggest that they make a logic table. You may also wish to point out the meaning of the word *nephew.*

WRITING EXERCISES allow students to describe more fully their thinking and understanding of the concepts they've learned. **Exercise 11** is a writing exercise.

1 ASSESSMENT

1. Twenty people were asked about the amount of time it takes them to commute to work.
   a. Make a frequency table for the data.
   b. Choose intervals for the data. Make a histogram. a–b. See back of book.

"How Many Minutes Do You Spend Commuting to Work?"

0	60	25	10
15	45	35	30
25	50	90	20
35	10	60	30
40	30	50	45

Teenagers' Preferred Exercise

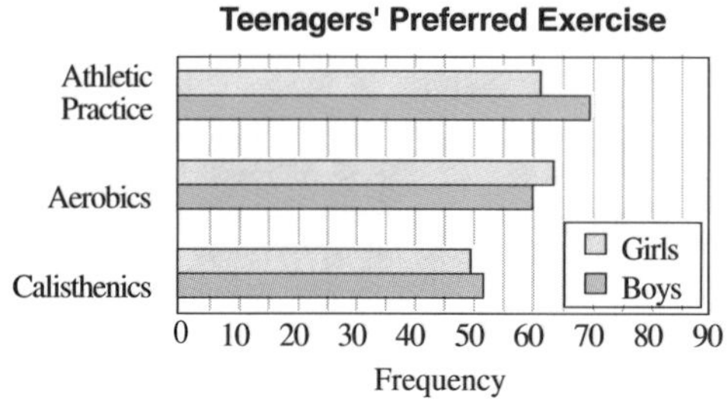

2. Use the graph above to answer the following questions.
   a. Who gets more exercise through athletic practice? boys
   b. Who gets less of their exercise through calisthenics? girls
   c. Which form of exercise do teenagers do most? athletic practice
   d. About how many girls were surveyed? 175
3. The Summer Street School holds a crafts fair every year. Their profits for the last five years are $425, $355, $390, $400, and $360. Make a line graph representing the profits. See back of book.
4. a. What kind of graph is better for showing changes over time?
   b. What kind of graph is better for comparing data?
   a. line graph b. bar graph
5. **Choose A, B, C, or D.** To best describe the favorite subject of seventh grade students, which measure would you use? C
   A. mean B. median
   C. mode D. range
6. Mark Lenzi and Xiong Ni competed for the gold medal at the 1996 Summer Olympic men's diving competition. Use the scores to create an appropriate graph to compare the two diver's scores for the six final dives. See back of book.

Dive	Lenzi	Xiong
1	75.60	75.60
2	68.40	77.19
3	62.10	72.00
4	79.05	78.30
5	79.20	79.20
6	92.40	87.72

7. Find the mean, median, mode, and range of the weights, in ounces, of one-month-old hamsters: 4, 1, 3, 2, 2, 2, 1, 1, 2, 1, 2, 3. 2; 2; 2; 3
8. Ella, Sara, and Tim have the last names Ellis, Syrio, and Trang. Syrio is Trang's nephew. No one has a first and a last name that begin with the same letter. What is the full name of each person? Tim Syrio, Ella Trang, and Sara Ellis
9. Create a stem-and-leaf plot for the following junior league bowling scores: 45, 56, 34, 55, 78, 21, 38, 66, 56, 41. See back of book.
10. Suppose you want to conduct a survey on how long people wait in doctors' offices. Would you have a random sample if you called all of Dr. Mengesha's patients? Explain. See below.

11. See back of book.

11. *Writing* What are some ways in which a graph may be misleading?

10. No; patients of other doctors would not have a chance to be surveyed.

CUMULATIVE REVIEW

Item	Review Topic	Ch
1	Line plots	1
2, 3	Stem-and-leaf plots	1
4	Order of operations	Precourse
5	Mode	1
6	Estimation	Precourse
7	Using logical reasoning	1
8, 9, 10	Bar graphs	1
11	Median	1

1 CUMULATIVE REVIEW

Choose the best answer.

1. Use the line plot. How many families own at least three bicycles? **A**

Number of Bicycles in a Family

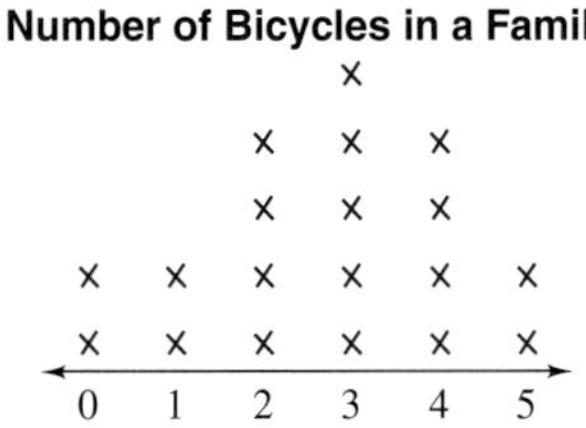

A. 11 B. 13 C. 15 D. 19

2. What is the range of the data in the stem-and-leaf plot? **B**

8	8
9	1 6
10	3 4 4 5
11	0

8 | 8 means 88

A. 88 B. 22
C. 104 D. 110

3. What could the data in the stem-and-leaf plot above most likely represent? **A**
   A. High temperatures for 8 days
   B. Number of hours 8 people spent watching television in one day
   C. Weight in pounds of Chicago Bears football players
   D. Number of books read in one week by members of the Mystery Club

4. Which symbol makes the sentence true? **C**

$3 \times 5 - 2 = 7 + (3 \blacksquare 2)$

A. + B. − C. × D. ÷

5. What is the mode of the data below? **B**
3 7 7 9 2 4 3 8 8 7 0 6

A. 6.5 B. 7 C. 8 D. 9

6. What is the best estimate of 12 × 37? **D**

A. 250 B. 300 C. 350 D. 400

7. When the soccer team stopped for lunch, eight players ordered pasta and salad while three players ordered salad only. There are 20 players on the team, and each player ordered at least one of these two items. How many players ordered pasta but no salad? **C**

A. 5 B. 12 C. 9 D. 17

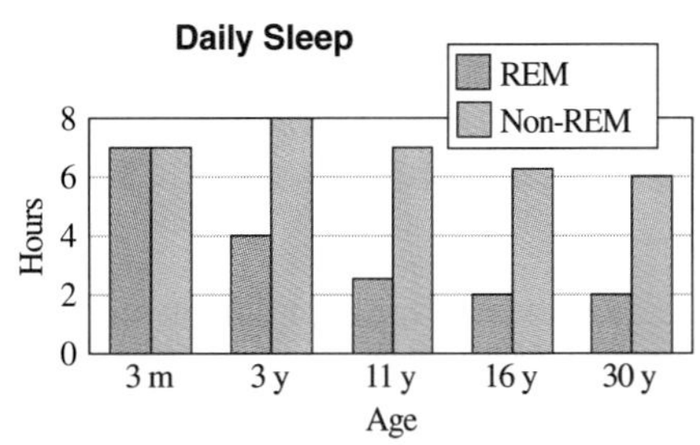

8. Use the bar graph above to compare the total number of hours slept daily by a 3-month-old to the total hours slept by a 30-year-old. **B**
   A. about half as much
   B. about twice as much
   C. about the same
   D. about three times as much

9. Use the bar graph to estimate the REM sleep for each age group. What is the mean of the data? **A**

A. 3.5 B. 2 C. 5 D. 2.5

10. In the bar graph, about how many more hours does a 3-month-old spend in REM sleep than a 30-year-old? **D**

A. 2 B. 3 C. 4 D. 5

11. What is the median of the data below? **C**
5 2 8 10 4 6 3 9 12 8

A. 5 B. 6.7 C. 7 D. 8

CUMULATIVE REVIEW

Chapter 1 Cumulative Review

Choose the best answer. Circle A, B, C, or D.

1. Replace each ▩ with +, −, ×, or ÷ to make a true statement.
3 ▩ 4 ▩ 3 = 4 ▩ 5
   A. ×, ÷, + B. ×, +, −
   C. +, ×, − (D.) ×, −, +

2. Which of the following is in order from least to greatest?
   A. 0.25, 0.52, 0.5 (B.) 5.0, 5.05, 5.5
   C. 2.16, 2.1, 2.165 D. 0.03, 0.3, 0.003

3. Estimate the area of the figure.

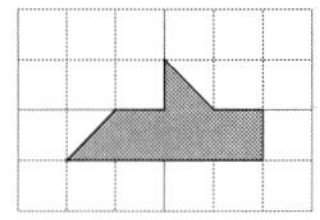

   A. 5 $units^2$ (B.) 4 $units^2$
   C. 3 $units^2$ D. 2 $units^2$

4. Which of the following is equivalent to 8 × 54?
   A. (8 × 5) + (8 × 4)
   (B.) (8 × 50) + (8 × 4)
   C. (5 × 8) + (40 × 8)
   D. (8 × 9) + (8 × 6)

5. Evaluate $s(72 + r)$ for $s = 0.1$ and $r = 32$.
   (A.) 10.4 B. 39.2
   C. 40 D. 104

6. Five friends recorded the number of football cards they have collected: 124, 256, 90, 144, 232. What is the range of the data?
   A. 108 B. 132
   (C.) 166 D. 169

7. Which of the following is true?
   A. A line plot shows the mean of a set of data.
   (B.) A stem-and-leaf plot lists each piece of data.
   C. A histogram shows either a positive or negative trend between two sets of data.
   D. A double bar graph compares changes over time of two sets of data.

8. Which is the median of the given data? 6, 7, 5, 4, 8, 9, 5, 3, 1, 10
   A. 5 (B.) 5.5
   C. 6 D. 9

9. For the data in Exercise 8, which is largest?
   A. mean B. median
   C. mode (D.) range

10. Which of the following is *not* true?
    A. Eliminating an outlier raises or lowers the mean.
    B. Eliminating an outlier does not change the mode.
    C. Eliminating an outlier can lower the range.
    (D.) Eliminating an outlier does not affect the mean, median, or mode.

Assessment

CUMULATIVE REVIEW

Chapter 1 Cumulative Review (continued)

11. What does the scatter plot show?

    A. no trend
    B. positive trend
    (C.) negative trend
    D. extreme trend

12. A stem-and-leaf plot of the data below would most likely have which numbers for the stems?
12.5, 13.2, 15.6, 14.4, 13.8,
12.3, 16.7, 15.9, 14.0, 15.6
    A. 0–19 (B.) 12–16
    C. 1.2–1.6 D. 10–16

13. What is the key for a stem-and-leaf plot of the data in Exercise 12?
    A. 10 | 1 means 10.1
    B. 12 | 5 means 125
    (C.) 12 | 3 means 12.3
    D. 16 | 7 means 1.67

14. What is the mean for the data in Exercise 12?
    (A.) 14.4 B. 14
    C. 13.6 D. 13

15. What is the median for the data in Exercise 12?
    A. 14.0 B. 14.1
    (C.) 14.2 D. 14.3

Bob and Karen's mother recorded the number of inches they grew over their first four years. She made a double line graph of the data. Use the graph to answer Exercises 16–19.

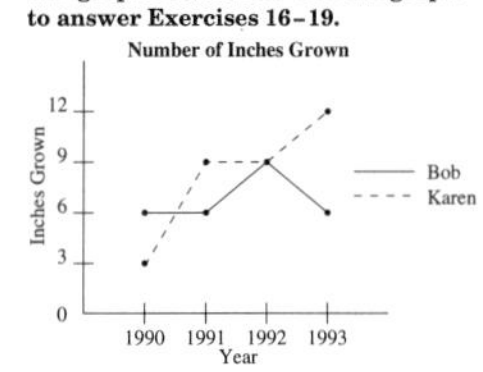

16. During which year did Bob grow more than Karen?
    (A.) 1990 B. 1991
    C. 1992 D. 1993

17. During which year was the difference in the amounts each grew the greatest?
    A. 1990 B. 1991
    C. 1992 (D.) 1993

18. What was Bob's average growth over the four years?
    A. 4.0 in. B. 5.0 in.
    (C.) 6.75 in. D. 7.1 in.

19. About how many inches in all did Karen grow over the four years?
    A. 30 in. (B.) 33 in.
    C. 35 in. D. 39 in.

20. Carla has $50 in $5-bills and $10-bills. She has 7 bills altogether. How many $5-bills does she have?
    A. two $5-bills B. three $5-bills
    (C.) four $5-bills D. five $5-bills

Resources

Teaching Resources

Chapter Support File, Ch. 1
• Cumulative Review

Teacher's Edition

See pp. 2C–D for Assessment Options.

2 Applications of Decimals

Chapter Overview

To accommodate flexible scheduling, most lessons are divided into parts. Assignment Options are given in the Teacher's Edition for each lesson.

Lesson 2-1 Data Analysis: Comparing and Rounding Decimals

Pages 50–53

NCTM 1, 3, 4, 13

Part 1 Comparing and Ordering Decimals
Part 2 Rounding Decimal Numbers

Key term: equivalent decimals

Alternative Activity 2-1

Journal

Lesson 2-2 Problem Solving: Using Estimation Strategies

Pages 54–58

NCTM 1, 2, 4, 5, 7, 13

Part 1 Estimating Sums and Differences
Part 2 Estimating Products and Quotients

Key term: compatible numbers

Journal **Project Link**

Math at Work

Lesson 2-3 Algebra: Adding and Subtracting Decimals

Pages 59–62

NCTM 2, 3, 4, 5, 9, 13

Part 1 Adding and Subtracting Decimals
Part 2 Properties of Addition

Key terms: identity property, commutative property, associative property

Alternative Activity 2-3

Checkpoint 1

Lesson 2-7 Technology: Terminating and Repeating Decimals

Pages 76–79

NCTM 1, 2, 3, 5, 6, 7

Part 1 Investigating Division on a Calculator
Part 2 Classifying Quotients

Key terms: terminating decimal, repeating decimal

Project Link

Checkpoint 2

Lesson 2-8 Algebra: Order of Operations and the Distributive Property

Pages 80–84

NCTM 2, 3, 4, 5, 7, 9

Part 1 Using the Order of Operations
Part 2 Using the Distributive Property

Key terms: order of operations, distributive property

Project Link

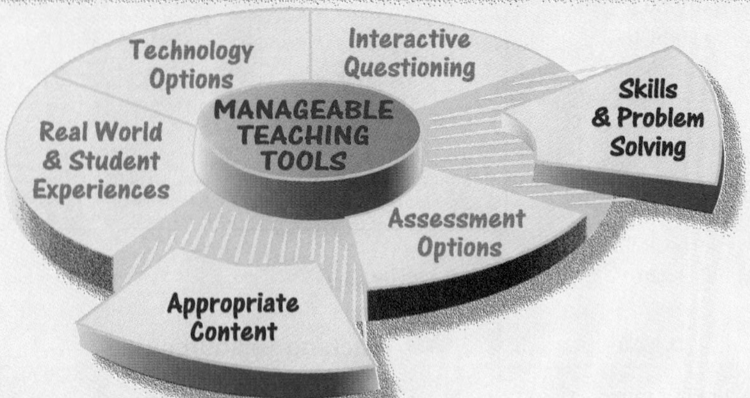

Pacing Options

This chart suggests pacing only for the core lessons and their parts. It is provided merely as a possible guide. It will help you determine how much time you have in your schedule to cover other features, such as the Chapter Project, Math Toolboxes, Wrap Up, and Assessment.

	1 Class Period	1 Class Period	1 Class Period	1 C… Per…
Traditional (40–45 min class periods)	2–1 (1) 2–1 (2)	2–2 (1)	2–2 (2)	2–3 (1)
Block Scheduling (90 min class periods)	2–1 (1) 2–1 (2) 2–2 (1)	2–2 (2) 2–3 (1) 2–3 (2)	2–4 2–5 (1) 2–5 (2)	2–6 (1) 2-…

CHAPTER PROJECT

Weighty Matters

Goal: Research, collect data, and use the data to calculate with decimals.

THEME: SCIENCE

NCTM STANDARDS

1 Problem Solving
2 Communication
3 Reasoning
4 Mathematical Connections
5 Number and Number Relationships
6 Number Systems and Number Theory
7 Computation and Estimation
8 Patterns and Functions
9 Algebra
10 Statistics
11 Probability
12 Geometry
13 Measurement

Pages 64–66	Lesson 2-4 Problem Solving Strategy
NCTM 1, 3, 4, 7	Too Much or Too Little Information Project Link

Pages 67–70	Lesson 2-5 Algebra: Multiplying Decimals
NCTM 1, 2, 3, 4, 5, 9	Part 1 Multiplying Decimals Part 2 Using Properties of Multiplication **Key terms:** identity property of multiplication, zero property, commutative property, associative property

Pages 72–74	Lesson 2-6 Dividing Decimals
NCTM 3, 4, 5, 7, 13	Part 1 Dividing a Decimal by a Whole Number Part 2 Dividing a Decimal by a Decimal

Optional Materials and Manipulatives

graph paper (2-1, 2-5, 2-8)
encyclopedia (2-4)

calculator (2-5, 2-6, 2-7)

Optional calculator use is integrated throughout the course.

ass iod	1 Class Period	1 Class Period	1 Class Period	1 Class Period	1 Class Period	1 Class Period	1 Class Period	1 Class Period	1 Class Period	1 Class Period
-4	2–5 1	2–5 2	2–6 1 2–6 2	2–7 1 2–7 2	2–8 1 2–8 2					
-8 2–8 2										

Meeting Individual Needs

Accommodating Diverse Learning Styles

In your Teacher's Edition, you will find suggestions as to how you can help students complete mathematical tasks in Chapter 2 by meeting individual needs and supporting various learning styles. Here are some examples:

VISUAL LEARNING
highlighting digits to use in front-end estimation *(p. 54)*

TACTILE LEARNING
creating models of decimal numbers *(p. 67)*

AUDITORY LEARNING
writing decimal numbers that are read aloud *(p. 50)*

KINESTHETIC LEARNING
acting out problems to help understand them *(p. 64)*

EARLY FINISHERS
Performance-Based Project, MathBlaster® Mystery, Interdisciplinary Units

GIFTED AND TALENTED
calculating what songs can fit on a tape *(p. 59)*

DIVERSITY comparing types of transportation in different countries *(p. 56)*

ACQUIRING ENGLISH PROFICIENCY (AEP)
creating mnemonics *(p. 81)*

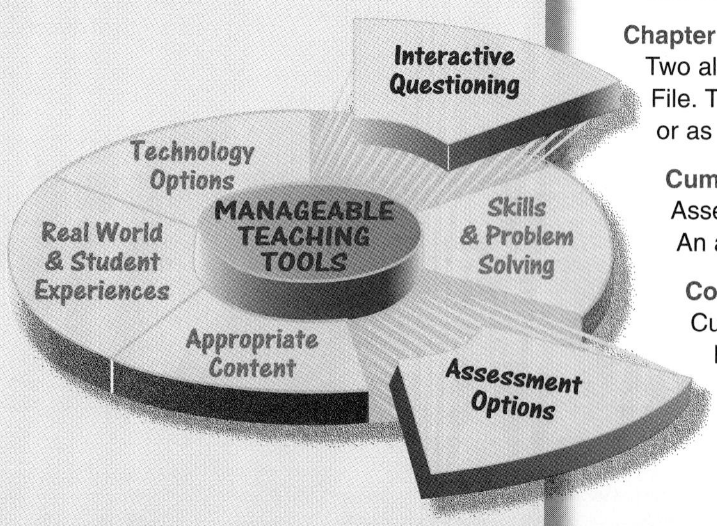

Assessing Progress

A broad range of assessment tools are available to reach a variety of learners.

INFORMAL ASSESSMENT

Informal assessments provide day-to-day feedback to help give you a picture of conceptual understanding and skill development.

ONGOING ASSESSMENT is built into lesson instruction and the Teaching Notes of the Teacher's Edition.

In the Teacher's Edition
Lesson Quiz for every lesson

In the Student Edition
On Your Own, Mixed Review, Journal, Portfolio, Project Link, Chapter Wrap Up

Look for **Interactive Questions** within lessons that

- **BUILD UNDERSTANDING** with labels such as **Analyze, Reasoning, Estimation, Writing, and Summarize**
- ✓ **CHECK UNDERSTANDING** with the **Try It Out** label.

FORMAL ASSESSMENT

Formal assessment can occur before and after the chapter, as well as at natural breaking points in the chapter.

Checkpoints
Two forms of each self-assessment Checkpoints are available: one in the Student Edition and another in the Chapter Support File in the Teaching Resources box.

- Mid-Chapter Checkpoint 1, page 62
- End-of-Chapter Checkpoint 2, page 79

Chapter 2 Assessment, page 88.
Two alternative forms are available in the Chapter Support File. They may be used after a chapter has been completed, or as a pre-test and post-test comparison.

Cumulative Review, page 89.
Assesses skills and concepts in Chapters 1–2. An alternative form is available in Chapter Support File.

Computer Item Generator for Chapter 2
Customized tests can be generated for each lesson and for mid-chapter and end-of-chapter assessments, and for pre- and post-test comparisons of achievement.

PERFORMANCE-BASED ASSESSMENT

The Chapter Project in the student edition provides a real-world connection to the math context of the chapter. The Teacher's Edition contains a scoring rubric.

A Performance Assessment with a scoring rubric can be found in the Chapter Support File in the Teaching Resources box.

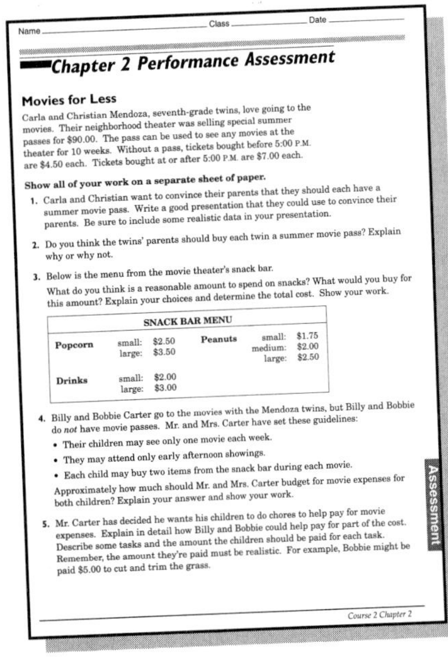

Name ______ Class ______ Date ______

Chapter 2 Performance Assessment

Movies for Less

Carla and Christian Mendoza, seventh-grade twins, love going to the movies. Their neighborhood theater was selling special summer passes for $90.00. The pass can be used to see any movies at the theater for 10 weeks. Without a pass, tickets bought before 5:00 P.M. are $4.50 each. Tickets bought at or after 5:00 P.M. are $7.00 each.

Show all of your work on a separate sheet of paper.

1. Carla and Christian want to convince their parents that they should each have a summer movie pass. Write a good presentation that they could use to convince their parents. Be sure to include some realistic data in your presentation.
2. Do you think the twins' parents should buy each twin a summer movie pass? Explain why or why not.
3. Below is the menu from the movie theater's snack bar. What do you think is a reasonable amount to spend on snacks? What would you buy for this amount? Explain your choices and determine the total cost. Show your work.

SNACK BAR MENU					
Popcorn	small: large:	$2.50 $3.50	**Peanuts**	small: medium: large:	$1.75 $2.00 $2.50
Drinks	small: large:	$2.00 $3.00			

4. Billy and Bobbie Carter go to the movies with the Mendoza twins, but Billy and Bobbie do *not* have movie passes. Mr. and Mrs. Carter have set these guidelines:
   - Their children may see only one movie each week.
   - They may attend only early afternoon showings.
   - Each child may buy two items from the snack bar during each movie.

   Approximately how much should Mr. and Mrs. Carter budget for movie expenses for both children? Explain your answer and show your work.
5. Mr. Carter has decided he wants his children to do chores to help pay for movie expenses. Explain in detail how Billy and Bobbie could help pay for part of the cost. Describe some tasks and the amount the children should be paid for each task. Remember, the amount they're paid must be realistic. For example, Bobbie might be paid $5.00 to cut and trim the grass.

Assessment

Course 2 Chapter 2

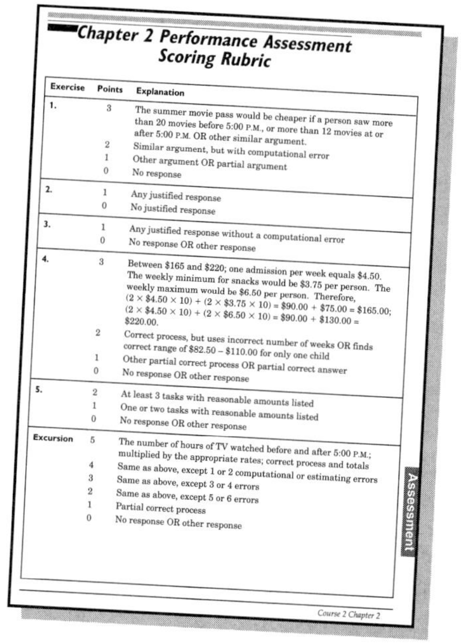

Chapter 2 Performance Assessment Scoring Rubric

Exercise	Points	Explanation
1.	3	The summer movie pass would be cheaper if a person saw more than 20 movies before 5:00 P.M., or more than 12 movies at or after 5:00 P.M. OR other similar argument.
	2	Similar argument, but with computational error
	1	Other argument OR partial argument
	0	No response
2.	1	Any justified response
	0	No justified response
3.	1	Any justified response without a computational error
	0	No response OR other response
4.	3	Between $165 and $220; one admission per week equals $4.50. The weekly minimum for snacks would be $3.75 per person. The weekly maximum would be $6.50 per person. Therefore, (2 × $4.50 × 10) + (2 × $3.75 × 10) = $90.00 + $75.00 = $165.00; (2 × $4.50 × 10) + (2 × $6.50 × 10) = $90.00 + $130.00 = $220.00.
	2	Correct process, but uses incorrect number of weeks OR finds correct range of $82.50 – $110.00 for only one child
	1	Other partial correct process OR partial correct answer
	0	No response OR other response
5.	2	At least 3 tasks with reasonable amounts listed
	1	One or two tasks with reasonable amounts listed
	0	No response OR other response
Excursion	5	The number of hours of TV watched before and after 5:00 P.M.; multiplied by the appropriate rates; correct process and totals
	4	Same as above, except 1 or 2 computational or estimating errors
	3	Same as above, except 3 or 4 errors
	2	Same as above, except 5 or 6 errors
	1	Partial correct process
	0	No response OR other response

Assessment

Course 2 Chapter 2

Correlation to Standardized Tests

Lesson		STANDARDIZED TEST ITEMS CAT5	Terra Nova	ITBS, Form M	MAT7	SAT9	Local Test
2-1	Data Analysis: Comparing and Rounding Decimals	CA1, 12, 27	27, 31, 42	CE8	CP3	PS3, 6, 11–13	
2-2	Problem Solving: Using Estimation Strategies	CA41	10–13	CE31, 33–35, 37–42, 45–52, PD4, 19	CP30–31, 33	PS41, 43	
2-3	Algebra: Adding and Subtracting Decimals	CA3, 8, 26, MC1–2, 6, 10, 14, 28, 31	1, 7, MC1, 3	PD12–17, MC3, 11, 16, 26, 28, 30, 41	PR3, 6, 18–19	PR9, 19–21	
2-4	Problem Solving Strategy: Too Much or Too Little Information	CA2		PD1, 6	CP45, 47	PS44	
2-5	Algebra: Multiplying Decimals	Ca11, 32, MC17, 22, 37	9, MC5	PD16–17, MC6, 13, 19, 35, 40	PR11, 20–21	PR10, 19, 22	
2-6	Dividing Decimals	CA26, MC5, 13, 24	33, 46, MC14	MC32, 36, 39	PR5, 10, 22 23		
2-7	Technology: Terminating and Repeating Decimals						
2-8	Algebra: Order of Operations and the Distributive Property	CA14, MC3, 9, 18, 26, 36, 41		CE19			

CA: Concepts and Applications PR: Math Procedures MC: Math Computation CE: Concepts and Estimation
PS: Problem Solving CP: Concepts and Problem Solving PD: Problem Solving and Data Interpretation

See page 2D for the level of each test referenced.

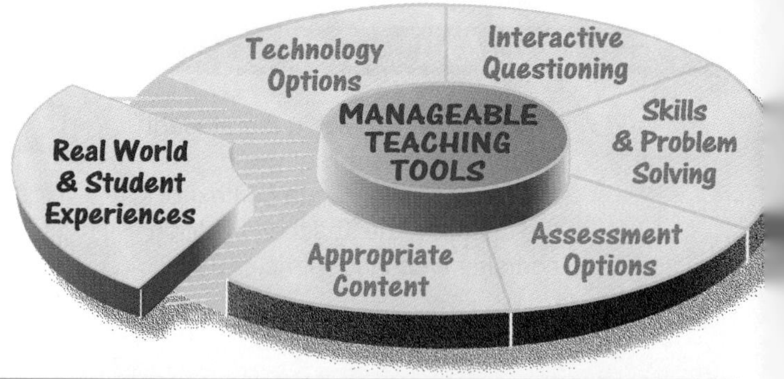

MAKING CONNECTIONS

TEAM TEACHING WITH PRENTICE HALL MATERIALS

MIDDLE GRADES MATH INTERDISCIPLINARY UNITS	*INTERDISCIPLINARY EXPLORATIONS*	*PRENTICE HALL SCIENCE* **L** Life Science **E** Earth Science **P** Physical Science
• **The Environment: Activities 2 & 6** • **The Arts: Activities 3**	• ***The Power of Patterns* pp. 38 & 39**	**L Sec. 1–3 Metric System** **E Sec. 1–3 Metric System** **P Sec. 1–3 Metric System** **Lab p. 34 (metric measuring)**

Lesson	Interdisciplinary Connections	Real World Connections	Math Integration
2-1	Sports Biology	Auto Racing Weather	Statistics
2-2	Nutrition Sports	Home Decorating Music Carpentry Weather Cooking	Statistics
2-3	Sports	Music Hobbies Cars Entertainment Decision Making	Algebra Geometry Statistics
2-4	Biology	Sewing Travel Money School Fair	Statistics
2-5	Sports	Food Exercise Wages	Algebra
2-6	Data Analysis	Exercise Computer Games Movies Gardening	Statistics
2-7	History	Technology Business	Data Analysis
2-8	Drama	Advertising Museum Admission Money Set Design	Algebra Data Analysis Geometry

School to Home

MATERIALS:
restaurant menu
merchandise catalog
newspaper
scissors
paper
pencils

English version is in the Chapter Support File. Spanish version is in the Spanish Resources.

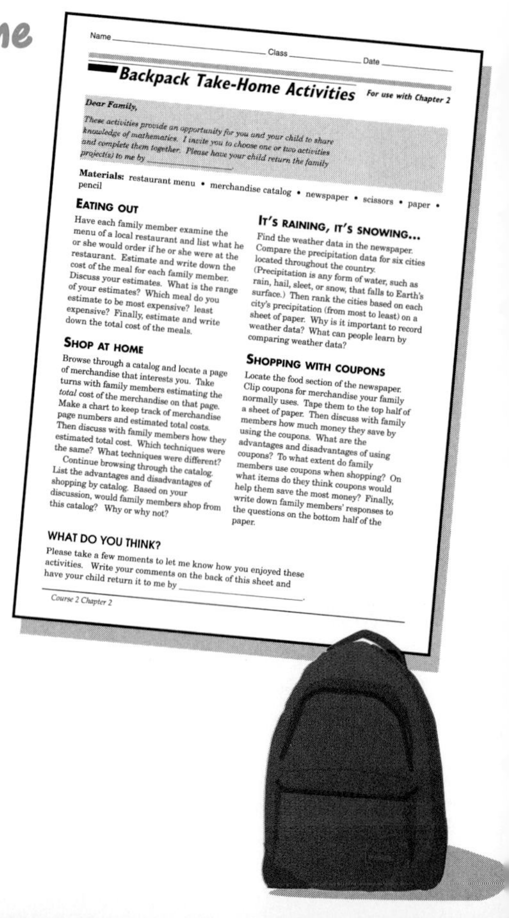

Name ______________ Class ________ Date ________

Backpack Take-Home Activities *For use with Chapter 2*

Dear Family,

These activities provide an opportunity for you and your child to share knowledge of mathematics. I invite you to choose one or two activities and complete them together. Please have your child return the family project(s) to me by ____________.

Materials: restaurant menu • merchandise catalog • newspaper • scissors • paper • pencil

EATING OUT

Have each family member examine the menu of a local restaurant and list what he or she would order if he or she were at the restaurant. Estimate and write down the cost of the meal for each family member. Discuss your estimates. What is the range of your estimates? Which meal do you estimate to be most expensive? least expensive? Finally, estimate and write down the total cost of the meals.

SHOP AT HOME

Browse through a catalog and locate a page of merchandise that interests you. Take turns with family members estimating the *total* cost of the merchandise on that page. Make a chart to keep track of merchandise page numbers and estimated total costs. Then discuss with family members how they estimated total cost. Which techniques were the same? What techniques were different?

Continue browsing through the catalog. List the advantages and disadvantages of shopping by catalog. Based on your discussion, would family members shop from this catalog? Why or why not?

IT'S RAINING, IT'S SNOWING...

Find the weather data in the newspaper. Compare the precipitation data for six cities located throughout the country. (Precipitation is any form of water, such as rain, hail, sleet, or snow, that falls to Earth's surface.) Then rank the cities based on each city's precipitation (from most to least) on a sheet of paper. Why is it important to record weather data? What can people learn by comparing weather data?

SHOPPING WITH COUPONS

Locate the food section of the newspaper. Clip coupons for merchandise your family normally uses. Tape them to the top half of a sheet of paper. Then discuss with family members how much money they save by using the coupons. What are the advantages and disadvantages of using coupons? To what extent do family members use coupons when shopping? On what items do they think coupons would help them save the most money? Finally, write down family members' responses to the questions on the bottom half of the paper.

WHAT DO YOU THINK?

Please take a few moments to let me know how you enjoyed these activities. Write your comments on the back of this sheet and have your child return it to me by ____________.

Course 2 Chapter 2

Using Technology to Enhance Instruction

For the Student

Multimedia Math Hot Pages™
This interactive software and video package on CD-ROM integrates solid math content through a variety of media.

- Hot Page™ 3-3
- Hot Page™ 3-5

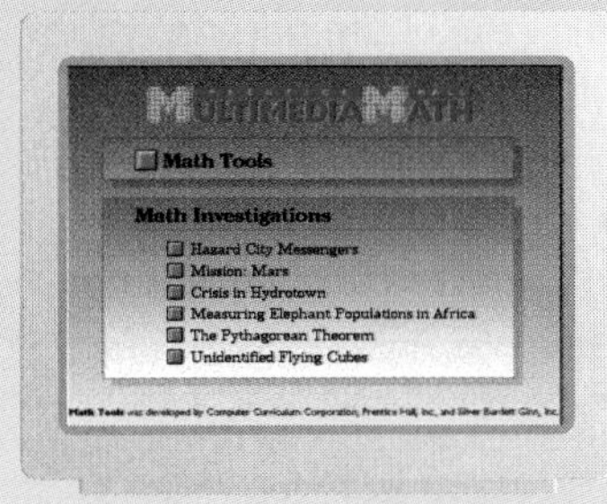

Multimedia Math Investigations
These in-depth interactive activities on CD-ROM develop real-world applications of mathematics. They allow students the opportunity to reinforce key concepts.

- Mission: Mars

MathBlaster® Mystery
This award-winning, interactive software program on CD-ROM can be used to maintain skills or to accommodate early finishers.

- Level: Earn 4 coins; Pay 4 coins
- Mission Mode (all lessons)
- Kitchen Comparisons (2-1, 2-5)
- Number Guesser (2-4, 2-7)
- Equation Maker (2-3, 2-6, 2-8)
- Word Problems (2-2, Problem Solving Practice)

Math Tools/Math Labs
This software, available on CD-ROM, includes on-screen Math Lab activities. Students use linkable, interactive tools to explore math concepts.

Interactive Student Tutorial
Available on CD-ROM, this test preparation program contains self-tests with questions in standardized test format. Software includes electronic versions of the text lessons and an on-line glossary.

Internet Connection

For Students

Support for the Chapter Project

A career-oriented link for Math at Work feature

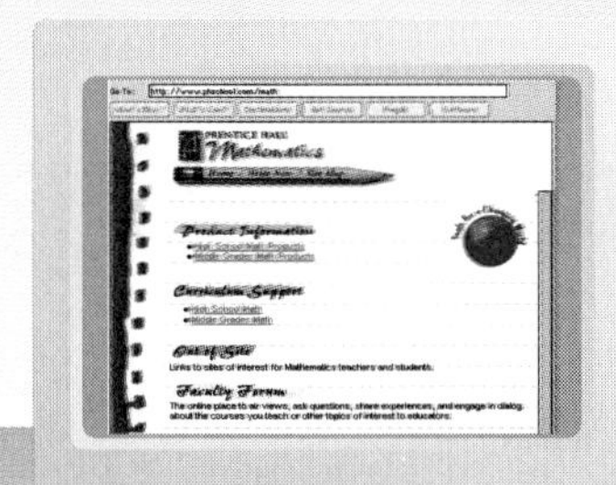

www.phschool.com/math

For teachers

Curriculum Support

Product Information

Regional Support Information

For the Teacher

Computer Item Generator with Standardized Test Practice
This software generates customized practice sheets and tests. It also generates unlimited practice sheets for the standardized tests listed on page 48D.

Resource Pro™ with Planning Express™
Available on CD-ROM, this software can be used to customize and plan lessons. It contains over 1,700 resource pages.

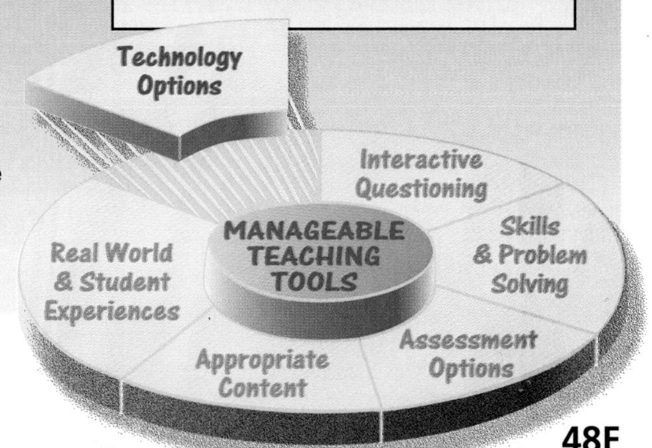

CHAPTER 2

Applications of Decimals

CONNECTING TO PRIOR LEARNING Bring to class a number of newspaper advertisements for sales. Ask students to identify the numbers with decimal points in them. Then ask them how they would find the individual cost of an item that the store has priced as a group.

CULTURAL CONNECTIONS Ask students to name a statue they have seen of an American they admire, such as Martin Luther King, Jr., or Abraham Lincoln. Have students describe what they admire about the person the statue represents and give their opinions of the statue itself.

INTERDISCIPLINARY CONNECTIONS Students can research well-known sculptures of people or animals. Ask students why some sculptures are better known than others. Have students present their findings and ideas to the class.

ABOUT THE PROJECT The Chapter Project allows students to apply their knowledge of decimals to making a table that shows the weights and costs of various statues.

Internet • For information and activities related to the Chapter Project, visit the Prentice Hall site at www.phschool.com/mgm2/ch2

Materials/Manipulatives

- newspaper advertisements

WHAT YOU WILL LEARN IN THIS CHAPTER

- How to compare decimals
- How to add, subtract, multiply, and divide decimals
- How to use the properties of addition and multiplication

LAUNCHING THE CHAPTER PROJECT

Ask students:

- *Have you ever used decimal numbers? Describe a situation in which you have used decimals.* **Answers may vary. Sample: finding the total of a few purchases**
- *How can you calculate the cost of a certain amount of a material if you know the price per pound and the weight?* **Multiply the price per pound and the weight**
- *How can two objects the same size have different weights?* **The materials in the objects are different.**

PROJECT NOTEBOOK Encourage students to keep all project-related materials in a separate folder or notebook.

TRACKING THE PROJECT You may wish to have students read Finishing the Chapter Project on page 85 to help them get an overview of the project. Set benchmark deadlines for students to show you their work in progress.

CHAPTER PROJECT

THEME: SCIENCE

Weighty Matters

Have you ever loved a pet so much that you wanted a statue made of it? Imagine a statue of your pet on the front steps of your home. "Gee, what a wise way to spend hard-earned money," your admiring neighbors would say. Or maybe not. In addition to being expensive, these statues would also be heavy. For instance, a 35-lb dog cast in gold would weigh about 670 lb.

Using Specific Gravity For the chapter project, you will find the weight of different animals and the weight of different metals. Your final project will be a table of animals with their weights, the weight of their statues in different materials, and the cost of the statues.

Steps to help you complete the project:

- How to analyze problems with too much or too little information

PROBLEM SOLVING

SCORING RUBRIC

3 You collected all the data required for the statues, and you displayed the data in an organized list or table. You accurately estimated the weight and cost of each statue. You offered an explanation for why you chose one statue to offer as a gift to a city, museum, park, or other organization.

2 You collected five animal weights, five specific gravity values, and at least two of the costs of the metals used. Most of your estimations of statue weights and costs were accurate, and you displayed the data in an organized manner.

1 You omitted some of the data, some of your calculations were inaccurate, or your presentation was not organized properly.

0 You neglected to collect a significant portion of the data, or you failed to complete and display all of the required calculations.

2-1 Teaching Notes

1 Focus

CONNECTING TO PRIOR KNOWLEDGE Ask students how they use decimals when they want to buy something from the store. **Answers may vary. Sample: The cost of items is in decimals. Money is in decimals.**

2 Teach

THINK AND DISCUSS

AUDITORY LEARNING Read a decimal aloud. Have students write each part of the number as you read it. Remind students to write the decimal point when you say the word *and.* Have students read the numbers back to you.

AEP Point out that numbers to the right of the decimal have a *-ths* ending.

Example 1 Students may want to stack the decimals so the place values line up. This will make it easier for students to see places they need to compare.

CONNECTING TO THE STUDENTS' WORLD
Example 2 Find the average yearly rainfall for your area. Compare it to the cities in the example.

EXTENSION **Example 3** Ask: *Would the answer be different if the digit in the ten-thousandths' place was a 9 instead of a 2? Explain.* **No; the digit in the ten-**

Lesson Planning Options

Prerequisite Skills

- knowledge of decimal place value (precourse)

Vocabulary/Symbols

equivalent decimals

Materials/Manipulatives

- graph paper

Resources

Student Edition

Skills Handbook, pp. 533, 534
Extra Practice, p. 515
Glossary/Study Guide

Teaching Resources

Chapter Support File, Ch. 2
- Lesson Planner 2-1
- Practice 2-1, Reteaching 2-1
- Alternative Activity 2-1
- Answer Masters 2-1

Teaching Aids Masters 20, 26
Glossary, Spanish Resources

Transparencies

9–11, 80, Minds on Math 2-1

Warm Up

Ask students to list each set of fractions in order from greatest to least.

$\frac{5}{6}, \frac{9}{10}, \frac{3}{5}$ $\frac{9}{10}, \frac{5}{6}, \frac{3}{5}$

$\frac{1}{6}, \frac{2}{3}, \frac{2}{7}$ $\frac{2}{3}, \frac{2}{7}, \frac{1}{6}$

$\frac{1}{4}, \frac{1}{3}, \frac{1}{5}$ $\frac{1}{3}, \frac{1}{4}, \frac{1}{5}$

DATA ANALYSIS Connection

2-1 Comparing and Rounding Decimals

What You'll Learn

1. To compare and order decimals
2. To round decimal numbers

...And Why

You can compare speed records and weather data.

Here's How

Look for questions that
- build understanding
- ✔ check understanding

THINK AND DISCUSS

1 Comparing and Ordering Decimals

In 1920, a gasoline-powered Dusenberg car set a one-mile speed record in auto racing at 155.046 mi/h (miles per hour). In 1997, a jet-propelled Thrust set the all-time record of 763.04 mi/h.

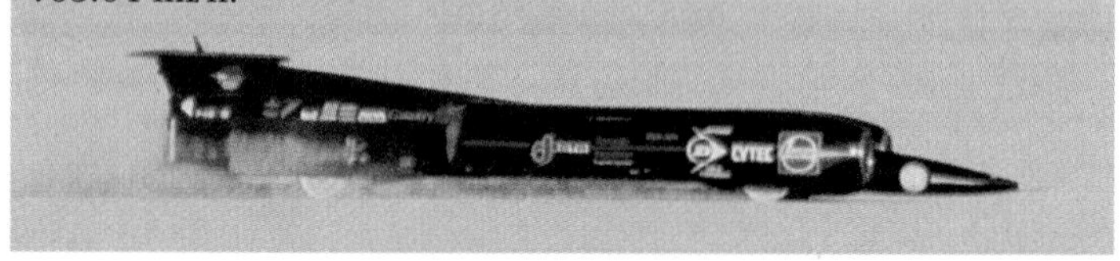

To read a decimal, find the value of the last digit on the right.

155.046 ← The last digit is in the thousandths' place.
↑ Read the decimal point as **"and."**

You read 155.046 as "one hundred fifty-five and forty-six thousandths."

hundreds	tens	ones	.	tenths	hundredths	thousandths	ten-thousandths	hundred-thousandths
1	5	5	.	0	4	6		
7	6	3	.	0	4			

1. *Reasoning* The digit 6 appears twice in the place value chart at the left. What is the value of the 6 each time it appears? **6 tens; 6 thousandths**

2. Dina read 12.0045 as "twelve and forty-five thousandths." Was she correct? Why or why not? **See left.**

2. No; 4 is in the thousandths place and 5 is in the ten-thousandths place. The value is twelve and forty-five ten-thousandths.

You can compare decimal numbers using models or a number line.

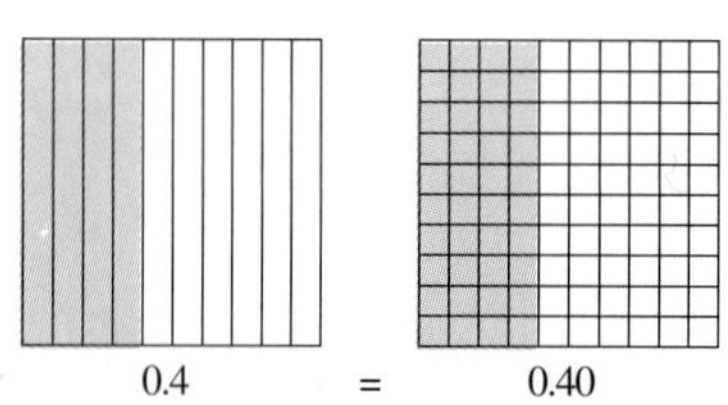

The numbers 0.4 and 0.40 are **equivalent decimals.** They name the same amount.

thousandths' place does not affect rounding to the hundredths' place.

■ ADDITIONAL EXAMPLES

FOR EXAMPLE 1

Order 0.9, 0.59, and 0.5 from least to greatest. Use a number line. **0.5, 0.59, 0.9**

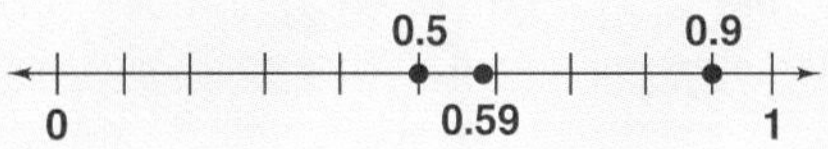

FOR EXAMPLE 2

Average Yearly Snowfall

City	Amount (in.)
Memphis, TN	5.5
El Paso, TX	5.2
Little Rock, AR	5.4

Order the cities according to the average yearly snowfall. **El Paso, Little Rock, Memphis**

FOR EXAMPLE 3

Round 2.85499 to the nearest thousandth. **2.855**

Question 6 Remind students not to write extra zeros at the end of a rounded decimal.

Question 7 It might help students to draw an arrow to the underlined number from the number at its right. This emphasizes the rounding relationship.

3.

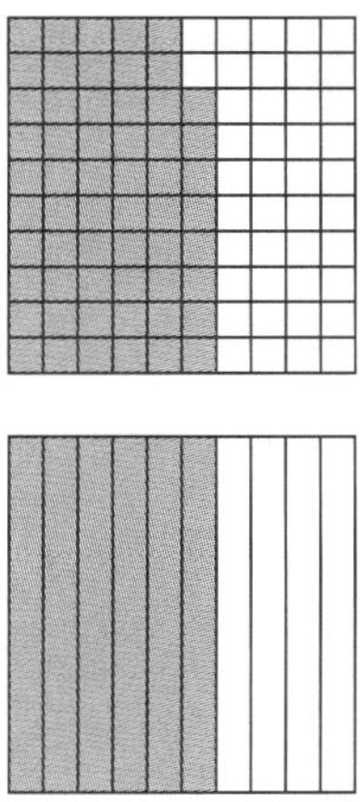

3. *Modeling* Draw models of 0.58 and 0.6. Which is greater? **See left for models; 0.6.**

■ EXAMPLE 1

Order 0.5, 0.8, and 0.25 from least to greatest. Use a number line.

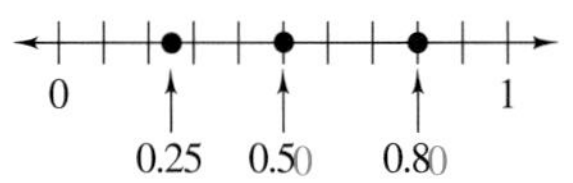

From least to greatest, the numbers are 0.25, 0.5, and 0.8.

4. *✔ Try It Out* Order the numbers from least to greatest.
   a. 2.6, 2.3, 2.7 **2.3, 2.6, 2.7**
   b. 7.58, 7.59, 7.54 **7.54, 7.58, 7.59**
   c. 4.9, 4.84, 4.87 **4.84, 4.87, 4.9**

You can also compare numbers using place value.

■ EXAMPLE 2 *Real-World Problem Solving*

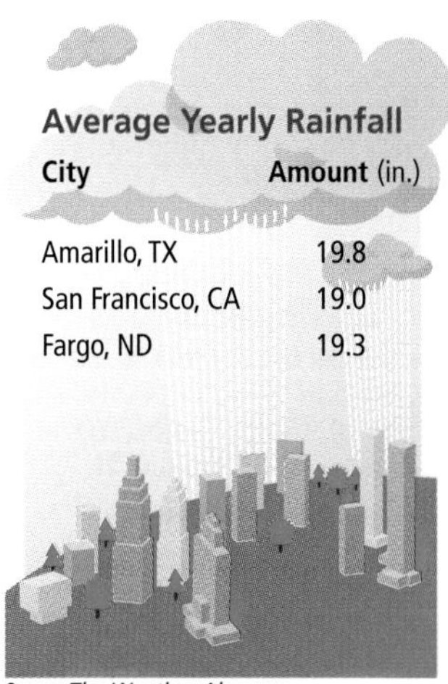

Average Yearly Rainfall

City	Amount (in.)
Amarillo, TX	19.8
San Francisco, CA	19.0
Fargo, ND	19.3

Source: *The Weather Almanac*

Weather Use the data at the left. Order the cities according to the average yearly rainfall.

Compare the numbers 19.8, 19.0, and 19.3.

19.8 19.0 19.3 ← The digits in the tens and ones places are the same.

Digits in the **tenths** place are different.

$0 < 3 < 8$ ← Compare the digits in the tenths place.

Therefore, $19.0 < 19.3 < 19.8$.

Ranked from least to greatest rainfall, the cities are San Francisco, Fargo, and Amarillo.

5. *Number Sense* Which decimal place must you use to compare 44.0174 and 44.0147? **thousandths**

Now you may assign Exercises 1–23.

2 *Rounding Decimal Numbers*

Rounding decimal numbers is similar to rounding whole numbers.

QUICKreview

Round up if the digit to the right is 5 or greater. Round down if the digit to the right is 4 or less.

■ EXAMPLE 3

Round 1.73628 to the nearest hundredth.

1.7<u>3</u>628 ← Look at the digit to the right of the hundredths place.
3 → 4 ← Since $6 > 5$, round the hundredths digit up.
1.74 ← Write the rounded number.

Technology Options

Prentice Hall Technology

Software for Learners
- Math Blaster® Mystery*
- Interactive Student Tutorial, Chapter 2*

Teaching Resource Software
- Computer Item Generator 2-1
- Resource Pro™ Chapter 2*

Internet • For related mathematics activities, visit the Prentice Hall site at www.phschool.com/math

**Available on CD-ROM only*

Assignment Options for Exercises On Your Own

To provide flexible scheduling, this lesson can be split into parts.

1 **Core** 1–11, 13–23
Extension 12

2 **Core** 24–34
Extension 35

Use Mixed Review to maintain skills.

CONNECTION TO BUSINESS Use this opportunity to show students how to write a check. When writing out the dollar amount, emphasize the word *and* goes only where the decimal point is.

ASSESSMENT Write decimals on index cards. Give one card to each student. Have them compare cards without talking to order themselves from least to greatest in a line. Once in line, have each student read their number aloud.

3 Practice/Assess

EXERCISES ***On Your Own***

CONNECTION TO BIOLOGY Exercise 24 Have students draw a period on a piece of paper. Next to the period, have students draw a segment 11.020 in. long. Let them compare the difference in size of the two spiders.

ERROR ALERT! Exercise 26 Some students may round with the underlined number.

Remediation: Have students circle the number to the right of the underlined number. Remind them the underlined number only changes if the circled number is five or greater.

OPEN-ENDED Exercise 34 Tell students to write 7.26 three times in a column. Then write 7.25 two times in the same column. Now write a number to the right of each number in the column that will make 7.26 and 7.25 round to 7.26.

pages 52–53 On Your Own

11. **John Olerud, Paul O'Neill, Alex Rodriguez, Edgar Martinez (1995), Edgar Martinez (1992), Julio Franco**
12. **No; the first two players would have the same rounded average and the last four players would have the same rounded average.**
23. **Tens, ones, and tenths are the same. 16.75 has 5 in the hundredths place, 16.746 has 4 in the hundredths place. 5 > 4, so 16.75 > 16.746**

Need Help? For practice in rounding decimals, see Skills Handbook page 534.

The symbol ≈ means "is approximately equal to." To the nearest hundredth, 1.73025 ≈ 1.73. To the nearest thousandth, 1.73025 ≈ 1.730.

6. Which is 1.37602 rounded to the nearest ten-thousandth, 1.3760 or 1.37600? Why?

6. 1.3760; when rounding, you drop all digits after the given place value if the next digit is 4 or less.

7. ✔ *Try It Out* Round each number to the indicated place.
   a. 3.<u>5</u>71 **3.6** b. 19.0<u>7</u>362 **19.07** c. 8.<u>0</u>15 **8.0** d. 4.75<u>1</u>8 **4.752**

Now you may assign Exercises 24–35.

EXERCISES ***On Your Own***

1. a. *Modeling* Look at the models at the right. Write the value of the shaded area of each model in words and as a decimal.
   b. Write a statement that compares the decimals from part (a) using <, >, or =. **0.36 < 0.52 < 0.64**

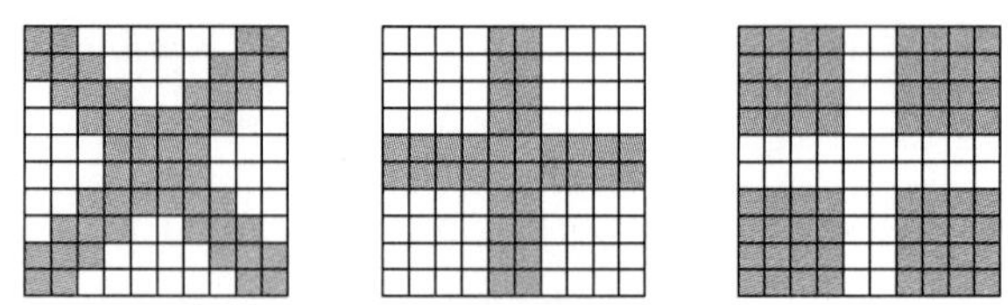

1a. fifty-two hundredths or 0.52; thirty-six hundredths or 0.36; sixty-four hundredths or 0.64

Use a number line to order the decimals from least to greatest.

2. 3.5, 3.2, 3.3 **3.2, 3.3, 3.5**
3. 9.4, 9.7, 9.42 **9.4, 9.42, 9.7**
4. 4.04, 4.01, 4.02 **4.01, 4.02, 4.04**
5. 0.32, 0.38, 0.29 **0.29, 0.32, 0.38**
6. 6.1, 6.3, 6.12 **6.1, 6.12, 6.3**
7. 1.6, 1.74, 1.30 **1.30, 1.6, 1.74**
8. 0.9, 1.38, 1.04 **0.9, 1.04, 1.38**
9. 5.43, 5.42, 5.51 **5.42, 5.43, 5.51**

Sports **Use the table at the right to answer Exercises 10–12.**

10. Who had the highest batting average? The lowest? **John Olerud; Julio Franco**
11. List the players in order from highest to lowest batting average. **See margin.**
12. *Reasoning* Suppose you rounded each batting average to the nearest hundredth. Could you accurately order the players from highest to lowest? Why or why not? **See margin.**

American League Batting Champions

Year	Player	Batting Average
1991	Julio Franco, Texas	.341
1992	Edgar Martinez, Seattle	.343
1993	John Olerud, Toronto	.363
1994	Paul O'Neill, New York	.359
1995	Edgar Martinez, Seattle	.356
1996	Alex Rodriguez, Seattle	.358

Source: *The Information Please Sports Almanac*

Open-ended **Write five numbers between the given numbers.** **13–16. Samples are given.**

13. 40 and 50 **41, 43, 44, 46, 48**
14. 18 and 19 **18.1, 18.5, 18.675, 18.8, 18.88**
15. 3.7 and 3.8 **3.701, 3.71, 3.75, 3.752, 3.79**
16. 7.08 and 7.09 **7.0802, 7.0805, 7.081, 7.082, 7.085**

WRAP UP

IDENTIFYING THE BIG IDEA Ask students to discuss how they can tell which of two decimals is greater.

JOURNAL Provide newspapers for students. Have students discuss their reasons with each other.

LESSON QUIZ

1. Compare using <, >, or =.
   1.59 ■ 1.5899 >
2. Use a number line to order the decimals from least to greatest.
   2.30, 2.28, 2.4 **2.28, 2.30, 2.4**
3. Identify the place value of the underlined digit. Then round the decimal to the indicated place. $0.368\underline{4}5$ **ten-thousandths'; 0.3685**

Compare using <, >, or =.

17. 0.167 g ■ 0.16 g >
18. 3.1309 m ■ 3.1903 m <
19. 45.715 mm ■ 45.175 mm >
20. 1.34 mL ■ 1.27 mL >
21. 2.6289 in. ■ 3.2895 in. <
22. 3.09725 mi ■ 3.07926 mi >
23. *Writing* Explain how you would determine which decimal is greater, 16.75 or 16.746. See margin p. 52.
24. *Biology* The smallest spider is a male *Patu marplesi* that is 0.017 in. across, about the size of a period. The largest spider is a male goliath bird-eating spider that is 11.020 in. across.
    a. Write each number in words.
    b. Round each number to the nearest hundredth. **0.02; 11.02**
    a. seventeen thousandths; eleven and twenty thousandths
25. Suppose you rounded 1.73648 to the nearest thousandth and wrote 1.736. Did you make a mistake? Why or why not?
    No; the next digit is 4, so you round down.

The goliath bird-eating spider is found in the rain forests of South America. This male is shown $\frac{1}{4}$ of its normal size.

Identify the place value of the underlined digit. Then round each decimal to the indicated place.

26. $0.76\underline{9}49$ **thousandths; 0.769**
27. $5.194\underline{3}8$ **ten-thousandths; 5.1944**
28. $0.5643\underline{9}1$ **hundred-thousandths; 0.56439**
29. $0.6\underline{1}34$ **hundredths; 0.61**
30. $3.24\underline{5}5$ **thousandths; 3.246**
31. $41\underline{5}.78201$ **ones; 416**
32. $8.\underline{7}247$ **tenths; 8.7**
33. $15.619\underline{4}03$ **ten-thousandths; 15.6194**
34. *Open-ended* Write five decimals that round to 7.26.
    Samples: 7.261, 7.264, 7.255, 7.259, 7.2599
35. a. Give an example of a situation when a rounded number is appropriate. **Sample: the height of the school in meters**
    b. Give an example of a situation when it is not appropriate to use a rounded decimal.
    Sample: the amount owed for three purchases

JOURNAL
Find a newspaper article that has a decimal. Do you think the decimal was rounded? Explain your reasoning.

Mixed Review

Find the mean, median, and mode of the given data. *(Lesson 1-4)*

36. 6 3 7 4 2 3 6 3 2
    4; 3; 3
37. 0.2 0.8 0.2 0.4 0.5 0.5 0.2
    0.4; 0.4; 0.2
38. a. Does Brand M cost twice as much as Brand N? Explain.
    b. Is this graph misleading? Explain. *(Lesson 1-2)* **See below.**
    Yes; the graph makes it appear that Brand N is much cheaper.

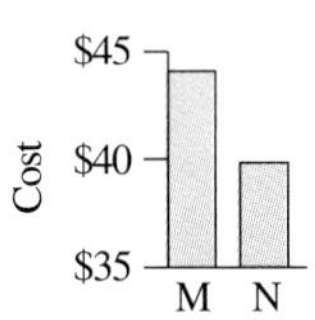

39. *Choose a Strategy* A list of consecutive whole numbers begins with 1 and ends with 113. How many digits are on the list? **231**

38a. No; the part of the graph from $0 to $35 is missing.

PRACTICE

Practice 2-1 *Comparing and Rounding Decimals*

Write five numbers between the given numbers. List the numbers in order from least to greatest. Answers will vary.

1. 30 and 35
2. 55 and 60
3. 15 and 17
4. 43 and 45
5. 8 and 9
6. 19 and 20
7. 1.3 and 1.4
8. 2.6 and 2.65

Identify the place value of the underlined digit. Then round each decimal to the indicated place.

9. $0.82\underline{7}65$ thousandths; 0.828
10. $8.\underline{7}59$ tenths; 8.8
11. $4.\underline{3}2457$ tenths; 4.3
12. $7.0\underline{0}92$ hundredths; 7.01
13. $0.7\underline{1}99$ hundredths; 0.72
14. $0.090\underline{9}9$ ten-thousandths; 0.0910
15. $5.123\underline{5}79$ ten-thousandths; 5.1236
16. $2.\underline{4}59$ tenths; 2.5
17. $5.00\underline{2}3$ thousandths; 5.002
18. $4.0\underline{2}39$ hundredths; 4.02
19. $0.0102\underline{0}6$ hundred-thou–sandths; 0.01021
20. $7.99\underline{9}905$ thousandths; 8.000

Compare using <, >, or =.

21. 0.23 [=] 0.230
22. 4.79 [<] 4.8
23. 1.92 [>] 1.09
24. 5.72 [>] 5.3
25. 4.706 [<] 4.71
26. 22.6 [=] 22.60
27. 8.09 [<] 8.90
28. 0.003 [<] 2.0030
29. 1.023 [<] 1.203
30. 10.4 [<] 10.41
31. 0.41 [>] 0.14
32. 4.390 [=] 4.3900
33. Write 5 decimals that round to 0.96. Answers may vary. Sample: 0.961, 0.962, 0.963, 0.9602, 0.9598
34. Each year, the North American continent moves approximately 1.2 in. farther away from Europe. Write three possible measurements that round to 1.2 in. Answers may vary. Sample: 1.15 in., 1.18 in., 1.21 in.
35. The length of each day of the year changes by about 0.00000002 s. Write a length of time that could be rounded up to this figure. Answers may vary. Sample: 0.0000000199 s

In copymaster and workbook formats

RETEACHING

Reteaching 2-1 *Comparing and Rounding Decimals*

To compare two decimals:

① Annex, or insert, zeros so both numbers have the same number of decimal places.
2.67 and 2.6 → 2.67 and 2.60

② Compare the two numbers without the decimal point.
267 is greater than 260.
Therefore, 2.67 is greater than 2.60.
2.67 > 2.6

To round a decimal to the nearest tenth:

① Look at the digit to the right of the tenths' place.
$9.1\underline{3}6$

② Since 3 ≤ 5, round down. Drop the digits 3 and 6. Write the rounded number.
9.1

Annex zeros so both numbers have the same number of decimal places. Then compare using <, >, or =.

1. 2.5 and 2.46 — 2.50 [>] 2.46
2. 0.05 and 0.5 — 0.05 [<] 0.50
3. 12.63 and 12.6 — 12.63 [>] 12.60
4. 7.35 and 8.2 — 7.37 [<] 8.20
5. 72.55 and 72.005 — 72.550 [>] 72.005
6. 125.25 and 152.5 — 125.25 [<] 152.50

Compare the decimals. Ring the greatest decimal in each group.

7. (3.5) 3.48 3.42
8. 15.03 (15.3) 15.00
9. 19.16 14.9 (19.4)
10. 23.905 (25.2) 23.56

Identify the place value of the underlined digit. Then round each decimal to the indicated place.

11. $15.\underline{7}94$ tenths; 15.8
12. $12\underline{1}.58$ ones; 122
13. $0.53\underline{2}4$ thousandths; 0.532
14. $6.4\underline{3}62$ hundredths; 6.44
15. $6.\underline{2}679$ tenths; 6.3
16. $7.83\underline{4}172$ thousandths; 7.834

ENRICHMENT

Minds on Math Transparency

2-1

The number on Luke's locker has three digits. The middle digit is twice the first digit. The last digit is one less than the middle digit. The sum of the digits is 14. What is the number?

365

See *Solution Key* for worked-out answers.

2-2 Teaching Notes

1 Focus

CONNECTING TO PRIOR KNOWLEDGE Ask students: *When would it be useful to estimate the sum of several numbers?* **Answers may vary. Sample: buying several things at a store** *Why wouldn't you just find the exact answer?* **Answers may vary. Sample: The computation would take too long and be too hard, all I needed was an approximate answer.**

2 Teach

THINK AND DISCUSS

VISUAL LEARNING When using front-end estimation, have students highlight the front-end digits in color.

Example 1 Ask students: *How will the answer change if you round to the nearest dollar?* **The estimate would be 2 + 1, or 3.**

EXTENSION Example 3 Ask students: *If carpet costs \$3.25 for a ft^2, estimate how much it would cost to carpet the living room.* **Answers may vary. The cost should be around \$325.**

Lesson Planning Options

Prerequisite Skills

- proficiency at rounding decimals (2-1)
- ability to add and subtract decimals with whole numbers (precourse)

Vocabulary/Symbols

compatible numbers

Resources

Student Edition

Skills Handbook, p. 534
Extra Practice, p. 515
Glossary/Study Guide

Teaching Resources

Chapter Support File, Ch. 2
- Lesson Planner 2-2
- Practice 2-2, Reteaching 2-2
- Answer Masters 2-2

Teaching Aids Masters 20, 26
Glossary, Spanish Resources

Transparencies

9–11, Minds on Math 2-2

Warm Up

Have students work in groups of three to determine how many times a watch beeps in $2\frac{1}{2}$ h and in $2\frac{1}{2}$ da, if the watch beeps every 15 min. **Including the beep at 0 min, the watch beeps 11 times in $2\frac{1}{2}$ h and 241 times in $2\frac{1}{2}$ da.**

2-2 Problem Solving: Using Estimation Strategies

What You'll Learn

1. To estimate sums and differences
2. To estimate products and quotients

...And Why

You can check reasonableness of answers.

Here's How

Look for questions that
- build understanding
- ✔ check understanding

THINK AND DISCUSS

1 Estimating Sums and Differences

You can estimate an answer before you calculate it to make sure your answer is reasonable. If the answer is close to the estimate, it is probably correct. Sometimes, an estimate is all you need.

You can use *rounding* to estimate sums and differences.

■ **EXAMPLE 1** *Real-World Problem Solving*

Food Use the menu board. Estimate the cost of a grilled cheese sandwich and a frozen yogurt.

$1.89 + 1.49 \approx 2 + 1.5$ ← Round to the nearest half-dollar.
$= 3.5$ ← Add.

The cost is about \$3.50.

1. *Look Back* Is this estimate more or less than the exact cost? How do you know? **More; each term in the sum has been rounded up.**
2. Estimate the difference between the prices of a taco and a grilled cheese sandwich to the nearest half-dollar. **\$1.50**
3. ✔ *Try It Out* If you have \$6, can you buy a taco, a frozen yogurt, and a large juice? Explain. **No; estimated cost is \$6.50. The actual cost is \$6.07.**

Another method of estimating is *front-end estimation.*

■ **EXAMPLE 2**

Estimate the cost of a slice of pizza and yogurt with granola.

Add the front-end digits. → 1.45 / $+\ 1.39$ ← **Estimate the total amount of cents to the nearest dollar.**

$2 + 1 = 3$ ← **Add.**

The total cost is about \$3.

4. *Reasoning* In Example 2, do you get the same answer if you use rounding? Why or why not? **Yes; each number rounds to \$1.50.**

ERROR ALERT! Questions 6–9 Students may use front-end estimation for all four questions. **Remediation:** Remind students that front-end estimation is most useful for sums. Because Questions 6 and 7 involve multiplication, and Questions 8 and 9 involve division, different strategies would give a closer estimate.

ADDITIONAL EXAMPLES

FOR EXAMPLE 1

Estimate the cost of a slice of pizza and a large juice. **$3**

FOR EXAMPLE 2

Estimate the cost of a taco and a small juice. **$4**

FOR EXAMPLE 3

Estimate the area of a kitchen that is 8.5 ft × 5.75 ft. **54 ft²**

FOR EXAMPLE 4

You saved $61.80. Based on the CD price list, how many CDs from category B could you buy? **4**

5. Answers may vary. Sample: Rounding; front-end estimation would give too great a difference.

5. ✔ *Try It Out* Which method of estimation would you use to find how much more a large juice costs than a small juice? Explain why you chose that method.
Now you may assign Exercises 1–16.

2 *Estimating Products and Quotients*

You can use rounding to estimate products.

QUICKreview

Area of a rectangle = length × width

EXAMPLE 3 *Real-World Problem Solving*

Home Decorating Estimate the area of a living room that is 10.5 ft × 9.25 ft.

$10.5 \approx 11$ ← Round each factor.
$9.25 \approx 9$
$11 \times 9 = 99$ ← Multiply.

The area of the living room is about 99 ft².

6. ✔ *Try It Out* Estimate 7.65 × 3.12. **24**

7. *Reasoning* You want to paint a wall that is 9.75 ft × 8.25 ft. Do you need to find an estimate or the exact area to decide how much paint to buy? **estimate**

Estimate quotients using two compatible numbers. **Compatible numbers** are numbers that are easy to divide mentally.

CD Price List

Category	Price
A	$23.95*
B	$15.95
C	$12.95
D	$ 7.95

*Double CD

EXAMPLE 4 *Real-World Problem Solving*

Music You've saved $50.25. Based on the chart at the left, about how many CDs from category D could you buy?

$7.95 \approx 8$ ← Round.
$50.25 \approx 48$ ← Choose a number that is close to 50.25 and divisible evenly by 8.
$48 \div 8 = 6$ ← Divide.

You can buy about 6 CDs from category D.

8. ✔ *Try It Out* About how many CDs in category B can you buy? Explain your choice of compatible numbers.
3; 3 CDs in category B cost about $48.

9. a. Is an estimate of the price good enough to decide if you have enough money to buy the CDs you want? Explain.
b. Is an estimate of the price good enough when you pay for your CDs? Why or why not? **a–b. See left.**

9a. Yes; you do not need to know exact cost, and it is faster to estimate.
b. No; you must pay the exact amount when buying CDs.

Technology Options

Prentice Hall Technology

Software for Learners
- Math Blaster® Mystery*
- Interactive Student Tutorial, Chapter 2*

Teaching Resource Software
- Computer Item Generator 2-2
- Resource Pro™ Chapter 2*

Internet • For related mathematics activities, visit the Prentice Hall site at www.phschool.com/math

*Available on CD-ROM only

Assignment Options for Exercises On Your Own

To provide flexible scheduling, this lesson can be split into parts.

1 **Core** 1–13
Extension 14–16

2 **Core** 17–28, 30, 31
Extension 29

Use Mixed Review to maintain skills.

Work Together

TACTILE LEARNING Have students cut out eight squares and label each with an activity number and bin weight. Students can put the squares in rows to model the problem and investigate the different combinations possible.

If you have block scheduling or extended class periods, organize students into five groups. Ask each group to create a table describing each estimation strategy. Have them choose one strategy and write a real-life situation using it. Have each group act out the situation for the class.

3 Practice/Assess

EXERCISES *On Your Own*

WRITING Exercise 11 Have students write the correct and incorrect calculations side by side and compare each step.

OPEN-ENDED Exercise 13 Have students trade problems to solve.

Exercises 14–16 Have students give the number the addends cluster around.

DIVERSITY Exercise 18 Ask if anyone in the class has been to Europe and ridden the TGV. Ask: *What is transportation like in other countries? How is it different than the transportation in your area?*

ASSESSMENT Exercises 20–28 Have students pick one of the exercises. Then

Work Together

Using Estimates

A science teacher is building shelves for the bins that hold equipment for 8 lab activities. Each shelf holds 55 lb.

Bin Weights

Activity	Bin Weight (lb)
Activity 1	16.8
Activity 2	16
Activity 3	12
Activity 4	14.98
Activity 5	15.26
Activity 6	13.8
Activity 7	17.1
Activity 8	15.04

10. a. Estimate the least number of shelves the teacher needs.

b. Explain which method you chose to estimate part (a) and why you chose that strategy.

11. *Reasoning* Which bins should share a shelf to distribute the weight as evenly as possible?

12. Is it reasonable to use estimates in this situation? Explain.

10a. 3; each bin is approximately 15 lb, so 3 bins can go on each shelf.
b. Answers may vary. Sample: Rounding to the nearest 5 lb; rounding is easier to compute.
11. Answers may vary. Sample: 17.1 and 16.8; 12, 14.98, and 16; 13.8, 15.04, and 15.26
12. Yes, if you round each weight to the nearest pound. Rounding to the nearest 5 pounds does not identify the heavier bins.

Now you may assign Exercises 17–31.

EXERCISES *On Your Own*

Estimate by rounding to the nearest half dollar.

1. \$10.13 + 1.46 **\$11.50**

2. \$9.82 − 1.76 **\$8**

3. \$11.53 + 7.23 **\$18.50**

4. \$14.17 − 10.92 **\$3**

5. \$21.18 − 17.92 **\$3**

6. *Weather* In Chicago, Illinois, the average wind speed is 10.4 mi/h. In Great Falls, Montana, the average wind speed is 13.1 mi/h. About how much greater is the average wind speed in Great Falls than in Chicago? **about 2.5 mi/h**

Use front-end estimation to find each sum.

7. 5.429 + 2.665 **8** **8.** 3.602 + 2.309 **6** **9.** 2.174 + 5.891 **8** **10.** 4.39 + 9.57 **14**

11. *Writing* Suppose you used a calculator to find 362.9 + 42.8 + 35.46. Your display reads 826.36.
a. Describe how you could have gotten this answer.
b. How could estimation help you discover your mistake?

a. You missed the decimal point in 42.8.
b. Using front-end estimation (in hundreds), the sum is about 450. So you added a number that is about 400 greater than what you needed.

12. Choose A, B, C, or D. The correct estimate of a sum is 900. Which numbers could have been used to get this estimate? **A**

A. 682.14 + 65.21 + 142.65
B. 734.3 + 201.79 + 55.22
C. 421.5 + 337.948 + 275.801
D. 225.06 + 275.8 + 269.7

solve the exercise using two strategies and decide which estimate they think is closer. Have them write a reason for their choice and then check their answer with a calculator.

CONNECTION TO STATISTICS Exercise 29 Students find estimates from data in a stem-and-leaf plot. After finding the estimates, tell students to find the actual values and compare.

WRAP UP

IDENTIFYING THE BIG IDEA Ask students to describe the different methods used to estimate decimal computations.

PROJECT LINK Tell students that one method for weighing small animals is to hold the animal while standing on a scale. Then subtract your weight from the total weight shown on the scale.

JOURNAL Help students get started by asking them to think about the different situations presented in the problems in this lesson. Or you may wish to put students in small groups to brainstorm ideas.

Math at Work

If you have extended class periods or block sheduling, have students discuss different types of detectives they have read about or may have seen in a movie or on television.

---

13. *Open-ended* Write a problem you could solve using front-end estimation. **Check student's work.**

The sample below shows the estimation technique called clustering. Use clustering to estimate each sum in Exercises 14–16.

Sample: $2.8 + 2.6 + 2.2 + 2.4 + 2.5 \approx 2.5 + 2.5 + 2.5 + 2.5 + 2.5$
$5 \times 2.5 = 12.5$ ← Multiply.

14. $6.3 + 5.9 + 6.09 + 6.33 + 5.68 + 6.1$ **36**

15. $14.25 + $13.75 + $14.53 + $13.69 **$56**

16. $33.15 + 37.95 + 34.63 + 36.29 + 34.08$ **175**

17. *Cooking* It took 75.75 lb of shredded cheese to make the world's largest burrito. Estimate how many 10-lb boxes of shredded cheese the cooks needed. **8 boxes**

18. *Travel* One of the world's fastest trains is France's TGV (*train à grande vitesse*, or train of great speed). It averages 132 mi/h. About how far could it travel in 4.75 h? **650 mi**

19. *Money* Apples cost $.69 per pound. Estimate the cost of a 3.75-lb bag of apples. **about $2.80**

Use any estimation strategy to calculate. Tell which strategy you used and why. **20–28. Answers may vary. Samples are given.**

20. $71.43 - 28.098$ **43.5; rounding to the nearest 0.5**
21. 24.32×179.12 **4,500; rounding to the nearest 5**
22. $345.124 \div 8.98$ **35; rounding to the nearest 10**
23. $726.27 + 685.8 + 699.05$ **2,100; front-end**
24. $3.963 \div 1.79$ **2; rounding to the nearest whole number**
25. 4.27×1.6 **8; rounding to the nearest whole number**
26. $9.355 - 0.8$ **8.5; rounding to the nearest 0.5**
27. $24.71 + 16.03$ **41; front-end**
28. $7.59 \div 2.143$ **4; rounding to the nearest whole number**

29. *Weather* Six students measured rainfall at their homes and plotted the data in the stem-and-leaf plot at the right.
 a. Estimate the range of the rainfall. **2 in.**
 b. Estimate the mean rainfall for the area. **1.5 in.**

Rainfall (in.)

0	5 9
1	6 7 3
2	4

2 | 4 means 2.4

30. *Sports* A bowling ball weighs 5.61 kg and a bowling pin weighs 1.57 kg. About how many bowling pins would it take to equal the weight of the bowling ball? **about 4 pins**

PRACTICE

Practice 2-2 Problem Solving: Using Estimation Strategies

Estimate by rounding to the nearest half-dollar.

1. \$4.85 + 1.47 = \$6.50
2. \$6.79 − 3.95 = \$3.00
3. \$14.19 + 5.59 = \$19.50
4. \$25.43 − 21.20 = \$4.50

Use front-end estimation to find each sum.

5. 4.76 + 6.15 — 11
6. 1.409 + 3.512 — 5
7. 2.479 + 6.518 — 9
8. 3.17 + 2.72 — 6
9. 9.87 + 2.16 — 12
10. 5.89 + 7.21 — 13

Use clustering to estimate each sum.

11. 8.9 + 9.01 + 9.3 + 8.7 + 9.15 — 45
12. 5.7 + 6.3 + 5.9 + 6.12 + 5.87 — 30
13. \$24.79 + \$25.79 + \$25.02 + \$24.10 + \$25.19 + \$24.59 — \$150
14. \$66.93 + \$72.18 + \$69.18 + \$71.94 + \$65.75 — \$350

Use any estimation strategy to calculate. Tell which strategy you used. Samples given.

15. 93.26 − 69.78 — 20; rounding
16. 51.12 × 87.906 — 4,500; rounding
17. 43.19 + 26.87 — 70; rounding
18. 457.03 + 592.8 — 1,100; rounding
19. 702 ÷ 61 — 12; compatible numbers
20. 81.19 × 38.69 — 3,200; rounding
21. 12.87 + 14.31 + 15.09 — 42; front-end est.
22. 536 ÷ 41 — 13; compatible numbers
23. 526.89 − 417.26 — 110; rounding

Find each estimate. Samples given.

24. A rare truffle once sold for \$13.20 for a 0.44 oz can. Approximately how much would 1 lb of this truffle cost? about \$480
25. The longest loaf of bread measured 1,405 ft $1\frac{3}{4}$ in. in length. It was cut into slices $\frac{1}{2}$ in. thick. How many slices were there? about 33,600 slices

Practice

In copymaster and workbook formats

RETEACHING

Reteaching 2-2 Problem Solving: Using Estimation Strategies

One way to estimate a sum, difference, or product is to round numbers to their greatest places. Then add, subtract, or multiply.

	Greatest Place	
1.6	ones	2
+ 4.4	ones	+ 4
		6 Estimate

	Greatest Place	
17.2	tens	20
× 7.3	ones	× 7
		140 Estimate

You get a better estimate if you round to the digit to the right of the greatest place.

\$24.27 − 8.79 ⟶ \$24.00 − 9.00 = \$15.00 Estimate

Estimate each sum, difference, or product. Estimates may vary. Samples given.

	Problem	Estimate
1.	9.265 + 6.840	9 + 7 = 16
2.	12.91 − 7.80	13 − 8 = 5
3.	\$16.49 − 5.25	\$16 − 5 = \$11
4.	2.362 + 0.815	2.4 + 0.8 = 3.2
5.	2.4 × 5.2	2 × 5 = 10
6.	6.5 × 0.9	7 × 1 = 7
7.	\$12.09 − 10.55	\$12 − 11 = \$1
8.	6.147 + 0.715	6.1 + 0.7 = 6.8
9.	65.4 − 22.2	70 − 20 = 50
10.	27.14 × 3.1	30 × 3 = 90

Reteaching

ENRICHMENT

Minds on Math Transparency

2-2

Marika called two of the members of her softball team to tell them their practice schedule for the week. Each of those team members called three other team members, and then each of those members called two more team members. How many team members were called? Do not include Marika.

20 team members

See *Solution Key* for worked-out answers.

LESSON QUIZ

Use any estimation strategy to calculate.
Answers may vary.

1. 76.44 − 29.621 **46**
2. 24.73 + 15.25 **40**
3. 3.81 × 1.9 **8**
4. 44.365 ÷ 8.97 **5**

31. *Entertainment* During the Singapore Food Festival, Simon Sang Koon Sung made 8,192 noodle strings from one piece of dough in 59.29 seconds. **160 noodles**
    a. Estimate the number of noodles he made per second.
    b. Explain how you found the estimate.
    Round 8,192 to 8,000. Round 59.29 to 50. Divide 8,000 by 50.

JOURNAL Describe a situation when you might use estimation to find an answer and a situation when you would need to find the actual answer.

Mixed Review

Order the numbers from greatest to least. *(Lesson 2-1)*

32. 0.04 0.040007 4.004 0.40 0.403
    4.004, 0.403, 0.40, 0.040007, 0.04
33. 7.618 7.681 7.6801 7.0681
    7.681, 7.6801, 7.618, 7.0681

Find each sum or difference. *(Previous Course)*

34. 738 + 187 + 232 **1,157**
35. 7,083 − 896 **6,187**
36. 693 + 14 **707**
37. 429 − 185 **244**
38. Identify the outlier of 8, 5, 10, 15, 7, 9, 3, 30, 3. *(Lesson 1-4)* **30**

CHAPTER PROJECT

PROJECT LINK: MEASURING

Find the weights of five animals. You can include the weight of a pet on your list, if you have one. **Check students' work.**

Math at Work

DETECTIVE

Most people think of a detective as a person in a trench coat looking for clues. In reality, detectives can work for government agencies, lawyers, or businesses. Detectives may gather information, trace debtors, or do background investigations.

Detectives use mathematics to locate stolen funds, develop financial profiles, or monitor expense accounts.

Internet Connection: Visit the FBI Home Page to learn more about investigative careers: www.fbi.gov/

2-3 Teaching Notes

1 Focus

CONNECTING TO PRIOR KNOWLEDGE Most students have added and subtracted decimals in the context of money. Ask students:

- *How much money would you spend if you bought a sandwich for $3.50 and a carton of milk for $.79?* **$4.29**
- *How much would the sandwich cost if you paid $0.35 less by leaving off the cheese?* **$3.15**

2 Teach

THINK AND DISCUSS

ERROR ALERT! Example 1 Students may forget to line up decimal points before adding decimals. Instead, they may line up the numbers by the first or last digit. **Remediation:** Have students use a place-value chart or draw a vertical line through the decimals as a reminder.

EXTENSION Example 2 Ask students to choose songs from the list to record on a 20-minute tape. Have them calculate how many minutes of music there would be on their tape. Then have them find how many minutes of silence.

ERROR ALERT! Example 2 Students may forget to regroup when subtracting.

ALGEBRA Connection

2-3 Adding and Subtracting Decimals

What You'll Learn

1. To add and subtract decimals
2. To use the properties of addition

...And Why

In business, people use decimals to find information about time as well as money.

Here's How

Look for questions that
- build understanding
- ✔ check understanding

THINK AND DISCUSS

1 *Adding and Subtracting Decimals*

When you add and subtract decimals, be sure to align the decimal points. It is a good idea to estimate before computing.

EXAMPLE 1

Find 2.31 + 19.1 + 1.882.

Estimate: $2.31 + 19.1 + 1.882 \approx 2 + 19 + 2 = 23$

$$\begin{array}{r} 2.310 \\ 19.100 \\ +\ 1.882 \\ \hline 23.292 \end{array}$$

Align the decimal points.
Insert zeros so each addend has the same number of decimal places.

Check 23.292 is reasonable since it is close to 23.

1. *Reasoning* How do you align the addends in 7.42 + 10? **Align 7 with the 0 of 10.**
2. ✔ *Try It Out* Find 9.75 + 14.851 + 2. **26.601**

EXAMPLE 2 *Real-World Problem Solving*

Music You have 8.34 min left on a tape. How much time will be left after taping *Born in the USA*?

Estimate: $8.34 - 4.65 \approx 8 - 5 = 3$

$$\begin{array}{r} \scriptstyle 7\ 12\ 14 \\ 8.34 \\ -\ 4.65 \\ \hline 3.69 \end{array}$$

← Regroup.

You have 3.69 min left on the tape.

4th of July Music

Title	Min
76 Trombones	3.12
Liberty Bell March	3.6
Stars & Stripes Forever	3.52
Born in the USA	4.65
America the Beautiful	3.63
Yankee Doodle Dandy	2.5
Star Spangled Banner	4.5

3. *Open-ended* Choose another song. Find the time that is left after recording the song you chose. **Check students' work.**
4. ✔ *Try It Out* Find 36.901 − 27.8241. **9.0769**

Now you may assign Exercises 1–17.

Lesson Planning Options

Prerequisite Skills

- know decimal place values (precourse)
- basic addition and subtraction skills (precourse)
- estimation skills (2-2)

Vocabulary/Symbols

identity property, commutative property, associative property

Resources

Student Edition

Skills Handbook, pp. 533, 534
Extra Practice, p. 515
Glossary/Study Guide

Teaching Resources

Chapter Support File, Ch. 2
- Lesson Planner 2-3
- Practice 2-3, Reteaching 2-3
- Alternative Activity 2-3
- Answer Masters 2-3

Teaching Aids Masters 20, 26
Glossary, Spanish Resources

Transparencies

9–11, 15, 81, Minds on Math 2-3

Warm Up

Ask each student to use mental math to express each mixed number as an improper fraction.

$40\frac{3}{8}$ $\frac{323}{8}$

$50\frac{1}{6}$ $\frac{301}{6}$

Remediation: Before subtracting, have students compare each top digit to its aligned bottom digit. If the top digit is less, have them draw a diagonal line through the digit to remind them they will need to regroup when they subtract.

DIVERSITY Example 2 Ask students:

- *Is there a 4th of July in other countries?* **yes**
- *Is it a national holiday?* **not usually**
- *What are similar holidays in other countries?* **Answers may vary. Samples: Cinco de Mayo in Mexico, Canada Day in Canada, Bastille Day in France**

ADDITIONAL EXAMPLES

FOR EXAMPLE 1

Find 2.15 + 7.632 + 16.5. **26.282**

FOR EXAMPLE 2

You have 5.08 min left at the end of a tape. How much time will you have after taping *Yankee Doodle Dandy?* **2.58 min**

FOR EXAMPLE 3

Use the properties of addition to find 0.25 + 6.7 + 1.75 + 0 mentally. **8.7**

VISUAL LEARNING and MENTAL MATH Question 6a Have students explore the Identity Property with base-ten blocks. Let each unit square represent 0.1. First have students model 5.2, 0, and 3.8. Count the total squares. Then model 5.2 and 3.8. Count these squares. Ask: *How do the totals compare?* **The totals are the same.** Have students also explore the Commutative

Technology Options

Prentice Hall Technology

Software for Learners
- Hot Page™ 3–3*
- Math Blaster® Mystery*
- Interactive Student Tutorial, Chapter 2*

Teaching Resource Software
- Computer Item Generator 2-3
- Resource Pro™ Chapter 2*

Internet • For related mathematics activities, visit the Prentice Hall site at www.phschool.com/math

**Available on CD-ROM only*

Assignment Options for Exercises On Your Own

To provide flexible scheduling, this lesson can be split into parts.

1 **Core** 1–12, 14–17
Extension 13

2 **Core** 18–22, 26–31
Extension 23–25

Use Mixed Review to maintain skills.

2 *Properties of Addition*

You can use the properties of addition to add decimals mentally. You can make general statements of properties using letters. This shows that a property is true for any value.

PROPERTIES OF ADDITION

Identity Property

The sum of zero and a is a.

Arithmetic: $5.6 + 0 = 5.6$ **Algebra:** $a + 0 = a$

Commutative Property

Changing the order of the addends does not change the sum.

Arithmetic: $1.2 + 3.4 = 3.4 + 1.2$

Algebra: $a + b = b + a$

Associative Property

Changing the grouping of the addends does not change the sum.

Arithmetic: $(2.5 + 6) + 4 = 2.5 + (6 + 4)$

Algebra: $(a + b) + c = a + (b + c)$

EXAMPLE 3

Use the properties of addition to find 0.7 + 12.5 + 1.3 mentally.

$$\begin{aligned} 0.7 + 12.5 + 1.3 &= 12.5 + 0.7 + 1.3 && \leftarrow \text{Commutative Property} \\ &= 12.5 + (0.7 + 1.3) && \leftarrow \text{Associative Property} \\ &= 12.5 + 2 \\ &= 14.5 \end{aligned}$$

5. ✔ *Try It Out* Explain which properties you would use to find 4.4 + 5.3 + 0.6. Then find the sum. **See left.**

5. Use the commutative property to switch the last two terms. Use the associative property to add 4.4 and 0.6. Add the result to 5.3. The sum is 10.3.

6. *Mental Math* Use mental math and the properties of addition to find each sum.
   a. 5.2 + 0 + 3.8 **9** b. 7.4 + 1.9 + 2.6 **11.9**

Now you may assign Exercises 1–31.

Property this way. If you do not have base-ten blocks, students may draw on graph paper letting one square equal 0.1.

ASSESSMENT Example 3 Group students in pairs. Give each pair six index cards. Have them write Identity Property, Commutative Property, or Associative Property on the front of three of the cards. Have them make up an example of each property and write each on the remaining three cards. Pairs exchange example cards. Students match the correct property with the correct example.

3 Practice/Assess

EXERCISES *On Your Own*

Exercises 1–12 Have students check the reasonableness of their answers by estimating the sums and differences.

CONNECTION TO GEOMETRY Exercise 15 Students may only add the two numbers written in the art. Remind them that perimeter means to add the lengths of all the sides. You may need to remind students that opposite sides of a rectangle are equal.

WRITING Exercise 22 Ask students: *What number is mentioned in the Identity Property?* 0 *What equals zero in this exercise?* 5.238 − 5.238

EXERCISES *On Your Own*

Find each sum or difference.

1. $4.56 + 2.9$ 7.46
2. $5.3 - 0.12$ 5.18
3. $12.46 - 7.2$ 5.26
4. $3.061 + 1.8$ 4.861
5. $0.56 + 0.8 + 3.1$ 4.46
6. $25.1 - 15.06$ 10.04
7. $3.102 - 0.89$ 2.212
8. $7 + 0.582$ 7.582
9. $102.8 + 3$ 105.8
10. $0.008 - 0.0002$ 0.0078
11. $0.1305 - 0.066$ 0.0645
12. $0.75 + 3.8 + 4$ 8.55
13. *Hobbies* The width of the tracks determines the size of model trains. Use the information at the right.
    a. *Estimation* Estimate the difference between the widths of the smallest gauge track and the largest gauge track. 4 cm
    b. *Decision Making* Suppose you plan to buy a train for a 5-year-old child. Which train would you purchase? Why? Answers may vary. Sample: G gauge; it is easier to hold.
14. *Cars* In 1976, Kitty Hambleton set the women's land-speed record. The mean of her two runs was 512.710 mi/h. Her faster run was at 524.016 mi/h. What was the difference between her fastest speed and her mean speed? 11.306 mi/h

N gauge
0.79375 cm wide

0 gauge
3.175 cm wide

G gauge
5.3975 cm wide

Geometry **Find the perimeter of each figure.**

15. 29.66 m

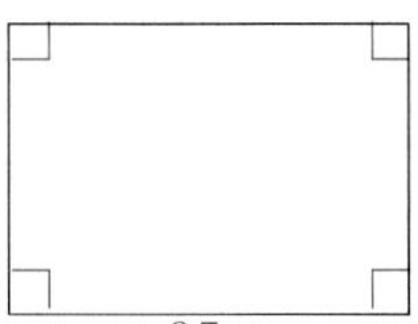

16. 9.2 ft

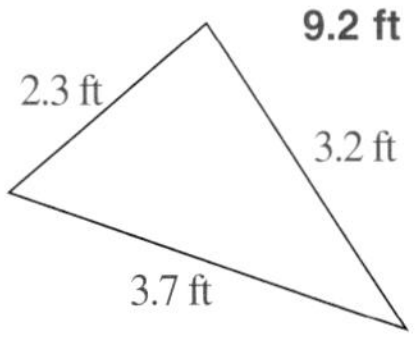

17. *Entertainment* Lisa, Ana, and Lisa's brother Jacob went roller skating. Admission was \$3.50 for those 12 and older, and \$1.75 for those under 12. The roller skates rented for \$2.75 a pair. Lisa and Ana are 13 years old, and Jacob is 10.
    a. How much more did Lisa pay than Jacob? \$1.75
    b. What was the total cost of admission? \$8.75
    c. How much did it cost for them all to rent roller skates? \$8.25

Identify each property shown.

18. $(46.8 + 32.7) + 7.3 = 46.8 + (32.7 + 7.3)$ associative prop. of addition
19. $60.2 + 0 = 60.2$ identity prop. of addition
20. $1.97 + 31.2 - 1.97 = 31.2 + 1.97 - 1.97$ commutative prop. of addition
21. $1.3 + (5.8 + 3.91) = (1.3 + 5.8) + 3.91$ associative prop. of addition

CHECKPOINT 1

Checkpoint 1

Lessons 2-1 through 2-3

Write five numbers between the given numbers. Sample answers are given.

1. 41 and 42 — 41.1, 41.2, 41.3, 41.4, 41.5
2. 5.1 and 5.2 — 5.11, 5.12, 5.13, 5.14, 5.15

Use any strategy to estimate.

3. $79.06 - 38.64$ — 40
4. \$5.78 + \$3.64 — \$10
5. $7.875 \div 3.91$ — 2
6. **Choose A, B, C, or D.** Which property of addition is shown?
   $78.96 + 0 = 78.96$
   (A.) Identity property B. Commutative property
   C. Associative property D. not here

Find each sum or difference.

7. $53.23 - 24.89$ — 28.34
8. $4.89 + 34.5 + 2.17$ — 41.56
9. $7.895 - 3.449$ — 4.446

PRACTICE

Practice 2-3 *Adding and Subtracting Decimals*

Identify each property shown in the equation.

1. (8.7 + 6.3) + 3.7 = 8.7 + (6.3 + 3.7) Associative property
2. 9.06 + 0 = 9.06 Identity property
3. 4.06 + 8.92 = 8.92 + 4.06 Commutative property
4. 0 + 7.13 = 7.13 + 0 Commutative property
5. (8.4 + 12.6) + 4.7 = 8.4 + (12.6 + 4.7) Associative property
6. 0 + 17.96 = 17.96 Identity property

Find each sum.

7. 4.6 + 8.79 13.39
8. 14.8 + 29.07 43.87
9. 20.16 + 15.703 35.863
10. 36.12 + 5.793 41.913
11. 8.9 + 2.14+ 7.1 18.14
12. 3.6 + 5.27+ 8.93 17.8
13. 107.5 + 6 113.5
14. 15.26 + 13.29+ 38.96 67.51
15. 46.21 + 53.942 100.152
16. 83.14 + 96.72 179.86
17. 58.01 + 74.94 132.95
18. 9 + 0.638 9.638

Find each difference.

19. 8.7 − 2.03 6.67
20. 53.86 − 4.02 49.84
21. 14.59 − 8.3 6.29
22. 27.13 − 18.9 8.23
23. 42.75 − 26.36 16.39
24. 53.86 − 16.47 37.39
25. 56.89 − 48.91 7.98
26. 23.5 − 18.079 5.421
27. 5.06 − 3.297 1.763
28. 3.4 − 2.768 0.632
29. 5.002 − 4.3 0.702
30. 0.2406 − 0.058 0.1826

Use the advertisement at the right. Find each cost.

31. 1 egg $.55
32. toast $.40
33. bacon $.75
34. milk $.50
35. 1 egg and milk $1.05
36. 1 egg and bacon $1.30

2 eggs, toast, bacon, milk	$2.75
1 egg, toast, bacon, milk	$2.20
toast, milk	$0.90
toast, bacon, milk	$1.65
1 egg, toast	$0.95

In copymaster and workbook formats

RETEACHING

Reteaching 2-3 *Adding and Subtracting Decimals*

Add 3.19 + 6.098 + 26.7.

Round to estimate.	Line up the decimal points.	Annex zeros. Then add.
3.19 → 3	3.19	3.190
6.098 → 6	6.098	6.098
+ 26.7 → + 27	+ 26.7	+ 26.700
36		35.988

Compare to make sure your answer is reasonable: 35.988 is close to 36.

Subtract 8.7 − 4.97.

Round to estimate.	Line up the decimal points.	Annex zeros. Then subtract.
8.7 → 9	8.7	8.70
− 4.97 → − 5	− 4.97	− 4.97
4		3.73

Compare to make sure your answer is reasonable: 3.73 is close to 4.

Estimate first. Then find each sum or difference.

1. 46.2 − 34.09 = 12.11
2. 3.31 + 9.075 = 12.385
3. 9.06 − 7.2 = 1.86
4. 84.32 + 6.94 = 91.26
5. 8.037 + 1.9 = 9.937
6. 10.6 − 4.59 = 6.01
7. 4.102 + 7.7 = 11.802
8. 5.4 − 1.6 = 3.8
9. 7.09 + 4.3 + 20.1 = 31.49
10. 0.392 − 0.26 = 0.132
11. 15.64 − 8.5 = 7.14
12. 8.709 + 3.2 = 11.909
13. 6 + 0.497 = 6.497
14. 95.1 + 6 = 101.1
15. 0.004 − 0.0005 = 0.0035
16. 0.2408 − 0.051 = 0.1898
17. 0.36 + 4.7 + 6 = 11.06
18. 5.306 − 0.78 = 4.526

ENRICHMENT

Minds on Math Transparency

2-3

Ulysses began with a number, multiplied his number by 2, divided the product by 5, and then added 9. The result was 19. With what number did Ulysses begin?

25

See *Solution Key* for worked-out answers.

WRAP UP

IDENTIFYING THE BIG IDEA Ask students to explain the steps involved in adding and subtracting decimals and in using properties of addition.

LESSON QUIZ

Find each sum or difference.

1. 0.009 − 0.0005 0.0085

2. 4.074 + 2.9 6.974

Use the properties of addition to find the value of each expression. State which properties you used.

3. 0.6 + 11.8 + 1.4 **13.8; commutative and associative properties**

4. 6.3 + 0 + 4.7 **11; all properties**

22. *Writing* How could you use the identity property to find 5.238 − 5.238 + 17.9?
5.238 − 5.238 = 0, so the sum is 17.9, by the identity property.

Use the properties of addition to find the value of each expression. State which properties you used.

23. 16.2 + 23.5 + 3.8 43.5; commutative, then associative
24. 24.4 + (5.6 + 11) 41; associative
25. 27.4 + 0 + 12.1 39.5; identity
26. 6.1 + 8.4 + 1.6 16.1; associative
27. 9.2 + 1.8 + 0 11; identity
28. (4.7 + 10.6) + 0.3 15.6; commutative, then associative
29. 8.5 + 6.3 + 1.5 16.3; commutative, then associative
30. (6.4 + 0.3) + 0.7 7.4; associative
31. 7 + 3.2 + 3 13.2; commutative, then associative

Mixed Review

Tell whether the questions are biased or fair. *(Lesson 1-7)*

32. Do you prefer tuna sandwiches or chicken sandwiches? fair
33. Do you like long, warm days of summer or dark, cold days of winter? biased

Find the value of each expression. *(Previous Course)*

34. 17 − 8 + 2 11
35. 15 − 11 + 4 − 3 5
36. 8 + 56 − 8 56
37. 18 − 2 − 5 + 1 12

38. *Consumer Issues* When you join the Teen Tape Club, you get 6 tapes for 1¢ each. You must buy 8 more tapes for $7.99 each. What is the average price of each tape? *(Lesson 1-4)* $4.57

✓ CHECKPOINT 1

Lessons 2-1 through 2-3

Compare using <, >, or =.

1. 4.406 ■ 4.4060 =
2. 6.621 ■ 6.612 >
3. 10.01 ■ 0.101 >
4. 5.034 ■ 5.304 <

5. a. Round to estimate $3.07 + $3.48 + $4.24. $10.50
   b. Use front-end estimation to find the sum again. $11
   c. Explain which strategy you would use when buying items. c. Answers may vary. Sample: Front-end estimation; it is better to have a high estimate than a low one when buying items.

6. **Choose A, B, C, or D.** Which property is shown? C
   7.65 + 1.43 + (1.07 + 8.92) = 7.65 + (1.43 + 1.07) + 8.92
   A. Identity B. Commutative C. Associative D. Not Here

Find each sum or difference.

7. 89.32 − 23.073 66.247
8. 2.99 + 3.08 + 18.5642 24.6342
9. 9.7418 − 4.603 5.1388

MATH TOOLBOX

In Lesson 2-3, students learned to add and subtract decimals. This toolbox helps students to explore compensation, which they can use to add and subtract decimals mentally.

ERROR ALERT! Students may confuse compensation with rounding and think that they are finding an estimate instead of an actual answer. **Remediation:** Point out to students that using compensation with simple whole-number sums and differences does not change the sum or difference. Students can see this for themselves by using compensation.

ASSESSMENT Exercises 1–4 Have partners compare their solutions. Ask students to describe to their partners their compensation strategies.

ADDITIONAL PROBLEM

Ask students to write a problem requiring the use of compensation in the solution. Students can exchange problems with a partner and solve.

MATH TOOLBOX EXPLORATION

Mental Math: Compensation

After Lesson 2-3

You can use compensation to find sums and differences. You use compensation to make problems easier to calculate mentally.

A sum remains the same if you add a number to one addend and subtract it from another addend.

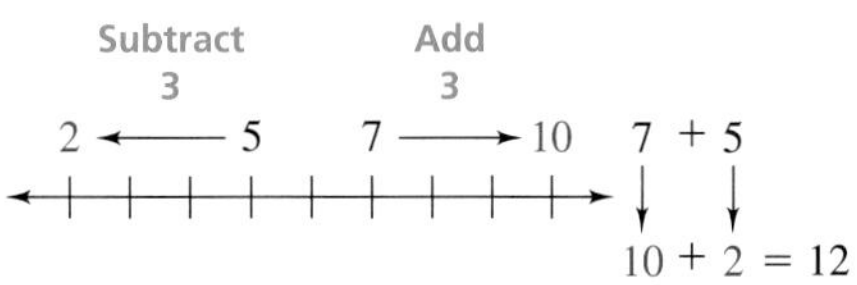

The difference between two numbers remains the same if you add (or subtract) the same number from both numbers.

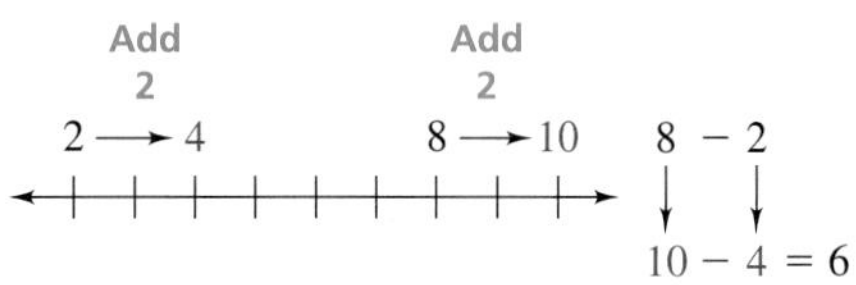

EXAMPLE

Find each sum or difference.

a. $4.6 + 3.9$

$4.6 + 3.9 + 5.4$

$+0.4$ $\quad -0.4$ ← Add 0.4 to one addend and subtract 0.4 from another addend.

$5 + 3.9 + 5 = 13.9$

b. $6.1 - 1.3$

$6.1 - 1.3$

$+0.7$ $\quad +0.7$ ← Add 0.7 to both numbers.

$6.8 - 2 = 4.8$

Use compensation to find each sum or difference.

1. $0.9 + 1.4$ **2.3**

2. $22 + 29 + 38$ **89**

3. $10.5 + 7.1 + 2.9$ **20.5**

4. $72 + 14$ **86**

5. $2.5 + 9.1$ **11.6**

6. $117 + 96$ **213**

7. $72.3 + 8.1 + 6.7$ **87.1**

8. $3.8 + 1.7$ **5.5**

9. $38 - 11$ **27**

10. $9.3 - 6.1$ **3.2**

11. $102 - 77$ **25**

12. $41.6 - 0.7$ **40.9**

13. $11.7 - 6.9$ **4.8**

14. $69 - 31$ **38**

15. $984 - 852$ **132**

16. $8.4 - 6.9$ **1.5**

17. $53 + 81 + 69$ **203**

18. $74.6 - 35.8$ **38.8**

19. $0.4 + 7.8$ **8.2**

20. $12.4 - 8.3$ **4.1**

2-4 Teaching Notes

1 Focus

CONNECTING TO PRIOR KNOWLEDGE Ask students to name the kind of information they might expect if they asked a friend for directions to his or her house. Then ask whether they would have problems if the information were too little or too much. **Answers may vary. Sample: It would be difficult to find a house without a street address.**

2 Teach

THINK AND DISCUSS

AEP Read the problem aloud to students. Reread it phrase by phrase and help students identify the information necessary to solve the problem. Help them identify key words.

KINESTHETIC LEARNING Ask students to form groups to act out the problem about the lemonade stand. Students may have trouble improvising the problem-solving dialogue, but acting out the preparations for the booth will help them focus on the relevant information.

ADDITIONAL PROBLEM

The eighth grade is selling crafts at Family Day. They sell key chains for $.79, pillows for $3.50, bracelets for $1.29, and bookmarks for $.29. Keisha sold 6 key chains and 3

Lesson Planning Options

Prerequisite Skills

- adding and subtracting decimals (2-3)

Materials/Manipulatives

- encyclopedia

Resources

Student Edition

Skills Handbook, p. 531
Extra Practice, p. 515
Glossary/Study Guide

Teaching Resources

Chapter Support File, Ch. 2
- Lesson Planner 2-4
- Practice 2-4, Reteaching 2-4
- Answer Masters 2-4

Glossary, Spanish Resources

Transparencies
Minds on Math 2-4

Warm Up

Have students work in pairs to determine all the different ways four people can be seated at a round dinner table. 6

PROBLEM SOLVING STRATEGY

2-4 Too Much or Too Little Information

Problem Solving Strategies

- Draw a Diagram
- Guess and Test
- Look for a Pattern
- Make a Model
- Make a Table
- Simulate a Problem
- Solve a Simpler Problem
- ✔ Too Much or Too Little Information
- Use Logical Reasoning
- Use Multiple Strategies
- Work Backward
- Write an Equation

THINK AND DISCUSS

Some problems may not contain enough information for you to solve them. Others may have more information than you need.

SAMPLE PROBLEM

Holdfield Middle School is sponsoring a Family Day. The seventh grade will be selling lemonade.

The class hopes to sell at least 100 cups of lemonade. Four 64-oz pitchers were borrowed to serve the lemonade. Three packages of 50 paper cups at $1.50 per package and fourteen 12-oz cans of frozen lemonade were bought for $.89 each. Each can makes 48 oz.

The charge for a 6-oz cup of lemonade is $.30. How much was spent on supplies?

READ
Read for understanding. Summarize the problem.

1. Think about what is asked, the information given, and which information to use.
   a. What do you need to find? **the price of all the supplies**
   b. Do you need all the facts to solve the problem? Explain. **See below.**

PLAN
Decide on a strategy.

To find the total cost of supplies, decide what the supplies are, and how much was spent on them.

2. How much was spent on lemonade? **$12.46**
3. How much was spent on paper cups? **$4.50**
4. How much was spent on pitchers? **$0**

SOLVE
Try the strategy.

Use this information to solve the problem.

5. What was the total cost of supplies? **$16.96**

1b. No; you only need to know how much each package of cups and each can of lemonade cost and how many of each had been bought.

bracelets. How much money did she collect? **$8.61**

ASSESSMENT Ask students: *You and two friends are going to the same four birthday parties. You have decided to share the cost of four T-shirts for gifts. One medium T-shirt and one small have stripes. The other two shirts are smalls and have college names on them. The striped shirts cost $14 each for size small and medium, and $17 for large and extra large. The college shirts cost $15 each for size small and medium, and $18 for large and extra large. How much does your share of the gifts cost?* **$19.33, rounded to the nearest cent**

3 Practice/Assess

EXERCISES *On Your Own*

ERROR ALERT! Students may try to always use all the numbers in a problem. **Remediation:** Tell students to always try to find the number or numbers that are not useful. Have students make a two-column list showing the information that is useful and the information that is not useful.

Exercise 2 Some students may assume that the $5 fish bowl contains 32 fish.

WRAP UP

IDENTIFYING THE BIG IDEA Ask students to explain how to decide whether a problem has too much or too little information.

LOOK BACK

Think about how you solved the problem.

To solve the problem, you selected some facts and ignored the rest.

6. What information didn't you need? **See back of book.**
7. Could you find the profit for the day? Why or why not?

7. No; you cannot find out how many cups of lemonade the class sold.

Now you may assign Exercises 1–7.

EXERCISES *On Your Own*

Solve if possible. If not, tell what information is needed.

1. *Sewing* A group of friends made a 4-yd long rectangular banner. They paid $3.75 per yard for the fabric and $9 for the trim to go around the banner's 10-yd perimeter. What was the width of the banner? **1 yd**
2. *Hobbies* A pet store has 32 tropical fish. The store charges $2.45 per fish and $5.00 for a fish bowl. How much will a fish bowl and some fish cost? **You need to know how many fish are bought.**
3. *Travel* The four members of the Coy family drove eight hours a day for three days. What is the average number of miles the family traveled each day? **You need to know the average speed the Coy family traveled.**

Use any strategy to solve each problem. If it is not possible to solve, tell what information is missing.

4. *School Fair* Central Middle School is having a heritage fair. Ed, Daria, Jarel, and Liz are each presenting an item. The items are maracas from Mexico, a sari from India, a game from Ghana, and a ram's horn from Israel. Jarel did not bring an item from Ghana or India. Daria did not bring an item from Ghana. Ed brought maracas. What items did the other students bring? **See above right.**
5. *Money* Lamarr sold frozen slush at a fair from 12 noon to 5 P.M. He charged $.50 for a small slush and $.75 for a large one. Twelve children bought a total of 15 small slushes and 24 adults bought a total of 28 large slushes. How much money did Lamarr collect? **$28.50**

4. Jarel presented the ram's horn; Daria presented the sari; Liz presented the game.

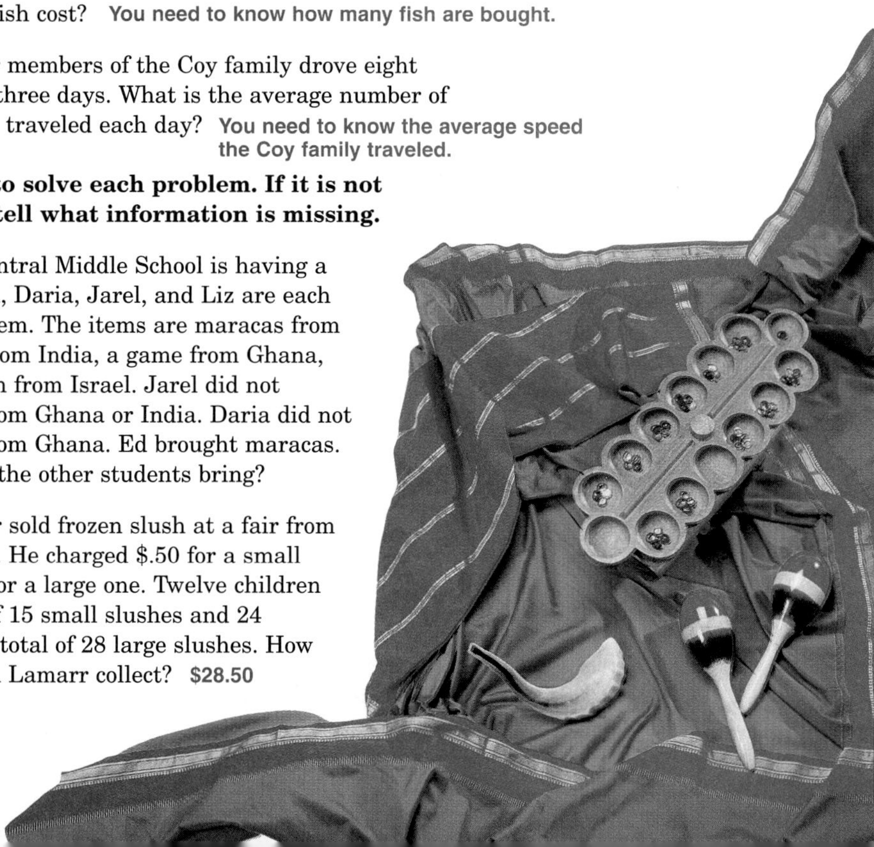

Technology Options

Prentice Hall Technology

Software for Learners
- Math Blaster® Mystery*
- Interactive Student Tutorial, Chapter 2*

Teaching Resource Software
- Computer Item Generator 2-4
- Resource Pro™ Chapter 2*

Internet • For related mathematics activities, visit the Prentice Hall site at www.phschool.com/math

**Available on CD-ROM only*

Assignment Options for Exercises On Your Own

Core 1–6
Extension 7

Use Mixed Review to maintain skills.

PRACTICE

Practice 2-4 *Problem-Solving Strategy: Too Much or Too Little Information*

Use any strategy to solve each problem. If it is not possible to solve, tell what needed information is missing.

1. Mary Jo wants to buy some stamps and three envelopes. Envelopes cost $.10 each, and stamps cost $.29 each. How much will the stamps and envelopes cost? need to know how many stamps
2. Royce earns $200 per week, plus $50 for every stereo system that he sells. Last week, he earned $850. How many stereo systems did Royce sell last week? 13 stereo systems
3. Four friends were standing in the lunch line. Tom was not last. Hank was in line immediately after Cindy. Tom and Beverly had at least one person between them. In what order were the four standing? Tom, Cindy, Hank, Beverly
4. A store had a grand-opening sale on Friday and Saturday. Over 400 people attended on Friday, and four times as many people attended on Saturday. If each person attending had to buy a ticket to enter, how many tickets were needed? need to know the exact number on Friday
5. You have a set of models of two-dimensional shapes. A balance scale balances with one triangle and three squares on one side, and one square, two circles, and one triangle on the other side. Each triangle weighs 2 kg. Each square weighs 3 kg. How much does each circle weigh? 3 kg
6. Rodrigo wants to double a recipe requiring 1 c milk and 3 c flour. How much cinnamon should he add? need to know the original amount of cinnamon
7. The Smythe children take turns picking which TV show to watch. Jo picks first since she is the youngest. Lyle picks immediately before Mark. Meg picks before Beth, but after Lyle. In what order do the children pick which TV show to watch? Jo, Lyle, Mark, Meg, Beth
8. The Hsu family pays $15 per month for trash pickup, plus $7 per large item. How much did they pay for trash pickup last year if they got rid of an old couch and a refrigerator? $194

Practice

In copymaster and workbook formats

RETEACHING

Reteaching 2-4 *Problem-Solving Strategy: Too Much or Too Little Information*

In physical education class, Shawn ran 6 laps around the track in 12 minutes. Robin ran 6 laps starting at 9 A.M. After fixing two shoelaces, Meera ran for 8 minutes. Who runs 6 laps in the least amount of time?

Read What does the problem ask you to find? *You need to find out which student runs 6 laps in the least amount of time.*

Plan First, decide what the key facts are. *Shawn runs 6 laps in 12 minutes.*

What information is not needed? *Meera fixing two shoelaces*

Do you have all the necessary information? *No. You need to know how many laps Meera ran and the time that Robin finished running.*

Solve Can you solve this problem? *No. There is too little information.*

Solve if possible. If not, tell what information is needed.

1. Every school day, Shawn swims 400 yards in 10 minutes. Robin swims 600 yards in 15 minutes. Meera swims 500 yards. Who swims for the greatest amount of time each week? You need to know how many minutes Meera swims.
2. Rog gets $30 for his birthday. He buys a fishbowl for $9.99. Goldfish cost $3.85 each and guppies are $1.99 each. How many goldfish can he buy? 5 goldfish
3. Maria bought some cans of paint. She spent $25.88 in all. How much did each can cost? You need to know how many cans of paint she bought.
4. Kendra spent $38.56 on school supplies. How much change did she get? You need to know how much money she gave the clerk.
5. Casey had a balance of $50.39 in his checking account. He made a deposit of $30.75. Then he wrote a check for $24.95. He spent $4.75 for lunch. What was his new checking balance? $56.19
6. Tom's scout troop hiked 3.8 miles in the morning. They took a 45-minute lunch break. In the afternoon, they hiked 4.7 miles. How many miles did the troop hike in all? 8.5 miles

Reteaching

ENRICHMENT

Minds on Math Transparency

2-4

Each girl in the Lynberg family has the same number of brothers as she has sisters. Each boy in the Lynberg family has twice as many sisters as he has brothers. How many girls and boys are there in the Lynberg family?

4 girls and 3 boys

See *Solution Key* for worked-out answers.

PROJECT LINK You may want to bring chemistry books to class so that students have another type of source in which to find the specific gravities.

LESSON QUIZ

Solve, if possible. If not, tell what information is needed.

1. Julia is fencing her rectangular yard. Her yard is 25 ft wide by 50 ft long. If the fence is 6 ft high, what length of fence does she need? **150 ft**
2. Peter drove for 4 h at 60 mi per hour before stopping to fill up his car with gas. How many miles to the gallon of gas did his car get? **Not possible; you need to know how many gallons of gas he purchased and if he started with a full tank.**

6. *Biology* The Chinese giant panda lives in bamboo forests. It spends about 10–12 h each day eating. About every 50 years, bamboo forests flower, seed, and die. As a result, many pandas die since the panda mainly eats bamboo. In 1983, before the most recent bamboo forest seeding and dying, about 1,000 pandas were alive. How many are left?
You need to know how many pandas died when bamboo flowered.

The giant panda is about 6 in. long and weighs about 3 lb at birth. Adult pandas can weigh up to 300 lb and stand 5 ft tall when upright.

7. James, Emily, and Marcia are working on a history project. One student is interviewing, one is researching, and one is writing. Their last names are Brown, Johnson, and Wong, but not in that order.
   - Emily's last name is not Brown.
   - The student whose last name is Wong and the girl who is doing research are neighbors.
   - James is not interviewing.
   - The student whose last name is Johnson likes to go camping with his father.

   What is each student's full name and what part of the history project is each working on? **James Johnson is writing; Emily Wong is interviewing; Marcia Brown is researching.**

Mixed Review

Estimate each sum or difference. *(Lesson 2-2)*

8. 52.039 + 12.99 **65**
9. 9.37 − 8.4 **1**
10. 1.562 − 0.91 **0.5**
11. 9.1 + 0.578 **9.5**

Make a stem-and-leaf plot for each set of data. *(Lesson 1-5)* **12–14. See back of book.**

12. 29 27 37 40 46 48
13. 1.3 2.2 1.7 1.4 1.3
14. 21 19 16 23 18 16

CHAPTER PROJECT

PROJECT LINK: RESEARCHING

Specific gravity describes how many times heavier a metal is than the weight of an equal volume of water. For example, the specific gravity of gold is about 19.3. If a cup of water weighs 8 ounces, then a cup of gold would weigh 8×19.3 ounces, or 154.4 ounces. Since mammals are made mostly of water, their specific gravity is about 1. Use an encyclopedia to find the specific gravity of four of these metals: lead, copper, zinc, aluminum, silver, iron, or nickel.

2-5 Teaching Notes

1 Focus

CONNECTING TO PRIOR KNOWLEDGE Ask students how to find the total cost of 5 footballs at $23.74 each. **$118.70** After students explain their methods, ask how they knew where to place the decimal point in the answer.

2 Teach

Work Together

TACTILE LEARNING Question 1 Have students use tracing paper laid over graph paper to create models for 0.2 and 0.9. Students can then cut out their models and overlap the rectangles to show the product. Lightly shading the rectangle with different colors will benefit students with a visual learning style. Students can repeat this procedure for 0.3 × 0.5 and 0.8 × 0.2.

Question 2 Select two sets of partners to share their models and discuss their conclusions.

THINK AND DISCUSS

Example 1 Be sure students understand that the only difference between the two products is the placement of the decimal point.

ALGEBRA Connection

2-5 Multiplying Decimals

What You'll Learn

1. To multiply decimals
2. To use the properties of multiplication

...And Why

You use decimals in calculations involving money and sports.

Here's How

Look for questions that
- build understanding
- ✔ check understanding

Work Together — *Modeling Decimal Multiplication*

Work with a partner to model multiplication of decimals. For example, the product of 0.7 and 0.4 is 0.28.

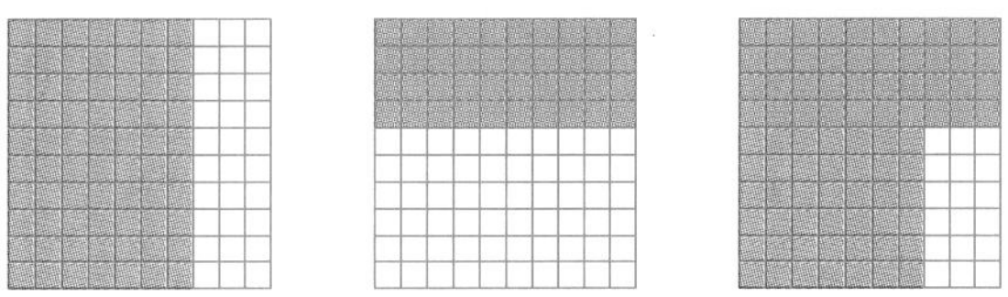

0.7 × 0.4 = 0.28

1. Draw models for 0.2 × 0.9, 0.3 × 0.5, and 0.8 × 0.2.
   See back of book for models; 0.18; 0.15; 0.16.
2. *Draw a Conclusion* In Exercise 1, is each product greater or less than each factor? What can you conclude about the product of decimals less than one? **Each product is less than each factor. The product of two numbers less than 1 is less than each factor.**

Need Help? For practice in multiplying whole numbers or decimals, see Skills Handbook pages 530 and 535.

THINK AND DISCUSS

1 *Multiplying Decimals*

When you multiply decimals, first multiply as if the factors were whole numbers. Then count the decimal places in both factors to find where to place the decimal point in the product.

■ EXAMPLE 1

Find each product.

a. 243 × 25

```
  243
 × 25
 1215
 486
 6075
```

b. 2.43 × 2.5

```
  2.43   ← two decimal places
 × 2.5   ← one decimal place
 1215
 486
 6.075   ← three decimal places
```

The products are 6,075 and 6.075.

Lesson Planning Options

Prerequisite Skills
- basic multiplication (precourse)

Vocabulary/Symbols
identity property of multiplication, zero property, commutative property, associative property

Materials/Manipulatives
- graph paper
- calculator

Resources

Student Edition

Skills Handbook, p. 535
Extra Practice, p. 515
Glossary/Study Guide

Teaching Resources

Chapter Support File, Ch. 2
- Lesson Planner 2-5
- Practice 2-5, Reteaching 2-5
- Answer Masters 2-5

Teaching Aids Masters 20, 26
Glossary, Spanish Resources

Transparencies
9–11, 81, Minds on Math 2-5

Warm Up

Ask students to find all possible number pairs for which the sum of two whole numbers is 63 and the difference between the numbers is less than 10. **31 and 32; 30 and 33; 29 and 34; 28 and 35; 27 and 36**

ERROR ALERT! Students may line up the decimal points instead of counting the number of places in both factors. **Remediation:** Remind students to make an estimate before giving an answer to a problem. Students might also put a circle around each numeral in a decimal place. Then count the circles to find the number of decimal places in the product.

AEP You can relate the Identity Property to the word *identical.* Say: *Multiplying a number by 1 or adding 0 to a number gives you an* identical *number.*

ADDITIONAL EXAMPLES

FOR EXAMPLE 1

Find each product.

a. 115 × 36 **4,140**

b. 1.15 × 3.6 **4.140**

FOR EXAMPLE 2

Find 10 × 7.1 × 0.1. **7.1**

ASSESSMENT Have students work in pairs to find 0.36 × 6.42. Ask the following:

- *Is the product less than or greater than 6.42?* **less than**
- *How many decimal places will the answer have?* **four**
- *What is the product?* **2.3112**

Technology Options

Prentice Hall Technology

Software for Learners

- Math Blaster® Mystery*
- Interactive Student Tutorial, Chapter 2*

Teaching Resource Software

- Computer Item Generator 2-5
- Resource Pro™ Chapter 2*

Internet • For related mathematics activities, visit the Prentice Hall site at www.phschool.com/math

**Available on CD-ROM only*

Assignment Options for Exercises On Your Own

To provide flexible scheduling, this lesson can be split into parts.

1 **Core** 1–15, 17–21
Extension 16

2 **Core** 22–31, 33
Extension 32

Use Mixed Review to maintain skills.

3. ✔ *Try It Out* Find each product.
   a. 37 × 9 **333** b. 1.43 × 0.81 **1.1583** c. 8.732 × 5.4 **47.1528**

There are several ways to use symbols to indicate multiplication. Four ways to write "Multiply 3.4 by 5" are shown below.

3.4 × 5   3.4 · 5   3.4(5)   (3.4)(5)

4. If the dot is not centered, you might mistake it for a decimal point.

4. *Think About It* Suppose you are indicating multiplication using a dot. Why is it important to use a *centered* dot?

Now you may assign Exercises 1–21.

2 *Using Properties of Multiplication*

The properties of multiplication can help you find products mentally.

PROPERTIES OF MULTIPLICATION

Identity Property

The product of one and a is a.

Arithmetic: $5 \times 1 = 5$ Algebra: $a \times 1 = a$

Zero Property

The product of zero and any number is zero.

Arithmetic: $5 \times 0 = 0$ Algebra: $a \times 0 = 0$

Commutative Property

Changing the order of factors doesn't change the product.

Arithmetic: $5 \times 2 = 2 \times 5$ Algebra: $a \times b = b \times a$

Associative Property

Changing the grouping of factors doesn't change the product.

Arithmetic: $(3 \times 2) \times 5 = 3 \times (2 \times 5)$
Algebra: $(a \times b) \times c = a \times (b \times c)$

5. *Reasoning* Carmela found the answer to 3.625 × 58.42 × 0 in less than one second. How did she do it?
   She used the zero property. The product is 0.

3 Practice/Assess

EXERCISES *On Your Own*

Exercises 4–15 Have students estimate their answers before multiplying.

KINESTHETIC LEARNING **Exercise 16** Using meter sticks, have groups of students test a can of new tennis balls. Drop each tennis ball from a height of 200 cm and measure how high each ball bounces. Record the results in a table. Ask: *Do the balls meet ITF standards?* Have the students leave the tennis balls out for three days. and measure the bounces again. Then ask: *Do the balls still bounce as high? Do they meet the standards?*

OPEN-ENDED **Exercise 17** Have students exchange and solve each other's problems.

REASONING **Exercise 21** Suggest that students struggling with this exercise review Example 1.

Exercises 22–31 Suggest students write the names of the properties of multiplication in the margin of their paper so they can refer to them quickly.

WRITING **Exercise 32** Before writing, suggest students create a table comparing the properties of multiplication and addition. This will help them organize the information.

■ **EXAMPLE 2**

Find $0.25 \times 3.58 \times 4$.

$0.25 \times 3.58 \times 4 = 3.58 \times 0.25 \times 4$ ← Commutative Property
$= 3.58 \times (0.25 \times 4)$ ← Associative Property
$= 3.58 \times 1$
$= 3.58$ ← Identity Property

6. ✔ *Try It Out* Use the commutative property to find $2.5 \times 6.3 \times 4$. 63

7. *Think About It* What property would you use first when finding $4.3 \times 2.5 \times 2$? Explain your reasoning.

7. Use the associative property to multiply 2.5 and 2; you don't need to multiply two decimal numbers.

Now you may assign Exercises 22–33.

EXERCISES *On Your Own*

Rewrite each equation with the decimal point in the correct place in the product.

1. $1.2 \times 49 = 588$
   $1.2 \times 49 = 58.8$
2. $27 \times 1.3 = 351$
   $27 \times 1.3 = 35.1$
3. $3.7 \times 6.4 = 2368$
   $3.7 \times 6.4 = 23.68$

Choose **Use a model, paper and pencil, or a calculator to find each product.**

4. 0.2×0.7 0.14
5. $0.4 \cdot 0.6$ 0.24
6. $0.3 \cdot 0.5$ 0.15
7. 27×817 22,059
8. 145×26 3,770
9. 1.3×0.05 0.065
10. $0.008(1.25)$ 0.01
11. $(41)(7.5)$ 307.5
12. $2.41 \cdot 0.17$ 0.4097
13. $8.7(0.45)$ 3.915
14. $(1.02)(3.6)$ 3.672
15. 0.45×1.5 0.675

16. *Sports* The International Tennis Federation (ITF) requires that a new tennis ball bounce between 0.53 and 0.58 of its original height when dropped on a hard surface.
   a. A new tennis ball is dropped from a height of 200 cm. Find the range of acceptable heights after the first bounce. 106 cm to 116 cm
   b. A tennis ball dropped from a height of 150 cm reached 79 cm after one bounce. Does the ball meet ITF standards? no

17. *Open-ended* Write a problem that you could solve using multiplication of decimals. Include your solution.
   Check students' work.

pages 69–70 On Your Own

21a. **Multiply the numbers as whole numbers. Then place the decimal point before the three digits on the right.**

PRACTICE

Practice 2-5 Multiplying Decimals

Use a model, paper and pencil, or a calculator to find each product.

1. 28×6 168
2. $7.3 \cdot 0.9$ 6.57
3. $58 \cdot 2.1$ 121.8
4. $15(187)$ 2,805
5. 6.6×25 165
6. $(1.8)(0.7)$ 1.26
7. $0.91 \cdot 2.7$ 2.457
8. $4.6(3.9)$ 17.94

Rewrite each equation with the decimal point in the correct place in the product.

9. $5.6 \times 1.2 = 672$ — $5.6 \times 1.2 = 6.72$
10. $3.7 \times 2.4 = 888$ — $3.7 \times 2.4 = 8.88$
11. $6.5 \times 2.5 = 1625$ — $6.5 \times 2.5 = 16.25$
12. $1.02 \times 6.9 = 7038$ — $1.02 \times 6.9 = 7.038$
13. $4.4 \times 6.51 = 28644$ — $4.4 \times 6.51 = 28.644$
14. $0.6 \times 9.312 = 55872$ — $0.6 \times 9.312 = 5.5872$

Name the property of multiplication shown.

15. $3 \times 4 = 4 \times 3$ Commutative Property
16. $9 \times (6 \times 3) = (9 \times 6) \times 3$ Associative Property
17. $2 \times 0 = 0$ Zero Property
18. $10 \times 1 = 10$ Identity Property

Use mental math and the properties of multiplication to find the value of each expression.

19. $0.4 \times 6.71 \times 5$ 13.42
20. $8.3 \times 2.1 \times 0 \times 4.6$ 0
21. $5.9 \times 0.3 \times 10$ 17.7
22. $(5.3 \times 2.5) \times 4$ 53
23. $0.3 \times 6.21 \times 10$ 18.63
24. $(7.5 \times 9.3) \times 4$ 279

Solve.

25. Al's Car Rental charges $122.50 for a 5-day rental and then $27.50 for each additional day. Dave's Car Rental charges a flat rate of $26.25 per day. Which company charges less for a 7-day car rental? Al's Car Rental is $6.25 cheaper.
26. Anitta works in a department store and earns $7.60 per hour. Last week she worked 39.5 hours. How much money did she earn for the week? $300.20

In copymaster and workbook formats

RETEACHING

Reteaching 2-5 Multiplying Decimals

Multiply 5.43×1.8.

First, make an estimate of the product. 5.43×1.8 round to → $5 \times 2 = 10$ Estimate

Step 1
Multiply as if the numbers were whole numbers.

Step 2
Count the total number of decimal places in the factors. 5.43×1.8 } 3 decimal places

Step 3
Place the decimal point in the product. $4344 + 543 = 9.774$ ← 3 decimal places

The multiplication is correct. Place a decimal point in the correct place.

1. 45.3×7.2 = 326.16
2. 12.2×3.8 = 46.36
3. 57.9×3.78 = 218.862
4. 88.9×6.54 = 581.406

Estimate the product. Then multiply.

5. 1.42×7.2 10.224
6. 2.2×4.1 9.02
7. 5.11×0.3 1.533
8. 3.68×5.8 21.344
9. 51.8×7.5 388.50
10. 34.2×5.1 174.42
11. 2.9×0.08 0.232
12. 3.62×0.18 0.6516
13. $2.8 \times 0.05 =$ 0.140
14. $1.45 \cdot 0.7 =$ 1.015
15. $(2.07)(4.9) =$ 10.143
16. $9.3(0.56) =$ 5.208
17. $0.006(3.75) =$ 0.0225
18. $3.8 \times 912 =$ 3,465.6

ENRICHMENT

Minds on Math Transparency

2-5

Six classmates are sitting at a rectangular table. Two are sitting along each long side. Stella and Troy are sitting at the short ends of the table. No girls are sitting next to each other. Melvin is at Dawnett's left. Ray is across from Melvin. Who is sitting at Diane's left?

Troy

See *Solution Key* for worked-out answers.

WRAP UP

IDENTIFYING THE BIG IDEA Have students explain how they use the properties of multiplication when they multiply with decimals. Then have them describe how they decide where to place the decimal point in a decimal product.

LESSON QUIZ

Use a model, paper and pencil, or a calculator to find each product.

1. 0.7(1.2) **0.84**
2. 2.1×1.05 **2.205**

Use the properties of multiplication to find the value of each expression.

3. $2 \times (4.5 \times 0.3)$ **2.7**
4. $2.18 \times 3.55 \times 0$ **0**

18. *Food* Rice costs $.69 per pound. Jerry bought 1.3 lb. How much did he pay? $0.90

19. *Exercise* Monina walks 3.5 mi/h. She took a 1.2 h walk. How far did she walk? 4.2 mi

20a. 0.15; 0.25; 0.10; 0.20; 0.15; 0.25; 0.1; 0.2

20. a. *Calculator* Find 0.5×0.3, 0.5×0.5, 0.5×0.2, and 0.5×0.4 without a calculator and then with a calculator.
    b. When the final digit in a decimal product is a zero, what does your calculator do?
    The calculator does not show the final 0.

21. a. *Reasoning* Suppose the decimal point key on your calculator is not working. How could you use the calculator to find the area of a room that is 12.5 ft × 15.75 ft? See margin p. 69.
    b. Find the area of the room. 196.875 ft^2

Complete. Name the property of multiplication shown.

22. $3.6 \times$ ■ $= 0$ 0; zero
23. ■ $\times 1 = 25.5$ 25.5; identity
24. ■ $\times 4 = 4 \times 3$ 3; commutative
25. $7.8 \times$ ■ $= 7.8$ 1; identity
26. $(2.5 \times$ ■$) \times 2.3 = 2.5 \times (1.4 \times 2.3)$ 1.4; associative
27. $9.1 \times (6.5 \times 2.7) = (9.1 \times$ ■ $) \times 2.7$ 6.5; associative

Mental Math **Use the properties of multiplication to find the value of each expression.**

28. $0.2 \times 3.41 \times 5$ 3.41
29. $1.09 \times 23.6 \times 0$ 0
30. $(2.3 \times 0.5) \times 4$ 4.6
31. $5 \times (4.3 \times 1)$ 21.5

32. *Writing* How are the identity properties of multiplication and of addition similar? How are they different? The result is equal to the initial number; the identity property for addition uses 0, the identity property for multiplication uses 1.

33. **Choose A, B, C, or D.** Which example shows the commutative property of multiplication? B
    A. $(8.76 \times 5.4) \times 3.9 = 8.76 \times (5.4 \times 3.9)$
    B. $5.61 \times 1.4 \times 8.9 = 5.61 \times 8.9 \times 1.4$
    C. $4.8 \times 0 \times 7.91 \times 5.742 \times 6.108 = 0$
    D. $0.53 \times 7.159 \times 1 = 0.53 \times 7.159$

Mixed Review

Round each decimal to the indicated place. (Lesson 2-1)

34. 33.51623 33.5162
35. 0.618736 0.619
36. 5.62849 5.628
37. 10.453 10.5

38. Use the line plot at the right. (Lesson 1-4)
    a. Find the mean, median, and mode of the data. 4.2; 4; 6
    b. Which measure is the greatest? mode
    c. Which measure is the least? median

Textbooks Brought Home

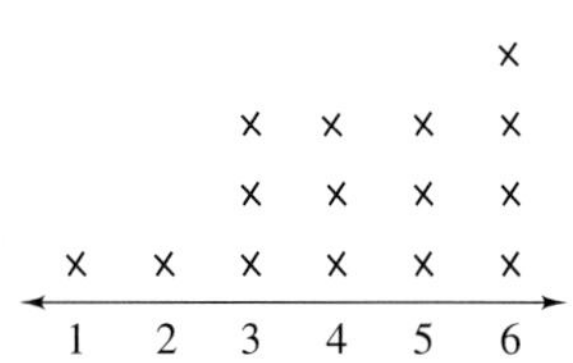

39. *Choose a Strategy* Devon earns $25.50 per day working in a shoe store. His boss pays him $.50 extra for each package of sports socks he sells. After 5 days of work, Devon earned $157.50. How many packages of sports socks did he sell? 60 packages

PROBLEM SOLVING PRACTICE ★★

This page provides problems for students to solve using their knowledge of rounding, estimation, median, range, metric units, and addition, subtraction, multiplication, and division of decimals. Encourage students to read each problem carefully. Also have them refer to the list of problem solving strategies to help them decide how to solve the problems. Point out that not all questions require a strategy for solving, nor are all strategies on the list used on this page.

ERROR ALERT! Exercise 3 Students may use the first and last numbers in the table to find the range. **Remediation:** Remind student to always order the data from least to greatest before finding median or range.

Exercise 4 Encourage students to use compensation as discussed in the Math Toolbox on page 63.

Exercise 8 Encourage students to find a range of possible travel miles for the club. Students can use the minimum and maximum to answer the question.

PROBLEM SOLVING PRACTICE ★★★★★

Read each question and choose the best answer.

1. The restaurant bill for Sam and four of his friends was $47.84. In order to determine the tip, Dave rounded this amount to the nearest dollar. What is this amount rounded to the nearest dollar? C

   A. $40.00 B. $47.00
   C. $48.00 D. $50.00

2. The table shows the number of hours of homework that each of six students did in one week. What was the median number of hours of homework? G

Hours of Homework

Student	Number of Hours
Lisi	4.5
Jareem	8
Marisa	10
Camille	6
Tyler	9.25
Lindy	5.5

   F. 6.5 G. 7 H. 7.5 J. 8

3. Use the table above. What was the range of hours of homework? C

   A. 4.5 B. 5 C. 5.5 D. 6

Please note that items 4–9 have *five* answer choices.

4. A bottle of apple juice holds 3.79 L. A bottle of orange juice holds 1.89 L. How much more does the bottle of apple juice hold? J

   F. 0.8 L G. 0.9 L H. 1.8 L
   J. 1.9 L K. 2.9 L

5. A bookstore received a carton that contained 12 copies of a dictionary. Each dictionary weighed 2.3 kg, and the carton weighed 1.3 kg. What is the total weight of the filled carton? D

   A. 26.3 kg B. 27.6 kg C. 27.9 kg
   D. 28.9 kg E. Not Here

6. For a class party, the student council purchased 42 balloons at $1.85 each. What is the best estimate of the total amount the student council paid for the balloons? H

   F. $70.00 G. $75.00 H. $80.00
   J. $90.00 K. $95.00

7. Jenny saved part of her allowance for four weeks. The first week Jenny saved $4.20, the second week she saved $3.85, the third week she saved $2.50, and the fourth week she saved $3.30. What was the total amount Jenny saved? C

   A. $12.85 B. $13.75 C. $13.85
   D. $13.86 E. Not Here

8. The hiking club went on a 7-day trip. Each day they hiked between 5.5 and 7.5 miles. It is reasonable to assume that during the 7 days the club hiked — G

   F. less than 35 miles
   G. between 35 and 55 miles
   H. exactly 55 miles
   J. more than 55 miles
   K. Not Here

9. Esther used rounding to estimate the sum of two prices. Her sum was $5. What numbers could she have added? D

   A. $4.23 + $7.80 B. $3.95 + $2.25
   C. $2.37 + $2.07 D. $2.35 + $2.73
   E. $3.59 + $2.78

2-6 Teaching Notes

1 Focus

CONNECTING TO PRIOR KNOWLEDGE *Ask students: If I want to drive 120 mi and my car gets 30 mi/gal, how many gallons of gas do I need in my car?* **4 gal** *Does division always come out evenly?* **no** *Are miles and gallons always whole numbers?* **no** *What must I be able to do if I want to know how many gallons I need to drive 2.5 mi?* **Answers may vary. Sample: Divide decimals.**

2 Teach

THINK AND DISCUSS

AEP VISUAL LEARNING Have students draw a colorful display to help them remember where each part of a division is. Students should write their example as a sentence and in a division house, using the same color for the matching parts.

CONNECTION TO TECHNOLOGY Have students explore division by 0 using a calculator. Have students divide 6 by 1, 0.5, 0.25, 0.1, and 0. Ask students how many empty glasses it takes to make six glasses of juice. Relate this to multiplying and dividing by zero.

Lesson Planning Options

Prerequisite Skills

- estimating quotients (2-2)

Materials/Manipulatives

- calculator

Resources

Student Edition

Skills Handbook, p. 537
Extra Practice, p. 515
Glossary/Study Guide

Teaching Resources

Chapter Support File, Ch. 2
- Lesson Planner 2-6
- Practice 2-6, Reteaching 2-6
- Answer Masters 2-6

Teaching Aids Masters 20, 26
Glossary, Spanish Resources

Transparencies

9, 10, 11, Minds on Math 2-6

Warm Up

Without actually dividing, which expression is the largest?
6.1 ÷ 2.8
12.6 ÷ 1.1
9.305 ÷ 2.99 **12.6 ÷ 1.1 is the largest because the approximate values of the three expressions respectively are 2, 13, and 3.**

2-6 Dividing Decimals

What You'll Learn

1. To divide decimals by whole numbers
2. To divide decimals by decimals

...And Why

You can find how to share costs when you buy items with others.

Here's How

Look for questions that
- build understanding
- ✔ check understanding

THINK AND DISCUSS

1 Dividing a Decimal by a Whole Number

Recall the names of the parts of a division problem.

$$6\overline{)18} = 3$$

divisor → 6; 3 ← quotient; 18 ← dividend

Estimation can help you avoid errors when you divide decimals.

■ **EXAMPLE 1** *Real-World Problem Solving*

Computers You and two friends are buying a new computer game for $40.95. How much is your share?

Estimate: 40.95 ÷ 3 ≈ 42 ÷ 3 = 14 ← Use compatible numbers.

```
   13.65   ← Place the decimal point in
3)40.95      the quotient. Then divide.
 -3
  10
 - 9
   19
 - 18
    15
  - 15
     0
```

Your share is $13.65.

1. ✔ *Try It Out* Find each quotient.
   a. 20.65 ÷ 5 **4.13** b. 9.868 ÷ 2 **4.934** c. 20.93 ÷ 7 **2.99**

Now you may assign Exercises 1–10.

2 Dividing a Decimal by a Decimal

Can you divide by zero? Consider these related problems.

6 ÷ 3 = 2	6 ÷ 0 $\stackrel{?}{=}$ 0 ← $\stackrel{?}{=}$ means deciding if equal or not.
2 × 3 = 6	0 × 0 ≠ 6 ← ≠ means not equal to.

The related division and multiplication problems show that division by zero does not make sense! So division by zero is undefined.

ERROR ALERT! Students may misplace the decimal in the quotient. **Remediation:** Stress to students to always write the decimal in the quotient first. Students may want to draw a light line that goes through the decimal in the dividend up through the quotient.

■ **ADDITIONAL EXAMPLES**

FOR EXAMPLE 1

You and three friends are buying a new video for $25.92. How much is your share? **$6.48**

FOR EXAMPLE 2

The Astronomy Club received $44.80 in change after they paid for their tickets to the planetarium. They divided the change evenly so every member received $3.20 for lunch money. How many members of the club visited the planetarium? **14 members**

FOR EXAMPLE 3

Find the quotient 0.68 ÷ 0.08. **8.5**

ASSESSMENT Have students make a list of the steps they use to find the quotient 1.25 ÷ 0.2. **6.25** Have students exchange lists, then follow the steps to check their validity.

3 Practice/Assess

EXERCISES *On Your Own*

Exercises 1–8 Remind students to estimate the quotient first, then use the estimate to check their final quotient.

Before you begin to divide decimals, rewrite the problem so the divisor is a whole number.

■ **EXAMPLE 2** *Real-World Problem Solving*

Need Help? For practice in dividing decimals, see Skills Handbook pages 537 and 539.

Exercise Suppose you ride your bicycle 25.75 mi in 2.5 h. Find your average speed in miles per hour.

Estimate: 25.75 ÷ 2.5 ≈ 25 ÷ 2.5 = 10

$$2.5\overline{)25.75} \rightarrow 25\overline{)257.5}$$

- Quotient: 10.3 — Multiply the divisor and dividend by 10.
- −25
- 07 5 — Since 7 is less than 25, put a zero in the quotient. Then bring down both 7 and 5.
- −7 5
- 0

Your average speed is 10.3 mi/h.

2. *Reasoning* If you multiplied 2.5 and 25.75 by 100 in the example above, will this affect the answer? Explain.
No; when you multiply and divide by the same number (100), the result does not change.

When you divide by a decimal, sometimes you need to use extra zeros in the dividend, the quotient, or both.

■ **EXAMPLE 3**

Find 0.14 ÷ 0.04.

$$0.04\overline{)0.14} \rightarrow 4\overline{)14.0}$$

- Quotient: 3.5 — Multiply the divisor and dividend by 100.
- −12
- 2 0 — Insert a zero after the dividend.
- −2 0
- 0

Check 0.04 × 3.5 = 0.14✓ — Multiply the quotient by the original divisor.

3. ✔ *Try It Out* Find $3.2\overline{)17.6}$. Check your answer. **5.5; 3.2 × 5.5 = 17.6**

Now you may assign Exercises 11–31.

EXERCISES *On Your Own*

Find each quotient. Check each answer.

1. 22.2 ÷ 3 **7.4**	**2.** $5\overline{)16.5}$ **3.3**	**3.** 14.49 ÷ 7 **2.07**	**4.** $4\overline{)5.16}$ **1.29**
5. 79.599 ÷ 13 **6.123**	**6.** $83\overline{)15.272}$ **0.184**	**7.** 22.568 ÷ 26 **0.868**	**8.** 0.0882 ÷ 6 **0.0147**

Technology Options

Prentice Hall Technology

Software for Learners
- Hot Page™ 3–5*
- Math Blaster® Mystery*
- Interactive Student Tutorial, Chapter 2*

Teaching Resource Software
- Computer Item Generator 2-6
- Resource Pro™ Chapter 2*

Internet • For related mathematics activities, visit the Prentice Hall site at www.phschool.com/math

**Available on CD-ROM only*

Assignment Options for Exercises On Your Own

To provide flexible scheduling, this lesson can be split into parts.

1 **Core** 1–9
Extension 10

2 **Core** 11–30
Extension 31

Use Mixed Review to maintain skills.

PRACTICE

Practice 2-6 Dividing Decimals

Circle A, B, or C. Estimate each quotient. Choose the best answer.

1. 10 ÷ 4.6 A. 0.23 (B.) 2.3 C. 33
2. 9.9 ÷ 2.7 A. 40 (B.) 4 C. 0.37
3. 43.68 ÷ 7.8 (A.) 6 B. 60 C. 0.56
4. 65.29 ÷ 8.5 A. 80 B. 72 (C.) 8

Use mental math to find each quotient.

5. 0.7 ÷ 100 0.007
6. 4.85 ÷ 0.1 48.5
7. 7.08 ÷ 10 0.708
8. 3.5 ÷ 0.1 35
9. 847 ÷ 0.01 84,700
10. 0.3 ÷ 0.1 3
11. 32.6 ÷ 0.01 3,260
12. 5.02 ÷ 0.1 50.2

Choose mental math, paper and pencil, or a calculator.

13. 2.1)12.6 6
14. 29.75 ÷ 0.7 42.5
15. 37 ÷ 0.2 185
16. 4.74 ÷ 0.06 79
17. 1.414 ÷ 1.4 1.01
18. 0.78)0.16614 0.213
19. 0.154 ÷ 5.5 0.028
20. 0.85)0.0527 0.062

Find each quotient. Check each answer.

21. 42.6 ÷ 6 7.1
22. 3)6.51 2.17
23. 106.4 ÷ 7 15.2
24. 8)31.2 3.9
25. 81.648 ÷ 14 5.832
26. 55.68 ÷ 32 1.74
27. 9)7.704 0.856
28. 7.518 ÷ 15 0.5012

Solve.

29. Alicia paid $1.32 for a bag of pinto beans. The beans cost $0.55 per lb. How much did the bag of pinto beans weigh? 2.4 lb
30. Nina and 3 friends ate lunch at a cafe. They decided to split the bill evenly. The total bill was $17.84. How much was each person's share? $4.46

Practice

In copymaster and workbook formats

RETEACHING

Reteaching 2-6 Dividing Decimals

Divide 38.25 ÷ 1.5.

First, estimate the quotient. Use compatible numbers. 38.25 ÷ 1.5 **Round to** 40 ÷ 2 = 20 **Estimate**

Step 1
If the divisor is a decimal, rewrite the problem with a whole number divisor. 1.5)38.25 → 1.5.)38.2.5 **Move 1 place each.**

Step 2
Place the decimal point in the quotient. The estimated quotient is 20. So place the first digit in the tens column of the quotient. 15)382.5 **Keep in line.**

Step 3
Divide. Then check.

```
     25.5
15)382.5
  - 30
     82
   - 75
      7 5
    - 7 5
        0
```

Multiply to check. 25.5 × 15 = 382.5 ✓

Rewrite each problem so the divisor is a whole number.

1. 5.1)351.9 51)3519
2. 1.8)14.9 18)149
3. 0.32)39.68 32)3968
4. 0.06)0.948 6)94.8
5. 0.8)2.112 8)21.12
6. 0.49)9.457 49)945.7

Divide. Check each quotient by multiplying.

7. 9)87.3 9.7
8. 18)8.28 0.46
9. 48)1.488 0.031
10. 2)15.8 7.9
11. 0.4)2.2 5.5
12. 0.09)0.99 11
13. 2.7)12.15 4.5
14. 0.14)28.14 201
15. 0.08)0.64 8

Reteaching

ENRICHMENT

Minds on Math Transparency

2-6

Ted told Frank that all of the markers in Ted's box were black except for two, all were red except for two, and all were purple except for two. How many markers were in Ted's box?

2 if none are black, red, or purple; otherwise 3: 1 black, 1 red, and 1 purple

See *Solution Key* for worked-out answers.

Exercise 10 Bring in a parsnip, or a picture of a parsnip, for students who have never seen one.

Exercise 16 Make sure students remember 0.003 is the dividend. They may be tempted to divide the larger number by the smaller one.

WRAP UP

IDENTIFYING THE BIG IDEA Have students describe the difference between dividing a decimal by a whole number and a decimal by a decimal.

LESSON QUIZ

Find each quotient. Check each answer with multiplication.

1. 4)66.16 16.54
2. 0.09 ÷ 0.36 0.25

9. *Movies* Akiko bought five tickets for $23.75. How much did each ticket cost? $4.75

10. *Food* The longest parsnip grown was 171.72 in. long. How long was it in yards? 4.77 yd

Choose **Use mental math, paper and pencil, or a calculator.**

11. 10.8 ÷ 2.7 4
12. 0.04)10 250
13. 0.3)135.6 452
14. 0.04)1 25
15. 59.2 ÷ 0.8 74
16. 0.003 ÷ 0.6 0.005
17. 0.34)0.00119 0.0035
18. 0.054 ÷ 0.72 0.075
19. 1.2)0.078 0.065
20. 2.245 ÷ 0.05 44.9
21. 0.04)0.1 2.5
22. 2.8 ÷ 0.25 11.2

23. a. Find each quotient.
    i. 75)300 4 ii. 7.5)300 40 iii. 0.75)300 400

    b. *Patterns* Describe what happens to a quotient when the dividend remains the same and the divisor decreases.

For each place the decimal point moves to the left in the divisor, the quotient increases 10-fold.

Mental Math **Find each quotient.**

24. 0.9 ÷ 100 0.009
25. 236.7 ÷ 0.1 2,367
26. 5.02 ÷ 0.01 502
27. 0.7 ÷ 10 0.07

28. *Gardening* After digging up lilac bushes in his garden, Julio used sod to cover the dirt. The sod cost $2.25/yd^2. He paid $31.50. How much sod did he buy? 14 yd^2

29. *Reasoning* Last week Sue's father drove 283.4 mi on 16.2 gal of gasoline. Sue says that he averaged about 1.75 mi/gal. Is her answer reasonable? Explain.
No; the quotient is about 17.5 mi/gal.

30. *Hobbies* Nikia bought 3.2 yd of fabric for a total price of $13.92. How much did the fabric cost per yard? $4.35 per yard

31. *Writing* Do you think there is a commutative property of division? Why or why not? Give examples.
No; 1 ÷ 10 is not the same as 10 ÷ 1.

Mixed Review

Find each sum. *(Lesson 2-3)*

32. 8.56 + 3.11 11.67
33. 9.843 + 8.2 18.043
34. 6.4 + 7.024 13.424
35. 17.1 + 3.09 20.19

36. a. Use the data below to draw a scatter plot. Graph the number of classes on the horizontal axis and hours of homework on the vertical axis. See margin p. 75.

Number of Classes	6	7	5	7	6	6	5	6	7	4	5
Hours of Homework	3	4	3.5	4.5	3.5	4	3	5	6	2	4

b. Do you see a trend? Explain. *(Lesson 1-9)*

b. Yes; the hours of homework increase with the number of classes

MATH TOOLBOX

In Lesson 2-5, students learned to multiply decimals. This toolbox helps students apply their knowledge of multiplying decimals to change from one metric measure to another.

ERROR ALERT! **Exercise 4–6** Students may have trouble converting from the left side of the chart to the right side using this multiplication method. **Remediation:** First have students convert the given measurement to the basic unit. Then rewrite the problem to convert from the basic unit to the new measurement.

ASSESSMENT Group students in pairs. Have one student write two units of measure. The partner writes the number needed to multiply the first unit by to change to the second unit. Have partners change roles. Repeat the process five more times.

■ ADDITIONAL PROBLEM

Complete the statement.

1. 850 cm = ■ km 0.0085

MATH TOOLBOX SKILLS REVIEW

The Metric System

After Lesson 2-6

The basic unit of length in the metric system is the meter. All the other units are based on the meter. In the chart below, each unit is 10 times the value of the unit to its left.

Unit	millimeter	centimeter	decimeter	meter	decameter	hectometer	kilometer
Symbol	mm	cm	dm	m	dam	hm	km
Value	0.001 m	0.01 m	0.1 m	1 m	10 m	100 m	1,000 m

The same prefixes are used with gram for measures of mass and liter for measures of capacity. For example, one thousand grams (symbol g) is a kilogram (symbol kg). One thousandth of a liter (symbol L) is a milliliter (symbol mL). (*Note:* A *capital* L is used for liters to avoid confusion with the number 1.)

To change a measure from one unit to another, start by finding the relationship between the two units.

■ EXAMPLE

Complete each equation.

a. 245 mL = ■ L
1 mL = 0.001 L
$245 \times 0.001 = 0.245$ ← To change mL to L, multiply by 0.001.
245 mL = 0.245 L

b. 2.3 kg = ■ g
1 kg = 1,000 g
$2.3 \times 1,000 = 2,300$ ← To change kg to g, multiply by 1,000.
2.3 kg = 2,300 g

Complete each statement.

1. ■ L = 90 mL 0.09
2. ■ g = 8 mg 0.008
3. 0.6 mL = ■ L 0.0006
4. ■ mg = 2.7 kg 2,700,000
5. 1,200 mL = ■ kL 0.0012
6. ■ km = 620,000 mm 0.62
7. 58 L = ■ mL 58,000
8. 7,800 g = ■ kg 7.8
9. ■ m = 850 cm 8.5
10. ■ cg = 80 g 8,000
11. 2.46 km = ■ mm 2,460,000
12. ■ L = 0.47 kL 470
13. ■ km = 309,000 cm 3.09
14. 240 kL = ■ L 240,000
15. 7 m = ■ km 0.007
16. *Language* Use a dictionary to find the meaning of each prefix in the chart above. *Milli-* means one thousandth; *centi-* means one hundredth; *deci-* means one tenth; *deca-* means ten; *hecto-* means hundred; *kilo-* means thousand.

Materials/Manipulatives

- dictionary

Resources

Teaching Resources
Teaching Aids Masters 3

Transparencies
13, 15

pages 70–74 On Your Own

36a. Number of Classes and Hours of Homework

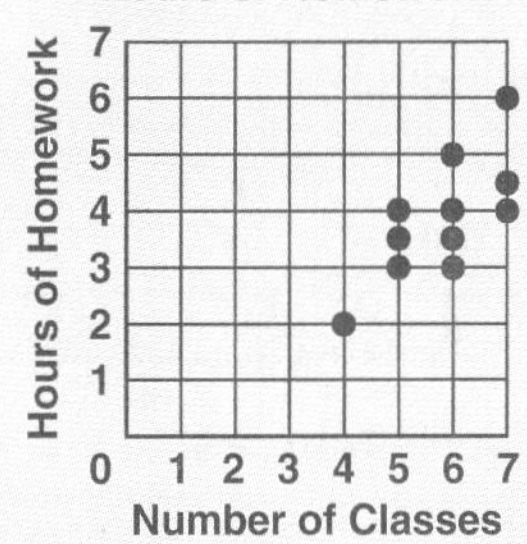

2-7 Teaching Notes

1 Focus

CONNECTING TO PRIOR KNOWLEDGE Ask students to find 1 ÷ 3 using paper and pencil. **0.3333** Ask: *How is this division problem different from the problems you did in Lesson 2-6?* **The decimal repeats and does not end.**

2 Teach

THINK AND DISCUSS

TACTILE LEARNING Question 1 Have students use base-ten blocks to model 6 ÷ 2 × 2. Divide six longs into two equal sections. **3 longs** Then multiply the longs in one section by 2. **6 longs** Ask students how this amount compares with the original amount of longs. **They are the same.**

ERROR ALERT! Students may misplace the bar when more than one digit repeats. **Remediation:** Explain that the bar covers only the repeating section or sequence of digits. This sequence can have any number of digits. Have students circle the sequence of digits each time it appears. For example, in 0.375637563756. . . , students circle 3756 each time it appears.

Lesson Planning Options

Prerequisite Skills

- division of decimals (2-6)
- rounding decimals (2-1)

Vocabulary/Symbols

terminating decimal, repeating decimal

Materials/Manipulatives

- calculator

Resources

Student Edition

Skills Handbook, pp. 532, 533
Extra Practice, p. 515
Glossary/Study Guide

Teaching Resources

Chapter Support File, Ch. 2
- Lesson Planner 2-7
- Practice 2-7, Reteaching 2-7
- Answer Masters 2-7

Glossary, Spanish Resources

Transparencies
15, Minds on Math 2-7

Warm Up

If Jack walks $\frac{3}{4}$ km in $\frac{1}{4}$ h, how far does he walk in 2 h? **6 km**

TECHNOLOGY

2-7 Terminating and Repeating Decimals

What You'll Learn

1. To investigate division using a calculator
2. To classify decimals as terminating or repeating

...And Why

You can understand how your calculator's memory retains calculations.

Here's How

Look for questions that
- build understanding
- ✓ check understanding

THINK AND DISCUSS

1 *Investigating Division on a Calculator*

Do you know how a scientific calculator's memory affects the answers it gives you? You can learn more about a calculator by exploring division.

1. Suppose you divide 8 by 6, then multiply the product by 6. What will be the result? **8**

2. a. *Calculator* Use your calculator to find 8 ÷ 6.
   b. Clear your calculator. Enter the result to part (a) and multiply by 6. **7.999999998**
   c. Does your answer to part (b) match your answer to Question 1? **no**

   2a. 1.333333333

3. Now find 8 ÷ 6 × 6 using these keystrokes: 8 [÷] 6 [×] 6.

When you find 8 ÷ 6, the calculator's memory holds more digits in its memory than are shown on the screen. When you continue calculations, you use all these digits without re-entering them.

4. a. *Calculator* Use each method to find 6 ÷ 9 + 5 ÷ 15.

   [(] 6 [÷] 9 [)] [+] [(] 5 [÷] 15 [)] [=] **1**   6 [÷] 9 [+] 5 [÷] 15 [=] **1**

   b. Are your results for both methods the same? **yes**

Now you may assign Exercises 1–8, 19.

2 *Classifying Quotients*

When you divide decimals, if the quotient stops it is a **terminating decimal.** When a digit or sequence of digits keeps repeating, it is a **repeating decimal.** You can write 0.666. . . as $0.\overline{6}$.

Terminating Decimals
3 ÷ 4 ⇒ 0.75
5 ÷ 8 ⇒ 0.625

Repeating Decimals
1 ÷ 3 ⇒ 0.333... ⇒ $0.\overline{3}$
2 ÷ 3 ⇒ 0.666... ⇒ $0.\overline{6}$

The bar shows that the digit repeats.

VISUAL LEARNING Questions 5 and 6 Have students highlight all the repeating numbers and then place the bar over the first set of repeating numbers.

■ ADDITIONAL EXAMPLE

FOR EXAMPLE
Find each quotient. Tell if the quotient is terminating or repeating.

a. 7 ÷ 16 **0.4375; terminating**

b. 2 ÷ 9 **0.222. . . ; repeating**

EXTENSION Ask: *How is a calculator useful when finding repeating decimal patterns?* **Answers may vary. Sample: Calculators can find a lot of decimal places quickly. This makes finding patterns easier.** *Are some patterns easier to find than others? Give examples.* **Answers may vary. Sample: When one number repeats, such as 0.3333. . . , it is much easier to see than when several numbers repeat, such as 0.257257. . . .**

ASSESSMENT Draw a long number line on the board with measurements to the tenths' place. Write repeating decimals on index cards and have each student choose a card. Each student writes the decimal in the appropriate location on the number line. The class verifies the placement of each decimal.

■ EXAMPLE

Find each quotient. Tell if the quotient is terminating or repeating.

a. 1 ÷ 4

```
   0.25
 4)1.00
  -8
   20
  -20
    0   <-- There is no remainder.
```

1 ÷ 4 = 0.25, a terminating decimal.

b. 9 ÷ 11

```
    0.8181
 11)9.0000
   -88
     20
    -11
     90
    -88
     20
    -11
      9   <-- There will always be a remainder.
```

9 ÷ 11 = 0.8181 . . . or $0.\overline{81}$, a repeating decimal.

WHAT? The number 142857 is called "roundabout." Does it look familiar? Check what happens when it's multiplied by 2. How about 3? What happens when it's multiplied by 7?

Source: *The Kids' World Almanac of Amazing Facts About Numbers, Math, and Money*

5. ✔ *Try It Out* Find each quotient. Put a bar over any repeating digit(s).
a. 5 ÷ 6 **$0.8\overline{3}$** **b.** 4 ÷ 9 **$0.\overline{4}$** **c.** 7 ÷ 8 **0.875** **d.** 50 ÷ 11 **$4.\overline{54}$**

6. a. Find 1 ÷ 7. What digits repeat? **0.1428571428571...; 142857**
b. Write the quotient of 1 ÷ 7 using a bar. **$0.\overline{142857}$**
c. *Calculator* Use a calculator to find 1 ÷ 7. How many of the digits can you see repeating in the display? **0.142857142; 3**

Now you may assign Exercises 9–18, 20–26.

EXERCISES *On Your Own*

Use a calculator to find each quotient.

1. 7 ÷ 12 + 4 ÷ 24 **0.75**
2. 5 ÷ 9 − 8 ÷ 36 **0.333333333**
3. 7 ÷ 11 − 3 ÷ 22 **0.5**
4. 5 ÷ 7 + 10 ÷ 35 **1**
5. 6 ÷ 13 + 1 ÷ 26 **0.5**
6. 41 ÷ 17 − 14 ÷ 34 **2**
7. 5 ÷ 7 + 14 ÷ 49 **1**
8. 23 ÷ 60 − 2 ÷ 15 **0.25**

Choose **Use a calculator or paper and pencil to find each quotient. Use a bar to show repeating decimals.**

9. 3 ÷ 8 **0.375**
10. 12 ÷ 13 **$0.\overline{923076}$**
11. 10 ÷ 3 **$3.\overline{3}$**
12. 155 ÷ 11 **$14.\overline{09}$**
13. 2 ÷ 7 **$0.\overline{285714}$**
14. 12 ÷ 5 **2.4**
15. 60 ÷ 11 **$5.\overline{45}$**
16. 42 ÷ 28 **1.5**
17. 50 ÷ 6 **$8.\overline{3}$**
18. 16 ÷ 5 **3.2**

Technology Options

Prentice Hall Technology

Software for Learners
- Math Blaster® Mystery*
- Interactive Student Tutorial, Chapter 2*

Teaching Resource Software
- Computer Item Generator 2-7
- Resource Pro™ Chapter 2*

Internet • For related mathematics activities, visit the Prentice Hall site at www.phschool.com/math

**Available on CD-ROM only*

Assignment Options for Exercises On Your Own

To provide flexible scheduling, this lesson can be split into parts.

1 Core 1–8
Extension 19

2 Core 9–18, 20–24, 26
Extension 25

Use Mixed Review to maintain skills.

3 Practice/Assess

EXERCISES *On Your Own*

Exercises 9–13 To encourage division practice, consider asking students to use pencil and paper for at least two problems.

CONNECTION TO TECHNOLOGY Exercise 19 Have students experiment with dividing decimals using a spreadsheet program and the numbers in the table.

DIVERSITY Exercises 22–24 Use the article to help stress to students that the same mathematical concepts are used all over the world and have withstood the test of time.

EXTENSION Exercises 22–24 If you have block scheduling or extended class periods, pair students and have them bring examples of circles to class to measure. Tell students:

- *Measure the distance around the circles (the circumference) and the distance across the circle (the diameter).*
- *Use a calculator to divide the circumference by the diameter.*
- *Compare your quotient with that of others.*

CONNECTION TO HISTORY Exercises 22–24 Have students investigate pi. Ask: *What is the value of pi written out to 15 decimal places?* **3.141592653589793**

WRITING Exercise 25 Encourage students to try to write the number using a bar. This will help them see that no specific sequence of digits repeats.

CHECKPOINT 2

Checkpoint 2

Lessons 2-4 through 2-7

Find each product or quotient. Use a bar to show repeating decimals.

1. 7.5×3 22.5
2. 3.1×6.9 21.39
3. $0.71 \cdot 50$ 35.5
4. $9 \div 5.5$ $1.\overline{63}$
5. $8 \div 1.5$ $5.\overline{3}$
6. $12.3 \div 6$ 2.05

Complete. Name the property of multiplication shown.

7. ■ $\times 1 = 36.4$ 36.4; Identity
8. ■ $\times 3.5 = 3.5 \times 1.8$ 1.8; Commutative
9. $9.6 \times$ ■ $= 0$ 0; Zero property
10. Each student in a class of 21 joined the baseball team or the soccer team but not both. Six students joined the band. Fifteen students joined the soccer team. How many joined the baseball team? 6 students

Assessment

pages 77–78 On Your Own

19a. Each successive divisor is one tenth of the one before it.

b. 0.0001; 0.00001; 0.000001; 0.5; 5; 50; 500; 5,000; 50,000; 500,000; 5,000,000; 50,000,000

c. As the divisors get closer to 0, the quotients get very large; the smaller the divisor, the more times it goes into the dividend.

20a. 0.04040404; 0.05050505; 0.06060606; the first two digits are repeated. The first digit is 0 and the second is the same as the dividend.

19. a. *Patterns* Look at the division problems at the right. What pattern do you see in the divisors?

b. Copy the table. Find the missing divisors. Find each quotient.

c. *Reasoning* As the divisor gets closer and closer to zero, what happens to the quotient? Why?

a–c. See margin.

Dividend		Divisor		Quotient
50	÷	100	=	■
50	÷	10	=	■
50	÷	1	=	■
50	÷	0.1	=	■
50	÷	0.01	=	■
50	÷	0.001	=	■
50	÷	■	=	■
50	÷	■	=	■
50	÷	■	=	■

20. a. *Patterns* Use your calculator to find $4 \div 99$, $5 \div 99$, and $6 \div 99$. What pattern do you see? **20a. See margin.**

b. Use your pattern to find $7 \div 99$, $8 \div 99$, and $9 \div 99$ without a calculator. $0.\overline{07}$; $0.\overline{08}$; $0.\overline{09}$

21. Divide 1 by each whole number from 10 to 20.

a. For which divisors do the digits in the quotients repeat? For which divisors do the digits terminate? **11, 12, 13, 14, 15, 18; 10, 16, 20**

b. For which divisors can't you tell if the digits of the quotient terminate or repeat? Why can't you tell? **17, 19; digits in the calculator display do not repeat, but fill all spaces.**

SLICES OF Pi

CIRCLES, computers, and "Star Trek" are all linked to one number, *pi. Pi*, or π, defines the relationship between a circle and its diameter.

Different approximations have been used for π. The Egyptians believed it to be 256 ÷ 81. The Chinese used 355 ÷ 113, and one estimate used in India was 62,832 ÷ 20,000. The Greek mathematician Archimedes proved that π is between 22 ÷ 7 and 223 ÷ 71.

In 1767, Johann Lambert proved that π is a decimal that neither terminates nor repeats. Because π never terminates nor repeats, the Star Trek crew used it to keep an evil computer busy until it could be disarmed.

Use the article to answer Exercises 22–24.

22. Is the Indian estimate a terminating or repeating decimal? **terminating**

23. Which of the two estimates of π given by Archimedes is closer to the value your calculator gives? **223 ÷ 71**

24. *Open-ended* Find two numbers not mentioned in the article whose quotient is about equal to π. **Sample: 371 ÷ 118**

25. *Writing* Is the number 3.03003000300003. . . a repeating decimal? Why or why not? **No; the numbers in the pattern do not repeat in the same order.**

26. *Mental Math* Find $7 \div 12$. Use it to find $70 \div 12$. $0.58\overline{3}$; $5.8\overline{3}$

WRAP UP

IDENTIFYING THE BIG IDEA Ask students to explain the difference between terminating decimals and repeating decimals.

PROJECT LINK You may wish to show students samples of metallic statues of different animals. These can be found in art books.

LESSON QUIZ

Use a calculator to find each quotient. Use a bar to show repeating decimals.

1. 7 ÷ 11 $0.\overline{63}$

2. 3 ÷ 4 0.75

3. 3 ÷ 7 $0.\overline{428571}$

PRACTICE

Practice 2-7 Terminating and Repeating Decimals

Write each repeating decimal using a bar.

1. 0.333 . . . $0.\overline{3}$
2. 0.125125 . . . $0.\overline{125}$
3. 0.8787 . . . $0.\overline{87}$
4. 3.5666 . . . $3.5\overline{6}$
5. 0.030030 . . . $0.\overline{030}$
6. 7.322322 . . . $7.\overline{322}$
7. 5.7745353 . . . $5.774\overline{53}$
8. 12.11222 . . . $12.11\overline{2}$

Write each repeating decimal without a bar.

9. $0.\overline{5}$ 0.555 . . .
10. $0.\overline{732}$ 0.732732 . . .
11. $5.8\overline{218}$ 5.8218218 . . .
12. $7.\overline{56}$ 7.5656 . . .
13. $0.9\overline{7}$ 0.9777 . . .
14. $0.\overline{003}$ 0.003003 . . .
15. $8.\overline{211}$ 8.211211 . . .
16. $24.\overline{48}$ 24.4848 . . .

Use a calculator to find each answer.

17. 1 ÷ 2 + 9 ÷ 6 2
18. 5 ÷ 3 + 32 ÷ 12 $4.\overline{3}$
19. 15 ÷ 9 − 24 ÷ 18 $0.\overline{3}$
20. 2 ÷ 14 + 10 ÷ 28 0.5
21. 10 ÷ 8 − 3 ÷ 24 1.125
22. 9 ÷ 13 − 27 ÷ 39 0
23. 35 ÷ 10 + 18 ÷ 12 5
24. 9 ÷ 11 − 7 ÷ 22 0.5
25. 7 ÷ 4 + 24 ÷ 40 2.35

Choose a calculator or paper and pencil to find each quotient. Use a bar to show repeating decimals.

26. 5 ÷ 8 0.625
27. 7 ÷ 8 0.875
28. 9 ÷ 16 0.5625
29. 7 ÷ 16 0.4375
30. 4 ÷ 9 $0.\overline{4}$
31. 5 ÷ 32 0.15625
32. 7 ÷ 12 $0.58\overline{3}$
33. 11 ÷ 32 0.34375
34. 5 ÷ 4 1.25
35. 5 ÷ 7 $0.\overline{714285}$
36. 2 ÷ 11 $0.\overline{18}$
37. 4 ÷ 7 $0.\overline{571428}$
38. 6 ÷ 13 $0.\overline{461538}$
39. 11 ÷ 3 $3.\overline{6}$
40. 8 ÷ 9 $0.\overline{8}$
41. 11 ÷ 9 $1.\overline{2}$
42. 7 ÷ 32 0.21875
43. 9 ÷ 32 0.28125
44. 5 ÷ 16 0.3125
45. 8 ÷ 15 $0.5\overline{3}$

In copymaster and workbook formats

Mixed Review

Find each difference. *(Lesson 2-3)*

27. 9.8 − 7.02 2.78 **28.** 190.76 − 178.5 12.26 **29.** 18.4 − 9.57 8.83 **30.** 10 − 4.139 5.861

Compare using <, >, or =. *(Lesson 2-1)*

31. 3.012 ■ 3.12 < **32.** 79.284 ■ 79.28 > **33.** 35.009 ■ 35.01 <

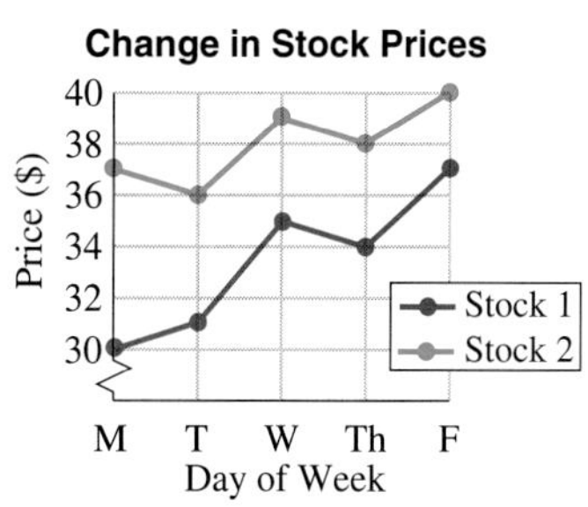

34. a. *Business* Use the line graph at the right. Find the change from Monday to Friday for each stock. See below.

b. You buy one stock on Monday and sell it on Friday. Which stock is the better choice? Explain. *(Lesson 1-3)* Stock 1; stock 1 increased by $4 more than stock 2.

35. A penny weighs about 0.1 oz. How much is a pound of pennies worth? *(Lesson 2-5)* $1.60

CHAPTER PROJECT

PROJECT LINK: CALCULATING

Use the weights of the different animals and the specific gravities of the different metals. Find the weight of a statue of each animal in each metal. Check students' work.

34a. Stock 1 incresed by $7; stock 2 increased by $3.

✓ CHECKPOINT 2 *Lessons 2-4 through 2-7*

Find each product or quotient. Use a bar to show repeating decimals.

1. 6 × 8.2 49.2 **2.** 4.5 ÷ 3 1.5 **3.** 9.1 · 2.4 21.84 **4.** 8.7 ÷ 4 2.175 **5.** 9.35 ÷ 6 $1.558\overline{3}$ **6.** 10.3 × 5.7 58.71

7. 7 ÷ 4.8 $1.458\overline{3}$ **8.** 17 · 0.61 10.37 **9.** 9.8 ÷ 3.7 $2.\overline{648}$ **10.** 1.36 × 8.94 12.1584 **11.** 15 ÷ 0.11 $136.\overline{36}$ **12.** 11.5 ÷ 3 $3.8\overline{3}$

13. a. *Open-ended* Write an expression with division and decimals. a–b. Check students' work.

b. Find the value of your expression. Is it a terminating decimal or a repeating decimal?

14. Each seventh-grade student is in one activity. Twelve of the students are on the student council. One is the president and one is the treasurer. Another 25 play sports, and 19 are in the band. Seven students work on the school paper. How many students are in seventh grade? 63 students

RETEACHING

Reteaching 2-7 Terminating and Repeating Decimals

A **terminating decimal** has a last digit, or terminates.

Examples: 0.3 2.57 0.008 (↑ ↑ ↑)

A **repeating decimal** has a digit or digits that repeat.
You can use a bar to show that digits repeat.

Examples: 0.444 . . . = $0.\overline{4}$ 0.020202 . . . = $0.\overline{02}$ 4.1232323 . . . = $4.1\overline{23}$

Some quotients are terminating decimals.
Some quotients are repeating decimals.

	3 ÷ 8	2 ÷ 9
Step 1 Annex zeros.	8)3.000 → 0.375 ← terminating decimal	9)2.000 → 0.222 ← repeating decimal
Step 2 Divide until the remainder is zero or until you see a pattern.	−24, 60, −56, 40, −40, 0 ← remainder zero	−18, 20, −18, 20, −18, 2 ← There is a pattern.
Step 3 If there is a pattern, use a bar to show repeating digits.	3 ÷ 8 = 0.375	2 ÷ 9 = 0.222 . . ., or $0.\overline{2}$

Write each repeating decimal using a bar.

1. 0.555 . . . $0.\overline{5}$
2. 0.6464 . . . $0.\overline{64}$
3. 2.7333 . . . $2.7\overline{3}$
4. 0.011011 . . . $0.\overline{011}$

Divide. Use a bar to show repeating decimals.

5. 4)3 0.75
6. 8)5 0.625
7. 6)5 $0.8\overline{3}$
8. 11)100 $9.\overline{09}$
9. 3)7 $2.\overline{3}$
10. 5)12 2.4
11. 9)16 $1.\overline{7}$
12. 15)4 $0.2\overline{6}$
13. 162 ÷ 10 16.2
14. 6 ÷ 11 $0.\overline{54}$
15. 10 ÷ 8 1.25
16. 9 ÷ 8 1.125

ENRICHMENT

Minds on Math Transparency

2-7

Tia has one less than twice the number of pets that Marcus has. Together they have 8 pets. How many pets does Marcus have?

3 pets

See *Solution Key* for worked-out answers.

2-8 Teaching Notes

1 Focus

CONNECTING TO PRIOR KNOWLEDGE
Group students in pairs. Give half the pairs scientific calculators that apply the Order of Operations. Give the other pairs basic calculators that do not apply the Order of Operations. Have students enter 8 ÷ 4 + 6 ÷ 2. The pairs with the scientific calculators will get 5. The pairs with the basic calculators will get 4. Ask:

- *Do you think there can be two answers?* **Answers may vary.**
- *Why do you think different calculators got different answers?* **Answers may vary.**
- *Could the calculators be working different problems?* **yes**

2 Teach

Work Together

Provide each pair of students with scissors and graph paper. Make sure they label their rectangles with a letter and the total area. Encourage students to make a table for recording their combinations.

Lesson Planning Options

Prerequisite Skills
- area of rectangle (precourse)
- basic decimal operations (2-1 to 2-7)

Vocabulary/Symbols
order of operations, distributive property

Materials/Manipulatives
- graph paper

Resources

Student Edition

Skills Handbook, p. 530
Extra Practice, p. 515
Glossary/Study Guide

Teaching Resources

Chapter Support File, Ch. 2
- Lesson Planner 2-8
- Practice 2-8, Reteaching 2-8
- Answer Masters 2-8

Teaching Aids Masters 1, 2, 19
Glossary, Spanish Resources

Transparencies
1, 7, 15, 81, Minds on Math 2-8

Warm Up

Ask students to evaluate each expression.
8 + 6 − 2 **12**
16 − 8 + 2 **10**
12 + 9 · 2 **30**

ALGEBRA Connection

2-8 Order of Operations and the Distributive Property

What You'll Learn

1. To use the order of operations
2. To use the distributive property

...And Why

You can use the distributive property to find products mentally.

Here's How

Look for questions that
- build understanding
- ✔ check understanding

Work Together

Exploring Area

Set Design Luther, Zia, Jon, and Rashanda painted scenery screens for the school play. Each screen was a rectangle 9 ft tall that could combine with other screens to make different scenes.

Work in pairs. Use graph paper to draw rectangles that have the following dimensions.

9×4 $\quad$ 9×5 $\quad$ 9×6 $\quad$ 9×7 $\quad$ 9×8

1. Cut out the rectangles. Find the area of each rectangle. **36; 45; 54; 63; 72**
2. *Number Sense* Combine any two rectangles. How does the area of the combined rectangle compare with the sum of the areas of the two original rectangles?

Check students' work for areas; the area of the combined rectangle is equal to the sum of the areas of the original rectangles.

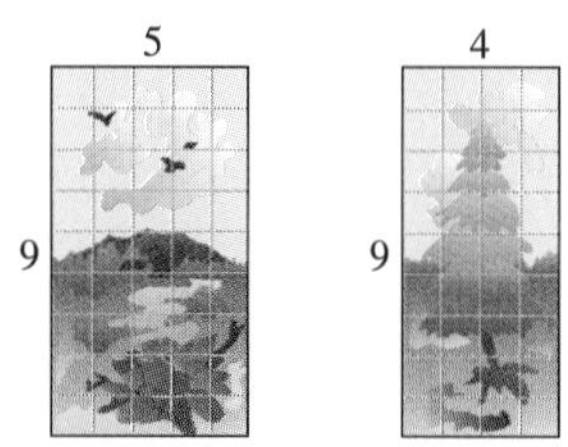

THINK AND DISCUSS

1 *Using the Order of Operations*

Suppose you combine the 9×4 and 9×5 scenery screens. You can find their area using $9 \times 4 + 9 \times 5$.

You use the order of operations to know what to do first in an expression with more than one operation.

ORDER OF OPERATIONS

1. Do all operations within grouping symbols first.
2. Multiply and divide in order from left to right.
3. Add and subtract in order from left to right.

THINK AND DISCUSS

AEP Many students use the mnemonic "Please Excuse My Dear Aunt Sally" to remember the Order of Operations. Have students create a mnemonic using vocabulary meaningful to them.

■ ADDITIONAL EXAMPLES

FOR EXAMPLE 1

Find the value of each expression.

a. $20 \div 2 + 3 \cdot 5$ **25**

b. $20 \div (2 + 3) \cdot 5$ **20**

FOR EXAMPLE 2

Find 7×72 mentally. **504**

FOR EXAMPLE 3

Find 4(4.8) mentally. **19.2**

VISUAL LEARNING Question 5 Students can show the distribution process by drawing arrows from the 9 to each of the two numbers in the parentheses.

$$9(4.2 - 2)$$

ERROR ALERT! Question 8 For expressions such as $3(2.5 + 5)$, students may multiply only the first number inside the parentheses, then add 5 to the product. **Remediation:** Have students do the computation two ways. First, they can use the distributive property to rewrite the expression and multiply. Then they can add the numbers

■ EXAMPLE 1

Find the value of each expression.

a. $30 \div 3 + 2 \cdot 6$

$30 \div 3 + 2 \cdot 6$ ← Divide and multiply.

$10 + 12$ ← Add.

22

b. $30 \div (3 + 2) \cdot 6$

$30 \div (3 + 2) \cdot 6$ ← Do operations within grouping symbols.

$30 \div 5 \cdot 6$ ← Divide.

$6 \cdot 6$ ← Multiply.

36

3. ✔ *Try It Out* Find the value of each expression.

a. $7 \cdot (0.5 + 2) - 1$ **16.5** **b.** $8 - 4 \times 1.5 + 3$ **5**

Now you may assign Exercises 1–22.

2 *Using the Distributive Property*

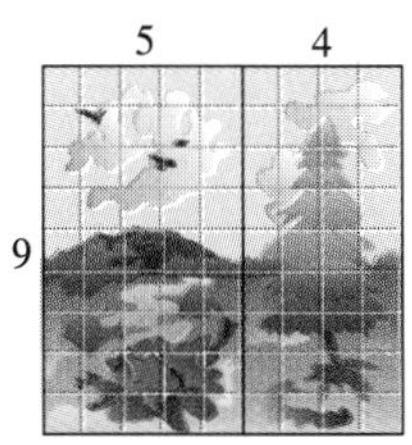

Another way to find the total area of the combined rectangles is to add the widths and multiply by the length.

4. a. What is the width of the combined rectangles? **9**

b. A numerical expression that describes the area by combining the widths first is $9 \cdot (4 + 5)$, or $9(4 + 5)$. Using the order of operations, what should you do first? **Add 4 and 5.**

c. What is the area of the combined rectangles? **81 units^2**

You can rewrite $9 \cdot 4 + 9 \cdot 5$ as $9(4 + 5)$ because they are equal expressions. This is an example of the distributive property. You can use the distributive property to evaluate expressions that have a number multiplying a sum or a difference.

DISTRIBUTIVE PROPERTY

Arithmetic:	**Algebra:**
$9(4 + 5) = 9 \cdot 4 + 9 \cdot 5$	$a(b + c) = a \cdot b + a \cdot c$
$5(8 - 2) = 5 \cdot 8 - 5 \cdot 2$	$a(b - c) = a \cdot b - a \cdot c$

5. ✔ *Try It Out* Rewrite $9(4.2 - 2)$ without parentheses.

$9 \times 4.2 - 9 \times 2$

Technology Options

Prentice Hall Technology

Software for Learners

- Math Blaster® Mystery*
- Interactive Student Tutorial, Chapter 2*

Teaching Resource Software

- Computer Item Generator 2-8
- Resource Pro™ Chapter 2*

Internet • For related mathematics activities, visit the Prentice Hall site at www.phschool.com/math

**Available on CD-ROM only*

Assignment Options for Exercises On Your Own

To provide flexible scheduling, this lesson can be split into parts.

1 **Core** 1–16
Extension 17–22

2 **Core** 23–27, 29–38
Extension 28

Use Mixed Review to maintain skills.

in parentheses and multiply the result. Point out that the result of the two methods must be the same.

Example 3 Some students may prefer to express 5.9 as 5 + 0.9 rather than 6 − 0.1. Explain that although this results in the same answer, it is easier to multiply by 0.1 than 0.9.

ASSESSMENT Have students form pairs. Give them the problem 4(3 + 2) − 4 ÷ 2. One student writes the first step in words. The partner does the first step and writes the second step in words. Students keep taking turns until the problem is solved and there is a description for each step.

3 Practice/Assess

EXERCISES *On Your Own*

Exercises 1–8 Before students compute the answers to each exercise, have them circle the operation they need to do first.

OPEN-ENDED Exercise 9 Students using division may become frustrated if their quotient is a decimal. Encourage students to work backward when writing a division problem and to choose numbers that divide easily.

Exercises 11–22 Encourage students who have trouble getting started to make a guess and then check.

Exercises 17–22 When the value of the expression is small, students may find the Zero Property for Multiplication helpful.

You can use the distributive property to multiply numbers mentally.

EXAMPLE 2

Find 6×53 mentally.

To find 6×53 mentally, think of 53 as 50 + 3.

$$\begin{aligned} 6 \times 53 &= 6(50 + 3) \\ &= 6 \cdot 50 + 6 \cdot 3 && \leftarrow \text{Use the distributive property.} \\ &= 300 + 18 && \leftarrow \text{Add.} \\ &= 318 \end{aligned}$$

6. ✔ *Try It Out* Find each product mentally using the distributive property.
   - a. 8×21 168
   - b. 14×9 126
   - c. 48×6 288
   - d. 7×92 644

You can also use the distributive property to multiply a whole number by a decimal.

EXAMPLE 3

Find 7(5.9) mentally.

To find 7×5.9 mentally, think of 5.9 as 6.0 − 0.1.

$$\begin{aligned} 7 \times 5.9 &= 7(6.0 - 0.1) \\ &= 7 \cdot 6.0 - 7 \cdot 0.1 && \leftarrow \text{Use the distributive property.} \\ &= 42 - 0.7 && \leftarrow \text{Subtract.} \\ &= 41.3 \end{aligned}$$

8a. Use the commutative property of multiplication to switch terms.

7. ✔ *Try It Out* What steps would you use to find 4×12.1 mentally using the distributive property and addition? **Multiply 4 by 12. Multiply 4 by 0.1. Add the results.**
8. a. *Explain* Why does $3(2.5 + 5) = (2.5 + 5)3$? **See left.**
   b. Complete: $(2.5 + 5)3 = (2.5)■ + (5)■$ **3 3**

Now you may assign Exercises 23–38.

EXERCISES *On Your Own*

Find the value of each expression.

1. $6 + 1 \times 5$ 11
2. $4 \div 2 + 9$ 11
3. $5 - 8 \div 4$ 3
4. $3 - 0 \cdot 11$ 3
5. $12 \div 6 - 1$ 1
6. $100 - 7 \cdot 9$ 37
7. $9 \div 2 + 8$ 12.5
8. $19 \div 4 \times 3$ 14.25

Remind them the product of zero and a number is zero. Suggest students try grouping numbers to make zeros.

MENTAL MATH Exercises 29–32 Have students rewrite the problems with the distributive property before using mental math. Have students share their strategies with the class.

RESEARCH Exercise 28d Give students a list of nearby museums and their telephone numbers. If there are no museums in your area, have students use the World Wide Web to research famous museums such as the Smithsonian Museum of Natural History and the Louvre.

WRAP UP

IDENTIFYING THE BIG IDEA Ask students to use the order of operations and the distributive property to explain why $5(3 + 6)$ and $5 \times 3 + 6$ are not equivalent, but $5(3 + 6)$ and $5 \times 3 + 5 \times 6$ are.

PROJECT LINK One source for the current prices of the metals is in the business section of newspapers that contain futures.

PORTFOLIO Share with students the criteria you use to assess their work in portfolios, as well as how you plan to use the results. Students should understand how the rubrics are used to assess their work, how each piece in the portfolio counts, and how the scores they get in their portfolios will affect their overall evaluation.

9. *Open-ended* Write an expression with three operations. Find the value of your expression. **Check students' work.**

10. **Choose A, B, C, or D.** Which expression has the greatest value? **B**

A. $(5 + 2) \div 7 + 9 \times 0.5 - 3$ B. $9 - 4 \cdot 2 + 1 \times 1.5 \div 0.3$
C. $7 \div 2 + 1.4 \times 3 - 6$ D. $8 + 1 - 10 \div 4 - 12 \div 4$

Insert +, −, ×, or ÷ to make each equation true.

11. $5 \blacksquare 3 + 2 = 17$ **×**
12. $1.1 \blacksquare 6 \times 0.3 = 2.9$ **+**
13. $30 - 6 \blacksquare 6 = 29$ **÷**
14. $23.1 \div 7 \blacksquare 3.3 = 6.6$ **+**
15. $48 \blacksquare 12 + 11 = 15$ **÷**
16. $21 \div 7 \blacksquare 4 = 12$ **×**

Place parentheses to make each statement true.

17. $4 + 4 \div 4 - 4 = 1$ **$4 + (4 \div 4) - 4 = 1$**
18. $4 \times 4 \div 4 + 4 = 2$ **$4 \times 4 \div (4 + 4) = 2$**
19. $4 + 4 + 4 \div 4 = 3$ **$(4 + 4 + 4) \div 4 = 3$**
20. $4 \times 4 - 4 + 4 = 4$ **$4 \times (4 - 4) + 4 = 4$**
21. $4 + 4 \times 4 - 4 = 28$ **$(4 + 4) \times 4 - 4 = 28$**
22. $4 + 4 \times 4 - 4 = 0$ **$(4 + 4) \times (4 - 4) = 0$**

23. *Advertising* Rashaun made a large poster for his school rummage sale. The poster measured 20 in. × 28.5 in.
    a. Use the distributive property to write an expression to find the area of the poster using mental math. **$20 \times (30 - 1.5)$**
    b. Find the area of Rashaun's poster. **570 in.^{2}**

Find the missing numbers.

24. $4(7 + 8) = 4(\blacksquare) + 4(\blacksquare)$ **7, 8**
25. $3(8.2 - 1.5) = (\blacksquare)8.2 - (\blacksquare)1.5$ **3, 3**
26. $\blacksquare(4.8) = 6(5) - 6(\blacksquare)$ **6, 0.2**
27. $\blacksquare(2.8 + 6.5) = 7(2.8) + 7(6.5)$ **7**

28a. $6 \times 5.25 + 6 \times 4.75 = 6 \times (5.25 + 4.75)$

28. Dustin and five of his friends went to the science museum. The admission fee was \$5.25 per person. The planetarium was an additional \$4.75 per person.
    a. Show how you would use the distributive property to find the admission fee for all of them. **See above.**
    b. Use the distributive property to find the additional planetarium cost. **\$28.50**
    c. How much did Dustin and his friends pay altogether? **c. \$60**
    d. *Research* Find the total admission fees to a local museum for three adults and four children. **Check students' work.**

Planetarium projectors are used to simulate views of the night sky.

Calculate mentally using the distributive property.

29. 6(3.9) **23.4** 30. 10.3(4) **41.2** 31. 7(2.6) **18.2** 32. 11.6(9) **104.4**

page 84 Mixed Review

44.
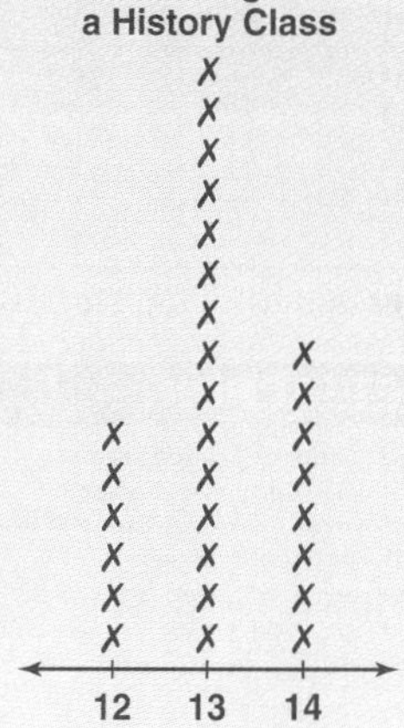

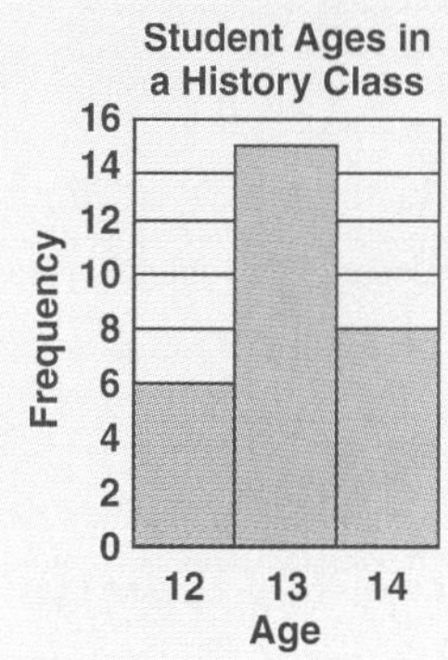

PRACTICE

Practice 2-8 Order of Operations and the Distributive Property

Find the value of each expression.

1. (8 + 2) × 9 **90**
2. 5 − 1 ÷ 4 **4.75**
3. (6 + 3) ÷ 18 **0.5**
4. 80 − 6 × 7 **38**
5. 4 × 6 + 3 **27**
6. 4 × (6 + 3) **36**
7. 35 − 6 × 5 **5**
8. 8 ÷ 3 + 6 **$8\frac{2}{3}$**

Find the missing numbers.

9. 5 (9 + 6) = 5 (■) + 5 (■) **9; 6**
10. 4 (9.7 − 8.1) = ■ (9.7) − ■ (8.1) **4; 4**
11. ■ (3.8) = 9 (4) − 9 (■) **9; 0.2**
12. ■ (17.1 + 12.6) = 6 (17.1) + 6 (12.6) **6**

Calculate mentally using the distributive property.

13. 3 (6.4) **19.2**
14. 5 (7.1) **35.5**
15. 5 (8.9) **44.5**
16. 6 (9.8) **58.8**
17. 4 (9.2) **36.8**
18. 9 (11.1) **99.9**
19. 7 (8.9) **62.3**
20. 8 (20.1) **160.8**

Place parentheses to make each sentence true.

21. 6 + 6 ÷ 6 × 6 + 6 = 24 **(6 + 6) ÷ 6 × (6 + 6) = 24**
22. 6 × 6 + 6 × 6 − 6 = 426 **6 × (6 + 6) × 6 − 6 = 426**
23. 6 + 6 ÷ 6 × 6 − 6 = 0 **(6 + 6) ÷ 6 × (6 − 6) = 0**
24. 6 − 6 × 6 + 6 ÷ 6 = 1 **(6 − 6) × 6 + 6 ÷ 6 = 1**
25. 6 + 6 ÷ 6 + 6 × 6 = 6 **(6 + 6) ÷ (6 + 6) × 6 = 6**
26. 6 − 6 ÷ 6 × 6 + 6 = 0 **(6 − 6) ÷ 6 × (6 + 6) = 0**

Circle A, B, C, or D. Ring the letter of the expression that has the greatest value.

27. A. 8.3 × 0.6 B. 8.3 + 0.6 (C.) 8.3 ÷ 0.6 D. 8.3 − 0.6
28. A. 6.1 + 1.2 (B.) 6.1 × 1.2 C. 6.1 − 1.2 D. 6.1 ÷ 1.2
29. A. 5.6 − 1.4 B. 5.6 ÷ 1.4 C. 5.6 + 1.4 (D.) 5.6 × 1.4
30. (A.) 0.9 ÷ 0.5 B. 0.9 × 0.5 C. 0.9 + 0.5 D. 0.9 − 0.5

Practice

In copymaster and workbook formats

RETEACHING

Reteaching 2-8 Order of Operations and the Distributive Property

You can remember the order of operations using this phrase:

Please, My Dear Aunt Sally

Parentheses Multiply Divide Add Subtract

First, do operations within parentheses.

7 + 8 × [(5 + 3)] − 1 3 ÷ [(5 − 2)] + 36
7 + 8 × 8 − 1 3 ÷ 3 + 36

Next, multiply and divide from left to right.

7 + [8 × 8] − 1 [3 ÷ 3] + 36
7 + 64 − 1 1 + 36

Then, add and subtract from left to right.

[7 + 64] − 1 [1 + 36]
71 − 1 37
70

Complete.

1. 3 + 2 × 4; 3 + **8**; **11**
2. 5 × 4 + 3 × 2; **20** + **6**; **26**
3. (5 × 4) + 3 − 2; **20 + 3 − 2**; **21**
4. 5 + 7 × 2; 5 + **14**; **19**
5. 8 × 6 + 4 × 4; **48** + **16**; **64**
6. (6 × 2) + (12 ÷ 2); **12** + **6**; **18**

Find the value of each expression.

7. 8 + 5 × 6 + 2 **40**
8. 7 − 4 + 5 × 3 **18**
9. 9 + 3 × 7 − 5 **25**
10. (15 + 9) ÷ (8 − 2) **4**
11. 80 − 6 × 7 **38**
12. 15 ÷ (5 − 2) **5**

Write the missing numbers.

13. 8(5 + 2) = [8] (5) + [8] (2)
14. [4] (5.6) = 4(6.0) − 4([0.4])
15. [5] (3.4 + 7) = 5(3.4) + 5(7)

Reteaching

ENRICHMENT

Minds on Math Transparency

2-8

Briton wants to place an even number of chairs along the walls in a rectangular room so that there are the same number of chairs along each wall. How can he do that? (Hint: a chair in a corner counts for two walls.)

Sample: Divide the chairs equally along four walls and if two chairs are left over, put them in opposite corners.

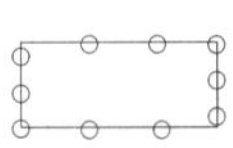

See *Solution Key* for worked-out answers.

LESSON QUIZ

1. Use the order of operations to find the value of the expression.
   6 + 14 ÷ 2 **13**
2. Calculate mentally using the distributive property.
   10.4(3) **31.2**

34. 3 × (5 + 5); 3 × 5 + 3 × 5; 30 units^2

Geometry **Write two expressions to find the total area of each figure. Find the area.**

33.

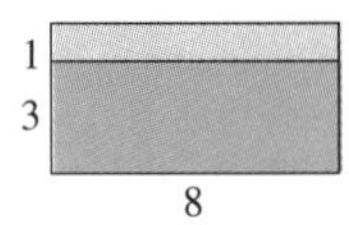

8 × (3 + 1); 8 × 3 + 8 × 1; 32 units^2

34.

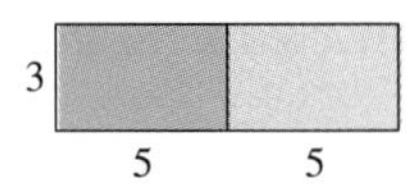

5 × (2 + 3); 5 × 2 + 5 × 3; 25 units^2

35.

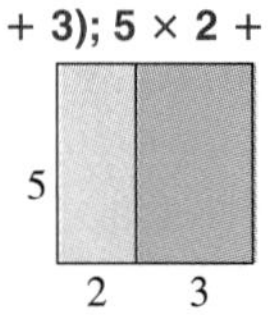

36. ***Money*** A caterer is buying lilies to use in centerpieces. Each centerpiece will have 3 lilies. There are a total of 10 tables. After a discount, each lily costs $.92. Use mental math to find the cost of the lilies. **$27.60**

37. ***Mental Math*** You want to buy 4 notebooks at $.89 each. Use mental math to find the total cost. **$3.56**

38. ***Writing*** Explain how you could use the distributive property to calculate 4(110.5) two different ways.
    You can use 4(110 + 0.5) or 4(111 − 0.5).

PORTFOLIO

For your portfolio, choose one or two items from your work for this chapter. Here are some possibilities:

- a journal entry
- corrected work
- part of your project

Explain why you have included each selection.

Mixed Review

Find each quotient. *(Lesson 2-6)*

39. 2.21 ÷ 1.7 **1.3**
40. 0.75 ÷ 0.5 **1.5**
41. 62 ÷ 2.5 **24.8**
42. 3.8 ÷ 4 **0.95**
43. 7.1 ÷ 0.8 **8.875**

Use the data at the right for Exercises 44–46. *(Lessons 1-1, 1-2)*

44. Make a line plot and a histogram of the data.
    See margin p. 83.
45. How many students are in the class? **29**
46. What is the range of ages of the students? **2**

Student Ages in a History Class

Age	Number of Students
12	6
13	15
14	8

47. ***Patterns*** Find the product of 4.2 × 10, 4.2 × 100, and 4.2 × 1,000. Predict 4.2 × 1,000,000. *(Lesson 2-5)*
    42; 420; 4,200; 4,200,000

CHAPTER PROJECT

PROJECT LINK: CALCULATING

Find the price of the different metals you used. Include the source of your information. Use this data to calculate how much each statue would cost. **Check students' work.**

Extra Practice, Lesson 2-8, page 515

FINISHING THE CHAPTER PROJECT

PROJECT DAY You may wish to plan a project day on which students share their completed projects. Encourage students to explain their process as well as their product.

PROJECT NOTEBOOK Ask students to review their project work and bring their notebooks up to date.

Have students review their methods for making their lists, calculating the weight of each statue, and calculating the cost of each statue.

SCORING RUBRIC

3 You collected all the data required for the statues, and you displayed the data in an organized list or table. You accurately estimated the weight and cost of each statue. You offered an explanation for why you chose one statue to offer as a gift to a city, museum, park, or other organization.

2 You collected five animal weights, five specific gravity values, and at least two of the costs of the metals used. Most of your estimations of statue weights and costs were accurate, and you displayed the data in an organized manner.

1 You omitted some of the data, some of your calculations were inaccurate, or your presentation was not organized properly.

0 You neglected to collect a significant portion of the data, or you failed to complete and display all of the required calculations.

FINISHING THE CHAPTER PROJECT

CHAPTER PROJECT

Weighty Matters

Using Specific Gravity The Project Link questions on pages 58, 66, 79, and 84 should help you to complete your project. Here is a checklist to help you gather together the parts of your project.

- ✓ the list of animals and their weights
- ✓ the list of different metals' specific gravity
- ✓ the weight of each statue in each metal
- ✓ the cost of each statue in each metal

Choose your favorite statue. Pretend that you are going to present this statue as a gift to a city, museum, or park. Explain why you chose that statue. How much would it weigh? How much would it cost?

Reflect and Revise

Review your project with a friend or someone at home. Are your lists complete? Are your calculations accurate? Are your numbers realistic? If necessary, make changes to improve your project.

Web Extension

Internet Connection

Prentice Hall's Internet site contains information you might find helpful as you complete your project. Visit www.phschool.com/mgm2/ch2 for some links and ideas related to specific gravity.

STUDENT SELF-ASSESSMENT SURVEY

Chapter 2 Student Self-Assessment Survey

1. Now that you have finished this chapter, think about what you have learned about working with decimals. Check each topic that you feel confident you understand.
   - _____ compare and order decimals (2-1)
   - _____ round decimals (2-1)
   - _____ estimate with decimals (2-2)
   - _____ add and subtract decimals; use the properties of addition (2-3)
   - _____ decide whether a problem has too little or too much information (2-4)
   - _____ multiply decimals; use the properties of multiplication (2-5)
   - _____ divide decimals by whole numbers and by decimals (2-6)
   - _____ classify decimals as terminating or repeating (2-7)
   - _____ use the distributive property and order of operations (2-8)
2. Before the Chapter Assessment, I need to review _____
3. **a.** Check one. In general, I thought this chapter was
   ___ a snap ___ easy ___ average ___ hard ___ a monster
   b. Why do you feel this way? _____
4. In this chapter, I did my best work on _____
5. In this chapter, I had trouble with _____
6. I think the hardest thing about working with decimals is _____
7. In this chapter, you investigated division on your calculator. Did you find this easy or confusing? _____ Explain. _____
8. List three places outside the classroom where people use decimals in everyday life. _____

Vocabulary/Symbols

associative property of addition, associative property of multiplication, compatible numbers, commutative property of addition, commutative property of multiplication, distributive property, equivalent decimals, identity property of addition, identity property of multiplication, order of operations, repeating decimal, terminating decimal, zero property of multiplication

Materials/Manipulatives

- calculator

Resources

Student Edition

Extra Practice, p. 515
Glossary/Study Guide

Teaching Resources

Chapter Support File, Ch. 2
- Student Self-Assessment Survey

Glossary, Spanish Resources
Tools for Studying Smarter

WRAP UP

Exercises 1–4 Remind students to compare the digits to the left of the decimal first.

Exercises 11–18 Have students list the estimation strategy they used.

ASSESSMENT Exercises 11–18 Have students try two or more of the estimation strategies for each problem. Then have them explain in writing the strategy they used for each problem and why it worked best.

WRITING Exercise 19 You may also want students to explain when to use rounding or front-end estimation to estimate the value of an expression. Have students provide examples for each method.

Exercises 20–44 Have students check the first problem in each section with a partner. Partners should refer to the lesson number listed by each section if their answers disagree.

2 WRAP UP

Rounding and Ordering Decimals — 2-1

To compare numbers, start from the left. Compare the first set of digits that are not the same.

When rounding numbers, round up if the digit to the right is 5 or greater. Round down if the digit to the right is 4 or less.

Compare using <, >, or =.

1. 0.168 ■ 0.1680 **=**
2. 5.6 ■ 5.592 **>**
3. 1.83 ■ 2.032 **<**
4. 11.26 ■ 11.206 **>**

Round each number to the underlined place value.

5. $17.8\underline{5}2$ **17.85**
6. $0.10\underline{3}8$ **0.104**
7. $10\underline{9}.71$ **110**
8. $1.\underline{3}601$ **1.4**
9. $\underline{5}.4972$ **5**
10. $8.194\underline{6}5$ **8.1947**

Estimation Strategies — 2-2

You can estimate decimals using rounding, front-end estimation, or compatible numbers.

Use any estimation strategy to calculate. Then tell which strategy you used.

11. $50.3 \div 6.9$ **7; compatible numbers**
12. $1.46 + 4.38$ **6; front-end**
13. $98.52 - 46.9074$ **51.5; rounding**
14. 6.9×8.92 **63; rounding**
15. $\$37.63 \div \$7.19$ **$5; compatible numbers**
16. $0.167 + 0.902$ **1; rounding**
17. $7.981 - 3.0189$ **5; front-end**
18. 1.7×78.43 **160; rounding**
19. *Writing* Explain when you would use compatible numbers to estimate the value of an expression. **Use compatible numbers to estimate a quotient.**

Addition and Subtraction of Decimals — 2-3

When adding or subtracting decimals, align the decimal points.

Use the **commutative property** to change the order in an expression. Use the **associative property** to change the grouping.

Find each sum or difference.

20. $8.62 + 9.4$ **18.02**
21. $10.87 - 6.9$ **3.97**
22. $4.6 - 3.87$ **0.73**
23. $8.04 + 9.1$ **17.14**
24. $7.4 + 9.2$ **16.6**
25. $11.47 - 9.03$ **2.44**
26. $0.54 + 0.027$ **0.567**
27. $3.09 - 2.975$ **0.115**

Remind students that the new mathematical terms in this chapter are defined in the Student Study Guide/Glossary in the back of the textbook.

CHAPTER ASSESSMENT • FORM A

Chapter 2 Assessment • Form A

	Answers
1. Round 0.237 to the nearest tenth.	**1.** 0.2
2. Round 1.7955 to the nearest thousandth.	**2.** 1.796
3. Round 0.8992 to the nearest hundredth.	**3.** 0.90
4. Order the numbers from least to greatest. 0.05, 0.5, 0.005, 0.505, 0.055	**4.** 0.005, 0.05, 0.055, 0.5, 0.505
5. Use rounding to estimate the product. 11.5×10.2	**5.** about 120
6. Use front-end estimation to estimate the sum. $5.312 + 3.726$	**6.** about 9
7. Identify the addition property shown. $(6.95 + 23.34) + 6.9 = 6.95 + (23.34 + 6.9)$	**7.** associative
8. Use the properties of addition to mentally evaluate. $6.3 + 19.6 + 1.4 + 3.7$	**8.** 31
9. Identify the multiplication property shown. $5.98 \times 0.3 = 0.3 \times 5.98$	**9.** commutative
10. Use mental math and the properties of multiplication to evaluate. $9.876 \times 3.5 \times 0$	**10.** 0
11. Three friends ate lunch together. Their total bill was $13.75. If the bill was divided evenly among the three friends, how much did each person pay, rounded to the nearest ten cents?	**11.** $4.60
12. Use mental math and the distributive property to evaluate 9(10.5).	**12.** 94.5

Assessment

CHAPTER ASSESSMENT • FORM A

Chapter 2 Assessment • Form A (continued)

Find each sum or difference.

13. $8.27 + 6.9 + 5$	**13.** 20.17
14. $19 - 12.735$	**14.** 6.265
15. $21.6 - 9.24$	**15.** 12.36
16. $0.68 + 5.681$	**16.** 6.361

Find each product or quotient.

17. 5.9×0.32	**17.** 1.888
18. 67.3×0.04	**18.** 2.692
19. $57.96 \div 2.8$	**19.** 20.7
20. $408.48 \div 8$	**20.** 51.06

Choose A, B, C, or D.

21. Which expression has the greatest value? **21.** C

A. $5 \times 1.3 + 1.3$ B. $14 \div 3.5 + 5$
C. $20 - 20 \div 2.5$ D. $6 + 5 \times 0.8$

Choose a Strategy

22. Solve if possible. If not, tell what information is needed. **22.** You need to know how much he gets paid for overtime.

Dale earns $5.25/h working as a baker's assistant. He gets paid extra for each hour that he works over 40 h. Last week he worked 46 h. How much did he earn last week?

Writing

23. Explain the difference between terminating and repeating decimals. Give an example of each type of decimal.
Sample: Terminating decimals end with a particular digit. Example: 4.5. Repeating decimals have a digit or sequence of digits that keeps repeating. Example: 8.333 . . . or $8.\overline{3}$

Problem Solving Strategies 2-4

Before you try to solve a problem, you must decide if you have too much or too little information.

Solve if possible. If not, tell what information is needed.

28. *Sports* In doubles tennis, the width of the court is 10.97 m. The net is between 0.91 m and 1.07 m tall. The court is 23.77 m long. Find the area of the court. $260.7569\ m^2$

29. *Clothing* Tamika bought a sweater on sale for half of the original $36 price. She also bought jeans on sale for $15. How much did she save by buying sale items? You need to know the original price of the jeans.

Multiplication of Decimals and the Order of Operations 2-5, 2-8

When you multiply decimals, put the decimal point in the proper place in the product.

Use the **order of operations** to simplify an expression. Use the **distributive property** to evaluate expressions that have a number multiplying a sum or a difference.

Find the value of each expression.

30. $7 \div 2 + 3 \times 4 - 10$ 5.5

31. $8.1 - (4.2 \times 0.25) \div 5$ 7.89

32. $(7.3 + 4) \div 4 + 0.3 \times 2$ 3.425

33. $(11.94 - 7.621) \times (3.45 + 6.1)$ 41.24645

34. $8 - 6.2 \div 5 + 0.7 \times 0.91$ 7.397

35. $61.152 \div 9.8 - (2.1 + 1.8) + 0.5$ 2.84

36. Choose A, B, C, or D. Which property is illustrated below?
$8.4 \times (7.23 \times 4.915) = (8.4 \times 7.23) \times 4.915$ C

A. Identity property
B. Distributive property
C. Associative property
D. Commutative property

Dividing Decimals 2-6, 2-7

When you divide decimals, if the quotient ends it is a **terminating decimal.** When a digit or sequence of digits keep repeating, it is a **repeating decimal.**

Find each quotient. Use a bar to indicate repeating digits.

37. $9.8 \div 5$ 1.96

38. $3.52 \div 0.6$ $5.8\overline{6}$

39. $1.67 \div 1.5$ $1.11\overline{3}$

40. $7 \div 4.4$ $1.5\overline{90}$

41. $8.25 \div 0.25$ 33

42. $2.54 \div 6.4$ 0.396875

43. $5.38 \div 11$ $0.4\overline{890}$

44. $18.5 \div 3.52$ $5.2556\overline{81}$

CHAPTER ASSESSMENT • FORM B

Chapter 2 Assessment • Form B

Choose the best answer. Circle A, B, C, or D.

1. Round 0.4671 to the nearest tenth.
   A. 0.467 **B.** 0.47 **C.** 0.4 **(D)** 0.5
2. Round 3.9844 to the nearest thousandth.
   (A) 3.984 **B.** 3.99 **C.** 4.0 **D.** 3.985
3. Round 9.67513 to the nearest hundredth.
   A. 9.675 **B.** 9.676 **(C)** 9.68 **D.** 9.67
4. Which of the following is in order from least to greatest?
   A. 0.012, 0.12, 0.102, 1.02 **B.** 2.09, 2.9, 2.29, 2.029
   (C) 0.506, 0.56, 0.6, 0.65 **D.** 0.89, 0.09, 0.8, 0.098
5. Use rounding to estimate the product.
   4.75×3.25
   A. 8 **B.** 9 **C.** 12 **(D)** 15
6. Use front-end estimation to estimate the sum.
   $3.796 + 7.812$
   A. 11.6 **B.** 10 **(C)** 12 **D.** 11
7. Identify the addition property shown.
   $89.032 + 0 = 89.032$
   A. associative **B.** commutative **C.** distributive **(D)** identity
8. Use the properties of addition to mentally evaluate.
   $4.5 + 9.4 + 5.5 + 10.6$
   A. 25 **(B)** 30 **C.** 35 **D.** 40
9. Use estimation to decide which of the following is the correct answer to $765.23 - 662.7$.
   A. 1.025 **B.** 113.5 **C.** 10.3 **(D)** 102.53
10. Identify the multiplication property shown.
    $(3 \times 4) \times 1 = 3 \times (4 \times 1)$
    A. identity **(B)** associative **C.** zero **D.** distributive
11. Use mental math and the properties of multiplication to evaluate $2 \times 4.78 \times 0.5$.
    A. 1 **B.** 2 **(C)** 4.78 **D.** 0.5

Assessment

CHAPTER ASSESSMENT • FORM B

Chapter 2 Assessment • Form B (continued)

12. Four friends agreed to divide the cost of a compact disc between them equally. The total cost was $18.31. How much did each of the friends pay, rounded to the nearest cent?
    A. $4.56 **B.** $4.57 **(C)** $4.58 **D.** $4.59
13. Use mental math and the distributive property to evaluate 3(15.9).
    (A) 47.7 **B.** 45 **C.** 27 **D.** 4.77
14. Evaluate 35.3×4.
    A. 39.3 **B.** 91.2 **(C)** 141.2 **D.** 142.2
15. Joey bought 3.8 lb of pears. How much did they cost to the nearest cent if the price was $1.29/lb?
    A. $4.52 **(B)** $4.90 **C.** $5.16 **D.** not here
16. Evaluate $27.9 \div 3$.
    A. 9.1 **(B)** 9.3 **C.** 91 **D.** 93
17. Evaluate $18.72 \div 7.2$.
    A. 26 **B.** 2.5 **(C)** 2.6 **D.** 0.26
18. Evaluate $9 + 18 \div 4.5$.
    A. 6 **(B)** 13 **C.** 31.5 **D.** 36
19. Jody ran 3.5 miles each day for 11 days. Kaitlin ran 5.8 miles for 7 days. How many more miles did Kaitlin run than Jody?
    A. 38.5 miles **B.** 9.3 miles **C.** 2.3 miles **(D)** 2.1 miles

Choose a Strategy

20. Sundi earns $6.50/h regular pay. She makes twice that amount for overtime. Last week she worked 5 h overtime. What additional information do you need to find out the total amount that Sundi earned last week?
    A. the number of days she worked
    (B) the number of regular hours she worked
    C. the number of hours she took for lunch
    D. the number of weeks she works in a year

Teaching Resources

Chapter Support File, Ch. 2, and Spanish Resources

Teacher's Edition

See pp. 48C–D for Assessment Options.

Teaching Resource Software

- Computer Item Generator, Ch. 2

ASSESSMENT

WRITING EXERCISES allow students to describe more fully their thinking and understanding of the concepts they've learned. **Exercise 9** is a writing exercise.

ENHANCED MULTIPLE CHOICE QUESTIONS are more complex than traditional multiple choice questions, which assess only one skill. Enhanced multiple choice questions assess the processes that students use, as well as the end results. They are written so that students can use more than one strategy to solve the problem. Using multiple strategies is encouraged by the National Council of Teachers of Mathematics (NCTM). **Exercise 11** is an enhanced multiple choice question.

Exercise 12 Before finding the value of the expressions, have students rewrite the expressions using the distributive property.

2 ASSESSMENT

1. Round each number to the underlined place value. a. 0.571 b. 26.1 c. 501.939
   a. $0.57\underline{1}034$ b. $26.\underline{0}95$
   c. $501.93\underline{8}6$ d. $1\underline{8}.419$
   e. $4\underline{6}7.15$ f. $43.5\underline{7}7$
   d. 18 e. 470 f. 43.58
2. Order the numbers from least to greatest: 8.05, 8.5, 8.059, 8.049, 8.0499. 8.049, 8.0499, 8.05, 8.059, 8.5
3. Use any method to estimate the value of each expression.
   a. $289.76 - 52$ 238 b. $8.7891 - 3.493$ 5.5
   c. $68.5 \div 7.02$ 10 d. $97.60 \cdot 3.4$ 300
   e. $7.532 + 2.19$ 10 f. 5.4×9.5 50
   3a–f. Answers may vary. Samples given.
4. Use front-end estimation to estimate the sum of the following grocery item prices: $7.99, $2.79, $4.15, $2.09. $17
5. Find each sum or difference.
   a. $9.53 + 3.29$ b. $8 - 6.1273$ 1.8727
   c. $10.5 - 9.67$ 0.83 d. $0.57 + 1.825$
   e. $9 - 5.018$ 3.982 f. $8.51 + 4$ 12.51
   5a. 12.82 d. 2.395
6. *Money* On her last bank statement, Rhea Medeiros had a balance of $213.15 in her checking account. She wrote one check for $68.94 and another for $128.36. What is her current balance? $15.85
   7a. comm. prop. of add. b. assoc. prop. of mult.
7. Identify each property shown.
   a. $9.5 + 6.1 + 2.3 = 9.5 + 2.3 + 6.1$
   b. $7.2 \times (1.6 \times 3.9) = (7.2 \times 1.6) \times 3.9$
   c. $8.329 + 0 + 1.74 = 8.329 + 1.74$
   d. $5.1(7.4 - 3.1) = 5.1(7.4) - 5.1(3.1)$
   c. identity prop. of add. d. distributive
8. Find each quotient. Use a bar to show repeating decimals.
   a. $1.9 \div 1.8$ $1.0\overline{5}$ b. $5.1 \div 3$ 1.7
   c. $1.2 \div 0.3$ 4 d. $1.58 \div 1.1$ $1.4\overline{36}$
9. *Writing* You have a choice of two jobs for the summer. You can work at a gas station at $5.20/h for 18 h/wk or you can babysit at $3.75/h for 25 h/wk. Which job should you choose? Explain your reasoning. See below left.
10. Find the value of each expression.
    a. $9.5 - 7.1 + 2.4 \times 0.5 - 1.3$ 2.3
    b. $8.25 \div 4 \times (0.6 - 0.54) + 8.3$ 8.42375
    c. $(7.2 + 3.6) \div 5 + 8.4 \times 0.6$ 7.2
    d. $5.82 + 10.24 \div 3.2 - 4.195$ 4.825
11. **Choose A, B, C, or D.** The weights of four bags of apples were 3.5, 3.8, 4.2, and 3.5 lb. What was the median weight? B
    A. 3.5 **B.** 3.65 **C.** 3.75 **D.** 3.8
12. Use the distributive property to find the value of each expression.
    a. 6(10.5) 63 b. 3(98) 294 c. (7.3)6 43.8
13. Solve the problem or tell what information is needed to solve.
    At the 1996 Summer Olympics, Denis Pankratov of Russia swam the 100-m butterfly in 52.27 seconds to win the gold medal. At the 1972 Summer Olympics, Mark Spitz won the same event. Who had the faster time, and how much faster was it?
    You need to know Mark Spitz's time.
14. Solve the problem or tell what information is needed to solve.
    You bought a case of 30 toys for your store at $3.95 each. They were delivered on Wednesday. A customer bought 3 toys for $4.99 each. How much profit did you make on the 3 toys? $3.12

9. Answers may vary. Sample: Work at the gas station; the total weekly pay is almost the same, but you spend less time working at the gas station.

CUMULATIVE REVIEW

Item	Review Topic	Ch
1, 2	Too little, too much much information	Precourse
3, 8	Analyzing graphs	1

Item	Review Topic	Ch
4	Multiplying decimals	2
5–6	Dividing decimals	2
7	Subtracting decimals	2

2 CUMULATIVE REVIEW

Choose the best answer.

1. Laura bought several tennis items at the sports store. She purchased a racket on sale for \$49.50, socks for \$8.50, and 3 cans of tennis balls for \$12.95. On sale, sunglasses were \$8.99. Laura spent \$4.89 more on a shirt than on a pair of shorts. What else do you need to know to determine how much Laura spent in all? A
   - **A.** the cost of the pair of shorts
   - **B.** the number of tennis balls in each can
   - **C.** the number of socks purchased
   - **D.** the original price of the racket

2. In the problem above, what information is not needed to solve the problem? B
   - **A.** the cost of the tennis balls
   - **B.** the original price of sunglasses
   - **C.** the sale price of the racket
   - **D.** how much more the shirt cost than the shorts

3. What does the stem-and-leaf plot *not* tell you? D

1	3 4 9
2	1 2 4 4
3	0 3

2 | 5 means 25

   - **A.** The greatest number is 33.
   - **B.** The mode is 24.
   - **C.** The median is 22.
   - **D.** There are 12 items of data.

4. Which kind of graph would best show the change in population of the United States from 1935 to 1995? A
   - **A.** line graph **B.** bar graph
   - **C.** scatter plot **D.** stem-and-leaf plot

5. Rendell bought 1.2 lb of peanuts at \$2.89/lb, 0.7 lb of cashews at \$4.59/lb, and two one-pound boxes of raisins for \$2.39 each. How much did he spend? C
   - **A.** \$9.87 **B.** \$12.26
   - **C.** \$11.46 **D.** \$12.31

6. What is the greatest number of movie tickets you can buy if you have \$33.48 and each movie ticket costs \$6.75? B
   - **A.** 3 **B.** 4 **C.** 5 **D.** 6

7. Eulalia received \$25.00 for her birthday. She paid \$6.89 for two magazines and repaid her brother \$4.25. How much money did Eulalia have left? E
   - **A.** \$20.75 **B.** \$18.11 **C.** \$12.86
   - **D.** \$11.14 **E.** Not Here

8. What information is *not* given by the bar graph below? C

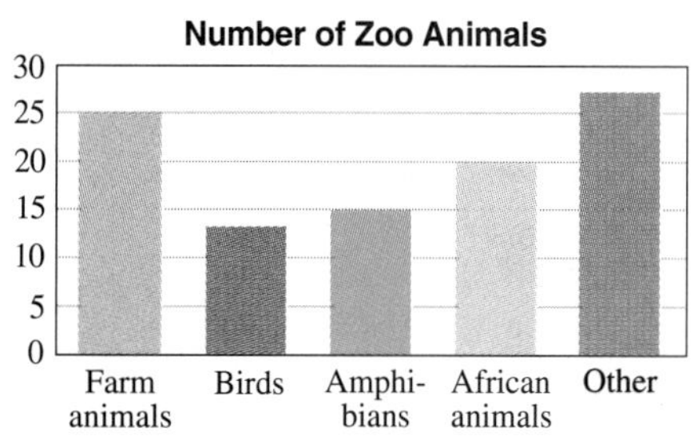

   - **A.** There are about the same number of birds as amphibians at the zoo.
   - **B.** There are more farm animals than African animals.
   - **C.** Reptiles are included in the "other" category.
   - **D.** There are fewer birds than farm animals at the zoo.

CUMULATIVE REVIEW

Chapter 2 Cumulative Review

Choose the best answer. Circle A, B, C, or D.

1. Which of the following shows the order from least to greatest for the mean, the median, and the mode of this set of data? 0, 1, 2, 2, 2, 3, 4, 7, 10, 11
   - Ⓐ mode, median, mean
   - **B.** median, mode, mean
   - **C.** mode, mean, median
   - **D.** mean, median, mode

2. You have saved \$35.75. About how many tapes can you buy if each tape costs \$8.47, tax included?
   - **A.** 2 tapes **B.** 3 tapes
   - Ⓒ 4 tapes **D.** 5 tapes

3. Identify the property of addition shown. $(1.5 + 2.5) + 3 = 1.5 + (2.5 + 3)$
   - Ⓐ associative **B.** distributive
   - **C.** commutative **D.** identity

4. Which expression is *not* the same as $2.7 \times 3.6 \div 9$?
   - **A.** $2.7 \div 9 \times 3.6$
   - Ⓑ $3.6 \times 9 \div 2.7$
   - **C.** $3.6 \times 2.7 \div 9$
   - **D.** $3.6 \div 9 \times 2.7$

5. What is the tenth digit in the quotient $120 \div 11$?
   - Ⓐ 0 **B.** 1
   - **C.** 8 **D.** 9

6. Sara saved \$12.50 for five weeks. Her brother saved \$13.75 for five weeks. How much more did her brother save?
   - Ⓐ \$6.25 **B.** \$62.50
   - **C.** \$6.88 **D.** \$68.75

7. A pumpkin weighs 23.8 lb. How many ounces does the pumpkin weigh? (There are 16 oz in a pound.)
   - **A.** 190.4 oz **B.** 285.6 oz
   - Ⓒ 380.8 oz **D.** not here

8. For a dance, the student government bought 178 carnations at \$.49 each. What is the best estimate of the total amount paid for the carnations?
   - **A.** \$70 Ⓑ \$90
   - **C.** \$100 **D.** \$120

9. Which would be true for a bar graph displaying the data in the table below?

Week	Income
1	\$28.50
2	\$30.00
3	\$17.00
4	\$41.50

   - **A.** There will be five bars.
   - **B.** The bar for week 3 will be taller than the bar for week 4.
   - **C.** The bar for week 4 will be the shortest bar.
   - Ⓓ The bars for weeks 1 and 2 will be about the same height.

Assessment

CUMULATIVE REVIEW

Chapter 2 Cumulative Review (continued)

10. Order 0.7, 0.77, and 0.07 from least to greatest.
    - **A.** 0.7, 0.07, 0.77 **B.** 0.07, 0.77, 0.7
    - Ⓒ 0.07, 0.7, 0.77 **D.** 0.77, 0.7, 0.07

11. Use the stem-and-leaf plot to find how many people exercise more than 10 h each week.

Hours of Exercise per Week

0	3 5 6
1	0 1 4 9
2	2 2 5 7 8
3	1 4

0 | 3 means 3

    - **A.** 12 people Ⓑ 10 people
    - **C.** 4 people **D.** 3 people

12. Which of the following uses the distributive property to find 7×57?
    - **A.** $7 \times 5 \times 7$
    - **B.** $7(50 \times 7)$
    - **C.** $(7 \times 50) + 7$
    - Ⓓ $(7 \times 50) + (7 \times 7)$

13. Tim's test grades in French class are 86, 96, 88, and 91. What score must Tim make on his next test to average 92?
    - **A.** 89 **B.** 93
    - **C.** 97 Ⓓ 99

14. Which two numbers have a sum of 36 and a product of 320?
    - **A.** 26 and 10 **B.** 32 and 10
    - Ⓒ 20 and 16 **D.** 8 and 40

15. Which equation is true?
    - Ⓐ $17 - 3 \times 5 = 2$
    - **B.** $20 - 5 \times 3 = 45$
    - **C.** $10 + 3 \times 2 = 26$
    - **D.** $6 + 5 \times 9 = 99$

16. Which decimal is between 46.7 and 47?
    - **A.** 44.1 Ⓑ 46.81
    - **C.** 46.34 **D.** 47.7

17. Which symbol makes the sentence true? $7 + 3 \times 2 = 5 \times 3 \blacksquare 2$
    - Ⓐ $-$ **B.** $\div$
    - **C.** $\times$ **D.** $+$

18. The Rory family drove 310 miles each day for four days. Then on Friday they drove 250 miles to Centerville. On Saturday they drove 150 miles to Westfield. What else do you need to know to determine how many miles they averaged each day for that one week?
    - **A.** number of miles driven back home
    - **B.** number of days in a week
    - **C.** distance from Centerville to Westfield
    - Ⓓ number of miles driven the seventh day

Choose a Strategy

19. Bertha, Burt, Barb, and Brenda entered a swimming contest. Burt finished last. Brenda finished between Burt and Barb. Bertha placed first. Who came in third?
    - Ⓐ Brenda **B.** Barb
    - **C.** Bertha **D.** Burt

Resources

Teaching Resources

Chapter Support File, Ch. 2
- Cumulative Review

Teacher's Edition

See pp. 48C–D for Assessment Options.

3 Algebra: Integers and Equations

Chapter Overview

To accommodate flexible scheduling, most lessons are divided into parts. Assignment Options are given in the Teacher's Edition for each lesson.

Lesson 3-1 Data Analysis: Evaluating and Writing Variable Expressions

Pages 92–96

NCTM 1, 2, 3, 4, 5, 7, 9, 13

Part 1 Evaluating Variable Expressions
Part 2 Writing Variable Expressions

Key terms: variable, variable expression

Alternative Activity 3-1

Lesson 3-2 Comparing and Ordering Integers

Pages 97–100

NCTM 1, 2, 3, 4, 5, 13

Part 1 Graphing and Ordering Integers
Part 2 Finding Absolute Value

Key terms: integers, absolute value

Journal

Project Link

Lesson 3-3 Using Models: Adding Integers

Pages 102–105

NCTM 1, 2, 4, 5, 7, 9, 13

Part 1 Adding Integers Using Models
Part 2 Addition Using Absolute Value

Lesson 3-7 Solving Equations by Multiplying and Dividing

Pages 122–125

NCTM 1, 2, 3, 4, 5, 7, 9, 13

Part 1 Solving Equations by Dividing
Part 2 Solving Equations by Multiplying

Key terms: Multiplicative Property of Equality, Division Property of Equality

Alternative Activity 3-7

Lesson 3-8 Writing Equations

Pages 126–129

NCTM 1, 2, 4, 7, 9, 13

Journal

Project Link

Checkpoint 2

Lesson 3-9 Algebra: Solving Two-Step Equations

Pages 130–133

NCTM 1, 2, 4, 7, 9

Alternative Activity 3-9

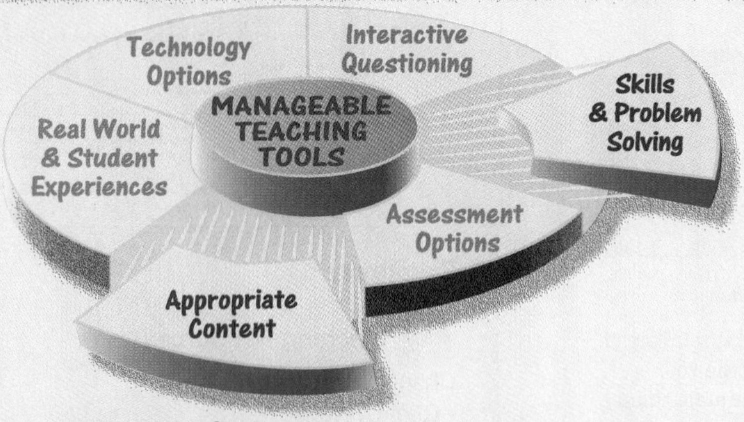

Pacing Options

This chart suggests pacing only for the core lessons and their parts. It is provided merely as a possible guide. It will help you determine how much time you have in your schedule to cover other features, such as the Chapter Project, Math Toolboxes, Wrap Up, and Assessment.

	1 Class Period	1 Class Period	1 Class Period	1 C… Pe…
Traditional (40–45 min class periods)	3–1 (1)	3–1 (2), 3–2 (1)	3–2 (2)	3–… (1)
Block Scheduling (90 min class periods)	3–1 (1), 3–1 (2), 3–2 (1)	3–2 (2), 3–3 (1), 3–3 (2)	3–4 (1), 3–4 (2), 3–5 (1)	3–5 (2) …

CHAPTER PROJECT

Board Walk

Goals: Design and create a board game using integers

THEME: RECREATION

NCTM STANDARDS

1 Problem Solving
2 Communication
3 Reasoning
4 Mathematical Connections
5 Number and Number Relationships
6 Number Systems and Number Theory
7 Computation and Estimation
8 Patterns and Functions
9 Algebra
10 Statistics
11 Probability
12 Geometry
13 Measurement

Pages 106–110	Lesson 3-4 Subtracting Integers
NCTM 1, 2, 3, 4, 5, 7, 8, 13	Part 1 Using Models to Subtract Integers Part 2 Using a Rule to Subtract Integers ▼ **Project Link** ☑ **Checkpoint 1**

Pages 112–116	Lesson 3-5 Multiplying and Dividing Integers
NCTM 1, 2, 4, 5, 7, 8, 13	Part 1 Multiplying Integers Part 2 Dividing Integers ▼ **Project Link** **Math at Work**

Pages 118–121	Lesson 3-6 Solving Equations by Adding and Subtracting
NCTM 1, 2, 3, 4, 5, 7, 9	Part 1 Using Models to Solve Equations Part 2 Using Inverse Operations **Key terms:** solution, Addition Property of Equality, Subtraction Property of Equality

Pages 134–136	Lesson 3-10 Problem Solving Strategy
NCTM 1, 3, 4, 13	Make a Table

Optional Materials and Manipulatives

clock or watch (3-1)
algebra tiles (3-3, 3-4, 3-6, 3-7, 3-9)
calculator (3-3, 3-6, 3-7, 3-9)
number cubes (3-3)

cardboard (3-5)
bag (3-3)
markers (3-5)

Optional calculator use is integrated throughout the course.

ss od	1 Class Period	1 Class Period	1 Class Period	1 Class Period	1 Class Period	1 Class Period	1 Class Period	1 Class Period	1 Class Period	1 Class Period
	3–4 ▼2	3–5 ▼1 3–5 ▼2	3–6 ▼1 3–6 ▼2	3–7 ▼1	3–7 ▼2	3–8	3–9	3–10		
3–8	3–9 3–10									

MEETING INDIVIDUAL NEEDS

Accommodating Diverse Learning Styles

In your Teacher's Edition, you will find suggestions as to how you can help students complete mathematical tasks in Chapter 3 by meeting individual needs and supporting various learning styles. Here are some examples:

VISUAL LEARNING
drawing tiles to answer questions *(p. 102)*

TACTILE LEARNING
modeling problems with algebra tiles *(p. 102)*

AUDITORY LEARNING
writing word phrases from taped dictation *(p. 94)*

KINESTHETIC LEARNING
measuring distances between students acting out a number line *(p. 98)*

EARLY FINISHERS
Performance-Based Project, MathBlaster® Mystery, Interdisciplinary Units

GIFTED AND TALENTED
rewriting problems so there is only one possible answer *(p. 135)*

DIVERSITY describing the stock market to students who are not familiar with it *(p. 114)*

ACQUIRING ENGLISH PROFICIENCY (AEP)
using cognates to learn math terms *(p. 119)*

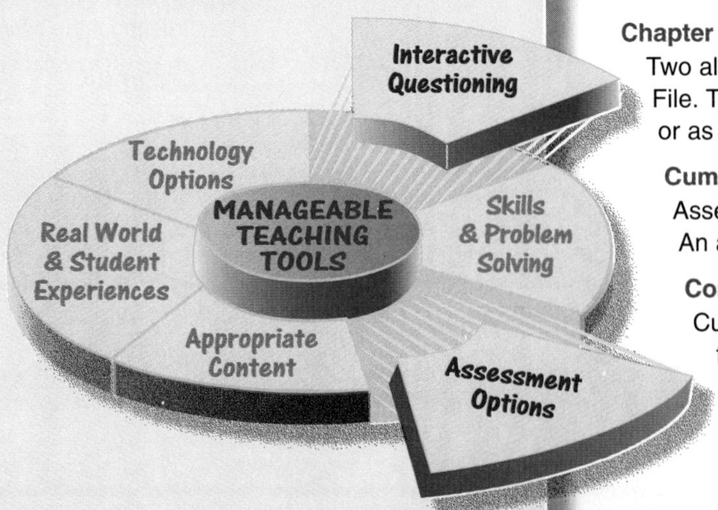

ASSESSING PROGRESS

A broad range of assessment tools are available to reach a variety of learners.

INFORMAL ASSESSMENT

Informal assessments provide day-to-day feedback to help give you a picture of conceptual understanding and skill development.

ONGOING ASSESSMENT is built into lesson instruction and the Teaching Notes of the Teacher's Edition.

In the Teacher's Edition
Lesson Quiz for every lesson

In the Student Edition
On Your Own, Mixed Review, Journal, Portfolio, Project Link, Chapter Wrap Up

Look for **Interactive Questions** within lessons that

- **BUILD UNDERSTANDING** with labels such as **Analyze, Reasoning, Estimation, Writing, and Summarize**
- ✔ **CHECK UNDERSTANDING** with the **Try It Out** label.

FORMAL ASSESSMENT

Formal assessment can occur before and after the chapter, as well as at natural breaking points in the chapter.

Checkpoints
Two forms of each self-assessment Checkpoints are available: one in the Student Edition and another in the Chapter Support File in the Teaching Resources box.

- Mid-Chapter Checkpoint 1, page 110
- End-of-Chapter Checkpoint 2, page 129

Chapter 3 Assessment, page 140.
Two alternative forms are available in the Chapter Support File. They may be used after a chapter has been completed, or as a pre-test and post-test comparison.

Cumulative Review, page 141.
Assesses skills and concepts in Chapters 1–3.
An alternative form is available in Chapter Support File.

Computer Item Generator for Chapter 3
Customized tests can be generated for each lesson and for mid-chapter and end-of-chapter assessments, and for pre- and post-test comparisons of achievement.

PERFORMANCE-BASED ASSESSMENT

CHAPTER PROJECT

The Chapter Project in the student edition provides a real-world connection to the math context of the chapter. The Teacher's Edition contains a scoring rubric.

A Performance Assessment with a scoring rubric can be found in the Chapter Support File in the Teaching Resources box.

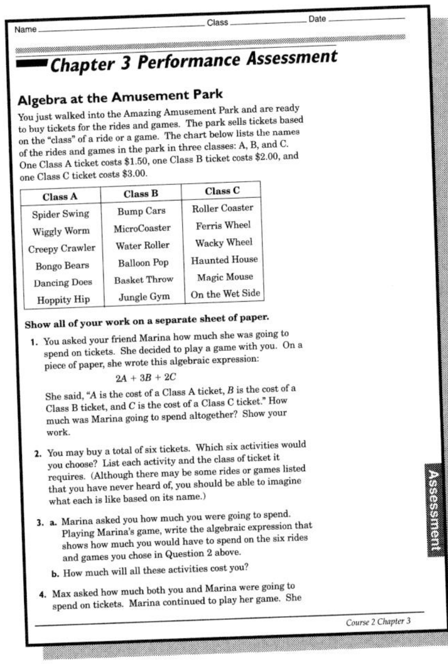

Name ______ Class ______ Date ______

Chapter 3 Performance Assessment

Algebra at the Amusement Park

You just walked into the Amazing Amusement Park and are ready to buy tickets for the rides and games. The park sells tickets based on the "class" of a ride or a game. The chart below lists the names of the rides and games in the park in three classes: A, B, and C. One Class A ticket costs $1.50, one Class B ticket costs $2.00, and one Class C ticket costs $3.00.

Class A	Class B	Class C
Spider Swing	Bump Cars	Roller Coaster
Wiggly Worm	MicroCoaster	Ferris Wheel
Creepy Crawler	Water Roller	Wacky Wheel
Bongo Bears	Balloon Pop	Haunted House
Dancing Does	Basket Throw	Magic Mouse
Hoppity Hip	Jungle Gym	On the Wet Side

Show all of your work on a separate sheet of paper.

1. You asked your friend Marina how much she was going to spend on tickets. She decided to play a game with you. On a piece of paper, she wrote this algebraic expression:

$$2A + 3B + 2C$$

She said, "A is the cost of a Class A ticket, B is the cost of a Class B ticket, and C is the cost of a Class C ticket." How much was Marina going to spend altogether? Show your work.

2. You may buy a total of six tickets. Which six activities would you choose? List each activity and the class of ticket it requires. (Although there may be some rides or games listed that you have never heard of, you should be able to imagine what each is like based on its name.)

3. a. Marina asked you how much you were going to spend. Playing Marina's game, write the algebraic expression that shows how much you would have to spend on the six rides and games you chose in Question 2 above.
   b. How much will all these activities cost you?

4. Max asked how much both you and Marina were going to spend on tickets. Marina continued to play her game. She

Assessment

Course 2 Chapter 3

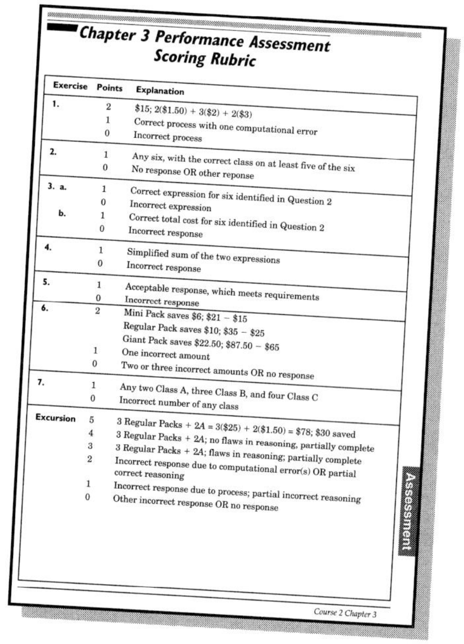

Chapter 3 Performance Assessment Scoring Rubric

Exercise	Points	Explanation
1.	2	$15; 2($1.50) + 3($2) + 2($3)
	1	Correct process with one computational error
	0	Incorrect process
2.	1	Any six, with the correct class on at least five of the six
	0	No response OR other reponse
3. a.	1	Correct expression for six identified in Question 2
	0	Incorrect expression
b.	1	Correct total cost for six identified in Question 2
	0	Incorrect response
4.	1	Simplified sum of the two expressions
	0	Incorrect response
5.	1	Acceptable response, which meets requirements
	0	Incorrect response
6.	2	Mini Pack saves $6; $21 − $15 Regular Pack saves $10; $35 − $25 Giant Pack saves $22.50; $87.50 − $65
	1	One incorrect amount
	0	Two or three incorrect amounts OR no response
7.	1	Any two Class A, three Class B, and four Class C
	0	Incorrect number of any class
Excursion	5	3 Regular Packs + 2A = 3($25) + 2($1.50) = $78; $30 saved
	4	3 Regular Packs + 2A; no flaws in reasoning, partially complete
	3	3 Regular Packs + 2A; flaws in reasoning; partially complete
	2	Incorrect response due to computational error(s) OR partial correct reasoning
	1	Incorrect response due to process; partial incorrect reasoning
	0	Other incorrect response OR no response

Assessment

Course 2 Chapter 3

Correlation to Standardized Tests

Lesson		CAT5	Terra Nova	ITBS, Form M	MAT7	SAT9	Local Test
		STANDARDIZED TEST ITEMS					
3-1	Data Analysis: Evaluating and Writing Variable Expressions	CA15	38	CE15	CP7, 44	PS12, 14	
3-2	Comparing and Ordering Integers	CA16, 34	28	CE1	CP15	PS1, 8, PR11	
3-3	Using Models: Adding Integers	MC11, 23, 30	2, MC2, 9, 12, 15	MC1, 24	CP1, 46	PS9, 42, PR15	
3-4	Subtracting Integers		MC15, 19	MC4, 9, 34	PR1, 15, CP46	PS7, PR18	
3-5	Multiplying and Dividing Integers	MC8, 38, 43, CA23, 35–36	6, 8, MC2, 4, 9, 15, 17	CE5, MC2, 5, 8, 12, 15, 18, 22, 25, 31	PR2–3, 7, 9, 16–17	PS40, 48, PR1–3, 16–17	
3-6	Solving Equations by Adding and Subtracting			CE17			
3-7	Solving Equations by Multiplying and Dividing		5	CE11, 13	CP12		
3-8	Writing Equations				CP27, 29, 43		
3-9	Solving Two-Step Equations		16, 30		CP42		
3-10	Problem Solving Strategy: Make a Table						

CA: Concepts and Applications PR: Math Procedures MC: Math Computation CE: Concepts and Estimation
PS: Problem Solving CP: Concepts and Problem Solving PD: Problem Solving and Data Interpretation

See page 2D for the level of each test referenced.

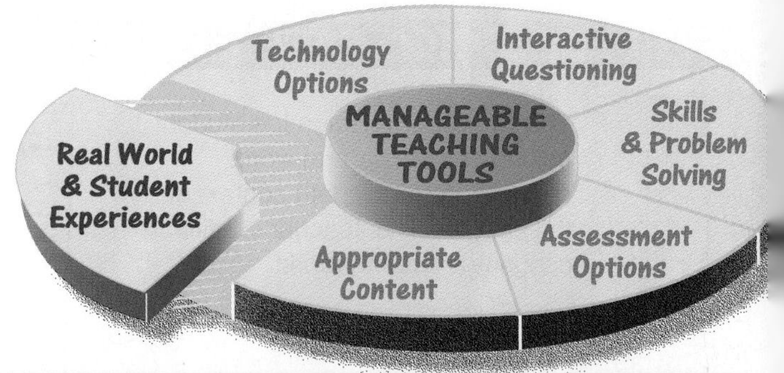

MAKING CONNECTIONS

TEAM TEACHING WITH PRENTICE HALL MATERIALS

MIDDLE GRADES MATH INTERDISCIPLINARY UNITS	INTERDISCIPLINARY EXPLORATIONS	PRENTICE HALL SCIENCE L Life Science E Earth Science P Physical Science
• **Agriculture: Activity 3**	• ***Riddles of the Pharaohs* p. 24**	**E Sec. 5–3 Layers of the Atmosphere (low temperatures)**

Lesson	Interdisciplinary Connections	Real World Connections	Math Integration
3-1	Health Language Biology	Entertainment Public Service Business	Algebra Measurement
3-2	Geography Science	Temperatures Astronomy Recreation	Algebra Measurement
3-3	Geography	Weather Entertainment Money	Algebra Measurement
3-4	Finance Science	Temperature Marathons	Algebra Measurement
3-5	Business Nutrition	Stock Market Hobbies Computer Software	Algebra Measurement
3-6	Business	Job Market Softball	Algebra
3-7	Algebra	Money Entertainment	Algebra Measurement
3-8	History Earth Science	Architecture Environment Astronomy Education	Algebra Measurement
3-9	History	Jobs Travel Entertainment	Algebra
3-10	Physical Science Sports Biology	Data Analysis Pen Pals Salaries Weather	Measurement

School to Home

MATERIALS:
newspaper
tape measure
almanac
paper
pencil

English version is in the Chapter Support File. Spanish version is in the Spanish Resources.

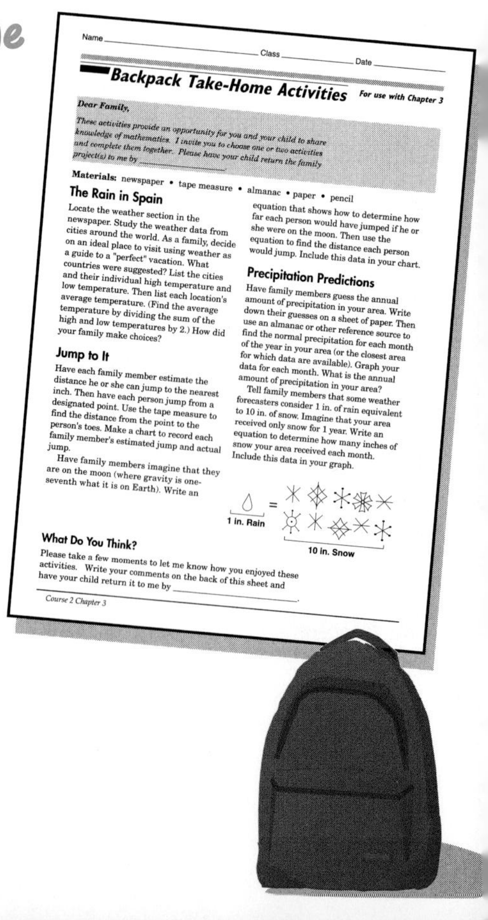

Name ______ Class ______ Date ______

Backpack Take-Home Activities *For use with Chapter 3*

Dear Family,

These activities provide an opportunity for you and your child to share knowledge of mathematics. I invite you to choose one or two activities and complete them together. Please have your child return the family project(s) to me by ______

Materials: newspaper • tape measure • almanac • paper • pencil

The Rain in Spain

Locate the weather section in the newspaper. Study the weather data from cities around the world. As a family, decide on an ideal place to visit using weather as a guide to a "perfect" vacation. What countries were suggested? List the cities and their individual high temperature and low temperature. Then list each location's average temperature. (Find the average temperature by dividing the sum of the high and low temperatures by 2.) How did your family make choices?

Jump to It

Have each family member estimate the distance he or she can jump to the nearest inch. Then have each person jump from a designated point. Use the tape measure to find the distance from the point to the person's toes. Make a chart to record each family member's estimated jump and actual jump.

Have family members imagine that they are on the moon (where gravity is one-seventh what it is on Earth). Write an equation that shows how to determine how far each person would have jumped if he or she were on the moon. Then use the equation to find the distance each person would jump. Include this data in your chart.

Precipitation Predictions

Have family members guess the annual amount of precipitation in your area. Write down their guesses on a sheet of paper. Then use an almanac or other reference source to find the normal precipitation for each month of the year in your area (or the closest area for which data are available). Graph your data for each month. What is the annual amount of precipitation in your area?

Tell family members that some weather forecasters consider 1 in. of rain equivalent to 10 in. of snow. Imagine that your area received only snow for 1 year. Write an equation to determine how many inches of snow your area received each month. Include this data in your graph.

1 in. Rain = 10 in. Snow

What Do You Think?

Please take a few moments to let me know how you enjoyed these activities. Write your comments on the back of this sheet and have your child return it to me by ______.

Course 2 Chapter 3

USING TECHNOLOGY TO ENHANCE INSTRUCTION

FOR THE STUDENT

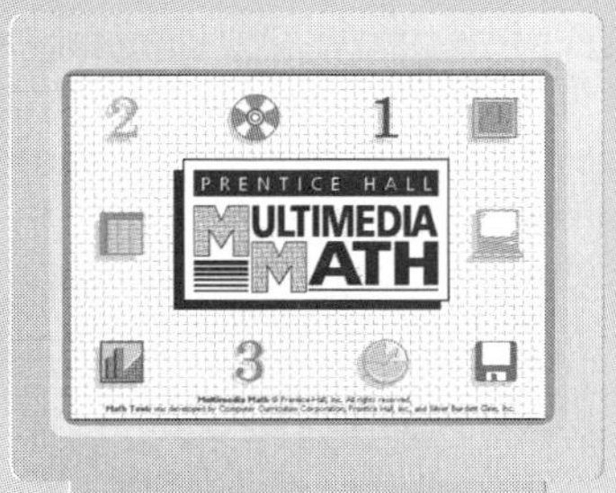

Multimedia Math Hot Pages™

This interactive software and video package on CD-ROM integrates solid math content through a variety of media.

- Hot Page™ 4-4
- Hot Page™ 4-6
- Hot Page™ 4-10

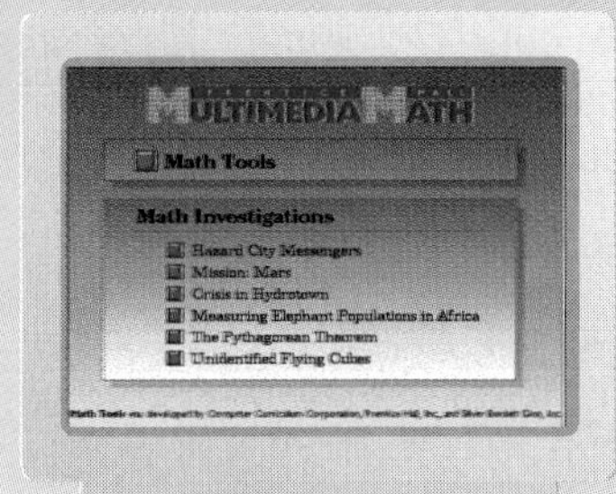

Multimedia Math Investigations

These in-depth interactive activities on CD-ROM develop real-world applications of mathematics. They allow students the opportunity to reinforce key concepts.

- Mission: Mars

MathBlaster® Mystery

This award-winning, interactive software program on CD-ROM can be used to maintain skills or to accommodate early finishers.

- Level: Earn 4 coins; Pay 4 coins
- Mission Mode (all lessons)
- Kitchen Comparisons (3-3, 3-7)
- Number Guesser (3-2, 3-5)
- Equation Maker (3-1, 3-4, 3-6, 3-9)
- Word Problems (3-8, 3-10, Problem Solving Practice)

Math Tools/Math Labs

This software, available on CD-ROM, includes on-screen Math Lab activities. Students use linkable, interactive tools to explore math concepts.

- Math Lab: Adding Integers (3-3)

Interactive Student Tutorial

Available on CD-ROM, this test preparation program contains self-tests with questions in standardized test format. Software includes electronic versions of the text lessons and an on-line glossary.

Internet Connection

For Students

Support for the Chapter Project

A career-oriented link for Math at Work feature

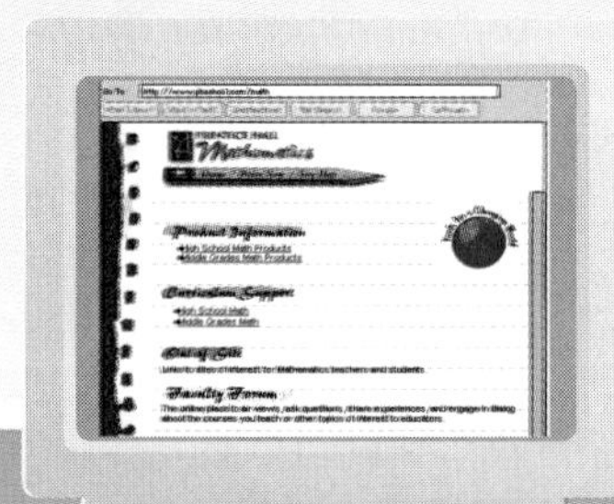

www.phschool.com/math

For teachers

Curriculum Support

Product Information

Regional Support Information

FOR THE TEACHER

Computer Item Generator with Standardized Test Practice

This software generates customized practice sheets and tests. It also generates unlimited practice sheets for the standardized tests listed on page 90D.

Resource Pro™ with Planning Express™

Available on CD-ROM, this software can be used to customize and plan lessons. It contains over 1,700 resource pages.

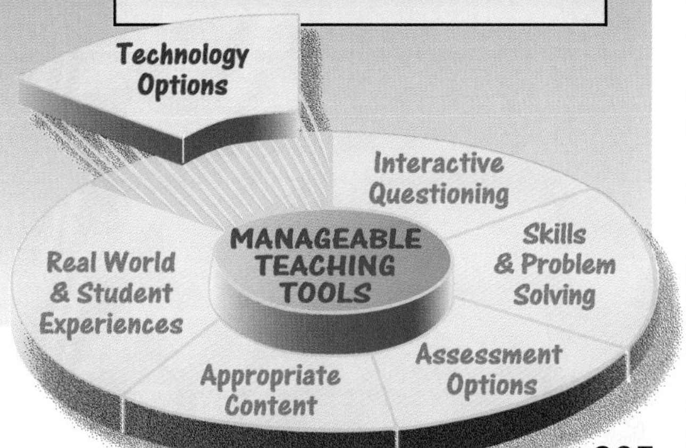

CHAPTER 3

EVALUATING AND WRITING VARIABLE EXPRESSIONS

CONNECTING TO PRIOR LEARNING Bring to class a report of winter low temperatures in the United States. Have students compare extremes, such as a low temperature in Florida and a below-zero temperature in Alaska.

CULTURAL CONNECTIONS Many sports, such as golf, use integers in some way. Golf is played in almost every country in the world. Challenge students to find other international sports that use integers.

INTERDISCIPLINARY CONNECTIONS Discuss with students how integers are used in geography. You can use integers to describe your elevation compared to sea level.

ABOUT THE PROJECT The Chapter Project gives students an opportunity to apply their knowledge of integers to design a game. The Project Link questions help students to organize and encourage them to use the game to reinforce their integer skills.

Internet • For information and activities related to the Chapter Project, visit the Prentice Hall site at www.phschool.com/mgm2/ch3

3 Algebra: Integers and Equations

WHAT YOU WILL LEARN IN THIS CHAPTER

- How to model and work with integers
- How to model, write, and solve equations
- How to use formulas in a spreadsheet

LAUNCHING THE CHAPTER PROJECT

Ask students:

- *Do you know what negative numbers are?*
- *Have you ever used a board game to practice a skill?*

PROJECT NOTEBOOK Encourage students to keep all project-related materials in a separate folder or notebook.

TRACKING THE PROJECT You may wish to have students read Finishing the Chapter Project on page 137 to help them get an overview of the project. Set benchmark deadlines for students to show you their work in progress.

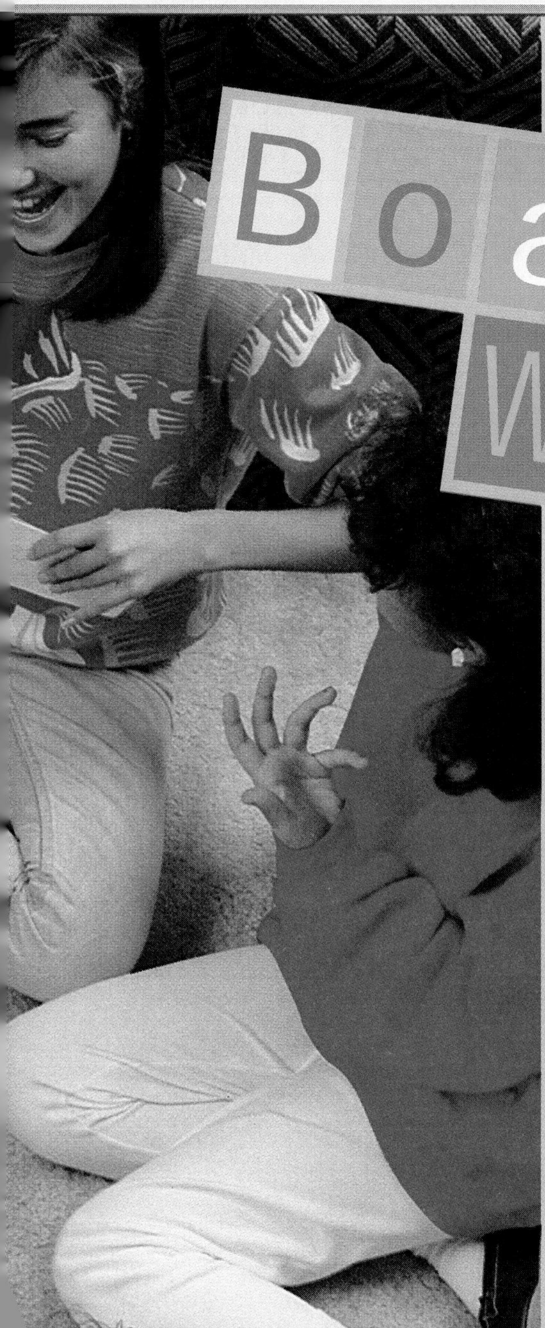

Board Walk

CHAPTER PROJECT

THEME: RECREATION

What makes a board game so much fun? You have challenges like road blocks or false paths that make you backtrack. Then you land on a lucky square that lets you leap forward past your opponent. Best of all, you are with your friends as you play!

Create a Board Game For this chapter project, you will use integers to create a game. Then you will play your game with friends or family for a trial run. Finally you will decorate your game and bring it to class to play.

Steps to help you complete the project:

p. 100 **Project Link:** *Making a Decision*
p. 110 **Project Link:** *Designing*
p. 116 **Project Link:** *Designing*
p. 129 **Project Link:** *Organizing*
p. 137 *Finishing the Chapter Project*

- How to solve problems by making a table

PROBLEM SOLVING

SCORING RUBRIC

3 You provided work to show that you thought about your game before putting it together. Your game includes opportunities to use addition, subtraction, and multiplication of positive and negative integers. Your finished game board is attractive, and your project includes rules that are easy to understand and follow.

2 You created a game that includes opportunities to add, subtract, and multiply positive and negative integers, but your finished product is not as well-planned or constructed as it could have been.

1 Your finished game is not well-thought-out or does not provide many opportunities to add, subtract, and multiply positive and negative integers.

0 You did not make a game, or you did not include the use of both positive and negative integers in your game.

3-1 Teaching Notes

1 Focus

CONNECTING TO PRIOR KNOWLEDGE Ask students to find the amount of money represented by 15 nickels. **$.75** If a new coin, called an *x*, has the same value as 3 nickels, what is the value of one *x*? **$.15** What is the value of five *x*'s? **$.75**

DIVERSITY Some students may not be comfortable calculating with U. S. currency. Encourage students to bring in coins from their native countries. Students can create their own math problems using the values of these coins.

2 Teach

Work Together

DIVERSITY Make students aware that heart rates will vary.

Each group of students needs a watch or clock with a second hand. Suggest that they begin timing their pulse when the second hand is at the 12 or 6, rather than at an irregular point on the clock.

Some students may have difficulty taking their pulse. Suggest they take their pulse three times and average the results. The inside of the wrist and the side of the neck are good places to take a pulse.

Lesson Planning Options

Prerequisite Skills
- decimal operations (2-1 to 2-8)
- basic arithmetic (precourse)

Vocabulary/Symbols
variable, variable expression

Materials/Manipulatives
- clock or watch

Resources

Student Edition

Skills Handbook, p. 530
Extra Practice, p. 516
Glossary/Study Guide

Teaching Resources

Chapter Support File, Ch. 3
- Lesson Planner
- Practice 3-1, Reteaching 3-1
- Alternative Activity 3-1
- Answer Masters 3-1

Teaching Aids Master 27
Glossary, Spanish Resources

Transparencies

15, Minds on Math 3-1

Warm Up

Ask students to find the number of quarts of yellow and blue paint needed to make 8 qt of green paint if the ratio of yellow to blue is 1 qt to 3 qt. **2 qt yellow, 6 qt blue**

3-1 Evaluating and Writing Variable Expressions

What You'll Learn

1. To evaluate variable expressions
2. To write variable expressions

...And Why

You can use variables and variable expressions to find the cost of a purchase of video tapes.

Here's How

Look for questions that
- build understanding
- ✔ check understanding

Work Together

Collecting Data

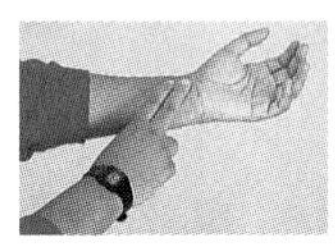

Work in a group. Find the number of times your heart beats in 15 s by taking a 15-s reading of your pulse. Each beat corresponds to one beat of your heart.

1. Record each person's 15-s rate. Calculate the beats per minute.
   1, 2a. Check students' work.
2. a. Use the heart rates you found in Question 1. How many times would each person's heart beat in 5 minutes? In 1 day? In 1 week?
   b. *Reasoning* Explain how you found the expected number of heartbeats in 5 minutes and in 1 day.
   See left.

2b. To find expected heart beats in 5 min, multiply the number of beats per minute by 5; to find expected heart beats in 1 day, multiply the number of beats per minute by 60 and then multiply the result by 24.

THINK AND DISCUSS

1 Evaluating Variable Expressions

A **variable** is a symbol that stands for a number. A **variable expression** is a group of numbers, variables, and operations.

variables →	g	z	x
variable expressions →	$13 - g$	$z \div 2$	$3x + 8$

You can use a variable expression to describe data. Suppose your heart beats 72 times in one minute.

$72m$ ← variable represents number of minutes; variable expression represents number of heartbeats in m minutes

The variable expression $72m$ means $72 \times m$ or $72 \cdot m$. To evaluate a variable expression, replace the variable with a number.

$72m = 72 \cdot 3$ ← Substitute 3 for m to find the number of heartbeats in three minutes.

$= 216$ ← Multiply.

THINK AND DISCUSS

Help students understand that we write variables in italics and unit abbreviations in regular type: 15*s* means 15 times the variable *s;* 15 s means 15 seconds.

TACTILE LEARNING **Example 1** Have students evaluate expressions such as $5x + 6$ by selecting a number card to cover the variable.

ADDITIONAL EXAMPLES

FOR EXAMPLE 1

Suppose you buy four cassette tapes and one \$18 video tape. Use the expression $4v + 18$. Find the total cost of your purchase if the cassette tapes cost \$8 each. **\$50**

FOR EXAMPLE 2

Write a variable expression for the cost of 9 packages of markers at *d* dollars each. **9*d***

AEP Encourage students having problems with the vocabulary of expressions to copy the chart onto a note card for future reference. They may want to color code the words that represent the different operations.

In 1997, the movie *Star Wars* overtook *E.T.* to become the top money-making movie of all time.

Source: *USA Today*

EXAMPLE 1 *Real-World Problem Solving*

Entertainment Suppose you want to buy two video tapes and a \$7 cassette tape. Use the variable expression $2v + 7$. Find the total cost of your purchase if the tapes cost \$9.95 each.

$$2v + 7 = 2 \cdot 9.95 + 7 \quad \leftarrow \text{Substitute 9.95 for } v.$$
$$= 19.9 + 7 \quad \leftarrow \text{Multiply.}$$
$$= 26.9 \quad \leftarrow \text{Simplify.}$$

The total cost of your purchase is \$26.90.

3. ✔ *Try It Out* Suppose the video tapes from Example 1 cost \$17.95 each. Find the total cost. **\$42.90**

Now you may assign Exercises 1–35, 50.

2 *Writing Variable Expressions*

The table shows some of the key words you can use in word phrases for variable expressions.

Key Words	Operation	Key Words	Operation
add	+	minus	−
plus	+	difference	−
sum	+	subtract	−
total	+	less than	−
increased by	+	less	−
more than	+	decreased by	−
product	×	quotient	÷
times	×	divide	÷
multiply	×		

Below are three ways you can write a word phrase for $x + 2$.

a number plus two

the sum of two and a number

a number increased by two

a–c. Answers may vary. Samples are given.

4. Write a word phrase for each variable expression.
   a. $5 + n$ b. $p \div 3$ c. $50.75 - c$

a. the sum of 5 and a number
b. a number divided by 3
c. 50.75 decreased by a number

5. **Choose A, B, or C.** Which variable expression corresponds to "3 less than a number"? **A**
   A. $n - 3$ B. $3 - n$ C. $3 < n$

Technology Options

Prentice Hall Technology

Software for Learners

- Math Blaster® Mystery*
- Interactive Student Tutorial, Chapter 3*

Teaching Resource Software

- Computer Item Generator 3-1*
- Resource Pro™ Chapter 3*

Internet • For related mathematics activities, visit the Prentice Hall site at www.phschool.com/math

**Available on CD-ROM only*

Assignment Options for Exercises On Your Own

To provide flexible scheduling, this lesson can be subdivided into parts.

1 **Core** 1–11, 13–24, 27–35
Extension 12, 25–26, 50

2 **Core** 36–48, 51–54
Extension 49, 55, 56

Use Mixed Review to maintain skills.

AUDITORY LEARNING Questions 4 and 5 Make an auditory tape of several word phrases, with and without variables. Students can practice writing the word phrases as you say them with the appropriate numerical or variable expression.

ERROR ALERT! Students may confuse *less than* with *is less than*. **Remediation:** Remind students that *is* means *equals*. They write "<" (is less than) in place of an equal sign. *Less than* means to subtract.

ERROR ALERT! Students may write subtraction expressions in the wrong order. **Remediation:** Have students substitute a number for each variable to see if the expression makes sense. It may be helpful for some students to circle *than* when they see it in a word phrase. The circle will signal students to reverse the order of the terms when writing the variable expression.

ASSESSMENT Ask students to use 5 and d to write four variable expressions using the four operations. Then have them rewrite the variable expressions as word phrases. Students can also evaluate the expressions using $d = 4$.

EXAMPLE 2 *Real-World Problem Solving*

Public Service Suppose your environmental club is putting up posters downtown. Write a variable expression for the cost of the posters at $4 per poster.

Words • $4 per poster times the number of posters

• Let p = the number of posters

Expression • $4 \cdot p$

A variable expression for the cost of the posters is $4p$.

6. ✔ *Try It Out* Suppose each of the nine students in the club is going to put up p posters. Write a variable expression for the total number of posters the students will put up. **9p**

Now you may assign Exercises 36–49, 51–56.

EXERCISES *On Your Own*

Mental Math **Evaluate each expression for $p = 4$, $n = 6$, and $s = 2$.**

1. $5p + 3$ **23**
2. $3p + n$ **18**
3. $p \times s$ **8**
4. $2 + 4n$ **26**
5. $n \div p$ $\frac{3}{2}$
6. $3s + n$ **12**
7. $p + s - n$ **0**
8. $n \div s$ **3**
9. $(p + n) \div s$ **5**
10. nps **48**

11. Complete the table. Substitute the value on the left for the variable in the expression at the top of each column. Then evaluate each expression.

	$t + 2$	$2t - 1$	$2(t - 1)$	$2(2t)$
$t = 1.7$	■ **3.7**	■ **2.4**	■ **1.4**	■ **6.8**
$t = 2.04$	■ **4.04**	■ **3.08**	■ **2.08**	■ **8.16**

12. Evaluate the expression $4 + 0.5n$ for $n = 3$. Tell what steps you followed. **5.5; first multiply 0.5 and 3, then add 4.**

Evaluate each expression for $a = 3$, $b = 7$, and $c = 4.2$.

13. $6c$ **25.2**
14. $a + 5$ **8**
15. $c - 4$ **0.2**
16. $0.5b$ **3.5**
17. $12 \div a$ **4**
18. $6 + b$ **13**
19. $10 - c$ **5.8**
20. $a \div 9$ $\frac{1}{3}$
21. $16.3 - b$ **9.3**
22. $2.5a$ **7.5**
23. $9.9 - a$ **6.9**
24. $c + 6.8$ **11**

25. a. From 1953 to 1991, Gwilym Hughes of Great Britain saw an average of 528 movies a year. The variable expression to show the number of movies he saw in y years is $528 \cdot$ ■. **y**
    b. Find the number of movies he saw in 38 years. **20,064 movies**

3 Practice/Assess

EXERCISES *On Your Own*

MENTAL MATH **Exercises 1–10** You may want to allow students to first rewrite the expression using the value of the variables. They can then use mental math to evaluate the expressions.

CONNECTING TO THE STUDENTS' WORLD **Exercise 25** Have students write a variable expression using the approximate number of movies they see in a year.

REASONING **Exercise 26** Group students into two teams to debate the question. Encourage students to give valid and specific reasons.

Exercise 50a Review with students how they found the value 0.05 for a nickel.

Exercise 50b Have students find the value of the pennies and nickels mentioned in the article.

ESTIMATION **Exercise 51** Remind students to estimate, rather than find, the exact expression. Encourage them to choose an estimation strategy such as rounding or front-end estimation. You may want to give them the hint to use p for the number of pages in the directory.

WRITING **Exercise 54** Although the word phrase for the expression will not be a complete sentence, stress that students should explain situations using correct grammar and punctuation.

26. *Reasoning* Do the variable expressions $k + 2$ and $m + 2$ represent the same amount? Explain. **Yes, if k and m represent the same quantity. No, if they represent different quantities.**

Evaluate.

27. $7p$ for $p = 2$ **14**
28. $m - 8$ for $m = 20$ **12**
29. $b \div 4$ for $b = 8$ **2**
30. $3t + 7$ for $t = 0$ **7**
31. $9 \cdot 3h$ for $h = 2$ **54**
32. $5w \div 2$ for $w = 10$ **25**
33. $12 - 4m$ for $m = 2$ **4**
34. $30 + 2q$ for $q = 12$ **54**
35. $7c \cdot 5$ for $c = 1$ **35**

Write each variable expression in words. **36–39. Answers may vary. Samples are given.**

36. $n + 2$ **two added to a number**
37. $n - 8.2$ **8.2 less than a number**
38. $6.5 - n$ **6.5 minus a number**
39. $4 \div n$ **4 divided by a number**

Write a variable expression for each word phrase. **46–48. Variables may vary. Samples are given.**

40. four more than s **$s + 4$**
41. the sum of r and c **$r + c$**
42. seven increased by y **42. $7 + y$**
43. the product of 7 and t **$7t$**
44. the quotient of p and 5 **44. $p \div 5$**
45. nine less than x **$x - 9$**
46. 6 increased by a number **$6 + n$**
47. 4 times a number **$4b$**
48. divide a number by 7 **48. $x \div 7$**

49. *Language* In the expressions at the right, the red numbers are *coefficients* and the blue numbers are *constants*.

$3x + 5$ $\quad 7a - 12$
$8 + 4y$ $\quad 6 - 9c$
$2m + 10$

   a. How are the variable and its coefficient related? **a. The variable is multiplied by the coefficient.**
   b. How is the constant related to the rest of the expression? **b. The constant and the rest of the expression are connected by a plus or a minus sign.**
   c. An expression may have one or more *terms*. Terms are separated by + or − signs. How many terms are in the expressions at the right? **two**

$ Minty Money $

The United States Mint makes all the United States coins at production facilities in Denver and Philadelphia. Federal Reserve banks then distribute the coins to the public.

The Denver and Philadelphia Mints together produced the following numbers of coins in 1995: 13,418,625,000 pennies; 1,623,366,110 nickels; 2,364,988,110 dimes; 2,070,174,110 quarters.

50. a. The variable expression for the value in dollars of n nickels is $0.05n$. Evaluate the expression using the number of nickels minted in 1995. **$81,168,305.50**
   b. Which would you rather have, the dollar value of the pennies minted in 1995 or the dollar value of the nickels? Why? **The dollar value of the pennies; the amount is greater.**

PRACTICE

Practice 3-1 *Evaluating and Writing Variable Expressions*

Evaluate each expression for $m = 7, r = 8$, and $t = 2$.

1. $5m - 6$ 29
2. $4t + 18$ 26
3. $4m + t$ 30
4. $r \div t$ 4
5. $m \times t$ 14
6. $35 \div m$ 5
7. $5t + 2m$ 24
8. $r \times m$ 56
9. $3m - 5t$ 11
10. $m + r - t$ 13
11. $(m \times r) \div t$ 28
12. mrt 112
13. Complete the table below. Substitute the value on the left for the variable in the expression at the top of each column. Then evaluate each expression.

	$w + 5$	$3(w + 4)$	$5w$	$8(3w)$	$3(w - 2)$
$w = 2.7$	7.7	20.1	13.5	64.8	2.1
$w = 9.05$	14.05	39.15	45.25	217.2	21.15

Write each variable expression in words. Answers may vary. Samples are given.

14. $n + 16$ 16 more than *n*
15. $3.2n$ 3.2 times *n*
16. $25.6 - n$ *n* less than 25.6
17. $n \div 24$ *n* divided by 24
18. $\frac{45}{n}$ 45 divided by *n*
19. $15.4 - n$ 15.4 less *n*

Write a variable expression for each word phrase.

20. seven more than *t* $t + 7$
21. the product of 12 and *d* $12d$
22. the sum of *s* and *t* $s + t$
23. the difference of *q* and 5 $q - 5$
24. 42 added to a number $a + 42$
25. 15 increased by *b* $15 + b$
26. Suki and four friends plan a surprise party. Each of them contributes the same amount of money *m* for food.
    a. Write a variable expression for the total amount of money contributed for food. $5m$
    b. Evaluate your expression for $m = \$5.25$. $26.25

In copymaster and workbook formats

RETEACHING

Reteaching 3-1 *Evaluating and Writing Variable Expressions*

To evaluate an *expression*, replace the *variable* with a number and compute.

Evaluate $5y - 8$ for $y = 7$.

$5y - 8$
$5 \times 7 - 8$ ← **Replace y with 7.**
$35 - 8 = 27$ ← **Compute.**

You can use key words to write a word phrase for a variable expression.

$a + 5$ → *a* plus 5 or *a* increased by 5
$2n$ → the product of 2 and *n* or 2 times *n*

Evaluate each expression for $m = 3$ and $x = 8$.

1. $4m + 9$
   Replace *m*: $4 \times$ 3 $+ 9$
   Compute: 12 $+ 9 =$ 21
2. $4x - 7$
   Replace *x*: $4 \times$ 8 $- 7$
   Compute: 32 $- 7 =$ 25
3. $5x + x$
   Replace *x*: $5 \times$ 8 $+$ 8
   Compute: 40 $+$ 8 $=$ 48
4. $x + 2m$
   Replace *x* and *m*: 8 $+ 2 \times$ 3
   Compute: 8 $+$ 6 $=$ 14

Evaluate each expression for $y = 4, z = 8$, and $p = 10$.

5. $3y + 6 =$ 18
6. $4z - 2 =$ 30
7. $p + 2p =$ 30
8. $3z \times z =$ 192
9. $5z - y =$ 36
10. $2p + y =$ 24
11. $8p - p =$ 70
12. $3y + 2z =$ 28

Write each variable expression in words. Answers may vary. Samples are given.

13. $9 + x$ 9 plus a number
14. $6x$ 6 times a number
15. $x - 8$ 8 less than a number
16. $\frac{x}{5}$ a number divided by 5

Write a variable expression for each word phrase. Use *x* as the variable.

17. a number plus 10 $x + 10$
18. 4 less than a number $x - 4$
19. 3 more than a number $x + 3$
20. 6 times a number $6x$

ENRICHMENT

Minds on Math Transparency

3-1

Lon, Jon, and Vaughn all live next to each other in three houses on the same street. Their houses are brown, white, and green. Lon does not live in the brown house. Vaughn's house is white and is next to Lon's house. Jon's house is next to the green house. What color is Lon's house? Where does Lon live in relationship to Jon and Vaughn?

Green; Lon lives between Jon and Vaughn.

See *Solution Key* for worked-out answers.

WRAP UP

IDENTIFYING THE BIG IDEA Ask students to consider the word phrase *the value of seven coins minus sixteen cents.* Have students describe how to translate the word phrase into a numerical expression, and explain how to evaluate the expression if the coins are dimes.

LESSON QUIZ

Evaluate.

1. $20p + 3$ for $p = 2$ **43**
2. $54 - 3 + m$ for $m = 1$ **52**
3. $4.2 + f$ for $f = 6.9$ **11.1**

Write a variable expression for each word phrase.

4. five less than *c* **$c - 5$**
5. the number of days in *w* weeks **$7w$**

51. *Estimation* This section of a page from a telephone directory shows 11 names in 1 in. Each page has four 10-inch columns. Write a variable expression for the approximate number of names in *p* pages of the directory. **p = number of pages in the directory, 440p**

6-4462 **Daalling V** 8 Everett All
2-3302 **Daavis K** 444 Greeley R
4-1775 **Dabady V** 94 Burnside All
2-0014 **Dabagh L** 13 Lancaster R
6-3356 **Dabagh W** Dr 521 Weston All
4-7322 **Dabar G** 98 River All
6-1530 **Dabarera F** 34 Roseland All
2-2279 **Dabas M** 17 Riverside R
4-9978 **D'Abate D** 86 Moss Hill Rd All
2-6745 **D'Abate G** 111 South Central R
4-5456 **Dabbous H** 670 Warren Dr All
6-3064 **Dabbraccio F** 151 Century All
6-2257 **Dabby D** 542 Walnut All
2-9987 **Dabcovich M G** 219 Green R
6-5643 **Dabcovich M** 72 Main All

52a. 275b

52. a. There are *b* books on one shelf in the library. Write a variable expression for the number of books on 275 shelves.
    b. Evaluate your expression for 25 books per shelf. **6,875**
53. *Biology* An adult human heart pumps about 599.4 gal of blood per hour.
    a. Write a variable expression for the number of gallons an adult heart pumps in *h* hours. **599.4h**
    b. Find the gallons of blood the heart pumps in one day. **14,385.6 gallons of blood**
54. *Writing* Write each variable expression at the right as a word phrase. Then make up a situation for each expression. **Answers may vary. See above right for samples. Check student's work.**

    $3 \div n \quad n \div 3 \quad 3n \quad 3 - n$

    54. 3 divided by a number; a number divided by 3; 3 times a number; the difference between 3 and a number.
55. **Choose A, B, C, or D.** What operations are in the variable expression for "twice a number increased by three"? **C**

    A. + and − B. × and − C. × and + D. ×, +, and −
56. *Business* Erik can mow one lawn each weekday after school and two lawns on Saturday.
    a. How many lawns can Erik mow in one week? **7 lawns**
    b. Write a variable expression for the number of lawns he can mow in *w* weeks. **7w**
    c. Suppose Erik earns an average of \$6 for each lawn. How much money can he make in one week? **\$42**
    d. Write a variable expression for the amount of money he can make in *w* weeks. **42w**

Mixed Review

Find the value of each expression. (Lesson 2-8)

57. $3(4 + 5) + 2(4 + 5)$ **45**
58. $3 + 7(1.2) + 7(0.5)$ **14.9**
59. $5(0.25 \times 40)$ **50**

Estimate each answer. (Lesson 2-2)

60. $239.6 - 118.43$ **120**
61. $26.92 + 13.267$ **40**
62. $765.7 - 66.7$ **700**
63. $29.5 + 32.3$ **62**
64. *Choose a Strategy* Karisha has read the first 79 pages of a book. When she has read 17 more pages, she will have read half of the book. How many pages are in the book? **192 pages**

Extra Practice, Lesson 3-1, page 516

3-2 Teaching Notes

1 Focus

CONNECTING TO PRIOR KNOWLEDGE Ask students: *Name some situations that could be described using numbers less than zero.* **Answers may vary. Sample: weight loss, bank withdrawals, temperature, coupon savings** *How have you seen these amounts represented mathematically?* **with a negative sign**

2 Teach

THINK AND DISCUSS

CONNECTING TO THE STUDENTS' WORLD Rather than using the temperatures and weather maps listed in the textbook, contact your local television station or newspaper for the record low temperatures in your state. Then replace St. Paul and Madison with cities from your own state. If your state does not experience temperatures below zero, ask the class: *Has anyone ever lived in a state that had temperatures below zero?* Then ask volunteers to research the record low temperatures for those states mentioned.

AEP Students may have difficulty understanding the difference between *negative* and *opposite*. Give them examples to show that all negative numbers are written with a negative symbol, and all opposites are written in pairs. It may help to visualize *oppo-* as two opposites.

3-2 Comparing and Ordering Integers

What You'll Learn

1. To graph and order integers
2. To find the opposite and absolute value of an integer

...And Why

You can compare temperatures.

Here's How

Look for questions that
- build understanding
- ✓ check understanding

THINK AND DISCUSS

1 Graphing and Ordering Integers

In January, the average daily high temperature measured in Celsius (°C) in Louisville, Kentucky, is about five degrees above zero. The average daily low temperature is about five degrees below zero.

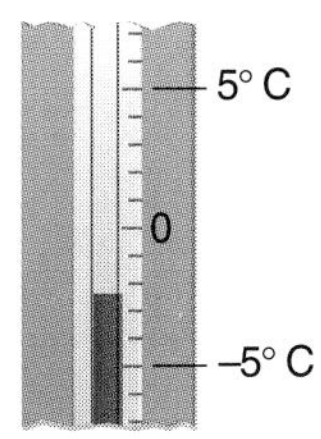

You can write the temperature above zero as +5°C or 5°C. You write the temperature below zero as −5°C. You read the numbers 5 and −5 as *positive* 5 and *negative* 5.

■ **EXAMPLE 1** *Real-World Problem Solving*

Weather Use the map at the left. Which city is colder, St. Paul or Madison?

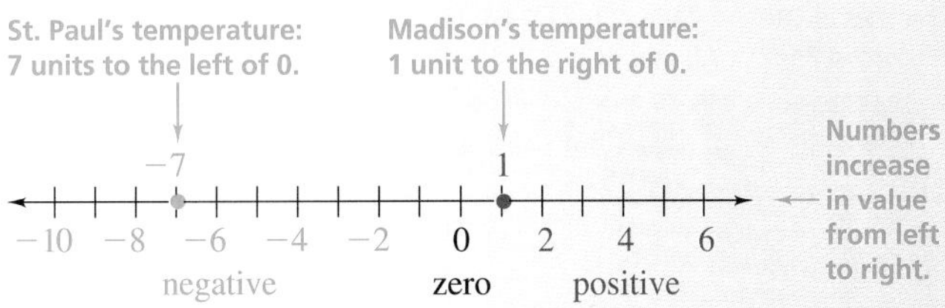

It is colder in St. Paul than it is in Madison.

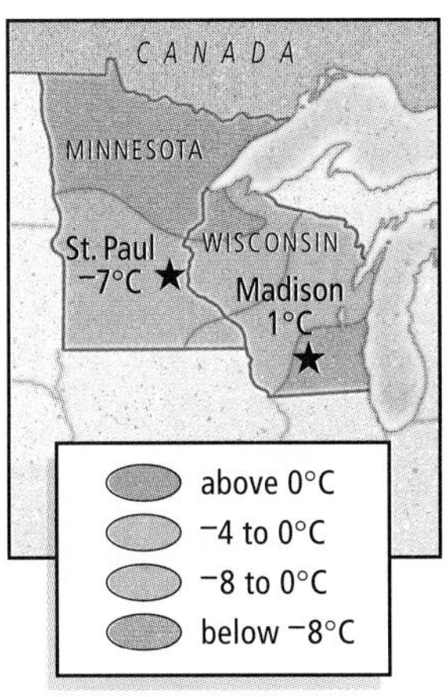

−8; it is farther to the left; see margin p. 99 for diagram.

1. a. ✓ *Try It Out* Graph the numbers −8 and 2 on a number line. Which number has the lesser value? Explain.
   b. Choose >, <, or =. Write a number sentence to compare −8 and 2. **−8 < 2**
2. *Think About It* Which number is greater, 247 or −247? Use a number line to explain your reasoning. **247; it is farther to the right; see left for diagram.**

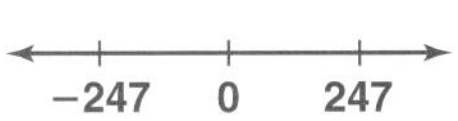

3. *Go a Step Further* Use a number line. Order −9, 6, 0, −4, and 1 from least to greatest. **−9, −4, 0, 1, 6**

Now you may assign Exercises 1–4, 6–9, 21–23, 48.

Lesson Planning Options

Prerequisite Skills
- comparing and ordering whole numbers (precourse)
- reading number lines and charts (precourse)

Vocabulary/Symbols
integers, absolute value

Resources

Student Edition

Skills Handbook, p. 528
Extra Practice, p. 516
Glossary/Study Guide

Teaching Resources

Chapter Support File, Ch. 3
- Lesson Planner 3-2
- Practice 3-2, Reteaching 3-2
- Answer Masters 3-2

Teaching Aids Master 26
Glossary, Spanish Resources

Transparencies

11, 82, Minds on Math 3-2

Warm Up

Divide. Round each quotient to the nearest hundredth.

$\frac{0.5952}{1.6}$ **0.372 which rounds to 0.37**

$\frac{10.5126}{2.1}$ **5.006 which rounds to 5.01**

KINESTHETIC LEARNING Example 2
Carefully draw a large number line from –10 to 10 on the board. Make each number 6 in. apart. Ask one student to stand by a given negative number and another student to stand by its opposite. A volunteer can measure the distance from each to zero to find the absolute values.

■ ADDITIONAL EXAMPLES

FOR EXAMPLE 1

On one winter day, the temperature in Anchorage, Alaska, was -20°F, and the temperature in Fairbanks, Alaska, was -40°F. Which city was colder? **Fairbanks**

FOR EXAMPLE 2

Find $|-5|$ and $|5|$. Use a number line.

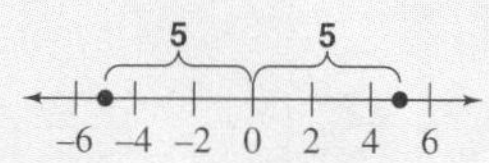

Both -5 and 5 are 5 units from 0, so $|-5| = 5$, and $|5| = 5$.

Technology Options

Prentice Hall Technology

Software for Learners
- Math Blaster® Mystery*
- Interactive Student Tutorial, Chapter 3*

Teaching Resource Software
- Computer Item Generator 3-2
- Resource Pro™ Chapter 3*

Internet • For related mathematics activities, visit the Prentice Hall site at www.phschool.com/math

**Available on CD-ROM only*

Assignment Options for Exercises On Your Own

To provide flexible scheduling, this lesson can be subdivided into parts.

1 **Core** 1–4, 6–9, 22, 23
Extension 21, 48

2 **Core** 5, 10–20, 24–46
Extension 47

Use Mixed Review to maintain skills.

QUICKreview

The whole numbers are 0, 1, 2, 3, ...

2 *Finding Absolute Value*

The numbers 3 and -3 are *opposites*. **Integers** are the set of whole numbers and their opposites. The **absolute value** of an integer is its distance from 0 on a number line. Distance is always positive. You write "the absolute value of -3" as $|-3|$.

■ EXAMPLE 2

Find $|-3|$ and $|3|$. Use a number line.

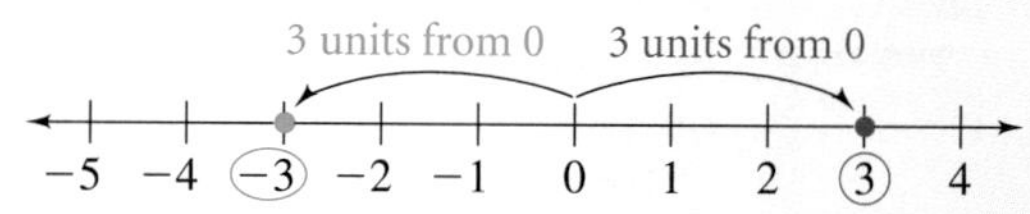

$|-3| = 3$; $|3| = 3$

4. ✔ *Try It Out* Write $|-4|$ in words. Then find $|-4|$. **the absolute value of −4; 4**

5. What two numbers have an absolute value of 1? **1 and −1**

6. *Reasoning* Can the absolute value of a number be -7? Why or why not? **No; distance cannot be negative.**

WEATHER For snowboarding you need snow! The average January snowfall for the cities listed at the right ranges from 23.7 inches in Caribou, Maine, to 2.2 inches in Barrow, Alaska.

Work Together

Comparing Temperatures

Weather Work with a partner. Use the table below of normal high and low temperatures in January for selected cities.
7–8. See margin p. 99.

7. Draw a number line. Use the normal high temperature for January. Arrange the cities above the number line from coldest to warmest.

8. Use the normal low temperature for January. Arrange the cities below the number line from coldest to warmest.

Normal Temperatures for January (°F)

City	High	Low
Barrow, AK	−7	−19
Bismarck, ND	20	−2
Caribou, ME	19	−2
Duluth, MN	16	−2
Omaha, NB	31	11

Source: National Climatic Data Center

9. *Analyze* Which city has the least variation in normal temperatures in January? Which has the greatest? How do you know? **Barrow, AK; Bismarck, ND; compare the distances between the high and the low temperature for each city on the number line.**

Now you may assign Exercises 5, 10–20, 24–47.

Work Together

Have students look at the range of temperatures and decide how to include all the numbers before they start drawing. They may want to turn their paper sideways.

ASSESSMENT Have students work with a partner. One student writes five integers on one side of a note card. The partner draws a number line on the other side of the card and orders the integers from least to greatest. The partner then finds the absolute value of each integer. Partners switch roles and repeat the activity.

3 Practice/Assess

EXERCISES *On Your Own*

ERROR ALERT! Exercises 12–20 Students may think $-6 > -3$ because -6 has the greater absolute value. **Remediation:** Have students use a number line to graph pairs of numbers such as -6 and -3. Generalize a rule about the position of the numbers: Greater numbers are to the *r*ight, and *l*esser numbers are to the *l*eft.

RESEARCH Exercise 23 Students may find pertinent information in sources such as *The World Almanac and Book of Facts*, encyclopedias, or on the Internet.

EXERCISES *On Your Own*

Name the integer represented by each point on the number line.

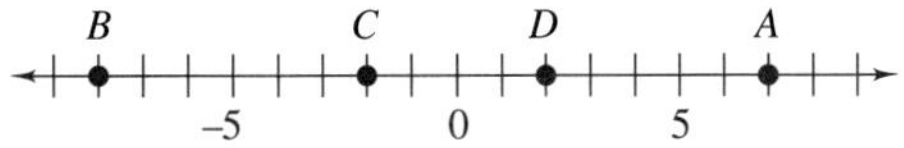

1. *A* 7 2. *B* −8 3. *C* −2 4. *D* 2

5. On the number line above, which two points are opposites? C and D

Write an integer to represent each situation.

6. *Geography* The city of New Orleans, Louisiana, is 8 ft below sea level. −8

7. *Temperature* In Miami, Florida, the average July temperature is 83°F. 83

8. *Astronomy* The surface temperature on the light side of the moon is 270°F. 270

9. *Geography* The Dead Sea is 1,312 ft below sea level. −1,312

Write the absolute value represented by each diagram.

10. Distance is 5 units from 0. |−5|

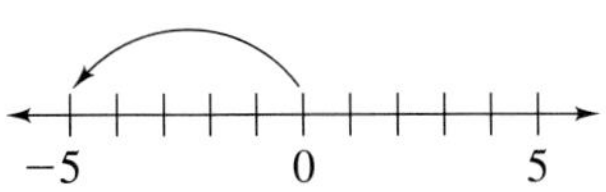

11. Distance is 7 units from 0. |7|

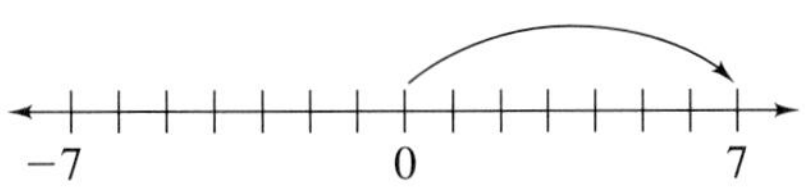

Compare. Use <, >, or =.

12. $0 \blacksquare -2$ (>) 13. $|-6| \blacksquare -3$ (>) 14. $-14 \blacksquare 14$ (<)

15. $-23 \blacksquare 0$ (<) 16. $-4 \blacksquare -5$ (>) 17. $17 \blacksquare -18$ (>)

18. $7 \blacksquare -12$ (>) 19. $10 \blacksquare |-10|$ (=) 20. $5 \blacksquare -1$ (>)

21. *Writing* Suppose a friend does not know how to order integers. Write an explanation for how to order the numbers from least to greatest: −32, 12, 0, −4, 22, −5. See margin.

22. *Science* Use the information at the right. Write integers to represent the temperatures on Mars. Label each temperature as high or low. −68; −176

23. *Research* Write integers to represent the high and low surface temperatures of two other planets. Check students' work.

Graph each integer and its opposite on a number line.

24. 2 25. −9 26. 12 27. −5

24–27. See margin.

The "Sojourner" robot investigated the surface of Mars in 1997. Scientists know that the surface temperature ranges from 68 degrees below zero during the day to 176 degrees below zero at night.

pages 97–98 Think and Discuss

1a.

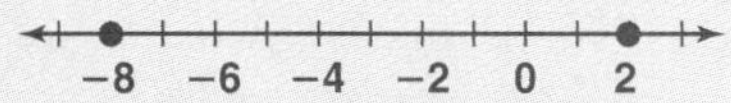

page 98 Work Together

7–8.

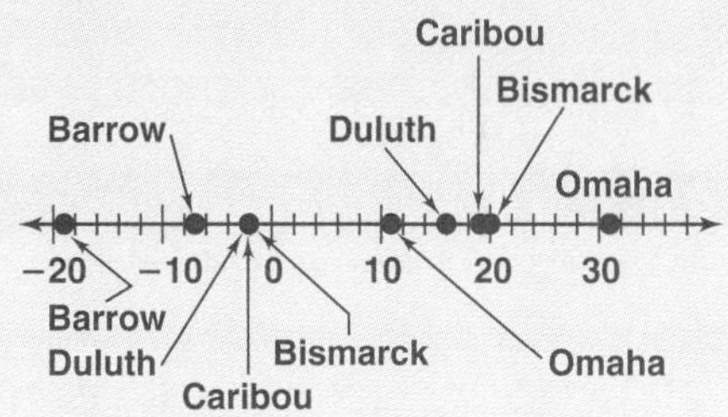

pages 99–100 On Your Own

21. Select the negative numbers first. Then order them from greatest to least absolute value. Then order the remaining numbers from least to greatest.

24.

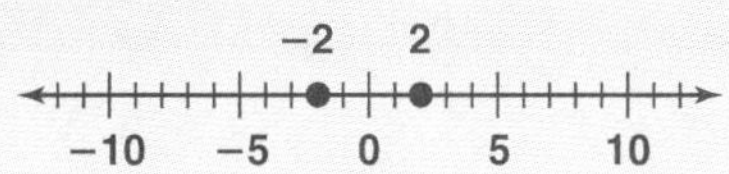

25.

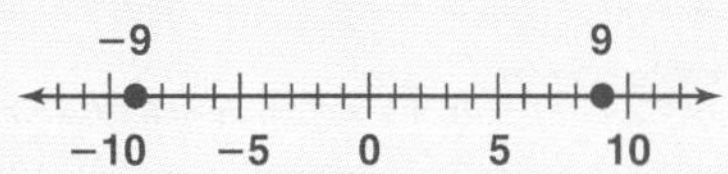

26.

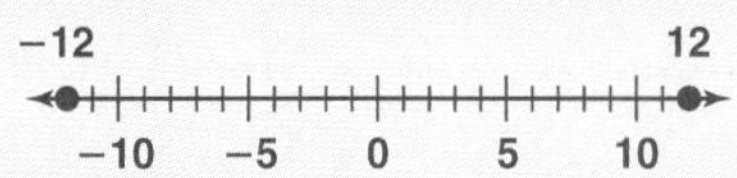

27.

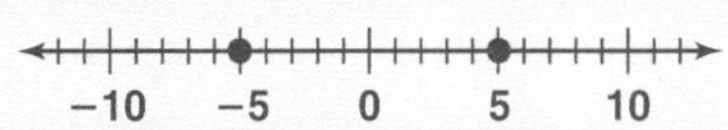

PRACTICE

Practice 3-2 *Comparing and Ordering Integers*

Name the integer represented by each point on the number line.

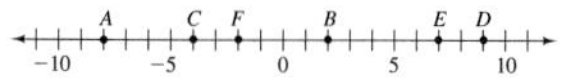

1. A −8 2. B 2 3. C −4 4. D 9 5. E 7 6. F −2

Compare. Use <, >, or =.

7. −8 [<] 8 8. 4 [>] −4 9. |5| [=] |−5| 10. −8 [<] 0

11. −6 [<] −2 12. −1 [>] −3 13. |−4| [>] 0 14. |−3| [>] 2

Graph each integer and its opposite on the number line.

15. −9

16. 5

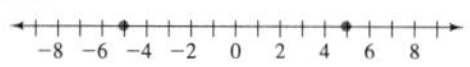

17. 6

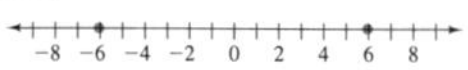

18. 7

19. 8

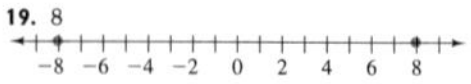

20. −2

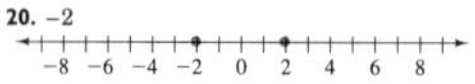

Find the value of each expression.

21. |2| 2 22. |−3| 3 23. |−38| 38 24. |−2 + 5| 3 25. |−44| 44

26. |5| + 4 9 27. |−5| + 4 9 28. |5 + 2| 7 29. |−16| 16 30. |3 − 7| 4

Write an integer to represent each situation.

31. A gain of 5 yards 5
32. A debt of $5 −5
33. 4 degrees below zero −4
34. A temperature of 100°F 100
35. 135 feet below sea level −135
36. A loss of $30 −30

Practice

In copymaster and workbook formats

RETEACHING

Reteaching 3-2 *Comparing and Ordering Integers*

The numbers 2 and −2 are opposites. The numbers 7 and −7 are opposites. Whole numbers and their opposites are called **integers**.

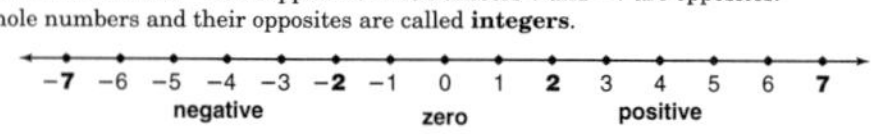

You can use the number line to compare integers.

−2 is less than 0.
−2 < 0

7 is greater than 2.
7 > 2

Numbers to the left are less. −2 is farther left than 0.	Numbers to the right are greater. 7 is farther right than 2.

The **absolute value** of an integer is its distance from zero on the number line. Distance is always positive.

The absolute value of −5 is 5.
|−5| = 5

The absolute value of 3 is 3.
|3| = 3

Compare using < or >.

1. 4 [>] 2 2. −3 [<] −2 3. 3 [>] −4
4. −1 [>] −2 5. 0 [<] 5 6. 0 [>] −4
7. −6 [<] 4 8. −8 [<] −2 9. 3 [>] 0
10. −7 [>] −10 11. −10 [<] 10 12. 1 [>] −1

Find each absolute value.

13. |−6| = 6 14. |3| = 3 15. |−8| = 8
16. |9| = 9 17. |−5| = 5 18. |0| = 0
19. |6| = 6 20. |−10| = 10 21. |−20| = 20

Use the number line above. Write the integers in order from least to greatest.

22. −4, 5, −2, 0, 1
−4, −2, 0, 1, 5

23. 6, −3, −5, 4, −6
−6, −5, −3, 4, 6

24. 3, −5, 4, −4, −7, 0
−7, −5, −4, 0, 3, 4

25. 1, 3, −7, −6, 5, −2
−7, −6, −2, 1, 3, 5

Reteaching

ENRICHMENT

Minds on Math Transparency

3-2

Janelle puts one piece of paper on top of another and cuts them both in half. She now has 4 pieces of paper. She stacks the pieces and cuts the stack in half to get 8 pieces of paper. Repeating this process, how many cuts will Janelle need to make in all to get 128 pieces of paper?

6 cuts

See *Solution Key* for worked-out answers.

WRAP UP

IDENTIFYING THE BIG IDEA Have students describe the difference between the absolute value of an integer and the opposite of an integer.

PROJECT LINK Have students brainstorm a list of decisions they need to make in order to design their game.

JOURNAL Students may wish to make a chart of similarities and differences.

LESSON QUIZ

Compare. Use <, >, or =.

1. 5 ■ −3 >
2. −9 ■ −6 <

Use a number line to find the opposite of the integer and the absolute value.

3. −7 7; 7
4. 4 −4; 4

Find the value of each expression.

28. $|8|$ 8 29. $|-11|$ 11 30. $|-16|$ 16 31. $|-1|$ 1 32. $|4|$ 4

33. $|4| + 3$ 7 34. $|-4| + 3$ 7 35. $|-1| + 3$ 4 36. $|-5| - 3$ 2 37. $|-2| + 2$ 4

Open-ended **Write an integer to make the statement true.** 38–46. Samples are given.

38. $-7 <$ ■ 0 39. $|12| <$ ■ 15 40. $-15 >$ ■ −16

41. $|-4| <$ ■ 5 42. ■ $= |-13|$ 13 43. $0 >$ ■ −2

44. $-357 <$ ■ −1 45. $|-253| <$ ■ 300 46. ■ $> |-6| + 1$ 8

47. Which integer is greater, −43 or 22? Which has the greater absolute value? Explain your reasoning. **22; −43; the absolute value of −43 is 43. The absolute value of 22 is 22. 43 > 22**

48. a. *Open-ended* Write three numbers that are between −3 and −4. **Numbers may vary. Sample: −3.1, −3.3, −3.55**
b. Are the numbers you wrote integers? Why or why not? **No; −4 and −3 are consecutive integers.**

JOURNAL
How is comparing and ordering integers similar to and different from comparing and ordering decimals? Give examples.

Mixed Review

Find each quotient. *(Previous Course)*

49. $8\overline{)296}$ 37 50. $5\overline{)3,245}$ 649 51. $93\overline{)6,882}$ 74 52. $82\overline{)22,960}$ 280 53. $71\overline{)39,902}$ 562

54. *Recreation* A family of four spends an average of $189.70 per day while on vacation. *(Lesson 3-1)*
a. Write a variable expression to express the amount a family would spend in any number of days. **d = number of days; 189.7d**
b. Use your expression to find the amount a family would spend in nine days. **$1,707.30**

CHAPTER PROJECT

PROJECT LINK: MAKING A DECISION

Choose a setting for your game board. Is the game in a cave, in a castle, in a person's digestive tract? Decide whether you want players to move by selecting cards, rolling number cubes, or both. Do you want the end of the game to be determined by the number of points someone has or by moving to an end square? **Check students' work.**

Extra Practice, Lesson 3-2, page 516

MATH TOOLBOX

In Lesson 3-2, students learned to order integers. This toolbox allows students to apply their knowledge to explore inequalities.

ERROR ALERT! Students may confuse the symbols "$<$" and "$\leq$". **Remediation:** Explain to students that the symbol "$<$" means *is less than*, "$\leq$" means *is less than or equal to*. The line under the symbol looks like half an equal sign and represents the possibility that the two numbers may be equal. It does not mean that the two numbers have to be equal.

ASSESSMENT Exercises 5–10 Have pairs of students compare their solutions. Ask students to describe to their partners the decisions they had to make to graph their number lines. If students find that their number lines are different, they can use the inequalities to check them by replacing the *x* in the inequality with the numbers on the lines that are different.

■ **ADDITIONAL PROBLEMS**

Which numbers are solutions of each inequality?

1. $x < -3$; $-5, -4, -3$ $-5, -4$

2. $x \geq -2$; $-3, -2, -1$ $-2, -1$

MATH TOOLBOX EXPLORATION

Exploring Inequalities

After Lesson 3-2

An *inequality* is a statement that compares two expressions. Sometimes an inequality contains a variable, like $x \geq 2$. All the values that make the inequality true are solutions of the inequality.

Inequality Symbols

- $<$ less than
- $>$ greater than
- $\leq$ less than or equal to
- $\geq$ greater than or equal to

■ **EXAMPLE 1**

Tell whether each number is a solution of $x \leq 2$: $-3, 0, 2, 4.5$.

$x \leq 2$ ← Use the inequality.

$-3 \leq 2$ $\quad 0 \leq 2$ $\quad 2 \leq 2$ $\quad 4.5 \leq 2$ ← Replace *x* with each number.

true $\quad$ true $\quad$ true $\quad$ false

The numbers -3, 0, and 2 are solutions of $x \leq 2$. The number 4.5 is not a solution.

You can graph solutions of an inequality on a number line.

■ **EXAMPLE 2**

Graph each inequality on a number line.

a. $x \geq -3$ $\qquad$ **b.** $x < 7$

Use a closed dot to show that *x* can equal -3.

Use an open dot to show that *x* cannot equal 7.

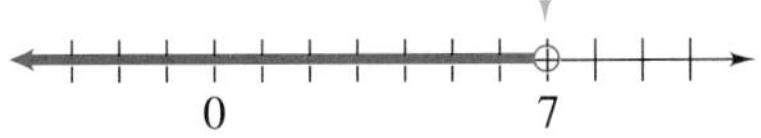

Which numbers are solutions of each inequality?

1. $x < 0$; $-3, 0, 5$ -3 $\quad$ **2.** $x > -4$; $-4, -2, 5$ $-2, 5$ $\quad$ **3.** $x \geq -7$; $-9, 0, 6$ $0, 6$ $\quad$ **4.** $x \leq 5$; $3, -1, -5$ $3, -1, -5$

Graph each inequality on a number line. 5–10. See margin.

5. $x \geq 8$ $\quad$ **6.** $x < -2$ $\quad$ **7.** $x \leq 1$ $\quad$ **8.** $x > -10$ $\quad$ **9.** $x < 3$ $\quad$ **10.** $x \geq -4$

11. *Writing* In your own words, tell how to graph an inequality on a number line. See margin.

Resources

Teaching Resources
Teaching Aids Master 26

Transparencies
11

page 101 Math Toolbox

5. 

6. 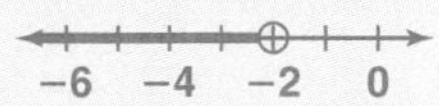

7. 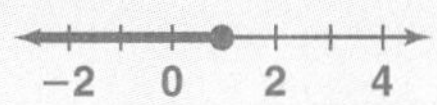

8. 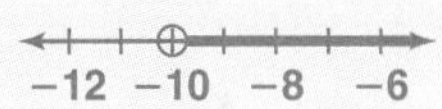

9. 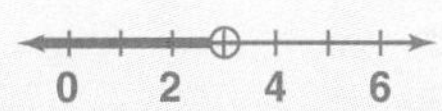

10. 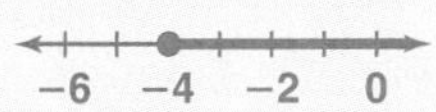

11. Answers may vary. Sample: Graph the number. Use an open dot for "greater than" or "less than" inequality. Use a closed dot for "greater than or equal to" or "less than or equal to" inequality. Shade the line to the left for "less than" or "less than or equal to" inequality. Shade the line to the right for "greater than" or "greater than or equal to" inequality.

1 Focus

CONNECTING TO PRIOR KNOWLEDGE Ask students questions to help them begin to develop an understanding of zero pairs. Use familiar situations and represent each with an integer. Ask students:

- *If you owe $7, how much money must you repay to owe $0?* $7; so −7 + 7 = 0
- *If the temperature is −3°F, how many degrees must the temperature rise to be 0°F?* 3°; so −3 + 3 = 0

2 Teach

THINK AND DISCUSS

VISUAL LEARNING Questions 3 and 4 It may be helpful for some students to draw a set of tiles for each question.

TACTILE LEARNING Question 5 Have students make stacks of one positive and one negative tile as they group zero pairs. Each stack represents zero. Students should only count the remaining unstacked tiles, noting whether they are positive or negative.

ERROR ALERT! Example 2 Students may choose the incorrect sign for the sum. **Remediation:** Have students circle the sign of the number with the greater absolute value. Explain that this is also the number that would require the greater amount of tiles.

Lesson Planning Options

Prerequisite Skills

- basic arithmetic (precourse)
- using a number line (precourse)
- absolute value (3-2)

Materials/Manipulatives

- algebra tiles
- bag
- number cubes
- calculator

Resources

Student Edition

Skills Handbook, p. 528
Extra Practice, p. 516
Glossary/Study Guide

Teaching Resources

Chapter Support File, Ch. 3
- Lesson Planner 3-3
- Practice 3-3, Reteaching 3-3
- Answer Masters 3-3

Teaching Aids Masters 26, 27
Glossary, Spanish Resources

Transparencies

11, 15, 83, Minds on Math 3-3

Warm Up

Evaluate $10 - \frac{c}{5}$ for $c = 10$. 8

2a.
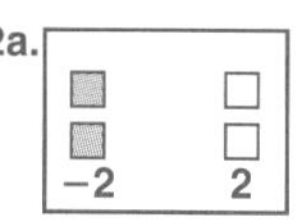

b.
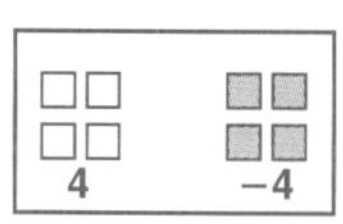

c.
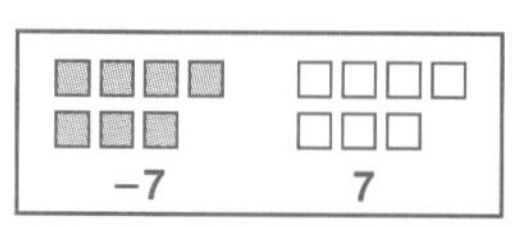

d.
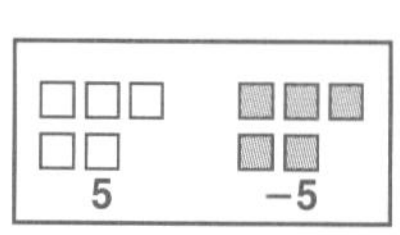

3-3 Using Models: Adding Integers

What You'll Learn

1. To use models to add integers
2. To use absolute value to add integers

...And Why

You can add integers to find how much you owe someone or how high a temperature is.

Here's How

Look for questions that
- build understanding
- ✔ check understanding

THINK AND DISCUSS

1 Adding Integers Using Models

Algebra tiles can help you understand integers.

▫ 1 positive   ■ −1 negative

1. *Modeling* Write the integer represented by each set of tiles.
   a. ▫▫ 2 b. ■■■ −3 c. ▫▫▫ 3 d. ■ −1
2. Draw a set of tiles to represent each integer and its opposite.
   a. −2 b. 4 c. −7 d. 5
   a–d. See left.

An equal number of positive and negative tiles represents zero.

▫■ ← a zero pair

You can write this as the number sentence $1 + (-1) = 0$.

3. *Think About It* Suppose you have 8 positive tiles. How many negative tiles do you need to represent zero? 8
4. Suppose you have 5 negative tiles. How many positive tiles do you need to represent zero? 5

EXAMPLE 1

Add $-8 + 3$.

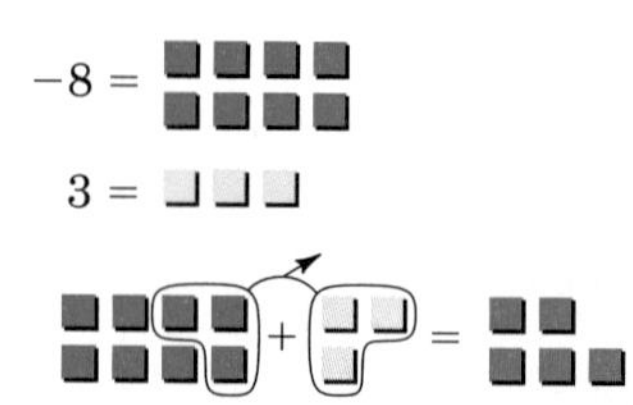

← Use tiles to represent each integer.
← Group and remove zero pairs.

$-8 + 3 = -5$ ← Simplify.

5. ✔ *Try It Out* Use tiles to find each sum.
   a. $5 + (-3)$ 2 b. $2 + (-5)$ −3 c. $-4 + (-3)$ −7

■ ADDITIONAL EXAMPLES

FOR EXAMPLE 1

Use tiles to add $4 + (-7)$. **−3**

FOR EXAMPLE 2

Use a number line to find $-6 + 8$. **2**

FOR EXAMPLE 3

The forecast for Kulusuk, Greenland, says the low temperature will be −13°F. The temperature is expected to rise only 6°F during the day. What is the expected high temperature? **−7°F**

Work Together

DIVERSITY Even though the activity does not state that the first partner with ten points is the winner, some students may interpret the directions this way. To make the activity less competitive, have the partners work together to determine which symbol to use. Each time they are correct, they receive one point. Repeat the activity until the team has 15 points.

EXTENSION If you have block scheduling or extended class periods, you can expand this activity by adding integers. One partner determines which number is greater, and the other partner finds the sum. Partners switch roles each time they choose new tiles. They receive one point for each correct answer until they have earned 20 points.

You can also use a number line to add integers.

■ EXAMPLE 2

Use a number line to find $-6 + 4$.

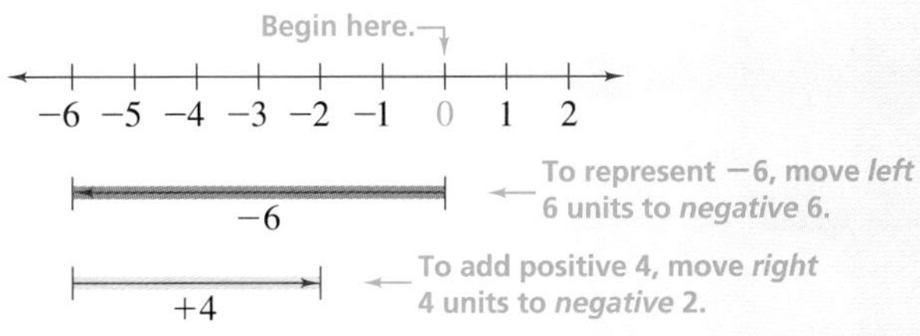

$-6 + 4 = -2$

PROBLEM SOLVING HINT

The first arrow below the number line represents the first integer in the expression.

a–c. See back of book.

6. ✓ *Try It Out* Draw a number line to find each sum.
   a. $-4 + 5$ b. $2 + (-5)$ c. $-1 + (-7)$

Now you may assign Exercises 1–22.

2 *Addition Using Absolute Value*

You can use absolute values to find the sum of two integers.

ADDING INTEGERS

The sum of two positive numbers is positive. The sum of two negative numbers is negative.

Examples: $3 + 5 = 8$ $-3 + (-5) = -8$

To add two numbers with different signs, find the *difference* between their absolute values. The sum has the same sign as the number with the greater absolute value.

Examples: $-3 + 5 = 2$ $3 + (-5) = -2$

■ EXAMPLE 3 *Real-World Problem Solving*

Weather During the day, the temperature in Fairbanks, Alaska, rose 17°F. The low temperature for the day was −18°F. What was the high temperature for the day?

$|-18| > |17|$ ← Compare the absolute values.

$|-18| - |17| = 18 - 17 = 1$ ← Find the difference.

$-18 + 17 = -1$ ← Because $|-18|$ is greater than $|17|$, the sum is negative.

The high temperature for the day was −1°F.

WHERE? January is the coldest month of the year in Fairbanks, Alaska, with an average daily temperature of −10°F. The average daily temperature in January in Honolulu, Hawaii, is 73°F.

Source: National Climatic Data Center and *USA Today Weather Almanac*

Technology Options

Prentice Hall Technology

Software for Learners

- Math Lab: Adding Integers
- Math Blaster® Mystery*
- Interactive Student Tutorial, Chapter 3*

Teaching Resource Software

- Computer Item Generator 3-3
- Resource Pro™ Chapter 3*

Internet • For related mathematics activities, visit the Prentice Hall site at www.phschool.com/math

**Available on CD-ROM only*

Assignment Options for Exercises On Your Own

To provide flexible scheduling, this lesson can be subdivided into parts.

1 **Core** 1–4, 6–22
Extension 5

2 **Core** 25–36, 38–47
Extension 23, 24, 37

Use Mixed Review to maintain skills.

ASSESSMENT Group students in pairs. Have each pair write three integer addition problems that have a sum equal to 5. Have partners use tiles to demonstrate the solution for the first problem, a number line for the second, and absolute values for the third. Have each pair share one of their sums with the class.

3 Practice/Assess

EXERCISES *On Your Own*

OPEN–ENDED Exercises 16–21 Encourage students to use a variety of combinations for each exercise. Suggest that students represent each integer at least once with tiles that are the same sign, and at least once with tiles that are opposite signs.

Exercise 5 Allow students to use tiles or to draw tiles to represent this exercise.

WRITING Exercise 24 Students may feel more comfortable writing about a specific problem such as $-3 + 8$.

MENTAL MATH Exercise 26 Ask students to give the values of $|-3|$ and (-3).

pages 104–105 On Your Own

16.
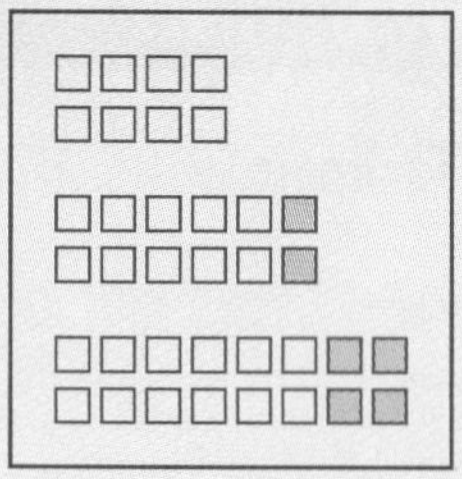

17.
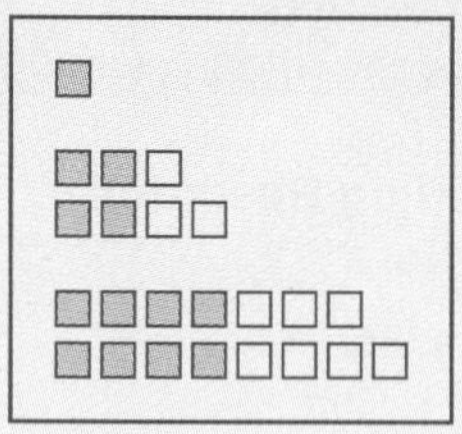

18.
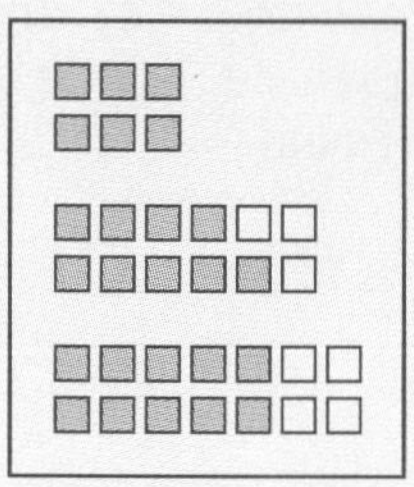

19.
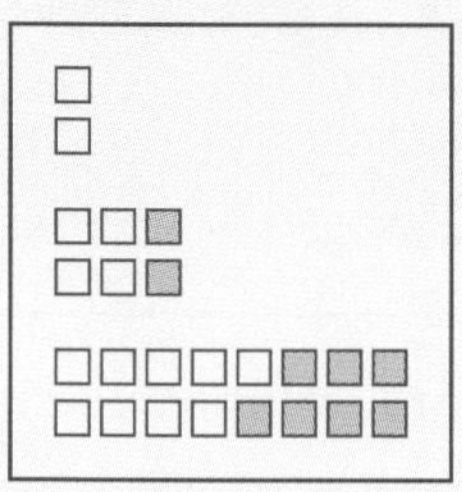

7. ✔ *Try It Out* Use absolute values to find each sum.
   a. $-19 + 34$ 15 b. $21 + (-39)$ −18 c. $-97 + (-65)$ −162

Work Together

Playing an Integer Game

Work with a partner. You will need two number cubes and a bag containing algebra tiles. Take turns rolling the number cubes.

The number you roll is the number of tiles you draw. For example, if you roll a 6 and a 1, you draw seven tiles from the bag. Place the tiles on the table without looking.

a–b. Check students' work.

8. a. Write the number represented by the tiles. Record it in a chart like the one at the right. Use <, >, or = to compare the values. The person with the lesser value scores 1 point.

Player 1	Player 2	Integer Sentence
−5	3	−5 < 3
■	■	■

   b. Repeat the activity until one of you has 10 points.

Now you may assign Exercises 23–47.

EXERCISES *On Your Own*

Write an expression for each model. Then find the sum.

1. 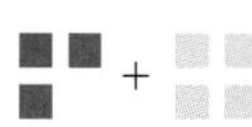
−3 + 4; 1

2. 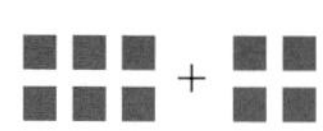
−6 + −4; −10

3. 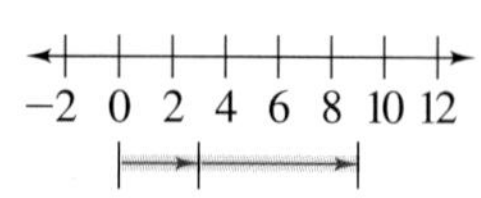

3 + 6; 9

4. 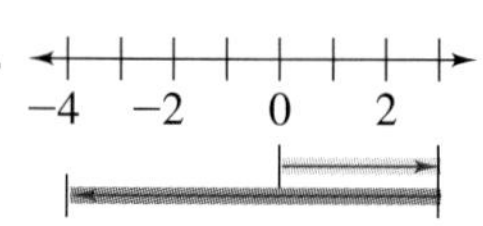

3 + (−7); −4

5. A set of tiles represents the integer 7. The set contains 4 negative tiles. How many positive tiles does it contain? 11

Find each sum.

6. $-5 + (-4)$ −9
7. $2 + (-8)$ −6
8. $-6 + 7$ 1
9. $12 + (-7)$ 5
10. $3 + (-3)$ 0
11. $-8 + (-1)$ −9
12. $7 + (-2)$ 5
13. $3 + (-12)$ −9
14. $-14 + 16$ 2
15. $-10 + 7$ −3

Open-ended **Sketch tiles to represent each integer in three different ways.** 16–19. See margin for samples.

16. 8
17. −1
18. −6
19. 2
20. 0
21. −9

20–21. See back of book for samples.

22. Nina uses the expression $t + 3$ to find the time in New York, where t stands for the time in Los Angeles. Find the time in New York when it is 5 P.M. in Los Angeles. 8 P.M.

WRAP UP

IDENTIFYING THE BIG IDEA Have students write the rules for adding two integers. Ask them to use −5, −3, 7, and 2 to give concrete examples of the rules using algebra tiles, a number line, and absolute value.

LESSON QUIZ

Find each sum. Support your answer by drawing tiles or a number line, or by using absolute value.

1. $5 + (-12)$ −7
2. $-7 + 13$ 6
3. $8 + 2$ 10
4. $-6 + (-8)$ −14

PRACTICE

Practice 3-3 *Using Models: Adding Integers*

Group zero pairs. Then write the addition equation for each model.

1. 4 + (−4) = 0
2. −3 + (−4) = −7
3. 7 + (−2) = 5
4. −5 + (−2) = −7
5. −4 + 2 = −2
6. 8 + (−4) = 4

Find each sum.

7. $-2 + (-3)$ −5
8. $8 - 7 + 4$ 5
9. $8 + (-5)$ 3
10. $15 + (-3)$ 12
11. $-16 + 8$ −8
12. $7 + (-10)$ −3
13. $-9 + (-5)$ −14
14. $-12 + 14$ 2

Sketch algebra tiles to represent each number in two different ways. Answers will vary. Samples given.

15. 1
16. 3
17. −2

Simplify each expression using mental math.

18. $3 + 8 + (-4)$ 7
19. $2 + |-3| + (-3)$ 2
20. $9 + 7 + (-6)$ 10
21. $56 + (-4) + (-58)$ −6
22. $-4 + 3 + (-2)$ −3
23. $|-8| + 15 + (-8)$ 15

Use absolute values to find each sum.

24. $43 + (-40)$ 3
25. $-12 + 12$ 0
26. $-25 + 16$ −9
27. $53 + (-33)$ 20
28. $127 + (-83)$ 44
29. $54 + (-96)$ −42
30. $-87 + (-56)$ −143
31. $-152 + 43$ −109

In copymaster and workbook formats

RETEACHING

Reteaching 3-3 *Using Models: Adding Integers*

To add integers using algebra tiles:	Add $-6 + (-2)$.	Add $-5 + 3$.
① Use algebra tiles to represent each integer.		
② Group zero pairs. An equal number of positive and negative tiles represent zero.	There are no zero pairs.	There are 3 zero pairs.
③ Simplify.	$-6 + (-2) = -8$	$-5 + 3 = -2$

Group zero pairs. Then complete the addition equation for each model.

1. 3 + −1 = 2
2. −2 + 5 = 3
3. −3 + 3 = 0

Find the sum.

4. $8 + (-2) =$ 6
5. $-9 + 4 =$ −5
6. $3 + (-2) =$ 1
7. $-1 + 11 =$ 10
8. $12 + 13 =$ 25
9. $-9 + 5 =$ −4
10. $7 + 2 =$ 9
11. $-1 + (-7) =$ −8
12. $-3 + 0 =$ −3
13. $-1 + (-1) =$ −2
14. $6 + 5 =$ 11
15. $3 + (-2) =$ 1
16. $-9 + 1 =$ −8
17. $-4 + (-1) =$ −5
18. $9 + (-2) =$ 7
19. $-5 + (-8) =$ −13
20. $23 + 0 =$ 23
21. $-17 + 2 =$ −15
22. $-11 + (-11) =$ −22
23. $-2 + 3 =$ 1
24. $-3 + 16 =$ 13

ENRICHMENT

Minds on Math Transparency 3-3

I am a three-digit number. The sum of my digits is 26. My last two digits are the same. What number am I?

899

See *Solution Key* for worked-out answers.

---

23. *Entertainment* How far below ground level will the roller coaster go? 35 ft

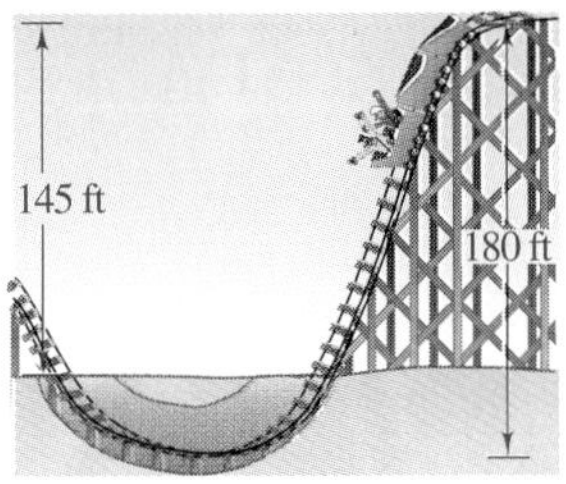

24. *Writing* Explain how you would find the sum of two integers that have different signs. See back of book.

Mental Math **Find the value of each expression.**

25. $4 + 7 + (-2)$ 9
26. $|-3| + 5 + (-3)$ 5
27. $28 + (-12) + (-26)$ −10

Evaluate each expression for $n = 6$.

28. $3.4 + n$ 9.4
29. $-3.4 + n$ 2.6
30. $-n + 3.4$ −2.6
31. $-n + (-3.4)$ −9.4

Use the associative property of addition to simplify.

32. $-3 + (-7 + 13)$ 3
33. $5 + (-5 + 12)$ 12
34. $-12 + (-8 + 6)$ −14
35. $(-4 + 10) + (-10)$ −4

Choose **Use a calculator, paper and pencil, or mental math. Write an expression for each situation. Find the value of the expression.**

36. *Money* On Friday Rosa borrowed \$10 from her sister. The next day she paid back \$5. Then on Monday she borrowed \$4 more. How much does Rosa owe? 10 − 5 + 4 = 9; \$9

37. *Weather* At midnight, the temperature was −12°F. By 6 A.M. the next morning the temperature had risen 19 degrees. What was the temperature at 6 A.M.? −12 + 19 = 7; 7°F

Find each sum.

38. $27 + (-24)$ 3
39. $42 + (-42)$ 0
40. $-15 + 20$ 5
41. $-13 + 7$ −6
42. $28 + (-32)$ −4
43. $126 + (-92)$ 34
44. $68 + (-72)$ −4
45. $-99 + 137$ 38
46. $-50 + 48$ −2
47. $74 + (-25)$ 49

Mixed Review

Make a stem-and-leaf plot for each data set. *(Lesson 1-5)*

48. 39, 37, 47, 50, 56, 58 See above right.

48.

3	7 9
4	7
5	0 6 8

5 | 0 means 50

49. 2.43, 2.44, 2.48, 2.57, 2.49, 2.62, 2.53, 2.50 See below.

Compare. Use <, >, or =. *(Lesson 3-2)*

50. −4 ■ −10 >
51. 5 ■ −6 >
52. |−3| ■ |3| =
53. |16| ■ |−23| <

54. *Choose a Strategy* The pages of a book are numbered from 1 to 128. How many page numbers contain the digit 6? 22 pages

49.

24	3 4 8 9
25	0 3 7
26	2

26 | 2 means 2.62

3-4 Teaching Notes

1 Focus

CONNECTING TO PRIOR KNOWLEDGE Ask students to think about how they used subtraction to add integers. Have them describe how they might model the subtraction of integers.

2 Teach

THINK AND DISCUSS

CONNECTION TO SCIENCE Discuss the difference between the Fahrenheit and Celsius temperature scales. Explain that water freezes at 32°F, or 0°C.

Example 2 Ask students: *Why are you able to add zero pairs and not affect the value of the answer?* **A number plus zero equals the same number.**

REASONING Example 2 Ask students: *Would the value of 4 − 6 change if you added only two positive tiles?* **yes** *Only two negative tiles?* **yes** *Explain.* **Two positive tiles would increase the value by 2. Two negative tiles would decrease the value by 2.**

ASSESSMENT Have students choose a number from 1 to 5. Then subtract 2, −3, 4, and −1 from the number they chose. When everyone has finished, have them find another student who started with the same number, and work with that partner to check each other's answer.

Lesson Planning Options

Prerequisite Skills

- finding opposites (3-2)
- adding integers (3-3)
- using inverse operations (precourse)

Materials/Manipulatives

- algebra tiles

Resources

Student Edition

Skills Handbook, p. 528
Extra Practice, p 516
Glossary/Study Guide

Teaching Resources

Chapter Support File, Ch. 3
- Lesson Planner 3-4
- Practice 3-4, Reteaching 3-4
- Answer Masters 3-4

Teaching Aids Masters 26, 27
Glossary, Spanish Resources

Transparencies
11, 15, 83, Minds on Math 3-4

Warm Up

Evaluate each expression:
24 − 6 ÷ 2 · 4 + 36 **48**
6 · (3 − 1) + 18 **30**
10 + 6 · 5 − 4 ÷ 2 **38**

3-4 Subtracting Integers

What You'll Learn

1. To use models to subtract integers
2. To use a rule to subtract integers

...And Why

You can subtract integers to find the difference in temperatures.

Here's How

Look for questions that
- build understanding
- ✔ check understanding

THINK AND DISCUSS

1 Using Models to Subtract Integers

The coldest recorded temperature for Sacramento is −5°C. The coldest recorded temperature for San Diego is −2°C. To find the difference in temperature of these California cities, you subtract.

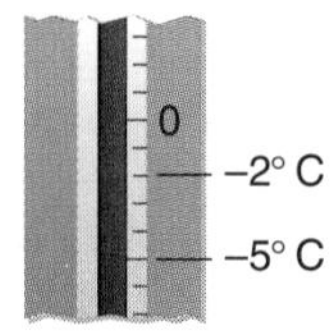

1. Which expression describes subtracting −2 from −5: −2 − (−5) *or* −5 − (−2)? **−5 − (−2)**

Algebra tiles can help you understand how to subtract integers.

EXAMPLE 1

Use algebra tiles to find −5 − (−2).

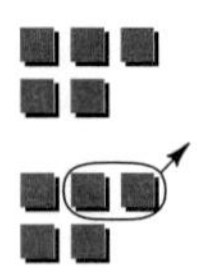

← Start with 5 negative tiles.

← Take away 2 negative tiles. There are 3 negative tiles left.

−5 − (−2) = −3

2. ✔ *Try It Out* Use algebra tiles to find each difference.
   a. −7 − (−2) **−5** b. 5 − 3 **2** c. −5 − (−4) **−1**

EXAMPLE 2

Find 4 − 6.

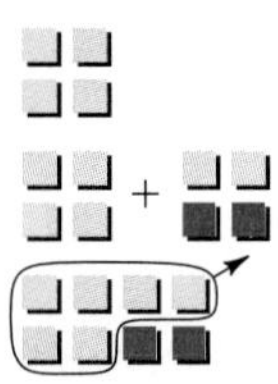

← Start with 4 positive tiles.

← There are not enough positive tiles to take 6 away. Add 2 zero pairs.

← Take away 6 positive tiles. There are 2 negative tiles left.

4 − 6 = −2

ADDITIONAL EXAMPLES

FOR EXAMPLE 1

Use algebra tiles to find $-10 - (-6)$. -4

FOR EXAMPLE 2

Use algebra tiles to find $3 - 8$. -5

FOR EXAMPLE 3

On a day in December, Lynn flew from Los Angeles to Beijing. The temperature in Los Angeles was 16°C when she left. The temperature was −6°C when she arrived. What is the difference between these temperatures? 22°

ERROR ALERT! Question 6a Students may confuse a positive number following a minus sign with the negative number. **Remediation:** Guide students to understand that the 7 in $3 - 7$ is a positive number. Point out that negative numbers following a minus sign are usually in parentheses. For example, in Question 6b: $-2 - (-8)$.

CONNECTION TO SCIENCE and BUSINESS
Before students work the exercises, you may want to discuss how people use subtraction of integers in the following career fields.

- **Science:** finding differences in temperatures, ocean tide levels, depths of mineral deposits
- **Business:** finding the difference in stock prices and interest rates, accounting debits and credits

WHERE? GEOGRAPHY Death Valley, in southeastern California, lies near the Nevada border. It is the hottest and driest region of North America.

Source: *Encyclopedia Brittanica*

3. ✔ *Try It Out* Use algebra tiles to find each difference.
   a. $4 - 7$ -3 b. $-1 - 5$ -6 c. $7 - (-5)$ 12 d. $-6 - 10$ -16

Now you may assign Exercises 1–15, 29.

2 *Using a Rule to Subtract Integers*

To subtract integers, look for a pattern in related addition and subtraction problems.

4. *Modeling* Use algebra tiles to find each difference and sum.
   a. $5 - 3$ 2; $5 + (-3)$ 2 b. $-9 - (-6)$ -3; $-9 + 6$ -3 c. $4 - (-5)$ 9; $4 + 5$ 9

5. *Patterns* What do you notice about the sums and differences in Question 4? They are the same.

The patterns you investigated in Questions 4 and 5 lead to a rule for subtraction.

SUBTRACTING INTEGERS

To subtract an integer, add its opposite.

Examples: $3 - 5 = 3 + (-5) = -2$
$-3 - 5 = -3 + (-5) = -8$

EXAMPLE 3 *Real-World Problem Solving*

Temperature The highest temperature recorded in the United States was 134°F, measured at Death Valley, California. The coldest temperature, −80°F, was recorded at Prospect Creek, Alaska. What is the difference between these temperatures?

$134 - (-80) = 134 + 80$ ← To subtract −80, add its opposite, 80.
$= 214$

The difference between the highest and lowest temperatures recorded in the United States is 214 degrees.

6. ✔ *Try It Out* Find each difference.
   a. $3 - 7$ -4 b. $-2 - (-8)$ 6 c. $17 - 9$ 8 d. $-23 - 18$ -41

7. Temperatures in Verkhoyansk, Russia, have ranged from a low of −90°F to a high of 98°F. Find the temperature range in Verkhoyansk. 188°F

Now you may assign Exercises 16–28, 30–71.

Technology Options

Prentice Hall Technology

Software for Learners
- Hot Page™ 4–4*
- Math Blaster® Mystery*
- Interactive Student Tutorial, Chapter 3*

Teaching Resource Software
- Computer Item Generator 3-4
- Resource Pro™ Chapter 3*

Internet • For related mathematics activities, visit the Prentice Hall site at www.phschool.com/math

*Available on CD-ROM only

Assignment Options for Exercises On Your Own

To provide flexible scheduling, this lesson can be subdivided into parts.

1 **Core** 1–15
Extension 29

2 **Core** 16–28, 30–36, 38–49, 54–70
Extension 37, 50–53, 71

Use Mixed Review to maintain skills.

ERROR ALERT! Students may fail to add the opposite of a number when subtracting integers. **Remediation:** Remind students that subtracting is the opposite of adding. Since they are performing the *opposite* operation, they first must find the *opposite* of the second number before they perform the operation.

3 Practice/Assess

EXERCISES *On Your Own*

Exercises 9–28 Encourage students to answer the exercises on paper by rewriting the differences as addition problems. Have them use algebra tiles or draw models to check answers.

AEP VISUAL LEARNING Exercise 30 Some students may not understand the term *ground level.* Draw a sketch showing a cross section of the snow and ground level. This will help students see that the lower temperature is above the level of the ground.

DIVERSITY Exercise 37 Have students with visual impairments work with a partner for these exercises. Have the partner describe the data in the charts to the visually impaired student.

pages 108–109 On Your Own

1.
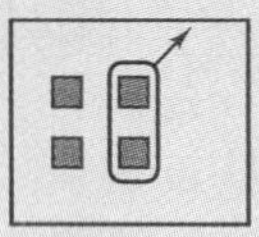

2.
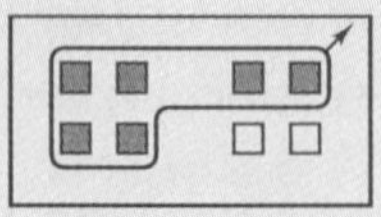

3.

4.
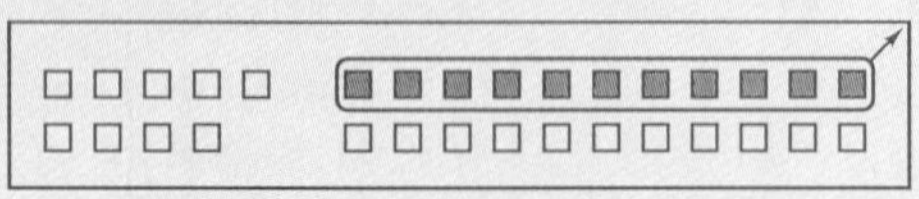

5.
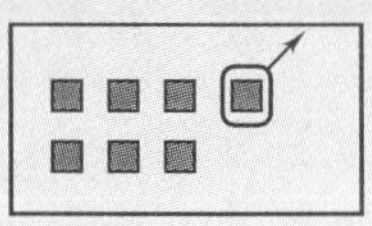

6.

7.
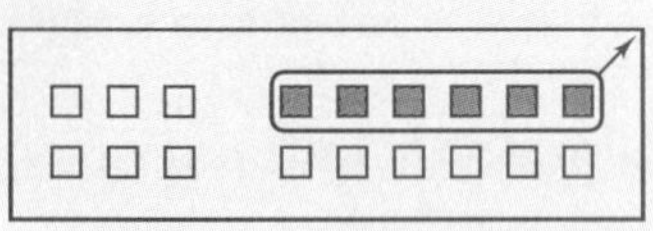

8.
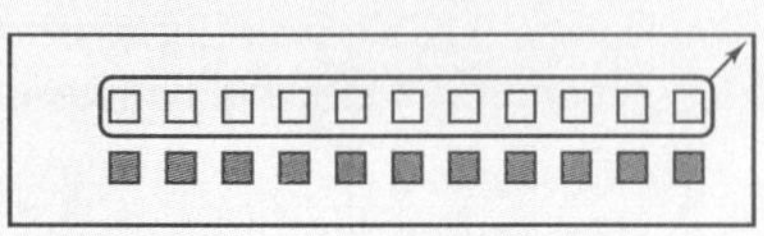

EXERCISES *On Your Own*

Draw models to find each difference. 1–8. See margin for diagrams.

1. $-4 - (-2)$ −2
2. $-4 - (-6)$ 2
3. $3 - 9$ −6
4. $9 - (-11)$ 20
5. $-7 - (-1)$ −6
6. $-8 - 12$ −20
7. $6 - (-6)$ 12
8. $0 - 11$ −11

Find each difference.

9. $12 - (-4)$ 16
10. $-7 - 3$ −10
11. $-15 - 2$ −17
12. $-3 - (-3)$ 0
13. $2 - 5$ −3
14. $1 - (-7)$ 8
15. $-5 - (-9)$ 4
16. $270 - 35$ 235
17. $47 - 151$ −104
18. $-3 - 9$ −12
19. $17 - (-8)$ 25
20. $20 - (-8)$ 28
21. $-14 - (-14)$ 0
22. $-100 - 150$ −250
23. $-10 - (-18)$ 8
24. $589 - 635$ −46
25. $-121 - 98$ −219
26. $0 - (-22)$ 22
27. $-54 - 82$ −136
28. $-8 - (-12)$ 4

29. **Choose A, B, C, or D.** At 8 P.M. the wind speed was 10 miles per hour (mi/h). The wind-chill temperature was −9°F. One hour later, the wind speed had increased to 25 mi/h. The wind-chill temperature had fallen to −29°F. Which number sentence below shows this change? B
    A. $29 + (-9) = 20$ B. $-29 - (-9) = -20$ C. $-9 - (-29) = 20$ D. $-29 - 9 = -38$

30. *Temperature* A scientist measured the temperature at the surface of a 7-inch-deep snowbank. The temperature was −27°F. At ground level the temperature was 24°F. How much warmer was the temperature at ground level? 51°F

Write the related addition expression for each subtraction expression. Then find its value.

31. $-9 - (-6)$ $-9 + 6$; −3
32. $6 - 11$ $6 + (-11)$; −5
33. $5 - (-3)$ $5 + 3$; 8
34. $-2 - (-5)$ $-2 + 5$; 3
35. $1 - (-9)$ $1 + 9$; 10
36. $-16 - 17$ $-16 + (-17)$; −33

37. *Finance* The chart at the right shows the changes in a stock price each day.
    a. The opening price of the stock on Monday was $25. What was the closing price on Tuesday? $30
    b. How much did the stock price change during the week? $13
    c. What was the average daily change? $2.60

Stock Activity

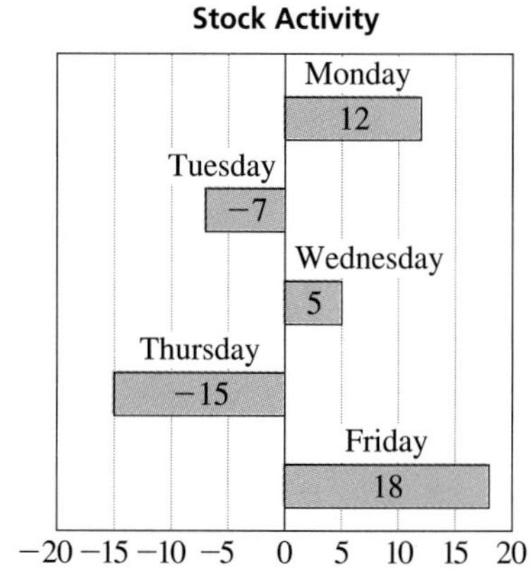

ESTIMATION Exercises 54–65 Remind students that their estimates may include a sign.

EXTENSION Exercises 66–69 You may want to give students the opportunity to subtract negative decimal numbers. For example:

- 68.7 − (−8.9) **77.6**
- −22.7 − 1.1 **−23.8**
- −30 − (−8.9) **−21.1**

CONNECTION TO SCIENCE Exercises 66–69 These exercises require students to compare the boiling points of different elements.

WRITING Exercise 70 Have students compare their explanations. Discuss the strategies that students mention.

REASONING Exercise 71 Encourage students to use algebra tiles to test examples for each sentence.

WRAP UP

IDENTIFYING THE BIG IDEA Ask students to use models to subtract integers. Have them describe a rule they can use to subtract integers.

PROJECT LINK Hint to students that they may want to determine the total number of spaces to include on the game board before they create rules for movement. For example, if there are only 12

Mental Math **Find the value of each expression.**

38. $-4 + 5 - (-4)$ 5 **39.** $-3 - (-3) + (-6)$ −6 **40.** $7 + (-7) + 5$ 5 **41.** $6 - 13 - (-13)$ 6

42. $-8 + 4 - (-8)$ 4 **43.** $-2 + (-3) - (-5)$ 0 **44.** $-11 - (-3) + 11$ 3 **45.** $-3 + 10 + (-7)$ 0

46. $21 - 12 + (-21)$ −12 **47.** $7 - (-4) - (-3)$ 14 **48.** $19 - (-7) + 1$ 27 **49.** $2 + 8 - (-2)$ 12

Without calculating, determine whether each difference is positive or negative.

50. $-18 - 25$ negative **51.** $9 - (-2)$ positive **52.** $46 - (-65)$ positive **53.** $-7 - (-13)$ positive

Estimation **Round each number. Then estimate the sum or difference.** 54–65. Estimates may vary. Samples are given.

54. $124 - 238$ −120 **55.** $-53 + (-110)$ −160 **56.** $122 - 16$ 100 **57.** $22 - (-7)$ 29

58. $-74 - 52$ −120 **59.** $-1{,}302 - 2{,}305$ −3,600 **60.** $16 - 23$ 0 **61.** $-52 - (-104)$ 52

62. $-78 + (-97)$ −180 **63.** $258 + (-167)$ 90 **64.** $-38 + 17$ −20 **65.** $-295 - (-82)$ −213

Science **Use the data at the right for Exercises 66–69.**

66. How much less than the boiling temperature of carbon is the boiling temperature of gold? **2,020°C**

67. How much greater than the boiling temperature of chlorine is the boiling temperature of iodine? **218.95°C**

68. How much less than the boiling temperature of mercury is the boiling temperature of helium? **625.514°C**

69. How much greater than the boiling temperature of helium is the boiling temperature of chlorine? **234.334°C**

Boiling Point

Element	Temperature (Celsius)
Carbon	4827
Chlorine	−34.6
Gold	2807
Helium	−268.934
Iodine	184.35
Mercury	356.58
Water	100

Source: *Information Please Almanac*

70. *Writing* In your own words, explain how you add and subtract integers. Use examples. **See margin.**

71. *Reasoning* Tell if each of the subtraction sentences would *always, sometimes,* or *never* be true. Support your answer with examples. **a–f. Numbers may vary. Samples are given.**

a. (positive) − (positive) = (positive) **b.** (negative) − (positive) = (negative)
c. (negative) − (negative) = (positive) **d.** (positive) − (negative) = (negative)
e. (negative) − (positive) = (positive) **f.** (positive) − (positive) = (negative)

a. sometimes; 2 − 1 = 1, 2 − 3 = −1 b. always; −1 − 1 = −2
c. sometimes; −2 − (−1) = −1, −2 − (−3) = 1 d. never; 1 − (−1) = 2
e. never; −1 − 1 = −2 f. sometimes; 2 − 1 = 1, 2 − 3 = −1

CHECKPOINT 1

Checkpoint 1

Lessons 3-1 through 3-4

Use the data from the table at the right for Exercises 1 and 2.

1. Write a variable expression to show the number of baseball cards in k packages. **8k**

2. Write a variable expression for the sum of the number of hockey cards in h packages and the number of basketball cards in b packages. **7h + 10b**

Sports Cards	
Sport	Cards per Package
Baseball	8
Basketball	10
Hockey	7
Football	12
Wrestling	5

Evaluate each expression for $s = 3$ and $t = 5$.

3. $st + 1$ 16 **4.** $t(s - 1)$ 10 **5.** $4t - 2.5s$ 12.5 **6.** $21 - s - t$ 13

Find the value of each expression.

7. $-8 + 10$ 2 **8.** $-6 - 12$ −18 **9.** $-25 + 14$ −11 **10.** $7 - (-6)$ 13

70. Check students' work. Sample: To add two integers with the same sign, find the sum of the absolute values. The sum has the same sign as both of the integers. Example: −4 + (−5) = −9. To add two integers with different signs, find the difference between the absolute values. The sum has the sign of the integer with the greater absolute value. Examples: −4 + 5 = 1 and 4 + (−5) = −1. To subtract an integer, add its opposite. Examples: −4 − 5 = −4 + (−5) = −9 and −4 − (−5) = −4 + 5 = 1

PRACTICE

Practice 3-4 Subtracting Integers

Use >, <, or = to complete each statement.

1. $-9 - (-11)$ [>] 0 2. $-17 + 20$ [>] 0 3. $11 - (-4)$ [>] 0 4. $-19 + 16$ [<] 0
5. $28 - 19$ [>] 0 6. $52 + (-65)$ [<] 0 7. $-28 - (-28)$ [=] 0 8. $-28 - (-53)$ [>] 0

Choose a calculator, paper and pencil, or mental math to subtract.

9. $9 - 26$ **−17**
10. $-4 - 15$ **−19**
11. $21 - (-7)$ **28**
12. $27 - (-16)$ **43**
13. $-16 - (-43)$ **27**
14. $47 - 19$ **28**
15. $-156 - 98$ **−254**
16. $-192 - 47$ **−239**
17. $0 - (-51)$ **51**
18. $-63 - 89$ **−152**
19. $-12 - (-21)$ **9**
20. $92 - (-16)$ **108**
21. $72 - 15$ **57**
22. $-86 - (-19)$ **−67**
23. $17 - (-46)$ **63**
24. $-78 - (-53)$ **−25**

Solve.

25. The highest and lowest temperatures ever recorded in Africa are 136°F and −11°F. The highest temperature was recorded in Libya, and the lowest temperature was recorded in Morocco. What is the difference in these temperature extremes? **147°F**

26. The highest and lowest temperatures ever recorded in South America are 120°F and −27°F. Both the highest and lowest temperatures were recorded in Argentina. What is the difference in these temperature extremes? **147°F**

Find each difference. Ignore any negative signs when placing the result in the puzzle.

Across	Down
1. $18 - (-8)$	2. $-72 - (-9)$
3. $-156 - 78$	3. $-125 - 88$
5. $451 - 110$	4. $58 - 11$
8. $120 - (-15)$	6. $592 - 175$
10. $-450 - 77$	7. $-93 - (-48)$
12. $-8 - 18$	9. $126 - 74$
14. $128 - (-375)$	11. $-112 - 98$
15. $94 - 13$	13. $-102 - (-743)$

1. 2	2. 6	■	3. 2	3	4. 4
■	5. 3	6. 4	1	■	7
7. 4	■	8. 1	3	9. 5	■
10. 5	11. 2	7	■	12. 2	13. 6
■	1	■	■	■	4
14. 5	0	3	■	15. 8	1

Practice

In copymaster and workbook formats

RETEACHING

Reteaching 3-4 Subtracting Integers

Subtract $6 - (-3)$ using algebra tiles.

① Start with 6 positive tiles.

② There are no negative tiles. Add 3 zero pairs.

③ Take away 3 negative tiles. There are 9 positive tiles left.

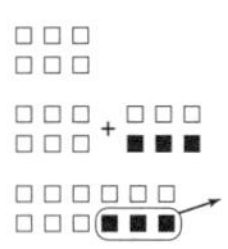

$6 - (-3) = 9$

You can also use this rule:
To subtract integers, add the opposite.

$6 - (-3)$ ← **The opposite of −3 is 3.**
$6 + 3$ ← **Add the opposite.**
$6 + 3 = 9$

Complete the subtraction equation for each model.

1. 
$-8 - 3 =$ **−11**

2. 
$8 - (-3) =$ **11**

3. 
$-4 - 2 =$ **−6**

Complete.

4. $-3 - 4$ Change to addition: $-3 +$ **(−4)** = **−7**
5. $5 - 2$ Change to addition: $5 +$ **(−2)** = **3**
6. $-6 - (-10)$ Change to addition: $-6 +$ **10** = **4**
7. $8 - (-2)$ Change to addition: $8 +$ **2** = **10**

Find each difference.

8. $4 - 5 =$ **−1**
9. $-5 - 4 =$ **−9**
10. $-8 - (-7) =$ **−1**
11. $19 - (-6) =$ **25**
12. $-10 - 12 =$ **−22**
13. $-12 - 10 =$ **−22**
14. $-4 - (-5) =$ **1**
15. $-2 - (-3) =$ **1**
16. $9 - (-7) =$ **16**
17. $0 - 3 =$ **−3**
18. $6 - 8 =$ **−2**
19. $0 - (-10) =$ **10**

Reteaching

ENRICHMENT

Minds on Math Transparency

3-4

The counting numbers are arranged in a triangle array as begun below. In what row is the number 50?

```
      1
     2 3
    4 5 6
  7 8 9 10
```

10th row

See *Solution Key* for worked-out answers.

spaces, they may not want to use "Fly in an airplane. Move +10 spaces."

LESSON QUIZ

1. 22 − 30 **−8**
2. 6 − (−8) **14**
3. −12 − 11 **−23**
4. −3 − (−1) **−2**

Mixed Review

Find each sum. *(Lesson 3-3)*

72. $-9 + 6$ **−3**
73. $15 + (-4)$ **11**
74. $90 + (-73)$ **17**
75. $-50 + (-22)$ **−72**
76. $84 + (-38)$ **46**

Divide. *(Lesson 2-6)*

77. $1.2 \div 0.6$ **2**
78. $39 \div 1.3$ **30**
79. $14.7 \div 3.5$ **4.2**
80. $45.14 \div 3.7$ **12.2**
81. $174.22 \div 3.1$ **56.2**

82. ***Choose a Strategy*** Dwana is in training for a marathon. The first week she runs 1 mi each day, the second week 2 mi each day, and the third week 3 mi each day. If she continues in this way, how many total miles will she have run at the end of 5 weeks? **105 mi**

CHAPTER PROJECT

PROJECT LINK: DESIGNING

Make a draft of your game board. Add details. Use integers to determine positive and negative points or positive and negative movement on the game board. Think of adventures and misadventures for your game like "Catch a falling star. Get +10 points" or "Fall off a cliff. Move −7 spaces."

Check student's work.

✓ CHECKPOINT 1

Lessons 3-1 through 3-4

Use the data from the table at the right.

1. a. Write a variable expression to find the plums in p boxes. **6p**
   b. Evaluate the expression from part (a) for $p = 4$; $p = 10$. **24; 60**
2. Write a variable expression for the sum of the number of apples in a bags and the number of tomatoes in t boxes. **10a + 8t**

Farmer's Market Produce

Produce	Package
Apples	10 per bag
Daisies	12 per bunch
Green beans	2-lb bag
Plums	6 per box
Tomatoes	8 per box

Evaluate each expression for $p = 7$ and $q = 6$.

3. $4(p - 2)$ **20**
4. $18 - 3q$ **0**
5. $pq \div 14$ **3**
6. $3.2(p + q)$ **41.6**

Find the value of each expression.

7. $-5 + 9$ **4**
8. $-6 + (-3)$ **−9**
9. $8 + (-4)$ **4**
10. $-27 + 4$ **−23**
11. $14 + (-23)$ **−9**
12. $3 - (-2)$ **5**
13. $-7 - (-4)$ **−3**
14. $-17 - 12$ **−29**
15. $14 - 19$ **−5**
16. $-23 - (-29)$ **6**

Extra Practice, Lesson 3-4, page 516

MATH TOOLBOX

In Lesson 3-4, students learned how to subtract integers. This toolbox allows students to apply their knowledge to using a computer spreadsheet format.

ERROR ALERT! Some students may have difficulty carrying the previous balance forward to the next row. **Remediation:** You may want to have students copy the spreadsheet onto their own paper and add a column between A and B headed "Previous Balance." This will allow students to start each new row with the final balance from the previous row.

ASSESSMENT Have students work in pairs to write their own beginning balance and entries for a checking account. Let them exchange "checkbook registers" with another pair, then find the account balance after each entry.

■ **ADDITIONAL PROBLEM**

Have students add an additional row to the spreadsheet. Have them use today's date, and post a deposit of $200 and a withdrawal of $100. Find the new balance.

50 + 200 − 100 = 150

MATH TOOLBOX

TECHNOLOGY

Using Spreadsheets

After Lesson 3-4

You can use a computer spreadsheet to keep track of the balance in a checking account. You add deposits and subtract checks. You can compute values in cells in a spreadsheet.

■ **EXAMPLE**

Use the spreadsheet. Find the balance after each entry.

	A	B	C	D
1	Date	Deposits	Checks	Balance
2				$350
3	4/29	$100		■
4	4/30		$400	■

Use the formula = D2+B3. The computer finds 350 + 100 = 450.

Use the formula = D3−C4. The computer finds 450 − 400 = 50.

The first balance is $450. The second balance is $50.

1. $224.02, = D2 − C3; −$15.38, = D3 − C4; $106.62, = D4 + B5; $51.97, = D5 − C6; $401.97, = D6 + B7; $238.17, = D7 − C8

Use the spreadsheet at the right.

	A	B	C	D
1	Date	Deposits	Checks	Balance
2				$250
3	11/3		25.98	■
4	11/9		239.40	■
5	11/10	122.00		■
6	11/13		54.65	■
7	11/20	350.00		■
8	11/29		163.80	■

1. Find the account balance after each entry. Write the formulas you used. See right.
2. **Choose A, B, C, or D.** Which formula could you use to find the balance in cell D9 regardless of whether a check had been written or a deposit had been made? D

   A. =D8−B9+C9 B. =D8−B9−C9
   C. =D8+B9+C9 D. =D8+B9−C9
3. *Reasoning* Suppose the balance in cell D9 is $130.34. Was the amount of a deposit entered into cell B9, or was the amount of a check entered into cell C9? Support your answer. Check in C9; the balance decreased.
4. *Writing* Consider your answer to Exercise 2. Explain why the formula you chose works, and give examples. See margin.

Materials/Manipulatives

- computer
- spreadsheet software

Resources

Teaching Resources

Teaching Aids Master 5

Transparencies

3

page 111 Math Toolbox

4. The formula = D8 + B9 − C9 starts with the previous balance (D8), adds any deposit (B9), and subtracts any checks (C9) to find the new balance. Check students' work for examples.

3-5 Teaching Notes

1 Focus

CONNECTING TO PRIOR KNOWLEDGE Have students recall what they know about the relationship between the multiplication and division of whole numbers. Ask students: *Use the multiplication sentence 3 · 4 = 12 to write two division sentences.*
12 ÷ 4 = 3; 12 ÷ 3 = 4

2 Teach

THINK AND DISCUSS

You may want to help students recall that 3 × (−4), 3 • (−4), (3)(−4), and 3(−4) are all ways to indicate multiplication.

Question 3 The patterns shown allow most students to formulate the algorithms for multiplication with ease. For some students, you may also wish to use tiles to model the product of two negative integers; however, this process may be challenging for some, because the two negative signs must be interpreted differently. For example, to use tiles to model –2(–5), have students remove 2 groups of 5 negative tiles. First, they must introduce 10 zero pairs. Then remove the 2 groups of 5 negative tiles. There are 10 positive tiles left, so –2(–5) = 10.

ERROR ALERT! Students may confuse the rules for adding with the rules for multiplying. **Remediation:** Have students make a chart to show the two operations and their different rules.

Lesson Planning Options

Prerequisite Skills

- multiplication of whole numbers (precourse)
- using the commutative property (2-5)
- using inverse operations (precourse)

Materials/Manipulatives

- cardboard
- markers

Resources

Student Edition

Skills Handbook, pp. 530, 531
Extra Practice, p. 516
Glossary/Study Guide

Teaching Resources

Chapter Support File, Ch. 3
- Lesson Planner 3-5
- Practice 3-5, Reteaching 3-5
- Answer Masters 3-5

Teaching Aids Masters 26, 27
Glossary, Spanish Resources

Transparencies
11, 15, Minds on Math 3-5

Warm Up

For 3 weeks, Jessica worked 2 hours per day, 4 days per week baby sitting. If she earned $3.50 per hour, how much did she earn in all? **$84.00**

3-5 Multiplying and Dividing Integers

What You'll Learn

1. To multiply integers
2. To divide integers

...And Why

Stockbrokers use integers to describe changes in the price of stock.

Here's How

Look for questions that
- build understanding
- ✔ check understanding

QUICK review

Commutative Property
ab = *ba*

3c.
−2 (3) = −6
−2 (2) = −4
−2 (1) = −2
−2 (0) = 0
−2 (−1) = 2
−2 (−2) = 4
−2 (−3) = 6
−2 (−4) = 8
−2 (−5) = 10

−4(3) = ■ −12
−4(2) = ■ −8
−4(1) = ■ −4
−4(0) = ■ 0
−4(−1) = ■ 4
−4(−2) = ■ 8
−4(−3) = ■ 12

THINK AND DISCUSS

1 Multiplying Integers

Suppose a cave explorer descends 4 ft/min for 3 min. You can use negative tiles to model the explorer's descent. Show 3 groups of 4 negative tiles.

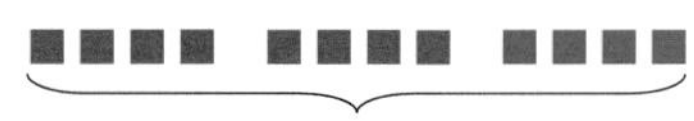

3(−4) = −12. The explorer descends 12 ft.

You can use the commutative property to find −4(3).

−4(3) = 3(−4) = −12

To use tiles to find −2(5), think −2(5) = 5(−2). Then model 5(−2). Show 5 groups of 2 negative tiles.

5(−2) = −10, so −2(5) = −10.

1. ✔ *Try It Out* Use tiles to find each product.
   a. −6(4) **−24** **b.** 3(−3) **−9** **c.** 4(−5) **−20**

2. Choose the correct word to complete the following statement:
   The sign of the product of two integers with different signs is *negative / positive.* **negative**

Patterns can help you find the product of two negative integers.

3. **a.** Copy and complete the table at the left.
   b. *Patterns* Describe the pattern you see in the products as you go from −4(3) to −4(−3). **See below.**
   c. Write a pattern like the one on the left to find −2(−5). Start with −2(3). **See above left.**
   d. Complete the following statement: **positive**
   The sign of the product of two negative integers is __?__.

b. Each time the second term decreases by 1, the product increases by 4.

Question 5 Once the grouping model for division is established using tiles, students can formulate the algorithms for division using related multiplication patterns. Most students find it difficult to model division completely with tiles, since there are two other cases. To model –6 ÷ (–3), begin with 6 negative tiles and have students make groups of 3 negative tiles. Since there are 2 groups, –6 ÷ (–3) = 2. To model 6 ÷ (–3), you cannot create –3 groups or groups of –3. Therefore, have students rewrite the problem as –3 · ■ = 6, and use the multiplication model discussed with Question 3.

AEP Students may not recall *inverse operations.* Relate *inverse* to *invert.* Tell students: *If you invert a shirt, you turn it inside-out, or to the opposite side. Therefore,* inverse *and* opposite *have similar meanings.*

Example 2 Ask students: *Why do you divide the sum by 5?* **To find an average, you divide by the number of data items, which is 5.**

■ **ADDITIONAL EXAMPLES**

FOR EXAMPLE 1

Find each product.

a. $-3(-3)$ **9**

b. $10(-5)$ **–50**

c. $6(3)$ **18**

d. $-4(9)$ **–36**

5c. When you multiply or divide two integers with the same sign, the product or quotient is positive. When you multiply or divide two integers with different signs, the product or quotient is negative.

WHAT?

Lechuguilla Cave in New Mexico is the deepest cave discovered in the United States.

Source: *The Guinness Book of Records*

MULTIPLYING INTEGERS

When you multiply two integers with the same sign, the product is positive.

Examples: $2 \cdot 6 = 12$ $\quad -2(-6) = 12$

When you multiply two integers with different signs, the product is negative.

Examples: $-2 \cdot 6 = -12$ $\quad 2(-6) = -12$

■ **EXAMPLE 1**

Find each product.

a. $5(3)$ $\quad 5(3) = 15$ ← Both factors are positive, so the product is positive.

b. $5(-3)$ $\quad 5(-3) = -15$ ← One factor is negative, so the product is negative.

c. $-5(3)$ $\quad -5(3) = -15$ ← One factor is negative, so the product is negative.

d. $-5(-3)$ $\quad -5(-3) = 15$ ← Both factors are negative, so the product is positive.

4. ✔ *Try It Out* Find each product.

a. $-6 \cdot 2$ **–12** **b.** $15(-8)$ **–120** **c.** $-12 \cdot 6$ **–72** **d.** $22(-41)$ **–902**

Now you may assign Exercises 1–17, 42.

2 *Dividing Integers*

You can use tiles to divide integers. To find $-6 \div 2$, use 6 negative tiles and make 2 equal groups.

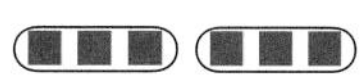

So, $-6 \div 2 = -3$.

5. ✔ *Try It Out* Use tiles to find each quotient.

a. $-8 \div 2$ **–4** **b.** $-6 \div 3$ **–2** **c.** $-10 \div 5$ **–2**

Multiplication and division are *inverse operations.*

6. a. *Patterns* Use inverse operations to find each quotient.

i. $3 \cdot 4 = 12$
$12 \div 4 = ■$ **3**
$12 \div 3 = ■$ **4**

ii. $3(-4) = -12$
$-12 \div (-4) = ■$ **3**
$-12 \div 3 = ■$ **–4**

iii. $(-3)(-4) = 12$
$12 \div (-4) = ■$ **–3**
$12 \div (-3) = ■$ **–4**

b. When two integers have the same sign, what is the sign of the quotient? When two integers have different signs, what is the sign of the quotient? **positive; negative**

c. Rewrite the Rules for Multiplying Integers to include dividing integers. **See above left.**

Technology Options

Prentice Hall Technology

Software for Learners

- Hot Page™ 4–6*
- Math Blaster® Mystery*
- Interactive Student Tutorial, Chapter 3*

Teaching Resource Software

- Computer Item Generator 3-5
- Resource Pro™ Chapter 3*

Internet • For related mathematics activities, visit the Prentice Hall site at www.phschool.com/math

**Available on CD-ROM only*

Assignment Options for Exercises On Your Own

To provide flexible scheduling, this lesson can be subdivided into parts.

1 Core 1–16, 42
Extension 17

2 Core 18–41, 43–57, 60
Extension 58, 59

Use Mixed Review to maintain skills.

FOR EXAMPLE 2

In one week, the Dow Jones Industrial Average fell 4 points on Monday, rose 2 points on Tuesday, rose 3 points on Wednesday, fell 1 point on Thursday, and rose 5 points on Friday. What was the average daily change? **+1, up 1 point**

DIVERSITY Some students may not have heard of the Stock Market or may not understand what stocks are. Ask if there is a student familiar with the Stock Market. Ask this student to explain what he or she knows about the Stock Market.

ASSESSMENT Have students work with a partner to memorize the rules for multiplying and dividing integers. Then have each partner write eight number sentences, one example for each rule. Partners can then exchange sentences to check for understanding. Have each pair post one of their examples on the board for the class to answer. Make sure the examples on the board illustrate each of the rules.

3 Practice/Assess

EXERCISES *On Your Own*

Exercises 1–6 You may want to have students include a reason for the sign of their answers. For example: $7(-4)$ is negative because only one factor is negative.

Exercise 17 Students may use -180 ft since the diver is below sea level. Point out that the diver is rising to the surface, a positive movement of 180 ft.

WHAT? The Dow Jones Industrial Average is based on the stock prices of 30 companies. Investors use the information to track market trends.

Source: *Encyclopedia Brittanica*

Some problems may require you to use more than one operation.

EXAMPLE 2 *Real-World Problem Solving*

Stock Market In one week, the Dow Jones Industrial Average rose 1 point on Monday, fell 3 points on Tuesday, rose 4 points on Wednesday, fell 4 points on Thursday, and fell 3 points on Friday. What was the average daily change?

$$\frac{1 + (-3) + 4 + (-4) + (-3)}{5} = \frac{-5}{5}$$ ← Find the sum of the changes and divide by 5.

The average daily change was -1 point, or down 1 point.

7 ✔ *Try It Out* Find the average of these winter temperatures.
$-12°$ $-8°$ $-6°$ $-3°$ $0°$ $3°$ $5°$ $-3°$

Now you may assign Exercises 18–41, 43–60.

EXERCISES *On Your Own*

Use tiles to find each product.

1. $7(-4)$ −28 **2.** $-4(4)$ −16 **3.** $-4(9)$ −36 **4.** $6(-3)$ −18 **5.** $3(-2)$ −6 **6.** $12(-1)$ −12

Multiply.

7. $-2(-13)$ 26 **8.** $-6 \cdot 12$ −72 **9.** $-5(-6)$ 30 **10.** $4(-9)$ −36 **11.** $12(-4)$ −48

12. $-15(-3)$ 45 **13.** $-36 \cdot 2$ −72 **14.** $102(-6)$ −612 **15.** $-35(24)$ −840 **16.** $27 \cdot 31$ 837

17. *Hobbies* Suppose a scuba diver is 180 ft below sea level and rises to the surface at a rate of 30 ft/min. How long will it take the diver to reach the surface? 6 min

Open-ended **Complete each number sentence. Then write two examples to illustrate each relationship.** 18–25. Numbers may vary. Samples are given.

18. (positive) · (positive) = ■ positive
$3 \times 2 = 6$; $1 \times 7 = 7$

19. (positive) · (negative) = ■ negative
$3 \times (-2) = -6$; $1 \times (-7) = -7$

20. (negative) · (positive) = ■ negative
$-3 \times 2 = -6$; $-1 \times 7 = -7$

21. (negative) · (negative) = ■ positive
$-3 \times (-2) = 6$; $-1 \times (-7) = 7$

22. (positive) ÷ (positive) = ■ positive
$6 \div 2 = 3$; $12 \div 3 = 4$

23. (positive) ÷ (negative) = ■ negative
$6 \div (-2) = -3$; $12 \div (-3) = -4$

24. (negative) ÷ (positive) = ■ negative
$-6 \div 2 = -3$; $-12 \div 3 = -4$

25. (negative) ÷ (negative) = ■ positive
$-6 \div (-2) = 3$; $-12 \div (-3) = 4$

Use tiles to find each quotient.

26. $-15 \div (5)$ −3 **27.** $-12 \div 6$ −2 **28.** $-9 \div 9$ −1 **29.** $-16 \div (2)$ −8 **30.** $-20 \div (4)$ −5

ALTERNATIVE METHOD Exercises 26–30 Some students may prefer to use inverse operations and the rules for multiplying to find the sign of the quotient. For example, they can rewrite $-15 \div 5$ as $5 \cdot ■ = -15$.

ESTIMATION Exercises 43–52 Have students write a number sentence to explain how they estimated each product or quotient.

CONNECTING TO THE STUDENTS' WORLD Exercise 58 Ask students: *What is your net gain or loss of calories during an average school day?* Have students keep a food journal so they can find the total number of calories they consume in a day. They can find the number of calories in the food they eat on nutritional labels or a calorie chart. Then have students record the amount of activity they do in a day, including walking to class. The library is a good source for books that include calorie expenditure for activities not listed on a calorie chart.

WRITING Exercise 60 Make sure students' explanations cover all possible combinations of two integers. It may help them to refer to their answers to Exercises 18–24.

WRAP UP

IDENTIFYING THE BIG IDEA Ask students to explain how to multiply and divide integers.

PROJECT LINK Encourage students to share ways to use multiplication of integers to make their game more interesting. For example: "You wrote three checks for $9 each, but you did not have any money in your checking account. Multiply $3 \cdot -9$."

Mental Math **Divide.**

31. $36 \div (-12)$ **−3**
32. $72 \div 9$ **8**
33. $39 \div (-3)$ **−13**
34. $0 \div (-2)$ **0**
35. $(-4 \cdot 6) \div (-3)$ **8**
36. $15 \div (-3)$ **−5**
37. $-50 \div (-5)$ **10**
38. $66 \div (-11)$ **−6**
39. $-72 \div 8$ **−9**
40. $-27 \div 9$ **−3**
41. Write two related division sentences for $7(-3) = -21$. **$-21 \div 7 = -3$; $-21 \div (-3) = 7$**
42. *Business* The price of a stock fell $2 each day for 8 days.
    a. What was the total change in the price of the stock? **−$16**
    b. Before the price of the stock started falling, its value was $38. What was the price of the stock after the drop? **$22**

Estimation **Estimate each product or quotient.** **43–52. Estimates may vary. Samples are given.**

43. $-24 \cdot 35$ **−800**
44. $428 \div (-58)$ **−7**
45. $-108(-55)$ **6,600**
46. $-58 \div (-9)$ **6**
47. $12 \cdot (-15)$ **−150**
48. $-265 \div (-129)$ **2**
49. $-72 \cdot 68$ **−4,900**
50. $64 \cdot 93$ **5,400**
51. $19 \div 4.7$ **4**
52. $-12(-14)$ **150**

Find the point on the number line that shows each product or quotient.

53. $-2 \cdot 0$ ***D***
54. $-16 \div (-2)$ ***G***
55. $(-1)(-1)$ ***E***
56. $-4(2)$ ***A***
57. $32 \div (-8)$ ***B***

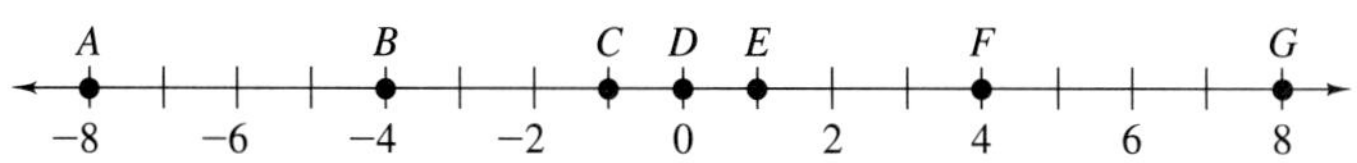

Use the table at the right for Exercises 58 and 59.

58. *Nutrition* Suppose you swam for 25 min. Then you ate 1 c of tomato soup, 3 oz of cheddar cheese, and 8 crackers.
    a. Find the number of calories you used while swimming and the number of calories you ate during lunch. **150 cal; 535 cal**
    b. Find the net gain or loss of calories. **385 cal**
59. *Open-ended* Select some foods for lunch and an activity for 40 min of exercise. Find the total number of calories you would eat during lunch. Find the number of calories you would use during exercise. What would be your net gain or loss of calories? **Check students' work.**
60. *Writing* Explain how to find the sign of the product or quotient of any two integers. **See margin.**

Food	Calories
Apple (1)	80
Banana (1)	100
Cheddar cheese (1 oz)	115
Lettuce, iceberg (1 c)	5
Mayonnaise (1 tbsp)	100
Milk, skim (1 c)	85
Orange juice (1 c)	120
Crackers (4)	50
Tomato soup (1 c)	90
Tuna (3 oz)	170

Activity	Calories used per minute
Walking	3
Skating	4
Tennis	5
Swimming	6

pages 114–115 On Your Own

60. The sign of the product or the quotient of two integers with the same sign is positive. The sign of the product or the quotient of two integers with different signs is negative.

PRACTICE

Practice 3-5 Multiplying and Dividing Integers

Complete each number sentence. Then write two examples to illustrate each relationship.

1. positive ÷ positive
   Positive; answers may vary.
2. negative · positive
   Negative; answers may vary.
3. positive · positive
   Positive; answers may vary.
4. negative ÷ negative
   Positive; answers may vary.
5. negative ÷ positive
   Negative; answers may vary.
6. positive · positive
   Positive; answers may vary.
7. positive ÷ negative
   Negative; answers may vary.
8. negative · negative
   Positive; answers may vary.

Estimate each product or quotient. Answers may vary. Samples given.

9. $-72 \cdot 57$ **−4,200**
10. $-92 \cdot (-41)$ **3,600**
11. $-476 \div 90$ **−5**
12. $-83 \cdot 52$ **−4,000**
13. $538 \div (-63)$ **−9**
14. $-803\,(-106)$ **80,000**
15. $49 \cdot 61$ **3,000**
16. $479 \div (-61)$ **−8**

Use the order of operations to evaluate.

17. $-36 \div 9 + 4(-7)$ **−32**
18. $-52 \div (-4) + (-3)(-6)$ **31**
19. $-13 + (-5)(-4)$ **7**
20. $-8(9) - 4(-7)$ **−44**
21. $-3(7 - 12) - 8$ **7**
22. $-24(-7 - 12)$ **456**
23. $-8(-7) - 12$ **44**
24. $-15(-8 - 9)$ **255**
25. $-8(46 - 92) + (-4)$ **364**
26. $7(-8 - 5)$ **−91**
27. $-9(-11 + 17)$ **−54**
28. $4(-4 + 7)$ **12**
29. $-15(-9 + 6)$ **45**
30. $43(8 - 9)$ **−43**
31. $83(-7 - 2) - (-4)$ **−743**

Find the point on the number line that shows each product or quotient.

32. $-4 \cdot 0$ **D** 33. $12 \div (-3)$ **B** 34. $(-2) \cdot (-2)$ **E** 35. $-6 \div 3$ **C** 36. $1 \cdot (-5)$ **A**

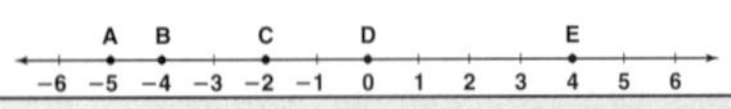

In copymaster and workbook formats

RETEACHING

Reteaching 3-5 Multiplying and Dividing Integers

To multiply integers:

- If the signs are alike, the product is positive.
  $2 \times 3 = 6$
  $-2 \times -3 = 6$
- If the signs are different, the product is negative.
  $2 \times -3 = -6$
  $-2 \times 3 = -6$

To divide integers:

- If the signs are alike, the quotient is positive.
  $6 \div 3 = 2$
  $-6 \div -3 = 2$
- If the signs are different, the quotient is negative.
  $6 \div -3 = -2$
  $-6 \div 3 = -2$

Study the sign patterns. Write positive or negative to complete each statement.

$7 \times 3 = 21$ $\quad$ $7 \times -3 = -21$
$-7 \times -3 = 21$ $\quad$ $-7 \times 3 = -21$

1. When both integers are positive, the product is **positive**.
2. When one integer is positive and one is negative, the product is **negative**.
3. When both integers are negative, the product is **positive**.

$21 \div 3 = 7$ $\quad$ $-21 \div -3 = 7$
$21 \div -3 = -7$ $\quad$ $-21 \div 3 = -7$

4. When both integers are positive, the quotient is **positive**.
5. When both integers are negative, the quotient is **positive**.
6. When one integer is positive and one is negative, the quotient is **negative**.

Tell whether each product or quotient will be *positive* or *negative*.

7. 4×7 **positive**
8. -4×7 **negative**
9. -4×-7 **positive**
10. 4×-7 **negative**
11. $-28 \div 4$ **negative**
12. $28 \div 4$ **positive**
13. $-28 \div -7$ **positive**
14. $28 \div -7$ **negative**
15. 10×-4 **negative**
16. $-25 \div 5$ **negative**
17. -2×-2 **positive**
18. $100 \div 10$ **positive**

ENRICHMENT

Minds on Math Transparency

3-5

Students from four classes of about the same size at Clinton Middle School are going on a tour of the historical center. The largest class going has 29 students. If the students divide into groups of 9 for the tour, there will be 2 students left over. If the students divide into groups of 15 for the tour, there will be 5 students left over. How many students are going on the tour?

110 students

See *Solution Key* for worked-out answers.

Math at Work

If you have block scheduling or extended class periods, have students work with spreadsheet software to add and subtract integers. Encourage students with programming skills to write a short program to find sums and differences.

LESSON QUIZ

1. $-3 \cdot -54$ **162**
2. $639 \div -9$ **−71**
3. Find the product of −33 and 42. Divide the product by −6. **231**

Mixed Review

Find each difference. *(Lesson 3-4)*

61. $8 - 1$ **7**
62. $3 - (-6)$ **9**
63. $-4 - (-9)$ **5**
64. $86 - (-17)$ **103**
65. $-23 - 9$ **−32**

Evaluate for $m = 1.8$ and $n = 4.6$. *(Lesson 3-1)*

66. $4m - n$ **2.6**
67. $4(n + m)$ **25.6**
68. $n - 5$ **−0.4**
69. $mn + 13$ **21.28**
70. $mn \div 2.3$ **3.6**
71. *Choose a Strategy* In how many ways can you order the letters A, B, C, and D? Do not repeat a letter in any arrangement. **24 ways**

CHAPTER PROJECT

PROJECT LINK: DESIGNING

Add details to your game board that require multiplication of integers. Use illustrations and color, and put a cardboard backing on the game board. **Check students' work.**

Math at Work

SOFTWARE DEVELOPER

Software developers create programs for computers. Computer software can consist of operating systems, which control the computer, or applications programs, which adapt the computer to perform a specific task, such as figuring a payroll, modeling a machine part, or running a video game.

Internet Connection

To find out more about computer software, visit this Web site: http://www.yahooligans.com/Computers__Games__and_Online/Software/

Extra Practice, Lesson 3-5, page 516

PROBLEM SOLVING PRACTICE ★★

This page provides problems for students to solve using their knowledge of tables, patterns, decimals, and dividing whole numbers. Allow students to use any method they find helpful.

Exercise 5 Students may think they need to know the number of bags of soil to solve the problem, if they do not notice the word *total.*

Exercise 7 Encourage students to draw a table to help them solve the problem. Students are more likely to recognize the pattern from a visual display than from the paragraph.

COOPERATIVE GROUPS Problem 2 Have students work with a partner. Have partners agree on a rule that describes the first three rows. Then they can take turns using the rule to find the numbers in the other rows.

PROBLEM SOLVING PRACTICE ★★★★★

Choose the best answer.

Balance Beam Competition

Gymnast	Score
Ruth	9.45
Davida	9.5
Shante	9.4
Lupe	9.55
Aun	9.05

1. The gymnasts' names will be posted on the bulletin board in order based on their scores from greatest to least. In what order will the names be listed? C

   A. Davida, Ruth, Lupe, Shante, Aun
   B. Lupe, Shante, Ruth, Davida, Aun
   C. Lupe, Davida, Ruth, Shante, Aun
   D. Aun, Shante, Ruth, Davida, Lupe

2. The marching band does a formation in which there are 48 students in the first row, 42 students in the second row, and 36 students in the third row. If the pattern continues, how many students are in the *seventh* row? H

   F. 24 G. 18 H. 12 J. 6

Please note that items 3–7 have *five* answer choices.

3. At the grocery store, Dan bought hamburger that weighed 1.42 lb, sausage that weighed 2.16 lb, and chicken that weighed 3.73 lb. How many pounds of meat did Dan purchase in all? D

   A. 3.58 lb B. 5.89 lb C. 6.31 lb
   D. 7.31 lb E. 7.41 lb

4. Tanya started her road trip with a full tank of gas. She drove 318 miles and then put 12 gallons of gas in her car. What was the average number of miles per gallon? F

   F. 26.5 G. 26
   H. 25.5 J. 25
   K. Not Here

5. At the gardening store, Ellen bought weed killer on sale for $4.97 a bottle, a gardening rake and a shovel for $8.25 each, and several bags of soil that cost a total of $37.50. Ellen had $85 before she made her purchases. What additional information do you need to find the total cost of her purchases? E

   A. the price of the rake
   B. the price of the shovel
   C. the original price of the weed killer
   D. the number of bags of soil
   E. the number of bottles of weed killer purchased

6. In the problem above, what information is *not* needed to solve the problem? J

   F. the sale price of the weed killer
   G. the combined cost of the rake and shovel
   H the total cost of the bags of soil
   J. the amount of money Ellen had before making the purchases
   K. Not Here

7. After 4 weeks, Kono had $25 in his savings account, after 5 weeks he had $31.25, and after 6 weeks he had $37.50. If the pattern continues, how much money will he have after 9 weeks? B

   A. $62.50 B. $56.25 C. $54.25
   D. $50.00 E. $43.75

3-6 Teaching Notes

1 Focus

CONNECTING TO PRIOR KNOWLEDGE Ask students:

- *How is the balance in a checkbook register related to the balance in the checking account?* **They should both show the same amount of money.**
- *What do you do in the checkbook register when you withdraw $20 from the bank?* **subtract $20** *When you deposit $30?* **add $30**

2 Teach

THINK AND DISCUSS

Begin a class discussion by asking students what they think the word *equation* means. Accept all reasonable answers, but focus the discussion on definitions that contain the concept of equality.

TACTILE LEARNING Use a balance-beam scale to illustrate the concepts presented in the opening paragraphs. Allow students to place tiles on the scale. Ask them to describe what must be true for the scale to balance. **Both sides must contain the same weight.** Have one student remove three tiles from one side of the scale. Ask the class what must be done to rebalance the scale. **Remove three tiles from the other side.**

Lesson Planning Options

Prerequisite Skills

- adding and subtracting integers (3-3, 3-4)
- using inverses (precourse)

Vocabulary/Symbols

solution, Addition Property of Equality, Subtraction Property of Equality

Materials/Manipulatives

- algebra tiles
- calculator

Resources

Student Edition

Skills Handbook, p. 531
Extra Practice, p. 516
Glossary/Study Guide

Teaching Resources

Chapter Support File, Ch. 3
- Lesson Planner 3-6
- Practice 3-6, Reteaching 3-6
- Answer Masters 3-6

Teaching Aids Masters 26, 27
Glossary, Spanish Resources

Transparencies
11, 12, 15, 83, Minds on Math 3-6

Warm Up

Find each sum or difference.

$27\frac{1}{8} - 12$ $15\frac{1}{8}$

$15\frac{3}{5} + 27$ $42\frac{3}{5}$

3-6 Solving Equations by Adding and Subtracting

What You'll Learn

1. To use models to solve equations
2. To use inverse operations to solve equations

...And Why

You can solve equations to find a predicted number of jobs.

Here's How

Look for questions that
- build understanding
- ✔ check understanding

THINK AND DISCUSS

1 *Using Models to Solve Equations*

Solving an equation is like balancing a scale. A scale balances when the weights on both sides are equal. An equation is true when the values on both sides are equal.

The green rectangular tile in the model at the right represents the variable in an equation. The value of the variable that makes the equation true is the **solution.**

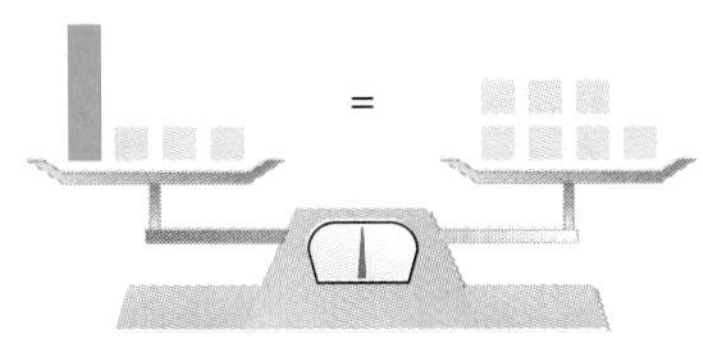

1. *Analyze* How would you remove weights to get the variable alone but keep the scale balanced? **Remove three yellow tiles from each side.**

To find the value of a variable, you need to get it alone on one side of the equal sign.

2a .

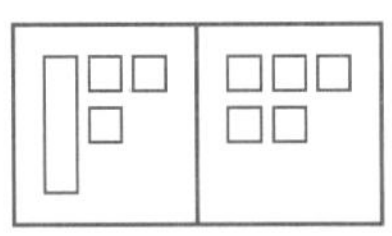

b.

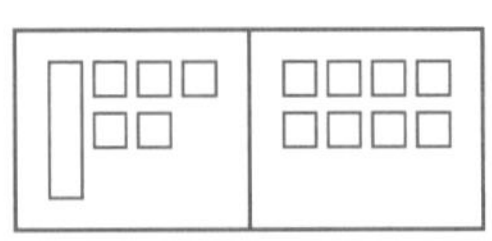

■ **EXAMPLE 1**

Use models to solve $x + 3 = 7$.

Model the equation. Remove 3 tiles from each side.

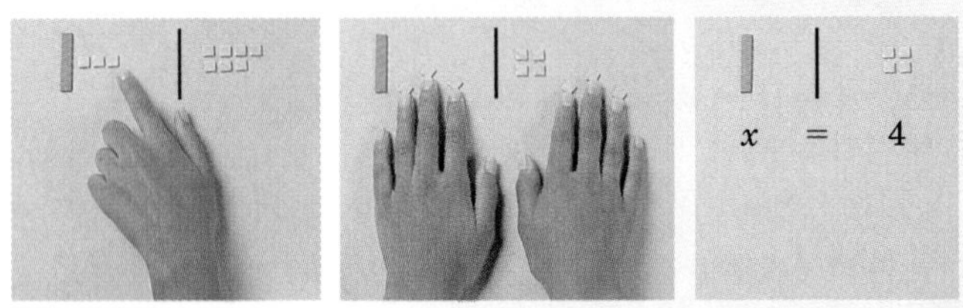

a–b. See left for diagrams.

2. ✔ *Try It Out* Model and solve each equation.
   a. $x + 3 = 5$ **2** b. $y + 5 = 8$ **3** c. $7 + a = 12$ **5**
   c. See margin p. 120 for diagrams.
3. *Go a Step Further* Complete each step of the equation at the right. **7; 7; 17**

$x + 7 = 24$
$x + 7 - ■ = 24 - ■$
$x = ■$

AEP *Cognates* are words that have similar spellings and meanings in different languages. Recognizing cognates can be a helpful strategy for those trying to learn a new language. Two English/Spanish cognates are *solution* and *solución*, and *balance* and *balanza*.

■ ADDITIONAL EXAMPLES

FOR EXAMPLE 1

Use models to solve $x + 2 = 5$. $x = 3$

FOR EXAMPLE 2

Model the equation and solve $n - 5 = -4$
$n = 1$

FOR EXAMPLE 3

Solve $-6 = x - 2$. Check your answer.
$x = -4$

Example 2 Make sure students understand that subtracting 4 was modeled by adding -4.

ALTERNATIVE METHOD Example 3 Some students may prefer to see you solve equations vertically. Present the following vertical method.

$$\begin{array}{rcr} -4 & = & x - 3 \\ +\ 3 & = & +\ 3 \\ \hline -1 & = & x + 0 \end{array}$$

Therefore, $-1 = x$.

ERROR ALERT! Some students may try to simplify across the equal sign. For example, in the equation $x - 6 = 6$, students may add -6 and 6 to get 0. **Remediation:** Have students draw a vertical line through the equal

A model can be especially helpful when you solve equations involving subtraction or negative integers.

■ EXAMPLE 2

Model the equation $n - 4 = -1$ and solve.

$n - 4 = -1$
$n + (-4) = -1$ ← Subtracting is the same as adding the opposite.

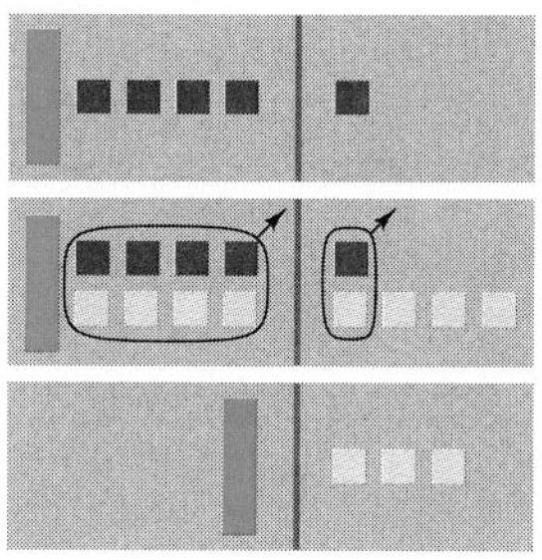

a–c. See left for diagrams.

4. ✔ *Try It Out* Model each equation. Then solve.
   a. $x - 4 = 5$ 9
   b. $y - 2 = 8$ 10
   c. $a - (-5) = -3$ −8

Now you may assign Exercises 1–28.

4a.

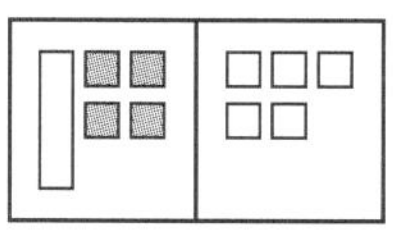

b.

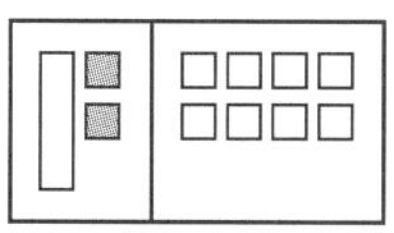

c.

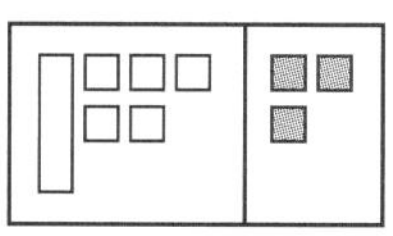

2 *Using Inverse Operations*

Addition and subtraction are inverse operations. You can add to undo subtraction and subtract to undo addition.

You can add or subtract the same number from each side of an equation. The result is an equation having the same solution.

■ EXAMPLE 3

Solve $-4 = x - 3$. Check your answer.

$-4 = x - 3$
$-4 + 3 = x - 3 + 3$ ← Since 3 is subtracted from the variable, add 3 to both sides of the equation.
$-1 = x$ ← Simplify.

Check: $-4 = x - 3$ ← Start with the original equation.
$-4 \stackrel{?}{=} -1 - 3$ ← Replace x with -1.
$-4 = -4$ ✔ ← Simplify.

5. *Error Alert* Stephen solved $x - 5 = -3$. His solution was $x = -8$. Find his mistake.
Stephen subtracted 5 instead of adding it.

Technology Options

Prentice Hall Technology

Software for Learners

- Math Blaster® Mystery*
- Interactive Student Tutorial, Chapter 3*

Teaching Resource Software

- Computer Item Generator 3-6
- Resource Pro™ Chapter 3*

Internet • For related mathematics activities, visit the Prentice Hall site at www.phschool.com/math

**Available on CD-ROM only*

Assignment Options for Exercises On Your Own

To provide flexible scheduling, this lesson can be subdivided into parts.

1 **Core** 1–16
Extension 17–28

2 **Core** 29–44, 47
Extension 45, 46

Use Mixed Review to maintain skills.

sign and extend the line into the work space below the equation. Tell them that a number cannot cross the "wall" from one side of the equation to the other. However, they can add or subtract equal amounts from each side of the equation.

ASSESSMENT Have students draw a balance scale and tiles to illustrate $8 + x = 15$. Then have them solve the equation. $x = 7$ Ask students to describe the method they used to find the solution.

3 Practice/Assess

EXERCISES *On Your Own*

MENTAL MATH Exercises 17–28 Have students record the property they use to solve each equation.

Exercises 41–44 Have students record the method they use to solve each equation. Ask them to justify their choice. You may want to ask them to use each method at least once.

Give students the opportunity to share their methods with the class.

REASONING Exercise 46 Encourage students to first solve the two equations to see if they are equivalent before trying to rewrite them. Some students may need to model the equations with tiles.

WRITING Exercise 47 Suggest students first try using the Subtraction Property and then write about adding the opposite.

pages 118–120 Think and Discuss

2c. 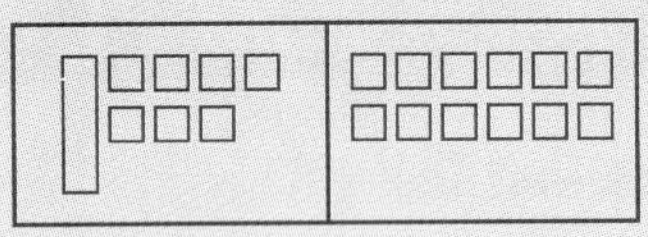

The following properties summarize how you can add or subtract to rewrite an equation.

PROPERTIES OF EQUALITY

Addition

You can add the same value to each side of an equation.

Arithmetic: Since $\frac{20}{2} = 10$, $\frac{20}{2} + 3 = 10 + 3$.

Algebra: If $a = b$, then $a + c = b + c$.

Subtraction

You can subtract the same value from each side of an equation.

Arithmetic: Since $\frac{20}{2} = 10$, $\frac{20}{2} - 3 = 10 - 3$.

Algebra: If $a = b$, then $a - c = b - c$.

6a–c. Answers may vary. Samples are given.

a. subtraction property of equality; subtract 19

b. addition property of equality; add 54

c. addition property of equality; add −15

6. State which property you would use to solve each equation. Then state what you would add or subtract. See left.

a. $x + 19 = 36$ **b.** $x - 54 = -28$ **c.** $x - (-15) = -4$

Now you may assign Exercises 29–47.

EXERCISES *On Your Own*

Write the equation represented by each model. Then solve.

1. 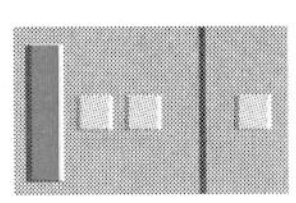
$x + 2 = 1$; -1

2. 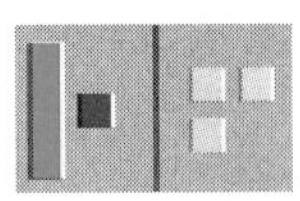
$x - 1 = 3$; 4

3. 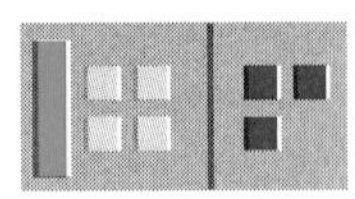
$x + 4 = -3$; -7

4. 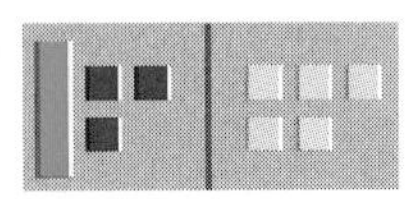
$x - 3 = 5$; 8

Use a model to solve each equation.

5. $x + 4 = 5$ 1 **6.** $x - 3 = -2$ 1 **7.** $x + 1 = -4$ −5 **8.** $-1 = 4 + n$ −5

9. $y + 1 = 9$ 8 **10.** $3 = a - 5$ 8 **11.** $2 + n = -3$ −5 **12.** $8 = p + 7$ 1

13. $-8 = (-7) + b$ −1 **14.** $-2 + m = -9$ −7 **15.** $d - (-1) = 5$ 4 **16.** $x - (-5) = 3$ −2

Mental Math **Solve each equation.**

17. $x + 6 = -6$ −12 **18.** $x - 6 = -6$ 0 **19.** $x + 6 = 6$ 0 **20.** $x - 6 = 6$ 12

21. $x - 3 = 0$ 3 **22.** $-5 = p + 8$ −13 **23.** $q - 6 = 4$ 10 **24.** $7 = 9 + y$ −2

25. $x - 2 = 1$ 3 **26.** $-7 = k + 4$ −11 **27.** $m - 4 = 12$ 16 **28.** $17 = 19 + t$ −2

WRAP UP

IDENTIFYING THE BIG IDEA Ask students to explain how to solve equations by adding and subtracting.

LESSON QUIZ

Use a model to solve each equation.

1. $x - 4 = 5$ $x = 9$
2. $8 + m = -6$ $m = -14$

Solve each equation.

3. $-6 = y - (-5)$ $y = -11$
4. $10 = k + 12$ $k = -2$

Solve each equation.

29. $16 = c + (-5)$ 21
30. $-11 = a - (-6)$ −17
31. $-7 + g = 10$ 17
32. $r + (-2) = -4$ −2
33. $9 + x = -4$ −13
34. $p + (-3) = 8$ 11
35. $5 + e = -7$ −12
36. $3 = -2 + k$ 5
37. $12 = q - (-7)$ 5
38. $8 + b = 0$ −8
39. $-1 = h - 5$ 4
40. $r - 54 = 74$ 128

Choose **Use a calculator, paper and pencil, or mental math. Solve each equation and check the solution.**

41. $n - 35 = 84$ 119
42. $166 = m + 97$ 69
43. $x + 25 = 16$ −9
44. $-17 = x + 6$ −23

45. *Business* The bar graph at the right shows the projected changes in employment for selected occupations.
    a. Which occupation expects the greatest increase in jobs from 1994 to 2005? Which expects the greatest decrease? See below.
    b. Which equation could you use to find the occupation that expects 17 more jobs per 100 than mathematician, $n - 17 = 5$ or $n + 17 = 5$? $n - 17 = 5$
    c. Which occupation expects 17 more jobs per 100 than mathematician? physician

    a. computer engineer; directory assistance operator

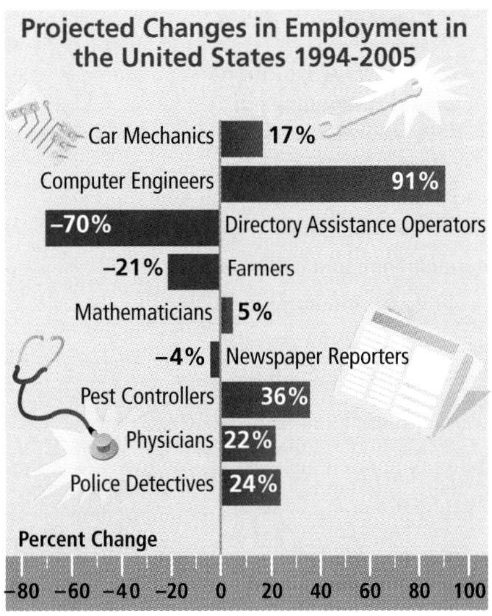

Source: *Monthly Labor Review*

46. *Reasoning* Can you rewrite the equation $5 + x = 4$ to become the equation $3 + x = 2$? Explain. Yes; use the subtraction property of equality to subtract 2 from each side.
47. *Writing* Explain how you could use the Addition Property of Equality to solve the equation $x + 15 = 34$. Add −15 to each side of the equation.

Mixed Review

Find each answer. *(Lesson 3-5)*

48. $54 \div (-9)$ −6
49. $-24 \div 3$ −8
50. $4(5)(-3)$ −60
51. $(15 \div 3)(-6)$ −30

52. *Choose a Strategy* The 16 teams in the summer softball league held a tournament. A team was eliminated after a single loss. How many games were played to determine the league championship? 15 games

PRACTICE

Practice 3-6 *Solving Equations by Adding and Subtracting*

Solve each equation. Use mental math to check the solution.

1. $n + 2 = 5$ 3
2. $x - 1 = -3$ −2
3. $7 = a + 2$ 5
4. $p + 2 = -6$ −8
5. $-9 = -4 + a$ −5
6. $-2 = c + 2$ −4
7. $x - (-3) = 7$ 4
8. $a + (-6) = 5$ 11
9. $10 = r - 5$ 15
10. $x + 10 = 2$ −8
11. $-5 + c = -1$ 4
12. $-12 = 7 + h$ −19
13. $16 + s = 6$ −10
14. $p + (-2) = 19$ 21
15. $r - 7 = -13$ −6
16. $25 = a - (-3)$ 22

Choose a calculator, paper and pencil, or mental math to solve each equation. Check the solution.

17. $t + 43 = 28$ −15
18. $-19 = r + 6$ −25
19. $25 = r + 7$ 18
20. $13 = 24 + c$ −11
21. $d - 19 = -46$ −27
22. $b + 27 = -18$ −45
23. $46 = f - 19$ 65
24. $z - 74 = -19$ 55

Circle A, B, C, or D in Exercises 25 and 26.

25. After driving 62.3 miles, the odometer on Mira's car read 20,186.7. Which equation could you use to find how many miles were on the odometer before driving 62.3 miles?
    A. $20{,}186.7 + 62.3 = m$
    B. $m + 20{,}186.7 = 62.3$
    (C.) $m + 62.3 = 20{,}186.7$
    D. $m - 62.3 = 20{,}186.7$
26. Michael bought a $25.00 gift for a friend. After he bought the gift, Michael had $176.89. Which equation could you use to find how much money Michael had before he bought the gift?
    A. g + $176.89 = $25.00
    (B.) g − $25.00 = $176.89
    C. g + $25.00 = $176.89
    D. $176.89 − $25.00 = g
27. In Exercise 25, find the odometer reading before the trip. 20,124.4
28. In Exercise 26, find how much money Michael had before he bought the gift. $201.89

Practice

In copymaster and workbook formats

RETEACHING

Reteaching 3-6 *Solving Equations by Adding and Subtracting*

Follow these steps to solve equations.

	Solve: $n + (-2) = 11$	Solve: $n - 6 = -36$
Step 1 Use the inverse operation on both sides of the equation.	$n + (-2) - (-2) = 11 - (-2)$	$n - 6 + 6 = -36 + 6$
Step 2 Simplify.	$n = 13$	$n = -30$
Step 3 Check.	$n + (-2) = 11$ $13 + (-2) \stackrel{?}{=} 11$ $11 = 11$ ✓	$n - 6 = -36$ $-30 - 6 \stackrel{?}{=} -36$ $-36 = -36$ ✓

Solve each equation. Check your answer.

1. $n + 6 = 8$
   $n + 6 - 6 = 8 -$ 6
   $n =$ 2
2. $n - 3 = 20$
   $n - 3 +$ 3 $= 20 + 3$
   $n =$ 23
3. $n - (-3) = -1$
   $n - (-3) +$ (−3) $= -1 +$ (−3)
   $n =$ −4
4. $-2 = n + 5$
   $-2 -$ 5 $= n + 5 -$ 5
   −7 $= n$
5. $n - (-4) = -2$
   $n - (-4) +$ (−4) $= -2 +$ (−4)
   $n =$ −6
6. $n - 16 = -23$
   $n - 16 +$ 16 $= -23 +$ 16
   $n =$ −7

Choose a calculator, pencil and paper, or mental math to solve each equation.

7. $n + 1 = 17$ 16
8. $n - (-6) = 7$ 1
9. $n - 8 = -12$ −4
10. $n - 19 = 34$ 53
11. $61 = n + 29$ 32
12. $n + 84 = 131$ 47
13. $-13 = n + 9$ −22
14. $-18 = n - (-5)$ −23

Reteaching

ENRICHMENT

Minds on Math Transparency

3-6

Jamil planted half of the plants in his garden in rows of 18 and the other half of the plants in rows of 24. If he planted a total of 14 rows, how many plants are in his garden?

288 plants

See *Solution Key* for worked-out answers.

3-7 Teaching Notes

1 Focus

CONNECTING TO PRIOR KNOWLEDGE
Ask students to recall the following:

- *What are inverse operations?* **operations that undo each other**
- *What operation could you use to solve an equation that contains addition?* **subtraction** *That contains subtraction?* **addition**
- *What operation could you use to solve an equation that contains multiplication?* **division** *That contains division?* **multiplication**

2 Teach

THINK AND DISCUSS

Question 1 Ask: *Are tiles practical for solving all equations? Explain.* **Answers may vary. Sample: No, if the numbers are large, there would be too many tiles.**

ERROR ALERT! **Example 2** Students may try to divide by 12 rather than −12. **Remediation:** Remind students that inverse

Lesson Planning Options

Prerequisite Skills

- multiplication and division of integers (3-5)

Vocabulary/Symbols

Multiplicative Property of Equality, Division Property of Equality

Materials/Manipulatives

- algebra tiles
- calculator

Resources

Student Edition

Skills Handbook, pp. 530, 531
Extra Practice, p. 516
Glossary/Study Guide

Teaching Resources

Chapter Support File, Ch. 3
- Lesson Planner 3-7
- Practice 3-7, Reteaching 3-7
- Alternative Activity 3-7
- Answer Masters 3-7

Teaching Aids Masters 26, 27
Glossary, Spanish Resources

Transparencies
11, 12, 15, 83, Minds on Math 3-7

Warm Up

Write and solve the proportion: The ratio of scouts to leaders is 25 to 1. If there are 125 scouts how many leaders are there?
5

3-7 Solving Equations by Multiplying and Dividing

What You'll Learn

1. To solve equations by dividing
2. To solve equations by multiplying

...And Why

You can solve equations to find the number of days a library book was late.

Here's How

Look for questions that
- build understanding
- ✔ check understanding

THINK AND DISCUSS

1 *Solving Equations by Dividing*

You can use algebra tiles to solve some equations that involve multiplication.

■ **EXAMPLE 1**

Use algebra tiles to solve the equation $3x = 21$.

$3x = 21$ ← Represent the equation.

$\frac{3x}{3} = \frac{21}{3}$ ← Divide each side into three equal groups.

$x = 7$ ← Simplify.

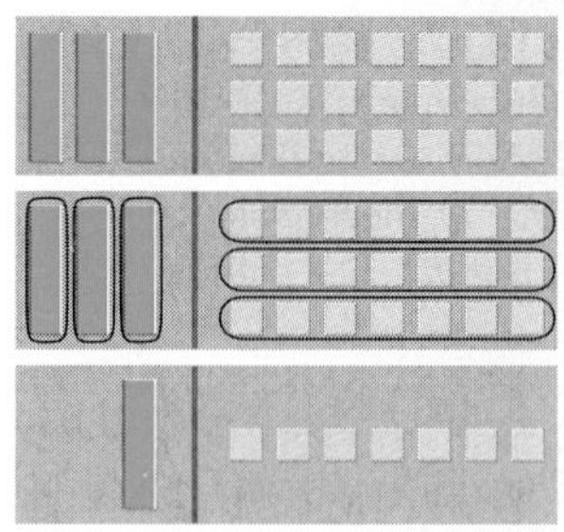

1. ✔ *Try It Out* Write the equation for each model. Then use algebra tiles to solve.

a. 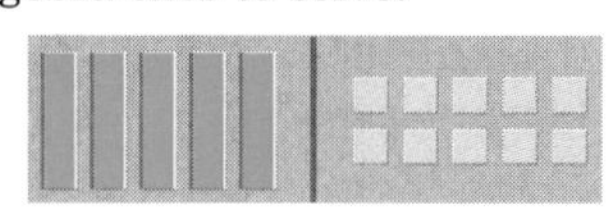

5x = 10; 2

b. 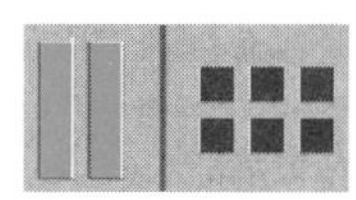

2x = −6; −3

Since multiplication and division are inverse operations, you can use division to undo multiplication.

■ **EXAMPLE 2**

Solve $-12x = 84$.

$-12x = 84$

$\frac{-12x}{-12} = \frac{84}{-12}$ ← Divide each side by −12.

$x = -7$ ← Simplify.

operations only undo each other if they use the same numbers. If they divide $-12x$ by 12, the result is $-1x$. Have students check their answers by replacing the variable with their solution.

AUDITORY LEARNING Read equations aloud. Call on students to tell the class what inverse operation they would use to solve the equation. When you read, it is helpful to include the operation rather than just reading the phrase. For example, for the phrase $6n$, read *six times n* rather than *six n*. For $\frac{x}{-6}$, read *x divided by negative six* rather than *x over negative six*.

ADDITIONAL EXAMPLES

FOR EXAMPLE 1

Use algebra tiles to solve the equation $4x = 8$. $x = 2$

FOR EXAMPLE 2

Solve $-15x = 90$. $x = -6$

FOR EXAMPLE 3

Karina wants to buy some small erasers. Each eraser costs 8¢. She only has 96¢ to spend. Solve the equation $8g = 96$ to find the number of erasers Karina can buy. 12

FOR EXAMPLE 4

Solve $\frac{z}{-6} = -6$. $z = 36$

2. ✔ *Try It Out* Solve each equation.
   a. $12x = 84$ 7 b. $12x = -84$ −7 c. $-12x = -84$ 7

EXAMPLE 3 *Real-World Problem Solving*

Money Suppose you return an overdue library book. Your fine is 78¢. The library charges 6¢ per day. Solve the equation $6d = 78$ to find the number of days the book was overdue.

$6d = 78$ ← Since 6 multiplies *d*, divide each side of the equation by 6.

$\frac{6d}{6} = \frac{78}{6}$ ← Simplify.

$d = 13$

Check: $6d = 78$ ← Replace *d* with 13.

$6 \cdot 13 \stackrel{?}{=} 78$ ← Simplify.

$78 = 78$ ✔

The book was 13 days overdue.

The most overdue library book in the United States was borrowed in 1823 and returned in 1968 by the borrower's great-grandson. The library waived the fine of $2,264.

Source: *The Guinness Book of Records*

3. ✔ *Try It Out* David's library charges 7¢ per day for overdue books. David has a fine of 98¢. Solve the equation $7d = 98$ to find the number of days his book was overdue. Check your answer. **14 days; 14 × 7 = 98 ✓**

Now you may assign Exercises 1–10, 18–20, 42.

2 *Solving Equations by Multiplying*

Just as you use division to undo multiplication, you can use multiplication to undo division.

EXAMPLE 4

Solve $\frac{s}{-4} = -5$.

$\frac{s}{-4} = -5$

$(-4)\frac{s}{-4} = (-4)(-5)$ ← Since −4 divides *s*, multiply each side of the equation by −4.

$s = 20$ ← Simplify.

4. $\frac{s}{-4} = -5$; $\frac{20}{-4} \stackrel{?}{=} -5$; $-5 = -5$ ✓

4. Check the solution to Example 4. **See above.**
5. ✔ *Try It Out* Solve and check each equation. **a. 72; $\frac{72}{8} = 9$ ✓**
   a. $\frac{x}{8} = 9$ b. $\frac{x}{6} = -15$ c. $\frac{x}{-5} = -23$
   b. −90; $\frac{-90}{6} = -15$ ✓
   c. 115; $\frac{115}{-5} = -23$ ✓

Technology Options

Prentice Hall Technology

Software for Learners
- Math Blaster® Mystery*
- Interactive Student Tutorial, Chapter 3*

Teaching Resource Software
- Computer Item Generator 3-7
- Resource Pro™ Chapter 3*

Internet • For related mathematics activities, visit the Prentice Hall site at www.phschool.com/math

**Available on CD-ROM only*

Assignment Options for Exercises On Your Own

To provide flexible scheduling, this lesson can be subdivided into parts.

1 **Core** 1–10, 19, 42
Extension 18, 20

2 **Core** 11–17, 21–41
Extension 43

Use Mixed Review to maintain skills.

ERROR ALERT! Students may not understand how multiplying or dividing both sides of an equation by the same number produces an equivalent equation.
Remediation: Illustrate the Multiplication and Division Properties of Equality using tiles and a balance-beam scale. Have a student place 2 tiles on each side of the scale. Another student multiplies each side by 3 and places 6 tiles in each side. Ask: *Did they keep the scale balanced?* **yes** *Would they keep the scale in balance if they divided both sides by 2?* **yes**

Example 4 Remind students that in the third step of the solution $-4 = \frac{-4}{1}$. So, $(-4)\frac{s}{-4} = (\frac{-4}{1})\frac{s}{-4} = \frac{-4s}{-4} = s$. Ask students to describe the goal of the operation. **to isolate the variable**

ASSESSMENT Have students solve the equations $10a = 10$ and $\frac{d}{6} = 12$. **$a = 1$; $d = 72$** Have them write three variations of each equation in which one or both of the numbers are negative. Ask them to describe how the signs of the numbers affect the equation's solution.

3 Practice/Assess

EXERCISES *On Your Own*

ESTIMATION Exercise 18 Watch for students who drop the negative sign when estimating.

REASONING Exercise 20 Make sure students provide two possible solutions.

The following properties summarize how you can use division and multiplication to rewrite equations.

PROPERTIES OF EQUALITY

Multiplication

You can multiply each side of an equation by the same value.

Arithmetic: Since $\frac{12}{2} = 6$, $\frac{12}{2} \cdot 2 = 6 \cdot 2$.

Algebra: If $a = b$, then $a \cdot c = b \cdot c$.

Division

You can divide each side of an equation by the same nonzero value.

Arithmetic: Since $3(2) = 6$, $3(2) \div 2 = 6 \div 2$.

Algebra: If $a = b$, then $a \div c = b \div c$.

a. division property **b. multiplication property** **c. division property**

6. Would you use the Division Property of Equality or the Multiplication Property of Equality to solve each equation?
   a. $5x = 95$ b. $\frac{x}{-12} = -24$ c. $-3x = 42$

Now you may assign Exercises 11–17, 21–41, 43.

EXERCISES *On Your Own*

Write the equation represented by each model. Then solve and check the equation.

1. 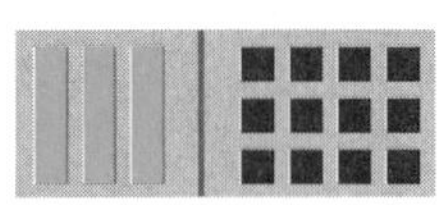
$3x = -12$; -4

2. 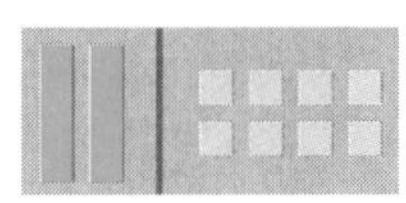
$2x = 8$; 4

Choose **Use models, paper and pencil, or mental math to solve each equation.**

3. $5b = -20$ **-4**
4. $35 = -7h$ **-5**
5. $-52 = 13e$ **-4**
6. $8p = -40$ **-5**
7. $12 = 6t$ **2**
8. $2x = 4$ **2**
9. $3x = -27$ **-9**
10. $-7y = -28$ **4**
11. $7 = d \div 4$ **28**
12. $\frac{m}{-5} = 3$ **-15**
13. $-6 = \frac{r}{10}$ **-60**
14. $z \div 8 = -3$ **-24**
15. $-14 = q \div -2$ **28**
16. $m \div -3 = 9$ **-27**
17. $\frac{t}{8} = 120$ **960**
18. *Estimation* What equation would you use to estimate the solution of $12x = -38$? Explain your choice. Then estimate the solution. **$12x = -36$; -36 is -3×12 and is close to -38; -3**

WRITING **Exercise 41** To help students begin, have them first correctly solve the equation. Then they can compare the incorrect and correct solutions.

WRAP UP

IDENTIFYING THE BIG IDEA Ask students to explain how to solve multiplication and division equations.

LESSON QUIZ

Use a calculator, paper and pencil, or mental math to solve each equation.

1. $-35 = -7x$ $x = 5$
2. $\frac{y}{-9} = 8$ $y = -72$
3. $-8c = 64$ $c = -8$
4. $n \div -5 = -13$ $n = 65$

19. *Entertainment* Dr. H. Howard Hughes of Fort Worth, Texas, saw 6,136 plays in 31 years. Solve the equation $31p = 6{,}136$ to find the average number of plays p he saw per year. about 198 plays per year

20. *Reasoning* For what values of x is $5|x| = 10$ true? -2 and 2

Choose **Use a calculator, paper and pencil, or mental math to solve each equation.**

25. −55 30. −6

21. $27 = -9w$ -3 22. $-3k = -18$ 6 23. $\frac{c}{6} = -1$ -6 24. $\frac{y}{-4} = -12$ 48 25. $\frac{n}{-5} = 11$

26. $t \div 6 = -10$ -60 27. $\frac{q}{-5} = 30$ -150 28. $8n = 112$ 14 29. $-4 = -2r$ 2 30. $-4y = 24$

31. $-7 = 7m$ -1 32. $3g = 42$ 14 33. $d \div 7 = -8$ -56 34. $\frac{n}{3} = 4$ 12 35. $-5 = \frac{a}{-9}$

36. $\frac{n}{3} = -42$ -126 37. $\frac{r}{-4} = -104$ 416 38. $7 = \frac{n}{9}$ 63 39. $\frac{x}{18} = -40$ -720 40. $\frac{x}{-78} = -63$

35. 45 40. 4,914

41. *Writing* Susan's solution for the equation $\frac{n}{-6} = 12$ is $n = -2$. Explain how Susan may have found this solution and how you would help her correct her mistake. Susan divided 12 by −6; you find the solution by multiplying 12 by −6 to get −72.

42. George Adrian of Indianapolis, Indiana, picked 15,830 pounds of apples in 8 hours. Solve $8a = 15{,}830$ to find the number of pounds of apples a he picked per hour. 1978.75 lb

43. **Choose A, B, C or D.** Which equation would you use to represent the following situation? A growing tree absorbs about 26 lb of carbon dioxide a year. How many years y would it take the tree to absorb 390 lb of carbon dioxide?

   A. $26 + y = 390$ B. $\frac{y}{26} = 390$ C. $26y = 390$ D. $\frac{26}{y} = 390$

   C

Mixed Review

46. zero property of multiplication
47. commutative property of addition

Name the property shown. *(Lessons 2-3, 2-5, and 2-8)* 46–47. See above.

44. $3(4 + 8) = 12 + 24$ distributive property 45. $21 \cdot 1 = 21$ identity property of multiplication 46. $0(17.56) = 0$ 47. $3 + 4 = 4 + 3$

Evaluate each expression for $m = 12$. *(Lesson 3-1)*

48. $32 - 2m$ 8 49. $5 + 6m$ 77 50. $2m + 10$ 34 51. $7m$ 84 52. $125 - 4m$ 77

53. *Choose a Strategy* A clock gains 4 min every hour. One day it is set to the correct time at 9:00 A.M. What is the correct time when the clock shows 1:00 P.M.? 12:45 P.M.

Extra Practice, Lesson 3-7, page 516

PRACTICE

Practice 3-7 *Solving Equations by Multiplying and Dividing*

Choose a calculator, paper and pencil, or mental math to solve each equation. Check the solution.

1. $9n = 126$ 14
2. $\frac{d}{3} = -81$ −243
3. $-2t = 56$ −28
4. $\frac{k}{-3} = 6$ −18
5. $-18 = \frac{y}{-2}$ 36
6. $y \div 16 = 3$ 48
7. $-56 = 8r$ −7
8. $9w = -63$ −7
9. $-3v = -48$ 16
10. $13 = x \div (-4)$ −52
11. $28 = -4a$ −7
12. $t \div (-42) = 3$ −126
13. $-19 = f \div 6$ −114
14. $75 = -5s$ −15
15. $\frac{q}{4} = 56$ 224
16. $18w = -36$ −2
17. $24 = f \div (-4)$ −96
18. $15 = -3j$ −5
19. $102k = 408$ 4
20. $\frac{b}{-96} = -3$ 288

Estimate the solution. Answers may vary. Samples given.

21. $\frac{x}{19} = -21$ −400
22. $\frac{x}{-22} = -63$ 1,200
23. $-41x = 161$ −4
24. $-98r = 1{,}200$ −12
25. $\frac{x}{91} = -98$ −9,100
26. $452 = -4x$ −110
27. $52x = -2{,}500$ −50
28. $79x = -6{,}380$ −80

Write an equation to represent each situation. Solve the equation.

29. One of the largest flowers, the Rafflesia, weighs about 15 lb. How many Rafflesia flowers can be placed in a container that can hold a maximum of 240 lb?
   $15n = 240$, $n = 16$; 16 flowers

30. "Heavy water" is a name given to a compound used in some nuclear reactors. Heavy water costs about \$1,500 per gallon. If a nuclear plant spent \$10,500 on heavy water, how many gallons of heavy water were bought?
   $\frac{10{,}500}{n} = 1{,}500$, $n = 7$; 7 gal

In copymaster and workbook formats

RETEACHING

Reteaching 3-7 *Solving Equations by Multiplying and Dividing*

Follow these steps to solve equations. ($\frac{t}{5}$ means $t \div 5$.)

	Solve: $\frac{t}{5} = -7$	Solve: $-2x = 8$
Step 1 Use the inverse operation on both sides of the equation.	$(5)\frac{t}{5} = (5)(-7)$	$\frac{-2x}{-2} = \frac{8}{-2}$
Step 2 Simplify.	$t = -35$	$x = -4$
Step 3 Check.	$\frac{t}{5} = -7$ $\frac{-35}{5} \stackrel{?}{=} -7$ $-7 = -7$ ✓	$-2x = 8$ $-2(-4) \stackrel{?}{=} 8$ $8 = 8$ ✓

Solve each equation. Check your answer.

1. $-5n = 30$; $\frac{-5n}{-5} = \frac{30}{-5}$; $n =$ −6
2. $\frac{a}{2} = -16$; $\frac{(2)a}{2} = (2)(-16)$; $a =$ −32
3. $-2w = -4$; $\frac{-2w}{-2} = \frac{-4}{-2}$; $w =$ 2
4. $8t = 32$; $\frac{8t}{8} = \frac{32}{8}$; $t =$ 4
5. $5 = g \div 6$; $6(5) = 6(g \div 6)$; 30 $= g$
6. $\frac{n}{-3} = 5$; $\frac{(-3)n}{(-3)} = (-3)(5)$; $n =$ −15

Choose a calculator, pencil and paper, or mental math to solve each equation.

7. $\frac{x}{4} = -1$ −4
8. $-5w = 125$ −25
9. $\frac{m}{-8} = 10$ −80
10. $-2 = x \div (-4)$ 8
11. $3y = 12$ 4
12. $-4t = -64$ 16
13. $9w = -81$ −9
14. $21 = -3z$ −7
15. $\frac{a}{-4} = 12$ −48
16. $-6b = 42$ −7
17. $-3 = \frac{c}{-8}$ 24
18. $5 = \frac{d}{7}$ 35
19. $2t = 38$ 19
20. $-9 = 9q$ −1
21. $n \div 6 = -3$ −18
22. $-8k = -40$ 5

ENRICHMENT

Minds on Math Transparency

3-7

I am a three-digit number. I am exactly divisible by 24 and by 36. When I am divided by 24, the quotient is 6 more than the quotient when I am divided by 36. What number am I?

432

See *Solution Key* for worked-out answers.

3-8 Teaching Notes

1 Focus

CONNECTING TO PRIOR KNOWLEDGE Have students brainstorm phrases or metaphors that describe the equal sign such as *is the same as.* Ask students: *Why is the equal sign important in an equation?* **An equal sign shows that two quantities are equivalent.**

2 Teach

THINK AND DISCUSS

Question 1 Remind students that terms such as *times, increased, less than,* and *divided by* help them decide which operation symbol to write in their equations. Students may want to review the chart on page 93.

ASSESSMENT After Try It Out, ask students to work with a partner to write the following statements as equations. Have them solve the equations.

- The product of 4 and a number equals 52. **$4n = 52; n = 13$**
- A number divided by 5 is 25. **$n \div 5 = 25; n = 125$**

AEP **Example 2** Before trying the real-world problem, students with language challenges may benefit from the following activity.

Lesson Planning Options

Prerequisite Skills

- integer operations (3-7)
- writing algebraic expressions (3-1)

Resources

Student Edition

Skills Handbook, pp. 530, 531
Extra Practice, p. 516
Glossary/Study Guide

Teaching Resources

Chapter Support File, Ch. 3
- Lesson Planner 3-8
- Practice 3-8, Reteaching 3-8
- Answer Masters 3-8

Teaching Aids Masters 26, 27
Glossary, Spanish Resources

Transparencies
11, 12, 15, Minds on Math 3-8

Warm Up

Order from least to greatest.
$\frac{1}{2}$, 0.25, $\frac{1}{6}$, -0.5, 0.3, -2
$-2, -0.5, \frac{1}{6}, 0.25, 0.3, \frac{1}{2}$

3-8 Writing Equations

What You'll Learn
- To write equations

...And Why
You can write and use equations to find the heights of buildings.

Here's How
Look for questions that
- build understanding
- ✔ check understanding

THINK AND DISCUSS

You can use what you learned about writing expressions to write equations. A word sentence translates to an equation the way a word expression translates to a mathematical expression.

EXAMPLE 1

Write and solve an equation for "Four times a number is ten."

Let n = the unknown number. ← Identify the variable.

$4n = 10$ ← Write an equation.

$\frac{4n}{4} = \frac{10}{4}$ ← Divide each side by 4.

$n = 2.5$ ← Simplify.

a–b. Variables may vary. Samples are given.

1. ✔ *Try It Out* Write and solve an equation for each sentence.
   a. Three less than a number is twelve. **$n - 3 = 12; 15$**
   b. A number divided by three equals twelve. **$\frac{n}{3} = 12; 36$**

You can write equations to solve some real-world problems.

HISTORY The first true skyscraper was built in Chicago in 1885 for the Home Insurance Corporation. It had 10 stories. The Sears Tower has 110 stories.

Source: *American Art and Architecture*

EXAMPLE 2 *Real-World Problem Solving*

Architecture The 553-m CN Tower in Toronto is 110 m taller than the Sears Tower in Chicago. Write and solve an equation to find the height of the Sears Tower.

Words • height of CN Tower | is | 110 m | more than | height of Sears Tower

• Height of CN Tower = 553
Let s = height of Sears Tower

Equation • $553 = 110 + s$

$553 = 110 + s$ ← Set up the equation.

$553 - 110 = 110 + s - 110$ ← Subtract 110 from each side.

$443 = s$ ← Simplify.

The Sears Tower is 443 m tall.

Write 7 + 5 = 12 on the board. Ask a student to read the equation aloud. Record the student's words. **Answers may vary. Sample:** ***7 plus 5 equals 12.*** Ask another student to read the equation in a different way. **Sample:** ***The sum of 7 and 5 is 12.*** Write 7 + *n* = 12. Have students read the new equation. Use other equations with all four operations for further practice.

Question 2 Ask students: *What does the variable represent in this problem?* **the number of students who attend school**

ADDITIONAL EXAMPLES

FOR EXAMPLE 1

Write and solve an equation for "Three times a number is twenty-seven." **$3n = 27$; $n = 9$**

FOR EXAMPLE 2

Jacob has saved \$38. He needs \$94 to buy a new bike. Write and solve an equation to find how much money Jacob still needs to save. **$s + 38 = 94$; $s = 56$**

Work Together

You may want to have students write each word sentence and equation on separate index cards. They can then move the cards around to match each word sentence with its equation.

2. ✔ *Try It Out* On Tuesday, 80 students were absent from Hartwell Middle School. There were 478 students present. Write and solve an equation to find how many students attend the school. **Variable may vary. Sample: $n - 80 = 478$; 558 students**

Work Together — *Matching Words and Equations*

Work with a partner. Match each word sentence with an equation.

3. Five less than a number equals three. **E**
4. Three times a number is negative five. **G**
5. A number minus three is five. **C**
6. Five is three more than a number. **A**
7. Three equals a number divided by negative five. **B**
8. The product of a number and five is negative three. **D**
9. Five plus a number is three. **H**

A. $5 = 3 + n$
B. $3 = \frac{n}{-5}$
C. $m - 3 = 5$
D. $5n = -3$
E. $p - 5 = 3$
F. $5 + 3 = n$
G. $3n = -5$
H. $5 + a = 3$
I. $y - 5 = -3$

Now you may assign Exercises 1–30.

EXERCISES *On Your Own*

Write a word sentence for each equation.

1. $67 = n + 15$
2. $13n = 69$
3. $\frac{n}{2} = 17$
4. $n - 16 = 12$
5. $18 = \frac{n}{3}$
6. $n - 2 = 34$
7. $-55 = 5n$
8. $17 + n = -12$

1. Sixty-seven is fifteen more than a number.
2. Thirteen times a number is sixty-nine.
3. Half a number is seventeen.
4. Twelve is sixteen less than a number.
5–8. See margin p. 128.

Write an equation. Then solve. **9–16. Variables may vary. Samples are given.**

9. The sum of 52 and a number is 75. **$52 + x = 75$; 23**
10. A number divided by 6 equals 8. **$\frac{n}{6} = 8$; 48**
11. Five times some number is 45. **$5n = 45$; 9**
12. Fifty-six is fourteen less than a number. **$56 = n - 14$; 70**
13. Ten times a number is sixty. **$10x = 60$; 6**
14. Negative two is ten less than a number. **$-2 = x - 10$; 8**
15. The product of negative one and a number is eight. **$-1n = 8$; -8**
16. Seven equals a number divided by negative three. **$7 = \frac{x}{-3}$; -21**

Technology Options

Prentice Hall Technology

Software for Learners
- Hot Page™ 4–10*
- Math Blaster® Mystery*
- Interactive Student Tutorial, Chapter 3*

Teaching Resource Software
- Computer Item Generator 3-8
- Resource Pro™ Chapter 3*

Internet • For related mathematics activities, visit the Prentice Hall site at www.phschool.com/math

**Available on CD-ROM only*

Assignment Options for Exercises On Your Own

Core 9–27, 30
Extension 1–8, 28, 29

Use Mixed Review to maintain skills.

3 Practice/Assess

EXERCISES *On Your Own*

ERROR ALERT! Exercises 14–16 Students may not include the correct signs in equations or solutions. **Remediation:** Have students first write the word sentence for each exercise. Then highlight or circle the word *negative* and immediately write a negative sign underneath it.

VISUAL LEARNING Exercises 19–26 Lining up the equation vertically with the word sentence helps students understand the origin of each symbol. Have students print the written sentence on the first line, then write the mathematical symbols underneath each word.

EXTENSION and CONNECTION TO SCIENCE Exercise 27 Encourage interested students to find the constellations Ptolmey named on a star chart.

WRITING Exercise 30 Before students begin to write, encourage them to solve and check the equations. Some students may try to use inverse operations to solve $150 \div 15 = g$. Explain they should only simplify this equation.

ESTIMATION Exercise 41 Review the strategies for estimating: rounding, front-end estimation, and clustering.

CHECKPOINT 2

Checkpoint 2 — *Lessons 3-5 through 3-8*

Multiply or divide.

1. $8(-9)$ — -72
2. $7(6)$ — 42
3. $-36 \div (-4)$ — 9
4. $-8 \div 2$ — -4

Solve each equation.

5. $n + 5 = -12$ — -17
6. $h - 7 = 11$ — 18
7. $y + (-8) = 15$ — 23
8. $6m = -54$ — -9
9. $-7d = 49$ — -7
10. $w \div (-4) = -10$ — 40
11. $\frac{p}{9} = -7$ — -63
12. $r \div (-3) = 20$ — -60

Write an equation. Then solve.

13. Twice a number is eighty. $2x = 80$; 40
14. Five less than a number is thirty. $n - 5 = 30$; 35

Assessment

pages 127–129 On Your Own

5. Eighteen is a number divided by three.
6. A number minus two is thirty-four.
7. Negative fifty-five is five times a number.
8. Seventeen more than a number is negative twelve.

page 129 Mixed Review

33. three hundred twelve million, two hundred ninety-one thousand, seven hundred forty-five
34. two billion, nine hundred thirty-three million, four hundred fifty-eight thousand, six hundred ninety-five
35. twenty-five million, seven hundred eighty-five thousand, four hundred fifty-six

Use the given word model to write an equation for each problem. Then solve the equation. 17–26. Variables may vary. Samples are given.

17. *Environment* The world's fastest-moving glacier is the Quarayaq in Greenland, which can flow 72.5 ft in one week. About how far can the glacier flow in one day? $7d = 72.5$; 10 ft

distance per week	$\div$	days in one week	$=$	distance per day

18. *Entertainment* You and three friends go to lunch and a matinee movie. The total cost of the outing is \$37. How much should each person contribute to share the cost evenly? $4c = 37$; \$9.25

number of people	$\times$	cost per person	$=$	total cost

Write an equation for Exercises 19–26. Then solve.

19. Four times what number is 52? $4n = 52$; 13
20. Seven subtracted from what number is 29? $n - 7 = 29$; 36
21. What number increased by 12 is 61? $x + 12 = 61$; 49
22. Six is what number divided by 9? $6 = x \div 9$; 54
23. What number added to 3 is -2? $3 + n = -2$; -5
24. Twenty-seven is 3 times what number? $27 = 3n$; 9
25. Thirteen times what number is 91? $13x = 91$; 7
26. Twelve is -7 plus what number? $12 = -7 + n$; 19
27. *Astronomy* Ptolemy, an astronomer who lived from about A.D. 85 to about A.D. 165, named 48 constellations. Today, there are 88 named constellations. How many constellations were *not* named by Ptolemy? 40 constellations

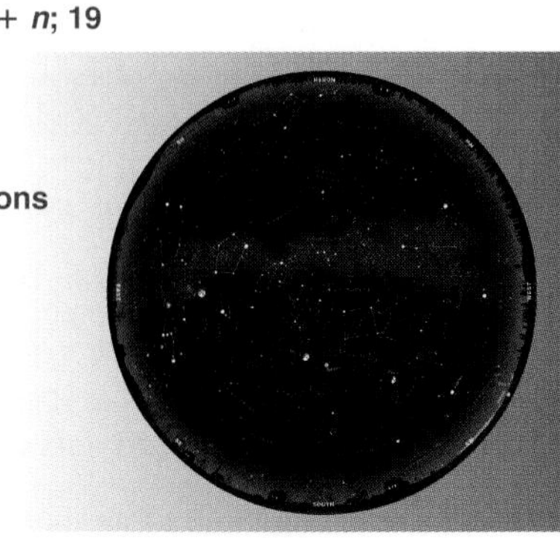

28. *Education* Hillary spends 3 h a week at soccer practice. She spends 2.5 times as long on her homework. How much time does she spend on her homework? 7.5 h
29. You are putting glasses on display shelves. You have 120 glasses. You know that each shelf holds 30 glasses. How many shelves will you need? 4 shelves
30. *Writing* One gum tree reached a height of 150 ft in 15 years. Cathy and Darla wrote different equations to find the yearly average growth of the tree, g. Cathy wrote $15g = 150$. Darla wrote $150 \div 15 = g$. Do these equations have the same solution? Explain. Yes; you get the second equation from the first by dividing each side by 15.

JOURNAL Write a problem you would use an equation to solve. Solve the problem. Explain the steps you used.

WRAP UP

IDENTIFYING THE BIG IDEA Ask students to explain how to write and solve one-step equations.

JOURNAL Encourage students to write a problem they might solve in everyday life outside math class.

PROJECT LINK Make sure students have all of the supplies they need to play the game. Have students trade rules with a partner to make sure the rules are easy to understand.

LESSON QUIZ

1. Write a word sentence for $28 = n - 4$. **28 is four less than a number.**
2. Write an equation for "The sum of 54 and a number is 46." Then solve. **$54 + n = 46$; $n = -8$**

Mixed Review

Write each number in words. *(Previous Course)* 33–35. See margin p. 128.

31. 836,001 — 31. eight hundred thirty-six thousand, one
32. 4,900,456 — 32. four million, nine hundred thousand, four hundred fifty-six
33. 312,291,745
34. 2,933,458,695
35. 25,785,456

Find the value of each expression. *(Lessons 2-3, 2-5, and 2-6)*

36. $6.2 + 7.4$ — 13.6
37. $8.3 - 2.9$ — 5.4
38. $2.4(5.2)$ — 12.48
39. $12.9 \div 4.3$ — 3
40. $2.7(3.4 - 1.9)$ — 4.05

41. *Estimation* Dalen bought three paperbacks at a used-book store. They cost \$2.53, \$2.65, and \$2.39. *(Lesson 2-2)*
    a. About how much does each paperback cost? **about \$2.50**
    b. Explain how you would estimate the total cost. **Each book is about \$2.50. The total cost is about 3×2.50.**

CHAPTER PROJECT

PROJECT LINK: ORGANIZING

Finish your game board, and write the rules of your game. Organize everything needed to play your game.

Check student's work.

✓ CHECKPOINT 2

Lessons 3-5 through 3-8

Multiply or divide.

1. $6(-7)$ — -42
2. $-3(-4)$ — 12
3. $15 \div (-3)$ — -5
4. $-28 \div 4$ — -7
5. $-9(6)$ — -54
6. $-32 \div (-8)$ — 4
7. $12(6)$ — 72
8. $-93 \div (-31)$ — 3
9. $106 \div 2$ — 53
10. $-8(11)$ — -88
11. $-12(-4)$ — 48
12. $84 \div (-12)$ — -7

Solve each equation.

13. $t \div 4 = 16$ — 64
14. $-5y = -50$ — 10
15. $\frac{p}{-3} = -6$ — 18
16. $f + (-6) = -13$ — -7
17. $r \div 7 = -6$ — -42
18. $-8d = 72$ — -9
19. $s + (-4) = 17$ — 21
20. $g - (-4) = -3$ — -7

21. **Choose A, B, C, or D.** Which equation means "Fifteen is three less than a number"? **B**
    A. $15 = 3 - n$
    B. $15 = n - 3$
    C. $15 - 3 = n$
    D. $3 - 15 = n$

Write an equation. Then solve.

22. Twenty is nine more than a number. **$20 = 9 + n$; 11**
23. Six less than a number is fifteen. **$x - 6 = 15$; 21**
24. Twice a number is sixty-two. **$2n = 62$; 31**
25. A number divided by thirteen is seven. **$\frac{x}{13} = 7$; 91**

Extra Practice, Lesson 3-8, page 516

PRACTICE

Practice 3-8 Writing Equations

Write an equation. Then solve. Equations may vary. Samples given.

1. The sum of 63 and some number is 82. $63 + n = 82$; 19
2. A number divided by negative 18 is 26. $n \div (-18) = 26$; -468
3. Nine times a number is 54. $9n = 54$; 6
4. Fifty-two divided by a number equals 4. $52 \div n = 4$; 13
5. A number divided by 8 equals 12. $\frac{n}{8} = 12$; 96
6. Sixty-eight is ninety-seven less than a number. $68 = n - 97$; 165
7. Forty-nine is thirteen less than a number. $49 = n - 13$; 62
8. Eighty-three times a number is 1,411. $83n = 1{,}411$; 17
9. Fifty-seven is 19 more than some number. $57 = n + 19$; 38
10. Seventy-five times a number is 1,800. $75n = 1{,}800$; 24
11. In order to make a teaspoon of honey, a honeybee must make 154 trips. If a honeybee made 924 trips, how many teaspoons of honey could it make? $154n = 924$; 6 teaspoons
12. Eight travelers sleeping in a hostel are snoring. The hostel has 15 sleeping travelers. How many travelers are not snoring? $8 + n = 15$; 7 travelers
13. On a trip, the Rodriguez family drove an average of 250 mi each day. If the family drove a total of 3,000 mi on their trip, how many days were they gone? $250d = 3{,}000$; 12 days
14. Maida has completed typing 6 pages of her term paper. If her term paper is 18 pages long, how many more pages does she have to type? $t + 6 = 18$; 12 pages
15. Hoshi plans to read 500 pages of a book in one week. He has completed 142 pages so far this week. How many more pages must he read? $142 + n = 500$; 358 pages
16. After withdrawing \$58, Martha had \$200 left in her savings account. How much money was in the account before the withdrawal? $x - 58 = 200$; \$258

Practice

In copymaster and workbook formats

RETEACHING

Reteaching 3-8 Writing Equations

Write and solve an equation for "A number divided by five is three."

Step 1

Identify the variable. Let n = the unknown number.

Step 2

Change the words into symbols to write the equation.

A number divided by five is three.

$n \div 5 = 3$

$\frac{n}{5} = 3$

Step 3

Solve the equation.

$5(\frac{n}{5}) = 5(3)$

$n = 15$

Complete the word sentence for each equation.

1. $x - 12 = 4$ — 12 less than x is equal to 4.
2. $\frac{45}{z} = 5$ — 45 divided by z is equal to 5.
3. $9w = 108$ — The product of 9 and w is equal to 108.
4. $y + 21 = 47$ — The sum of y and 21 is equal to 47.

Write an equation. Then solve.

5. A number doubled is 26. $2x = 26$; 13
6. Subtract 8 from a number, the result is 5. $x - 8 = 5$; 13
7. A number subtracted from 30 is 10. $30 - x = 10$; 20
8. The product of a number and 8 is 72. $8x = 72$; 9
9. The sum of 17 and a number is 77. $17 + x = 77$; 60
10. Negative five is five less than a number. $-5 = x - 5$; 0
11. A number divided by 3 equals 36. $x \div 3 = 36$; 108
12. Six times some number is 30. $6x = 30$; 5
13. If you triple my age, you will get 39. $3x = 39$; 13
14. If my age is divided by 2, the result is 18. $x \div 2 = 18$; 36

Reteaching

ENRICHMENT

Minds on Math Transparency

3-8

Kira is fertilizing her garden. She wants to add 2 tsp of fertilizer to 1 gal of water. She has a 3-gal bucket and a 7-gal bucket. How can she use these buckets to measure 1 gal of water?

Sample: Fill the 7-gal bucket. Then fill the 3-gal bucket twice from the 7-gal bucket to leave 1 gal of water.

See *Solution Key* for worked-out answers.

3-9 Teaching Notes

1 Focus

CONNECTING TO PRIOR KNOWLEDGE
Have students review the methods for solving one-step equations using these examples: $3x = -45$, $\frac{1}{4}y = 3$, $m + 4 = -9$, $p - 6 = 5$ $x = -15$; $y = 12$; $m = -13$; $p = 11$ Remind students how to use inverse operations to solve equations.

2 Teach

THINK AND DISCUSS

Review the concept of order of operations before beginning this lesson. Explain that to solve an equation using inverse operations, you also reverse the order of operations.

KINESTHETIC LEARNING If you have block scheduling or extended class periods, have students act out the equation $2x + 1 = 7$ using play money. Write a giant equal sign on the board and ask for four volunteers. Have three students stand on the left side of the equal sign, and one stand on the right. Give the student on the right side $7. Hand one of the students on the left side $1, and give the other two students empty paper bags. Explain that the bags contain the same amount of money, but the exact amount is unknown. Ask students to find how much money should be in each bag.

Lesson Planning Options

Prerequisite Skills

- integer operations (3-8)
- solving one-step equations (3-6, 3-7)

Materials/Manipulatives

- algebra tiles
- calculator

Resources

Student Edition

Skills Handbook, pp. 530, 531
Extra Practice, p. 516
Glossary/Study Guide

Teaching Resources

Chapter Support File, Ch. 3
- Lesson Planner 3-9
- Practice 3-9, Reteaching 3-9
- Alternative Activity 3-9
- Answer Masters 3-9

Teaching Aids Masters 26, 27
Glossary, Spanish Resources

Transparencies
11, 12, 15, Minds on Math 3-9

Warm Up

The short sides of a kite measure 54 cm each, and the long sides each measure 78 cm. What is the perimeter of the kite? 264 cm

ALGEBRA Connection

3-9 Solving Two-Step Equations

What You'll Learn

- To solve two-step equations

...And Why

Understanding how to solve two-step equations allows you to apply your knowledge of algebra to more situations.

Here's How

Look for questions that
- build understanding
- ✔ check understanding

THINK AND DISCUSS

You can use algebra tiles to solve some two-step equations. The tiles below show how to solve $2x + 1 = 7$.

$2x + 1 = 7$ ← Represent the equation.

$2x + 1 - 1 = 7 - 1$
$2x = 6$ ← Remove 1 tile from each side.

$\frac{2x}{2} = \frac{6}{2}$ ← Divide each side into two equal groups.

$x = 3$ ← Simplify.

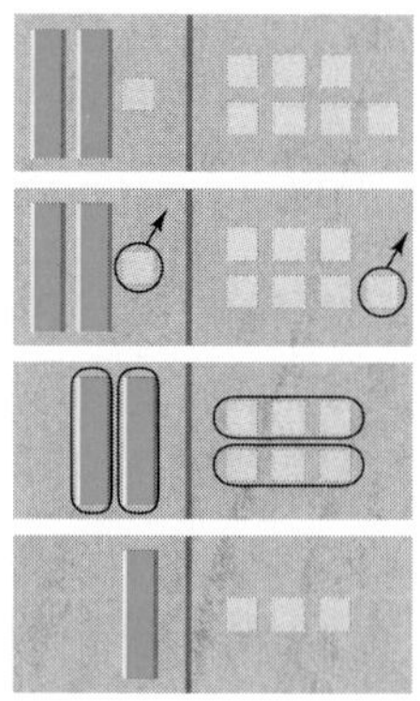

1. ✔ *Try It Out* Use algebra tiles to solve each equation.
   a. $3x - 1 = 8$ 3
   b. $4x + 2 = 14$ 3
   c. $2x - 3 = -9$ −3

You can use inverse operations to solve two-step equations.

SOLVING A TWO-STEP EQUATION

Step 1 Undo addition or subtraction.
Step 2 Undo multiplication or division.

EXAMPLE 1

Solve $5n - 7 = -22$.

$5n - 7 = -22$
$5n - 7 + 7 = -22 + 7$ ← Add 7 to each side.
$5n = -15$ ← Simplify.
$\frac{5n}{5} = \frac{-15}{5}$ ← Divide each side by 5.
$n = -3$ ← Simplify.

CONNECTION TO TECHNOLOGY and ALTERNATIVE METHOD Example 3 Some students may become intimidated by the parentheses in the example. To help them, have them solve the equation without the parentheses by pressing the equal sign between operations. For example: to solve $\frac{n}{3} + 2 = 6$, students can enter 6 [−] 2 [=] × 3 [=]. This allows students to enter the operations in the same order they would use when solving with pencil and paper.

ADDITIONAL EXAMPLES

FOR EXAMPLE 1

Solve $6r + 2 = 26$. $r = 4$

FOR EXAMPLE 2

Solve and check $\frac{a}{3} + 4 = 10$. $a = 18$

ERROR ALERT! Students may perform the multiplication or division before the addition or subtraction. **Remediation:** Remind students to reverse the order of operations because they are working with inverses. Have students circle the multiplication or division signs in an equation to remind them to undo these operations first.

---

2. *Try It Out* Solve each equation.
   a. $2n + 5 = 7$ **1** b. $2n = 5 + -7$ **−1** c. $2n - 5 = 7$ **6**

HISTORY

The earliest mathematical records that archaeologists have found come from Babylon, now central Iraq. About 300 clay tablets, dating about 2100 B.C. to A.D. 300, include many equations and their solutions.

EXAMPLE 2

Solve and check $\frac{n}{3} + 2 = 6$.

$\frac{n}{3} + 2 = 6$

$\frac{n}{3} + 2 - 2 = 6 - 2$ ← Subtract 2 from each side.

$\frac{n}{3} = 4$ ← Simplify.

$(3)\frac{n}{3} = (3)(4)$ ← Multiply each side by 3.

$n = 12$ ← Simplify.

Check: $\frac{n}{3} + 2 = 6$

$\frac{12}{3} + 2 \stackrel{?}{=} 6$ ← Replace *n* with 12.

$6 = 6$ ✓ ← Simplify.

3. a. *Reasoning* Which two operations would you use to solve $\frac{n}{3} - 2 = 6$? **addition and multiplication**
   b. Solve $\frac{n}{3} - 2 = 6$. **24**

To solve an equation like $\frac{n}{3} + 2 = 6$ using a calculator, think of the equation like this.

$\frac{n}{3} + 2 - 2 = 6 - 2$ ← Subtract 2 from each side.

$(3)\frac{n}{3} = (3)(6 - 2)$ ← Multiply each side by 3.

$n = (3)(6 - 2)$ ← Simplify the left side.

3 [×] [(] 6 [−] 2 [)] [=] 12 ← Use a calculator.

4. *Try It Out* Show the calculator sequence you would use to solve each equation.
   a. $2n + 3 = 11$ **[(] 11 [−] 3 [)] [÷] 2 [=]**
   b. $\frac{n}{5} - 2 = 8$ **[(] 8 [+] 2 [)] [×] 5 [=]**
   c. $3n + 17 = -4$ **[(] 4 [+/−] [−] 17 [)] [÷] 3 [=]**
5. *Explain* Describe how you would use a calculator to solve $12x - 35 = 76$. **Add 35 and 76. Then divide by 12.**

Now you may assign Exercises 1–50.

EXERCISES *On Your Own*

Write and solve the equation represented by each model.

1. 

3x − 2 = −5; −1

2. 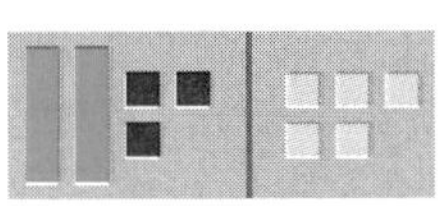

2x − 3 = 5; 4

3. 

2x + 2 = 4; 1

Technology Options

Prentice Hall Technology

Software for Learners

- Math Blaster® Mystery*
- Interactive Student Tutorial, Chapter 3*

Teaching Resource Software

- Computer Item Generator 3-9
- Resource Pro™ Chapter 3*

Internet • For related mathematics activities, visit the Prentice Hall site at www.phschool.com/math

**Available on CD-ROM only*

Assignment Options for Exercises On Your Own

Core 1–45, 50
Extension 46–49

Use Mixed Review to maintain skills.

CONNECTION TO SCIENCE Scientists use two-step equations to calculate rates and patterns of growth or decay.

ASSESSMENT Ask students to write a two-step equation and trade with a partner to solve. They should use algebra tiles to model the equation and then solve it on paper. Have them show their work step-by-step.

3 Practice/Assess

EXERCISES *On Your Own*

MENTAL MATH Exercises 8–14 You may wish to have students support their answers by writing down the operations they used to solve the equation. For example: to solve $3x + 6 = 12$, the student would write "subtract 6, divide by 3."

AEP Exercises 37–41 Students may confuse the meaning of the words *twice* and *half.* Have students write *twice* twice. Then write *half* and draw a vertical line between the "a" and the "l" to cut the word in half.

WRITING Exercise 49 Ask students to include the rules they used to decide which operation to undo first. They may want to include an additional example for their friend that shows an equation with division and addition. Have students trade notes to check for clarity.

Use a model to solve each equation. Then check your solution.

4. $2n + 6 = -8$ −7; 2(−7) + 6 = −8 ✓
5. $2x - 6 = 18$ 12; 2 × 12 − 6 = 18 ✓
6. $y - 11 = -36$ −25; −25 − 11 = −36 ✓
7. $3x - 2 = 4$ 2; 3 × 2 − 2 = 4 ✓

Mental Math **Solve each equation.**

8. $\frac{x}{3} + 9 = 9$ 0
9. $3x + 6 = 12$ 2
10. $2y - 10 = -2$ 4
11. $10t - 10 = 90$ 10
12. $5c + 5 = 0$ −1
13. $5d - 8 = 12$ 4
14. $4g + 7 = 35$ 7
15. $2p - 7 = 13$ 10

16. **Choose A, B, C, or D.** Which calculator sequence shows how to find the solution to $5x + 12 = 67$? A
    A. (67 − 12) ÷ 5 =
    B. 67 − 12 ÷ 5 =
    C. 67 ÷ 5 − 12 =
    D. 67 + 12 × 5 =

Solve each equation. Then check your solution.

17. $8r - 8 = -32$ −3; 8(−3) − 8 = −32 ✓
18. $\frac{n}{4} + 2 = 4$ 8; $\frac{8}{4} + 2 = 4$ ✓
19. $-9h + 5 = 32$ −3; −9(−3) + 5 = 32 ✓
20. $5t + 12 = 67$ 11; 5 × 11 + 12 = 67 ✓
21. $\frac{m}{-11} + 1 = -10$ 121; $\frac{121}{-11} + 1 = -10$ ✓
22. $\frac{n}{8} + 4 = 13$ 72; $\frac{72}{8} + 4 = 13$ ✓
23. $7r - 6 = -104$ −14; 7(−14) − 6 = −104 ✓
24. $4k + 5 = 41$ 9; 4 × 9 + 5 = 41 ✓
25. $3t - 6 = -15$ −3; 3(−3) − 6 = −15 ✓
26. $-6y + 2 = -4$ 1; −6 × 1 + 2 = −4 ✓
27. $10q + 3 = -27$ −3; 10(−3) + 3 = −27 ✓
28. $-5h - 2 = 8$ −2; −5(−2) − 2 = 8 ✓
29. $8a - 1 = 23$ 3; 8 × 3 − 1 = 23 ✓
30. $\frac{m}{-10} - 5 = 9$ −140; $\frac{-140}{-10} - 5 = 9$ ✓
31. $\frac{x}{-7} + 3 = -2$ 35; $\frac{35}{-7} + 3 = -2$ ✓
32. $\frac{b}{-8} - 4 = 3$ −56; $\frac{-56}{-8} - 4 = 3$ ✓

Calculator **Write a calculator sequence to solve each equation. Then solve.**

33. $4n - 6 = -12$ (12 +/− + 6) ÷ 4 =; −1.5
34. $\frac{w}{2} - 7 = -1$ (1 +/− + 7) × 2 =; 12
35. $\frac{n}{3} + 5 = 10$ (10 − 5) × 3 =; 15
36. $-2g + 8 = 12$ (12 − 8) ÷ 2 +/− =; −2

Match each sentence with a two-step equation.

37. Half a number plus three equals five. E
38. Three times a number minus four equals twelve. B
39. Twice a number plus three equals negative 1. A
40. Two less than a number divided by three equals negative five. D
41. Ten less than negative two times a number equals twenty. G
42. Seventeen more than a number times negative three equals twelve. F

A. $2c + 3 = -1$
B. $3x - 4 = 12$
C. $\frac{3}{z} - 4 = 8$
D. $\frac{b}{3} - 2 = -5$
E. $\frac{n}{2} + 3 = 5$
F. $-3a + 17 = 12$
G. $-2y - 10 = 20$

WRAP UP

IDENTIFYING THE BIG IDEA Have students write a step-by-step explanation for solving a two-step equation such as $3b - 14 = 13$.

LESSON QUIZ

Solve each equation.

1. $5k - 12 = 53$ **$k = 13$**
2. $\frac{e}{-5} + 2 = -10$ **$e = 60$**
3. $-6h + 7 = 43$ **$h = -6$**
4. $\frac{y}{3} - 4 = -8$ **$y = -12$**

43. *Jobs* Jim earns \$5/h helping a disabled man. He pays \$1 in bus fare each way. To find the number of hours he must work to make \$20, solve the equation $5h - 2 = 20$. **4.4 h**

44. *Travel* Best Deal Auto Rental offers a daily rate of \$38 plus \$.30/mile. After a one-day rental, the bill was \$74. Solve the equation $38 + 0.3m = 74$ to find the number of miles driven. **120 mi**

45. *Entertainment* Movie Madness video rental rents movies at \$3.95 for the first night, plus \$1.25 for each additional night. When he returned his movie, Ravi paid \$7.70. Solve the equation $3.95 + 1.25n = 7.7$ to find the number of extra nights Ravi kept the movie. **3 extra nights**

Write an equation. Then solve.

46. Two times a number plus five equals seventeen. **$2n + 5 = 17$; 6**

47. Three times a number minus fifty-one equals zero. **$3n - 51 = 0$; 17**

48. Three less than five times a number equals twenty-seven. **$5n - 3 = 27$; 6**

49. Five less than half a number equals negative fifteen. **$\frac{n}{2} - 5 = -15$; −20**

50. *Writing* Suppose a friend was absent from today's class. Write a note to your friend explaining how to solve the equation $5x - 23 = -13$. **Add 23 to each side. Then divide each side by 5.**

Mixed Review

Find the value of each expression. (Lesson 2-8)

51. $36 \div (2 + 4) \times 4 - 5$ **19**

52. $36 \div 2 + 4 \times 4 - 2$ **32**

53. $36 \div 2 + 4 \times (4 - 2)$ **26**

Use the spreadsheet. (Lesson 1-3)

	A	B	C
1	3	6	12
2	7	14	28
3	11	22	44

54. Which cell contains the value 12? **C1**

55. What is the value in cell B3? **22**

56. *Choose a Strategy* Every white cat at a pet show was long-haired. Half of all black cats were long-haired. Half of all long-haired cats were white. There were 40 black cats and 30 white cats. How many long-haired cats were neither black nor white? **10 cats**

PRACTICE

Practice 3-9 *Solving Two-Step Equations*

Solve each equation. Use mental math to check the solution.

1. $7m + 8 = 71$ 9
2. $\frac{y}{7} + 6 = 11$ 35
3. $12y + 2 = 146$ 12
4. $\frac{m}{9} - 17 = 21$ 342
5. $\frac{y}{-12} + 1 = 6$ −60
6. $2a - 1 = 19$ 10
7. $\frac{c}{9} - 8 = 17$ 225
8. $-4t + 16 = 24$ −2
9. $4f + 11 = -29$ −10
10. $\frac{g}{17} - 8 = -6$ 34
11. $13n - 9 = 17$ 2
12. $5v - 42 = 73$ 23
13. $\frac{b}{-2} - 8 = -6$ −4
14. $3d + 14 = 11$ −1
15. $\frac{z}{17} - 1 = 8$ 153
16. $\frac{e}{5} - 14 = 21$ 175
17. $\frac{f}{-9} + 4 = 2$ 18
18. $-2y + 16 = 10$ 3
19. $4w - 26 = 82$ 27
20. $\frac{j}{19} - 2 = -5$ −57

Write a calculator sequence to solve each equation. Then solve.

21. $3n - 8 = 4$
 [(] 4 [+] 8 [)] [÷] 3 [=]; 4
22. $\frac{n}{5} - 4 = 11$
 [(] 11 [+] 4 [)] [×] 5 [=]; 75
23. $2n - 3 = 9$
 [(] 9 [+] 3 [)] [÷] 2 [=]; 6
24. $1 + \frac{n}{4} = 9$
 [(] 9 [−] 1 [)] [×] 4 [=]; 32

Match each sentence with a two-step equation.

25. Half a number minus five equals fifteen. E
26. Five more than half of a number equals fifteen. C
27. Two less than three times a number equals twelve. B
28. Eight less than the quotient of a number and four equals negative five. F
29. Three times a number increased by two equals twelve. D
30. Eight fewer than four times a number equals negative five. A

A. $4n - 8 = -5$
B. $3n - 2 = 12$
C. $\frac{n}{2} + 5 = 15$
D. $3n + 2 = 12$
E. $\frac{n}{2} - 5 = 15$
F. $\frac{n}{4} - 8 = -5$

In copymaster and workbook formats

RETEACHING

Reteaching 3-9 *Solving Two-Step Equations*

The marbles and boxes represent this equation.

$2x + 3 = 7$

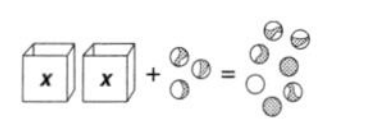

The variable x stands for the number of marbles (unseen) in each box.

There are the same number of marbles on each side and the same number of marbles in each box.

To solve the equation, follow these steps.

Step 1

Subtract the extra marbles from both sides.

$2x + 3 - 3 = 7 - 3$

$2x = 4$

Step 2

Divide the number of marbles by 2, the number of boxes.

$\frac{2x}{2} = \frac{4}{2}$

$x = 2$

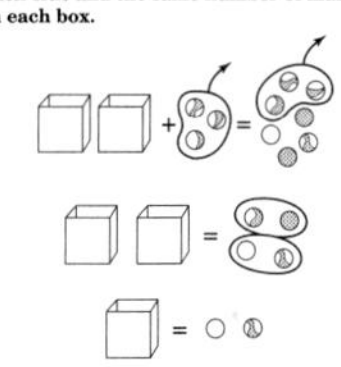

Write an equation. Use the picture to help solve.

1. 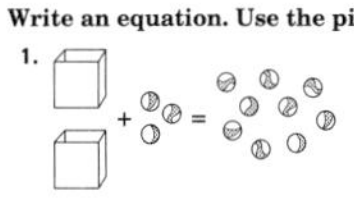

 2x + 3 = 9
 $x =$ 3

2. 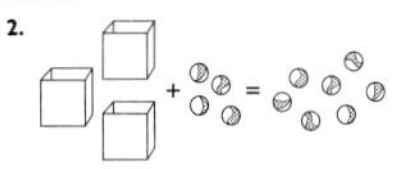

 3x + 4 = 7
 $x =$ 1

Complete to solve each equation.

3. $5x + 7 = 2$
 $5x + 7 -$ 7 $= 2 -$ 7
 $\frac{5x}{\boxed{5}} = \frac{-5}{\boxed{5}}$
 $x =$ −1

4. $2x - 1 = 9$
 $2x - 1 +$ 1 $= 9 +$ 1
 $\frac{2x}{\boxed{2}} = \frac{10}{\boxed{2}}$
 $x =$ 5

Solve each equation.

5. $4x + 7 = 15$ 2
6. $3b - 5 = 13$ 6
7. $5t - 2 = -17$ −3
8. $3z + 1 = 16$ 5
9. $7h - 9 = -2$ 1
10. $2k + 12 = -2$ −7

ENRICHMENT

Minds on Math Transparency

3-9

Find the value of this expression.

$1 + 1 \times 1 \div 1 - 1 \div 1 + 1 \times (1 - 1) + 1$

2

See *Solution Key* for worked-out answers.

3-10 Teaching Notes

1 Focus

CONNECTING TO PRIOR KNOWLEDGE
Ask students:

- *Name different visual displays used to organize information.* **bar graph, line graph, table, circle graph**
- *Describe what a table looks like.* **columns and rows with headings, different entries at each intersection**

2 Teach

THINK AND DISCUSS

ERROR ALERT! Some students may duplicate solutions in their tables. **Remediation:** Encourage them to use patterns when creating the tables.

DIVERSITY Question 3 Some students may know the value of a coin, but not the name. Show students examples of the coins when setting up the table. Label the value of each coin in the headings.

TACTILE LEARNING Question 3 Some students are comfortable with the visual display in a table, but others may need to hold the coins to understand the different combinations. Pair students to work on extending the table. Have one student record the data, while the other uses play money to try the different combinations of change.

Lesson Planning Options

Prerequisite Skills

- constructing and using tables (precourse)
- making change (precourse)

Student Edition

Skills Handbook, p. 528
Extra Practice, p. 516
Glossary/Study Guide

Teaching Resources

Chapter Support File, Ch. 3
- Lesson Planner 3-10
- Practice 3-10, Reteaching 3-10
- Answer Masters 3-10

Glossary, Spanish Resources

Transparencies
Minds on Math 3-10

Warm Up

Arrange the numbers 3, 4, 6, and 9 to create four numbers that are greater than 9,000 and less than 9,500. **9,346; 9,364; 9,436; 9,463**

PROBLEM SOLVING STRATEGY

READ PLAN SOLVE LOOK BACK

3-10 Make a Table

Problem Solving Strategies

- Draw a Diagram
- Guess and Test
- Look for a Pattern
- Make a Model
- ✔ Make a Table
- Simulate a Problem
- Solve a Simpler Problem
- Too Much or Too Little Information
- Use Logical Reasoning
- Use Multiple Strategies
- Work Backward
- Write an Equation

THINK AND DISCUSS

When a problem requires you to look at a lot of possibilities, you can organize the information in a table.

SAMPLE PROBLEM

Sheila works at a variety store after school. Three children bought the same items. Sheila gave each child 45¢ in change. She used a different combination of coins each time. Then Sheila wondered how many ways she could make 45¢ in change without using pennies.

READ
Read for understanding. Summarize the problem.

1. Restate what you are to find in your own words. **the number of different ways you can make 45¢ with quarters, dimes and nickels**
2. What information will you need to use to solve the problem? **how much each coin is worth**

PLAN
Decide on a strategy.

Making a table of the coins and their values will help you find all the possible coin combinations that total value 45¢. A table will also help you avoid using the same combination more than once.

SOLVE
Try the strategy.

3. a. Copy and complete the table. Extend the table until you have found all possible combinations. **See margin p. 137.**

Coin	Number of Coins (Value)			
Quarter	1(25¢)	1(25¢)	1(25¢)	0(0¢)
Dime	0(0¢)	1(10¢)	2(20¢)	■
Nickel	4(20¢)	2(10¢)	0(0¢)	■
Total value	45¢	45¢	45¢	■

b. How many different ways can Sheila make 45¢ in change without using pennies? **8 ways**

LOOK BACK
Think about how you solved the problem.

4. How did the table help you organize the information? **Answers m vary. Sample: The table helps you to make sure you include all possibiliti**
5. Make a table to show all the ways of making 60¢ in change without using pennies. **See margin p. 137.**

Now you may assign Exercises 1–10.

ASSESSMENT Have students work with a partner to find the number of possible combinations of coins that can make 35¢. Students may use quarters, dimes, nickels, and up to ten pennies. 15

■ ADDITIONAL PROBLEM

For his trip, Karl packed a red shirt, a striped shirt, a white shirt, a pair of blue jeans, and a pair of black jeans. Make a table to find out how many different outfits he could wear if he chose a shirt and a pair of jeans from his suitcase. 6

3 Practice/Assess

EXERCISES *On Your Own*

EXTENSION **Exercise 3** Three combinations correctly answer this question. Have students add an additional piece of information that will restrict the question so that there is only one answer. For example: If Kim bought nine books, how many of each kind of book did she buy?

WRAP UP

IDENTIFYING THE BIG IDEA Ask students to describe how to solve a problem by making a table. Have them give a specific example.

PORTFOLIO Share with students the criteria you use to assess their work in portfolios, as well as how you plan to use the results. Students should understand how you use the rubrics to assess their work, how each piece in the portfolio counts, and how

EXERCISES *On Your Own*

Make a table to solve each problem.

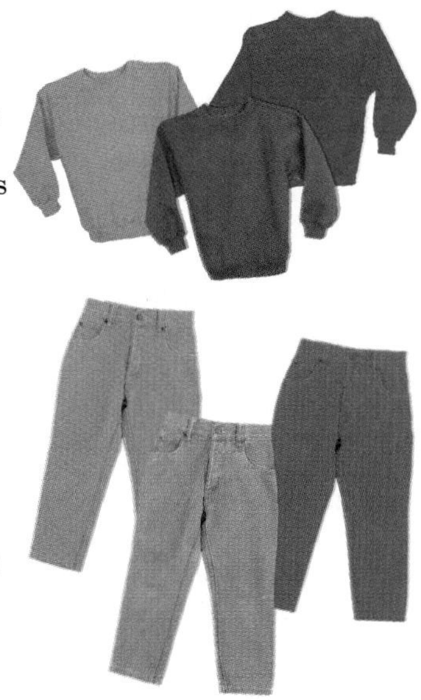

1. Each day Jamal selects a pair of jeans and a sweatshirt from his wardrobe.
   a. How many different combinations of jeans and sweatshirts can Jamal make with his clothes? 9 combinations
   b. Describe any patterns or shortcuts you found that helped you solve the problem. Check students' work.
2. Karen remembers that the three digits in her locker combination are 3, 5, and 7, but she has forgotten the order of the numbers. What is the maximum number of combinations she must check in order to open her lock? 6 combinations
3. The local library sponsored a used book sale to raise money. The books were priced at \$.60 for paperback books and \$1.00 for hardcover books. Kim spent \$4.40. How many of each kind of book did she buy? 4 paperback and 2 hardcover books

Use any strategy to solve each problem. Show all your work.

4. Hanon and Oliver collected \$29 for tickets to the science museum. Adult's tickets cost \$7, and children's tickets cost \$5. How many adults and how many children plan to visit the museum? 2 adults and 3 children
5. a. The town of Dornville is 15 mi south of Chester. Topson is 12 mi north of Dornville. Ludberg is 4.5 mi north of Topson. What is the order of the towns from north to south? Lundberg, Chester, Topson, Dornville
   b. What is the distance between Dornville and Ludberg? 16.5 mi
6. Without looking, Ruben drew one marble at a time from a bowl containing red, green, blue, and white marbles. He was told to stop when he had one marble of each color. What is the least number of marbles he could have selected? 4 marbles
7. A science teacher discovered that students had used, and misplaced, several of his weights. He can find the 9 mg, 7 mg, 2 mg, and 5 mg weights. How can he use these weights to find out if a piece of copper wire weighs 1 mg? See margin p. 137.

Technology Options

Prentice Hall Technology

Software for Learners

- Math Blaster® Mystery*
- Interactive Student Tutorial, Chapter 3*

Teaching Resource Software

- Computer Item Generator 3-10
- Resource Pro™ Chapter 3*

Internet • For related mathematics activities, visit the Prentice Hall site at www.phschool.com/math

**Available on CD-ROM only*

Assignment Options for Exercises On Your Own

Core 1–9, 11, 12
Extension 10

Use Mixed Review to maintain skills.

PRACTICE

Practice 3-10 *Problem-Solving Strategy: Make a Table*

Make a table to solve each problem.

1. At a yard sale, Rhonda bought 9 items costing either \$.50 or \$.75. If she spent a total of \$5.00, how many items of each price did Rhonda buy?
   7 of \$.50 and 2 of \$.75
2. You have a penny, a nickel, and a dime. Name the different amounts of money that are possible using one or more of these coins.
   1¢, 5¢, 6¢, 10¢, 11¢, 15¢, 16¢
3. Vijay bought 11 tickets for a waterslide. The tickets were \$6 for adults and \$4 for children. Vijay paid \$60 for the tickets. For how many adults and how many children did he buy tickets?
   8 adults and 3 children
4. A certain kind of sports car is available in red, white, black, or silver. The upholstery is available in leather, vinyl, or cloth. The dealer keeps one of each possible type on the lot. How many sports cars are on the lot?
   12 cars

Use any strategy to solve each problem. Show all your work.

5. Over the summer three friends saved a total of \$180. Marti saved twice as much as Paula and \$10 more than Oscar. How much did each save?
   \$76; \$38; \$66
6. Find two integers whose sum is 5 and whose product is −36.
   −4 and 9
7. A ball is dropped from a height of 16 ft. Each time it hits the ground it bounces three-fourths of its previous height. The ball is caught when the height of its bounce is $6\frac{3}{4}$ ft. What is the total vertical distance the ball traveled?
   $64\frac{3}{4}$ ft
8. Mai and Juan are friends. They live at corners of the blocks as shown below. How many different routes can Juan take to Mai's house? He only travels west or north and does not retrace his steps.

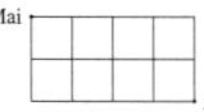

   15 routes
9. How many rectangles are in the figure below?

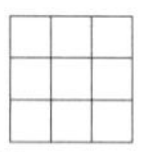

   36 rectangles

Practice

In copymaster and workbook formats

RETEACHING

Reteaching 3-10 *Problem-Solving Strategy: Make a Table*

Amanda decided to donate \$.10 to the school fund Monday and to double her contribution each day for 5 days. How much will she give in all?

Read What do you need to find out? *You need to find out how much money Amanda will contribute in 5 days.*

Plan You can make a table to help organize information to solve the problem.

Solve

Day	1	2	3	4	5
Amount	\$.10	\$.20	\$.40	\$.80	\$1.60

To find how much Amanda will give in all, find the sum for the 5 days. \$.10 + \$.20 + \$.40 + \$.80 + \$1.60 = \$3.10

Look Back How could you use models to solve the problem? *Use dimes to model the problem and count the dimes.*

Complete each table to solve.

1. How much will Amanda give in all if she doubles her contribution every day for 7 days? \$12.70

Day	5	6	7
Amount	\$1.60	\$3.20	\$6.40

2. Adult tickets at the zoo cost \$5. Children's tickets are \$3. Four people go to the zoo and spend \$14. How many adults and how many children go to the zoo?
   3 children, 1 adult

Children	Adults	Cost
0	4	\$20
1	3	\$18
2	2	\$16
3	1	\$14
4	0	\$12

Make a table to solve each problem.

3. Sean spends \$8 on snacks for himself and 4 friends. A bag of popcorn costs \$1 and a fruit cup costs \$2. He buys 1 item for each person. How many bags of popcorn and fruit cups does he buy?
   2 bags of popcorn, 3 fruit cups
4. Ming is planning a design with sequins for a T-shirt. The first row has 5 sequins. Each row has 4 more sequins than the row before it. How many sequins will be in the 8th row? How many are needed for all for 8 rows?
   33 sequins; 152 sequins

Reteaching

ENRICHMENT

Minds on Math Transparency

3-10

Trevor has 8 square tables. One person can sit at each side of each table. Trevor wants to arrange the tables so that each table shares a side with at least one other table. He wants to be able to seat 18 people. How could Trevor arrange the tables? Find as many arrangements as you can.

Sample:

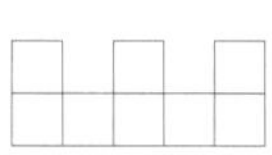

Course 2 Minds on Math Transparency 53

See *Solution Key* for worked-out answers.

the scores they get in their portfolios will affect their overall evaluation.

LESSON QUIZ

Make a table to solve each problem.

1. How many different ways are there to make 20¢ using dimes, nickels, and pennies? **9**
2. The school gift shop sells T-shirts for \$10 and caps for \$4. The shop made \$48 on Thursday. How many of each item did they sell? **There are 3 combinations: 4 shirts and 2 caps; 2 shirts and 7 caps; 12 caps.**

8. *Biology* In spring, a female crocodile lays 30 to 70 eggs. After 90 days the eggs hatch. Baby crocodiles are about 12 in. long when they hatch and grow about 10 in. a year. How old is a crocodile that is about 32 in. long? **2 yr old**
9. *Physical Science* A ball drops 16 ft and hits the ground. It bounces one-half its previous height on each bounce. The ball is caught when the height of its bounce is 2 ft. What is the total vertical distance the ball travels? **42 ft**
10. *Sports* A weight lifter can lift 80 kg plus the weight of the bar. He has 5 kg, 10 kg, and 25 kg weights. The bar will hold up to seven weights on each side. Each side must have the same weights. How many different combinations of weights can be placed on the bar for a total of 80 kg? **6 ways**
11. During a 10-minute period in a busy office building, an elevator started at the ground floor, rose 8 floors, rose 7 floors, descended 3 floors, rose 5 floors, descended 1 floor, rose 2 floors, rose 8 floors, and descended 11 floors. On which floor was the elevator at the end of the 10-minute period? **15th floor**
12. Jaleesa has three pen pals. She writes back the same week that she gets a letter. Robby writes every four weeks, Emma every three weeks, and Takashi every five weeks. Jaleesa wrote to all of her pen pals this week. How many weeks will it be before she writes to them all in the same week again? **60 weeks**

PORTFOLIO

Select one or two items from your work for this chapter. Consider:
- work with manipulatives
- work you found challenging
- cooperative work

Explain why you have included each selection that you make.

Mixed Review

13. a. *Data Analysis* Use the data to find the mean, median, and mode. (Lesson 1-4) **about \$41,167; \$25,000; \$14,000**
    b. Suppose you were a worker earning \$14,000. Would you use the mean or the median to convince your boss that you should be given a raise? Why? (Lesson 1-8) **Mean; the gap between your salary and the mean is the greatest.**

Yearly Salary

Name	Salary
Sylvia	\$ 14,000
Jose	\$ 23,000
Yukiko	\$ 27,000
Brisa	\$ 14,000
Elki	\$ 65,000
Anitha	\$104,000

Order from least to greatest. (Lesson 2-1)

14. 0.234, 0.243, 0.23, 0.24 **0.23, 0.234, 0.24, 0.243**
15. 0.368, 0.3681, 0.36792, 0.3 **0.3, 0.36792, 0.368, 0.3681**
16. *Weather* Between 1862 and 1866 British scientist James Glaisher made 28 balloon flights to gather weather data. During one flight, temperature went from 19°C to –8°C. What was the temperature range? (Lesson 3-4) **27°C**

FINISHING THE CHAPTER PROJECT

PROJECT DAY You may wish to plan a project day on which students share their completed projects. Encourage students to explain their process as well as their product.

PROJECT NOTEBOOK Ask students to review their project work and bring their notebooks up to date.

- Have students review their methods for designing and revising the game.
- Encourage students to play each other's games to check for clarity and completeness.

SCORING RUBRIC

3 You provided work to show that you thought about your game before putting it together. Your game includes opportunities to use addition, subtraction, and multiplication of positive and negative integers. Your finished game board is attractive, and your project includes rules that are easy to understand and follow.

2 You created a game that includes opportunities to add, subtract, and multiply positive and negative integers, but your finished product is not as well-planned or constructed as it could have been.

1 Your finished game is not well-thought-out or does not provide many opportunities to add, subtract, and multiply positive and negative integers.

0 You did not make a game, or you did not include the use of both positive and negative integers in your game.

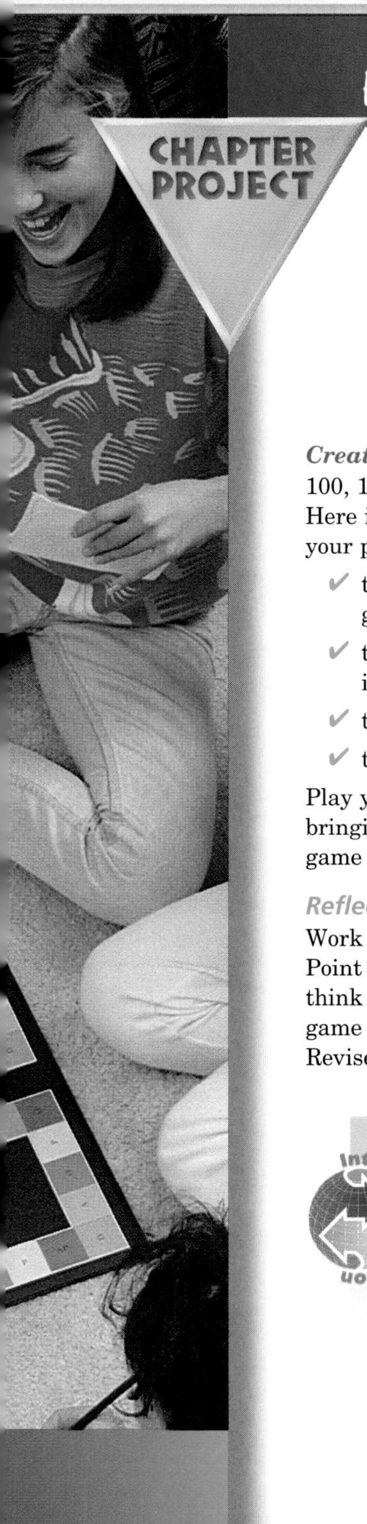

FINISHING THE CHAPTER PROJECT

CHAPTER PROJECT

Board Walk

Create a Board Game The Project Link questions on pages 100, 110, 116, and 129 should help you complete your project. Here is a checklist to help you gather together the parts of your project.

- ✔ the setting for your game, and how moves and the end of game are determined
- ✔ the rough draft of your game board with ways to use integers
- ✔ the details for using multiplication of integers
- ✔ the final game board and the rules for your game

Play your game so you can make final revisions before bringing it to school. Is the game too easy or too hard? Is the game interesting enough? What should you add or change?

Reflect and Revise

Work (or play) in small groups to test each other's games. Point out to each other the features of the games that you think are well-designed. What part of the mathematics of the game works well? What do you like about playing the game? Revise your game based on comments from your group.

Web Extension

Prentice Hall's Internet site contains information you might find helpful as you complete your project. Visit www.phschool.com/mgm2/ch3 for some links and ideas related to creating a board game.

page 134 Think and Discuss

3a.

Quarter	Dime	Nickel	Total Value
0 (0¢)	4 (40¢)	1 (5¢)	45¢
0 (0¢)	3 (30¢)	3 (15¢)	45¢
0 (0¢)	2 (20¢)	5 (25¢)	45¢
0 (0¢)	1 (10¢)	7 (35¢)	45¢
0 (0¢)	0 (0¢)	9 (45¢)	45¢

5.

Quarter	Dime	Nickel
2 (50¢)	1 (10¢)	0 (0¢)
2 (50¢)	0 (0¢)	2 (10¢)
1 (25¢)	3 (30¢)	1 (5¢)
1 (25¢)	2 (20¢)	3 (15¢)
1 (25¢)	1 (10¢)	5 (25¢)
1 (25¢)	0 (0¢)	7 (35¢)
0 (0¢)	6 (60¢)	0 (0¢)
0 (0¢)	5 (50¢)	2 (10¢)
0 (0¢)	4 (40¢)	4 (20¢)
0 (0¢)	3 (30¢)	6 (30¢)
0 (0¢)	2 (20¢)	8 (40¢)
0 (0¢)	1 (10¢)	10 (50¢)
0 (0¢)	0 (0¢)	12 (60¢)

pages 135–136 On Your Own

7. Place the 7 mg and 5 mg weights on one side and 9 mg, 2 mg, and the wire on the other. If the weights balance, the wire weighs 1 mg.

STUDENT SELF-ASSESSMENT SURVEY

Chapter 3 Student Self-Assessment Survey

1. Now that you have finished this chapter, think about what you have been introduced to in algebra. Check each topic that you feel confident you understand.
   - ______ write and evaluate variable expressions (3-1)
   - ______ graph and order integers (3-2)
   - ______ find the opposite and absolute value of an integer (3-2)
   - ______ model addition of integers (3-3)
   - ______ add integers (3-3)
   - ______ model subtraction of integers (3-4)
   - ______ subtract integers (3-4)
   - ______ multiply and divide integers (3-5)
   - ______ solve one-step addition and subtraction equations (3-6)
   - ______ solve one-step multiplication and division equations (3-7)
   - ______ write and solve one-step equations (3-8)
   - ______ solve two-step equations (3-9)
   - ______ solve problems by making tables (3-10)
2. Before the Chapter Assessment, I need to review ______________________
3. **a.** Check one. In general, I thought this chapter was
   ____ a snap ____ easy ____ average ____ hard ____ a monster
   b. Why do you feel this way? ______________________
4. In this chapter, I did my best work on ______________________
5. In this chapter, I had trouble with ______________________
6. This chapter is an introduction to algebra. Based on this chapter, do you think you will like doing more work in algebra? Explain. ______________________
7. Before doing this chapter, you did chapters on decimals and on interpreting data. How would you compare this chapter with those chapters, both in difficulty and in how much you liked them? ______________________
8. Did you use a computer spreadsheet in this chapter? ______
   What are some situations in which people use spreadsheets outside the classroom? ______________________

Vocabulary/Symbols

absolute value, Addition Property of Equality, Division Property of Equality, integers, Multiplicative Property of Equality, solution, Subtraction Property of Equality, variable, variable expression

Materials/Manipulatives

- calculator
- algebra tiles

Resources

Student Edition

Extra Practice, p. 516
Glossary/Study Guide

Teaching Resources

Chapter Support File, Ch. 3
- Student Self-Assessment Survey

Glossary, Spanish Resources
Tools for Studying Smarter

WRAP UP

Exercise 19 Encourage students to draw or use models to help support their answer.

WRITING **Exercise 33** Encourage students to actually find the sum and product of -5 and 8. Then they can describe the process they used to determine the sign.

Exercises 34–41 Have students support their answers by drawing the models, writing out what they would enter in the calculator, or showing all the steps in a pencil and paper solution.

ASSESSMENT You may want to have students work in pairs. For each exercise, have one partner use a model or a number line to solve the problem. Have the other partner use mental math or pencil and paper. Then have partners compare results.

3 WRAP UP

Variable Expressions — 3-1

A **variable** is a symbol that stands for a number. A **variable expression** contains at least one variable. To evaluate an expression, you replace the variable with a number and simplify.

Evaluate each expression for $x = 3$ and $y = 5$.

1. $6x + 9$ 27
2. $3 + 8y$ 43
3. xy 15
4. $2x + y$ 11
5. $3x - y$ 4
6. $2y - 3x$ 1

Write a variable expression for each word phrase.

7. n less than 8 $8 - n$
8. the product of 6 and c $6c$
9. 6 more than twice n $6 + 2n$

Integers, Opposites, and Absolute Value — 3-2

Opposites are two numbers that are the same distance from 0 on a number line, but in opposite directions. The set of **integers** is the set of whole numbers and their opposites. The **absolute value** of an integer is its distance from 0 on a number line.

11.
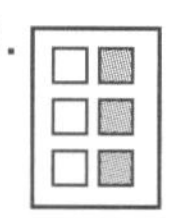

10. What integer represents 9°F below zero? -9
11. Draw a model for zero using 6 tiles.
12. Write the absolute value of each integer.
    a. -5 5 **b.** 2 2 **c.** -17 17
13. Order the integers from least to greatest.
    7 -6 0 -3 1 $-6, -3, 0, 1, 7$

Compare. Use <, >, or =.

14. -7 ■ 7 <
15. $|-3|$ ■ $|3|$ =
16. -12 ■ 0 <
17. $|-9|$ ■ -4 >
18. 8 ■ -15 >

19. **Choose A, B, C, or D.** Which number of tiles could you use to model -5? B
    A. 4 tiles **B.** 9 tiles **C.** 10 tiles **D.** 12 tiles

Adding and Subtracting Integers — 3-3, 3-4

The sum of two positive integers is positive. The sum of two negative integers is negative. To find the sum of two integers with *different* signs, *subtract* their absolute values. The sum has the same sign as the integer with the greater absolute value.

To subtract an integer, add its opposite.

Remind students that the new mathematical terms in this chapter are defined in the Glossary/Study Guide in the back of the book.

Write an expression for each model. Then find its value.

20. 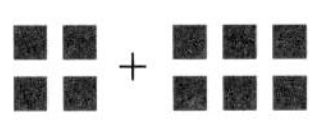

$-4 + (-6); -10$

21. 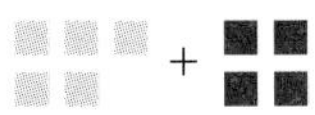

$5 + (-4); 1$

22. 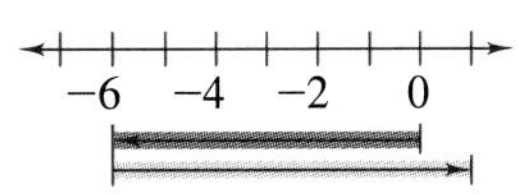

$-6 + 7; 1$

Find each sum or difference.

23. $-4 + 7$ 3
24. $-14 + (-8)$ −22
25. $3 - 8$ −5
26. $17 - (-12)$ 29
27. $15 + (-18)$ −3

Multiplying and Dividing Integers 3-5

The product or quotient of two integers with the *same* sign is *positive*.

The product or quotient of two integers with *different* signs is *negative*.

Find each product or quotient.

28. $-5 \cdot 6$ −30
29. $-14 \cdot (-6)$ 84
30. $125 \div (-5)$ −25
31. $-98 \div (-49)$ 2
32. $-15 \div 3$ −5

33. *Writing* Explain how to determine the signs of each of the following: the sum of −5 and 8 and the product of −5 and 8.
See back of book.

Solving Equations with Integers 3-6, 3-7, 3-8, 3-9

To solve an equation using addition or subtraction, add or subtract the same value from both sides of the equation.

To solve an equation using multiplication or division, multiply or divide both sides of the equation by the same nonzero value.

Choose **Use models, a calculator, or paper and pencil to solve and check.**

34. $x - (-2) = -4$ −6
35. $2y = 8$ 4
36. $\frac{q}{5} = 7$ 35
37. $3m + 4 = -2$ −2
38. $t + 4 = -5$ −9
39. $\frac{w}{2} = -7$ −14
40. $-8g = -24$ 3
41. $3d - 4 = 17$ 7

42. Write an equation for the statement "Four more than a number is negative seven." Solve the equation.
$4 + n = -7; -11$

Problem Solving Strategies 3-10

You can use the strategy Make a Table to solve problems.

43. Tadeo sold banners for a school fund raiser. Small banners cost \$1.25. The large ones cost \$1.75. How many of each size could he sell for \$20? Write all the possible solutions.

Large	Small
0 (\$0)	16 (\$20)
5 (\$8.75)	9 (\$11.25)
10 (\$17.50)	2 (\$2.50)

CHAPTER ASSESSMENT • FORM A

Chapter 3 Assessment • Form A

Compare. Use >, <, or =. Answers

1. $|-4|$ ▩ $|1|$ — 1. >
2. −2 ▩ −6 — 2. >
3. Order −8, 3, 0, −1 and −12 from least to greatest. — 3. −12, −8, −1, 0, 3

Use mental math to find each sum or difference.

4. $-2 - (-3)$ — 4. 1
5. $10 + (-6) + (-3)$ — 5. 1

Simplify using mental math.

6. $-7 + 3 - (-7)$ — 6. 3
7. $12 - 7 + (-12)$ — 7. −7

Estimate each product or quotient.

8. $89(-71)$ — 8. about −6,300
9. $-104 \div 4$ — 9. about −25

Solve each equation.

10. $-7 + n = 0$ — 10. 7
11. $4y = -28$ — 11. −7
12. $\frac{z}{3} = -5$ — 12. −15

Write an equation. Then solve.

13. The sum of 45 and some number is 53. — 13. $45 + n = 53; 8$
14. A number divided by 7 equals 1. — 14. $\frac{x}{7} = 1; 7$

Evaluate for $a = -2$ and $b = 8$.

15. $5(a + b)$ — 15. 30
16. $ab \div 4$ — 16. −4
17. $a - b$ — 17. −10
18. $2b + 5$ — 18. 21

Assessment

CHAPTER ASSESSMENT • FORM A

Chapter 3 Assessment • Form A (continued)

Solve each equation.

19. $3x + 4 = -14$ — 19. −6
20. $\frac{x}{-6} - 12 = 12$ — 20. −144

Write a variable expression for each word phrase.

21. five less than *y* — 21. $y - 5$
22. the product of a number and 78 — 22. $78n$
23. the quotient of a number and 9 — 23. $n \div 9$
24. ten increased by a number — 24. $10 + n$

Choose A, B, C, or D.

25. Which equation would you use to represent the following situation? Julie has some money. Cara has \$7 more than the amount Julie has. Together they have \$40. — 25. C
   A. $7 + n = 40$
   B. $n - 7 = 40$
   C. $7 + n + n = 40$
   D. $n + n = 40$

Choose a Strategy

26. Make a table of heads and tails to show all possible ways three coins can land after being tossed in the air. — 26. Possible combinations:

Coin 1	H	H	H	H	T	T	T	T
Coin 2	H	H	T	T	T	T	H	H
Coin 3	H	T	T	H	T	H	H	T

Writing

27. Is the addition sentence (negative) + (negative) = (negative) *always*, *sometimes*, or *never* true? Support your answer with examples.
Always; samples: $(-2) + (-4) = -6$,
$(-10) + (-5) = -15$

CHAPTER ASSESSMENT • FORM B

Chapter 3 Assessment • Form B

Choose the best answer. Circle A, B, C, or D.

1. Which number is *not* greater than $|-8|$?
   A. $|-10|$ Ⓑ $|-6|$ C. $|-18|$ D. $|20|$
2. Which number is less than -4?
   A. -1 B. 0 Ⓒ -9 D. $|-4|$
3. Which list shows the integers in order from least to greatest?
   A. $-3, -5, 0$ B. $-5, 0, -3$ C. $0, -3, -5$ Ⓓ $-5, -3, 0$
4. Simplify $-9 - (-9)$ using mental math.
   A. -18 B. 18 Ⓒ 0 D. -81
5. Simplify $-15 + (-2) - (-15)$ using mental math.
   A. 32 B. 2 Ⓒ -2 D. -32
6. Which expression is equivalent to $48 - (-29)$?
   A. $-29 + 48$ Ⓑ $48 + 29$ C. $-48 - 29$ D. $48 + (-29)$
7. Simplify $-3 + 7 + (-4)$.
   A. 14 Ⓑ 0 C. -6 D. -14
8. Estimate $104(-99)$.
   Ⓐ about $-10{,}000$ B. about 0
   C. about 200 D. about $-90{,}000$
9. Estimate $-571 \div 32$.
   A. about -540 Ⓑ about -20
   C. about -600 D. about 20
10. Solve $-10 + x = 0$.
    Ⓐ 10 B. 0 C. -10 D. $\frac{1}{10}$
11. Solve $9n = -63$.
    A. -567 B. 7 Ⓒ -7 D. 567
12. Solve $\frac{y}{-5} = 0$.
    Ⓐ 0 B. 5 C. -5 D. -0

Assessment

CHAPTER ASSESSMENT • FORM B

Chapter 3 Assessment • Form B (continued)

13. Which of the following shows an equation for "the sum of -23 and some number is -4"?
    A. $-23 + n = 4$ B. $23 + n = 4$ Ⓒ $-23 + n = -4$ D. $23 + (-4) = n$
14. Which of the following shows an equation for "a number times 7 equals -35"?
    A. $7n = 35$ B. $\frac{7}{n} = 35$ Ⓒ $7n = -35$ D. $7(-35) = n$
15. Which equation would you use to represent the following situation? Jan has some money. Carl has \$5 less than the amount Jan has. Together they have \$19.
    A. $5 + n = 19$ Ⓑ $n - 5 + n = 19$
    C. $n - 5 = 19$ D. $5 - n + n = 19$
16. Solve $-9 + 2x = 31$.
    A. -40 Ⓑ 20 C. -16 D. -20
17. Solve $\frac{y}{-4} + 24 = 24$.
    A. -4 B. -12 Ⓒ 0 D. 12
18. Evaluate the expression $2g + h$ for $g = -2$ and $h = 3$.
    A. 7 B. 1 Ⓒ -1 D. -7
19. Which expression shows the number of inches in y yards?
    Ⓐ $36y$ B. $12y$ C. $3y$ D. $y + 36$
20. **Choose A, B, or C.** The addition sentence (positive) $-$ (negative) $=$ (negative) is ▒.
    A. always true B. sometimes true Ⓒ never true

Choose a Strategy

21. How many combinations of pennies, nickels, dimes, and quarters could Joe use to give \$.27 in change?
    A. 6 B. 4 C. 8 Ⓓ 13

Teaching Resources

Chapter Support File, Ch. 3, and Spanish Resources

Teacher's Edition

See pp. 90C–D for Assessment Options.

Teaching Resource Software

- Computer Item Generator, Ch. 3

ASSESSMENT

OPEN-ENDED PROBLEMS allow for more than one solution. Students must construct their own responses instead of choosing from possible answers. The student responses will help you determine the depth of their understanding and any possible areas of difficulty. **Exercise 1** is an open-ended problem.

WRITING EXERCISES allow students to describe more fully their thinking and understanding of the concepts they've learned. **Exercise 7** is a writing exercise.

ENHANCED MULTIPLE CHOICE QUESTIONS are more complex than traditional multiple choice questions, which assess only one skill. Enhanced multiple choice questions assess the processes that students use, as well as the end result. They are written so that students can use more than one strategy to solve the problem. Using multiple strategies is encouraged by the National Council of Teachers of Mathematics (NCTM). **Exercises 8 and 15** are enhanced multiple choice questions.

3 ASSESSMENT

1a–d. Samples are given.

1. *Open-ended* Complete with an integer that makes each statement true.
   a. $-1 < \blacksquare$ **1** b. $\blacksquare > -7$ **10**
   c. $|-13| > \blacksquare$ **0** d. $-17 < \blacksquare$ **−5**
2. Draw models to represent each integer in two different ways.
   a. 8 b. -1 c. -5 d. 0
   2a–d. See back of book.
3. Write the integers in order from least to greatest. **−7, −3, −2, 0, 5**
   $-2 \quad 5 \quad 0 \quad -7 \quad -3$
4. Find each sum.
   a. $7 + (-1)$ **6** b. $-3 + 2$ **−1**
   c. $-4 + (-2)$ **−6** d. $-11 + (-5)$ **−16**
   e. $-8 + (-5)$ **−13** f. $5 + (-7)$ **−2**
5. *Mental Math* Find the value of each expression.
   a. $-3 + 5$ **2** b. $-2 + (-2)$ **−4**
   c. $-4 - 9$ **−13** d. $-11 + 15$ **4**
   e. $8 + (-8) + 4$ **4** f. $7 - 13 + (-7)$ **−13**
6. Find the value of each expression.
   a. $6(-11)$ **−66** b. $-63 \div (-7)$ **9**
   c. $48 \div (-3)$ **−16** d. $-8(-9)$ **72**
   e. $22(4) \div -8$ **−11** f. $(-2 \cdot 8) \div 4$ **−4**
7. *Writing* Explain the steps you would use to solve the equation $5y + 2 = 17$. **See below.**
8. **Choose A, B, C, or D.** Kira had \$58.25 after buying a calculator. Which equation could you use to find how much money Kira had to start with if the calculator cost \$13.45? **A**
   A. $m - \$13.45 = \$58.25$
   B. $m + \$13.45 = \$58.25$
   C. $m + \$58.25 = \$13.45$
   D. $\$58.25 - \$13.45 = m$
9. Solve each equation.
   a. $x + 3 = 9$ **6** b. $a - 4 = -1$ **3**
   c. $c - 2 = 5$ **7** d. $y + 1 = -12$ **−13**
   e. $n + (-4) = -10$ **−6** f. $z - (-2) = -8$ **−10**
10. Write an equation. Then solve.
    a. A number divided by 7 equals 3.
    b. Six less than a number is 52.
    c. A number times 6 equals -48.
    d. Five more than a number is -14.
    10a–d. See below.
11. Solve each equation.
    a. $6n = -42$ **−7** b. $m \div 8 = 8$ **64**
    c. $g \div 2 = -11$ **−22** d. $-9x = -180$ **20**
    e. $-12c = -132$ **11** f. $\frac{h}{7} = -14$ **−98**
12. A submarine was at a depth of 250 m below sea level. It rose 75 m. Then it dove 20 m. Use an integer to describe the new depth of the submarine. **−195**
13. Jamie has a coordinated wardrobe consisting of four blouses, three skirts, and two pairs of slacks. How many different two-piece outfits can she make? **20 outfits**
14. Solve each equation.
    a. $4d - 3 = 9$ **3** b. $7z + 2 = -19$ **−3**
    c. $9g + 1 = 82$ **9** d. $\frac{x}{5} - 8 = -1$ **35**
    e. $49 + 6t = 25$ **−4** f. $7 + 13m = 13.5$ **0.5**
15. **Choose A, B, C, or D.** Which equation has the same solution as $5a - 1 = 9$? **D**
    A. $10a - 15 = -4$ B. $6a + 4 = 8$
    C. $13a + 1 = 14$ D. $2a - 1 = 3$
16. Evaluate for $b = -3$ and $c = 4$.
    a. $b + c$ **1** b. $-2b$ **6** c. $3c - 10$
    d. bc **−12** e. $c - b$ **7** f. $b - c$
    g. $\frac{b}{c}$ **$-\frac{3}{4}$** h. $2c - 13$ **−5** j. $-4 - b$
    16c. 2 f. −7 j. −1

10a. $\frac{n}{7} = 3$; 21 b. $x - 6 = 52$; 58 c. $6n = -48$; −8 d. $5 + x = -14$; −19

7. Subtract 2 from each side. Then divide each side by 5.

CUMULATIVE REVIEW

Item	Review Topic	Ch
1	Multiplying decimals	2
2	Estimation	2
3	Modeling integers	3
4	Solving equations	3
5	Conducting a survey	1
6	Distributive Property	2

Item	Review Topic	Ch
7, 9	Writing variable expressions	3
8	Making a table	3
10	Stem-and-leaf plots	1
11	Mean	1
12	Estimating integer multiplication	3

3 CUMULATIVE REVIEW

Choose A, B, C, or D.

1. *Entertainment* Zoom Video charges \$3.75 per day for overdue videos. Carli had a video that was due on Sunday. She returned it the following Friday. How much did she owe? C

   A. \$3.75 B. \$22.50 C. \$18.75 D. \$15

2. *Estimation* Estimate to determine which sum is between 21 and 22. B

   A. $13.71 + 1.5 + 8.2$
   B. $6.75 + 9.02 + 5.838$
   C. $5.99 + 2.69 + 15.49$
   D. $3.772 + 12.04 + 4.009$

3. Which set of tiles does *not* represent the integer -2? D

   A. 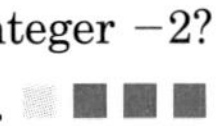
   B. 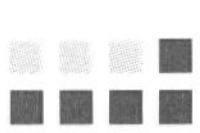
   C. 
   D. 

4. What is the solution of the equation $-15 = m - 9$? A

   A. -6 B. -24 C. 24 D. 6

5. Which is the best survey question to find how much time students spend on their math homework? B

   A. How long did your homework take you last night?
   B. How many hours did you spend on math homework last week?
   C. Which homework takes you more time, math or history?
   D. Did you do last night's math homework?

6. Which expression *cannot* be rewritten using the distributive property? C

   A. $3(2 + 8)$ B. $9(14 - 6)$
   C. $5(2 \cdot 3)$ D. $(18 - 9)7$

7. *Cooking* Suppose s represents the cups of sugar in a recipe. The amount of flour is one-half cup more than twice the amount of sugar. Which variable expression represents the amount of flour? D

   A. $\frac{1}{2} + s$ B. $\frac{1}{2} + \frac{s}{2}$
   C. $2(s + \frac{1}{2})$ D. $\frac{1}{2} + 2s$

8. *Money* Kali has \$3. How many different lunches of one sandwich and one drink can he order? A

Tuna	\$2.50
Hot dog	\$1.75
Roast Beef	\$2.95
Milk	\$.60
Lemonade	\$.50

   A. 3 B. 4 C. 5 D. 6

9. What variable expression is described by the word phrase "increase r by 2"? C

   A. $2r$ B. $r - 2$ C. $r + 2$ D. $r \cdot 2$

10. In the stem-and-leaf plot below, the stem represents the tens digit. What does the stem and leaf plot *not* tell you? D

1	3 4 9
2	1 2 4 4
3	0 3

1 | 3 means 13

   A. The greatest number is 33.
   B. The mode is 24.
   C. The median is 22.
   D. There are 12 items of data.

11. The mean of six numbers is 6. Five of the numbers are 5, 9, 3, 1, and 10. What is the sixth number? C

   A. 0 B. 4 C. 8 D. 12

12. What is the best estimate of $12(-17)$? A

   A. -200 B. -150 C. 150 D. 200

CUMULATIVE REVIEW

Chapter 3 Cumulative Review

Choose the best answer. Circle A, B, C, or D.

1. Find the mean and median of these bowling scores.

   123 138 142 133

   A. 134 and 19 B. 123 and 142
   C. 135 and 135.5 D. 134 and 135.5

The table below shows the results of a survey on students' favorite types of music. Use the table for Exercises 2–4.

Favorite Type of Music	
Music	Number of Students
Jazz	12
Rock	15
Classical	8
Country	12

2. How many types of music were chosen by more than 10 students?

   A. 1 B. 3
   C. 4 D. 39

3. Which type of music is the mode?

   A. jazz B. rock
   C. classical D. country

4. What kind of graph would best show the music data above?

   A. line graph B. bar graph
   C. scatter plot D. histogram

5. Order from least to greatest.

   0.586 0.865 0.658 0.568

   A. 0.865, 0.658, 0.568, 0.586
   B. 0.658, 0.568, 0.865, 0.586
   C. 0.586, 0.568, 0.658, 0.865
   D. 0.568, 0.586, 0.658, 0.865

6. Pierre drove 305.8 miles on one tank of gas. Then he filled the tank with 11 gallons of gas. What was the average number of miles per gallon?

   A. 27.8 B. 28
   C. 30 D. not here

7. Which multiplication property is shown? $8(6.3) = 8(6) + 8(0.3)$

   A. Identity property
   B. Commutative property
   C. Associative property
   D. Distributive property

8. Use mental math to find $5.3 + 6.2 + 4.7 + 4.8$.

   A. 20.0 B. 21.0
   C. 22.0 D. 23.0

9. Mark bought a hamburger special for \$4.95. His brother bought a chicken special for \$5.50. If the tax was \$.55, how much change did they get back from a \$20 bill?

   A. \$10 B. \$9
   C. \$9.50 D. \$8

10. What sequence of digits repeats in $6 \div 11$?

   A. 183 B. 45
   C. 611 D. 54

11. Which of the following is true?

   A. $5 + (5 \div 5) - 5 = 1$
   B. $5 \times (5 + 5) - 5 = 25$
   C. $5 - 5 \times (5 - 5) = 0$
   D. $5 \div 5 + 5 + 5 = 75$

Assessment

CUMULATIVE REVIEW

Chapter 3 Cumulative Review (continued)

12. Solve the equation $4y - 6 = -18$.

   A. 3 B. 6
   C. -3 D. -6

13. Evaluate $8n - 3m$ for $n = 4$ and $m = 3$.

   A. 23 B. 50
   C. 41 D. 10

14. The German Club members had a bake sale. They sold small cookies for \$.35 and large cookies for \$1.00. The ingredients cost \$4.95. Which expression shows how much money they made from the sale of the cookies?

   A. $(0.35 + 1) - 4.95n$
   B. $0.35n + m - 4.95$
   C. $1.35n - 4.95$
   D. $1.35n + 4.95$

15. Which of the following is equivalent to $-|-7|$?

   A. $|7|$ B. $-|7|$
   C. 7 D. $-(-7)$

16. Which of the expressions below is *not* equivalent to $-8 - (-8)$?

   A. $-8 + 8$ B. 0
   C. $8 - 8$ D. $-8 + (-8)$

17. Use mental math to simplify $-4 + (-6) - (-4) - (-7)$.

   A. -21 B. 21
   C. 1 D. 0

18. Jason opened his savings account with \$100. In one week he withdrew \$45 to buy presents and \$20 to buy a new shirt. He deposited \$125 the next week. Which expression could Jason use to show how much money he had after the second deposit?

   A. $100 - 65$
   B. $(100 + 125) - (45 + 20)$
   C. $(100 - 45 + 20) + 125$
   D. $100 + 125 - 45 + 20$

19. Shayna opened a new bank account. She deposited \$75.50 on Monday, withdrew \$15.75 on Tuesday, withdrew \$35.48 on Wednesday, deposited \$50.36 on Thursday, and withdrew \$60.91 on Friday. What was her balance on Friday?

   A. \$15.46 B. \$74.63
   C. \$13.72 D. \$238.00

20. Solve $\frac{3n}{5} - 9 = 0$.

   A. -15 B. 5.4
   C. 15 D. 135

21. Sandra has \$.50 in change in her pocket. How many possible combinations of coins could she have if she has no pennies and no half-dollars?

   A. 8 combinations
   B. 9 combinations
   C. 10 combinations
   D. 11 combinations

Resources

Teaching Resources

Chapter Support File, Ch. 3
- Cumulative Review

Teacher's Edition

See pp. 90C–D for Assessment Options.

4 Fractions and Number Theory

Chapter Overview

To accommodate flexible scheduling, most lessons are divided into parts. Assignment Options are given in the Teacher's Edition for each lesson.

Lesson 4-1 Geometry: Relating Fractions to Models
Pages 144–146

NCTM 2, 4, 5, 12

Part 1 Fractions and Models
Part 2 Modeling Mixed Numbers
Key term: mixed number

Lesson 4-2 Equivalent Fractions
Pages 147–151

NCTM 1, 2, 3, 5, 7, 8, 9, 13

Part 1 Identifying Factors and Multiples
Part 2 Writing Equivalent Fractions
Key terms: multiple, least common multiple (LCM), factor, equivalent fractions

Math at Work

Lesson 4-3 Measurement: Comparing and Ordering Fractions
Pages 152–154

NCTM 1, 3, 5, 7, 13

Part 1 Comparing Fractions
Part 2 Ordering Fractions
Key term: least common denominator (LCD)

Journal

Project Link

Lesson 4-7 Problem Solving Strategy
Pages 168–170

NCTM 1, 4, 5, 7, 8

Look for a Pattern

Lesson 4-8 Measurement: Mixed Numbers and Improper Fractions
Pages 172–175

NCTM 1, 2, 3, 4, 5, 13

Part 1 Mixed Numbers to Improper Fractions
Part 2 Improper Fractions to Mixed Numbers
Key term: improper fractions

Journal

Checkpoint 2

Lesson 4-9 Fractions and Decimals
Pages 176–180

NCTM 1, 2, 3, 4, 5, 13

Part 1 Writing Fractions as Decimals
Part 2 Changing Decimals to Fractions

Alternative Activity 4-9

Project Link

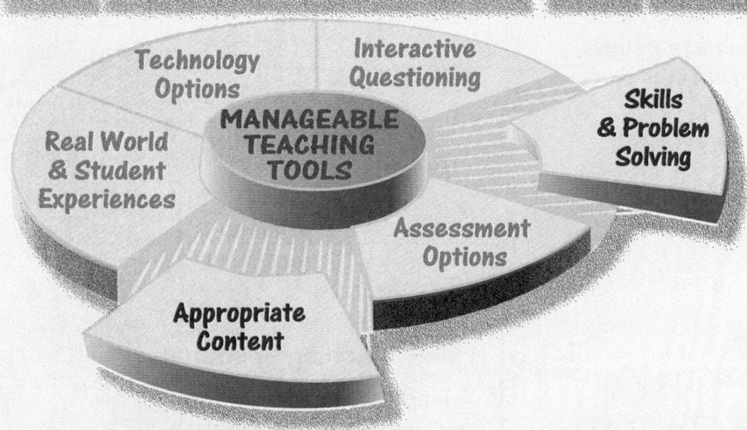

Pacing Options

This chart suggests pacing only for the core lessons and their parts. It is provided merely as a possible guide. It will help you determine how much time you have in your schedule to cover other features, such as the Chapter Project, Math Toolboxes, Wrap Up, and Assessment.

	1 Class Period	1 Class Period	1 Class Period	1
Traditional (40–45 min class periods)	4–1 (1) 4–1 (2)	4–2 (1) 4–2 (2)	4–3 (1)	
Block Scheduling (90 min class periods)	4–1 (1) 4–1 (2) 4–2 (1)	4–2 (2) 4–3 (1) 4–3 (2)	4–4 (1) 4–4 (2) 4–5 (1)	4– (2)

CHAPTER PROJECT

Making the Measure

Goals: Invent a new unit of measure for a ruler and measure different lengths with it

THEME: MEASUREMENT

NCTM STANDARDS

1 Problem Solving
2 Communication
3 Reasoning
4 Mathematical Connections
5 Number and Number Relationships
6 Number Systems and Number Theory
7 Computation and Estimation
8 Patterns and Functions
9 Algebra
10 Statistics
11 Probability
12 Geometry
13 Measurement

Pages	Lesson
Pages 155–158	**Lesson 4-4 Technology: Exponents and Order of Operations**
NCTM 2, 3, 4, 5, 7, 8, 12	Part 1 Standard and Exponential Forms Part 2 Using the Order of Operations **Key terms:** exponent, base, power **Alternative Activity** 4-4
Pages 160–163	**Lesson 4-5 Geometry: Prime Factorization**
NCTM 3, 4, 5, 6, 13	Part 1 Finding Prime Factorization Part 2 Finding the GCF **Key terms:** composite, prime, prime factorization, factor tree, greatest common factor (GCF) **Journal** **Checkpoint 1**
Pages 164–167	**Lesson 4-6 Data Analysis: Simplifying Fractions**
NCTM 1, 3, 4, 5, 8, 13	Part 1 Writing Fractions in Simplest Form Part 2 Using the GCF to Simplify Fractions **Key term:** simplest form **Alternative Activity** 4-6 **Project Link**

Optional Materials and Manipulatives

pattern blocks (4-1)
ruler (4-2)
calculator (4-4, 4-7, 4-9)

graph paper (4-5)
newspaper (4-8)

Optional calculator use is integrated throughout the course.

...ss ...od	1 Class Period	1 Class Period	1 Class Period	1 Class Period	1 Class Period	1 Class Period	1 Class Period	1 Class Period	1 Class Period	1 Class Period
...-4 2	4–5 1, 4–5 2	4–6 1, 4–6 2	4–7	4–8 1	4–8 2	4–9 1	4–9 2			
4–8 2	4–9 1, 4–9 2									

Meeting Individual Needs

Accommodating Diverse Learning Styles

In your Teacher's Edition, you will find suggestions as to how you can help students complete mathematical tasks in Chapter 4 by meeting individual needs and supporting various learning styles. Here are some examples:

VISUAL LEARNING
coloring parts of circles different colors *(p. 149)*

TACTILE LEARNING
measuring fractions of cups of water *(p. 152)*

AUDITORY LEARNING
writing symbols for less than, greater than, and equal to from dictation *(p. 152)*

KINESTHETIC LEARNING
modeling fractions by standing and sitting to represent the numerators and denominators (*p. 145)*

EARLY FINISHERS
Performance-Based Project, MathBlaster® Mystery, Interdisciplinary Units

GIFTED AND TALENTED
writing fraction questions based on research *(p. 178)*

DIVERSITY discussing occupations that require varying work schedules *(p. 147)*

ACQUIRING ENGLISH PROFICIENCY (AEP)
practicing saying fractions out loud *(p. 144)*

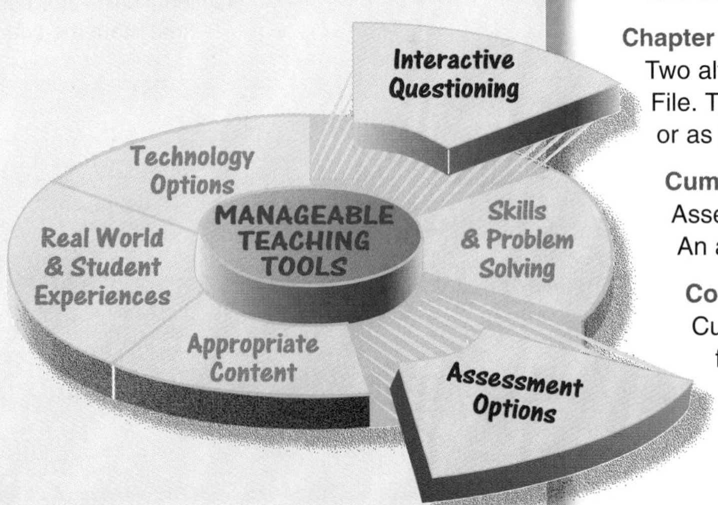

Assessing Progress

A broad range of assessment tools are available to reach a variety of learners.

INFORMAL ASSESSMENT

Informal assessments provide day-to-day feedback to help give you a picture of conceptual understanding and skill development.

ONGOING ASSESSMENT is built into lesson instruction and the Teaching Notes of the Teacher's Edition.

In the Teacher's Edition
Lesson Quiz for every lesson

In the Student Edition
On Your Own, Mixed Review, Journal, Portfolio, Project Link, Chapter Wrap Up

Look for **Interactive Questions** within lessons that

- **BUILD UNDERSTANDING** with labels such as Analyze, Reasoning, Estimation, Writing, and Summarize
- ✓ **CHECK UNDERSTANDING** with the Try It Out label.

FORMAL ASSESSMENT

Formal assessment can occur before and after the chapter, as well as at natural breaking points in the chapter.

Checkpoints
Two forms of each self-assessment Checkpoints are available: one in the Student Edition and another in the Chapter Support File in the Teaching Resources box.

- Mid-Chapter Checkpoint 1, page 163
- End-of-Chapter Checkpoint 2, page 175

Chapter 4 Assessment, page 184.
Two alternative forms are available in the Chapter Support File. They may be used after a chapter has been completed, or as a pre-test and post-test comparison.

Cumulative Review, page 185.
Assesses skills and concepts in Chapters 1–4. An alternative form is available in Chapter Support File.

Computer Item Generator for Chapter 4
Customized tests can be generated for each lesson and for mid-chapter and end-of-chapter assessments, and for pre- and post-test comparisons of achievement.

CHAPTER PROJECT

The Chapter Project in the student edition provides a real-world connection to the math context of the chapter. The Teacher's Edition contains a scoring rubric.

A Performance Assessment with a scoring rubric can be found in the Chapter Support File in the Teaching Resources box.

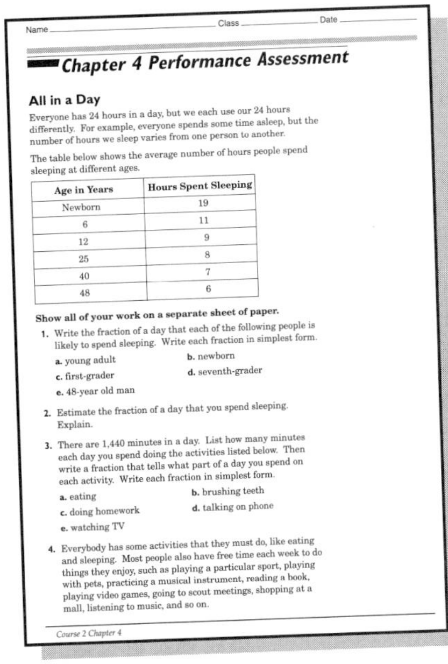

Name ______ Class ______ Date ______

Chapter 4 Performance Assessment

All in a Day

Everyone has 24 hours in a day, but we each use our 24 hours differently. For example, everyone spends some time asleep, but the number of hours we sleep varies from one person to another.

The table below shows the average number of hours people spend sleeping at different ages.

Age in Years	Hours Spent Sleeping
Newborn	19
6	11
12	9
25	8
40	7
48	6

Show all of your work on a separate sheet of paper.

1. Write the fraction of a day that each of the following people is likely to spend sleeping. Write each fraction in simplest form.
   a. young adult
   b. newborn
   c. first-grader
   d. seventh-grader
   e. 48-year old man
2. Estimate the fraction of a day that you spend sleeping. Explain.
3. There are 1,440 minutes in a day. List how many minutes each day you spend doing the activities listed below. Then write a fraction that tells what part of a day you spend on each activity. Write each fraction in simplest form.
   a. eating
   b. brushing teeth
   c. doing homework
   d. talking on phone
   e. watching TV
4. Everybody has some activities that they must do, like eating and sleeping. Most people also have free time each week to do things they enjoy, such as playing a particular sport, playing with pets, practicing a musical instrument, reading a book, playing video games, going to scout meetings, shopping at a mall, listening to music, and so on.

Course 2 Chapter 4

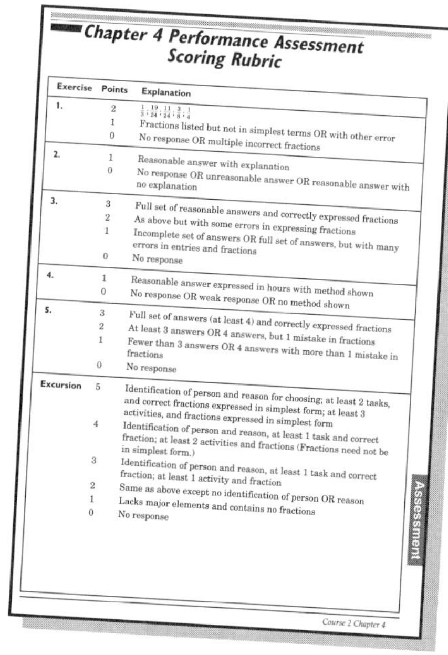

Chapter 4 Performance Assessment Scoring Rubric

Exercise	Points	Explanation
1.	2	$\frac{1}{3}$; $\frac{19}{24}$; $\frac{11}{24}$; $\frac{3}{8}$; $\frac{1}{4}$
	1	Fractions listed but not in simplest terms OR with other error
	0	No response OR multiple incorrect fractions
2.	1	Reasonable answer with explanation
	0	No response OR unreasonable answer OR reasonable answer with no explanation
3.	3	Full set of reasonable answers and correctly expressed fractions
	2	As above but with some errors in expressing fractions
	1	Incomplete set of answers OR full set of answers, but with many errors in entries and fractions
	0	No response
4.	1	Reasonable answer expressed in hours with method shown
	0	No response OR weak response OR no method shown
5.	3	Full set of answers (at least 4) and correctly expressed fractions
	2	At least 3 answers OR 4 answers, but 1 mistake in fractions
	1	Fewer than 3 answers OR 4 answers with more than 1 mistake in fractions
	0	No response
Excursion	5	Identification of person and reason for choosing; at least 2 tasks, and correct fractions expressed in simplest form; at least 3 activities, and fractions expressed in simplest form
	4	Identification of person and reason, at least 1 task and correct fraction; at least 2 activities and fractions (Fractions need not be in simplest form.)
	3	Identification of person and reason, at least 1 task and correct fraction; at least 1 activity and fraction
	2	Same as above except no identification of person OR reason
	1	Lacks major elements and contains no fractions
	0	No response

Assessment

Course 2 Chapter 4

Correlation to Standardized Tests

Lesson		STANDARDIZED TEST ITEMS: CAT5	Terra Nova	ITBS, Form M	MAT7	SAT9	Local Test
4-1	Geometry: Relating Fractions to Models	CA4		CE7			
4-2	Equivalent Fractions	CA5, 25, 40	20, 29, 37	CE9, 21			
4-3	Measurement: Comparing and Ordering Fractions	CA43		CE6, 29	CP6	PS2	
4-4	Technology: Exponents and Order of Operations		47	CE27	CP8		
4-5	Geometry: Prime Factorization		54		CP9		
4-6	Data Analysis: Simplifying Fractions						
4-7	Problem Solving Strategy: Look for a Pattern		48	CE14	CP13	PS19–20	
4-8	Measurement: Mixed Numbers and Improper Fractions	MC34			CP4	PS4–5	
4-9	Fractions and Decimals		49	CE10			

CA: Concepts and Applications
PS: Problem Solving
PR: Math Procedures
CP: Concepts and Problem Solving
MC: Math Computation
PD: Problem Solving and Data Interpretation
CE: Concepts and Estimation

See page 2D for the level of each test referenced.

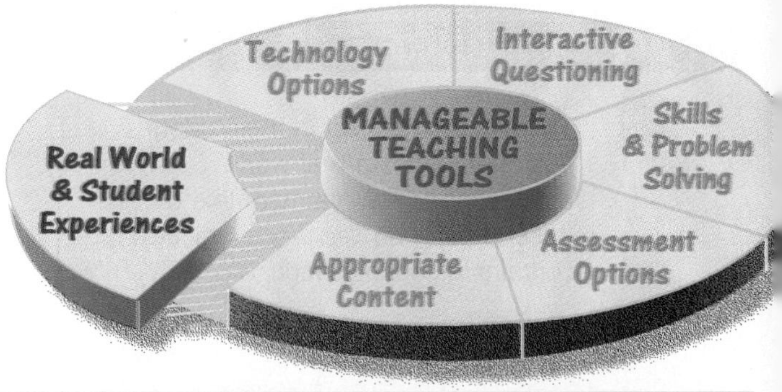

MAKING CONNECTIONS

TEAM TEACHING WITH PRENTICE HALL MATERIALS

MIDDLE GRADES MATH INTERDISCIPLINARY UNITS	INTERDISCIPLINARY EXPLORATIONS
• **The Environment: Activity 9** • **Advancements in Industry: Activity 5**	• ***The Power of Patterns* pp. 10–13**

Lesson	Interdisciplinary Connections	Real World Connections	Math Integration
4-1	Music	Quilting Baking	Geometry
4-2	Number Theory	Volunteer Work Homework Medicine Carpentry	Algebra Measurement
4-3	Science	Psychology Cooking Carpentry	Measurement
4-4	Geography Language Biology	Allowances	Geometry Measurement
4-5	Number Theory	Charity	Geometry Measurement
4-6	Social Studies Geography Anatomy	Entertainment Time Management Travel	Measurement
4-7	Foreign Languages Health	Cars Entertainment Exercise	Measurement
4-8	Nutrition	Travel Cooking Carpentry	Measurement
4-9	Sports Science	Batting Averages Population Basketball	Measurement

School to Home

MATERIALS:
cookbook
graph paper
colored pencils
newspaper
catalogs
paper
pencil

English version is in the Chapter Support File. Spanish version is in the Spanish Resources.

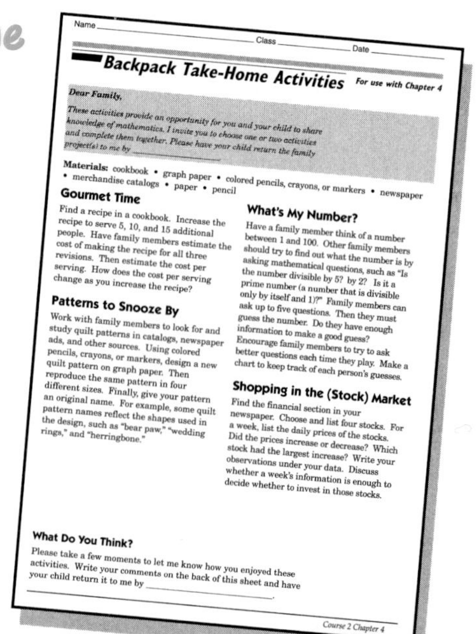

Name ____ Class ____ Date ____

Backpack Take-Home Activities *For use with Chapter 4*

Dear Family,

These activities provide an opportunity for you and your child to share knowledge of mathematics. I invite you to choose one or two activities and complete them together. Please have your child return the family project(s) to me by ____

Materials: cookbook • graph paper • colored pencils, crayons, or markers • newspaper • merchandise catalogs • paper • pencil

Gourmet Time

Find a recipe in a cookbook. Increase the recipe to serve 5, 10, and 15 additional people. Have family members estimate the cost of making the recipe for all three revisions. Then estimate the cost per serving. How does the cost per serving change as you increase the recipe?

Patterns to Snooze By

Work with family members to look for and study quilt patterns in catalogs, newspaper ads, and other sources. Using colored pencils, crayons, or markers, design a new quilt pattern on graph paper. Then reproduce the same pattern in four different sizes. Finally, give your pattern an original name. For example, some quilt pattern names reflect the shapes used in the design, such as "bear paw," "wedding rings," and "herringbone."

What's My Number?

Have a family member think of a number between 1 and 100. Other family members should try to find out what the number is by asking mathematical questions, such as "Is the number divisible by 5? by 2? Is it a prime number (a number that is divisible only by itself and 1)?" Family members can ask up to five questions. Then they must guess the number. Do they have enough information to make a good guess? Encourage family members to try to ask better questions each time they play. Make a chart to keep track of each person's guesses.

Shopping in the (Stock) Market

Find the financial section in your newspaper. Choose and list four stocks. For a week, list the daily prices of the stocks. Did the prices increase or decrease? Which stock had the largest increase? Write your observations under your data. Discuss whether a week's information is enough to decide whether to invest in those stocks.

What Do You Think?

Please take a few moments to let me know how you enjoyed these activities. Write your comments on the back of this sheet and have your child return it to me by ____.

Course 2 Chapter 4

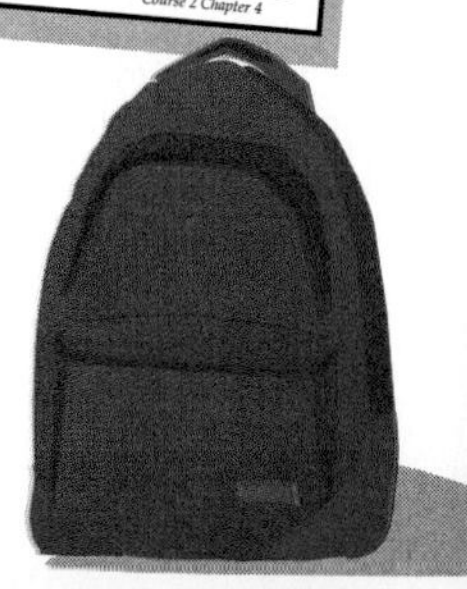

Using Technology to Enhance Instruction

For the Student

Multimedia Math Hot Pages™

This interactive software and video package on CD-ROM integrates solid math content through a variety of media.

- Hot Page™ 3-8
- Hot Page™ 7-1
- Hot Page™ 7-6
- Hot Page™ 7-7

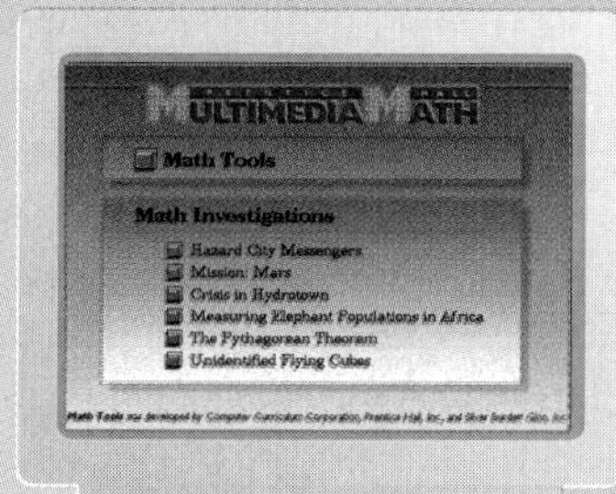

Multimedia Math Investigations

These in-depth interactive activities on CD-ROM develop real-world applications of mathematics. They allow students the opportunity to reinforce key concepts.

- Unidentified Flying Cubes
- Hazard City Messengers

MathBlaster® Mystery

This award-winning, interactive software program on CD-ROM can be used to maintain skills or to accommodate early finishers.

- Level: Earn 4 coins; Pay 4 coins
- Mission Mode (all lessons)
- Kitchen Comparisons (4-1, 4-9)
- Number Guesser (4-2, 4-5, 4-7)
- Equation Maker (4-4, 4-6)
- Word Problems (4-3, 4-8, Problem Solving Practice)

Math Tools/Math Labs

This software, available on CD-ROM, includes on-screen Math Lab activities. Students use linkable, interactive tools to explore math concepts.

- Math Lab: Prime and Composite Numbers (4-5)

Interactive Student Tutorial

Available on CD-ROM, this test preparation program contains self-tests with questions in standardized test format. Software includes electronic versions of the text lessons and an on-line glossary.

Internet Connection

For Students

Support for the Chapter Project

A career-oriented link for Math at Work feature

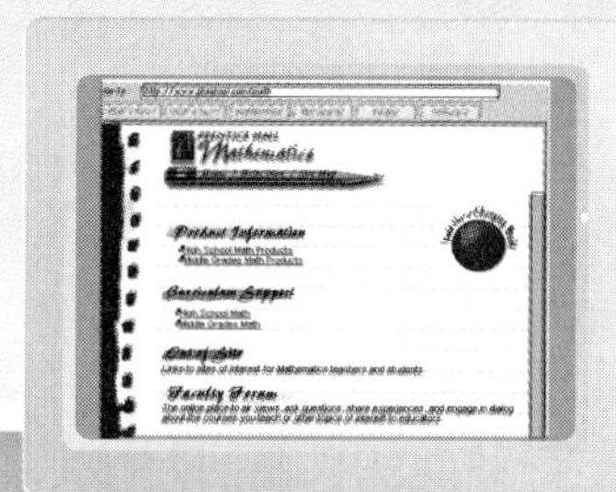

www.phschool.com/math

For teachers

Curriculum Support

Product Information

Regional Support Information

For the Teacher

Computer Item Generator with Standardized Test Practice

This software generates customized practice sheets and tests. It also generates unlimited practice sheets for the standardized tests listed on page 142D.

Resource Pro™ with Planning Express™

Available on CD-ROM, this software can be used to customize and plan lessons. It contains over 1,700 resource pages.

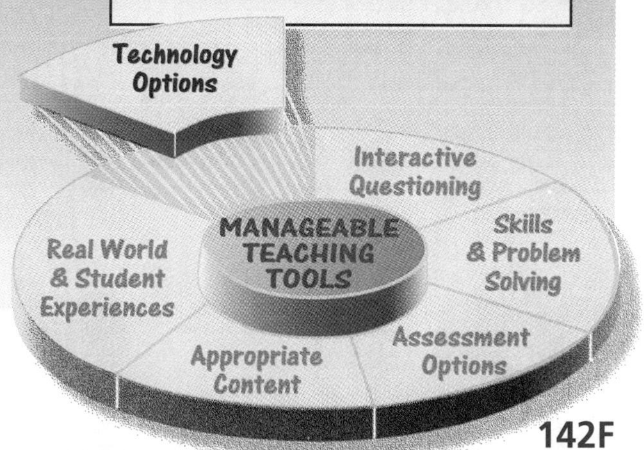

CHAPTER 4

FRACTIONS AND NUMBER THEORY

CONNECTING TO PRIOR LEARNING Ask students: *Name different types of measuring devices you have used.* **Answers may vary. Sample: measuring cup, scale, centimeter ruler, yardstick** Ask: *Have any of these devices been marked in increments that show fractions of the whole?* **yes**

CULTURAL CONNECTIONS The United States relies mainly on the customary system of measurement. Most other countries use the metric system. Increasing global trade and the influence of immigrants may speed the United States' adoption of the metric system.

INTERDISCIPLINARY CONNECTIONS Artists use measurement when they draw the human body. One rule artists use to find the distance from the top of the head to the waistline is to multiply the head-length by 3. Have students research other measurement rules used by artists.

ABOUT THE PROJECT The Chapter Project allows students to use their knowledge of fractions and number theory to make a unique ruler. The Project Link questions help them evaluate the usefulness of their ruler.

Internet • For information and activities related to the Chapter Project, visit the Prentice Hall site at www.phschool.com/mgm2/ch4

4 Fractions and Number Theory

WHAT YOU WILL LEARN IN THIS CHAPTER

- How to model and write fractions
- How to use exponents with the order of operations
- How to write fractions as decimals and decimals as fractions

LAUNCHING THE CHAPTER PROJECT

Ask students:

- *Have you ever compared units of measure?*
- *How did the units of measure we use now develop?*
- *What are some advantages and disadvantages of using the yard as a primary unit of measure?*

PROJECT NOTEBOOK Encourage students to keep all project-related materials in a separate folder or notebook.

TRACKING THE PROJECT You may wish to have students read Finishing the Chapter Project on page 181 to help them get an overview of the project. Set benchmark deadlines for students to show you their work in progress.

CHAPTER PROJECT

THEME: MEASUREMENT

Making the Measure

In the high jump, as in most sports, a consistent system of measurement allows athletes to make comparisons. It took the decree of a king to create one such system!

Back in the 12th century, King Henry I of England decided that a yard was the distance from the tip of his nose to the end of his thumb. How far is it from the tip of your nose to the end of your thumb? Is it more than a yard or less? Is it the same distance for everyone?

Invent Your Own Ruler For the chapter project, you will design a new system for measuring distance. Your final project will be a new ruler, together with a report on its usefulness.

Steps to help you complete the project:

p. 154 **Project Link:** *Designing*

p. 167 **Project Link:** *Measuring*

p. 180 **Project Link:** *Analyzing*

p. 181 *Finishing the Chapter Project*

How to solve problems by looking for a pattern

PROBLEM SOLVING

SCORING RUBRIC

3 You constructed and labeled your ruler carefully, and it accurately shows fractions of your basic measurement unit. You used your ruler to accurately measure at least eight objects over a wide range of lengths. You described how your ruler could be used to measure fractional units, or you compared your measurement system to other measurement systems.

2 You constructed a ruler that includes fractional units, but it is not as accurate as it could have been. You measured and listed the lengths of several short objects and several long objects.

1 You constructed your ruler carelessly, or you made and recorded inaccurate measurements.

0 You did not create your own unit of measure, or you didn't use fractional units, or you made very few measurements.

4-1 Teaching Notes

1 Focus

CONNECTING TO PRIOR KNOWLEDGE Ask students to recall situations in which they have described parts of a whole. **Answers may vary. Sample: number of slices of pizza** Have students name ways they refer to these parts. **Sample: half of a pizza**

2 Teach

Work Together

If you have block scheduling or extended class periods, have students create other shapes using trapezoids, triangles, and parallelograms. Ask: *Would you use the same method to answer the (b) questions?* **yes**

AEP Some students may not feel comfortable saying fractions before the class because of language difficulties. Have students practice in pairs, pointing to fractions and saying them out loud.

THINK AND DISCUSS

ERROR ALERT! Example 1 Students may write the wrong number in the denominator. **Remediation:** Students can use the mnemonic "*whole* sounds like a *hole* under the ground" to remind themselves that the *whole* is in the denominator.

Lesson Planning Options

Prerequisite Skills

- using fraction models (precourse)

Vocabulary/Symbols

mixed number

Materials/Manipulatives

- pattern blocks

Resources

Student Edition

Skills Handbook, p. 528
Extra Practice, p. 517
Glossary/Study Guide

Teaching Resources

Chapter Support File, Ch. 4
- Lesson Planner 4-1
- Practice 4-1, Reteaching 4-1
- Answer Masters 4-1

Teaching Aids Masters 8, 10, 20–25
Glossary, Spanish Resources

Transparencies

9, 10, 18–25, Minds on Math 4-1

Warm Up

Use the digits 0 through 9 to complete the following addition sentence. Use each number only once. (2 has been placed for you.)

2 + ■■ + ■■■ = ■■■■

Answers may vary. Sample:
2 + 64 + 987 = 1,053
2 + 87 + 946 = 1,035

GEOMETRY Connection

4-1 Relating Fractions to Models

What You'll Learn

1. To use models to explore fractions
2. To model mixed numbers

...And Why

Models can help you understand the meaning of fractions and mixed numbers.

Here's How

Look for questions that
- build understanding
- ✔ check understanding

Work Together

Modeling Fractions

Work with a partner. You can use pattern blocks to explore fractions that are part of a whole. A yellow hexagon represents one whole.

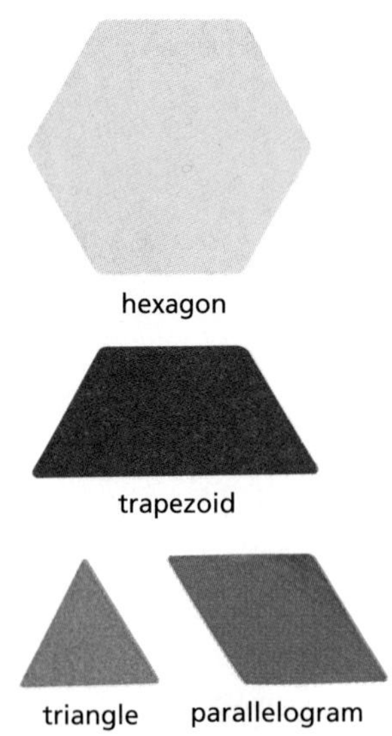

1. a. How many trapezoids make up one hexagon? **two**
   b. What part of a whole is one trapezoid? $\frac{1}{2}$
2. a. How many triangles make up one hexagon? **six**
   b. What part of a whole is one triangle? $\frac{1}{6}$
3. a. How many parallelograms make up one hexagon? **three**
   b. What part of a whole is one parallelogram? $\frac{1}{3}$

THINK AND DISCUSS

1 *Fractions and Models*

Fractions describe parts of a whole or members of a group.

■ **EXAMPLE 1**

Write the fraction that each model represents.

a.

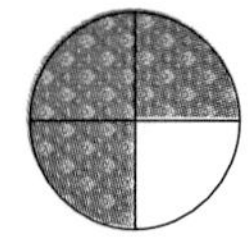

Three parts of a whole that has four parts is represented by $\frac{3}{4}$.

b.

Three members of a group of four items is also represented by $\frac{3}{4}$.

KINESTHETIC LEARNING Have a group of students model fractions. The whole group stands. Then the number of students that represent the numerator sit down.

ADDITIONAL EXAMPLES

FOR EXAMPLE 1

Write the fraction the model represents. $\frac{2}{5}$

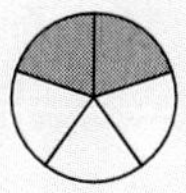

FOR EXAMPLE 2

Write the mixed number the model represents. $2\frac{5}{8}$

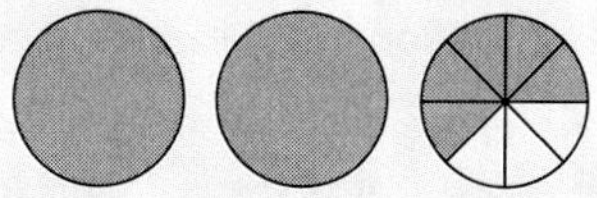

ASSESSMENT Have students choose a fraction or mixed number and represent it by drawing a model. Students exchange models with a partner and identify the partner's fraction by looking at the model.

3 Practice/Assess

EXERCISES *On Your Own*

OPEN-ENDED **Exercise 5** Point out that the quilt square can consist of any number of smaller shapes, but to represent a fraction, the shapes must be the same size.

WRITING **Exercise 6** Students may need to trace the circle on graph paper to see that the sections are not equal.

4. Answers may vary. Sample:

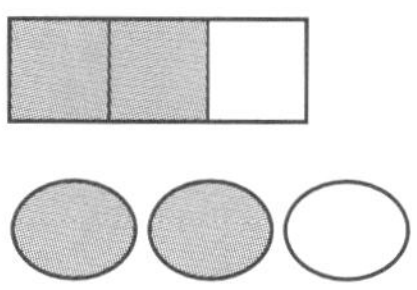

4. ✔ *Try It Out* Draw two models, one that shows $\frac{2}{3}$ as parts of a whole, and one that shows $\frac{2}{3}$ as part of a group.

Now you may assign Exercises 1–6.

2 *Modeling Mixed Numbers*

You can use models to represent fractions that are mixed numbers. A **mixed number** is the sum of a whole number and a fraction.

EXAMPLE 2

Write the mixed number that the model represents.

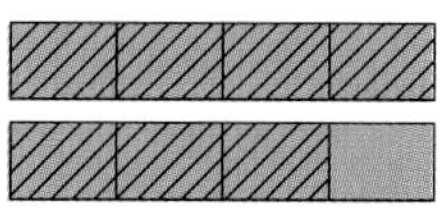

The model represents $1\frac{3}{4}$.

On Your Own

5. Answers may vary. Sample:

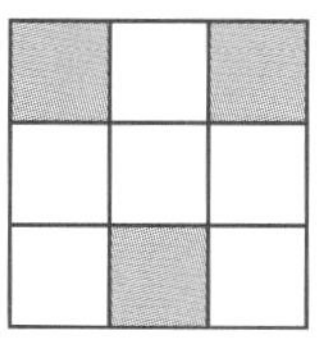

5. ✔ *Try It Out* Write the mixed number that each model represents.

a. $1\frac{3}{4}$

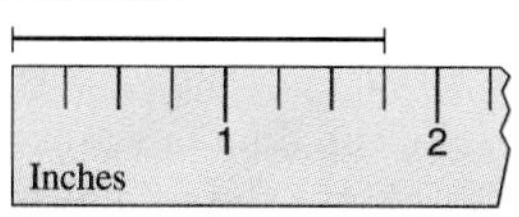

b. $2\frac{5}{8}$

Now you may assign Exercises 7–10.

EXERCISES *On Your Own*

Write a fraction for each model.

1. $\frac{1}{2}$

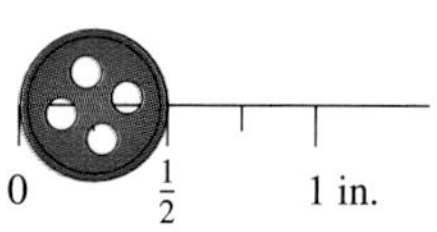

2. $\frac{2}{9}$

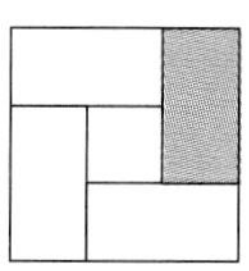

3. $\frac{3}{8}$

4. a. *Quilting* What fraction of each quilt square is purple?
   b. What fraction of each quilt square is blue?

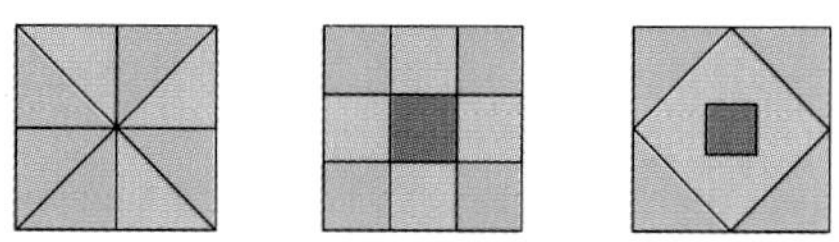

4a. $\frac{3}{8}$ $\frac{5}{9}$ $\frac{1}{2}$
b. $\frac{5}{8}$ $\frac{4}{9}$ $\frac{1}{2}$

5. *Open-ended* Design a quilt square in which $\frac{1}{3}$ of the square is green.
   See above for sample diagram.

Technology Options

Prentice Hall Technology

Software for Learners
- Hot Page™ 7–1*
- Math Blaster® Mystery*
- Interactive Student Tutorial, Chapter 4*

Teaching Resource Software
- Computer Item Generator 4-1
- Resource Pro™ Chapter 4*

Internet • For related mathematics activities, visit the Prentice Hall site at www.phschool.com/math

**Available on CD-ROM only*

Assignment Options for Exercises On Your Own

To provide flexible scheduling, this lesson can be split into parts.

1 **Core** 1–5
Extension 6

2 **Core** 7–9
Extension 10

Use Mixed Review to maintain skills.

PRACTICE

Practice 4-1 *Relating Fractions to Models*

Write a fraction for each model.

1. $\frac{3}{4}$ 2. $\frac{7}{12}$ 3. $\frac{1}{4}$

Write a mixed number for each model.

4. $3\frac{3}{4}$ 5. $1\frac{5}{6}$ 6. $2\frac{2}{3}$

Write the fraction or a mixed number represented by the shaded parts.

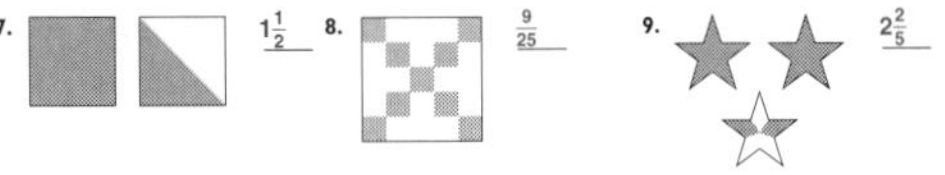

7. $1\frac{1}{2}$ 8. $\frac{9}{25}$ 9. $2\frac{2}{5}$

Practice

10. One brand of cheese comes in packages of 12 slices. Anna used 7 slices for grilled cheese sandwiches.
 a. What part of the package did she use? $\frac{7}{12}$
 b. What part of the package was left over? $\frac{5}{12}$

There are 24 hours in a day. For Exercises 11–14, write the fraction for each. Answers may vary.

11. number of whole hours you slept last night ____
12. number of whole hours you spent at school today ____
13. number of whole hours you spend doing homework ____
14. number of whole hours you spend watching TV ____
15. What part of the alphabet consists of vowels? $\frac{5}{26}$
16. Use your first name. Write a fraction for the part of your name made of vowels. Write a fraction for the part of your name made of consonants.
 Answers may vary.

In copymaster and workbook formats

RETEACHING

Reteaching 4-1 *Relating Fractions to Models*

You can use fractions and models to describe parts of a whole or members of a group. You can also use both to represent mixed numbers. A **mixed number** is the sum of a whole number and a fraction.

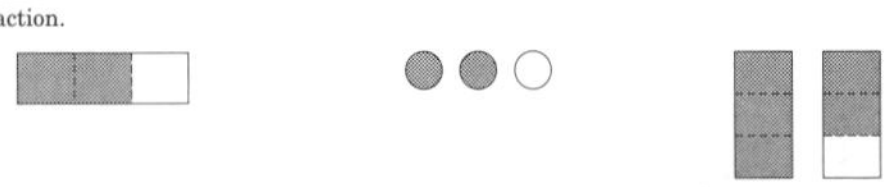

Two shaded parts of a whole that has three parts is represented by $\frac{2}{3}$.

Two shaded items of a group of three items is represented by $\frac{2}{3}$.

All three parts of the first figure and two parts of the second figure are shaded. The model represents $1\frac{2}{3}$.

Write a fraction or mixed number for each model.

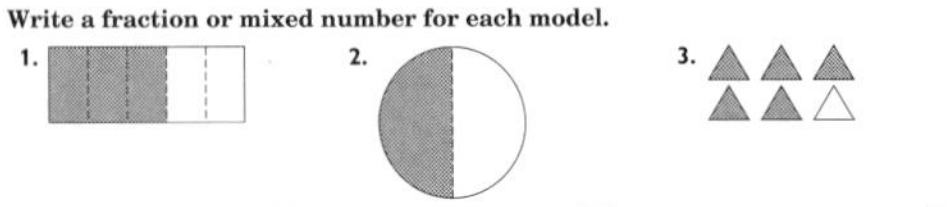

1. 3 parts shaded [3] / 5 parts total [5]
2. 1 part shaded [1] / 2 parts total [2]
3. 5 items shaded [5] / 6 items total [6]

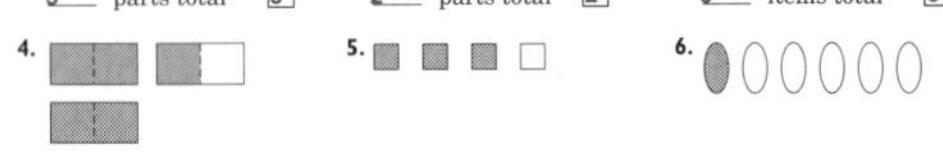

4. $2\frac{1}{2}$ 5. $\frac{3}{4}$ 6. $\frac{1}{6}$

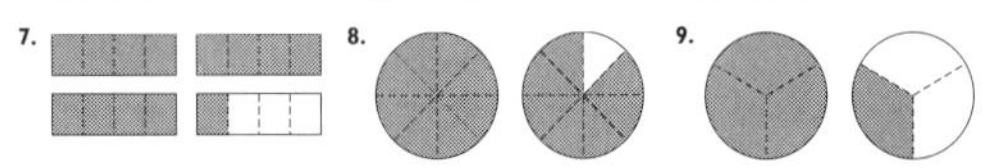

7. $3\frac{1}{4}$ 8. $1\frac{7}{8}$ 9. $1\frac{1}{3}$

ENRICHMENT

Minds on Math Transparency

4-1

Draw exactly four triangles to make the figure below.

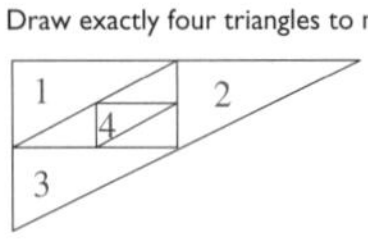

Sample shown.

See *Solution Key* for worked-out answers.

146

WRAP UP

IDENTIFYING THE BIG IDEA Ask students how to relate fractions and models.

LESSON QUIZ

Write a fraction or mixed number for each model.

1. 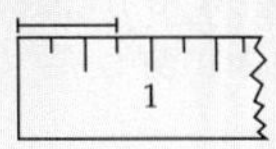 $\frac{3}{4}$

2. 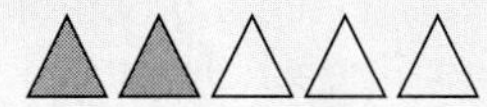 $\frac{2}{5}$

3. 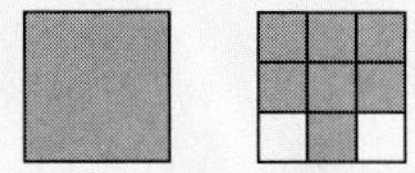 $1\frac{7}{9}$

6. *Writing* Jason described the shaded region at the right as $\frac{1}{3}$ of a circle. Is he correct? Why or why not?
 No. The three parts are not equal.

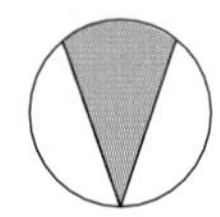

Write a fraction or a mixed number for each model.

7.  $\frac{5}{6}$

8. 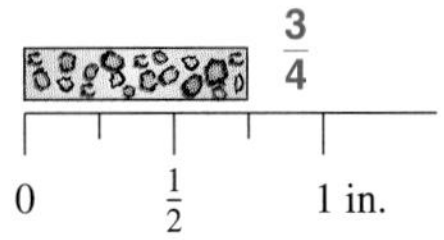

$\frac{3}{4}$

9. 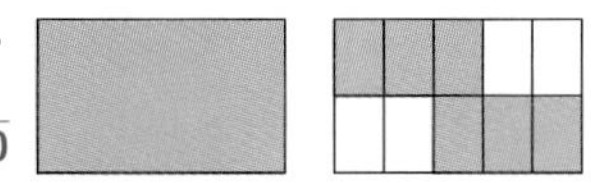 $1\frac{6}{10}$

10. a. *Music* List the denominators of the fractions in the table. 2, 4, 8

Symbol	𝅝	𝅗𝅥	♩	♪	𝅘𝅥𝅯	𝅘𝅥𝅰
Name	whole note	half note	quarter note	eighth note	■ sixteenth note	■ thirty-second note
Value	1	$\frac{1}{2}$	$\frac{1}{4}$	$\frac{1}{8}$	■ $\frac{1}{16}$	■ $\frac{1}{32}$
Model					■	■

b. Each denominator is twice the preceding one; see table for names.

b. *Patterns* Describe the pattern of the denominators. Based on this pattern, what do you think are the names of the last two notes in the table?

c. Copy and complete the last two rows of the table.

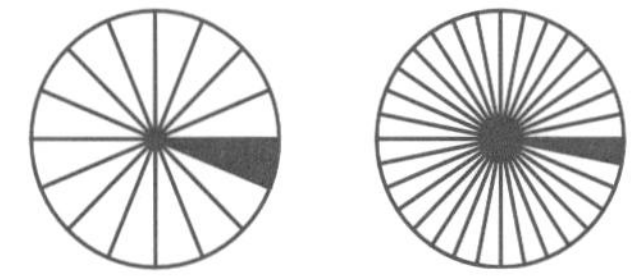

Mixed Review

Write a variable expression for each phrase. (Lesson 3-1)

11. twice a number decreased by four
 $2n - 4$
12. three more than half a number
 $\frac{1}{2}n + 3$

Compare. Use <, >, or =. (Lessons 3-2, 3-3, 3-4, 3-5)

13. $5 - (-8)$ ■ 13 =
14. $3.5(-3)$ ■ $7 - 11$ <
15. $6 \div (-2)$ ■ -4 >
16. -1 ■ $-5 - 6$ >

17. A team of bakers at the Shiwassee County Fairgrounds, Michigan, created a 100-tier cake. At 30.85 m, it was the tallest in the world. About how tall was each tier? (Lesson 2-2) about 0.31 m

Extra Practice, Lesson 4-1, page 517

4-2 Teaching Notes

1 Focus

CONNECTING TO PRIOR KNOWLEDGE Draw two equal-size pizzas on the board. Divide one pizza into 4 equal slices and the other into 8 equal slices. Ask: *If you ate half a pizza, from which pizza would you get the most?* **Both $\frac{2}{4}$ and $\frac{4}{8}$ equal $\frac{1}{2}$, so you would get the same amount from each pizza.**

2 Teach

THINK AND DISCUSS

DIVERSITY Some students or family members may volunteer or work on a varied schedule. If there is time, allow students to discuss occupations that require a varied schedule, such as nursing or waiting tables.

AEP Students may have difficulty differentiating between factors and multiples. Give them a list that shows the factor pairs that equal 12 compared with the multiples of 12. Allow them to keep the list for reference. Also suggest that students use the mnemonic "You *multiply* to get *multiples*."

REASONING Question 3 Have students find the LCD of 6 and 9 using zero as a multiple. Ask them to explain the results.

4-2 Equivalent Fractions

What You'll Learn

1. To find the factors and multiples of a number
2. To write equivalent fractions

...And Why

Using factors and multiples, you can find many ways to write one fraction.

Here's How

Look for questions that
- build understanding
- ✔ check understanding

THINK AND DISCUSS

1 *Identifying Factors and Multiples*

Suppose you and a friend do volunteer work at the animal shelter. Both of you are at the shelter today. You volunteer every third day and your friend volunteers every fourth day. After how many days will you both be at the center on the same day?

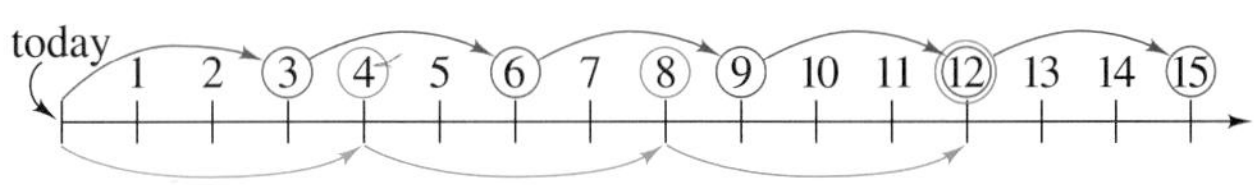

You will see each other at the shelter 12 days from today.

The diagram above shows multiples of 3 and 4. A **multiple** of a number is the product of the number and a nonzero whole number.

The **least common multiple (LCM)** of two numbers is the least number that is a multiple of both. The LCM of 3 and 4 is 12.

■ **EXAMPLE 1**

Find the least common multiple of 6 and 9.

multiples of 6: 6, 12, 18, 24, 30, 36
multiples of 9: 9, 18, 27, 36

← List the first several multiples of 6 and 9.

The LCM of 6 and 9 is 18.

1. Find the first four multiples of each number.
   a. 5 **5, 10, 15, 20** b. 8 **8, 16, 24, 32** c. 11 **11, 22, 33, 44**
2. ✔ *Try It Out* Find the LCM of each pair of numbers.
   a. 4, 10 **20** b. 5, 7 **35** c. 12, 15 **60**
3. *Reasoning* Zero is not considered a multiple of a number other than itself. Why does this make sense? **Answers may vary. Sample: The product of any number and zero is zero.**

Lesson Planning Options

Prerequisite Skills

- multiplying whole numbers (precourse)
- dividing whole numbers (precourse)

Vocabulary/Symbols

multiple, least common multiple (LCM), factor, equivalent fractions

Materials/Manipulatives

- ruler

Resources

Student Edition

Skills Handbook, p. 530
Extra Practice, p. 517
Glossary/Study Guide

Teaching Resources

Chapter Support File, Ch. 4
- Lesson Planner 4-2
- Practice 4-2, Reteaching 4-2
- Answer Masters 4-2

Teaching Aids Masters 8, 10, 20–25
Glossary, Spanish Resources

Transparencies

9, 10, 15, 18–25, 84, Minds on Math 4-2

Warm Up

In 1990, a disc jockey broadcast her show for $27\frac{1}{2}$ h each week. About how many hours did she broadcast that year? **about 1,500 h**

■ ADDITIONAL EXAMPLES

FOR EXAMPLE 1

Find the least common multiple of 6 and 10. **30**

FOR EXAMPLE 2

Find the factors of 36. **1, 2, 3, 4, 6, 9, 12, 18, and 36**

FOR EXAMPLE 3

Use a table of multiples to find three fractions equivalent to $\frac{4}{5}$. **Answers may vary. Sample:** $\frac{8}{10}, \frac{12}{15}, \frac{16}{20}$

FOR EXAMPLE 4

Find four fractions equivalent to $\frac{32}{48}$. **Answers may vary. Sample:** $\frac{16}{24}, \frac{8}{12}, \frac{4}{6}, \frac{2}{3}$

TACTILE LEARNING Encourage students to use fraction bars to compare equivalent fractions.

ERROR ALERT! Some students may have difficulty remembering which part of the fraction is the numerator and which is the denominator. **Remediation:** Suggest to students a mnemonic such as: The n*u*merator is *u*p and the *d*enominator is *d*own. Stress the "u" in the words up and numerator, and the "d" in down and denominator.

Technology Options

Prentice Hall Technology

Software for Learners

- Math Blaster® Mystery*
- Interactive Student Tutorial, Chapter 4*

Teaching Resource Software

- Computer Item Generator 4-2
- Resource Pro™ Chapter 4*

Internet • For related mathematics activities, visit the Prentice Hall site at www.phschool.com/math

**Available on CD-ROM only*

Assignment Options for Exercises On Your Own

To provide flexible scheduling, this lesson can be split into parts.

1 **Core** 1–15, 17–28
Extension 16

2 **Core** 29–53
Extension 54

Use Mixed Review to maintain skills.

A **factor** is a whole number that divides another whole number with no remainder.

■ EXAMPLE 2

Find the factors of 30.

$30 = 1 \times 30, 2 \times 15, 3 \times 10, \text{ and } 5 \times 6$ ← Find all the pairs of numbers with a product of 30.

The factors of 30 are 1, 2, 3, 5, 6, 10, 15, and 30.

4. ✔ *Try It Out* Find the factors of 8. **1, 2, 4, 8**

Now you may assign Exercises 1–28.

2 *Writing Equivalent Fractions*

QUICKreview

$\frac{2}{3}$ ← numerator / ← denominator

Fractions that are equal are **equivalent fractions.**

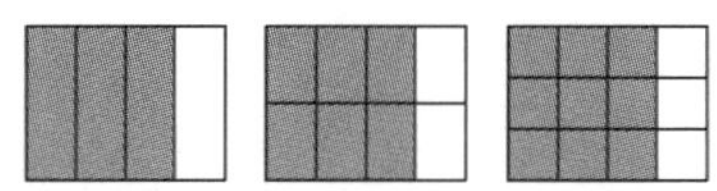

$\frac{3}{4} = \frac{6}{8} = \frac{9}{12}$

You can find equivalent fractions by multiplying the numerator and denominator by the same number.

$$\frac{2}{3} \xrightarrow{\times 2} = \frac{4}{6}$$

■ EXAMPLE 3

Use a table of multiples to find three fractions equivalent to $\frac{3}{4}$.

	× 2	× 3	× 4
3	6	9	12
4	8	12	16

Multiples in the same column will form fractions equivalent to $\frac{3}{4}$.

Three fractions equivalent to $\frac{3}{4}$ are $\frac{6}{8}, \frac{9}{12}$, and $\frac{12}{16}$.

5. ✔ *Try It Out* Find two other fractions equivalent to $\frac{3}{4}$.

6. *Open-ended* You can write 2 as the fraction $\frac{2}{1}$. Write three other fractions equivalent to 2.

7. *Error Analysis* Shana wrote that $\frac{5}{6} = \frac{5+4}{6+4} = \frac{9}{10}$. Is her answer reasonable? Explain.

5. Answers may vary. Sample: $\frac{15}{20}$ **and** $\frac{18}{24}$

6. Answers may vary. Sample: $\frac{4}{2}, \frac{6}{3}$, **and** $\frac{8}{4}$

7. No; to find a fraction equivalent to a given fraction, you multiply the numerator and denominator by the same number. You don't add the same number to the numerator and denominator.

VISUAL LEARNING Example 3 Have students draw 4 equal-size circles. Have them divide the circles into 4, 8, 12, and 16 equal parts. Then have students shade $\frac{3}{4}$ of each circle by coloring 3, 6, 9, and 12 parts respectively. Label each circle with the appropriate fraction equivalent to $\frac{3}{4}$.

ASSESSMENT Have each student write four fractions equivalent to $\frac{8}{12}$. Ask students to exchange fractions with a partner and compare.

3 Practice/Assess

EXERCISES *On Your Own*

MENTAL MATH Exercises 1–6 Have students check whether each factor on their list forms a pair with another factor.

Exercises 7–12 Students may forget to list the given number as the first multiple. Encourage them to begin their multiples table by multiplying by 1.

Exercise 15 Have students look at the lists of factors given throughout this lesson for help.

Exercises 39–50 Students can use the multiplication table given for Exercises 34–38 to answer most of these exercises. Encourage students to use factors and multiples by having them write "÷ ■" or "× ■" for each exercise.

WRITING Exercise 52 Challenge students to write about ways to find an equivalent fraction using both factors and multiples.

Another way to find equivalent fractions is to divide the numerator and the denominator by the same nonzero number.

■ EXAMPLE 4

Find three fractions equivalent to $\frac{24}{30}$.

Factors of 24: 1, 2, 3, 4, 6, 8, 12, 24
Factors of 30: 1, 2, 3, 5, 6, 10, 15, 30
← Find common factors.

$\frac{24}{30} = \frac{12}{15}$ (÷ 2 numerator and denominator) $\qquad$ $\frac{24}{30} = \frac{8}{10}$ (÷ 3 numerator and denominator) $\qquad$ $\frac{24}{30} = \frac{4}{5}$ (÷ 6 numerator and denominator)

Three fractions equivalent to $\frac{24}{30}$ are $\frac{12}{15}$, $\frac{8}{10}$, and $\frac{4}{5}$.

8. ✔ *Try It Out* Use division to find two fractions equivalent to $\frac{30}{36}$.

8. Answers may vary. Sample: $\frac{15}{18}$ and $\frac{5}{6}$

Now you may assign Exercises 29–54.

EXERCISES *On Your Own*

Mental Math **List the factors of each number.**

1. 17 **1, 17**
2. 18 **1, 2, 3, 6, 9, 18**
3. 32 **1, 2, 4, 8, 16, 32**
4. 42 **1, 2, 3, 6, 7, 14, 21, 42**
5. 23 **1, 23**
6. 70 **1, 2, 5, 7, 10, 14, 35, 70**

Write the first five multiples of each number.

7. 7 **7, 14, 21, 28, 35**
8. 4 **4, 8, 12, 16, 20**
9. 9 **9, 18, 27, 36, 45**
10. 13 **13, 26, 39, 52, 65**
11. 18 **18, 36, 54, 72, 90**
12. 32 **32, 64, 96, 128, 160**

13. Describe the relationship between 15, 5, and 3 using the words *factor* and *multiple*.
Sample: 3 and 5 are factors of 15; 15 is a multiple of both 3 and 5.

14. *Number Sense* What number is a factor of all other numbers? **1**

15. Mr. Quaid's class has 24 students, and Mrs. Carlson's class has 30 students. Each class is divided into several teams. What is the greatest number of people on a team if both classes have teams that are equal in size? **6 people**

16. *Number Theory* A number n is a multiple of 2. Is $n + 1$ a multiple of 2? Explain using examples.
No. Example: 4 is a multiple of 2, but 5 is not.

Find the LCM of each pair of numbers.

17. 4, 6 **12** 18. 9, 12 **36** 19. 8, 5 **40** 20. 14, 21 **42** 21. 3, 8 **24** 22. 2, 5 **10**

23. 5, 10 **10** 24. 15, 18 **90** 25. 10, 6 **30** 26. 15, 9 **45** 27. 12, 16 **48** 28. 24, 8 **24**

OPEN-ENDED Exercise 53 Ask students to share their equivalent fractions with the class by writing them on the board. Then have them discuss the strategies they used to find the fractions.

CONNECTING TO THE STUDENTS' WORLD
Exercise 54 If students have access to a sliding door, have them measure its thickness. Then have them measure the track. Ask them to write down and compare the measurements. Ask students what would happen if the track was too narrow or too wide.

WRAP UP

IDENTIFYING THE BIG IDEA Ask students to explain how to find factors and multiples. Have students define equivalent fractions and explain how they use factors and multiples to find equivalent fractions.

Math at Work

If you have block scheduling or extended class periods, consider having each member of the class create a case study of an imaginary child with a common illness. Have students include the child's symptoms, age, weight, and any known allergies. Tell students to research several brands of medicine and make a table of the recommended doses. Have students conclude their case studies with a diagnosis and recommendation for

Write two equivalent fractions for each model. 29–31. Samples are given.

29. 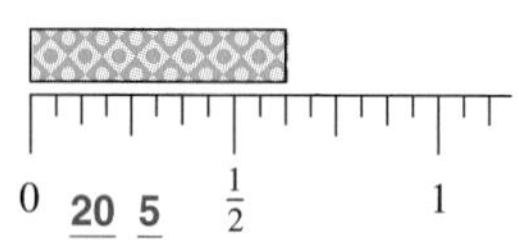

$\frac{20}{32}, \frac{5}{8}$

30. 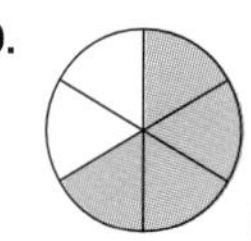
$\frac{2}{3}, \frac{8}{12}$

31. 

$\frac{2}{4}, \frac{3}{6}$

32. a. Write the first four multiples of 8 and 12.
b. Use multiples to write three fractions equivalent to $\frac{8}{12}$.
c. Find the factors of 8 and 12. What are the common factors?
d. Use common factors to find two fractions equivalent to $\frac{8}{12}$.

32a. 8: 8, 16, 24, 32
12: 12, 24, 36, 48
b. $\frac{16}{24}, \frac{24}{36}, \frac{32}{48}$
c. 8: 1, 2, 4, 8
12: 1, 2, 3, 4, 6, 12
The common factors are 1, 2, and 4.
d. $\frac{4}{6}, \frac{2}{3}$

33. a. Takala had 20 homework problems. She finished 15 of them while she was at the library. What fraction of the problems did she have left to do at home? $\frac{5}{20}$
b. Write a fraction equivalent to your answer in part (a) using common factors. $\frac{1}{4}$

Use the multiplication table below for Exercises 34–38. Find the number that makes each statement true.

	1	2	3	4	5	6	7	8	9
5	5	10	15	20	25	30	35	40	45
6	6	12	18	24	30	36	42	48	54
7	7	14	21	28	35	42	49	56	63
8	8	16	24	32	40	48	56	64	72

34. $\frac{5}{6} = \frac{20}{■}$ 24
35. $\frac{25}{40} = \frac{■}{32}$ 20
36. $\frac{7}{8} = \frac{35}{■}$ 40
37. $\frac{■}{72} = \frac{30}{48}$ 45
38. $\frac{20}{28} = \frac{■}{49}$ 35

Find each missing number.

39. $\frac{18}{■} = \frac{6}{7}$ 21
40. $\frac{5}{8} = \frac{■}{32}$ 20
41. $\frac{■}{6} = \frac{4}{1}$ 24
42. $\frac{5}{7} = \frac{25}{■}$ 35
43. $\frac{■}{72} = \frac{7}{8}$ 63
44. $\frac{■}{49} = \frac{3}{7}$ 21
45. $\frac{■}{64} = \frac{5}{8}$ 40
46. $\frac{6}{7} = \frac{■}{28}$ 24
47. $\frac{35}{■} = \frac{7}{8}$ 40
48. $\frac{10}{■} = \frac{5}{8}$ 16
49. $\frac{7}{8} = \frac{21}{■}$ 24
50. $\frac{35}{■} = \frac{7}{1}$ 5

51. **Choose A, B, C, or D.** Which square does *not* have the same fraction shaded as the others? D

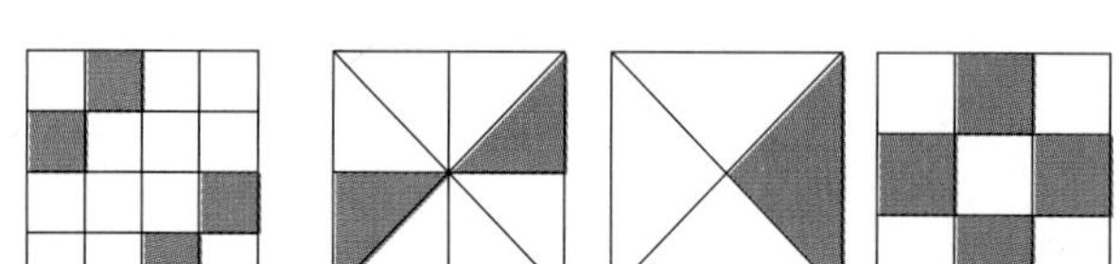

A B C D

treatment. If medicine is recommended, include dosage. Have volunteers share their case studies with the class.

LESSON QUIZ

1. Find three fractions equivalent to $\frac{5}{7}$.
   Sample: $\frac{10}{14}, \frac{15}{21}, \frac{20}{28}$
2. Use division to find three fractions equivalent to $\frac{24}{30}$. $\frac{12}{15}, \frac{8}{10}, \frac{4}{5}$

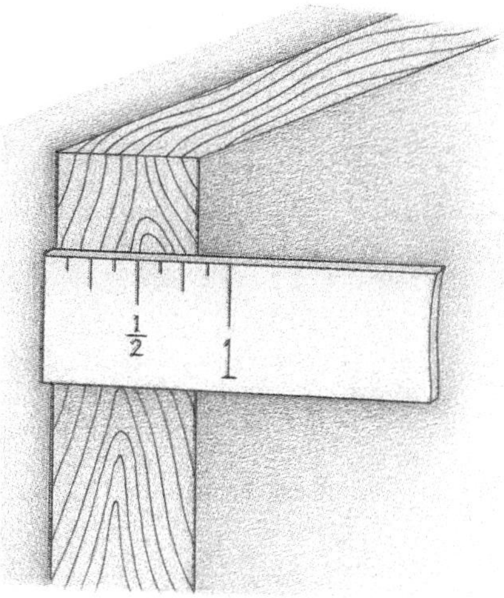

52. *Writing* Explain to someone who has been absent from class how to find fractions equivalent to $\frac{6}{18}$. **See below.**

53. *Open-ended* Write a fraction. Then find two fractions equivalent to your fraction. **Sample:** $\frac{5}{6}$; $\frac{10}{12}$ and $\frac{15}{18}$

54. a. Measure the thickness of the door at the right to the nearest $\frac{1}{4}$ inch. **a.** $\frac{3}{4}$ **in.** **b.** $\frac{7}{8}$ **in.**
    b. Measure the thickness of the door to the nearest $\frac{1}{8}$ inch.
    c. *Reasoning* You have a sliding door with the thickness shown at the right. Would you use your answer to part (a) or part (b) if you were making a track for the door to slide in? Explain.
    Part (b); you need a groove that is larger than the width of the door.

Mixed Review

Solve each equation. *(Lesson 3-9)*

55. $8m + 3 = 19$ **2**
56. $-5t + 7 = 62$ **−11**
57. $\frac{s}{2} - 4 = 11$ **30**
58. $\frac{n}{3} + 2 = -4$ **−18**

Find each sum or difference. *(Lesson 2-3)*

59. $14.02 + 3.6$ **17.62**
60. $0.83 - 0.75$ **0.08**
61. $45.79 - 2.3$ **43.49**
62. $7.077 + 25.3$ **32.377**
63. $25.98 - 8.89$ **17.09**

52. Sample: Multiply or divide the numerator and the denominator by the same whole number.

Math at Work

PEDIATRICIAN

A pediatrician uses math skills when reading a patient's medical profile and to interpret test results. Logical reasoning and problem-solving skills are essential to make a diagnosis and determine the proper treatment for a child who is ill.

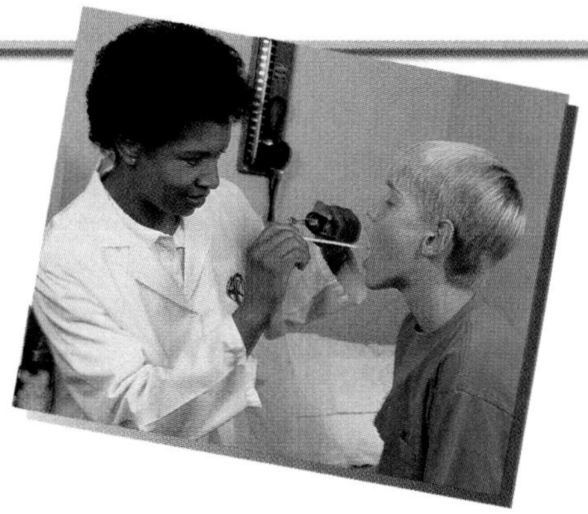

Internet Connection

Visit this Web site on Pediatrics to find more information:

www.yahoo.com/Health/Medicine/Pediatrics

PRACTICE

Practice 4-2 Equivalent Fractions

1. a. Write the first five multiples of 6 and 9. 6: 6, 12, 18, 24, 30; 9: 9, 18, 27, 36, 45
   b. What is the smallest multiple that 6 and 9 have in common? 18
2. a. Write the factors of 6 and the factors of 9. 6: 1, 2, 3, 6; 9: 1, 3, 9
   b. What factors do 6 and 9 have in common? 1, 3

Match each fraction in the column on the left with its equivalent in the column on the right.

3. $\frac{3}{8}$ H — A. $\frac{3}{5}$
4. $\frac{7}{12}$ F — B. $\frac{7}{8}$
5. $\frac{6}{10}$ A — C. $\frac{6}{12}$
6. $\frac{14}{16}$ B — D. $\frac{5}{6}$
7. $\frac{1}{2}$ C — E. $\frac{21}{28}$
8. $\frac{3}{4}$ E — F. $\frac{14}{24}$
9. $\frac{2}{3}$ G — G. $\frac{14}{21}$
10. $\frac{25}{30}$ D — H. $\frac{9}{24}$

11. Name two fractions that are modeled. $\frac{12}{20}, \frac{3}{5}$

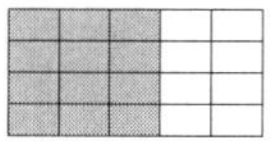

Find the number that makes a true statement.

12. $\frac{10}{16} = \frac{x}{8}$ 5
13. $\frac{16}{24} = \frac{2}{x}$ 3
14. $\frac{15}{25} = \frac{x}{5}$ 3
15. $\frac{21}{35} = \frac{3}{x}$ 5
16. $\frac{8}{32} = \frac{1}{x}$ 4
17. $\frac{x}{36} = \frac{7}{9}$ 28

Solve.

18. Which of the following numbers, 2, 3, 4, 5, 6, 8, 9, and 10, are factors of 2,910? 2, 3, 5, 6, 10
19. The Rano family decided to wrap presents together. Kim wrapped three presents for her grandmother. Her mother wrapped two presents. Her sister wrapped one present. What fraction of their grandmother's presents did each family member wrap? Kim: $\frac{1}{2}$; Mother: $\frac{1}{3}$; sister: $\frac{1}{6}$

In copymaster and workbook formats

RETEACHING

Reteaching 4-2 Equivalent Fractions

The **least common multiple (LCM)** of two numbers is the least number that is a multiple of both. To find the LCM of 8 and 10:

① List the first several multiples. — multiples of 8: 8, 16, 24, 32, **40**, 48; multiples of 10: 10, 20, 30, **40**, 50, 60

② Find the least multiple common to both lists. — The LCM of 8 and 10 is 40.

Fractions that are equal are **equivalent fractions.**

You can find equivalent fractions by multiplying the numerator and denominator by the same number or by dividing both by the same nonzero number.

$\frac{1}{4} = \frac{3}{12}$ (×3, ×3) — $\frac{1}{4}$ is equivalent to $\frac{3}{12}$.

$\frac{4}{6} = \frac{2}{3}$ (÷2, ÷2) — $\frac{4}{6}$ is equivalent to $\frac{2}{3}$.

Complete the list of the first five multiples of each number. Then find the LCM of each pair of numbers.

1. a. multiples of 4: 4, 8, 12, 16, 20
   b. multiples of 5: 5, 10, 15, 20, 25
   c. LCM of 4 and 5: 20
2. a. multiples of 18: 18, 36, 54, 72, 90
   b. multiples of 12: 12, 24, 36, 48, 60
   c. LCM of 18 and 12: 36
3. a. multiples of 6: 6, 12, 18, 24, 30
   b. multiples of 4: 4, 8, 12, 16, 20
   c. LCM of 6 and 4: 12
4. a. multiples of 10: 10, 20, 30, 40, 50
   b. multiples of 15: 15, 30, 45, 60, 75
   c. LCM of 10 and 15: 30

Find the LCM of each pair of numbers.

5. 10, 12 60
6. 8, 12 24
7. 25, 10 50
8. 10, 16 80

Find each missing number.

9. $\frac{3}{4} = \frac{15}{\boxed{20}}$
10. $\frac{18}{24} = \frac{\boxed{9}}{12}$
11. $\frac{18}{\boxed{30}} = \frac{3}{5}$
12. $\frac{\boxed{12}}{16} = \frac{6}{8}$

Reteaching

ENRICHMENT

Minds on Math Transparency

4-2

In the equations below, □ represents a two-digit number and △ represents a three-digit number. What numbers do they represent?

248 − □ = △

64 + □ = △

□ represents 92 and △ represents 156

See *Solution Key* for worked-out answers.

4-3 Teaching Notes

1 Focus

CONNECTING TO PRIOR KNOWLEDGE Ask students: *Name some strategies you can use to compare the decimal numbers 1.3 and 1.24.* **Answers may vary. Sample: Use a model; draw a number line.** Explain to the class that they can compare fractions using similar strategies.

2 Teach

THINK AND DISCUSS

AUDITORY LEARNING Have students practice writing the correct symbols as you read sentences that contain the terms *less than, greater than, or equal to.*

TACTILE LEARNING Example 2 Ask students to bring measuring cups to class to use to compare fractions. Have them measure water. Then pour the water into transparent containers of the same size. Label each container with the appropriate fraction, and order them from least to greatest.

ERROR ALERT! Question 4 Students might forget to write the original fractions after they order them using the LCD. **Remediation**: Before students rename fractions with the LCD, have them draw a box around the original fractions. After they order the fractions for their answers, they can find the original fractions inside each box.

Lesson Planning Options

Prerequisite Skills

- comparing and ordering whole numbers (3-2)
- writing equivalent fractions (4-2)

Vocabulary/Symbols

least common denominator (LCD)

Resources

Student Edition

Skills Handbook, p. 528
Extra Practice, p. 517
Glossary/Study Guide

Teaching Resources

Chapter Support File, Ch. 4
- Lesson Planner 4-3
- Practice 4-3, Reteaching 4-3
- Answer Masters 4-3

Teaching Aids Masters 10, 20–25
Glossary, Spanish Resources

Transparencies

9, 10, 15, 18–25, Minds on Math 4-3

Warm Up

Separate the digits 1 through 9 into three groups which have the same sum. **1, 5, 9; 2, 6, 7; 3, 4, 8**

MEASUREMENT Connection

4-3 Comparing and Ordering Fractions

What You'll Learn

1. To compare fractions
2. To order fractions

...And Why

You can compare amounts in recipes.

Here's How

Look for questions that
- build understanding
- check understanding

1. Set A: $\frac{7}{12}$ and $\frac{5}{6}$; Set B: $\frac{5}{12}$ and $\frac{2}{3}$

2a. $\frac{5}{6} > \frac{7}{12}$

b. $\frac{5}{12} < \frac{2}{3}$

WHAT?

People remember:
- three fourths of what they say
- one tenth of what they hear
- nine tenths of what they do

THINK AND DISCUSS

1 Comparing Fractions

1–2. See left.

1. Name the fractions represented by the fraction models below.

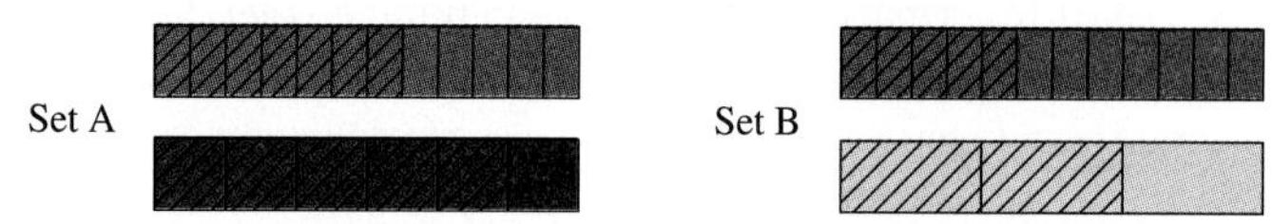

2. a. Use greater than (>) to compare the fractions in set A.
   b. Use less than (<) to compare the fractions in set B.

A number line helps you compare fractions too.

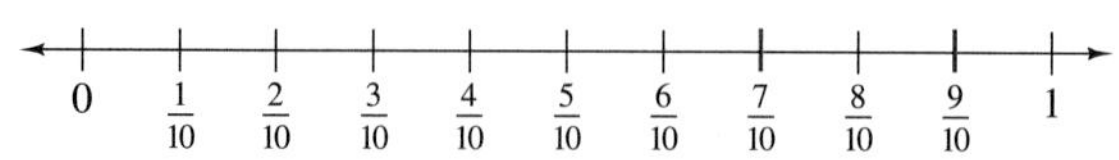

As you can see, if the denominators are the same, the numerators determine which is greater. So $\frac{7}{10} < \frac{9}{10}$, or $\frac{9}{10} > \frac{7}{10}$.

To compare fractions with different denominators, write them using the same denominator. Then, compare the numerators.

The **least common denominator (LCD)** of two fractions is the least common multiple of their denominators.

EXAMPLE 1 *Real-World Problem Solving*

Do people remember more of what they say or do?

Rewrite $\frac{3}{4}$ and $\frac{9}{10}$ using the LCD. The LCD of 4 and 10 is 20.

$$\frac{3}{4} = \frac{3 \cdot 5}{4 \cdot 5} = \frac{15}{20}$$

$$\frac{9}{10} = \frac{9 \cdot 2}{10 \cdot 2} = \frac{18}{20}$$

Write equivalent fractions.

Since $15 < 18$, $\frac{15}{20} < \frac{18}{20}$, and $\frac{3}{4} < \frac{9}{10}$.

People remember more of what they do than what they say.

3. ✔ *Try It Out* Compare each pair of fractions.
   a. $\frac{3}{4}$ ■ $\frac{5}{6}$ **<** b. $\frac{1}{6}$ ■ $\frac{2}{9}$ **<** c. $\frac{4}{10}$ ■ $\frac{3}{8}$ **>**

Now you may assign Exercises 1–22.

ADDITIONAL EXAMPLES

FOR EXAMPLE 1

During a fund raiser, three eighths of the students bought a cap, and one third of the students bought a T-shirt. Did more students buy a cap or a T-shirt? $\frac{3}{8} > \frac{1}{3}$; more students bought a cap than a T-shirt.

FOR EXAMPLE 2

Giselda wants to paint the dog house. In the storeroom, she finds $\frac{3}{5}$ gal of blue paint, $\frac{2}{3}$ gal of yellow paint, and $\frac{1}{2}$ gal of red paint. Of which color paint is there the greatest amount? yellow The least? red

3 Practice/Assess

EXERCISES *On Your Own*

ASSESSMENT **Exercises 3–7** Before beginning these exercises, have students write the steps they will use to compare the fractions. Then, after they have followed the steps, have them compare their work and answers with a partner.

WRAP UP

IDENTIFYING THE BIG IDEA Have students explain how to order fractions with the same denominator and fractions with different denominators.

2 *Ordering Fractions*

You can use the LCD to order more than two fractions.

EXAMPLE 2 ***Real-World Problem Solving***

Cooking Compare the amounts of sugar, oatmeal, and oil in the recipe at the left. Which has the greatest? The least?

Order $\frac{1}{2}$, $\frac{2}{3}$, and $\frac{1}{4}$.

The LCD of the denominators 2, 3, and 4 is 12.

$\frac{1}{2} = \frac{1 \cdot 6}{2 \cdot 6} = \frac{6}{12}$

$\frac{2}{3} = \frac{2 \cdot 4}{3 \cdot 4} = \frac{8}{12}$ ← Use the LCD to find equivalent fractions.

$\frac{1}{4} = \frac{1 \cdot 3}{4 \cdot 3} = \frac{3}{12}$

$\frac{3}{12} < \frac{6}{12} < \frac{8}{12}$ so $\frac{1}{4} < \frac{1}{2} < \frac{2}{3}$.

Oatmeal has the greatest amount, and oil has the least.

4a. $\frac{3}{8}, \frac{2}{5}, \frac{1}{2}$ b. $\frac{1}{3}, \frac{7}{12}, \frac{6}{9}$ c. $\frac{1}{15}, \frac{1}{5}, \frac{2}{6}$

4. ✓ *Try It Out* Order from least to greatest.

a. $\frac{3}{8}, \frac{1}{2}, \frac{2}{5}$ b. $\frac{6}{9}, \frac{1}{3}, \frac{7}{12}$ c. $\frac{1}{5}, \frac{2}{6}, \frac{1}{15}$

Now you may assign Exercises 23–39.

EXERCISES *On Your Own*

Write two fractions for the models and compare them.

1.

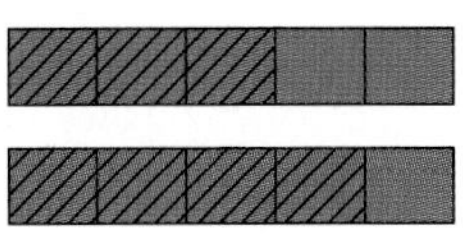

$\frac{3}{5} < \frac{4}{5}$

2.

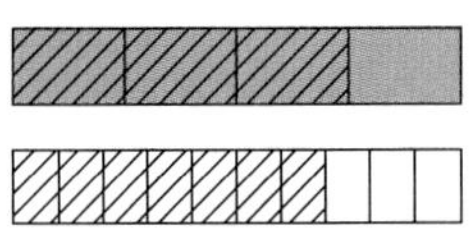

$\frac{3}{4} > \frac{7}{10}$

Compare. Use <, >, or =.

3. $\frac{5}{12}$ ■ $\frac{7}{12}$ < **4.** $\frac{5}{6}$ ■ $\frac{3}{6}$ > **5.** $\frac{1}{3}$ ■ $\frac{3}{4}$ < **6.** $\frac{5}{6}$ ■ $\frac{3}{5}$ > **7.** $\frac{3}{8}$ ■ $\frac{2}{3}$ <

8. $\frac{6}{7}$ ■ $\frac{4}{5}$ > **9.** $\frac{2}{3}$ ■ $\frac{5}{8}$ > **10.** $\frac{5}{6}$ ■ $\frac{7}{10}$ > **11.** $\frac{3}{8}$ ■ $\frac{3}{5}$ < **12.** $\frac{7}{12}$ ■ $\frac{5}{9}$ >

13. $\frac{3}{8}$ ■ $\frac{5}{8}$ < **14.** $\frac{2}{3}$ ■ $\frac{3}{5}$ > **15.** $\frac{1}{8}$ ■ $\frac{3}{16}$ < **16.** $\frac{3}{4}$ ■ $\frac{3}{10}$ > **17.** $\frac{4}{5}$ ■ $\frac{2}{3}$ >

Which fractional part would you prefer? Explain.

18–21. Answers may vary. Samples are given.

18. $\frac{2}{3}$ or $\frac{2}{5}$ of an apple to eat
$\frac{2}{3}$, since there is more fruit.

19. $2\frac{1}{2}$ or $2\frac{3}{4}$ h of homework
$2\frac{1}{2}$, since it is less homework.

20. $\frac{1}{6}$ or $\frac{1}{12}$ year for vacation
$\frac{1}{6}$, since it would be a longer vacation.

21. *Writing* Describe an easy way to compare two fractions that have the same *numerator*, like $\frac{4}{5}$ and $\frac{4}{7}$.
The fraction with the greater denominator has the lesser value.

Technology Options

Prentice Hall Technology

Software for Learners
- Math Blaster® Mystery*
- Interactive Student Tutorial, Chapter 4*

Teaching Resource Software
- Computer Item Generator 4-3
- Resource Pro™ Chapter 4*

Internet • For related mathematics activities, visit the Prentice Hall site at www.phschool.com/math

**Available on CD-ROM only*

Assignment Options for Exercises On Your Own

To provide flexible scheduling, this lesson can be split into parts.

1 **Core** 1–21
Extension 22

2 **Core** 23–38
Extension 39

Use Mixed Review to maintain skills.

PRACTICE

Practice 4-3 Comparing and Ordering Fractions

Write the two fractions modeled and compare them.

1. $\frac{4}{5}, \frac{5}{6}; \frac{4}{5} < \frac{5}{6}$
2. $\frac{7}{8}, \frac{2}{3}; \frac{7}{8} > \frac{2}{3}$
3. $\frac{9}{10}, \frac{7}{8}; \frac{9}{10} > \frac{7}{8}$

Find the LCD of each pair of fractions.

4. $\frac{5}{8}, \frac{5}{6}$ 24
5. $\frac{5}{12}, \frac{7}{8}$ 24
6. $\frac{9}{10}, \frac{1}{2}$ 10
7. $\frac{2}{3}, \frac{3}{4}$ 12
8. $\frac{1}{6}, \frac{3}{10}$ 30
9. $\frac{1}{4}, \frac{2}{15}$ 60
10. $\frac{5}{6}, \frac{8}{15}$ 30
11. $\frac{7}{12}, \frac{9}{20}$ 60

Compare. Use <, >, or =.

12. $\frac{7}{8} > \frac{3}{8}$
13. $\frac{4}{5} > \frac{1}{2}$
14. $\frac{6}{12} = \frac{4}{8}$
15. $\frac{7}{15} < \frac{11}{15}$
16. $\frac{4}{5} > \frac{6}{10}$
17. $\frac{7}{12} < \frac{2}{3}$
18. $\frac{8}{15} > \frac{1}{2}$
19. $\frac{10}{15} = \frac{8}{12}$
20. $\frac{4}{9} < \frac{7}{9}$
21. $\frac{2}{5} > \frac{3}{8}$
22. $\frac{1}{2} < \frac{11}{20}$
23. $\frac{7}{16} < \frac{1}{2}$

Order from least to greatest.

24. $\frac{1}{4}, \frac{1}{3}, \frac{1}{6}$ — $\frac{1}{6}, \frac{1}{4}, \frac{1}{3}$
25. $\frac{1}{2}, \frac{5}{6}, \frac{7}{8}$ — $\frac{1}{2}, \frac{5}{6}, \frac{7}{8}$
26. $\frac{1}{4}, \frac{2}{5}, \frac{3}{8}$ — $\frac{1}{4}, \frac{3}{8}, \frac{2}{5}$
27. $\frac{7}{8}, \frac{5}{9}, \frac{2}{3}$ — $\frac{5}{9}, \frac{2}{3}, \frac{7}{8}$
28. $\frac{3}{8}, \frac{5}{6}, \frac{1}{2}$ — $\frac{3}{8}, \frac{1}{2}, \frac{5}{6}$
29. $\frac{9}{10}, \frac{11}{12}, \frac{15}{16}$ — $\frac{9}{10}, \frac{11}{12}, \frac{15}{16}$
30. $\frac{3}{4}, \frac{1}{2}, \frac{7}{8}$ — $\frac{1}{2}, \frac{3}{4}, \frac{7}{8}$
31. $\frac{5}{9}, \frac{2}{3}, \frac{7}{12}$ — $\frac{5}{9}, \frac{7}{12}, \frac{2}{3}$
32. $\frac{15}{16}, \frac{7}{8}, \frac{1}{2}$ — $\frac{1}{2}, \frac{7}{8}, \frac{15}{16}$

Solve.

33. A pattern requires a seam of at least $\frac{5}{8}$ in. Rachel sewed a seam $\frac{1}{2}$ in. wide. Did she sew the seam wide enough? Explain.
    No; $\frac{1}{2}$ is less than $\frac{5}{8}$.

34. Marc needs $\frac{3}{4}$ c of milk for a recipe. He has $\frac{2}{3}$ c. Does he have enough? Explain.
    No; $\frac{2}{3}$ is less than $\frac{3}{4}$.

35. Monica is growing three bean plants as part of a science experiment. Plant A is $\frac{1}{2}$ in. tall. Plant B is $\frac{3}{4}$ in. tall. Plant C is $\frac{3}{8}$ in. tall. Order the plants from shortest to tallest.
    Plant C, Plant A, Plant B

36. During a rainstorm Willow received $\frac{7}{16}$ in. of rain and Riverton received $\frac{5}{8}$ in. of rain. Which community received more rain?
    Riverton

Practice

In copymaster and workbook formats

RETEACHING

Reteaching 4-3 Comparing and Ordering Fractions

Follow these steps to *compare* $\frac{2}{5}$ and $\frac{3}{10}$ (unlike denominators).

① Find the **least common denominator (LCD).** The denominators are 5 and 10. The LCD of 5 and 10 is their least common multiple.

② Write the equivalent fractions using the LCD. $\frac{2}{5} = \frac{4}{10}$ and $\frac{3}{10} = \frac{3}{10}$

③ Compare the numerators. $4 > 3$

So, $\frac{4}{10} > \frac{3}{10}$ and $\frac{2}{5} > \frac{3}{10}$.

Follow these steps to *order* the fractions $\frac{1}{2}, \frac{3}{5}$, and $\frac{2}{3}$.

① Find the LCD. The LCD of 2, 5, and 3 is 30.

② Write equivalent fractions using the LCD.

$$\frac{1}{2} = \frac{1 \cdot 15}{2 \cdot 15} = \frac{15}{30}$$
$$\frac{3}{5} = \frac{3 \cdot 6}{5 \cdot 6} = \frac{18}{30}$$
$$\frac{2}{3} = \frac{2 \cdot 10}{3 \cdot 10} = \frac{20}{30}$$

③ Order the fractions using their numerators. $\frac{15}{30} < \frac{18}{30} < \frac{20}{30}$

So, $\frac{1}{2} < \frac{3}{5} < \frac{2}{3}$.

Find each missing number. Then compare the fractions. Use <, >, or =.

1. $\frac{2}{3}$ and $\frac{3}{5}$
   a. $\frac{2}{3} = \frac{10}{15}, \frac{3}{5} = \frac{9}{15}$
   b. $\frac{2}{3} > \frac{3}{5}$
2. $\frac{1}{2}$ and $\frac{5}{8}$
   a. $\frac{1}{2} = \frac{4}{8}, \frac{5}{8} = \frac{5}{8}$
   b. $\frac{1}{2} < \frac{5}{8}$
3. $\frac{3}{4}$ and $\frac{9}{12}$
   a. $\frac{3}{4} = \frac{9}{12}, \frac{9}{12} = \frac{9}{12}$
   b. $\frac{3}{4} = \frac{9}{12}$

Compare. Use <, >, or =.

4. $\frac{3}{5} < \frac{4}{5}$
5. $\frac{3}{4} < \frac{7}{8}$
6. $\frac{8}{12} = \frac{2}{3}$
7. $\frac{1}{2} < \frac{9}{16}$
8. $\frac{2}{3} > \frac{1}{2}$
9. $\frac{5}{9} = \frac{10}{18}$
10. $\frac{6}{7} > \frac{5}{6}$
11. $\frac{3}{8} < \frac{3}{5}$

Order from least to greatest.

12. $\frac{1}{2}, \frac{4}{5}, \frac{1}{4}$ — $\frac{1}{4}, \frac{1}{2}, \frac{4}{5}$
13. $\frac{2}{3}, \frac{3}{8}, \frac{1}{2}$ — $\frac{3}{8}, \frac{1}{2}, \frac{2}{3}$
14. $\frac{5}{6}, \frac{7}{8}, \frac{1}{4}$ — $\frac{1}{4}, \frac{5}{6}, \frac{7}{8}$
15. $\frac{1}{2}, \frac{5}{8}, \frac{5}{6}$ — $\frac{1}{2}, \frac{5}{8}, \frac{5}{6}$
16. $\frac{7}{10}, \frac{2}{3}, \frac{1}{5}$ — $\frac{1}{5}, \frac{2}{3}, \frac{7}{10}$
17. $\frac{2}{3}, \frac{1}{4}, \frac{11}{12}$ — $\frac{1}{4}, \frac{2}{3}, \frac{11}{12}$

ENRICHMENT

Minds on Math Transparency

4-3

A worm is trying to crawl out of a 3-ft deep hole. If the worm crawls up 7 in. and then falls down 2 in. each hour, how many hours will it take the worm to crawl out of the hole?

more than 6 but less than 7 hours

See *Solution Key* for worked-out answers.

JOURNAL Have students use the steps used in Exercises 3–7.

PROJECT LINK Have students brainstorm what materials to use and what size to make their rulers.

LESSON QUIZ

1. Compare. Use <, >, or =.
   $\frac{3}{5}$ ■ $\frac{4}{9}$ >
2. Order from least to greatest.
   $\frac{7}{9}, \frac{5}{6}, \frac{2}{3}$ — $\frac{2}{3}, \frac{7}{9}, \frac{5}{6}$

22. *Reasoning* You want to nail a board that is $\frac{1}{2}$ in. thick onto a wall. You can choose from nails that are $\frac{3}{8}$ in. long and $\frac{3}{4}$ in. long. Which size nail is the better choice? Explain. $\frac{3}{4}$ in.; the other nail will not reach the wall through the board.

28–31. See back of book.

Order from least to greatest.

23. $\frac{3}{4}, \frac{2}{3}, \frac{5}{6}$ — 23. $\frac{2}{3}, \frac{3}{4}, \frac{5}{6}$
24. $\frac{3}{8}, \frac{1}{4}, \frac{2}{3}$ — 24. $\frac{1}{4}, \frac{3}{8}, \frac{2}{3}$
25. $\frac{4}{9}, \frac{2}{3}, \frac{1}{2}$ — 25. $\frac{4}{9}, \frac{1}{2}, \frac{2}{3}$
26. $\frac{1}{3}, \frac{5}{6}, \frac{3}{8}$ — 26. $\frac{1}{3}, \frac{3}{8}, \frac{5}{6}$
27. $\frac{1}{8}, \frac{1}{6}, \frac{1}{9}$ — 27. $\frac{1}{9}, \frac{1}{8}, \frac{1}{6}$
28. $\frac{9}{16}, \frac{3}{6}, \frac{5}{8}$
29. $\frac{3}{15}, \frac{3}{10}, \frac{3}{5}$
30. $\frac{5}{8}, \frac{7}{9}, \frac{3}{4}$
31. $\frac{3}{5}, \frac{1}{2}, \frac{2}{3}$
32. $\frac{6}{10}, \frac{7}{12}, \frac{5}{8}$ — 32. $\frac{7}{12}, \frac{6}{10}, \frac{5}{8}$
33. $\frac{5}{6}, \frac{4}{5}, \frac{3}{4}$ — 33. $\frac{3}{4}, \frac{4}{5}, \frac{5}{6}$
34. $\frac{8}{9}, \frac{7}{12}, \frac{3}{4}$ — 34. $\frac{7}{12}, \frac{3}{4}, \frac{8}{9}$

Estimation **Match each fraction with a point on the number line.**

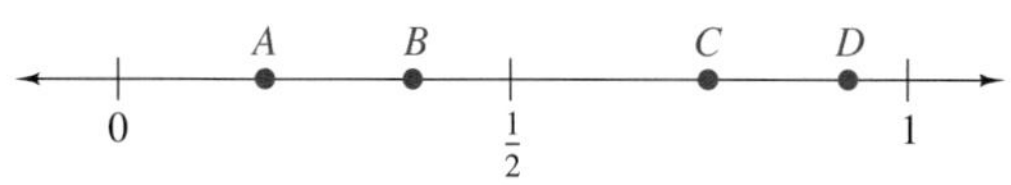

35. $\frac{3}{8}$ B
36. $\frac{11}{12}$ D
37. $\frac{3}{4}$ C
38. $\frac{3}{16}$ A

39. *Reasoning* For a party, a class ordered the same number of cheese pizzas, vegetable pizzas, and meatball pizzas. The leftovers were $\frac{5}{8}$ of a cheese pizza, $\frac{2}{3}$ of a vegetable pizza, and $\frac{3}{4}$ of a meatball pizza. Which type was most popular? Explain.
    Cheese, since that was the pizza with the least amount of leftovers.

JOURNAL Explain how to compare fractions that have different denominators.

Mixed Review

Find each sum. (Lesson 3-3)

40. $-3 + 7$ 4
41. $5 + (-2)$ 3
42. $6 + (-8)$ −2
43. $-9 + (-4)$ −13
44. $-1 + 7$ 6
45. $3 + (-7)$ −4

Find each product or quotient. (Lessons 2-5, 2-6)

46. 9.4×0.3 2.82
47. $1.02 \div 0.3$ 3.4
48. 8.07×14.2 114.594
49. $85.92 \div 4.8$ 17.9
50. $63.18 \div 8.1$ 7.8

51. *Choose a Strategy* In a science class the number of bacteria in a jar doubles each day. If the jar is full on the 28th day, on what day was it half full? on the 27th day

CHAPTER PROJECT

PROJECT LINK: DESIGNING

Design a new unit for measuring length. What will you call it? Make a ruler one unit long based on your new measurement. Use it to measure the length of a classroom door. Estimate the length of your classroom using your measuring unit. What is the length of a bicycle or a car?

Check student's work.

4-4 Teaching Notes

1 Focus

CONNECTING TO PRIOR KNOWLEDGE Review with students the formula for finding the area of a rectangle, $A = lw$. Have them use the formula to find the area of a square with sides of 5 cm. Point out that since the sides of a square are the same length, they can write the formula for the area of a square as $A = s^2$. Ask: *Did you multiply the 5 by 2 to find the area?* **no** *What do you think the digit 2 in the formula means?* **Answers may vary. Sample: Use the length of the side as a factor two times.**

2 Teach

Work Together

REASONING Question 2 Have students compare the suggested allowance for nine weeks to a $1 per week allowance for nine weeks. **The suggested allowance is $1.22 greater.**

THINK AND DISCUSS

ERROR ALERT! Question 3 Students might multiply the base by the exponent. **Remediation:** Have students draw the same number of empty boxes as the power given in the problem and put a multiplication sign between each box. Then fill in each box with the base.

TECHNOLOGY

4-4 Exponents and Order of Operations

What You'll Learn

- 1 To write numbers with exponents
- 2 To evaluate expressions with exponents using the order of operations

...And Why

Using exponents is an efficient way of writing products of the same factor.

Here's How

Look for questions that
- build understanding
- ✔ check understanding

Work Together

Exploring Exponents

Luis and Sofia suggested that their allowance be changed. They wanted 2¢ the first week, with their allowance to be doubled each week. Their parents investigated the suggestion using this table.

Week	Cents
one	$2 = ■$
two	$2 \times 2 = ■$
three	$2 \times 2 \times 2 = ■$
four	$2 \times 2 \times 2 \times 2 = ■$

1. a. Complete the table to find how many cents Luis and Sofia would be paid each of the first four weeks. **2, 4, 8, 16**
   b. How much would they be paid the seventh week? The tenth week? **$1.28; $10.24**
2. *Reasoning* Do you think their parents will agree with their suggestion? Explain.
   No; the allowance will rise very rapidly.

THINK AND DISCUSS

1 Standard and Exponential Forms

In the Work Together you multiplied 2 by itself several times. You can use an **exponent** to indicate repeated multiplication.

$$\text{base} \rightarrow 2^4 = \underbrace{2 \times 2 \times 2 \times 2}_{\text{The base is used as a factor four times.}}$$
(exponent ↓ points to the 4)

A number expressed using an exponent is a **power.** You read 2^4 as "two to the fourth power." Both 2^4 and 16 have the same value.

exponential expression → $2^4 = 16$ ← the value of the expression

3. ✔ *Try It Out* What are the base and the exponent of each expression?
   a. 10^2 **10; 2** b. 3^5 **3; 5** c. 12^7 **12; 7**

Lesson Planning Options

Prerequisite Skills
- multiplying whole numbers (precourse)

Vocabulary/Symbols

exponent, base, power

Materials/Manipulatives
- calculator

Resources

Student Edition

Skills Handbook, p. 530
Extra Practice, p. 517
Glossary/Study Guide

Teaching Resources

Chapter Support File, Ch. 4
- Lesson Planner 4-4
- Practice 4-4, Reteaching 4-4
- Alternative Activity 4-4
- Answer Masters 4-4

Glossary, Spanish Resources

Transparencies
15, Minds on Math 4-4

Warm Up

Determine if and where Will and Pedro will meet if they start driving at the same intersection. Pedro travels 2 blocks east, 2 blocks south, 2 blocks east, and 2 blocks north, while Will starts traveling 2 blocks north, 4 blocks east, and 2 blocks south.
Yes, they will meet 4 blocks east.

■ **ADDITIONAL EXAMPLES**

FOR EXAMPLE 1

The Glencove neighborhood has an area of $(1.3)^2$ km^2. Evaluate $(1.3)^2$. **1.69 km^2**

FOR EXAMPLE 2

Simplify $2^3 \times (9 - 3)^2$. **288**

FOR EXAMPLE 3

Simplify each expression.

a. $(-4)^2$ **16**

b. -4^2 **−16**

AEP Some students may have difficulty reading exponential numbers. Relate *squared* to the exponent 2. Remind students that a square is two-dimensional. Relate *cubed* to the exponent 3. Demonstrate that a cube is three-dimensional.

AUDITORY LEARNING Example 2 Inform students that one way to remember the order of operations is to use a mnemonic phrase, such as: *P*lease(*P*arenthesis) *E*xcuse (*E*xponents) *M*y (*M*ultiply) *D*ear (*D*ivide) *A*unt (*A*dd) *S*ally (*S*ubtract). Challenge the class to come up with its own mnemonic.

Example 3 Have students make a chart that shows the results of multiplying with negative signs.

$(-) \cdot (-) = (+)$

$(-) \cdot (-) \cdot (-) = (-)$

$(-) \cdot (-) \cdot (-) \cdot (-) = (+)$

Have students summarize their results. **When there is an even number of negative signs, the result is positive. When there is**

Technology Options

Prentice Hall Technology

Software for Learners

- Hot Page™ 3–8*
- Math Blaster® Mystery*
- Interactive Student Tutorial, Chapter 4*

Teaching Resource Software

- Computer Item Generator 4-4
- Resource Pro™ Chapter 4*

Internet • For related mathematics activities, visit the Prentice Hall site at www.phschool.com/math

**Available on CD-ROM only*

Assignment Options for Exercises On Your Own

To provide flexible scheduling, this lesson can be split into parts.

1 **Core** 1–23
Extension 24

2 **Core** 25–42
Extension 43

Use Mixed Review to maintain skills.

Gibraltar

Gibraltar is the smallest colony in the world. It is located at the mouth of the Mediterranean, off the coast of Spain.

There are special exponent keys on a scientific calculator. These can help you find the value of an exponential expression.

■ **EXAMPLE 1** *Real-World Problem Solving*

Gibraltar has an area of $(1.5)^2$ mi^2. Evaluate $(1.5)^2$.

1.5 [x^2] 2.25 ← Use the [x^2] key to square numbers.

The area of Gibraltar is 2.25 mi^2.

You can use the [y^x] key to raise a number to any power.

4^3 → 4 [y^x] 3 [=] *64*

2.3 [y^x] 2; 2.3 [x^2]; 2.3 [×] 2.3

4. *Think About It* Describe three ways you can use your calculator to find the value of 2.3^2.

Now you may assign Exercises 1–24.

2 *Using the Order of Operations*

To evaluate expressions that contain exponents, you must include exponents in the order of operations.

ORDER OF OPERATIONS

1. Do all operations within grouping symbols first.
2. Evaluate any term with exponents.
3. Multiply and divide in order from left to right.
4. Add and subtract in order from left to right.

■ **EXAMPLE 2**

Simplify $3^4 \times (7 - 2)^3$.

$3^4 \times (7 - 2)^3 = 3^4 \times 5^3$ ← Do operations in parentheses.

$= 81 \times 125$ ← Evaluate exponential expressions.

$= 10{,}125$ ← Multiply.

5. ✔ *Try It Out* Which operation happens first? Explain.
   a. $(3^2 + 5) - 2$ **b.** $3^2 + 5 - 2$ **c.** $(3 + 5)^2 - 2$

5a. 3^2; within the parentheses, evaluate the term with an exponent first.
b. 3^2; since there are no grouping symbols, evaluate the term with an exponent.
c. 3 + 5; do operations in parentheses first.

A scientific calculator follows the order of operations. Here are the keystrokes to find the value of the expression in Example 2.

3 [y^x] 4 [×] [(] 7 [−] 2 [)] [y^x] 3 [=] *10125*

6. ✔ *Try It Out* What key strokes would you use to find the value of $(1.5 + 21)^2 \div 72$?
   Answers may vary. Sample: [(] 1.5 [+] 21 [)] [x^2] [÷] 72 [=]

an odd number of negative signs, the result is negative.

ASSESSMENT Have students work in pairs. Each partner writes an expression that involves order of operations with exponents. Partners exchange problems and simplify. Allow partners to check each other's work. Ask for volunteers to share their expressions with the class.

3 Practice/Assess

EXERCISES *On Your Own*

OPEN-ENDED Exercise 19 Have students use trial and error. Remind them they can use different bases and exponents.

WRITING Exercise 24d Remind students that to write a general rule is to give a brief summary.

WRAP UP

IDENTIFYING THE BIG IDEA Ask students to explain what it means to find the value of a number to a certain power. Have them list the order of operations. Then ask them to explain what would happen if they did not follow the order of operations.

When you use an exponent with a negative number as the base, it is important to use grouping symbols to avoid confusion.

■ EXAMPLE 3

Simplify each expression.

a. $(-5)^4 = (-5)(-5)(-5)(-5)$
$= 625$

b. $-5^4 = -(5 \cdot 5 \cdot 5 \cdot 5)$
$= -625$

7. ✔ *Try It Out* Simplify each expression.
a. -2^3 **−8** b. $(-2)^3$ **−8** c. -2^4 **−16** d. $(-2)^4$ **16**

Now you may assign Exercises 25–43.

EXERCISES *On Your Own*

Write each expression using exponents.

1. $7 \times 7 \times 7$ **7^3**
2. $4 \times 4 \times 4 \times 4 \times 4 \times 4$ **4^6**
3. $0.3 \times 0.3 \times 0.3 \times 0.3 \times 0.3$ **0.3^5**

Write each expression as a product of repeated factors. Then evaluate each expression. **4–15. See margin for products.**

4. 4^5 **1,024**
5. 5^3 **125**
6. 13^6 **4,826,809**
7. 0.2^4 **0.0016**
8. 3^3 **27**
9. 9^6 **531,441**
10. 11^3 **1,331**
11. 6^5 **7,776**
12. 1.7^3 **4.913**
13. 8^4 **4,096**
14. 5^5 **3,125**
15. 0.6^2 **0.36**

16. a. *Geometry* How many small squares are on one side of the square at the right? **3**
b. How many small squares make up the whole square? **9**
c. *Language* Why do you think 3^2 is referred to as "3 squared"? **See margin.**

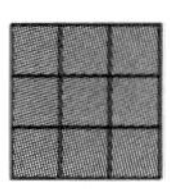

Values: 10; 100; 1,000; 10,000; 100,000

17. a. Copy and complete the table at the right.
b. *Patterns* What pattern do you see with powers of 10? **See margin.**
c. Use your pattern to find the value of 10^{12}. **1,000,000,000,000**

	Value	Number of Zeros
10^1	■	1
10^2	■	■ **2**
10^3	■	■ **3**
10^4	■	■ **4**
10^5	■	■ **5**

18. *Calculator* Use a calculator. Find 5^1, 17^1, and 3.2^1. What do you notice?
5, 17, 3.2; Any number raised to the first power equals itself.

19. *Open-ended* Write two numbers using exponents that are between the values of 5^2 and 5^3. **Answers may vary. Sample: 4^3, 6^2**

20. a. Without calculating, predict which is greater, 2^6 or 6^2. **2^6**
b. *Calculator* Find 2^6 and 6^2. Was your prediction correct? Explain. **64, 36; yes; the greater number of factors increases the value very rapidly.**

pages 157–158 On Your Own

4. $4 \times 4 \times 4 \times 4 \times 4$
5. $5 \times 5 \times 5$
6. $13 \times 13 \times 13 \times 13 \times 13 \times 13$
7. $0.2 \times 0.2 \times 0.2 \times 0.2$
8. $3 \times 3 \times 3$
9. $9 \times 9 \times 9 \times 9 \times 9 \times 9$
10. $11 \times 11 \times 11$
11. $6 \times 6 \times 6 \times 6 \times 6$
12. $1.7 \times 1.7 \times 1.7$
13. $8 \times 8 \times 8 \times 8$
14. $5 \times 5 \times 5 \times 5 \times 5$
15. 0.6×0.6

16c. Answers may vary. Sample: It can be modeled by a square whose side is 3 units long.

17b. The number of zeros is the same as the exponent.

PRACTICE

Practice 4-4 Exponents and Order of Operations

Write each expression using exponents.

1. $3 \times 3 \times 3 \times 3 \times 3$ 3^5
2. $2.7 \times 2.7 \times 2.7$ 2.7^3
3. $11.6 \times 11.6 \times 11.6 \times 11.6$ 11.6^4
4. $2 \times 2 \times 2 \times 2 \times 2 \times 2$ 2^6
5. $8.3 \times 8.3 \times 8.3 \times 8.3 \times 8.3$ 8.3^5
6. $4 \times 4 \times 4 \times 4 \times 4 \times 4 \times 4 \times 4$ 4^8

Write each expression as the product of repeated factors. Then evaluate each expression.

7. 0.5^3 $0.5 \times 0.5 \times 0.5$; 0.125
8. 4^5 $4 \times 4 \times 4 \times 4 \times 4$; 1,024
9. 2.7^2 2.7×2.7; 7.29
10. 2^3 $2 \times 2 \times 2$; 8
11. 5^6 $5 \times 5 \times 5 \times 5 \times 5 \times 5$; 15,625
12. 8.1^3 $8.1 \times 8.1 \times 8.1$; 531.441

Choose a calculator, paper and pencil, or mental math to evaluate each expression.

13. -4^3 −64
14. $8^3 + 9$ 521
15. $11 + 6^3$ 227
16. $14 + 16^2$ 270
17. $8 + 6^4$ 1,304
18. $2^5 + 2^3$ 40
19. $3^2 \cdot 5^4$ 5,625
20. $6^2 - 2^4$ 20
21. $4(0.9 + 1.3)^3$ 42.592
22. $3(1.5 - 0.2)^3$ 6.591
23. $3^5 - (4^2 + 5)$ 222
24. $(3^3 + 6) - 7$ 26
25. $5(0.3 \cdot 1.2)^2$ 0.648
26. $18 \div (1.4 - 0.4)^2$ 18
27. $5(4 + 2)^2$ 180
28. $(8 - 6.7)^3$ 2.197

Circle A, B, or C.

29. 2^4 ■ 4^2
 A. > B. < (C.) =
30. 3^6 ■ 6^3
 (A.) > B. < C. =
31. 2^5 ■ 5^2
 (A.) > B. < C. =

In copymaster and workbook formats

RETEACHING

Reteaching 4-4 Exponents and Order of Operations

You can use a shortcut to indicate repeated multiplication. The **exponent** tells how many times the **base** is used as a factor.

5^4 is called an **exponential expression** and 625 is the **value of the expression.**

$5 \times 5 \times 5 \times 5 = 5^4 = 625$ (exponent: 4; base: 5)

You can use this sentence to remember the order of operations for expressions with exponents. → **P**lease **E**xcuse **M**y **D**ear **A**unt **S**ally.

$2^2 + 4(7 - 3) + 6 = 2^2 + 4(4) + 6$	**P**	Do all operations within **P**arentheses first.
$= 4 + 4(4) + 6$	**E**	**E**valuate any terms with **E**xponents.
$= 4 + 16 + 6$	**M-D**	**M**ultiply and **D**ivide in from left order to right.
$= 26$	**A-S**	**A**dd and **S**ubtract in order from left to right.

Write each expression using exponents.

1. $6 \times 6 \times 6 \times 6 \times 6$ 6^5
2. $0.2 \times 0.2 \times 0.2$ 0.2^3
3. $9 \times 9 \times 9 \times 9$ 9^4
4. $12 \times 12 \times 12 \times 12 \times 12$ 12^5

Write each expression as a product of repeated factors. Then evaluate each expression.

5. 12^2 12×12; 144
6. 8^3 $8 \times 8 \times 8$; 512
7. 0.4^3 $0.4 \times 0.4 \times 0.4$; 0.064
8. 5^5 $5 \times 5 \times 5 \times 5 \times 5$; 3,125
9. 3^6 $3 \times 3 \times 3 \times 3 \times 3 \times 3$; 729
10. 1.4^2 1.4×1.4; 1.96

Evaluate each expression.

11. $7^2 + 3^3$ 76
12. $8 + 4^2$ 24
13. $5(0.2 + 0.8)^{10}$ 5
14. $(9 - 7)^2$ 4
15. $(8^2 + 16) \div 2$ 40
16. $5^3 + 100$ 225
17. $(4 + 7)^2 - 8$ 113
18. $(9 - 3)^2 + 6 \times 2$ 48

Reteaching

ENRICHMENT

Minds on Math Transparency

4-4

Paulette has six marbles that are the same size. Five of her marbles weigh the same. The other marble is heavier than the rest. Hahn is trying to determine which marble is heavier than the rest by using a balance scale and only two weighings. How can he do this?

Sample: Put 3 marbles on each side of the scale and find the heavier group of 3. From these 3, put 1 marble on each side of the scale. If either is heavier, the scale will show which. If not, the marble left off the scale is heavier.

See *Solution Key* for worked-out answers.

LESSON QUIZ

Evaluate each expression.

1. 6^3 216
2. $(-3)^5$ −243
3. $10^3 + 7^2$ 1,049
4. $(12 - 3^2) \times 5 + 6$ 21

Match the fact with the power.

21. wheels on a unicycle C
22. planets in the solar system B
23. freezing point of water in °F A

A. 2^5
B. 3^2
C. 1^{17}

24. a. Look at the chart below. What exponent completes it?

Value	16	8	4	2	1
Power of 2	2^4	2^3	2^2	2^1	$2^{■}$ 0

b. *Calculator* Check your prediction on your calculator. Check students' work.
c. *Patterns* Find 3^0, 4^0, 5^0, 10^0. What do you notice? 1, 1, 1, 1; they are all equal to 1.
d. *Writing* Write a general rule to describe your discovery. Any number raised to the 0 power equals 1.

Choose **Use your calculator, paper and pencil, or mental math to evaluate each expression.**

25. $2^5 \times 4^2$ 512
26. $12 + 5^3$ 137
27. -7^4 −2,401
28. $3(0.5 + 2.5)^2$ 27
29. $(-5)^5$ −3,125
30. $10^2 + 6^2$ 136
31. $(10 + 6)^2$ 256
32. $8 + 3^4$ 89
33. $3(4^2 - 10)$ 18
34. $(5 - 2^2) - 1$ 0
35. $4^3 + 14 \div 7$ 66
36. $(20 \div 10)^2$ 4

Evaluate each expression for $m = 3$, $n = 2$, and $r = 4$.

37. $m^2 + n^2$ 13
38. $(m + n)^2$ 25
39. $(-r)^3$ −64
40. $-m^3$ −27
41. $m^4 - r^2$ 65
42. $n^2(m + r)$ 28

43. a. What is the base of $(7 - 9)^4$? The exponent? $(7 - 9)$; 4
 b. Evaluate $(7 - 9)^4$. 16

Mixed Review

Find the value of each expression *(Lesson 2-8)*

44. $12 + 3 - 6$ 9
45. $2 - 5 \times 3 \times 3$ −43
46. $27 - 2 \times 8 \div 2$ 19
47. $17 - (2 + 6) \times 2$ 1

Compare. Use <, >, or =. *(Lesson 2-1)*

48. 22.168 ■ 22.1168 >
49. 3.899 ■ 3.8899 >
50. 9.3742 ■ 9.3842 <

51. *Biology* A honeybee hive contains 35,000 cells. How many cells are there in 50 hives? *(Lesson 3-5)* 1,750,000

Extra Practice, Lesson 4-4, page 517

MATH TOOLBOX

In Examples 2 and 3 of Lesson 4-5, students learn how to find the greatest common factor of two numbers. This toolbox shows students how to use divisibility tests to determine the factors of a number.

ERROR ALERT! Students may assume that a number is divisible by all numbers that are factors of the sum of the digits. For example, because the sum of the digits in 927 is 18, they may assume that 927 is divisible by 2, 3, 6, and 9. **Remediation:** Point out to students that we only use the *sum* divisibility test for 3 and other powers of 3. Ask them to use the sum divisibility test on 999. Check for divisibility by 3, 9, and 27.

ASSESSMENT Have small groups of students discuss how they know that a number divisible by 9 is also divisible by 3, and that a number divisible by 10 is also divisible by 2 and 5. Have the groups look for other such connections. **Answers may vary.** **Sample: A number that is divisible by 2 and 3 is also divisible by 6.**

ADDITIONAL PROBLEMS

Test whether each number is divisible by 2, 3, 4, 5, 8, 9, and/or 10.

1. 320 **2, 4, 5, 8, 10**

2. 7,542 **2, 3, 9**

MATH TOOLBOX

SKILLS REVIEW

Divisibility Tests

Before Lesson 4-5

You can use divisibility tests to simplify fractions. A number is *divisible* by another if the remainder is zero. You can combine divisibility tests to develop tests for other numbers.

Number	Divisibility Test
2	The ones digit is 0, 2, 4, 6, or 8.
3	The sum of digits is divisible by 3.
4	The number formed by the last two digits is divisible by 4.
5	The ones digit is 0 or 5.
8	The number formed by the last three digits is divisible by 8.
9	The sum of digits is divisible by 9.
10	The ones digit is 0.

EXAMPLE

Use the divisibility tests to determine by which numbers 30 is divisible.

The ones digit of 30 is 0, so 30 is divisible by 2, 5, and 10. The sum of the digits is $3 + 0 = 3$, so it is divisible by 3.

Test whether each number is divisible by 2, 3, 4, 5, 8, 9, and/or 10.

1. 36 **2.** 324 **3.** 150 **4.** 840 **5.** 2,235 **6.** 2,724

7. 6,168 **8.** 810 **9.** 3,864 **10.** 1,430 **11.** 2,421 **12.** 6,720

13. 875 **14.** 81,816 **15.** 7,848 **16.** 625 **17.** 4,725 **18.** 4,104

19. a. Complete: Since 54 is divisible by 2 and 3, it must also be divisible by ■. **6**

b. *Reasoning* Write a divisibility test for 15. **b–c. See margin.**

c. *Reasoning* Write a divisibility test for 12.

20. *Writing* In her notes, Michiko wrote "14 can be divided by 4, but 14 is not divisible by 4." Is she correct? Explain. **Yes; a number is divisible by 4 if the remainder is 0.**

1. 2, 3, 4, 9
2. 2, 3, 4, 9
3. 2, 3, 5, 10
4. 2, 3, 4, 5, 8, 10
5. 3, 5
6. 2, 3, 4
7. 2, 3, 4, 8
8. 2, 3, 5, 9, 10
9. 2, 3, 4, 8
10. 2, 5, 10
11. 3, 9
12. 2, 3, 4, 5, 8, 10
13. 5
14. 2, 3, 4, 8
15. 2, 3, 4, 8, 9
16. 5
17. 3, 5, 9
18. 2, 3, 4, 8, 9

Resources

Transparencies
15

page 159 Math Toolbox

19b. The number must end in 5 or 0 and the sum of the digits must be divisible by 3.

c. The number formed by the last two digits must be divisible by 4 and the sum of the digits must be divisible by 3.

4-5 Teaching Notes

1 Focus

CONNECTING TO PRIOR KNOWLEDGE
Write the numbers 1 through 10 on the board. Ask students to name two possible categories for the numbers. **Answers may vary. Sample: even/odd, single digit/double digit, prime/composite**

2 Teach

Work Together

AEP Help students understand the definition of orientation in the context of this activity. Hold up a rectangular piece of paper in several ways to help explain the context.

THINK AND DISCUSS

Question 4 Have students explain why each number is prime or composite.

REASONING **Question 5** Explain that if one number does not fit the criteria, you cannot use the word *all*.

AUDITORY LEARNING **Example 1** Have students describe the factor tree out loud using terms such as *tree top*, *branches*, and *leaves*. Ask:

Lesson Planning Options

Prerequisite Skills
- identifying factors (4-2)
- dividing whole numbers (precourse)

Vocabulary/Symbols
composite, prime, prime factorization, factor tree, greatest common factor (GCF)

Materials/Manipulatives
- graph paper

Resources

Student Edition
Skills Handbook, p. 531
Extra Practice, p. 517
Glossary/Study Guide

Teaching Resources
Chapter Support File, Ch. 4
- Lesson Planner 4-5
- Practice 4-5, Reteaching 4-5
- Answer Masters 4-5

Teaching Aids Masters 1, 2
Glossary, Spanish Resources

Transparencies
1, 15, 85, Minds on Math 4-5

Warm Up
A piece of rope 68 in. long is to be cut into two pieces. How long will each piece be if one piece is cut three times longer than the other piece? **17 in. and 51 in.**

GEOMETRY Connection

4-5 Prime Factorization

What You'll Learn
1. To find the prime factorization of a number
2. To find the greatest common factor (GCF) of two numbers

...And Why
Learning how to find the greatest common factor of two numbers will help you compute with fractions.

Here's How
Look for questions that
- build understanding
- ✔ check understanding

Work Together

Finding Factors

Work with a partner. The 4 by 6 and the 6 by 4 rectangles in the photograph are considered the same.

2a. 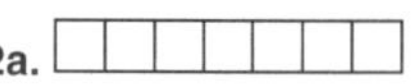

1. a. Use graph paper. Draw all the rectangles with an area of 24 square units. **See below left.**
   b. List the dimensions of the rectangles.
   1 × 24, 2 × 12, 3 × 8, 4 × 6
2. a. Now draw all the rectangles with an area of 7 square units.
   b. List the dimensions of the rectangles. **1 × 7**
3. *Explain* How do the dimensions you found relate to the factors of each number? **The dimensions are the factors.**

1a. 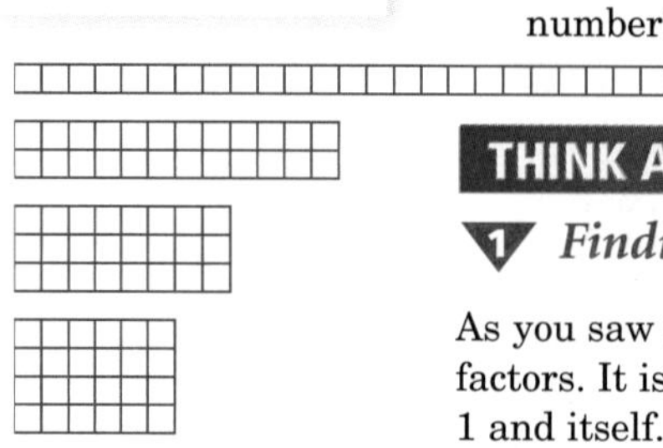

THINK AND DISCUSS

1 Finding Prime Factorization

As you saw in the Work Together, twenty-four has more than two factors. It is a **composite** number. Seven has exactly two factors, 1 and itself. It is a **prime** number. The number 1 has exactly one factor, 1, and is neither prime nor composite.

4. Tell whether each number is prime or composite.
   a. 11 **prime** b. 12 **composite** c. 13 **prime** d. 14 **composite** e. 15 **composite**
5. *Reasoning* Are all even numbers composite? Explain.
   No; 2 is a prime number.

To write the **prime factorization** of a composite number, you write the number as the product of its prime factors. A *factor tree* can help you find the prime factors of a number.

- *How is the tree arranged?* **The number is the tree top. The branches connect the factors, or leaves, to the tree top.**
- *How do you know when to end a factor tree?* **when every leaf is a prime number**
- *How many leaves will all prime numbers have?* **2**

■ ADDITIONAL EXAMPLES

FOR EXAMPLE 1

Write the prime factorization of 90.
$2 \cdot 3^2 \cdot 5$

FOR EXAMPLE 2

Find the GCF of 32 and 48. **16**

FOR EXAMPLE 3

What is the greatest common factor of 24 and 56? **8**

ERROR ALERT! Example 2 Some students may use both matching prime numbers when finding the GCF. **Remediation:** Have students circle each matching pair of common factors. Tell students they may write only one factor from each circle. They should have no more factors than circles.

EXTENSION Have students write the prime factorizations of 10,800 and 7,200 to find their GCF. **360**

ASSESSMENT and KINESTHETIC LEARNING Have students form horizontal factor trees using their arms as branches. One student says a composite number and holds out both arms. Another student says one factor and holds one hand of the first student. Another student says the other number of the factor pair and holds the other hand. Students repeat this until the factor tree is complete.

■ EXAMPLE 1

Use a factor tree to write the prime factorization of 60.

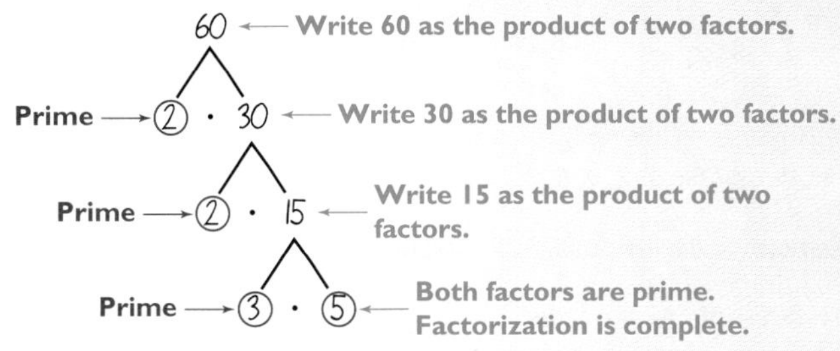

$60 = 2 \cdot 2 \cdot 3 \cdot 5$, or $2^2 \cdot 3 \cdot 5$

6a.

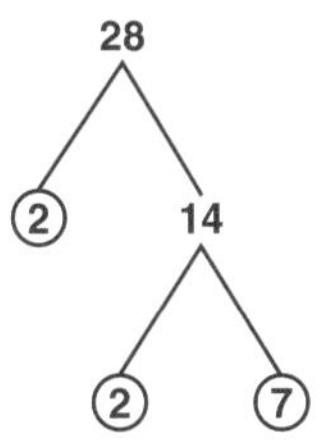

6. a. ✔ *Try It Out* Use a factor tree to write the prime factorization of 28.
   b. Write the prime factorization of 28 using exponents. **$2^2 \cdot 7$**

Now you may assign Exercises 1–21.

2 *Finding the GCF*

The greatest number that is a factor of two or more numbers is the **greatest common factor** or **GCF.** You can use the prime factorizations of two numbers to find their GCF.

■ EXAMPLE 2

Find the GCF of 24 and 36.

Step 1 Write the prime factorization of each number. Identify the common prime factors.

$24 = 2 \cdot 2 \cdot 2 \cdot 3$
$36 = 2 \cdot 2 \cdot 3 \cdot 3$

Both 24 and 36 have the factors $2 \cdot 2 \cdot 3$.

Step 2 Find the product of the common prime factors.

$2 \cdot 2 \cdot 3 = 12$

The GCF of 24 and 36 is 12.

7. ✔ *Try It Out* Use prime factorizations to find the GCF of each pair of numbers.
   a. 16, 24 **8** b. 15, 25 **5** c. 9, 45 **9** d. 10, 8 **2**

8. *Go a Step Further* Write two pairs of numbers with a GCF of 4. **Answers may vary. Samples: 12 and 20; 8 and 28**

Technology Options

Prentice Hall Technology

Software for Learners
- Math Lab: Prime and Composite Numbers*
- Math Blaster® Mystery*
- Interactive Student Tutorial, Chapter 4*

Teaching Resource Software
- Computer Item Generator 4-5
- Resource Pro™ Chapter 4*

Internet • For related mathematics activities, visit the Prentice Hall site at www.phschool.com/math

**Available on CD-ROM only*

Assignment Options for Exercises On Your Own

To provide flexible scheduling, this lesson can be split into parts.

1 **Core** 1–20
Extension 21

2 **Core** 22–34
Extension 35–37

Use Mixed Review to maintain skills.

Then each student at the end of a branch says his or her number aloud.

3 Practice/Assess

EXERCISES *On Your Own*

MENTAL MATH Exercises 1–6 Remind students to use the divisibility rules of two, three, and five.

Exercise 7 If you have block scheduling or extended class periods, have students list all prime numbers less than 250.

WRITING Exercise 20 Encourage students to include the Commutative Property of Multiplication in their answers.

REASONING Exercise 22 Have students list factors of several prime numbers and compare lists.

REASONING Exercise 35 Review why different numbers are in different parts of the Venn diagram. Review the definitions of *intersection* and *LCM*.

WRAP UP

IDENTIFYING THE BIG IDEA Have students explain how to find the GCF of two numbers using factor trees, lists of factors, and mental math. Have them explain which method they prefer and why.

CHECKPOINT 1

Checkpoint 1

Lessons 4-1 through 4-5

Write two fractions equivalent to the given fraction. Sample answers given.

1. $\frac{7}{8}$ $\frac{14}{16}, \frac{21}{24}$
2. $\frac{10}{30}$ $\frac{1}{3}, \frac{2}{6}$
3. $\frac{14}{18}$ $\frac{7}{9}, \frac{28}{36}$
4. $\frac{3}{5}$ $\frac{6}{10}, \frac{9}{15}$
5. $\frac{9}{21}$ $\frac{3}{7}, \frac{6}{14}$

6. **Circle A, B, C, or D.** Which fraction is greatest?
   A. $\frac{8}{10}$ (B.) $\frac{7}{8}$ C. $\frac{12}{18}$ D. $\frac{5}{6}$

Find the value of each expression.

7. $20 - 3^2$ 11
8. $2^3 + 10^2$ 108
9. $(8 - 1)^2$ 49
10. $(-3)^3$ −27

Tell whether each number is prime or composite. Then find the GCF of each pair of numbers.

11. 2, 14 prime, composite; 2
12. 15, 18 both composite; 3
13. 20, 35 both composite; 5
14. 7, 13 both prime; 1

pages 162–163 On Your Own

37. No; when the composite number is a multiple of the prime number, their GCF is the prime number.

Another way to find the GCF is to list the factors of each number.

■ EXAMPLE 3

What is the greatest common factor of 28 and 42?

List the factors of 28 and 42 to find the GCF.

Factors of 28: 1, 2, 4, 7, 14, 28

Factors of 42: 1, 2, 3, 6, 7, 14, 21, 42

14 is the greatest common factor.

The GCF of 28 and 42 is 14.

9. ✔ *Try It Out* List the factors to find the GCF of 54 and 72.

9. Factors of 54: 1, 2, 3, 6, 9, 18, 27, 54
   Factors of 72: 1, 2, 3, 4, 6, 8, 9, 12, 18, 24, 36, 72
   The GCF of 54 and 72 is 18.

Now you may assign Exercises 22–37.

EXERCISES *On Your Own*

Mental Math **Is each number prime or composite?**

1. 104 composite
2. 88 composite
3. 165 composite
4. 47 prime
5. 77 composite
6. 69 composite
7. *Number Sense* List all the prime numbers less than 50. 2, 3, 5, 7, 11, 13, 17, 19, 23, 29, 31, 37, 41, 43, 47

Use a factor tree to write the prime factorization of each number. Write the prime factorization using exponents where possible.

8. 45 $3^2 \cdot 5$
9. 64 2^6
10. 84 $2^2 \cdot 3 \cdot 7$
11. 111 $3 \cdot 37$
12. 100 $2^2 \cdot 5^2$
13. 52 $2^2 \cdot 13$
14. 65 $5 \cdot 13$
15. 132 $2^2 \cdot 3 \cdot 11$
16. 48 $2^4 \cdot 3$
17. 60 $2^2 \cdot 3 \cdot 5$
18. 72 $2^3 \cdot 3^2$
19. 75 $5^2 \cdot 3$

20. *Writing* Sal and Marla made the two factor trees at the right of the prime factors of 24. Are both correct? Explain.
Yes; the first choice of factors does not affect the final result.

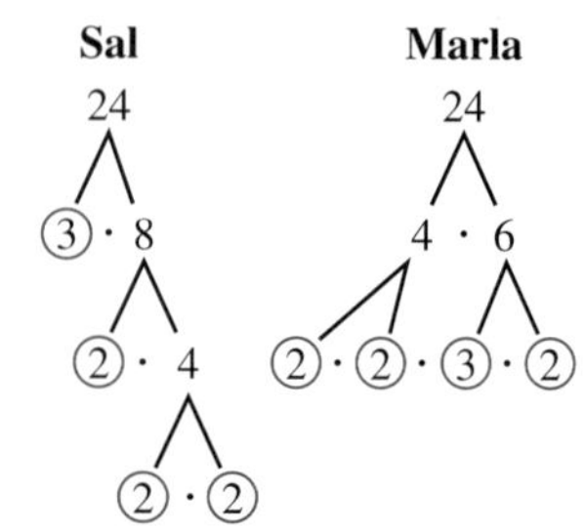

21. *Number Theory* If n is a number, is $2n$ prime or composite? Justify your answer. See below.
22. *Reasoning* What is the GCF of two prime numbers? 1

Find the GCF of each pair of numbers.

23. 75, 90 15
24. 38, 76 38
25. 100, 75 25
26. 12, 15 3
27. 77, 121 11
28. 32, 18 2
29. 54, 80 2
30. 22, 121 11
31. 16, 80 16
32. 10, 85 5
33. 98, 105 7
34. 52, 26 26

21. $2n$ is composite unless $n = 1$; for $n > 1$, $2n$ has at least three factors (1, 2, and n), so it is not prime.

JOURNAL Have students make a list of vocabulary terms from the chapter. The list may include *factors*, *multiples*, *LCD*, *exponents*, *factor trees*, *prime factorization*, and *GCF*. Have students use the terms to explain prime and composite numbers.

LESSON QUIZ

1. Is 243 prime or composite? **composite**
2. Use a factor tree to write the prime factorization of 112. **$2^4 \cdot 7$**
3. Find the GCF of 30 and 125. **5**

PRACTICE

Practice 4-5 *Prime Factorization*

Determine whether each number is prime or composite.

1. 97 prime 2. 63 composite 3. 29 prime 4. 120 composite

Use a factor tree to find the prime factors of each number. Then write the prime factorization, using exponents where possible.

5. 42 $2 \cdot 3 \cdot 7$ 6. 130 $2 \cdot 5 \cdot 13$ 7. 78 $2 \cdot 3 \cdot 13$ 8. 126 $2 \cdot 3^2 \cdot 7$

9. 125 5^3 10. 90 $2 \cdot 3^2 \cdot 5$ 11. 92 $2^2 \cdot 23$ 12. 180 $2^2 \cdot 3^2 \cdot 5$

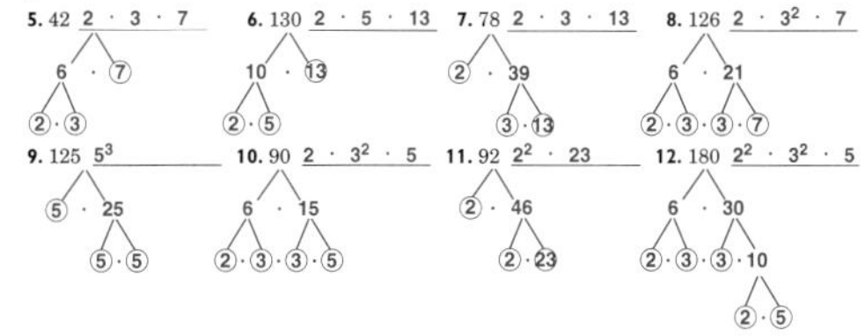

Use a calculator to find the number with the given prime factorization.

13. $3^2 \cdot 11^2$ 1,089 14. $2^2 \cdot 3 \cdot 5^3$ 1,500 15. $3^2 \cdot 5^2 \cdot 7^3$ 77,175

Make lists of factors for each set of numbers. Then find the GCF.

16. 16, 20	16: 1, 2, 4, 8, 16	20: 1, 2, 4, 5, 10, 20	GCF = 4
17. 24, 30	24: 1, 2, 3, 4, 6, 8, 12, 24	30: 1, 2, 3, 5, 6, 10, 15, 30	GCF = 6
18. 10, 25	10: 1, 2, 5, 10	25: 1, 5, 25	GCF = 5
19. 15, 24	15: 1, 3, 5, 15	24: 1, 2, 3, 4, 6, 8, 12, 24	GCF = 3

Find the GCF for each pair of numbers.

20. 45, 60 15 21. 18, 42 6 22. 32, 80 16

23. 20, 65 5 24. 24, 90 6 25. 17, 34 17

26. 14, 35 7 27. 51, 27 3 28. 42, 63 21

Practice

In copymaster and workbook formats

35. *Reasoning* The prime factors of 18 and 24 are at the right.
   a. Find the product of the factors that are in the intersection of both circles. Is this the GCF or the LCM? **6; GCF**
   b. Find the product of the factors in both circles. Is this the GCF or the LCM? **72; LCM**

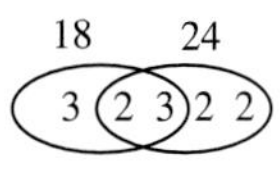

36. *Reasoning* Find two composite numbers with a GCF of 1. **Answers may vary. Sample: 4 and 9**
37. *Number Sense* Will a prime number and a composite number always have a GCF of 1? Explain. **See margin p. 162.**

JOURNAL
Explain the difference between a prime and a composite number.

Mixed Review

Find the value of each expression. *(Lessons 3-3, 3-4)*

38. $8-(-14)$ **22** 39. $-25+46$ **21** 40. $-31-(-18)$ **−13** 41. $29+(-74)$ **−45**

42. *Charity* In 1997, Princess Diana auctioned some of her dresses to raise money for charity. *(Lessons 1-4, 1-5, 2-3)*
   a. The highest price for a dress was \$222,500, and the lowest price was \$19,000. What was the range of prices? **\$203,500**
   b. The 97 dresses sold for a total of \$3.25 million. What was the mean price? Round your answer to the nearest dollar. **\$33,505**
   c. Sales of the catalog raised another \$2.5 million for charity. What was the total amount that was raised for charity? **\$5.75 million**

RETEACHING

Reteaching 4-5 *Prime Factorization*

A **prime number** has exactly two factors, 1 and itself. 2 and 7 are prime numbers. 2 is the smallest prime number.

$2 \times 1 = 2$ $7 \times 1 = 7$

Every **composite number** can be written as a product of two or more prime numbers. This is called the **prime factorization** of the number.

$60 = 2 \cdot 2 \cdot 3 \cdot 5 = 2^2 \cdot 3 \cdot 5$
$40 = 2 \cdot 2 \cdot 2 \cdot 5 = 2^3 \cdot 5$

You can use a *factor tree* and division to find the prime factorization of a number.

① Divide by a factor other than 1 and the number itself. Record the divisor and the quotient in the factor tree.

② Continue dividing until all the factors are prime numbers.

③ Use exponents to write the prime factorization.

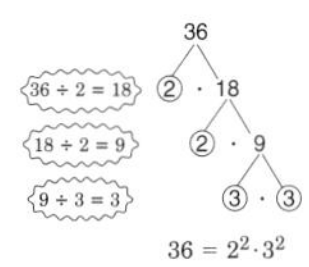

$36 = 2^2 \cdot 3^2$

Complete each factor tree. Then write the prime factorization using exponents where possible.

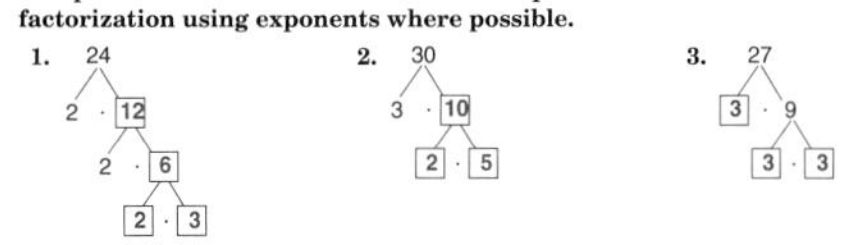

1. $2^3 \cdot 3$ 2. $2 \cdot 3 \cdot 5$ 3. 3^3

Write the prime factorization of each number. Use exponents where possible.

4. 20 = $2^2 \cdot 5$ 5. 54 = $2 \cdot 3^3$ 6. 40 = $2^3 \cdot 5$

7. 48 = $2^4 \cdot 3$ 8. 56 = $2^3 \cdot 7$ 9. 150 = $2 \cdot 3 \cdot 5^2$

✓ CHECKPOINT 1 — Lessons 4-1 through 4-5

Write two fractions equivalent to the given fraction. **1–6. Answers may vary. Samples are given.**

1. $\frac{3}{4}$ **$\frac{6}{8}, \frac{9}{12}$** 2. $\frac{16}{32}$ **$\frac{1}{2}, \frac{2}{4}$** 3. $\frac{15}{20}$ **$\frac{3}{4}, \frac{6}{8}$** 4. $\frac{7}{9}$ **$\frac{14}{18}, \frac{21}{27}$** 5. $\frac{4}{5}$ **$\frac{8}{10}, \frac{12}{15}$** 6. $\frac{6}{8}$ **$\frac{3}{4}, \frac{9}{12}$**

7. **Choose A, B, C, or D.** Which fraction has the greatest value? **D**
   A. $\frac{5}{8}$ B. $\frac{7}{10}$ C. $\frac{8}{12}$ D. $\frac{12}{15}$

Find the value of each expression.

8. 8^2+11 **75** 9. 5^3-7^2 **76** 10. $(9-3)^2$ **36** 11. $(-2)^4$ **16** 12. $(-5)^3$ **−125** 13. -3^4 **−81**

Tell whether each number is prime or composite. Then find the GCF of each pair of numbers.

14. 12, 9 **comp., comp.; 3** 15. 121, 11 **comp., prime; 11** 16. 15, 3 **comp., prime; 3** 17. 6, 8 **comp., comp.; 2** 18. 9, 27 **comp., comp.; 9** 19. 3, 45 **prime, comp.; 3**

ENRICHMENT

Minds on Math Transparency 4-5

A drop of water drips from a leaky faucet every 8 seconds. It takes 6 drops to make a milliliter of water. How many liters drip from this faucet in a week?

12.6 liters

See *Solution Key* for worked-out answers.

Extra Practice, Lesson 4-5, page 517

4-6 Teaching Notes

1 Focus

CONNECTING TO PRIOR KNOWLEDGE Ask students: *Name some fractions equivalent to $\frac{1}{2}$.* **Answers may vary. Sample: $\frac{2}{4}$, $\frac{3}{6}$** *Why do we use $\frac{1}{2}$ more often than the other equivalent fractions?* **Answers may vary. Sample: Simpler fractions are easier to work with.**

2 Teach

THINK AND DISCUSS

DIVERSITY Question 1 Some students may not be familiar with the people in the frequency table. Ask students to expand the table by mentioning leaders they know and the countries they represent.

VISUAL LEARNING Example 1 Have students write all the factors of 12 and 24. Have them circle or highlight all the common factors. Students then simplify the fraction using each of the common factors. Ask: *Which common factor reduced the fraction to simplest form?* **12**

Example 2 Ask students: *Which divisibility tests might be helpful for simplifying $\frac{18}{30}$?* **Answers may vary: Sample: dividing by 2 because the numerator and denominator are even; dividing by 3 because the digits of each number add to a multiple of 3**

Lesson Planning Options

Prerequisite Skills

- dividing whole numbers (precourse)
- finding the greatest common factor (4-5)
- prime factorization (4-5)

Vocabulary/Symbols

simplest form

Resources

Student Edition

Skills Handbook, p. 531
Extra Practice, p. 517
Glossary/Study Guide

Teaching Resources

Chapter Support File, Ch. 4
- Lesson Planner 4-6
- Practice 4-6, Reteaching 4-6
- Alternative Activity 4-6
- Answer Masters 4-6

Teaching Aids Masters 10, 20–25
Glossary, Spanish Resources

Transparencies
15, 18–25, Minds on Math 4-6

Warm Up

Trent is on a CD-buying spree. He bought 2 CDs one week, 6 the following week, and 10 in the third week. If he continues this pattern, how many CDs will he buy in the seventh week? **26**

DATA ANALYSIS Connection

4-6 Simplifying Fractions

What You'll Learn

- 1 To write fractions in simplest form
- 2 To use the greatest common factor (GCF) to write fractions in simplest form

...And Why

You can use fractions in surveys.

Here's How

Look for questions that
- build understanding
- ✔ check understanding

THINK AND DISCUSS

1 *Writing Fractions in Simplest Form*

Social Studies Jeremy conducted a survey for his social studies class. He asked 24 people to identify the country each of the people in the table below are from. The frequency table shows the number of correct responses. (Try it yourself. The answers are at the bottom left of the page.)

World Leader Survey

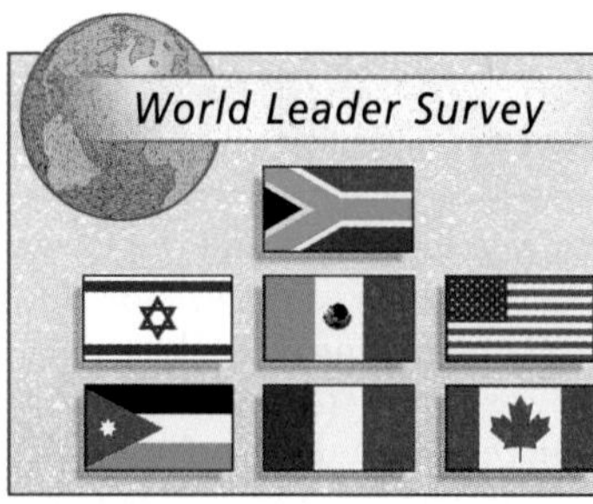

LEADER	FREQUENCY
Jacques Chirac	15
Benjamin Netanyahu	16
Ernesto Zedillo	20
King Hussein	12
Bill Clinton	24
Nelson Mandela	21
Jean Crétien	18

1. Jeremy wrote the fraction $\frac{12}{24}$ to report the fraction of people who identified that King Hussein is from Jordan. Jeremy's brother thinks he should use the fraction $\frac{1}{2}$. Which fraction do you think Jeremy should use? Why?
Check students' work.

A fraction is in simplest form when the only factor common to both the numerator and the denominator is 1.

■ **EXAMPLE 1**

Simplify $\frac{12}{24}$.

$\frac{12 \div 2}{24 \div 2} = \frac{6}{12}$ ⟶ $\frac{6 \div 6}{12 \div 6} = \frac{1}{2}$

Divide the numerator and denominator by a common factor.

If necessary, divide again by another common factor.

In simplest form, $\frac{12}{24}$ is $\frac{1}{2}$.

(Jacques Chirac: France; Ernesto Zedillo: Mexico; Benjamin Netanyahu: Israel; King Hussein: Jordan; Bill Clinton: United States; Nelson Mandela: South Africa; Jean Crétien: Canada)

ERROR ALERT! Example 2 Students may think the GCF is 3. The largest *prime* factor is 3. **Remediation:** Have students highlight all the common prime factors in the numerator and denominator. Remind them that *all* these common factors multiply to get the GCF.

ADDITIONAL EXAMPLES

FOR EXAMPLE 1

Simplify $\frac{20}{30}$. $\frac{2}{3}$

FOR EXAMPLE 2

Simplify $\frac{28}{36}$. $\frac{7}{9}$

FOR EXAMPLE 3

Write $\frac{45}{60}$ in simplest form. $\frac{3}{4}$

Example 3 If you have block scheduling or extended class periods, have students work with a partner to simplify fractions such as $\frac{720}{1,080}$. $\frac{2}{3}$ Have each pair make a list of the divisibility tests they used and tell how they simplified the fraction. Encourage students to share their strategies with the class.

3 Practice/Assess

EXERCISES *On Your Own*

ASSESSMENT Exercises 1–12 Have students show at least two methods for simplifying any three of these exercises. Then have students explain in writing which method they preferred for each exercise.

WRITING Exercise 13 Have students use correct terminology such as *common factor* in their writing.

Pictured above are Ernesto Zedillo (top) and Nelson Mandela.

2. ✔ *Try It Out* Write each fraction in simplest form.
   a. $\frac{6}{8}$ $\frac{3}{4}$ b. $\frac{8}{12}$ $\frac{2}{3}$ c. $\frac{10}{15}$ $\frac{2}{3}$ d. $\frac{7}{14}$ $\frac{1}{2}$
3. Use the table in Example 1. What fraction of the people recognized the countries that Ernesto Zedillo and Nelson Mandela are from? Write each fraction in simplest form. $\frac{5}{6}$, $\frac{7}{8}$

Now you may assign Exercises 1–15.

2 *Using the GCF to Simplify Fractions*

You can divide the numerator and the denominator of a fraction by their GCF to write the fraction in simplest form in one step.

EXAMPLE 2

Simplify $\frac{18}{30}$.

$18 = 2 \cdot 3 \cdot 3$
$30 = 2 \cdot 3 \cdot 5$ ← The GCF is 2 · 3, which is 6.

$\frac{18 \div 6}{30 \div 6} = \frac{3}{5}$ ← Divide the numerator and denominator by the GCF.

4. ✔ *Try It Out* Write $\frac{36}{96}$ in simplest form by using the GCF of 36 and 96. $\frac{36 \div 12}{96 \div 12} = \frac{3}{8}$

You can also simplify a fraction using the prime factorization of the numerator and denominator.

EXAMPLE 3

Write $\frac{42}{105}$ in simplest form.

$\frac{42}{105} = \frac{2 \cdot 3 \cdot 7}{3 \cdot 5 \cdot 7}$ ← Write the prime factorization of the numerator and the denominator.

$= \frac{2 \cdot \cancel{3}^1 \cdot \cancel{7}^1}{\cancel{3}_1 \cdot 5 \cdot \cancel{7}_1}$ ← Divide numerator and denominator by the common factors.

$= \frac{2}{5}$ ← Write the fraction in simplest form.

5–6. See left.

5. ✔ *Try It Out* Use prime factorization to write each fraction in simplest form.
   a. $\frac{18}{48}$ b. $\frac{99}{132}$ c. $\frac{60}{75}$
6. *Think About It* When would you prefer to simplify a fraction by dividing by the GCF? When would you prefer to use prime factorization?

Now you may assign Exercises 16–38.

5a. $\frac{2 \cdot 3 \cdot 3}{2 \cdot 2 \cdot 2 \cdot 2 \cdot 3} = \frac{3}{8}$
b. $\frac{3 \cdot 3 \cdot 11}{2 \cdot 2 \cdot 3 \cdot 11} = \frac{3}{4}$
c. $\frac{2 \cdot 2 \cdot 3 \cdot 5}{3 \cdot 5 \cdot 5} = \frac{4}{5}$
6. Answers may vary. Sample: Dividing by the GCF is easier when you can use mental math. Using prime factorization is easier when the numerator and denominator have many factors.

Technology Options

Prentice Hall Technology

Software for Learners
- Math Blaster® Mystery*
- Interactive Student Tutorial, Chapter 4*

Teaching Resource Software
- Computer Item Generator 4-6
- Resource Pro™ Chapter 4*

Internet • For related mathematics activities, visit the Prentice Hall site at www.phschool.com/math

**Available on CD-ROM only*

Assignment Options for Exercises On Your Own

To provide flexible scheduling, this lesson can be split into parts.

1 **Core** 1–14
Extension 15

2 **Core** 16–33, 35–38
Extension 34

Use Mixed Review to maintain skills.

CONNECTING TO THE STUDENTS' WORLD **Exercise 15** Have students find the average amount of time they spend per day on at least five activities. Have them write a fraction in simplest form to express how much time they spend per day on each activity.

CONNECTION TO SCIENCE **Exercise 34** Have students find out the total number of bones a domestic cat has. Have them find the fraction, in simplest form, of the bones that are in the cat's tail.

Exercise 36 Students may want to include reasons why Alex might have made the mistakes.

WRAP UP

IDENTIFYING THE BIG IDEA Ask students to explain why it is useful to write fractions in simplest form. Have them give some real-life examples to support their answer. Then have them explain how to write a fraction in simplest form.

PROJECT LINK Point out to students that on an inch ruler, the $\frac{1}{2}$-in. marks are longer than the $\frac{1}{4}$-in. marks to make reading the ruler easier. Encourage them to use marks of different sizes to measure the objects.

pages 166–167 On Your Own

37. Asia $\frac{121}{200}$, Africa $\frac{16}{125}$, Europe $\frac{63}{500}$, Latin America $\frac{21}{250}$, North America $\frac{13}{250}$, Australia and New Zealand $\frac{1}{200}$

EXERCISES *On Your Own*

Write each fraction in simplest form.

1. $\frac{24}{32}$ $\frac{3}{4}$
2. $\frac{18}{27}$ $\frac{2}{3}$
3. $\frac{20}{24}$ $\frac{5}{6}$
4. $\frac{10}{12}$ $\frac{5}{6}$
5. $\frac{33}{39}$ $\frac{11}{13}$
6. $\frac{8}{18}$ $\frac{4}{9}$
7. $\frac{16}{28}$ $\frac{4}{7}$
8. $\frac{21}{28}$ $\frac{3}{4}$
9. $\frac{18}{30}$ $\frac{3}{5}$
10. $\frac{25}{35}$ $\frac{5}{7}$
11. $\frac{9}{15}$ $\frac{3}{5}$
12. $\frac{6}{28}$ $\frac{3}{14}$

13. *Writing* Which of the following fractions is in simplest form: $\frac{9}{16}$, $\frac{10}{24}$, $\frac{14}{35}$? Explain how you know. $\frac{9}{16}$; a fraction is in simplest form when the GCF of the numerator and denominator is 1.

14. *Entertainment* Larry surveyed some students to find their music preferences. His results are at the right. Larry wanted to write the results in fraction form for a news article. What fractions should Larry use? Rock $\frac{3}{5}$, Country/Western $\frac{4}{15}$, Classical $\frac{2}{15}$

Student Music Preferences

Musical Format	Number
Rock	18
Country/Western	8
Classical	4

15. On an average school day, Josephina spends 7 hours in school, 1 hour delivering newspapers, 2 hours doing her homework, 3 hours reading or talking on the phone, and 8 hours asleep. Write a fraction in simplest form to express how much time she spends on each activity each day. school $\frac{7}{24}$, delivering papers $\frac{1}{24}$, homework $\frac{1}{12}$, reading or talking on the phone $\frac{1}{8}$, sleep $\frac{1}{3}$

Find the GCF of the numerator and denominator of each fraction. Then write each fraction in simplest form.

16. $\frac{27}{72}$ 9; $\frac{3}{8}$
17. $\frac{42}{63}$ 21; $\frac{2}{3}$
18. $\frac{35}{49}$ 7; $\frac{5}{7}$
19. $\frac{12}{75}$ 3; $\frac{4}{25}$
20. $\frac{24}{60}$ 12; $\frac{2}{5}$
21. $\frac{15}{105}$ 15; $\frac{1}{7}$
22. $\frac{12}{57}$ 3; $\frac{4}{19}$
23. $\frac{28}{96}$ 4; $\frac{7}{24}$
24. $\frac{75}{125}$ 25; $\frac{3}{5}$
25. $\frac{108}{120}$ 12; $\frac{9}{10}$
26. $\frac{63}{81}$ 9; $\frac{7}{9}$
27. $\frac{125}{200}$ 25; $\frac{5}{8}$
28. $\frac{42}{64}$ 2; $\frac{21}{32}$
29. $\frac{35}{95}$ 5; $\frac{7}{19}$
30. $\frac{25}{80}$ 5; $\frac{5}{16}$
31. $\frac{18}{48}$ 6; $\frac{3}{8}$
32. $\frac{20}{54}$ 2; $\frac{10}{27}$
33. $\frac{17}{51}$ 17; $\frac{1}{3}$

34. *Anatomy* An adult has 206 bones. Of these, 106 are in the feet, ankles, wrists, and hands. What fraction of the bones are in the feet, ankles, wrists, and hands? Write your answer in simplest form. $\frac{53}{103}$ of the bones

35. **Choose A, B, C, or D.** Which fraction is *not* in simplest form? B

A. $\frac{5}{16}$ B. $\frac{7}{35}$ C. $\frac{9}{70}$ D. $\frac{10}{169}$

36. *Error Alert* Alex used the method below to write $\frac{54}{64}$ in simplest form. Is he correct? Explain.

$\frac{54}{64} = \frac{5\not{4}}{6\not{4}} = \frac{5}{6}$ No; he is not dividing by factors.

LESSON QUIZ

Write each fraction in simplest form.

1. $\frac{15}{25}$ $\frac{3}{5}$
2. $\frac{18}{72}$ $\frac{1}{4}$
3. On Saturday, Austin spent 4 h playing basketball and 2 h studying. Write two fractions in simplest form to express how much of Saturday Austin spent on each activity. **basketball: $\frac{1}{6}$; studying: $\frac{1}{12}$**

The Global Village

Think of Earth as a global village of only a thousand people. Then 605 of those people would be from Asia, 128 from Africa, 126 from Europe, 84 from Latin America, 52 from North America, and 5 from Australia and New Zealand.

Only 70 people in the village would be over 65, but 320 would be under 15.

37. What fraction of the people in the global village are from each area? Write each fraction in simplest form. **See margin p. 166.**

38. What fraction of the people are under 15? Adults over 65? Adults under 65? Write each fraction in simplest form. **$\frac{8}{25}$; $\frac{7}{100}$; $\frac{61}{100}$**

Mixed Review

Open-ended **Write a fraction equivalent to the given fraction.** *(Lesson 4-2)* **39–44. Answers may vary. Samples are given.**

39. $\frac{3}{4}$ **$\frac{6}{8}$, $\frac{9}{12}$**
40. $\frac{12}{15}$ **$\frac{4}{5}$, $\frac{24}{30}$**
41. $\frac{45}{63}$ **$\frac{5}{7}$, $\frac{10}{14}$**
42. $\frac{6}{9}$ **$\frac{2}{3}$, $\frac{4}{6}$**
43. $\frac{7}{14}$ **$\frac{1}{2}$, $\frac{2}{4}$**
44. $\frac{3}{8}$ **$\frac{6}{16}$, $\frac{12}{32}$**

Find the value of each expression. *(Lessons 3-2, 4-4)*

45. $(2 + 5)^2$ **49**
46. $-|10|$ **−10**
47. $2^4 + (3 \cdot 5)$ **31**
48. $(4 - 7)^3$ **−27**
49. $|-8|$ **8**

Choose **Use a calculator or paper and pencil to find each quotient. Use a bar to show repeating decimals.** *(Lesson 2-7)*

50. $9 \div 4$ **2.25**
51. $11 \div 3$ **$3.\overline{6}$**
52. $34 \div 8$ **4.25**
53. $37 \div 6$ **$6.1\overline{6}$**
54. $21 \div 4$ **5.25**

55. *Choose a Strategy* Mrs. Brown has retired to Florida. Her children enjoy visiting her. Melvin visits her every three months, Lillian every four months, and Whitney every five months. If all the children visited her in June, in how many months will they all visit her in the same month again? **in 60 months or 5 years**

CHAPTER PROJECT

PROJECT LINK: MEASURING

So you can measure very short lengths with your ruler, mark it to show equal fractions of a unit. What fractions do the marks on your ruler show? Explain why you chose them. Use the fractions on your ruler to measure several small objects.

Check students' work.

Extra Practice, Lesson 4-6, page 517

PRACTICE

Practice 4-6 *Simplifying Fractions*

Write each fraction in simplest form.

1. $\frac{8}{12}$ **$\frac{2}{3}$**
2. $\frac{9}{15}$ **$\frac{3}{5}$**
3. $\frac{16}{20}$ **$\frac{4}{5}$**
4. $\frac{20}{25}$ **$\frac{4}{5}$**
5. $\frac{15}{18}$ **$\frac{5}{6}$**
6. $\frac{14}{30}$ **$\frac{7}{15}$**
7. $\frac{11}{44}$ **$\frac{1}{4}$**
8. $\frac{24}{36}$ **$\frac{2}{3}$**
9. $\frac{12}{16}$ **$\frac{3}{4}$**
10. $\frac{34}{68}$ **$\frac{1}{2}$**
11. $\frac{28}{42}$ **$\frac{2}{3}$**
12. $\frac{30}{65}$ **$\frac{6}{13}$**

Write each fraction in simplest form. Give the GCF of the numerator and denominator.

13. $\frac{18}{45}$ **$\frac{2}{5}$** GCF = **9**
14. $\frac{66}{121}$ **$\frac{6}{11}$** GCF = **11**
15. $\frac{36}{102}$ **$\frac{6}{17}$** GCF = **6**
16. $\frac{125}{200}$ **$\frac{5}{8}$** GCF = **25**
17. $\frac{36}{64}$ **$\frac{9}{16}$** GCF = **4**
18. $\frac{65}{90}$ **$\frac{13}{18}$** GCF = **5**
19. $\frac{45}{72}$ **$\frac{5}{8}$** GCF = **9**
20. $\frac{35}{85}$ **$\frac{7}{17}$** GCF = **5**
21. $\frac{30}{42}$ **$\frac{5}{7}$** GCF = **6**

Solve.

22. Emily exercised from 4:05 P.M. to 4:32 P.M. For what part of an hour did Emily exercise? Write the fraction in the simplest form. **$\frac{9}{20}$ h**
23. Luis rode his bike after school for 48 min. For what part of an hour did he ride his bike? Write the fraction in the simplest form. **$\frac{4}{5}$ h**
24. Philip played video games for 55 min before dinner. For what part of an hour did he play? **$\frac{11}{12}$ h**
25. What part of an hour is your school lunch time? **Answers may vary.**
26. Survey 12 people to find their favorite kind of pizza from the following choices. Write the results in fraction form. Then shade the pizza shape using different colors to indicate their choices.

Pizza Favorites

Cheese **Answers may vary.**
Sausage
Pepperoni
Mushroom

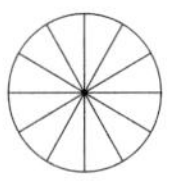

In copymaster and workbook formats

RETEACHING

Reteaching 4-6 *Simplifying Fractions*

A fraction is in **simplest form** when the only factor common to both the numerator and denominator is 1.

To write $\frac{18}{24}$ in the simplest form:

① Divide the numerator and denominator by a common factor. $\frac{18 \div 2}{24 \div 2} = \frac{9}{12}$

② Continue dividing by common factors until the only common factor is 1. $\frac{9 \div 3}{12 \div 3} = \frac{3}{4}$ The only factor common to 3 and 4 is 1.

In simplest form $\frac{18}{24}$ is $\frac{3}{4}$.

You can use the greatest common factor (GCF) to write a fraction in simplest form. Divide the numerator and the denominator by the GCF.

The GCF of 18 and 24 is 6.

$\frac{18}{24} = \frac{18 \div 6}{24 \div 6} = \frac{3}{4}$

Complete to write each fraction in simplest form.

1. $\frac{10}{20} = \frac{10 \div \boxed{2}}{20 \div 2} = \frac{\boxed{5} \div \boxed{5}}{10 \div \boxed{5}} = \frac{1}{2}$
2. $\frac{24}{60} = \frac{24 \div 6}{60 \div \boxed{6}} = \frac{\boxed{4} \div \boxed{2}}{10 \div \boxed{2}} = \frac{2}{5}$

Find the GCF of the numerator and denominator of each fraction. Then write each fraction in simplest form.

3. $\frac{12}{14} = \frac{6}{7}$ GCF = **2**
4. $\frac{9}{15} = \frac{3}{5}$ GCF = **3**
5. $\frac{35}{42} = \frac{5}{6}$ GCF = **7**
6. $\frac{40}{50} = \frac{4}{5}$ GCF = **10**

Write each fraction in simplest form.

7. $\frac{42}{60} = \frac{7}{10}$
8. $\frac{20}{36} = \frac{5}{9}$
9. $\frac{18}{20} = \frac{9}{10}$
10. $\frac{9}{27} = \frac{1}{3}$
11. $\frac{42}{56} = \frac{3}{4}$
12. $\frac{16}{72} = \frac{2}{9}$
13. $\frac{24}{40} = \frac{3}{5}$
14. $\frac{18}{32} = \frac{9}{16}$
15. $\frac{25}{75} = \frac{1}{3}$
16. $\frac{65}{75} = \frac{13}{15}$
17. $\frac{40}{60} = \frac{2}{3}$
18. $\frac{50}{95} = \frac{10}{19}$

Reteaching

ENRICHMENT

Minds on Math Transparency

4-6

A number is divided by 6. When 8 is added to the doubled quotient, the answer is 24. What is the number?

48

See *Solution Key* for worked-out answers.

4-7 Teaching Notes

1 Focus

CONNECTING TO PRIOR KNOWLEDGE Ask students to name some common number patterns. **Answers may vary. Sample: odd or even numbers; multiples of 2, 5, or 10**
When do you use number patterns in everyday life? **Answers may vary. Sample: counting pairs of objects; counting the value of nickels or dimes**

2 Teach

THINK AND DISCUSS

DIVERSITY The exercise may frustrate students who have a short attention span if they don't quickly recognize a pattern. These students can work with a partner to discuss patterns they think they have found.

AEP Review the meaning of the term *one's digit*. Then write several numbers on the board. Circle the one's digit of each number with a different color.

ASSESSMENT Have students choose a power of 3 between 30 and 50. Have them find the one's digit of their expression, and explain how they found it. Then make a chart of the one's digits on the board. Each student writes their own power of 3 in the appropriate place on the chart.

Lesson Planning Options

Prerequisite Skills

- knowing place values (precourse)
- multiplying exponents (4-4)

Materials/Manipulatives

- calculator

Resources

Student Edition
Skills Handbook, p. 528
Glossary/Study Guide

Teaching Resources
Chapter Support File, Ch. 4
- Lesson Planner 4-7
- Practice 4-7, Reteaching 4-7
- Answer Masters 4-7

Teaching Aids Masters 2, 19
Glossary, Spanish Resources

Transparencies
1, 7, Minds on Math 4-7

Warm Up

In Jocepheen's class, 4 out of 5 children study music. If 30 children are in the class, how many study music? **24**

PROBLEM SOLVING STRATEGY

READ PLAN SOLVE LOOK BACK

4-7 Look for a Pattern

Problem Solving Strategies
- Draw a Diagram
- Guess and Test
- ✓ Look for a Pattern
- Make a Model
- Make a Table
- Simulate a Problem
- Solve a Simpler Problem
- Too Much or Too Little Information
- Use Logical Reasoning
- Use Multiple Strategies
- Work Backward
- Write an Equation

THINK AND DISCUSS

You can solve a problem by solving a series of simpler problems. Then you look for a pattern.

SAMPLE PROBLEM

What is the ones digit of 3^{50} when you find the value of the expression?

READ
Read for understanding. Summarize the problem.

Think about the information you are given.
a. the product of fifty 3s. b. The number is too big.

1. a. What is the meaning of the expression 3^{50}?
   b. Why is it not easy to evaluate 3^{50} with paper and pencil?
   c. What happens when you try to evaluate 3^{50} with a calculator?
   The calculator displays a string of numbers followed by E23.

PLAN
Decide on a strategy.

Look for a pattern of the ones digits of the powers of 3 instead of using paper and pencil or a calculator.

2. What is the ones digit in 3^2, 3^3, and 3^4? **9; 7; 1**

SOLVE
Try the strategy.

You need to look for a pattern, so it is a good idea to organize your answers in a table.

3. a. Copy and complete the table at the right.
   b. Circle the ones digit of each number in the Value column. What pattern do you see?
   c. What is the fiftieth number in the pattern? **9**
   d. What is the ones digit of 3^{50}? **9**

b. Answers may vary. Sample: The pattern 3, 9, 7, 1 repeats.

Power	Value	Power	Value
3^1	■ **3**	3^6	■
3^2	■ **9**	3^7	■
3^3	■ **27**	3^8	■
3^4	■ **81**	3^9	■
3^5	■	3^{10}	■

243; 729; 2,187; 6,561; 19,683; 59,049

■ **ADDITIONAL PROBLEM**

What is the one's digit of 8^{23}? 2

3 Practice/Assess

EXERCISES *On Your Own*

ERROR ALERT! Exercise 3 Some students may interpret the parentheses as a signal to multiply and find the answer −427. **Remediation:** Have students rewrite −1 in *b*lue because it is the *b*ase. Have students write 427 in *p*urple because it is the *p*ower. Ask students: *What is the result when you raise 1 to any power?* 1 Then have students recall the pattern for multiplying negative numbers. Ask: *Will a negative number multiplied an odd number of times be negative or positive?* **negative**

TACTILE LEARNING Exercise 4 Have groups of students make squares of different sizes with 25 algebra tiles. Ask them to discover the length each side must be to form a square. Then have them recall the formula for finding the area of a square.

Exercise 10 For students having difficulty getting started, ask them to write five multiples of 10 and five multiples of 6.

Exercise 12 Challenge students to use a Venn Diagram to solve the problem.

Exercise 13 Students may find it helpful to draw a diagram.

LOOK BACK
Think about how you solved the problem.

4. How did looking for a pattern help in solving this problem? Check students' work.
5. Explain how you can find the ones digit of any power of 4. See below.

Now you may assign Exercises 1–15.

EXERCISES *On Your Own*

Look for a pattern to solve each problem. Show your work.

The sequence of ones digits repeats the pattern 7, 9, 3, 1.

1. a. Find a pattern for the ones digits of the powers of 7. Describe the pattern you find.
   b. What is the ones digit of 7^{21}? 7
2. a. Find the sum of the first one hundred odd numbers. That is, find the sum $1 + 3 + 5 + 7 + \ldots + 199$. 10,000
   b. Describe how you solved part (a).
3. What is the value of $(-1)^{427}$? −1

Use any strategy to solve each problem. Show your work.

4. **Choose A, B, C, or D.** How long is one side of the seventh square in this pattern? D

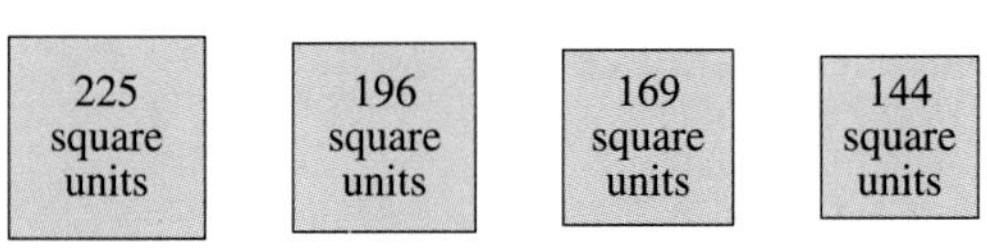

   A. 121 B. 81 C. 40.5 D. 9
5. *Cars* A new car comes in five different exterior colors and three different interior colors. How many different color combinations are available? 15
6. Nita, a six-year-old, can stretch her legs to take two steps at one time. How many different ways can she climb the six steps on her porch using any combination of one or two steps? 13 ways

7. Jiro has four ways to walk to school and two ways to walk to his after-school job. He does not like to take the same path every day. How many school days elapse before Jiro must repeat a path if he goes to his job every day? 8

5. Answers may vary. Sample: Make a table of the powers of 4. The table shows a repeating pattern of 4s and 6s. The last digit of every even power of 4 is 6. The last digit of every odd power is 4.

2b. Answers may vary. Sample: The first odd number is 1^2, the sum of the first two is 2^2, of the first three is 3^2, etc. So the sum of the first 100 odd numbers is 100^2.

Technology Options

Prentice Hall Technology

Software for Learners
- Hot Page™ 7–7*
- Math Blaster® Mystery*
- Interactive Student Tutorial, Chapter 4*

Teaching Resource Software
- Computer Item Generator 4-7
- Resource Pro™ Chapter 4*

Internet • For related mathematics activities, visit the Prentice Hall site at www.phschool.com/math

**Available on CD-ROM only*

Assignment Options for Exercises On Your Own
Core 1–14
Extension 15
Use Mixed Review to maintain skills.

PRACTICE

Practice 4-7 Problem-Solving Strategy: Look for a Pattern

Look for a pattern to solve each problem.

1. Find a pattern for the units digit of the powers of 7. What is the units digit of 7^{34}?
   pattern: 7, 9, 3, 1, 7, 9, 3, 1, . . .; 9
2. Find the sum of the two hundred even numbers from 0 to 398.
   39,800
3. The figures at the right represent the first three *rectangular numbers*. Describe the pattern. Find the value of the eighth rectangular number.
   Answers may vary. Sample: the value of the nth rectangular number is $n(n + 1)$; 72

4. The same cube is shown from three different angles. What color is on the bottom in the first position? (HINT: Cut out a model.)
   red

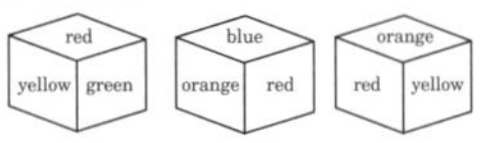

Use any strategy to solve each problem. Show all your work.

5. What is the greatest number of pieces of pizza you can form if you use five straight cuts acrcss the pizza? 16 pieces
6. In this puzzle, each letter represents a digit. If a letter is used more than once, it represents the same digit each time. A true addition problem must result when you substitute digits for letters. (There is more than one answer possible.)

```
  SEVEN
+ EIGHT
 TWELVE
```

Sample answers:

```
  63, 732      85, 254
+ 39, 841    + 50, 671
 103, 573     135, 925
```

7. In a class of 34 students, 12 play the piano, 16 play football, and 12 play neither. How many play both piano and football?
   6 students
8. What is the units digit of 6^6? 6

Practice

In copymaster and workbook formats

RETEACHING

Reteaching 4-7 Problem Solving Strategy: Look for a Pattern

When solving a problem it may be helpful to look for a pattern.

Look at the three drawings of boxes. How many boxes should there be in the next drawing?

Read Think about the information you are given. You know there are 2 boxes in the first drawing, 4 boxes in the second, and 8 boxes in the third.

Plan You know the number of boxes in each drawing. It makes sense to look for a pattern.

Solve There is a pattern. The number of boxes doubles each time. The next drawing should have 16 boxes.

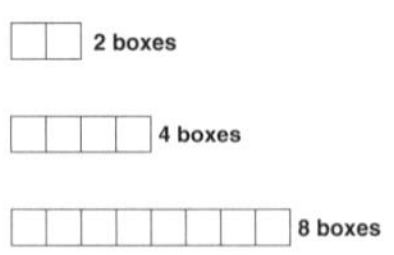

Look Back Is there another pattern possible?

For Exercises 1–2, describe each pattern and draw the next arrangement of boxes.

1. 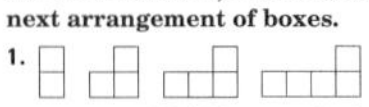

   Pattern: Add 1 box on the left each time.

2. 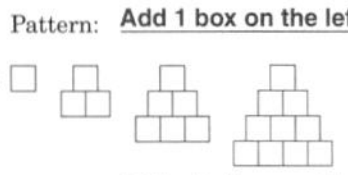

   Pattern: At the bottom, add a new row with 1 more box each time.

3. Look for a pattern to find the value of $(-1)^{100}$.
   a. $(-1)^1 =$ −1 b. $(-1)^2 =$ 1 c. $(-1)^3 =$ −1
   d. $(-1)^4 =$ 1 e. $(-1)^{100} =$ 1
4. Describe the pattern you used in Exercise 3. −1 to any even power is 1.
5. A winter coat is on sale. Look for a pattern in the prices to predict the price of the coat on the tenth day.
   $88.50

Winter Coat Sale Price	
Day 1—$129.00	Day 2—$124.50
Day 3—$120.00	Day 4—$115.50

ENRICHMENT

Minds on Math Transparency

4-7

Kirk's family drove 400 mi on the first day of their vacation. Each day after that they drove half the distance they drove the day before. Their total trip was 775 mi long. How long did it take them to make the trip?

5 days

See *Solution Key* for worked-out answers.

WRAP UP

IDENTIFYING THE BIG IDEA Have students explain how finding a pattern can help them solve problems. Ask them to give examples.

LESSON QUIZ

1. Find a pattern for the one's digit of the powers of 2. **2, 4, 8, 6, . . .**
2. What is the one's digit of 2^{25}? **2**
3. What is the one's digit of 2^{40}? **6**
4. What is the one's digit of 2^{34}? **4**

8. *Entertainment* The Drama Club presented two performances of the play *The Wizard of Oz*, one on Friday night and one on Saturday night. Twice as many people came to see the play on Saturday as on Friday. If 495 people saw the play altogether, how many came on each night?
   165 people on Friday, 330 people on Saturday
9. It takes two minutes to make one cut through a log. How long will it take to cut a ten-foot log into four equal pieces?
   6 minutes
10. There are two blinking neon signs on one block. One blinks on every 10 s, while the other blinks on every 6 s. How many times per minute do they blink together?
    two times
11. Show how to cut a round pizza into eleven pieces with exactly four straight cuts.

11. Sample:

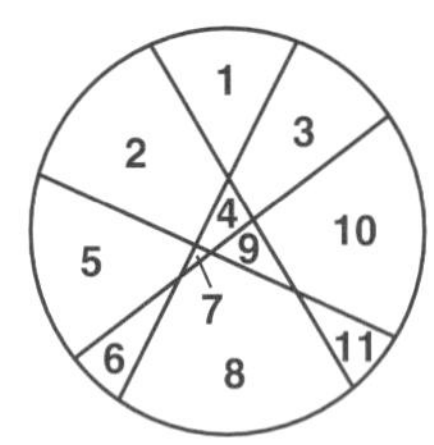

12. In a class of 30 students, 18 students study Spanish, 15 study French, and 5 study neither Spanish nor French. How many students study both Spanish and French?
    8 students
13. Five pears weigh the same as three apples and two strawberries. An apple weighs the same as 21 strawberries. How many strawberries weigh the same as a pear?
    13 strawberries
14. Suppose three students fill four Thanksgiving food baskets in twelve minutes. How many baskets can four students fill in eighteen minutes?
    8 baskets
15. *Health* Suppose that in 1 hour a 125-lb person burns 110 calories by walking 2 mi/h, 180 calories by walking 3 mi/h, or 260 calories by walking 4 mi/h. How many calories do you think a 125-lb person would burn in 1 hour by walking 5 mi/h?
    about 350 calories

Mixed Review

Solve each equation. *(Lesson 3-7)*

16. $x \div 50 = 4$ **200**
17. $-2z = -12$ **6**
18. $-7y = 105$ **−15**
19. $-10x = 10$ **−1**
20. $y \div 9 = -3$ **−27**

Estimate. Use any method. *(Lesson 2-2)*

21. $4.29 + $3.88 + $1.01 **$9**
22. $5.7621 - 2.497$ **4**
23. $2.4 + 2.71 + 2.359$ **7**

24. Write an equation for the statement "two times n plus seven equals eleven." Solve the equation. *(Lesson 3-9)* **$2n + 7 = 11$; 2**

PROBLEM SOLVING PRACTICE ★★

This page provides problems for students to solve using their knowledge of equations, expressions, integers, exponents, and factors. Allow students to use any method they find helpful.

Exercises 1 and 2 Have students check their answers by choosing values for the variables, then substituting the values into the expressions.

Exercise 4 Have students first identify the variable for which they are solving before they begin work.

COOPERATIVE GROUPS Let students work in small groups for Problems 8–10. Group members work together to determine which problem-solving strategy is best for each problem.

PROBLEM SOLVING PRACTICE ★★★★★

Choose the best answer.

1. Which equation is equivalent to $8p + 4.5 = 32$? C

   A. $8p + 4.5 = 32 + 4.5$
   B. $8p = 36.5$
   C. $8p = 27.5$
   D. $6p = 32 - 2$

2. Which expression is equivalent to $9m + 9n$? J

   F. $18(m + n)$ G. $(m + n)$
   H. $m + n$ J. $9(m + n)$

3. Scores in a golf tournament were reported by the number of strokes each player was above or below par. The scores for 6 players at the end of the tournament were −12, +2, −7, +4, −4, and −3. What are the golfers' scores in order from the least number under par to the greatest number over par? A

   A. −12, −7, −4, −3, +2, +4
   B. +2, −3, −4, +4, −7, −12
   C. +4, +2, −3, −4, −7, −12
   D. −3, −4, −7, −12, +2, +4

4. The cost for renting a boat for a day is found by using this formula:

   $$C = 15 + 10h,$$

   where C is the total cost of renting the boat, $15 is the maintenance fee for the boat, and h is the number of hours the boat is rented. Using this formula, what would it cost to rent a boat for 6 hours? G

   F. $100 G. $75 H. $60 J. $45

5. If $4t + 13.7 = 29.9$, what is the value of t? C

   A. 64.8 B. 10.5 C. 4.05 D. 3.55

6. What factors represent $2^3 \times 4^2$? H

   F. $3 \times 3 \times 2 \times 2$
   G. 6×8
   H. $2 \times 2 \times 2 \times 4 \times 4$
   J. $2 \times 2 \times 4 \times 2$

7. Which numbers are between 6^3 and 6^4? D

   A. 3^6 and 4^6 B. 5^3 and 5^4
   C. 7^2 and 7^3 D. 4^5 and 5^4

Please note that items 8–10 have *five* answer choices.

8. Mountain climbers hiked down 1,800 feet from the top of a mountain every day. How far down from the top of the mountain are the climbers after six days? H

   F. 1,806 ft G. 12,600 ft
   H. 10,800 ft J. 9,000 ft
   K. Not Here

9. Medium beverages cost $1.39 and small beverages cost $.89. Which equation could be used to find the total cost in dollars d of any number of medium beverages m and any number of small beverages s? C

   A. $d = (\$1.39 + m) \times (\$.89 + s)$
   B. $d = (m \times \$.89) + (s \times \$1.39)$
   C. $d = (m \times \$1.39) + (s \times \$.89)$
   D. $d = (\$.89 + \$1.39) \times (m \times s)$
   E. $d = (\$1.39 + \$.89) + (m \times s)$

10. What is the prime factorization of 6,000? J

    F. $10 \cdot 20 \cdot 30$ G. $10^2 \cdot 60$
    H. $2^2 \cdot 3 \cdot 5^4$ J. $2^4 \cdot 3 \cdot 5^3$
    K. Not Here

4-8 Teaching Notes

1 Focus

CONNECTING TO PRIOR KNOWLEDGE Ask a volunteer to measure some object in the classroom that will result in a mixed number. Ask students to name situations in which they have used mixed numbers. **Answers may vary. Sample: in recipes, to measure distance or weight**

DIVERSITY Students that are comfortable with the metric system may give measurements in centimeters as a decimal number. Point out that they can write most decimal numbers that are greater than 1 as a mixed number.

2 Teach

THINK AND DISCUSS

ERROR ALERT! Example 1 Students may rewrite 2 as $\frac{2}{4}$. **Remediation:** Ask students to write 2 as $\frac{2}{1}$. Then have them find the LCM of 1 and 4 before they write equivalent fractions.

AUDITORY LEARNING Example 1 Have students listen as you read the mixed number aloud. Ask them to listen for the word *and*. Explain that the plus sign is one mathematical symbol for *and*.

Lesson Planning Options

Prerequisite Skills

- writing equivalent fractions (4-2)
- adding fractions with common denominators (precourse)

Vocabulary/Symbols

improper fractions

Materials/Manipulatives

- newspaper

Resources

Student Edition

Skills Handbook, p. 531
Extra Practice, p. 517
Glossary/Study Guide

Teaching Resources

Chapter Support File, Ch. 4
- Lesson Planner 4-8
- Practice 4-8, Reteaching 4-8
- Answer Masters 4-8

Teaching Aids Masters 8, 10, 21–25
Glossary, Spanish Resources

Transparencies
15, 18–25, Minds on Math 4-8

Warm Up

Write $\frac{29,716}{52,003}$ in simplest form. $\frac{4}{7}$

MEASUREMENT Connection

4-8 Mixed Numbers and Improper Fractions

What You'll Learn

1. To change a mixed number to an improper fraction
2. To change an improper fraction to a mixed number

...And Why

Cooks use mixed numbers and improper fractions when calculating servings.

Here's How

Look for questions that
- build understanding
- ✔ check understanding

THINK AND DISCUSS

1 Mixed Numbers to Improper Fractions

An **improper fraction** has a numerator that is greater than or equal to its denominator. You can use models to understand the connection between mixed numbers and improper fractions.

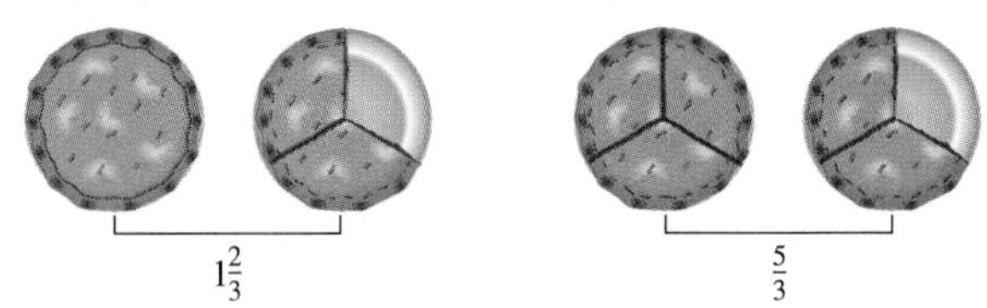

A number line can also help you understand improper fractions and mixed numbers. The number line shows that $1\frac{1}{4} = \frac{5}{4}$.

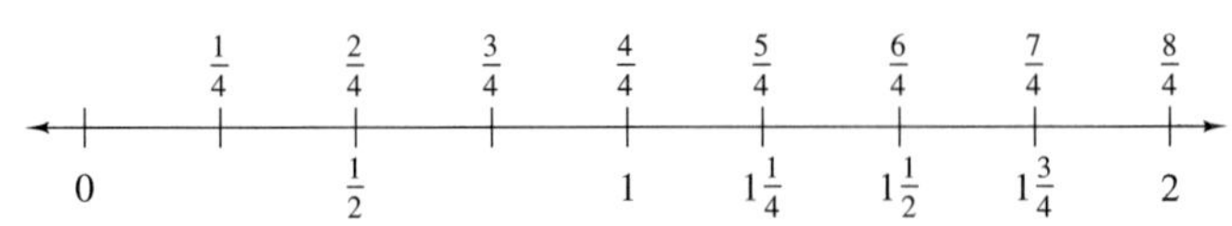

1. Use the number line to write two other mixed numbers as improper fractions.
   Answers may vary. Sample: $1\frac{1}{2} = \frac{6}{4}$, $1\frac{3}{4} = \frac{7}{4}$

You can change a mixed number to an improper fraction using equivalent fractions.

EXAMPLE 1

Write $2\frac{3}{4}$ as an improper fraction.

$2\frac{3}{4} = 2 + \frac{3}{4}$ ← Write the mixed number as a sum.

$= \frac{8}{4} + \frac{3}{4}$ ← Write 2 as the fraction $\frac{8}{4}$.

$= \frac{8 + 3}{4}$ ← Add the numerators.

$2\frac{3}{4} = \frac{11}{4}$

2. *Look Back* Why is $\frac{8}{4}$ a good choice as the equivalent fraction for $\frac{2}{1}$? **Answers may vary. Sample: The denominator is the same as the fraction $\frac{3}{4}$.**

ADDITIONAL EXAMPLES

FOR EXAMPLE 1

Write $3\frac{2}{5}$ as an improper fraction. $\frac{17}{5}$

FOR EXAMPLE 2

Write $5\frac{4}{7}$ as an improper fraction. $\frac{39}{7}$

FOR EXAMPLE 3

Write $\frac{42}{9}$ as a mixed number in simplest form. $4\frac{2}{3}$

ASSESSMENT Question 3 Have students work in pairs. One partner uses the method in Example 1, the other uses the method in Example 2. They compare answers. Partners alternate using the methods. Each student uses a different color pencil so it is obvious which method they used.

Example 2 Point out that these steps are a shortcut to the steps in Example 1. When writing a mixed number as an improper fraction, students should make sure that the denominator of the mixed number is the same as the denominator of the improper fraction.

Question 5 Ask students: *Will the mixed number always have the same denominator as the improper fraction?* **no** *Explain.* **If you simplify the fraction, the denominator will change.**

3. ✔ *Try It Out* Write each mixed number as an improper fraction.
   a. $1\frac{2}{3}$ $\frac{5}{3}$ b. $2\frac{2}{3}$ $\frac{8}{3}$ c. $3\frac{2}{3}$ $\frac{11}{3}$ d. $4\frac{2}{3}$ $\frac{14}{3}$

4. *Patterns* Describe the pattern you see in the numerators of the fractions you wrote for Question 3. **Answers may vary. Sample: Each numerator is 3 greater than the previous one.**

Here is another way to write mixed numbers as improper fractions.

EXAMPLE 2

Write $4\frac{2}{3}$ as an improper fraction.

Multiply the denominator by the whole number. Add the numerator.

$$4\frac{2}{3} = \frac{(3 \times 4) + 2}{3} = \frac{14}{3}$$

Write the result over the denominator, which stays the same.

5. ✔ *Try It Out* Write each mixed number as an improper fraction.
   a. $3\frac{4}{5}$ $\frac{19}{5}$ b. $2\frac{5}{8}$ $\frac{21}{8}$ c. $3\frac{1}{4}$ $\frac{13}{4}$ d. $1\frac{7}{8}$ $\frac{15}{8}$

Now you may assign Exercises 1–24.

2 *Improper Fractions to Mixed Numbers*

To change an improper fraction to a mixed number, divide the numerator by the denominator.

EXAMPLE 3

Write $\frac{30}{8}$ as a mixed number in simplest form.

$$8\overline{)30} = 3 \text{ R } 6$$

denominator → 8; 3 ← whole number; 24; 6 ← remainder

$$\frac{30}{8} = 3\frac{6}{8} \quad \leftarrow \text{Write } \frac{\text{remainder}}{\text{denominator}}.$$

$$= 3\frac{3}{4} \quad \leftarrow \text{Simplify the fraction.}$$

6. ✔ *Try It Out* Write each fraction as a mixed number.
   a. $\frac{12}{5}$ $2\frac{2}{5}$ b. $\frac{8}{6}$ $1\frac{1}{3}$ c. $\frac{15}{12}$ $1\frac{1}{4}$ d. $\frac{25}{4}$ $6\frac{1}{4}$

Now you may assign Exercises 25–49.

Technology Options

Prentice Hall Technology

Software for Learners
- Hot Page™ 7–6*
- Math Blaster® Mystery*
- Interactive Student Tutorial, Chapter 4*

Teaching Resource Software
- Computer Item Generator 4-8
- Resource Pro™ Chapter 4*

Internet • For related mathematics activities, visit the Prentice Hall site at www.phschool.com/math

**Available on CD-ROM only*

Assignment Options for Exercises On Your Own

To provide flexible scheduling, this lesson can be split into parts.

1 **Core** 1–19, 21–24
Extension 20

2 **Core** 25–42, 44–49
Extension 43

Use Mixed Review to maintain skills.

3 Practice/Assess

EXERCISES *On Your Own*

Exercises 1–18 Have students check their answers using this checklist. If the answer to each question is "yes," the answer is reasonable.

- Is the denominator in the improper fraction the same as the denominator in the mixed number?
- Is the numerator in the improper fraction larger than the numerator in the mixed number?
- Did you remove the whole number after you changed the mixed number to an improper fraction?

WRITING Exercise 19 Have students look up the word *improper* in the dictionary.

RESEARCH Exercise 20 Suggest students find mixed numbers in the cooking, business, or real estate section of the newspaper. Have students bring newspaper clippings to share with the class.

REASONING and TACTILE LEARNING Exercise 43 Students can measure water in a quarter cup measure to find the answer.

CHECKPOINT 2

Checkpoint 2 *Lessons 4-6 through 4-8*

Write each fraction in simplest form.

1. $\frac{12}{20}$ $\frac{3}{5}$
2. $\frac{15}{18}$ $\frac{5}{6}$
3. $\frac{24}{36}$ $\frac{2}{3}$
4. $\frac{45}{60}$ $\frac{3}{4}$
5. $\frac{20}{48}$ $\frac{5}{12}$

Write each mixed number as an improper fraction and each improper fraction as a mixed number.

6. $\frac{34}{6}$ $5\frac{4}{6}$ or $5\frac{2}{3}$
7. $4\frac{1}{5}$ $\frac{21}{5}$
8. $\frac{65}{8}$ $8\frac{1}{8}$
9. $1\frac{3}{10}$ $\frac{13}{10}$
10. $3\frac{6}{7}$ $\frac{27}{7}$

Solve.

11. A child's book has pages numbered from 1 to 63. The odd-numbered pages are printed in red, and the even-numbered pages are printed in blue. How many page numbers are printed in blue? 31 numbers

EXERCISES *On Your Own*

Write each mixed number as an improper fraction.

1. $2\frac{3}{8}$ $\frac{19}{8}$
2. $5\frac{3}{4}$ $\frac{23}{4}$
3. $1\frac{1}{12}$ $\frac{13}{12}$
4. $4\frac{3}{5}$ $\frac{23}{5}$
5. $1\frac{3}{7}$ $\frac{10}{7}$
6. $4\frac{5}{8}$ $\frac{37}{8}$
7. $3\frac{2}{5}$ $\frac{17}{5}$
8. $2\frac{11}{12}$ $\frac{35}{12}$
9. $5\frac{2}{3}$ $\frac{17}{3}$
10. $3\frac{1}{4}$ $\frac{13}{4}$
11. $2\frac{4}{9}$ $\frac{22}{9}$
12. $4\frac{7}{10}$ $\frac{47}{10}$
13. $4\frac{7}{8}$ $\frac{39}{8}$
14. $3\frac{1}{6}$ $\frac{19}{6}$
15. $8\frac{3}{7}$ $\frac{59}{7}$
16. $2\frac{5}{12}$ $\frac{29}{12}$
17. $6\frac{1}{7}$ $\frac{43}{7}$
18. $3\frac{5}{12}$ $\frac{41}{12}$

19. *Writing* How can you tell if a fraction is an improper fraction?
The fraction is improper if the numerator is greater than or equal to the denominator.

20. *Research* Find a mixed number in a newspaper. State your source, then write it as an improper fraction. **Check students' work.**

Write the length of each line segment below as a mixed number and as an improper fraction.

21. 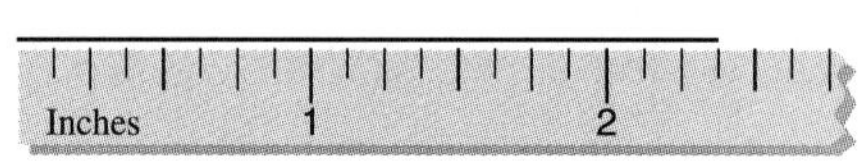

$2\frac{3}{8}$, $\frac{19}{8}$

22. 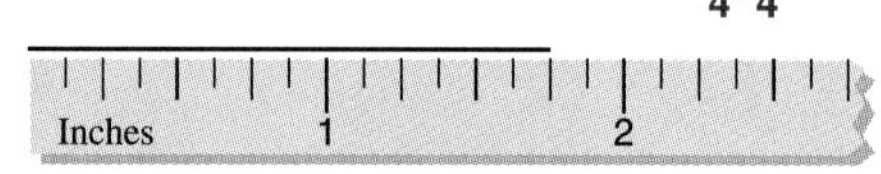

$1\frac{3}{4}$, $\frac{7}{4}$

23. 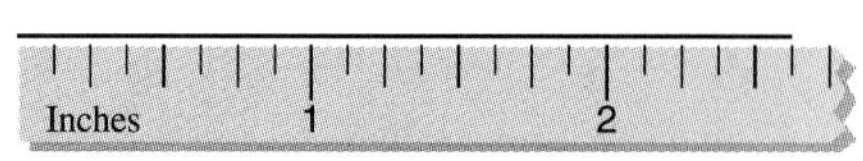

$2\frac{5}{8}$, $\frac{21}{8}$

24. 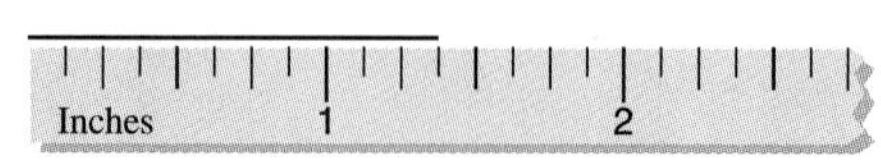

$1\frac{3}{8}$, $\frac{11}{8}$

Write each improper fraction as a whole number or a mixed number in simplest form.

25. $\frac{16}{3}$ $5\frac{1}{3}$
26. $\frac{21}{3}$ 7
27. $\frac{42}{4}$ $10\frac{1}{2}$
28. $\frac{31}{12}$ $2\frac{7}{12}$
29. $\frac{32}{8}$ 4
30. $\frac{49}{6}$ $8\frac{1}{6}$
31. $\frac{84}{7}$ 12
32. $\frac{45}{10}$ $4\frac{1}{2}$
33. $\frac{18}{3}$ 6
34. $\frac{15}{8}$ $1\frac{7}{8}$
35. $\frac{9}{2}$ $4\frac{1}{2}$
36. $\frac{42}{7}$ 6
37. $\frac{22}{5}$ $4\frac{2}{5}$
38. $\frac{17}{6}$ $2\frac{5}{6}$
39. $\frac{27}{4}$ $6\frac{3}{4}$
40. $\frac{19}{12}$ $1\frac{7}{12}$
41. $\frac{18}{4}$ $4\frac{1}{2}$
42. $\frac{21}{9}$ $2\frac{1}{3}$

43. *Reasoning* A recipe calls for $1\frac{3}{4}$ c of flour. Darrell and Tanisha have only a quarter cup measure. How many times will they fill it for the recipe? **7**

44. *Carpentry* Pearl kept track of the time she worked on her carpentry project. She worked a total of 345 min. Use mixed numbers to write Pearl's time in hours. **$5\frac{3}{4}$ hours**

45. *Travel* It took the Brook family 3 h 45 min to travel from their home to their cousins' home for Thanksgiving. Write the time as a mixed number and as a fraction in simplest form. **$3\frac{3}{4}$ h, $\frac{15}{4}$ h**

46. *Cooking* A cooking class served $25\frac{1}{4}$ loaves of banana bread at a faculty breakfast. Each loaf was cut into eight equal slices. How many slices of banana bread did they serve? **202 slices**

WRAP UP

IDENTIFYING THE BIG IDEA Have students explain how to write a mixed number as an improper fraction and how to write an improper fraction as a mixed number. Then have them compare these two forms of rational numbers.

JOURNAL Students may want to explain why we call improper fractions *improper*.

LESSON QUIZ

Write each mixed number as an improper fraction.

1. $6\frac{5}{7}$ $\frac{47}{7}$
2. $8\frac{2}{9}$ $\frac{74}{9}$

Write each improper fraction as a mixed number in simplest form.

3. $\frac{23}{5}$ $4\frac{3}{5}$
4. $\frac{38}{4}$ $9\frac{1}{2}$

PRACTICE

Practice 4-8 Mixed Numbers and Improper Fractions

1. Write a mixed number and an improper fraction for the model below. $2\frac{3}{4}$; $\frac{11}{4}$

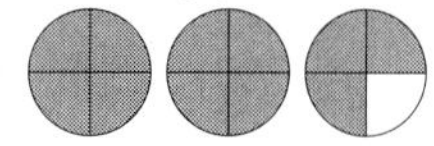

Write each mixed number as an improper fraction.

2. $2\frac{3}{8}$ $\frac{19}{8}$ 3. $5\frac{1}{3}$ $\frac{16}{3}$ 4. $1\frac{7}{10}$ $\frac{17}{10}$ 5. $3\frac{4}{9}$ $\frac{31}{9}$

6. $4\frac{5}{8}$ $\frac{37}{8}$ 7. $3\frac{5}{12}$ $\frac{41}{12}$ 8. $1\frac{15}{16}$ $\frac{31}{16}$ 9. $2\frac{3}{10}$ $\frac{23}{10}$

Write each improper fraction as a whole number or a mixed number in simplest form.

10. $\frac{25}{3}$ $8\frac{1}{3}$ 11. $\frac{42}{7}$ 6 12. $\frac{18}{4}$ $4\frac{1}{2}$ 13. $\frac{28}{6}$ $4\frac{2}{3}$

14. $\frac{27}{12}$ $2\frac{1}{4}$ 15. $\frac{11}{6}$ $1\frac{5}{6}$ 16. $\frac{20}{3}$ $6\frac{2}{3}$ 17. $\frac{34}{8}$ $4\frac{1}{4}$

18. $\frac{125}{5}$ 25 19. $\frac{34}{7}$ $4\frac{6}{7}$ 20. $\frac{40}{6}$ $6\frac{2}{3}$ 21. $\frac{84}{12}$ 7

The distance around an indoor running track is $\frac{1}{16}$ mi.

22. Juan jogged around the track 40 times. How far did he jog? $2\frac{1}{2}$ mi

23. Aaron walked around the track 36 times. How far did he walk? $2\frac{1}{4}$ mi

The distance around an outdoor running track is $\frac{1}{6}$ mile.

24. Aruna jogged around the track 16 times. How far did she jog? $2\frac{2}{3}$ mi

25. Theresa walked around the track 22 times. How far did she walk? $3\frac{2}{3}$ mi

26. Shade the figures below to represent $3\frac{5}{8}$. How many eighths are shaded? 29

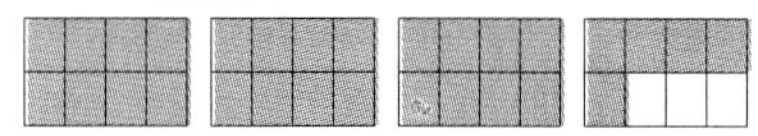

In copymaster and workbook formats

47. **Choose A, B, C, or D.** A length of material measures between 3 and $3\frac{1}{4}$ feet. What length could it be? C

A. $\frac{26}{7}$ B. $\frac{11}{3}$ C. $\frac{25}{8}$ D. $\frac{18}{5}$

48. Each pizza delivered to a class party was divided into 8 equal slices. After the party, there were 2 slices from one pizza, 3 slices from each of two other pizzas, and 5 slices from another pizza left on the table. Write the amount of leftover pizza as a mixed number. $1\frac{5}{8}$

49. *Reasoning* Use the digits 2, 5, and 9 to write a fraction with the greatest possible value. Then write the fraction as a mixed number. $\frac{95}{2}$, $47\frac{1}{2}$

JOURNAL Write an explanation for writing $4\frac{5}{9}$ as an improper fraction.

Mixed Review

Find each sum or difference. (Lessons 3-3, 3-4)

50. $6 + (-7)$ -1 51. $8 - (-5)$ 13 52. $-12 + (-3)$ -15 53. $-20 - 4$ -24 54. $-5 - (-1)$ -4

55. Alan has lumber 63 in. long, 84 in. long, and 105 in. long. He plans to cut all the lumber into pieces of equal length. What is the longest length he can cut without having any left over? (Lesson 4-5) 21 in.

✓ CHECKPOINT 2

Lessons 4-6 through 4-8

Write each fraction in simplest form.

1. $\frac{36}{48}$ $\frac{3}{4}$ 2. $\frac{42}{63}$ $\frac{2}{3}$ 3. $\frac{30}{45}$ $\frac{2}{3}$ 4. $\frac{18}{20}$ $\frac{9}{10}$ 5. $\frac{12}{54}$ $\frac{2}{9}$ 6. $\frac{35}{50}$ $\frac{7}{10}$

Write each improper fraction as a mixed number and each mixed number as an improper fraction.

7. $\frac{29}{6}$ $4\frac{5}{6}$ 8. $\frac{82}{5}$ $16\frac{2}{5}$ 9. $4\frac{1}{9}$ $\frac{37}{9}$ 10. $1\frac{9}{10}$ $\frac{19}{10}$ 11. $\frac{33}{12}$ $2\frac{3}{4}$ 12. $2\frac{5}{6}$ $\frac{17}{6}$

13. a. *Writing* Would you prefer to list factors or use prime factorization to simplify $\frac{375}{1,000}$? Why? Answers may vary. Sample: Prime factorization; there are many factors.

b. Use your choice to simplify $\frac{375}{1,000}$. $\frac{3}{8}$

14. A street has a building for every number. How many buildings are on the odd-numbered side of a street that starts at number 107 and ends with 189? 42

RETEACHING

Reteaching 4-8 Mixed Numbers and Improper Fractions

An **improper fraction** is greater than or equal to 1. Its numerator is greater than or equal to its denominator.

Improper fractions: $\frac{6}{4}$ $\frac{8}{8}$ $\frac{10}{8}$ $\frac{7}{2}$

A mixed number is the sum of a whole number and a fraction.

Mixed numbers: $1\frac{2}{3}$ $5\frac{4}{9}$ $3\frac{1}{2}$

To write a mixed number as an improper fraction:

① Write the mixed number as a sum. $3\frac{1}{2} = 3 + \frac{1}{2}$

② Write both numbers as fractions. $= \frac{6}{2} + \frac{1}{2}$

③ Add the fractions. $= \frac{7}{2}$

To write an improper fraction as a mixed number:

① Divide the numerator by the denominator. $\frac{7}{2}$ Think: $7 \div 2$ $2\overline{)7}$ quotient 3, -6, remainder 1

② Write the whole number, then the remainder over the divisor. $\frac{7}{2} = 3\frac{1}{2}$

Write each mixed number as an improper fraction.

1. $3\frac{1}{4} = \frac{13}{4}$ 2. $2\frac{2}{3} = \frac{8}{3}$ 3. $1\frac{3}{8} = \frac{11}{8}$ 4. $5\frac{2}{7} = \frac{37}{7}$

5. $6\frac{3}{4} = \frac{27}{4}$ 6. $1\frac{1}{9} = \frac{10}{9}$ 7. $4\frac{1}{2} = \frac{9}{2}$ 8. $3\frac{4}{5} = \frac{19}{5}$

9. $5\frac{1}{6} = \frac{31}{6}$ 10. $3\frac{1}{3} = \frac{10}{3}$ 11. $5\frac{7}{8} = \frac{47}{8}$ 12. $4\frac{1}{8} = \frac{33}{8}$

Write each improper fraction as a whole number or a mixed number in simplest form.

13. $\frac{14}{4} = 3\frac{1}{2}$ 14. $\frac{12}{2} = 6$ 15. $\frac{22}{5} = 4\frac{2}{5}$ 16. $\frac{16}{3} = 5\frac{1}{3}$

17. $\frac{47}{8} = 5\frac{7}{8}$ 18. $\frac{56}{7} = 8$ 19. $\frac{17}{4} = 4\frac{1}{4}$ 20. $\frac{21}{6} = 3\frac{1}{2}$

21. $\frac{13}{5} = 2\frac{3}{5}$ 22. $\frac{23}{4} = 5\frac{3}{4}$ 23. $\frac{13}{9} = 1\frac{4}{9}$ 24. $\frac{14}{2} = 7$

Reteaching

ENRICHMENT

Minds on Math Transparency

4-8

Five friends are seated in a row at a concert. Shayla is sitting next to Suki. Sam is in the middle of the row and sitting next to Suki and Sari. Shar is sitting on the right end of the row. Who is sitting on the left end of the row?

Shayla

See *Solution Key* for worked-out answers.

4-9 Teaching Notes

1 Focus

CONNECTING TO PRIOR KNOWLEDGE
Ask students:

- *How would you express $\frac{1}{2}$ of a dollar as a decimal?* $.50
- *What fraction of a dollar is $.25?* $\frac{1}{4}$

2 Teach

Work Together

EXTENSION Suggest that students estimate each fraction by covering up the one's digit in the numerator and denominator. Then they can reduce the remaining fraction.

ERROR ALERT! Question 3 Some students may think Heather Boyer hit the ball a greater fraction of times at bat because she has more hits. **Remediation:** Remind students she came to bat fewer times. Ask students to find a common denominator to help compare fractions that are close in value.

THINK AND DISCUSS

KINESTHETIC LEARNING Question 7 To help students understand the meaning of repeating decimals, write $0.\overline{45}$ on the board. Give each student an index card. Half the students write 4 on their cards. The other half write 5 on their cards. Arrange students around the room to model the decimal. The

Lesson Planning Options

Prerequisite Skills
- dividing whole numbers (precourse)
- rounding decimals (2-2)

Materials/Manipulatives
- calculator

Resources

Student Edition
Skills Handbook, pp. 532, 533
Extra Practice, p. 517
Glossary/Study Guide

Teaching Resources
Chapter Support File, Ch. 4
- Lesson Planner 4-9
- Practice 4-9, Reteaching 4-9
- Alternative Activity 4-9
- Answer Masters 4-9

Teaching Aids Masters 20–25
Glossary, Spanish Resources

Transparencies
9, 10, 15, 18–25, Minds on Math 4-9

Warm Up
Because of mishandling, $\frac{3}{10}$ of a crate of oranges was ruined. If the crate originally weighed 50 lb, how many pounds of oranges were good? 35 lb

4-9 Fractions and Decimals

What You'll Learn
1. To change fractions to decimals
2. To change decimals to fractions in simplest form

...And Why
Fractions and decimals are used to compute statistics.

Here's How
Look for questions that
- build understanding
- ✔ check understanding

Work Together
Ordering Fractions

The white blur of the softball speeds toward you. Your body leans, your arms and wrist snap the bat around. Pow! The ball rockets into center field for a hit.

It doesn't happen every time at bat. In fact, few players get a hit more than $\frac{1}{3}$ of the time.

Top Five Georgia Bulldogs Hitters, 1997

Player	Hits	Times at Bat	Fraction of Times Player Got a Hit
Jessi Cerra	47	164	$\frac{47}{164}$
Chrissy Gavin	35	137	$\frac{35}{137}$
Heather Boyer	32	93	$\frac{32}{93}$
Sabrina Touchberry	30	100	$\frac{30}{100}$
Caroline Patrick	23	85	$\frac{23}{85}$

1. In what order are the five players listed? decreasing order of the number of hits
2. Who had more times at bat, Sabrina Touchberry or Heather Boyer? Sabrina Touchberry
3. Do you think Sabrina Touchberry or Heather Boyer had hits a greater fraction of her times at bat? Why? Heather Boyer, because $\frac{32}{93} > \frac{30}{100}$.
4. *Explain* Was Sabrina Touchberry or Heather Boyer more likely to get a hit when she came to bat? Heather Boyer had a hit more than $\frac{1}{3}$ of the time, while Sabrina Touchberry got a hit less than $\frac{1}{3}$ of the time. So Heather Boyer is more likely to get a hit.

person representing the decimal point and the pair holding the first 4 and 5 stand in front of the written $0.\overline{45}$. (You or a student can represent the decimal point.) Have the final pair holding a 4 and a 5 give their index cards to the students in the first pair holding the corresponding cards. Repeat the process until only the first pair remains.

ADDITIONAL EXAMPLES

FOR EXAMPLE 1

Jacob hit the ball $\frac{7}{27}$ of the time at bat. Write Jacob's batting average as a decimal rounded to the nearest thousandth. **0.259**

FOR EXAMPLE 2

Change $\frac{7}{11}$ to a decimal. **$0.\overline{63}$**

FOR EXAMPLE 3

Write 0.275 as a fraction in simplest form. **$\frac{11}{40}$**

3 Practice/Assess

EXERCISES *On Your Own*

ASSESSMENT Exercises 1–6 Have students write the calculation method they use as they answer the first row of questions. They should use each calculation method at least once. When they have finished, ask them to order the decimals from least to greatest and check with a partner. **0.15, 0.375, 0.4, $0.8\overline{3}$, $0.91\overline{6}$, 1.5**

THINK AND DISCUSS

1 *Writing Fractions as Decimals*

Batting averages are usually expressed as decimals. Change the fraction $\frac{\text{hits}}{\text{times at bat}}$ to a decimal by dividing the numerator by the denominator.

EXAMPLE 1 *Real-World Problem Solving*

Sports Write Heather Boyer's batting average as a decimal. Round your answer to the nearest thousandth.

Heather Boyer got a hit $\frac{32}{93}$ of the time.

32 ÷ 93 = 0.344086021 ← Use a calculator to divide the numerator by the denominator.

≈ 0.344 ← Round to the nearest thousandth.

Heather Boyer's batting average is .344.

5a. 0.287, 0.255, 0.300, 0.271
b. Heather Boyer, Sabrina Touchberry, Jessi Cerra, Caroline Patrick, Chrissy Gavin
c. In decimal form; you don't need to find a common demoninator.

5. a. *Try It Out* Change the fraction for each of the other players' batting averages on page 176 to a decimal. Round each average to the nearest thousandth.
   b. List the five players in order from highest to lowest batting average.
   c. *Think About It* Is it easier to compare batting averages in fraction form or in decimal form? Why?

6. *Reasoning* Why do you need to know what place to round the decimal to in Example 1?
   Answers may vary. Sample: The decimal does not terminate.

Sometimes when you change a fraction to a decimal, the result is a repeating decimal. To show that a decimal repeats, you use a bar over the digits that repeat.

EXAMPLE 2

Change each fraction to a decimal.

a. $\frac{5}{11}$

$\frac{5}{11} = 5 \div 11$
$= 0.454545454\ldots$
$= 0.\overline{45}$

b. $\frac{2}{3}$

$\frac{2}{3} = 2 \div 3$
$= 0.666666666\ldots$
$= 0.\overline{6}$

Technology Options

Prentice Hall Technology

Software for Learners
- Hot Page™ 8–11*
- Math Blaster® Mystery*
- Interactive Student Tutorial, Chapter 4*

Teaching Resource Software
- Computer Item Generator 4-9
- Resource Pro™ Chapter 4*

Internet • For related mathematics activities, visit the Prentice Hall site at www.phschool.com/math

**Available on CD-ROM only*

Assignment Options for Exercises On Your Own

To provide flexible scheduling, this lesson can be split into parts.

1 **Core** 1–23
Extension 24

2 **Core** 25–44
Extension 45

Use Mixed Review to maintain skills.

CONNECTION TO SCIENCE and EXTENSION Exercise 19 Encourage students to research what happens to Greenland icebergs that don't float into the Atlantic Ocean. Have them use their discoveries to write a question with a fraction as an answer. Then change their fraction to a decimal and present the results to the class.

CONNECTING TO THE STUDENTS' WORLD Exercise 20 Students can list all living members of their own or another family. Include parents, guardians, step-parents, siblings, aunts, uncles, cousins, grandparents, and great grandparents. Ask: *What fraction of your family is under 18?* Have students compare this fraction to the states in the Population Chart.

ESTIMATION Exercise 20b Have students check their answers by finding the number that is one third of the total population for each state. This will help them determine whether the number of people under 18 is less than or greater than one third.

WRITING Exercise 23 Suggest students interview relatives or neighbors about everyday situations involving fractions or decimals.

7. ✔ *Try It Out* Write each fraction as a decimal. Use a bar to show repeating digits.
   a. $\frac{2}{11}$ $0.\overline{18}$ b. $\frac{5}{15}$ $0.\overline{3}$ c. $\frac{5}{9}$ $0.\overline{5}$ d. $\frac{7}{12}$ $0.58\overline{3}$

Now you may assign Exercises 1–24.

2 *Changing Decimals to Fractions*

QUICKreview

A terminating decimal is a decimal that ends.

You can change a terminating decimal to a fraction by writing the decimal as a number over some power of 10, like 10, 100, or 1,000.

■ EXAMPLE 3

Write 1.325 as a fraction in simplest form.

Read the number as one and three hundred twenty-five *thousandths*. The number in the denominator is *1,000*. Write $1\frac{325}{1{,}000}$.

$$1\frac{325}{1{,}000} = 1\frac{325 \div 25}{1{,}000 \div 25} \quad \leftarrow \text{Use the GCF to write the fraction in simplest form.}$$
$$= 1\frac{13}{40}$$

8. ✔ *Try It Out* Write each decimal as a fraction in simplest form.
   a. 0.6 $\frac{3}{5}$ b. 2.48 $2\frac{12}{25}$ c. 0.79 $\frac{79}{100}$ d. 0.525 $\frac{21}{40}$

Now you may assign Exercises 25–45.

EXERCISES *On Your Own*

Choose **Use a calculator, paper and pencil, or mental math to write each fraction as a decimal. Use a bar to show any repeating digits.**

1. $\frac{2}{5}$ 0.4 2. $\frac{5}{6}$ $0.8\overline{3}$ 3. $\frac{3}{20}$ 0.15 4. $\frac{3}{8}$ 0.375 5. $\frac{11}{12}$ $0.91\overline{6}$ 6. $\frac{3}{2}$ 1.5

7. $\frac{6}{8}$ 0.75 8. $\frac{4}{15}$ $0.2\overline{6}$ 9. $\frac{5}{12}$ $0.41\overline{6}$ 10. $\frac{6}{11}$ $0.\overline{54}$ 11. $\frac{1}{6}$ $0.1\overline{6}$ 12. $\frac{4}{5}$ 0.8

13. $\frac{25}{33}$ $0.\overline{75}$ 14. $\frac{9}{16}$ 0.5625 15. $\frac{21}{30}$ 0.7 16. $\frac{10}{45}$ $0.\overline{2}$ 17. $\frac{72}{80}$ 0.9 18. $\frac{5}{24}$ $0.208\overline{3}$

Greenland

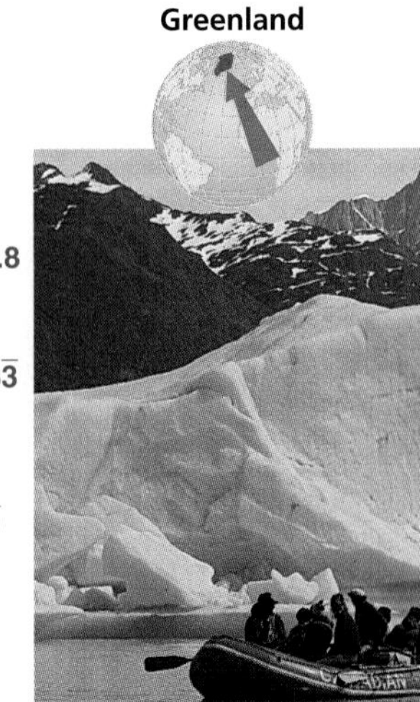

19. *Science* About 12,500 icebergs break away from Greenland each year. Of these, about 375 float into the Atlantic Ocean.
   a. What fraction of the icebergs that break away from Greenland each year float into the Atlantic Ocean? Write your answer in simplest form. $\frac{3}{100}$
   b. Change your answer from part (a) to a decimal. 0.03
   c. What fraction of the icebergs *don't* float into the Atlantic Ocean? Write your answer in simplest form. $\frac{97}{100}$

Exercises 25–42 Remind students to write their fractions in simplest form.

Exercise 45 Suggest that students read 2.63 as 2 *and* 63 hundredths. Point out that this is a mixed number. The whole number is 2, the fraction is $\frac{63}{100}$.

WRAP UP

IDENTIFYING THE BIG IDEA Have students tell how to express fractions as decimals and decimals as fractions. Then have students give a real-life example that illustrates why this skill is useful.

PORTFOLIO Share with students the criteria you will use to assess their work in portfolios, as well as how you plan to use the results. Students should understand how the rubrics are used to assess their work, how each piece in the portfolio counts, and how the scores they get in their portfolios will affect their overall evaluation.

PROJECT LINK Have students exchange their measuring systems with a partner to discover advantages and disadvantages of each system.

---

20. Use the table at the right. **a, c. See below right.**
  a. Write a fraction showing $\frac{\text{number of people under 18}}{\text{total population}}$ for each state.
  b. *Estimation* For most of the states, would $\frac{1}{2}$, $\frac{1}{3}$, or $\frac{1}{4}$ best describe the fraction of the population that is under 18? $\frac{1}{4}$
  c. *Calculator* Change each fraction from part (a) to a decimal. Round to the nearest thousandth.
  d. Write the states from least to greatest based on the part of the population that is under 18. **FL, KY, NY, MD, ME, OH, CA, OK, AK, WY**

Population Chart

State	Total Population (thousands)	Number of People Under 18 (thousands)
ME	1,235	310
NY	18,055	4,366
OH	10,939	2,819
CA	30,380	8,163
MD	4,860	1,201
KY	3,713	875
OK	3,175	875
WY	460	154
AK	570	180
FL	13,277	2,998

Source: *Statistical Abstract of the United States*

21. **Choose A, B, C, or D.** Which has the greatest value? **C**
  A. 0.668 B. $\frac{4}{6}$ C. $\frac{5}{7}$ D. 0.68

22. a. *Calculator* Change each fraction in the table below to a decimal. Use a bar to show repeating decimals.

Basketball Players' Statistics

Player	Free Throws	Attempts	Fraction	
A	52	96	$\frac{52}{96}$	$0.541\overline{6}$
B	75	120	$\frac{75}{120}$	0.625
C	51	99	$\frac{51}{99}$	$0.\overline{51}$
D	92	150	$\frac{92}{150}$	$0.61\overline{3}$

  b. List the players in order from highest to lowest free-throw average. **B, D, A, C**

20a. $\frac{310}{1,235}$, $\frac{4,366}{18,055}$, $\frac{2,819}{10,939}$, $\frac{8,163}{30,380}$, $\frac{1,201}{4,860}$, $\frac{875}{3,713}$, $\frac{875}{3,175}$, $\frac{154}{460}$, $\frac{180}{570}$, $\frac{2,998}{13,277}$

c. 0.251, 0.242, 0.258, 0.269, 0.247, 0.236, 0.276, 0.335, 0.316, 0.226

23. *Writing* Describe some everyday situations in which you need to change fractions to decimals. **Check students' work.**

24. a. Write $3\frac{5}{8}$ as an improper fraction. $\frac{29}{8}$
  b. Change your answer from part (a) to a decimal. **3.625**

Write each decimal as a fraction in simplest form.

25. 0.6 $\frac{3}{5}$ 26. 0.125 $\frac{1}{8}$ 27. 0.66 $\frac{33}{50}$ 28. 2.5 $2\frac{1}{2}$ 29. 3.75 $3\frac{3}{4}$ 30. 0.32 $\frac{8}{25}$

31. 0.19 $\frac{19}{100}$ 32. 0.8 $\frac{4}{5}$ 33. 0.965 $\frac{193}{200}$ 34. 1.6 $1\frac{3}{5}$ 35. 4.305 $4\frac{61}{200}$ 36. 1.27 $1\frac{27}{100}$

37. 0.65 $\frac{13}{20}$ 38. 0.394 $\frac{197}{500}$ 39. 1.69 $1\frac{69}{100}$ 40. 0.78 $\frac{39}{50}$ 41. 0.568 $\frac{71}{125}$ 42. 0.35 $\frac{7}{20}$

43. Write in order from least to greatest.
  $\frac{2}{3}$, 0.67, $\frac{5}{9}$, 0.58, $\frac{7}{12}$ $\frac{5}{9}$, 0.58, $\frac{7}{12}$, $\frac{2}{3}$, 0.67

PRACTICE

Practice 4-9 *Fractions and Decimals*

Choose a calculator, paper and pencil, or mental math to write each fraction as a decimal. Use a bar to indicate repeating digits.

1. $\frac{3}{5}$ 0.6
2. $\frac{7}{8}$ 0.875
3. $\frac{7}{9}$ $0.\overline{7}$
4. $\frac{5}{16}$ 0.3125
5. $\frac{1}{6}$ $0.1\overline{6}$
6. $\frac{5}{8}$ 0.625
7. $\frac{1}{3}$ $0.\overline{3}$
8. $\frac{2}{3}$ $0.\overline{6}$
9. $\frac{9}{10}$ 0.9
10. $\frac{7}{11}$ $0.\overline{63}$
11. $\frac{9}{20}$ 0.45
12. $\frac{3}{4}$ 0.75
13. $\frac{4}{9}$ $0.\overline{4}$
14. $\frac{9}{11}$ $0.\overline{81}$
15. $\frac{11}{20}$ 0.55
16. $\frac{9}{2}$ 4.5
17. $\frac{5}{4}$ 1.25
18. $\frac{11}{8}$ 1.375
19. $\frac{11}{12}$ $0.91\overline{6}$
20. $\frac{8}{15}$ $0.5\overline{3}$

Write each decimal as a fraction in simplest form.

21. 0.6 $\frac{3}{5}$
22. 0.45 $\frac{9}{20}$
23. 0.62 $\frac{31}{50}$
24. 0.8 $\frac{4}{5}$
25. 0.325 $\frac{13}{40}$
26. 0.725 $\frac{29}{40}$
27. 4.75 $4\frac{3}{4}$
28. 0.33 $\frac{33}{100}$
29. 0.925 $\frac{37}{40}$
30. 3.8 $3\frac{4}{5}$
31. 4.7 $4\frac{7}{10}$
32. 0.05 $\frac{1}{20}$
33. 0.65 $\frac{13}{20}$
34. 0.855 $\frac{171}{200}$
35. 0.104 $\frac{13}{125}$
36. 0.47 $\frac{47}{100}$
37. 0.894 $\frac{447}{500}$
38. 0.276 $\frac{69}{250}$
39. 1.84 $1\frac{21}{25}$
40. 2.59 $2\frac{59}{100}$

Use the chart at the right for Exercises 41 and 42.

41. In which year did about $\frac{1}{10}$ of the families have four or more children? 1970
42. In which year did about $\frac{1}{25}$ of the families have four or more children? 1980

Year	Number of families (thousands)	Families with 4 or more children (thousands)
1970	51,586	5,055
1975	55,712	3,844
1980	59,550	2,441
1985	62,706	1,881
1990	66,090	1,851

Practice

In copymaster and workbook formats

RETEACHING

Reteaching 4-9 *Fractions and Decimals*

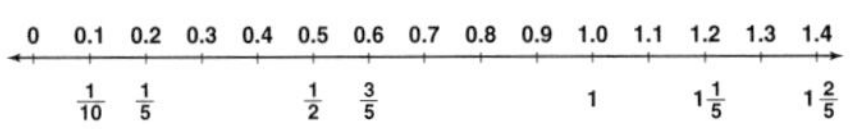

To change a fraction to a decimal, divide the numerator by the denominator.

$\frac{3}{5}$ Think: 3 ÷ 5

$$\begin{array}{r} 0.6 \\ 5\overline{)3.0} \\ -\,30 \\ \hline 0 \end{array}$$

$\frac{3}{5} = 0.6$

To change a decimal to a fraction:

① Read the decimal to find the denominator. Write the decimal digits over 10, 100, or 1,000.

0.65 is 65 *hundredths* → $\frac{65}{100}$

② Use the GCF to write the fraction in simplest form.

The GCF of 65 and 100 is 5.

$\frac{65}{100} = \frac{65 \div 5}{100 \div 5} = \frac{13}{20}$

Divide to write each fraction as a decimal.

1. $\frac{4}{5}$ = 0.8
2. $\frac{3}{4}$ = 0.75
3. $\frac{1}{8}$ = 0.125
4. $\frac{1}{4}$ = 0.25
5. $\frac{2}{5}$ = 0.4
6. $\frac{7}{10}$ = 0.7
7. $\frac{5}{8}$ = 0.625
8. $\frac{1}{5}$ = 0.2
9. $\frac{3}{8}$ = 0.375

Write each decimal as a fraction in simplest form.

10. 0.4 = $\frac{2}{5}$
11. 0.75 = $\frac{3}{4}$
12. 1.5 = $1\frac{1}{2}$
13. 0.35 = $\frac{7}{20}$
14. 2.7 = $2\frac{7}{10}$
15. 1.8 = $1\frac{4}{5}$
16. 0.625 = $\frac{5}{8}$
17. 0.78 = $\frac{39}{50}$
18. 0.88 = $\frac{22}{25}$

Choose A, B, or C. Find the equivalent fraction or decimal.

19. 0.95 A. $\frac{45}{50}$ (B) $\frac{19}{20}$ C. $\frac{9}{10}$
20. $\frac{21}{25}$ A. 0.21 B. 0.42 (C) 0.84
21. 0.76 (A) $\frac{19}{25}$ B. $\frac{3}{4}$ C. $\frac{76}{10}$
22. $\frac{19}{50}$ (A) 0.38 B. 0.038 C. 3.8

ENRICHMENT

Minds on Math Transparency

4-9

I am an integer 28 units from my opposite value on the number line. I am not 14. What integer am I?

–14

See *Solution Key* for worked-out answers.

LESSON QUIZ

Write each fraction as a decimal. Use a bar to indicate any repeating digits.

1. $\frac{5}{16}$ 0.3125
2. $\frac{10}{12}$ $0.8\overline{3}$

Write each decimal as a fraction in simplest form.

3. 0.84 $\frac{21}{25}$
4. 0.425 $\frac{17}{40}$

44. In an experiment with seeds from wild plants, a botanist gathered the data below on the number of seeds planted and the number that sprouted for each variety.

Seed Type	A	B	C	D	E	F	G	H	I
Number Sprouted	15	5	22	17	18	21	14	18	8
Number Planted	48	20	44	35	52	63	55	35	15

a. *Calculator* Write a fraction showing $\frac{\text{number sprouted}}{\text{number planted}}$, then change the fraction to a decimal. Round to the nearest hundredth. See right.

b. Place the seed types into 3 groups: those that sprout about $\frac{1}{2}$ of the time, those that sprout about $\frac{1}{3}$ of the time, and those that sprout about $\frac{1}{4}$ of the time. C, D, H, I; A, E, F; B, G

c. Which type(s) of seeds would you prefer to plant? Why? See right.

45. In 1990, the average number of people per household was 2.63. Write this number as a mixed number and as an improper fraction. $2\frac{63}{100}$, $\frac{263}{100}$

44a. $\frac{15}{48} = 0.31$, $\frac{5}{20} = 0.25$, $\frac{22}{44} = 0.5$, $\frac{17}{35} = 0.49$, $\frac{18}{52} = 0.35$, $\frac{21}{63} = 0.33$, $\frac{14}{55} = 0.25$, $\frac{18}{35} = 0.51$, $\frac{8}{15} = 0.53$

PORTFOLIO

For your portfolio, choose one or two items from your work for this chapter. Here are some possibilities:
- cooperative work
- work you found challenging
- part of your project

Explain why you have included each selection.

44c. Answers may vary. Sample: C, D, H, I; you want to plant the seeds that are more likely to sprout.

Mixed Review

Write each mixed number as an improper fraction. (Lesson 4-8)

46. $1\frac{2}{3}$ $\frac{5}{3}$
47. $2\frac{4}{5}$ $\frac{14}{5}$
48. $6\frac{4}{9}$ $\frac{58}{9}$
49. $3\frac{1}{12}$ $\frac{37}{12}$
50. $4\frac{2}{7}$ $\frac{30}{7}$
51. $2\frac{3}{11}$ $\frac{25}{11}$

Find each quotient. (Lesson 2-6)

52. 0.45 ÷ 9 0.05
53. 0.64 ÷ 0.8 0.8
54. 1.75 ÷ 0.05 35
55. 3.06 ÷ 0.3 10.2

56. Find the mean, median, and mode of the following scores: 93, 80, 77, 93, 69, 90, 85, 88. (Lesson 1-4) 84.375; 86.5; 93

57. *Choose a Strategy* Six building blocks are cubes with edges of 1 cm, 2 cm, 3 cm, 4 cm, 5 cm, and 6 cm. Can you use all the blocks to make two towers of the same height? Explain.

57. Answers may vary. Sample: No; the sum of the heights of the cubes is 21 cm, which also must be the sum of the heights of the two towers. Since the heights of the two towers must be equal whole numbers, it is not possible.

CHAPTER PROJECT

PROJECT LINK: ANALYZING

Is your system as good as the other systems you have used to measure lengths? What are the advantages and disadvantages of your system and the other systems?

Check students' work.

Extra Practice, Lesson 4-9, page 517

FINISHING THE CHAPTER PROJECT

PROJECT DAY You may wish to plan a project day on which students share their completed projects. Encourage students to explain their process as well as their product.

PROJECT NOTEBOOK Ask students to review their project work and bring their notebooks up to date.

SCORING RUBRIC

3 You constructed and labeled your ruler carefully, and it accurately shows fractions of your basic measurement unit. You used your ruler to accurately measure at least eight objects over a wide range of lengths. You described how your ruler could be used to measure fractional units, or you compared your measurement system to other measurement systems.

2 You constructed a ruler that includes fractional units, but it is not as accurate as it could have been. You measured and listed the lengths of several short objects and several long objects.

1 You constructed your ruler carelessly, or you made and recorded inaccurate measurements.

0 You did not create your own unit of measure, or you didn't use fractional units, or you made very few measurements.

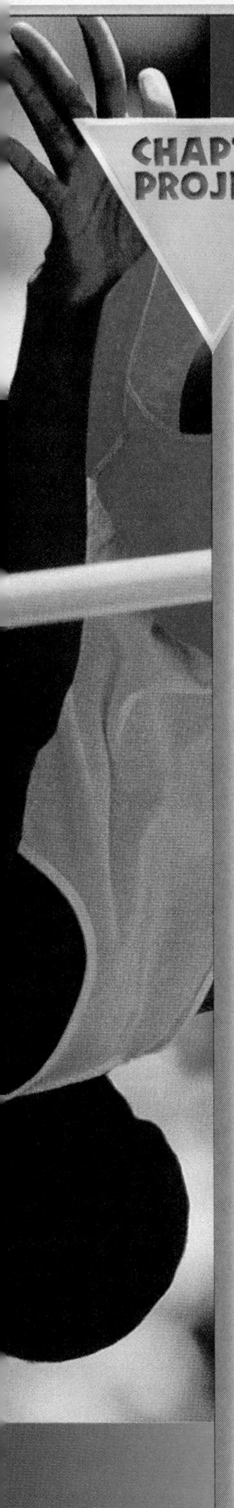

FINISHING THE CHAPTER PROJECT

CHAPTER PROJECT

making THE measure

Invent Your Own Ruler The Project Link questions on pages 154, 167, and 180 should help you to complete your project. Here is a checklist to help you gather together the parts of your project.

- ✔ the actual ruler
- ✔ the name of your unit of measurement
- ✔ the list of objects and their lengths that you have measured with your unit
- ✔ an explanation of how to measure in fractional units
- ✔ your analysis of measurement systems

Be prepared to demonstrate your ruler to the class. Show how to measure a wide range of lengths using your ruler. Include some actual measurements to show how useful your system is.

Reflect and Revise

Discuss the usefulness of your ruler with a friend or family member. Does it allow you to measure long and short lengths? Can you measure in fractions of units? If necessary, make changes to improve your project.

Web Extension

Internet Connection

Prentice Hall's Internet site contains information you might find helpful as you complete your project. Visit www.phschool.com/mgm2/ch4 for some links and ideas related to measurement.

Materials/Manipulatives

- cardboard or thick paper
- yard stick or other straightedge

STUDENT SELF-ASSESSMENT SURVEY

Chapter 4 Student Self-Assessment Survey

1. Now that you have finished this chapter, think about what you have learned about fractions. Check each topic that you feel confident you understand.
   - ______ make models for fractions and mixed numbers (4-1)
   - ______ find the factors and multiples of a number (4-2)
   - ______ write equivalent fractions (4-2)
   - ______ compare and order fractions (4-3)
   - ______ write numbers with exponents (4-4)
   - ______ evaluate expressions with exponents using the order of operations (4-4)
   - ______ find prime factorizations and the GCF of two numbers (4-5)
   - ______ write fractions in simplest form (4-6)
   - ______ solve problems by looking for a pattern (4-7)
   - ______ write a mixed number as an improper fraction (4-8)
   - ______ write an improper fraction as a mixed number (4-8)
   - ______ change fractions to decimals and decimals to fractions (4-9)
2. Before the Chapter Assessment, I need to review ______________________
3. a. Check one. In general, I thought this chapter was
   ____ a snap ____ easy ____ average ____ hard ____ a monster
   b. Why do you feel this way? ______________________
4. In this chapter, I did my best work on ______________________
5. In this chapter, I had trouble with ______________________
6. Check each one that applies. Now that I've spent some time studying fractions, I think they are
   ____ important ____ boring ____ useful ____ fun
   ____ a waste of time ____ confusing ____ tricky ____ interesting
7. Name three occupations in which people need to use fractions.
   ____

Assessment

Vocabulary/Symbols

base, composite, equivalent fractions, exponent, factor, factor tree, greatest common factor (GCF), improper fractions, least common denominator (LCD), least common multiple (LCM), mixed number, multiple, power, prime, prime factors, simplest form

Resources

Student Edition

Extra Practice, p. 517

Glossary/Study Guide

Teaching Resources

Chapter Support File, Ch. 4
- Student Self-Assessment Survey

Glossary, Spanish Resources

Tools for Studying Smarter

WRAP UP

ASSESSMENT Exercise 4–10 After students find each answer on their own, have them compare strategies and results with a partner. If they differ in strategy, ask them to decide which strategy is best.

Exercises 17–22 Have students explain why each number is prime or composite.

Exercises 23–28 Students should show their work or explain in words how to find each fraction's simplest form.

Exercises 37–42 Remind students that they can express a decimal written in the hundredths' place using a fraction with a denominator of 100. A decimal to the tenths' place, written as a fraction, will have 10 as a denominator.

Remind students that the new mathematical terms in this chapter are defined in the Glossary/Study Guide in the back of the book.

4 WRAP UP

The Meaning of Fractions 4-1

Fractions are used to describe parts of a whole and members of a group.

Write a fraction for each model.

1. $\frac{2}{5}$

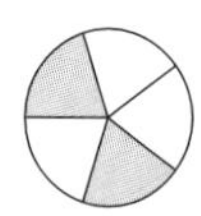

2. $\frac{4}{7}$

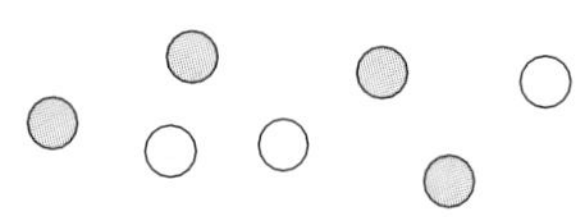

3. $\frac{3}{4}$

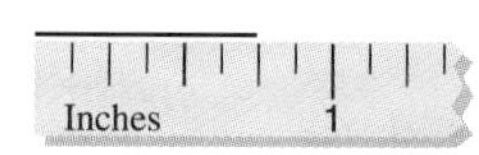

Equivalent Fractions and Comparing Fractions 4-2, 4-3

To find **equivalent fractions,** multiply or divide the numerator and denominator by the same nonzero number. To compare fractions, first find a common denominator.

Order from least to greatest.

4. $\frac{3}{8}, \frac{1}{2}, \frac{1}{4}$ See right. — 4. $\frac{1}{4}, \frac{3}{8}, \frac{1}{2}$ 5. $\frac{1}{6}, \frac{7}{12}, \frac{3}{4}$
5. $\frac{3}{4}, \frac{7}{12}, \frac{1}{6}$
6. $\frac{2}{5}, \frac{1}{3}, \frac{7}{15}$ — $\frac{1}{3}, \frac{2}{5}, \frac{7}{15}$
7. $\frac{6}{10}, \frac{4}{5}, \frac{8}{20}$ — $\frac{8}{20}, \frac{6}{10}, \frac{4}{5}$
8. $\frac{6}{7}, \frac{8}{10}, \frac{3}{4}$ — $\frac{3}{4}, \frac{8}{10}, \frac{6}{7}$
9. $\frac{4}{6}, \frac{9}{12}, \frac{3}{5}$ — $\frac{3}{5}, \frac{4}{6}, \frac{9}{12}$

10. **Choose A, B, C, or D.** Which fraction is *not* equivalent to $\frac{4}{7}$? B

A. $\frac{24}{42}$ B. $\frac{48}{74}$ C. $\frac{16}{28}$ D. $\frac{20}{35}$

Exponents 4-4

You use an **exponent** to show repeated multiplication.

Write each expression as a product of repeated factors. Then evaluate each expression.

11. 2^3 — $2 \times 2 \times 2; 8$
12. -3^4 — $-(3 \times 3 \times 3 \times 3); -81$
13. 6^2 — $6 \times 6; 36$
14. 0.2^3 — $0.2 \times 0.2 \times 0.2; 0.008$
15. 0.12^2 — $0.12 \times 0.12; 0.0144$
16. $(-3)^4$ — 16. $-3 \times -3 \times -3 \times -3; 81$

Prime Factorization and Simplifying Fractions 4-5, 4-6

A **prime number** has exactly two factors, 1 and the number itself. If a number has more than two factors, then it is **composite.**

To write the **prime factorization** of a composite number, you write the number as the product of its prime factors.

A fraction is in **simplest form** when the only factor common to both the numerator and the denominator is 1.

Identify each number as prime or composite. Then write the prime factorization of each number.

17. 73 prime; $1 \cdot 73$
18. 110 composite; $2 \cdot 5 \cdot 11$
19. 16 composite; $2 \cdot 2 \cdot 2 \cdot 2$
20. 87 composite; $3 \cdot 29$
21. 121 composite; $11 \cdot 11$
22. 28 composite; $2 \cdot 2 \cdot 7$

Write each fraction in simplest form.

23. $\frac{24}{48}$ $\frac{1}{2}$
24. $\frac{33}{132}$ $\frac{1}{4}$
25. $\frac{54}{72}$ $\frac{3}{4}$
26. $\frac{24}{60}$ $\frac{2}{5}$
27. $\frac{32}{36}$ $\frac{8}{9}$
28. $\frac{84}{144}$ $\frac{7}{12}$

Problem Solving Strategies 4-7

You can use patterns to help you solve problems.

29. A grocer is stacking boxes of cereal as part of a display. Each row has one less than the row beneath it. The top row will have one box. How many boxes will be in 20 rows? 210 boxes

Mixed Numbers and Improper Fractions 4-8

The numerator of an **improper fraction** is greater than or equal to the denominator.

Write each mixed number as an improper fraction and each improper fraction as a mixed number in simplest form.

30. $4\frac{5}{8}$ $\frac{37}{8}$
31. $\frac{23}{5}$ $4\frac{3}{5}$
32. $5\frac{7}{9}$ $\frac{52}{9}$
33. $3\frac{2}{3}$ $\frac{11}{3}$
34. $\frac{15}{8}$ $1\frac{7}{8}$
35. $\frac{28}{6}$ $4\frac{2}{3}$

36. *Writing* Explain how to write an improper fraction as a mixed number in simplest form. Include an example.
Check students' work.

Fractions and Decimals 4-9

To write a fraction as a decimal, divide the numerator by the denominator.

To write a decimal as a fraction, first write a fraction with a denominator that is a power of ten. Then, simplify the fraction.

Write each fraction as a decimal, and each decimal as a fraction in simplest form.

37. 0.05 $\frac{1}{20}$
38. $\frac{75}{100}$ 0.75
39. 0.24 $\frac{6}{25}$
40. $\frac{7}{8}$ 0.875
41. 2.96 $2\frac{24}{25}$
42. $\frac{5}{6}$ $0.8\overline{3}$

CHAPTER ASSESSMENT • FORM A

Chapter 4 Assessment • Form A

Answers

1. Write a fraction for the shaded part of this figure. — 1. $\frac{1}{2}$

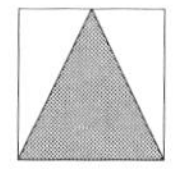

2. Write three fractions that are equivalent to $\frac{1}{3}$. — 2. $\frac{2}{6}, \frac{3}{9}, \frac{4}{12}$ (Answers will vary.)

3. Write the mixed number for each model. — 3. a. $2\frac{4}{6}$ or $2\frac{2}{3}$ b. $3\frac{1}{4}$

a. 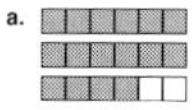

b. 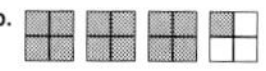

4. What factors do 12 and 15 have in common? — 4. 1, 3
5. Write $6 \times 6 \times 6 \times 6$ using an exponent. — 5. 6^4
6. Compare using <, >, or =. $\frac{7}{12}$ ■ $\frac{5}{9}$ — 6. >
7. Find the GCF of 27 and 36. — 7. 9
8. Find two prime numbers that are larger than 17. — 8. Answers may vary. Sample: 19, 23
9. Find two composite numbers that are greater than 17. — 9. Answers may vary. Sample: 18, 20
10. The sum of what two prime numbers equals 16? — 10. 11, 5 or 13, 3
11. Write the prime factorization of 52. — 11. $2^2 \cdot 13$
12. Write $3\frac{3}{10}$ as an improper fraction. — 12. $\frac{33}{10}$
13. Write $\frac{52}{6}$ as a mixed number in simplest form. — 13. $8\frac{2}{3}$
14. Write $\frac{63}{81}$ in simplest form. — 14. $\frac{7}{9}$
15. Simplify $\frac{35}{42}$. — 15. $\frac{5}{6}$

Assessment

CHAPTER ASSESSMENT • FORM A

Chapter 4 Assessment • Form A (continued)

16. Find the missing number. $\frac{?}{56} = \frac{5}{7}$ — 16. 40
17. Use a factor tree to write the prime factorization of 60. — 17. $2^2 \cdot 3 \cdot 5$

Sample:

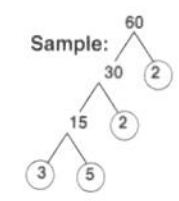

18. Find the GCF of the numerator and denominator of $\frac{42}{56}$, and write the fraction in simplest form. — 18. GCF = 14; $\frac{3}{4}$
19. Order from least to greatest. $\frac{7}{11}, \frac{5}{6}, \frac{2}{8}$ — 19. $\frac{2}{8}, \frac{7}{11}, \frac{5}{6}$
20. Evaluate the expression $(s + t)^2$ for $s = 7$ and $t = 4$. — 20. 121
21. Write $\frac{6}{15}$ as a decimal. — 21. 0.4
22. Write 0.56 as a fraction in simplest form. — 22. $\frac{14}{25}$

Choose A, B, C, or D.

23. Which of the following is *not* equivalent to $\frac{78}{45}$? — 23. D

A. $1\frac{11}{15}$ B. $\frac{26}{15}$ C. $1\frac{33}{45}$ D. $\frac{13}{9}$

Choose a Strategy

24. Find the 100th decimal digit in the decimal equivalent of $\frac{12}{37}$. — 24. 3

Writing

25. Describe the pattern in the decimal values of these fractions: $\frac{2}{9}, \frac{4}{9}, \frac{6}{9}, \frac{8}{9}$.
Sample: They are repeating decimals with digits corresponding to the numerators.

CHAPTER ASSESSMENT • FORM B

Chapter 4 Assessment • Form B

Choose the best answer. Circle A, B, C, or D.

1. What fraction of the figure below is shaded?

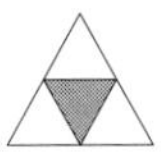

A. $\frac{1}{2}$ B. $\frac{1}{3}$ (C.) $\frac{1}{4}$ D. $\frac{1}{5}$

2. Which of the following pairs of fractions are equivalent to $\frac{2}{5}$?

A. $\frac{4}{10}, \frac{6}{12}$ B. $\frac{6}{15}, \frac{5}{18}$ (C.) $\frac{4}{10}, \frac{8}{20}$ D. $\frac{10}{25}, \frac{12}{35}$

3. What is the mixed number for the figure below?

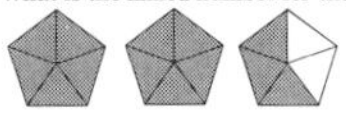

A. $\frac{12}{5}$ (B.) $2\frac{3}{5}$ C. 13 D. $2\frac{1}{3}$

4. What factors do 24 and 32 have in common?

(A.) 1, 2, 4, 8 B. 1, 2, 3, 8 C. 2, 4, 6, 8 D. 4, 6, 8, 12

5. Find the missing number. $\frac{12}{20} = \frac{?}{10}$

A. 15 (B.) 6 C. 22 D. 28

6. Which of $\frac{1}{2}, \frac{3}{5}, \frac{7}{15}$, and $\frac{15}{31}$ is greatest?

A. $\frac{15}{31}$ (B.) $\frac{3}{5}$ C. $\frac{1}{2}$ D. $\frac{7}{15}$

7. Which of the number pairs are both composite numbers?

A. 39, 31 B. 17, 29 (C.) 27, 51 D. 63, 13

8. Which of the number pairs are both prime numbers?

A. 54, 34 B. 33, 23 C. 37, 49 (D.) 41, 19

9. What is the GCF of 84 and 144?

A. 3 B. 6 C. 9 (D.) 12

10. What is the value of $x^2 + y^2$ for $x = 2$ and $y = 3$?

A. 8 (B.) 13 C. 25 D. 36

Assessment

CHAPTER ASSESSMENT • FORM B

Chapter 4 Assessment • Form B (continued)

11. What are the prime factors of 90?

A. 2, 5, 9 B. 2, 3, 4, 15 (C.) 2, 3, 5 D. 6, 15

12. What is $4\frac{6}{7}$ as an improper fraction?

A. $\frac{28}{7}$ (B.) $\frac{34}{7}$ C. $\frac{48}{7}$ D. $\frac{24}{7}$

13. What is $\frac{40}{6}$ as a mixed number in simplest form?

A. $6\frac{1}{6}$ B. $6\frac{4}{6}$ C. $6\frac{2}{6}$ (D.) $6\frac{2}{3}$

14. Which is equivalent to $\frac{10}{16}$?

A. 0.116 (B.) 0.625 C. 1.16 D. 10.16

15. Which of the following is *not* equivalent to $\frac{10}{16}$?

(A.) $\frac{2}{3}$ B. $\frac{30}{48}$ C. $\frac{15}{24}$ D. $\frac{5}{8}$

16. Find the missing number. $\frac{?}{29} = \frac{3}{87}$

(A.) 1 B. 3 C. 9 D. 27

17. What numbers are missing from this factor tree?

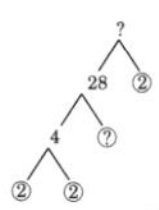

A. 1, 56 B. 8, 7 C. 58, 14 (D.) 56, 7

18. Which number is the GCF of the numerator and denominator of $\frac{48}{64}$?

(A.) 16 B. 8 C. 24 D. 32

19. What is $\frac{1}{16}$ written as a decimal?

A. 0.25 B. 0.375 (C.) 0.0625 D. 0.03125

20. Which of the following is equivalent to 3.65?

(A.) $3\frac{13}{20}$ B. $3\frac{5}{65}$ C. $\frac{365}{10}$ D. $3\frac{3}{5}$

Choose a Strategy

21. What is the 100th decimal digit in the decimal equivalent of $\frac{5}{37}$?

A. 0 (B.) 1 C. 3 D. 5

Teaching Resources

Chapter Support File, Ch. 4, and Spanish Resources

Teacher's Edition

See pp. 142C–D for Assessment Options.

Teaching Resource Software

- Computer Item Generator, Ch. 4

ASSESSMENT

ENHANCED MULTIPLE CHOICE QUESTIONS are more complex than traditional multiple choice questions, which assess only one skill. Enhanced multiple choice questions assess the processes that students use, as well as the end result. They are written so that students can use more than one strategy to solve the problem. Using multiple strategies is encouraged by the National Council of Teachers of Mathematics (NCTM). **Exercise 9** is an enhanced multiple choice question.

WRITING EXERCISES allow students to describe more fully their understanding of the concepts they've learned. **Exercise 12** is a writing exercise.

Exercise 14 Point out to students that there is only one *greatest* possible number of crew members, and they should use the GCF to find it. Students should also use the *greatest* number of crew members to find the number of coin types that each crew member will have.

4 ASSESSMENT

1. What fraction does the shaded part of the model represent? $\frac{3}{8}$

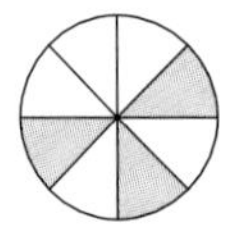

2. Draw models to represent $\frac{3}{4}$ and $2\frac{3}{5}$. See back of book.

3. Write two fractions equivalent to each given fraction. Samples are given.

a. $\frac{1}{3}$ $\frac{2}{6}, \frac{3}{9}$ b. $\frac{15}{24}$ $\frac{5}{8}, \frac{10}{16}$ c. $\frac{4}{5}$ $\frac{8}{10}, \frac{12}{15}$ d. $\frac{16}{28}$ $\frac{4}{7}, \frac{8}{14}$

4. Compare. Use <, >, or =.

a. $\frac{2}{9}$ ■ $\frac{8}{9}$ < b. $\frac{5}{16}$ ■ $\frac{3}{8}$ < c. $\frac{13}{20}$ ■ $\frac{5}{8}$ >

5. Find the value of each expression.

a. $(3^2 + 1) \div 5$ 2 b. $5^2 - 7^2$ −24

c. $(6 - 9)^3$ −27 d. $54 \div 3^2$ 6

6b. 1, 2, 3, 4, 6, 9, 12, 18, 36

6. List the factors of each number.

a. 27 1, 3, 9, 27 b. 36 c. 100 See below. d. 25 1, 5, 25

7. Tell whether each number is prime or composite.

a. 17 prime b. 75 composite c. 49 composite d. 83 prime

8. Find the GCF of each pair of numbers.

a. 32, 40 8 b. 55, 15 5

c. 36, 57 3 d. 24, 68 4

9. **Choose A, B, C, or D.** Which statement is *always* true? D

A. Two is a composite number.

B. Any factor of a whole number is greater than any multiple of a whole number.

C. A number is divisible by 3 if its last digit is divisible by 3.

D. One is neither a composite nor a prime number.

10. Use a factor tree to write the prime factorization of 42. Check students' work for diagram; 2 × 3 × 7.

11. Write the first four multiples of 27. 27, 54, 81, 108

12. *Writing* Explain how to use prime factorization to write a fraction in simplest form. Check students' work.

13. Write each fraction in simplest form.

a. $\frac{12}{18}$ $\frac{2}{3}$ b. $\frac{27}{54}$ $\frac{1}{2}$ c. $\frac{36}{96}$ $\frac{3}{8}$ d. $\frac{7}{42}$ $\frac{1}{6}$

14. The Fair-Share Salvage crew found a sunken pirate ship that had a chest containing 168 gold and 200 silver coins. All crew members received an equal share of each kind of coin. There were no coins left over. What is the greatest possible number of crew members? How many of each type of coin does each crew member get? 8 crew members; 21 gold and 25 silver coins

15. Write each mixed number as an improper fraction.

a. $5\frac{2}{3}$ $\frac{17}{3}$ b. $4\frac{5}{6}$ $\frac{29}{6}$ c. $8\frac{7}{10}$ $\frac{87}{10}$ d. $3\frac{2}{5}$ $\frac{17}{5}$

16. Write each improper fraction as a whole number or a mixed number.

a. $\frac{12}{5}$ $2\frac{2}{5}$ b. $\frac{30}{9}$ $3\frac{1}{3}$ c. $\frac{48}{12}$ 4 d. $\frac{42}{30}$ $1\frac{2}{5}$

17. Write each fraction as a decimal.

a. $\frac{2}{16}$ 0.125 b. $\frac{6}{15}$ 0.4 c. $\frac{5}{4}$ 1.25 d. $\frac{8}{25}$ 0.32

18. Write each decimal as a fraction.

a. 0.2 $\frac{1}{5}$ b. 1.3 $\frac{13}{10}$ c. 0.35 $\frac{7}{20}$ d. 3.62 $\frac{181}{50}$

19. Find the value of the expression $1 - 2 + 3 - 4 + 5 - \ldots - 50$. Explain how you found your answer. −25; check students' work for reasoning.

20. In one week, $\frac{5}{8}$ of the mail the Franklin family received was advertisements and $\frac{1}{5}$ of the mail was from friends. What is the least number of pieces of mail they could have received? 40 pieces

6c. 1, 2, 4, 5, 10, 20, 25, 50, 100

Cumulative Review

Item	Review topic	Ch
1	Relating fractions to models	4
2	Adding decimals	2
3	Displaying data	1
4	Writing expressions	3
5, 7	Comparing fractions and mixed numbers	4

Item	Review topic	Ch
6	Number theory	4
8	Exponents	4
9	Recognizing patterns	4
10	Solving equations	3
11, 12	Estimating decimals	2

4 Cumulative Review

Choose the best answer.

1. A hexagon represents one whole. Which mixed number is shown? D

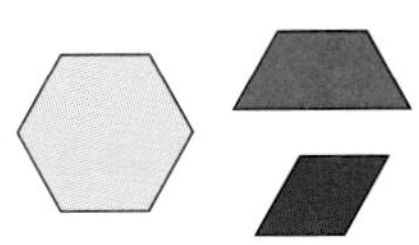

A. $3\frac{2}{3}$ B. $5\frac{1}{2}$ C. $2\frac{1}{3}$ D. $1\frac{5}{6}$

2. How much will a $3.99 sandwich and $1.19 juice cost? A

A. $5.18 B. $4.18
C. $5.08 D. $4.08

3. You have data about the age and height of some trees. How would you display the data to find a relationship between the age and height of a tree? C

A. double bar graph
B. frequency table
C. scatter plot
D. line plot

4. Which expression represents "3 less than w"? D

A. $3 - w$ B. $w \div 3$
C. $3 \div w$ D. $w - 3$

5. Which fraction is *not* equivalent to $\frac{9}{12}$? D

A. $\frac{24}{32}$ B. $\frac{6}{8}$ C. $\frac{15}{20}$ D. $\frac{16}{24}$

6. Which statement is *false*? B

A. The GCF of two prime numbers is 1.
B. Any fraction with composite numbers in the numerator and denominator is *not* in simplest form.
C. More than half of the numbers between 1 and 100 are composite.
D. The GCF of a number and twice that number is the number itself.

7. You want to buy two tickets that regularly cost $354 each. From which airline should you buy your tickets? D

Airline	Price Offer
A	"Buy 1 ticket, get the 2nd at $\frac{1}{2}$ off"
B	"$\frac{1}{4}$ off the price of all tickets"
C	"Get $\frac{1}{2}$ off any ticket over $400"
D	"$89 off each ticket"

8. How is the product $5 \times 5 \times 5 \times 5$ expressed as a power? A

A. 5^4 B. 4^5 C. 4×5 D. 10^2

9. What is the next fraction in the pattern $\frac{1}{2}, \frac{3}{4}, \frac{9}{8}, \frac{27}{16}, \ldots$? B

A. $\frac{36}{24}$ B. $\frac{81}{32}$ C. $\frac{54}{48}$ D. $\frac{40}{25}$

10. If $\frac{b}{6} - 3 = 9$, what is the value of b? D

A. 2 B. 24 C. 36 D. 72

11. A video store offered movies on sale at 3 for $42.50. Scott wants to purchase 5 videos. It is reasonable to assume that the cost of the 5 videos is C

A. exactly $42.50
B. between $40 and $60
C. between $60 and $80
D. more than $80

12. The book sale at Meyer Middle School made $552.78. This money will be divided equally among three grades. What is the best estimate of the amount each class will receive? B

A. $170 B. $180 C. $190 D. $200

CUMULATIVE REVIEW

Chapter 4 Cumulative Review

Choose the best answer. Circle A, B, C, or D.

1. Which is the next figure in the pattern below?

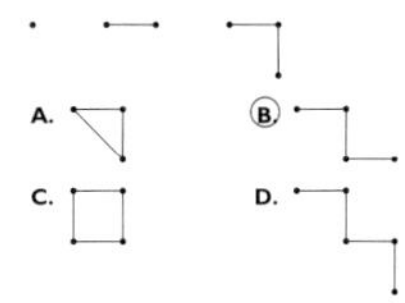

2. Which numbers are in order from least to greatest?
(A) 1.1, 1.2, 1.25, 1.415
B. 0.2, 0.02, 2.2, 0.22
C. 0.3, 0.6, 0.51, 0.65
D. 3.5, 3.41, 3.02, 3.6

3. Which shows the associative property?
A. $3.5 \times 6.7 = 6.7 \times 3.5$
B. $17.6 \times 1 = 17.6$
(C) $3 \times (4.7 \times 2.8) = (3 \times 4.7) \times 2.8$
D. $8.54 \times 0 = 0$

4. Karl's video scores for five games were 38, 57, 48, 62, and 55. What is his mean score?
A. 24 B. 38
(C) 52 D. 55

5. Which difference is greatest?
A. $2.5 - 2.3$
(B) $5.5 - 4.15$
C. $3.75 - 2.95$
D. $8.05 - 7.85$

6. Which number is the outlier?
25 34 63 27 31
A. 34 B. 25
(C) 63 D. 36

7. Which equation is true?
A. $7 - (-3) = -10$
B. $8 - 12 = (-2)(-2)$
C. $18 \div (-2) = 9$
(D) $(-1)(-2)(-4) = -16 \div 2$

8. Solve $4m - 6 = 14$.
A. 2 B. 3
C. 4 (D) 5

9. Ten identical coins weigh 34.5 g. How much does one coin weigh?
A. 0.345 g (B) 3.45 g
C. 345 g D. not here

10. Which variable expression is represented by "six less than twice a number"?
(A) $2m - 6$ B. $m - 6$
C. $2m + 6$ D. $6 < 2m$

11. What is the mode of this data?
0.12 0.21 0.15 0.51
0.51 0.25 0.52
A. 0.25 B. 0.40
(C) 0.51 D. 0.52

12. Which sum is positive?
A. $-56 + (-4)$ B. $81 + (-90)$
(C) $-48 + 55$ D. $-76 + 45$

Assessment

CUMULATIVE REVIEW

Chapter 4 Cumulative Review (continued)

13. Which question is biased?
A. Do you prefer a bird or a fish as a pet?
B. Do you prefer to eat spaghetti or shrimp?
(C) Do you prefer long, cold winters or short, pleasant summers?
D. Do you prefer red or green for the team color?

14. Which equation has the same solution as $6a + 3 = 21$?
A. $2a - 3 = 7$ B. $5a + 1 = 21$
C. $6a - 21 = 9$ (D) $16 - a = 13$

15. Brandon read the first 85 pages of a book. When he reads 53 more pages, he will have read half the book. How many pages are in the book?
A. 69 pages B. 138 pages
(C) 276 pages D. 414 pages

16. Evaluate $48 \div (3 \times 4) - 6$.
A. -3 (B) -2
C. 14 D. 42

17. Which word phrase is represented by $3 + 2m$?
A. the product of three and twice a number
B. the sum of a number and three
C. the difference of twice a number and three
(D) the sum of three and twice a number

18. Which of the following is equivalent to $4^2 - 2^4$?
A. $2^6 - 6^2$ B. $5^3 - 3^5$
C. $8^2 - 2^8$ (D) $2^4 - 4^2$

19. What fraction of this figure is represented by the shaded region?

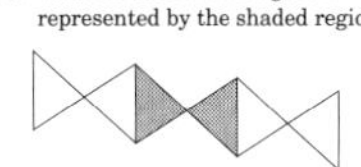

A. $\frac{1}{6}$ (B) $\frac{1}{3}$
C. $\frac{1}{4}$ D. $\frac{2}{3}$

20. Which of the following is equivalent to $\frac{7}{8}$?
A. $\frac{14}{18}$ B. $\frac{28}{30}$
(C) $\frac{35}{40}$ D. $\frac{21}{28}$

21. Which fraction is greatest?
A. $\frac{2}{5}$ B. $\frac{1}{6}$
C. $\frac{6}{10}$ (D) $\frac{14}{18}$

22. What is the GCF of 84 and 126?
(A) 42 B. 21
C. 18 D. 7

23. The jerseys of the members of one team are numbered 01 to 42. How many jerseys contain the digit 0?
A. 9 jerseys B. 10 jerseys
C. 12 jerseys (D) 13 jerseys

24. What is $5\frac{2}{3}$ as an improper fraction?
A. $\frac{10}{3}$ B. $\frac{15}{3}$
(C) $\frac{17}{3}$ D. $\frac{52}{3}$

Resources

Teaching Resources

Chapter Support File, Ch. 4
- Cumulative Review

Teacher's Edition

See pp. 142C–D for Assessment Options.

5 Applications of Fractions

Chapter Overview

To accommodate flexible scheduling, most lessons are divided into parts. Assignment Options are given in the Teacher's Edition for each lesson.

Pages	Lesson	NCTM	Parts
188–191	**Lesson 5-1** Estimating with Fractions and Mixed Numbers	2, 4, 5, 7, 13	Part 1 Estimating Sums and Differences Part 2 Estimating Products and Quotients **Journal**
193–196	**Lesson 5-2** Adding and Subtracting Fractions	1, 2, 3, 4, 5, 7, 13	Part 1 Adding Fractions Part 2 Subtracting Fractions **Project Link**
197–199	**Lesson 5-3** Adding and Subtracting Mixed Numbers	1, 2, 4, 5, 7, 13	Part 1 Adding Mixed Numbers Part 2 Subtracting Mixed Numbers
214–216	**Lesson 5-7** Problem Solving Strategy	1, 3, 4, 13	Work Backward
218–221	**Lesson 5-8** Measurement: Changing Units in the Customary System	1, 2, 4, 5, 7, 13	Part 1 Changing Units of Length and Capacity Part 2 Changing Units of Weight **Checkpoint 2**
222–224	**Lesson 5-9** Algebra: Solving Equations with Fractions by Multiplying and Dividing	2, 4, 5, 7, 9	Part 1 Solving Equations by Multiplying Part 2 Solving Equations by Dividing **Alternative Activity** 5-9 **Project Link**

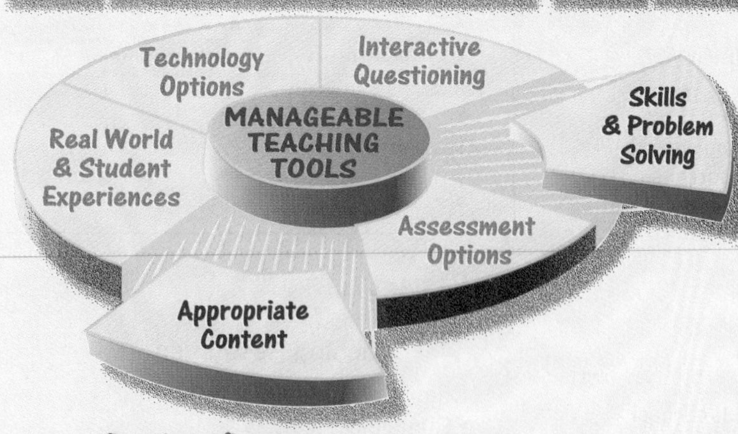

Pacing Options

This chart suggests pacing only for the core lessons and their parts. It is provided merely as a possible guide. It will help you determine how much time you have in your schedule to cover other features, such as the Chapter Project, Math Toolboxes, Wrap Up, and Assessment.

	1 Class Period	1 Class Period	1 Class Period	1
Traditional (40–45 min class periods)	5-1 (1) 5-1 (2)	5-2 (1) 5-2 (2)	5-3 (1) 5-3 (2)	
Block Scheduling (90 min class periods)	5-1 (1) 5-1 (2) 5-2 (1) 5-2 (2)	5-3 (1) 5-3 (2) 5-4 (1)	5-4 (2) 5-5 (1) 5-5 (2)	5

CHAPTER PROJECT

Toss and Turn!

Goals: Modify a pancake recipe to feed the whole class

THEME: COOKING

NCTM STANDARDS

1 Problem Solving
2 Communication
3 Reasoning
4 Mathematical Connections
5 Number and Number Relationships
6 Number Systems and Number Theory
7 Computation and Estimation
8 Patterns and Functions
9 Algebra
10 Statistics
11 Probability
12 Geometry
13 Measurement

Pages 200–204	Lesson 5-4 Algebra: Solving Equations with Fractions by Adding and Subtracting
NCTM 1, 5, 7, 9, 13	Part 1 Solving Equations by Adding Part 2 Solving Equations by Subtracting **Alternative Activity** 5-4 **Journal** **Math at Work** **Checkpoint 1**

Pages 205–209	Lesson 5-5 Geometry: Multiplying Fractions and Mixed Numbers
NCTM 1, 2, 4, 5, 7, 12, 13	Part 1 Multiplying Fractions Part 2 Multiplying Mixed Numbers **Project Link**

Pages 210–212	Lesson 5-6 Dividing Fractions and Mixed Numbers
NCTM 2, 4, 5, 7, 13	Part 1 Dividing Fractions Part 2 Dividing Mixed Numbers **Key term:** reciprocals

Optional Materials and Manipulatives

fraction bars (5-2, 5-4)
graph paper (5-4)

paper for models (5-5)
colored pencils (5-5)

Optional calculator use is integrated throughout the course.

...ss ...od	1 Class Period	1 Class Period	1 Class Period	1 Class Period	1 Class Period	1 Class Period	1 Class Period	1 Class Period	1 Class Period	1 Class Period
	5–5 1	5–5 2	5–6 1	5–6 2	5–7	5–8 1, 5–8 2	5–9 1, 5–9 2			
5–8 2	5–9 1, 5–9 2									

MEETING INDIVIDUAL NEEDS

Accommodating Diverse Learning Styles

In your Teacher's Edition, you will find suggestions as to how you can help students complete mathematical tasks in Chapter 5 by meeting individual needs and supporting various learning styles. Here are some examples:

VISUAL LEARNING
making a time line to show the order of events *(p. 214)*

TACTILE LEARNING
modeling fractions with graph paper or colored tiles *(p. 188)*

AUDITORY LEARNING
explaining to other students how a model is helpful *(p. 200)*

KINESTHETIC LEARNING
modeling examples with giant fraction bars *(p. 197)*

EARLY FINISHERS
Performance-Based Project, MathBlaster® Mystery, Interdisciplinary Units

GIFTED AND TALENTED
analyzing how estimates relate to exact values *(p. 190)*

DIVERSITY solving problems of making change using foreign coins *(p. 195)*

ACQUIRING ENGLISH PROFICIENCY (AEP)
creating mnemonics to remember numerator and denominator *(p. 188)*

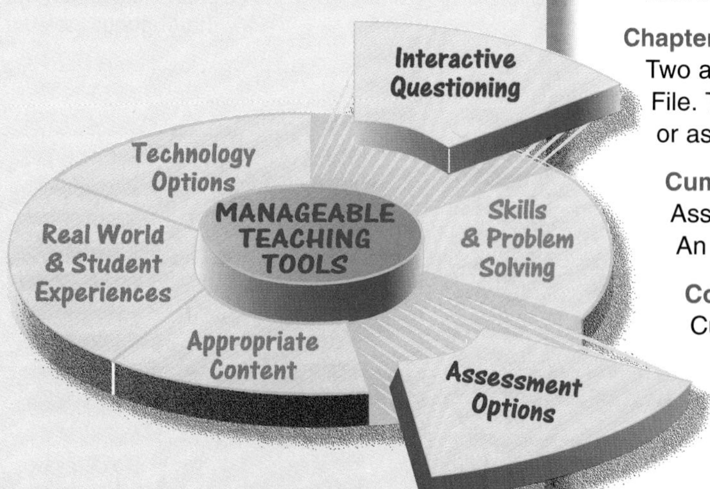

ASSESSING PROGRESS

A broad range of assessment tools are available to reach a variety of learners.

INFORMAL ASSESSMENT

Informal assessments provide day-to-day feedback to help give you a picture of conceptual understanding and skill development.

ONGOING ASSESSMENT is built into lesson instruction and the Teaching Notes of the Teacher's Edition.

In the Teacher's Edition
Lesson Quiz for every lesson

In the Student Edition
On Your Own, Mixed Review, Journal, Portfolio, Project Link, Chapter Wrap Up

Look for **Interactive Questions** within lessons that

- **BUILD UNDERSTANDING** with labels such as **Analyze, Reasoning, Estimation, Writing, and Summarize**
- ✔ **CHECK UNDERSTANDING** with the **Try It Out** label.

FORMAL ASSESSMENT

Formal assessment can occur before and after the chapter, as well as at natural breaking points in the chapter.

Checkpoints
Two forms of each self-assessment Checkpoints are available: one in the Student Edition and another in the Chapter Support File in the Teaching Resources box.

- Mid-Chapter Checkpoint 1, page 204
- End-of-Chapter Checkpoint 2, page 221

Chapter 5 Assessment, page 228.
Two alternative forms are available in the Chapter Support File. They may be used after a chapter has been completed, or as a pre-test and post-test comparison.

Cumulative Review, page 229.
Assesses skills and concepts in Chapters 1–5. An alternative form is available in Chapter Support File.

Computer Item Generator for Chapter 5
Customized tests can be generated for each lesson and for mid-chapter and end-of-chapter assessments, and for pre- and post-test comparisons of achievement.

PERFORMANCE-BASED ASSESSMENT

CHAPTER PROJECT

The Chapter Project in the student edition provides a real-world connection to the math context of the chapter. The Teacher's Edition contains a scoring rubric.

A Performance Assessment with a scoring rubric can be found in the Chapter Support File in the Teaching Resources box.

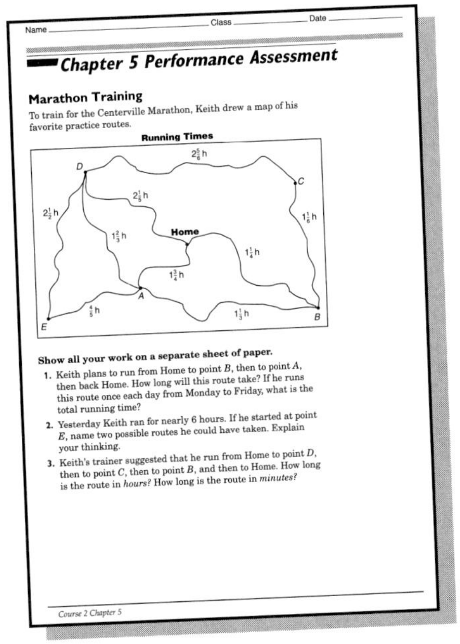

Name ______ Class ______ Date ______

Chapter 5 Performance Assessment

Marathon Training

To train for the Centerville Marathon, Keith drew a map of his favorite practice routes.

Show all your work on a separate sheet of paper.

1. Keith plans to run from Home to point B, then to point A, then back Home. How long will this route take? If he runs this route once each day from Monday to Friday, what is the total running time?
2. Yesterday Keith ran for nearly 6 hours. If he started at point E, name two possible routes he could have taken. Explain your thinking.
3. Keith's trainer suggested that he run from Home to point D, then to point C, then to point B, and then to Home. How long is the route in *hours?* How long is the route in *minutes?*

Course 2 Chapter 5

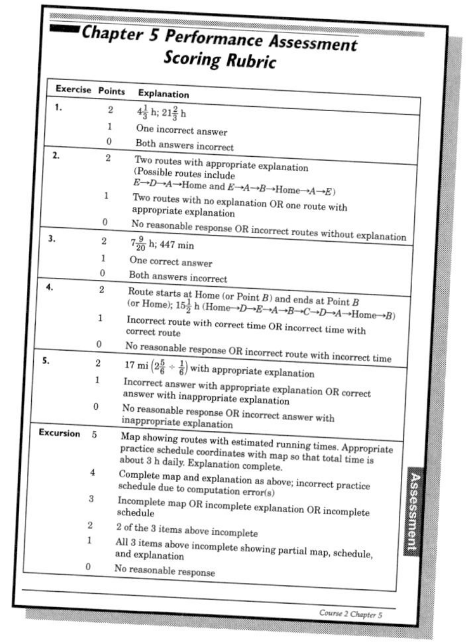

Chapter 5 Performance Assessment Scoring Rubric

Exercise	Points	Explanation
1.	2	$4\frac{1}{3}$ h; $21\frac{2}{3}$ h
	1	One incorrect answer
	0	Both answers incorrect
2.	2	Two routes with appropriate explanation (Possible routes include $E \to D \to A \to$ Home and $E \to A \to B \to$ Home $\to A \to E$)
	1	Two routes with no explanation OR one route with appropriate explanation
	0	No reasonable response OR incorrect routes without explanation
3.	2	$7\frac{9}{20}$ h; 447 min
	1	One correct answer
	0	Both answers incorrect
4.	2	Route starts at Home (or Point B) and ends at Point B (or Home); $15\frac{1}{2}$ h (Home $\to D \to E \to A \to B \to C \to D \to A \to$ Home $\to B$)
	1	Incorrect route with correct time OR incorrect time with correct route
	0	No reasonable response OR incorrect route with incorrect time
5.	2	17 mi $\left(2\frac{5}{6} \div \frac{1}{6}\right)$ with appropriate explanation
	1	Incorrect answer with appropriate explanation OR correct answer with inappropriate explanation
	0	No reasonable response OR incorrect answer with inappropriate explanation
Excursion	5	Map showing routes with estimated running times. Appropriate practice schedule coordinates with map so that total time is about 3 h daily. Explanation complete.
	4	Complete map and explanation as above; incorrect practice schedule due to computation error(s)
	3	Incomplete map OR incomplete explanation OR incomplete schedule
	2	2 of the 3 items above incomplete
	1	All 3 items above incomplete showing partial map, schedule, and explanation
	0	No reasonable response

Assessment

Course 2 Chapter 5

Correlation to Standardized Tests

Lesson		STANDARDIZED TEST ITEMS CAT5	Terra Nova	ITBS, Form M	MAT7	SAT9	Local Test
5-1	Estimating with Fractions and Mixed Numbers		14	CE32, 36, 44		PR14	
5-2	Adding and Subtracting Fractions	CA22, MC4, 16, 25, 39–40	MC8	MC7, 14, 20–21, 27, 38	PR13, 24	PR4–7, 23–25	
5-3	Adding and Subtracting Mixed Numbers	MC21, 27, 44	4, MC6–7	MC33	PR8	PR26	
5-4	Algebra: Solving Equations with Fractions by Adding and Subtracting			CE30	CP28	PS13	
5-5	Geometry: Multiplying Fractions with Mixed Numbers	CA19–21, MC12, 19, 33	9, MC18	CE26, MC10, 17, 23, 29		PR8, 27–28	
5-6	Dividing Fractions and Mixed Numbers	MC29, 35	MC7, 11	MC37,42			
5-7	Problem Solving Strategy: Work Backward	CA39			CP48, 52		
5-8	Measurement: Changing Units in the Customary System	CA29		CE2, 4, 25	CP20	PS34, 37	
5-9	Algebra: Solving Equations with Fractions by Multiplying and Dividing			CE30	PR12		

CA: Concepts and Applications
PS: Problem Solving
PR: Math Procedures
CP: Concepts and Problem Solving
MC: Math Computation
PD: Problem Solving and Data Interpretation
CE: Concepts and Estimation

See page 2D for the level of each test referenced.

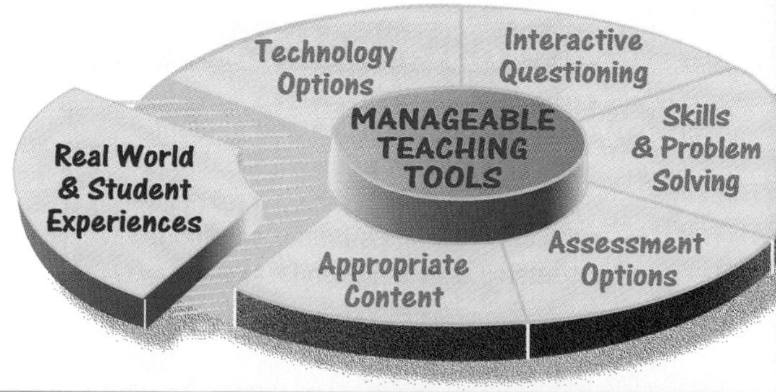

MAKING CONNECTIONS

TEAM TEACHING WITH PRENTICE HALL MATERIALS

INTERDISCIPLINARY EXPLORATIONS

- ***Back to the Thirties*** **pp. 16 & 17**
- ***Wagons West*** **p. 39**

PRENTICE HALL SCIENCE

L Life Science **E** Earth Science **P** Physical Science

P Sec. 12-2 Measuring Motion

Lesson	Interdisciplinary Connections	Real World Connections	Math Integration
5-1	Music	Swimming Weather Cooking School Fair	Measurement
5-2	History	Carpentry Cooking	Measurement
5-3	Sports	Hiking Masonry Mechanics Advertising	Measurement
5-4	Sports	Commercial Fishing Environment Carpentry	Algebra Measurement
5-5	Biology Geography	Cooking Jogging	Geometry Measurement
5-6	Biology	Sewing Meal Planning School Store	Measurement
5-7	Business Sports	Time Management Entertainment Money	Geometry
5-8	Sports Geography Earth Science	Carpentry Cooking Hobbies Canoeing	Measurement
5-9	Business Sports Geography	Money Videos	Algebra

School to Home

MATERIALS:
newspaper
tape measure
paper
pencil

English version is in the Chapter Support File. Spanish version is in the Spanish Resources.

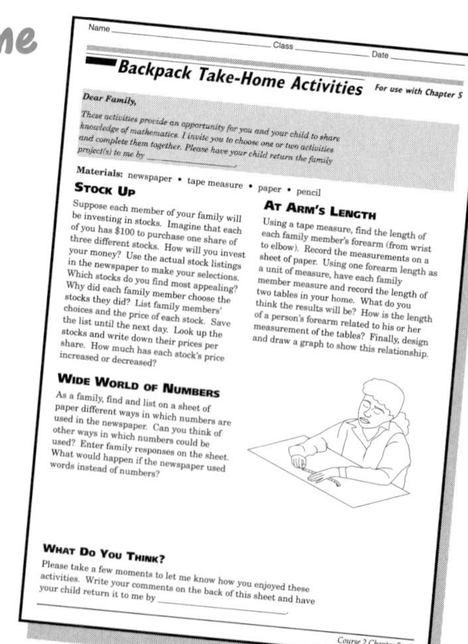
Name ______ Class ______ Date ______

Backpack Take-Home Activities *For use with Chapter 5*

Dear Family,

These activities provide an opportunity for you and your child to share knowledge of mathematics. I invite you to choose one or two activities and complete them together. Please have your child return the family project(s) to me by ______.

Materials: newspaper • tape measure • paper • pencil

STOCK UP

Suppose each member of your family will be investing in stocks. Imagine that each of you has $100 to purchase one share of three different stocks. How will you invest your money? Use the actual stock listings in the newspaper to make your selections. Which stocks do you find most appealing? Why did each family member choose the stocks they did? List family members' choices and the price of each stock. Save the list until the next day. Look up the stocks and write down their prices per share. How much has each stock's price increased or decreased?

AT ARM'S LENGTH

Using a tape measure, find the length of each family member's forearm (from wrist to elbow). Record the measurements on a sheet of paper. Using one forearm length as a unit of measure, have each family member measure and record the length of two tables in your home. What do you think the results will be? How is the length of a person's forearm related to his or her measurement of the tables? Finally, design and draw a graph to show this relationship.

WIDE WORLD OF NUMBERS

As a family, find and list on a sheet of paper different ways in which numbers are used in the newspaper. Can you think of other ways in which numbers could be used? Enter family responses on the sheet. What would happen if the newspaper used words instead of numbers?

WHAT DO YOU THINK?

Please take a few moments to let me know how you enjoyed these activities. Write your comments on the back of this sheet and have your child return it to me by ______.

Course 2 Chapter 5

Using Technology to Enhance Instruction

For the Student

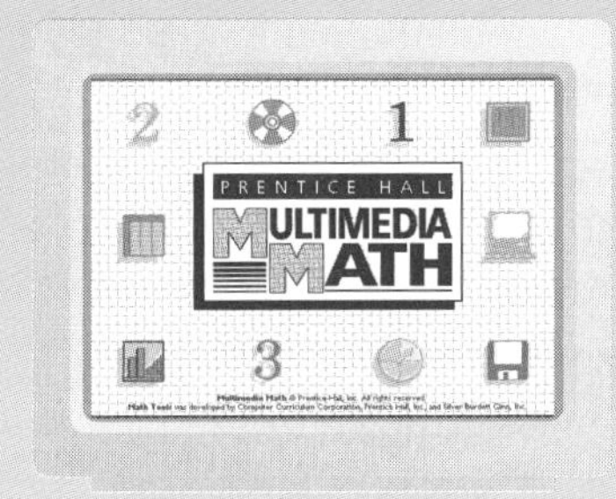

Multimedia Math Hot Pages™

This interactive software and video package on CD-ROM integrates solid math content through a variety of media.

- Hot Page™ 8-4
- Hot Page™ 8-6

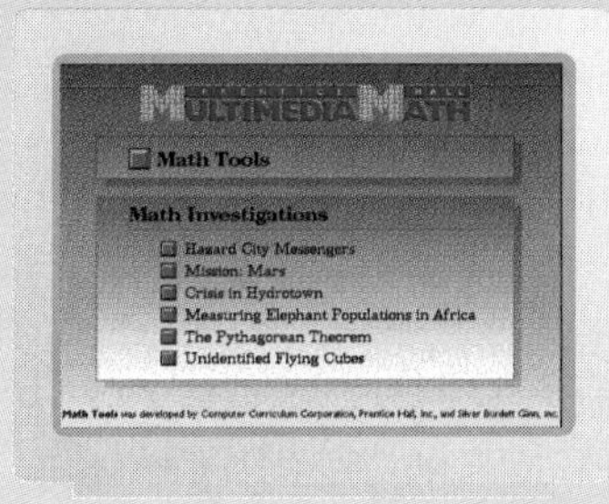

Multimedia Math Investigations

These in-depth interactive activities on CD-ROM develop real-world applications of mathematics. They allow students the opportunity to reinforce key concepts.

- Measuring Elephant Populations in Africa

MathBlaster® Mystery

This award-winning, interactive software program on CD-ROM can be used to maintain skills or to accommodate early finishers.

- Level: Earn 4 coins; Pay 4 coins
- Mission Mode (all lessons)
- Kitchen Comparisons (5-2, 5-6)
- Number Guesser (5-8)
- Equation Maker (5-3, 5-4, 5-9)
- Word Problems (5-1, 5-5, 5-7, Problem Solving Practice)

Math Tools/Math Labs

This software, available on CD-ROM, includes on-screen Math Lab activities. Students use linkable, interactive tools to explore math concepts.

Interactive Student Tutorial

Available on CD-ROM, this test preparation program contains self-tests with questions in standardized test format. Software includes electronic versions of the text lessons and an on-line glossary.

Internet Connection

For Students

Support for the Chapter Project
A career-oriented link for Math at Work feature

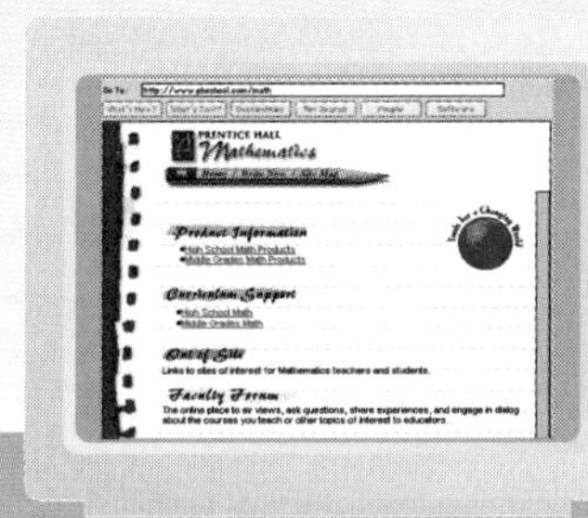

www.phschool.com/math

For teachers

Curriculum Support
Product Information
Regional Support Information

For the Teacher

Computer Item Generator with Standardized Test Practice

This software generates customized practice sheets and tests. It also generates unlimited practice sheets for the standardized tests listed on page 186D.

Resource Pro™ with Planning Express™

Available on CD-ROM, this software can be used to customize and plan lessons. It contains over 1,700 resource pages.

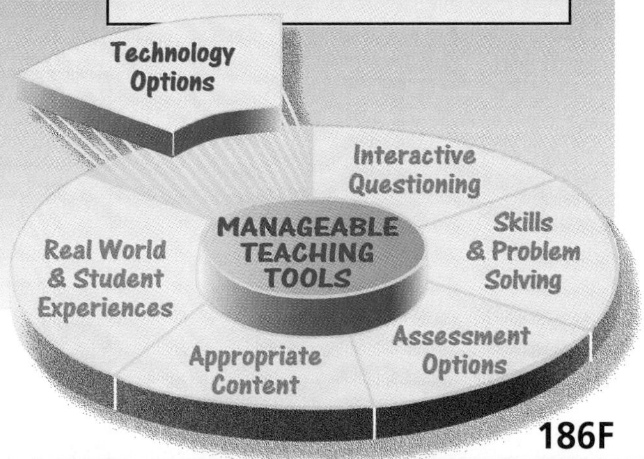

CHAPTER 5

APPLICATIONS OF FRACTIONS

CONNECTING TO PRIOR LEARNING Ask students if they have ever seen fractions used in directions. **Answers may vary. Sample: yes, in directions for building model airplanes, or doghouses, or baking a cake** As students provide examples, ask them to say what would happen if they used the wrong fraction or the wrong unit of measure. You may want to bring some sets of directions to class for students to study.

CULTURAL CONNECTIONS Other countries have their own foods that are similar to pancakes. Have students research to find examples of these. **Answers may vary. Sample: China, rice cakes; France, crepes; Germany, *Pfannkuchen***

INTERDISCIPLINARY CONNECTIONS Ask: *What would happen if a chemist did not understand fractions and used the wrong amounts while mixing chemicals?* **Answers may vary. Sample: The chemist may cause injury or blow up the lab.**

ABOUT THE PROJECT The Chapter Project provides students with the opportunity to apply their knowledge of fractions to writing and using a recipe.

Internet • For information and activities related to the Chapter Project, visit the Prentice Hall site at www.phschool.com/mgm2/ch5

WHAT YOU WILL LEARN IN THIS CHAPTER

- How to model operations with fractions
- How to solve equations with fractions
- How to change between customary units of measure

LAUNCHING THE CHAPTER PROJECT

Ask students:

- *Have you ever prepared food from a recipe? If so, did you have to change anything about the recipe?*
- *How would you adapt recipes that make four servings to feed eight people?*
- *How are fractions used in recipes?*

PROJECT NOTEBOOK Encourage students to keep all project-related materials in a separate folder or notebook.

TRACKING THE PROJECT You may wish to have students read Finishing the Chapter Project on page 225 to help them get an overview of the project. Set benchmark deadlines for students to show their work in progress.

- How to solve problems by working backward

CHAPTER PROJECT

THEME: COOKING

Did you ever make pancakes? The recipe can be pretty simple—an egg, some pancake mix, milk, and maybe some oil. Or forget the mix and start from scratch! Either way, you can vary the ingredients to suit your tastes. Do you want to include some wheat germ? How about some pecans, or maybe some fruit? Bananas are always in season!

Write Your Own Recipe For the chapter project, you will write your own recipe for pancakes. Your final product will be a recipe that will feed everyone in your class.

Steps to help you complete the project:

p. 196 **Project Link:** *Interviewing*
p. 209 **Project Link:** *Researching*
p. 224 **Project Link:** *Calculating*
p. 225 *Finishing the Chapter Project*

SCORING RUBRIC

3 Your pancake recipe works. You provided step-by-step explanations of how you calculated the amounts of ingredients required for your family and for your whole class. You provided evidence that either you tested your recipe by making it for your family or you interviewed someone with cooking experience to make sure your recipe made sense.

2 You wrote a pancake recipe and explained how you calculated the amounts of ingredients required for your family and the class, but either some of your calculations were inaccurate or you didn't verify that your recipe made sense.

1 You wrote a pancake recipe but didn't calculate the amounts of ingredients required for either your family or the whole class.

0 You did not write a pancake recipe.

5-1 Teaching Notes

1 Focus

CONNECTING TO PRIOR KNOWLEDGE Ask students to name some estimation techniques. **Answers may vary. Sample: rounding, compatible numbers** Have students describe situations in which these techniques are useful. **Answers may vary. Sample: estimating tax on a purchase**

2 Teach

THINK AND DISCUSS

AEP Students may have difficulty remembering which numbers are *numerators* and which are *denominators.* Encourage students to create mnemonics such as *The denominator is down.*

TACTILE LEARNING To help students understand that fractions such as $\frac{2}{5}$, $\frac{3}{7}$, and $\frac{5}{9}$ are approximately $\frac{1}{2}$, invite students to represent the fractions using fraction bars, graph paper, colored tiles, or other objects.

Example 2 Point out that when we round up a mixed number, we add 1 to the whole number part.

Lesson Planning Options

Prerequisite Skills

- comparing fractions (4-3)
- rounding (precourse)

Resources

Student Edition

Skills Handbook, pp. 530, 531
Extra Practice, p. 518
Glossary/Study Guide

Teaching Resources

Chapter Support File, Ch. 5
- Lesson Planner 5-1
- Practice 5-1, Reteaching 5-1
- Answer Masters 5-1

Teaching Aids Masters 3, 20–25
Glossary, Spanish Resources

Transparencies

9, 10, 15, 18–25, Minds on Math 5-1

Warm Up

Estimate the sum or difference.

$5\frac{1}{6} + 3\frac{4}{9} = ■$ $8\frac{1}{2}$

$7\frac{5}{6} - 3\frac{15}{16} = ■$ 4

5-1 Estimating with Fractions and Mixed Numbers

What You'll Learn

1. To estimate sums and differences
2. To estimate products and quotients

...And Why

You can use estimates to check the reasonableness of an answer and when exact calculations are not necessary.

Here's How

Look for questions that
- build understanding
- ✔ check understanding

THINK AND DISCUSS

1 Estimating Sums and Differences

To estimate sums and differences of fractions, round them to 0, $\frac{1}{2}$, or 1. You can think of a number line as you round the fractions.

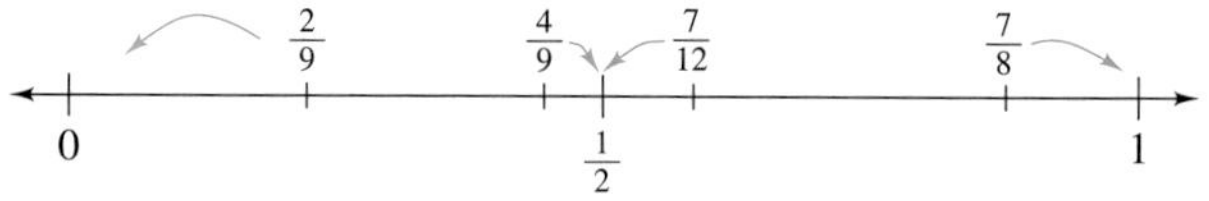

Round to 0 when the numerator is very small compared to the denominator.

Round to $\frac{1}{2}$ when the denominator is about twice the numerator.

Round to 1 when the numerator and denominator are nearly equal.

■ **EXAMPLE 1**

Estimate $\frac{7}{8} + \frac{4}{9}$.

$\frac{7}{8} + \frac{4}{9} \approx 1 + \frac{1}{2} = 1\frac{1}{2}$ ← Round each fraction. Then add.

1. ✔ *Try It Out* Estimate each sum or difference.
   a. $\frac{5}{12} + \frac{1}{15}$ $\frac{1}{2}$ b. $\frac{3}{5} - \frac{1}{8}$ $\frac{1}{2}$ c. $\frac{7}{8} + \frac{7}{9}$ 2 d. $\frac{7}{8} - \frac{5}{9}$ $\frac{1}{2}$

When a sum or difference involves mixed numbers, you get a reasonable estimate by rounding to the nearest whole number.

■ **EXAMPLE 2** *Real-World Problem Solving*

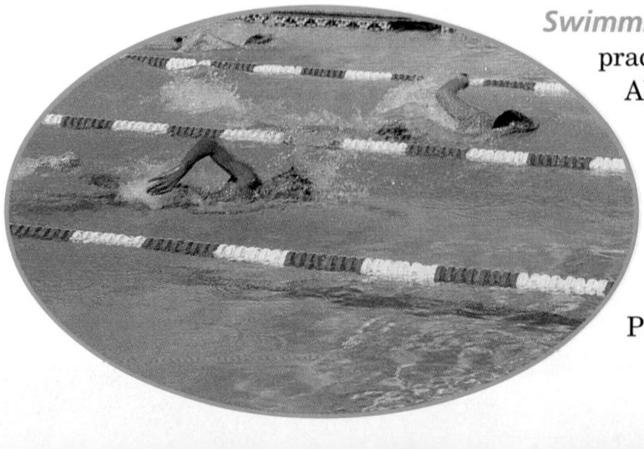

Swimming In the week before the swim meet, Paulo practiced by swimming $8\frac{1}{5}$ mi. Allen swam $4\frac{1}{2}$ mi. About how many more miles did Paulo swim?

Estimate $8\frac{1}{5} - 4\frac{1}{2}$.

$8\frac{1}{5} - 4\frac{1}{2}$ ← If the fractional part is greater than or equal to $\frac{1}{2}$, round up.

$8 - 5 = 3$

Paulo swam about 3 mi farther.

ERROR ALERT! Example 2 Students may not round $4\frac{1}{2}$ to 5. **Remediation:** Explain that you can round to $\frac{1}{2}$ when you estimate with fractions. Because mixed numbers contain whole numbers, you round only to whole numbers.

ADDITIONAL EXAMPLES

FOR EXAMPLE 1

Estimate $\frac{7}{12} + \frac{12}{13}$. **$1\frac{1}{2}$**

FOR EXAMPLE 2

Aaron spent $2\frac{7}{8}$ h doing homework. Jerome spent $1\frac{1}{9}$ h doing homework. About how many more hours did Aaron spend than Jerome? **about 2 h**

FOR EXAMPLE 3

Estimate $3\frac{1}{12} \cdot 5\frac{11}{12}$. **18**

FOR EXAMPLE 4

Estimate $23\frac{8}{9} \div 6\frac{1}{7}$. **4**

Example 4 Point out that using compatible numbers for estimating quotients of mixed numbers is similar to using compatible numbers for dividing whole numbers.

ERROR ALERT! Example 4 Students who have difficulty remembering their multiplication facts may make errors selecting compatible numbers. **Remediation:** Allow these students to keep a multiplication table handy for reference.

---

2. ✔ *Try It Out* Estimate each sum or difference.
   a. $7\frac{4}{5} + 2\frac{1}{3}$ **10** b. $1\frac{7}{8} + 3\frac{2}{5}$ **5** c. $4\frac{1}{8} - 1\frac{8}{9}$ **2** d. $8\frac{9}{16} - 3\frac{7}{8}$ **5**

Now you may assign Exercises 1–14.

2 *Estimating Products and Quotients*

To estimate a product of mixed numbers, round to the nearest whole number.

EXAMPLE 3

Estimate $2\frac{2}{5} \cdot 6\frac{1}{10}$.

$2\frac{2}{5} \cdot 6\frac{1}{10}$ ← Round.

$2 \cdot 6 = 12$ ← Multiply.

3. ✔ *Try It Out* Estimate each product.
   a. $3\frac{5}{6} \cdot 5\frac{1}{8}$ **20** b. $8\frac{1}{8} \cdot 5\frac{11}{12}$ **48** c. $2\frac{3}{5} \cdot 1\frac{2}{5}$ **3** d. $5\frac{3}{4} \cdot 4\frac{11}{12}$ **30**

4. *Look Back* Is the actual product in Example 3 *greater than* 12 or *less than* 12? Explain. **Greater; $2\frac{2}{5} > 2$ and $6\frac{1}{10} > 6$.**

QUICKreview

72 ÷ 9 = 8

dividend divisor quotient

To estimate a quotient of mixed numbers, you can use compatible numbers. First round the divisor. Then find a compatible number for the dividend.

EXAMPLE 4

Estimate $43\frac{1}{4} \div 5\frac{7}{8}$.

$43\frac{1}{4} \div 5\frac{7}{8}$ ← $5\frac{7}{8}$ rounds to 6. 42 is compatible with 6, and is close to $43\frac{1}{4}$.

$42 \div 6 = 7$ ← Find the quotient.

5. *Think About It* What compatible numbers would you use to estimate each quotient?
   a. $21\frac{1}{2} \div 5\frac{1}{5}$ b. $34\frac{1}{3} \div 6\frac{5}{8}$ c. $42\frac{1}{3} \div 7\frac{1}{4}$ d. $70\frac{3}{5} \div 9\frac{2}{5}$

5a. 20 ÷ 5
b. 35 ÷ 7
c. 42 ÷ 7
d. 72 ÷ 9

6. ✔ *Try It Out* Estimate each quotient.
   a. $35\frac{3}{4} \div 5\frac{11}{12}$ b. $22\frac{7}{8} \div 3\frac{5}{6}$ c. $44\frac{1}{8} \div 6\frac{1}{2}$ d. $8\frac{1}{8} \div 3\frac{1}{8}$

6a. 6
b. 6
c. 6
d. 3

7. *Reasoning* Victor estimated $87\frac{3}{4} \div 10\frac{5}{8}$. His answer was 8. Is this answer reasonable? Explain.

7. Answers may vary. Sample: Yes; $10\frac{5}{8}$ rounds to 11, and $87\frac{3}{4}$ rounds to 88, and $\frac{88}{11} = 8$.

Now you may assign Exercises 15–45.

Technology Options

Prentice Hall Technology

Software for Learners

- Math Blaster® Mystery*
- Interactive Student Tutorial, Chapter 5*

Teaching Resource Software

- Computer Item Generator 5-1
- Resource Pro™ Chapter 5*

Internet • For related mathematics activities, visit the Prentice Hall site at www.phschool.com/math

**Available on CD-ROM only*

Assignment Options for Exercises On Your Own

To provide flexible scheduling, this lesson can be subdivided into parts.

1 **Core** 1–13
Extension 14

2 **Core** 15–41, 43–45
Extension 42

Use Mixed Review to maintain skills.

Question 5 Point out that students do not need to find each estimated quotient. They need to identify only the compatible numbers they would use.

CONNECTION TO HOUSEHOLD Ask students to name items bought at the grocery store by weight. Stress that students can find approximate costs of these items by estimating products.

ASSESSMENT Question 6 Have students explain how they estimated the quotient in part (a).

3 Practice/Assess

EXERCISES *On Your Own*

REASONING Exercise 14c Suggest that students find the exact sum. Then have them compare both estimates to the exact sum.

WRITING Exercise 25 Tell students to make the first number they choose much greater than the second number. If the first number is less, students may have difficulty estimating the difference and the quotient.

EXTENSION Exercise 42 Ask students:

- *Will your estimate be greater than or less than the exact distance? Explain.* **The estimate will be less because you round down.**
- *When will an estimate be greater than the exact value?* **when you estimate by rounding up**

pages 190–191 On Your Own

14c. The numbers are close to 0, so rounding to the nearest whole number gives you no idea how large their sum is.

25. Sample: $3\frac{7}{8}$ and $2\frac{2}{5}$; for sum, difference and product, round to the nearest whole numbers, 4 and 2. 4 and 2 are also the compatible numbers for division.

26. Yes; each of the first two recipes requires less than 1 c of pasta. The 3rd recipe requires less than 2 c. The sum is less than 4 c.

page 191 Mixed Review

51. Positive trend; as people grow older, they grow taller. After you stop growing, the height remains the same.

52. No trend; there is no relation between height and income.

53. Positive trend; you are likely to get better income with greater experience.

EXERCISES *On Your Own*

Estimate each sum or difference.

1. $\frac{1}{7} + \frac{3}{8}$ $\frac{1}{2}$
2. $\frac{2}{3} + \frac{9}{10}$ 2
3. $9\frac{1}{11} - 3\frac{7}{9}$ 5
4. $5\frac{3}{5} + 3\frac{2}{3}$ 10
5. $4\frac{1}{2} - 1\frac{24}{25}$ 3
6. $\frac{3}{5} - \frac{1}{2}$ 0
7. $7\frac{2}{3} - 2\frac{11}{12}$ 5
8. $\frac{1}{7} + \frac{3}{8}$ $\frac{1}{2}$
9. $\frac{3}{4} + \frac{5}{6}$ 2
10. $\frac{3}{4} - \frac{1}{5}$ 1

Music **Use the table for Exercises 11–13. The table shows the weight of the bells of Boston's Old North Church. The bells are in order from smallest to largest.**

Tone	F	E	D	C	B flat	A	G	low F
Weight in tons	$\frac{3}{10}$	$\frac{3}{10}$	$\frac{7}{20}$	$\frac{2}{5}$	$\frac{11}{25}$	$\frac{19}{40}$	$\frac{3}{5}$	$\frac{3}{4}$

11. Estimate the total weight of the two largest bells. 2 tons
12. Estimate the total weight of all eight bells. $4\frac{1}{2}$ tons
13. Estimate the difference in the weights of the largest and smallest bell. $\frac{1}{2}$ ton
14. a. Estimate $\frac{1}{8} + \frac{2}{5}$ by rounding each fraction to the nearest whole number. 0
    b. Estimate the sum by rounding each fraction to 0, $\frac{1}{2}$, or 1. $\frac{1}{2}$
    c. *Reasoning* Why is the estimation method used in part (b) more appropriate than the method used in part (a)? See margin.

HISTORY Lanterns were set in the Old North Church to signal Paul Revere to start his ride in April of 1775. This was the start of the American Revolution.

Estimate each product or quotient.

15. $2\frac{1}{8} \cdot 3\frac{6}{7}$ 8
16. $5\frac{2}{9} \cdot 4\frac{9}{10}$ 25
17. $10\frac{7}{8} \div 3\frac{1}{9}$ 3
18. $7\frac{3}{5} \div 1\frac{1}{2}$ 4
19. $3\frac{2}{5} \cdot 7\frac{9}{20}$ 21
20. $3\frac{3}{8} \cdot 5\frac{1}{6}$ 15
21. $36\frac{1}{3} \div 4\frac{2}{5}$ 9
22. $1\frac{7}{10} \cdot 8\frac{1}{12}$ 16
23. $5\frac{3}{4} \cdot 2\frac{2}{3}$ 18
24. *Weather* The average annual rainfall in Nashville, Tennessee, is about $47\frac{3}{10}$ in. Estimate the average monthly rainfall. 4 in.

WRAP UP

IDENTIFYING THE BIG IDEA Ask students: *How do you estimate with fractions and mixed numbers?*

JOURNAL Ask students to think of situations in which they do not need an exact answer, only an estimate.

LESSON QUIZ

Estimate each answer.

1. $6\frac{4}{5} + 9\frac{1}{6}$ 16
2. $53\frac{14}{15} \div 8\frac{11}{12}$ 6
3. $12\frac{1}{7} - 2\frac{6}{7}$ 9
4. $4\frac{11}{12} \cdot 5\frac{3}{12}$ 25

PRACTICE

Practice 5-1 *Estimating with Fractions and Mixed Numbers*

Estimate each sum or difference. Estimates may vary.

1. $\frac{1}{6} + \frac{5}{8}$ $\frac{1}{2}$
2. $\frac{7}{8} - \frac{1}{16}$ 1
3. $\frac{9}{10} + \frac{7}{8}$ 2
4. $\frac{1}{12} + \frac{9}{10}$ 1
5. $\frac{1}{10} + \frac{5}{6}$ 1
6. $\frac{4}{5} - \frac{1}{6}$ 1
7. $\frac{11}{12} - \frac{5}{16}$ $\frac{1}{2}$
8. $\frac{15}{16} + \frac{11}{12}$ 2
9. $2\frac{1}{6} + 7\frac{1}{9}$ 9
10. $4\frac{9}{10} - 3\frac{5}{8}$ $1\frac{1}{2}$
11. $4\frac{7}{8} + 8\frac{1}{5}$ 13
12. $14\frac{7}{9} - 9\frac{1}{8}$ 6
13. $14\frac{3}{4} + 9\frac{7}{8}$ 25
14. $7\frac{11}{15} - 6\frac{7}{16}$ $1\frac{1}{2}$
15. $3\frac{11}{15} - 2\frac{9}{10}$ 1
16. $8\frac{7}{8} - \frac{11}{12}$ 8

Estimate each product or quotient. Estimates may vary.

17. $13\frac{1}{8} \div 6\frac{1}{5}$ 2
18. $5\frac{1}{6} \cdot 8\frac{4}{5}$ 45
19. $8\frac{1}{6} \div 1\frac{9}{10}$ 4
20. $1\frac{9}{10} \cdot 4\frac{7}{8}$ 10
21. $27\frac{6}{7} \div 3\frac{2}{3}$ 7
22. $20\frac{4}{5} \cdot 2\frac{2}{7}$ 42
23. $9\frac{1}{3} \div 2\frac{7}{8}$ 3
24. $16\frac{1}{9} \cdot 2\frac{1}{8}$ 32
25. $19\frac{4}{5} \div 4\frac{5}{8}$ 4
26. $9\frac{2}{13} \div 3\frac{1}{18}$ 3
27. $42\frac{1}{6} \div 6\frac{1}{16}$ 7
28. $3\frac{9}{10} \cdot 8\frac{7}{8}$ 36
29. $15\frac{1}{20} \cdot 3\frac{1}{10}$ 45
30. $72\frac{2}{15} \div 8\frac{3}{4}$ 8
31. $3\frac{5}{6} \cdot 10\frac{1}{12}$ 40
32. $36\frac{1}{4} \div 5\frac{15}{16}$ 6

Solve each problem.

33. Each dress for a wedding party requires $7\frac{1}{8}$ yd of material. Estimate the amount of material you would need to make 6 dresses. about 42 yd
34. A fabric store has $80\frac{3}{8}$ yd of a particular fabric. About how many pairs of curtains could be made from this fabric if each pair requires $4\frac{1}{8}$ yd of fabric? about 20 pairs
35. Adam's car can hold $16\frac{1}{10}$ gal of gasoline. About how many gallons are left if he started with a full tank and has used $11\frac{9}{10}$ gal? about 4 gal
36. Julia bought stock at $\$28\frac{1}{8}$ per share. The value of each stock increased by $\$6\frac{5}{8}$. About how much is each share of stock now worth? about \$35

Practice

In copymaster and workbook formats

RETEACHING

Reteaching 5-1 *Estimating with Fractions and Mixed Numbers*

You can estimate sums, differences, and products by rounding.

- Round *proper* fractions to 0, $\frac{1}{2}$, or 1.
- Round mixed numbers to the nearest whole number.

Estimate the sum:	Estimate the difference:	Estimate the product:
$\frac{5}{6} + \frac{7}{12}$	$3\frac{5}{6} - 2\frac{1}{3}$	$4\frac{1}{3} \times 2\frac{2}{3}$
$1 + \frac{1}{2} = 1\frac{1}{2}$	$4 - 2 = 2$	$4 \times 3 = 12$

You can estimate a quotient by using compatible numbers.

Estimate: $15\frac{3}{8} \div 4\frac{1}{8}$

Think: $15\frac{3}{8}$ is close to 16.
16 is divisible by 4.
$15\frac{3}{8} \div 4\frac{1}{8} \approx 16 \div 4 = 4$

Circle the better estimate.

1. $\frac{1}{2} + \frac{3}{8}$ 1 (circled) or $\frac{1}{2}$
2. $\frac{9}{10} - \frac{7}{8}$ 0 (circled) or $\frac{1}{2}$
3. $\frac{5}{8} + \frac{3}{7}$ $\frac{1}{2}$ or 1 (circled)
4. $\frac{8}{9} - \frac{1}{9}$ $\frac{1}{2}$ or 1 (circled)
5. $\frac{5}{8} + \frac{8}{9}$ 1 or $1\frac{1}{2}$ (circled)
6. $\frac{5}{6} + \frac{11}{12}$ $1\frac{1}{2}$ or 2 (circled)

Estimate each sum or difference.

7. $\frac{1}{2} + \frac{3}{7}$ 1
8. $\frac{5}{9} - \frac{3}{7}$ 0
9. $4\frac{2}{3} - \frac{1}{2}$ 4
10. $6\frac{7}{8} + 4\frac{4}{9}$ 12
11. $5\frac{8}{9} + 3\frac{1}{3}$ 9
12. $11\frac{1}{5} - 4\frac{1}{12}$ 7

Circle the better choice to estimate each product or quotient.

13. $5\frac{1}{4} \cdot 2\frac{1}{8}$ $5 \cdot 2$ (circled) or $5 \cdot 3$
14. $13\frac{1}{4} \div 3\frac{7}{8}$ $12 \div 4$ (circled) or $15 \div 3$
15. $6\frac{3}{4} \cdot 8\frac{7}{8}$ $7 \cdot 8$ or $7 \cdot 9$ (circled)
16. $21\frac{1}{2} \div 4\frac{1}{4}$ $20 \div 4$ (circled) or $24 \div 4$
17. $4\frac{13}{15} \cdot 7\frac{2}{9}$ $5 \cdot 7$ (circled) or $4 \cdot 8$
18. $38\frac{5}{6} \div 5\frac{1}{3}$ $35 \div 5$ or $40 \div 5$ (circled)

Estimate each product or quotient.

19. $6\frac{1}{4} \cdot 3\frac{5}{6}$ 24
20. $9\frac{1}{2} \div 2\frac{5}{8}$ 3
21. $2\frac{1}{7} \cdot 3\frac{5}{7}$ 8
22. $9\frac{4}{5} \cdot 4\frac{5}{6}$ 50
23. $15\frac{1}{2} \div 3\frac{5}{7}$ 4
24. $11\frac{1}{9} \cdot 2\frac{7}{8}$ 33

ENRICHMENT

Minds on Math Transparency 5-1

How many whole numbers that are made up of the digits 1, 2, 3, 4, and 5, each used at most once, are multiples of 8?

27

25. *Writing* Write two mixed numbers. Explain how you would estimate their sum, difference, product, and quotient.
25–26. See margin p. 190.
26. *Cooking* You want to make three kinds of pasta salad. One recipe requires $\frac{2}{3}$ c. Another requires $\frac{3}{4}$ c. The third requires $1\frac{2}{3}$ c. You have 4 c of pasta. Do you have enough? Explain.

Estimate each answer.

27. $5\frac{1}{8} - 2\frac{6}{7}$ 2
28. $1\frac{5}{8} \cdot 3\frac{1}{3}$ 6
29. $\frac{5}{6} + \frac{7}{9}$ 2
30. $16\frac{1}{7} \div 3\frac{3}{5}$ 4
31. $4\frac{2}{3} \cdot 5\frac{1}{3}$ 25
32. $7\frac{1}{6} + \frac{8}{10}$ 8
33. $\frac{8}{9} \div \frac{19}{20}$ 1
34. $6\frac{2}{9} - 5\frac{9}{10}$ 0
35. $29\frac{5}{6} \cdot 1\frac{13}{25}$ 60
36. $20\frac{7}{8} \div 1\frac{1}{12}$
37. $\frac{49}{50} - \frac{1}{2}$ $\frac{1}{2}$
38. $9\frac{3}{5} \div 4\frac{1}{2}$ 2
39. $\frac{5}{12} - \frac{2}{5}$ 0
40. $3\frac{2}{3} \cdot 5\frac{1}{2}$ 24
41. $\frac{27}{50} + \frac{47}{99}$ 1

36. 21

42. *Jogging* Suppose you jog $16\frac{1}{4}$ times around an indoor track that is 125 yd long. Have you jogged more than a mile? Explain. (*Hint:* 1 mi = 1,760 yd) yes; 16 × 125 = 2,000
43. *Cooking* Your recipe for a loaf of bread calls for $2\frac{3}{4}$ c of flour. You want to triple the recipe. The label on a two-pound bag of flour says that it contains about 7 c. Will that be enough flour to make three loaves of bread? Explain.

43. No; $2\frac{3}{4}$ is almost 3, so the triple recipe will use almost 9 c of flour.

44. *School Fair* Donnat and Alex are making place mats for a school fair. Each mat uses $14\frac{3}{4}$ in. of fabric. They have fabric that is $89\frac{3}{4}$ in. long. About how many place mats can they make? 6 mats
45. **Choose A, B, C, or D.** Which is between 6 and 7? C
 A. $\frac{1}{2} \cdot 14\frac{1}{2}$ B. $2 \cdot 3\frac{15}{16}$ C. $5\frac{11}{12} + \frac{24}{25}$ D. $7\frac{8}{9} - \frac{1}{2}$

JOURNAL Describe a situation where it would be appropriate to find a sum by using estimation.

Mixed Review

Divide. *(Lesson 2-6)*

46. $0.768 \div 1.6$ 0.48
47. $8.19 \div 9$ 0.91
48. $74.2 \div 0.53$ 140
49. $760.38 \div 0.38$ 2001
50. $903.6 \div 25.1$ 36

Explain why you would or would not expect to see a trend in the scatter plots described in Exercises 51–53. *(Lesson 1-9)*
51–53. See margin p. 190.

51. height and age
52. height and income
53. age and income

54. *Fund-Raising* The school band sold 116 tickets to their concert. They spent \$50 on refreshments and ended up with \$327. How much did each ticket cost? *(Lesson 2-6)* \$3.25

See *Solution Key* for worked-out answers.

MATH TOOLBOX

In the Work Together of Lesson 5-2, students use models to add and subtract fractions. This toolbox shows students how to find and use the correct models.

ERROR ALERT! Students may have trouble finding equivalent fractions when adding and subtracting fractions. **Remediation:** Have students compare several models that show equivalent fractions. Lead students to understand that multiplying or dividing the numerator and denominator of a fraction by the same number results in an equivalent fraction.

ASSESSMENT Have each student explain to a partner how to use models to find one of the sums or differences in the exercises. Students can compare strategies and results.

ADDITIONAL PROBLEMS

Use models to find each sum or difference.

1. $\frac{3}{4} - \frac{1}{8}$ $\frac{5}{8}$
2. $\frac{1}{3} + \frac{4}{9}$ $\frac{7}{9}$

Resources

Teaching Resource

Teaching Aids Masters 8–10, 20–25

Transparencies

9, 10, 18–25

MATH TOOLBOX SKILLS REVIEW

Using Fraction Models

Before Lesson 5-2

You can use models to add and subtract fractions.

EXAMPLE 1

Find $\frac{3}{10} + \frac{1}{10}$.

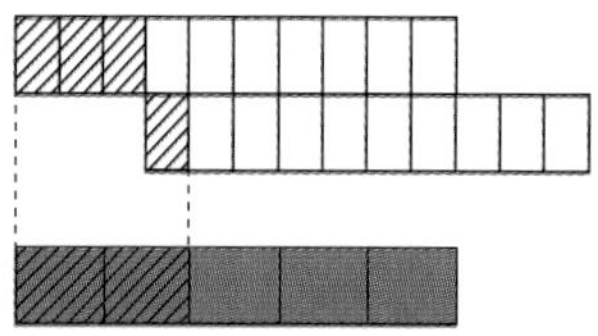

To add, align the right side of the shaded part of the first model with the left side of the second one.

Find a model that represents the sum of the shaded parts. If you have more than one model to choose from, use the one with the largest sections.

$\frac{3}{10} + \frac{1}{10} = \frac{2}{5}$

EXAMPLE 2

Find $\frac{3}{4} - \frac{1}{3}$.

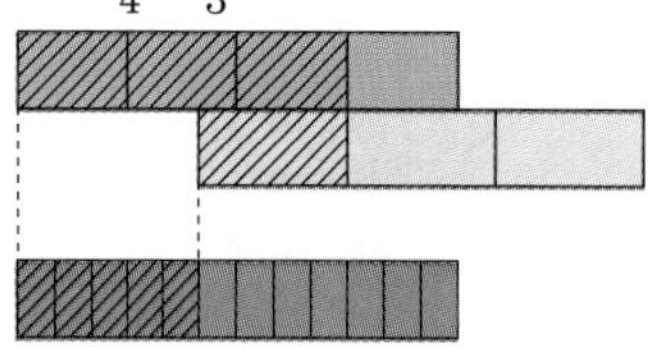

To subtract, align the right ends of the shaded part of each model.

Find the model that represents the difference.

$\frac{3}{4} - \frac{1}{3} = \frac{5}{12}$

Write a number sentence for each model.

1. 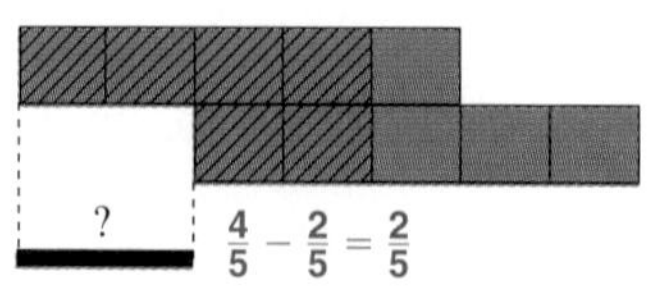

$\frac{4}{5} - \frac{2}{5} = \frac{2}{5}$

2. 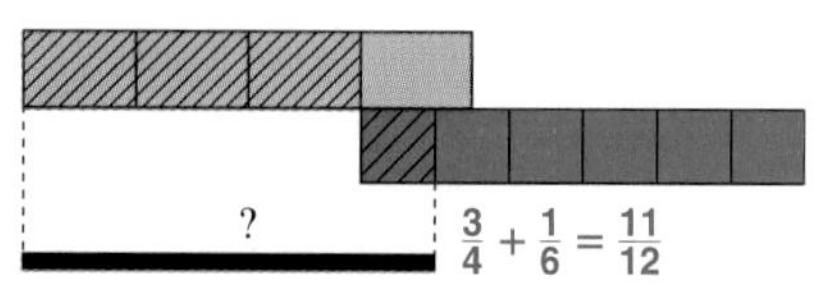

$\frac{3}{4} + \frac{1}{6} = \frac{11}{12}$

Use models to find each sum or difference.

3. $\frac{3}{8} + \frac{3}{8}$ $\frac{3}{4}$
4. $\frac{5}{6} - \frac{1}{6}$ $\frac{2}{3}$
5. $\frac{9}{10} - \frac{7}{10}$ $\frac{1}{5}$
6. $\frac{1}{6} + \frac{5}{6}$ 1
7. $\frac{2}{5} + \frac{1}{2}$ $\frac{9}{10}$
8. $\frac{3}{4} + \frac{1}{8}$ $\frac{7}{8}$
9. $\frac{4}{5} - \frac{1}{2}$ $\frac{3}{10}$
10. $\frac{7}{10} - \frac{1}{5}$ $\frac{1}{2}$
11. $\frac{5}{6} + \frac{1}{2}$ $\frac{4}{3}$
12. $\frac{5}{8} + \frac{1}{4}$ $\frac{7}{8}$
13. $\frac{2}{3} - \frac{1}{6}$ $\frac{1}{2}$
14. $\frac{9}{10} - \frac{1}{2}$ $\frac{2}{5}$

5-2 Teaching Notes

1 Focus

CONNECTING TO PRIOR KNOWLEDGE Draw a pizza on a piece of poster board and cut it out. Then cut out $\frac{1}{4}$ of the pizza. Ask students: *How much of the pizza is missing?* $\frac{1}{4}$ Cut off another $\frac{1}{4}$ of the pizza. Ask the question again. $\frac{1}{2}$

2 Teach

Work Together

AUDITORY LEARNING Question 2 To help students relate the model to the number sentence, urge students to say each number sentence quietly.

THINK AND DISCUSS

AUDITORY LEARNING Examples 1 and 2 Have students name a fruit for each denominator. When the denominators are the same, they might say: *Two apples plus four apples equals how many apples?* When the denominators are different, they may say: *Four apples plus two oranges equals how many whats?* Stress that you cannot add two kinds of fruit and have one kind of fruit as the result. These questions may help students

5-2 Adding and Subtracting Fractions

What You'll Learn

1. To add fractions
2. To subtract fractions

...And Why

When using customary units, you frequently use fractions.

Here's How

Look for questions that
- build understanding
- ✔ check understanding

2. $\frac{1}{4} + \frac{1}{3} = \frac{7}{12}$; $\frac{1}{2} - \frac{1}{3} = \frac{1}{6}$

Need Help? For practice in adding and subtracting fractions, see Skills Handbook page 540.

Work Together

Using Models

Work with a partner. Use the models shown to answer the questions below.

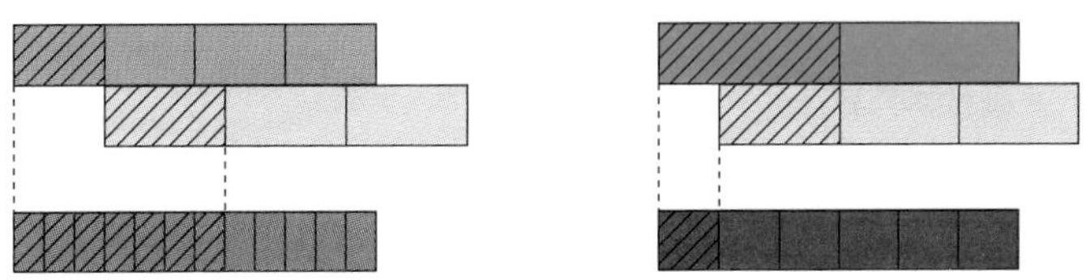

1. Which model shows addition? Subtraction? **first model; second model**
2. Write a number sentence for each model. **See left.**
3. *Modeling* Use fraction models to find two or more sums or differences that equal $\frac{1}{3}$. **Answers may vary. See margin p.195 for sample.**

THINK AND DISCUSS

1 Adding Fractions

To find the sum of two fractions that have the same denominator, you add their numerators.

EXAMPLE 1

Find $\frac{2}{9} + \frac{4}{9}$.

Estimate: $\frac{2}{9} + \frac{4}{9} \approx 0 + \frac{1}{2} = \frac{1}{2}$

$$\frac{2}{9} + \frac{4}{9} = \frac{2+4}{9}$$ ← Add the numerators.

$$= \frac{6}{9}$$

$$= \frac{2}{3}$$ ← Simplify the fraction. The answer is close to the estimate.

4. ✔ *Try It Out* Find each sum.

a. $\frac{2}{5} + \frac{2}{5}$ $\frac{4}{5}$ b. $\frac{1}{8} + \frac{3}{8}$ $\frac{1}{2}$ c. $\frac{1}{3} + \frac{2}{3}$ 1 d. $\frac{9}{10} + \frac{3}{10}$ $1\frac{1}{5}$

Lesson Planning Options

Prerequisite Skills

- calculating LCD (4-3)
- writing number sentences (3-1)

Materials/Manipulatives

- fraction bars

Resources

Student Edition

Skills Handbook, p. 540
Extra Practice, p. 518
Glossary/Study Guide

Teaching Resources

Chapter Support File, Ch. 5
- Lesson Planner 5-2
- Practice 5-2, Reteaching 5-2
- Answer Masters 5-2

Teaching Aids Masters 8, 10, 20–25
Glossary, Spanish Resources

Transparencies

9, 10, 15, 18–25, Minds on Math 5-2

Warm Up

Find the sum or difference. If possible, write each answer in lowest terms.

$\frac{4}{5} + \frac{2}{5} = ■$ $1\frac{1}{5}$

$7\frac{5}{6} - 5\frac{2}{6} = ■$ $2\frac{3}{6} = 2\frac{1}{2}$

decide when they must find the LCD before adding or subtracting.

Example 2 Have students recall how they used the LCD to compare and order fractions. Remind students that they can compare fractions easily if the fractions have the same denominator. They can also add or subtract fractions more easily if the fractions have the same denominator.

ERROR ALERT! Example 2 Students may add the denominators. **Remediation:** Model the example using fraction bars to show students that the sum cannot be $\frac{6}{8}$.

ADDITIONAL EXAMPLES

FOR EXAMPLE 1

Find $\frac{3}{10} + \frac{6}{10}$. $\frac{9}{10}$

FOR EXAMPLE 2

Find $\frac{3}{5} + \frac{1}{4}$. $\frac{17}{20}$

FOR EXAMPLE 3

A carpenter needs a board that is $\frac{5}{8}$ ft long to make a shelf. He has a piece of board $\frac{2}{3}$ ft long. How much of the board must he cut off? $\frac{1}{24}$ ft

Technology Options

Prentice Hall Technology

Software for Learners

- Hot Page™ 8–4*
- Math Blaster® Mystery*
- Interactive Student Tutorial, Chapter 5*

Teaching Resource Software

- Computer Item Generator 5-2
- Resource Pro™ Chapter 5*

Internet • For related mathematics activities, visit the Prentice Hall site at www.phschool.com/math

**Available on CD-ROM only*

Assignment Options for Exercises On Your Own

To provide flexible scheduling, this lesson can be subdivided into parts.

1 **Core** 1–12
Extension 13

2 **Core** 14–42
Extension 43–47

Use Mixed Review to maintain skills.

WHO? HISTORY The ancient Egyptians represented all fractions, except $\frac{2}{3}$, as a *unit fraction* or the sum of unit fractions. A unit fraction, such as $\frac{1}{2}$, is a fraction with a numerator of 1. The Egyptians would write $\frac{3}{4}$ as $\frac{1}{2} + \frac{1}{4}$.

To find the sum of two fractions that have different denominators, you first find their LCD.

EXAMPLE 2

Find the sum $\frac{4}{5} + \frac{2}{3}$.

Estimate: $\frac{4}{5} + \frac{2}{3} \approx 1 + \frac{1}{2} = 1\frac{1}{2}$

$$\frac{4}{5} = \frac{4 \cdot 3}{5 \cdot 3} = \frac{12}{15}$$
$$\frac{2}{3} = \frac{2 \cdot 5}{3 \cdot 5} = \frac{10}{15}$$
← The LCD is 15. Write the fractions with the same denominator.

$$= \frac{22}{15}$$
← Add the numerators.

$$= 1\frac{7}{15}$$
← Write the answer as a mixed number. The answer is close to the estimate.

5. ✓ *Try It Out* Find each sum.
a. $\frac{1}{3} + \frac{1}{8}$ $\frac{11}{24}$
b. $\frac{3}{4} + \frac{3}{8}$ $1\frac{1}{8}$
c. $\frac{1}{4} + \frac{5}{6}$ $1\frac{1}{12}$
d. $\frac{2}{3} + \frac{3}{5}$ $1\frac{4}{15}$

Now you may assign Exercises 1–13.

2 *Subtracting Fractions*

You also use the LCD to subtract fractions with different denominators.

EXAMPLE 3 *Real-World Problem Solving*

Carpentry A cabinet maker needs a board that is $\frac{11}{16}$ in. thick. How much must he decrease the thickness of a board that is $\frac{7}{8}$ in. thick?

Find $\frac{7}{8} - \frac{11}{16}$.

Estimate: $\frac{7}{8} - \frac{11}{16} \approx 1 - \frac{1}{2} = \frac{1}{2}$

$$\frac{7}{8} - \frac{11}{16} = \frac{7 \cdot 2}{8 \cdot 2} - \frac{11}{16}$$
$$= \frac{14}{16} - \frac{11}{16}$$
← The LCD is 16. Write the fractions with the same denominator.

$$= \frac{3}{16}$$
← Subtract the numerators. The answer is close to the estimate.

The cabinet maker should decrease the thickness of the board by $\frac{3}{16}$ in.

6. ✓ *Try It Out* Find each difference.
a. $\frac{3}{4} - \frac{1}{8}$ $\frac{5}{8}$
b. $\frac{4}{5} - \frac{2}{3}$ $\frac{2}{15}$
c. $\frac{5}{6} - \frac{1}{4}$ $\frac{7}{12}$
d. $\frac{3}{4} - \frac{3}{5}$ $\frac{3}{20}$

Now you may assign Exercises 14–47.

3 Practice/Assess

EXERCISES *On Your Own*

ASSESSMENT Exercise 6 To assess students' understanding, ask:

- *Will the sum be a fraction or a mixed number?* **a mixed number** *Explain.* **The sum will be greater than 1.**
- *What is the denominator of the sum?* **40**

Exercise 12 Suggest that students draw pictures of fraction bars to show why the answer is not correct.

WRITING Exercise 42d Prompt students' thinking by asking: *What should be the sum of all four fractions?* **1**

REASONING Exercises 43–46 Students may wish to write fractions such as $-\frac{2}{3}$ as $\frac{-2}{3}$.

DIVERSITY Exercise 56 Recent immigrants may not be familiar with the denominations of coins used in the United States. Some countries use a 20-cent coin instead of a quarter. If you have block scheduling or extended class periods, invite students who have foreign coins to bring them to class. Challenge students to solve change problems using a 20-cent coin instead of a quarter.

EXERCISES *On Your Own*

Find each sum.

1. $\frac{1}{7}+\frac{4}{7}$ **$\frac{5}{7}$**
2. $\frac{1}{5}+\frac{3}{5}$ **$\frac{4}{5}$**
3. $\frac{2}{3}+\frac{1}{2}$ **$1\frac{1}{6}$**
4. $\frac{7}{12}+\frac{1}{6}$ **$\frac{3}{4}$**
5. $\frac{3}{3}+\frac{5}{8}$ **$1\frac{5}{8}$**
6. $\frac{4}{5}+\frac{7}{8}$ **$1\frac{27}{40}$**
7. $\frac{1}{2}+\frac{4}{5}$ **$1\frac{3}{10}$**
8. $\frac{4}{3}+\frac{2}{3}$ **2**
9. $\frac{3}{2}+\frac{1}{4}$ **$1\frac{3}{4}$**
10. $\frac{5}{6}+\frac{7}{8}$ **$1\frac{17}{24}$**

11. One third of the students in your class got an A on a test. One fourth of them got a B.
    a. What fraction of the students got an A or a B? **$\frac{7}{12}$**
    b. Did a majority of the students get As and Bs? Explain. **yes; $\frac{7}{12} > \frac{1}{2}$**

12. *Error Analysis* What is the error in $\frac{2}{8}+\frac{3}{8}=\frac{5}{16}$? **You do not add the denominators.**

13. Allen and Meda have recipes for three kinds of cookies. The recipes call for $\frac{1}{2}$ c, $\frac{2}{3}$ c, and $\frac{3}{4}$ c of sugar. They have 2 c of sugar. Allen says that isn't enough sugar for one batch of each recipe. Is he correct? Explain. **No; $\frac{1}{2}+\frac{2}{3}+\frac{3}{4}=1\frac{11}{12}$, so 2 c is enough.**

Find each difference.

14. $\frac{4}{5}-\frac{1}{5}$ **$\frac{3}{5}$**
15. $\frac{7}{10}-\frac{1}{10}$ **$\frac{3}{5}$**
16. $\frac{7}{10}-\frac{1}{6}$ **$\frac{8}{15}$**
17. $\frac{7}{10}-\frac{1}{5}$ **$\frac{1}{2}$**
18. $\frac{9}{10}-\frac{2}{5}$ **$\frac{1}{2}$**
19. $\frac{2}{3}-\frac{1}{4}$ **$\frac{5}{12}$**
20. $\frac{5}{6}-\frac{1}{3}$ **$\frac{1}{2}$**
21. $\frac{11}{12}-\frac{3}{4}$ **$\frac{1}{6}$**
22. $\frac{3}{5}-\frac{1}{4}$ **$\frac{7}{20}$**
23. $\frac{7}{6}-\frac{3}{4}$ **$\frac{5}{12}$**

24. Hal is using nails that are $\frac{5}{6}$ in. long to nail $\frac{1}{4}$-in. thick plywood to a beam. How much of the nail extends into the beam? **$\frac{7}{12}$ in.**

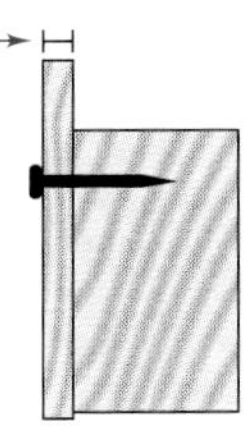

25. a. You rowed two thirds of a mile. Your friend rowed eight tenths of a mile. Who rowed farther? How much farther? **a. your friend; $\frac{2}{15}$ mi**
    b. Which operation did you use to solve the problem? Why? **Subtraction; to find the difference of the distances, you subtract.**

Find each sum or difference.

26. $\frac{7}{12}-\frac{1}{12}$ **$\frac{1}{2}$**
27. $\frac{1}{4}+\frac{1}{3}$ **$\frac{7}{12}$**
28. $\frac{2}{3}-\frac{1}{8}$ **$\frac{13}{24}$**
29. $\frac{1}{3}-\frac{1}{4}$ **$\frac{1}{12}$**
30. $\frac{1}{3}+\frac{5}{12}$ **$\frac{3}{4}$**
31. $\frac{5}{6}+\frac{3}{4}$ **$1\frac{7}{12}$**
32. $\frac{1}{5}+\frac{3}{10}$ **$\frac{1}{2}$**
33. $\frac{1}{2}-\frac{1}{8}$ **$\frac{3}{8}$**
34. $\frac{1}{2}+\frac{5}{6}$ **$1\frac{1}{3}$**
35. $\frac{7}{6}-\frac{3}{4}$ **$\frac{5}{12}$**
36. $\frac{1}{2}-\frac{1}{3}$ **$\frac{1}{6}$**
37. $\frac{3}{5}+\frac{3}{4}$ **$1\frac{7}{20}$**
38. $\frac{1}{3}-\frac{1}{5}$ **$\frac{2}{15}$**
39. $\frac{1}{5}+\frac{3}{8}$ **$\frac{23}{40}$**
40. $\frac{3}{4}-\frac{3}{10}$ **$\frac{9}{20}$**

41. Sally has to walk $\frac{7}{10}$ mi from her home to the bus stop. She has to walk $\frac{1}{4}$ mi from her home to the subway station. How much farther is it to the bus stop than to the station? **$\frac{9}{20}$ mi**

page 193 Work Together

3.

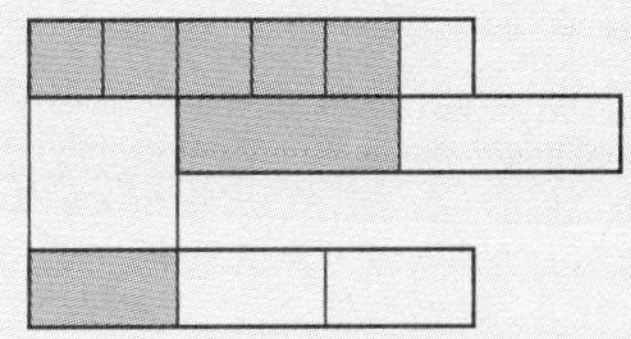

$\frac{5}{6}-\frac{1}{2}=\frac{1}{3}$

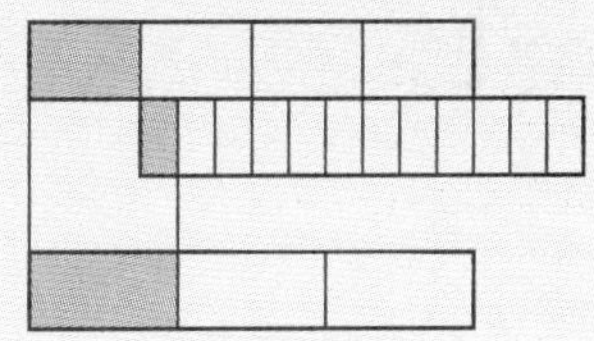

$\frac{1}{4}+\frac{1}{12}=\frac{1}{3}$

page 196 Mixed Review

56.

half-dollars	quarters	dimes	nickels
1	0	1	1
1	0	0	3
0	2	1	1
0	2	0	3
0	1	4	0
0	1	3	2
0	1	2	4
0	1	1	6
0	1	0	8
0	0	6	1
0	0	5	3
0	0	4	5
0	0	3	7
0	0	2	9
0	0	1	11
0	0	0	13

PRACTICE

Practice 5-2 Adding and Subtracting Fractions

Write a number sentence for each model shown.

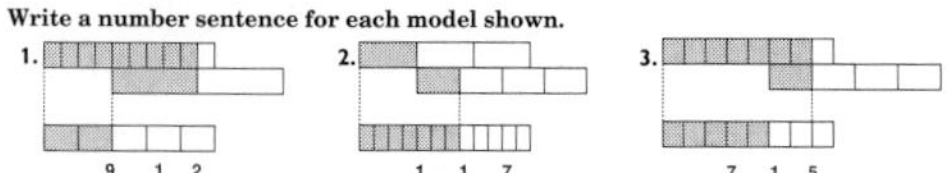

1. $\frac{9}{10} - \frac{1}{2} = \frac{2}{5}$ 2. $\frac{1}{3} + \frac{1}{4} = \frac{7}{12}$ 3. $\frac{7}{8} - \frac{1}{4} = \frac{5}{8}$

Find each sum or difference.

4. $\frac{1}{6} + \frac{7}{8}$ $1\frac{1}{24}$
5. $\frac{9}{10} - \frac{1}{6}$ $\frac{11}{15}$
6. $\frac{4}{5} + \frac{9}{10}$ $1\frac{7}{10}$
7. $\frac{1}{6} + \frac{1}{6}$ $\frac{1}{3}$
8. $\frac{1}{10} + \frac{2}{5}$ $\frac{1}{2}$
9. $\frac{8}{9} - \frac{2}{9}$ $\frac{2}{3}$
10. $\frac{5}{6} + \frac{1}{12}$ $\frac{11}{12}$
11. $\frac{2}{3} - \frac{1}{2}$ $\frac{1}{6}$
12. $\frac{3}{10} + \frac{3}{10}$ $\frac{3}{5}$
13. $\frac{7}{9} - \frac{1}{3}$ $\frac{4}{9}$
14. $\frac{3}{4} - \frac{1}{4}$ $\frac{1}{2}$
15. $\frac{3}{8} + \frac{5}{12}$ $\frac{19}{24}$
16. $\frac{1}{5} + \frac{3}{4}$ $\frac{19}{20}$
17. $\frac{1}{3} + \frac{1}{2}$ $\frac{5}{6}$
18. $\frac{11}{12} - \frac{3}{4}$ $\frac{1}{6}$
19. $\frac{1}{8} + \frac{1}{12}$ $\frac{5}{24}$
20. $\frac{7}{10} - \frac{1}{3}$ $\frac{11}{30}$
21. $\frac{5}{8} + \frac{1}{4}$ $\frac{7}{8}$

Use the table at the right for Exercises 22–27. Tell which two snacks combine to make each amount.

22. $\frac{5}{6}$ c sesame sticks, dried apricots
23. $\frac{1}{2}$ c peanuts, chocolate chips
24. $\frac{3}{4}$ c pretzels, chocolate chips
25. $\frac{11}{12}$ c raisins, sesame sticks
26. 1 c peanuts, pretzels
27. $\frac{19}{24}$ c pretzels, dried apricots; or chocolate chips, sesame sticks

Snack	Serving Amount
Raisins	$\frac{1}{4}$ c
Peanuts	$\frac{3}{8}$ c
Chocolate chips	$\frac{1}{8}$ c
Sesame sticks	$\frac{2}{3}$ c
Mini pretzels	$\frac{5}{8}$ c
Dried apricots	$\frac{1}{6}$ c

In copymaster and workbook formats

RETEACHING

Reteaching 5-2 Adding and Subtracting Fractions

Follow these steps to add or subtract fractions with different denominators.

		Add: $\frac{1}{3} + \frac{1}{6}$	Subtract: $\frac{11}{12} - \frac{1}{6}$
Step 1	Write the fractions with the same denominator.	$\frac{2}{6} + \frac{1}{6}$	$\frac{11}{12} - \frac{2}{12}$
Step 2	Add or subtract the numerators.	$\frac{2}{6} + \frac{1}{6} = \frac{3}{6}$	$\frac{11}{12} - \frac{2}{12} = \frac{9}{12}$
Step 3	Simplify the fraction.	$\frac{3}{6} = \frac{1}{2}$	$\frac{9}{12} = \frac{3}{4}$

Complete to find each sum or difference.

1. $\frac{3}{10} + \frac{2}{5}$; $\frac{3}{10} + \frac{4}{10} = \frac{7}{10}$
2. $\frac{1}{4} + \frac{3}{6}$; $\frac{3}{12} + \frac{6}{12} = \frac{9}{12} = \frac{3}{4}$
3. $\frac{5}{8} + \frac{1}{4}$; $\frac{5}{8} + \frac{2}{8} = \frac{7}{8}$
4. $\frac{3}{4} - \frac{1}{2}$; $\frac{3}{4} - \frac{2}{4} = \frac{1}{4}$
5. $\frac{5}{9} - \frac{1}{3}$; $\frac{5}{9} - \frac{3}{9} = \frac{2}{9}$
6. $\frac{3}{5} - \frac{1}{3}$; $\frac{9}{15} - \frac{5}{15} = \frac{4}{15}$

Find each sum or difference. Write it in simplest form.

7. $\frac{4}{5} + \frac{4}{5}$ $1\frac{3}{5}$
8. $\frac{7}{8} - \frac{5}{8}$ $\frac{1}{4}$
9. $\frac{5}{6} - \frac{2}{3}$ $\frac{1}{6}$
10. $\frac{5}{12} - \frac{1}{4}$ $\frac{1}{6}$
11. $\frac{7}{8} + \frac{1}{4}$ $1\frac{1}{8}$
12. $\frac{3}{4} - \frac{1}{8}$ $\frac{5}{8}$
13. $\frac{2}{5} + \frac{1}{10}$ $\frac{1}{2}$
14. $\frac{7}{12} - \frac{1}{3}$ $\frac{1}{4}$
15. $\frac{3}{5} + \frac{7}{15}$ $1\frac{1}{15}$
16. $\frac{1}{2} + \frac{9}{10}$ $1\frac{2}{5}$
17. $\frac{5}{6} - \frac{1}{4}$ $\frac{7}{12}$
18. $\frac{9}{10} - \frac{1}{2}$ $\frac{2}{5}$

Choose A, B, C, or D for each sum or difference.

19. $\frac{5}{8} + \frac{1}{2}$ A. $\frac{6}{8}$ B. $\frac{6}{10}$ (C.) $1\frac{1}{8}$ D. 1
20. $\frac{2}{5} - \frac{3}{10}$ A. $\frac{5}{15}$ B. $\frac{1}{5}$ C. $\frac{7}{10}$ (D.) $\frac{1}{10}$
21. $\frac{5}{6} - \frac{7}{12}$ (A.) $\frac{1}{4}$ B. $\frac{1}{2}$ C. $\frac{2}{6}$ D. $\frac{1}{3}$
22. $\frac{7}{8} + \frac{1}{3}$ A. $\frac{13}{24}$ (B.) $1\frac{5}{24}$ C. $\frac{8}{11}$ D. $1\frac{7}{24}$

Reteaching

ENRICHMENT

Minds on Math Transparency

5-2

Show how a square could have one of the points below on each of its sides without touching the rectangle.

Sample is shown.

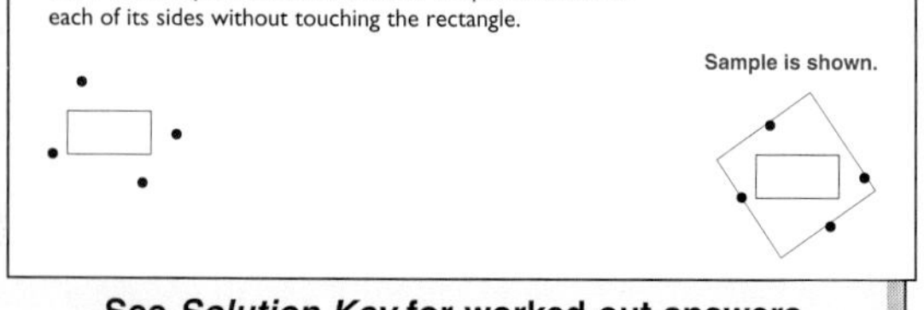

See *Solution Key* for worked-out answers.

WRAP UP

IDENTIFYING THE BIG IDEA Ask students: *How do you add and subtract fractions with different denominators?*

PROJECT LINK Tell students that they can usually find a recipe for pancakes on a pancake-mix box. The boxes also list optional ingredients that you can add to the mix.

LESSON QUIZ

Find each sum or difference.

1. $\frac{4}{15} + \frac{7}{15}$ $\frac{11}{15}$
2. $\frac{1}{10} + \frac{1}{5}$ $\frac{3}{10}$
3. $\frac{8}{9} - \frac{4}{9}$ $\frac{4}{9}$
4. A loaf of French bread is $\frac{9}{10}$ m long. After you cut off a piece $\frac{1}{5}$ m long, how much remains? $\frac{7}{10}$ m

42. Use the circle graph at the right.
    a. What fraction of takeout food is eaten at home or in a car? $\frac{7}{10}$
    b. How much greater is the fraction of takeout food eaten at home than at work? $\frac{7}{20}$
    c. What fraction of the takeout food is eaten at home, in a car, or at work? $\frac{17}{20}$
    d. *Writing* Describe two ways to get the answer to part (c). See below right.

Reasoning **Use what you know about addition of integers to predict whether each sum will be positive, negative, or zero. Explain your reasoning.** 43–46. See right.

43. $-\frac{2}{3} + \frac{5}{6}$
44. $-\frac{4}{5} + \frac{8}{10}$
45. $-\frac{7}{8} + \frac{3}{4}$
46. $-\frac{3}{4} + \frac{3}{5}$

47. *Calculator* You can use this key sequence to find $\frac{3}{5} + \frac{1}{4}$.

    3 ÷ 5 + 1 ÷ 4 =

    The answer the calculator displays, 0.85, can be rewritten as the fraction $\frac{85}{100}$ which simplifies to $\frac{17}{20}$.
    a. Write the key sequence you could use to find $\frac{7}{8} - \frac{3}{5}$.
    b. Use your key sequence to find $\frac{7}{8} - \frac{3}{5}$. 0.275
    a. 7 ÷ 8 − 3 ÷ 5

42d. Add the three fractions for the food eaten at home, in a car, and at work; subtract the fraction for "other" from 1.

43. positive; $\frac{2}{3} < \frac{5}{6}$
44. 0; $\frac{8}{10} = \frac{4}{5}$
45. negative; $\frac{7}{8} > \frac{3}{4}$
46. negative; $\frac{3}{4} > \frac{3}{5}$

Mixed Review

Multiply or divide. *(Lesson 3-5)*

48. $5 \cdot (-11)$ −55
49. $-84 \div 12$ −7
50. $-3 \cdot (-9)$ 27
51. $-13 \cdot 5$ −65
52. $-63 \div (-7)$ 9

Find the value of each expression. *(Lesson 2-8)*

53. $7 \cdot 3 + 8 \cdot 2$ 37
54. $8 - 2 + 3 \cdot 4$ 18
55. $82 - 43 - 6 \div 6$ 38

56. *Choose a Strategy* Find the ways a clerk can give change for a dollar for a $.35 purchase without using pennies. See margin p. 195.

CHAPTER PROJECT

PROJECT LINK: INTERVIEWING

Interview some people who know how to make pancakes or start with a recipe in a cookbook. Use that information to write your own recipe. Most of the ingredients should involve fractions. Include things that you like, such as fruits or nuts.

Check students' work.

Extra Practice, Lesson 5-2, page 518

1 Focus

CONNECTING TO PRIOR KNOWLEDGE Ask students: *If you add two fractions, how can the sum be a mixed number?* **The sum can be a mixed number when it is greater than 1.**

2 Teach

THINK AND DISCUSS

ERROR ALERT! Example 1 Students often forget to add or subtract the whole number part of the mixed number. **Remediation:** Encourage students to use estimation to determine if their answers are reasonable.

AEP Discuss the meaning of the term *mixed number.* Explain that a mixed number consists of a whole number and a fraction.

KINESTHETIC LEARNING Example 2 Have students make a set of giant fraction bars using strips of heavy paper. Each unit should be 1 yd long. Make enough thirds, quarters, and twelfths for students to be able to model Example 2. Then have groups of students take turns modeling the example by standing in an open area of the classroom with the correct number of fraction bars.

5-3 Adding and Subtracting Mixed Numbers

What You'll Learn

1. To add mixed numbers
2. To subtract mixed numbers

...And Why

You can find the space needed for newspaper ads.

Here's How

Look for questions that
- build understanding
- ✔ check understanding

THINK AND DISCUSS

1 Adding Mixed Numbers

To add mixed numbers that have common denominators, you add the whole numbers and then you add the fractions.

EXAMPLE 1

Find $1\frac{2}{5} + 2\frac{4}{5}$.

Estimate: $1\frac{2}{5} + 2\frac{4}{5} \approx 1 + 3 = 4$

$$\begin{array}{r} 1\frac{2}{5} \\ +\ 2\frac{4}{5} \\ \hline \end{array}$$

$= 3\frac{6}{5}$ ← Add the whole numbers. Add the fractions.

$= 3 + 1\frac{1}{5}$ ← Rename $\frac{6}{5}$: $\frac{6}{5} = \frac{5}{5} + \frac{1}{5} = 1\frac{1}{5}$

$= 4\frac{1}{5}$ ← Add the whole numbers. The answer is close to the estimate.

1. ✔ *Try It Out* Find $6\frac{3}{8} + 4\frac{7}{8}$. **$11\frac{1}{4}$**

Fractions in mixed numbers may have different denominators. Use the LCD to rewrite the fractions with common denominators.

EXAMPLE 2 *Real-World Problem Solving*

Hiking You hiked $2\frac{2}{3}$ mi from the campground to Jewel Pond and then $3\frac{1}{4}$ mi to Lookout Ledge. How far did you hike?

Find $2\frac{2}{3} + 3\frac{1}{4}$.

Estimate: $2\frac{2}{3} + 3\frac{1}{4} \approx 3 + 3 = 6$

$2\frac{2}{3} + 3\frac{1}{4} = 2\frac{8}{12} + 3\frac{3}{12}$ ← The LCD is 12.

$= 5 + \frac{11}{12}$ ← Add the whole numbers. Add the fractions.

$= 5\frac{11}{12}$ ← The answer is close to the estimate.

You hiked $5\frac{11}{12}$ mi.

Lesson Planning Options

Prerequisite Skills
- calculating LCD (4-3)
- simplifying fractions (4-6)

Materials/Manipulatives
- calculator

Resources

Student Edition

Skills Handbook, p. 540
Extra Practice, p. 518
Glossary/Study Guide

Teaching Resources

Chapter Support File, Ch. 5
- Lesson Planner 5-3
- Practice 5-3, Reteaching 5-3
- Answer Masters 5-3

Teaching Aids Masters 8, 10, 20–25
Glossary, Spanish Resources

Transparencies

9, 10, 15, 18–25, Minds on Math 5-3

Warm Up

What is $\frac{175}{80}$ expressed as a decimal? **2.1875**

Example 3 Some students may be more accustomed to using the term *borrow* than the term *rename* when subtracting fractions. Use both terms until they are familiar with *rename.*

ADDITIONAL EXAMPLES

FOR EXAMPLE 1

Find the sum $3\frac{1}{4} + 4\frac{2}{3}$. **$7\frac{11}{12}$**

FOR EXAMPLE 2

On Saturday you hiked $4\frac{3}{8}$ mi. On Sunday you hiked $3\frac{5}{8}$ mi. How far did you hike that weekend? **8 mi**

FOR EXAMPLE 3

Find the difference $4\frac{1}{6} - 1\frac{5}{8}$. **$2\frac{13}{24}$**

3 Practice/Assess

EXERCISES *On Your Own*

ASSESSMENT Have students work in pairs. Each student writes a real-world problem using mixed numbers. There must be two questions to answer: one involving addition, and one involving subtraction. Have students exchange problems with their partners and solve.

Technology Options

Prentice Hall Technology

Software for Learners

- Math Blaster® Mystery*
- Interactive Student Tutorial, Chapter 5*

Teaching Resource Software

- Computer Item Generator 5-3
- Resource Pro™ Chapter 5*

Internet • For related mathematics activities, visit the Prentice Hall site at www.phschool.com/math

**Available on CD-ROM only*

Assignment Options for Exercises On Your Own

To provide flexible scheduling, this lesson can be subdivided into parts.

1 **Core** 1–11, **Extension** 12

2 **Core** 13–46, **Extension** 47

Use Mixed Review to maintain skills.

2. ✔ *Try It Out* Find each sum.
   a. $4\frac{3}{4} + 3\frac{1}{2}$ **$8\frac{1}{4}$** b. $1\frac{5}{6} + 4\frac{2}{3}$ **$6\frac{1}{2}$** c. $2\frac{1}{3} + 6\frac{4}{5}$ **$9\frac{2}{15}$** d. $3\frac{1}{6} + 8\frac{7}{8}$ **$12\frac{1}{24}$**

Now you may assign Exercises 1–12.

2 *Subtracting Mixed Numbers*

When you subtract mixed numbers, you may need to rename before subtracting.

EXAMPLE 3

Find the difference $6\frac{1}{8} - 2\frac{3}{4}$.

Estimate: $6\frac{1}{8} - 2\frac{3}{4} \approx 6 - 3 = 3$

$6\frac{1}{8} - 2\frac{3}{4} = 6\frac{1}{8} - 2\frac{6}{8}$ ← The LCD is 8.

$= 5\frac{9}{8} - 2\frac{6}{8}$ ← Rename $6\frac{1}{8}$: $6\frac{1}{8} = 5 + 1\frac{1}{8} = 5\frac{9}{8}$.

$= 3\frac{3}{8}$ ← Subtract the whole numbers. Subtract the fractions. The answer is close to the estimate.

3. ✔ *Try It Out* Find each difference.
   a. $5\frac{1}{2} - 3\frac{3}{4}$ **$1\frac{3}{4}$** b. $2\frac{7}{8} - 1\frac{1}{4}$ **$1\frac{5}{8}$** c. $6\frac{1}{2} - 1\frac{7}{8}$ **$4\frac{5}{8}$** d. $10\frac{1}{3} - 7\frac{3}{4}$ **$2\frac{7}{12}$**

Now you may assign Exercises 13–47.

EXERCISES *On Your Own*

Find each sum.

1. $6\frac{2}{5} + 1\frac{4}{5}$ **$8\frac{1}{5}$**
2. $5\frac{2}{3} + 7\frac{1}{3}$ **13**
3. $9\frac{1}{2} + 9\frac{1}{3}$ **$18\frac{5}{6}$**
4. $7\frac{1}{6} + 8\frac{1}{8}$ **$15\frac{7}{24}$**
5. $6\frac{1}{2} + 4\frac{5}{6}$ **$11\frac{1}{3}$**
6. $8\frac{3}{4} + 8\frac{1}{8}$ **$16\frac{7}{8}$**
7. $5\frac{5}{9} + 9\frac{1}{3}$ **$14\frac{8}{9}$**
8. $8\frac{2}{3} + 5\frac{1}{4}$ **$13\frac{11}{12}$**
9. $17\frac{3}{4} + 3\frac{3}{8}$ **$21\frac{1}{8}$**
10. $17\frac{2}{5} + 11\frac{3}{4}$ **$29\frac{3}{20}$**
11. *Masonry* A brick is $1\frac{7}{8}$ in. high. How high is a stack of 2 bricks? A stack of 4 bricks? **$3\frac{3}{4}$ in.; $7\frac{1}{2}$ in.**
12. *Writing* Explain the steps you would use to find $3\frac{2}{3} + 4\frac{1}{2}$. **See back of book.**

Find each difference.

13. $8\frac{4}{5} - 4\frac{1}{5}$ **$4\frac{3}{5}$**
14. $3\frac{1}{3} - 1\frac{2}{3}$ **$1\frac{2}{3}$**
15. $7\frac{2}{3} - 1\frac{1}{6}$ **$6\frac{1}{2}$**
16. $15 - 3\frac{3}{4}$ **$11\frac{1}{4}$**
17. $15\frac{3}{4} - 8\frac{3}{8}$ **17. $7\frac{3}{8}$**
18. $9\frac{1}{2} - \frac{2}{3}$ **$8\frac{5}{6}$**
19. $14 - 5\frac{1}{5}$ **$8\frac{4}{5}$**
20. $6\frac{9}{10} - 3\frac{2}{5}$ **$3\frac{1}{2}$**
21. $15\frac{1}{3} - 9\frac{1}{2}$ **$5\frac{5}{6}$**
22. $6\frac{3}{8} - 2\frac{3}{4}$ **22. $3\frac{5}{8}$**
23. *Mechanic* A piece of tubing $8\frac{5}{8}$ in. long is cut from a piece $23\frac{1}{2}$ in. long. How much is left? **$14\frac{7}{8}$ in.**
24. One bag of corn chips contains $1\frac{5}{8}$ oz. Another contains $1\frac{3}{4}$ oz. Which contains more? How much more does it contain? **24. $1\frac{3}{4}$ oz; $\frac{1}{8}$ oz**

CONNECTION TO MECHANICS Exercise 23 Ask students who have worked on cars to explain to the class why car engines contain tubing.

Exercise 47 Ask students why the parentheses are not necessary in this exercise. **Following the order of operations, we perform the two divisions first.** Ask when the parentheses would be necessary. **if we multiply or divide the two fractions**

WRAP UP

IDENTIFYING THE BIG IDEA Ask students: *How do you add and subtract mixed numbers?*

LESSON QUIZ

Find each sum or difference.

1. $3\frac{1}{4} - \frac{3}{4}$ **$2\frac{1}{2}$**
2. $5\frac{4}{9} - 2\frac{2}{3}$ **$2\frac{7}{9}$**
3. $12\frac{3}{5} + 6\frac{4}{5}$ **$19\frac{2}{5}$**
4. $2\frac{4}{5} + 3\frac{1}{10}$ **$5\frac{9}{10}$**

PRACTICE

Practice 5-3 *Adding and Subtracting Mixed Numbers*

Find each sum.

1. $5\frac{1}{3} + 3\frac{2}{3}$ 9
2. $7\frac{1}{4} + 4\frac{3}{8}$ $11\frac{5}{8}$
3. $2\frac{1}{8} + 6\frac{5}{8}$ $8\frac{3}{4}$
4. $8\frac{1}{5} + 4\frac{3}{10}$ $12\frac{1}{2}$
5. $9\frac{1}{6} + 6\frac{1}{4}$ $15\frac{5}{12}$
6. $3\frac{2}{3} + 10\frac{5}{6}$ $14\frac{1}{2}$

Find each difference.

7. $6\frac{11}{12} - 4\frac{5}{12}$ $2\frac{1}{2}$
8. $12 - 5\frac{3}{10}$ $6\frac{7}{10}$
9. $14\frac{1}{2} - 7\frac{1}{5}$ $7\frac{3}{10}$
10. $9 - 5\frac{5}{6}$ $3\frac{1}{6}$
11. $13\frac{3}{4} - 10\frac{1}{2}$ $3\frac{1}{4}$
12. $15\frac{1}{6} - 6\frac{5}{12}$ $8\frac{3}{4}$

Find each sum or difference.

13. $1\frac{1}{6} - \frac{3}{4}$ $\frac{5}{12}$
14. $4\frac{1}{2} - 2\frac{7}{8}$ $1\frac{5}{8}$
15. $9\frac{3}{4} + 7\frac{7}{8}$ $17\frac{5}{8}$
16. $5\frac{1}{6} - 4\frac{7}{12}$ $\frac{7}{12}$
17. $9\frac{8}{15} + 11\frac{5}{12}$ $20\frac{19}{20}$
18. $\frac{14}{15} - \frac{1}{2}$ $\frac{13}{30}$
19. $\frac{7}{12} + \frac{5}{6}$ $1\frac{5}{12}$
20. $1\frac{4}{9} + 3\frac{1}{6}$ $4\frac{11}{18}$
21. $3\frac{1}{2} - 2\frac{1}{4}$ $1\frac{1}{4}$

Circle A, B, C, or D. Which of the following represents each period of time as a fraction in lowest terms?

22. 8:00 A.M. to 9:20 A.M.
(A.) $1\frac{1}{3}$ h B. $1\frac{1}{2}$ h C. $\frac{1}{3}$ h D. $1\frac{2}{3}$ h

23. 9:00 A.M. to 2:45 P.M.
A. $5\frac{2}{3}$ h B. $7\frac{3}{4}$ h C. $4\frac{3}{4}$ h (D.) $5\frac{3}{4}$ h

24. 11:00 A.M. to 3:55 P.M.
A. $3\frac{11}{12}$ h (B.) $4\frac{11}{12}$ h C. $4\frac{55}{60}$ h D. $4\frac{11}{10}$ h

25. 8:30 A.M. to 10:40 P.M.
A. $2\frac{1}{6}$ h B. $2\frac{1}{5}$ h (C.) $14\frac{1}{6}$ h D. $14\frac{2}{3}$ h

26. 5:30 P.M. to 10:45 P.M.
A. $4\frac{3}{4}$ h (B.) $5\frac{1}{4}$ h C. $6\frac{1}{6}$ h D. $5\frac{1}{5}$ h

27. 7:20 A.M. to 11:00 A.M.
(A.) $3\frac{2}{3}$ h B. $3\frac{1}{15}$ h C. $2\frac{1}{3}$ h D. $4\frac{1}{4}$ h

Practice

In copymaster and workbook formats

Find the value of each expression. 26. $21\frac{1}{8}$ 29. $7\frac{1}{12}$ 34. $2\frac{1}{8}$ 37. $13\frac{17}{20}$

25. $8\frac{2}{5} - 5\frac{3}{5}$ **$2\frac{4}{5}$**
26. $12\frac{7}{8} + 8\frac{1}{4}$
27. $4\frac{2}{3} - \frac{5}{6}$ **$3\frac{5}{6}$**
28. $13\frac{5}{8} + 5\frac{1}{2}$ **$19\frac{1}{8}$**
29. $1\frac{3}{4} + 5\frac{1}{3}$
30. $2\frac{1}{8} + 4\frac{7}{8}$ **7**
31. $10 - \frac{5}{6}$ **$9\frac{1}{6}$**
32. $3\frac{5}{8} + 2\frac{1}{4}$ **$5\frac{7}{8}$**
33. $18\frac{1}{8} - 9\frac{3}{4}$ **$8\frac{3}{8}$**
34. $16\frac{7}{8} - 14\frac{3}{4}$
35. $24 - 9\frac{3}{5}$ **$14\frac{2}{5}$**
36. $19\frac{3}{4} + 6\frac{2}{5}$ **$26\frac{3}{20}$**
37. $25\frac{1}{4} - 11\frac{2}{5}$
38. $30\frac{2}{3} + 12\frac{3}{4}$
39. $25\frac{7}{8} - 9\frac{4}{5}$
40. $4\frac{2}{3} + 6 + 3\frac{1}{3}$ **14**
41. $8\frac{2}{5} - 3\frac{2}{3} + 2$ **$6\frac{11}{15}$**
42. $8\frac{2}{5} - (3\frac{2}{3} + 2)$ **$2\frac{11}{15}$**
43. $3\frac{1}{3} - 1\frac{1}{4} - 1\frac{1}{5}$

38. $43\frac{5}{12}$ 39. $16\frac{3}{40}$

43. $\frac{53}{60}$

44. a. *Advertising* A company placed ads in a newspaper that require $4\frac{1}{2}$ c.i. (column inches), $5\frac{3}{4}$ c.i., $3\frac{1}{4}$ c.i., $4\frac{3}{4}$ c.i., and $5\frac{3}{4}$ c.i. What is the total number of column inches? **24 c.i.**
   b. At \$20 per column inch, what is the total cost of the ads? **\$480**

45. *Construction* A bolt must go through a sign that is $\frac{5}{8}$ in. **$2\frac{7}{16}$ in.** thick and a support that is $1\frac{1}{2}$ in. thick. An additional $\frac{5}{16}$ in. is needed for the washer and nut. How long should the bolt be?

46. Your punch bowl holds 6 qt. Is it large enough to hold all the ingredients called for in the recipe at the right? Explain. **See below.**

Lemon Raspberry Fizz

47. *Calculator* You can use this key sequence to find $5\frac{1}{2} + 4\frac{3}{4}$.

(5 + 1 ÷ 2) + (4 + 3 ÷ 4) = 10.25

The calculator display 10.25 can be written as $10\frac{1}{4}$.

a. Write a key sequence you can use to find $4\frac{1}{8} - 1\frac{3}{4}$.
b. Use your key sequence to find $4\frac{1}{8} - 1\frac{3}{4}$. **2.375**

a. (4 + 1 ÷ 8) − (1 + 3 ÷ 4) =

Mixed Review

Write the prime factorization of each number. *(Lesson 4-5)*

48. 54 **2×3^3**
49. 104 **$2^3 \times 13$**
50. 128 **2^7**
51. 70 **$2 \times 5 \times 7$**
52. 100 **$2^2 \times 5^2$**

Order from least to greatest. *(Lesson 2-1)*

53. 0.438, 0.431, 0.4, 0.43 **0.4, 0.43, 0.431, 0.438**
54. 11.2, 11.02, 11.201, 11.1 **11.02, 11.1, 11.2, 11.201**
55. 75.3, 75.09, 75.98 **75.09, 75.3, 75.98**

56. *Choose a Strategy* An ice machine makes 50 ice cubes/h. Each ice cube uses 0.025 L of water. How much water is used to make ice cubes in one day? **30 L**

46. Yes; the total of all the ingredients is $5\frac{11}{12}$ qt.

RETEACHING

Reteaching 5-3 *Adding and Subtracting Mixed Numbers*

Follow these steps to add or subtract mixed numbers with different denominators.

		Add: $2\frac{2}{5} + 1\frac{3}{4}$	Subtract: $4\frac{1}{3} - 2\frac{5}{6}$
Step 1	Write the fractions with the same denominator.	$2\frac{8}{20} + 1\frac{15}{20}$	$4\frac{2}{6} - 2\frac{5}{6}$
Step 2	Rename, if necessary.		$3\frac{8}{6} - 2\frac{5}{6}$
Step 3	Add or subtract the whole numbers. Add or subtract the fractions.	$2\frac{8}{20} + 1\frac{15}{20} = 3\frac{23}{20}$	$3\frac{8}{6} - 2\frac{5}{6} = 1\frac{3}{6}$
Step 4	Simplify.	$3\frac{23}{20} = 4\frac{3}{20}$	$1\frac{3}{6} = 1\frac{1}{2}$

Complete to find each sum or difference.

1. $4\frac{3}{4} - 2\frac{3}{8}$
   $4\frac{6}{8} - 2\frac{3}{8} = 2\frac{3}{8}$
2. $4\frac{7}{12} + 2\frac{5}{6}$
   $4\frac{7}{12} + 2\frac{10}{12} = 6\frac{17}{12}$
   $= 7\frac{5}{12}$
3. $4\frac{1}{3} - 1\frac{3}{5}$
   $4\frac{5}{15} - 1\frac{9}{15}$
   $= 3\frac{20}{15} - 1\frac{9}{15}$
   $= 2\frac{11}{15}$

Find each sum or difference. Write it in simplest form.

4. $2\frac{3}{5} + 1\frac{1}{10}$ $3\frac{7}{10}$
5. $2\frac{5}{6} + 3\frac{4}{9}$ $6\frac{5}{18}$
6. $5 - 3\frac{7}{10}$ $1\frac{3}{10}$
7. $3\frac{1}{6} - 2\frac{1}{3}$ $\frac{5}{6}$
8. $4\frac{3}{4} - 1\frac{2}{3}$ $3\frac{1}{12}$
9. $3\frac{1}{2} + 4\frac{1}{3}$ $7\frac{5}{6}$
10. $3\frac{3}{10} + 1\frac{3}{5}$ $4\frac{9}{10}$
11. $6\frac{1}{3} + 7\frac{1}{4}$ $13\frac{7}{12}$
12. $4\frac{3}{5} + 6\frac{7}{10}$ $11\frac{3}{10}$
13. $7\frac{15}{16} - 2\frac{3}{8}$ $5\frac{9}{16}$
14. $4 - 2\frac{3}{10}$ $1\frac{7}{10}$
15. $5\frac{1}{4} - 1\frac{3}{8}$ $3\frac{7}{8}$
16. $2\frac{1}{2} + 5\frac{3}{5}$ $8\frac{1}{10}$
17. $7\frac{1}{4} - 3\frac{3}{5}$ $3\frac{13}{20}$
18. $5 - 2\frac{5}{8}$ $2\frac{3}{8}$
19. $9\frac{3}{5} + 1\frac{7}{10}$ $11\frac{3}{10}$
20. $6 - 5\frac{5}{6}$ $\frac{1}{6}$
21. $4\frac{7}{10} + 4\frac{1}{2}$ $9\frac{1}{5}$

ENRICHMENT

Minds on Math Transparency

5-3

Write the numbers 2, 3, 4, 5, 6, 7, 8, 9, and 10 in the squares, using each number only once, so that the numbers in the squares on each of the four circles have a sum of 27.

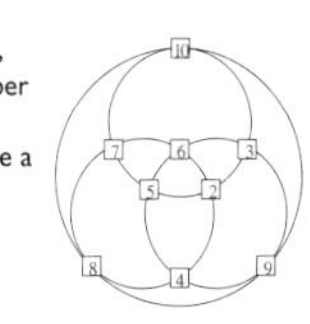

Sample answer is shown.

See *Solution Key* for worked-out answers.

5-4 Teaching Notes

1 Focus

CONNECTING TO PRIOR KNOWLEDGE
Write $a + 5 = 14$ on the board. Tell students: *You have $5 and want to buy something that costs $14.* Ask:

- *How does the equation represent the statement?* **Answers may vary. Sample: Some amount plus $5 will be enough to buy the item that costs $14.**
- *What does the variable "a" stand for in the equation?* **the additional amount you need to buy the item**

2 Teach

Work Together

AUDITORY LEARNING Questions 1 and 3
Ask those students who find the models helpful to explain them to those who do not understand how the models work.

Lesson Planning Options

Prerequisite Skills

- solving whole number equations (3-6 and 3-7)
- adding and subtracting fractions (5-2)

Materials/Manipulatives

- fraction bars
- graph paper

Resources

Student Edition

Skills Handbook, p. 540
Extra Practice, p. 518
Glossary/Study Guide

Teaching Resources

Chapter Support File, Ch. 5
- Lesson Planner 5-4
- Practice 5-4, Reteaching 5-4
- Alternative Activity 5-4
- Answer Masters 5-4

Teaching Aids Masters 20–25
Glossary, Spanish Resources

Transparencies
9, 10, 12, 15, 18–25,
Minds on Math 5-4

Warm Up

A ski shop has 28 pairs of gloves on sale. There are 7 pairs of leather gloves and 12 pairs of wool gloves. What fraction of the pairs on sale are wool? $\frac{3}{7}$

ALGEBRA Connection

5-4 Solving Equations with Fractions by Adding and Subtracting

What You'll Learn

1. To solve one-step equations by adding
2. To solve one-step equations by subtracting

...And Why

Knowing how to solve more kinds of equations allows you to use algebra in more situations.

Here's How

Look for questions that
- build understanding
- ✔ check understanding

4.

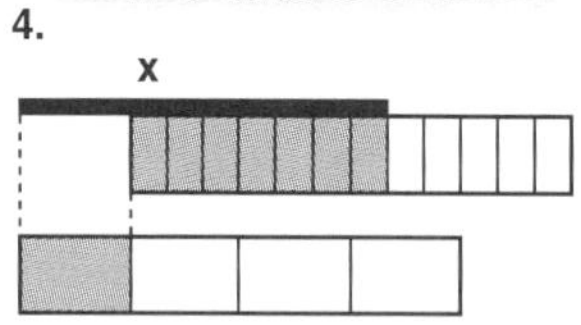

Work Together

Modeling Equations

1. At the right is a model of one of the following equations. Which equation do you think it is? **B**

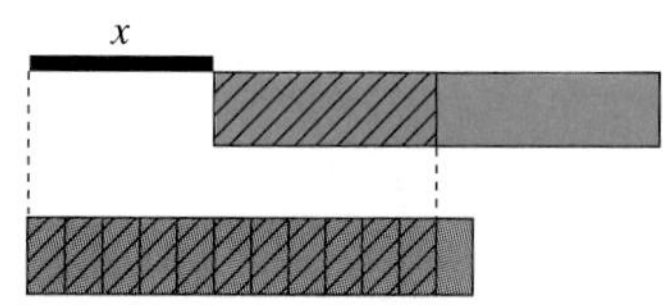

A. $x + \frac{11}{12} = \frac{1}{2}$ **B.** $x + \frac{1}{2} = \frac{11}{12}$ **C.** $x - \frac{1}{2} = \frac{11}{12}$

2. What is the solution of the equation modeled above? $\frac{5}{12}$

3. **a.** Complete: The model at the right represents the equation $x - \blacksquare = \blacksquare$. $\frac{3}{5}$; $\frac{3}{10}$
   b. What is the solution of the equation? $\frac{9}{10}$

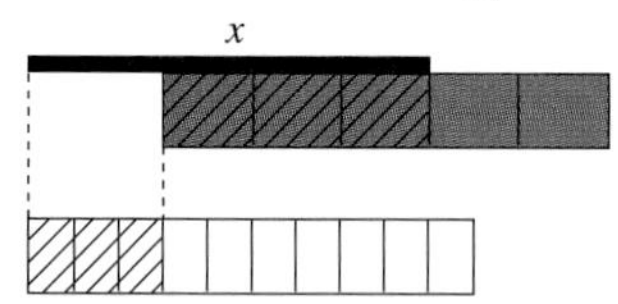

4. *Modeling* Model and solve the equation $x - \frac{7}{12} = \frac{1}{4}$. **See left for model; $\frac{5}{6}$**

THINK AND DISCUSS

1 Solving Equations by Adding

If an equation involves subtraction, use addition to "undo" it.

QUICKreview

Addition and subtraction are inverse operations. Addition "undoes" subtraction, and subtraction "undoes" addition.

■ **EXAMPLE 1**

Solve $n - \frac{1}{2} = 4\frac{3}{4}$.

$n - \frac{1}{2} = 4\frac{3}{4}$

$n - \frac{1}{2} + \frac{1}{2} = 4\frac{3}{4} + \frac{1}{2}$ ← Add $\frac{1}{2}$ to each side.

$n = 4\frac{3}{4} + \frac{2}{4}$ ← Find a common denominator.

$n = 4\frac{5}{4} = 5\frac{1}{4}$ ← Add the numerators. Rewrite $4\frac{5}{4}$ as $5\frac{1}{4}$.

5. ✔ *Try It Out* Solve each equation.
   a. $g - \frac{1}{4} = 3\frac{1}{2}$ $3\frac{3}{4}$ **b.** $2\frac{1}{2} = k - 4\frac{1}{3}$ $6\frac{5}{6}$ **c.** $x - \frac{2}{5} = \frac{5}{6}$ $1\frac{7}{30}$

Now you may assign Exercises 1–8.

THINK AND DISCUSS

Example 1 Remind students that you solve a variable equation by isolating the variable on one side of the equal sign.

Question 5b Make sure students realize that they can swap the left and right sides of this equation if they wish. This will neither change the answer nor the process for solving the equation.

Example 2 Remind students to watch for fractions that may need writing whenever they subtract. You may want to review the process for writing mixed numbers.

ERROR ALERT! Example 2 Students may forget to find the LCD to subtract the fractions because they are focusing on solving the equation. **Remediation:** Ask students to write and solve the subtraction problem separately and in vertical form.

ADDITIONAL EXAMPLES

FOR EXAMPLE 1

Solve $x - \frac{3}{5} = 8\frac{1}{4}$. $x = 8\frac{17}{20}$

FOR EXAMPLE 2

Solve $x + \frac{1}{4} = 3\frac{1}{2}$. $x = 3\frac{1}{4}$

FOR EXAMPLE 3

Star needs $6\frac{1}{2}$ lb of gravel to put on the bottom of her new fish tank. A friend gives her $1\frac{3}{4}$ lb. How much more gravel must Star buy? $4\frac{3}{4}$ lb

2 *Solving Equations by Subtracting*

Use subtraction to "undo" addition.

EXAMPLE 2

Solve $s + \frac{1}{3} = 2\frac{1}{6}$.

$$s + \frac{1}{3} = 2\frac{1}{6}$$
$$s + \frac{1}{3} - \frac{1}{3} = 2\frac{1}{6} - \frac{1}{3} \quad \leftarrow \text{Subtract } \tfrac{1}{3} \text{ from each side.}$$
$$s = 2\frac{1}{6} - \frac{2}{6} \quad \leftarrow \text{Find a common denominator.}$$
$$s = 1\frac{7}{6} - \frac{2}{6} \quad \leftarrow \text{Rewrite } 2\tfrac{1}{6} \text{ as } 1\tfrac{7}{6}.$$
$$= 1\frac{5}{6} \quad \leftarrow \text{Subtract.}$$

6a. $5\frac{3}{10}$

b. $2\frac{5}{12}$

c. $\frac{1}{12}$

6. ✔ *Try It Out* Solve each equation.
   a. $r + 4\frac{2}{5} = 9\frac{7}{10}$ **b.** $2\frac{2}{3} = p + \frac{1}{4}$ **c.** $\frac{1}{4} = \frac{1}{6} + m$

You use fractions in equations to solve many everyday problems.

EXAMPLE 3 *Real-World Problem Solving*

Commercial Fishing A fisherman caught $1\frac{1}{4}$ tons of fish. His boat holds $2\frac{3}{4}$ tons. How many more tons can he catch?

Words • tons of fish to be caught + tons of fish already caught = capacity of boat

• Let t = tons of fish to be caught
Tons of fish already caught $= 1\frac{1}{4}$
Capacity of boat $= 2\frac{3}{4}$

Equation • $t + 1\frac{1}{4} = 2\frac{3}{4}$

$$t + 1\frac{1}{4} = 2\frac{3}{4}$$
$$t + 1\frac{1}{4} - 1\frac{1}{4} = 2\frac{3}{4} - 1\frac{1}{4} \quad \leftarrow \text{Subtract } 1\tfrac{1}{4} \text{ from each side.}$$
$$t = 1\frac{2}{4}$$
$$t = 1\frac{1}{2} \quad \leftarrow \text{Simplify } 1\tfrac{2}{4}.$$

The fisherman can catch $1\frac{1}{2}$ tons more of fish.

7. *Look Back* Suppose the boat holds $3\frac{3}{8}$ tons. How many tons more could the fisherman catch if he already has $1\frac{1}{4}$ tons of fish? $2\frac{1}{8}$

Now you may assign Exercises 9–39.

Technology Options

Prentice Hall Technology

Software for Learners
- Math Blaster® Mystery*
- Interactive Student Tutorial, Chapter 5*

Teaching Resource Software
- Computer Item Generator 5-4
- Resource Pro™ Chapter 5*

Internet • For related mathematics activities, visit the Prentice Hall site at www.phschool.com/math

**Available on CD-ROM only*

Assignment Options for Exercises On Your Own

To provide flexible scheduling, this lesson can be subdivided into parts.

1 **Core** 1–7
Extension 8

2 **Core** 9–35, 37, 38
Extension 36, 39

Use Mixed Review to maintain skills.

Example 3 Help students understand the problem by first reading it aloud, replacing the fractions with whole numbers. Have students write the words and the equation for the whole number problem. Then read the problem again with mixed numbers.

EXTENSION Example 3 Show students how they can check their work by substituting the answer into the original equation. Once they simplify, the two sides of the equation should be equal.

3 Practice/Assess

EXERCISES *On Your Own*

ASSESSMENT Exercise 5 Ask students to write a short paragraph about how to solve this equation.

AEP Exercise 7 Make sure students understand that *then* tells them that the level was $10\frac{1}{3}$ ft after the water level had dropped.

ESTIMATION Exercise 8 Suggest that students round the fractions to 0, $\frac{1}{2}$, or 1. Have them rewrite the equation with rounded numbers. $r - \frac{1}{2} = 0$ Then have them solve this equation.

Exercise 26 Students may discover they can answer the question by substituting 1 for *n* in each equation. Then they can study the incorrect equations to see which would be correct if *n* was less than 1.

pages 201–202 On Your Own

36. $1 - p = \frac{1}{10} + \frac{2}{3} + \frac{1}{10}$; $\frac{2}{15}$ of the stadium
37. $\frac{1}{4} + r = \frac{2}{3}$; $\frac{5}{12}$ of trash
38. You need to "undo" each operation in both kinds of equations. The equations with fractions and mixed numbers need an extra step to find the LCD.

EXERCISES *On Your Own*

Write and solve an equation for each model.

1. $x - \frac{3}{4} = \frac{1}{12}$; $\frac{5}{6}$

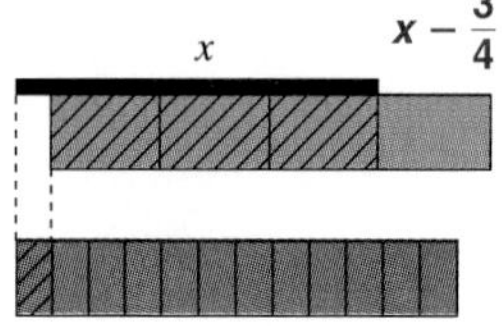

2. $x + \frac{3}{5} = \frac{9}{10}$; $\frac{3}{10}$

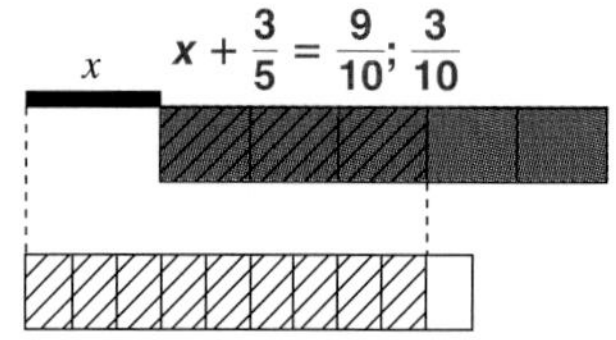

Solve each equation.

3. $q - \frac{1}{4} = 2\frac{1}{8}$ $2\frac{3}{8}$
4. $t - 2\frac{1}{5} = 4\frac{3}{10}$ $6\frac{1}{2}$
5. $\frac{1}{4} = b - \frac{1}{3}$ $\frac{7}{12}$
6. $a - \frac{7}{8} = 1\frac{1}{4}$ $2\frac{1}{8}$
7. ***Environment*** In the recent dry spell, the water level of Bailey's Pond decreased $1\frac{3}{4}$ ft. The pond was then only $10\frac{1}{3}$ ft deep. Write and solve an equation to find the depth before the dry spell. $d - 1\frac{3}{4} = 10\frac{1}{3}$; $12\frac{1}{12}$ ft
8. ***Estimation*** Is the solution of $r - \frac{4}{7} = \frac{2}{99}$ closest to 0, $\frac{1}{2}$, or 1? Explain. $\frac{1}{2}$; the solution is $\frac{2}{99} + \frac{4}{7} \approx 0 + \frac{1}{2} = \frac{1}{2}$.

Solve each equation.

9. $x + \frac{1}{2} = \frac{5}{8}$ $\frac{1}{8}$
10. $p + \frac{4}{5} = 6\frac{1}{5}$ $5\frac{2}{5}$
11. $\frac{1}{2} + d = 7\frac{5}{6}$ $7\frac{1}{3}$
12. $3\frac{9}{10} = s + 1\frac{1}{5}$ $2\frac{7}{10}$
13. Jathan's height on his last birthday was $51\frac{1}{2}$ in. When he measured his height this year, he was $52\frac{1}{4}$ in. tall.
    a. Write an equation that you can use to find how many inches Jathan grew this year. $51\frac{1}{2} + h = 52\frac{1}{4}$
    b. How many inches did Jathan grow this year? $\frac{3}{4}$ in.

Solve each equation.

14. $j + \frac{3}{4} = \frac{7}{8}$ $\frac{1}{8}$
15. $\frac{1}{6} = g - \frac{7}{8}$ $1\frac{1}{24}$
16. $\frac{5}{8} + t = 9\frac{3}{4}$ $9\frac{1}{8}$
17. $6\frac{1}{2} = m + 2\frac{7}{8}$ $3\frac{5}{8}$
18. $\frac{2}{5} + m = 1\frac{1}{2}$ $1\frac{1}{10}$
19. $a - \frac{7}{8} = 1\frac{1}{4}$ $2\frac{1}{8}$
20. $p + \frac{4}{5} = 6\frac{1}{5}$ $5\frac{2}{5}$
21. $\frac{2}{3} = p - \frac{2}{9}$ $\frac{8}{9}$
22. $w - 3\frac{1}{2} = 1\frac{3}{4}$ $5\frac{1}{4}$
23. $x + \frac{1}{2} = \frac{11}{22}$ 0
24. $z - 1\frac{3}{4} = 4\frac{1}{2}$ $6\frac{1}{4}$
25. $10 = y + 2\frac{2}{3}$ $7\frac{1}{3}$
26. **Choose A, B, or C.** For which equation is n less than 1? B

    A. $\frac{3}{4} + n = 1\frac{4}{5}$ B. $n + 1\frac{2}{7} = 1\frac{4}{9}$ C. $2\frac{3}{4} = 1\frac{3}{5} + n$

MENTAL MATH Exercises 27–34 Caution students not to add or subtract until they decide how to "undo" the operation in each exercise.

DIVERSITY Exercise 36 Some students may not be familiar with baseball. Ask a student who is familiar with baseball seating to explain to the class the different categories of seats in a baseball stadium.

CONNECTION TO HOUSEHOLD Exercise 37 Have students estimate what fraction of their household trash they recycle. Ask students: *How could your household increase the fraction of trash they recycle?* **Answers may vary. Sample: Start a compost pile.**

WRITING Exercise 38 Be sure students provide examples of each situation.

OPEN-ENDED Exercise 39c Suggest that students think of hobbies or activities they enjoy that could involve fraction equations.

Wrap Up

IDENTIFYING THE BIG IDEA Ask students: *How do you solve equations containing fractions?*

JOURNAL Suggest students think of activities they perform at the beginning and end of their day.

Mental Math **Solve each equation.** 30. $1\frac{1}{4}$ 34. $6\frac{1}{10}$

27. $y + \frac{1}{2} = 1\frac{1}{2}$ 1

28. $k - \frac{3}{8} = \frac{5}{8}$ 1

29. $\frac{3}{4} + a = \frac{3}{4}$ 0

30. $x + 2\frac{1}{2} = 3\frac{3}{4}$

31. $z + \frac{7}{9} = 4$ $3\frac{2}{9}$

32. $4\frac{3}{4} = v - 1\frac{1}{2}$ $6\frac{1}{4}$

33. $s - \frac{2}{9} = \frac{1}{3}$ $\frac{5}{9}$

34. $7\frac{3}{10} = 1\frac{1}{5} + b$

Solve each problem by writing and solving an equation. 35. $b + 3\frac{3}{4} = 5\frac{1}{4}$; $1\frac{1}{2}$ ft

35. *Carpentry* Charley had a board that was $5\frac{1}{4}$ ft long. While making a fence, he cut a piece $3\frac{3}{4}$ ft long from the board. What was the length of the piece of board that remained?

36. *Sports* At one baseball stadium, $\frac{1}{10}$ of the seats are box seats, $\frac{2}{3}$ are general admission, and $\frac{1}{10}$ are bleacher seats. The rest are premium seats. What fraction of the total are premium seats?

37. *Environment* The average U.S. household recycles about $\frac{1}{4}$ of its trash. How much would an average household have to increase its recycling to reach the goal of recycling $\frac{2}{3}$ of the trash?

38. *Writing* How is solving equations that involve fractions and mixed numbers similar to solving equations that involve integers? How is it different?

36–38. See margin p. 202.

a–b. Answers may vary. Samples are given.

39. a. *Open-ended* Write an equation that can be solved by addition and that has the solution $\frac{2}{5}$.
 b. Write an equation that can be solved by subtraction and that has the solution $\frac{2}{5}$.
 c. Write word problems for the equations you wrote for parts (a) and (b). a. $x - \frac{1}{4} = \frac{3}{20}$ b. $x + \frac{1}{2} = \frac{9}{10}$
 c. Check students' work.

JOURNAL
Describe several pairs of your daily activities that are inverses of each other. Describe some activities that have no inverse.

Mixed Review

40. Use the data at the right to create a graph. Predict the life expectancy for males and females in 2010. *(Lesson 1-9)* See margin.

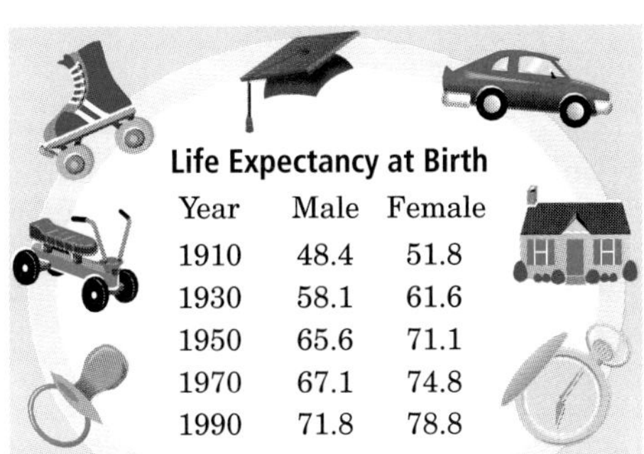

Life Expectancy at Birth

Year	Male	Female
1910	48.4	51.8
1930	58.1	61.6
1950	65.6	71.1
1970	67.1	74.8
1990	71.8	78.8

Solve. *(Lesson 3-7)*

41. $\frac{x}{-3} = -8$ 24

42. $-20 = \frac{y}{4}$ −80

43. $-3z = 39$ −13

44. $x \div (-7) = 77$ −539

45. $-81 = -3k$ 27

46. *Choose a Strategy* Antwan bought six pairs of socks and a $5 scarf. He paid $12.74 for everything. How much did each pair of socks cost? $1.29

CHECKPOINT 1

Checkpoint 1 *Lessons 5-1 through 5-4*

Estimate each answer.

1. $4\frac{4}{5} + 2\frac{7}{8}$ 8
2. $8\frac{1}{8} - 2\frac{6}{7}$ 5
3. $6\frac{3}{10} \div 1\frac{9}{10}$ 3
4. $3\frac{1}{12} \times 1\frac{7}{9}$ 6

5. **Circle A, B, C, or D. Which is between 10 and 11?**

A. $29\frac{3}{4} \div 3\frac{7}{8}$ B. $2 \cdot 4\frac{5}{8}$
(C) $7\frac{2}{7} + 3\frac{1}{5}$ D. $13\frac{3}{4} - \frac{7}{8}$

Find each sum or difference.

6. $\frac{2}{5} + \frac{3}{10}$ $\frac{7}{10}$
7. $\frac{2}{3} + 4\frac{2}{5}$ $5\frac{1}{15}$
8. $\frac{1}{3} - \frac{2}{9}$ $\frac{1}{9}$
9. $8\frac{7}{10} - 3\frac{1}{3}$ $5\frac{11}{30}$

Solve each equation.

10. $\frac{5}{6} = t + \frac{1}{2}$ $\frac{1}{3}$
11. $n - 2\frac{1}{5} = \frac{4}{5}$ 3
12. $2\frac{4}{5} + n = \frac{2}{3}$ $-2\frac{2}{15}$
13. $x + \frac{3}{10} = \frac{4}{5}$ $\frac{5}{10}$ or $\frac{1}{2}$

pages 203 Mixed Review

40.

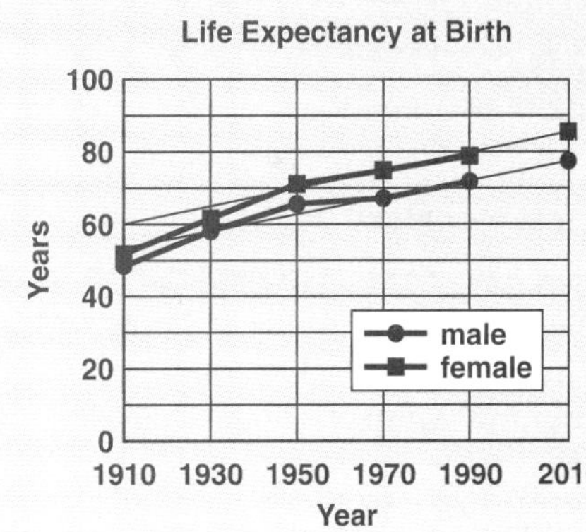

Predictions may vary. Sample: 77.4 years; 85.5 years

PRACTICE

Practice 5-4 *Solving Equations with Fractions by Adding and Subtracting*

Write and solve the equation represented by each model.

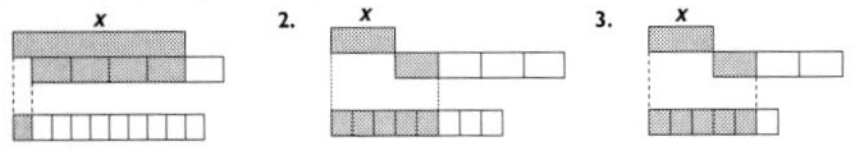

1. $x - \frac{4}{5} = \frac{1}{10}$; $\frac{9}{10}$
2. $x + \frac{1}{4} = \frac{5}{8}$; $\frac{3}{8}$
3. $x + \frac{1}{3} = \frac{5}{6}$; $\frac{1}{2}$

Solve each equation.

4. $m + \frac{7}{8} = 1\frac{1}{2}$ $\frac{5}{8}$
5. $j - \frac{1}{4} = \frac{7}{8}$ $1\frac{1}{8}$
6. $t + \frac{9}{10} = 1\frac{4}{5}$ $\frac{9}{10}$
7. $k - \frac{5}{6} = \frac{11}{12}$ $1\frac{3}{4}$
8. $\frac{7}{8} = n + \frac{1}{4}$ $\frac{5}{8}$
9. $\frac{1}{5} = a - \frac{9}{10}$ $1\frac{1}{10}$
10. $b + \frac{7}{10} = 1\frac{1}{2}$ $\frac{4}{5}$
11. $c - \frac{7}{8} = \frac{5}{8}$ $1\frac{1}{2}$
12. $w + 2\frac{1}{4} = 5\frac{5}{8}$ $3\frac{3}{8}$
13. $x - 1\frac{3}{5} = 2\frac{7}{10}$ $4\frac{3}{10}$
14. $\frac{2}{9} = z - \frac{2}{3}$ $\frac{8}{9}$
15. $\frac{1}{2} = d + \frac{1}{6}$ $\frac{1}{3}$
16. $4\frac{3}{4} + q = 5\frac{7}{8}$ $1\frac{1}{8}$
17. $9\frac{1}{4} = h - 1\frac{3}{4}$ 11
18. $e + 6\frac{3}{4} = 9\frac{7}{8}$ $3\frac{1}{8}$
19. $f - 5\frac{1}{2} = 8\frac{2}{3}$ $14\frac{1}{6}$
20. $u + 7\frac{1}{6} = 9\frac{5}{12}$ $2\frac{1}{4}$
21. $e - 4\frac{1}{6} = 7\frac{5}{6}$ 12
22. $i + 7\frac{1}{3} = 9\frac{11}{12}$ $2\frac{7}{12}$
23. $k - 8\frac{1}{5} = 7\frac{2}{5}$ $15\frac{3}{5}$
24. $p + 4\frac{2}{9} = 11\frac{1}{3}$ $7\frac{1}{9}$

Solve each problem by writing and solving an equation. Equations may vary.

25. Lacey had a ribbon $5\frac{7}{8}$ yd long. She used $1\frac{1}{2}$ yd for a belt for a dress. What length of the ribbon remains? $5\frac{7}{8} - 1\frac{1}{2} = x$; $4\frac{3}{8}$ yd
26. The depth of a river at one spot is normally $16\frac{3}{4}$ ft deep. The water rose $5\frac{1}{2}$ ft during a flood. What was the depth of the river at that spot during the flood? $16\frac{3}{4} + 5\frac{1}{2} = x$; $22\frac{1}{4}$ ft
27. Katrina rode her bicycle $6\frac{3}{4}$ mi before she realized she forgot her lock. She rode $2\frac{1}{2}$ mi toward home before she met Magda. How far does Katrina need to ride before she is home? $6\frac{3}{4} - 2\frac{1}{2} = x$; $4\frac{1}{4}$ mi
28. A shoreline is washing away at a rate of $1\frac{7}{10}$ ft each year. A house is $225\frac{9}{10}$ ft from the water. If erosion continues at the same rate, how far from the water will the house be next year? $225\frac{9}{10} - 1\frac{7}{10} = x$; $224\frac{1}{5}$ ft

In copymaster and workbook formats

RETEACHING

Reteaching 5-4 *Solving Equations with Fractions by Adding and Subtracting*

To solve equations, remember that subtraction "undoes" addition and addition "undoes" subtraction.

$n + 4\frac{1}{4} = 5\frac{3}{4}$ ← **Addition equation: use subtraction to solve.**

$n + 4\frac{1}{4} - 4\frac{1}{4} = 5\frac{3}{4} - 4\frac{1}{4}$ ← **Subtract $4\frac{1}{4}$ from each side.**

$n = 1\frac{2}{4} = 1\frac{1}{2}$ ← **Simplify.**

$n - 1\frac{3}{4} = \frac{1}{2}$ ← **Subtraction equation: use addition to solve.**

$n - 1\frac{3}{4} + 1\frac{3}{4} = \frac{1}{2} + 1\frac{3}{4}$ ← **Add $1\frac{3}{4}$ to each side.**

$n = \frac{2}{4} + 1\frac{3}{4}$ ← **Find a common denominator.**

$n = 1\frac{5}{4} = 2\frac{1}{4}$ ← **Simplify.**

Complete to solve each equation.

1. $x + \frac{1}{5} = \frac{3}{5}$
   $x + \frac{1}{5} - \frac{1}{5} = \frac{3}{5} - \frac{1}{5}$
   $x = \frac{2}{5}$
2. $\frac{1}{4} + t = 1\frac{3}{4}$
   $\frac{1}{4} - \frac{1}{4} + t = 1\frac{3}{4} - \frac{1}{4}$
   $t = 1\frac{2}{4} = 1\frac{1}{2}$
3. $\frac{7}{8} = w - \frac{3}{8}$
   $\frac{7}{8} + \frac{3}{8} = w - \frac{3}{8} + \frac{3}{8}$
   $1\frac{1}{4} = \frac{10}{8} = w$
4. $h - 2\frac{1}{3} = \frac{2}{3}$
   $h - 2\frac{1}{3} + 2\frac{1}{3} = \frac{2}{3} + 2\frac{1}{3}$
   $h = 3$

Solve each equation.

5. $a + 1\frac{2}{5} = 4\frac{4}{5}$ $3\frac{2}{5}$
6. $2\frac{3}{4} = f - \frac{1}{4}$ 3
7. $\frac{5}{9} + k = 1\frac{7}{9}$ $1\frac{2}{9}$
8. $z - \frac{3}{5} = \frac{9}{10}$ $1\frac{1}{2}$
9. $4\frac{2}{3} + s = 6$ $1\frac{1}{3}$
10. $\frac{5}{8} = b - \frac{1}{8}$ $\frac{3}{4}$
11. $3\frac{5}{6} + m = 10\frac{2}{3}$ $6\frac{5}{6}$
12. $n - 1\frac{1}{3} = \frac{1}{2}$ $1\frac{5}{6}$
13. $\frac{3}{5} = t + \frac{1}{3}$ $\frac{4}{15}$
14. $z + 1\frac{2}{7} = 2\frac{5}{7}$ $1\frac{3}{7}$
15. $r - 3\frac{1}{2} = 4\frac{3}{8}$ $7\frac{7}{8}$
16. $x + \frac{7}{9} = 2\frac{2}{3}$ $1\frac{8}{9}$
17. $3\frac{5}{9} = r + 2\frac{1}{6}$ $1\frac{7}{18}$
18. $k - 2\frac{3}{10} = \frac{4}{5}$ $3\frac{1}{10}$
19. $2\frac{1}{4} = m + 1\frac{1}{6}$ $1\frac{1}{12}$

Reteaching

ENRICHMENT

Minds on Math Transparency

5-4

What will row 50 of the pattern below look like?

$1 + 2 = 3$
$4 + 5 + 6 = 7 + 8$
$9 + 10 + 11 + 12 = 13 + 14 + 15$
$16 + 17 + 18 + 19 + 20 = 21 + 22 + 23 + 24$

$2{,}500 + 2{,}501 + \ldots + 2{,}550 = 2{,}551 + \ldots + 2{,}600$

See *Solution Key* for worked-out answers.

Math at Work

If you have block scheduling or extended class periods, challenge small groups of students to write new lyrics to a song they know. Tell students to choose words with syllables that fit the rhythm of the music. Students may want to end pairs of lines with rhyming words. If possible, borrow song books from a music teacher for examples. Also, consider asking a musician to give students a five-minute lesson on writing song lyrics to music.

LESSON QUIZ

Solve each equation.

1. $x + \frac{1}{3} = \frac{3}{4}$ $x = \frac{5}{12}$
2. $y - \frac{2}{5} = \frac{9}{10}$ $y = 1\frac{3}{10}$
3. $a + 2\frac{3}{4} = 7\frac{1}{4}$ $a = 4\frac{1}{2}$
4. $b - 6\frac{3}{8} = 2\frac{1}{2}$ $b = 8\frac{7}{8}$

✓ CHECKPOINT 1 — Lessons 5-1 through 5-4

Estimate each answer.

1. $\frac{1}{2} + \frac{2}{5}$ 1
2. $\frac{1}{8} + \frac{5}{12}$ $\frac{1}{2}$
3. $4\frac{2}{5} - 1\frac{1}{4}$ 3
4. $8\frac{1}{3} \cdot 2\frac{4}{5}$ 24
5. $28\frac{3}{4} + 2\frac{7}{8}$ 32

Find each sum or difference.

6. $\frac{3}{4} + \frac{7}{8}$ $1\frac{5}{8}$
7. $\frac{2}{3} - \frac{5}{8}$ $\frac{1}{24}$
8. $\frac{1}{6} + \frac{3}{8}$ $\frac{13}{24}$
9. $\frac{5}{6} - \frac{1}{9}$ $\frac{13}{18}$
10. $\frac{1}{2} + \frac{1}{6}$ $\frac{2}{3}$
11. $7\frac{1}{2} - 3\frac{3}{7}$ $4\frac{1}{14}$
12. $\frac{4}{5} + 3\frac{2}{3}$ $4\frac{7}{15}$
13. $13\frac{3}{8} - 7\frac{1}{2}$ $5\frac{7}{8}$
14. $7\frac{2}{5} - 1\frac{2}{3}$ $5\frac{11}{15}$
15. $5\frac{1}{2} + 7\frac{5}{8}$ $13\frac{1}{8}$

Write an equation for each model.

16. 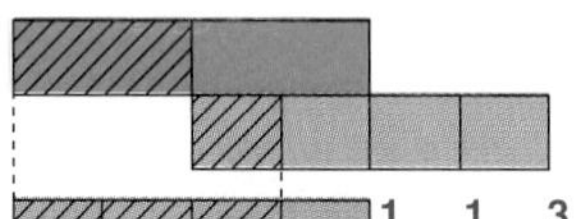 $\frac{1}{2} + \frac{1}{4} = \frac{3}{4}$

17. 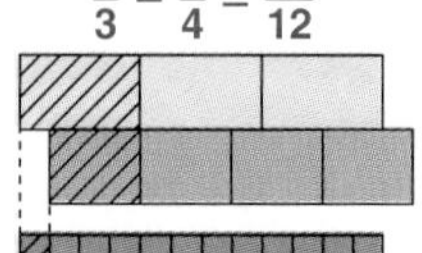 $\frac{1}{3} - \frac{1}{4} = \frac{1}{12}$

18. 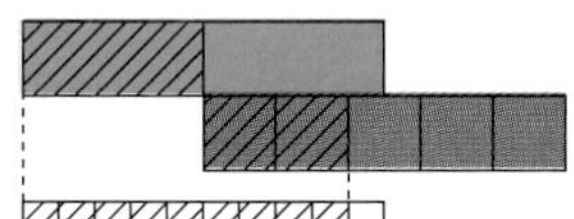 $\frac{1}{2} + \frac{2}{5} = \frac{9}{10}$

Solve each equation.

19. $\frac{3}{8} = t - \frac{3}{4}$ $1\frac{1}{8}$
20. $n + 2\frac{1}{3} = 3\frac{4}{5}$ $1\frac{7}{15}$
21. $3\frac{1}{2} + a = 5\frac{3}{10}$ $1\frac{4}{5}$
22. $p - 3\frac{3}{4} = 15\frac{1}{8}$ $18\frac{7}{8}$
23. $b + \frac{1}{2} = \frac{3}{5}$ $\frac{1}{10}$
24. $\frac{3}{8} + f = \frac{7}{12}$ $\frac{5}{24}$
25. $5\frac{3}{5} = d - 2\frac{1}{4}$ $7\frac{17}{20}$
26. $h - 8\frac{1}{3} = 1\frac{4}{5}$ $10\frac{2}{15}$

Math at Work

SONGWRITER

Songwriters need to know what types of music are "in" and compose songs that will sell. Then the songwriter must find a publisher willing to find an artist to record it. Producers and record companies decide if they will promote a song as a potential hit.

Songwriters use mathematics to understand complex rhythms and produce lyrics to all kinds of music.

Internet Connection

To learn more, check out this Web site on Songwriting, Composition, and Performing: www.studyweb.com/music/songs.htm

5-5 Teaching Notes

1 Focus

CONNECTING TO PRIOR KNOWLEDGE

Make statements such as: *I used half a dozen eggs in this recipe* or *Joanne used one fourth of her $20 to buy supplies.* Ask students to find the amounts you referred to in each statement, and to explain how they found the amounts. Relate the statements to the expressions $\frac{1}{2}$ of 12 and $\frac{1}{4}$ of 20.

2 Teach

Work Together

Question 4 Students may believe that a product is always larger than either of its two factors. Discuss the size of the product after students have found $\frac{1}{12}$ using their model. Ask students: *Is the product of two numbers always larger than the numbers being multiplied?* **no** *Name some situations in which the product is smaller.* **Answers may vary. Samples: when at least one of the numbers is less than 1; when one of the numbers is negative**

THINK AND DISCUSS

Example 2 Some students may refer to dividing by the GCF as *canceling.* Explain that this word can mean both *dividing to equal 1*

GEOMETRY Connection

5-5 Multiplying Fractions and Mixed Numbers

What You'll Learn

1. To multiply fractions
2. To multiply mixed numbers

...And Why

You can multiply fractions to find land area or to change the number of servings of a recipe.

Here's How

Look for questions that
- build understanding
- ✔ check understanding

Work Together — *Modeling Multiplication of Fractions*

Work with a partner. Use paper folding to find $\frac{1}{3}$ of $\frac{1}{4}$, or $\frac{1}{3} \cdot \frac{1}{4}$.

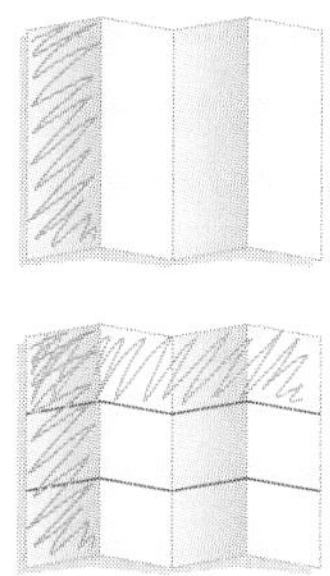

1. Fold a sheet of paper as shown. Shade $\frac{1}{4}$ of it.
2. Now fold the paper as shown in the second picture. Shade $\frac{1}{3}$ of it as shown.
   1–2. Check students' work.
3. a. Count the total number of rectangles made by the folds. **12 rectangles**
   b. How many did you shade twice? **1**
   c. What fraction of all the rectangles is this? $\mathbf{\frac{1}{12}}$
4. Use your model to complete: $\frac{1}{3} \cdot \frac{1}{4} = \blacksquare$. $\mathbf{\frac{1}{12}}$
5. *Modeling* Pick two fractions from $\frac{1}{3}$, $\frac{2}{3}$, or $\frac{3}{4}$. Use paper folding and shading to find their product.
   Answers may vary. Sample: $\frac{1}{3} \cdot \frac{3}{4} = \frac{1}{4}$

THINK AND DISCUSS

1 Multiplying Fractions

To multiply fractions, you multiply their numerators and multiply their denominators.

EXAMPLE 1

Find $\frac{7}{8} \cdot \frac{2}{3}$.

$$\frac{7}{8} \cdot \frac{2}{3} = \frac{7 \cdot 2}{8 \cdot 3}$$ ← Multiply numerators. ← Multiply denominators.

$$= \frac{14}{24}$$ ← Find the two products.

$$= \frac{7}{12}$$ ← Write $\frac{14}{24}$ in simplest form.

6. ✔ *Try It Out* Find each product.
   a. $\frac{3}{5} \cdot \frac{1}{4}$ $\mathbf{\frac{3}{20}}$ b. $\frac{5}{6} \cdot \frac{4}{5}$ $\mathbf{\frac{2}{3}}$ c. $\frac{3}{10} \cdot \frac{5}{8}$ $\mathbf{\frac{3}{16}}$ d. $\frac{3}{4} \cdot \frac{4}{3}$ **1**

Lesson Planning Options

Prerequisite Skills

- simplifying fractions (4-6)
- writing mixed numbers as improper fractions (4-8)

Materials/Manipulatives

- paper for models
- colored pencils
- calculator

Resources

Student Edition

Skills Handbook, p. 530
Extra Practice, p. 518
Glossary/Study Guide

Teaching Resources

Chapter Support File, Ch. 5
- Lesson Planner 5-5
- Practice 5-5, Reteaching 5-5
- Answer Masters 5-5

Teaching Aids Masters 8, 10, 20–25
Glossary, Spanish Resources

Transparencies

9, 10, 15, 18–25, Minds on Math 5-5

Warm Up

As Marques walks along the hike and bike trail, he begins to plan his new book about hikes in Yosemite, Bryce Canyon, Yellowstone, and Big Bend National Parks. He cannot decide the order to write the four parks in the book. How many orders are possible? **24**

and *subtracting to 0.* Urge students to use the phrase *dividing by the GCF.*

CONNECTION TO BIOLOGY Example 2 Challenge students to use a balance-beam scale to find an item in the classroom that weighs $\frac{1}{15}$ oz. Give all students an opportunity to feel the weight of the object so that they can appreciate how tiny the bee hummingbird is.

ADDITIONAL EXAMPLES

FOR EXAMPLE 1

Find $\frac{5}{6} \cdot \frac{3}{4}$. $\frac{5}{8}$

FOR EXAMPLE 2

A sheet of art paper weighs $\frac{7}{9}$ oz. If you tear off $\frac{1}{4}$ of the sheet, what will the remaining $\frac{3}{4}$ weigh? Find the product of $\frac{3}{4}$ and $\frac{7}{9}$. $\frac{7}{12}$ oz

FOR EXAMPLE 3

What is $\frac{5}{8}$ of 24? 15

FOR EXAMPLE 4

Find $2\frac{1}{7} \cdot 2\frac{1}{3}$. 5

KINESTHETIC LEARNING Example 3 Choose 28 students to stand in a grid of 4 rows and 7 columns. If you do not have 28 students, use desks or chairs in their place. Point to 3 of the 7 columns. Direct students in these 3 columns to raise their hands. Have students count the 12 raised hands.

ERROR ALERT! Example 4 Some students may find the product of the whole numbers

Technology Options

Prentice Hall Technology

Software for Learners

- Hot Page™ 8–6*
- Math Blaster® Mystery*
- Interactive Student Tutorial, Chapter 5*

Teaching Resource Software

- Computer Item Generator 5-5
- Resource Pro™ Chapter 5*

Internet • For related mathematics activities, visit the Prentice Hall site at www.phschool.com/math

**Available on CD-ROM only*

Assignment Options for Exercises On Your Own

To provide flexible scheduling, this lesson can be subdivided into parts.

1 **Core** 1–23
Extension 24

2 **Core** 25–42, 44–46
Extension 43

Use Mixed Review to maintain skills.

7. *Look Back* Why is the figure below a model of the product in Example 1?

$\frac{7}{8}$ of the columns are shaded and $\frac{2}{3}$ of the rows are shaded. The area shaded twice is $\frac{7}{8} \cdot \frac{2}{3} = \frac{7}{12}$.

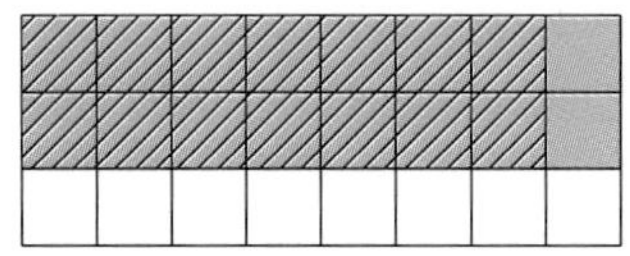

When a numerator and a denominator have a common factor, you can simplify before multiplying.

EXAMPLE 2 *Real-World Problem Solving*

Biology The largest hummingbird is the giant hummingbird of South America. It weighs $\frac{2}{3}$ oz. The smallest hummingbird is the bee hummingbird of Cuba. It has only one tenth the weight of a giant hummingbird. What is the weight of a bee hummingbird?

Find the product of $\frac{1}{10}$ and $\frac{2}{3}$.

$$\frac{1}{10} \cdot \frac{2}{3} = \frac{1}{_5\cancel{10}} \cdot \frac{\cancel{2}^1}{3} \quad \leftarrow \text{Divide a numerator and a denominator by their GCF, which is 2.}$$

$$= \frac{1 \cdot 1}{5 \cdot 3} \quad \leftarrow \text{Multiply the numerators.} \leftarrow \text{Multiply the denominators.}$$

$$= \frac{1}{15} \quad \leftarrow \text{Simplify.}$$

A bee hummingbird weighs $\frac{1}{15}$ oz.

8. ✔ *Try It Out* Find each product.

a. $\frac{1}{2} \cdot \frac{2}{3}$ $\frac{1}{3}$ b. $\frac{3}{4} \cdot \frac{2}{5}$ $\frac{3}{10}$ c. $\frac{2}{3} \cdot \frac{3}{8}$ $\frac{1}{4}$ d. $\frac{2}{5} \cdot \frac{3}{8}$ $\frac{3}{20}$

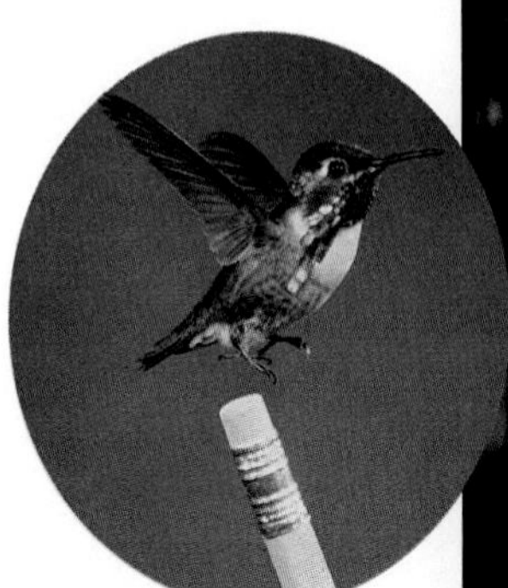

and the product of the fractions and then add the two products. **Remediation:** Remind students that when multiplying two-digit numbers, you do not just multiply the tens by the tens and the ones by the ones. You must multiply everything by everything.

ASSESSMENT Question 10 Have students write a note to their partner explaining how to find the product of $2\frac{1}{3} \cdot 4\frac{5}{8}$. Have partners exchange notes and follow each other's directions to see if the explanation is clear.

3 Practice/Assess

EXERCISES *On Your Own*

ERROR ALERT! Some students introduce mistakes when they try to divide by common factors mentally. **Remediation:** Encourage students to show their work on paper when dividing the numerator and the denominator by the GCF.

CONNECTION TO GEOGRAPHY Exercise 23a Have students examine a globe. Encourage students to estimate what fraction of the surface area of Earth is water, land, and desert.

MENTAL MATH Exercises 25–39 Encourage students to use each of the three calculation methods for at least two exercises. You may need to help students identify exercises that they can answer reasonably using mental math. For example, Exercises 26 and 30.

When multiplying a fraction by a whole number, write the whole number as a fraction with a denominator of 1.

■ EXAMPLE 3

What is $\frac{3}{7}$ of 28?

Find $\frac{3}{7} \cdot 28$.

Estimate: $\frac{3}{7} \cdot 28 \approx \frac{1}{2} \cdot 28 = 14$

$\frac{3}{7} \cdot 28 = \frac{3}{7} \cdot \frac{28}{1}$ ← Write 28 as $\frac{28}{1}$.

$= \frac{3 \cdot \cancel{28}^{4}}{{}_{1}\cancel{7} \cdot 1}$ ← Divide a numerator and denominator by their GCF, which is 7.

$= \frac{12}{1}$ ← Multiply.

$= 12$ ← Simplify.

9. ✔ *Try It Out* Find $\frac{4}{5}$ of 30. **24**

Now you may assign Exercises 1–24.

2 *Multiplying Mixed Numbers*

To multiply mixed numbers, first write them as improper fractions.

■ EXAMPLE 4

Find $2\frac{3}{5} \cdot 4\frac{1}{2}$.

Estimate: $2\frac{3}{5} \cdot 4\frac{1}{2} \approx 3 \cdot 5 = 15$

$2\frac{3}{5} \cdot 4\frac{1}{2} = \frac{13}{5} \cdot \frac{9}{2}$ ← Write mixed numbers as improper fractions.

$= \frac{13 \cdot 9}{5 \cdot 2}$ ← Multiply the numerators. ← Multiply the denominators.

$= \frac{117}{10}$

$= 11\frac{7}{10}$ ← Write as a mixed number in simplest form.

10. ✔ *Try It Out* Find $2\frac{1}{3} \cdot 4\frac{5}{8}$. **$10\frac{19}{24}$**

You can multiply mixed numbers on your calculator. For instance, you can use this key sequence to find $2\frac{3}{5} \cdot 4\frac{1}{2}$.

(2 + 3 ÷ 5) × (4 + 1 ÷ 2) = 11.7

You can write the answer 11.7 as the mixed number $11\frac{7}{10}$.

11. *Calculator* Use a calculator to find $3\frac{1}{2} \cdot 1\frac{3}{4}$. **$6\frac{1}{8}$**

Now you may assign Exercises 25–46.

WRITING Exercise 44 Suggest that students choose two fractions to multiply and then add, before writing their answer. Students can practice recognizing the difference between the two operations.

DIVERSITY Exercise 45 Some students may not be familiar with Sloppy Joes. Invite students to describe them and list as many ingredients as they can remember. If possible, ask your school cafeteria to serve Sloppy Joes.

ESTIMATION Exercises 47–51 Remind students that rounding or front-end estimation is easier to use for addition, subtraction, and multiplication, but that for division they should use compatible numbers. You may need to review finding compatible numbers.

WRAP UP

IDENTIFYING THE BIG IDEA Ask students: *How do you multiply fractions? How is multiplying mixed numbers different from multiplying fractions?*

PROJECT LINK Have several cookbooks available for students to compare recipes. Urge students to have an adult present when making their pancakes.

pages 208–209 On Your Own

44. When you multiply two fractions, you multiply the numerators and multiply the denominators. When you add fractions, you write them with a common denominator and add only the numerators.

EXERCISES *On Your Own*

Write a multiplication sentence for each model.

1. 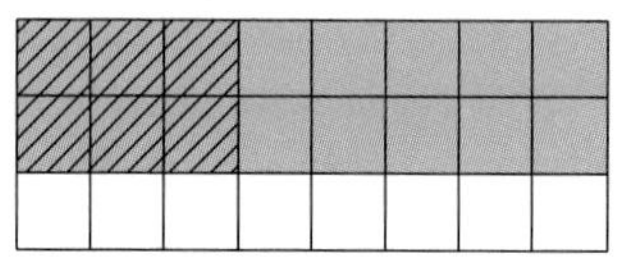
$\frac{3}{8} \cdot \frac{2}{3} = \frac{6}{24}$

2. 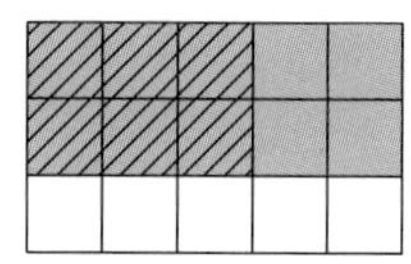
$\frac{3}{5} \cdot \frac{2}{3} = \frac{6}{15}$

3. $\frac{5}{6} \cdot \frac{3}{4} = \frac{15}{24}$
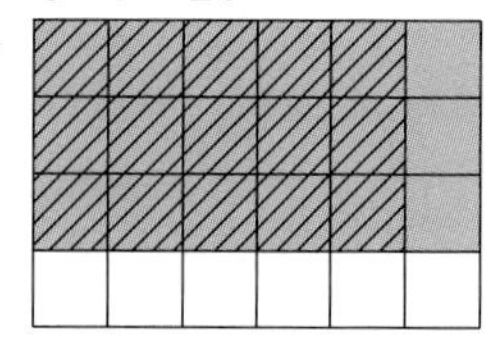

Draw a sketch or use a model to find each product.

4. $\frac{1}{2} \cdot \frac{1}{3}$ $\frac{1}{6}$
5. $\frac{1}{4} \cdot \frac{3}{5}$ $\frac{3}{20}$
6. $\frac{2}{3} \cdot \frac{3}{4}$ $\frac{1}{2}$
7. $\frac{1}{3} \cdot \frac{5}{6}$ $\frac{5}{18}$

Find each product.

8. $\frac{1}{4} \cdot \frac{8}{9}$ $\frac{2}{9}$
9. $\frac{7}{8} \cdot \frac{4}{5}$ $\frac{7}{10}$
10. $\frac{2}{5} \cdot \frac{15}{16}$ $\frac{3}{8}$
11. $\frac{1}{3} \cdot 12$ 4
12. $\frac{1}{4} \cdot 4$ 1
13. $\frac{3}{4} \cdot \frac{3}{2}$ $1\frac{1}{8}$
14. $\frac{2}{3} \cdot \frac{2}{5}$ $\frac{4}{15}$
15. $\frac{2}{5} \cdot \frac{2}{5}$ $\frac{4}{25}$
16. $\frac{1}{4}$ of 12 3
17. $\frac{3}{4}$ of 20 15
18. $\frac{3}{4} \cdot 16$ 12
19. $\frac{5}{8} \cdot \frac{3}{5}$ $\frac{3}{8}$
20. $\frac{3}{8} \cdot \frac{2}{5}$ $\frac{3}{20}$
21. $\frac{3}{10}$ of 60 18
22. $\frac{2}{3} \cdot \frac{3}{4}$ $\frac{1}{2}$

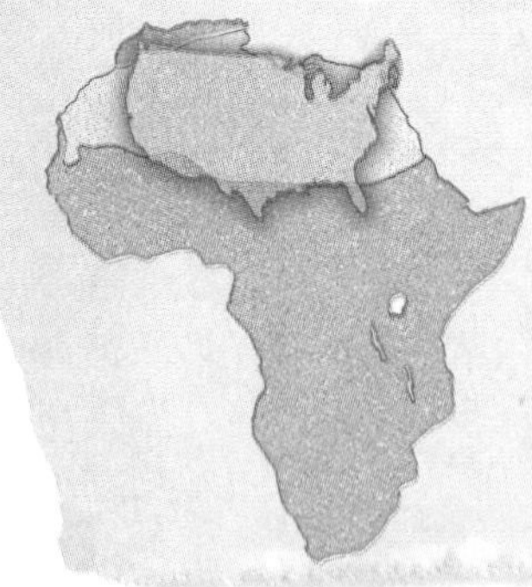

What's *on* Earth?

EARTH has almost 200 million square miles of surface area. What is it really like? A little more than seven tenths of that area is water. What remains is land. But nearly one fifth of the land is desert. The largest desert is the Sahara Desert, which is $3\frac{1}{2}$ million square miles. The Sahara is roughly equal to the land area of the United States!

23. a. *Geography* About how many square miles of Earth's surface is water? 140,000,000 mi^2
    b. About how many square miles is desert? 12,000,000 mi^2

24. The length of a nail should be three times the thickness of the board being fastened with it. How long a nail should be used with boards of each thickness?
    a. $\frac{3}{8}$ in. $1\frac{1}{8}$ in. b. $\frac{1}{2}$ in. $1\frac{1}{2}$ in. c. $\frac{5}{8}$ in. $1\frac{7}{8}$ in. d. $\frac{3}{4}$ in. $2\frac{1}{4}$ in. e. $\frac{7}{8}$ in. $2\frac{5}{8}$ in.

LESSON QUIZ

Find each product.

1. Find $\frac{3}{8} \cdot \frac{1}{2}$. $\frac{3}{16}$
2. Find $\frac{5}{16} \cdot \frac{4}{5}$. $\frac{1}{4}$
3. What is $\frac{5}{6}$ of 36? 30
4. Find $3\frac{1}{3} \cdot 2\frac{7}{10}$. 9

Choose **Use a calculator, paper and pencil, or mental math to find each product.**

25. $3 \cdot 2\frac{3}{8}$ $7\frac{1}{8}$
26. $\frac{3}{4}$ of 20 15
27. $10 \cdot 1\frac{4}{5}$ 18
28. $6\frac{2}{3} \cdot 3\frac{1}{3}$ $22\frac{2}{9}$
29. $2 \cdot 3\frac{2}{3}$ $7\frac{1}{3}$
30. $\frac{1}{2}$ of $6\frac{1}{2}$ $3\frac{1}{4}$
31. $\frac{1}{3} \cdot 2\frac{2}{5}$ $\frac{4}{5}$
32. $\frac{7}{8} \cdot 32$ 28
33. $\frac{1}{2} \cdot \frac{4}{5}$ $\frac{2}{5}$
34. $3\frac{1}{6} \cdot 4\frac{3}{4}$
35. $4\frac{3}{8} \cdot \frac{5}{7}$ $3\frac{1}{8}$
36. $3\frac{4}{9} \cdot 2\frac{1}{4}$ $7\frac{3}{4}$
37. $2\frac{1}{4} \cdot 5\frac{1}{6}$ $11\frac{5}{8}$
38. $4\frac{3}{8} \cdot 16$ 70
39. $1\frac{7}{8} \cdot \frac{8}{15}$

34. $15\frac{1}{24}$ 39. 1

Find the area of each rectangle.

40. $1\frac{1}{2}$ mi; $3\frac{1}{2}$ mi — $5\frac{1}{4}$ mi^2

41. $4\frac{2}{3}$ yd; $7\frac{1}{3}$ yd — $34\frac{2}{9}$ yd^2

42. $5\frac{1}{4}$ in.; $6\frac{1}{8}$ in. — $32\frac{5}{32}$ in.^{2}

43. (1 + 1 ÷ 4) × (3 + 1 ÷ 5) =

43. *Calculator* Write a key sequence to find $1\frac{1}{4} \cdot 3\frac{1}{5}$.

44. *Writing* How does multiplying two fractions differ from adding them? See margin p. 208.

45. *Cooking* A recipe for Sloppy Joes serves 100 people. It calls for $11\frac{1}{2}$ lb of tomato puree. How much puree would you need to serve 300 people? $34\frac{1}{2}$ lb

46. *Jogging* A track around a football field is about $\frac{1}{4}$ mi. Franklin jogged around the track $3\frac{3}{4}$ times. What distance did he jog? $\frac{15}{16}$ mi

Mixed Review

Estimate. *(Lesson 2-2)*

47–51. Estimates may vary. Samples are given.

47. $19.5 + 56.13$ 76
48. $34.3 - 18.9$ 15
49. 26.7×9.9 270
50. $119 \div 23$ 6
51. $204 \div 0.48$ 400

52. *Choose a Strategy* You regularly buy a monthly magazine at a newsstand for \$3.99. The subscription rate is \$1.50 per issue. How much can you save in a year by subscribing? \$29.88

CHAPTER PROJECT

PROJECT LINK: RESEARCHING

Test your recipe by making pancakes for your family. (You may ask some cooks to review your recipe if you do not have an opportunity to cook.) Revise if necessary. Adjust quantities so you have the right amount to feed your family. Check students' work.

Extra Practice, Lesson 5-5, page 518

PRACTICE

Practice 5-5 *Multiplying Fractions and Mixed Numbers*

Write a multiplication sentence for each model. Write the product as a fraction in simplest form.

1.  $\frac{1}{2} \cdot \frac{3}{7} = \frac{3}{14}$
2.  $\frac{2}{3} \cdot \frac{3}{4} = \frac{6}{12} = \frac{1}{2}$
3. 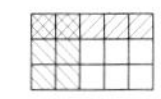 $\frac{1}{3} \cdot \frac{2}{5} = \frac{2}{15}$

Find each product.

4. $\frac{5}{6} \cdot \frac{3}{5}$ $\frac{1}{2}$
5. $\frac{7}{8} \cdot \frac{4}{5}$ $\frac{7}{10}$
6. $\frac{9}{10} \cdot \frac{5}{12}$ $\frac{3}{8}$
7. $\frac{5}{8} \cdot \frac{3}{5}$ $\frac{3}{8}$
8. $\frac{1}{6}$ of 36 6
9. $\frac{2}{3}$ of 36 24
10. $\frac{5}{9} \cdot 36$ 20
11. $\frac{3}{4} \cdot 36$ 27
12. $5 \cdot \frac{3}{4}$ $3\frac{3}{4}$
13. $2 \cdot \frac{9}{10}$ $1\frac{4}{5}$
14. $8 \cdot \frac{9}{10}$ $7\frac{1}{5}$
15. $4 \cdot \frac{7}{12}$ $2\frac{1}{3}$
16. $\frac{1}{4} \cdot 3\frac{1}{3}$ $\frac{5}{6}$
17. $\frac{5}{6}$ of $1\frac{3}{5}$ $1\frac{1}{3}$
18. $\frac{4}{5} \cdot 2\frac{5}{6}$ $2\frac{4}{15}$
19. $\frac{1}{8}$ of $1\frac{4}{5}$ $\frac{9}{40}$
20. $3 \cdot 4\frac{1}{2}$ $13\frac{1}{2}$
21. $4 \cdot 2\frac{2}{3}$ $10\frac{2}{3}$
22. $5 \cdot 2\frac{1}{4}$ $11\frac{1}{4}$
23. $3 \cdot 2\frac{2}{3}$ 8
24. $4\frac{1}{2} \cdot 1\frac{1}{6}$ $5\frac{1}{4}$
25. $3\frac{2}{3} \cdot 1\frac{1}{2}$ $5\frac{1}{2}$
26. $4\frac{1}{6} \cdot 2\frac{2}{5}$ 10
27. $3\frac{1}{4} \cdot 2\frac{1}{6}$ $7\frac{1}{24}$

Find the area of each rectangle.

28. $3\frac{1}{4}$ yd; $6\frac{1}{2}$ yd — $21\frac{1}{8}$ yd^2

29. $5\frac{1}{4}$ in.; $5\frac{1}{4}$ in. — $27\frac{9}{16}$ in.^{2}

30. $6\frac{1}{2}$ ft; $7\frac{3}{4}$ ft — $50\frac{3}{8}$ ft^2

31. $9\frac{1}{2}$ yd; 4 yd — 38 yd^2

Practice

In copymaster and workbook formats

RETEACHING

Reteaching 5-5 *Multiplying Fractions and Mixed Numbers*

Follow these steps to multiply fractions and mixed numbers.

		Multiply: $\frac{3}{4} \cdot \frac{2}{5}$	Multiply: $2\frac{2}{3} \cdot 1\frac{5}{8}$
Step 1	Rewrite each mixed number as an improper fraction if necessary.		$\frac{8}{3} \cdot \frac{13}{8}$
Step 2	Multiply numerators. Multiply denominators.	$\frac{3 \cdot 2}{4 \cdot 5} = \frac{6}{20}$	$\frac{8 \cdot 13}{3 \cdot 8} = \frac{104}{24}$
Step 3	Simplify, if necessary.	$\frac{6}{20} = \frac{3}{10}$	$\frac{104}{24} = 4\frac{1}{3}$

Complete to find and simplify each product.

1. $\frac{1}{5} \cdot \frac{2}{3}$ — $\frac{1 \cdot 2}{5 \cdot 3} = \frac{2}{15}$ — Product $\frac{2}{15}$
2. $\frac{1}{4} \cdot 4\frac{1}{8}$ — $\frac{1}{4} \cdot \frac{33}{8} = \frac{33}{32}$ — Product $1\frac{1}{32}$
3. $2\frac{3}{4} \cdot 1\frac{2}{3}$ — $\frac{11}{4} \cdot \frac{5}{3} = \frac{55}{12}$ — Product $4\frac{7}{12}$

Find each product. Write the product in simplest form.

4. $\frac{5}{8} \cdot \frac{2}{5}$ $\frac{1}{4}$
5. $\frac{2}{3} \cdot 9$ 6
6. $\frac{5}{12} \cdot \frac{3}{10}$ $\frac{1}{8}$
7. $\frac{3}{4} \cdot 1\frac{4}{5}$ $1\frac{7}{20}$
8. $\frac{1}{2} \cdot 5\frac{1}{6}$ $2\frac{7}{12}$
9. $3\frac{4}{5} \cdot \frac{1}{6}$ $\frac{19}{30}$
10. $1\frac{2}{3} \cdot 5$ $8\frac{1}{3}$
11. $1\frac{3}{4} \cdot 3\frac{1}{7}$ $5\frac{1}{2}$
12. $2\frac{3}{5} \cdot \frac{1}{4}$ $\frac{13}{20}$
13. $2\frac{3}{5} \cdot \frac{7}{8}$ $2\frac{11}{40}$
14. $4\frac{1}{5} \cdot \frac{5}{7}$ 3
15. $\frac{1}{2} \cdot 2\frac{1}{8}$ $1\frac{1}{16}$
16. $3\frac{5}{6} \cdot 2\frac{1}{4}$ $8\frac{5}{8}$
17. $2\frac{5}{7} \cdot 1\frac{1}{3}$ $3\frac{13}{21}$
18. $7\frac{2}{3} \cdot 2\frac{1}{7}$ $16\frac{3}{7}$
19. $5\frac{1}{2} \cdot 2\frac{2}{3}$ $14\frac{2}{3}$
20. $\frac{5}{6} \cdot 3\frac{3}{5}$ 3
21. $7\frac{3}{4} \cdot 2$ $15\frac{1}{2}$

ENRICHMENT

Minds on Math Transparency

5-5

I am a fraction in simplest form. I am greater than $\frac{1}{3}$ and less than $\frac{1}{2}$. The sum of all of my digits is 8. The difference between my numerator and denominator is 7. What fraction am I?

$\frac{5}{12}$

See *Solution Key* for worked-out answers.

5-6 Teaching Notes

1 Focus

CONNECTING TO PRIOR KNOWLEDGE
Write 18 ÷ 3 on the board. Tell students: *I can cut an 18-ft rope into 3-ft sections.* Ask: *How does the expression on the board relate to what I said?* **18 represents the total length, 3 represents the lengths of the sections.** Write 12 × $\frac{1}{4}$ on the board. Ask: *Does the $\frac{1}{4}$ relate to the 18 or the 3 in the first expression?* **the 3**

2 Teach

THINK AND DISCUSS

Encourage students to discuss why the quotient of 4 ÷ $\frac{2}{3}$ is greater than 4. **Answers may vary. Sample: The question is asking how many pieces smaller than 1 fit into 4 ones.**

TACTILE LEARNING Question 1 Have pairs of students use models to convince themselves that dividing by $\frac{2}{3}$ is the same as multiplying by $\frac{3}{2}$.

AEP Question 2 Students may not understand the term *reciprocal.* Say fractions aloud and ask students to determine the reciprocals.

Example 1 Remind students to find the reciprocal of only the divisor.

Lesson Planning Options

Prerequisite Skills
- multiplying fractions (5-5)
- writing mixed numbers as improper fractions (4-8)

Vocabulary/Symbols
reciprocals

Materials/Manipulatives
- calculator

Resources

Student Edition
Skills Handbook, p. 531
Extra Practice, p. 518
Glossary/Study Guide

Teaching Resources
Chapter Support File, Ch. 5
- Lesson Planner 5-6
- Practice 5-6, Reteaching 5-6
- Answer Masters 5-6

Teaching Aids Masters 8, 10, 20–25
Glossary, Spanish Resources

Transparencies
9, 10, 15, 18–25, Minds on Math 5-6

Warm Up
Write each number as an improper fraction.
$4\frac{1}{5}$ **$\frac{21}{5}$**
$3\frac{7}{8}$ **$\frac{31}{8}$**

5-6 Dividing Fractions and Mixed Numbers

What You'll Learn
1. To divide fractions
2. To divide mixed numbers

...And Why
You can find the number of costumes you can make from a piece of fabric.

Here's How
Look for questions that
- build understanding
- ✔ check understanding

THINK AND DISCUSS

1 Dividing Fractions

"What is $4 \div \frac{2}{3}$?" is the same as asking, "How many two thirds are in four wholes?" To find how many two thirds are in 4, draw 4 rectangles and divide them into thirds.

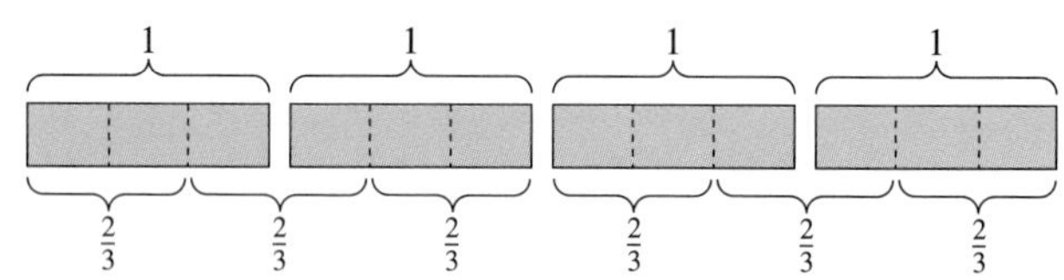

You can see that there are 6 two thirds in four wholes.

1. Complete each statement.
   a. $4 \div \frac{2}{3} = ■$ **6** b. $4 \cdot \frac{3}{2} = ■$ **6** c. $4 \div \frac{2}{3} = 4 \cdot \frac{■}{■}$ **$\frac{3}{2}$**

The numbers $\frac{2}{3}$ and $\frac{3}{2}$ are **reciprocals** because their product is 1. To divide by $\frac{2}{3}$, you can multiply by $\frac{3}{2}$. To find the reciprocal of a fraction, interchange the numerator and denominator.

$\frac{2}{3} \rightleftarrows \frac{3}{2}$

2. ✔ *Try It Out* Find the reciprocal of each fraction.
   a. $\frac{3}{5}$ **$\frac{5}{3}$** b. $\frac{1}{2}$ **2** c. $\frac{9}{4}$ **$\frac{4}{9}$** d. $\frac{5}{2}$ **$\frac{2}{5}$**

To divide by a fraction, multiply by the reciprocal of the fraction.

EXAMPLE 1

Find $\frac{2}{3} \div \frac{5}{6}$.

$\frac{2}{3} \div \frac{5}{6} = \frac{2}{3} \cdot \frac{6}{5}$ ← Multiply by the reciprocal of $\frac{5}{6}$ which is $\frac{6}{5}$.

$= \frac{2 \cdot \cancel{6}^{2}}{_{1}\cancel{3} \cdot 5}$ ← The GCF is 3.

$= \frac{4}{5}$ ← Simplify.

3. ✔ *Try It Out* Find each quotient.
   a. $\frac{3}{4} \div \frac{1}{4}$ **3** b. $\frac{3}{10} \div \frac{3}{5}$ **$\frac{1}{2}$** c. $\frac{3}{4} \div \frac{1}{8}$ **6** d. $\frac{2}{3} \div \frac{2}{3}$ **1**

ERROR ALERT! Question 5 Students may write the reciprocal of a mixed number incorrectly. For example, they may write the reciprocal of $2\frac{2}{3}$ as $2\frac{3}{2}$. **Remediation:** Give students practice finding reciprocals of mixed numbers. Have students first write an improper fraction and then its reciprocal.

■ ADDITIONAL EXAMPLES

FOR EXAMPLE 1

Find $\frac{5}{12} \div \frac{2}{3}$. $\frac{5}{8}$

FOR EXAMPLE 2

Jamie must cut a 42-in. ribbon into pieces that are each $5\frac{1}{4}$ in. long. How many pieces of ribbon can he cut? 8

ASSESSMENT Have students write a list of steps explaining how to find $4\frac{3}{4} \div 6\frac{1}{3}$. Have partners trade lists and check by following the steps. If the list of steps is correct, they should find $\frac{3}{4}$.

3 Practice/Assess

EXERCISES ***On Your Own***

Exercises 5 and 6 Remind students to find the improper fraction before finding the reciprocal.

MENTAL MATH Exercises 7–11 Encourage students to first find the reciprocal of the divisor using mental math.

To divide with fractions and whole numbers, first write the whole number as a fraction with a denominator of 1. Then multiply by the reciprocal of the divisor. For example,

$$\frac{3}{5} \div 2 = \frac{3}{5} \div \frac{2}{1} = \frac{3}{5} \cdot \frac{1}{2} = \frac{3}{10}$$

4. ✔ *Try It Out* Find each quotient.
   a. $\frac{3}{4} \div 3$ $\frac{1}{4}$ b. $\frac{3}{4} \div 6$ $\frac{1}{8}$ c. $10 \div \frac{3}{5}$ $16\frac{2}{3}$ d. $2 \div \frac{4}{3}$ $1\frac{1}{2}$

Now you may assign Exercises 1–23.

2 *Dividing Mixed Numbers*

To divide mixed numbers, rewrite them as improper fractions.

■ EXAMPLE 2 *Real-World Problem Solving*

Sewing Joanne has $13\frac{1}{2}$ yd of material to make costumes. Each costume takes $2\frac{1}{4}$ yd. How many costumes can she make?

You need to find the quotient of $13\frac{1}{2} \div 2\frac{1}{4}$.

Estimate: $13\frac{1}{2} \div 2\frac{1}{4} \approx 14 \div 2 = 7$

$13\frac{1}{2} \div 2\frac{1}{4} = \frac{27}{2} \div \frac{9}{4}$ ← Write the mixed numbers as improper fractions.

$= \frac{27}{2} \cdot \frac{4}{9}$ ← Multiply by the reciprocal of $\frac{9}{4}$.

$= \frac{^{3}\cancel{27} \cdot \cancel{4}^{2}}{_{1}\cancel{2} \cdot \cancel{9}_{1}}$ ← Divide 27 and 9 by 9, their GCF. Divide 4 and 2 by 2, their GCF.

$= \frac{6}{1} = 6$ ← Simplify.

Joanne can make six costumes.

5. ✔ *Try It Out* Another costume takes $2\frac{2}{3}$ yd of material. How many can be made from $13\frac{1}{3}$ yd of material? 5 costumes

Now you may assign Exercises 24–41.

EXERCISES ***On Your Own***

Find the reciprocal of each number.

1. $\frac{3}{4}$ $\frac{4}{3}$
2. 5 $\frac{1}{5}$
3. $\frac{1}{7}$ 7
4. $\frac{5}{4}$ $\frac{4}{5}$
5. $2\frac{1}{6}$ $\frac{6}{13}$
6. $4\frac{5}{8}$ $\frac{8}{37}$

Mental Math **Find each quotient.**

7. $8 \div \frac{1}{2}$ 16
8. $5 \div \frac{1}{3}$ 15
9. $2 \div \frac{1}{9}$ 18
10. $10 \div \frac{1}{10}$ 100
11. $\frac{3}{2} \div \frac{1}{2}$ 3

Technology Options

Prentice Hall Technology

Software for Learners

- Math Blaster® Mystery*
- Interactive Student Tutorial, Chapter 5*

Teaching Resource Software

- Computer Item Generator 5-6
- Resource Pro™ Chapter 5*

Internet • For related mathematics activities, visit the Prentice Hall site at www.phschool.com/math

**Available on CD-ROM only*

Assignment Options for Exercises On Your Own

To provide flexible scheduling, this lesson can be subdivided into parts.

1 **Core** 1–22
Extension 23

2 **Core** 24–40
Extension 41

Use Mixed Review to maintain skills.

PRACTICE

Practice 5-6 *Dividing Fractions and Mixed Numbers*

Find the reciprocal of each number.

1. $\frac{1}{2}$ 2
2. $\frac{3}{4}$ $\frac{4}{3}$
3. $\frac{7}{8}$ $\frac{8}{7}$
4. $\frac{9}{16}$ $\frac{16}{9}$
5. $\frac{4}{5}$ $\frac{5}{4}$
6. $1\frac{1}{4}$ $\frac{4}{5}$
7. $2\frac{1}{3}$ $\frac{3}{7}$
8. $3\frac{2}{5}$ $\frac{5}{17}$
9. $2\frac{9}{10}$ $\frac{10}{29}$
10. $3\frac{1}{6}$ $\frac{6}{19}$

Choose a calculator, paper and pencil, or mental math to find each quotient.

11. $\frac{3}{4} \div \frac{1}{4}$ 3
12. $\frac{7}{8} \div \frac{1}{4}$ $3\frac{1}{2}$
13. $\frac{5}{6} \div \frac{1}{12}$ 10
14. $\frac{1}{12} \div \frac{5}{6}$ $\frac{1}{10}$
15. $4 \div \frac{1}{3}$ 12
16. $6 \div \frac{3}{4}$ 8
17. $5 \div \frac{9}{10}$ $5\frac{5}{9}$
18. $8 \div \frac{2}{3}$ 12
19. $\frac{4}{5} \div 2$ $\frac{2}{5}$
20. $\frac{7}{8} \div 3$ $\frac{7}{24}$
21. $\frac{5}{6} \div 5$ $\frac{1}{6}$
22. $\frac{4}{9} \div 8$ $\frac{1}{18}$
23. $1\frac{1}{2} \div \frac{2}{3}$ $2\frac{1}{4}$
24. $1\frac{1}{2} \div \frac{3}{2}$ 1
25. $\frac{3}{4} \div 1\frac{1}{3}$ $\frac{9}{16}$
26. $2\frac{1}{2} \div 1\frac{1}{4}$ 2
27. $2\frac{1}{2} \div 2\frac{1}{4}$ $1\frac{1}{9}$
28. $1\frac{3}{4} \div \frac{3}{4}$ $2\frac{1}{3}$
29. $1\frac{7}{10} \div \frac{1}{2}$ $3\frac{2}{5}$
30. $3\frac{1}{4} \div 1\frac{1}{3}$ $2\frac{7}{16}$
31. $4\frac{1}{2} \div 2\frac{1}{2}$ $1\frac{4}{5}$
32. $6 \div 3\frac{4}{5}$ $1\frac{11}{19}$
33. $4\frac{3}{4} \div \frac{7}{8}$ $5\frac{3}{7}$
34. $5\frac{5}{6} \div 1\frac{1}{3}$ $4\frac{3}{8}$
35. $3\frac{3}{8} \div 1\frac{1}{4}$ $2\frac{7}{10}$
36. $6\frac{1}{2} \div 1\frac{1}{2}$ $4\frac{1}{3}$
37. $2\frac{9}{10} \div 1\frac{3}{4}$ $1\frac{23}{35}$
38. $7\frac{5}{8} \div 4\frac{1}{2}$ $1\frac{25}{36}$

Solve each problem.

39. Rosa makes $2\frac{1}{2}$ c of pudding. How many $\frac{1}{3}$ c servings can she get from the pudding?
$7\frac{1}{2}$ servings

40. One type of lightning bug glows once every $1\frac{1}{2}$ s. How many times can it glow in 1 min?
40 times

41. Bea can run $\frac{1}{6}$ mi in 2 min. How long should it take her to run 2 mi?
24 min

42. Joe drives 20 mi in $\frac{1}{2}$ h. How long will it take him to drive 50 mi?
$1\frac{1}{4}$ h

In copymaster and workbook formats

RETEACHING

Reteaching 5-6 *Dividing Fractions and Mixed Numbers*

To find the **reciprocal** of a fraction, switch the numerator and the denominator.

Examples: The reciprocal of $\frac{1}{4}$ is $\frac{4}{1}$. The reciprocal of $\frac{7}{5}$ is $\frac{5}{7}$.

Follow these steps to divide fractions and mixed numbers.

		Divide: $\frac{2}{3} \div \frac{1}{4}$	Divide: $3\frac{3}{4} \div 1\frac{2}{5}$
Step 1	Rewrite mixed numbers as improper fractions as needed.		$\frac{15}{4} \div \frac{7}{5}$
Step 2	Multiply by the reciprocal of the divisor.	$\frac{2}{3} \cdot \frac{4}{1}$	$\frac{15}{4} \cdot \frac{5}{7}$
Step 3	Multiply numerators. Multiply denominators.	$\frac{2 \cdot 4}{3 \cdot 1} = \frac{8}{3}$	$\frac{15 \cdot 5}{4 \cdot 7} = \frac{75}{28}$
Step 4	Simplify.	$\frac{8}{3} = 2\frac{2}{3}$	$\frac{75}{28} = 2\frac{19}{28}$

Find the reciprocal of each number.

1. $\frac{7}{8}$ $\frac{8}{7}$
2. $\frac{1}{6}$ $\frac{6}{1}$
3. $\frac{8}{3}$ $\frac{3}{8}$
4. $\frac{9}{10}$ $\frac{10}{9}$

Write each mixed number as an improper fraction. Then find the reciprocal.

5. $1\frac{1}{2}$ $\frac{3}{2}; \frac{2}{3}$
6. $2\frac{1}{3}$ $\frac{7}{3}; \frac{3}{7}$
7. $1\frac{4}{5}$ $\frac{9}{5}; \frac{5}{9}$
8. $2\frac{3}{4}$ $\frac{11}{4}; \frac{4}{11}$

Complete to find each quotient. Write the quotient in simplest form.

9. $\frac{2}{3} \div \frac{3}{8}$
$\frac{2}{3} \cdot \frac{8}{3} = \frac{16}{9}$
Quotient $1\frac{7}{9}$

10. $10 \div \frac{7}{8}$
$\frac{10}{1} \div \frac{7}{8} = \frac{10}{1} \cdot \frac{8}{7}$
$= \frac{80}{7}$
Quotient $11\frac{3}{7}$

11. $3\frac{3}{5} \div 1\frac{1}{5}$
$\frac{18}{5} \div \frac{6}{5} = \frac{18}{5} \cdot \frac{5}{6}$
$= \frac{90}{30}$
Quotient 3

12. $\frac{1}{5} \div \frac{1}{2} = \frac{2}{5}$
13. $\frac{3}{8} \div \frac{2}{3} = \frac{9}{16}$
14. $8 \div \frac{4}{5} = 10$
15. $6 \div \frac{3}{4} = 8$
16. $1\frac{1}{8} \div 2\frac{2}{5} = \frac{15}{32}$
17. $3\frac{1}{5} \div 2\frac{2}{3} = 1\frac{1}{5}$

Reteaching

ENRICHMENT

Minds on Math Transparency

5-6

I am a two-digit number. My square is a number with its first two digits identical and its last two digits identical. What number am I?

88

See *Solution Key* for worked-out answers.

212

WRITING Exercise 23 Have students refer to Exercises 7–11. Ask: *What makes these exercises easy to divide mentally?* **Answers may vary. Sample: The numerators of the divisors are all 1.**

LESSON QUIZ

Find each quotient.

1. $\frac{3}{5} \div \frac{1}{2}$. $1\frac{1}{5}$
2. $\frac{4}{9} \div 3$. $\frac{4}{27}$
3. $5\frac{1}{4} \div 3\frac{1}{2}$. $1\frac{1}{2}$

WRAP UP

IDENTIFYING THE BIG IDEA Ask students: *How is dividing fractions and mixed numbers related to multiplying fractions and mixed numbers?*

Find each quotient.

12. $\frac{4}{5} \div \frac{1}{4}$ $3\frac{1}{5}$
13. $15 \div \frac{3}{4}$ 20
14. $\frac{7}{8} \div 3$ $\frac{7}{24}$
15. $\frac{2}{9} \div \frac{2}{3}$ $\frac{1}{3}$
16. $\frac{3}{4} \div \frac{8}{9}$ $\frac{27}{32}$
17. $\frac{3}{4} \div \frac{3}{5}$ $1\frac{1}{4}$
18. $6 \div \frac{1}{7}$ 42
19. $\frac{5}{16} \div \frac{1}{2}$ $\frac{5}{8}$
20. $\frac{5}{6} \div \frac{3}{4}$ $1\frac{1}{9}$
21. $42 \div \frac{7}{9}$ 54

22. A new gas line will be installed along a $\frac{3}{4}$-mi. long street. It takes a day to install $\frac{1}{8}$ mi. How long will the project take? **6 days**

23. *Writing* Explain how to find the reciprocal of a fraction or whole number. **Answers may vary. Sample: To find the reciprocal of a fraction, switch the numerator with the denominator. For a whole number, write it as a fraction, then flip the numerator and the denominator.**

Choose **Use a calculator, paper and pencil, or mental math to find each quotient.**

24. $2\frac{1}{6} \div \frac{5}{6}$ $2\frac{3}{5}$
25. $\frac{3}{4} \div 3$ $\frac{1}{4}$
26. $\frac{1}{4} \div \frac{2}{3}$ $\frac{3}{8}$
27. $4\frac{3}{4} \div 1\frac{1}{4}$ $3\frac{4}{5}$
28. $\frac{7}{12} \div 2\frac{1}{6}$ $\frac{7}{26}$
29. $1\frac{1}{5} \div 2\frac{3}{10}$ $\frac{12}{23}$
30. $\frac{7}{9} \div \frac{1}{4}$ $3\frac{1}{9}$
31. $\frac{2}{3} \div 4\frac{1}{12}$ $\frac{8}{49}$
32. $8\frac{1}{3} \div 2\frac{1}{2}$ $3\frac{1}{3}$
33. $2\frac{2}{3} \div 5\frac{1}{9}$
34. $8\frac{2}{5} \div \frac{3}{10}$ 28
35. $4\frac{7}{8} \div 3\frac{1}{4}$ $1\frac{1}{2}$
36. $11 \div \frac{1}{9}$ 99
37. $1\frac{2}{3} \div \frac{9}{10}$ $1\frac{23}{27}$
38. $\frac{2}{5} \div \frac{4}{7}$ $\frac{7}{10}$

33. $\frac{12}{23}$

39. *Biology* A killer whale can swim 40 mi in $1\frac{1}{4}$ h. How far can the whale swim in 1 h? **32 mi**

40. *Meal Planning* One serving of cereal contains $1\frac{1}{2}$ oz. How many servings are in a $19\frac{1}{2}$-oz box? **13 servings**

41. *Calculator* You can use this key sequence to find $2\frac{1}{2} \div \frac{5}{6}$.

(2 + 1 ÷ 2) ÷ (5 ÷ 6) =

Write and use a key sequence to find $13\frac{7}{8} \div 6\frac{1}{6}$.
(13 + 7 ÷ 8) ÷ (6 + 1 ÷ 6) =; 2.25

Mixed Review

Write each fraction as a decimal. Use a bar to indicate any repeating digits. *(Lesson 4-9)*

42. $\frac{4}{5}$ 0.8
43. $\frac{3}{8}$ 0.375
44. $\frac{2}{9}$ $0.\overline{2}$
45. $\frac{8}{3}$ $2.\overline{6}$
46. $\frac{2}{32}$ 0.0625
47. $\frac{7}{24}$ $0.291\overline{6}$

Write each decimal as a fraction in simplest form. *(Lesson 4-9)*

48. 0.4 $\frac{2}{5}$
49. 0.625 $\frac{5}{8}$
50. 5.75 $5\frac{3}{4}$
51. 2.38 $2\frac{19}{50}$
52. 0.55 $\frac{11}{20}$
53. 4.305 $4\frac{61}{200}$

54. *School Store* At the school store, notebooks cost \$1.75, pencils \$.05, pens \$1, and folders \$.75. How much would two notebooks and four pencils cost? *(Lessons 2-3, 2-5)* **\$3.70**

Extra Practice, Lesson 5-6, page 518

In Lesson 5-6, students learned how to write the division of fractions and mixed numbers on paper. This toolbox shows students how to divide fractions and mixed numbers using the Explorer fraction calculator.

ERROR ALERT! Students may have difficulty following the steps on the fraction calculator. **Remediation:** Have students do the examples with a partner, one step at a time. If their answers are different from those given, they will be able to determine at which step they made a mistake.

ASSESSMENT Exercise 10 Have each student explain aloud to a partner, step by step, how to find the difference. Students should agree on their answers and their steps.

ADDITIONAL PROBLEMS

Find the value of each expression.

1. $2\frac{3}{4} + 4\frac{5}{8}$. $7\frac{3}{8}$
2. $6\frac{4}{5} - 3\frac{3}{4}$. $3\frac{1}{20}$
3. $11\frac{6}{7} \cdot 4\frac{8}{9}$. $57\frac{61}{63}$
4. $37\frac{1}{2} \div 6\frac{2}{3}$. $5\frac{5}{8}$

MATH TOOLBOX TECHNOLOGY

Using a Fraction Calculator

After Lesson 5-6

You can use a fraction calculator to compute with fractions. A fraction calculator will give you your result in fraction form.

EXAMPLE 1

Find $3\frac{4}{5} + 2\frac{5}{8}$.

3 UNIT 4 / 5 + 2 UNIT 5 / 8 = 5u57/40 Ab/c 6u17/40

The sum is $6\frac{17}{40}$.

To simplify an answer, you may need to use SIMP = more than once.

EXAMPLE 2

Find $9\frac{3}{8} \cdot 4\frac{2}{3}$.

9 UNIT 3 / 8 × 4 UNIT 2 / 3 =

1050/24 Ab/c 43u18/24 SIMP = 43u9/12 SIMP = 43u3/4

The product is $43\frac{3}{4}$.

EXAMPLE 3

Find $5\frac{3}{4} \div 1\frac{7}{8}$.

5 UNIT 3 / 4 ÷ 1 UNIT 7 / 8 =

184/60 Ab/c 3u4/60 SIMP = 3u2/30 SIMP = 3u1/15

The product is $3\frac{1}{15}$.

Find the value of each expression.

1. $8\frac{7}{10} + 9\frac{1}{5}$ $17\frac{9}{10}$
2. $14\frac{5}{12} - 6\frac{5}{8}$ $7\frac{19}{24}$
3. $11\frac{4}{5} + 8\frac{1}{4}$ $20\frac{1}{20}$
4. $9\frac{3}{4} \cdot 4\frac{5}{6}$ $47\frac{1}{8}$
5. $17\frac{3}{8} \div 5\frac{3}{4}$ $3\frac{1}{46}$
6. $13\frac{5}{12} - 4\frac{7}{8}$ 6. $8\frac{13}{24}$
7. $7\frac{2}{3} \cdot 10\frac{1}{4}$ $78\frac{7}{12}$
8. $18\frac{3}{10} \div 10\frac{1}{2}$ 8. $1\frac{26}{35}$
9. $17\frac{11}{12} \cdot 21\frac{3}{8}$ $382\frac{31}{32}$
10. $28\frac{7}{16} - 19\frac{5}{8}$ $8\frac{13}{16}$

11. a. *Writing* Suppose a student calculated $4\frac{2}{3} + 5\frac{3}{4}$. The student's answer was 17u11/12. Why is this answer not reasonable? **You can estimate the sum to be about 11. The answer is much larger than the estimate.**

    b. What error may the student have made when entering the fractions in the calculator? **The student probably did not press the unit key between 5 and 3.**

Resources

Transparencies
15

5-7 Teaching Notes

1 Focus

CONNECTING TO PRIOR KNOWLEDGE Ask the class: *Suppose you spent $2 in the cafeteria at lunch and loaned $1 to a friend. You now have $5. How much money did you have to start with?* **$8** Ask students how they found the answer. Tell students that we call this strategy *work backward.*

2 Teach

THINK AND DISCUSS

Students can assume that the theater is next door to the restaurant, and that there are no unexpected delays.

ERROR ALERT! Students may add the 15 min as the whole number 15, not as $\frac{1}{4}$. **Remediation:** Have students write all numbers and their units. Stress that all units must be the same, as in adding and subtracting fractions. Urge students to draw analog clock faces to diagram the time. Help them see that 15 min is $\frac{1}{4}$ h.

AEP VISUAL LEARNING Students may have difficulty understanding the sequence of events in the paragraph. Have students work with a partner to draw a time line showing the order in which the events took place. Record the amount of time required above each event.

Lesson Planning Options

Prerequisite Skills

- reading time on an analog clock (precourse)
- adding and subtracting fractions (5-2)

Resources

Student Edition

Skills Handbook, p. 540
Extra Practice, p. 518
Glossary/Study Guide

Teaching Resources

Chapter Support File, Ch. 5
- Lesson Planner 5-7
- Practice 5-7, Reteaching 5-7
- Answer Masters 5-7

Glossary, Spanish Resources

Transparencies
87, Minds on Math 5-7

Warm Up

Ayesha had some extra spending money. She spent $\frac{4}{5}$ of it on lunch and a movie and had $1.67 left. How much money did she have to begin with? **$8.35**

PROBLEM SOLVING STRATEGY

5-7 Work Backward

Problem Solving Strategies

Draw a Diagram
Guess and Test
Look for a Pattern
Make a Model
Make a Table
Simulate a Problem
Solve a Simpler Problem
Too Much or Too Little Information
Use Logical Reasoning
Use Multiple Strategies
✔ Work Backward
Write an Equation

THINK AND DISCUSS

To solve some problems, you may need to work backward.

SAMPLE PROBLEM

Mrs. Ruiz is taking her son Javier and his friends to dinner, and then to a concert that starts at 8:00 P.M. It will take $\frac{3}{4}$ h to pick up his friends and get to the restaurant next to the theater and $1\frac{1}{4}$ h to eat and walk to the theater. They want to be at the theater 15 min before the concert starts. When should they leave home?

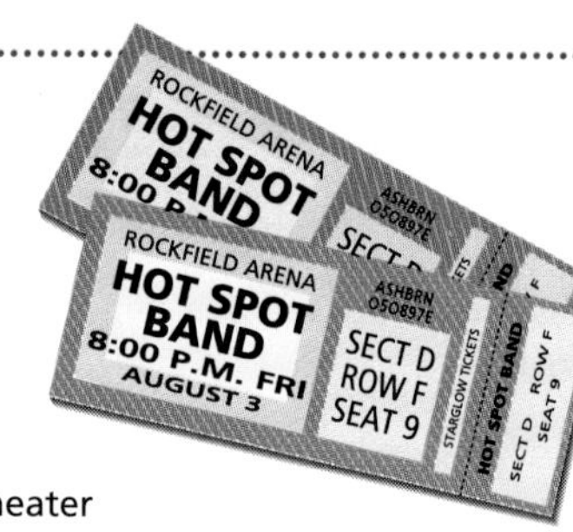

READ
Read for understanding. Summarize the problem.

b. See below.
c. $\frac{3}{4}$ h; $1\frac{1}{4}$ h; $\frac{1}{4}$ h
d. See below.

1. Think about the information you are given.
   a. At what time does the concert start? **8:00 P.M.**
   b. What activities are planned between the time Mrs. Ruiz and Javier leave home and the time the concert starts?
   c. What amount of time is planned for each activity?
   d. Summarize the goal of the problem in your own words.

   b. **picking up friends, eating dinner, waiting for start of concert**

PLAN
Decide on a strategy.

You know that a series of events must *end* at 8:00 P.M. It makes sense to work backward to find when the events must *begin.*

SOLVE
Try the strategy.

2. a. Write the time for each event.

concert starts **8:00 P.M.** | arrive at theater **7:45 P.M.** | arrive at dinner **6:30 P.M.** | leave home **5:45 P.M.**

   b. What is the solution to the problem? **5:45 P.M.**

1d. When Mrs. Ruiz and Javier need to leave to complete all the activities before the 8:00 P.M. concert.

■ **ADDITIONAL PROBLEM**

After school today, Jackie spent $1\frac{1}{4}$ h at track practice and then $\frac{1}{2}$ h in the school library. It took him 15 min to walk home. He arrived home at 5:00 P.M. At what time did he start? **3:00 P.M.**

ASSESSMENT Have students work with a partner to write a problem they can solve by working backward. Let pairs exchange problems to practice the strategy and to check for understanding.

3 Practice/Assess

EXERCISES *On Your Own*

ALTERNATE METHOD Exercise 2a Show students how they could use the Guess-and-Check strategy to solve this problem. Use an initial guess of 100. Have students compare the two methods and list the pros and cons of each.

CONNECTION TO GEOMETRY Exercise 5 Students use their knowledge of area to answer questions about tiling a floor. If necessary, review with the class how to find the area of a rectangle.

WRAP UP

IDENTIFYING THE BIG IDEA Ask students: *When would you use the Work Backward strategy to solve a problem?*

LOOK BACK

Think about how you solved the problem.

3. Show how to check your solution by working *forward*. **See back of book.**
4. a. Think of 15 min as $\frac{1}{4}$ h. Find the sum $\frac{3}{4} + 1\frac{1}{4} + \frac{1}{4}$. **$2\frac{1}{4}$ h**
   b. How could you use your answer to part (a) to solve the problem in a different way? **See below.**

Now you may assign Exercises 1–11.

EXERCISES *On Your Own*

Think and Discuss

4b. Subtract $2\frac{1}{4}$ h from 8:00 P.M. to find the time to leave home.

Work backward to solve each problem.

1. Look back at the Sample Problem.
   a. Suppose that the concert starts at 8:30 P.M. At what time should Mrs. Ruiz and Javier leave home? **6:15 P.M.**
   b. Suppose that the concert starts at 8:00 P.M., but it takes only 20 min to pick up Javier's friends. At what time should Mrs. Ruiz and Javier leave home? **6:10 P.M.**
2. a. *Entertainment* The new movie that opened yesterday was so boring that $\frac{1}{2}$ of the people in the theater at the start of the movie left after the first 45 min. In the next 15 min, $\frac{1}{2}$ of the remaining people left. In the next $\frac{1}{4}$ h, 18 more people left. Only 36 of the people who were there at the start stayed to see the end of the movie. How many people were in the theater at the start of the movie? **216 people**
   b. Which parts of the given information were not needed to solve the problem? **You do not need to know the exact time people left.**
3. If you start with a number, add 5, then multiply by 7, the result is 133. What was the original number? **14**

Use any strategy to solve each problem. Show your work.

4. Mia has ten coins that have a total value of $.65. She has no pennies. None of the coins is greater than a quarter. What are the coins? **3 dimes and 7 nickels**
5. a. *Business* The manager of a department store plans to make an electronic game shop in a section of the store that is 12 ft wide and 20 ft long. Using the pattern shown at the right, the manager wants to cover the floor with tiles that measure 1 ft on each side. How many black tiles will be needed? How many white tiles will be needed? **132 tiles; 108 tiles**
   b. How can you use areas of rectangles to check that you found the correct number of tiles? **See back of book.**

Technology Options

Prentice Hall Technology

Software for Learners

- Math Blaster® Mystery*
- Interactive Student Tutorial, Chapter 5*

Teaching Resource Software

- Computer Item Generator 5-7
- Resource Pro™ Chapter 5*

Internet • For related mathematics activities, visit the Prentice Hall site at www.phschool.com/math

**Available on CD-ROM only*

Assignment Options for Exercises On Your Own

Core 1–10
Extension 11

Use Mixed Review to maintain skills.

PRACTICE

Practice 5-7 Problem-Solving Strategy: Work Backward

Work backward to solve each problem.

1. A fast-growing mushroom doubled in size every day. After 30 days, it measured 6 in. tall. On which day did it measure $1\frac{1}{2}$ in. tall? 28th day
2. If you start with a number, subtract 14, then divide by 12, the result is 248. What was the original number? 2,990
3. Mrs. Wainright is in a car pool. It takes her 20 min to pick up her passengers. From her last stop, it takes her 45 min to drive to the office. The group likes to arrive 10 min before office hours begin. If office hours start at 8:30 A.M., what time should Mrs. Wainright leave her apartment? 7:15 A.M.

Use any strategy to solve each problem. Show your work.

4. James went shopping one Saturday afternoon. He spent $\frac{1}{2}$ of the money he had on a new stereo system. He spent half of the money he had left on a new suit. Half of what remained, he spent on a new sweater. Half of what remained, he spent on a new CD. If he went home with $15, how much money did he have to begin with? $240
5. At a middle school, half the students leave immediately after school because they walk home. After 5 min, $\frac{1}{4}$ of the students remaining are gone, riding home on their bicycles. After another 5 min, $\frac{3}{4}$ of those remaining depart on buses. At this time, 51 students remain for after-school activities. How many students attend the middle school? 544 students
6. Trish spent a fourth of her money on a new book. She paid a friend $3.50 that she had borrowed. Later she spent $4.75 on a pair of earrings. When she arrived home, she had $18.00. How much money did she have to start with? $35
7. During one day, Howard wrote checks for $125.00, $98.57, and $23.46. He made a deposit of $475.00. If his account now has $472.96, how much was in the account at the start of the day? $244.99
8. If you start with a number, add $\frac{2}{5}$, then multiply by 7, the result is $6\frac{3}{10}$. What was the original number? $\frac{1}{2}$

Practice

In copymaster and workbook formats

RETEACHING

Reteaching 5-7 Problem-Solving Strategy: Work Backward

Ramón began his shopping trip by cashing his paycheck. While shopping, he noted what he spent. At the end of the day, he had $49.50 left. What was the amount of his paycheck?

Videotape	$13.95
Sweater	45.99
Shirt	17.99
Pants	32.45

Read What information are you given? *You know how much Ramón had left and how much he spent.*

Plan It makes sense to *work backward* to find the amount Ramón began with.

Solve Add the amount spent to the amount left. Ramón's paycheck was for $159.88.

Look Back You can check your answer by *working forward.* Begin with $159.88. Subtract each amount Ramón spent.

Amount left	$49.50
Amount spent	32.45
	17.99
	45.99
	13.95
	$159.88

Work backward to solve each problem.

1. Madeline took her month's allowance to the amusement park. She had $1.50 left at the end of the day. She made a list of her expenses.

Rides	$3.50
Food	2.50
Admission	1.50
Toss-a-ring	2.00

How much was her allowance?

Allowance: $11.00

2. Dana left nuts out for the chipmunks. She kept track of how many each chipmunk took.

Curlytail	15
Whitefoot	22
Squeaker	19
Stripes	32

If there were 12 nuts left, how many did she start with?

Total nuts: 100

3. Suzy multiplied her age by 2, subtracted 5, divided by 3, and added 9. The result was 20. How old is she? 19 years old

4. Each time a ball bounces it returns to a height $\frac{2}{3}$ the height of the previous bounce. After the third bounce, the ball returns to a height of 4 ft. From what height was it dropped? $13\frac{1}{2}$ ft

ENRICHMENT

Minds on Math Transparency

5-7

A gross is a dozen dozen. A great gross is a dozen gross. How many objects are in a great gross?

1,728 objects

See *Solution Key* for worked-out answers.

216

LESSON QUIZ

Work backward to solve each problem.

1. Erin gets cash from the bank machine. She then spends $12.54 at the grocery store, $8.77 at the gas station, and $3.05 at the video store. She has $15.64 left. How much did Erin get from the bank? $40
2. On the last day of a semester, there were 314 students in a college class. During the semester, 16 students joined the class, and 37 students dropped out. How many students were enrolled in the class on the first day of the semester? 335

6. *Money* Rosita saved $60 to spend on basketball cards. She plans to buy the cards at the sale advertised on the sign at the right. What is the least expensive way to buy five cards? **Buy 3 cards for $9 each, buy the 4th card for $7 and the 5th for $9.**

7. Darren spent one third of his money on lunch. At lunch, his friend gave him $2.50 to repay a loan. Then Darren spent $3.25 for a movie ticket and $.75 for a snack. He had $4.90 left. How much money did Darren have before lunch? **$9.60**
8. *Sports* Janelle practiced gymnastics 28 h in one week. Each day she practiced one hour more than the day before. How many hours did she practice on the fifth day? **5 h**
9. Chloe and Lavanna started work on the same day. Chloe will earn a salary of $28,000 the first year. She will then receive a $4,000 raise each year that follows. Lavanna's salary for the first year is $41,000, followed by a $1,500 yearly raise. In what year will Chloe's salary be more than Lavanna's? **7th year**
10. At a fund-raising event attended by 150 people, $2,000 was collected for charity. Suppose 25 people gave nothing. How much was the average donation from those who gave? **$16**
11. *Money* Lydia went shopping with $35 in her wallet. She bought a sweater that was on sale for half price, using a coupon for an additional $5 off the sale price. Lydia had $10.50 left. What was the original price of the sweater? **$59**

Mixed Review

Find each sum or difference. *(Lessons 5-2, 5-3)*

12. $\frac{3}{8} + \frac{2}{5}$ $\frac{31}{40}$
13. $3\frac{3}{4} - 2\frac{5}{8}$ $1\frac{1}{8}$
14. $9\frac{1}{4} + 7\frac{5}{6}$ $17\frac{1}{12}$
15. $11\frac{7}{8} - 2\frac{2}{3}$ $9\frac{5}{24}$
16. $10 - 8\frac{1}{6}$ $1\frac{5}{6}$

Evaluate each expression for $a = 4$, $b = 6$, and $c = 5.6$. *(Lesson 3-1)*

17. $8c$ 44.8
18. $3a + 7a$ 40
19. $\frac{c}{a}$ 1.4
20. $3b - a$ 14
21. $2(c - a)$ 3.2
22. $\frac{b - c}{8}$ 0.05

23. *Food* You go out to lunch with two friends. Together you order a plate of nachos for $6.99 and a large pizza for $11.97. *(Lessons 2-3, 2-6)*
    a. How much does this lunch cost? **$18.96**
    b. What is your share? **$6.32**

PROBLEM SOLVING PRACTICE ★★

This page provides problems for students to solve using their knowledge of fractions, decimals, expressions, and estimating products. Allow students to use any method they find helpful.

Exercise 4 Students may find the formula confusing. Have them read the formula aloud, beginning with The cost of a museum tour is, then substituting number of students for *s* and number of teachers for *t*.

Exercise 5 Challenge students to name the property they use to find the equivalent expression.

USING MANIPULATIVES Exercises 6 and 8 Students may want to use fraction bars to model the fractions and mixed numbers.

PROBLEM SOLVING PRACTICE ★★★★★

Choose the best answer.

1. For the first half of the baseball season, Karen got a hit $\frac{11}{35}$ of the times she was at bat. To the nearest thousandth, what is this fraction expressed as a decimal? B

   A. 0.310 B. 0.314 C. 0.315 D. 0.320

2. After three hours, the biking club had ridden $35\frac{1}{4}$ miles, after four hours they had ridden 47 miles, and after five hours they had ridden $58\frac{3}{4}$ miles. If this pattern continues, how many miles will they have ridden after seven hours? H

   F. $70\frac{1}{2}$ miles G. $75\frac{3}{4}$ miles
   H. $82\frac{1}{4}$ miles J. 94 miles

3. If $d - \frac{5}{8} = 4\frac{3}{4}$, what is the value of d? B

   A. $3\frac{2}{3}$ B. $5\frac{3}{8}$
   C. $5\frac{5}{8}$ D. $5\frac{23}{24}$

4. The cost for a museum tour is found by using the formula:

   $$(s \times 1.25) + (t \times 2.25) + 40$$

   In this formula s is the number of students, t is the number of teachers, and \$40 is the basic cost of the tour. Using the formula, what would it cost for 35 students and 3 teachers to take the tour? H

   F. \$50.50 G. \$83.75
   H. \$90.50 J. \$98.44

5. Which expression is equivalent to $6.5 + (4.6 \times 8.2)$? D

   A. $(6.5 + 4.6) \times 8.2$
   B. $6.5 \times (4.6 + 8.2)$
   C. $(6.5 + 4.6) \times (6.5 \times 8.2)$
   D. $(8.2 \times 4.6) + 6.5$

6. Dorie has plants with heights $4\frac{5}{8}$ in., $4\frac{3}{16}$ in., $4\frac{3}{4}$ in., $4\frac{13}{16}$ in., and $4\frac{1}{2}$ in. She wants to arrange the plants on her windowsill from tallest to shortest. Which is the correct order? H

   F. $4\frac{13}{16}$ in., $4\frac{5}{8}$ in., $4\frac{3}{4}$ in., $4\frac{3}{16}$ in., $4\frac{1}{2}$ in.
   G. $4\frac{3}{4}$ in., $4\frac{5}{8}$ in., $4\frac{1}{2}$ in., $4\frac{13}{16}$ in., $4\frac{3}{16}$ in.
   H. $4\frac{13}{16}$ in., $4\frac{3}{4}$ in., $4\frac{5}{8}$ in., $4\frac{1}{2}$ in., $4\frac{3}{16}$ in.
   J. $4\frac{13}{16}$ in., $4\frac{3}{16}$ in., $4\frac{5}{8}$ in., $4\frac{3}{4}$ in., $4\frac{1}{2}$ in

7. Jeff is making a taco pie using a recipe that calls for $1\frac{1}{8}$ pounds of ground turkey. Jeff buys a package of ground turkey that is labeled 1.17 pounds. In order to determine if he has enough meat, Jeff writes $1\frac{1}{8}$ as a decimal. Which decimal is equivalent to $1\frac{1}{8}$? A

   A. 1.125 B. 1.25
   C. 1.8 D. 1.875

Please note that items 8–9 have *five* answer choices.

8. Jose needs a board that measures $2\frac{3}{4}$ ft to make a shelf. He has a board that is 5 ft long. What length is left after he cuts the board? F

   F. $2\frac{1}{4}$ ft G. $3\frac{1}{4}$ ft H. $7\frac{1}{4}$ ft
   J. $7\frac{3}{4}$ ft K. Not Here

9. During a four-week period, Laron earned \$12.75, \$31.43, \$27.89, and \$21.14 at his part-time job. The best estimate of the amount of money he earned during the four weeks is— C

   A. \$70 B. \$80 C. \$90
   D. \$100 E. \$110

5-8 Teaching Notes

1 Focus

CONNECTING TO PRIOR KNOWLEDGE Have students record their height on a piece of paper. Ask: *Who recorded their height in inches? Who recorded their height in feet and inches?* Explain that each way is correct. Ask students: *What would you need to know to compare a height in feet with a height in inches?* **the number of inches in a foot**

DIVERSITY Help students who used metric measurements in the Connecting to Prior Knowledge activity convert their heights to the customary system by showing them a meter stick and a ruler.

2 Teach

THINK AND DISCUSS

VISUAL LEARNING Students must have a sense of the size of each unit to help them determine whether they are converting to a smaller or larger unit. Have students bring to class objects or pictures of objects that are the lengths, weights, and capacities listed in the chart. Point out that the chart lists the smaller units on the left.

Lesson Planning Options

Prerequisite Skills

- measuring in the customary system (precourse)
- multiplying and dividing with fractions and mixed numbers (5-5 and 5-6)

Materials/Manipulatives

- calculator

Resources

Student Edition

Skills Handbook, pp. 541–543
Extra Practice, p. 518
Glossary/Study Guide

Teaching Resources

Chapter Support File, Ch. 5
- Lesson Planner 5-8
- Practice 5-8, Reteaching 5-8
- Answer Masters 5-8

Teaching Aids Master 3
Glossary, Spanish Resources

Transparencies
13, 15, Minds on Math 5-8

Warm Up

Find the greatest common factor (GCF) for each pair of numbers.
18 and 30 **6**
14 and 63 **7**

MEASUREMENT Connection

5-8 Changing Units in the Customary System

What You'll Learn

1. To change units of length and capacity
2. To change units of weight

...And Why

To use the customary system of measurement, you must be able to change units.

Here's How

Look for questions that
- build understanding
- ✔ check understanding

THINK AND DISCUSS

1 *Changing Units of Length and Capacity*

When a measure involves mixed units, it may be helpful to change to a mixed number involving just one unit.

■ **EXAMPLE 1** *Real-World Problem Solving*

Carpentry Sarah has a board that is 10 ft long. She plans to cut a piece that is 5 ft 3 in. long from the board. What will be the length of the remaining piece?

You need to subtract 5 ft 3 in. from 10 ft.

$5 \text{ ft } 3 \text{ in.} = 5\frac{3}{12} \text{ ft} = 5\frac{1}{4} \text{ ft}$ ← Write 3 in. as a fraction of a foot.

$10 - 5\frac{1}{4} = 9\frac{4}{4} - 5\frac{1}{4}$ ← Write 10 as $9\frac{4}{4}$. Then subtract.

$= 4\frac{3}{4}$

The remaining piece will be $4\frac{3}{4}$ ft long.

1 ft 7 in. or $1\frac{7}{12}$ ft 1. ✔ *Try It Out* Suppose Sarah cut 8 ft 5 in. from the 10 ft board. What would be the length of the remaining piece?

To change from a smaller unit to a larger unit, you *divide*.

Customary Units of Measure

Length	
12 inches (in.) = 1 foot (ft)	
3 feet = 1 yard (yd)	
5,280 feet = 1 mile (mi)	
Weight	
16 ounces (oz) = 1 pound (lb)	
2,000 pounds = 1 ton (T)	
Capacity	
8 fluid ounces (fl oz) = 1 cup (c)	
2 cups = 1 pint (p)	
2 pints = 1 quart (qt)	
4 quarts = 1 gallon (gal)	

■ **EXAMPLE 2** *Real-World Problem Solving*

How many one-cup servings are in a 36-fl oz bottle of juice?

Think of the relationship between fluid ounces and cups. 8 fl oz = 1 c (÷ 8)

To change 36 fl oz to cups, divide 36 fl oz by 8.

$36 \div 8 = 4.5$ ← Use mental math.

There are $4\frac{1}{2}$ one-cup servings in the 36-fl oz bottle.

2. ✔ *Try It Out* How many one-cup servings are in a 50-fl oz bottle of juice? **$6\frac{1}{4}$ servings**

Now you may assign Exercises 1–5, 26–28, 31–32.

EXTENSION Example 2 Challenge students to use the nutrition label on a bottle of juice to identify the serving size. Have them convert to find the number of servings per bottle. Use the label to check.

ADDITIONAL EXAMPLES

FOR EXAMPLE 1

Tenisha has 4 yd of ribbon. She plans to use 1 yd 2 ft to decorate a homecoming mum. What will be the length of the remaining piece of ribbon? **$2\frac{1}{3}$ yd**

FOR EXAMPLE 2

How many gallons are in 65 qt? **$16\frac{1}{4}$ gal**

FOR EXAMPLE 3

The social studies book weighs $8\frac{1}{2}$ lb, and the math book weighs 112 oz. Which book will be easier to carry? **The math book will be easier, the social studies book weighs 136 oz.**

VISUAL LEARNING Using a yardstick, point out that as units get smaller, you need more to fill the same space, so you multiply. As units get larger, you need fewer to fill the same space, so you divide.

Work Together

KINESTHETIC LEARNING Questions 4–7 If you have block scheduling or extended class periods, have students use measuring cups and water to perform conversions.

2 *Changing Units of Weight*

To change from a larger unit to a smaller unit, you *multiply*.

EXAMPLE 3 *Real-World Problem Solving*

The lighter the frame of a mountain bike, the easier it is to cycle. Which bike shown in the ad will be easier to cycle?

Think of the relationship between pounds and ounces. 1 lb = 16 oz (× 16)

To change $4\frac{1}{4}$ lb to ounces, multiply $4\frac{1}{4}$ lb by 16.

$$4\frac{1}{4} \cdot 16 = \frac{17}{\cancel{4}_1} \cdot \frac{\cancel{16}^4}{1} = 68$$

← Write $4\frac{1}{4}$ as an improper fraction. Then multiply.

The $4\frac{1}{4}$-lb bike weighs 68 oz, so it is lighter than the 76-oz bike.

3. ✔ *Try It Out* Find the number of ounces for each weight.

a. $4\frac{5}{8}$ lb **74 oz** b. $3\frac{7}{16}$ lb **55 oz** c. $9\frac{3}{4}$ lb **156 oz**

Work Together *Adjusting a Recipe*

Cooking Work in pairs. Suppose that you operate a catering service. You have a basic recipe for split pea soup that serves eight. Copy and complete the chart below to adjust the recipe for 16, 24, 32, and 48 servings. Whenever possible, change an amount to a larger unit of measure.

Answers			Number of Servings				
		Ingredient	8	16	24	32	48
$1\frac{1}{8}$ qt; $1\frac{11}{16}$ qt; $2\frac{1}{4}$ qt; $3\frac{3}{8}$ qt	4.	Dried split peas	$2\frac{1}{4}$ c	■	■	■	■
1 gal; $1\frac{1}{2}$ gal; 2 gal; 3 gal	5.	Water	2 qt	■	■	■	■
$1\frac{1}{2}$ c; $2\frac{1}{4}$ c; 3 c; $1\frac{1}{8}$ qt	6.	Chopped onion	$\frac{3}{4}$ c	■	■	■	■
1 pt; $1\frac{1}{2}$ pt; 1 qt; $1\frac{1}{2}$ qt	7.	Chopped celery	1 c	■	■	■	■
4 lb; 6 lb; 8 lb; 12 lb	8.	Ham shank	2 lb	■	■	■	■
$\frac{1}{2}$ lb; $\frac{3}{4}$ lb; 1 lb; $1\frac{1}{2}$ lb	9.	Sliced carrot	$\frac{1}{4}$ lb	■	■	■	■

Now you may assign Exercises 6–25, 29–30.

Technology Options

Prentice Hall Technology

Software for Learners
- Math Blaster® Mystery*
- Interactive Student Tutorial, Chapter 5*

Teaching Resource Software
- Computer Item Generator 5-8
- Resource Pro™ Chapter 5*

Internet • For related mathematics activities, visit the Prentice Hall site at www.phschool.com/math

**Available on CD-ROM only*

Assignment Options for Exercises On Your Own

To provide flexible scheduling, this lesson can be subdivided into parts.

1 **Core** 1–5, 26–28
Extension 31–32

2 **Core** 6–25
Extension 29, 30

Use Mixed Review to maintain skills.

ASSESSMENT When partners have completed the Work Together, have them compare their answers with another pair. If their answers disagree, help them determine whether the mistake is the result of a calculation error or a misunderstanding of the conversion process.

ERROR ALERT! Students may have trouble differentiating between 8 fl oz in 1 c and 16 oz in 1 lb. **Remediation:** Invite students to create a mnemonic or a rhyme they can use to remember which unit equals 8 fl oz and which unit equals 16 oz.

3 Practice/Assess

EXERCISES *On Your Own*

WRITING Exercise 29 This exercise will help students organize their thinking about changing measurements from one unit to another. Carefully check students' answers to determine whether you need to reteach.

CONNECTION TO EARTH SCIENCE
Exercises 31 and 32 Challenge students to use an atlas to find the highest elevation they have visited. Encourage students to make a classroom display recording these high-elevation places.

WRAP UP

IDENTIFYING THE BIG IDEA Tell students: *Describe a situation where it would be useful to convert measurements. Explain how to perform the conversion.*

CHECKPOINT 2

Checkpoint 2 *Lessons 5-5 through 5-8*

Find each product or quotient.

1. $\frac{9}{10} \cdot \frac{5}{6}$ $\frac{3}{4}$
2. $\frac{5}{6} \div \frac{1}{12}$ 10
3. $2\frac{3}{4} \div \frac{3}{8}$ $7\frac{1}{3}$
4. $1\frac{3}{5} \cdot 2\frac{7}{9}$ $4\frac{4}{9}$

Complete.

5. 24 in. = 2 ft
6. $4\frac{3}{4}$ lb = 76 oz
7. 5 pt = $2\frac{1}{2}$ qt
8. If you start with a number, add 7, then divide by 3, the result is 19. What was the original number? 50

Assessment

pages 220–221 On Your Own

29. Answers may vary. Sample: A larger unit contains many small units. So you multiply the number of larger units by the number of smaller units in each larger unit. 1 gal contains 4 qt, so $2\frac{1}{2}$ gal contains $2\frac{1}{2} \times 4 = 10$ qt. A smaller unit is a fractional part of a larger unit. So to find the number of larger units, you need to multiply the number of smaller units by the fraction, or divide by the number of smaller units in each large one. 1 yd contains 3 ft, so 18 ft are equivalent to $18 \div 3 = 6$ yd.

27. Yes; 1 gal = 16 c, so 4 gal = 64 c.

EXERCISES *On Your Own*

Tell whether you would *multiply* or *divide* to change from one unit of measure to the other.

1. gallons to quarts multiply
2. cups to pints divide
3. quarts to cups multiply
4. fluid ounces to cups divide

Mental Math **Complete.**

5. 4 ft 6 in. = ■ ft $4\frac{1}{2}$
6. $\frac{3}{4}$ lb = ■ oz 12
7. 500 lb = ■ T $\frac{1}{4}$
8. $1\frac{1}{5}$ T = ■ lb 2,400
9. Yung Mi has three packages of walnuts that weigh 12 oz, 32 oz, and $1\frac{1}{2}$ lb. How many pounds of walnuts does she have altogether? $4\frac{1}{4}$ lb

Choose **Use a calculator, paper and pencil, or mental math to change from one unit of measure to the other.**

10. $5\frac{1}{4}$ gal = ■ qt 21
11. 5,250 lb = ■ T $2\frac{5}{8}$
12. 4 yd 2 ft = ■ yd $4\frac{2}{3}$
13. ■ gal = 36 pt $4\frac{1}{2}$
14. 26 in. = ■ ft $2\frac{1}{6}$
15. 4 c = ■ fl oz 32
16. 68 oz = ■ lb $4\frac{1}{4}$
17. 36 oz = ■ lb $2\frac{1}{4}$
18. $3\frac{1}{2}$ mi = ■ ft 18,480
19. 16 ft = ■ yd $5\frac{1}{3}$
20. $4\frac{1}{2}$ qt = ■ c 18
21. 2,800 lb = ■ T $1\frac{2}{5}$
22. 1 ft 9 in. = ■ ft $1\frac{3}{4}$
23. ■ pt = 14 fl oz $\frac{7}{8}$
24. 3 lb 12 oz = ■ lb $3\frac{3}{4}$
25. 7 pt = ■ qt $3\frac{1}{2}$
26. *Geography* The length of the Amazon River in South America is about 4,000 mi. How many feet is this? 21,120,000 ft
27. Will 4 gal of milk make 64 one-cup servings? Explain. See above.
28. *Hobbies* Jim has a pattern that requires $1\frac{3}{4}$ yd of 60-in. canvas. At a sale, he finds a remnant of 60-in. canvas that is $5\frac{1}{2}$ ft long. Will this be enough? Explain. Yes; $1\frac{3}{4}$ yd = $5\frac{1}{4}$ ft.
29. *Writing* Explain why you multiply to change from a larger unit to a smaller unit and divide to change from a smaller unit to a larger unit. Include examples. See margin.
30. a. *Calculator* In one day, people in the United States discard an average of 200,000 tons of food. Suppose that a garbage truck can hold 12,000 lb of this food. How many trucks are needed to haul all of it?
    b. Suppose that garbage trucks carrying all the discarded food are lined up bumper to bumper. Each truck is 25 ft long. About how long is the line of trucks in miles?
    a. 33,334 trucks b. about 158 mi

The Amazon River Basin contains $\frac{1}{5}$ of the world's fresh river water and $\frac{1}{3}$ of its forests. It may produce up to $\frac{1}{2}$ of the oxygen added to the atmosphere each year.

Source: *Curious Facts*

LESSON QUIZ

Tell whether you multiply or divide to change from one measure to the other. Then complete.

1. $3\frac{2}{3}$ yd = ■ ft **multiply; 11 ft**
2. 260 oz = ■ lb **divide; $16\frac{1}{4}$ lb**
3. 10 gal = ■ c **multiply; 160 c**

Climb or Dive?

WHAT IS THE TALLEST MOUNTAIN IN THE WORLD? Mount Everest can claim the world's highest elevation above sea level. As shown at the right, however, Hawaii's Mauna Kea is truly the world's tallest mountain, although much of it is hidden in the Pacific Ocean.

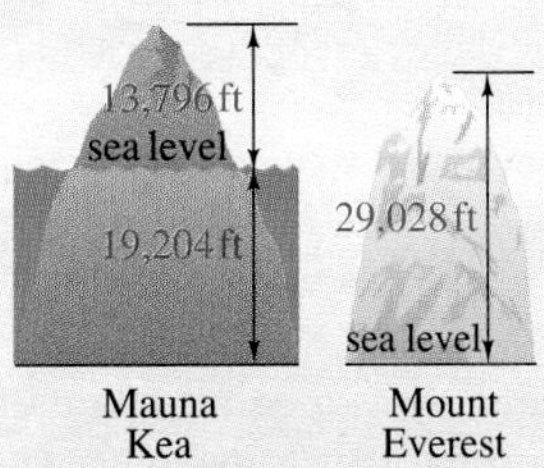

So what is the *lowest* elevation on Earth? Located between Israel and Jordan, the Dead Sea is 1,312 ft below sea level. For the oceans, the lowest elevation is the Marianas Trench. It lies 36,198 ft below the surface of the Pacific Ocean. If Mount Everest were placed in the Marianas Trench, its peak would be about $1\frac{1}{3}$ mi below sea level.

31. a. *Earth Science* How many miles high is Mauna Kea? **about $6\frac{1}{4}$ mi**
    b. About how many miles taller than Mount Everest is Mauna Kea? **about $\frac{3}{4}$ mi**

32. About how many miles in elevation separate the highest and lowest elevations on Earth? **12.5 mi**

Mixed Review

Solve using mental math. *(Lesson 3-6)*

33. $x + 42 = 83$ **41**
34. $b - (-2) = 7$ **5**
35. $z - 92 = 138$ **230**
36. $m + 4 = -4$ **−8**

37. *Canoeing* Laura and Leslie rented a canoe for $3\frac{1}{2}$ hours. The canoe rental is $2.20 per hour. How much should each pay? *(Lessons 5-5, 5-6)* **$3.85**

✓ CHECKPOINT 2

Lessons 5-5 through 5-8

Find each product or quotient.

1. $\frac{4}{5} \cdot \frac{5}{8}$ **$\frac{1}{2}$**
2. $\frac{1}{3} \div \frac{4}{9}$ **$\frac{3}{4}$**
3. $\frac{5}{6} \div 6\frac{2}{3}$ **$\frac{1}{8}$**
4. $7\frac{1}{2} \cdot 3\frac{4}{7}$ **$26\frac{11}{14}$**
5. $8\frac{1}{2} \div \frac{1}{4}$ **34**
6. Alicia has a job interview at 8:30 A.M. She needs 15 min to eat breakfast, $\frac{1}{2}$ h to get dressed, and 40 min to drive to the interview. What is the latest time that she should get up? **7:05 A.M.**

Complete.

7. 28 in. = ■ ft **$2\frac{1}{3}$**
8. $8\frac{1}{2}$ lb = ■ oz **136**
9. 15 qt = ■ gal **$3\frac{3}{4}$**
10. 7 yd 2 ft = ■ yd **$7\frac{2}{3}$**

PRACTICE

Practice 5-8 Changing Units in the Customary System

Tell whether you would multiply or divide to change from one unit of measure to the other.

1. tons to pounds **multiply**
2. pints to quarts **divide**
3. feet to yards **divide**
4. gallons to pints **multiply**
5. cups to quarts **divide**
6. pounds to ounces **multiply**

Choose a calculator, paper and pencil, or mental math to change from one unit of measure to the other.

7. 9 qt = **$2\frac{1}{4}$** gal
8. $2\frac{1}{4}$ t = **4,500** lb
9. $3\frac{1}{2}$ yd = **126** in.
10. 4 yd = **12** ft
11. 60 c = **15** qt
12. $1\frac{3}{4}$ gal = **14** pt
13. 246 in. = **$20\frac{1}{2}$** ft
14. 1,750 oz = **$109\frac{3}{8}$** lb
15. $\frac{3}{4}$ t = **24,000** oz
16. 84 ft = **28** yd
17. 198 in. = **$5\frac{1}{2}$** yd
18. 11,880 ft = **$2\frac{1}{4}$** mi
19. 480 fl oz = **30** pt
20. $\frac{1}{4}$ gal = **32** fl oz
21. $1\frac{1}{2}$ pt = **24** fl oz
22. $\frac{1}{2}$ mi = **2,640** ft
23. $\frac{1}{10}$ mi = **6,336** in.
24. 3 mi = **5,280** yd
25. 2 lb 6 oz = **$2\frac{3}{8}$** lb
26. 2 qt 8 fl oz = **$2\frac{1}{4}$** qt
27. 4 yd 2 ft = **$4\frac{2}{3}$** yd

Find the perimeter of each rectangle in feet and in inches.

28. $6\frac{1}{2}$ ft by $2\frac{1}{4}$ ft — **$17\frac{1}{2}$ ft; 210 in.**
29. 6 ft 3 in. by 5 ft 2 in. — **$22\frac{5}{6}$ ft; 274 in.**
30. 426 in. by 352 in. — **$129\frac{2}{3}$ ft; 1,556 in.**

In copymaster and workbook formats

RETEACHING

Reteaching 5-8 Changing Units in the Customary System

Length	Weight	Capacity
12 inches (in.) = 1 foot (ft) 3 ft = 1 yard (yd) 5,280 ft = 1 mile (mi)	16 ounces (oz) = 1 pound (lb) 2,000 lb = 1 ton (t)	8 fluid ounces (fl oz) = 1 cup (c) 2 c = 1 pint (pt) 2 pt = 1 quart (qt) 4 qt = 1 gallon (gal)

To change to a *larger* unit, divide.

66 in. = ■ (1 ft is larger than 1 in. 12 in. = 1 ft)

$66 \div 12 = \frac{66}{12} = 5\frac{6}{12} = 5\frac{1}{2}$

66 in. = $5\frac{1}{2}$ ft

To change to a *smaller* unit, multiply.

$3\frac{1}{2}$ qt = ■ pt (1 pt is smaller than 1 qt. 1 qt = 2 pt)

$3\frac{1}{2} \cdot 2 = \frac{7}{2} \cdot \frac{2}{1} = \frac{14}{2} = 7$

$3\frac{1}{2}$ qt = 7 pt

Multiply to change to a smaller unit. Write the fact you used.

1. $3\frac{1}{2}$ ft = **42 in.** — **1 ft = 12 in.**
2. $1\frac{1}{2}$ c = **12 oz** — **1 c = 8 fl oz**
3. 5 lb = **80 oz** — **1 lb = 16 oz**
4. $5\frac{1}{2}$ qt = **11 pt** — **1 qt = 2 pt**
5. $3\frac{1}{4}$ gal = **13 qt** — **1 gal = 4 qt**
6. 4 pt = **8 c** — **1 pt = 2 c**
7. 2 mi = **10,560 ft** — **1 mi = 5,280 ft**
8. 6 qt = **12 pt** — **1 qt = 2 pt**
9. $1\frac{1}{2}$ t = **3,000 lb** — **1 t = 2,000 lb**

Divide to change to a larger unit. Write the fact you used.

10. 24 oz = **3 c** — **1 c = 8 fl oz**
11. 32 oz = **2 lb** — **1 lb = 16 oz**
12. 10 qt = **$2\frac{1}{2}$ gal** — **1 gal = 4 qt**
13. 3 c = **$1\frac{1}{2}$ pt** — **1 pt = 2 c**
14. 4,000 lb = **2 t** — **1 t = 2,000 lb**
15. 17 oz = **$1\frac{1}{16}$ lb** — **1 lb = 16 oz**
16. 7 pt = **$3\frac{1}{2}$ qt** — **1 qt = 2 pt**
17. 27 ft = **9 yd** — **1 yd = 3 ft**
18. 30 in. = **$2\frac{1}{2}$ ft** — **1 ft = 12 in.**

Reteaching

ENRICHMENT

Minds on Math Transparency

5-8

Place the digits 2, 4, 5, and 7 in the boxes to make the equation true.

$\frac{3}{6} = \frac{9}{18} = \frac{\square\square}{\square\square}$

$\frac{27}{54}$

See *Solution Key* for worked-out answers.

5-9 Teaching Notes

1 Focus

CONNECTING TO PRIOR KNOWLEDGE
Invite students to write examples on the board of multiplication and division equations involving whole numbers. Have the class solve the equations. Ask students: *Do you think the method for solving the equations would be different if you replaced the whole numbers with fractions?*

2 Teach

THINK AND DISCUSS

Example 1 You may need to rewrite $\frac{1}{4}s$ as $\frac{1}{4} \times \frac{s}{1}$ before changing to $\frac{s}{4}$. Remind students that $1 \times s$ is the same as s.

ERROR ALERT! Example 1 Because students think of s as being multiplied by $\frac{1}{4}$, they may divide both sides by 4. They may also attempt to solve mentally because 4 divides easily into 44. **Remediation:** Remind students that to divide by a fraction they must multiply by the reciprocal. Point out that multiplying by 4 is the same as dividing by $\frac{1}{4}$. Encourage students to use substitution to check their answers.

ASSESSMENT Have students solve $7n = 23$ and $\frac{1}{8}y = 5$. **$n = 3\frac{2}{7}$; $y = 40$** Students show each step of their solution, then exchange with a partner to compare steps and solutions.

Lesson Planning Options

Prerequisite Skills
- solving whole number equations (3-6 and 3-7)
- multiplying fractions and mixed numbers (5-5)

Materials/Manipulatives
- calculator

Resources

Student Edition
Skills Handbook, p. 530
Extra Practice, p. 518
Glossary/Study Guide

Teaching Resources
Chapter Support File, Ch. 5
- Lesson Planner 5-9
- Practice 5-9, Reteaching 5-9
- Alternative Activity 5-9
- Answer Masters 5-9

Teaching Aids Masters 20–25
Glossary, Spanish Resources

Transparencies
9, 10, 12, 15, 18–25,
Minds on Math 5-9

Warm Up
Find the least common denominator (LCD) for each set of fractions.

$\frac{1}{4}$ and $\frac{1}{6}$ **12** $\frac{3}{10}$ and $\frac{3}{8}$ **40**

ALGEBRA Connection

5-9 Solving Equations with Fractions by Multiplying and Dividing

What You'll Learn
1. To solve equations using multiplication
2. To solve equations using division

...And Why
You can extend your knowledge of how to solve equations.

Here's How
Look for questions that
- build understanding
- ✔ check understanding

THINK AND DISCUSS

1 Solving Equations by Multiplying

You have solved equations using multiplication and division. Now apply your knowledge to equations with fractions.

EXAMPLE 1 *Real-World Problem Solving*

Money Paper money is printed in sheets of 32 bills. Inspectors check about one fourth of the sheets. If an inspector checked 44 sheets, how many sheets were printed?

Words • one fourth of sheets printed = sheets checked

• Let s = number of sheets printed

Equation • $\frac{1}{4}s = 44$

$\frac{s}{4} = 44$ ← Write $\frac{1}{4}s$ as $\frac{s}{4}$.

$4 \cdot \frac{s}{4} = 4 \cdot 44$ ← Since s is divided by 4, multiply each side by 4.

$s = 176$

176 sheets were printed.

1. ✔ *Try It Out* Solve each equation.
   a. $\frac{1}{3}s = 5$ **15** b. $\frac{1}{2}s = \frac{3}{4}$ **$1\frac{1}{2}$** c. $\frac{s}{8} = 2\frac{1}{3}$ **$18\frac{2}{3}$** d. $\frac{s}{8} = 6\frac{3}{4}$ **54**

Now you may assign Exercises 1–8.

2 Solving Equations by Dividing

The solution of an equation may be a fraction or a mixed number.

EXAMPLE 2

Solve $32c = 130$.

$32c = 130$

$\frac{32c}{32} = \frac{130}{32}$ ← Divide each side by 32.

$c = \frac{65}{16} = 4\frac{1}{16}$ ← Simplify and write as a mixed number.

ADDITIONAL EXAMPLES

FOR EXAMPLE 1

At the pet store, $\frac{1}{7}$ of the snakes are shedding. Holly counts 4 shedding snakes. How many snakes does the pet store have? $\frac{1}{7}s = 4$; $s = 28$

FOR EXAMPLE 2

Solve $12d = 140$. $d = 11\frac{2}{3}$

3 Practice/Assess

EXERCISES *On Your Own*

AUDITORY LEARNING Exercises 6 and 7 Have students work in pairs. One partner reads the question aloud, the other listens and writes the equation.

OPEN-ENDED Exercise 8 Suggest that students think of x as a group of people or a set of objects.

ESTIMATION Exercise 19 Ask: *Is 49 being divided by a number greater than or less than 49?*

WRAP UP

IDENTIFYING THE BIG IDEA Ask students to describe how to solve equations with fractions by multiplying and dividing.

PORTFOLIO Share with students the criteria you will use to assess their work in portfolios, as well as how you plan to use the

---

a. $8\frac{3}{5}$ 2. ✔ *Try It Out* Solve each equation.

a. $5x = 43$ b. $8a = 50$ $6\frac{1}{4}$ c. $32 = 6d$ $5\frac{1}{3}$ d. $4r = 3$ $\frac{3}{4}$

Now you may assign Exercises 9–43.

EXERCISES *On Your Own*

Solve each equation.

1. $\frac{y}{6} = 5$ 30
2. $\frac{1}{8}d = 5\frac{1}{4}$ 42
3. $\frac{t}{5} = 3\frac{7}{10}$ $18\frac{1}{2}$
4. $16 = \frac{1}{3}e$ 48
5. $8\frac{3}{4} = \frac{p}{6}$ $52\frac{1}{2}$

6. *Business* On a recent day, a store manager noted that 65 customers bought at least eight items. This was one fifth of the total number of customers that day. Write and solve an equation to find the total number of customers. $\frac{1}{5}c = 65$; 325 customers

7. *Sports* It took Ruthene $\frac{1}{4}$ h to run 2 mi. What was her average speed? 8 mi/h

8. *Open-ended* Write a problem that can be solved using the equation $\frac{1}{5}x = 28$. Sample: One-fifth of a shipment of fruit is 28 tons of pineapples. What is the weight of the entire shipment of fruit?

Solve each equation.

9. $4a = 9$ $2\frac{1}{4}$
10. $2q = 17$ $8\frac{1}{2}$
11. $6g = 16$ $2\frac{2}{3}$
12. $10w = 4$ $\frac{2}{5}$
13. $8n = 15$ $1\frac{7}{8}$

Mental Math **Solve each equation.**

14. $\frac{x}{6} = 2$ 12
15. $3p = 9$ 3
16. $12f = 2$ $\frac{1}{6}$
17. $\frac{1}{3}b = 12$ 36
18. $12k = 8$ $\frac{2}{3}$

19. *Estimation* Carl and Ed each estimated the solution of $20g = 49$. Carl's estimate was $\frac{2}{5}$. Ed's estimate was $2\frac{1}{2}$.
    a. Whose estimate is correct? How do you think he made the estimate? Ed's; 49 is about 50, so the solution is $\frac{50}{20} = 2\frac{1}{2}$.
    b. What error do you think the other person made? Carl divided 20 by 50 instead of 50 by 20.

Choose **Use a calculator, paper and pencil, or mental math to solve each equation.**

20. $\frac{1}{5}s = 16$ 80
21. $9a = 20$ $2\frac{2}{9}$
22. $48q = 36$ $\frac{3}{4}$
23. $\frac{1}{28} = \frac{1}{4}z$ $\frac{1}{7}$
24. $3w = 5$ $1\frac{2}{3}$
25. $14n = 60$ $4\frac{2}{7}$
26. $\frac{s}{8} = 128$ 1,024
27. $88 = 22c$ 4
28. $\frac{w}{7} = 628$ 4,396
29. $36m = 4$ $\frac{1}{9}$
30. $37p = 407$ 11
31. $\frac{1}{55}b = 78$ 4,290
32. $\frac{n}{12} = 10$ 120
33. $117 = \frac{1}{9}u$ 1,053
34. $5 = \frac{w}{10}$ 50

35. *Writing* How is solving the equation $4y = 24$ similar to solving $24y = 4$? How is it different? See back of book.

Technology Options

Prentice Hall Technology

Software for Learners

- Math Blaster® Mystery*
- Interactive Student Tutorial, Chapter 5*

Teaching Resource Software

- Computer Item Generator 5-9
- Resource Pro™ Chapter 5*

Internet • For related mathematics activities, visit the Prentice Hall site at www.phschool.com/math

**Available on CD-ROM only*

Assignment Options for Exercises On Your Own

To provide flexible scheduling, this lesson can be subdivided into parts.

1. **Core** 1–7; **Extension** 8
2. **Core** 9–42; **Extension** 43

Use Mixed Review to maintain skills.

PRACTICE

Practice 5-9 Solving Equations with Fractions by Mutliplying and Dividing

Choose a calculator, paper and pencil, or mental math to solve each equation.

1. $4y = 9$ $2\frac{1}{4}$	2. $\frac{d}{9} = 16$ 144	3. $\frac{1}{5}a = 47$ 235
4. $51m = 3$ $\frac{1}{17}$	5. $\frac{x}{9} = 4$ 36	6. $5j = 50$ 10
7. $16b = 2$ $\frac{1}{8}$	8. $\frac{1}{4}c = 9$ 36	9. $\frac{z}{12} = 8$ 96
10. $11e = 15$ $1\frac{4}{11}$	11. $50p = 75$ $1\frac{1}{2}$	12. $19 = \frac{1}{6}q$ 114
13. $\frac{k}{29} = 71$ 2,059	14. $15v = 34$ $2\frac{4}{15}$	15. $\frac{1}{16}t = 24$ 384
16. $96 = 8v$ 12	17. $\frac{x}{19} = 56$ 1,064	18. $8f = 12$ $1\frac{1}{2}$
19. $\frac{g}{58} = 29$ 1,682	20. $26i = 50$ $1\frac{12}{13}$	21. $\frac{k}{12} = 144$ 1,728
22. $18m = 30$ $1\frac{2}{3}$	23. $\frac{1}{20}n = 75$ 1,500	24. $\frac{r}{25} = 100$ 2,500
25. $\frac{1}{6}s = 12$ 72	26. $21u = 42$ 2	27. $\frac{x}{18} = 36$ 648
28. $\frac{y}{15} = 27$ 405	29. $15z = 27$ $1\frac{4}{5}$	30. $\frac{1}{9}a = 51$ 459

Practice

Solve.

31. If $\frac{1}{3}$ of a number is 21, what is the number? 63

32. If 8 times a number is 15, what is the number? $1\frac{7}{8}$

33. On a certain day, 240 cars along a certain stretch of highway had two or more people in them. If this was $\frac{2}{5}$ of the cars along that stretch of road, how many cars were there? 600 cars

34. In a store, $\frac{1}{6}$ of the slacks on a rack were black. If there were 8 pairs of black slacks, how many pairs of slacks were on that rack? 48 pairs of slacks

In copymaster and workbook formats

RETEACHING

Reteaching 5-9 Solving Equations with Fractions by Multiplying and Dividing

When solving an equation that involves multiplication or division, remember that division "undoes" multiplication and multiplication "undoes" division.

Solve:	Solve:
$\frac{w}{3} = 8$	$4b = 26$
$3 \cdot \frac{w}{3} = 3 \cdot 8$ ← **Since w is divided by 3, multiply by 3 to solve.**	$\frac{4b}{4} = \frac{26}{4}$ ← **Since b is multiplied by 4, divide by 4 to solve.**
$w = 24$	$b = \frac{26}{4} = 6\frac{1}{2}$ ← **Simplify.**

Complete to solve each equation.

1. $5a = 3$; $\frac{5a}{\boxed{5}} = \frac{3}{\boxed{5}}$; $a = \frac{3}{5}$
2. $9y = 5$; $\frac{9y}{\boxed{9}} = \frac{5}{\boxed{9}}$; $y = \frac{5}{9}$
3. $\frac{t}{3} = 2$; $\frac{t}{3} \cdot \boxed{3} = 2 \cdot \boxed{3}$; $t = 6$
4. $6m = 22$; $\frac{6m}{6} = \frac{\boxed{22}}{6}$; $m = 3\frac{2}{3}$
5. $\frac{1}{3}n = 4$; $\frac{1}{3}n \cdot \boxed{3} = 4 \cdot \boxed{3}$; $n = 12$
6. $\frac{c}{4} = 5$; $\frac{c}{4} \cdot \boxed{4} = 5 \cdot \boxed{4}$; $c = 20$

Solve each equation.

7. $4b = 16$ 4	8. $\frac{x}{6} = 3$ 18	9. $3z = 11$ $3\frac{2}{3}$
10. $10n = 25$ $2\frac{1}{2}$	11. $\frac{a}{4} = 2$ 8	12. $\frac{1}{2}x = 24$ 48
13. $7c = 3\frac{1}{2}$ $\frac{1}{2}$	14. $8 = \frac{s}{5}$ 40	15. $26p = 39$ $1\frac{1}{2}$
16. $15y = 12$ $\frac{4}{5}$	17. $\frac{n}{12} = 3\frac{3}{4}$ 45	18. $15 = \frac{1}{5}t$ 75
19. $21m = 7$ $\frac{1}{3}$	20. $\frac{1}{6} = \frac{1}{2}b$ $\frac{1}{3}$	21. $48z = 120$ $2\frac{1}{2}$

ENRICHMENT

Minds on Math Transparency

5-9

Cameron invited 17 friends to his party. He assigned each friend an integer from 2 to 18 and kept the number 1 for himself. During one dance, everyone was dancing with a partner. Cameron noticed that the sum of each couple's numbers was a perfect square. What was Cameron's partner's number during this dance?

15

See *Solution Key* for worked-out answers.

results. Students should understand how the rubrics are used to assess their work, how each piece in the portfolio counts, and how the scores they get in their portfolios will affect their overall evaluation.

PROJECT LINK Ask students why the number of eggs must be a whole number. **You cannot add $\frac{1}{2}$ of an egg.**

DIVERSITY Many people do not eat eggs. Discuss ways to substitute for eggs in recipes.

LESSON QUIZ

Solve each equation.

1. $\frac{1}{5}y = 18$ $y = 90$
2. $14x = 158$ $x = 11\frac{2}{7}$

Estimation **Estimate the solution of each equation. Explain how you made your estimate.** 36–40. Answers may vary. Samples are given.

36. $23q = 400$ 16; divide 400 by 25.
37. $9a = 121$ 12; divide 120 by 10.
38. $\frac{1}{21}n = 12$ 200; multiply 10 by 20.
39. $82 = \frac{1}{9}t$ 39. 800; multiply 80 by 10.
40. $2\frac{5}{6} = \frac{1}{7}x$ 40. 21; multiply 3 by 7.

Solve each problem by writing and solving an equation.

41. Mount McKinley, the tallest mountain in North America, is 20,320 ft tall. The Petronas Tower in Kuala Lampur, the world's tallest building, is 1,483 ft tall. About how many times as tall as the Petronas Tower is Mount McKinley? 13.7 times

42. *Geography* About one eighth of the total area of the New England states is covered by water. This is about 9,000 mi^2. What is the total area of the New England states? 72,000 mi^2

43. *Open-ended* Write two different equations that have the solution $5\frac{1}{2}$. One should require division to solve, and one should require multiplication to solve. Answers may vary. Samples: $2q = 11$; $n \div 2\frac{3}{4} = 2$

PORTFOLIO
Select one or two items from your work for this chapter. Consider:
- cooperative work
- work you found challenging
- part of your project

Explain why you have included each selection that you make.

Mixed Review

44–48. Estimates may vary. Samples are given.
Estimate each answer. (Lesson 5-1)

44. $12\frac{1}{2} - 5\frac{2}{3}$ 6
45. $16\frac{1}{2} \div \frac{3}{4}$ 17
46. $\frac{1}{2} + \frac{5}{12}$ 1
47. $21\frac{1}{8} \cdot 3\frac{1}{3}$ 63
48. $\frac{7}{8} - \frac{1}{6}$ 1

Compare. Use <, >, or =. (Lesson 3-2)

49. -15 ■ 0 <
50. 7 ■ -7 >
51. 23 ■ $|-23|$ =
52. -5 ■ -6 >
53. $|10|$ ■ -10 >

54. *Videos* In a video store, $\frac{1}{4}$ of the movies are comedies, $\frac{1}{6}$ are romances, and $\frac{1}{2}$ are thrillers. What fraction of the movies are not comedies, romances, or thrillers? (Lesson 5-2) $\frac{1}{12}$

CHAPTER PROJECT

PROJECT LINK: CALCULATING

Now that you have a good pancake recipe for feeding your family, adjust it to serve the number of people that are in your class. Remember to keep the number of eggs as a whole number, even though most of the other ingredients use fractions. Did you multiply fractions or divide fractions to get the class recipe? Explain. Multiply; the class is larger than the family.

Extra Practice, Lesson 5-9, page 518

FINISHING THE CHAPTER PROJECT

PROJECT DAY You may wish to plan a project day on which students share their completed projects. Encourage students to explain their process as well as their product.

PROJECT NOTEBOOK Ask students to review their project work and bring their notebooks up to date.

Have students review their methods for conducting their interviews, writing their recipes, and calculating a recipe to feed the entire class.

SCORING RUBRIC

3 Your pancake recipe works. You provided step-by-step explanations of how you calculated the amounts of ingredients required for your family and for your whole class. You provided evidence that either you tested your recipe by making it for your family or you interviewed someone with cooking experience to make sure your recipe made sense.

2 You wrote a pancake recipe and explained how you calculated the amounts of ingredients required for your family and the class, but either some of your calculations were inaccurate or you didn't verify that your recipe made sense.

1 You wrote a pancake recipe but didn't calculate the amounts of ingredients required for either your family or the whole class.

0 You did not write a pancake recipe.

FINISHING THE CHAPTER PROJECT

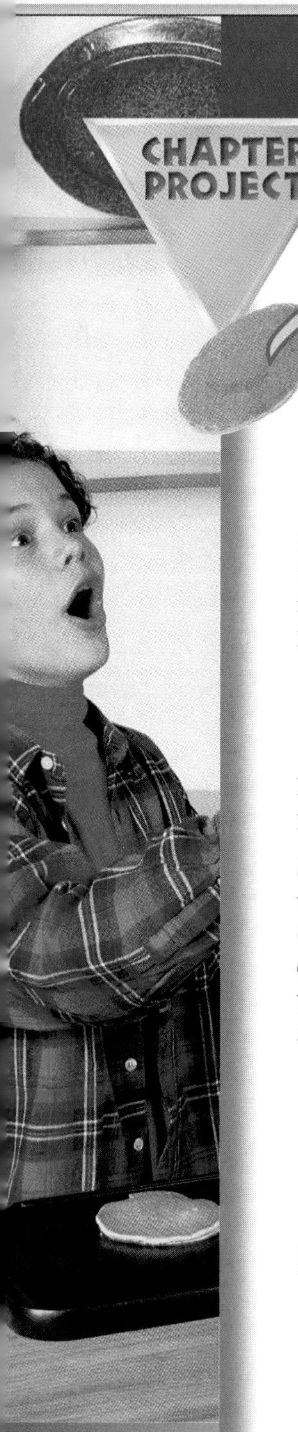

CHAPTER PROJECT

Toss and Turn

Write Your Own Recipe The Project Link questions on pages 196, 209, and 224 should help you complete your project. Here is a checklist to help you gather together the parts of your project.

- ✔ the people you interviewed
- ✔ your recipe for feeding your family
- ✔ your recipe for feeding the whole class

Present your recipe to your class. Sell them on how tasty your pancakes are!

Reflect and Revise

With an adult, make a batch of your pancakes for your family. Get their comments and change your recipe as needed.

Think about the math that you used to complete this project. What have you learned in this chapter that helped you? What advice did you get from others to create a great recipe?

Web Extension

Prentice Hall's Internet site contains information you might find helpful as you complete your project. Visit www.phschool.com/mgm2/ch5 for some links and ideas related to cooking.

STUDENT SELF-ASSESSMENT SURVEY

Chapter 5 Student Self-Assessment Survey

1. Now that you have finished this chapter, think about what you have learned about fractions. Check each topic that you feel confident you understand.
   ______ make estimates using fractions (5-1)
   ______ add and subtract fractions (5-2)
   ______ add and subtract mixed numbers (5-3)
   ______ solve equations by adding or subtracting fractions (5-4)
   ______ multiply fractions and mixed numbers (5-5)
   ______ divide fractions and mixed numbers (5-6)
   ______ solve problems by working backward (5-7)
   ______ change customary units of length, weight, and capacity (5-8)
   ______ solve one-step multiplication and division equations (5-9)
2. Before the Chapter Assessment, I need to review ______
3. a. Check one. In general, I thought this chapter was
   ___ a snap ___ easy ___ average ___ hard ___ a monster
   b. Why do you feel this way? ______
4. In this chapter, I did my best work on ______
5. In this chapter, I had trouble with ______
6. Check each one that applies. Now that I've spent some time working with fractions, I think they are
   ___ important ___ boring ___ useful ___ fun
   ___ a waste of time ___ confusing ___ tricky ___ interesting
7. List three situations outside the classroom where you could use fractions in your daily life. ______

Assessment

Vocabulary/Symbols

reciprocals

Resources

Student Edition

Extra Practice, p. 518
Glossary/Study Guide

Teaching Resources

Chapter Support File, Ch. 5
- Student Self-Assessment Survey

Glossary, Spanish Resources
Tools for Studying Smarter

WRAP UP

ESTIMATION Exercises 1–5 Encourage students to support their answers by writing the values they used to find their estimates.

Exercises 6–15 Have students estimate the sums and differences to make sure their answers are reasonable.

ASSESSMENT Exercises 16–23 and 44–53 Have students write the operation used to "undo" the operation in each equation before they solve.

Exercises 36–43 Have students make a table showing the relationships between the units. They can refer to the table while working on the exercises.

5 WRAP UP

Estimating with Fractions and Mixed Numbers 5-1

To estimate sums and differences of fractions, round to 0, $\frac{1}{2}$, or 1.

To estimate sums, differences, products, and quotients of mixed numbers, round to the nearest whole number.

1–5. Estimates may vary. Samples are given.

Estimate each answer.

1. $\frac{1}{8} + \frac{4}{5}$ 1
2. $\frac{5}{8} + 1\frac{2}{3}$ 2
3. $\frac{2}{5} - \frac{1}{4}$ $\frac{1}{2}$
4. $3\frac{1}{8} \cdot 9\frac{9}{10}$ 30
5. $12\frac{2}{5} \div 3\frac{8}{9}$ 3

Adding and Subtracting Fractions 5-2, 5-3

To add or subtract fractions, first find a common denominator and then add or subtract the numerators.

To add or subtract mixed numbers, add or subtract the whole numbers and then add or subtract the fractions. You may need to rename a mixed number before subtracting.

Find each sum or difference.

6. $\frac{3}{5} + \frac{3}{5}$ $1\frac{1}{5}$
7. $\frac{3}{4} - \frac{1}{8}$ $\frac{5}{8}$
8. $\frac{1}{2} + \frac{2}{5}$ $\frac{9}{10}$
9. $\frac{5}{8} - \frac{3}{16}$ $\frac{7}{16}$
10. $\frac{2}{3} + \frac{3}{4}$ $1\frac{5}{12}$
11. $2\frac{1}{3} + \frac{3}{4}$ $3\frac{1}{12}$
12. $16\frac{4}{5} - 9\frac{2}{3}$ $7\frac{2}{15}$
13. $8\frac{1}{6} + 7\frac{3}{12}$ $15\frac{5}{12}$
14. $11\frac{5}{6} - 5\frac{3}{8}$ $6\frac{11}{24}$
15. $3\frac{1}{3} - 2\frac{3}{4}$ $\frac{7}{12}$

Solving Equations with Fractions by Adding and Subtracting 5-4

Use addition to "undo" subtraction and use subtraction to "undo" addition.

16. $1\frac{7}{8} + n = 3\frac{3}{4}$ $1\frac{7}{8}$
17. $q - 3\frac{1}{5} = 5\frac{3}{10}$ $8\frac{1}{2}$
18. $1\frac{1}{2} = \frac{2}{5} + a$ $1\frac{1}{10}$
19. $2\frac{7}{10} = g - 2\frac{1}{4}$ $4\frac{19}{20}$
20. $m - \frac{3}{10} = \frac{4}{5}$ $1\frac{1}{10}$
21. $9\frac{1}{3} = k + \frac{3}{4}$ $8\frac{7}{12}$
22. $2\frac{1}{3} = x - 5\frac{1}{4}$ $7\frac{7}{12}$
23. $4\frac{1}{2} + m = 6\frac{2}{5}$ $1\frac{9}{10}$

Multiplying and Dividing Fractions and Mixed Numbers 5-5, 5-6

To multiply fractions, you multiply their numerators and then multiply their denominators.

To divide fractions, you multiply by the **reciprocal** of the divisor. To find $\frac{2}{3} \div \frac{5}{6}$, you multiply $\frac{2}{3} \cdot \frac{6}{5}$.

Remind students that the new mathematical terms in this chapter are defined in the Glossary/Study Guide in the back of the book.

Find each product or quotient.

24. $\frac{3}{5} \cdot \frac{1}{2}$ $\frac{3}{10}$
25. $\frac{2}{3} \cdot \frac{3}{8}$ $\frac{1}{4}$
26. $\frac{3}{5} \cdot 1\frac{1}{2}$ $\frac{9}{10}$
27. $2\frac{2}{3} \cdot 3\frac{3}{8}$ 9
28. $8\frac{5}{6} \cdot 10\frac{3}{4}$ $94\frac{23}{24}$
29. $\frac{2}{5} \div \frac{4}{5}$ $\frac{1}{2}$
30. $\frac{2}{3} \div \frac{4}{3}$ $\frac{1}{2}$
31. $5\frac{1}{4} \div \frac{7}{8}$ 6
32. $4\frac{4}{5} \div 1\frac{1}{3}$ $3\frac{3}{5}$
33. $1\frac{1}{3} \div 4\frac{4}{5}$ $\frac{5}{18}$

Problem Solving Strategies 5-7

To solve some problems you may have to work backward.

34. Lien wants to be at school at 7:30 A.M. It takes her $\frac{3}{4}$ h to get dressed, $\frac{1}{2}$ h to fix and eat breakfast, and 15 min to walk to school. What time should she get up? 6:00 A.M.

35. John bought a pair of shoes during a "$\frac{1}{4}$-off" sale. The original price was $34. After he paid for the shoes he had $14.26. How much money did he start with? $39.76

Changing Units in the Customary System 5-8

To change from a larger unit to a smaller unit, you *multiply*. To change from a smaller unit to a larger unit, you *divide*.

Complete.

36. 30 in. = ■ ft $2\frac{1}{2}$
37. 54 oz = ■ lb $3\frac{3}{8}$
38. 20 yd = ■ ft 60
39. $3\frac{1}{2}$ c = ■ fl oz 28
40. 4 ft 8 in. = ■ ft $4\frac{2}{3}$
41. $3\frac{3}{4}$ tons = ■ lb 7,500
42. 2 lb 4 oz = ■ lb $2\frac{1}{4}$
43. 78 in. = ■ ft $6\frac{1}{2}$

Solving Equations with Fractions by Multiplying and Dividing 5-9

Use multiplication to "undo" division and use division to "undo" multiplication.

Solve each equation.

44. $\frac{1}{5}g = 10$ 50
45. $\frac{3}{4} = 3t$ $\frac{1}{4}$
46. $5p = 18$ $3\frac{3}{5}$
47. $\frac{x}{5} = \frac{1}{4}$ $1\frac{1}{4}$
48. $\frac{7}{8} = \frac{s}{4}$ $3\frac{1}{2}$
49. $\frac{x}{7} = 3$ 21
50. $12p = 78$ $6\frac{1}{2}$
51. $\frac{1}{4}t = 3\frac{5}{8}$ $14\frac{1}{2}$
52. $15 = 18d$ $\frac{5}{6}$
53. $\frac{1}{10}y = \frac{2}{5}$ 4

54. Write an equation and solve. The 70 students graduating are $\frac{1}{5}$ of the total school population. How many students attend the school? $\frac{1}{5}s = 70$; 350 students

CHAPTER ASSESSMENT • FORM A

Chapter 5 Assessment • Form A

Answers

1. Estimate the sum $\frac{5}{9} + 2\frac{3}{4}$. — 1. 3 or $3\frac{1}{2}$
2. Find the sum $\frac{5}{8} + \frac{1}{4}$. — 2. $\frac{7}{8}$
3. Irene bought $4\frac{1}{2}$ lb of apples and $2\frac{7}{8}$ lb of pears. How many more pounds of apples than pears did she buy? — 3. $1\frac{5}{8}$ lb
4. Find the difference $\frac{2}{3} - \frac{5}{12}$. — 4. $\frac{1}{4}$
5. Four pumpkins weigh $7\frac{1}{8}$ lb, $11\frac{3}{4}$ lb, $6\frac{7}{8}$ lb, and $9\frac{1}{4}$ lb. What is the total weight of the pumpkins? — 5. 35 lb
6. Complete. $1\frac{1}{4}$ mi = ■ ft. — 6. 6,600
7. Solve $\frac{s}{8} = 307$. — 7. 2,456
8. Is the actual product $2\frac{7}{8} \times 4\frac{2}{3}$ greater than or less than 15? — 8. less than
9. A recipe calls for 1 c of butter or margarine. You have $\frac{1}{3}$ c of butter and $\frac{3}{4}$ c of margarine. Do you have enough butter and margarine together for the recipe? — 9. yes
10. A map shows three trails of $3\frac{1}{10}$ mi, $1\frac{1}{4}$ mi, and $2\frac{3}{5}$ mi. How many miles in all will you hike if you hike the entire length of each trail? — 10. $6\frac{19}{20}$ mi
11. Solve $n - \frac{2}{3} = 5\frac{1}{6}$. — 11. $5\frac{5}{6}$
12. Juan needs to use $\frac{2}{3}$ of a can of pizza sauce to make 2 pizzas. The can contains 1 lb 2 oz of sauce. How many ounces does Juan need for the pizzas? — 12. 12 oz
13. Find $\frac{7}{9} \div 3$. — 13. $\frac{7}{27}$
14. One serving from a $12\frac{1}{4}$-oz can of tuna is $3\frac{1}{2}$ oz. How many servings can you get from one can? — 14. $3\frac{1}{2}$ servings

Assessment

CHAPTER ASSESSMENT • FORM A

Chapter 5 Assessment • Form A (continued)

15. Solve $24m = 6$. — 15. $\frac{1}{4}$
16. A ride on the roller coaster takes $2\frac{1}{2}$ min. Antonio rode 6 times. For how many minutes did he ride? — 16. 15 min
17. Solve $\frac{5}{6} + f = 4\frac{1}{2}$ — 17. $3\frac{2}{3}$
18. Find the quotient $3\frac{2}{3} \div 5\frac{1}{2}$. — 18. $\frac{2}{3}$
19. What is the area of a rectangle with a length of $\frac{3}{8}$ ft and a width of $\frac{8}{9}$ ft? — 19. $\frac{1}{3}$ ft²
20. Find the product $2\frac{1}{5} \cdot 3\frac{3}{4}$. — 20. $8\frac{1}{4}$
21. Solve $3\frac{2}{3} \times t = 22$. — 21. 6
22. Complete. 1 yd 1 ft = ■ yd — 22. $1\frac{1}{3}$

Choose A, B, C, or D.

23. A recipe calls for $1\frac{3}{4}$ c of flour. If you make $3\frac{1}{2}$ times the recipe, how much flour will you need? — 23. C

A. $1\frac{3}{4}$ c **B.** $4\frac{1}{4}$ c **C.** $6\frac{1}{8}$ c **D.** $8\frac{1}{6}$ c

Choose a Strategy

24. Joanne received her allowance money on Monday. She spent one half of her allowance on lunch that week and loaned $5 to her brother. On Friday, she had $3 left. How much was her allowance? — 24. $16

Writing

25. To find $\frac{1}{2}$ of a circle, think of two equal parts. To find $\frac{1}{3}$ of a circle, think of three equal parts. Does thinking of five equal parts help you find $\frac{1}{3}$ of $\frac{1}{2}$? Explain why or why not.

No; divide a circle into two equal parts. Then divide each of these into three equal parts. You now have six, not five, equal parts.

CHAPTER ASSESSMENT • FORM B

Chapter 5 Assessment • Form B

Choose the best answer. Circle A, B, C, or D.

1. Find the sum $\frac{5}{6} + \frac{1}{8}$.
   A. $\frac{5}{48}$ B. $\frac{3}{7}$ C. $\frac{17}{24}$ (D) $\frac{23}{24}$
2. Find the product $1\frac{3}{8} \times 2\frac{1}{2}$.
   A. $2\frac{3}{16}$ (B) $3\frac{7}{16}$ C. $1\frac{1}{8}$ D. $3\frac{7}{8}$
3. Solve $y + 1\frac{3}{8} = 7$.
   (A) $5\frac{5}{8}$ B. $8\frac{3}{8}$ C. $9\frac{5}{8}$ D. $5\frac{1}{11}$
4. How many gallons are in 108 quarts?
   (A) 27 gal B. 54 gal C. 216 gal D. 432 gal
5. Estimate the sum $4\frac{2}{5} + 5\frac{5}{9}$.
   A. 9 (B) 10 C. 11 D. 20
6. Which of the following is closest to the actual product of $3\frac{4}{5} \cdot 1\frac{1}{3}$?
   A. 3 B. 6 C. 4 (D) 5
7. Estimate $\frac{2}{3}$ of 119.
   A. 40 B. 60 (C) 80 D. 100
8. A recipe calls for 2 lb of ground beef. You have one package of ground beef that weighs $1\frac{1}{3}$ lb and another that weighs $\frac{3}{4}$ lb. How much ground beef will you have left after making the recipe?
   A. 1 lb B. $\frac{1}{6}$ lb C. $\frac{1}{8}$ lb (D) $\frac{1}{12}$ lb
9. To get to the library, you must travel $\frac{1}{2}$ mi down one street, $\frac{3}{5}$ mi down another street, and $1\frac{1}{10}$ mi down a third street. How many miles must you travel in all to get to the library?
   (A) $2\frac{1}{5}$ mi B. $1\frac{1}{5}$ mi C. $1\frac{1}{10}$ mi D. $\frac{9}{10}$ mi
10. Solve $n + \frac{3}{8} = 2\frac{1}{2}$.
   A. $2\frac{7}{8}$ B. $2\frac{5}{8}$ C. $2\frac{3}{8}$ (D) $2\frac{1}{8}$

Assessment

CHAPTER ASSESSMENT • FORM B

Chapter 5 Assessment • Form B (continued)

11. Katy used $\frac{3}{4}$ of a 6-ft board for a science fair project. How many inches did she use?
   A. 4.5 in. B. 18 in. (C) 54 in. D. 75 in.
12. Find $\frac{7}{10} \div 7$.
   (A) $\frac{1}{10}$ B. 1 C. 4.9 D. 10
13. A grocer is dividing a 25-lb box of green beans into packages. How many $1\frac{1}{2}$-lb packages of green beans can he make?
   A. 25 packages B. 17 packages (C) 16 packages D. 15 packages
14. Find the difference $\frac{5}{9} - \frac{1}{6}$.
   A. $\frac{5}{54}$ B. $\frac{4}{9}$ (C) $\frac{7}{18}$ D. $\frac{13}{18}$
15. Solve $45n = 9$.
   A. 405 B. 5 (C) $\frac{1}{5}$ D. $\frac{1}{15}$
16. An exercise bicycle is on sale for $\frac{3}{4}$ of the original price of $244. What is the sale price of the bicycle?
   A. $60 B. $61 C. $181 (D) $183
17. Solve $\frac{x}{6} = 9$.
   A. $1\frac{1}{2}$ B. 3 C. 15 (D) 54

Choose a Strategy

18. May has some money in her savings account. She spent half of her savings on records. She gave $15 to a fund for needy children. She has $25 left. How much did May have in her savings account?
   A. $70 (B) $80 C. $90 D. $100

Teaching Resources

Chapter Support File, Ch. 5, and Spanish Resources

Teacher's Edition

See pp. 186C–D for Assessment Options.

Teaching Resource Software

- Computer Item Generator, Ch. 5

ASSESSMENT

ENHANCED MULTIPLE CHOICE QUESTIONS are more complex than traditional multiple choice questions, which assess only one skill. Enhanced multiple choice questions assess the processes that students use, as well as the end result. They are written so that students can use more than one strategy to solve the problem. Using multiple strategies is encouraged by the National Council of Teachers of Mathematics (NCTM). **Exercise 4** is an enhanced multiple choice question.

Exercise 11 Have students write a check for each equation.

5 ASSESSMENT

1. Estimate each answer.
   a. $\frac{7}{8} + \frac{15}{16}$ **2**
   b. $\frac{3}{5} - \frac{1}{2}$ **0**
   c. $7\frac{1}{8} + 2\frac{3}{4}$ **10**
   d. $8\frac{3}{8} - 5\frac{1}{3}$ **3**
   e. $4\frac{5}{8} \cdot 2\frac{1}{10}$ **10**
   f. $43\frac{1}{2} \div 5\frac{1}{5}$ **9**
   g. $23\frac{1}{3} \div 6\frac{2}{5}$ **4**
   h. $2\frac{1}{2} \cdot 10\frac{1}{4}$ **30**
2. You jog $8\frac{1}{2}$ times around the block. The distance around the block is 770 yd. About how many miles have you jogged? (1 mi = 1,760 yd) **about 3.7 mi**
3. Find each sum or difference.
   a. $\frac{15}{16} - \frac{3}{16}$ **$\frac{3}{4}$**
   b. $\frac{1}{4} + \frac{2}{3}$ **$\frac{11}{12}$**
   c. $\frac{1}{2} - \frac{3}{8}$ **$\frac{1}{8}$**
   d. $\frac{2}{3} + \frac{5}{6}$ **$1\frac{1}{2}$**
   e. $8\frac{2}{5} + 5\frac{3}{5}$ **14**
   f. $7\frac{5}{8} - 4\frac{1}{8}$ **$3\frac{1}{2}$**
   g. $4\frac{3}{4} + 5\frac{1}{5}$ **$9\frac{19}{20}$**
   h. $9\frac{3}{8} - 5\frac{1}{4}$ **$4\frac{1}{8}$**
   i. $1\frac{2}{3} - \frac{3}{4}$ **$\frac{11}{12}$**
   j. $4\frac{2}{3} + 1\frac{5}{6}$ **$6\frac{1}{2}$**
4. **Choose A, B, C, or D.** In which equation is the value of x less than 1? **D**
   A. $\frac{3}{8} = x - \frac{3}{4}$
   B. $x - \frac{1}{3} = \frac{3}{4}$
   C. $x - 1\frac{1}{3} = 2\frac{1}{3}$
   D. $x + 1\frac{1}{5} = 1\frac{3}{5}$
5. Jake worked $12\frac{1}{2}$ h at $4.50 per hour. After he was paid, he spent $24 for a shirt. He now has $89.23. How much money did he have before he was paid? **$56.98**
6. In March, a puppy weighed $4\frac{3}{4}$ lb. In August, it weighed $5\frac{7}{8}$ lb. How much weight did the puppy gain? **$1\frac{1}{8}$ lb**
7. Pamela is planning to make a dress. She needs to buy $2\frac{3}{4}$ yd of fabric that costs $8 per yard and $1\frac{2}{3}$ yd of fabric that costs $6 per yard. How much will the fabric cost? **$32**
8. Martha rides her bicycle $1\frac{1}{2}$ mi to school. At the end of the day, she stops at a park that is on her way home. The park is $\frac{7}{9}$ mi from school. How far is it from Martha's house? **$\frac{13}{18}$ mi**
9. Find each product or quotient.
   a. $\frac{4}{5} \cdot \frac{1}{4}$ **$\frac{1}{5}$**
   b. $\frac{4}{5} \div \frac{1}{4}$ **$3\frac{1}{5}$**
   c. $\frac{3}{4} \cdot \frac{2}{3}$ **$\frac{1}{2}$**
   d. $\frac{1}{4} \div \frac{4}{5}$ **$\frac{5}{16}$**
   e. $1\frac{2}{3} \cdot 1\frac{1}{4}$ **$2\frac{1}{12}$**
   f. $1\frac{2}{3} \div 1\frac{1}{4}$ **$1\frac{1}{3}$**
   g. $150 \div 2\frac{2}{3}$ **$56\frac{1}{4}$**
   h. $5\frac{3}{8} \cdot 3\frac{3}{4}$ **$20\frac{5}{32}$**
10. Complete.
   a. 38 in. = ■ ft **$3\frac{1}{6}$**
   b. 60 oz = ■ lb **$3\frac{3}{4}$**
   c. $3\frac{3}{4}$ qt = ■ c **15**
   d. $1\frac{2}{3}$ mi = ■ ft
   e. $5\frac{1}{2}$ yd = ■ in. **198**
   f. 50 fl oz = ■ c
   10d. 8,800 10f. $6\frac{1}{4}$
11. Solve.
   a. $15k = 33$ **$2\frac{1}{5}$**
   b. $12 = 8x$ **$1\frac{1}{2}$**
   c. $\frac{y}{12} = 2\frac{1}{2}$ **30**
   d. $\frac{1}{4}m = 10$ **40**
   e. $w + 4\frac{3}{5} = 6\frac{1}{2}$ **$1\frac{9}{10}$**
   f. $k - 2\frac{3}{4} = 9$
   g. $7\frac{1}{3} = 4\frac{1}{2} + p$
   h. $10\frac{3}{4} = n - \frac{5}{8}$
   f–h. See below.
12. You are an employee at a store that is having a "$\frac{1}{3}$-off" sale. Employees get an additional $\frac{1}{5}$ off the sale price. How much would you pay for a jacket that originally cost $60? **$32**
13. A brick is $1\frac{7}{8}$ in. high. Mortar that is $\frac{3}{8}$ in. thick is spread on each row of bricks. How many rows of bricks are needed to reach the top of a $7\frac{1}{2}$ ft doorway? **40 rows**
14. Kimo has $1\frac{1}{2}$ lb of salmon. He wants each person to get a 6-oz serving. How many people can he feed? **4 people**

11f. $11\frac{3}{4}$ g. $2\frac{5}{6}$ h. $11\frac{3}{8}$

Item	Review Topic	Ch
1	Adding fractions	5
2	Estimating sums	Precourse
3,4,10,11	Reading expressions	Precourse
5	Rounding decimals	2
6	Dividing fractions	5

Item	Review Topic	Ch
7	Multiplying fractions	5
8	Ordering decimals	2
9	Finding sums and products of integers	3
12	Reading charts of data	1

5 CUMULATIVE REVIEW

Choose the best answer.

1. Which sum is closest to 1? C
   A. $\frac{1}{3} + \frac{1}{5}$ B. $\frac{5}{8} + \frac{5}{9}$
   C. $\frac{2}{3} + \frac{4}{11}$ D. $\frac{3}{4} + \frac{3}{5}$

2. You want to buy some birthday presents for your little brother. You have $21. You know you will need about $1 for sales tax. What should you buy? A
   A. book and video
   B. model and video
   C. book and soccer ball
   D. model and soccer ball

Possible Gifts

Item	Cost
Book	$7.95
Model	$8.99
Video	$11.49
Soccer ball	$12.50

3. Which expression has the greatest value? D
   A. $3.4 \cdot 7 + 3.4 \cdot 9$ B. $3.4\,(7 + 9)$
   C. $3.4 \cdot 8 + 3.4 \cdot 8$ D. $3.4\,(17)$

4. Which expression has a value that is closest to -10? B
   A. $3 - (-6)$ B. $-6 - 3$
   C. $6 - (-3)$ D. $-3 - (-6)$

5. Which decimal is *not* 4.01 when rounded to the nearest hundredth? B
   A. 4.0086 B. 4.0049
   C. 4.0149 D. 4.0140

6. Henry plans to build a set of steps for his attic stairway. The steps must reach a height of $8\frac{1}{2}$ ft. Each step can be no more than $7\frac{3}{4}$ in. high. What is the least number of steps he must build? D
   A. 11 B. 12
   C. 13 D. 14

7. Estimate $6\frac{3}{4} \cdot 3\frac{1}{5}$. B
   A. 18 B. 21 C. 24 D. 27

8. The swimmers in the 100-meter backstroke finished with times of 59.27, 59.32, 58.72, 58.8, and 58.99 seconds. The times will be announced in order from the fastest (least) time to the slowest (greatest) time. In what order will the times be announced? D
   A. 58.99, 58.8, 58.72, 59.32, 59.27
   B. 59.32, 59.27, 58.99, 58.8, 58.72
   C. 58.99, 58.8, 58.72, 59.32, 59.27
   D. 58.72, 58.8, 58.99, 59.27, 59.32

9. Which pair of numbers has a product that is greater than their sum? A
   A. $-1, -3$ B. $-1, 3$
   C. $1, -3$ D. $1, 3$

10. Which variable expression can be described by the word phrase "r increased by 2"? C
   A. $2r$ B. $r - 2$ C. $r + 2$ D. $r \cdot 2$

11. Which expression has the greatest value? D
   A. $-5 + |-4|$ B. $|-5| + -4$
   C. $-5 + -4$ D. $|-5| + |-4|$

12. The chart shows the changes in Bill's weight over 6 months. What was his average weight change per month? B
   A. -3 lb
   B. -2 lb
   C. -1 lb
   D. 2 lb

Month	Weight change (lb)
Jan.	-5
Feb.	$+2$
Mar.	-6
Apr.	$+3$
May	-5
June	-1

CUMULATIVE REVIEW

Chapter 5 Cumulative Review

Choose the best answer. Circle A, B, C, or D.

1. You buy a sandwich for $2.89, a drink for $.95, and an apple for $.75. Estimate to the nearest dollar how much change you will get back from a ten-dollar bill.
   A. about $4 (B.) about $5
   C. about $6 D. about $7

2. When multiplying 0.23×1.492, how many decimal places does the answer have?
   A. 2 places B. 3 places
   C. 4 places (D.) 5 places

3. Kate divided 0.54 by 0.9 and got 6 for the answer. This answer is not correct. Which answer below is correct?
   A. 60 (B.) 0.6
   C. 0.06 D. 0.006

4. Which of the following is equivalent to $5(52) + 27 \div 9$?
   (A.) $5(50 + 2) + 3$
   B. $5(50 - 2) + 3$
   C. $(260 + 27) \div 9$
   D. $260 \div 3$

5. Which is greatest, 4^3, 8^2, 3^4, or 2^6?
   A. 4^3 B. 8^2
   (C.) 3^4 D. 2^6

6. What is the units digit when you evaluate 3^{17}?
   A. 1 (B.) 3
   C. 7 D. 9

7. What is the value of $5 + 3 \times 4$?
   A. 12 (B.) 17
   C. 19 D. 32

8. This data represent the number of magazines sold in the last five days.
   153 217 182 150 298
   What is the mean?
   A. 145 B. 153
   C. 182 (D.) 200

9. Harold entered the elevator on the tenth floor. He rode 26 floors up, 32 floors down, 28 floors up, then 17 floors down. On which floor is he now?
   A. floor 5 (B.) floor 15
   C. floor 40 D. floor 113

10. Which statement is true?
   A. $-27 > -20$ B. $-15 > 15$
   (C.) $-6 > -9$ D. $0 > 17$

11. Enise wants to be in school at 8:00 A.M. It takes her $\frac{1}{2}$ h to get dressed, $\frac{1}{3}$ h to fix and eat breakfast, and 20 min to bike to school. What time should she get up?
   (A.) 6:50 A.M. B. 6:30 A.M.
   C. 6:00 A.M. D. 7:30 A.M.

12. What is the solution of $30y = -60$?
   A. -30 (B.) -2
   C. 2 D. 30

Assessment

CUMULATIVE REVIEW

Chapter 5 Cumulative Review (continued)

13. How many feet are in 12 yd 2 ft?
   A. $12\frac{2}{3}$ ft B. 26 ft
   C. 36 ft (D.) 38 ft

14. You are to show the increase in the number of televisions sold in your state each year from 1990 to the present. Which type of graph will best show this data?
   A. bar graph B. histogram
   C. scatter plot (D.) line graph

15. Which fractions are equivalent fractions?
   (A.) $\frac{24}{36}, \frac{2}{3}$ B. $\frac{8}{9}, \frac{40}{54}$
   C. $\frac{3}{4}, \frac{33}{34}$ D. $\frac{15}{18}, \frac{12}{15}$

16. Which is the greatest common factor, or GCF, of 36 and 24?
   A. 3 B. 6
   C. 9 (D.) 12

17. What are the prime factors of 156?
   A. 2, 3, 39 (B.) 2, 2, 3, 13
   C. 3, 4, 13 D. 2, 6, 13

18. Which number is prime?
   (A.) 67 B. 123
   C. 456 D. 785

19. Which number is equivalent to $\frac{56}{9}$?
   A. $\frac{18}{3}$ B. $6\frac{2}{3}$
   C. $\frac{9}{56}$ (D.) $6\frac{2}{9}$

20. Which list is in order from greatest to least?
   A. $\frac{3}{8}, \frac{1}{4}, \frac{4}{5}$ B. $2\frac{1}{2}, 2\frac{5}{6}, 2\frac{9}{10}$
   (C.) $\frac{7}{6}, \frac{1}{2}, \frac{1}{3}$ D. $\frac{5}{8}, \frac{5}{6}, \frac{5}{9}$

21. Which decimal is closest to $\frac{7}{19}$?
   A. 0.36 B. 0.372
   C. 0.37 (D.) 0.368

22. Estimate the sum $7\frac{3}{4} + 3\frac{9}{10} + 1\frac{1}{5}$ by rounding to the nearest whole number.
   A. 14 (B.) 13
   C. 12 D. 11

23. This year, about $\frac{3}{4}$ of the seventh-grade students went on a field trip. If there are 242 students in the seventh grade, about how many students went on the field trip?
   A. 312 students B. 240 students
   C. 200 students (D.) 180 students

24. One serving of nuts is $\frac{3}{4}$ oz. How many servings are in a $13\frac{1}{2}$-oz can?
   A. 20 servings B. 19 servings
   (C.) 18 servings D. 16 servings

Resources

Teaching Resources

Chapter Support File, Ch. 5
- Cumulative Review

Teacher's Edition

See pp. 186C–D for Assessment Options.

Mid-Course Skills Assessment

A broad range of assessment tools are available to reach a variety of learners. Options for Formal and Informal Assessment appear on the **Assessing Progress** pages that precede each chapter.

Computer Item Generator

With the Computer Item Generator, you can customize assessment and create customized practice worksheets.

Standardized Test Preparation

You may wish to take advantage of the Standardized Test Preparation component that is available on the Computer Item Generator and the Resource Pro™ CD-ROM. With this component, you can generate tests to help students prepare for these standardized tests:

CAT5 California Achievement Test, 5th Edition
ITBS Iowa Test of Basic Skills, Form M
MAT7 Metropolitan Achievement Test, 7th Edition
SAT9 Stanford Achievement Test, 9th Edition
Terra Nova Comprehensive Test of Basic Skills, 5th Edition

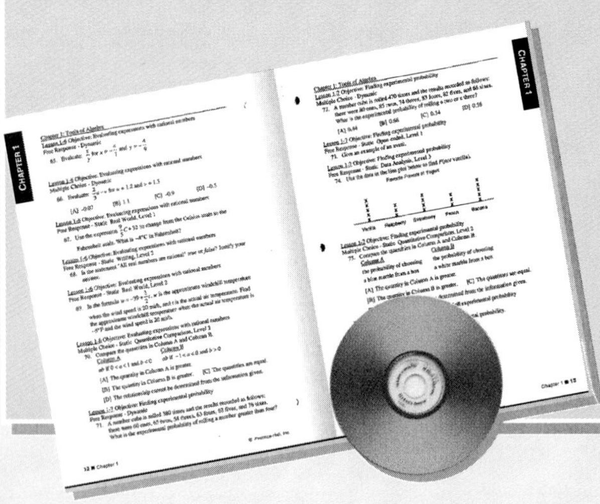

Mid-Course Assessment

The Mid-Course Assessment is available in the *Cumulative Assessment* booklet in the Teaching Resources.

Structure The Mid-Course Assessment is a two-page, multiple-choice test. The test assesses student progress on the skills and concepts covered in Chapters 1–5 of *Prentice Hall Middle Grades Math* Course 2. The test contains 3–5 test items from each chapter.

Scoring Usually, 75% correct should demonstrate that the student has sufficient mastery of the content to be able to succeed in this program. However, you may wish to set your own criteria.

Progress and Remediation Chart To assist you in assessing the skill level of your students, a Progress and Remediation Chart appears with the Mid-Course Assessment. This chart identifies the skills and concepts assessed, student achievement on the assessment, and suggests where remediation, if necessary, is found within the *Prentice Hall Middle Grades Math* program.

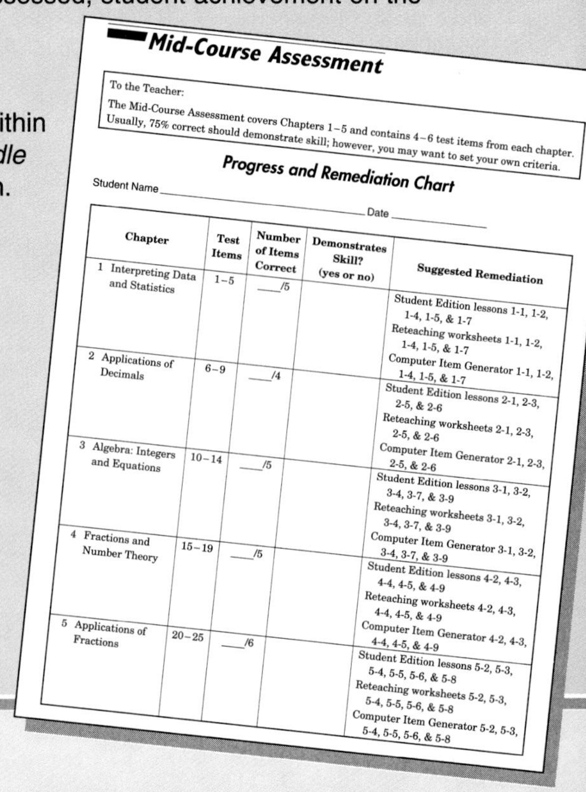

Mid-Course Assessment

To the Teacher:

The Mid-Course Assessment covers Chapters 1–5 and contains 4–6 test items from each chapter. Usually, 75% correct should demonstrate skill; however, you may want to set your own criteria.

Progress and Remediation Chart

Student Name ______________________ Date __________

Chapter	Test Items	Number of Items Correct	Demonstrates Skill? (yes or no)	Suggested Remediation
1 Interpreting Data and Statistics	1–5	____/5		Student Edition lessons 1-1, 1-2, 1-4, 1-5, & 1-7 Reteaching worksheets 1-1, 1-2, 1-4, 1-5, & 1-7 Computer Item Generator 1-1, 1-2, 1-4, 1-5, & 1-7
2 Applications of Decimals	6–9	____/4		Student Edition lessons 2-1, 2-3, 2-5, & 2-6 Reteaching worksheets 2-1, 2-3, 2-5, & 2-6 Computer Item Generator 2-1, 2-3, 2-5, & 2-6
3 Algebra: Integers and Equations	10–14	____/5		Student Edition lessons 3-1, 3-2, 3-4, 3-7, & 3-9 Reteaching worksheets 3-1, 3-2, 3-4, 3-7, & 3-9 Computer Item Generator 3-1, 3-2, 3-4, 3-7, & 3-9
4 Fractions and Number Theory	15–19	____/5		Student Edition lessons 4-2, 4-3, 4-4, 4-5, & 4-9 Reteaching worksheets 4-2, 4-3, 4-4, 4-5, & 4-9 Computer Item Generator 4-2, 4-3, 4-4, 4-5, & 4-9
5 Applications of Fractions	20–25	____/6		Student Edition lessons 5-2, 5-3, 5-4, 5-5, 5-6, & 5-8 Reteaching worksheets 5-2, 5-3, 5-4, 5-5, 5-6, & 5-8 Computer Item Generator 5-2, 5-3, 5-4, 5-5, 5-6, & 5-8

Mid-Course Assessment

Choose the best answer. Circle A, B, C, or D.

1. Which intervals would you use for a histogram given the following data?

   10, 8, 12, 15, 13, 7, 19, 5, 14, 6, 12, 15, 2, 13, 16, 3

   A. 0–5, 6–10, 11–15, 16–19
   B. 0–8, 9–16, 16–24
   C. 0–4, 6–10, 12–16, 18–20
   (D) 1–5, 6–10, 11–15, 16–20

2. According to the graph, for which city does the average snowfall exceed the average precipitation?

Average Annual Precipitation and Snowfall

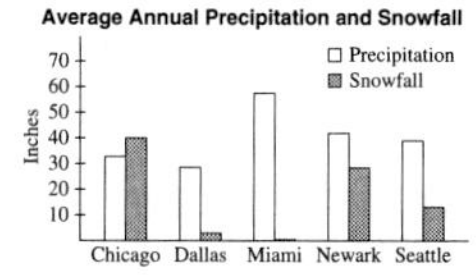

   (A) Chicago B. Dallas
   C. Miami D. Seattle

Use the stem-and-leaf plot below to answer Exercises 3 and 4.

0	2 6
1	4 7 8 9
2	0 0 1 3 6 8
3	2 3 5 7

0 | 2 means 2

3. Find the mean, median, and mode for the data. Which is their order from least to greatest?

   A. mean, median, mode
   B. mean, mode, median
   (C) mode, median, mean
   D. mode, mean, median

4. What is the range of the data?

   A. 5 B. 30
   (C) 35 D. 37

5. Which statement is true?

   A. A sample cannot provide enough information to draw conclusions about a population.
   B. A representative sample rarely has the same characteristics as the population.
   C. The most accurate way to collect data about a population is to gather information from a sample.
   (D) In a random sample each object in the population has an equal chance of being included in the sample.

6. Which number is 1.92509 rounded to the nearest ten-thousandth?

   (A) 1.9251 B. 1.9250
   C. 1.93000 D. 1.90000

7. Find the value of $(3.1 + 9.8) + 0.9$.

   A. 138 (B) 13.8
   C. 12.9 D. 12

8. Find the product. 2.4×0.06

   A. 0.0144 (B) 0.144
   C. 1.44 D. 14.4

9. Find the quotient. $0.45 \div 9$

   A. 5 B. 0.5
   (C) 0.05 D. 0.005

10. Which variable expression could you use to find the number of pencils in b boxes if there are 12 pencils in a box?

    A. $b + 12$ B. $b - 12$
    C. $\frac{b}{12}$ (D) $12b$

Mid-Course Assessment (continued)

11. Which of the following is in order from least to greatest?

    (A) $-9, -5, 0, |-2|$
    B. $|-5|, -4, 2, 6.7$
    C. $1.5, 0.9, -4, -6$
    D. $-1, 0, -0.3, 7$

12. Evaluate $-3 - (-9) + 4$.

    A. −10 B. −8
    (C) 10 D. 8

13. Solve the equation $-9x = -72$.

    A. −9 B. −8
    (C) 8 D. 9

14. Solve $\frac{x}{5} + 8 = 3$.

    A. 1 B. 0
    C. −1 (D) −25

15. Find the LCM of 16 and 20.

    A. 20 B. 40
    C. 60 (D) 80

16. Order these fractions from least to greatest.
    $\frac{2}{5}, \frac{1}{3}$, and $\frac{3}{8}$

    A. $\frac{3}{8}, \frac{2}{5}, \frac{1}{3}$ (B) $\frac{1}{3}, \frac{3}{8}, \frac{2}{5}$
    C. $\frac{3}{8}, \frac{1}{3}, \frac{2}{5}$ D. $\frac{2}{5}, \frac{3}{8}, \frac{1}{3}$

17. Evaluate $2^4 \times 3^2$.

    (A) 144 B. 96
    C. 72 D. 48

18. Find the GCF of 48 and 60.

    A. 20 B. 40
    C. 60 (D) 12

19. Write $\frac{8}{15}$ as a decimal.

    A. 1.875 B. 0.5
    C. 0.53 (D) $0.5\overline{3}$

20. Find the sum. $\frac{5}{6} + \frac{1}{3}$

    A. $\frac{4}{9}$ B. $\frac{2}{3}$
    (C) $1\frac{1}{6}$ D. $\frac{6}{7}$

21. Find the difference. $8\frac{1}{4} - 5\frac{3}{5}$

    A. $3\frac{13}{20}$ B. $3\frac{2}{9}$
    (C) $2\frac{13}{20}$ D. $2\frac{2}{9}$

22. Solve $x - \frac{5}{6} = 2\frac{1}{3}$.

    A. $1\frac{1}{2}$ B. $2\frac{2}{3}$
    C. 3 (D) $3\frac{1}{6}$

23. Find the product. $3 \cdot 4\frac{3}{4}$

    A. $\frac{12}{19}$ B. $8\frac{1}{4}$
    C. $12\frac{3}{4}$ (D) $14\frac{1}{4}$

24. Find the quotient. $2\frac{2}{3} \div 2\frac{2}{5}$

    (A) $1\frac{1}{9}$ B. $1\frac{13}{27}$
    C. $4\frac{1}{5}$ D. $6\frac{2}{5}$

25. Complete. $4\frac{1}{3}$ yd = ■ in.

    A. 13 B. 52
    C. 144 (D) 156

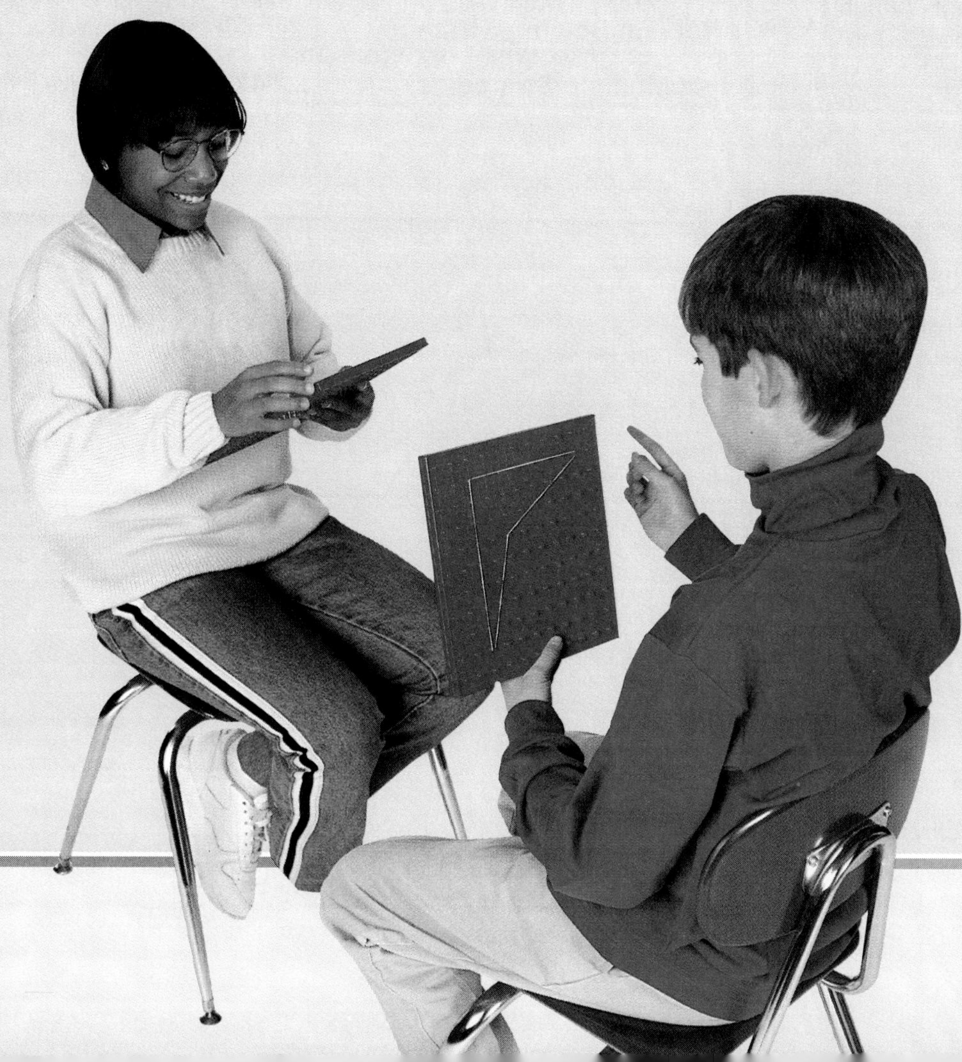

6 Using Proportions and Percents

Chapter Overview

To accommodate flexible scheduling, most lessons are divided into parts. Assignment Options are given in the Teacher's Edition for each lesson.

Pages	Lesson	NCTM	Content
232–236	**Lesson 6-1** Data Analysis: Exploring Ratios Using Data	1, 2, 3, 4, 5, 13	**Part 1** Writing Ratios **Part 2** Writing Equal Ratios **Key term:** ratio **Alternative Activity** 6-1 **Project Link**
237–240	**Lesson 6-2** Unit Rates and Proportional Reasoning	1, 2, 3, 4, 5, 7, 13	**Part 1** Finding Unit Rates **Part 2** Comparing Unit Prices **Key terms:** rate, unit rate, unit price **Journal**
241–244	**Lesson 6-3** Algebra: Proportions	1, 4, 5, 6, 7, 12, 13	**Part 1** Using Cross Products **Part 2** Solving Proportions **Key terms:** proportion, cross products **Alternative Activity** 6-3 **Checkpoint 1**
260–263	**Lesson 6-7** Percents, Fractions, and Decimals	1, 2, 4, 5, 6, 7, 13	**Part 1** Rewriting Percents and Fractions **Part 2** Percents and Decimals **Project Link**
264–266	**Lesson 6-8** Problem Solving Strategy	1, 3, 4, 5, 6, 8, 12	**Use Multiple Strategies**
267–270	**Lesson 6-9** Data Analysis: Finding Percent of a Number	1, 2, 3, 4, 5, 7, 13	**Part 1** Using Percents to Find Part of a Whole **Part 2** Finding Discount Prices **Journal** **Checkpoint 2**

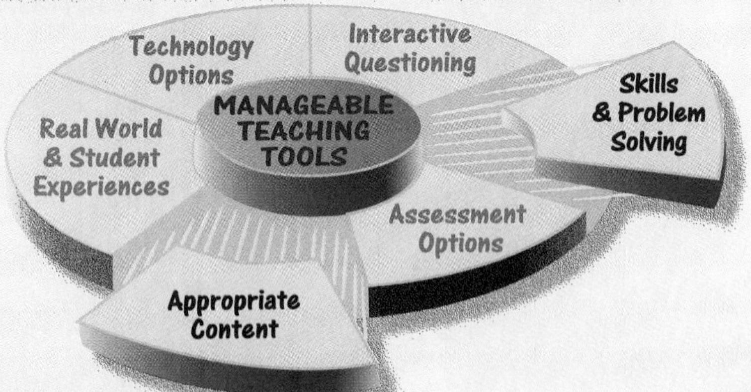

Pacing Options

This chart suggests pacing only for the core lessons and their parts. It is provided merely as a possible guide. It will help you determine how much time you have in your schedule to cover other features, such as the Chapter Project, Math Toolboxes, Wrap Up, and Assessment.

	1 Class Period	1 Class Period	1 Class Period
Traditional (40–45 min class periods)	6–1 (1) 6–1 (2)	6–2 (1) 6–2 (2)	6–3 (1)
Block Scheduling (90 min class periods)	6–1 (1) 6–1 (2) 6–2 (1)	6–2 (2) 6–3 (1) 6–3 (2)	6–4 (1) 6–4 (2) 6–5

CHAPTER PROJECT

Chills and Thrills

Goals: Students graph the results of a survey and make projections from the results.

THEME: BUSINESS

NCTM STANDARDS

1 Problem Solving
2 Communication
3 Reasoning
4 Mathematical Connections
5 Number and Number Relationships
6 Number Systems and Number Theory
7 Computation and Estimation
8 Patterns and Functions
9 Algebra
10 Statistics
11 Probability
12 Geometry
13 Measurement

Lesson 6-4 Geometry: Using Similar Figures

Pages 245–249

NCTM 1, 2, 3, 4, 5, 6, 7, 12

Part 1 Discovering Properties of Similar Figures
Part 2 Finding Measures Using Proportions

Key terms: similar, is similar to (~)

Project Link

Lesson 6-5 Geometry: Exploring Maps and Scale Drawings

Pages 251–254

NCTM 1, 2, 3, 4, 5, 6, 12, 13

Key term: scale drawing

Math at Work

Lesson 6-6 Modeling Percents

Pages 256–259

NCTM 1, 2, 4, 5, 6, 7, 13

Part 1 Modeling Percents
Part 2 Writing Percents Using Equal Ratios

Key term: percent

Lesson 6-10 Algebra: Using Proportions with Percents

Pages 271–274

NCTM 1, 4, 5, 7

Part 1 Finding a Percent
Part 2 Using Percents to Find a Whole

Lesson 6-11 Algebra: Finding Percent of Change

Pages 276–280

NCTM 1, 4, 5, 7, 9, 13

Part 1 Finding the Percent of Increase
Part 2 Finding the Percent of Decrease

Key term: percent of change

Alternative Activity 6-11

Project Link

Optional Materials and Manipulatives

newspaper (6-2, 6-7)
stopwatch or timer (6-2)
scissors (6-4)
ruler (6-4, 6-5, 6-11)

yardstick or meterstick (6-5)
graph paper (6-6)
rubber band (6-11)
small weights (6-11)

Optional calculator use is integrated throughout the course.

ss d	1 Class Period	1 Class Period	1 Class Period	1 Class Period	1 Class Period	1 Class Period	1 Class Period	1 Class Period	1 Class Period	1 Class Period	1 Class Period
	6–4 2	6–5	6–6 1	6–6 6–7 2 1	6–7 2	6–8	6–9 6–9 1 2	6–10 1	6–10 2	6–11 1	6–11 2
6–8	6–9 6–9 1 2	6–10 6–10 1 2	6–11 6–11 1 2								

MEETING INDIVIDUAL NEEDS

Accommodating Diverse Learning Styles

In your Teacher's Edition, you will find suggestions as to how you can help students complete mathematical tasks in Chapter 6 by meeting individual needs and supporting various learning styles. Here are some examples:

VISUAL LEARNING
drawing models of ratios *(p. 233)*

TACTILE LEARNING
modeling unit rates with colored counters *(p. 238)*

AUDITORY LEARNING
naming factor pairs of 100 *(p. 258)*

KINESTHETIC LEARNING
timing jumping-jack and sit-up rates *(p. 237)*

EARLY FINISHERS
Performance-Based Project, MathBlaster® Mystery, Interdisciplinary Units

GIFTED AND TALENTED
measuring the height of a flag pole using similar triangles and shadows *(p. 248)*

DIVERSITY making conjectures about demographics *(p. 232)*

ACQUIRING ENGLISH PROFICIENCY (AEP)
drawing pictures to explain cross products *(p. 241)*

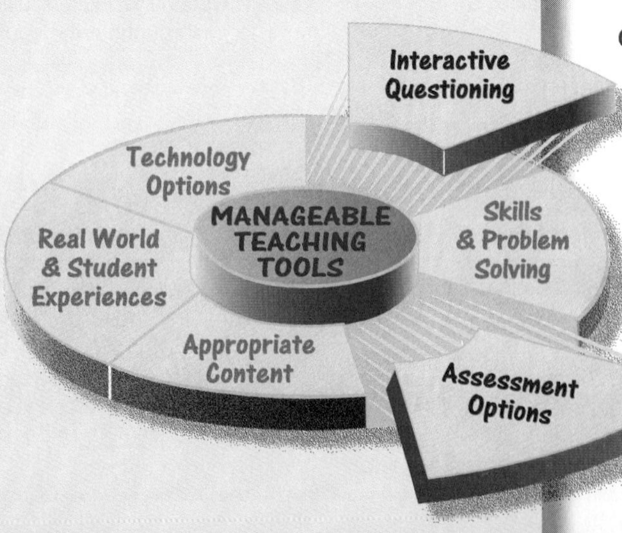

ASSESSING PROGRESS

A broad range of assessment tools are available to reach a variety of learners.

INFORMAL ASSESSMENT

Informal assessments provide day-to-day feedback to help give you a picture of conceptual understanding and skill development.

ONGOING ASSESSMENT is built into lesson instruction and the Teaching Notes of the Teacher's Edition.

In the Teacher's Edition
Lesson Quiz for every lesson

In the Student Edition
On Your Own, Mixed Review, Journal, Portfolio, Project Link, Chapter Wrap Up

Look for **Interactive Questions** within lessons that

- **BUILD UNDERSTANDING** with labels such as **Analyze, Reasoning, Estimation, Writing, and Summarize**
- ✔ **CHECK UNDERSTANDING** with the **Try It Out** label.

FORMAL ASSESSMENT

Formal assessment can occur before and after the chapter, as well as at natural breaking points in the chapter.

Checkpoints
Two forms of each self-assessment Checkpoints are available: one in the Student Edition and another in the Chapter Support File in the Teaching Resources box.

- Mid-Chapter Checkpoint 1, page 244
- End-of-Chapter Checkpoint 2, page 270

Chapter 6 Assessment, page 284.
Two alternative forms are available in the Chapter Support File. They may be used after a chapter has been completed, or as a pre-test and post-test comparison.

Cumulative Review, page 285.
Assesses skills and concepts in Chapters 1–6. An alternative form is available in Chapter Support File.

Computer Item Generator for Chapter 6
Customized tests can be generated for each lesson and for mid-chapter and end-of-chapter assessments, and for pre- and post-test comparisons of achievement.

PERFORMANCE-BASED ASSESSMENT

CHAPTER PROJECT The Chapter Project in the student edition provides a real-world connection to the math context of the chapter. The Teacher's Edition contains a scoring rubric.

A Performance Assessment with a scoring rubric can be found in the Chapter Support File in the Teaching Resources box.

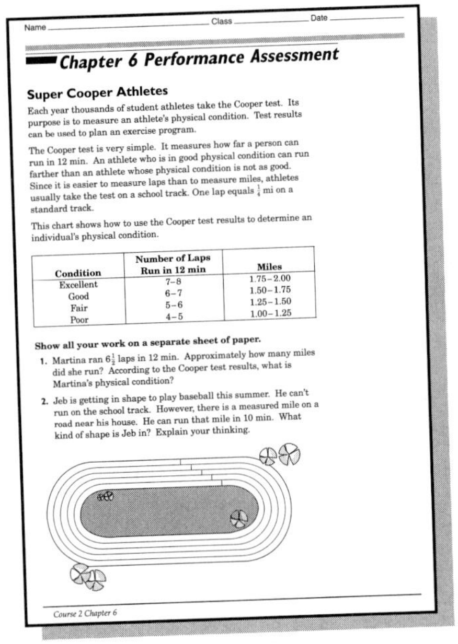

Name ______ Class ______ Date ______

Chapter 6 Performance Assessment

Super Cooper Athletes

Each year thousands of student athletes take the Cooper test. Its purpose is to measure an athlete's physical condition. Test results can be used to plan an exercise program.

The Cooper test is very simple. It measures how far a person can run in 12 min. An athlete who is in good physical condition can run farther than an athlete whose physical condition is not as good. Since it is easier to measure laps than to measure miles, athletes usually take the test on a school track. One lap equals $\frac{1}{4}$ mi on a standard track.

This chart shows how to use the Cooper test results to determine an individual's physical condition.

Condition	Number of Laps Run in 12 min	Miles
Excellent	7–8	1.75–2.00
Good	6–7	1.50–1.75
Fair	5–6	1.25–1.50
Poor	4–5	1.00–1.25

Show all your work on a separate sheet of paper.

1. Martina ran $6\frac{1}{2}$ laps in 12 min. Approximately how many miles did she run? According to the Cooper test results, what is Martina's physical condition?
2. Jeb is getting in shape to play baseball this summer. He can't run on the school track. However, there is a measured mile on a road near his house. He can run that mile in 10 min. What kind of shape is Jeb in? Explain your thinking.

Course 2 Chapter 6

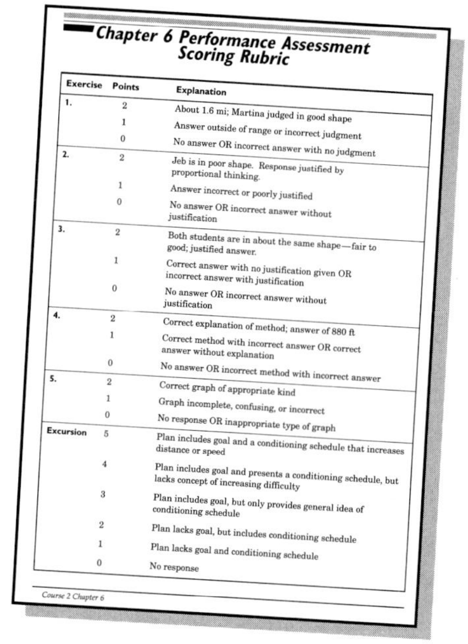

Chapter 6 Performance Assessment Scoring Rubric

Exercise	Points	Explanation
1.	2	About 1.6 mi; Martina judged in good shape
	1	Answer outside of range or incorrect judgment
	0	No answer OR incorrect answer with no judgment
2.	2	Jeb is in poor shape. Response justified by proportional thinking.
	1	Answer incorrect or poorly justified
	0	No answer OR incorrect answer without justification
3.	2	Both students are in about the same shape—fair to good; justified answer.
	1	Correct answer with no justification given OR incorrect answer with justification
	0	No answer OR incorrect answer without justification
4.	2	Correct explanation of method; answer of 880 ft
	1	Correct method with incorrect answer OR correct answer without explanation
	0	No answer OR incorrect method with incorrect answer
5.	2	Correct graph of appropriate kind
	1	Graph incomplete, confusing, or incorrect
	0	No response OR inappropriate type of graph
Excursion	5	Plan includes goal and a conditioning schedule that increases distance or speed
	4	Plan includes goal and presents a conditioning schedule, but lacks concept of increasing difficulty
	3	Plan includes goal, but only provides general idea of conditioning schedule
	2	Plan lacks goal, but includes conditioning schedule
	1	Plan lacks goal and conditioning schedule
	0	No response

Course 2 Chapter 6

Correlation to Standardized Tests

Lesson		STANDARDIZED TEST ITEMS CAT5	Terra Nova	ITBS, Form M	MAT7	SAT9	Local Test
6-1	Data Analysis: Exploring Ratios Using Data			CE24			
6-2	Unit Rates and Proportional Reasoning	CA37	39		CP50		
6-3	Algebra: Proportions		21		CP16		
6-4	Geometry: Using Similar Figures						
6-5	Geometry: Exploring Maps and Scale Drawings				CP18	PS39	
6-6	Modeling Percents				CP5		
6-7	Algebra: Percents, Fractions, and Decimals	CA7, 40			CP2		
6-8	Problem Solving Strategy: Use Multiple Strategies				CP39, PR14	PS10, 38	
6-9	Data Analysis: Finding the Percent of a Number	CA33, MC7, 15, 20, 32, 42	3, MC10, 13, 16, 20			PR29	
6-10	Algebra: Using Proportions with Percents					PR30	
6-11	Algebra: Finding Percent of Change						

CA: Concepts and Applications
PS: Problem Solving
PR: Math Procedures
CP: Concepts and Problem Solving
MC: Math Computation
PD: Problem Solving and Data Interpretation
CE: Concepts and Estimation

See page 2D for the level of each test referenced.

MAKING CONNECTIONS

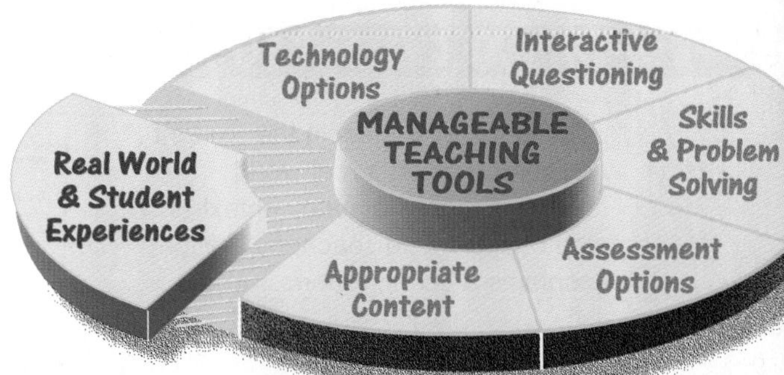

TEAM TEACHING WITH PRENTICE HALL MATERIALS

MIDDLE GRADES MATH INTERDISCIPLINARY UNITS

- **Agriculture: Activities 6–8, 10, 12**
- **Health, Exercise, and Fitness: Activities 2, 4–6, 10**
- **Advancements in Industry: Activities 1–3, 6, 9, 11**

INTERDISCIPLINARY EXPLORATIONS

- ***A Nation of Immigrants* pp. 16–18**
- ***Wagons West* pp. 24 & 25**
- ***Back to the Thirties* p. 28**

PRENTICE HALL SCIENCE

L Life Science **E** Earth Science **P** Physical Science

E Lab: Constructing a Telescope p. 42

P Sec. 12-2 Measuring Motion Lab p. 524 (relative humidity)

Lesson	Interdisciplinary Connections	Real World Connections	Math Integration
6-1	Social Studies Biology Sports	Transportation Cars Money	Measurement Data Analysis
6-2	History Sports Geography	Consumer Issues Data Collection	Statistics Measurement
6-3	History Physical Science	Aviation Entertainment Travel	Geometry Measurement
6-4	Social Studies	Geysers	Geometry
6-5	Geography History Art	Drafting Architecture Amusement Parks	Geometry Measurement
6-6	Biology	Education Volunteering	Measurement
6-7	Biology	Nutrition	Measurement
6-8	Social Studies	Consumer Issues Cooking Jobs	Geometry Measurement
6-9	Social Studies	Consumer Issues Hobbies Maps	Data Analysis Geometry Measurement
6-10	Social Studies Biology	Hiking Education Automobiles	Algebra
6-11	Zoology Social Studies Sports	Consumer Issues Business Medicine	Statistics Measurement

School to Home

MATERIALS:
newspapers
magazines
scissors
tape
paper
pencil

English version is in the Chapter Support File. Spanish version is in the Spanish Resources.

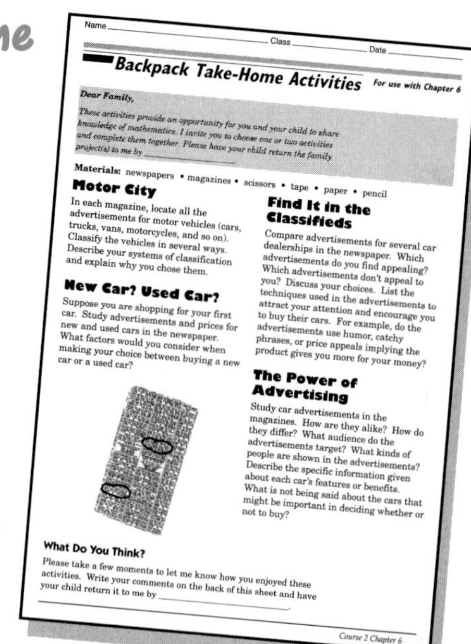

Name ______ Class ______ Date ______

Backpack Take-Home Activities *For use with Chapter 6*

Dear Family,

These activities provide an opportunity for you and your child to share knowledge of mathematics. I invite you to choose one or two activities and complete them together. Please have your child return the family project(s) to me by ______.

Materials: newspapers • magazines • scissors • tape • paper • pencil

Motor City

In each magazine, locate all the advertisements for motor vehicles (cars, trucks, vans, motorcycles, and so on). Classify the vehicles in several ways. Describe your systems of classification and explain why you chose them.

New Car? Used Car?

Suppose you are shopping for your first car. Study advertisements and prices for new and used cars in the newspaper. What factors would you consider when making your choice between buying a new car or a used car?

Find It in the Classifieds

Compare advertisements for several car dealerships in the newspaper. Which advertisements do you find appealing? Which advertisements don't appeal to you? Discuss your choices. List the techniques used in the advertisements to attract your attention and encourage you to buy their cars. For example, do the advertisements use humor, catchy phrases, or price appeals implying the product gives you more for your money?

The Power of Advertising

Study car advertisements in the magazines. How are they alike? How do they differ? What audience do the advertisements target? What kinds of people are shown in the advertisements? Describe the specific information given about each car's features or benefits. What is not being said about the cars that might be important in deciding whether or not to buy?

What Do You Think?

Please take a few moments to let me know how you enjoyed these activities. Write your comments on the back of this sheet and have your child return it to me by ______.

Course 2 Chapter 6

USING TECHNOLOGY TO ENHANCE INSTRUCTION

FOR THE STUDENT

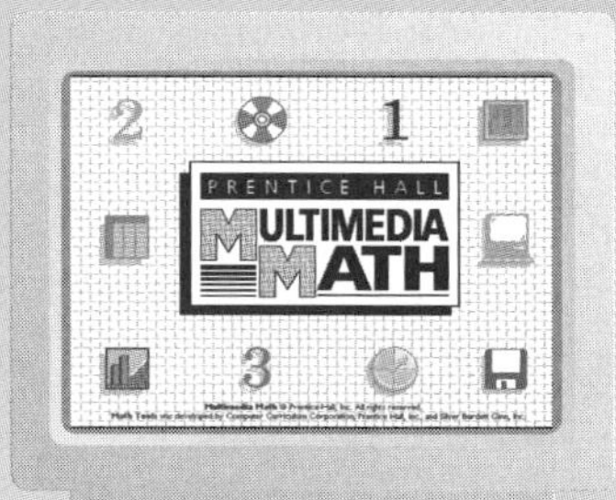

Multimedia Math Hot Pages™

This interactive software and video package on CD-ROM integrates solid math content through a variety of media.

- Hot Page™ 9-2
- Hot Page™ 9-5

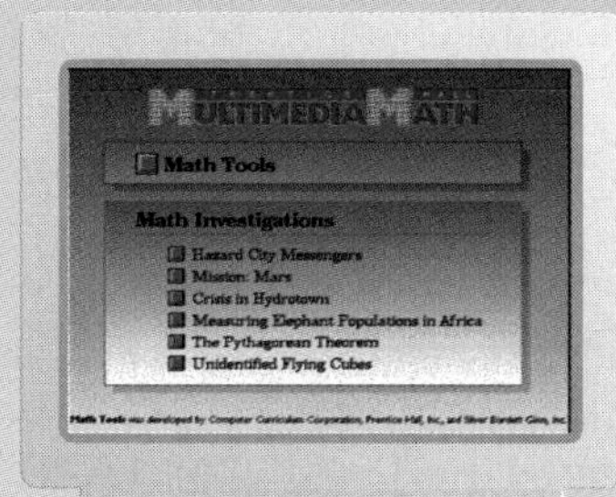

Multimedia Math Investigations

These in-depth interactive activities on CD-ROM develop real-world applications of mathematics. They allow students the opportunity to reinforce key concepts.

- Hazard City Messengers
- Crisis in Hydrotown

MathBlaster® Mystery

This award-winning, interactive software program on CD-ROM can be used to maintain skills or to accommodate early finishers.

- Level: Earn 4 coins; Pay 4 coins
- Mission Mode (all lessons)
- Kitchen Comparisons (6-2, 6-6, 6-10)
- Number Guesser (6-4, 6-8)
- Equation Maker (6-3, 6-7, 6-9)
- Word Problems (6-1, 6-5, 6-11, Problem Solving Practice)

Math Tools/Math Labs

This software, available on CD-ROM, includes on-screen Math Lab activities. Students use linkable, interactive tools to explore math concepts.

- Math Lab: Fractions, Decimals, and Percents (6-7)

Interactive Student Tutorial

Available on CD-ROM, this test preparation program contains self-tests with questions in standardized test format. Software includes electronic versions of the text lessons and an on-line glossary.

Internet Connection

For Students

Support for the Chapter Project
A career-oriented link for Math at Work feature

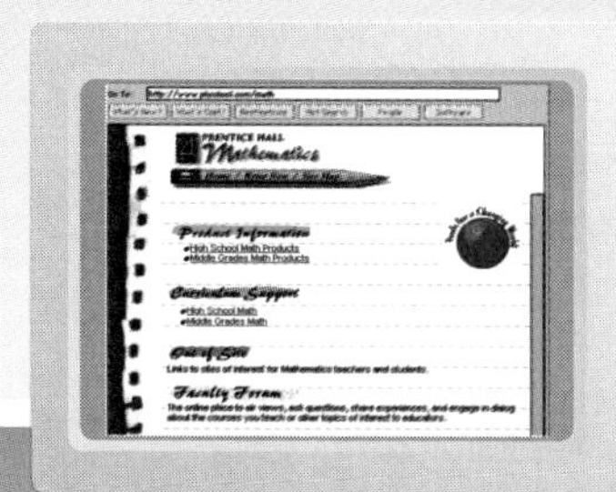

www.phschool.com/math

For teachers

Curriculum Support
Product Information
Regional Support Information

FOR THE TEACHER

Computer Item Generator with Standardized Test Practice

This software generates customized practice sheets and tests. It also generates unlimited practice sheets for the standardized tests listed on page 230D.

Resource Pro™ with Planning Express™

Available on CD-ROM, this software can be used to customize and plan lessons. It contains over 1,700 resource pages.

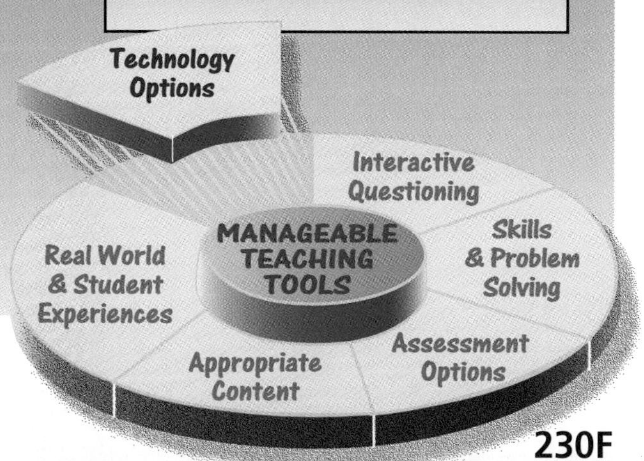

CHAPTER 6

USING PROPORTIONS AND PERCENTS

CONNECTING TO PRIOR LEARNING Ask students to describe the results of surveys they have seen in newspapers and magazines. You may want to bring some examples to class. Then ask students: *How are survey results expressed?* **percents, fractions, proportions** Then ask: *How are survey results displayed?* **table, charts, graphs**

CULTURAL CONNECTIONS Discuss with students the fact that there are amusement parks all over the world. Rides are also included in all types of celebrations, from World Fairs to Brazil's Carnival.

INTERDISCIPLINARY CONNECTIONS Ask: *How can businesses use surveys to increase their sales?* **Answers may vary. Sample: A business can survey its customers about what services the customers would like. The business can then adjust their services to fit the customers' responses.**

ABOUT THE PROJECT The Chapter Project gives students the opportunity to apply their knowledge of proportions and percents to conduct a survey and write a recommendation.

Internet • For information and activities related to the Chapter Project, visit the Prentice Hall site at www.phschool.com/mgm2/ch6

6 Using Proportions and Percents

WHAT YOU WILL LEARN IN THIS CHAPTER

- How to use proportions to solve problems
- How to find the scale for maps and scale drawings
- How to model and write percents

LAUNCHING THE CHAPTER PROJECT

Ask students:

- *Have you ever taken part in a survey?*
- *How can surveys make general conclusions based on the answers of a small group of people?*
- *How would you design a survey to make it accurate and useful?*

PROJECT NOTEBOOK Encourage students to keep all project-related materials in a separate folder or notebook.

TRACKING THE PROJECT You may wish to have students read Finishing the Chapter Project on page 281 to help them get an overview of the project. Set benchmark deadlines for students to show you their work in progress.

chills and *thrills*

CHAPTER PROJECT

THEME: BUSINESS

Your world is spinning. You are screaming. And you are loving every minute of it! Even though you are scared, you know that you will come to a safe stop at the end of the ride.

Clearly, a successful amusement park attraction like the one shown here, which is Paramount Park's ride Top Gun, must be both fun and safe. Planners of amusement parks use a lot of math to create thrills but avoid any spills.

Take a Survey For the chapter project you will decide which rides are likely to be most popular. Your final product will be a recommendation about which rides to include in a proposed amusement park for your town.

Steps to help you complete the project:

p. 236 **Project Link:** *Taking a Survey*
p. 249 **Project Link:** *Graphing*
p. 263 **Project Link:** *Calculating*
p. 280 **Project Link:** *Researching*
p. 281 *Finishing the Chapter Project*

- How to use multiple strategies to solve problems

PROBLEM SOLVING

SCORING RUBRIC

3 You conduct a survey and complete a graph showing the amusement park preferences of a reasonable sample of people. You describe these preferences using both ratios and percents, and you correctly use these values to estimate the projected number of people in a larger population who would prefer each ride.

2 You provide a graph of your survey data and the percentage of people who prefer each ride. You attempt to use the survey data to estimate the preferences of a larger population.

1 You don't gather adequate data from your survey, you incorrectly calculate percentages, or you don't make any projections for a larger population.

0 You fail to complete a survey, graph the results, or make any calculations based on these results.

6-1 Teaching Notes

1 Focus

CONNECTING TO PRIOR KNOWLEDGE
Draw one triangle and two squares. Ask students: *What fraction of objects are squares?* $\frac{2}{3}$ Then draw one more triangle and one more square. Ask: *What fraction of objects are squares?* $\frac{3}{5}$

2 Teach

THINK AND DISCUSS

ASSESSMENT Have students work with a partner to answer the following:

- *What is the ratio of males to females for the 60–64 age group in 1990?* **87 : 100**
- *What is the ratio of females to males for the 30–34 age group in 1980?* **100 : 99**
- *What is the ratio of males to the entire 10–14 age group in 1990?* **105 : 205**

DIVERSITY Some students may help take care of grandparents or other elderly relatives. Ask: *What might explain the lower rate of males to females in the 60–64 age group?* **Answers may vary. Sample: Women often live longer than men.**

Lesson Planning Options

Prerequisite Skills

- writing equivalent fractions (4-2)
- simplifying fractions (4-6)
- writing fractions as decimals (4-9)

Vocabulary/Symbols

ratio

Resources

Student Edition

Skills Handbook, p. 528
Extra Practice, p. 519
Glossary/Study Guide

Teaching Resources

Chapter Support File, Ch. 6
- Lesson Planner 6-1
- Practice 6-1, Reteaching 6-1
- Alternative Activity 6-1
- Answer Masters 6-1

Teaching Aids Masters 1–3, 19
Glossary, Spanish Resources

Transparencies
1, 7, 15, Minds on Math 6-1

Warm Up

Estimate the width and length in feet of three specific rectangular items in the classroom. Use the measurements to find the area of each item. **Answers may vary.**

DATA ANALYSIS Connection

6-1 Exploring Ratios Using Data

What You'll Learn

1. To write ratios
2. To find equal ratios

...And Why

You can use a ratio to describe a group of people in terms of age and gender.

Here's How

Look for questions that
- build understanding
- ✔ check understanding

THINK AND DISCUSS

1 *Writing Ratios*

A **ratio** is a comparison of two numbers by division. You can write a ratio three ways.

3 to 4 $\qquad$ 3 : 4 $\qquad$ $\frac{3}{4}$

The table below shows the ratio of males to females for different years and different age groups.

Ratio of Males to Females by Age Group

Year	10–14	30–34	60–64
1970	104 : 100	97 : 100	88 : 100
1980	104 : 100	99 : 100	86 : 100
1990	105 : 100	100 : 100	87 : 100

Source: *Statistical Abstract of the United States*

1. *Think About It* Write each ratio for the year 1990 in two other ways. **See margin p. 234.**

EXAMPLE 1 *Real-World Problem Solving*

Data Analysis The United States Census Bureau predicts that in the year 2010 there will be about 64 males for every 100 females who are 75 years old or older. Write this information as a ratio in three ways.

males → 64 to 100 ← females
males → 64 : 100 ← females
$\frac{64}{100}$ ← $\frac{\text{males}}{\text{females}}$

2. *Error Alert* A student reported the ratio of males to females as 100 : 64. Explain why this is incorrect. **The student reported the ratio of females to males.**
3. ✔ *Try It Out* The United States Census Bureau predicts that by the year 2010 there will be about 73 million people under the age of 18 and 39 million people 65 and older. Use this information to write a ratio in three ways. **Answers may vary. Sample: $\frac{73}{39}$ or 73 : 39 or 73 to 39**

VISUAL LEARNING Have students draw models of at least three ratios described in the table. Have students use small units so the models fit on notebook paper. Ask students to explain how their drawings illustrate the ratios.

ADDITIONAL EXAMPLES

FOR EXAMPLE 1

Robert predicts that his baseball team will win about 2 out of every 3 games they play this year. Write this information as a ratio in three ways. **2 to 3; 2 : 3; $\frac{2}{3}$**

FOR EXAMPLE 2

Ms. Burn's class has a ratio of 13 male students to 14 female students. The entire school population has 273 male students and 294 female students. Is this the same as the ratio in Ms. Burn's class? **yes** Explain. **Answers may vary. Sample: The school's male to female ratio is 0.93. Ms. Burn's male to female class ratio is also 0.93.**

FOR EXAMPLE 3

Find two ratios equal to $\frac{16}{10}$. **Answers may vary. Sample: $\frac{32}{20}$ and $\frac{8}{5}$**

FOR EXAMPLE 4

An average adult male gorilla living in the wild weighs about 350 lb. In zoos, an adult male gorilla can weigh about 750 lb. Write a ratio in simplest form to compare the weights of the gorillas in the two different habitats. **$\frac{7}{15}$**

You can use a decimal to express and compare ratios.

EXAMPLE 2 *Real-World Problem Solving*

Social Studies An official United States flag has a length-to-width ratio of 19 : 10. The largest U.S. flag measures 505 ft by 255 ft. Is this an official U.S. flag?

official flag		largest flag
$\frac{19}{10}$	← length / width →	$\frac{505}{255}$
$\frac{19}{10} = 1.9$	← Write as a decimal. Round if necessary. →	$\frac{505}{255} \approx 1.98$

The ratio 1.98 is not equal to the ratio 1.9, so the largest flag is not an official United States flag.

The largest United States flag is shown on the Ellipse in Washington, D.C., on Flag Day, June 14. It weighs 2,720 lb.

Source: *The Guinness Book of Records*

4. ✔*Try It Out* Express each ratio as a decimal. Round to the nearest hundredth, if necessary.
   a. $\frac{3}{4}$ **0.75** b. 16 to 5 **3.2** c. 8 : 9 **0.89** d. $\frac{7}{3}$ **2.33**

Now you may assign Exercises 1–20.

2 *Writing Equal Ratios*

To find equal ratios, multiply or divide the numerator and denominator of the ratio by the same nonzero number.

EXAMPLE 3

Find two ratios equal to $\frac{12}{15}$.

Multiply both numerator and denominator by 2.

$$\frac{12}{15} = \frac{12 \times 2}{15 \times 2} = \frac{24}{30}$$

Divide both numerator and denominator by 3.

$$\frac{12}{15} = \frac{12 \div 3}{15 \div 3} = \frac{4}{5}$$

Two ratios equal to $\frac{12}{15}$ are $\frac{24}{30}$ and $\frac{4}{5}$.

5. ✔*Try It Out* Write two ratios equal to $\frac{10}{16}$. **Answers may vary. Sample: $\frac{20}{32}$ and $\frac{5}{8}$**

6. *Go a Step Further* Use what you know about fractions. Tell which ratio in Example 3 is written in simplest form. **$\frac{4}{5}$**

Technology Options

Prentice Hall Technology

Software for Learners
- Math Blaster® Mystery*
- Interactive Student Tutorial, Chapter 6*

Teaching Resource Software
- Computer Item Generator 6-1
- Resource Pro™ Chapter 6*

Internet • For related mathematics activities, visit the Prentice Hall site at www.phschool.com/math

**Available on CD-ROM only*

Assignment Options for Exercises On Your Own

To provide flexible scheduling, this lesson can be split into parts.

1 **Core** 1–8, 10, 11
Extension 9, 12

2 **Core** 13–19, 21–34
Extension 20, 35

Use Mixed Review to maintain skills.

CONNECTION TO SOCIAL STUDIES
Example 2 Have students measure pictures of flags from other countries and states. Ask them to write the length-to-width ratio three ways and as a decimal. Then have them compare their ratio to the ratio of an official United States flag.

Work Together

If you have block scheduling or extended class periods, have students graph their results. Encourage students to use different types of graphs to represent their data. For example, they could select from a histogram, bar graph, or scatter plot.

3 Practice/Assess

EXERCISES *On Your Own*

Exercise 9 Encourage students to rewrite the two ratios so that they both contain the same number of blue marbles. **1 : 4, 4 : 10**

WRITING Exercise 12 Students may need to convert each ratio to a decimal to help them compare.

pages 232–234 Think and Discuss

1. 105 to 100 or $\frac{105}{100}$; 100 to 100 or $\frac{100}{100}$; 87 to 100 or $\frac{87}{100}$.

8c. You can multiply the number of students in your school by the ratio for August in part b.

EXAMPLE 4 *Real-World Problem Solving*

Biology A brown bear weighs about 325 lb. A polar bear weighs about 1,000 lb. Write a ratio in simplest form to compare the weights of the bears.

$\frac{325}{1,000} = \frac{325 \div 25}{1,000 \div 25} = \frac{13}{40}$ ← Divide the numerator and the denominator by 25.

The ratio of the weight of the brown bear to the weight of the polar bear is 13 to 40.

7. ✔ *Try It Out* Write each ratio in simplest form.
   a. $\frac{25}{75}$ $\frac{1}{3}$
   b. $\frac{110}{20}$ $\frac{11}{2}$
   c. 42 : 66 7 : 11
   d. 84 to 48 7 to 4

Work Together *Finding Ratios Using Data*

8. a. *Data Collection* Survey your class to find the month of each person's birthday. a–b. Check students' work.
   b. Write the ratio of the number of people born in each month to the number of people in class.
   c. How do you think you could use the data to estimate the number of students in your school who were born in August? See margin.

Now you may assign Exercises 13–35.

EXERCISES *On Your Own*

Write the ratio for each situation in three ways.

1. About 1 out of 4 people swims at least six times each year. Sample: 1 : 4, 1 to 4, $\frac{1}{4}$
2. About 24 out of 25 Californians live in a metropolitan area. Sample: 24 to 25, 24 : 25, $\frac{24}{25}$

Write each ratio in two other ways.

3. 12 : 4 12 to 4, $\frac{12}{4}$
4. 8 to 10 8 : 10, $\frac{8}{10}$
5. $\frac{5}{4}$ 5 to 4, 5 : 4
6. 13 : 8 13 to 8, $\frac{13}{8}$
7. 21 : 28 21 to 28, $\frac{21}{28}$
8. $\frac{8}{18}$ 8 to 18, 8 : 18
9. **Choose A, B, C, or D.** A bag contains red, blue, and yellow marbles. The ratio of red marbles to blue marbles is 1 : 4. The ratio of blue marbles to yellow marbles is 2 : 5. What is the ratio of red marbles to yellow marbles? B
   A. 1 : 5 B. 1 : 10 C. 1 : 2 D. 1 : 12

ERROR ALERT! Exercises 13–18 Students may have difficulty remembering which number goes inside the division house. **Remediation:** Tell students that the first number is the owner of the house and the second number is the visitor. So students write the first number inside the division house, and enter it first in the calculator. The second number is outside the house, and they enter it second in the calculator.

REASONING Exercise 20c Students may want to use a simpler problem to help answer this question. For example, they may compare two squares, one with a side of 2 in. and another with a side of 3 in. Ask:

- *What is the ratio of the sides?* 2 : 3
- *What is the ratio of the areas?* 4 : 9
- *Are the ratios equivalent?* no
- *How are the numbers in the area ratio related to the numbers in the sides ratio?* **The numbers in the area ratio are the squares of the numbers in the sides ratio.**

REASONING Exercise 35b Point out that the amount of antifreeze and water must total 15 qt together. Have students write the equation $2a + w = 15$. They can use Guess and Test to find an answer that makes the equation true.

Write each ratio in three ways.

10. A baseball team won 7 out of 15 games.
   a. wins to total games 7 : 15, 7 to 15, $\frac{7}{15}$
   b. wins to losses **7 : 8, 7 to 8, $\frac{7}{8}$**

11. A running club has 23 girls and 19 boys.
   a. girls to boys 23 : 19, 23 to 19, $\frac{23}{19}$
   b. boys to total number 19 : 42, 19 to 42, $\frac{19}{42}$

12. *Writing* Sara's math class included 15 girls and 10 boys. Sara said the ratio of girls to boys was 3 to 2. Two new students, a girl and a boy, enrolled in the class. Sara says the ratio is still 3 to 2. Is she correct? Why or why not? No; the new ratio is 16 : 11.

Express each ratio as a decimal. Round to the nearest tenth, if necessary.

13. 7 : 8 0.9
14. 18 to 5 3.6
15. $\frac{8}{3}$ 2.7
16. $\frac{14}{19}$ 0.7
17. 12 : 25 0.5
18. $\frac{110}{105}$ 1.0

19. *Transportation* Train A can travel 225 miles in 3 hours. Train B can travel 455 miles in 7 hours.
   a. Write a ratio of miles : hours for each train. 225 : 3, 455 : 7
   b. Express each ratio as a decimal. 75, 65
   c. Write a sentence to compare Train A to Train B. Answers may vary. Sample: Train A travels 75 mi/h while Train B travels 65 mi/h

20. *Sports* A softball diamond measures 65 ft by 65 ft. A baseball diamond measures 90 ft by 90 ft. Write a ratio in simplest form for each of the following.
   a. the length of a side of a softball diamond to the length of a side of a baseball diamond $\frac{13}{18}$
   b. the area of a softball diamond to the area of a baseball diamond $\frac{169}{324}$
   c. *Reasoning* Why do you think the ratio of the sides and the ratio of the areas are not the same? The ratio of areas is the square of the ratio of sides.

21–26. Answers may vary. Samples are given.

Open-ended **Write two other ratios equal to each ratio.**

21. 26 : 54 13 : 27, 78 : 162
22. 12 to 44 6 to 22, 3 to 11
23. $\frac{212}{100}$ $\frac{106}{50}$, $\frac{53}{25}$
24. $\frac{21}{3}$ $\frac{7}{1}$, $\frac{14}{2}$
25. $\frac{18}{36}$ $\frac{9}{18}$, $\frac{3}{6}$
26. 1 : 6 2 : 12, 3 : 18

Write each ratio in simplest form.

27. 25 : 10 5 : 2
28. 7 to 63 1 to 9
29. $\frac{2}{100}$ $\frac{1}{50}$
30. 48 to 12 4 to 1
31. 17 : 34 1 : 2
32. $\frac{9}{27}$ $\frac{1}{3}$

33. *Cars* A jack for a car requires a force of 120 lb to lift a 3,000 lb car. What is the ratio of the car's weight to the force required to lift the car? Write the ratio in simplest form. 25 to 1

PRACTICE

Practice 6-1 Exploring Ratios Using Data

Write a ratio in three ways for each situation.

1. Ten years ago in Louisiana, in 1988, schools averaged 182 pupils for every 10 teachers.
   182 to 10; 182 : 10; $\frac{182}{10}$
2. In a recent year, 41 out of 250 people in the labor force belonged to a union.
   41 to 250; 41 : 250; $\frac{41}{250}$
3. Between 1899–1900, 284 out of 1,000 people in the United States were 5–17 years old.
   284 to 1,000; 284 : 1,000; $\frac{284}{1,000}$
4. In a recent year, 7 out of 10 people with Japanese heritage who lived in the United States lived in either Hawaii or California.
   7 to 10; 7 : 10; $\frac{7}{10}$

Use the chart below for Exercises 5–6.

The seventh-grade classes were asked whether they wanted chicken or pasta served at their awards banquet.

Room Number	Chicken	Pasta
201	10	12
202	8	17
203	16	10

5. In room 201, what is the ratio of students who prefer chicken to students who prefer pasta?
   10 : 12; or 5 : 6
6. Combine the totals for all three rooms. What is the ratio of the number of students who prefer pasta to the number of students who prefer chicken?
   39 : 34

Write each ratio in simplest form.

7. $\frac{2}{6}$ $\frac{1}{3}$
8. 3:21 1:7
9. 16 to 20 4 to 5
10. $\frac{3}{30}$ $\frac{1}{10}$
11. 12 to 18 2 to 3
12. 81:27 3:1
13. $\frac{6}{28}$ $\frac{3}{14}$
14. 49 to 14 7 to 2

Choose A, B, C, or D.

15. A bag contains green, yellow, and orange marbles. The ratio of green marbles to yellow marbles is 2 : 5. The ratio of yellow marbles to orange marbles is 3 : 4. What is the ratio of green marbles to orange marbles? D
    A. 5 : 2 B. 15 : 8 C. 5 : 4 D. 3 : 10

Practice

In copymaster and workbook formats

RETEACHING

Reteaching 6-1 Exploring Ratios Using Data

A **ratio** is a comparison of two numbers by division. You can write a ratio three ways.

Compare the number of red tulips to the number of yellow tulips.

6 to 2, 6 : 2, or $\frac{6}{2}$

To find equal ratios, multiply or divide *each part* of the ratio by the same nonzero number.

$\frac{6}{2} = \frac{6 \times 2}{2 \times 2} = \frac{12}{4}$ ← **Multiply by 2.**

The ratio $\frac{3}{1}$ is in **simplest form.**

$\frac{6}{2} = \frac{6 \div 2}{2 \div 2} = \frac{3}{1}$ ← **Divide by 2.**

Use the drawings at the top of the page. Write each ratio in three ways.

1. yellow tulips to red tulips
   2 to 6; 2 : 6; $\frac{2}{6}$
2. white mums to orange mums
   3 to 5; 3 : 5; $\frac{3}{5}$
3. red tulips to orange mums
   6 to 5; 6 : 5; $\frac{6}{5}$
4. yellow tulips to white mums
   2 to 3; 2 : 3; $\frac{2}{3}$
5. red tulips to all flowers
   6 to 16; 6 : 16; $\frac{6}{16}$
6. orange mums to all flowers
   5 to 16; 5 : 16; $\frac{5}{16}$
7. tulips to mums
   8 to 8; 8 : 8; $\frac{8}{8}$
8. white mums to tulips
   3 to 8; 3 : 8; $\frac{3}{8}$
9. yellow tulips to all flowers
   2 to 16; 2 : 16; $\frac{2}{16}$
10. yellow tulips to orange mums
    2 to 5; 2 : 5; $\frac{2}{5}$

Write two other ratios equal to each ratio. Samples are shown.

11. $\frac{5}{10}$ $\frac{1}{2}$, $\frac{10}{20}$
12. 2:5 4 : 10, 6 : 15
13. 18 to 30 3 to 5, 36 to 60

Write each ratio in simplest form.

14. $\frac{8}{16}$ $\frac{1}{2}$
15. 8 to 2 4 to 1
16. 10:15 2 : 3
17. $\frac{48}{24}$ $\frac{2}{1}$
18. $\frac{6}{100}$ $\frac{3}{50}$
19. 8:18 4 : 9

ENRICHMENT

Minds on Math Transparency

6-1

Take nine toothpicks and form this pattern. Move three toothpicks and make five triangles.

Sample shown.

See *Solution Key* for worked-out answers.

WRAP UP

IDENTIFYING THE BIG IDEA Ask students to explain the meaning of a ratio. Then have students explain the different ways to express equal ratios.

PROJECT LINK Have students research amusement park advertisements, brochures, etc., to make a list of choices for the survey. Make sure students allow for additional rides to be included by those being surveyed.

LESSON QUIZ

1. Write $\frac{9}{17}$ in two other ways. **9 to 17; 9 : 17**
2. Write 11 : 27 as a decimal. Round to the nearest tenth. **0.4**
3. Write 56 to 16 in simplest form. **7 to 2**

34. Use the chart below.

a. Which two rooms have the same ratio of girls to boys? **101 and 107**
b. The students in Room 101 and Room 104 have one class together. What is the ratio of girls to boys for the combined class? Write the ratio in simplest form. **7 : 12**

35. *Cars* Antifreeze protects a car's radiator from freezing during the winter. One brand of antifreeze recommends mixing at least 2 parts antifreeze with every 1 part water for protection to −82°F.

a. Which of the ratios of antifreeze to water at the right provide protection to −82°F? **8 : 4**
b. *Reasoning* A car's radiator can hold 15 qt. How much antifreeze and how much water should be added to give protection to −82°F? **10 qt antifreeze, 5 qt water**

Ratio of Antifreeze to Water

Antifreeze (qt)	:	Water (qt)
8	:	4
7.5	:	3
12	:	8
3.5	:	1
9	:	18

Mixed Review

Estimate. *(Lesson 2-2)*

36. 412 • (83) **400 × 85 = 34,000**
37. 654 ÷ 48 **650 ÷ 50 = 13**
38. 28.7 ÷ 5.4 **30 ÷ 5 = 6**
39. 22.7 + 23.5 + 23.1 **23 + 23 + 23 = 69**

Solve. *(Lessons 3-6, 3-7)*

40. $72 = 8x$ **9**
41. $6 + y = 51$ **45**
42. $-5 = \frac{q}{7}$ **−35**
43. $-3 + r = -57$ **−54**
44. $x - 34 = -37$ **−3**

45. *Money* A swimsuit that has a regular price of $38.00 is now on sale for $\frac{1}{4}$ off. What is its sale price? *(Lesson 5-5)* **$28.50**

CHAPTER PROJECT

PROJECT LINK TAKING A SURVEY

What's your favorite amusement park ride? Conduct a survey to find out which rides are most popular. Keep track of the number of people you survey as well as their responses. **Check students' work.**

6-2 Teaching Notes

1 Focus

CONNECTING TO PRIOR KNOWLEDGE
Collect sale ads from grocery stores, discount stores, and drug stores. Ask students working in groups to cut out the ads for similar products from different stores. Students compare prices as well as sizes of the products.

2 Teach

Work Together

DIVERSITY Pair students together with similar reading ability. This may help to eliminate teasing or embarrassment.

AEP You may want to write a passage that consists of common, easily recognized words. An alternative is to have students read a passage from a familiar book.

THINK AND DISCUSS

EXTENSION and KINESTHETIC LEARNING
Example 1 Group students in pairs. One partner can do three timed activities, such as jumping-jacks, sit-ups, and walking around the room. The other partner can time the first activity for one minute, the second for two minutes, and the third for three minutes. Partners work together to find the unit rate for each activity.

6-2 Unit Rates and Proportional Reasoning

What You'll Learn

1. To find unit rates
2. To compare unit prices

...And Why

People compare prices to make wise purchasing decisions.

Here's How

Look for questions that
- build understanding
- ✔ check understanding

Work Together

Comparing Ratios

Suppose you plan to try out for a part in a radio advertisement. The casting director is looking for someone who can speak clearly but also very fast.

1. Work with a partner. Time each other as you read a newspaper article aloud as clearly and as fast as you can. After two minutes, count the number of words that you read.
   1–2. Check students' work.
2. *Analyze* Write a ratio comparing the number of words you read to your time. Then write a ratio for your partner's reading. Which ratio is greater? Explain how you know.

THINK AND DISCUSS

1 *Finding Unit Rates*

A **rate** is a ratio that compares two quantities measured in different units. In the Work Together, suppose you read 233 words in two minutes. Your reading rate would be $\frac{233\text{ words}}{2\text{ min}}$.

A **unit rate** is a rate that has a denominator of 1.

$$\frac{\text{words}}{\text{minutes}} \rightarrow \frac{233}{2} \overset{\div 2}{=} \frac{116.5}{1}$$

The unit rate is $\frac{116.5\text{ words}}{1\text{ min}}$, or 116.5 words/min (words per minute).

3. a. ✔ *Try It Out* Use the data you collected in the Work Together. Find the unit reading rates for your partner and yourself. **a–b. Check students' work.**
   b. Suppose you and your partner continued reading for 5 min. About how many words would each of you read?
4. *Go a Step Further* You measure the speed of a car in miles per hour. How is speed an example of a rate?
   Answers may vary. See above left for sample.

4. Speed is a ratio that compares a quantity measured in miles to a quantity measured in hours.

WHO? HISTORY
During a speech in December, 1961, President John F. Kennedy delivered a passage at the rate of 327 words/min. At the time, this was the fastest rate recorded for a public speaker.

Source: *The Guinness Book of Records*

Lesson Planning Options

Prerequisite Skills
- comparing decimals (2-1)
- writing fractions as decimals (4-9)

Vocabulary/Symbols
rate, unit rate, unit price

Materials/Manipulatives
- newspaper
- calculator
- stopwatch or timer

Resources

Student Edition

Skills Handbook, p. 528
Extra Practice, p. 519
Glossary/Study Guide

Teaching Resources

Chapter Support File, Ch. 6
- Lesson Planner 6-2
- Practice 6-2, Reteaching 6-2
- Answer Masters 6-2

Teaching Aids Masters 1–3, 19
Glossary, Spanish Resources

Transparencies
1, 7, 15, Minds on Math 6-2

Warm Up

Write five equivalent equations for each equation below.
$15 = 8 + n$ and $c - 19 = 4$
Answers may vary. Sample:
$14 = 9 + n$; $c = 23$

■ ADDITIONAL EXAMPLES

FOR EXAMPLE 1

Sarah drives 210 mi to her cousin's house in 3 h 23 min. About how fast is her average speed? **1.03 mi/min or about 62 mi/h**

FOR EXAMPLE 2

One blank video tape costs $1.98 and a pack of three video tapes is $4.98. Which is the better buy and why? **The pack of three tapes is the better buy; each tape costs $1.66.**

TACTILE LEARNING Organize students in small groups. Give each group 30 red counters and 6 green counters. Have students find the unit rate for the number of red counters to the number of green counters. Students should separate the counters into piles, each containing 1 green counter. How many red counters are in each pile? **Each pile has 5 red counters for each green.**

Question 5 Have students find estimates before they do the calculations. $\frac{30}{10} = 3$; $\frac{7{,}000}{200} = 35$ Ask students: *Why is estimating the answer first a good idea?* **Answers may vary. Sample: An estimate helps you check for errors such as pressing the wrong keys on the calculator.**

ASSESSMENT Question 5 Have students write a checklist of the steps used to find unit rates. Students trade with a partner and use their partner's checklist to answer Question 5. Have students check their partner's unit rates.

Technology Options

Prentice Hall Technology

Software for Learners

- Hot Page™ 9–2*
- Math Blaster® Mystery*
- Interactive Student Tutorial, Chapter 6*

Teaching Resource Software

- Computer Item Generator 6-2
- Resource Pro™ Chapter 6*

Internet • For related mathematics activities, visit the Prentice Hall site at www.phschool.com/math

**Available on CD-ROM only*

Assignment Options for Exercises On Your Own

To provide flexible scheduling, this lesson can be split into parts.

1 Core 1–6, 16, 24, 28
Extension 23

2 Core 7–14, 15, 17–22, 26
Extension 25, 27

Use Mixed Review to maintain skills.

Sometimes measures are written in mixed units. For example, time may be written in *minutes* and *seconds*. To find a unit rate of time, you first need to change the total time to seconds.

■ EXAMPLE 1 *Real-World Problem Solving*

Sports At the 1993 World Championships, Maria Mutola of Mozambique set a new world record for the women's 1,000-meter race. Her time was 2 min 29.34 s. About how fast was her average speed?

$2 \text{ min } 29.34 \text{ s} = 2 \times 60 \text{ s} + 29.34 \text{ s}$ ← Write the time in seconds.
$= 149.34 \text{ s}$

Write the ratio of meters to seconds. Find the unit rate.

$\frac{\text{meters}}{\text{seconds}} \rightarrow \frac{1{,}000}{149.34} = 1{,}000 \div 149.34 = 6.696129637$

$\approx 6.70 \text{ m/s}$ ← Round to the nearest hundredth.

Maria Mutola's average speed was about 6.7 m/s.

a. $4.25/h **b. 45 words/min**

5. ✔ *Try It Out* Write the unit rate for each situation.
   a. earn $34 in 8 h
   b. type 6,750 words in 2 h 30 min

Now you may assign Exercises 1–6, 16, 23–24, 28.

2 *Comparing Unit Prices*

A **unit price** is the price per unit of an item. To calculate a unit price, divide the price of the item by the size of the item.

■ EXAMPLE 2 *Real-World Problem Solving*

Consumer Issues A 10.2 fl oz bottle of Shine shampoo costs $5.98. The 16 fl oz bottle costs $9.95. Which size is the better buy?

$\frac{\text{price}}{\text{size}} \rightarrow \frac{\$5.98}{10.2 \text{ fl oz}} \approx \$.59/\text{fl oz}$
$\frac{\text{price}}{\text{size}} \rightarrow \frac{\$9.95}{16 \text{ fl oz}} \approx \$.62/\text{fl oz}$
← Find the unit price of each item.

Since $.59 < $.62, the 10.2 fl oz bottle is the better buy.

6. ✔ *Try It Out* You can buy 28 fl oz of fruit juice for $1.69 or 64 fl oz for $3.19. Which size is the better buy? **64 fl oz**

Now you may assign Exercises 7–15, 17–22, 25–27.

Question 6 If you have block scheduling or extended class periods, have students calculate the unit prices of the products they cut from the ads in Connecting to Prior Knowledge. Ask: *Why might you not choose the better buy?* **Answers may vary. Sample: The more expensive product tastes better.**

3 Practice/Assess

EXERCISES *On Your Own*

ERROR ALERT! **Exercises 7–14** Students may write the price and size in the wrong order. **Remediation:** Have students set up the ratio by first writing word ratio $\frac{\text{price}}{\text{size}}$. Then have students write the actual price and size in the appropriate places.

WRITING **Exercise 23c** Point out that the Chamber of Commerce or an almanac may contain this information. However, students' answers should include how to make their own estimation.

EXERCISES *On Your Own*

Write the unit rate for each situation.

1. travel 1,200 mi in 4 h **300 mi/h**
2. score 98 points in 6 games **16.3 points/game**
3. earn $145 in 25 h **$5.80/h**
4. write 11 pages in 2 h **5.5 pages/h**
5. run 400 m in 1 min 32 s **4.3 m/s**
6. make 686 cars in 56 days **12.25 cars/day**

Find each unit price.

7. $12 for 4 yd **$3/yd**
8. $9 for 5 fl oz **$1.80/fl oz**
9. $9.87 for 3 gal **$3.29/gal**
10. $3.45 for 2 lb **$1.73/lb**
11. 4 m for $10 **$2.50/m**
12. 20 lb for $7 **$.35/lb**
13. 7 oz for $6.65 **$.95/oz**
14. 3 qt for $4.49 **$1.50/qt**

Choose **Use a calculator, paper and pencil, or mental math.**

15. A 17-min telephone call from Boston to Chicago costs $2.38. What is the cost per minute? **$.14/min**
16. A plane travels 2,250 km in 3 h. What is its average speed? **750 km/h**

Find each unit price. Then determine the better buy.

17. detergent: 32 fl oz for $1.99
    50 fl oz for $2.49
    $.06/oz, $.05/oz; 50 fl oz
18. crackers: 12 oz for $2.69
    16 oz for $3.19
    $.22/oz, $.20/oz; 16 oz
19. juice: 48 fl oz for $2.15
    64 fl for $2.89
    $.04/oz, $.05/oz; 48 fl oz
20. popcorn: 15 oz for $1.69
    30 oz for $2.99
    $.11/oz, $.10/oz; 30 oz
21. ribbon: 1 yd for $.49
    3 yd for $1.95
    $.49/yd, $.65/yd; 1 yd
22. walnuts: 1 lb for $3.49
    10 oz for $2.49
    $.22/oz, $.25/oz; 1 lb

23. a. *Geography* *Population density* is the average number of people per unit of area. Alaska has the lowest population density of any state in the United States. What is its population density? Round to the nearest person per square mile. **1 person/mi^2**

    b. *Reasoning* New Jersey has 1,071 people/mi^2. It has the highest population density of any state. Can you conclude that 1,071 people live in every square mile in New Jersey? Explain. **See margin.**
    c. *Writing* Explain how you could find the population density of your city or town. **Find the ratio of the population of the city or town to its area.**

pages 239–240 On Your Own

23b. No; this is the average. There will be some square miles with more people and some with fewer.

page 240 Mixed Review

35. 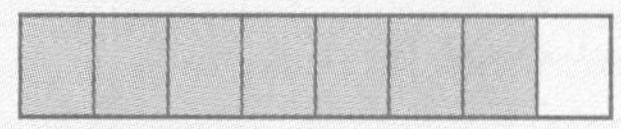
36. 
37. 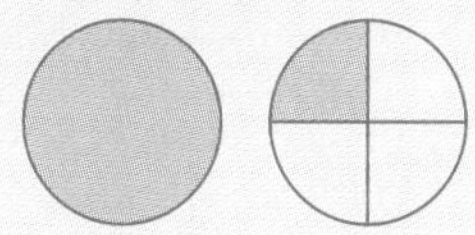
38. 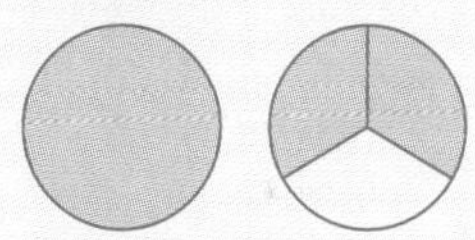
39. 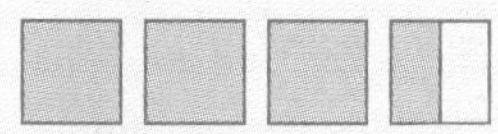
40. 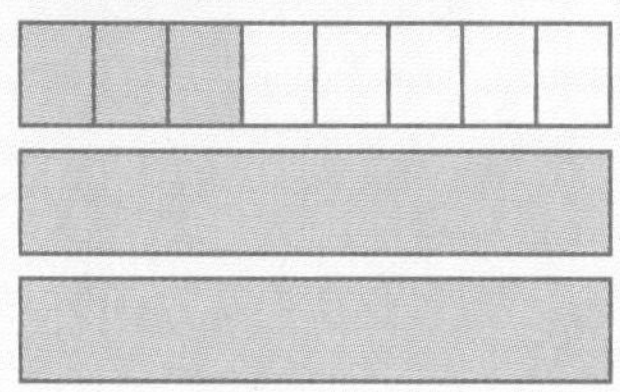

PRACTICE

Practice 6-2 Unit Rates and Proportional Reasoning

Write the unit rate for each situation.

1. travel 250 mi in 5 h
   50 mi/h
2. earn $75.20 in 8 h
   $9.40/h
3. read 80 pages in 2 h
   40 pages/h
4. type 8,580 words in 2 h 45 min
   52 words/min or 3,120 words/h
5. manufacture 2,488 parts in 8 h
   311 parts/h
6. 50 copies of a book on 2 shelves
   25 books/shelf
7. $30 for 6 books
   $5/book
8. 24 points in 3 games
   8 points/game

Find each unit price. Then determine the better buy.

9. paper: 100 sheets for $.99
   500 sheets for $4.29
   $.0099/sheet; $.00858/sheet; 500 sheets
10. peanuts: 1 lb for $1.29
    12 oz for $.95
    $.080625/lb; $.07917/lb; 12 oz
11. crackers: 15 oz for $1.79
    12 oz for $1.49
    $.1193/oz; $.1242/oz; 15 oz
12. apples: 3 lb for $1.89
    5 lb for $2.49
    $.63/lb; $.498/lb; 5 lb
13. mechanical pencils: 4 for $1.25
    25 for $5.69
    $.3125/pencil; $.2276/pencil; 25 pencils
14. bagels: 4 for $.89
    6 for $1.39
    $.2225/bagel; $.2317/bagel; 4 bagels
15. orange juice: 12 oz for $1.49
    16 oz for $1.89
    $.12417/oz; $.118125/oz; 16 oz
16. socks: 3 pairs for $4.29
    8 pairs for $10.79
    $1.43/pair; 1.34875/pair; 8 pairs
17. a. Yolanda and Yoko ran in a 100-yd dash. When Yolanda crossed the finish line, Yoko was 10 yd behind her. The girls then repeated the race, with Yolanda starting 10 yd behind the starting line. If each girl ran at the same rate as before, who won the race? By how many yards?
    Yolanda; 1 yd
    b. Assuming the girls run at the same rate as before, how far behind the starting line should Yolanda be in order for the two to finish in a tie?
    $11\frac{1}{9}$ yd, or 11 yd 4 in.

In copymaster and workbook formats

RETEACHING

Reteaching 6-2 Unit Rates and Proportional Reasoning

A **rate** is a ratio that compares two quantities measured in different units.

The cost for 10 copies is $1.50.

The rate is $1.50/10 copies ($1.50 per 10 copies).

A **unit rate** is the rate for one unit of a given quantity. You can compare using unit rates.

To find the unit rate for 10 copies:

$$\$1.50/10 \text{ copies} = \frac{\$1.50}{10} = \frac{\$1.50 \div 10}{10 \div 10} = \frac{\$.15}{1}$$

The unit rate is $.15 per copy. This is also the *unit price*.

COPY CENTER Color Copies	
1 copy	$0.25
10 copies	$1.50
25 copies	$2.50
50 copies	$4.50
100 copies	$6.00

For the better buy, compare unit rates.

The unit price for 10 copies is $.15/copy.

The unit price for 1 copy is $.25/copy.

Since $.15 < $.25, the 10-copy price is the better buy.

Use the Copy Center chart. Find the unit rate.

1. 25 copies
   $\frac{\$2.50}{25} = \frac{\$2.50 \div \boxed{25}}{25 \div \boxed{25}} =$ $.10/copy
2. 100 copies
   $\frac{\$6.00}{100} = \frac{\$6.00 \div \boxed{100}}{100 \div \boxed{100}} =$ $.06/copy
3. 50 copies
   $\frac{\$4.50}{50} = \frac{\$4.50 \div \boxed{50}}{50 \div \boxed{50}} =$ $.09/copy

Write the unit rate for each situation.

4. drive 1,800 mi in 30 h 60 mi/h
5. 390 mi on 15 gal of gasoline 26 mi/gal
6. jog 4,000 m in 12 min $333\frac{1}{3}$ m/min
7. $25.50 for 17 tickets $1.50/ticket
8. 456 mi on 12 gal of gasoline 38 mi/gal
9. 54 c of flour for 12 cakes 4.5 c/cake

Find each unit price. Then determine the better buy.

10. juice: 18 oz for $1.26
    8 oz for $.70
    $.07/oz; $.0875/oz; 18 oz
11. cloth: 2 yd for $3.15
    6 yd for $7.78
    $1.58/yd; $1.30/yd; 6 yd
12. socks: 2 pairs for $3.50
    6 pairs for $9.00
    $1.75/pair; $1.50/pair; 6 pairs
13. pecans: 1 lb for $4.80
    2 oz for $1.00
    $.30/oz; $.50/oz; 1 lb

Reteaching

ENRICHMENT

Minds on Math Transparency

6-2

How can you use one 2 and one 6 to make 64?

$2^6 = 64$

See *Solution Key* for worked-out answers.

WRAP UP

IDENTIFYING THE BIG IDEA Have students define *rate*, *unit rate*, and *unit price*. Ask them to explain what these terms have in common with ratios.

JOURNAL Remind students that they need to convert 40 min to h. Have students draw an analog clock and shade the area for 40 min. Then they can easily convert to a fraction.

LESSON QUIZ

1. Anthony took 1 wk 2 da to drive 1,413 mi. What was his rate of travel in miles per day? **157 mi/da**
2. A 20-lb bag of dog food costs $21.50. A 30-lb bag of dog food costs $32.90. Which bag is the better buy? **20-lb bag**

24. A school has 35 teachers and 945 students. What is the student-to-teacher ratio? Write your answer as a unit rate.
    27 students/teacher
25. *Sports* Use the table below.

Running Records

Distance	Time	Record Holder
200 m	19.32 s	Michael Johnson, USA
400 m	43.29 s	Butch Reynolds, USA
800 m	1 min 41.24 s	Wilson Kipketer, Kenya

Source: *ESPN*

a. 10.35 m/s, 9.24 m/s, 7.90 m/s

a. Find the average speed for each record holder. Round to the nearest hundredth of a meter per second.
b. *Reasoning* Is it fair to compare the speeds? Explain.
   Answers may vary. Sample: No; different races require different strategies.

26. *Consumer Issues* One brand of cereal costs $1.79 for a 7.2-oz box. A larger box that weighs 1 lb 4.25 oz costs $3.69. Which size is the better buy? Why? **The larger box; its unit price is $.18, while the smaller box has a unit price of $.25.**
27. a. *Consumer Issues* The 64-oz bottle of Stain-Free detergent is on sale this week for $4.99. The 36-oz bottle is not on sale. It costs $3.29. Which is the better buy?
    b. The 12-oz bottle of Stain-Free detergent costs $.75 every day. Of the three bottles, which is the best buy? **12-oz bottle**
    27a. 64-oz bottle

> **JOURNAL**
> Suppose a plane travels 1,824 mi in 4 h 40 min. Explain how to find its speed in miles per minute. Then explain how to find its speed in miles per hour.

28. *Data Collection* Have a member of your family count the number of times you blink in 3 min.
    a. What is your blinking rate in blinks per minute?
    b. About how many times will you blink in an hour?
    a–b. Check students' work.

Mixed Review

Round to the nearest hundredth. *(Lesson 2-1)*

29. 4.883 **4.88**
30. 6.1252 **6.13**
31. 21.457 **21.46**
32. 124.309 **124.31**
33. 1.0008 **1.00**
34. 7.90345 **7.90**

Draw a model for each fraction or mixed number. *(Lesson 4-1)* **35–40. See margin p. 239.**

35. $\frac{7}{8}$
36. $\frac{3}{5}$
37. $1\frac{1}{4}$
38. $1\frac{2}{3}$
39. $3\frac{1}{2}$
40. $2\frac{3}{8}$

41. *Choose a Strategy* A class of 23 students includes 11 students who are in the Computer Club and 14 who are in the Math Club. Five students belong to both clubs. How many students are not members of either club? **3 students**

Extra Practice, Lesson 6-2, page 519

6-3 Teaching Notes

1 Focus

CONNECTING TO PRIOR KNOWLEDGE
Have students write variable equations in which the variable is multiplied on the board. **Answers may vary. Sample: $3x = 12$** Ask:

- *What must every equation have?* **an equal sign**
- *How do you undo the multiplication?* **You divide each side of the equation by the number that is multiplied in the equation.**

2 Teach

THINK AND DISCUSS

AEP Proportion is *proporción* in Spanish. Have students define and/or draw a picture for the words *cross* and *product.*

VISUAL LEARNING Question 2 Using the numerators from each pair as widths and the denominators as lengths, have students draw rectangles on graph paper. The ratios are proportional if the rectangles are similar.

ASSESSMENT Group students in pairs. Have each student write two equal ratios and then use them to write a proportion. Next, students erase one of the numbers in their proportion and replace it with a variable. Have partners exchange proportions and solve.

ALGEBRA Connection

6-3 Proportions

What You'll Learn

1. To use cross products
2. To use proportions to solve problems

...And Why

You can use proportions to calculate the amount of time a trip takes.

Here's How

Look for questions that
- build understanding
- ✓ check understanding

THINK AND DISCUSS

1 Using Cross Products

A **proportion** is an equation stating that two ratios are equal. The equation $\frac{6}{8} = \frac{9}{12}$ is a proportion. **$\frac{3}{4} = \frac{3}{4}$; they are equal**

1. a. *Number Sense* Write both sides of the proportion $\frac{6}{8} = \frac{9}{12}$ as fractions in simplest form. What do you notice?
   b. Find the product of 6 and 12; of 8 and 9. What do you notice? **72, 72; they are equal**

In the proportion $\frac{6}{8} = \frac{9}{12}$, the products 6×12 and 8×9 are called **cross products.** The cross products of a proportion are always equal. You can use cross products to find if two ratios form a proportion.

$$\frac{6}{8} = \frac{9}{12}$$

■ **EXAMPLE 1**

Which pairs of ratios could form a proportion?

a. $\frac{5}{9}, \frac{30}{54}$ b. $\frac{7}{8}, \frac{55}{65}$

a.		b.
$\frac{5}{9} \stackrel{?}{=} \frac{30}{54}$	← Write a proportion. →	$\frac{7}{8} \stackrel{?}{=} \frac{55}{65}$
$5 \cdot 54 \stackrel{?}{=} 9 \cdot 30$	← Write cross products. →	$7 \cdot 65 \stackrel{?}{=} 8 \cdot 55$
$270 = 270$	← Multiply. →	$455 \neq 440$
Yes, $\frac{5}{9}$ and $\frac{30}{54}$ form a proportion.		No, $\frac{7}{8}$ and $\frac{55}{65}$ do not form a proportion.

2. ✓ *Try It Out* Which pairs of ratios could form a proportion?
   a. $\frac{3}{8}, \frac{6}{16}$ **yes** b. $\frac{6}{9}, \frac{4}{6}$ **yes** c. $\frac{4}{8}, \frac{5}{9}$ **no** d. $\frac{6}{10}, \frac{9}{15}$ **yes**

Now you may assign Exercises 1–9.

2 Solving Proportions

You can use cross products to solve a proportion that contains a variable.

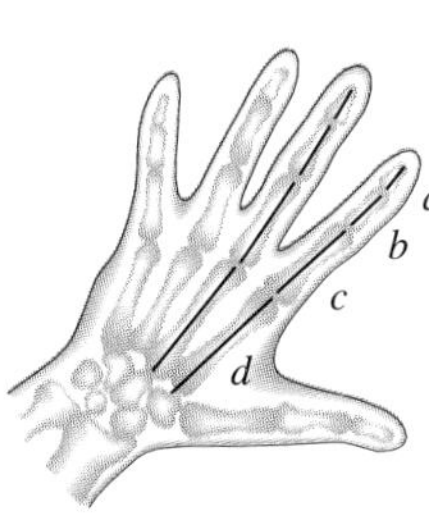

WHAT? The bones in your fingers are examples of a very special ratio called the golden ratio. For the bones, the following proportion is true:

$\frac{a}{b} = \frac{b}{c}$ and $\frac{b}{c} = \frac{c}{d}$

Source: *Fascinating Fibonaccis*

Lesson Planning Options

Prerequisite Skills
- multiplying decimals (2-5)
- solving equations by dividing (3-7)

Vocabulary/Symbols
proportion, cross products

Materials/Manipulatives
- calculator

Resources

Student Edition

Skills Handbook, p. 530
Extra Practice, p. 519
Glossary/Study Guide

Teaching Resources

Chapter Support File, Ch. 6
- Lesson Planner 6-3
- Practice 6-3, Reteaching 6-3
- Alternative Activity 6-3
- Answer Masters 6-3

Glossary, Spanish Resources

Transparencies
15, Minds on Math 6-3

Warm Up

Write three fractions equivalent to $\frac{4}{12}$. **Answers may vary. Sample: $\frac{1}{3}, \frac{2}{6}, \frac{8}{24}$**

ADDITIONAL EXAMPLES

FOR EXAMPLE 1

Which pairs of ratios could form a proportion?

a. $\frac{6}{7}, \frac{42}{56}$ **no**

b. $\frac{6}{10}, \frac{15}{25}$ **yes**

FOR EXAMPLE 2

Solve $\frac{6}{8} = \frac{9}{a}$. **$a = 12$**

FOR EXAMPLE 3

About how many hours would it take the Concorde to fly 2,130 mi? **about 2.2 h**

Example 2 Remind students that $15n$ means $15 \cdot n$.

Example 3 Have students estimate first. $4 \times 6{,}000 \div 4{,}000 = 6$

3 Practice/Assess

EXERCISES *On Your Own*

ALTERNATIVE METHOD Exercises 1–6 Some students may prefer to reduce the two fractions to see if they are equivalent. Others may prefer to change both fractions to decimals. Point out that both methods are acceptable. However, cross products are necessary for Exercises 10–24.

Technology Options

Prentice Hall Technology

Software for Learners

- Math Blaster® Mystery*
- Interactive Student Tutorial, Chapter 6*

Teaching Resource Software

- Computer Item Generator 6-3
- Resource Pro™ Chapter 6*

Internet • For related mathematics activities, visit the Prentice Hall site at www.phschool.com/math

**Available on CD-ROM only*

Assignment Options for Exercises On Your Own

To provide flexible scheduling, this lesson can be split into parts.

1 **Core** 1–8
Extension 9

2 **Core** 10–25, 28, 29
Extension 26, 27

Use Mixed Review to maintain skills.

EXAMPLE 2

Solve $\frac{n}{9} = \frac{10}{15}$.

$$\frac{n}{9} = \frac{10}{15}$$

$$15n = 9 \cdot 10 \quad \text{← Write the cross products.}$$

$$15n = 90 \quad \text{← Multiply.}$$

$$\frac{15n}{15} = \frac{90}{15} \quad \text{← Divide each side by 15.}$$

$$n = 6$$

3. ✔ *Try It Out* Use cross products to solve each proportion.

a. $\frac{3}{4} = \frac{t}{8}$ **6** **b.** $\frac{x}{2} = \frac{12}{5}$ **$\frac{24}{5} = 4.8$** **c.** $\frac{2}{c} = \frac{13}{39}$ **6** **d.** $\frac{1.2}{1.7} = \frac{3.6}{m}$ **5.1**

You can use proportions and cross products to solve problems.

The Concorde stretches about 10 in. as it travels at about twice the speed of sound, its top speed.

Sources: Air France and *3-2-1 Contact*

EXAMPLE 3 *Real-World Problem Solving*

Aviation The Concorde flies the 3,630 mi from New York to Paris in about 3.75 h. About how many hours would it take the Concorde to fly 5,687 mi from Paris to Rio de Janeiro?

Let n represent the number of hours it takes to fly from Paris to Rio de Janeiro.

$$\frac{\text{mi}}{\text{h}} \rightarrow \frac{3{,}630}{3.75} = \frac{5{,}687}{n} \leftarrow \frac{\text{mi}}{\text{h}} \quad \text{← Write the cross products.}$$

$$3{,}630n = 3.75 \cdot 5{,}687$$

$$\frac{3{,}630n}{3{,}630} = \frac{3.75 \cdot 5{,}687}{3{,}630} \quad \text{← Divide each side by 3,630.}$$

3.75 [×] 5687 [÷] 3630 [=] 5.875 ← Use a calculator.

$$n \approx 5.9$$

The Concorde would take about 5.9 h to fly from Paris to Rio de Janeiro.

4. ✔ *Try It Out* You burn about 200 calories by walking for 60 min. About how many do you burn if you walk for 15 min? **about 50 calories**

Now you may assign Exercises 10–29.

EXERCISES *On Your Own*

Which pairs of ratios could form a proportion?

1. $\frac{45}{9}, \frac{10}{2}$ **yes** 2. $\frac{6}{8}, \frac{4}{3}$ **no** 3. $\frac{40}{12}, \frac{95}{4}$ **no** 4. $\frac{8}{18}, \frac{20}{45}$ **yes** 5. $\frac{21}{24}, \frac{56}{64}$ **yes** 6. $\frac{16}{9}, \frac{48}{27}$ **yes**

EXTENSION and CONNECTION TO GEOMETRY Exercises 7 and 8 Have students find the area of each triangle. Then write the ratio of the base to the area. Ask: *Is the ratio of the base to the area the same in each pair of figures?* no

ERROR ALERT! Exercises 10–24 Students may carelessly multiply the wrong terms when trying to find the cross product.
Remediation: Have students draw an oval around each pair of numbers they are to multiply. Make sure the ovals cross. After they have multiplied, have students highlight the number next to the variable. This will help them remember which number to divide by.

WRITING Exercise 25b Encourage students to write the units beside each number in the given proportion: $\frac{2 \text{ meters}}{3 \text{ minutes}} = \frac{n \text{ minutes}}{240 \text{ meters}}$. This will help them notice that the units do not line up correctly.

CONNECTION TO HISTORY Exercise 27 Have students find the ratio of votes that the winner received to votes the opponent received in another Presidential election.

OPEN-ENDED Exercise 29 Challenge students to set up each of the three proportions differently. Then have them color corresponding units with the same color.

Geometry Show that the ratio base b to height h is the same in each pair of figures.

7. $\frac{27}{18} = \frac{9}{6}$

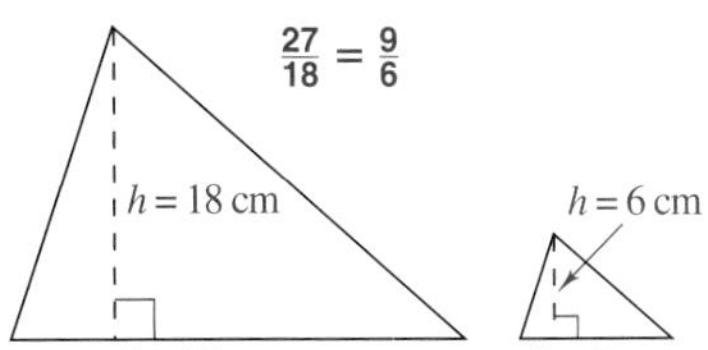

8.

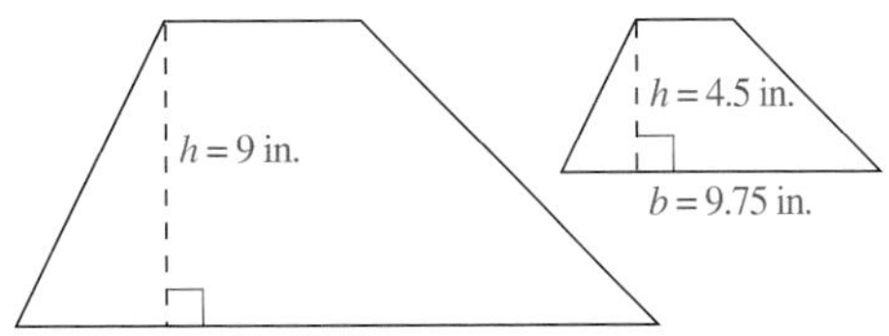

$\frac{19.5}{9} = \frac{9.75}{4.5}$

9. *Number Sense* Do the ratios $\frac{a}{b}$ and $\frac{a+b}{b}$ form a proportion? Substitute several values for a and b to support your answer.
No; check students' work.

Choose Use a calculator, paper and pencil, or mental math. Solve each proportion.

10. $\frac{6}{9} = \frac{a}{12}$ 8
11. $\frac{20}{n} = \frac{4}{5}$ 25
12. $\frac{3}{x} = \frac{19}{38}$ 6
13. $\frac{0.5}{7} = \frac{t}{42}$ 3
14. $\frac{p}{12} = \frac{7.5}{8}$ 11.25
15. $\frac{2}{45} = \frac{s}{30}$ $1.\overline{3}$
16. $\frac{56}{35} = \frac{8}{k}$ 5
17. $\frac{y}{18} = \frac{14}{9}$ 28
18. $\frac{0.5}{z} = \frac{2.5}{6}$ 1.2
19. $\frac{3}{1.2} = \frac{b}{6}$ 15
20. $\frac{24}{17} = \frac{108}{m}$ 76.5
21. $\frac{6}{25} = \frac{n}{80}$ 19.2
22. $\frac{7}{9} = \frac{g}{22.5}$ 17.5
23. $\frac{k}{49.5} = \frac{11}{18}$ 30.25
24. $\frac{6}{13} = \frac{7.8}{t}$ 16.9

25. *Entertainment* A video cassette recorder uses 2 m of tape in 3 min when set on extended play.
   a. The tape is about 240 m long. How many hours can you record using extended play? 6 h
   b. *Writing* To solve part (a), one student wrote the proportion $\frac{2}{3} = \frac{n}{240}$. Explain why this proportion is incorrect, and help the student write a correct proportion. Answers may vary. Sample: If the left side of a proportion compares meters to minutes, the right side should also, as in $\frac{2}{3} = \frac{240}{m}$.

26. *Travel* A Boeing 747 airplane takes about $4\frac{3}{4}$ h to fly 2,475 mi from New York City to Los Angeles. About how many hours will it take the Boeing 747 to fly 5,470 mi from Los Angeles to Tokyo? Round to the nearest tenth. 10.5 h

27. *History* Franklin D. Roosevelt won his first election for President in 1932 with about 22,800,000 votes. The ratio of the number of votes he received to the number of votes the other candidates received was 4 : 3. About how many votes did the other candidates receive?
about 17,100,000 votes

CHECKPOINT 1

Checkpoint 1 *Lessons 6-1 through 6-3*

Write two ratios equal to the given ratio. Answers will vary. Samples:

1. 4 : 60 1:15, 2:30
2. $\frac{4}{6}$ $\frac{2}{3}$, $\frac{12}{18}$
3. 3 to 15 1 to 5, 6 to 30
4. **Circle A, B, C, or D.** Which car gets the greatest mileage per gallon of fuel?
   (A.) 230 mi/6 gal B. 190 mi/6.5 gal C. 235 mi/7 gal D. 270 mi/8.5 gal

Solve each proportion.

5. $\frac{6}{9} = \frac{x}{108}$ 72
6. $\frac{x}{5} = \frac{81}{45}$ 9
7. $\frac{15}{24} = \frac{5}{x}$ 8
8. A jet airplane takes 45 min to fly 495 mi from Dallas to Kansas City. Suppose another jet travels at the same rate from New York to Los Angeles, a distance of 2,786 mi. How long will the flight take? Round to the nearest minute. 253 min

PRACTICE

Practice 6-3 Proportions

Choose a calculator, paper and pencil, or mental math. Which pairs of ratios form a proportion?

1. $\frac{12}{16}, \frac{30}{40}$ yes
2. $\frac{8}{12}, \frac{15}{21}$ no
3. $\frac{27}{21}, \frac{81}{56}$ no
4. $\frac{45}{24}, \frac{75}{40}$ yes
5. $\frac{5}{9}, \frac{80}{117}$ no
6. $\frac{15}{25}, \frac{75}{125}$ yes

Choose a calculator, paper and pencil, or mental math. Find the value of *n* in each proportion.

7. $\frac{n}{14} = \frac{20}{35}$ 8
8. $\frac{9}{6} = \frac{21}{n}$ 14
9. $\frac{24}{n} = \frac{16}{10}$ 15
10. $\frac{3}{4} = \frac{n}{10}$ 7.5
11. $\frac{n}{4} = \frac{17}{3}$ $22\frac{2}{3}$
12. $\frac{25}{n} = \frac{9}{8}$ $22\frac{2}{9}$

Choose A, B, or C.

13. A contractor estimates it will cost $2,400 to build a deck to a customer's specifications. Which proportion would help you find how much it would cost to build five similar decks? C

 A. $\frac{1}{5} = \frac{n}{\$2{,}400}$ B. $\frac{1}{\$2{,}400} = \frac{n}{5}$ C. $\frac{1}{\$2{,}400} = \frac{5}{n}$

14. A recipe requires 3 c of flour to make 27 dinner rolls. Which of the proportions would help you find the flour needed to make 9 rolls? C

 A. $\frac{3}{9} = \frac{n}{27}$ B. $\frac{3}{27} = \frac{9}{n}$ C. $\frac{27}{3} = \frac{9}{n}$

Choose a calculator, paper and pencil, or mental math.

15. Mandy runs 4 km in 18 min. She plans to run in a 15 km race. How long will it take her to complete the race?
 67.5 min
16. Ken's new car can go 26 mi/gal of gas. The car's gasoline tank holds 14 gal. How far will he be able to go on a full tank?
 364 mi
17. Eleanor can complete two skirts in 15 days. How long will it take her to complete eight skirts?
 60 d
18. Three eggs are required to make two dozen muffins. How many eggs are needed to make 12 dozen muffins?
 18 eggs

Practice

In copymaster and workbook formats

RETEACHING

Reteaching 6-3 Proportions

A **proportion** is an equation stating that two ratios are equal. $\frac{100}{2} = \frac{200}{4}$

In a proportion, the **cross products** are equal. $\frac{100}{2} = \frac{200}{4}$

$100 \cdot 4 = 200 \cdot 2$

$400 = 400$

Solve. $\frac{5}{15} = \frac{n}{3}$

① Write the cross products. $5 \cdot 3 = 15 \cdot n$

② Simplify. $15 = 15n$

③ Solve the equation. $n = 1$

Complete the cross products to determine which pairs of ratios could form a proportion. Then write *yes* or *no*.

1. $\frac{3}{10} \stackrel{?}{=} \frac{6}{20}$
 $3 \cdot 20 =$ 60
 $10 \cdot 6 =$ 60
 yes
2. $\frac{12}{24} \stackrel{?}{=} \frac{2}{4}$
 $12 \cdot 4 =$ 48
 $24 \cdot \boxed{2} =$ 48
 yes
3. $\frac{8}{5} \stackrel{?}{=} \frac{16}{8}$
 $8 \cdot \boxed{8} =$ 64
 $5 \cdot \boxed{16} =$ 80
 no

Can the pair of ratios form a proportion? Write *yes* or *no*.

4. $\frac{7}{5}, \frac{21}{15}$ yes
5. $\frac{16}{3}, \frac{5}{1}$ no
6. $\frac{12}{9}, \frac{4}{3}$ yes

Complete to solve each proportion.

7. $\frac{4}{24} = \frac{n}{6}$
 $4 \cdot$ 6 $= 24 \cdot$ n
 $n =$ 1
8. $\frac{15}{5} = \frac{6}{n}$
 $15n$ = $5 \cdot 6$
 $n =$ 2
9. $\frac{n}{3} = \frac{27}{9}$
 $n \cdot 9$ = $3 \cdot 27$
 $n =$ 9

Solve each proportion.

10. $\frac{25}{35} = \frac{n}{7}$ 5
11. $\frac{4.2}{7} = \frac{6}{n}$ 10
12. $\frac{n}{15} = \frac{20}{50}$ 6
13. $\frac{2}{5} = \frac{n}{15}$ 6
14. $\frac{3.6}{200} = \frac{n}{100}$ 1.8
15. $\frac{6}{n} = \frac{4}{8}$ 12
16. $\frac{16}{11} = \frac{96}{n}$ 66
17. $\frac{3}{7} = \frac{n}{5}$ $2\frac{1}{7}$
18. $\frac{2}{n} = \frac{1}{11}$ 22

ENRICHMENT

Minds on Math Transparency

6-3

If it takes Evelyn one minute to cut one board, how long will it take her to cut a 10-ft long board into 10 equal pieces?

9 min

See *Solution Key* for worked-out answers.

WRAP UP

IDENTIFYING THE BIG IDEA Have students define *proportion* and explain how to tell if two ratios are in proportion. Then have them give examples of situations they can solve using proportions.

LESSON QUIZ

Which pairs of ratios could form a proportion?

1. $\frac{9}{13}, \frac{18}{26}$ yes
2. $\frac{30}{16}, \frac{45}{12}$ no

Solve each proportion.

3. $\frac{48}{42} = \frac{8}{n}$ $n = 7$
4. $\frac{y}{12.5} = \frac{7.2}{9}$ $y = 10$

Physical Science **Use the data at the right. Round your answers to the nearest pound.**

Weight Comparison Chart	
Planet	Weight (lb)
Earth	100
Mercury	37
Venus	88
Mars	38
Jupiter	264
Saturn	115
Uranus	117
Neptune	118
Pluto	5

28. NASA designed two *Viking* spacecraft to travel to Mars and send information about the planet back to Earth. *Viking 1* weighed 275 lb and *Viking 2* weighed 272 lb on Earth. Use proportions to find how much they weighed on Mars.
 Viking 1: 105 lb; Viking 2: 103 lb
29. *Open-ended* Choose three other planets. Find how much each *Viking* spacecraft would have weighed on each planet.
 Check students' work.

Mixed Review

Find the mean and median of each set of data. *(Lesson 1-4)*

30. 14 20 5 17 15 16 17 18 13 17
 15.2; 16.5
31. 2.7 3.5 7.8 9 2.1 3.2 5.7 5 6.9
 5.1; 5

Compare. Use >, <, or =. *(Lesson 4-3)*

32. $\frac{3}{4}$ ■ $\frac{5}{16}$ >
33. $\frac{3}{5}$ ■ $\frac{2}{3}$ <
34. $\frac{1}{2}$ ■ $\frac{7}{14}$ =
35. $\frac{8}{12}$ ■ $\frac{4}{6}$ =
36. $\frac{1}{5}$ ■ $\frac{2}{12}$ >
37. $\frac{6}{8}$ ■ $\frac{5}{9}$ >

38. *Choose a Strategy* Jenny, Bruce, and Mia ate salad, chicken, or tofu for lunch. Mia didn't eat chicken or tofu. Bruce didn't eat chicken. What did each person eat?
 Jenny ate chicken, Bruce ate tofu, and Mia ate salad.

CHECKPOINT 1

Lessons 6-1 through 6-3

Write two ratios equal to each ratio. 1–6. Answers may vary. Samples are given.

1. 2 : 50
 1 : 25, 4 : 100
2. $\frac{3}{5}$ $\frac{6}{10}, \frac{12}{20}$
3. 4 to 12
 2 to 6, 1 to 3
4. $\frac{6}{9}$ $\frac{2}{3}, \frac{12}{18}$
5. $\frac{20}{3}$ $\frac{40}{6}, \frac{60}{9}$
6. 100 : 25
 4 : 1, 200 : 50

Solve each proportion.

7. $\frac{3}{8} = \frac{57}{d}$ 152
8. $\frac{4}{3} = \frac{m}{21}$ 28
9. $\frac{x}{15} = \frac{5}{6}$ 12.5
10. $\frac{30}{c} = \frac{5}{4}$ 24
11. $\frac{15}{20} = \frac{4}{t}$ 5.3
12. $\frac{21}{7} = \frac{g}{20}$ 60

13. **Choose A, B, C, or D.** Which has the most calories per ounce? C

 A. beef: 185 calories in 3 ounces
 B chicken: 240 calories in 6.2 ounces
 C. cheese: 230 calories in 2 ounces
 D. yogurt: 230 calories in 8 ounces

14. *Travel* A train in Japan takes 50 min to travel 106.3 mi from Morica to Sendi. Suppose a train travels 416 mi from Washington, D.C., to Boston, MA, at the same rate. How long would the trip take? Round to the nearest minute. 196 min

Extra Practice, Lesson 6-3, page 519

6-4 Teaching Notes

1 Focus

CONNECTING TO PRIOR KNOWLEDGE
Show a variety of coins. Ask:

- *What is similar about a nickel, a dime, and a quarter?* **Answers may vary. Sample: They are made of metal, have shape of circle, face is on one side.**
- *How are these coins similar to a plate?* **Answers may vary. Sample: shape of circle**

2 Teach

THINK AND DISCUSS

TACTILE LEARNING Have students trace, label, and cut out the figures. Encourage students to flip, turn, and slide the figures in order to explore the meaning of *similar.*

VISUAL LEARNING Bring to class enlarged and reduced photocopies of different geometric figures. Let students place one copy over another of different size and hold the two copies up to the light. Then align angles to see that they are congruent.

AEP Students may confuse the term *congruent* with *corresponding* when referring to sides of similar figures. Show students a picture of nonsimilar figures that contain a congruent side. Then show a picture of two similar figures. Point out that even though the

GEOMETRY Connection

6-4 Using Similar Figures

What You'll Learn

- 1 To discover the properties of similar figures
- 2 To use proportions to find missing lengths in similar figures

...And Why

Proportions and similar triangles can help you find lengths that you cannot measure directly.

Here's How

Look for questions that
- build understanding
- ✔ check understanding

THINK AND DISCUSS

1 *Discovering Properties of Similar Figures*

The word **similar** is often used in everyday language to compare things. Explore the figures below to discover the mathematical definition of similar.

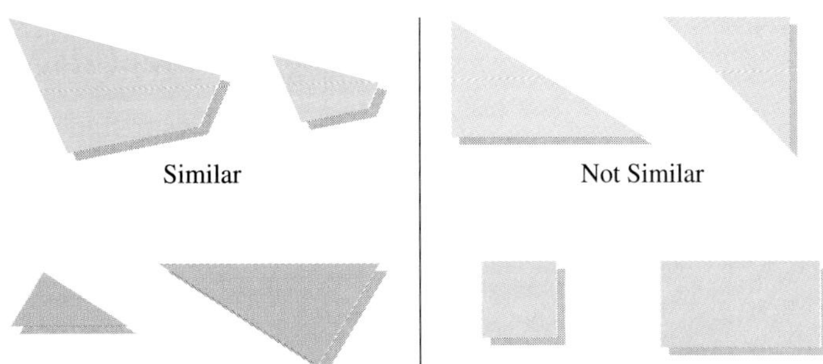
Similar — Not Similar — Similar — Not Similar

1. a. *Visual Thinking* Are similar figures the same shape? **yes**
   b. Do similar figures have to be the same size? **no**

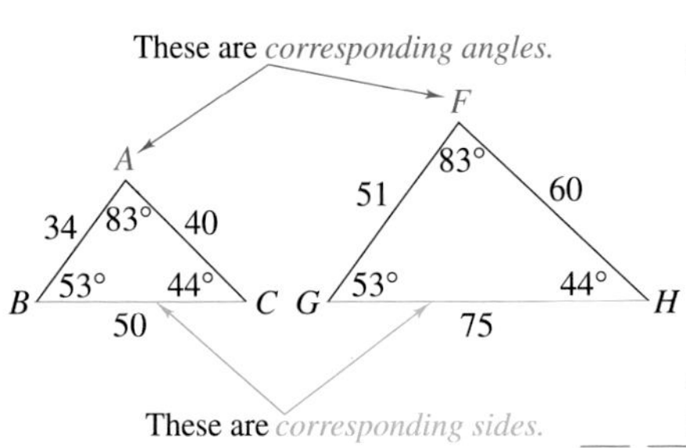

2. a. Look at the similar triangles at the left. What appears to be true of corresponding angles? **2a. They are equal.**
   b. List the pairs of corresponding angles. **b. $\angle A$, $\angle F$; $\angle B$, $\angle G$; $\angle C$, $\angle H$**
   c. *Draw a Conclusion* Complete the sentence: The measures of the corresponding angles of similar figures are __?__. **equal**

$\triangle ABC$ refers to triangle ABC. You write the segment from B to C as $\overline{BC}$.

3. a. List all the pairs of corresponding sides of the triangles. **$\overline{AC}$, $\overline{FH}$; $\overline{AB}$, $\overline{FG}$; $\overline{BC}$, $\overline{GH}$**
   b. Write the ratios of the length of each side of $\triangle ABC$ to the length of the corresponding side of $\triangle FGH$. What is true of these ratios? **40 : 60; 34 : 51; 50 : 75**
   c. *Draw a Conclusion* Complete the sentence: The ratios of the lengths of corresponding sides of similar figures are __?__. **equal**

Lesson Planning Options

Prerequisite Skills
- solving proportions (6-3)

Vocabulary/Symbols
similar, is similar to (~)

Materials/Manipulatives
- scissors
- ruler
- calculator

Resources

Student Edition
Skills Handbook, p. 528
Extra Practice, p. 519
Glossary/Study Guide

Teaching Resources
Chapter Support File, Ch. 6
- Lesson Planner 6-4
- Practice 6-4, Reteaching 6-4
- Answer Masters 6-4

Teaching Aids Masters 1–3, 19
Glossary, Spanish Resources

Transparencies
1, 7, 88, Minds on Math 6-4

Warm Up
Write three proportions that have cross products of 12. **Answers may vary. Sample: $\frac{1}{3} = \frac{4}{12}$**

corresponding sides are in the same position, they are not congruent.

ERROR ALERT and VISUAL LEARNING Some students may incorrectly write proportions using names of the sides of the triangles. **Remediation:** Help students see that the side with endpoints of first two letters in *CAT* correspond to the side with endpoints of first two letters in *DOG*. The sides with the second and third letters of each name as endpoints correspond, as do the sides with the first and last letters as endpoints.

■ ADDITIONAL EXAMPLES

FOR EXAMPLE 1

Suppose *DG* is 40. Find *CT*. **32**

FOR EXAMPLE 2

A 5-ft-tall boy standing near a tree has a shadow 12 ft long. The tree has a shadow 48 ft long. What is the height of the tree? **20 ft**

Example 1 Ask students:

- *Why can't you use the ratio $\frac{CT}{DG}$ to solve for x?* **The measurement of both these sides is unknown.**
- *How do you choose which corresponding sides to use in the proportion?* **You must compare a ratio with two known values to a ratio in which there is one unknown value.**

Technology Options

Prentice Hall Technology

Software for Learners

- Math Blaster® Mystery*
- Interactive Student Tutorial, Chapter 6*

Teaching Resource Software

- Computer Item Generator 6-4
- Resource Pro™ Chapter 6*

Internet • For related mathematics activities, visit the Prentice Hall site at www.phschool.com/math

**Available on CD-ROM only*

Assignment Options for Exercises On Your Own

To provide flexible scheduling, this lesson can be split into parts.

1 Core 1–6
Extension 7

2 Core 9–12
Extension 8, 13

Use Mixed Review to maintain skills.

SIMILAR FIGURES

Similar figures have two important properties.

- The corresponding angles have the same measure.
- The ratios of the lengths of corresponding sides are equal.

The symbol for *is similar to* is ~. For the triangles on page 245 you can write $\triangle ABC \sim \triangle FGH$. The length of $\overline{AB}$, written *AB*, is the distance from *A* to *B*.

Now you may assign Exercises 1–7.

2 *Finding Measures Using Proportions*

You can use proportions to find missing measures in similar figures since the corresponding sides are proportional.

■ EXAMPLE 1

$\triangle CAT \sim \triangle DOG$. Find *CA*.

$\frac{CA}{DO} = \frac{AT}{OG}$ ← Write a proportion.

$\frac{x}{50} = \frac{24}{30}$ ← Substitute.

$30x = 50 \cdot 24$ ← Write the cross products.

$\frac{30x}{30} = \frac{1{,}200}{30}$ ← Divide each side by 30.

$x = 40$ ← Solve for *x*.

CA is 40 cm.

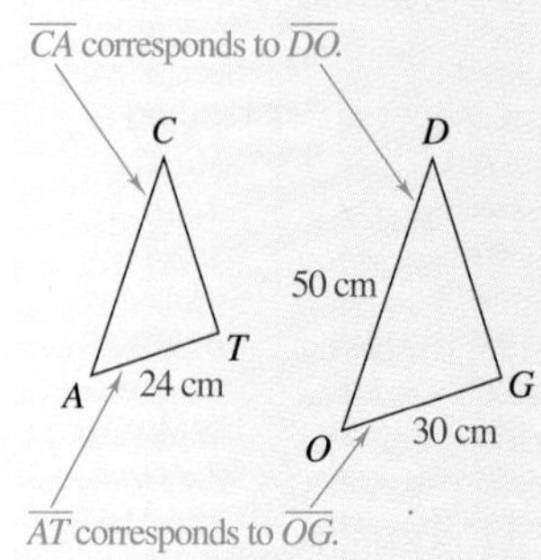

4. ✓ *Try It Out* Use the diagram in Example 1.
   a. *AT* corresponds to ■. ***OG***
   b. $\frac{AT}{OG} = \frac{CT}{■}$ ***DG***
   c. Suppose *CT* is 36 cm. Find the length of its corresponding side. **45 cm**
   d. Is the ratio of the perimeters of $\triangle CAT$ and $\triangle DOG$ equal to the ratio of a pair of corresponding sides? Explain. **Yes; check students' work for reasoning.**

WHO? Gottfried Liebniz (1646–1716) was the first person to use the symbol ~ to mean similarity. He taught himself Latin at age 8 and began studying Greek at age 12.

Source: *The History of Mathematics*

Example 2 Most students find it helpful to label each part of their proportion. They can write $\frac{\text{height of man}}{\text{height of geyser}} = \frac{\text{shadow of man}}{\text{shadow of geyser}}$. Then they can substitute the known measurements in the appropriate places. Using only the labels *height* and *shadow* may cause confusion because there are two heights and two shadows in the problem.

ASSESSMENT Have students work in pairs. Have them draw two figures that appear to be similar and two figures that are not similar. Then have them explain to their partner why the pairs of figures are similar or not similar.

If you have block scheduling or extended class periods, have students cut out figures from magazines or sale ads that appear to be similar. Have them measure the figures. Then they may use proportions to find out whether or not the figures are similar.

Work Together

Have students write the measure of each side inside each rectangle so they can easily recall the numbers to use for their proportions.

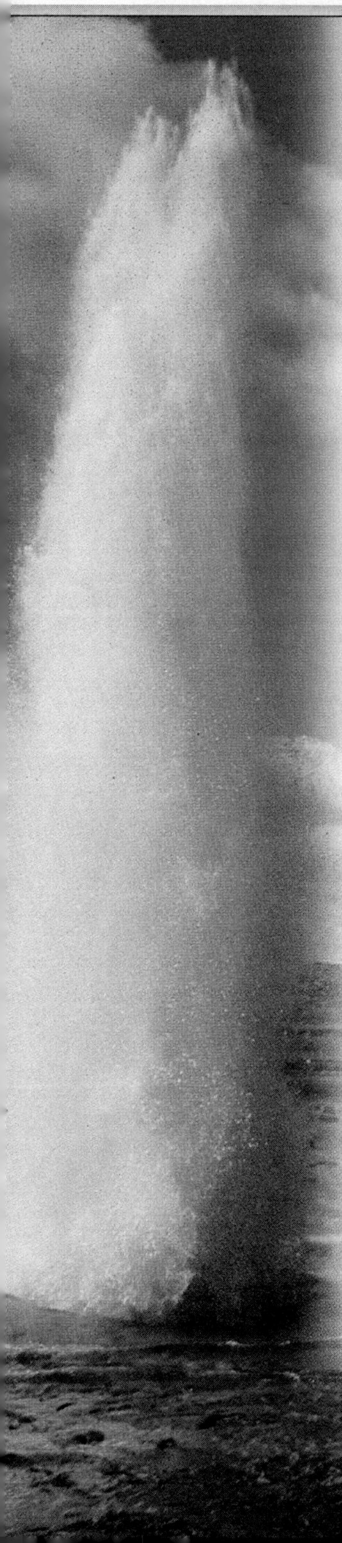

You can use proportions and similar triangles to measure distances that you would be unable to measure directly.

■ EXAMPLE 2 *Real-World Problem Solving*

Measurement A 6-ft-tall man standing near a geyser has a shadow 4.5 ft long. The geyser has a shadow 15 ft long. What is the height of the geyser?

Draw and label a diagram.

x corresponds to 6 ft.

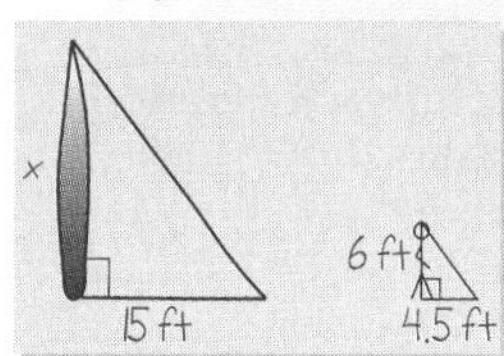

15 ft corresponds to 4.5 ft.

$\frac{x}{6} = \frac{15}{4.5}$ ← Write a proportion.

$4.5x = 6 \cdot 15$ ← Write the cross products.

$\frac{4.5x}{4.5} = \frac{6 \cdot 15}{4.5}$ ← Divide each side by 4.5.

$x = 20$ ← Solve for *x*.

The height of the geyser is 20 ft.

5. ✔ ***Try It Out*** Suppose a 6-ft-tall man has a shadow 5 ft long and a geyser has a shadow 30 ft long. How tall is the geyser? **36 ft**

Work Together *Exploring Similar Rectangles*

Similar figures can nest inside of each other like the rectangles at the right. The diagonals of similar figures will align.

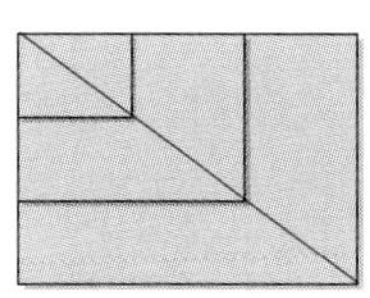

6. a. Draw rectangles with the dimensions 2 in. by 3 in., 4 in. by 5 in., 1 in. by $1\frac{1}{2}$ in., 4 in. by 6 in., and 6 in. by $7\frac{1}{2}$ in. **Check students' work.**
   b. ***Analyze*** Cut out the rectangles and stack them to determine which rectangles are similar. Make a list for each group of similar rectangles. **See below.**
   c. Use proportions to confirm that the rectangles in each of your lists are similar. **Check students' work.**

b. 2×3, $1 \times 1\frac{1}{2}$, and 4×6 are similar; 4×5 and $6 \times 7\frac{1}{2}$ are similar.

Now you may assign Exercises 8–13.

3 Practice/Assess

EXERCISES *On Your Own*

Exercise 1 Point out that many times you cannot judge similarity by appearance. It is important not to assume too much, especially on standardized tests.

CONNECTING TO THE STUDENTS' WORLD Exercises 2–6 Have students think about objects that can shrink or enlarge. For example, a shrunken sweater might be similar to the original sweater. Most copiers can enlarge the print on a piece of paper. The enlarged print is similar to the original print.

WRITING Exercise 7 Have the class brainstorm different real-world examples. The list may include doll houses, floor plans, or models.

EXTENSION Exercise 12 Have students go outside and measure the shadow of a meterstick. Then have them measure the shadow of the school flagpole. They can then use similar triangles to determine the height of the flagpole.

REASONING Exercise 13 Point out that the ratio 4 : 9 can be written as $\frac{4}{9}$. They can use $\frac{4}{9}$ to write proportions with the sides of the small triangle. For example, $\frac{4}{9} = \frac{10}{x}$.

pages 248–249 On Your Own

2. Similar; corresponding angles are equal and the ratios of corresponding sides are equal.
3. Not similar; number of sides are different.
4. Similar; corresponding angles are equal and the ratios of corresponding sides are equal.
5. Not similar; the ratios of corresponding sides are not equal.

EXERCISES *On Your Own*

1. Judging by appearance, is $LMNO \sim PQRS$? Justify your answer. **No; the sides are not proportional.**

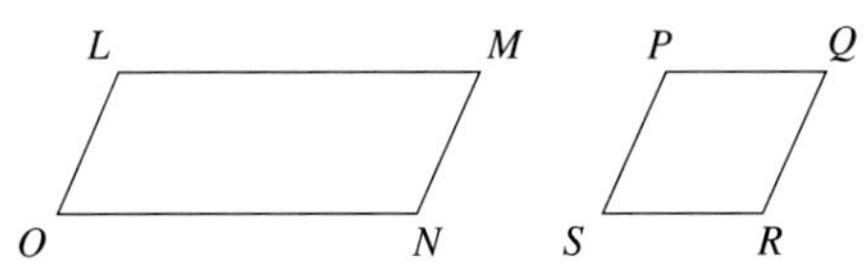

Explain why each pair of figures *are* similar or *are not* similar. **See margin.**

2.

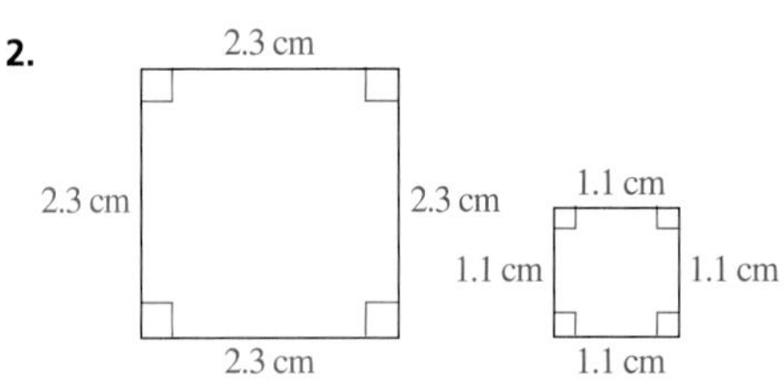

3.

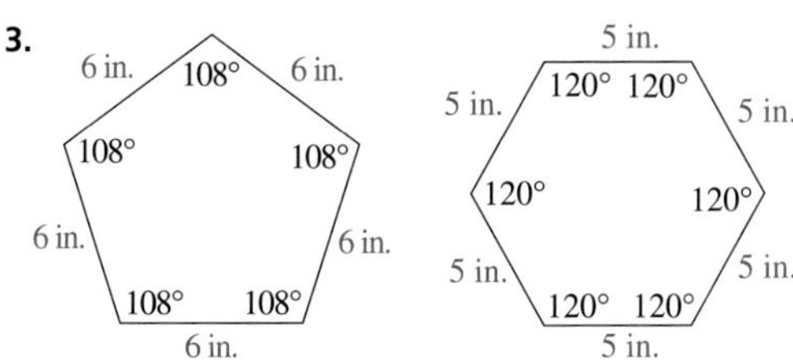

4.

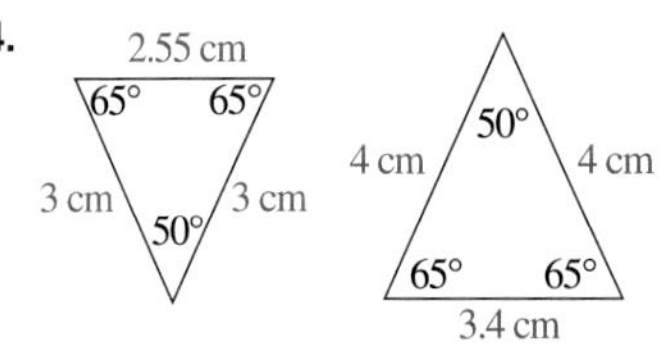

5.

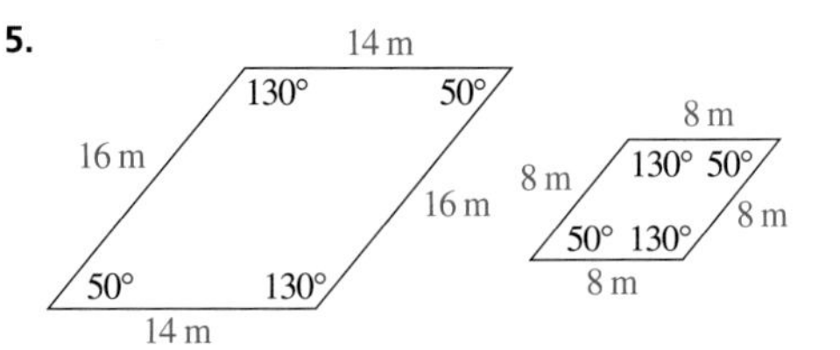

6. $\triangle ABC \sim \triangle PQR$. Complete.
   a. $\angle A$ corresponds to __?__. $\angle P$
   b. $\angle Q$ corresponds to __?__. $\angle B$
   c. $\overline{AC}$ corresponds to __?__. $\overline{PR}$
   d. $\overline{PQ}$ corresponds to __?__. $\overline{AB}$
   e. What is the ratio of the lengths of the corresponding sides? **3 : 2**

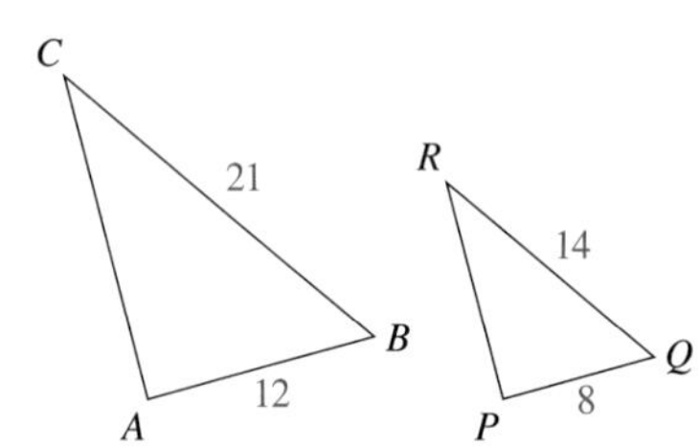

7. *Writing* Give three examples of real-world objects that are similar. **Check students' work.**
8. *Social Studies* Students at the Horace Mann Middle School want to enlarge a copy of the flag of the Philippines. To enlarge the flag so that the longest side measures 6 ft, how wide will the students need to make the flag? **4 ft**

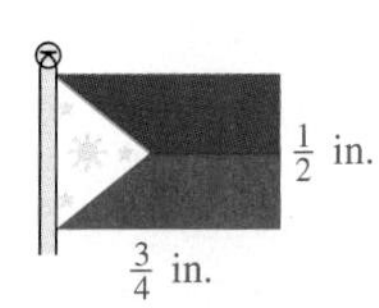

Philippines

Wrap Up

IDENTIFYING THE BIG IDEA Ask students to describe similar figures using some or all of the following terms: *ratio*, *proportion*, *corresponding angles*, *corresponding sides*, *congruent*, and *same shape*.

PROJECT LINK Have students make a chart of each type of graph they have studied so far. Have them include a brief description of each type of graph.

LESSON QUIZ

1. Rectangle $ABCD$ has a length of 10 and a width of 3. Rectangle $LMNO$ has a length of 12 and a width of 3.6. Are the rectangles similar? yes
2. Suppose a 4-ft-tall boy has a shadow 3 ft long and a telephone pole has a shadow 18 ft long. How tall is the telephone pole? 24 ft

Choose **Use a calculator, paper and pencil, or mental math. The pairs of figures below are similar. Find each value of x.**

9. 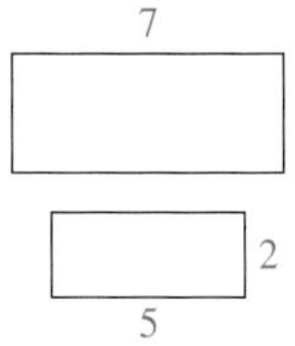

2.8

10. 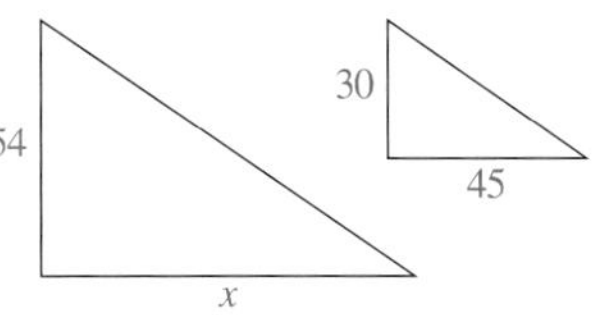

81

11. 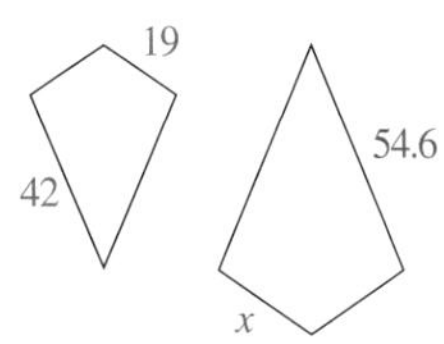

24.7

12. Isabel wants to know the height of a Saguaro cactus. The triangle formed by the cactus and its shadow is similar to the triangle Isabel forms with her shadow. How tall is the cactus? 125 in. or 10 ft 5 in.

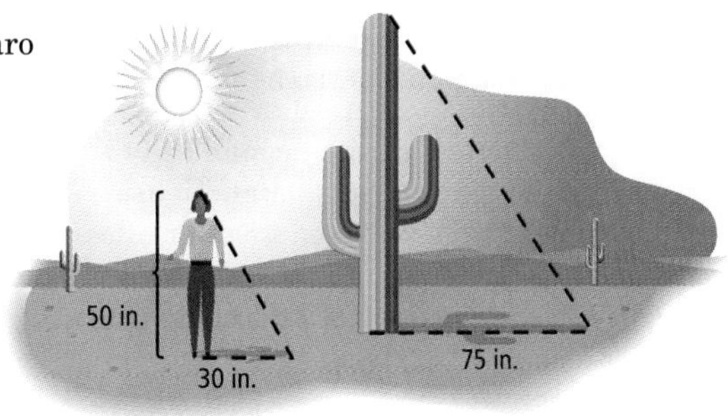

13. *Reasoning* The ratio of the corresponding sides of two similar triangles is 4 : 9. The sides of the smaller triangle are 10 cm, 16 cm, and 18 cm. Find the perimeter of the larger triangle. 99 cm

Mixed Review

Solve each equation. *(Lesson 3-6)*

14. $x - 4 = -12$ −8
15. $-8 = y + 6$ −14
16. $p - (-2) = 5$ 3
17. $11 = 17 + q$ −6

Write each number as an improper fraction. *(Lesson 4-8)*

18. $3\frac{1}{5}$ $\frac{16}{5}$
19. $2\frac{3}{4}$ $\frac{11}{4}$
20. $3\frac{7}{8}$ $\frac{31}{8}$
21. $2\frac{1}{6}$ $\frac{13}{6}$
22. $4\frac{5}{12}$ $\frac{53}{12}$
23. $3\frac{4}{7}$ $\frac{25}{7}$

24. *Estimation* Keisha earns \$4.95 an hour and works 19 hours a week. Estimate her pay for the week. *(Lesson 2-2)* \$100

CHAPTER PROJECT

PROJECT LINK: GRAPHING

Use the survey results from the Project Link on page 236. Decide which type of graph will best display your results. Then graph your data. Add a title and any other necessary information to your graph. Check students' work.

PRACTICE

Practice 6-4 *Using Similar Figures*

$\triangle MNO \sim \triangle JKL$. Find each of the corresponding parts.

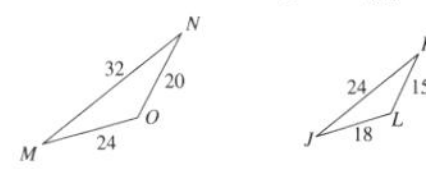

1. $\angle M$ corresponds to $\angle J$.
2. $\angle L$ corresponds to $\angle O$.
3. $\overline{ON}$ corresponds to $\overline{LK}$.
4. $\angle K$ corresponds to $\angle N$.
5. $\overline{JL}$ corresponds to $\overline{MO}$.
6. $\overline{MN}$ corresponds to $\overline{JK}$.
7. What is the ratio of the lengths of the corresponding sides? 4 : 3 or 3 : 4

Choose a calculator, paper and pencil, or mental math. The pairs of figures below are similar. Use proportions to find the values of x and y.

8. 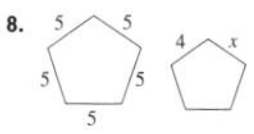

4

9. 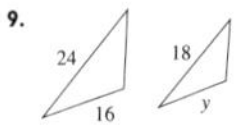

12

10. 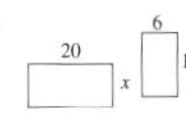

$8\frac{4}{7}$

11. 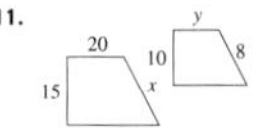

$x = 12$; $y = 13\frac{1}{3}$

12. 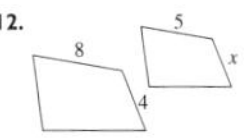

2.5

13. 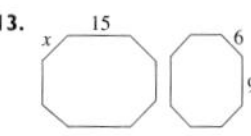

10

Draw lines to show how to divide the figure at the right into 12 pieces as described in Exercises 14 and 15. Each new piece must have the same size and shape as the other new pieces. Sample answers shown.

14. The shapes should be rectangles.

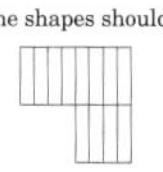

15. The shapes should be triangles.

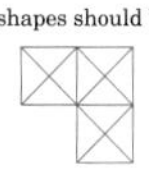

In copymaster and workbook formats

RETEACHING

Reteaching 6-4 *Using Similar Figures*

Similar figures have two important properties:

- The corresponding angles are congruent.
- The ratios of the lengths of corresponding sides are proportional.

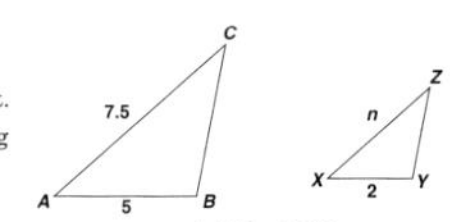

$\triangle ABC \sim \triangle XYZ$

You can use proportions to find missing lengths in similar (~) figures.

① Find the corresponding sides.
$\overline{AB}$ corresponds to $\overline{XY}$.
$\overline{AC}$ corresponds to $\overline{XZ}$.
$\overline{BC}$ corresponds to $\overline{YZ}$.

② Write ratios of their lengths in a proportion.
$\frac{AB}{XY} = \frac{AC}{XZ}$

③ Substitute the information you know.
$\frac{5}{2} = \frac{7.5}{n}$

④ Write cross products. Solve for n.
$5n = 2 \cdot 7.5$
$n = 3$
The length of $\overline{XZ}$ is 3 units.

The figures are similar. Find the corresponding sides. Then complete the proportion and solve for n.

1. $\overline{AB}$ corresponds to $\overline{QR}$.
$\overline{BC}$ corresponds to $\overline{RS}$.
$\overline{CA}$ corresponds to $\overline{SQ}$.

2. $\frac{CA}{SQ} = \frac{BC}{RS}$
$\frac{8}{20} = \frac{12}{n}$
$n =$ 30

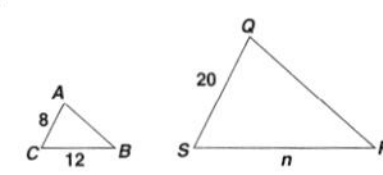

The figures are similar. Find the value of each x.

3. 80

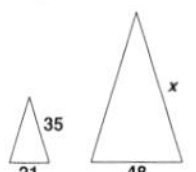

4. 7.5

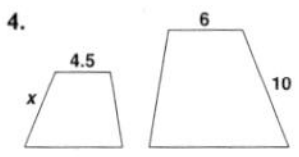

Reteaching

ENRICHMENT

Minds on Math Transparency

6-4

Two bricks have the same weight. One brick is cut into quarters. The whole brick is then placed on one side of a scale. Three-fourths of the other brick is placed on the other side of the scale along with a $\frac{3}{4}$-lb weight to balance the scale. How much do each of the bricks weigh?

3 lb

See *Solution Key* for worked-out answers.

In Lesson 6-4, students learned the properties of similar figures and how to use proportions to find missing lengths in similar figures. This toolbox shows students how to create similar figures using geometry software on a computer.

ERROR ALERT! Some students may have difficulty using the software. **Remediation:** Have students complete Step 1 and Step 2 with a partner. Pair students who are less proficient on the computer with those who are comfortable using the software. Each student should know the procedure after they have worked through the steps together.

ASSESSMENT Exercise 2 Have students in small groups describe their results. If students' results differ, have them follow the steps again and compare their work.

ADDITIONAL PROBLEM

Draw a quadrilateral and label it *DEFG*. Draw a point *H* not on the quadrilateral. Create a quadrilateral *HJKL* similar to quadrilateral *DEFG*. **Check students' work.**

Materials/Manipulatives

- geometry software
- computer

MATH TOOLBOX TECHNOLOGY

Creating Similar Figures

After Lesson 6-4

Using the computer is a great way to explore similar figures. For this activity you need geometry software.

Follow these steps to draw two similar triangles like those at the right.

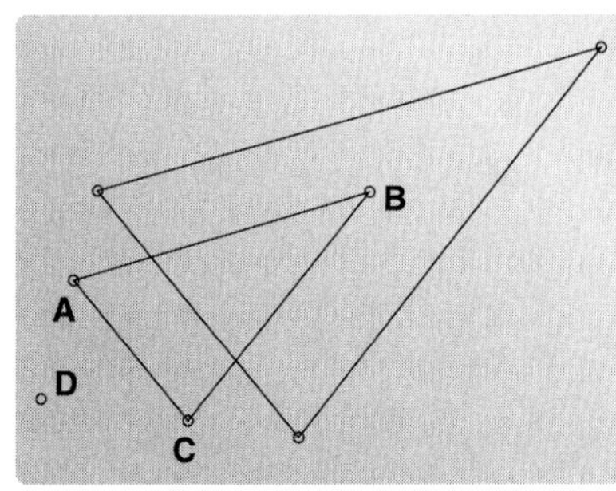

Step 1 Draw a triangle and label it *ABC*. Draw a point *D* not on the triangle.

Step 2 Create a triangle similar to $\triangle ABC$ by using the *dilation* command. To use this command, you will need to enter a *scale factor* and name one point as the *center* of the dilation. Use 2 as a scale factor and name point *D* as the center.

1. Change the shape of $\triangle ABC$ by dragging point *A*, *B*, or *C*. What happens to the larger triangle each time? **The triangle changes its shape and stays similar to $\triangle ABC$.**
2. *Explore* Drag point *D* to different locations. Describe what happens in each case below.
   a. *D* is inside $\triangle ABC$. **$\triangle ABC$ is inside its image.**
   b. *D* is on $\overline{AB}$. **$\overline{AB}$ lies on its image.**
   c. *D* is on top of point *C*. **The image of point *C* is *C*.**
3. Use the software to draw $\overleftrightarrow{AD}$ (line *AD*), $\overleftrightarrow{BD}$, and $\overleftrightarrow{CD}$.
   a. What do you notice about the lines and the larger triangle? **Each line passes through a vertex of $\triangle ABC$ and its image.**
   b. Why do you think that point *D* is called the center of the dilation? **Every line connecting a point and its image passes through *D*.**
4. Create a third triangle similar to $\triangle ABC$. This time use 0.5 as the scale factor. Keep *D* as the center. What do you notice about the new triangle? **The image is smaller than $\triangle ABC$.**
5. a. *Open-ended* Create more triangles similar to $\triangle ABC$ by choosing other scale factors. Again, keep *D* as the center. **Check students' work.**
   b. *Writing* Explain how your choice of scale factor affects the final figure. **The larger the scale factor, the larger the image triangle. If the scale factor is less than 1, the image triangle is smaller than the original.**

6-5 Teaching Notes

1 Focus

CONNECTING TO PRIOR KNOWLEDGE Ask students: *What drawings have you seen that represent something very large in real life?* **Answers may vary. Sample: maps, floor plans** Then have students quickly sketch a rough drawing of the classroom. Ask: *Could an architect use your drawing to build an identical classroom?* **No, the picture is not exactly similar to the room.**

2 Teach

THINK AND DISCUSS

DIVERSITY Many students have lived in more than one place. Have students use an atlas to find the distance from their previous country, state, or city to where they live now.

Ask: *Suppose you want to draw a map to scale to show this distance. What ratio could you use to reduce the actual distance to fit on notebook paper?* **Answers may vary. Sample: $\frac{1 \text{ in.}}{100 \text{ mi}}$**

Question 1 Ask students: *Why is it likely that the distance by road is longer than the distance calculated from the map?* **Answers may vary. Sample: The distance calculated from the map is a straight line. Roads are seldom a straight line.**

GEOMETRY Connection

6-5 Exploring Maps and Scale Drawings

What You'll Learn

- To use proportions to solve problems involving scale

...And Why

You can use proportion and scale changes to make maps or draw architectural plans.

Here's How

Look for questions that
- build understanding
- ✔ check understanding

THINK AND DISCUSS

A **scale drawing** is an enlarged or reduced drawing of an object. Maps and floor plans are smaller than the actual size. A scale drawing of a human cell is larger than the actual size.

You use a map's scale and proportions to find actual distances.

■ **EXAMPLE 1** *Real-World Problem Solving*

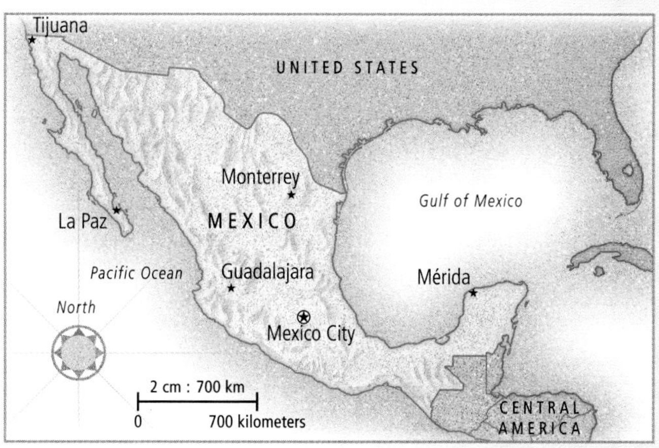

Geography The map distance from Tijuana to Monterrey is 5.1 cm. Use a proportion to find the actual distance.

$$\frac{\text{map (cm)}}{\text{actual (km)}} \rightarrow \frac{2}{700} = \frac{5.1}{n} \leftarrow \frac{\text{map (cm)}}{\text{actual (km)}}$$

$2n = 700(5.1)$ ← Write cross products.

$\frac{2n}{2} = \frac{700(5.1)}{2}$ ← Divide each side by 2.

$n = 1{,}785$ ← Simplify.

The distance from Tijuana to Monterrey is about 1,785 km.

1. ✔ *Try It Out* Find the actual distance between each pair of cities.
   a. Tijuana and Mexico City **2,240 km**
   b. Guadalajara and Merida **1,400 km**

HISTORY The first known map was made in Babylon more than 4,000 years ago. It was scratched into a clay tablet and then baked. The map would fit in the palm of your hand.

Source: *Britannica Junior Encyclopedia*

Lesson Planning Options

Prerequisite Skills

- simplifying fractions (4-6)
- writing and solving proportions (6-3)

Vocabulary/Symbols

scale drawing

Materials/Manipulatives

- ruler
- yardstick or meterstick

Resources

Student Edition

Skills Handbook, p. 530
Extra Practice, p. 519
Glossary/Study Guide

Teaching Resources

Chapter Support File, Ch. 6
- Lesson Planner 6-5
- Practice 6-5, Reteaching 6-5
- Answer Masters 6-5

Teaching Aids Masters 1–3, 19
Glossary, Spanish Resources

Transparencies

1, 7, 15, 89, Minds on Math 6-5

Warm Up

Find three integers whose sum is 12 and whose product is 42. **2, 3, 7**

ADDITIONAL EXAMPLES

FOR EXAMPLE 1

The map distance from Mexico City to Merida is 2.9 cm. Use a proportion to find the actual distance. **about 1,015 km**

FOR EXAMPLE 2

The actual length of the wheel base for a mountain bike is 260 cm. The length of the wheel base in a drawing is 4 cm. Find the scale of the drawing. **1 cm : 65 cm**

ASSESSMENT and CONNECTION TO GEOGRAPHY Display a map of your state and assign students to groups of four. Ask students to find and explain the scale on the map. Then have them use proportions to find the actual distance between two cities. Have students share their findings.

Work Together

KINESTHETIC LEARNING Have students get estimates using their own feet or arms before using metersticks or yardsticks.

3 Practice/Assess

EXERCISES *On Your Own*

ERROR ALERT! Exercises 3 and 5 Students may use the given numbers in their proportions and not convert mm to cm. **Remediation:** Have students write the proportion $\frac{2\text{ cm}}{15\text{ km}} = \frac{\blacksquare\text{ cm}}{\blacksquare\text{ km}}$. Highlight the cm in both ratios. Tell students to carefully fill in the boxes and make sure the units of measure match.

Technology Options

Prentice Hall Technology

Software for Learners
- Hot Page™ 9–5*
- Math Blaster® Mystery*
- Interactive Student Tutorial, Chapter 6*

Teaching Resource Software
- Computer Item Generator 6-5
- Resource Pro™ Chapter 6*

Internet • For related mathematics activities, visit the Prentice Hall site at www.phschool.com/math

**Available on CD-ROM only*

Assignment Options for Exercises On Your Own

Core 1–12, 14–22
Extension 13

Use Mixed Review to maintain skills.

You can use the GCF to find the scale of a drawing.

EXAMPLE 2 *Real-World Problem Solving*

Drafting The actual length of the wheel base for the all-terrain vehicle is 234 cm. Find the scale of the drawing.

$$\frac{\text{scale length}}{\text{actual length}} \rightarrow \frac{3}{234} = \frac{1}{78} \leftarrow$$ Divide both measures by the GCF, 3.

The scale is 1 cm : 78 cm.

2. ✔ *Try It Out* Suppose the length of a room in an architectural drawing is 10 in. Its actual length is 15 ft. What is the scale of the drawing? (*Hint*: Convert feet to inches before finding the scale.) **1 in. : 18 in. or 1 in. : 1.5 ft**

Work Together *Exploring Scale Drawings*

Work in a group. Make a scale drawing of your classroom.

3. *Reasoning* How did you decide on the scale for your drawing? **Check students' work.**

4. Yes; the drawings are all similar.

4. *Analyze* Compare your group's drawing with those of other groups. Do the scale drawings have the same shape even if the scales are not the same? Explain.

Now you may assign Exercises 1–22.

EXERCISES *On Your Own*

The scale of a map is 2 cm : 15 km. Find the actual distances for the following map distances.

1. 8 cm **60 km**
2. 1.3 cm **9.75 km**
3. 5 mm **3.75 km**
4. 24.4 cm **183 km**
5. 8 mm **6 km**
6. 15.5 cm **116.25 km**

A scale drawing has a scale of $\frac{1}{2}$ in. : 10 ft. Find the length on the drawing for each actual length.

7. 20 ft **1 in.**
8. 15 ft **$\frac{3}{4}$ in.**
9. 5 ft **$\frac{1}{4}$ in.**
10. 45 ft **$2\frac{1}{4}$ in.**
11. $1\frac{1}{2}$ ft **0.075 in.**
12. 13.5 ft **0.675 in.**

13. *Reasoning* Ramon is drawing a map of his town on a sheet of paper that is 11 in. × 17 in. From east to west the town is 13 mi. From north to south the town is 19 mi. To make the map as large as possible, what scale should Ramon use? **1 in. : 1.2 mi**

Exercises 7–12 Have students use the proportion $\frac{0.5 \text{ in.}}{10 \text{ ft}} = \frac{\text{scale}}{\text{actual}}$. The *actual* lengths are given, so the variable will replace *scale*.

REASONING Exercise 13 Encourage students to compare the two possible ratios 11 in. : 13 mi and 17 in. : 19 mi. Suggest they might want to change each ratio into a decimal. Ask: *To make sure the whole town fits on the paper, would you choose the smaller or the larger scale?* **the smaller scale**

WRITING Exercise 15 It might be helpful to provide the distances of some common routes to school.

RESEARCH Exercise 16 Students may get information from hobby or home improvement stores or model home builders.

WRAP UP

IDENTIFYING THE BIG IDEA Ask students to explain how they use proportions to find actual sizes or distances from a scale drawing.

Math at Work

If you have block scheduling or extended class periods, consider having each member of the class find a picture of a roller coaster or other amusement park ride. Have them estimate the scale of the picture. Then have them draw an enlargement or reduction of the ride in the picture using a ruler to make measurements. Display the pictures and sketches the students create.

14. *Architecture* The scale drawing shows the first floor of a house. The dimensions of the carport are 20 ft by 25 ft.

a. Complete: The scale is ■ : 5 ft. **$\frac{1}{4}$ in.**

b. Copy the floor plan on your paper. Write the actual dimensions in place of the scale dimensions. **See margin.**

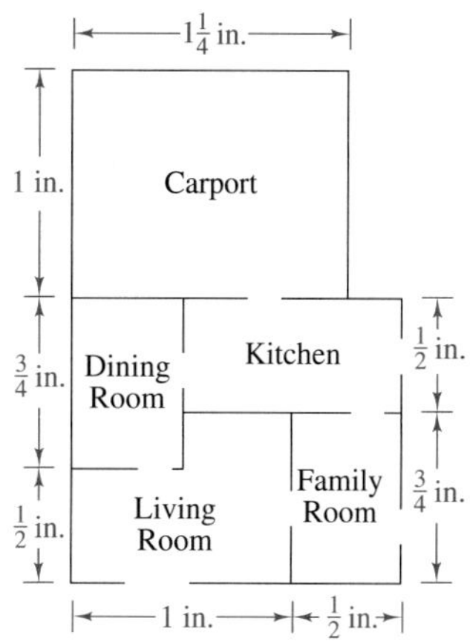

15. *Writing* Describe what you would do to draw a map of the route from your home to school. What scale would you use? **Check students' work.**

16. *Research* Find an item that someone would want a scale drawing of.

a. Make a scale drawing of your item. Include the scale on the drawing. **a–b. Check students' work.**

b. Write a paragraph describing the item and the reasons a scale drawing of it is useful.

17. *Geography* The cities of Indianapolis, Indiana, and Brownsville, Texas, are 1,166 mi apart.

a. A map of the United States has a scale of 1 in. : 250 mi. How far apart are the cities on the map? **4.7 in.**

b. Suppose the cities are 6 in. apart on a map. What is the scale of the map? **1 in. : 194.3 mi**

Far-Out Clothes

Computers help designers improve space suits for future space travelers.

Clothes designed for space must allow astronauts to move and breathe in an airless environment. An astronaut's suit must protect the astronaut from the sun's harsh rays.

For a computer image that is $\frac{1}{8}$ of the actual size, the designer knows that all other dimensions will have the same ratio.

Use the article for Exercises 18 and 19.

18. Suppose the computer image of the pants of a space suit is 5 in. long. How long are the pants? **40 in.**

19. An astronaut's arm is 24 in. long. Find the arm length in the computer image for a space suit. **3 in.**

pages 252–254 On Your Own

14b.

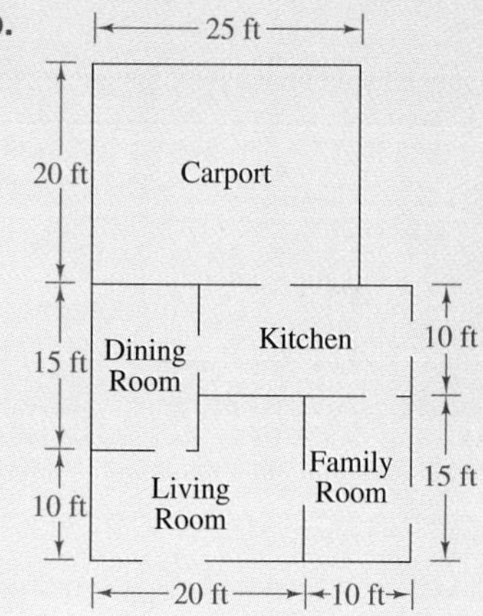

PRACTICE

Practice 6-5 *Exploring Maps and Scale Drawings*

The scale of a map is 2 cm : 21 km. Find the actual distances for the following map distances.

1. 9 cm 94.5 km
2. 12.5 cm 131.25 km
3. 14 mm 14.7 km
4. 3.6 m 3,780 km
5. 4.5 cm 47.25 km
6. 7.1 cm 74.55 km
7. 7.18 cm 75.39 km
8. 25 cm 262.5 km
9. 1 cm 10.5 km

A scale drawing has a scale of $\frac{1}{4}$ in. : 12 ft. Find the length on the drawing for each actual length.

10. 8 ft $\frac{1}{6}$ in.
11. 30 ft $\frac{5}{8}$ in.
12. 15 ft $\frac{5}{16}$ in.
13. 56 ft $1\frac{1}{6}$ in.
14. 18 ft $\frac{3}{8}$ in.
15. 20 ft $\frac{5}{12}$ in.
16. 40 ft $\frac{5}{6}$ in.
17. 80 ft $1\frac{2}{3}$ in.

Use a metric ruler to find the approximate distance between the towns.

18. Hitchcockburg to Kidville 80 km
19. Dodgetown to Earp City 50 km
20. Dodgetown to Kidville 54 km
21. Kidville to Earp City 96 km
22. Dodgetown to Hitchcockburg 46 km
23. Earp City to Hitchcockburg 20 km

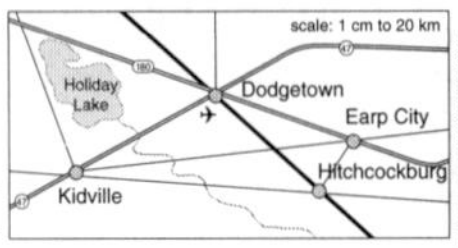

Practice

Solve.

24. The scale drawing shows a two-bedroom apartment. The master bedroom is 9 ft × 12 ft. Use an inch ruler to measure the drawing.
    a. The scale is 1 in. : 12 ft
    b. Write the actual dimensions in place of the scale dimensions. Check students' work.

In copymaster and workbook formats

RETEACHING

Reteaching 6-5 *Exploring Maps and Scale Drawings*

A **scale drawing** is an enlarged or reduced drawing of an object. A map is a scale drawing. On this map, the pool is 3 cm from the horse corral. What is the actual distance from the corral to the pool?

① Use the scale. Write a ratio of distance on the map to actual distance.

$\frac{\text{map (cm)}}{\text{actual (m)}} \quad \frac{2}{100}$

② Write a proportion using the scale.

$\frac{\text{map (cm)}}{\text{actual (m)}} \quad \frac{2}{100} = \frac{3}{n}$

③ Use cross products. Solve for n.

$2n = 100 \cdot 3$
$n = 150$ m

The pool is 150 m from the corral.

Use the information on the map. Write and solve a proportion to find the distance.

1. On the map, the mess hall is 4 cm from the pool. What is the actual distance from the pool to the mess hall?
   $\frac{\text{map}}{\text{actual}} \quad \frac{2}{100} = \frac{4}{n}$
   $n =$ 200 m
2. The lodge is 2 cm from the horse corral on the map. What is the actual distance from the corral to the lodge?
   $\frac{\text{map}}{\text{actual}} \quad \frac{2}{100} = \frac{2}{n}$
   $n =$ 100 m
3. The pool is actually 225 m from the lodge. How far would the pool be from the lodge on the map?
   $\frac{\text{map}}{\text{actual}} \quad \frac{2}{100} = \frac{n}{225}$
   $n =$ 4.5 cm
4. The mess hall is 150 m from the lodge. How far would the mess hall be from the lodge on the map?
   $\frac{\text{map}}{\text{actual}} \quad \frac{2}{100} = \frac{n}{150}$
   $n =$ 3 cm
5. A volleyball court will be built 175 m from the lodge. How far would the volleyball court be from the lodge on the map?
   $\frac{2}{100} = \frac{n}{175}$; 3.5 cm

ENRICHMENT

Minds on Math Transparency

6-5

Use the pattern in the equations below to find the sum of the first 100 odd numbers.

1 = 1
1 + 3 = 4
1 + 3 + 5 = 9
1 + 3 + 5 + 7 = 16
1 + 3 + 5 + 7 + 9 = 25

100^2, or 10,000

See *Solution Key* for worked-out answers.

LESSON QUIZ

The scale of a map is 3 cm : 14 km.

1. Find the actual distance for the map distance 9.3 cm. 43.4 km
2. Find the distance on the map if the actual distance is 70 km. 15 cm

Measure the length of the segment shown in each figure. Find the scale of each drawing.

20.

1 in. : 19.2 in.

21.

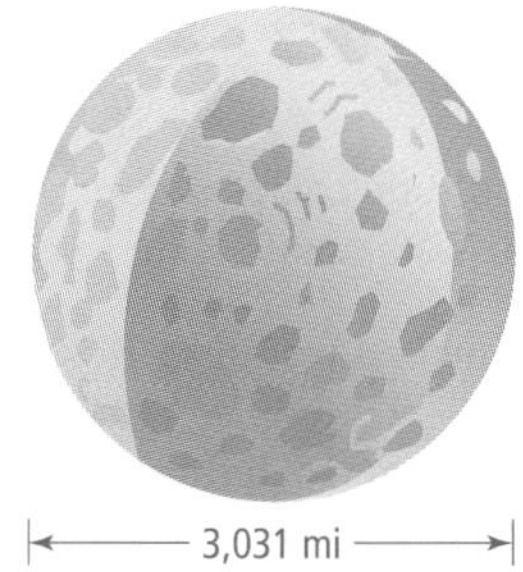

1 in. : 1,865 mi

22.

1 cm : 0.6 cm

Mixed Review

23. *Geometry* Find the values of x and y in the similar triangles at the right. *(Lesson 6-4)*
    40, 32

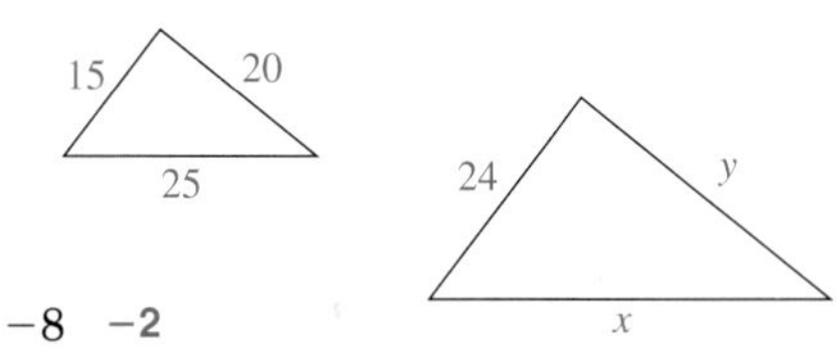

Solve each equation. *(Lesson 3-9)*

24. $3x + 2 = 17$ 5
25. $\frac{x}{5} + 5 = 21$ 80
26. $2a - 4 = -8$ −2

27. *Choose a Strategy* Jordan has a collection of nickels, dimes, and quarters totaling 8 coins. More than $\frac{1}{2}$ of his coins are quarters and less than $\frac{1}{4}$ are dimes. What are the possible amounts of money Jordan has?
    $1.45, $1.65

Math at Work

AMUSEMENT PARK DESIGNER

An amusement park designer considers the architecture and technology of the rides, the landscape of the park, lighting, and sound. To create exciting rides and interesting fun parks, a designer creates scale drawings and models.

Internet Connection

Find out more about amusement park opportunities at this Web site: http://www.napha.org

PROBLEM SOLVING PRACTICE ★★

This page provides problems for students to solve using their knowledge of decimals, fractions, ratios, and statistics. Allow students to use any method they find helpful.

Exercise 1 Have students show the proportion they use to solve the problem.

Exercise 5 Caution students to pay attention to the order in which the ratio is requested.

Exercise 7 Tell students to write an expression that would determine the total cost of the party supplies. Students can use the blanks in their expressions to answer the question.

USING MANIPULATIVES Exercise 8 Students can use fraction bars or a measuring stick to model the solution for the problem.

Exercise 9 Students need to find the mean, median, and mode to solve this problem.

PROBLEM SOLVING PRACTICE ★★★★★

Choose the best answer.

1. A blue shark swam 7.26 miles in ten minutes. What is the speed of the shark in miles per hour (mi/h)? B

   A. 0.726 mi/h B. 43.56 mi/h
   C. 48.16 mi/h D. 72.6 mi/h

2. Carlos bought school supplies with a $10 bill. He received $1.82 in change. How much did the supplies cost? F

   F. $8.18 G. $8.28
   H. $9.28 J. $11.82

3. Franklin volunteers time at the local library. Before returning books to the shelves, he puts them in order from least to greatest book number. Which list shows the correct order? D

   A. 808.81, 808.8, 813.082, 813
   B. 808.81, 808.8, 813, 813.082
   C. 813.082, 813, 808.81, 808.8
   D. 808.8, 808.81, 813, 813.082

4. Sandra scored 97, 88, 79 and 92 on four math tests. What was her mean (average) score? G

   F. 84 G. 89 H. 91 J. 92

5. On Monday, 30 students were in math class. On Tuesday, only 25 students were in math class. What is the ratio of Tuesday's attendance to Monday's attendance? B

   A. 6 to 5 B. 5 to 6 C. 5 to 11 D. 11 to 5

6. Litisha went to 12 movies in three months. Each movie admission cost $5.25. Which is the best estimate of the total amount Litisha paid for admission? H

   F. $50 G. $55 H. $60 J. $70

Please note that items 7–10 have *five* answer choices.

7. For a party, Andrew paid $1.29 for streamers, $.39 for each package of balloons, $2.58 for two gallons of fruit punch, and $1.35 each for four packages of crackers. What additional information do you need to find how much Andrew spent? B

   A. the price of one gallon of punch
   B. the number of packages of balloons
   C. the number of packages of streamers
   D. the price of two packages of cookies
   E. the number of students in the class

8. Carmela cut a length of ribbon into three equal pieces. Each piece measured $\frac{3}{4}$ yd. How long was the original length of ribbon? H

   F. $\frac{1}{4}$ yd G. $1\frac{1}{2}$ yd
   H. $2\frac{1}{4}$ yd J. 3 yd
   K. Not Here

9. Which of the following is true for the given data? 1, 2, 5, 3, 9, 7, 2 B

   A. mean < mode B. median < mean
   C. mode > median D. mean = mode
   E. median = mean

10. Luisa was reading a biography for her history class. After five days she had read 325 pages. On the sixth day, Luisa read 57 pages. A reasonable conclusion would be that Luisa read — H

    F. less than 50 pages each day
    G. between 50 and 60 pages each day
    H. between 55 and 65 pages each day
    J. more than 60 pages each day
    K. Not Here

6-6 Teaching Notes

1 Focus

CONNECTING TO PRIOR KNOWLEDGE Ask students to recall situations in which percents were used. **Answers may vary. Sample: grades, weather reports, sales** Ask students what they think of when someone mentions 50%. **Answers may vary. Sample: low test score, half of something**

2 Teach

THINK AND DISCUSS

AEP Point out that *percent* means "per one hundred," just as there are 100 cents in a dollar. Forty-nine cents is 49% of a dollar. Also relate *cent* in percent to *century*, 100 years. Challenge students to find other times when 100 and *cent* are related.

Question 1 Ask: *What are two ways to find the unshaded part?* **Find the sum of the three shaded parts and subtract from 100; count the unshaded squares.**

ASSESSMENT Write a percent on an index card. Write the equivalent fraction with 100 as a denominator on another index card. Give each student a card. Have students find their "match." Have students with matching cards draw models of the percents.

Lesson Planning Options

Prerequisite Skills

- writing equivalent fractions (4-3)
- writing fractions as decimals (4-9)

Vocabulary/Symbols

percent

Materials/Manipulatives

- graph paper

Resources

Student Edition

Skills Handbook, p. 533
Extra Practice, p. 519
Glossary/Study Guide

Teaching Resources

Chapter Support File, Ch. 6
- Lesson Planner 6-6
- Practice 6-6, Reteaching 6-6
- Answer Masters 6-6

Teaching Aids Masters 20, 25
Glossary, Spanish Resources

Transparencies
9, 10, Minds on Math 6-6

Warm Up

Use a graph with 100 squares to draw and shade squares that spell a 3-letter word. Estimate what fraction of the grid is unshaded. **Answers may vary.**

6-6 Modeling Percents

What You'll Learn

1. To model percents
2. To write percents using equal ratios

...And Why

Reporters use percents to describe consumer trends.

Here's How

Look for questions that
- build understanding
- ✔ check understanding

THINK AND DISCUSS

1 Modeling Percents

A **percent** is a ratio that compares a number to 100. You can write the ratio $\frac{25}{100}$ as 25%.

EXAMPLE 1

The figure at the right contains 100 squares. Write a ratio and a percent to describe each shaded part.

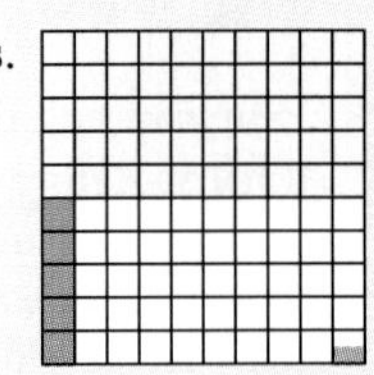

yellow: $\frac{50}{100} = 50\%$ blue: $\frac{5}{100} = 5\%$

red: $\frac{0.5}{100} = 0.5\%$

1. *Go a Step Further* Write a ratio and a percent to describe the unshaded part of the figure in Example 1.

1. $\frac{44.5}{100}$, 44.5%

You can model percents even when you divide a figure into fewer than 100 parts.

QUICKreview

To find equal ratios, multiply the numerator and denominator by the same non-zero number.

$\frac{a}{b} = \frac{a \cdot c}{b \cdot c}$

EXAMPLE 2

What percent does each shaded area represent?

a.
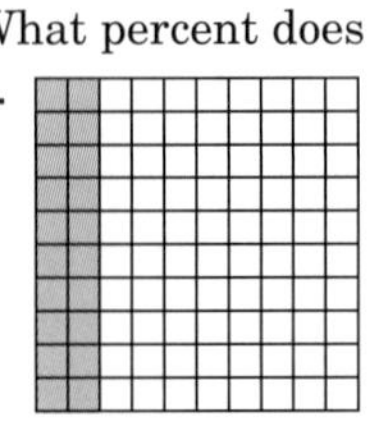
b.
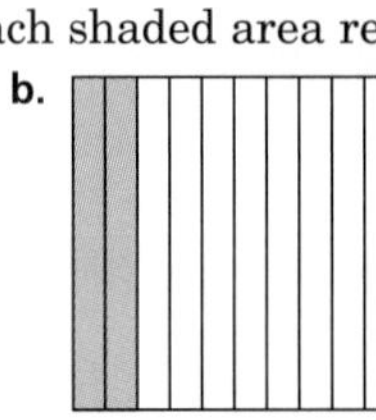
c.
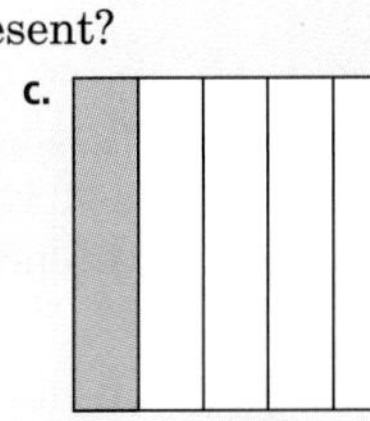

a. $\frac{20}{100} = 20\%$ b. $\frac{2}{10} = \frac{20}{100} = 20\%$ c. $\frac{1}{5} = \frac{20}{100} = 20\%$

2. ✔ *Try It Out* What percent does the shaded area represent in the figure at the right? **75%**

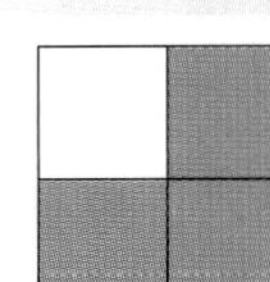

Example 2 Ask: *When can you simply take the numerator and put a percent sign next to it?* **when the denominator is 100**

ADDITIONAL EXAMPLES

FOR EXAMPLE 1

Write a ratio and a percent to describe the total of the parts shaded yellow or blue.
$\frac{55}{100}$; 55%

FOR EXAMPLE 2

What percent does each unshaded area represent? **a. 80% b. 80% c. 80%**

FOR EXAMPLE 3

In some department stores, they mark up prices 105%. Draw a model to represent 105%.

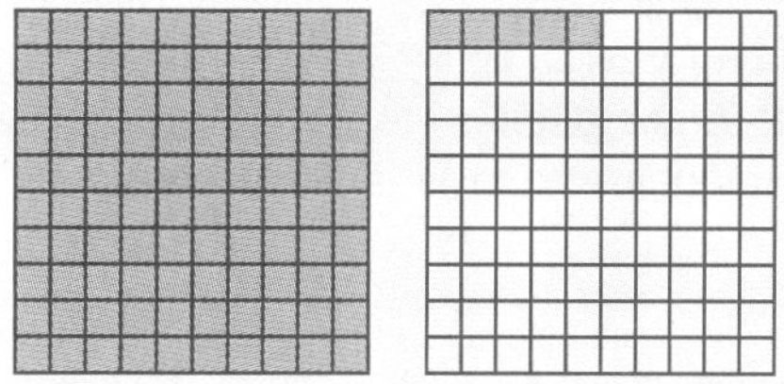

FOR EXAMPLE 4

Write $\frac{23}{25}$ as a percent. **92%**

Question 3 Have students review how to model mixed numbers. Ask: *How are the models for $2\frac{3}{4}$ and 275% similar?* **Both have two whole figures shaded and one figure with $\frac{3}{4}$ shaded.** *How are they different?* **Each figure in $2\frac{3}{4}$ has 4 parts. 275% has 100 parts.**

You use more than one figure to model percents greater than 100%.

EXAMPLE 3 *Real-World Problem Solving*

Biology The number of nesting pairs of bald eagles in the lower 48 states increased 185% between 1963 and 1981. Draw a model to represent 185%.

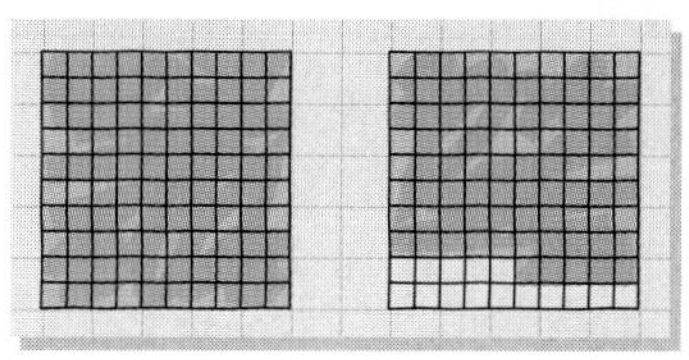

1. Draw two figures.
2. Shade one whole figure. Shade 85% of the second figure.

3. ✔ *Try It Out* Between 1981 and 1994 the number of nesting pairs of bald eagles increased 275%. Use graph paper to model 275%. **See back of book.**

Now you may assign Exercises 1–29.

2 *Writing Percents Using Equal Ratios*

Other than 1, the factors of 100 are 2, 4, 5, 10, 20, 25, and 50. Ratios that have these numbers as the denominator are easy to write as percents by finding equal ratios.

EXAMPLE 4

Write $\frac{3}{5}$ as a percent.

$\frac{3}{5} = \frac{3 \cdot 20}{5 \cdot 20}$ ← Since 5 · 20 = 100, use 20 to write a ratio equal to $\frac{3}{5}$.

$= \frac{60}{100}$ ← Multiply.

$= 60\%$ ← Write as a percent.

4. ✔ *Try It Out* Write each ratio as a percent.
   a. $\frac{6}{25}$ **24%** b. $\frac{3}{4}$ **75%** c. $\frac{1}{50}$ **2%** d. $\frac{19}{20}$ **95%**

5. *Go a Step Further* According to a news report, the prices on consumer goods rose a tenth of a percent during the month of March. Write the percent in numerals. **0.1%**

Now you may assign Exercises 30–51.

Technology Options

Prentice Hall Technology

Software for Learners
- Math Blaster® Mystery*
- Interactive Student Tutorial, Chapter 6*

Teaching Resource Software
- Computer Item Generator 6-6
- Resource Pro™ Chapter 6*

Internet • For related mathematics activities, visit the Prentice Hall site at www.phschool.com/math

**Available on CD-ROM only*

Assignment Options for Exercises On Your Own

To provide flexible scheduling, this lesson can be split into parts.

1 **Core** 1–11, 16–27
Extension 12–15, 28, 29

2 **Core** 30–47, 49–51
Extension 48

Use Mixed Review to maintain skills.

AUDITORY LEARNING Example 4 Have a student name the factor pairs of 100. Repeat until students can quickly name every pair.

3 Practice/Assess

EXERCISES *On Your Own*

TACTILE LEARNING Exercises 9–11 Let students use play or real coins. Students may want to make a chart of the value of a dollar in cents and the value of each coin in cents.

OPEN-ENDED Exercise 28 Tell students that they may have to distort their letter by making it wider than they normally would.

WRITING Exercise 29 Students may have difficulty visualizing a situation less than 1%. Show them a meterstick and point out the size of a millimeter.

ERROR ALERT! Exercises 30–47 Students might forget to first write each fraction as an equivalent fraction with a denominator of 100.

Remediation: For each exercise, tell students to first write: fraction $= \frac{\blacksquare}{100}$. Then have them replace the box with the correct number and simplify the fraction.

WRAP UP

IDENTIFYING THE BIG IDEA Have students define *percent*. Ask them to explain how to find the percent of a figure that is shaded. Then have them explain how to rewrite a ratio as a percent.

pages 258–259 On Your Own

16. 

17. 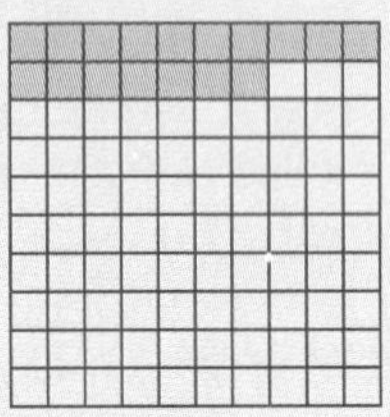

18. 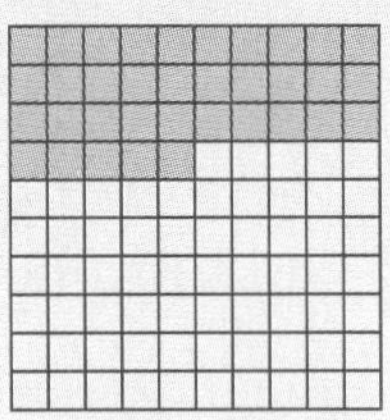

19. 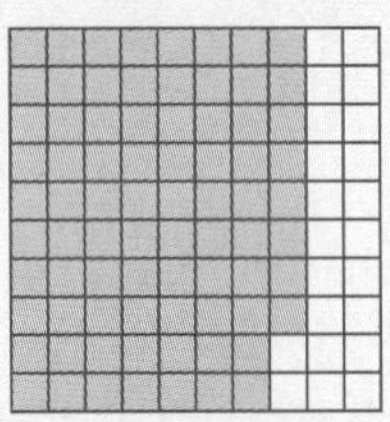

20. 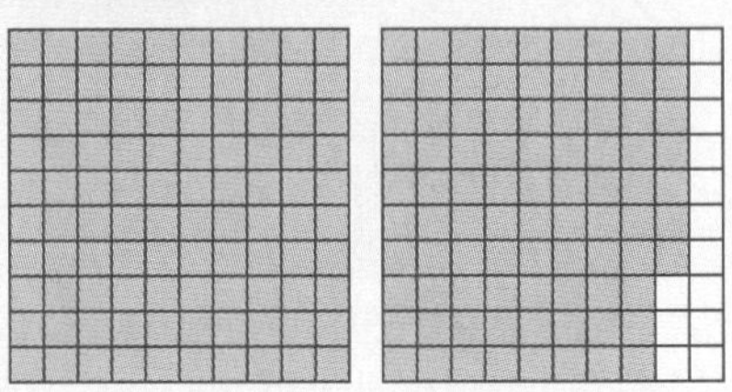

EXERCISES *On Your Own*

Write the percent of each figure that is shaded.

1. 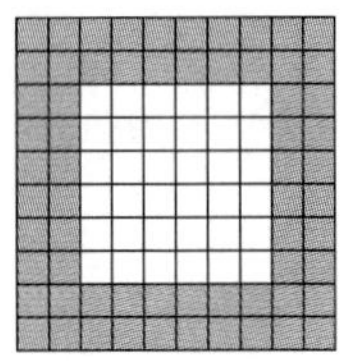
64%

2. 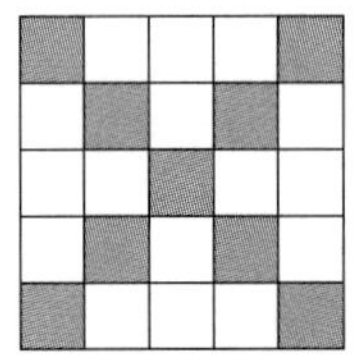
36%

3. 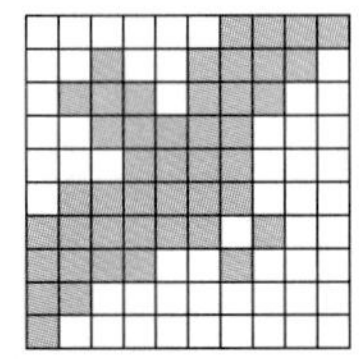
45%

4. 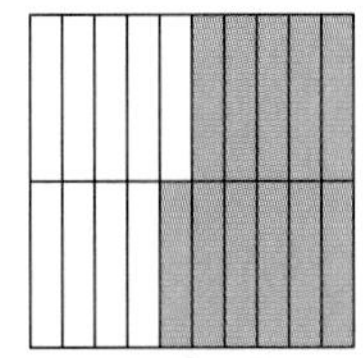
55%

5. 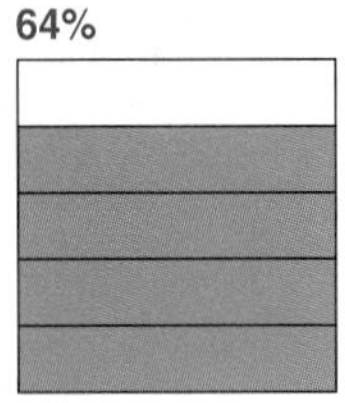
80%

6. 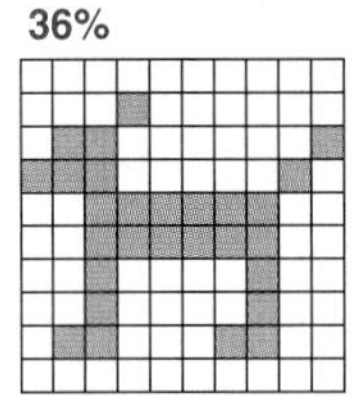
28%

7. 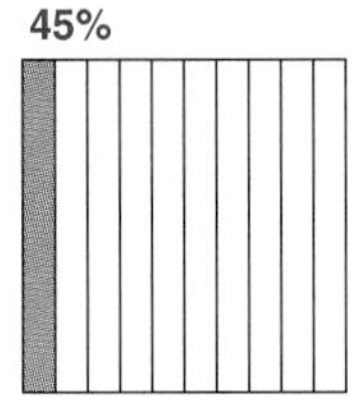
10%

8. 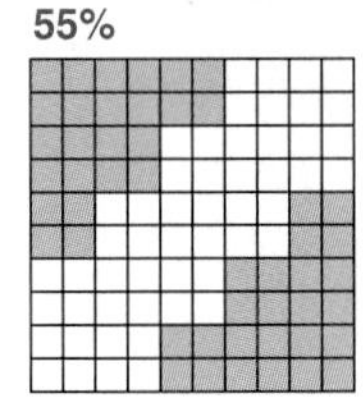
48%

Find what percent of a dollar each set of coins makes.

9. 2 quarters 50%

10. 5 quarters and 2 dimes 145%

11. 3 quarters, 2 dimes, and 1 nickel 100%

Estimate the percent that is shaded in each figure.

12. 
about 20%

13. 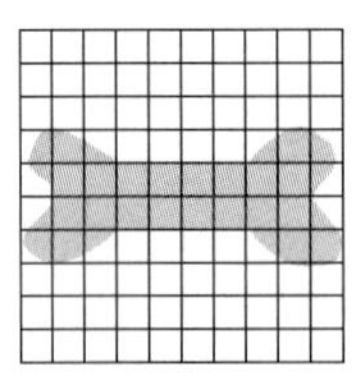
about 25%

14. 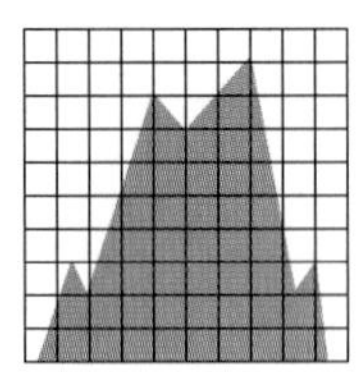
about 45%

15. 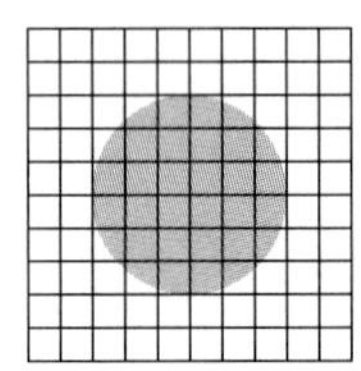
about 25%

Draw figures on 10 × 10 squares of graph paper to represent each of the following percents. 16–20. See margin.

16. 234% 17. 17% 18. 35% 19. 78% 20. 187% 21. 10%

22. 1.5% 23. 65.5% 24. 115% 25. 8% 26. 25% 27. 90.5%

21–27. See back of book.

28. a. *Open-ended* Draw and shade the first letter of your name on a 10 × 10 square of graph paper so that *more than* 30% is shaded. a–b. Check students' work.
   b. Draw and shade the last letter of your name on a 10 × 10 square of graph paper so that *less than* 30% is shaded.

LESSON QUIZ

Write the percent of each figure that is shaded.

1.

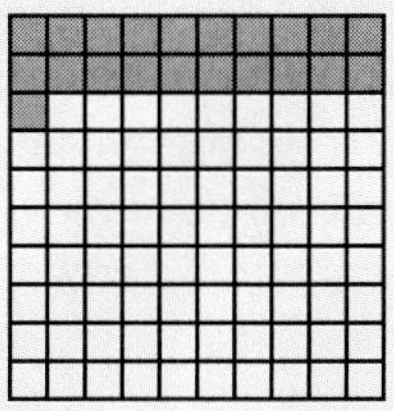

21%

2.

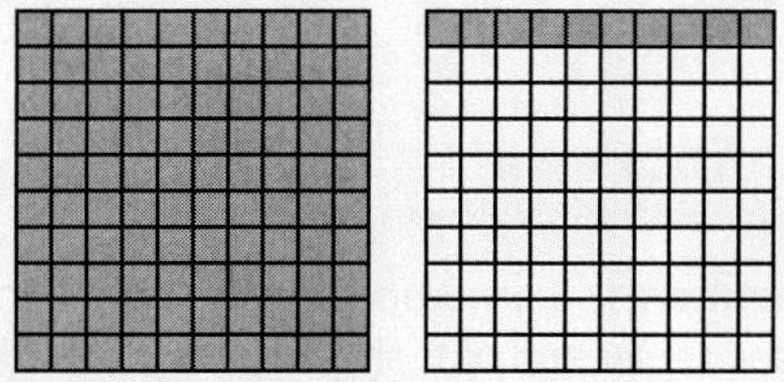

110%

Write each ratio as a percent.

3. $\frac{1}{10}$ 10%

4. $\frac{11}{50}$ 22%

29. *Writing* Describe one situation that requires a percent less than 1% and one that requires a percent greater than 100%. **Check students' work.**

Write each ratio as a percent.

30. $\frac{19}{25}$ 76% 31. $\frac{3}{5}$ 60% 32. $\frac{1}{2}$ 50% 33. $\frac{21}{25}$ 84% 34. $\frac{7}{10}$ 70% 35. $\frac{7}{20}$ 35%

36. $\frac{24}{25}$ 96% 37. $\frac{4}{5}$ 80% 38. $\frac{1}{4}$ 25% 39. $\frac{3}{10}$ 30% 40. $\frac{3}{25}$ 12% 41. $\frac{1}{5}$ 20%

42. $\frac{11}{20}$ 55% 43. $\frac{7}{8}$ 87.5% 44. $\frac{9}{50}$ 18% 45. $\frac{2}{5}$ 40% 46. $\frac{9}{10}$ 90% 47. $\frac{7}{50}$ 14%

48. a. What percent of the square at the right does the yellow part represent? the green part? $33\frac{1}{3}\%$, $66\frac{2}{3}\%$
   b. Write ratios to represent each section. $\frac{1}{3}$, $\frac{2}{3}$

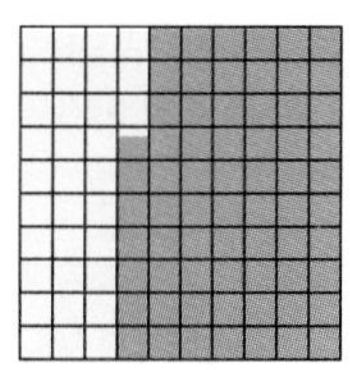

Write each percent in numerals.

49. *Money* Over a six-month period the price of gasoline rose six tenths of a percent. **0.6%**

50. *Education* Between 1974 and 1994 the cost of four years of education at a public university rose almost one hundred thirty-four percent. **134%**

51. *Volunteering* Since 1984, job inquiries to the Peace Corps have increased one hundred seventy-six percent. **176%**

Mixed Review

Find each sum or difference. *(Lesson 5-3)*

52. $7\frac{4}{5} + 9\frac{7}{10}$ $17\frac{1}{2}$ 53. $17\frac{2}{9} - 12\frac{1}{3}$ $4\frac{8}{9}$ 54. $8\frac{1}{12} + 12\frac{6}{11}$ $20\frac{83}{132}$ 55. $21\frac{2}{5} + 15\frac{1}{4}$ $36\frac{13}{20}$ 56. $9\frac{3}{11} - 8\frac{3}{8}$ $\frac{79}{88}$

Complete. *(Lessons 3-3, 3-4, and 3-5)*

57. $-4 \cdot 3 = 3 \cdot ■$ -4 58. $5 - (-2) = 5 + ■$ 2 59. $4 + 7 + (-4) = 7 + ■$ 0

60. *Automobiles* The gas tank of Gina's car holds 13.5 gal of gas. The gas tank of Karen's car holds 13.25 gal of gas. Whose car holds more gas? How many more quarts of gas does it hold? *(Lessons 2-1 and 5-8)* **Gina's car; 1 qt**

61. *Choose a Strategy* Seven teams are in the tennis-doubles playoffs. Each team plays every other team twice. What is the total number of matches played? **42 matches**

PRACTICE

Practice 6-6 Modeling Percents

Shade each grid to represent each of the following percents.

1. 53% 2. 123% 3. 71%

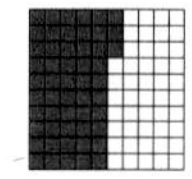

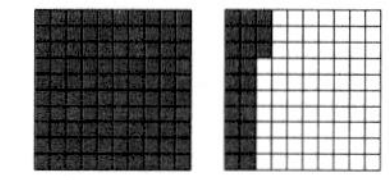

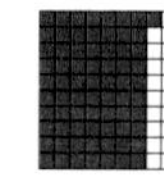

Rewrite each ratio as a percent.

4. $\frac{4}{5}$ 80% 5. $\frac{3}{5}$ 60% 6. $\frac{9}{10}$ 90% 7. $\frac{3}{10}$ 30%

8. $\frac{6}{25}$ 24% 9. $\frac{7}{100}$ 7% 10. $\frac{9}{50}$ 18% 11. $\frac{9}{25}$ 36%

12. $\frac{2}{5}$ 40% 13. $\frac{7}{10}$ 70% 14. $\frac{4}{25}$ 16% 15. $\frac{16}{25}$ 64%

16. $\frac{11}{20}$ 55% 17. $\frac{19}{20}$ 95% 18. $\frac{27}{50}$ 54% 19. 41 : 50 82%

Write the percent of each figure that is shaded.

20. 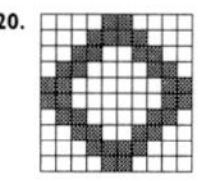 36%

21. 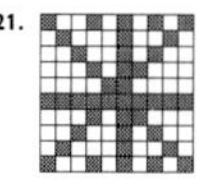 40%

22. 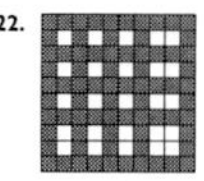 75%

Complete the following.

Ancient Egyptians did not write the fraction $\frac{4}{5}$ as "$\frac{4}{5}$". Instead, they used unit fractions. The numerator of a unit fraction is always 1. No denominator used to represent a given fraction can be repeated. For this reason, Egyptians would have written $\frac{4}{5}$ as $\frac{1}{2} + \frac{1}{5} + \frac{1}{10}$ and not as $\frac{1}{2} + \frac{1}{10} + \frac{1}{10} + \frac{1}{10}$. Write each of the following as a sum of unit fractions.

23. $\frac{3}{4}$ $\frac{1}{2} + \frac{1}{4}$ 24. $\frac{5}{8}$ $\frac{1}{2} + \frac{1}{8}$ 25. $\frac{9}{10}$ Sample: $\frac{1}{2} + \frac{1}{3} + \frac{1}{15}$

26. $\frac{7}{12}$ $\frac{1}{2} + \frac{1}{12}$ 27. $\frac{11}{12}$ Sample: $\frac{1}{2} + \frac{1}{3} + \frac{1}{12}$ 28. $\frac{11}{15}$ Sample: $\frac{1}{2} + \frac{1}{5} + \frac{1}{30}$

In copymaster and workbook formats

RETEACHING

Reteaching 6-6 Modeling Percents

A **percent** is a ratio that compares a number to 100. The figure at the right contains 25 squares. $\frac{9}{25}$ of the squares are shaded.

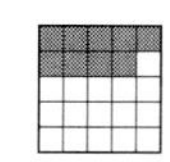

To write $\frac{9}{25}$ as a percent, follow these steps.

① Write a ratio with a denominator of 100 that is equal to $\frac{9}{25}$. $\frac{9}{25} = \frac{9 \cdot 4}{25 \cdot 4} = \frac{36}{100}$

② Write the ratio as a percent. $\frac{36}{100} = 36\%$

36% of the squares are shaded.

Write the percent of each figure that is shaded.

1. 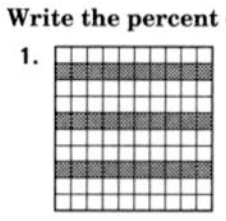 30%

2. 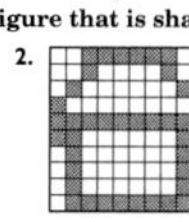 40%

3. 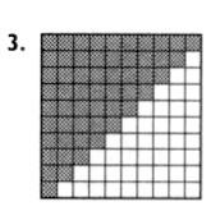 55%

4. 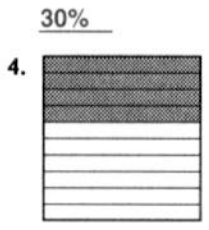 40%

5. 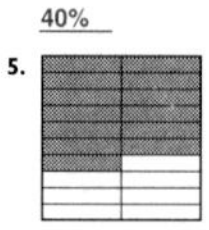 65%

6. 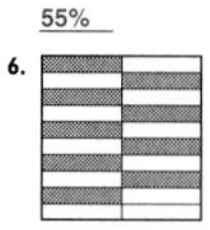 45%

Write each ratio as a percent.

7. $\frac{3}{5}$ 60% 8. $\frac{17}{100}$ 17% 9. $\frac{18}{25}$ 72% 10. $\frac{13}{20}$ 65%

11. $\frac{8}{10}$ 80% 12. $\frac{1}{4}$ 25% 13. $\frac{17}{50}$ 34% 14. $\frac{11}{25}$ 44%

15. $\frac{7}{20}$ 35% 16. $\frac{21}{25}$ 84% 17. $\frac{3}{10}$ 30% 18. $\frac{16}{25}$ 64%

19. $\frac{2}{5}$ 40% 20. $\frac{99}{100}$ 99% 21. $\frac{11}{20}$ 55% 22. $\frac{13}{25}$ 52%

23. $\frac{1}{10}$ 10% 24. $\frac{39}{50}$ 78% 25. $\frac{19}{20}$ 95% 26. $\frac{6}{25}$ 24%

Reteaching

ENRICHMENT

Minds on Math Transparency

6-6

Cameron has twice as many books as Kathi. Morey has one-third as many as Kira. Kira has 4 more books than Cameron. If Kathi has 16 books, how many books does Morey have?

12 books

See *Solution Key* for worked-out answers.

6-7 Teaching Notes

1 Focus

CONNECTING TO PRIOR KNOWLEDGE Ask: *How can 50%, $\frac{1}{2}$, or 0.50 be used in a sentence about a shirt sale?* **Answers may vary. Sample: The shirt is 50% off. The shirt is $\frac{1}{2}$ off. You save $.50 out of every $1.00.**

2 Teach

THINK AND DISCUSS

Question 1 Encourage students to check the reasonableness of their answers. Have them find half of the denominator. If the numerator is less than half of the denominator, then the percent should be less than 50%. If the numerator is greater than half, then the percent should be greater than 50%.

Question 2 Make sure students remove the percent sign after they express the percent as a fraction.

KINESTHETIC LEARNING **Example 3** Have students stand and represent digits and the decimal point. Then students change places to show the decimal point moving two places to the right. Include the percent sign.

Lesson Planning Options

Prerequisite Skills

- simplifying fractions (4-6)
- multiplying by powers of 10 (precourse)

Materials/Manipulatives

- newspaper

Resources

Student Edition

Skills Handbook, p. 538
Extra Practice, p. 519
Glossary/Study Guide

Teaching Resources

Chapter Support File, Ch. 6
- Lesson Planner 6-7
- Practice 6-7, Reteaching 6-7
- Answer Masters 6-7

Teaching Aids Masters 10, 20–25
Glossary, Spanish Resources

Transparencies

9, 10, 18–25, Minds on Math 6-7

Warm Up

Write five fractions that are greater than $\frac{1}{2}$ and less than 1. Write each fraction as a decimal.
Answers may vary. Sample: $\frac{3}{5}, \frac{5}{8}, \frac{2}{3}, \frac{3}{4}, \frac{7}{8}$; 0.6, 0.625, 0.6$\overline{6}$, 0.75, 0.875

6-7 Percents, Fractions, and Decimals

What You'll Learn

1. To write fractions as percents and percents as fractions
2. To write decimals as percents and percents as decimals

...And Why

You can understand the relationship between fractions, decimals, and percents by writing each in the other forms.

Here's How

Look for questions that
- build understanding
- ✔ check understanding

THINK AND DISCUSS

1 Rewriting Percents and Fractions

You can write any ratio or fraction as a percent.

■ **EXAMPLE 1** *Real-World Problem Solving*

Nutrition Forty-five calories in a slice of cheese pizza are from fat. There are 160 total calories in a slice of cheese pizza. What percent of the calories are from fat?

$\frac{45}{160} = 45 \div 160$ ← Write the ratio as a division sentence.
$= 0.28125$ ← Divide.
$= 28.125\%$ ← Express as a percent.

Fat accounts for about 28% of the calories in one slice of cheese pizza.

1. ✔ *Try It Out* Write each fraction as a percent.
   a. $\frac{8}{25}$ 32% b. $\frac{3}{5}$ 60% c. $\frac{9}{75}$ 12% d. $\frac{45}{50}$ 90%

You can rewrite a percent as a fraction.

■ **EXAMPLE 2** *Real-World Problem Solving*

Biology An elephant sleeps about 15% of a day. What fraction of a day does an elephant sleep?

$15\% = \frac{15}{100}$ ← Write 15% as a fraction with 100 as the denominator.
$= \frac{15 \div 5}{100 \div 5}$ ← Divide the numerator and denominator by the GCF, 5.
$= \frac{3}{20}$ ← Simplify the fraction.

An elephant sleeps about $\frac{3}{20}$ of every day.

2. ✔ *Try It Out* Express each percent as a fraction in simplest form.
   a. 95% $\frac{19}{20}$ b. 8% $\frac{2}{25}$ c. 79% $\frac{79}{100}$ d. 4.5% $\frac{9}{200}$

Now you may assign Exercises 1–12, 14–30.

ASSESSMENT Question 4 Have students trade answers with a partner. Have them check their partner's work by changing the answer to a percent. The percent should match the given one.

■ **ADDITIONAL EXAMPLES**

FOR EXAMPLE 1

Ashley sleeps 8 h a day. There are 24 h in a day. What percent of a day does Ashley spend sleeping? **about 33.3%**

FOR EXAMPLE 2

An elephant is awake about 85% of a day. What fraction of a day is an elephant awake? $\frac{17}{20}$

FOR EXAMPLE 3

Write 0.8485 as a percent. Round to the nearest tenth of a percent. **84.9%**

FOR EXAMPLE 4

Write 179% as a decimal. **1.79**

ERROR ALERT! and AUDITORY LEARNING Students may not be sure about when to move the decimal point left or right. **Remediation:** Tell students to think of the decimal point and the percent as two signs who only speak "sign language." When a percent sign is written to the right of a number, the decimal point moves two places closer so they can speak in sign. When the percent sign is removed, the decimal point returns home by moving two spaces to the left.

Need Help? For practice in multiplying or dividing by a power of 10, see Skills Handbook p. 538.

2 *Percents and Decimals*

To write a decimal as a percent, multiply it by 100, or move the decimal point two places to the right.

$$0.45 \times 100 \longrightarrow 0.45. \longrightarrow 45\%$$

■ **EXAMPLE 3**

Write each decimal as a percent. Round to the nearest tenth of a percent, if necessary.

a. 0.4 — $0.4 \times 100 = 40$, so $0.4 = 40\%$

b. 0.7593 — $0.7593 \times 100 = 75.93$, so $0.7593 = 75.9\%$

c. 1.05 — $1.05 \times 100 = 105$, so $1.05 = 105\%$

3. ✓*Try It Out* Write each decimal as a percent.

a. 0.31 **31%** **b.** 0.67328 **67.328%** **c.** 2.34 **234%** **d.** 0.001 **0.1%**

To write a percent as a decimal, divide it by 100, or move the decimal point two places to the left.

$$264.5\% \longrightarrow 264.5 \div 100 \longrightarrow 2.64.5 \longrightarrow 2.645$$

■ **EXAMPLE 4**

Write each percent as a decimal.

a. 2% — $2 \div 100 = 0.02$, so $2\% = 0.02$

b. 67.5% — $67.5 \div 100 = 0.675$, so $67.5\% = 0.675$

c. 125% — $125 \div 100 = 1.25$, so $125\% = 1.25$

4. ✓*Try It Out* Write each percent as a decimal.

a. 3% **0.03** **b.** 0.7% **0.007** **c.** 98% **0.98** **d.** 275% **2.75**

Now you may assign Exercises 13, 30–62.

EXERCISES *On Your Own*

Choose **Use paper and pencil or mental math to write each percent as a fraction in simplest form.**

1. 45% $\frac{9}{20}$ **2.** 62.5% $\frac{5}{8}$ **3.** 180% $\frac{9}{5}$ **4.** 12% $\frac{3}{25}$ **5.** 6% $\frac{3}{50}$ **6.** 20% $\frac{1}{5}$

7. 7.5% $\frac{3}{40}$ **8.** 240% $\frac{12}{5}$ **9.** 0.1% $\frac{1}{1000}$ **10.** 56% $\frac{14}{25}$ **11.** 85% $\frac{17}{20}$ **12.** 37.5% $\frac{3}{8}$

Technology Options

Prentice Hall Technology

Software for Learners

- Math Lab: Fractions, Decimals, and Percents
- Math Blaster® Mystery*
- Interactive Student Tutorial, Chapter 6*

Teaching Resource Software

- Computer Item Generator 6-7
- Resource Pro™ Chapter 6*

Internet • For related mathematics activities, visit the Prentice Hall site at www.phschool.com/math

**Available on CD-ROM only*

Assignment Options for Exercises On Your Own

To provide flexible scheduling, this lesson can be split into parts.

1 **Core** 1–12, 14–29
Extension 30

2 **Core** 31, 32–43, 45–60, 62
Extension 13, 44, 61

Use Mixed Review to maintain skills.

3 Practice/Assess

EXERCISES *On Your Own*

WRITING Exercise 31 Have students express both values as a fraction. Remind them that $0.4 = \frac{4}{10}$ and $0.4\% = \frac{0.4}{100}$. Make sure they include the decimal point in 0.4%.

MENTAL MATH Exercises 45–60 Repeat the Assessment activity. This time have students check their partner's work by changing the answer to a decimal. The decimal should match the one given for each exercise.

DIVERSITY and CONNECTING TO THE STUDENTS' WORLD Exercise 61 Some students may not have experience reading nutritional labels. Bring to class samples of nutrition labels from popular foods students eat. Have them find the percent of various nutrients contained in these foods.

OPEN-ENDED Exercise 62 Consider allowing students to choose decimals or fractions from newspapers and then convert them to percents.

WRAP UP

IDENTIFYING THE BIG IDEA Have students explain how fractions, decimals, and percents can be interchanged.

PROJECT LINK Encourage students to use their graphs to estimate the percents. Remind them to use the total number of people surveyed.

13. **Choose A, B, C, or D.** Use the figure at the right. Which set of numbers below represents the shaded area? B

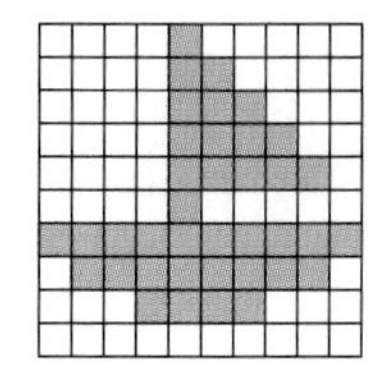

A. $3.8\%, \frac{38}{100}, 0.38$
B. $38\%, \frac{38}{100}, 0.38$
C. $38\%, \frac{38}{100}, 0.038$
D. $0.38\%, \frac{38}{100}, 0.038$

Write each fraction as a percent. Round to the nearest tenth of a percent, if necessary.

14. $\frac{27}{50}$ 54%
15. $\frac{17}{20}$ 85%
16. $\frac{33}{40}$ 82.5%
17. $\frac{5}{8}$ 62.5%
18. $\frac{8}{50}$ 16%
19. $\frac{19}{4}$ 475%
20. $\frac{125}{625}$ 20%
21. $\frac{101}{100}$ 101%
22. $\frac{18}{36}$ 50%
23. $\frac{7}{8}$ 87.5%
24. $\frac{3}{17}$ 17.6%
25. $\frac{6}{10}$ 60%
26. $\frac{67}{68}$ 98.5%
27. $\frac{4}{50}$ 8%
28. $\frac{8}{5}$ 160%
29. $\frac{10}{12}$ 83.3%

30c. Spaghetti with meatballs; a higher percent of its calories comes from carbohydrates.

30. *Nutrition* Runners usually eat foods high in carbohydrates before a race. A gram of fat has 9 calories. A gram of protein and a gram of carbohydrates each have 4 calories.
   a. How many calories does one serving of macaroni and cheese have? How many does one serving of spaghetti with meatballs have?
   b. What percent of the calories in each meal is carbohydrates? Round to the nearest percent.
   c. Which meal is the better choice for a runner? Why?

a. 525 calories; 340 calories b. 30%; 46% c. See above right.

31. *Writing* Does 0.4 equal 0.4%? Explain.
No; 0.4% is 0.004, which is less than 0.4.

Choose **Use paper and pencil or mental math to write each percent as a decimal.**

32. 130% 1.3
33. 32% 0.32
34. 2.5% 0.025
35. 88% 0.88
36. 125% 1.25
37. 345% 3.45
38. 34.678% 0.34678
39. 3% 0.03
40. 0.95% 0.0095
41. 12% 0.12
42. 19.1% 0.191
43. 0.09% 0.0009

44. *Nutrition* The Deluxe brand vitamin tablet supplies 0.5% of the *recommended daily allowance* (RDA) for phosphorus.
   a. Write the percent as a fraction. $\frac{1}{200}$
   b. Write the percent as a decimal. 0.005
   c. Which way do you prefer to see the number for the Recommended Daily Allowance for phosphorus, as a fraction, as a decimal, or as a percent? Why?
   Check students' work.

LESSON QUIZ

1. Write 55% as a fraction in simplest form. $\frac{11}{20}$
2. Write $\frac{9}{13}$ as a percent. Round to the nearest tenth of a percent. 69.2%
3. Write 9.8% as a decimal. 0.098
4. Write 0.8 as a percent. 80%

PRACTICE

Practice 6-7 *Percents, Fractions, and Decimals*

Choose a calculator, paper and pencil, or mental math. Write each percent as a fraction in simplest form and as a decimal.

1. 65% $\frac{13}{20}$; 0.65 2. 37.5% $\frac{3}{8}$; 0.375 3. 80% $\frac{4}{5}$; 0.8 4. 25% $\frac{1}{4}$; 0.25
5. 18% $\frac{9}{50}$; 0.18 6. 46% $\frac{23}{50}$; 0.46 7. 87% $\frac{87}{100}$; 0.87 8. 8% $\frac{2}{25}$; 0.08
9. 43% $\frac{43}{100}$; 0.43 10. 55% $\frac{11}{20}$; 0.55 11. 94% $\frac{47}{50}$; 0.94 12. 36% $\frac{9}{25}$; 0.36

Write each number as a percent. Round to the nearest tenth of a percent where necessary.

13. $\frac{7}{10}$ 70% 14. 0.635 63.5% 15. 3.7 370% 16. $\frac{8}{15}$ 53.3%
17. $\frac{7}{50}$ 14% 18. 0.56 56% 19. 4.13 413% 20. $\frac{3}{8}$ 37.5%
21. $\frac{7}{12}$ 58.3% 22. 0.387 38.7% 23. 2.83 283% 24. $\frac{2}{9}$ 22.2%

Write each number as a percent. Place the number into the puzzle without using the percent sign or decimal point.

Across

1. 1.34
3. $\frac{53}{100}$
5. $5\frac{13}{20}$
7. $\frac{228}{200}$
9. 0.0456
10. 0.63
11. $\frac{11}{2,000}$
13. 0.58
14. 0.00905
16. 0.605

Down

2. 3.46
4. 0.324
5. $\frac{1}{2}$
6. 0.515
8. $\frac{33}{200}$
9. 43.8
10. $\frac{659}{1,000}$
12. 5.435
15. $\frac{14}{25}$

1. 1	2. 3	4	■	■
■	4	■	3. 5	4. 3
5. 5	6	6. 5	■	2
0	■	7. 1	8. 1	4
■	9. 4	5	6	■
10. 6	3	■	11. 5	12. 5
13. 5	8	■	■	4
14. 9	0	15. 5	■	3
■	■	16. 6	0	5

Practice

In copymaster and workbook formats

RETEACHING

Reteaching 6-7 *Percents, Fractions, and Decimals*

You can use a proportion to write a fraction as a percent.

$\frac{3}{5} = \frac{n}{100}$ ← **Write a proportion.**

$5n = 3 \cdot 100$ ← **Cross multiply.**

$n = 60$ ← **Solve for n.**

$\frac{3}{5} = 60\%$

To write a percent as a fraction, write a fraction with 100 as the denominator.

$45\% = \frac{45}{100}$ ← **Denominator 100**

$= \frac{45 \div 5}{100 \div 5} = \frac{9}{20}$ ← **Simplify.**

$45\% = \frac{9}{20}$

To write a decimal as a percent, multiply by 100.

Write 0.85 as a percent.

$0.85 \cdot 100 = 85$

$0.85 = 85\%$

To write a percent as a decimal, divide by 100.

Write 46% as a decimal.

$46 \div 100 = 0.46$

$46\% = 0.46$

Complete to write each fraction as a percent.

1. $\frac{5}{8} = \frac{n}{\boxed{100}}$
   $5 \cdot \boxed{100} = 8 \cdot n$
   $n = 62.5$
   $\frac{5}{8} = 62.5\%$
2. $\frac{3}{20} = \frac{n}{\boxed{100}}$
   $3 \cdot \boxed{100} = 20 \cdot \boxed{n}$
   $n = 15$
   $\frac{3}{20} = 15\%$
3. $\frac{7}{25} = \frac{\boxed{n}}{100}$
   $7 \cdot 100 = 25n$
   $n = 28$
   $\frac{7}{25} = 28\%$

Write each fraction as a percent.

4. $\frac{3}{4}$ 75% 5. $\frac{12}{25}$ 48% 6. $\frac{4}{5}$ 80% 7. $\frac{23}{4}$ 575%

Write each percent as a fraction in simplest form.

8. 45% $\frac{9}{20}$ 9. 60% $\frac{3}{5}$ 10. 16% $\frac{4}{25}$ 11. 25% $\frac{1}{4}$
12. 37.5% $\frac{3}{8}$ 13. 99% $\frac{99}{100}$ 14. 40% $\frac{2}{5}$ 15. 86% $\frac{43}{50}$

Write each percent as a decimal or each decimal as a percent.

16. 35% 0.35 17. 48% 0.48 18. 116% 1.16 19. 8% 0.08
20. 12% 0.12 21. 5.5% 0.055 22. 400% 4 23. 0.6% 0.006
24. 0.39 39% 25. 0.735 73.5% 26. 0.86 86% 27. 3.4 340%
28. 0.4 40% 29. 0.6 60% 30. 0.004 0.4% 31. 6 600%

ENRICHMENT

Minds on Math Transparency

6-7

Use a whole number, a fraction, and one plus sign to make four 2s add to 23.

$22 + \frac{2}{2}$

Course 2 Minds on Math Transparency 61

See *Solution Key* for worked-out answers.

Mental Math **Write each number as a percent.**

45. 0.5 50% 46. 0.9002 90.02% 47. 0.0028 0.28% 48. 1.25 125%
49. 0.0033 0.33% 50. 2.89 289% 51. 0.375 37.5% 52. 2.5 250%
53. 0.987 98.7% 54. 10.05 1,005% 55. 0.009 0.9% 56. 0.155 15.5%
57. 10 1,000% 58. 0.00675 0.675% 59. 67.8 6,780% 60. 37.5 3,750%

61. *Nutrition* The label at the right gives nutritional information for one serving of oatmeal.
   a. Write each percent as a fraction and as a decimal. See below.
   b. How many servings of oatmeal would you need to eat in order to have all the recommended vitamin A for a day? 25 servings
62. *Open-ended* Find five examples of percents used in a newspaper. Display your examples in class. Check students' work.

61a. $\frac{1}{10}$, 0.1; $\frac{3}{20}$, 0.15; $\frac{1}{25}$, 0.04; $\frac{1}{50}$, 0.02; $\frac{3}{100}$, 0.03

Mixed Review

Find the number with the given prime factorization. *(Lessons 4-4 and 4-5)*

63. $5^2 \cdot 7^2$ 1,225 64. $2^4 \cdot 3$ 48 65. $2 \cdot 5^3 \cdot 13$ 3,250 66. $2^2 \cdot 5 \cdot 7$ 140 67. $3 \cdot 5^2$ 75

Solve. *(Lesson 3-7)*

68. $-13t = 52$ −4 69. $-5x = -30$ 6 70. $-2 = \frac{x}{24}$ −48 71. $2f = -9$ −4.5 72. $\frac{g}{-17} = -51$ 867

73. *Choose a Strategy* There are 43 students in the chorus. Ten of them also play in the orchestra. There are 52 students in the orchestra. Eight orchestra members belong to both the chorus and the chess club. How many students belong to both the orchestra and the chorus but *not* to the chess club? 2

CHAPTER PROJECT

PROJECT LINK: CALCULATING

Use the results of your survey from the Project Link on page 236. Write ratios of the number of people who prefer each ride to the total number of people surveyed. Find the percent of people who prefer each ride.

Check students' work.

Extra Practice, Lesson 6-7, page 519

6-8 Teaching Notes

1 Focus

CONNECTING TO PRIOR KNOWLEDGE Have students look at the list of Problem Solving Strategies. Ask them to choose a strategy and give an example of a question that can be solved using the strategy. Encourage them to look at previous problem solving lessons for ideas.

2 Teach

THINK AND DISCUSS

VISUAL LEARNING Some students may find it helpful to draw a diagram of the problem. Have them read the problem carefully. They might label the diagram to show both boys' houses, the state park halfway between the houses, and the distances and rates.

Question 2 Point out that the strategy Working Backward is often used in problems involving arrival times.

ASSESSMENT Ask: *What strategies did you use to solve the problem?* **Answers may vary. Sample: Write an equation and work backward.**

Lesson Planning Options

Prerequisite Skills

- solving equations using division (3-7)
- writing improper fractions as mixed numbers (4-8)

Resources

Student Edition

Skills Handbook, p. 528
Extra Practice, p. 519
Glossary/Study Guide

Teaching Resources

Chapter Support File, Ch. 6
- Lesson Planner 6-8
- Practice 6-8, Reteaching 6-8
- Answer Masters 6-8

Glossary, Spanish Resources

Transparencies

Minds on Math 6-8

Warm Up

Use four different integers to complete the equation. Ask them to find as many different solutions as they can.

(■ · ■) + (■ · ■) = 18

Answers may vary. Sample: (3 · 4) + (1 · 6) = 18

PROBLEM SOLVING STRATEGY

6-8 Use Multiple Strategies

Problem Solving Strategies

- Draw a Diagram
- Guess and Test
- Look for a Pattern
- Make a Model
- Make a Table
- Simulate a Problem
- Solve a Simpler Problem
- Too Much or Too Little Information
- Use Logical Reasoning
- ✔ Use Multiple Strategies
- Work Backward
- Write an Equation

THINK AND DISCUSS

Sometimes you may need to use more than one strategy to solve a problem.

SAMPLE PROBLEM

Jack and his cousin Sam live in Texas. Their homes are 40 mi apart. One day, Jack suggested that they ride their bicycles to a state park halfway between their homes. Sam averages 10 mi/h on his bicycle, and Jack averages 12 mi/h. To meet at 1 P.M., what time should each boy leave home?

READ
Read for understanding. Summarize the problem.

Read the problem carefully.

1. a. How far apart do Jack and Sam live? **40 mi**
   b. What rate does each boy average when riding his bicycle? **Sam 10 mi/h, Jack 12 mi/h**

PLAN
Decide on a strategy.

Decide on strategies.

Write an equation to find how long each boy should ride. Work backward to find what time each boy should leave his home.

SOLVE
Try the strategy.

Each boy travels halfway, which is 20 mi. Let x represent the number of hours that Jack should ride his bicycle.

$$12x = 20$$
$$\frac{12x}{12} = \frac{20}{12}$$
$$x = 1\frac{2}{3}$$

Jack should ride his bicycle $1\frac{2}{3}$ h, which is 1 h 40 min.

Work backward to find what time Jack should leave home.

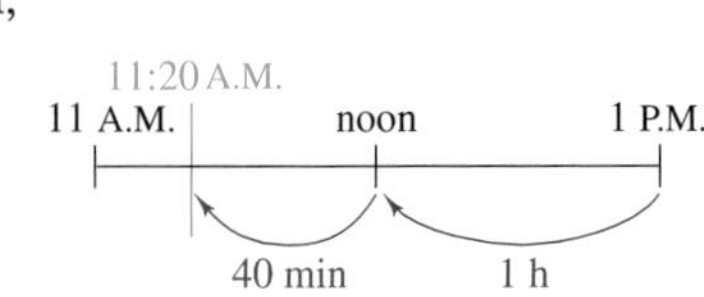

Jack should leave at 11:20 A.M.

■ ADDITIONAL PROBLEM

Ashley and Samantha are going to the beach for vacation. Ashley will fly the 560 mi and Samantha will take the train. They want to arrive at their terminals at the same time. At 6:30 A.M. Samantha boards a train that will travel 40 mi/h. Ashley's plane will travel at 224 mi/h. Which flight would Ashley take to arrive at the same time as Samantha: 4:00 P.M., 5:00 P.M., or 6:00 P.M.? **6:00 P.M.**

3 Practice/Assess

EXERCISES *On Your Own*

Exercises 1–3 Have students name the strategies they use.

Exercise 5 Students can make a diagram to solve this problem.

ERROR ALERT! **Exercise 6** Students may count too quickly and miss some of the overlapping triangles. **Remediation:** Suggest students find a base and count all the triangles made with that base before going on to another base.

Exercise 7 Point out $2\frac{1}{2}$ times the recipe should make 5 dozen cookies.

2. When should Sam leave his home to meet Jack?
   11:00 A.M. 3. Check students' work.

LOOK BACK
Think about how you solved the problem.

3. Did you solve the problem correctly? Add the traveling time to the starting time for Jack and Sam. Will both boys arrive at the state park at 1:00 P.M.? You will have to think, "One hour past 12:00 can be expressed as 1:00 or 13:00."

Now you may assign Exercises 1–12.

EXERCISES *On Your Own*

Use multiple strategies to solve each problem. Show all your work.

1. a. A fenced-in rectangular area has a perimeter of 40 ft. The fence has a post every 4 ft. How many posts are there? **10**
   b. There must be a post at each corner. What do you think the length and width of the field are?
   c. Are there any other possible answers to part (b)? Explain. **Yes; check students' work for reasoning.**
   b. 8 ft × 12 ft or 4 ft × 16 ft
2. A kite and its tail total 27 ft in length. The tail is five times as long as the body. How long is the kite's tail? **22.5 ft**
3. A grocer stacks oranges in the shape of a square pyramid. How many oranges will she use if one side of the base has 6 oranges? **91**

Aerodynamics The smaller the ratio of the weight of a kite to its surface area, the better the kite will fly.

Use any strategy to solve each problem. Show your work.

4. *Consumer Issues* Susan, the Science Club treasurer, found that the bill for 18 sweatshirts ordered by the club had two digits blurred by water damage. Susan was sure that the first and last digits were the same. What do you think the total price is? Explain your choice.
   $■68.9■ **$268.92; 18 divides into this number without any remainder.**
5. *Social Studies* At the beginning of every new term, each of the nine judges on the Supreme Court shakes hands with every other judge. How many handshakes take place? **36**
6. *Geometry* How many triangles are in the design at the right? **35**

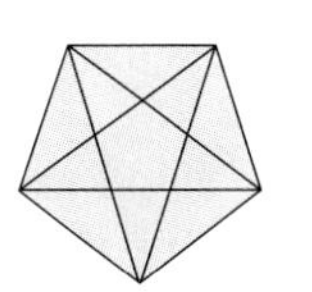

7. *Cooking* A recipe that makes 2 dozen raisin bars calls for $\frac{3}{4}$ c. of flour. How much flour will be needed to make 5 dozen? **$1\frac{7}{8}$c**

Technology Options

Prentice Hall Technology

Software for Learners
- Math Blaster® Mystery*
- Interactive Student Tutorial, Chapter 6*

Teaching Resource Software
- Computer Item Generator 6-8
- Resource Pro™ Chapter 6*

Internet • For related mathematics activities, visit the Prentice Hall site at www.phschool.com/math

**Available on CD-ROM only*

Assignment Options for Exercises On Your Own

Core 1–8, 10–12
Extension 9

Use Mixed Review to maintain skills.

PRACTICE

Practice 6-8 Problem-Solving Strategy: Use Multiple Strategies

Choose any strategy to solve. Show all your work.

1. Find four consecutive numbers that have a sum of 118.
   28, 29, 30, 31
2. Use the digits 3, 6, 7, and 8. Find all of the four-digit numbers that are divisible by 6. Use a digit only once in each number.
   3,678; 3,768; 3,786; 3,876; 6,378; 6,738; 7,368;
   7,386; 7,638; 7,836; 8,376; 8,736
3. A baby was 20 in. long at birth. The baby's body was 10 in. longer than the length of her head. How long was her head?
   5 in.
4. Frank and Ernest live 220 mi apart. They decide to meet at noon one Saturday at a restaurant exactly halfway between them. Frank will drive at a constant speed of 55 mi/h. Ernest will only drive at a constant speed of 50 mi/h. In order to meet at noon, when should each person leave home?
   Frank: 10:00 A.M.; Ernest: 9:48 A.M.
5. Find three consecutive numbers that have a sum of 381.
   126, 127, 128
6. Use the digits 1, 2, 7, and 8. Find all of the four-digit numbers that are divisible by 4. Use a digit only once in each number.
   1,728; 1,872; 7,128; 7,812; 8,172; 8,712
7. Samuel had a board 5 ft long that he cut into two pieces. One piece was 8 in. longer than the other. How long was the shorter board?
   26 in.
8. A fenced-in yard has length of 80 ft and width 120 ft. The fence has a post every 4 ft. How many posts are there?
   100 posts

In copymaster and workbook formats

RETEACHING

Reteaching 6-8 Problem-Solving Strategy: Use Multiple Strategies

Mario weighs 40 lb more than Lisa. Together they weigh 280 lb. How much does Mario weigh?

Read Read the problem carefully. How much do Mario and Lisa weigh? How much more does Mario weigh than Lisa?

Plan Think about strategies you could use: Make a table to list the possibilities.

Guess and test to find the correct answer.

Solve

Lisa	80	100	120	140
Mario	120	140	160	180

Use the table. If Lisa weighs 80 lb and Mario weighs 120 lb, together they weigh 200 lb, which is not enough.

If Lisa weighs 120 lb and Mario weighs 160 lb, together they weigh 280 lb, which is the correct amount.

Look Back Is Mario's weight 40 lb more than Lisa's? *Yes.* Is the sum of the weights 280 lb? *Yes.*

Use multiple strategies to solve each problem.

1. Kiandra spent $\frac{1}{2}$ of her money on a CD and $\frac{1}{3}$ on a movie and popcorn. She now had $4. How much money did she start with?
   $24
2. Jamil plays checkers with a computer. If Jamil wins, he gets 5 points. If the computer wins, it gets 2 points. They play 49 games and end with a tie score. How many games did the computer win?
   35 games
3. Rex and Cara biked a total of 40 mi for the school bikeathon. Cara biked 8 mi more than Rex. How many miles did each person ride?
   Rex rode 16 mi; Cara rode 24 mi
4. The product of two whole numbers is 72. What is the greatest sum possible for the two numbers?
   73 (1 and 72)
5. If you spin this spinner three times and find the total of your spins, how many different totals are possible?
   10

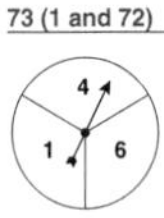

Reteaching

ENRICHMENT

Minds on Math Transparency

6-8

A father wants to give some land to his three children. He gives $\frac{1}{2}$ of the land to the oldest child, $\frac{1}{3}$ of the land to his second child, $\frac{1}{9}$ of the land to his youngest child. Then he keeps 1 acre for himself. How many acres of land does each child get?

The oldest child gets 9 acres, the second child gets 6 acres, and the youngest child gets 2 acres.

See *Solution Key* for worked-out answers.

WRAP UP

IDENTIFYING THE BIG IDEA Have students explain why multiple strategies are needed to solve some problems. Then have them give a real-world example.

LESSON QUIZ

1. Find a two-digit even number between 50 and 100 such that the difference of the digits is a prime number and the sum of the digits is also prime. **Answers may vary. Sample: 52**
2. A boat and a trailer total 40 ft in length. The trailer is 8 ft longer than the length of the boat. How long are the boat and the trailer? **boat, 16 ft; trailer, 24 ft**

8. *Jobs* Carla and Tanya were paid $45.00 for painting a fence. Carla worked 6 h, and Tanya worked 9 h. How much is Tanya's share of the money? **$27**

9. *Patterns* Examine the list at the right and look for a pattern.
   a. Write the sixth row.
   b. What is the last number in the 11th row? in the 23rd row? **21; 45**
   c. What is the sum of the numbers in the 4th row? in the 10th row? **16; 100**
   d. *Reasoning* How can you find the sum of any row when you know the row number? **The sum is the square of the row number.**

row 1	1
row 2	1 3
row 3	1 3 5
row 4	1 3 5 7
row 5	1 3 5 7 9
row 6	■

1 3 5 7 9 11

10. *Money* Trevor has $8 in his savings account and adds $1 each week. Aretha has $12 in her savings account and adds $3 each week. After how many weeks will Aretha's account have twice as much money as Trevor's? **4 weeks**

11. Alvin, Breon, and Carl work as an artist, a banker, and a conductor. Alvin and the artist play tennis together. The conductor helped Carl plant his garden. Breon is not the conductor, and he does not know Alvin. What does each person do for a living?
    Alvin is the conductor, Breon is the banker, and Carl is the artist.

12. A box contains the five disks below. Suppose you draw three disks at random and add the numbers together. How many different totals are possible? What are they?
    8 ways; 5,7,8,10,11,13,15,16

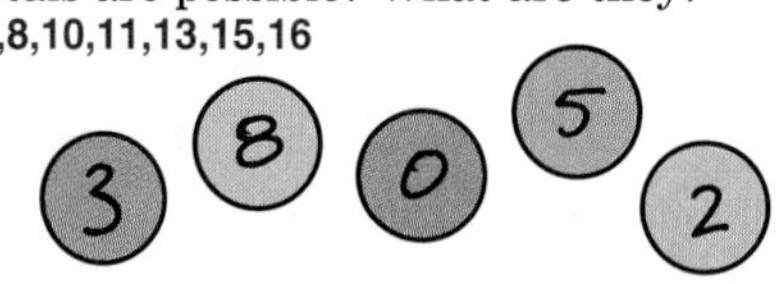

Mixed Review

Find each product. *(Lesson 5-5)*

13. $\frac{2}{5} \cdot \frac{5}{12}$ **$\frac{1}{6}$**
14. $\frac{6}{14} \cdot \frac{12}{18}$ **$\frac{2}{7}$**
15. $\frac{3}{7} \cdot 15$ **$6\frac{3}{7}$**
16. $\frac{4}{5} \cdot 2\frac{3}{4}$ **$2\frac{1}{5}$**
17. $2\frac{2}{3} \cdot 2\frac{1}{4}$ **6**

Write as a ratio in three ways. *(Lesson 6-1)*

18. 3 students to 8 students **3 : 8, 3 to 8, $\frac{3}{8}$**
19. 2 wins to 11 losses **2 : 11, 2 to 11, $\frac{2}{11}$**
20. 180 lb to 150 lb **180 : 150, 180 to 150, $\frac{180}{150}$**
21. a. Mariko found s shells on the beach. She shared them equally with her brother. The variable expression to show the number of shells each person had is $s \div$ ■. **2**
    b. Evaluate the expression for $s = 14$. *(Lesson 3-1)* **7**

6-9 Teaching Notes

1 Focus

CONNECTING TO PRIOR KNOWLEDGE Ask students:

- *What percent is a common tip for a waiter or waitress?* **15%**
- *Write 15% as a fraction.* $\frac{15}{100}$
- *What is $\frac{15}{100}$ of a meal costing \$20?* **\$3**

2 Teach

THINK AND DISCUSS

AEP Relate *percent* to other words containing *cent* that have a meaning connected with 100. For example: A *cent* is $\frac{1}{100}$ of a dollar, and a *century* is 100 years.

EXTENSION **Question 6** Have students interview a store manager. Some possible questions: *What are your responsibilities? How do you use percents in your job?*

TACTILE LEARNING **Example 2** Have students cut out sale ads offering percent discounts. Ask students to group the ads according to the percent. Have them calculate the amount of savings on each item. Then organize the ads by the amount of savings.

DATA ANALYSIS Connection

6-9 Finding Percent of a Number

What You'll Learn

1. To use a percent to find part of a whole
2. To find discount prices

...And Why

Retail store managers use proportions and survey data to predict customer buying patterns.

Here's How

Look for questions that
- build understanding
- ✓ check understanding

6. Answers may vary. Sample: Percents; the manager could reasonably assume the same percents would apply to the general population.

7c. Answers may vary. Sample: Use a decimal when working on a calculator; use a fraction when working with fractional amounts or when mental computations are easy.

WHERE? In 1996, toy sales in the United States totaled \$20.7 billion, or about \$357 per person. In Japan, toy sales totaled \$7.9 billion, or about \$390 per person.

Source: U.S. Toy Manufacturers Association

THINK AND DISCUSS

1 *Using Percents to Find Part of a Whole*

You can use a graph to present percent data.

1. What did most people have on their gift list? **clothing**
2. What do about $\frac{1}{3}$ of the people have on their list? $\frac{1}{4}$ of the people? **music; jewelry**
3. How many people answered the survey? **1,012 adults**
4. Why do you think the sum of the percents is greater than 100%? **People could choose more than one item.**

Gifts Holiday Shoppers Plan to Buy

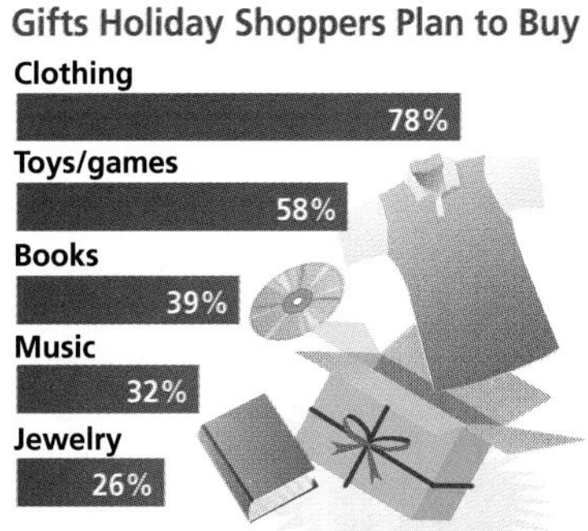

Survey of 1,012 adults

Source: *USA Today*

■ **EXAMPLE 1** *Real-World Problem Solving*

Use the graph above. Find the number of the people surveyed who have clothing on their gift lists.

$78\% = 0.78$ ← Change the percent to a decimal.

$0.78 \times 1{,}012 = 789.36$ ← Multiply.

About 789 people have clothing on their gift lists.

5. ✓ *Try It Out* Use the graph. About how many people have music on their gift list? **about 324 people**

6. *Go a Step Further* Would a department store manager be more interested in the percents or in the actual number of people who responded in each category? Explain.

6. See above left. **7b. $0.25 \times 44 = 11$; $\frac{1}{4} \times 44 = 11$**

7. a. Write 25% as a decimal and a fraction. **0.25; $\frac{1}{4}$**
   b. Use both the decimal and the fraction to find 25% of 44.
   c. *Reasoning* When would you use a decimal to find a percent? When would you use a fraction? **See above left.**

Now you may assign Exercises 1–27.

Lesson Planning Options

Prerequisite Skills

- multiplying decimals (2-5)
- writing percents as decimals (6-7)

Materials/Manipulatives

- calculator

Resources

Student Edition

Skills Handbook, p. 535
Extra Practice, p. 519
Glossary/Study Guide

Teaching Resources

Chapter Support File, Ch. 6
- Lesson Planner 6-9
- Practice 6-9, Reteaching 6-9
- Answer Masters 6-9

Glossary, Spanish Resources

Transparencies

15, Minds on Math 6-9

Warm Up

Without computing, explain why 40% of 22 is less than 11. **11 is half, or 50%, of 22, so 40% of 22 must be less than 11.**

ALTERNATIVE METHOD Question 8b Have students calculate 25% of the original price. Point out this is the savings amount. Then have them subtract the savings amount from the original price. Have them find the answer again by computing 75% of the original price. Compare the two answers. They should be the same. Ask: *Which method do you prefer?* **Answers may vary. Sample: finding 75% because it has fewer steps**

■ ADDITIONAL EXAMPLES

FOR EXAMPLE 1

Use the graph. Find the number of people surveyed who have books on their gift lists. **395**

FOR EXAMPLE 2

At another store, the telephone sells for 30% off the original price of $24. Find the sale price of the telephone. **$16.80**

3 Practice/Assess

EXERCISES *On Your Own*

ASSESSMENT Exercises 1–15 Write the correct answers for each problem on the board. Do not put them in order. Have students check their work by matching their answers to the answers on the board. If they cannot find their answer, have students check with a partner to find their mistake.

Technology Options

Prentice Hall Technology

Software for Learners
- Math Blaster® Mystery*
- Interactive Student Tutorial, Chapter 6*

Teaching Resource Software
- Computer Item Generator 6-9
- Resource Pro™ Chapter 6*

Internet • For related mathematics activities, visit the Prentice Hall site at www.phschool.com/math

**Available on CD-ROM only*

Assignment Options for Exercises On Your Own

To provide flexible scheduling, this lesson can be split into parts.

1 **Core** 1–25
Extension 26, 27

2 **Core** 28, 29, 35, 36
Extension 30–34

Use Mixed Review to maintain skills.

2 *Finding Discount Prices*

Advertisements that say "40% off" or "Price reduced 40%" tell you the percent a price was reduced. This is the sale price or discount price.

■ EXAMPLE 2 *Real-World Problem Solving*

Consumer Issues Find the sale price of the telephone. Round to the nearest cent.

$100\% - 40\% = 60\%$ ← The sale price is 60% of the original price.

$60\% = 0.6$ ← Write the percent as a decimal.

$0.6 \times 24 = 14.4$ ← Multiply.

The sale price of the telephone is $14.40.

8. ✔ *Try It Out* Sneakers that cost $48.99 go on sale for 25% off. **8a. 75%** **b. $36.74**
   a. What percent of the original price is the sale price?
   b. What is the sale price? Round to the nearest cent.

Now you may assign Exercises 28–36.

EXERCISES *On Your Own*

Find each answer.

1. 6% of 90 **5.4**	2. 125% of 64 **80**	3. 12.5% of 56 **7**	4. 12% of 230 **27.6**	5. 75% of 240 **180**
6. 18% of 90 **16.2**	7. 3% of 12 **0.36**	8. 150% of 17 **25.5**	9. 7% of 300 **21**	10. 60% of 120 **72**
11. 11% of 121 **13.31**	12. 27% of 120 **32.4**	13. 98% of 65 **63.7**	14. 20% of 80 **16**	15. 15% of 45 **6.75**

Choose **Use a calculator, paper and pencil, or mental math to solve each problem.**

16. Find 37.5% of 12. **4.5**	17. What is 8% of 25? **2**	18. Find 30% of 40. **12**
19. What is 25% of 95? **23.75**	20. Find 190% of 13. **24.7**	21. What is 20% of 20? **4**
22. Find 30% of 120. **36**	23. Find 12% of 33. **3.96**	24. What is 120% of 34? **40.8**

25. *Social Studies* Mesa, Arizona, is one of the fastest-growing cities in the United States. In 1994, the population was almost 500% of its 1970 total of 63,000.
   a. Write an expression to find the population in 1994. $\frac{500}{100} \times 63{,}000$
   b. Find the population in 1994. **315,000**

ERROR ALERT! Exercises 1–15 Some students may not convert the percent to a decimal before multiplying. **Remediation:** Have students estimate the answers by sketching a bar and shading the percent in the problem. Tell them to imagine the whole bar represents the whole—the number after the *of*—and the shaded part represents the part—the number they want. By estimating the amount shaded, they can see if they remembered to convert the percent to a decimal by moving the decimal two places to the right before multiplying.

MENTAL MATH Exercises 16–24 Have students check the reasonableness of their answers by using mental math to calculate 10%, 50%, and 100%. For example: 10% of 90 is 9, so 6% of 90 should be less than 9.

EXTENSION and CONNECTION TO SOCIAL STUDIES Exercise 25 Have students research to find the population of their own city or town in 1970 and 1994. Ask students to find the percent of change by writing the fraction $\frac{\text{1994 population}}{\text{1970 population}}$ and changing it to a percent.

REASONING Exercise 26a Challenge students to reduce $\frac{110}{100}$ to a mixed number. $\frac{110}{100} = \frac{11}{10} = 1\frac{1}{10}$

ALTERNATIVE METHOD and OPEN-ENDED Exercise 34 Many sale circulars show the sale price rather than the percent of discount. If the circular lists the sale price, ask students to calculate the percent of the discount by writing the fraction $\frac{\text{sale price}}{\text{original price}}$. Remind them to subtract their percent from 100.

26. a. *Reasoning* The number of students in this year's seventh grade class is 110% of the number in last year's class. When you write 110% as a ratio, what number is in the denominator? Why? **See below.**
    b. Do you think there will be more or fewer students in this year's class? Why? **more; 110 > 100**
    c. There were 260 students in last year's class. How many students are in this year's class? **286 students**

26a. 100; the denominator in a percent ratio is always 100.

27. *Data Analysis* 150 high school students were surveyed about their foreign language classes. The graph at the right shows their responses.
    a. How many students take French? What percent of the 150 students surveyed is that? **35 students; 23.3%**
    b. Find the percent of students taking each language. **See below.**
    c. *Estimation* The high school population is 2,500. Use the percents you found in parts (a) and (b). Estimate the total number of students at the school taking each language.

French students, 583; German students, 283; Spanish students, 1,133.

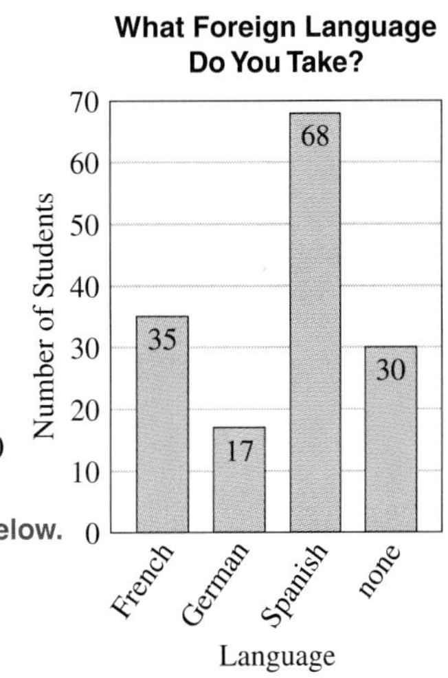

27b. French, 23.3%; German, 11.3%; Spanish, 45.3%

28. *Technology* The regular price of a calculator is $15.40. It is on sale for 30% off of the regular price. Find the sale price. **$10.78**

29. **Choose A, B, C, or D.** Which expression will *not* help you find the price of a $60 item on sale for 25% off? **D**

    A. 60 − 0.25(60) B. 0.75(60)
    C. 60(1 − 0.25) D. 60 − 0.75(60)

Hobbies **Use the advertisement at the right for Exercises 30–33.**

30. a. What percent of the original price of the calico fabric is the sale price? **70%**
    b. What is the sale price? **$3.98/yd**

31. What is the sale price of the children's patterns? **$2.49**

32. Find the sale price of the scissors. **$9.74**

33. Which costs less on sale, the calico or the cotton knit fabric? How much less? **the calico fabric; $.21/yd**

34. *Open-ended* Find a sale circular. Choose five items from the circular. Calculate the sale price of each item based on the original price of the item and the percent discount. **Check students' work.**

CHECKPOINT 2

Checkpoint 2

Lessons 6-4 through 6-9

1. The scale drawing for a house uses a scale of $\frac{1}{2}$ in. : 2 ft. If the length of a room is $2\frac{3}{4}$ in. on the drawing, what is the actual length of the room? 11 ft
2. The triangles on the right are similar. Find x. 10

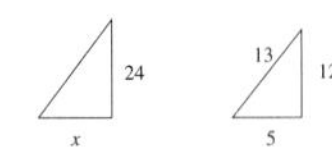

Write each fraction as a percent.

3. $\frac{18}{20}$ 90%
4. $\frac{9}{8}$ 112.5%
5. $\frac{1}{125}$ 0.8%
6. What percent of 84 is 21? 25%
7. 12 is what percent of 30? 40%
8. What is 200% of 30? 60
9. What is 80% of 26? 20.8
10. At the school pep rally, 208 students are wearing red. If there are 260 students at the rally, what percent are wearing red? 80%

PRACTICE

Practice 6-9 Finding the Percent of a Number

Find each answer.

1. What is 20% of 560? 112
2. What is 42% of 200? 84
3. What is 9% of 50? 4.5
4. Find 40% of 70. 28
5. What is 25% of 80? 20
6. What is 50% of 80? 40
7. What is 40% of 200? 80
8. Find 5% of 80. 4
9. What is 75% of 200? 150

Choose a calculator, paper and pencil, or mental math to solve.

10. What is 14% of 120? 16.8
11. Find 30% of 180. 54
12. What is 62.5% of 24? 15
13. What is 34% of 50? 17
14. What is 25% of 240? 60
15. Find 85.5% of 23. 19.665
16. What is 120% of 56? 67.2
17. Find 80% of 90. 72
18. What is 42% of 120? 50.4

Farmer Jones raised a watermelon that weighed 20 lb. From his experience with raising watermelons, he estimated that 95% of the watermelon's weight is water.

19. How much of the watermelon is water? 19 lb
20. How much of the watermelon is not water? 1 lb
21. The watermelon was shipped off to market. There it sat, until it had dehydrated (lost water) and only 90% of the watermelon's weight was water. If the watermelon is now only 90% water, what percent of it is not water? 10 %
22. The solid part of the watermelon still weighs the same. What was the weight of the watermelon at this point? 10 lb

Solve.

23. A bicycle goes on sale at 75% of its original price of $160. What is its sale price? $120

Practice

In copymaster and workbook formats

RETEACHING

Reteaching 6-9 Finding the Percent of a Number

	Find 12% of 50.	Find 150% of 90.
① Write the percent as a decimal.	0.12	1.5
② Multiply.	0.12 · 50 = 6	1.5 · 90 = 135
	12% of 50 is 6.	150% of 90 is 135.

Complete to find each answer.

1. 15% of 80
   15% = 0.15
   0.15 · 80 = 12
2. 4% of 70
   4% = 0.04
   0.04 · 70 = 2.8
3. 70% of 20
   70% = 0.7
   0.7 · 20 = 14

Find each answer.

4. 10% of 80 8
5. 20% of 80 16
6. 50% of 80 40
7. 75% of 80 60
8. 9% of 70 6.3
9. 2% of 66 1.32
10. 28% of 50 14
11. 75% of 20 15
12. 16% of 35 5.6
13. 94% of 22 20.68
14. 33% of 50 16.5
15. 40% of 45 18
16. 120% of 30 36
17. 110% of 70 77
18. 160% of 200 320
19. 180% of 250 450
20. 145% of 78 113.1
21. 187% of 40 74.8
22. 164% of 350 574
23. 125% of 230 287.5

Solve.

24. Pablo's weekly salary is $105. Each week he saves 60% of his salary. How much does he save each week? $63
25. The sixth-grade class is selling magazine subscriptions to raise money for charity. They give 55% of the money they raise to the homeless. If they raise $2,670, how much do they give to the homeless? $1,468.50

ENRICHMENT

Minds on Math Transparency

6-9

I am a 2-digit number. I am the difference of two numbers whose sum is 36. The larger of these numbers is twice the smaller. What number am I?

12

See *Solution Key* for worked-out answers.

WRITING **Exercise 35** Students can refer to the ads they used for Exercise 34.

WRAP UP

IDENTIFYING THE BIG IDEA Ask students to explain how to find the percent of a number.

JOURNAL Ask students to consider the reason it is important to evaluate the amount they will spend, as well as the amount they will save.

LESSON QUIZ

1. Find 40% of 90. 36
2. What is 8% of 19? 1.52
3. Find 120% of 45. 54
4. The regular price of a backpack is $32. It is on sale for 15% off the regular price. Find the sale price. $27.20

35. *Writing* Write a word problem about finding the sale price of an item. Solve your problem. Check students' work.
36. *Technology* The price of a new version of a computer game is 120% of the price of the original version. The original version cost $48. What is the cost of the new version? $57.60

JOURNAL How could you use percents during a store-wide clearance sale to make wise buying decisions?

Mixed Review

Write each fraction in simplest form. (Lesson 4-6)

37. $\frac{8}{10}$ $\frac{4}{5}$
38. $\frac{4}{12}$ $\frac{1}{3}$
39. $\frac{5}{100}$ $\frac{1}{20}$
40. $\frac{16}{24}$ $\frac{2}{3}$
41. $\frac{10}{70}$ $\frac{1}{7}$
42. $\frac{18}{54}$ $\frac{1}{3}$

Complete. (Lesson 5-8)

43. 6 ft 3 in. = ■ ft $6\frac{1}{4}$
44. 4 lb 2 oz = ■ oz 66
45. $5\frac{1}{2}$ c = ■ fl oz 44
46. 3 yd = ■ ft 9
47. *Choose a Strategy* A student spends $\frac{3}{8}$ of her money on a sweatshirt and $\frac{1}{2}$ of the remaining amount on a cassette. She now has $15. How much money did she have originally? $48

✓ CHECKPOINT 2

Lessons 6-4 through 6-9

Write each fraction as a percent.

1. $\frac{4}{5}$ 80%
2. $\frac{1}{250}$ 0.4%
3. $\frac{1}{3}$ $33\frac{1}{3}\%$
4. $\frac{14}{25}$ 56%
5. $\frac{13}{25}$ 52%
6. $\frac{3}{15}$ 20%

Write each percent as a decimal and as a fraction.

7. 17% 0.17, $\frac{17}{100}$
8. 29% 0.29, $\frac{29}{100}$
9. 135% 1.35, $1\frac{7}{20}$
10. 77% 0.77, $\frac{77}{100}$
11. 98% 0.98, $\frac{49}{50}$
12. 45% 0.45, $\frac{9}{20}$

Find each answer.

13. What is 29% of 58? 16.82
14. 60 is what percent of 35? 171%
15. What is 90% of 16? 14.4
16. *Geometry* $\Delta ABC \sim \Delta FDE$. Find x and y. 10, 6

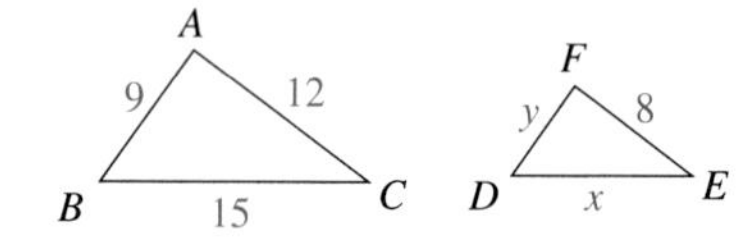

17. *Maps* A map's scale is 1 in. : 15 mi. Two towns are 3.5 in. apart on the map. What is the actual distance? 52.5 mi
18. A club has 100 members. Each of the 5 officers calls 6 other members to help them decorate for a club party. What percent of the club members help decorate? 35%

Extra Practice, Lesson 6-9, page 519

6-10 Teaching Notes

1 Focus

CONNECTING TO PRIOR KNOWLEDGE Review cross products with the class. Ask students: *Solve the proportion* $\frac{25}{100} = \frac{14}{x}$. $x = 56$ Then ask: *What percent is represented by the fraction* $\frac{25}{100}$? **25%**

2 Teach

THINK AND DISCUSS

AEP AUDITORY LEARNING Students may benefit from memorizing the basic percent proportion. Have them practice reciting $\frac{\text{percent}}{100} = \frac{\text{part}}{\text{whole}}$.

TACTILE LEARNING Examples 1 and 2 Have students write $\frac{\text{percent}}{100}$ on an index card. Have them write $\frac{\text{part}}{\text{whole}}$ on another index card. Place the two cards side-by-side. These are the two ratios in a percent proportion. Have them cut several index cards in half. Write *x* on one of the halves to stand for the unknown. They can use the other halves to write the numbers given in the problem. For Example 1, students can place the *x* card over the word *percent*. Then they can place the number 18 over the word *part*, and the number 25 over the word *whole*. Have them check the set up of their proportion before continuing to solve.

ALGEBRA Connection

6-10 Using Proportions with Percents

What You'll Learn

1. To find what percent one number is of another
2. To find a number when you know a percent and a part

...And Why

Business people use percents to advertise sales.

Here's How

Look for questions that
- build understanding
- ✔ check understanding

THINK AND DISCUSS

1 *Finding a Percent*

You can use models to understand the relationship of one number to another. You can use your model to write a proportion to express the relationship as a percent.

■ **EXAMPLE 1** *Real-World Problem Solving*

Eighteen students in a class of 25 students plan to go on a class hiking trip. What percent of the students plan to go on the trip?

Model the relationship.

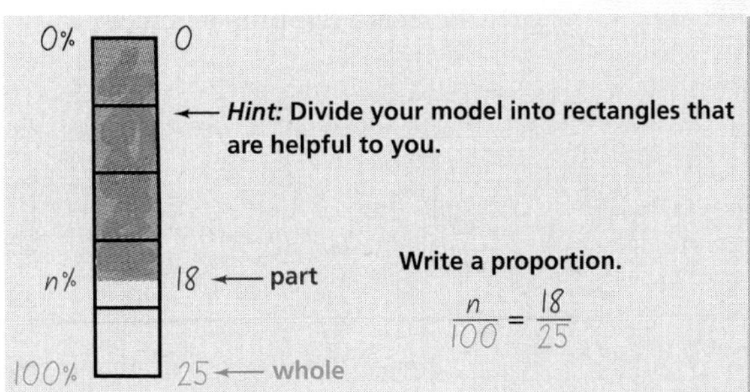

Solve the proportion.

$\frac{n}{100} = \frac{18}{25}$ ← Simplify by multiplying each side by 100.

$n = \frac{1800}{25}$ ← Divide.

$n = 72$

72% of the class plan to go on the trip.

1. **Look Back** The model in Example 1 has five equal rectangles. What percent does each rectangle represent? **20%**

2a–b. See margin p. 273 for models.

2. ✔ **Try It Out** Draw a model for each problem. Then solve.
   a. What percent of 90 is 36? **40%**
   b. What percent of 60 is 15? **25%**

Now you may assign Exercises 1–2, 5–15.

Lesson Planning Options

Prerequisite Skills
- modeling fractions (4-1)
- solving proportions (6-3)

Materials/Manipulatives
- calculator

Resources

Student Edition

Skills Handbook, pp. 530, 531
Extra Practice, p. 519
Glossary/Study Guide

Teaching Resources

Chapter Support File, Ch. 6
- Lesson Planner 6-10
- Practice 6-10, Reteaching 6-10
- Answer Masters 6-10

Glossary, Spanish Resources

Transparencies
15, Minds on Math 6-10

Warm Up

Use mental math to find each product or quotient.

8.75×100 **875**
9.6×100 **960**
$4.6 \div 10$ **0.46**
0.94×100 **94**
$4.06 \div 100$ **0.0406**

ASSESSMENT Ask students to fold a piece of paper in thirds. Have them copy the headings from the bottom of page 272: *Finding a Part, Finding a Percent, and Finding a Whole.* Ask students to draw a model to represent the problems given under each heading. They solve the exercises by cross multiplying. Have them use their model to check solutions.
5, 20, 25

ADDITIONAL EXAMPLES

FOR EXAMPLE 1

Seventeen students in a class of 20 students plan to go on a class biking trip. What percent of the students plan to go on the trip? **85%**

FOR EXAMPLE 2

14 is 12.5% of what number? **112**

EXTENSION and CONNECTION TO ALGEBRA
Students may want to solve the problems algebraically. Have them translate the problem into an equation and then solve. Remind them *is* means "=", *of* means "·", and *percent* should be written as a fraction with 100 for a denominator and a variable for the numerator. For example: The sentence *5 is what percent of 25?* becomes $5 = n \cdot 25$. Then have students solve for *n*. **20%**

Technology Options

Prentice Hall Technology

Software for Learners
- Math Blaster® Mystery*
- Interactive Student Tutorial, Chapter 6*

Teaching Resource Software
- Computer Item Generator 6-10
- Resource Pro™ Chapter 6*

Internet • For related mathematics activities, visit the Prentice Hall site at www.phschool.com/math

**Available on CD-ROM only*

Assignment Options for Exercises On Your Own

To provide flexible scheduling, this lesson can be split into parts.

1 **Core** 1, 2, 5–12, 14, 15
Extension 13

2 **Core** 3, 4, 16–25, 27
Extension 26

Use Mixed Review to maintain skills.

2 *Using Percents to Find a Whole*

Sometimes you are asked to find the whole when you know a part and what percent the part is of the whole.

EXAMPLE 2

29 is 72.5% of what number?

Model the relationship.

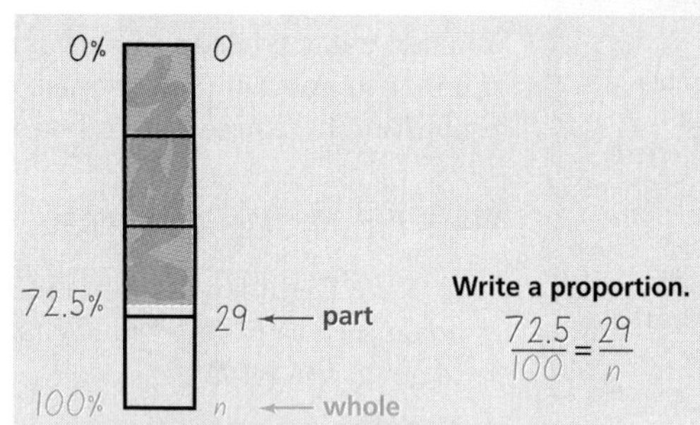

Solve the proportion.

$$\frac{72.5}{100} = \frac{29}{n}$$
$$72.5n = 29 \cdot 100 \quad \leftarrow \text{Write cross products.}$$
$$n = \frac{29 \cdot 100}{72.5} \quad \leftarrow \text{Divide each side by 72.5.}$$
$$n = 40 \quad \leftarrow \text{Find the value of the expression.}$$

29 is 72.5% of 40.

3. *Look Back* The model in Example 2 has four equal rectangles. What percent does each rectangle represent? **25%**

4. *✓Try It Out* A sweater is on sale for $34. This is 75% of the original price. Find the original price. **$45.33**

Here is a summary of what you have learned.

PERCENTS AND PROPORTIONS

Finding a Part	Finding a Percent	Finding a Whole
20% of 25 is what number?	5 is what percent of 25?	20% of what number is 5?
$\frac{20}{100} = \frac{n}{25} \begin{array}{l}\leftarrow \text{part} \\ \leftarrow \text{whole}\end{array}$	$\frac{n}{100} = \frac{5}{25} \begin{array}{l}\leftarrow \text{part} \\ \leftarrow \text{whole}\end{array}$	$\frac{20}{100} = \frac{5}{n} \begin{array}{l}\leftarrow \text{part} \\ \leftarrow \text{whole}\end{array}$

Now you may assign Exercises 3–4, 16–27.

3 Practice/Assess

EXERCISES *On Your Own*

ERROR ALERT! Exercises 6–11 Some students may have difficulty writing the proportion correctly. **Remediation:** Have students identify the part and the whole by looking for the words *of* and *is.* We write the word *of* immediately before the number representing the *whole.* The word *is* comes before or after the number representing the *part.* For example: In "what percent of 10 is 15?" *10* is the *whole*, and *15* is the *part.*

CONNECTION TO SOCIAL STUDIES
Exercise 14 Have students research to find the number of new members in the House of Representatives for the current year. Ask: *What percent are new?*

Exercises 19–24 If you have block scheduling or extended class periods, have students rewrite these exercises. After they have solved their proportions, have them rewrite each problem with a different number missing. For Exercise 19, students could write: *108 is 225% of what number?* Have them trade with a partner to solve the rewritten exercises.

Exercise 26 Point out $10,930.95 is the sale price, not the amount of discount.

WRITING Exercise 27c Ask students to consider the differences between saving $30 and saving 30%.

EXERCISES *On Your Own*

Write a proportion and solve each problem.

1. $\frac{n}{100} = \frac{12}{15}$; $n = 80$

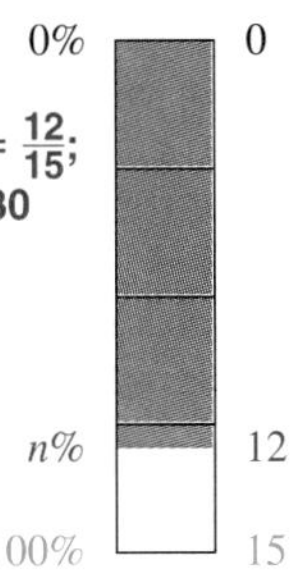

2. $\frac{n}{100} = \frac{17}{68}$; $n = 25$

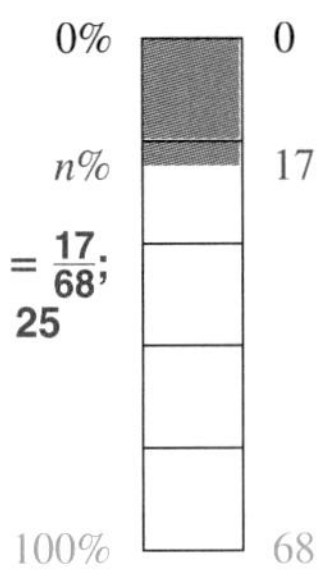

3. $\frac{75}{100} = \frac{6}{n}$; $n = 8$

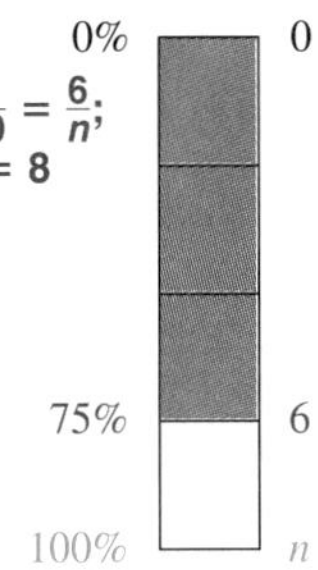

4. $\frac{60}{100} = \frac{30}{n}$; $n = 50$

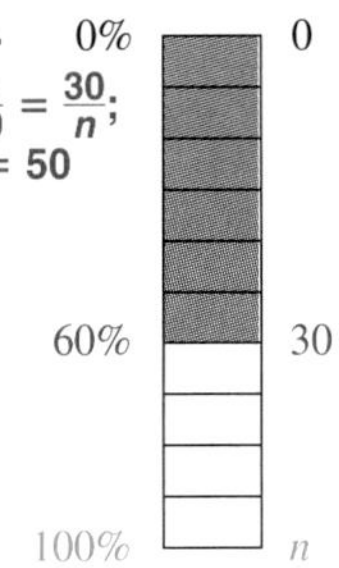

5. **Choose A, B, C, or D.** Choose the proportion that will help you find what percent 13 is of 20. A

A. $\frac{13}{20} = \frac{n}{100}$ B. $\frac{n}{20} = \frac{13}{100}$ C. $\frac{13}{n} = \frac{100}{20}$ D. $\frac{n}{13} = \frac{20}{100}$

Choose **Use a calculator, paper and pencil, or mental math to solve each problem.**

6. 24 is what percent of 32? 75%
7. What percent of 230 is 23? 10%
8. What percent of 25 is 23? 92%
9. 5 is what percent of 15? $33\frac{1}{3}$%
10. What percent of 400 is 8? 2%
11. What percent of 20 is 25? 125%
12. a. 50 is what percent of 75? $66\frac{2}{3}$%
    b. 75 is what percent of 50? 150%
    c. Which results in a percent greater than 100%, your answer to part (a) or to part (b)? Why? b; 75 > 50
13. What percent of the numbers from 1 to 20 are prime? 40%

Choose **Use a calculator, paper and pencil, or mental math to solve each problem. Round your answer to the nearest percent.**

14. *Social Studies* In 1996, voters elected 79 new members to the House of Representatives. The total number of representatives is 435. What percent were new? 18%
15. *Biology* The blood of an 85-lb German shepherd dog weighs about 6 lb. What percent of the dog's body weight is her blood? 7%

pages 271–272 Think and Discuss

2a. 40%,

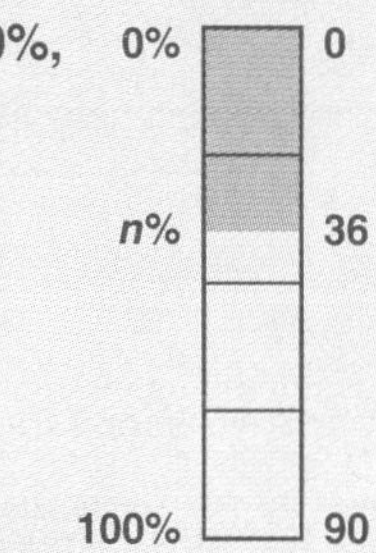

b. 25%,

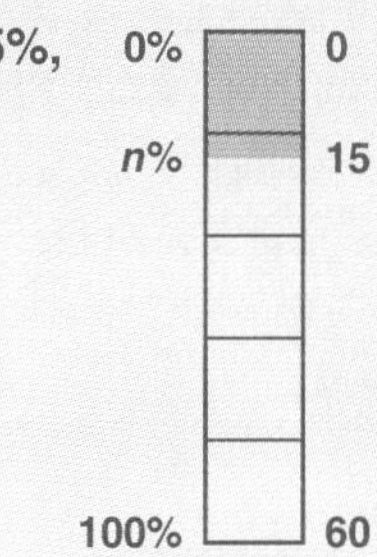

PRACTICE

Practice 6-10 Using Proportions with Percents

Write a proportion and solve.

1. 48 is 60% of what number? 80
2. What is 175% of 85? 148.75
3. What percent of 90 is 50? 55.6%
4. 76 is 80% of what number? 95
5. What is 50% of 42.88? 21.44
6. 96 is 160% of what number? 60
7. What percent of 24 is 72? 300%
8. What is 85% of 120? 102
9. What is 80% of 12? 9.6
10. 56 is 75% of what number? $74\frac{2}{3}$
11. What percent of 80 is 50? 62.5%
12. 85 is what percent of 200? 42.5%

Choose a calculator, paper and pencil, or mental math to solve.

13. The sale price of a bicycle is $120. This is 75% of the original price. Find the original price. $160
14. The attendance at the Brown family reunion was 160 people. This was 125% of last year's attendance. How many people attended the reunion last year? 128 people
15. A company has 875 employees. On "Half-Price Wednesday," 64% of the employees eat lunch at the company cafeteria. How many employees eat lunch at the cafeteria on Wednesdays? 560 employees
16. There are 1,295 students attending a small university. There are 714 women enrolled. What percentage of students are women? 55%

In copymaster and workbook formats

RETEACHING

Reteaching 6-10 Using Proportions with Percents

You can use proportions to solve percent problems. Remember, the percent is compared to 100.

Finding the part:	Finding the whole:	Finding the percent:
10% of 40 is _?_.	20% of _?_ is 8.	_?_ % of 25 is 20.
$\frac{10}{100} = \frac{n}{40}$	$\frac{20}{100} = \frac{8}{n}$	$\frac{n}{100} = \frac{20}{25}$
$100 \cdot n = 10 \cdot 40$, $n = 4$	$20 \cdot n = 100 \cdot 8$, $n = 40$	$25 \cdot n = 100 \cdot 20$, $n = 80$
10% of 40 is 4.	20% of 40 is 8.	80% is 20 of 25.

Complete to find the whole.

1. 75% of _?_ is 12? $\frac{75}{100} = \frac{12}{n}$; $75 \cdot n = 100 \cdot 12$; $n = 16$
2. 20% of _?_ is 82? $\frac{20}{100} = \frac{82}{n}$; $20 \cdot n = 100 \cdot 82$; $n = 410$
3. 5% of _?_ is 9? $\frac{5}{100} = \frac{9}{n}$; $5n = 100 \cdot 9$; $n = 180$

Complete to solve for *n*.

4. 60 is 5% of *n*: $\frac{5}{100} = \frac{60}{n}$; $5n = 100 \cdot 60$; $n = 1{,}200$
5. 6% of *n* is 4.8: $\frac{6}{100} = \frac{4.8}{n}$; $6n = 100 \cdot 4.8$; $n = 80$
6. 51 is 170% of *n*: $\frac{170}{100} = \frac{51}{n}$; $170n = 100 \cdot 51$; $n = 30$

Solve for *n*.

7. 12% of *n* is 9 75
8. 49% of *n* is 26.95 55
9. 18% of *n* is 27 150

Write a proportion and solve.

10. What is 210% of 44? 92.4
11. What is 30% of 200? 60
12. 64 is what percent of 80? 80%

Reteaching

ENRICHMENT

Minds on Math Transparency

6-10

How many different squares are shown in the figure below?

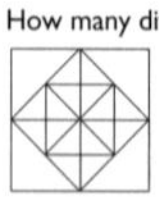

15 squares

See *Solution Key* for worked-out answers.

274

WRAP UP

IDENTIFYING THE BIG IDEA Have students describe the three basic types of percent problems. Then have them explain how to use proportions to solve each type.

LESSON QUIZ

1. 20 is what percent of 80? 25%
2. What percent of 220 is 11? 5%
3. What is 42% of 50? 21
4. 160% of what number is 48? 30

Match each question with the proportion you could use to solve it.

16. What is 40% of 15? C
17. 15 is what percent of 40? A
18. 40% of what number is 15? B

A. $\frac{15}{40} = \frac{n}{100}$ B. $\frac{40}{100} = \frac{15}{n}$ C. $\frac{40}{100} = \frac{n}{15}$

Write a proportion and solve. See below right.

19. What is 225% of 48?
20. 48 is what percent of 144? $\frac{n}{100} = \frac{48}{144}$, $33\frac{1}{3}\%$
21. 80% of what number is 15? $\frac{80}{100} = \frac{15}{n}$, 18.75
22. What percent of 25 is 21? $\frac{n}{100} = \frac{21}{25}$, 84%
23. 12% of what number is 42? $\frac{12}{100} = \frac{42}{n}$, 350
24. 68% of what number is 50? $\frac{68}{100} = \frac{50}{n}$, 73.5

19. $\frac{225}{100} = \frac{n}{48}$, 108

Choose **Use a calculator, paper and pencil, or mental math to solve each problem.**

25. *Education* The average daily attendance at Randolph Middle School is 92% of the school's enrollment. The average attendance is 422 students. How many students are enrolled? 459 students
26. *Automobiles* A car dealer advertises "All cars 19% off sticker price every day!" A buyer pays $10,930.95 for a car on the lot. What is the sticker price? $13,495
27. a. *Entertainment* A television is on sale for $449.95. This is $30 off the original price. Find the percent discount. 6.25%
    b. Find the original price of the television. $479.95
    c. *Writing* Which do you think is more effective in an advertisement, saying "Save $30" or using percents? Why? Check students' work.

Mixed Review

Solve each equation. *(Lesson 5-4)*

28. $y + \frac{1}{2} = \frac{7}{8}$ $\frac{3}{8}$
29. $x - \frac{3}{10} = 6$ $6\frac{3}{10}$
30. $a - \frac{3}{4} = \frac{1}{2}$ $1\frac{1}{4}$

Use the graph for Exercises 31 and 32. *(Lesson 1-7)*

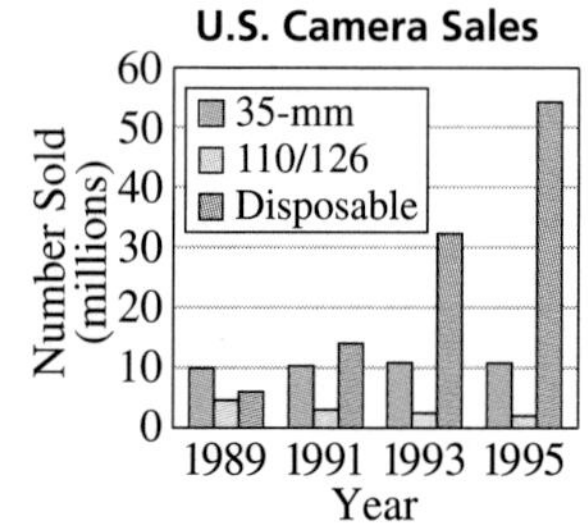

31. About how many cameras were sold in 1995? about 68,000,000
32. What percent of the cameras sold in 1995 were disposable? about 80%
33. *Choose a Strategy* Myra and Leah leave home at the same time walking in opposite directions. They each walk at the rate of 6 mi/h. How far apart are they after 20 min? 4 mi

Extra Practice, Lesson 6-10, page 519

MATH TOOLBOX

In Lesson 6-10, students learned how to find the percent one number is of another. This toolbox shows students how to apply their knowledge to compute tips using mental math.

ERROR ALERT! Students may miss the connection between the tax and the amount of the tip in Example 1. **Remediation:** Point out to students the tax amount is a known percent of the total. They can use the known percent (the tax) to find an unknown percent (the tip) by multiplying.

ASSESSMENT **Exercise 5** Have students compare their meal cost, tax, and tip with the results of a partner. Students can check each other's answer with a calculator or pencil and paper.

■ **ADDITIONAL PROBLEMS**

Calculate an approximate 15% tip for each situation.

1. A restaurant bill is $36.75, including a 5% tax of $1.75. $5.25
2. A taxi fare is $41.60. $6.30

MATH TOOLBOX

EXPLORATION

Mental Computation of Tips

After Lesson 6-10

You can use mental math to calculate most tips.

■ **EXAMPLE 1**

Entertainment A restaurant bill is $23.84, which includes a 5% tax of $1.14. Calculate a tip of about 15%.

tax → 5% tip → 15% = 3(5%) ← The tip will be about 3 times the tax.

$3(1.14) \approx 3(1.10) = 3.30$ ← Multiply.

The tip will be about $3.30.

If you live in a state where tax is not 5%, or if you want to tip for something that isn't taxed, here is another way to calculate a tip.

■ **EXAMPLE 2**

Consumer Issues A taxi fare is $35.75. Calculate a 15% tip.

$35.75 \div 10 = 3.575$ ← Divide by 10 to find 10%.

$3.575 \approx 3.6$ ← Round if necessary.

$3.6 \div 2 = 1.8$ ← Divide by 2 to find 5%.

$3.6 + 1.8 = 5.4$ ← Add to find 15%.

The tip will be about $5.40.

Calculate an approximate 15% tip for each situation. Tell which method you used and why. 1–4. Check students' work for methods and reasoning.

1. The taxi fare to the airport is $15.40.
   $2.25
2. A dinner bill is $64.56, including 7% tax of $4.22.
   $9.00
3. The bill for lunch is $19.68, including 5% tax of $.94.
   $3.00
4. A hired car for the spring dance costs $38.
   $5.70
5. *Open-ended* Create a pizza from the menu at the right. Find the cost of your meal including 5% tax and 15% tip.
   5–6. Check students' work.
6. *Writing* Which method of mental computation do you prefer for finding tips? Explain why.

Basic cheese pizza	**$5.99**
Toppings	**Cost**
Eggplant	$.40
Extra cheese	$.29
Ham	$.35
Onions	$.20
Peppers	$.35
Sausage	$.40
Tomatoes	$.49

6-11 Teaching Notes

1 Focus

CONNECTING TO PRIOR KNOWLEDGE
Ask students: *List some changes you have experienced this year that involve increases and decreases.* **Answers may vary. Sample: height, temperature, allowance, price of hamburgers** Discuss some of the changes these may have in common.

2 Teach

THINK AND DISCUSS

AEP Have students draw a number line. Ask them to draw an arrow pointing to the right. Label it *increase.* Draw an arrow pointing to the left. Label it decrease. Note the word *decrease* and the word *down* begin with the same letter.

VISUAL LEARNING Example 1 To help show the percent of change, students can draw bars to model the problem. One bar represents the percents; the other represents the prices. Comparison bars can help students understand their answers.

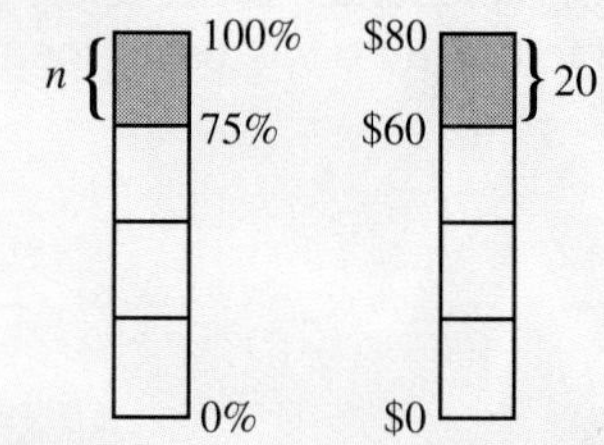

Lesson Planning Options

Prerequisite Skills
- solving proportions (6-3)

Vocabulary/Symbols
percent of change

Materials/Manipulatives
- rubber band
- ruler
- small weights

Resources

Student Edition
Skills Handbook, p. 534
Extra Practice, p. 519
Glossary/Study Guide

Teaching Resources
Chapter Support File, Ch. 6
- Lesson Planner 6-11
- Practice 6-11, Reteaching 6-11
- Alternative Activity 6-11
- Answer Masters 6-11

Teaching Aids Masters 3, 5
Glossary, Spanish Resources

Transparencies
3, 15, Minds on Math 6-11

Warm Up

Use the numbers below to write as many proportions as you can.
5, 24, 15, 8
$\frac{5}{15} = \frac{8}{24}$, $\frac{15}{5} = \frac{24}{8}$, $\frac{5}{8} = \frac{15}{24}$, $\frac{8}{5} = \frac{24}{15}$

ALBEBRA Connection

6-11 Finding Percent of Change

What You'll Learn

1. To find percent of increase
2. To find percent of decrease

...And Why

You can track population growth by finding a percent of change.

Here's How

Look for questions that
- build understanding
- ✔ check understanding

Biology Pythons can grow as long as 33 ft and have been known to swallow prey weighing up to 120 lb.

Source: *The Guinness Book of Animal Facts and Feats*

THINK AND DISCUSS

1 *Finding the Percent of Increase*

Zoologists use mathematics when they study animals. This table shows the length, in inches, of a python called Scooter.

Year	Start of Year	End of Year	Change
1st	20	40	20
2nd	40	50	10
3rd	50	64	14
4th	64	80	16
5th	80	100	20
6th	100	121	21

1. **Choose A, B, or C.** Which equation would you use to find the number in the Change column? **C**
   A. (Start of Year) + (End of Year) = (Change)
   B. (Start of Year) − (End of Year) = (Change)
   C. (End of Year) − (Start of Year) = (Change)
2. Copy and complete the table above. **See table.**
3. The drawing shows Scooter's growth during both her first and fifth years. In which year was Scooter's growth more noticeable? Why? **1st; Scooter's length almost doubled.**

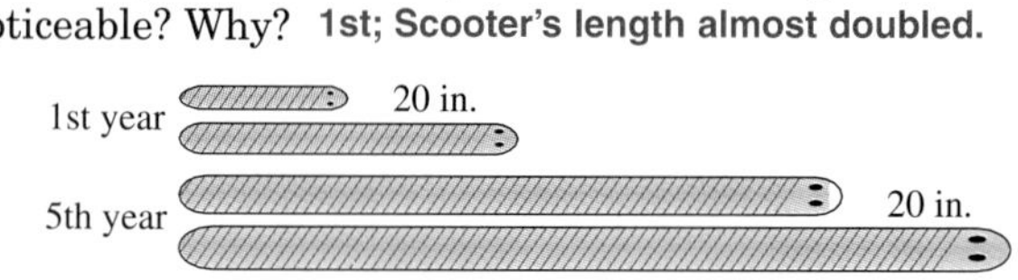

Although Scooter grew 20 inches both years, this number does not give all the information about her growth. **Percent of change** is the percent something increases or decreases from its original measure or amount. Finding it requires two steps.

Step 1 Subtract to find the amount of change.

Step 2 Use the proportion $\frac{\text{amount of change}}{\text{original amount}} = \frac{\text{percent of change}}{100}$.

100% is the same as the original size so they are at the top of each bar. The size change is in brackets is the percent increase or percent decrease.

ADDITIONAL EXAMPLES

FOR EXAMPLE 1

Suppose Scooter's growth chart for her second year shows 52 in. at the end of the year. Find the percent of increase in Scooter's growth for her second year. **30%**

FOR EXAMPLE 2

Find the percent of decrease in the price of the aquarium if the sale price is $59. **26.25%**

ASSESSMENT Write the numbers 40 and 50 on the board. Have half the class find the percent of decrease from 50 to 40. **20% decrease** Have the other half of the class find the percent of increase from 40 to 50. **25% increase** Ask:

- *How are the problems different?* **Answers may vary. Sample: For the percent of increase the original number is 40, for the percent of decrease the original number is 50.**
- *How are the problems alike?* **Answers may vary. Sample: The original numbers in both problems are the same.**

Work Together

Point out to students the original length of the rubber band should be the same for every weight.

Scooter's growth is an example of *percent of increase.*

EXAMPLE 1 *Real-World Problem Solving*

Zoology Find the percent of increase in Scooter's growth for her second year.

$50 - 40 = 10$ ← Find the amount of change.

$\frac{\text{amount of change}}{\text{original amount}} \rightarrow \frac{10}{40} = \frac{n}{100}$ ← Write a proportion.

$40n = 10 \cdot 100$ ← Write cross products.

$n = \frac{10 \cdot 100}{40}$ ← Divide each side by 40.

$n = 25$ ← Simplify.

The percent of increase in Scooter's growth was 25%.

4. ✔ *Try It Out* Find each percent of increase.
   a. 2 to 3 **50%** b. 3 to 5 **$66\frac{2}{3}$%** c. 4 to 9 **125%**

5. Find the percent of increase in Scooter's growth for each year shown in the table. **100%, 25%, 28%, 25%, 25%, 21%**

Now you may assign Exercises 1–20.

2 *Finding the Percent of Decrease*

A decreased price on a sale item is an example of *percent of decrease.*

EXAMPLE 2 *Real-World Problem Solving*

Consumer Issues Find the percent of decrease in the price of the aquarium.

$80 - 60 = 20$ ← Find the amount of change.

$\frac{\text{amount of change}}{\text{original amount}} \rightarrow \frac{20}{80} = \frac{n}{100}$ ← Write a proportion.

$0.25 = \frac{n}{100}$ ← Simplify the left side.

$n = 25$ ← Use mental math to multiply each side by 100.

The percent of decrease in the price is 25%.

6. ✔ *Try It Out* Find each percent of decrease. Round to the nearest tenth of a percent, if necessary.
   a. Original price: $125; sale price: $100 **20%**
   b. Original price: $8.99; sale price: $6.49 **27.8%**

Technology Options

Prentice Hall Technology

Software for Learners
- Math Blaster® Mystery*
- Interactive Student Tutorial, Chapter 6*

Teaching Resource Software
- Computer Item Generator 6-11
- Resource Pro™ Chapter 6*

Internet • For related mathematics activities, visit the Prentice Hall site at www.phschool.com/math

**Available on CD-ROM only*

Assignment Options for Exercises On Your Own

To provide flexible scheduling, this lesson can be split into parts.

1 **Core** 1–15, 17–20
Extension 16

2 **Core** 21–35, 37–55, 57
Extension 36, 56

Use Mixed Review to maintain skills.

3 Practice/Assess

EXERCISES *On Your Own*

ERROR ALERT! Exercises 1–15 Students may put the greater amount in the denominator instead of the original amount. **Remediation:** Have students copy the exercise. Ask them to label the first number *original amount.* Then have students check their proportions with a partner before calculating the percent of increase.

Exercise 16 Some students may not understand how to find the numbers for column C. Explain that if they look at the sales column, they can find the amount of change by finding the difference from the previous year.

CONNECTION TO STATISTICS Exercise 17 Point out that this problem relates to population statistics. Have students look up *statistics* in the dictionary. Ask them to think of ways that we use population statistics in our society. **Answers may vary. Sample: setting insurance rates, building apartments, planning highways**

CONNECTING TO THE STUDENTS' WORLD Exercise 19 Have students find the most recent increase in minimum wage. Ask: *What is the percent of increase?* **Answers may vary.**

7. *Think About It* Find each percent of change. State whether the change is an increase or a decrease.
   a. 5 to 2 — 60% decrease
   b. 7 to 9 — 28.6% increase
   c. 6 to 14 — 133.3% increase
   d. 19 to 3 — 84.2% decrease

Work Together

Exploring Percent of Change

Work in pairs. Measure the length of a rubber band. Hang several different weights on the rubber band, one at a time, and measure the new length of the rubber band each time.

8. Record your results in a table. Make a graph of the data of weights to length of the rubber band.

8–9. Check students' work.

9. Find the percent of change in the rubber band's length for each weight. Round to the nearest percent.

Now you may assign Exercises 21–57.

EXERCISES *On Your Own*

Find each percent of increase. Round to the nearest tenth.

1. 60 to 75 — 25%
2. 88 to 99 — 12.5%
3. 120 to 240 — 100%
4. 75 to 90 — 20%
5. 15 to 35 — 133.3%
6. 2 to 7 — 250%
7. 12 to 63 — 425%
8. 15 to 18 — 20%
9. 120 to 125 — 4.2%
10. 0.6 to 2.2 — 266.7%
11. 15 to 60 — 300%
12. 135 to 200 — 48.1%
13. 4 to 5 — 25%
14. 12 to 18 — 50%
15. $13\frac{1}{2}$ to 25 — 85.2%

16. *Business* The Tots and Tykes Toy Store opened five years ago. The owner uses a computer to track yearly income, but the program she uses has a bug. Some cells print @@@ instead of numbers. Copy and complete the spreadsheet.

	A	B	C	D
1	Year	Sales ($)	Change from Last Year ($)	Change from Last Year (%)
2	1	200,000	(not open last year)	(not open last year)
3	2	240,000	40,000	@@@ 20%
4	3	300,000	@@@ $60,000	@@@ 25%
5	4	330,000	@@@ $30,000	@@@ 10%

Find each percent of increase. Round to the nearest tenth.

17. *Social Studies* The population of Fresno, California, was 578,000 in 1980. In 1994, the population was 835,000. 44.5%

CONNECTION TO SPORTS Exercise 40 Have students consult an almanac to find the names of football players who may have gained this much yardage in two consecutive seasons.

Exercises 41–55 If you have block scheduling or extended class periods, have students write a brief word problem to describe several of the exercises.

Exercise 56 Point out the original amount is the previous day's attendance.

WRAP UP

IDENTIFYING THE BIG IDEA Have students explain percent of change and the differences and similarities between percent of decrease and percent of increase.

PROJECT LINK Explain how to use survey results to make predictions. Show students how to apply the survey percent to the larger school population.

PORTFOLIO Share with students the criteria you use to assess their work in portfolios, as well as how you plan to use the results. Students should understand how the rubrics are used to assess their work, how each piece in the portfolio counts, and how the scores they get in their portfolios affect their overall evaluation.

18. *Medicine* Heart surgeons performed 62 heart transplants in 1981. They performed 2,342 in 1994. 3,677.4%

19. *Business* A restaurant worker earning $5.15/h receives a raise. He now earns $6.00/h. 16.5%

20. *Aquaculture* Fish farms in Dutch Harbor, Alaska, raised 106.3 million fish in 1985. In 1993, the same farms raised 793.9 million fish. 646.8%

Find each percent of decrease. Round to the nearest tenth.

21. 150 to 147 2%	**22.** 60 to 54 10%	**23.** 75 to 25 66.7%	**24.** 8.4 to 6.3 25%	**25.** 480 to 300 37.5%
26. 10 to 7 30%	**27.** 25 to 12 52%	**28.** 85 to 60 29.4%	**29.** 5 to 3 40%	**30.** 29 to 25 13.8%
31. 9 to 2 77.8%	**32.** 110 to 88 20%	**33.** 1000 to 643 35.7%	**34.** 100 to 85 15%	**35.** 70 to 63 10%

36. a. *Business* The My-T-shirt store bought 5 dozen T-shirts for $4.29 each. The store owner decided to sell the T-shirts for $6.59 each. What was the percent of increase in the price of the T-shirts? 53.6%

b. *Consumer Issues* After a month, the remaining 2 dozen T-shirts went on sale for $4.59 each. What was the percent of decrease in the price of the T-shirts? 30.3%

Find each percent of decrease. Round to the nearest tenth.

37. *Mining* In 1990, the value of all the lead mined in the United States was $491 million. In 1994, the value was $286 million. 41.8%

38. *Social Studies* George Bush won the 1988 presidential election with 48,881,221 votes. He lost the 1992 election with 38,117,331 votes. 22%

39. *Nutrition* In 1970, the average person in the United States ate 79.6 lb of beef. In 1994, each person ate 63.6 lb of beef. 20.1%

40. *Sports* A football player gained 1,200 yd last season and 900 yd this season. 25%

Find each percent of change. Round to the nearest tenth. State whether the change is an *increase* or a *decrease*.

41. 50 to 45 10% decrease	**42.** 75 to 70 6.7% decrease	**43.** 530 to 600 13.2% increase	**44.** 25 to 35 40% increase	**45.** 13 to 15 15.4% increase
46. 56 to 78 39.3% increase	**47.** 900 to 630 30% decrease	**48.** 6 to 9 50% increase	**49.** 89 to 110 23.6% increase	**50.** 12.5 to 8.4 32.8% decrease
51. 27 to 20 25.9% decrease	**52.** 16 to 54 237.5% increase	**53.** 105 to 76 27.6% decrease	**54.** 16 to 100 525% increase	**55.** 30 to 16 46.7% decrease

PRACTICE

Practice 6-11 *Finding Percent of Change*

Find the percent of change. State whether each change is an increase or a decrease.

1. A $50 coat is put on sale for $35. decrease of 30%
2. Mayelle earns $18,000 a year. After a raise, she earns $19,500. increase of about 8.3%
3. Last year Anthony earned $24,000. After a brief lay-off this year, Anthony's income is $18,500. decrease of 22.9%
4. In 1981, about $1.1 million was lost due to fires. In 1988, the loss was about $9.6 million. increase of 773%
5. In a recent year, certain colleges and universities received about $268 million in aid. Ten years later, they received about $94 million. decrease of 65%
6. A coat regularly costing $125 is put on sale for $75. decrease of 40%
7. Suppose that at a job interview, you are told that you would receive a 10% increase in your salary at the end of each of the first three years. How much would your starting salary have changed at the end of the third year? increase of 33.1%
8. Four years ago there were 35 students in the school band. Since then 12 students have joined the band. increase of 34%

Practice

9. Complete the table.

Enrollment in Center City Schools From 1990 to 1995

Year	Enrollment	Change from Last Year (Number of Students)	Change from Last Year (%)	Increase or Decrease
1990	18,500	—	—	—
1991	19,300	800	4%	increase
1992	19,700	400	2%	increase
1993	19,500	200	1%	decrease
1994	19,870	370	2%	increase
1995	19,200	670	3%	decrease

In copymaster and workbook formats

RETEACHING

Reteaching 6-11 *Finding Percent of Change*

Percent of change is the percent something increases or decreases from its original amount.

	Find the percent of increase from 12 to 18.	Find the percent of decrease from 20 to 12.
① Subtract to find the amount of change.	$18 - 12 = 6$	$20 - 12 = 8$
② Write a proportion. $\frac{\text{change}}{\text{original}} = \frac{\text{percent}}{100}$	$\frac{6}{12} = \frac{n}{100}$ $6 \cdot 100 = 12n$	$\frac{8}{20} = \frac{n}{100}$ $8 \cdot 100 = 20n$
③ Solve for n.	$n = 50$	$n = 40$
	The percent of increase is 50%.	The percent of decrease is 40%.

State whether the change is *increase* or *decrease*. Complete to find the percent of change.

1. 40 to 60
   $60 - 40 = 20$
   $\frac{20}{40} = \frac{n}{100}$
   $20 \cdot 100 = 40n$
   $n = 50$
   increase 50%
2. 15 to 9
   $15 - 9 = 6$
   $\frac{6}{15} = \frac{n}{100}$
   $6 \cdot 100 = 15n$
   $n = 40$
   decrease 40%
3. 0.4 to 0.9
   $0.9 - 0.4 = 0.5$
   $\frac{0.5}{0.4} = \frac{n}{100}$
   $0.5 \cdot 100 = 0.4n$
   $n = 125$
   increase 125%

Find each percent of increase.

4. 16 to 40 150%
5. 22 to 66 200%
6. 4 to 8 100%
7. 20 to 22 10%
8. 9 to 18 100%
9. 28 to 35 25%
10. 80 to 112 40%
11. 150 to 165 10%

Find each percent of decrease.

12. 20 to 15 25%
13. 100 to 57 43%
14. 52 to 26 50%
15. 90 to 45 50%
16. 140 to 126 10%
17. 75 to 72 4%
18. 1000 to 990 1%
19. 420 to 357 15%

ENRICHMENT

Minds on Math Transparency

6-11

Fill in the boxes with the numbers 1 through 10 so that the number below any two numbers is the difference of those numbers. The order in which the numbers are subtracted does not have to be the same in each case.

8 10 3 9
2 7 6
5 1
4

Sample answer is shown.

See *Solution Key* for worked-out answers.

280

LESSON QUIZ

Find each percent of change and state whether it is an increase or a decrease. Round to the nearest tenth.

1. 13 to 25 **92.3%; increase**
2. 9.5 to 7.2 **24.2%; decrease**
3. 38 to 32 **15.8%; decrease**
4. 70 to 82 **17.1%; increase**

56. *Entertainment* The local community theater keeps track of the attendance at their productions. Copy and complete the table below for two weeks of shows. **% Change: 4% increase, 7.7% decrease, 16.7% decrease, 30% increase, 15.4% increase**

Day	Number	Change	% Change
F	125	opening night	no change
Sa	130	+5	■
Su	120	−10	■
Th	100	■ −20	■
F	130	■ +30	■
Sa	150	■ +20	■

57. *Writing* Describe how you would find the percent of change in the number of students in your school from last year to this year. See margin p. 281.

PORTFOLIO

For your portfolio, choose one or two items from your work for this chapter. Here are some possibilities:
- drawings you have made
- corrected work
- part of your project

Explain why you have included each selection.

Mixed Review

Evaluate for $m = 8$ and $n = -2$. (Lessons 3-1 and 3-3)

58. $6m + 8 + 5n$ **46**
59. $18 - 3(m + n)$ **0**
60. $-mn + 2$ **18**
61. $n - (m - 3)$ **−7**

Write each fraction as a decimal. Use a bar to indicate any repeating digits. (Lesson 4-9)

62. $\frac{19}{25}$ **0.76**
63. $\frac{2}{10}$ **0.2**
64. $\frac{8}{12}$ **$0.\overline{6}$**
65. $\frac{3}{18}$ **$0.1\overline{6}$**
66. $\frac{7}{9}$ **$0.\overline{7}$**
67. $\frac{4}{6}$ **$0.\overline{6}$**

Write the unit rate. (Lesson 6-2)

68. 408 mi traveled on 12 gal of gasoline **34 mi/gal**
69. $16.45 for 7 lb of fish **$2.35/lb**
70. A student is participating in a 50-mi fund-raising walk. She walks 40% of the distance the first day and $\frac{1}{3}$ of the remaining distance the second day. How many more miles does she have to walk? (Lessons 6-7, 5-5) **20 mi**

CHAPTER PROJECT

PROJECT LINK: RESEARCHING

Find the number of students in your school. Assuming that all the students in your school visit the park, predict how many students would choose each ride as their favorite.

Check students' work.

Extra Practice, Lesson 6-11, page 519

FINISHING THE CHAPTER PROJECT

PROJECT DAY You may wish to plan a project day on which students share their completed projects. Encourage students to explain their process as well as their product.

PROJECT NOTEBOOK Ask students to review their project work and bring their notebooks up to date.

Have students review their methods for conducting their surveys, making graphs, and making projections for the project.

SCORING RUBRIC

3 You conduct a survey and complete a graph showing the amusement park preferences of a reasonable sample of people. You describe these preferences using both ratios and percents, and you correctly use these values to estimate the projected number of people in a larger population who would prefer each ride.

2 You provide a graph of your survey data and the percentage of people who prefer each ride. You attempt to use the survey data to estimate the preferences of a larger population.

1 You don't gather adequate data from your survey, you incorrectly calculate percentages, or you don't make any projections for a larger population.

0 You fail to complete a survey, graph the results, or make any calculations based on these results.

FINISHING THE CHAPTER PROJECT

CHAPTER PROJECT

chills and thrills

Take a Survey The Project Link questions on pages 236, 249, 263, and 280 should help you to complete your project. Here is a checklist to help you gather together the parts of your project.

- ✔ the results of your survey
- ✔ the graph of your results
- ✔ the percent of people who preferred each ride
- ✔ the projected number of people who would prefer each ride

Pretend that your town has a limited amount of space for rides in a proposed amusement park. Which rides would you recommend they include? Explain your reasoning.

Be sure all of your work is neat and clear. After all, you *do* want the town to use your recommendations!

Reflect and Revise

Review your project with a friend or someone at home. Is your graph complete? Are your calculations accurate? Are your projections realistic? If necessary, make changes to improve your project.

Web Extension

Internet Connection

Prentice Hall's Internet site contains information you might find helpful as you complete your project. Visit www.phschool.com/mgm2/ch6 for some links and ideas related to amusement parks.

pages 278–280 On Your Own

57.

$$\frac{\#\text{ students this year} - \#\text{ students last year}}{\#\text{ students last year}} \times 100$$

STUDENT SELF-ASSESSMENT SURVEY

Chapter 6 Student Self-Assessment Survey

1. Now that you have finished this chapter, think about what you have learned about proportions. Check each topic you feel confident you understand.
   - _____ find equal ratios (6-1)
   - _____ find unit rates and unit prices (6-2)
   - _____ use cross products to solve a proportion (6-3)
   - _____ use proportions to find missing lengths in similar figures (6-4)
   - _____ solve problems involving scale (6-5)
   - _____ write percents using equal ratios (6-6)
   - _____ change among fractions, decimals, and percents (6-7)
   - _____ use more than one strategy to solve problems (6-8)
   - _____ find the percent of a number (6-9)
   - _____ find discount prices (6-9)
   - _____ find what percent a number is of another (6-10)
   - _____ find a number given a percent of the number (6-10)
   - _____ find percent of change (6-11)
2. Before the Chapter Assessment, I need to review _____
3. a. Check one. In general, I thought this chapter was
   _____ a snap _____ easy _____ average _____ hard _____ a monster
   b. Why do you feel this way? _____
4. In this chapter I did my best work on _____
5. In this chapter I had trouble with _____
6. Check each one that applies. Now that I've spent some time studying proportions, I think they are
   _____ important _____ boring _____ useful _____ fun
   _____ a waste of time _____ confusing _____ tricky _____ interesting
7. Did you use a computer to explore percent of change? _____
   If yes, did you find the computer helpful? _____
   Explain. _____

Assessment

Vocabulary/Symbols

cross products, is similar to (~), percent, percent of change, proportion, rate, ratio, scale drawing, similar, unit price, unit rate

Resources

Student Edition

Extra Practice, p. 519
Glossary/Study Guide

Teaching Resources

Chapter Support File, Ch. 6
- Student Self-Assessment Survey

Glossary, Spanish Resources
Tools for Studying Smarter

WRAP UP

ASSESSMENT Exercises 3–6 For these exercises, have students work with a partner. One student solves the odd-numbered exercises while the partner solves the even-numbered exercises. Then partners trade papers and check each other's work with a calculator. They can substitute the solution for *n* in the proportion, and express each ratio as a decimal. If the solution for *n* is correct, the decimals should be equal.

VISUAL LEARNING Exercises 11 and 12 Encourage students to use a ruler to make sketches to help solve the problems.

ASSESSMENT Exercises 16–21 List the solutions to these proportions in random order on the board. If students cannot find their solutions posted, have them work with a partner to correct their error.

Exercise 23 Encourage students to draw models of the lots before answering this question.

6 WRAP UP

Ratios, Rates, and Proportions — 6-1, 6-2, 6-3

A **ratio** is a comparison of two numbers.

A **rate** is a ratio comparing two quantities that are measured in different units.

A **proportion** is an equation stating that two ratios are equal.

1. In the 1996 Summer Olympics, the United States won 101 medals, including 44 gold medals. Write the ratio of gold medals to total medals in three ways. **44 : 101, 44 to 101, $\frac{44}{101}$**

2. A 10-oz box of cereal costs \$2.79. A 13-oz box of the same brand of cereal costs \$3.99. Find the unit price for each item and tell which is the better buy. **\$.28/oz, \$.31/oz; 10 oz box**

Find the value of *n* in each proportion.

3. $\frac{3}{7} = \frac{n}{28}$ **12**
4. $\frac{3}{5} = \frac{15}{n}$ **25**
5. $\frac{n}{18} = \frac{12}{72}$ **3**
6. $\frac{32}{n} = \frac{4}{17}$ **136**
7. $\frac{1.5}{1.2} = \frac{5}{n}$ **4**

8. A local lumberyard sells a total of 250,000 board feet of hardwood each year. The ratio of softwood to hardwood is 5 : 3.
   a. Write and solve a proportion to find the amount of softwood sold per year. $\frac{5}{3} = \frac{n}{250{,}000}$; **416,667 board feet**
   b. Write and solve a proportion to find the total amount of lumber sold per year. $\frac{3}{250{,}000} = \frac{8}{n}$; **666,667 board feet**

Similarity and Scale Drawings — 6-4, 6-5

If two figures are **similar,** corresponding angles are congruent and the ratios of the lengths of corresponding sides are equal.

A **scale drawing** is an enlarged or reduced drawing of an object.

Each pair of figures is similar. Find *x* and *y*.

9. 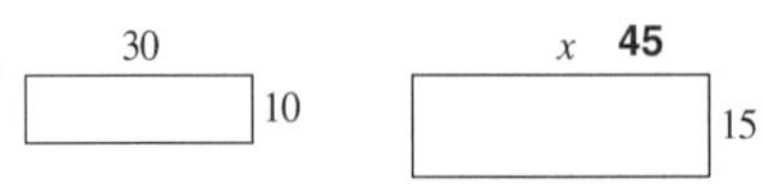

10. 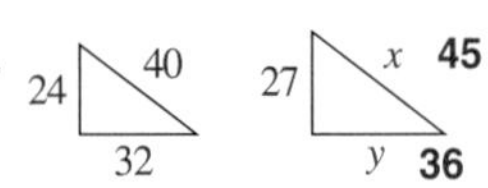

11. The scale on a map is 1.5 in. : 500 mi. The map distance from Chicago to Tokyo is 12 in. Find the actual distance between the cities. **4,000 mi**

12. A drawing's scale is 0.5 in. : 10 ft. A room is 15 ft long. How long is the room in the drawing? **0.75 in.**

WRITING Exercise 27 Suggest students consider their work in Exercises 24–26.

Remind students that the new mathematical terms in this chapter are defined in the Glossary/Study Guide in the back of the book.

Percent and Proportions 6-6, 6-7, 6-9, 6-10

A **percent** is a ratio that compares a number to 100.

13. Write $\frac{3}{8}$ as a percent. 37.5%

14. Write 1.8% as a decimal. 0.018

15. Write $62\frac{1}{2}\%$ as a fraction. $\frac{5}{8}$

Write a proportion and solve.

16. What percent of 40 is 28? $\frac{x}{100} = \frac{28}{40}$; 70%

17. 38 is 80% of what number? $\frac{38}{x} = \frac{80}{100}$; 47.5

18. What is 60% of 420? $\frac{60}{100} = \frac{x}{420}$; 252

19. 80% of 15 is what number? $\frac{80}{100} = \frac{x}{15}$; 12

20. 54 is 75% of what number? $\frac{54}{x} = \frac{75}{100}$; 72

21. 36 is what percent of 180? $\frac{36}{180} = \frac{x}{100}$; 20%

22. *Consumer Issues* A bicycle store is having a sale. Zara buys a bike marked 15% off. She pays \$45 less than the original price. What was the original price of the bicycle? \$300

Problem Solving Strategies 6-8

Sometimes you use more than one strategy to solve a problem.

23. Choose A, B, C, or D. A rectangular lot is worth \$9,000. What is the value of a similar lot whose length and width are each 50% greater than the dimensions of the first lot? D

A. \$2,250 B. \$4,000 C. \$13,000 D. \$20,250

Percent of Change 6-11

A **percent of change** is the percent something increases or decreases from its original measure or amount.

Find the percent of change. State whether the change is an *increase* or a *decrease.* Round to the nearest percent.

24. old: \$90; new: \$75 17% decrease

25. old: 3.5 ft; new: 4.2 ft 20% increase

26. old: 120 lb; new: 138 lb 15% increase

27. *Writing* When you find percent of change, how do you know whether the percent of change is an increase or a decrease?

27. Answers may vary. Sample: If the new value is greater than the previous value, then the change is an increase; otherwise, it is a decrease.

28. An answering machine costs \$54 on sale. The original price is \$80. Find the percent of change. 32.5% decrease

29. The sale price of a game is \$24.95. Its original price was \$36.00. Find the percent of change. Round to the nearest percent. 31% decrease

CHAPTER ASSESSMENT • FORM A

Chapter 6 Assessment • Form A

Answers

1. There are 14 boys and 16 girls in a class. What is the ratio of girls to boys? Write a ratio in simplest terms. — 1. $\frac{8}{7}$

2. Use mental math to decide which pairs of ratios form a proportion. — 2. B and C

A. $\frac{5}{9}, \frac{10}{20}$ B. $\frac{8}{3}, \frac{24}{9}$ C. $\frac{12}{15}, \frac{16}{20}$

3. Solve $\frac{n}{6} = \frac{25}{30}$. — 3. 5

4. **Choose A, B, C, or D.** Which could you use to find the price/oz of 16 oz of juice that cost \$1.59? — 4. A

A. $\frac{16}{1.59} = \frac{1}{n}$ B. $\frac{16}{n} = \frac{1.59}{1}$

C. $1.59n = 16$ D. $1.59 \times 16 = n$

5. Alonso can jog 2 mi in 15 min. Estimate how long it will take him to jog 3 mi. — 5. about 22 min

6. These triangles are similar. Find the values of x and y. — 6. $x = 26, y = 24$

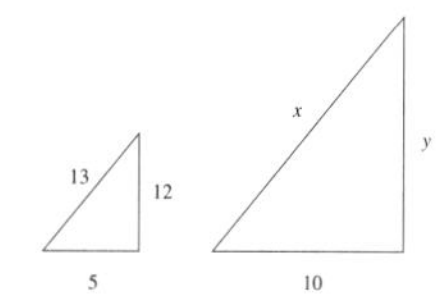

7. The scale of a map is $\frac{1}{2}$ in. : 5 mi. Find the actual length of a hiking trail that measures $6\frac{1}{5}$ in. on the map. — 7. 62 mi

8. Write $\frac{9}{10}$ as a percent. — 8. 90%

9. What percent of a dollar is a nickel? — 9. 5%

10. Which is a better buy, 6 apples for \$1.74 or 5 apples for \$1.20? — 10. 5 apples for \$1.20

Assessment

CHAPTER ASSESSMENT • FORM A

Chapter 6 Assessment • Form A (continued)

11. In one class, 55% of the students earned a grade of A on the last test. What fraction of the students earned an A? — 11. $\frac{55}{100} = \frac{11}{20}$

12. Write 0.675 as a percent. — 12. 67.5%

13. Write $7\frac{1}{4}\%$ as a decimal. — 13. 0.0725

14. What is 35% of 10? — 14. 3.5

15. What percent of 50 is 30? — 15. 60%

16. The price of a new model car is 112% of the price of last year's model. The new model costs \$10,080. Use a proportion to find the cost of last year's model. — 16. \$9,000

17. The price of a certain book was \$5.95. This book now costs \$6.59. Find the percent of increase in the price of the book. Round to the nearest percent. — 17. 11%

18. Lee bought a shirt for \$15.60, which was 35% off the original price. What was the original price? — 18. \$24.00

Choose a Strategy

19. Find three consecutive even numbers that have a sum of 36. — 19. 10, 12, 14

Writing

20. Can you make two similar triangles using exactly 9 toothpicks? If so, explain how.

Yes. Use 3 toothpicks to make one triangle. Use 6 toothpicks to make a second triangle with 2 toothpicks for each side.

CHAPTER ASSESSMENT • FORM B

Chapter 6 Assessment • Form B

Choose the best answer. Circle A, B, C, or D.

1. There are 18 red marbles and 24 blue marbles in a bag. In simplest form, what is the ratio of red marbles to blue marbles?
   A. $\frac{4}{3}$ B. $\frac{24}{18}$ C. $\frac{9}{12}$ (D) $\frac{3}{4}$
2. Which is the same price as 3 lb of roast beef for $4.20?
   A. 2 lb for $2.89 B. 1 lb for $1.45
   (C) 5 lb for $7.00 D. 10 lb for $14.95
3. Use mental math to decide which pair of ratios form a proportion.
   A. $\frac{4}{5}, \frac{2}{3}$ B. $\frac{5}{8}, \frac{6}{10}$ C. $\frac{7}{16}, \frac{8}{14}$ (D) $\frac{3}{4}, \frac{12}{16}$
4. Solve $\frac{n}{9} = \frac{7}{3}$.
   (A) 21 B. 6 C. 18 D. 14
5. Willa can run 7 mi in one hour. Estimate how long it takes her to run 1 mi.
   A. about 7 min (B) about 8 min C. about 10 min D. about 14 min
6. The triangles below are similar. What are the values of x and y?

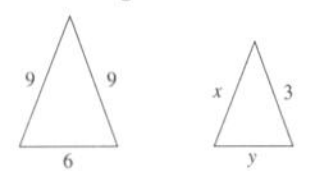

   A. $x = 9, y = 2$ (B) $x = 3, y = 2$ C. $x = 9, y = 3$ D. $x = 3, y = 6$
7. The scale of a map is $\frac{1}{4}$ in. : 4 mi. Find the actual length of a hiking trail that measures $1\frac{3}{4}$ in. on the map.
   A. 7 mi B. 14 mi (C) 28 mi D. 16 mi
8. Which expression is *not* equal to $\frac{5}{8}$?
   A. 0.625 B. 62.5% C. $\frac{10}{16}$ (D) 15 : 16
9. What percent of a dollar is a quarter?
   A. 5% B. 10% (C) 25% D. 50%

Assessment

CHAPTER ASSESSMENT • FORM B

Chapter 6 Assessment • Form B (continued)

10. In a class of 20, 85% of the students passed a test. How many students passed the test?
    A. 3 B. 4 C. 16 (D) 17
11. What is 0.001 written as a percent?
    (A) 0.1% B. 1% C. 10% D. 100%
12. The price of a certain tool went up 150%. Which decimal represents 150%?
    A. 0.015 B. 0.15 (C) 1.5 D. 15.0
13. Which is the same as twenty-five percent of forty?
    (A) 10% of 100 B. 20% of 80
    C. 50% of 50 D. 125% of 400
14. 30 is what percent of 90?
    A. 33% (B) $33\frac{1}{3}$% C. 34% D. $35\frac{1}{2}$%
15. Out of 24 students, 20 received an A on a math test. What percent got an A?
    A. $16\frac{2}{3}$% B. 80% C. $83\frac{1}{2}$% (D) $83\frac{1}{3}$%
16. The price of a jacket was $59.99. This jacket now costs $69.99. Estimate the percent of increase in the price of the jacket.
    A. about 10% (B) about 15%
    C. about 20% D. about 25%
17. Judy bought sneakers for $35.00, which was 30% off the original price. What was the original price?
    A. $116.67 (B) $50.00
    C. $65.00 D. $10.50
18. A load of 2 bags of lime weighs 49 lb. How many pounds will 18 bags weigh?
    A. 134 lb (B) 441 lb
    C. 268 lb D. 882 lb
19. Find three consecutive odd numbers that have a sum of 57.
    A. 17, 18, 19 B. 18, 19, 20
    (C) 17, 19, 21 D. 18, 20, 22

Teaching Resources

Chapter Support File, Ch. 6, and Spanish Resources

Teacher's Edition

See pp. 230C–D for Assessment Options.

Teaching Resource Software

- Computer Item Generator, Ch. 6

ASSESSMENT

Exercises 8 and 9 Remind students to *remove* the percent sign when changing a percent to a decimal or fraction. However, students must *include* the percent sign when changing a decimal or fraction to a percent.

WRITING EXERCISES allow students to describe more fully their thinking and understanding of the concepts they've learned. **Exercise 13** is a writing exercise.

6 ASSESSMENT

1. Write a ratio for the following information in three ways: 49 out of 50 homes have at least one television. **$\frac{49}{50}$, 49 : 50, 49 to 50**
2. Engineers tested four cars to find their fuel efficiency. Which car gets the most miles per gallon? **C**

Car	Miles	Gallons Used
A	225	14
B	312	15
C	315	10
D	452	16

3. Find each unit rate.
   a. Dontay runs 2.3 km in 7 min. **0.33 km/min**
   b. Carol earns $36.00 in 9 h. **$4/h**
   c. Sumako pays $5.89 for 60 lb. **$.10/lb**
4. Find the value of n in each proportion.
   a. $\frac{6}{5} = \frac{n}{7}$ **8.4** b. $\frac{3}{7} = \frac{8}{n}$ **18.7**
   c. $\frac{n}{4} = \frac{9}{32}$ **1.125** d. $\frac{3.5}{n} = \frac{14}{15}$ **3.75**
5. The ratio of teachers to students in Jefferson Middle School is 2 to 25. There are 350 students in the school. Find the number of teachers. **28 teachers**
6. A map with a scale 2 in. : 350 mi shows two cities to be 5 in. apart. How many miles apart are the cities? **875 mi**
7. A hot-air balloon is 2,100 ft above the ground. The balloon can descend at the rate of 1.5 ft/s. If the balloon is scheduled to land at 3:30 P.M., when should the balloonist start descending? **3:06 P.M.**
8. Write each decimal as a percent and each percent as a decimal.
   a. 5% **0.05** b. 0.3 **30%** c. 125% **1.25**
   d. 0.0045 **0.45%** e. 0.39% **0.0039** f. 3.4 **340%**
9. Write each fraction as a percent and each percent as a fraction in simplest form.
   a. 35% **$\frac{7}{20}$** b. $\frac{3}{4}$ **75%** c. 2% **$\frac{1}{50}$**
   d. $\frac{7}{8}$ **87.5%** e. 125% **$\frac{5}{4}$** f. $\frac{6}{5}$ **120%**

10 Use graph paper to model each percent.
   a. 34% b. 285% c. $12\frac{1}{2}$%
   See back of book.

11. The two triangles are similar. Find x and y. **12, 14**

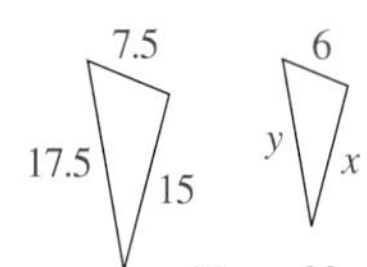

12. See back of book for model; $\frac{25}{100} = \frac{30}{x}$, 120.

12. Draw a model and write a proportion to find 25 percent of what number is 30.
13. *Writing* The price of a popular cassette was $8.95 last week. This week the price is $7.16. Explain how to find the percent of decrease in price. **See back of book.**
14. Write a proportion and solve.
    a. Find 35% of 150. **$\frac{35}{100} = \frac{n}{150}$; 52.5**
    b. What percent of 80 is 50? **b–d, f.**
    c. 40 is what percent of 25? **See below.**
    d. 60 is 80% of what number?
    e. What is 225% of 15? **$\frac{225}{100} = \frac{n}{15}$; 33.75**
    f. 400 is 150% of what number?
15. Shea bought a sweater for $18.75, which was 25% off the original price. What was the original price? **$25**
16. In 1994 there were about 2.1 million registered nurses in the United States. By the year 2005, the United States Labor Department predicts there will be 2.4 million registered nurses. What is the percent of change? Round to the nearest tenth of a percent. **14.3% increase**

14b. $\frac{n}{100} = \frac{50}{80}$; 62.5% c. $\frac{40}{25} = \frac{n}{100}$; 160%
d. $\frac{60}{n} = \frac{80}{100}$; 75 f. $\frac{400}{n} = \frac{150}{100}$; $266\frac{2}{3}$

CUMULATIVE REVIEW

Item	Review Topic	Ch
1, 3, 4 7, 14	Expressions and equations	3
2, 11, 12	Percents and proportions	6
5	Multiplying fractions	5
6, 9	Interpreting and displaying data	1

Item	Review Topic	Ch
8	Comparing fractions and decimals	4
10, 15	Decimal operations	2
11	Proportions	6
13	Scientific notation	Precourse

6 CUMULATIVE REVIEW

Choose the best answer.

1. Which equation is represented by the model shown? D

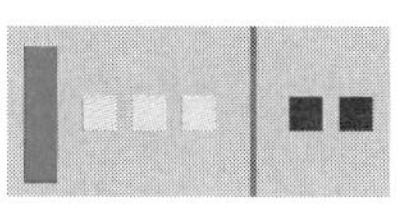

A. $x + 3 = 2$ B. $-3x = -2$
C. $x - 3 = -2$ D. $x + 3 = -2$

2. Which number is closest to 35% of 1,291? B

A. 400 B. 450 C. 500 D. 550

3. Which equation is *not* equivalent to $2x - 3 = 5$? B

A. $2x = 8$ B. $4x - 3 = 10$
C. $2x - 4 = 4$ D. $x - 1.5 = 2.5$

4. Which expression equals $3 \times 3 \times 3 \times 3$? A

A. 3^4 B. 4^3 C. 5×3 D. 3^3

5. Which point on the number line shows the product $\left(1\frac{7}{8}\right)\left(2\frac{1}{5}\right)$? C

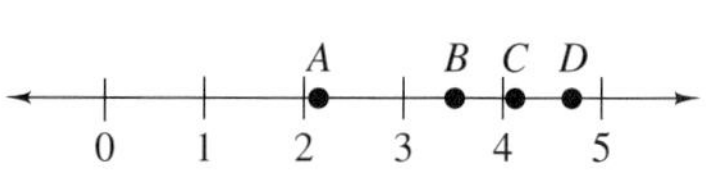

6. Find the median of the data in the stem-and-leaf plot. D

7	0 0 5 8
8	1 5 6 9 9
9	4

7 | 0 means 70.

A. 81.7 B. 89 C. 85 D. 83

7. Which expression has the greatest value? A

A. $32 - (-12)$ B. $32 - |-12|$
C. $-32 - (-12)$ D. $|-32 - (-12)|$

8. Which fraction is closest in value to 0.46? B

A. $\frac{19}{50}$ B. $\frac{22}{50}$ C. $\frac{25}{50}$ D. $\frac{28}{50}$

9. Which type of graph would best display the following data on the number of viewers (in millions) watching television during prime time? C

Mon., 91.9 Tue., 89.8 Wed., 93.9
Thu., 93.9 Fri., 78.0 Sat., 77.1
Sun., 87.7

A. scatter plot B. double line
C. bar D. double bar

10. Dyani paid for food at a delicatessen with a \$10 bill. She bought a sandwich for \$2.45, a salad for \$1.25, and a drink for \$.89. How much change did she receive? B

A. \$4.59 B. \$5.41 C. \$6.30 D. \$14.59

11. Which statement is *not* true? D

A. $\frac{12}{16} = \frac{9}{12}$ B. $\frac{12 + 16}{16} = \frac{9 + 12}{12}$
C. $\frac{12}{9} = \frac{16}{12}$ D. $\frac{12 + 1}{16} = \frac{9 + 1}{12}$

12. What is $\frac{5}{8}$ written as a percent? B

A. 16% B. $62\frac{1}{2}$% C. 160% D. 625%

13. Write the numbers 0.361×10^7, 4.22×10^7, and 13.5×10^6 in order from least to greatest. C

A. $13.5 \times 10^6, 0.361 \times 10^7, 4.22 \times 10^7$
B. $4.22 \times 10^7, 13.5 \times 10^6, 0.361 \times 10^7$
C. $0.361 \times 10^7, 13.5 \times 10^6, 4.22 \times 10^7$
D. $13.5 \times 10^6, 4.22 \times 10^7, 0.361 \times 10^7$

14. Find the value of $\frac{2m}{m + 2n}$ when $m = -4$ and $n = 3$. B

A. −8 B. −4 C. 0 D. 4

15. Which is the best estimate of $92.56 \cdot 37.1$? B

A. 2,700 B. 3,600 C. 4,000 D. 4,500

CUMULATIVE REVIEW

Chapter 6 Cumulative Review

Choose the best answer. Circle A, B, C, or D.

1. Which point on the number line shows the product $(-5) \times 2$?

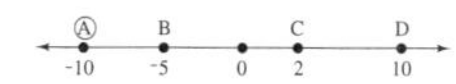

2. Which equation is *not* equivalent to $2x - 4 = 9$?

A. $-4 + 2x = 9$ B. $2x - 9 = 4$
C. $-9 + 2x = 4$ (D.) $4 - 2x = 9$

3. Solve $\frac{x}{6} = -8$.

A. −2 (B.) −48
C. 14 D. −8

4. Solve $-9m = -63$.

A. −72 B. −54
C. 567 (D.) 7

5. Joey spends 4 h/wk mowing lawns. This is one half of the time he spends doing homework. Which of the following equations could be used to find how much time Joey spends doing homework?

A. $x = \frac{1}{2} + 4$ (B.) $\frac{1}{2}x = 4$
C. $x = \frac{1}{2} \cdot 4$ D. $4x = \frac{1}{2}$

6. Which decimal is equal to $\frac{3}{8}$?

A. 0.125 (B.) 0.375
C. 0.38 D. 0.83

7. What is the LCD for $\frac{2}{9}$ and $\frac{5}{6}$?

A. 9 (B.) 18
C. 27 D. 54

8. Which number is closest to $1\frac{1}{2}$?

A. $\frac{9}{5}$ B. $1\frac{1}{3}$
(C.) $\frac{8}{5}$ D. $\frac{9}{10}$

9. Estimate how many $\frac{1}{3}$-lb boxes can be filled from a $5\frac{3}{4}$-lb bag of rice.

A. about 10 B. about 12
C. about 15 (D.) about 18

10. Solve $\frac{2}{3}x + 9 = -3$.

(A.) −18 B. −9
C. −8 D. −4

11. Which number is *not* the same as $2\frac{4}{5}$?

A. $2\frac{8}{10}$ (B.) 28%
C. 2.8 D. $\frac{14}{5}$

Assessment

CUMULATIVE REVIEW

Chapter 6 Cumulative Review (continued)

12. $\triangle ABC$ is similar to $\triangle DEF$. What is the value of x?

A. 1.5 B. 2
(C.) 2.5 D. 5

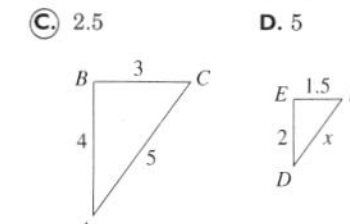

13. What is $\frac{45}{90}$ in simplest form?

A. $\frac{9}{18}$ B. $\frac{15}{30}$
C. $\frac{3}{6}$ (D.) $\frac{1}{2}$

14. Jason bought $4\frac{2}{3}$ yd of rope to make a swing. What is this number as an improper fraction?

A. $\frac{6}{3}$ (B.) $\frac{14}{3}$
C. $\frac{7}{2}$ D. $\frac{12}{3}$

15. What is the next fraction in this pattern?

$\frac{4}{2}, \frac{6}{3}, \frac{8}{4}, \frac{10}{5}, \ldots$

A. $\frac{11}{5}$ B. $\frac{12}{5}$
(C.) $\frac{12}{6}$ D. $\frac{11}{6}$

16. Bob spent $\frac{5}{6}$ h doing his homework. His brother Gene spent $\frac{3}{4}$ h, his sister Shirley spent $\frac{4}{5}$ h, and his sister Mary Jane spent $\frac{2}{3}$ h doing homework. Who spent the most time doing homework?

(A.) Bob B. Gene
C. Shirley D. Mary Jane

17. The pages in a book are numbered from 1 to 250. How many pages contain the digit 5 at least once?

A. 20 B. 25
C. 45 (D.) 44

18. The ratio of boys to girls in Austin Middle School is 9 to 10. There are 189 boys in the school. How many girls are there?

A. 1,890 B. 189
(C.) 210 D. 21

19. A certain radio is on sale for 15% off the regular price of \$29.99. About how much is the sale price of the radio?

A. \$15.00 B. \$18.00
(C.) \$25.00 D. \$30.00

20. At one store, the same socks are packaged four different ways. Which is the best buy?

A. 1 for \$1.29 B. 2 for \$2.49
(C.) 4 for \$4.79 D. 6 for \$7.39

Resources

Teaching Resources

Chapter Support File, Ch. 6
• Cumulative Review

Teacher's Edition

See pp. 230C–D for Assessment Options.

7 Investigating Geometry

Chapter Overview

To accommodate flexible scheduling, most lessons are divided into parts. Assignment Options are given in the Teacher's Edition for each lesson.

Pages 288–290	Lesson 7-1 Exploring Visual Patterns
NCTM 1, 4, 5, 7, 8, 12	**Math at Work**

Pages 291–295	Lesson 7-2 Algebra: Classifying and Measuring Angles
NCTM 2, 3, 4, 12, 13	Part 1 Measuring and Describing Angles Part 2 Pairs of Angles **Key terms:** angle, acute, right, obtuse, straight angles, adjacent angles, complementary, supplementary **Alternative Activity** 7-2 **Journal** **Project Link**

Pages 297–301	Lesson 7-3 Algebra: Triangles
NCTM 1, 2, 3, 4, 12, 13	Part 1 Classifying Triangles Part 2 Angles and Triangles **Checkpoint 1**

Pages 314–317	Lesson 7-7 Circles
NCTM 2, 3, 4, 5, 9, 12, 13	Part 1 Parts of a Circle Part 2 Inscribed Polygons **Key terms:** circle, center, radius, diameter, central angle, chord, arc, semicircle, endpoints, compass, inscribed polygon **Alternative Activity** 7-7

Pages 318–322	Lesson 7-8 Data Analysis: Circle Graphs
NCTM 2, 3, 4, 5, 12, 13	Part 1 Reading Circle Graphs Part 2 Making Circle Graphs **Key terms:** circle graphs, sectors **Project Link** **Checkpoint 2**

Pages 323–326	Lesson 7-9 Constructing Bisectors
NCTM 2, 4, 12, 13,	Part 1 Segment Bisectors Part 2 Angle Bisectors **Key terms:** midpoint, segment bisector, perpendicular lines, perpendicular bisector, straightedge, bisector

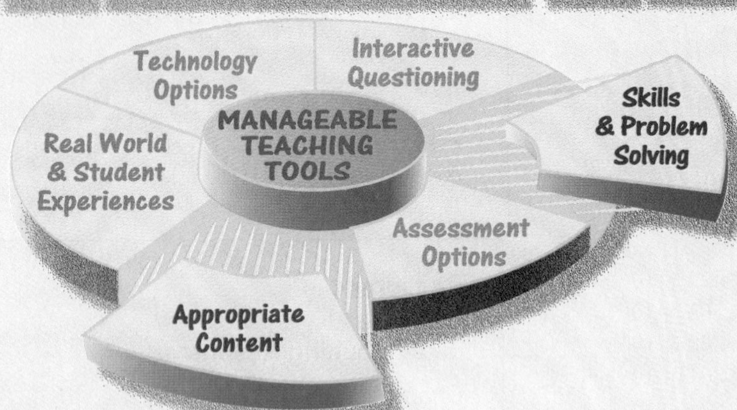

Pacing Options

This chart suggests pacing only for the core lessons and their parts. It is provided merely as a possible guide. It will help you determine how much time you have in your schedule to cover other features, such as the Chapter Project, Math Toolboxes, Wrap Up, and Assessment.

	1 Class Period	1 Class Period	1 Class Period	1
Traditional (40–45 min class periods)	7–1	7–2 7–2 1 2	7–3 7–3 1 2	
Block Scheduling (90 min class periods)	7–1 7–2 7–2 1 2	7–3 7–3 7–4 1 2	7–5 7–6 7–6 1 2	7

CHAPTER PROJECT

Raisin the Roof

Goal: Students build geometric shapes with raisins and toothpicks.

THEME: CONSTRUCTION

NCTM STANDARDS

1 Problem Solving	6 Number Systems and Number Theory	10 Statistics
2 Communication	7 Computation and Estimation	11 Probability
3 Reasoning	8 Patterns and Functions	12 Geometry
4 Mathematical Connections	9 Algebra	13 Measurement
5 Number and Number Relationships		

Pages 302–304	Lesson 7-4 Problem Solving Strategy
NCTM 1, 4, 5, 12, 13	Draw a Diagram ▼ Project Link

Pages 305–307	Lesson 7-5 Congruent Triangles
NCTM 1, 2, 3, 5, 9, 12	**Key terms:** congruent (≅), congruent polygons, corresponding parts **Alternative Activity** 7-5

Pages 308–312	Lesson 7-6 Polygons and Quadrilaterals
NCTM 2, 3, 4, 6, 7, 12	**Part 1** Classifying Polygons **Part 2** Special Quadrilaterals **Key terms:** polygon, regular polygon, quadrilaterals, parallel, trapezoid, parallelogram, rectangle, rhombus, square, diagonals **Journal** ▼ **Project Link**

Optional Materials and Manipulatives

protractor (7-2, 7-3, 7-4, 7-7)
scissors (7-3, 7-6)
paper for cutting and folding (7-3)
dot paper (7-6)

compass (7-7, 7-8, 7-9)
calculator (7-8)
straightedge (7-9)
tracing paper (7-9)

graph paper (7-9)
Optional calculator use is integrated throughout the course.

ss d	1 Class Period	1 Class Period	1 Class Period	1 Class Period	1 Class Period	1 Class Period	1 Class Period	1 Class Period	1 Class Period	1 Class Period
	7–6 ▼1	7–6 ▼2	7–7 ▼1	7–7 ▼2	7–8 ▼1 7–8 ▼2	7–9 ▼1	7–9 ▼2			
-8	7–9 ▼1 7–9 ▼2									

Meeting Individual Needs

Accommodating Diverse Learning Styles

In your Teacher's Edition, you will find suggestions as to how you can help students complete mathematical tasks in Chapter 7 by meeting individual needs and supporting various learning styles. Here are some examples:

VISUAL LEARNING
modeling angles with pencils *(p. 292)*

TACTILE LEARNING
measuring angles with a protractor *(p. 292)*

AUDITORY LEARNING
creating mnemonics for complementary and supplementary *(p. 292)*

KINESTHETIC LEARNING
creating patterns using arms *(p. 288)*

EARLY FINISHERS
Performance-Based Project, MathBlaster® Mystery, Interdisciplinary Units

GIFTED AND TALENTED
drawing regular polygons to see the relationship between sides and angles *(p. 309)*

DIVERSITY sharing knowledge of road signs from other countries *(p. 308)*

ACQUIRING ENGLISH PROFICIENCY (AEP)
reading and discussing problems *(p. 302)*

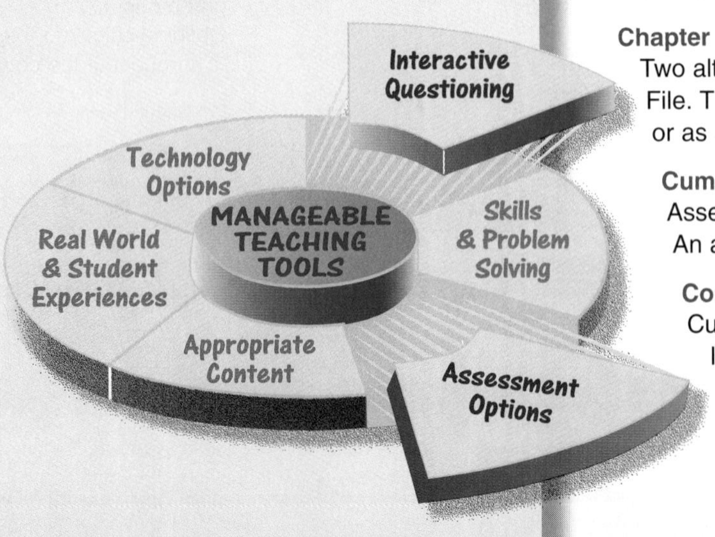

Assessing Progress

A broad range of assessment tools are available to reach a variety of learners.

INFORMAL ASSESSMENT

Informal assessments provide day-to-day feedback to help give you a picture of conceptual understanding and skill development.

ONGOING ASSESSMENT is built into lesson instruction and the Teaching Notes of the Teacher's Edition.

In the Teacher's Edition
Lesson Quiz for every lesson

In the Student Edition
On Your Own, Mixed Review, Journal, Portfolio, Project Link, Chapter Wrap Up

Look for **Interactive Questions** within lessons that

- **BUILD UNDERSTANDING** with labels such as **Analyze, Reasoning, Estimation, Writing, and Summarize**
- ✔ **CHECK UNDERSTANDING** with the **Try It Out** label.

FORMAL ASSESSMENT

Formal assessment can occur before and after the chapter, as well as at natural breaking points in the chapter.

Checkpoints
Two forms of each self-assessment Checkpoints are available: one in the Student Edition and another in the Chapter Support File in the Teaching Resources box.

- Mid-Chapter Checkpoint 1, page 301
- End-of-Chapter Checkpoint 2, page 322

Chapter 7 Assessment, page 332.
Two alternative forms are available in the Chapter Support File. They may be used after a chapter has been completed, or as a pre-test and post-test comparison.

Cumulative Review, page 333.
Assesses skills and concepts in Chapters 1–7. An alternative form is available in Chapter Support File.

Computer Item Generator for Chapter 7
Customized tests can be generated for each lesson and for mid-chapter and end-of-chapter assessments, and for pre- and post-test comparisons of achievement.

PERFORMANCE-BASED ASSESSMENT

CHAPTER PROJECT The Chapter Project in the student edition provides a real-world connection to the math context of the chapter. The Teacher's Edition contains a scoring rubric.

A Performance Assessment with a scoring rubric can be found in the Chapter Support File in the Teaching Resources box.

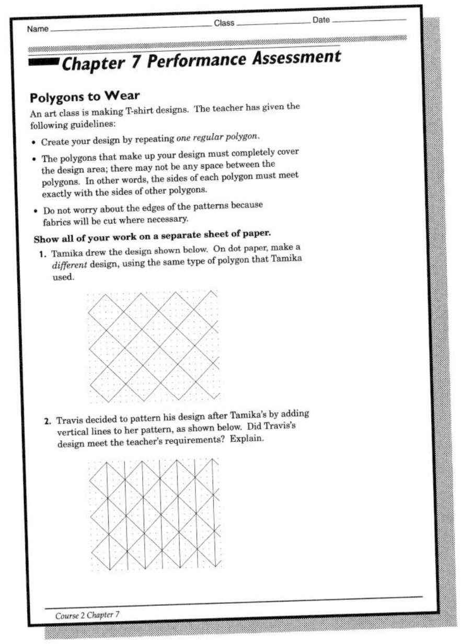

Name ______ Class ______ Date ______

Chapter 7 Performance Assessment

Polygons to Wear

An art class is making T-shirt designs. The teacher has given the following guidelines:

- Create your design by repeating *one regular polygon*.
- The polygons that make up your design must completely cover the design area; there may not be any space between the polygons. In other words, the sides of each polygon must meet exactly with the sides of other polygons.
- Do not worry about the edges of the patterns because fabrics will be cut where necessary.

Show all of your work on a separate sheet of paper.

1. Tamika drew the design shown below. On dot paper, make a *different* design, using the same type of polygon that Tamika used.

2. Travis decided to pattern his design after Tamika's by adding vertical lines to her pattern, as shown below. Did Travis's design meet the teacher's requirements? Explain.

Course 2 Chapter 7

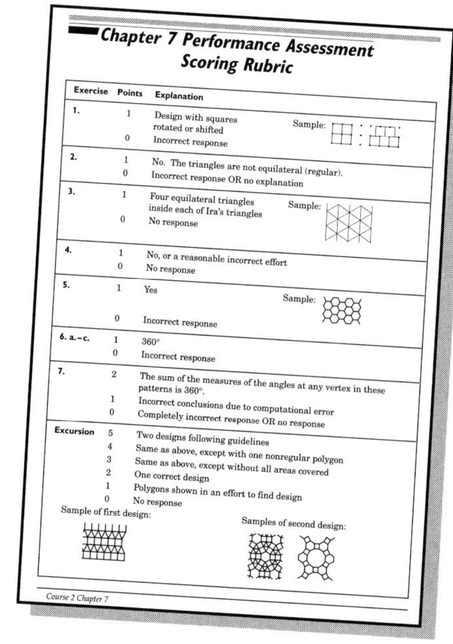

Chapter 7 Performance Assessment Scoring Rubric

Exercise	Points	Explanation
1.	1	Design with squares rotated or shifted (Sample:)
	0	Incorrect response
2.	1	No. The triangles are not equilateral (regular).
	0	Incorrect response OR no explanation
3.	1	Four equilateral triangles inside each of Ira's triangles (Sample:)
	0	No response
4.	1	No, or a reasonable incorrect effort
	0	No response
5.	1	Yes (Sample:)
	0	Incorrect response
6. a.–c.	1	360°
	0	Incorrect response
7.	2	The sum of the measures of the angles at any vertex in these patterns is 360°.
	1	Incorrect conclusions due to computational error
	0	Completely incorrect response OR no response
Excursion	5	Two designs following guidelines
	4	Same as above, except with one nonregular polygon
	3	Same as above, except without all areas covered
	2	One correct design
	1	Polygons shown in an effort to find design
	0	No response

Sample of first design:

Samples of second design:

Course 2 Chapter 7

Correlation to Standardized Tests

Lesson		STANDARDIZED TEST ITEMS CAT5	Terra Nova	ITBS, Form M	MAT7	SAT9	Local Test
7-1	Exploring Visual Patterns		34	CE3	CP14, 53		
7-2	Algebra: Classifying and Measuring Angles	CA50	32, 36, 55	CE20		PS28	
7-3	Algebra: Triangles				CP32	PS32	
7-4	Problem Solving Strategy: Draw a Diagram	CA49		PD9	CP10, 49, 54	PS46	
7-5	Congruent Triangles	CA45					
7-6	Polygons and Quadrilaterals	CA6, 46	56		CP51		
7-7	Circles	CA30			CP21	PS27	
7-8	Data Analysis: Circle Graphs	CA19–21		PD32–35			
7-9	Constructing Bisectors			CE28			

CA: Concepts and Applications
PS: Problem Solving
PR: Math Procedures
CP: Concepts and Problem Solving
MC: Math Computation
PD: Problem Solving and Data Interpretation
CE: Concepts and Estimation

See page 2D for the level of each test referenced.

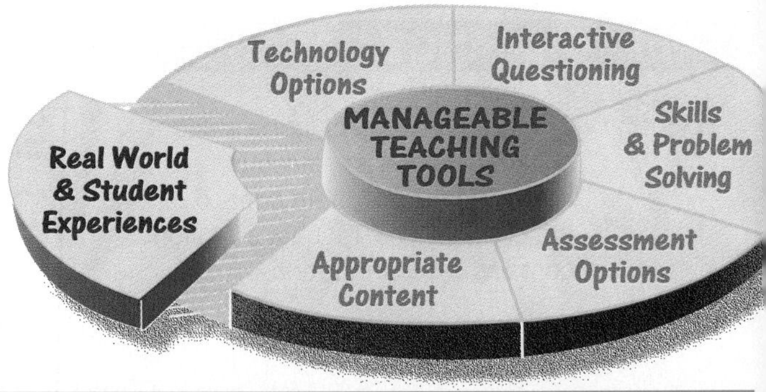

MAKING CONNECTIONS

TEAM TEACHING WITH PRENTICE HALL MATERIALS

MIDDLE GRADES MATH INTERDISCIPLINARY UNITS	INTERDISCIPLINARY EXPLORATIONS	PRENTICE HALL SCIENCE L Life Science E Earth Science P Physical Science
• **The Environment: Activity 8** • **The Arts: Activity 5** • **Advancements in Industry: Activities 7, 8, & 12**	• ***A Nation of Immigrants*** **pp. 37 & 40**	**E Sec. 13-2 (shapes of crystals)**

Lesson	Interdisciplinary Connections	Real World Connections	Math Integration
7-1	Architecture	Quilts	Geometry
7-2	Science	Physical Therapy Elephants Ivory	Geometry Measurement
7-3	Architecture Geometry	Music Social Studies Transportation Ecology	Geometry Measurement
7-4	Geometry	Table Tennis Gardening Music Bicycling	Geometry Measurement
7-5	Geometry	Puzzles	Algebra Geometry
7-6	Social Studies	Road Signs	Geometry
7-7	Construction	Shopping Tunnels	Algebra Measurement
7-8	Ecology	Automobiles Population Statistics Shopping	Geometry Measurement
7-9	History	Entertainment Raffle Tickets Safety	Geometry Measurement

School to Home

MATERIALS:
paper
pencil

English version is in the Chapter Support File. Spanish version is in the Spanish Resources.

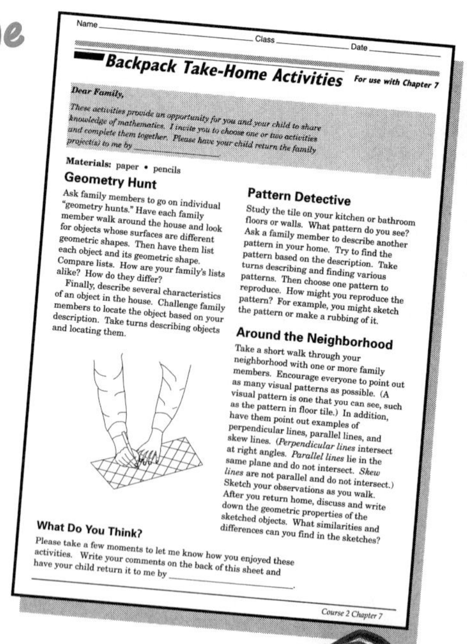
Name ______ Class ______ Date ______

Backpack Take-Home Activities *For use with Chapter 7*

Dear Family,

These activities provide an opportunity for you and your child to share knowledge of mathematics. I invite you to choose one or two activities and complete them together. Please have your child return the family project(s) to me by ______

Materials: paper • pencils

Geometry Hunt

Ask family members to go on individual "geometry hunts." Have each family member walk around the house and look for objects whose surfaces are different geometric shapes. Then have them list each object and its geometric shape. Compare lists. How are your family's lists alike? How do they differ?

Finally, describe several characteristics of an object in the house. Challenge family members to locate the object based on your description. Take turns describing objects and locating them.

Pattern Detective

Study the tile on your kitchen or bathroom floors or walls. What pattern do you see? Ask a family member to describe another pattern in your home. Try to find the pattern based on the description. Take turns describing and finding various patterns. Then choose one pattern to reproduce. How might you reproduce the pattern? For example, you might sketch the pattern or make a rubbing of it.

Around the Neighborhood

Take a short walk through your neighborhood with one or more family members. Encourage everyone to point out as many visual patterns as possible. (A visual pattern is one that you can see, such as the pattern in floor tile.) In addition, have them point out examples of perpendicular lines, parallel lines, and skew lines. (*Perpendicular lines* intersect at right angles. *Parallel lines* lie in the same plane and do not intersect. *Skew lines* are not parallel and do not intersect.) Sketch your observations as you walk. After you return home, discuss and write down the geometric properties of the sketched objects. What similarities and differences can you find in the sketches?

What Do You Think?

Please take a few moments to let me know how you enjoyed these activities. Write your comments on the back of this sheet and have your child return it to me by ______.

Course 2 Chapter 7

Using Technology to Enhance Instruction

For the Student

Multimedia Math Hot Pages™

This interactive software and video package on CD-ROM integrates solid math content through a variety of media.

- Hot Page™ 2-3
- Hot Page™ 2-6
- Hot Page™ 9-12

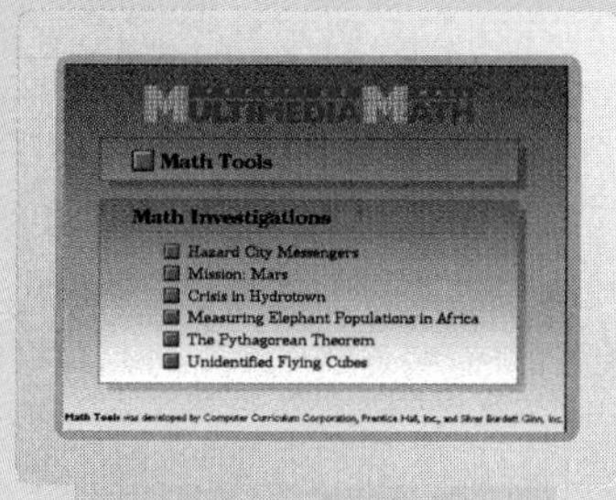

Multimedia Math Investigations

These in-depth interactive activities on CD-ROM develop real-world applications of mathematics. They allow students the opportunity to reinforce key concepts.

- Mission: Mars
- Unidentified Flying Cubes

MathBlaster® Mystery

This award-winning, interactive software program on CD-ROM can be used to maintain skills or to accommodate early finishers.

- Level: Earn 4 coins; Pay 4 coins
- Mission Mode (all lessons)
- Kitchen Comparisons (7-2, 7-9)
- Number Guesser (7-1, 7-7)
- Equation Maker (7-5, 7-8)
- Word Problems (7-3, 7-4, 7-6, Problem Solving Practice)

Math Tools/Math Labs

This software, available on CD-ROM, includes on-screen Math Lab activities. Students use linkable, interactive tools to explore math concepts.

- Math Lab: Congruent Triangles (7-5)

Interactive Student Tutorial

Available on CD-ROM, this test preparation program contains self-tests with questions in standardized test format. Software includes electronic versions of the text lessons and an on-line glossary.

Internet Connection

For Students

Support for the Chapter Project

A career-oriented link for Math at Work feature

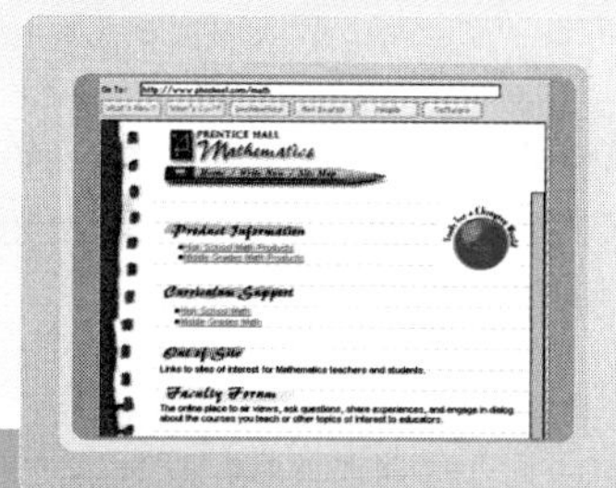

www.phschool.com/math

For teachers

Curriculum Support

Product Information

Regional Support Information

For the Teacher

Computer Item Generator with Standardized Test Practice

This software generates customized practice sheets and tests. It also generates unlimited practice sheets for the standardized tests listed on page 286D.

Resource Pro™ with Planning Express™

Available on CD-ROM, this software can be used to customize and plan lessons. It contains over 1,700 resource pages.

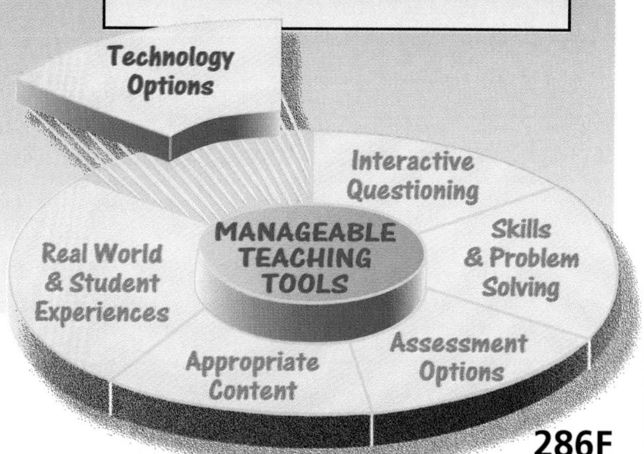

CHAPTER 7 INVESTIGATING GEOMETRY

CONNECTING TO PRIOR LEARNING Ask students: *Name some geometric shapes you have seen in buildings and bridges.* **Answers may vary. Sample: triangles, rectangles, squares** Then ask: *Why do we use some shapes more than others in construction?* **Answers may vary. Sample: Some shapes fit together better than others.**

CULTURAL CONNECTIONS Ask students to research the architecture of towers and bridges in other countries. For example, have students research the shapes in the structure of the Eiffel Tower in Paris.

INTERDISCIPLINARY CONNECTIONS Ask: *What geometric shapes might an artist use?* **Answers may vary. Sample: Artists use circles and rectangles in drawings and sculptures.**

ABOUT THE PROJECT The Chapter Project gives students the opportunity to apply their knowledge of geometry to make a tower with toothpicks and raisins that is strong enough to hold a baseball.

Internet • For information and activities related to the Chapter Project, visit the Prentice Hall site at www.phschool.com/mgm2/ch7

7 Investigating Geometry

WHAT YOU WILL LEARN IN THIS CHAPTER

- How to classify geometric figures
- How to make circle graphs
- How to construct bisectors

LAUNCHING THE CHAPTER PROJECT

Ask students:

- *Have you ever built a tower before?*
- *How can you make sure that the tower is sturdy?*
- *How can you use geometry in building a structure?*

PROJECT NOTEBOOK Encourage students to keep all project-related materials in a separate folder or notebook.

TRACKING THE PROJECT You may wish to have students read Finishing the Chapter Project on page 329 to help them get an overview of the project. Set benchmark deadlines for students to show you their work in progress.

• How to solve problems by drawing diagrams

CHAPTER PROJECT

Raisin' the Roof

THEME: CONSTRUCTION

Look around you. Triangles are everywhere in construction! You see them in bridges, in buildings, in scaffolding; even in bicycle frames! This project will give you a greater appreciation of the importance of triangles in construction. You might also develop a taste for raisins!

Build a Tower For the chapter project, you will use toothpicks and raisins to build geometric shapes. Your final product will be a tower strong enough to support a baseball.

Steps to help you complete the project:

p. 295 Project Link: *Researching*
p. 304 Project Link: *Analyzing*
p. 312 Project Link: *Creating*
p. 322 Project Link: *Measuring*
p. 329 *Finishing the Chapter Project*

SCORING RUBRIC

3 You provide several sample pictures showing the use of triangles in construction. You draw and describe how you strengthened your toothpick-and-raisin constructions. You sketch and build a tower that is at least four inches tall and can support a baseball. Your explanations, drawings, and construction are neat and clean.

2 You provide a picture showing triangles in construction. You explain how you strengthened your toothpick-and-raisin constructions, and you build a tower that is at least four inches tall and can support a baseball.

1 You build a tower but you don't provide any evidence that you tested toothpick-and-raisin constructions beforehand.

0 Your preliminary tests and your tower are incomplete or missing.

7-1 Teaching Notes

1 Focus

CONNECTING TO PRIOR KNOWLEDGE Ask students to describe the number pattern 3, 9, 15, 21, . . . **add 6** Ask students to brainstorm a list of events that repeat in a pattern. Choose a response that you can use to introduce visual patterns.

2 Teach

Work Together

KINESTHETIC LEARNING Have students work in groups of four. Each group stands in a line and creates a repeating pattern with their arms. Choose two groups to show their pattern while the rest of the class determines the next figure in the pattern.

THINK AND DISCUSS

DIVERSITY Some students may have difficulty differentiating the colors in the quilting pattern. It may be easier to show them a high-contrast photocopy of the student page and allow them to distinguish the shades of gray.

ERROR ALERT! **Question 3** Students may draw conclusions about the pattern too quickly and assume that the outside shape in the fourth shape is a triangle. **Remediation:**

Lesson Planning Options

Prerequisite Skill

- looking for patterns (4-7)

Resources

Student Edition

Skills Handbook, p. 528
Extra Practice, p. 520
Glossary/Study Guide

Teaching Resources

Chapter Support File, Ch. 7
- Lesson Planner 7-1
- Practice 7-1, Reteaching 7-1
- Answer Masters 7-1

Teaching Aids Masters 1, 2, 19
Glossary, Spanish Resources

Transparencies
1, 7, Minds on Math 7-1

Warm Up

On Jim's vacation, he collected the same number of shells each day for 7 days. When he came home, he gave away 14 shells and had 28 left over. How many shells did he collect each day of his vacation?
6 shells

7-1 Exploring Visual Patterns

What You'll Learn

▼ To continue visual patterns

...And Why

Many patterns, such as those on quilts, involve geometric figures.

Here's How

Look for questions that
- build understanding
- ✔ check understanding

WHERE? Geometric patterns are important in many quilt designs.

Work Together — *Extending Geometric Patterns*

1. a. Sketch the next figure for this pattern.

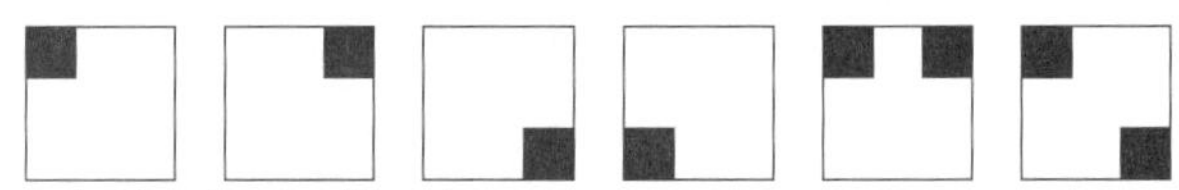

a–b. See back of book.

b. What might be the eighth and ninth figures in the pattern? Can you sketch more than one possibility? Explain.

2. a. Sketch the next two figures for this pattern.

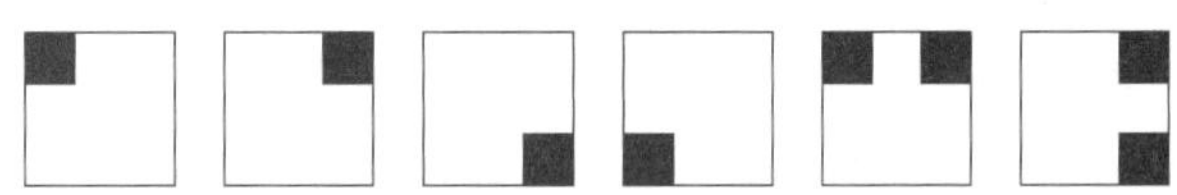

b. What might be the ninth and tenth figures in the pattern?
a–b. See back of book.

THINK AND DISCUSS

Many patterns involve geometric figures.

EXAMPLE — *Real-World Problem Solving*

Crafts Three parts of a quilt square called Dutchman's Puzzle are shown at the right. What design completes the quilt square?

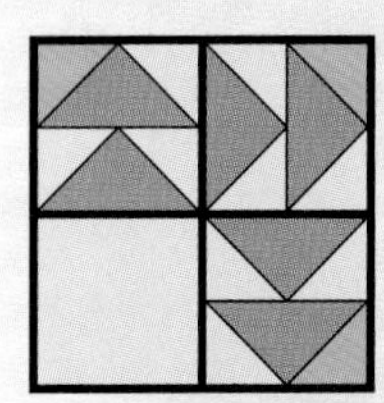

The triangle pattern is turned 90° clockwise going from A to B, from B to C, and from C to D.

Encourage students to list each shape in each figure of the pattern vertically. Then ask them to describe how each list differs to determine a pattern.

■ ADDITIONAL EXAMPLE

FOR EXAMPLE

Draw the next figure for the pattern.

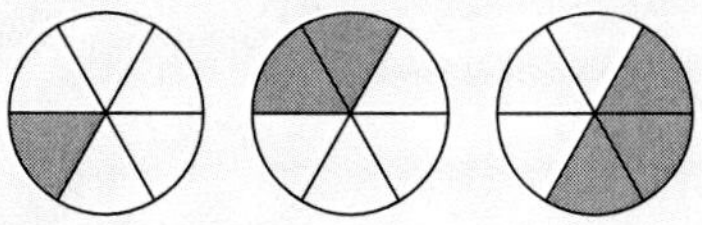

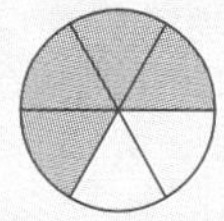

3 Practice/Assess

EXERCISES *On Your Own*

WRITING Exercise 1 Some students may need help seeing the relationship between the number of dots in the figure and the dimensions of the figure.

ASSESSMENT Exercise 3 Ask students to describe the pattern and explain how they chose their answer.

WRAP UP

IDENTIFYING THE BIG IDEA Ask students: *What is a pattern? How do you find the next figure in a pattern?*

PROJECT LINK If you have block scheduling or extended class periods, invite the school librarian to

3\. ✔ *Try It Out* Draw the next two figures for each pattern below.

a.

b.

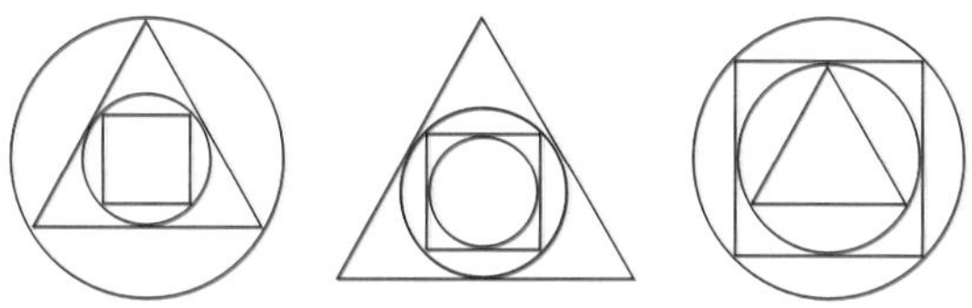

3a.

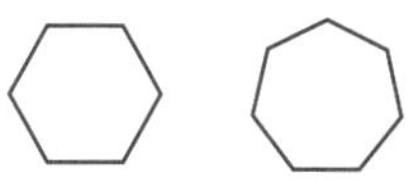

b.

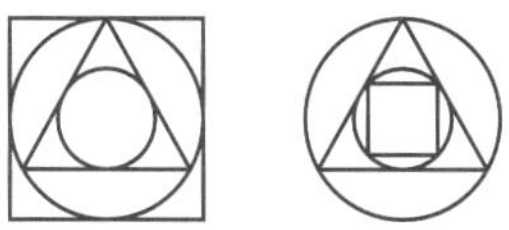

Now you may assign Exercises 1–6.

EXERCISES *On Your Own*

1. a. Draw the next two figures for the pattern.

1a.

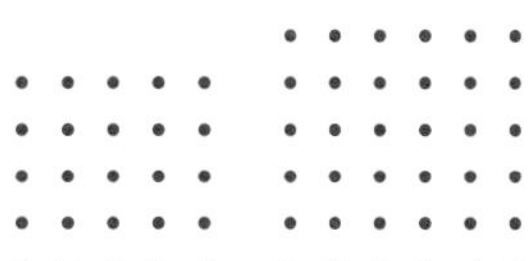

b. *Writing* Describe the twentieth figure for the pattern.
20 x 20 square array of dots

Choose the figure that continues each pattern.

2.

C

A.  **B.** 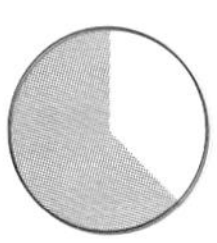 **C.** 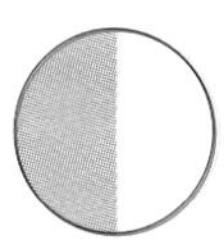 **D.** 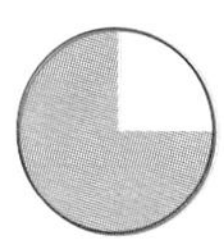

3.

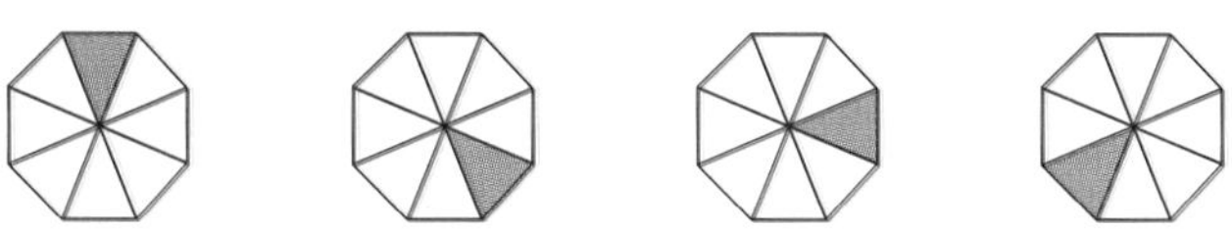

C

A. 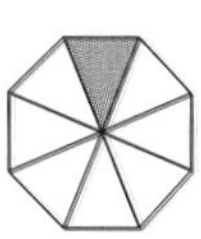 **B.** 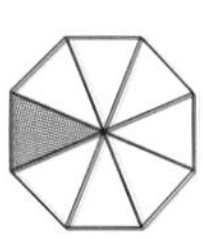 **C.** 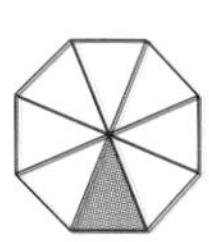 **D.** 

Technology Options

Prentice Hall Technology

Software for Learners

- Math Blaster® Mystery*
- Interactive Student Tutorial, Chapter 7*

Teaching Resource Software

- Computer Item Generator 7-1
- Resource Pro™ Chapter 7*

Internet • For related mathematics activities, visit the Prentice Hall site at www.phschool.com/math

**Available on CD-ROM only*

Assignment Options for Exercises On Your Own

Core 1–5
Extension 6

Use Mixed Review to maintain skills.

PRACTICE

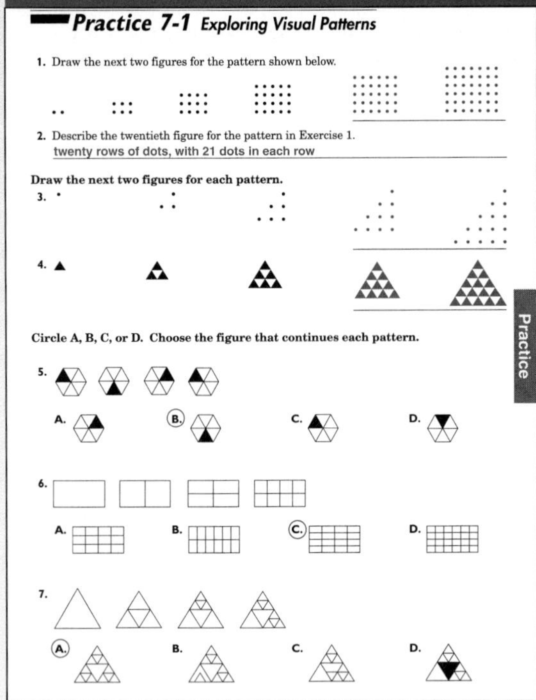
Practice 7-1 Exploring Visual Patterns

1. Draw the next two figures for the pattern shown below.
2. Describe the twentieth figure for the pattern in Exercise 1.
   twenty rows of dots, with 21 dots in each row

Draw the next two figures for each pattern.

3.

4.

Circle A, B, C, or D. Choose the figure that continues each pattern.

5. A. (B.) C. D.

6. A. B. (C.) D.

7. (A.) B. C. D.

In copymaster and workbook formats

RETEACHING

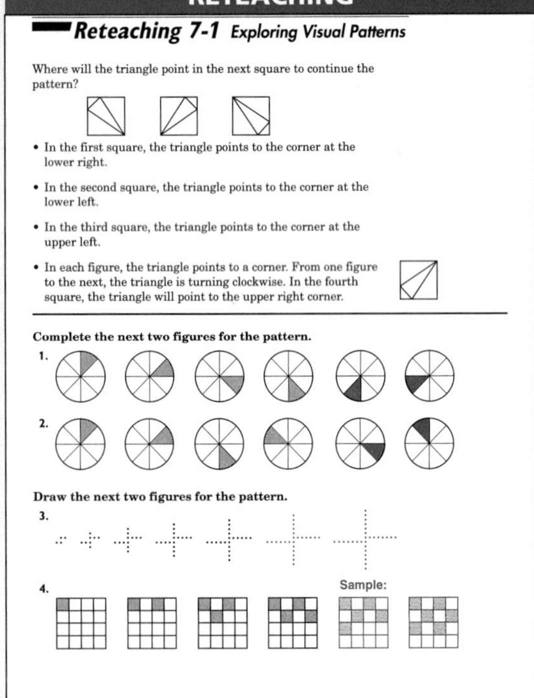
Reteaching 7-1 Exploring Visual Patterns

Where will the triangle point in the next square to continue the pattern?

- In the first square, the triangle points to the corner at the lower right.
- In the second square, the triangle points to the corner at the lower left.
- In the third square, the triangle points to the corner at the upper left.
- In each figure, the triangle points to a corner. From one figure to the next, the triangle is turning clockwise. In the fourth square, the triangle will point to the upper right corner.

Complete the next two figures for the pattern.

1.

2.

Draw the next two figures for the pattern.

3.

4. Sample:

ENRICHMENT

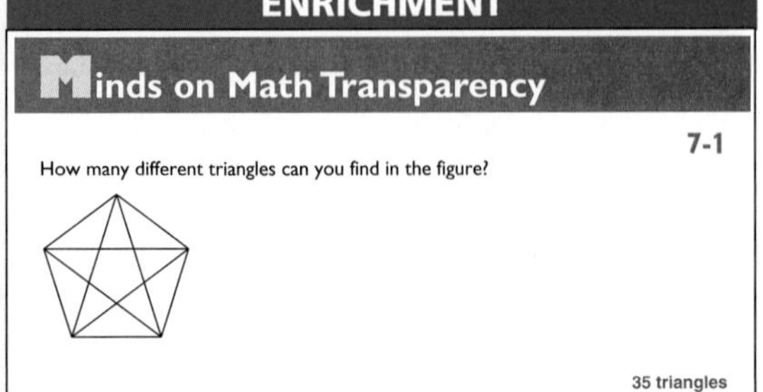
Minds on Math Transparency

7-1

How many different triangles can you find in the figure?

35 triangles

See *Solution Key* for worked-out answers.

class. Have the librarian show students how to use the library catalogs to search for books on bridges and towers.

Math at Work

If you have block scheduling or extended class periods, suggest students contact the American Institute of Architectural Students. AIAS explores and shares information on architecture and education through its journal, CRIT. The journal address is: AIAS, 1735 New York Avenue, NW, Washington DC 20006.

LESSON QUIZ

Draw the next two figures in the pattern.

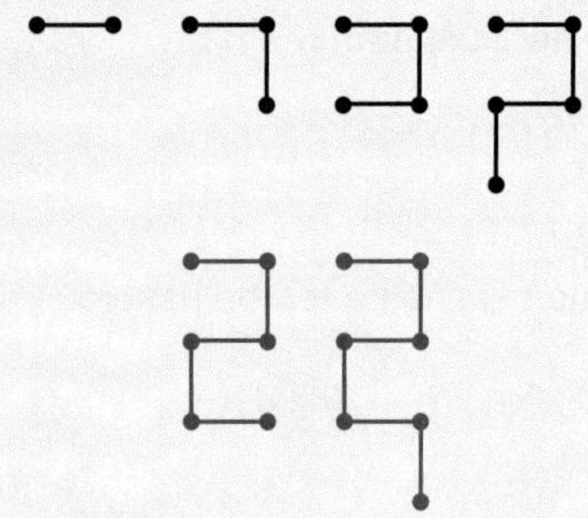

4. Copy the figures on dot paper. Draw two figures that continue the pattern. **See back of book.**

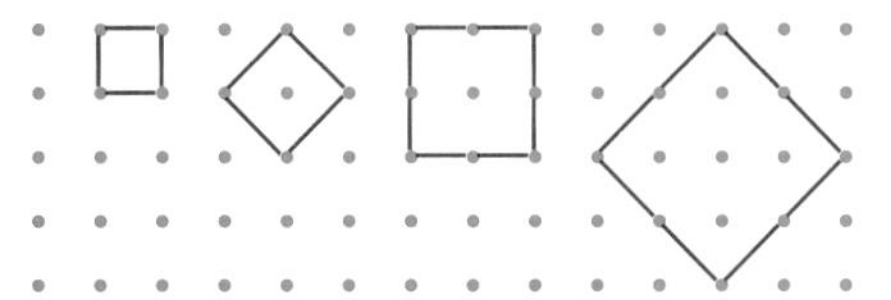

5. Copy the first four figures of the patterns in the Work Together activity. Decide on a way to continue the pattern that is different from Questions 1 and 2. Draw at least the next four figures in your pattern.

   5. Answers may vary. Sample:

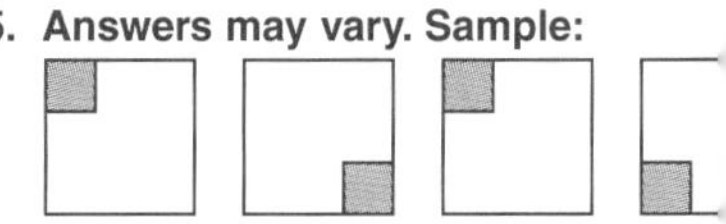

6. *Open-Ended* Draw the first four figures of your own pattern of geometric figures. **Check students' work.**

Mixed Review

Write each fraction in simplest form. *(Lesson 4-6)*

7. $\frac{10}{25}$ **$\frac{2}{5}$** 8. $\frac{14}{32}$ **$\frac{7}{16}$** 9. $\frac{9}{21}$ **$\frac{3}{7}$** 10. $\frac{48}{80}$ **$\frac{3}{5}$** 11. $\frac{28}{35}$ **$\frac{4}{5}$** 12. $\frac{20}{60}$ **$\frac{1}{3}$**

Find the percent of change. State whether the change is an increase or a decrease. Round to the nearest percent. *(Lesson 6-11)*

13. old: \$5.75; new: \$6.25 **9% increase**
14. old: 380 ft; new: 320 ft **16% decrease**
15. old: 3.95 lb; new: 4.25 lb **8% increase**
16. *Choose a Strategy* Jareem has two pairs of slacks to wear with any of three shirts. How many outfits does he have? **6 outfits**

Math at Work

ARCHITECT

Do you have an eye for design? If you choose a career as an architect, then you will design buildings such as homes, schools, and offices. After consulting with a client, an architect uses creativity to plan a beautiful and useful building. In preparing complex blueprints, an architect needs to understand spatial relationships.

Internet Connection

Find out more about architecture at the Web site: http://arc.futurescan.com/

7-2 Teaching Notes

1 Focus

CONNECTING TO PRIOR KNOWLEDGE Ask students when they have heard or read the word angle. Have students look around the room and point out angles they see. Invite students to describe other angles outside the classroom.

2 Teach

THINK AND DISCUSS

REASONING Question 1 Point out that in a three-letter name of an angle, the vertex must be the middle letter. Have students draw and label an angle that matches the name $\angle CDE$.

ERROR ALERT! Example 1 Some students may incorrectly line up the protractor on the angle or read the number from the wrong row of numbers. **Remediation:** Demonstrate how to use a protractor. Show students how to avoid common mistakes such as incorrectly lining up the protractor on the angle.

Question 2 Use a protractor to draw an angle with measure 110° and an angle with measure 70°. **Answers may vary.**

ESTIMATION Question 4a Urge students to compare the angle to an angle whose measure they know, such as 45°, 90°, or 180°.

ALGEBRA Connection

7-2 Classifying and Measuring Angles

What You'll Learn

1. To measure and classify angles
2. To work with pairs of angles

...And Why

Measuring angles is important in careers like carpentry and physical therapy.

Here's How

Look for questions that
- build understanding
- ✔ check understanding

THINK AND DISCUSS

1 Measuring and Describing Angles

Recall that segments and rays are both parts of lines.

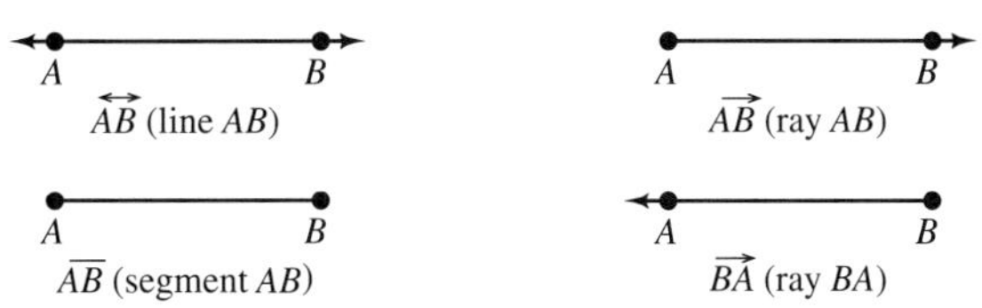

An **angle** is made up of two rays (the *sides* of the angle) with a common endpoint (the *vertex* of the angle). You can call the angle shown $\angle DCE$, $\angle ECD$, $\angle C$, or $\angle 1$.

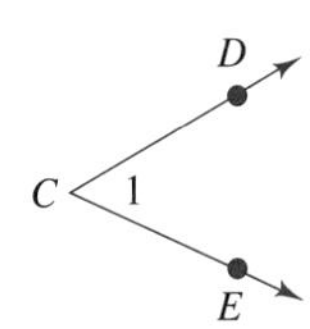

1. *Reasoning* Can you call the angle $\angle CDE$? Explain.
   No; the middle letter must name the vertex.

You can use a protractor to measure angles. You can write the "measure of $\angle X$" as $m\angle X$.

EXAMPLE 1

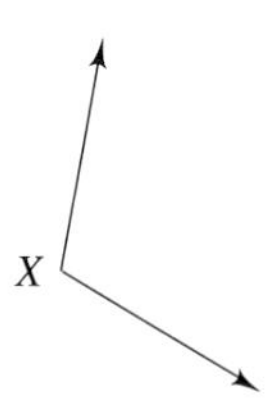

What is the measure of $\angle X$ at the left?

Step 1 Place the center point of your protractor on the vertex of the angle.

Step 2 Make sure that one side of the angle passes through zero on the protractor scale.

Step 3 Read the scale where it intersects the second side of the angle.

$m\angle X = 110°$

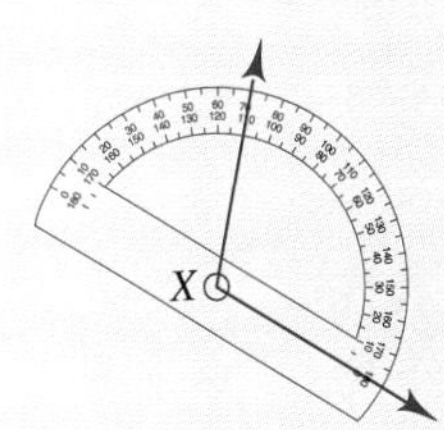

2. *Think About It* Why was the scale reading of 110° on the protractor chosen rather than 70°?
   You read from the scale with zero at the first side of the angle.

Lesson Planning Options

Prerequisite Skill
- solving equations (3-6)

Vocabulary/Symbols
angle, vertex, adjacent angles, acute, right, obtuse, straight angles, complementary, supplementary,

Materials/Manipulatives
- protractor

Resources

Student Edition

Skills Handbook, p. 528
Extra Practice, p. 520
Glossary/Study Guide

Teaching Resources

Chapter Support File, Ch. 7
- Lesson Planner 7-2
- Practice 7-2, Reteaching 7-2
- Alternative Activity 7-2
- Answer Masters 7-2

Teaching Aids Masters 3, 6
Glossary, Spanish Resources

Transparencies
4, 90, Minds on Math 7-2

Warm Up

What property is illustrated?
$(a + b) + c = a + (b + c)$
Associative Property of Addition

AEP **AUDITORY LEARNING** **Question 7** Students may confuse the terms *complementary* and *supplementary.* Invite students to suggest mnemonics they can use to remember how complementary angles and supplementary angles differ. For example, *complementary* is before *supplementary* alphabetically, and 90 is before 180 numerically.

■ ADDITIONAL EXAMPLES

FOR EXAMPLE 1

Use a protractor to find the measure of ∠*DCE* in Question 1. **55°**

FOR EXAMPLE 2

Find the measures of ∠1, ∠2, and ∠3 if *m*∠4 = 135°. ***m*∠1 = 45°; *m*∠2 = 135°; *m*∠3 = 45°**

AEP Some students may confuse *complement* with *compliment.* Tell students: *I like to receive compliments.* Relate *I* with the *i* in compl*i*ment.

TACTILE LEARNING Have students use a ruler to draw adjacent pairs of angles. Then use a protractor to measure the angles and determine which are complementary and which are supplementary.

VISUAL LEARNING Have students work in pairs. One student uses two pencils to model angles that are acute, right, obtuse, or straight. The partner names the type of angle.

Technology Options

Prentice Hall Technology

Software for Learners
- Math Blaster® Mystery*
- Interactive Student Tutorial, Chapter 7*

Teaching Resource Software
- Computer Item Generator 7-2
- Resource Pro™ Chapter 7*

Internet • For related mathematics activities, visit the Prentice Hall site at www.phschool.com/math

**Available on CD-ROM only*

Assignment Options for Exercises On Your Own

To provide flexible scheduling, this lesson can be subdivided into parts.

1 **Core** 1–13, 21, 22, 29–32
Extension 33

2 **Core** 14–20, 23, 24, 27–28
Extension 25, 26

Use Mixed Review to maintain skills.

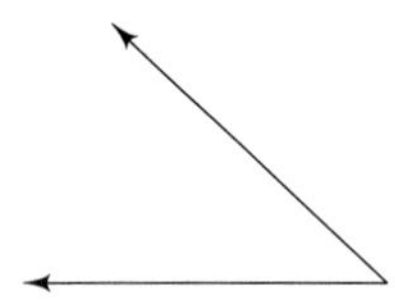

3. *Think About It* How would you measure an angle with sides that do not extend to the scale of the protractor?
Use a straightedge to extend the sides of the angle.

4. a. *Estimation* Estimate the measure of the angle at the left.
b. *Try It Out* Measure the angle. **b. 42°**
4a. Answers may vary. Sample: 45°

You can classify angles by their measures.

QUICK review

The symbol ⌉ indicates a right angle.

acute angle	**right angle**	**obtuse angle**	**straight angle**
measures less than 90°	measures 90°	measures greater than 90° and less than 180°	measures 180°

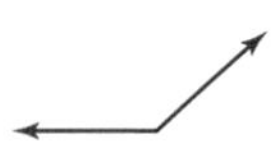

obtuse

5. *Try It Out* Use your protractor to draw a 140° angle. Then classify the angle.

Now you may assign Exercises 1–13, 21–22, 29–30.

2 *Pairs of Angles*

Two **adjacent angles** share a vertex and one side but have no common interior points.
∠*ABD* and ∠*DBC* are adjacent angles.

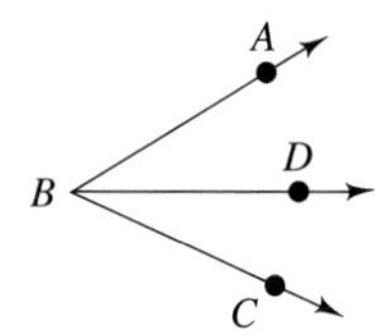

6. *Try It Out* Are ∠*ABD* and ∠*ABC* adjacent angles? Why or why not? **No; all interior points of ∠*ABD* are in the interior of ∠*ABC*.**

If the sum of the measures of two angles is 90°, the angles are **complementary.**

If the sum of the measures of two angles is 180°, the angles are **supplementary.**

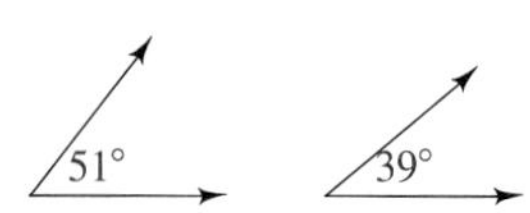

complementary

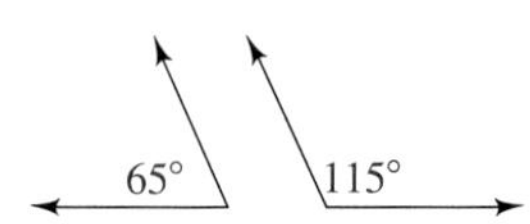

supplementary

7. *Try It Out* The measure of ∠1 is 56°. What is the measure of its complement? Of its supplement? **34°; 124°**

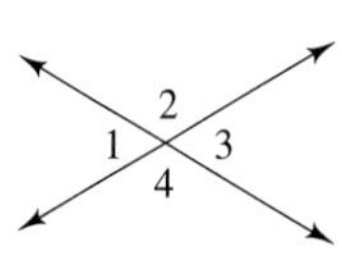

8. Name the pairs of adjacent angles in the figure at the left.
∠1 and ∠2, ∠2 and ∠3, ∠3 and ∠4, ∠1 and ∠4

The pairs of angles that are not adjacent are *vertical angles.* ∠1 and ∠3 are vertical angles. ∠2 and ∠4 are vertical angles.

9. *Analyze* Measure the angles in the figure at the left. Make a conjecture about the measures of vertical angles.
60°, 120°, 60°, 120°; Vertical angles have equal measures.

ERROR ALERT! Students may have difficulty remembering the difference between *obtuse* and *acute* angles. **Remediation:** Explain that acute can mean "sharp." Acute angles look like sharp points. Obtuse angles look like they open out.

ASSESSMENT Have students draw several intersecting lines. Then ask students to label angles that are *acute, obtuse, straight, right, vertical, adjacent, supplementary,* or *complementary.* Ask students to explain some of their answers.

EXTENSION Ask students whether they think angles can have measures larger than 180°. Have students look up the meaning of reflex angle. **angle with a measure of more than 180° but less than 360°** Discuss with students any difficulties they may encounter when trying to name a reflex angle.

3 Practice/Assess

EXERCISES *On Your Own*

ERROR ALERT! Exercise 18 Students may identify any two angles sharing a common side as adjacent angles. **Remediation:** Draw pairs of angles such as those shown. Help students see that for two angles to be adjacent, they must have the same vertex. Also relate adjacent angles to adjacent yards. A fence separates two yards, and the yards do not overlap.

■ EXAMPLE 2

Find the measures of $\angle 1$, $\angle 2$, and $\angle 3$ if $m\angle 4 = 128°$.

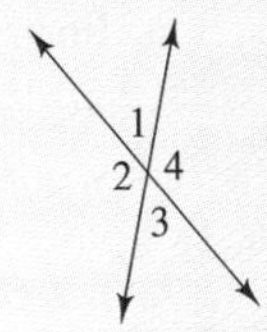

$m\angle 1 + 128° = 180°$ ← $\angle 1$ and $\angle 4$ are supplementary.

$m\angle 1 = 180° - 128°$

$m\angle 1 = 52°$

$m\angle 2 = 128°$ ← $\angle 2$ and $\angle 4$ are vertical angles.

$m\angle 3 = 52°$ ← $\angle 1$ and $\angle 3$ are vertical angles.

10. ✔ *Try It Out* The measure of an angle formed by two intersecting lines is 40°. What are the measures of the other three angles? 140°, 40°, 140°

Now you may assign Exercises 14–20, 23–28.

EXERCISES *On Your Own*

Classify each angle as acute, right, obtuse, or straight.

1. $m\angle A = 45°$ acute

2. $m\angle B = 180°$ straight

3. $m\angle C = 90°$ right

4. $m\angle D = 150°$ obtuse

Estimate the measure of each angle. Then classify the angle. 5–8. Estimates may vary. Samples are given.

5. 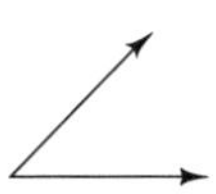
50°; acute

6. 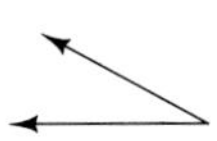
30°; acute

7. 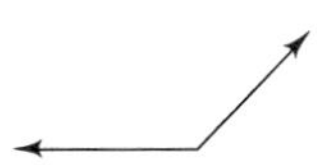
130°; obtuse

8. 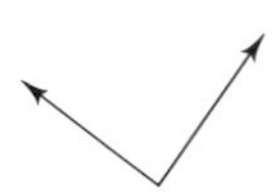
90°; right

9. *Physical Therapy* Physical therapists use *goniometers* to measure the amount of motion a person has in a joint, like an elbow or a knee. The goniometer has a built-in protractor. Estimate the measure of the angle in the photograph. about 65°

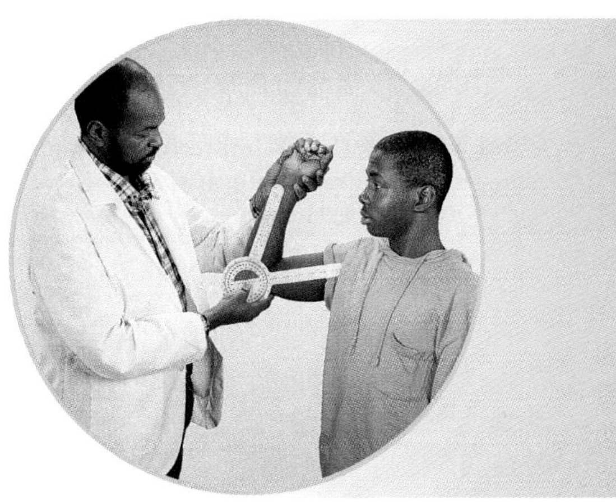

Use dot paper or graph paper to draw angles with the following measures *without* using a protractor.
10–13. See margin.

10. 90° **11.** 180°

12. 45° **13.** 135°

pages 293–295 On Your Own

10. 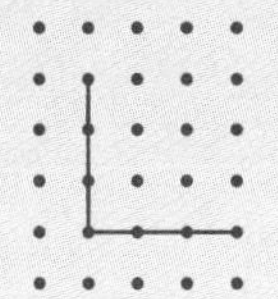

11. 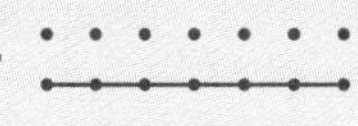

12. 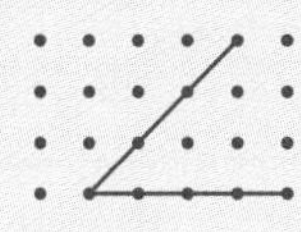

13. 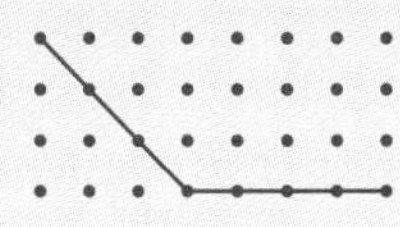

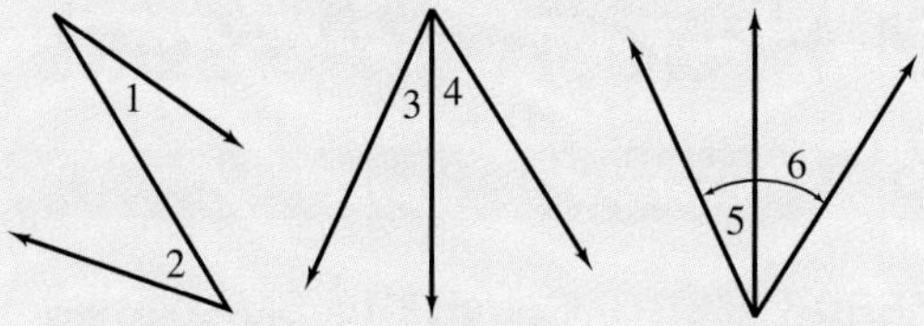

WRITING Exercise 21 Invite students to describe how they would avoid making the same mistake. Ask: *Could you make this mistake drawing an angle with measure 90°? Explain.* **No, the 90° marks on the two scales of the protractor coincide.**

ESTIMATION Exercises 29–32 Ask students to explain how they decide whether or not each estimate is reasonable.

WRAP UP

IDENTIFYING THE BIG IDEA Ask students to name and describe the four types of angles and the two types of adjacent angles.

JOURNAL Suggest students walk around the school building and look for angles. Ask them to describe where they see acute and obtuse angles.

LESSON QUIZ

1. Estimate the measure of ∠*D*. **170°**

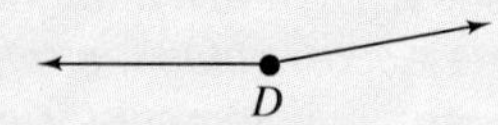

Use the figure at the right to name the following.
14–20. Answers may vary. Samples are given.

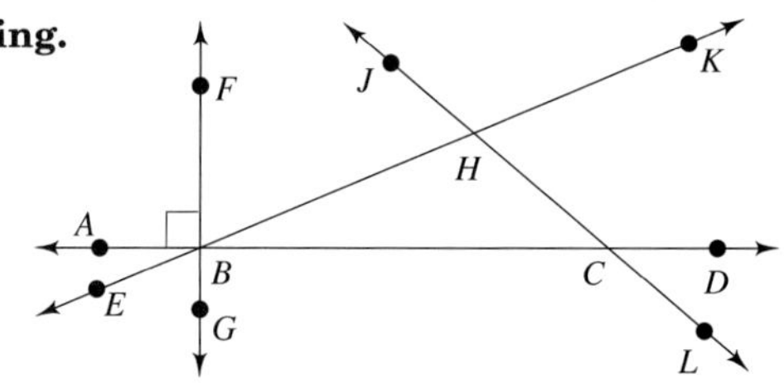

14. four lines
$\overleftrightarrow{AD}$, $\overleftrightarrow{EK}$, $\overleftrightarrow{FG}$, $\overleftrightarrow{JL}$

15. three segments
$\overline{AB}$, $\overline{BC}$, $\overline{CD}$

16. four rays
$\overrightarrow{AB}$, $\overrightarrow{HK}$, $\overrightarrow{HL}$, $\overrightarrow{BF}$

17. four right angles
∠*ABF*, ∠*FBC*, ∠*CBG*, ∠*ABG*

18. two pairs of adjacent supplementary angles
∠*ABF* and ∠*FBC*, ∠*JCB* and ∠*JCD*

19. two pairs of obtuse vertical angles
∠*JHK* and ∠*BHC*, ∠*FBE* and ∠*HBG*

20. two pairs of complementary angles
∠*FBH* and ∠*HBC*, ∠*ABE* and ∠*EBG*

21. *Writing* One student measured ∠*ABC* and said that *m*∠*ABC* = 60°. Explain the mistake that he made. **He read from the wrong set of numbers on the protractor.**

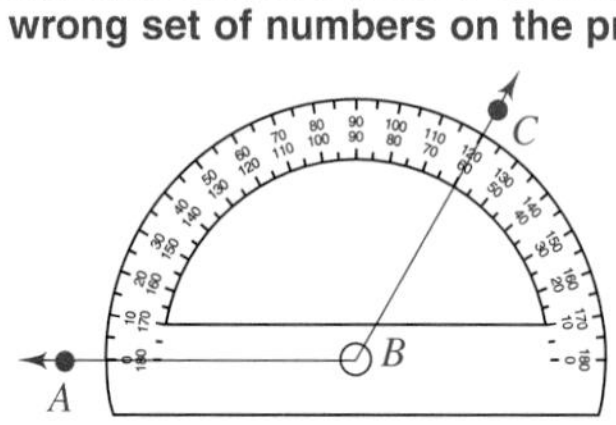

22. Use a protractor to find *m*∠*A*, *m*∠*B*, *m*∠*C*, and *m*∠*D*. **m∠A = 100°, m∠B = 115°, m∠C = 75°, m∠D = 70°**

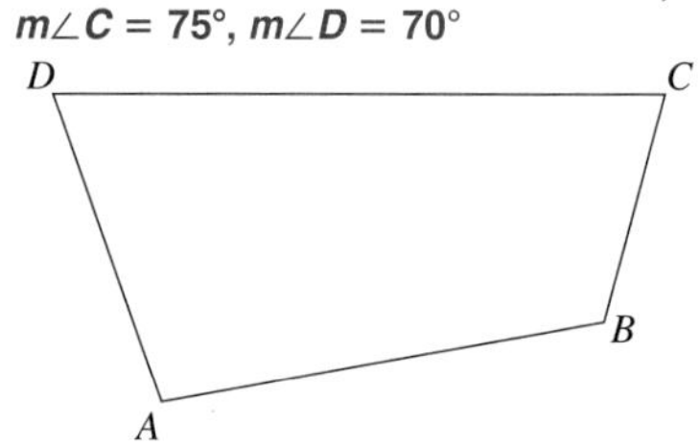

23. ∠*A* and ∠*B* are supplementary angles. If *m*∠*A* = 15°, what is *m*∠*B*? **165°**

24. ∠*C* and ∠*D* are complementary angles. If *m*∠*C* = 50°, what is *m*∠*D*? **40°**

25. Use a protractor to draw two complementary angles, one of which has measure 25°.

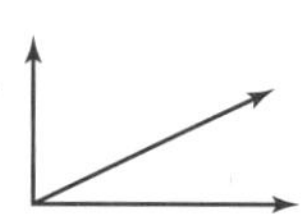

26. Use a protractor to draw two supplementary angles, one of which has measure 55°.

27. ∠1 and ∠2 are vertical angles. If *m*∠1 = 75°, what is *m*∠2? **75°**

28. Draw vertical angles, ∠1 and ∠2, that are complementary.

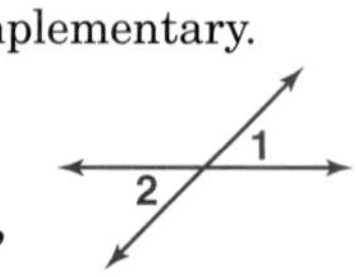

Tell whether the estimate for each angle measure is reasonable. If it is not reasonable, give a better estimate.

31. Not reasonable; estimates may vary. Sample: 140°

29. 120°

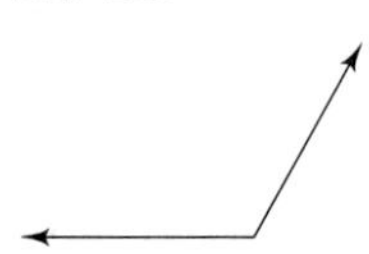

reasonable

30. 60°

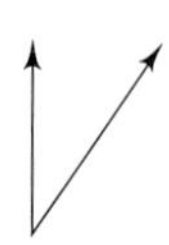

reasonable

31. 45°

32. 90°

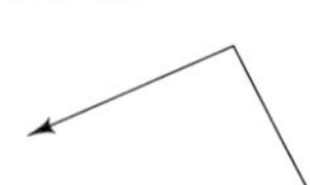

reasonable

JOURNAL
Describe the use of acute angles and obtuse angles in buildings.

294

2. Find the measures of ∠1 and ∠2.
$m\angle 1 = 43°$; $m\angle 2 = 133°$

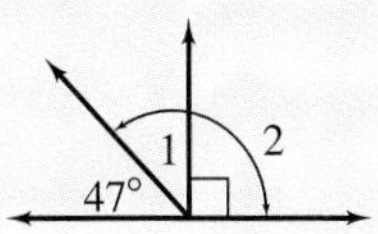

IVORY ID

Ivory smugglers try to slip illegal elephant ivory into the United States by labeling the ivory as mammoth tusks. Ed Espinoza of the United States Fish and Wildlife Service has found a way to identify whether ivory tusks are from prehistoric mammoths or from elephants.

The flat edges of tusks contain distinctive markings. When Ed Espinoza and a team of scientists photocopied and measured these markings, they found that markings from mammoth tusks create angles that measure 90° or less. Markings from elephants create angles that measure 115° or more.

33. These are photocopies of two ivory tusks. Identify which comes from a mammoth and which comes from an elephant.

a. 
mammoth

b. 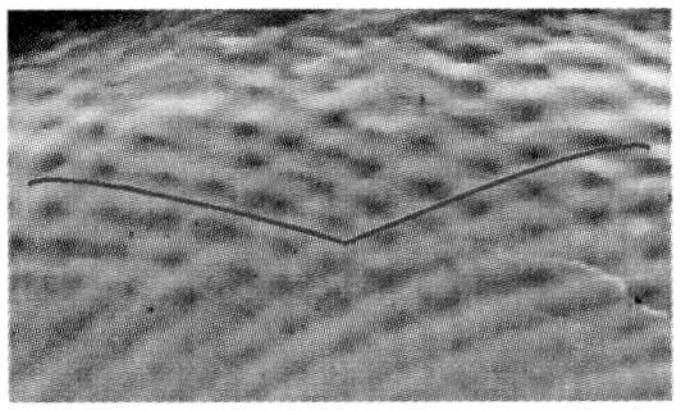
elephant

Mixed Review

Find each product. *(Lesson 5-5)*

34. $\frac{4}{5} \cdot \frac{2}{5}$ $\frac{8}{25}$ 35. $\frac{8}{14} \cdot \frac{7}{8}$ $\frac{1}{2}$ 36. $\frac{5}{6} \cdot 14$ 37. $\frac{8}{9} \cdot \frac{11}{12}$ $\frac{22}{27}$ 38. $\frac{5}{16} \cdot \frac{2}{5}$ $\frac{1}{8}$ 39. $\frac{8}{9} \cdot \frac{3}{4}$ $\frac{2}{3}$

36. $\frac{35}{3}$, or $11\frac{2}{3}$

40. Jack, Barbara, Sally, and Michelle have 25 dimes, 35 nickels, 267 pennies, and 7 quarters, respectively. Who has the most money? The least? *(Lessons 3-2, 3-5)*
Sally; Barbara and Michelle

CHAPTER PROJECT

PROJECT LINK: RESEARCHING

Find pictures of structures such as bridges and towers that use triangles in their construction. Use the pictures to get ideas for the design of your tower. Check students' work.

PRACTICE

Practice 7-2 *Classifying and Measuring Angles*

Estimate the measure of each angle. Then classify the angle.
Accept any reasonable estimates.

1. 90°, right 2. 135°, obtuse 3. 45°, acute

Classify each angle as *acute*, *right*, *obtuse*, or *straight*.

4. $m\angle A = 180°$ straight
5. $m\angle B = 43°$ acute
6. $m\angle C = 127°$ obtuse
7. $m\angle D = 90°$ right

Use the diagram at the right. Name each of the following.
Answers may vary. Sample answers shown.

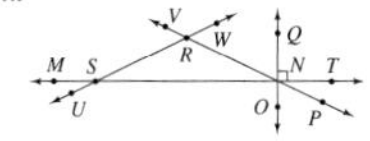

8. four lines $\overleftrightarrow{RU}$, $\overleftrightarrow{ST}$, $\overleftrightarrow{RP}$, $\overleftrightarrow{QO}$
9. three segments $\overline{RN}$, $\overline{RP}$, $\overline{QN}$
10. four rays $\overrightarrow{RW}$, $\overrightarrow{RS}$, $\overrightarrow{RV}$, $\overrightarrow{RP}$
11. four right angles ∠QNT, ∠TNO, ∠QNS and ∠SNO
12. two pairs of obtuse vertical angles ∠MSW and ∠UST, ∠SRP and ∠VRW
13. two pairs of adjacent supplementary angles ∠MSR and ∠MSU, ∠MSR and ∠RST
14. two pairs of complementary angles ∠QNR and ∠RNS, ∠TNP and ∠PNO

15. Use a protractor to find $m\angle A$, $m\angle B$, $m\angle C$, and $m\angle D$.

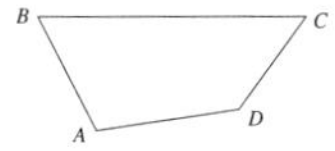

$m\angle A = 110°$
$m\angle B = 62°$
$m\angle C = 53°$
$m\angle D = 135°$

16. Use a protractor. Draw two vertical angles. One angle has a measure of 45°.

17. Use the dot grid to draw two supplementary angles, one of which is 45°. Do not use a protractor.

In copymaster and workbook formats

RETEACHING

Reteaching 7-2 *Classifying and Measuring Angles*

An **angle** is made up of two rays (the *sides* of the angle) with a common endpoint (the *vertex* of the angle).
You can name this angle ∠A, ∠BAC, or ∠CAB.

∠A is an **acute** angle because its measure is less than 90°. If an angle has a measure greater than 90° and less than 180°, it is an **obtuse angle.**

acute less than 90°
obtuse greater than 90° less than 180°

You can measure an angle using a protractor.
Write the measure of ∠A as $m\angle A$.
To measure an angle:

① Place the center point of your protractor on the vertex of the angle.
② Line up one side of the angle with zero on the protractor scale.
③ Read the scale at the second side of the angle. Since ∠A is an acute angle, read 80° and not 100°.

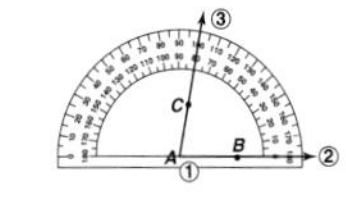

$m\angle A = 80°$

Measure each angle. Then circle *acute* or *obtuse*.

1. $m\angle B = 120°$ acute (obtuse)
2. $m\angle S = 50°$ (acute) obtuse
3. $m\angle Y = 60°$ (acute) obtuse
4. $m\angle N = 110°$ acute (obtuse)

Classify each angle with the given measure as *acute* or *obtuse*.

5. 45° acute
6. 148° obtuse
7. 4° acute
8. 106° obtuse
9. 65° acute
10. 179° obtuse
11. 23° acute
12. 115° obtuse

Reteaching

ENRICHMENT

Minds on Math Transparency

7-2

I am a three-digit number. When you reverse my digits, a larger number is formed. The product of me and the new number is 65,125. What number am I?

125

See *Solution Key* for worked-out answers.

Exercise 4 Make sure students extend the rays of the angles they draw far enough so that the angles can be measured with the protractor.

ASSESSMENT Exercise 4 Have students compare their results with a partner. Then challenge each pair to write a rule that describes their results. Pairs can share their rules with the class.

MATH TOOLBOX

In Lesson 7-2, students learned how to measure and classify angles. This toolbox shows students how to identify supplementary and congruent angles formed by parallel lines and a transversal.

ERROR ALERT! Students may draw lines that are not exactly parallel. **Remediation:** Have students use the opposite sides of a straightedge, or draw their lines on graph paper.

Materials/Manipulatives

- protractor

Resources

Teaching Aids Master 3

MATH TOOLBOX EXPLORATION

Parallel Lines

After Lesson 7-2

You can use a piece of notebook paper and your protractor to investigate the angles formed by a line that crosses two parallel lines.

Parallel lines are lines in a plane that do not intersect no matter how far they are extended. You can think of a plane as a flat surface. The lines on notebook paper are parts of parallel lines.

On a clean sheet of notebook paper, draw a diagram like the one at the right. The diagram shows two parallel lines and a *transversal* that crosses them.

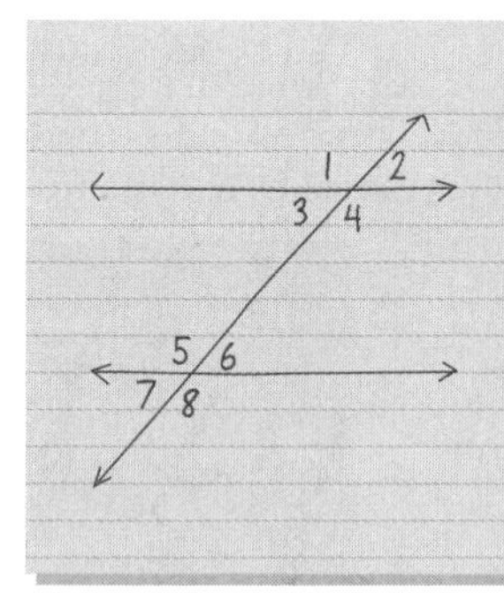

1. Use your protractor to measure each numbered angle.
   $m\angle 1 = 132°$, $m\angle 2 = 48°$, $m\angle 3 = 48°$, $m\angle 4 = 132°$, $m\angle 5 = 132°$, $m\angle 6 = 48°$, $m\angle 7 = 48°$, $m\angle 8 = 132°$
2. Which angles have the same measure as $\angle 1$?
   $\angle 4$, $\angle 5$, $\angle 8$
3. Which angles are supplementary to $\angle 1$?
   $\angle 2$, $\angle 3$, $\angle 6$, $\angle 7$
4. a. Draw another pair of parallel lines. Use your protractor to draw a transversal that makes a right angle with one of your parallel lines.
   b. Measure all of the angles. What do you notice?
   All angles are 90°.

4a.

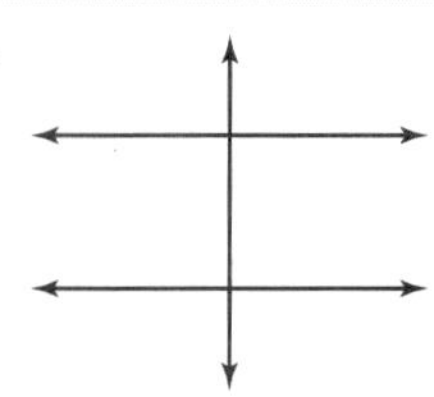

In each diagram, lines ℓ and m are parallel. Which numbered angles have the same measure as $\angle 1$? Which numbered angles are supplements of $\angle 1$?

5.

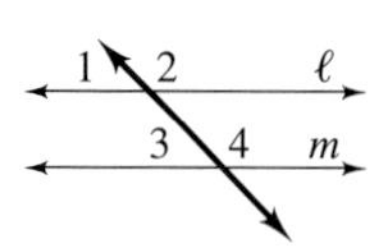

$\angle 3$; $\angle 2$, $\angle 4$

6.

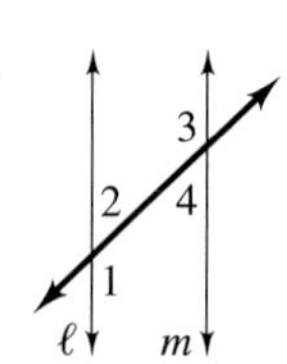

$\angle 3$; $\angle 2$, $\angle 4$

7.

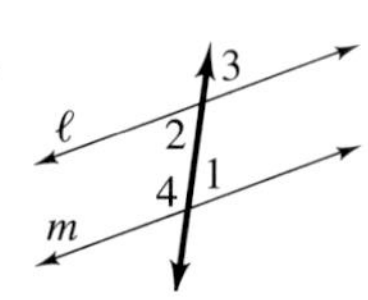

$\angle 2$, $\angle 3$; $\angle 4$

8.

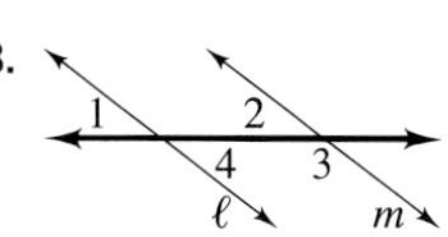

$\angle 2$, $\angle 4$; $\angle 3$

9. In the diagram at the right, lines ℓ and m are parallel and lines n and q are parallel. The measure of $\angle 4$ is 58°. Find the measures of the numbered angles.
   $m\angle 1 = 122°$, $m\angle 2 = 58°$, $m\angle 3 = 122°$

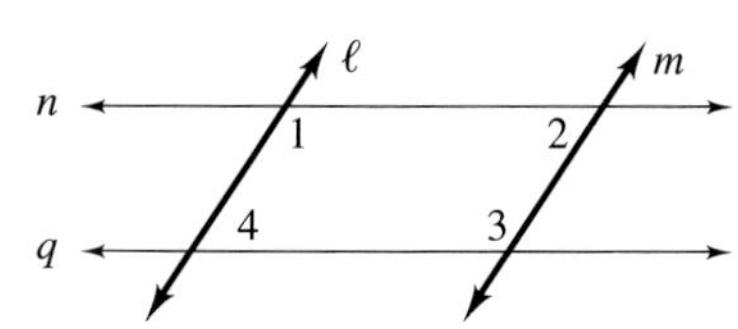

7-3 Teaching Notes

1 Focus

CONNECTING TO PRIOR KNOWLEDGE
Invite students to draw triangles on the board with sides of different lengths. Then consider the lengths of the sides and the angles formed and their relationship to each other. Ask students to make conjectures about how they can describe different triangles. Then sort triangles into different types.

2 Teach

Work Together

Have students work in groups of three or four. Have students cut out triangles of different shapes or supply them with triangles. Make sure students put all vertices together so that the angles are adjacent. Suggest that students draw a line or use the edge of a ruler to help them line up the angles.

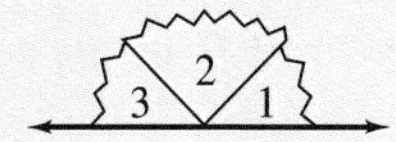

THINK AND DISCUSS

AEP Have students draw and label an *acute angle*, a *right angle*, and an *obtuse angle* with long sides. Have students draw a

---

ALGEBRA Connection

7-3 Triangles

What You'll Learn

- 1 To classify triangles by sides and by angles
- 2 To find the measure of one angle of a triangle, given the other two measures

...And Why

Triangles and the measures of their angles appear everywhere, from architecture to designing flags.

Here's How

Look for questions that
- build understanding
- ✔ check understanding

QUICK review

Congruent segments are segments that have the same length. Congruent angles are angles that have the same measure.

Work Together — *Investigating Angles of a Triangle*

Cut out a paper triangle that is a different shape from those of the other members of your group.

Step 1 Number the angles of the triangle and tear them off the triangle.

Step 2 Place the three angles side-by-side to form adjacent angles with no angles overlapping.

1. Compare your results with those of your group. Make a conjecture about the sum of the angles.
   The measures of the angles of a triangle total 180°.

THINK AND DISCUSS

1 *Classifying Triangles*

You can classify triangles by the number of congruent sides or by angle measures.

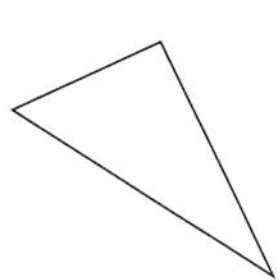
scalene triangle
no congruent sides

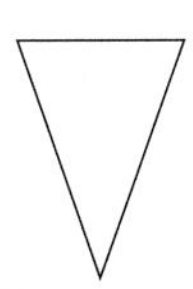
isosceles triangle
at least two congruent sides

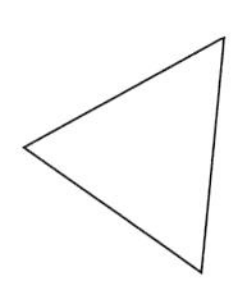
equilateral triangle
three congruent sides

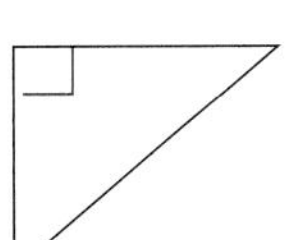
right triangle
one right angle

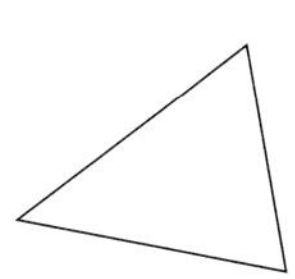
acute triangle
three acute angles

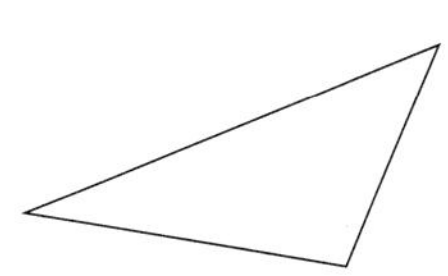
obtuse triangle
one obtuse angle

Lesson Planning Options

Prerequisite Skill

- solving equations using subtraction (3-6)

Materials/Manipulatives

- scissors
- protractor

Resources

Student Edition
Skills Handbook, p. 528
Extra Practice, p. 520
Glossary/Study Guide

Teaching Resources
Chapter Support File, Ch. 7
- Lesson Planner 7-3
- Practice 7-3, Reteaching 7-3
- Answer Masters 7-3

Teaching Aids Masters 3, 7–9
Glossary, Spanish Resources

Transparencies
16, 17, Minds on Math 7-3

Warm Up

Two men, both working at the same rate, take 3 h 15 min to mend a fence. If just one of them were to work alone at the same job and at the same rate, how long would he take to mend the fence?
6 h 30 min

line that crosses both sides of the angle to form a triangle. Have students label the triangles as *acute*, *right*, or *obtuse*.

EXAMPLE 2 Ask: *Is it possible for a triangle to have two right angles? Why?* **No, two right angles measure 180°, leaving zero degrees for the third angle.** Ask: *Is it possible for a triangle to have two obtuse angles? Why?* **No, two obtuse angles have a total measure of more than 180°.**

ADDITIONAL EXAMPLES

FOR EXAMPLE 1

Classify the triangle by its sides and angles.

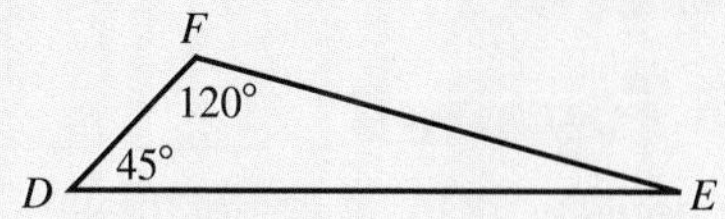

scalene; obtuse

FOR EXAMPLE 2

Find the measure of $\angle E$ of $\triangle DEF$ in For Example 1. **15°**

FOR EXAMPLE 3

The measure of one angle of an isosceles triangle is 30°. The other two angles are congruent. Find the measure of the two congruent angles. **75°.**

TACTILE LEARNING Have students work in pairs. Give each pair several straws or strips of paper that are of three different lengths.

Technology Options

Prentice Hall Technology

Software for Learners

- Hot Page™ 2–3*
- Math Blaster® Mystery*
- Interactive Student Tutorial, Chapter 7*

Teaching Resource Software

- Computer Item Generator 7-3
- Resource Pro™ Chapter 7*

Internet • For related mathematics activities, visit the Prentice Hall site at www.phschool.com/math

Assignment Options for Exercises On Your Own

To provide flexible scheduling, this lesson can be subdivided into parts.

1 **Core** 1–9, 17
Extension 24

2 **Core** 10–16, 18, 19, 21–23
Extension 20

Use Mixed Review to maintain skills.

Now you may assign Exercises 1–9, 17, 24.

EXAMPLE 1 *Real-World Problem Solving*

Architecture The building in the center of this photograph is the Transamerica Building in San Francisco. Classify the front of the Transamerica Building.

The front of the Transamerica Building is an acute isosceles triangle.

2. ✔ *Try It Out* Classify each triangle by its sides.

a. **equilateral**

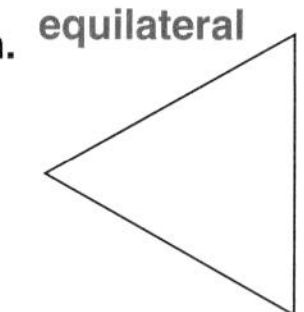

b. **isosceles**

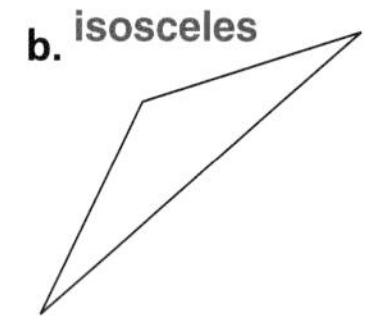

c. **scalene**

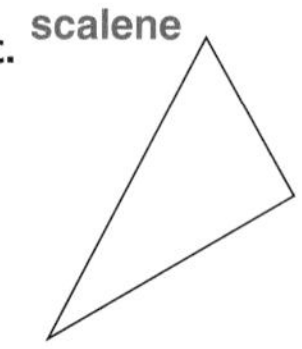

3. ✔ *Try It Out* Classify each triangle in Question 2 by its angles. **3a. acute b. obtuse c. right**

2 *Angles and Triangles*

In the Work Together activity you discovered that the following statement is true for all triangles.

The sum of the measures of the angles of a triangle is 180°.

EXAMPLE 2

Find the measure of $\angle C$.

$$m\angle C + 53^\circ + 61^\circ = 180^\circ$$
$$m\angle C + 114^\circ = 180^\circ$$
$$m\angle C = 180^\circ - 114^\circ$$
$$m\angle C = 66^\circ$$

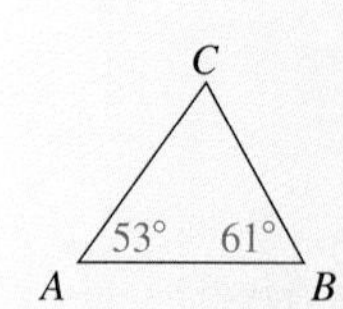

4. ✔ *Try It Out* The measures of two angles of a triangle are 48° and 37°. What is the measure of the third angle? **95°**

Have the students form and identify different types of triangles such as acute isosceles triangles and right scalene triangles.

AUDITORY LEARNING **Example 3** Have students work in pairs. One student reads the description of ΔABC. The partner listens, then draws the sides and angles of the triangle.

ERROR ALERT! Students may think that large triangles have larger angle measures than small triangles. **Remediation:** Photocopy a triangle and an enlargement of the same triangle. Have a volunteer demonstrate with a protractor that the angle measures of the corresponding angles are the same, regardless of the size of the triangle.

ASSESSMENT Assign partners to answer the following questions. Have them use a protractor and a ruler to draw triangles to support their answers.

- *Can an isosceles triangle be a right triangle?* **yes**
- *Can a scalene triangle be an acute triangle?* **yes**
- *Can a right triangle be an equilateral triangle?* **no**

TACTILE LEARNING Call out the various triangle classifications and have students model the triangles using geoboards.

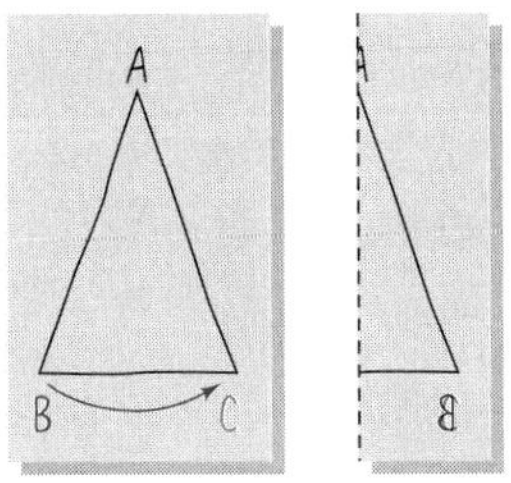

The diagram at the left shows the two congruent sides of an isosceles triangle folded on top of one another. When two sides of a triangle are congruent, two angles are congruent.

EXAMPLE 3

Triangle ABC is isosceles. Side AB is congruent to side AC, so $\angle B$ is congruent to $\angle C$. Find the measure of $\angle A$.

Since $\angle B$ is congruent to $\angle C$, $\angle C$ has the measure 40°.

$$m\angle A + 40° + 40° = 180°$$
$$m\angle A + 80° = 180°$$
$$m\angle A = 180° - 80°$$
$$m\angle A = 100°$$

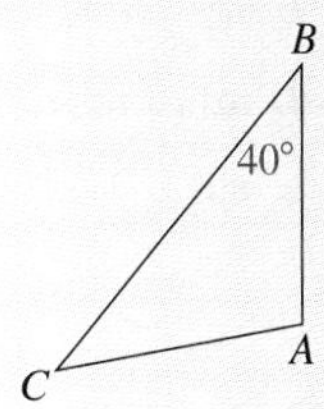

6a. They are congruent.
b. Yes; they are congruent.
c. 60°; 60 + 60 + 60 = 180

5. ✔ *Try It Out* One angle of an isosceles triangle has the measure 120°. Find the measure of the two congruent angles. **30°**

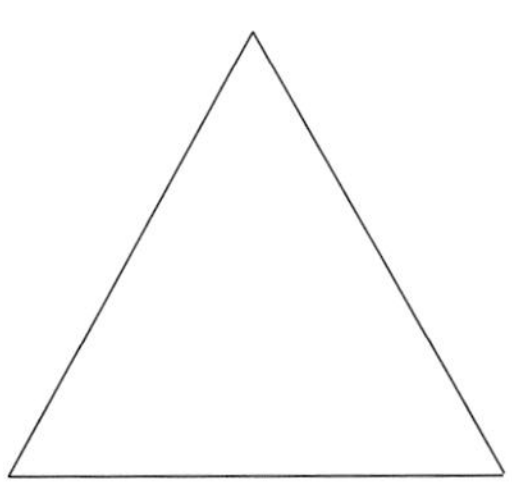

6. a. *Make a Model* Trace the equilateral triangle at the left. Fold the triangle so that one side matches another side. What is true of the angles that match?
   b. If you fold the triangle so that a different pair of sides match, do you get the same result? What is true of the three angles of an equilateral triangle?
   c. *Draw a Conclusion* What is the measure of each angle of an equilateral triangle? Explain. **a–c. See above left.**

Now you may assign Exercises 10–16, 18–23.

EXERCISES *On Your Own*

Judging by appearance, classify each triangle by its sides. Name any congruent sides.

1. 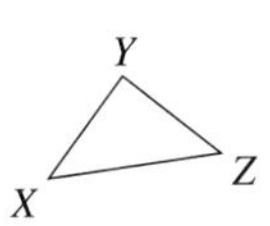

isosceles; $\overline{XY}$, $\overline{YZ}$

2. 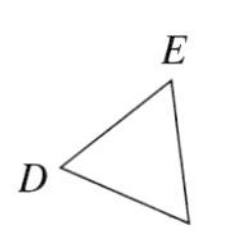

equilateral; $\overline{DE}$, $\overline{DF}$, $\overline{EF}$

3. 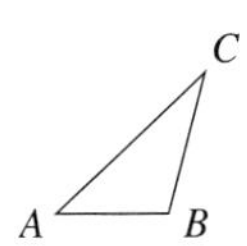

scalene

4. 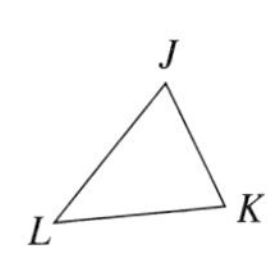

isosceles; $\overline{JL}$, $\overline{KL}$

Judging by appearance, classify each triangle above by its angles. Name any obtuse or right angles.

5. Exercise 1 **Right; $\angle Y$ is a right angle.**
6. Exercise 2 **acute**
7. Exercise 3 **Obtuse; $\angle B$ is obtuse.**
8. Exercise 4 **acute**

3 Practice/Assess

EXERCISES *On Your Own*

CONNECTION TO MUSIC Exercise 9 Challenge interested students to conjecture why a musical triangle is equilateral. Have students conjecture how the sound produced by the triangle relates to its size, shape, and type of metal.

CONNECTION TO SOCIAL STUDIES Exercise 17 If you have block scheduling or extended class periods, have students research to find other flags that contain triangles. **Answers may vary. Sample: Georgia, Ohio, Jamaica** Students can also design their own flags, featuring the types of triangles they have learned.

WRITING Exercise 18 Suggest that students try to draw each triangle mentioned. They can then compare the triangles using their own words or definitions.

OPEN-ENDED Exercise 24 Make sure students recognize that there are an infinite number of ways to draw each triangle.

WRAP UP

IDENTIFYING THE BIG IDEA Ask students how they can classify triangles by sides and angles.

CHECKPOINT 1

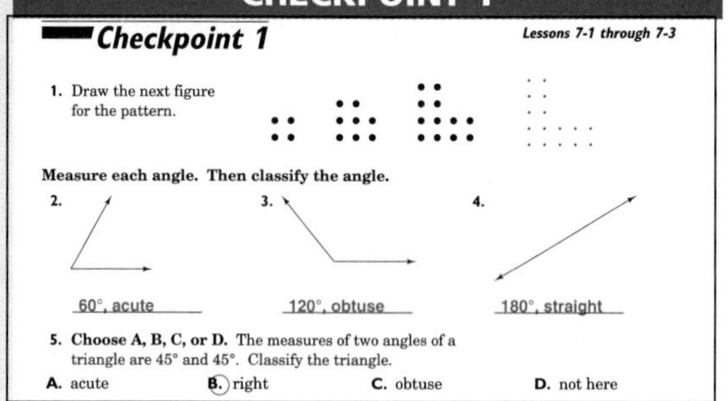
Checkpoint 1 *Lessons 7-1 through 7-3*

1. Draw the next figure for the pattern.

Measure each angle. Then classify the angle.

2. 60°, acute
3. 120°, obtuse
4. 180°, straight

5. Choose A, B, C, or D. The measures of two angles of a triangle are 45° and 45°. Classify the triangle.

A. acute B. right C. obtuse D. not here

pages 299–301 On Your Own

17. The two green triangles are scalene right triangles. The other triangles are acute isosceles triangles.

19c. No; two angles of an isosceles triangle are congruent.

d. Yes; since it is not equilateral or isosceles, it must be scalene.

20b. They are complementary; yes; the right angle measures 90°, so the sum of the measures of the other two angles must be 90°.

24. Answers may vary. Sample:

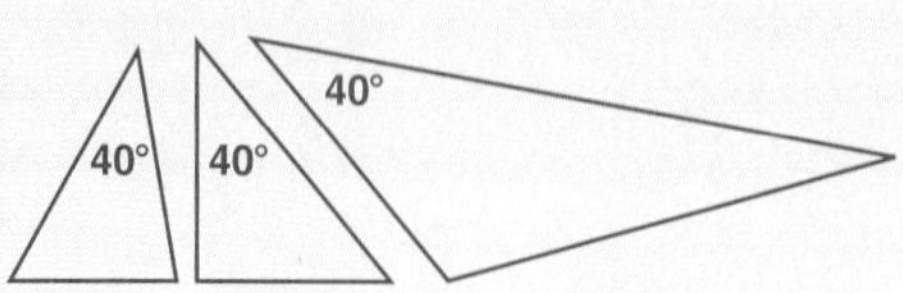

9. *Music* In an orchestra, a triangle is a percussion instrument that is made of a thin steel rod. Does a musical triangle look like a scalene triangle, an isosceles triangle, or an equilateral triangle? **equilateral triangle**

10. **Choose A, B, or C.** The measures of two angles of a triangle are 35° and 50°. Classify the triangle. **C**

A. acute B. right C. obtuse

Find each missing angle measure.

11. **80°**

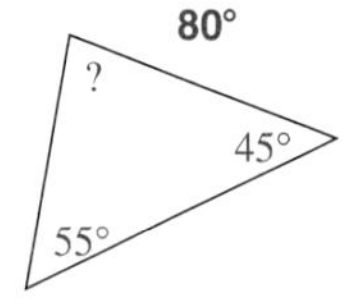

12. **64°**

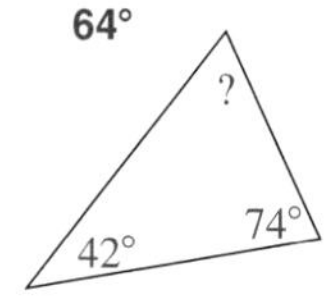

13. **44°**

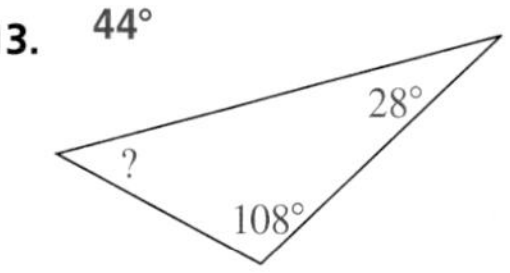

14. **38°**

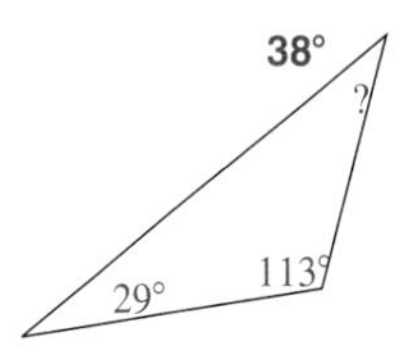

15. **60°**

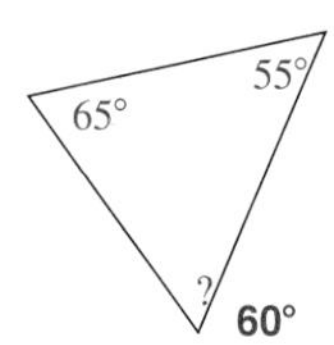

16. **93°**

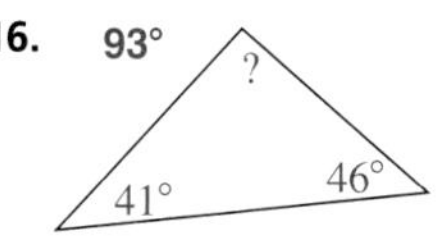

17. *Social Studies* Classify the triangles in the flag of Guyana. **See margin.**

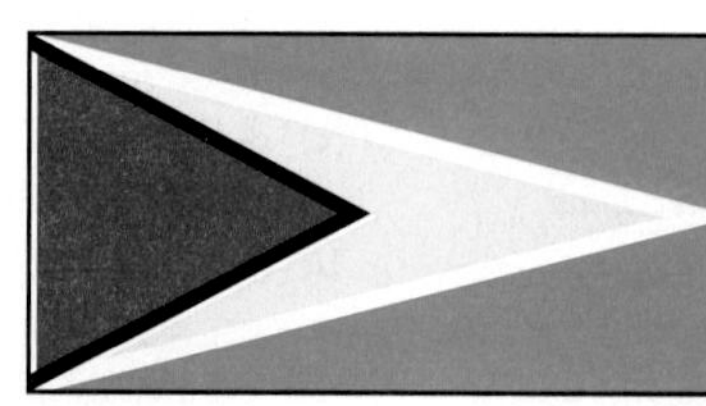

Guyana

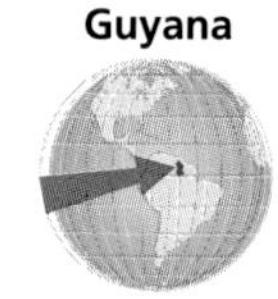

a. See below right.

18. a. *Writing* Can an equilateral triangle be a right triangle? Why or why not?
    b. Can an obtuse triangle have a right angle? Why or why not? **No; the sum of an obtuse angle and a right angle is greater than 180°.**

18a. No; all angles of an equilateral triangle are acute, and none is a right angle.

19. *Reasoning* The measures of the angles of a triangle are 50°, 60°, and 70°.
    a. Classify the triangle by its angles. **acute**
    b. Can the triangle be equilateral? Why or why not? **No; the angles of an equilateral triangle are congruent.**
    c. Can the triangle be isosceles? Why or why not?
    d. Can you classify the triangle by its sides? Why or why not? **c–d. See margin.**

20. The triangles shown at the right are all right triangles.
    a. What is the sum of the measures of the two acute angles in each triangle? **90°**
    b. What is the relationship of the two acute angles in these triangles? Is this true for all right triangles? Explain. **See margin.**

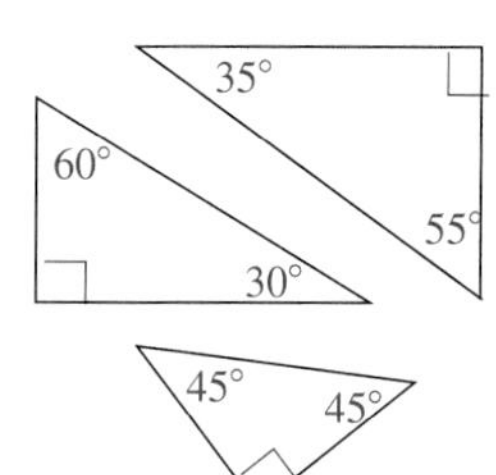

LESSON QUIZ

1. Classify the triangle by its sides and angles. Then find the measure of $\angle L$.

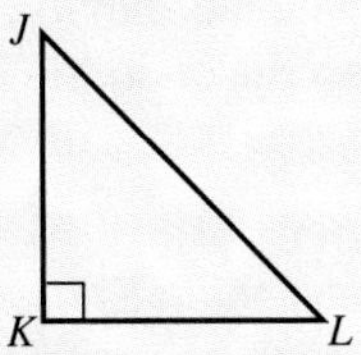

isosceles; right; 45°

2. The measures of two angles of a triangle are 40° and 55°. Find the measure of the third angle. **85°**
3. The measure of one acute angle of a right triangle is 20°. Find the measure of the other acute angle. **70°**

Find the missing angle measures for each isosceles triangle.

21. 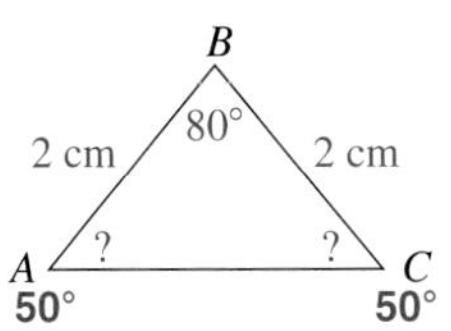

50° 50°

22. 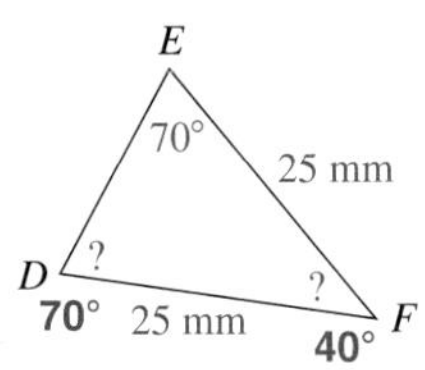

70° 40°

23. 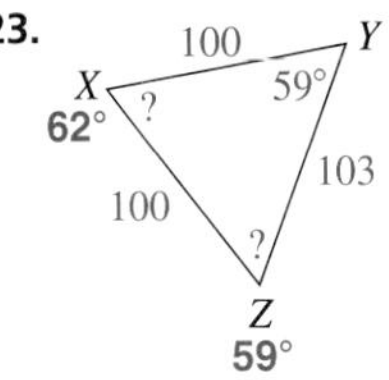

62° 59°

24. *Open-Ended* Use your protractor to draw acute, right, and obtuse triangles that each contain a 40° angle. Label the triangles and the 40° angles. **See margin p. 300.**

Mixed Review

Evaluate each expression. *(Lesson 4-4)*

25. 4^3 **64** 26. 2^6 **64** 27. 7^2 **49** 28. 6^4 **1,296** 29. 5^7 **78,125** 30. 10^6 **1,000,000**

Write each quotient as a decimal. Use a bar to show repeating decimals. *(Lesson 2-7)*

31. $5 \div 3$ **$1.\overline{6}$** 32. $7 \div 16$ **0.4375** 33. $15 \div 18$ **$0.8\overline{3}$** 34. $10 \div 6$ **$1.\overline{6}$** 35. $21 \div 8$ **2.625**

36. *Transportation* A taxi charges $2.10 for the first $\frac{1}{5}$ mi and $.50 for each additional $\frac{1}{5}$ mi. Find the cost of a 10-mi ride. *(Lessons 5-3, 5-5)* **$26.60**

✓ CHECKPOINT 1 — *Lessons 7-1 through 7-3*

1. Draw the next figure for the pattern at the right.

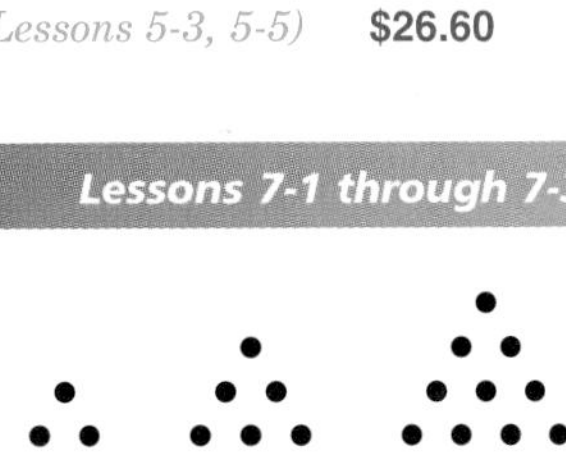

Classify the angle with the given measure.

2. 23° **acute** 3. 117° **obtuse** 4. 90° **right** 5. 180° **straight**

1. 

Judging by appearance, classify each triangle by its sides and angles.

6. 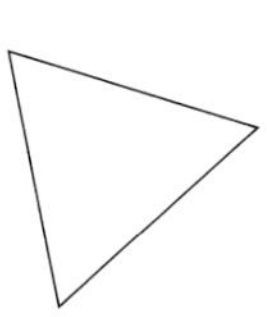
equilateral, acute

7. 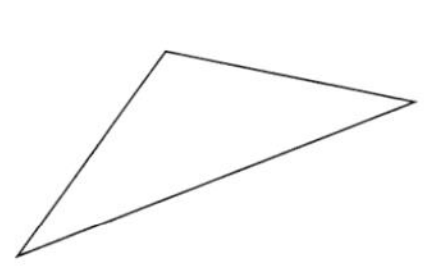
isosceles, obtuse

8. 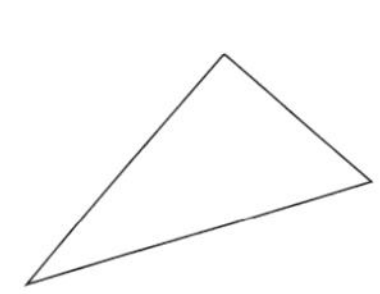
scalene, right

Extra Practice, Lesson 7-3, page 520

PRACTICE

Practice 7-3 *Triangles*

Find each missing angle measure.

1. 25°, 30° — 125°
2. 51°, 62° — 67°
3. 23°, 121° — 36°

Find the missing angle measures for each isosceles triangle.

4. 3 cm, 3 cm, 53° — 53° and 74°
5. 5 in., 5 in., 63° — 54° and 63°
6. 47°, 43 mm, 43 mm — 47° and 86°

Circle A, B, C, or D. Classify each triangle.

7. The measures of two angles are 45° and 45°.
   A. acute (B.) right C. obtuse D. cannot be determined
8. The measures of two angles are 15° and 47°.
   A. acute B. right (C.) obtuse D. cannot be determined
9. The measures of two angles are 53° and 76°.
   (A.) acute B. right C. obtuse D. cannot be determined
10. The measure of one angle is 18°.
   A. acute B. right C. obtuse (D.) cannot be determined
11. The measure of one angle is 90°.
   A. acute (B.) right C. obtuse D. cannot be determined
12. The measure of one angle is 115°.
   A. acute B. right (C.) obtuse D. cannot be determined
13. The measures of the angles of a triangle are 40°, 50°, and 90°.
   a. Classify the triangle by its angles. right
   b. Can the triangle be equilateral? Why or why not? No; sides are not congruent.
   c. Can the triangle be isosceles? Why or why not? No; no two angles are congruent.
   d. Can you classify the triangle by its sides? Why or why not? Yes, the triangle is scalene; no two sides are congruent if no two angles are congruent.

Practice

In copymaster and workbook formats

RETEACHING

Reteaching 7-3 *Triangles*

Classifying Triangles by Angles	Classifying Triangles by Sides
Acute triangle: three acute angles	**Equilateral triangle:** three congruent sides
Right triangle: one right angle	**Isosceles triangle:** at least two congruent sides
Obtuse triangle: one obtuse angle	**Scalene triangle:** no congruent sides

The sum of the measures of the angles of a triangle is 180°.

Find the measure of $\angle A$.

$$m\angle A + 40° + 78° = 180°$$
$$m\angle A + 118° = 180°$$
$$m\angle A = 180° - 118°$$
$$m\angle A = 62°$$

C 78°, A, B 40°

$m\angle A = 62°$

Judging by appearence, classify each triangle by its sides and then by its angles.

1. scalene; obtuse
2. equilateral; acute
3. isosceles; right
4. isosceles; obtuse
5. scalene; acute
6. isosceles; acute

Find each missing angle measure.

7. 29°, 46° — 105°
8. 73°, 73° — 34°
9. 39°, 51° — 90°

ENRICHMENT

Minds on Math Transparency

7-3

I am a two-digit odd number. My cube is a five-digit number. The digits in my cube are all different and are also different from my digits. What number am I?

27

See *Solution Key* for worked-out answers.

7-4 Teaching Notes

1 Focus

CONNECTING TO PRIOR KNOWLEDGE Ask students: *Describe a time when you have used a diagram to explain something to someone.* **Answers may vary. Sample: drawing a map to give directions**

2 Teach

THINK AND DISCUSS

ERROR ALERT! Question 2 Students may draw an incorrect diagram because they misinterpret or misread the information given. **Remediation:** Encourage students to write down important given information, such as *isosceles triangle* and *30°*. Review the definition of *isosceles triangle*. Remind students how isosceles triangles look when drawn in a diagram.

ASSESSMENT Ask students to write an explanation of why more than one diagram matches the description in the sample problem.

AEP AUDITORY LEARNING Pair students who are not proficient in English with those who are. Have each pair read the problem and questions softly. Encourage them to discuss all vocabulary terms to be sure they both understand them.

Lesson Planning Options

Prerequisite Skills

- drawing angles (7-2)
- classifying triangles (7-3)

Materials/Manipulatives

- protractor

Resources

Student Edition

Skills Handbook, p. 531
Extra Practice, p. 520
Glossary/Study Guide

Teaching Resources

Chapter Support File, Ch. 7
- Lesson Planner 7-4
- Practice 7-4, Reteaching 7-4
- Answer Masters 7-4

Glossary, Spanish Resources

Transparencies

Minds on Math 7-4

Warm Up

In a bag of groceries, there are 6 tomatoes, 5 celery stalks, and 2 onions. What is the ratio of onions to tomatoes? **2 : 6 or 1 : 3** What is the ratio of celery stalks to onions? **5 : 2**

PROBLEM SOLVING STRATEGY

READ PLAN SOLVE LOOK BACK

7-4 Draw a Diagram

Problem Solving Strategies

- ✓ Draw a Diagram
- Guess and Test
- Look for a Pattern
- Make a Model
- Make a Table
- Simulate a Problem
- Solve a Simpler Problem
- Too Much or Too Little Information
- Use Logical Reasoning
- Use Multiple Strategies
- Work Backward
- Write an Equation

THINK AND DISCUSS

Drawing a diagram can help you visualize the relationships described in a problem. Be sure to read the problem carefully. There may be more than one diagram that satisfies the given information.

SAMPLE PROBLEM

A furniture maker is designing a table for a customer who likes his furniture to be mathematical! So the furniture maker plans to make the table top an isosceles triangle. One angle of the table top measures 30°. What are the measures of the other two angles of the table top?

READ
Read for understanding. Summarize the problem.

1. Think about the information you are given and what you need to find.
   a. What is the measure of one angle of the triangle? **30°**
   b. What kind of triangle is involved in this problem? **isosceles**
   c. What is special about the angles of this kind of triangle? **c. Two of its angles are congruent.**
   d. Summarize the goal of this problem. **Find the two missing angle measures.**

PLAN
Decide on a strategy.

A good strategy to use here is to *draw a diagram*. The 30° angle could be one of the two congruent angles in the triangle or it could an angle that is not congruent to another angle.

SOLVE
Try the strategy.

2. Draw a diagram that shows the 30° angle as one of the two congruent angles.
   a. What is the measure of the angle that is congruent to the given angle? **30°**
   b. What is the measure of the third angle? **120°**
3. Draw a diagram that shows the 30° angle in a different location. What are the measures of the other angles? **75°, 75°**
4. Are there any other ways an isosceles triangle can have a 30° angle? Why or why not? **No; the 30° angle can be one of the two congruent angles or the third angle.**

■ ADDITIONAL PROBLEM

An isosceles triangle has a perimeter of 14 cm. One of its sides measures 4 cm. Find the measures of the other two sides. 4 cm and 6 cm, or 5 cm and 5 cm

EXTENSION Challenge students to write triangle problems that have two possible answers. Students can exchange problems and try to solve them.

3 Practice/Assess

EXERCISES *On Your Own*

Exercise 1 Have students share their methods for keeping track of the information in terms of distance and time.

Exercise 4 Clarify by suggesting that if the pencils cost $.07 each, you would buy 7 pencils. If they cost $.08 each, you would buy 8 pencils.

WRAP UP

IDENTIFYING THE BIG IDEA Ask students: *How can drawing diagrams help you solve problems?*

PROJECT LINK Encourage students to review their research on using triangles to build bridges and towers. Have students make notes about foundations and the weight supported by geometric shapes.

5. Write a solution to the original question by summarizing what you have found. The measures of the other two angles of the triangle can be either 30° and 120° or 75° and 75°.

LOOK BACK
Think about how you solved the problem.

6. Describe how drawing a diagram helped you solve the problem. The diagram helped to see the different possible places for the 30° angle.

Now you may assign Exercises 1–11.

EXERCISES *On Your Own*

Draw a diagram to help you solve each problem.

1. Each morning Jacob walks to school. At 8:20 A.M. he passes a stoplight that is two blocks from home. He walks another block and reaches the town library at 8:24 A.M. At this point he is three blocks from school and half the way there. If Jacob walks at the same pace all the way to school, at what time does he arrive at school? Explain your answer.
8:36 A.M.; he walks one block in 4 min and has 3 blocks, or 12 min, to go at 8:24 A.M.
2. At the first meeting of the Table Tennis Club, the seven members decided to have a tournament in which every player will play a game against every other player. How many games will there be in the tournament? 21 games

Use any strategy to solve each problem. Show your work.

3. The diagram shows part of a design made by using toothpicks to form triangles. The top row uses three toothpicks. The second row uses six toothpicks. The third row uses nine toothpicks, and so on.

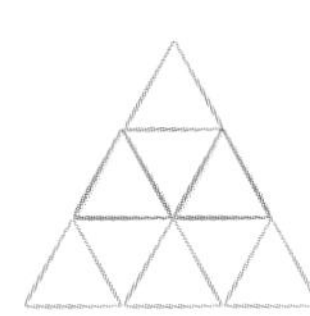

   a. If you decide to continue the design so that it has seven rows, how many toothpicks do you need altogether? 84 toothpicks
   b. Which row will use 24 toothpicks? row 8
4. Suppose you buy several pencils at a discount store. All the pencils are the same price, and you buy as many pencils as the cost (in cents) of each pencil. The pencils cost a total of $1.44. How many pencils did you buy? 12 pencils
5. *Gardening* Each year Brandon plants tulip bulbs in a square flower bed. This year Brandon's flower bed has 29 more bulbs than it had last year. If the flower bed is still square, how many tulip bulbs are in it this year? 225 tulip bulbs

Technology Options

Prentice Hall Technology

Software for Learners
- Math Blaster® Mystery*
- Interactive Student Tutorial, Chapter 7*

Teaching Resource Software
- Computer Item Generator 7-4
- Resource Pro™ Chapter 7*

Internet • For related mathematics activities, visit the Prentice Hall site at www.phschool.com/math

**Available on CD-ROM only*

Assignment Options for Exercises On Your Own

Core 1–9, 11
Extension 10

Use Mixed Review to maintain skills.

PRACTICE

Practice 7-4 Problem-Solving Strategy: Draw a Diagram

Use a diagram to help you solve each problem.

1. One angle of an isosceles triangle measures 56°. What are the measures of the other two angles? 56° and 68°, or 62° and 62°
2. The eight members of the Ping Pong Paddlers Club have a tournament in which every player plays a game against every other player. How many games are there in the tournament? 28 games
3. Moranda took a train trip to visit her cousin. By 10:15 the train had traveled 20 mi. By 10:30 the train had traveled an additional 10 mi. Moranda is now halfway to her cousin's town. At what time will she reach her cousin's town if the train's speed is constant? 11:15
4. Desmond's cat Calico likes to play on stairs. Starting at the bottom landing, Calico jumped up 4 steps, then down 2. Then Calico jumped up 5 steps and fell down 3. In two more jumps of 4 steps and then 5 steps, Calico reached the top of the stairs. How many stairs are in the staircase? 13 steps

Use any strategy to solve each problem.

5. Carla is five years older than her sister Julie. The product of their ages is 234. How old is Julie? 13
6. Ms. Spender bought pens for her class. The pens all cost the same price. She bought as many pens as the cost (in cents) of each pen. She spent a total of \$56.25. How many pens did she buy? 75 pens
7. If the pattern at the right continues, how many dots will there be in the fifth figure? 35 dots

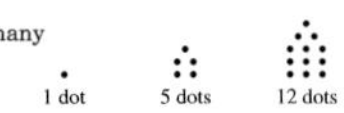

8. Frank, Bill, and Pam each ordered a salad at a restaurant. A spinach salad, a chef's salad, and a tuna salad were ordered. Bill did not order the spinach salad. Pam sat to the right of the one who ordered the spinach salad and to the left of the one who ordered the chef's salad. Who ordered which salad? Frank—spinach; Bill—chef's; Pam—tuna

In copymaster and workbook formats

RETEACHING

Reteaching 7-4 Problem-Solving Strategy: Draw a Diagram

One acute angle of a right triangle is 35°. What is the measure of the other acute angle?

Read What kind of triangle is given? *A right triangle is given.* What do you know about a right triangle? *It has one 90° angle and two acute angles.* What are you given? *You are given one acute angle that measures 35°.* What do you want to find? *You want to find the measure of the other acute angle.*

Plan A good strategy for this problem is to draw a diagram. Show a right triangle with the acute angle labeled and the right angle marked.

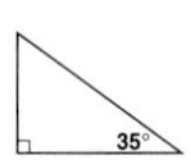

Solve Remember that the sum of the angle measures of a triangle is 180°. The diagram reminds you that the right angle measures 90°.

$$180° - (90° + 35°) = 180° - 125°$$
$$= 55°$$

The measure of the third angle is 55°.

Look Back Check by adding: 55° + 35° + 90° = 180°

Draw a diagram to help solve each problem.

1. One acute angle of a right triangle is 42°. What is the measure of the other acute angle? 48°
2. One of the two equal angles of an isosceles triangle is 48°. What are the measures of the other two angles? 48°, 84°
3. A square garden is enclosed by a fence that has 9 posts on each side. How many posts are there in all? 32 posts
4. A piece of string is cut in half. Then each piece is cut in half. Each of those pieces is cut in half. How many cuts were made? 7 cuts
5. Sean planned to bike 120 mi on his vacation. On the first day he biked $\frac{1}{2}$ of the distance. On the next day he biked $\frac{1}{4}$ of the remaining distance. How far did he have left to go? 45 mi
6. Newtown is 522 km west of Jamesburg. Pottsville is 356 km east of Jamesburg and 928 km east of Mayfield. How far and in what direction is Newtown from Mayfield? 50 km east

Reteaching

ENRICHMENT

Minds on Math Transparency

7-4

I am an acute angle. My supplement and my complement are themselves supplementary angles. What's my measure?

45°

See *Solution Key* for worked-out answers.

LESSON QUIZ

Draw a diagram to help you solve each problem.

1. Six people each shake hands with every other person. How many handshakes occur? 15
2. The city closes a road for repairs. To go from one end of the closed portion of road to the other, a cyclist follows the detour. The cyclist travels east for 2 blocks, north for 3 blocks, west for 1 block, south for 1 block, and west for 1 block. How many blocks long is the closed portion of the road? 2

6. Shana climbed a set of stairs and stopped at the middle step. She then walked down 2 steps, up 4 steps, down 3 steps, and up 5 steps, and she was at the top of the stairs. How many steps are in the set of stairs? 9 steps
7. Rosa, Alberto, and Vernesha are in a band together. They play guitar, piano, and drums. Alberto is the cousin of the guitar player. Rosa lives next door to the drummer and two blocks from the guitar player. Who plays which instrument? Rosa plays piano, Alberto plays drums, and Vernesha plays guitar.
8. Raphael has \$1.55 in dimes and quarters. Find all the possible combinations of coins that Raphael might have. 5 quarters and 3 dimes, 3 quarters and 8 dimes, 1 quarter and 13 dimes
9. How many angles are shown in the figure at the right? How many of them are obtuse? 6 angles; 3 obtuse angles

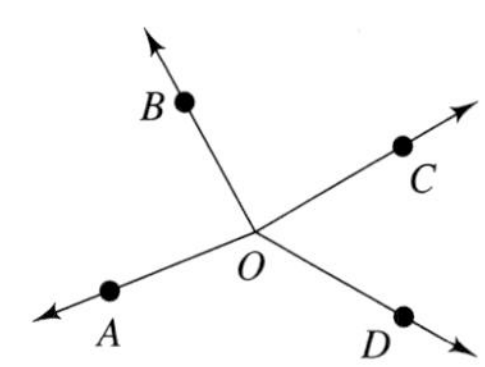

10. The Martin Luther King School library has 8 tables and 42 chairs. There are several small tables with 4 chairs each and some large tables with 6 chairs each. How many tables of each type are in the library? 3 small tables, 5 large tables
11. How many triangles are shown in the figure at the right? 13 triangles

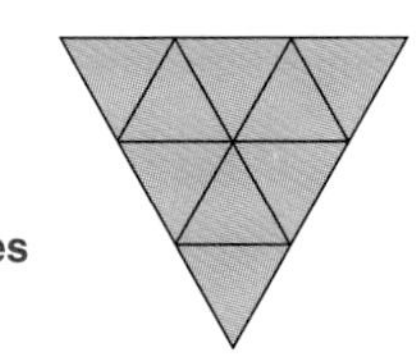

Mixed Review

Find each quotient. *(Lesson 5-6)*

12. $\frac{2}{3} \div \frac{8}{9}$ $\frac{3}{4}$
13. $3\frac{3}{4} \div \frac{5}{6}$ $\frac{9}{2}$, or $4\frac{1}{2}$
14. $12 \div 3\frac{1}{2}$ $\frac{24}{7}$, or $3\frac{3}{7}$
15. $1\frac{5}{9} \div 2\frac{1}{3}$ $\frac{2}{3}$
16. $7\frac{1}{4} \div 8\frac{1}{3}$ $\frac{87}{100}$

Solve each equation. *(Lesson 3-9)*

17. $6x + 7 = 13$ 1
18. $-3d + 5 = 17$ −4
19. $4r - 12 = -2$ $2\frac{1}{2}$
20. $-6p - 8 = -20$ 2

21. *Choose a Strategy* Bicycling burns 11 calories/minute, running 14 calories/minute, and dancing 8 calories/minute. Would you burn more calories by running for 15 minutes 3 days a week or bicycling 40 minutes 2 days a week? bicycling

CHAPTER PROJECT

PROJECT LINK: ANALYZING

Use toothpicks and raisins to build a triangle and a square. Gently wiggle each figure. Which is more rigid? Add toothpicks to strengthen the weaker one. Describe how you did it.

Check students' work for construction and reasoning; triangle.

7-5 Teaching Notes

1 Focus

CONNECTING TO PRIOR KNOWLEDGE
Have students list pairs of objects that are exactly the same shape and size. Then have students brainstorm pairs of objects that are exactly the same shape but of different sizes.

2 Teach

Work Together

VISUAL LEARNING and ERROR ALERT!
Question 1 Some students may not see that two figures are congruent if the figures are not facing the same direction. **Remediation:** Draw congruent scalene triangles on two transparencies. Display the transparencies so the triangles are not facing the same direction. Rotate or flip one transparency to overlap the triangles showing the corresponding vertices aligned.

THINK AND DISCUSS

State the six congruences of corresponding parts of the triangles. Then rotate one triangle to show that the vertices cannot match in any other way. Show students that the order of the letters in the name of the triangles tells us which vertices correspond.

7-5 Congruent Triangles

What You'll Learn

- To identify and work with congruent figures

...And Why

Congruent figures are used in crafts and manufacturing.

Here's How

Look for questions that
- build understanding
- ✔ check understanding

Work Together — *Exploring Congruent Figures*

1. Match the figures that appear to have the same size and shape. **a and g, b and d, c and f, e and h**

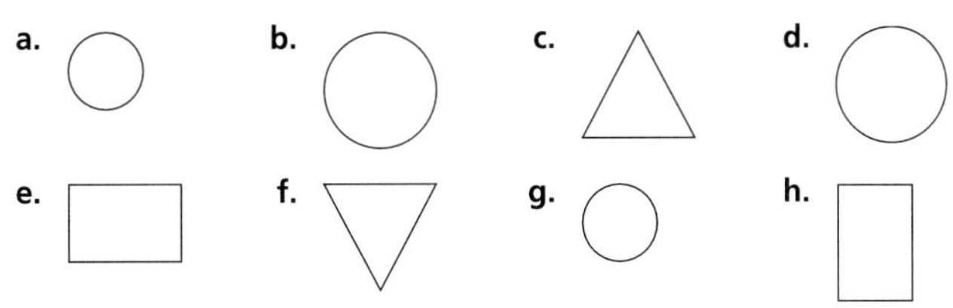

2. How could you check that your answers to Question 1 are correct? **Answers may vary. Sample: Trace one and place it over its match.**
3. Suppose you trace a polygon and match your tracing with another polygon that has the same size and shape. What would be true of the matching angles and segments? **They would be congruent.**

THINK AND DISCUSS

Figures that have the same size and shape are **congruent.** In the pinwheel at the left, all the triangles of the same color are congruent.

A *polygon* is a closed plane figure formed by three or more line segments that do not cross. **Congruent polygons** have congruent *corresponding parts* (sides and angles). You can write the symbol ≅ for "is congruent to."

$\overline{AB} \cong \overline{ED}$ $\angle A \cong \angle E$
$\overline{BC} \cong \overline{DF}$ $\angle B \cong \angle D$
$\overline{CA} \cong \overline{FE}$ $\angle C \cong \angle F$
$\triangle ABC \cong \triangle EDF$

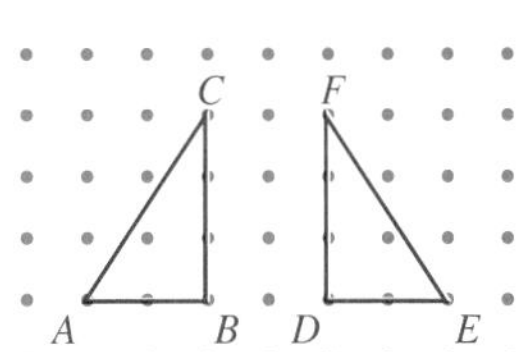

You name corresponding vertices in the same order.

Lesson Planning Options

Prerequisite Skill
- naming segments and angles (precourse)

Vocabulary/Symbols
congruent (≅), polygons, congruent polygons, corresponding parts

Resources

Student Edition
Skills Handbook, p. 528
Extra Practice, p. 520
Glossary/Study Guide

Teaching Resources
Chapter Support File, Ch. 7
- Lesson Planner 7-5
- Practice 7-5, Reteaching 7-5
- Alternative Activity 7-5
- Answer Masters 7-5

Teaching Aids Masters 1–3, 19
Glossary, Spanish Resources

Transparencies
1, 7, Minds on Math 7-5

Warm Up

Use calculators to check the pattern. Explain why the pattern works.
(15,873 × 7) × 2 = (222,222)
(15,873 × 7) × 3 = (333,333)
(15,873 × 7) × 4 = (444,444)
because (15,873 × 7) × 1 = (111,111)

AEP Use the symbol for congruent (≅) to help students understand the meaning of the word. The symbol includes the symbol for similar (same shape) and the symbol for equal (same quantity or measure).

ASSESSMENT Question 4 Tell students: $FE = 4$ ft and $m\angle E = 75°$. Have students find TR and $m\angle R$. Have them share their answers and reasoning with a partner.

ADDITIONAL EXAMPLE

FOR EXAMPLE

Triangles *PQR* and *STU* are congruent.

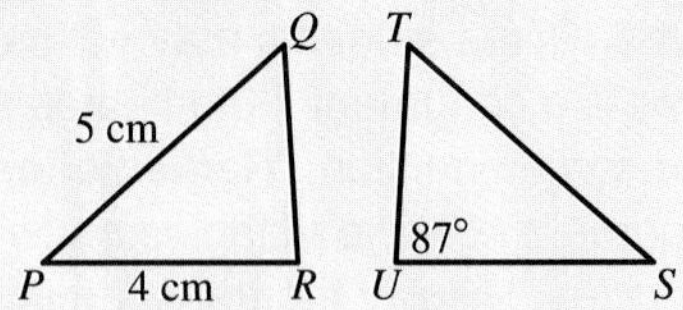

a. Write six congruences involving corresponding parts of the triangles.
$\overline{PQ} \cong \overline{ST}$ $\angle P \cong \angle S$
$\overline{QR} \cong \overline{TU}$ $\angle Q \cong \angle T$
$\overline{RP} \cong \overline{US}$ $\angle R \cong \angle U$

b. Find ST and $m\angle R$. $ST = 5$ cm; $m\angle R = 87°$

Technology Options

Prentice Hall Technology

Software for Learners
- Math Lab: Congruent Triangles
- Math Blaster® Mystery*
- Interactive Student Tutorial, Chapter 7*

Teaching Resource Software
- Computer Item Generator 7-5
- Resource Pro™ Chapter 7*

Internet • For related mathematics activities, visit the Prentice Hall site at www.phschool.com/math

Available on CD-ROM only

Assignment Options for Exercises On Your Own

Core 1–10
Extension 11

Use Mixed Review to maintain skills.

EXAMPLE

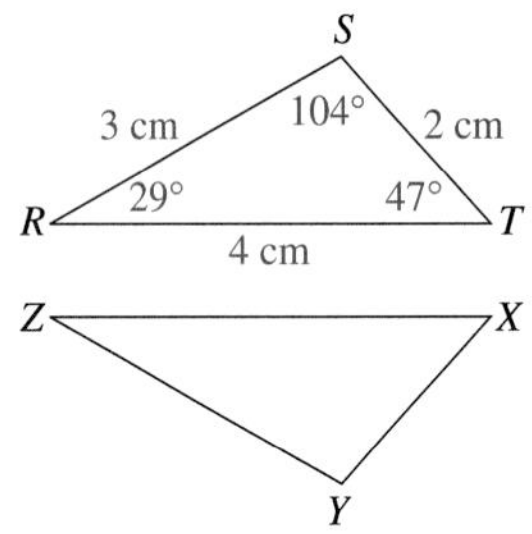

a. The triangles shown at the left are congruent. Write six congruences involving corresponding parts of the triangles.

$\angle X \cong \angle T$ $\angle Y \cong \angle S$ $\angle Z \cong \angle R$
$\overline{XY} \cong \overline{TS}$ $\overline{ZY} \cong \overline{RS}$ $\overline{ZX} \cong \overline{RT}$

b. Find ZY and $m\angle X$.

$ZY = 3$ cm ← Because $\overline{ZY} \cong \overline{RS}$, $ZY = RS$.
$m\angle T = 47°$ ← Because $\angle X \cong \angle T$, $m\angle X = m\angle T$.

4a. $\overline{FD} \cong \overline{TS}$, $\overline{FE} \cong \overline{TR}$, $\overline{DE} \cong \overline{SR}$, $\angle D \cong \angle S$, $\angle E \cong \angle R$, $\angle F \cong \angle T$

4. a. ✔ *Try It Out* Write six congruences involving corresponding sides and angles.
b. $\triangle DEF \cong$ ■ $\triangle SRT$
c. $\triangle EFD \cong$ ■ $\triangle RTS$
d. $\triangle DFE \cong$ ■ $\triangle STR$

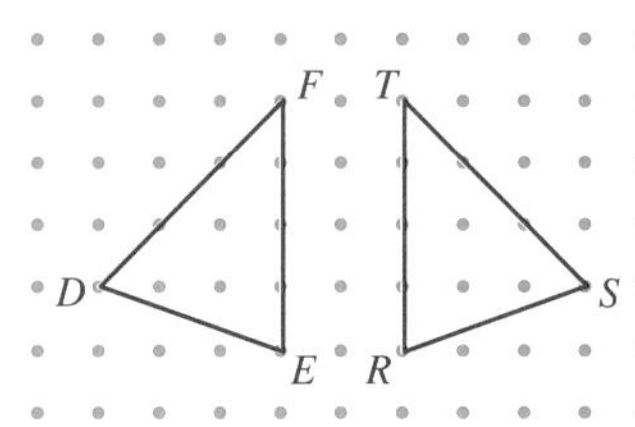

Now you may assign Exercises 1–11.

EXERCISES *On Your Own*

1. List the pairs of triangles that appear to be congruent. **a and f, b and e, c and d**

a.
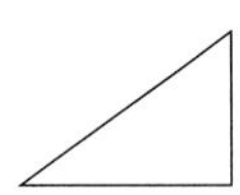
b.
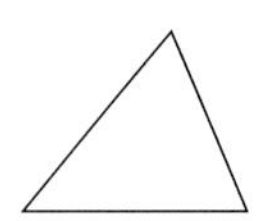
c.
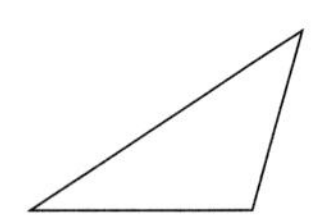
d.
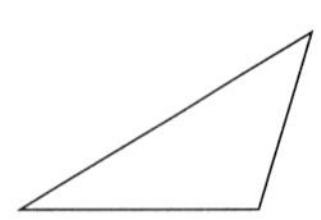
e.
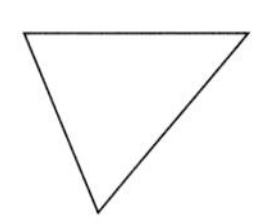
f.
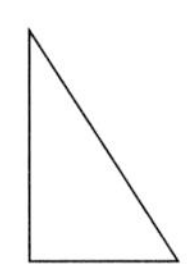

Complete. (Be sure that you name corresponding vertices in the same order.)

2. $\triangle ABC \cong$ ■ $\triangle SRT$

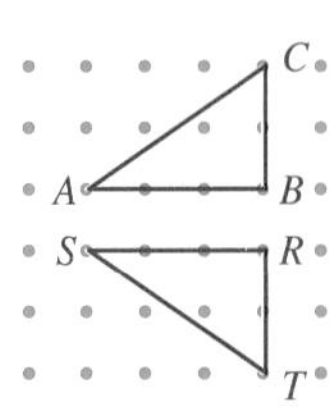

3. $\triangle ABC \cong$ ■ $\triangle FDE$

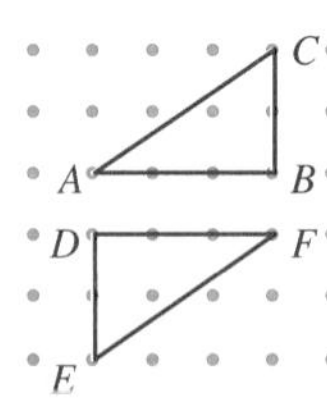

4. $\triangle ABC \cong$ ■ $\triangle ZXY$

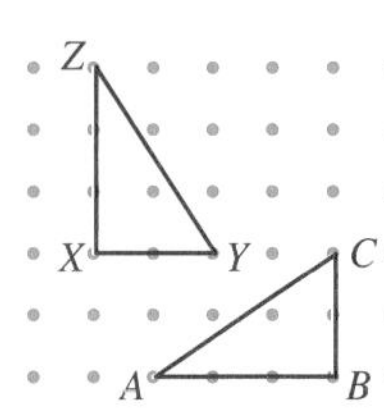

3 Practice/Assess

EXERCISES *On Your Own*

OPEN-ENDED Exercise 6 Have students consider when they might need to know that two shapes are identical.

WRITING Exercise 8 Remind students that the order of the letters in the names of the triangles tells us which vertices correspond.

WRAP UP

IDENTIFYING THE BIG IDEA Ask students to describe what they know about the sides and angles of congruent triangles.

LESSON QUIZ

$\triangle ABC \cong \triangle PQR$.

1. Which angle is congruent to $\angle B$? $\angle Q$
2. Which side is congruent to $\overline{AC}$? $\overline{PR}$

5. $\triangle DEF \cong \triangle CLK$. Complete each congruence statement.
   a. $\angle D \cong$ ■ $\angle C$ b. $\angle E \cong$ ■ $\angle L$ c. $\angle F \cong$ ■ $\angle K$
   d. $\overline{DE} \cong$ ■ $\overline{CL}$ e. $\overline{EF} \cong$ ■ $\overline{LK}$ f. $\overline{DF} \cong$ ■ $\overline{CK}$

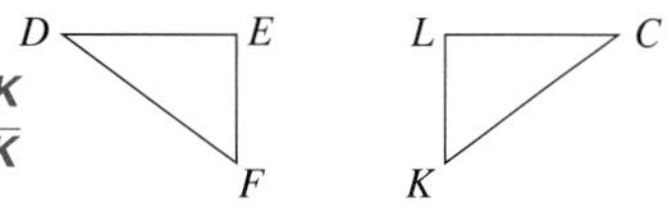

6. *Open-ended* Describe a real-life application of congruent figures. **Answers may vary. Sample: The floor and the ceiling of a classroom are usually congruent.**

7. $\overline{XY} \cong \overline{RB}$, $\overline{YZ} \cong \overline{BP}$, $\overline{XZ} \cong \overline{RP}$, $\angle X \cong \angle R$, $\angle Y \cong \angle B$, $\angle Z \cong \angle P$

7. Assume that $\triangle XYZ \cong \triangle RBP$. Write six congruences involving corresponding sides and angles.

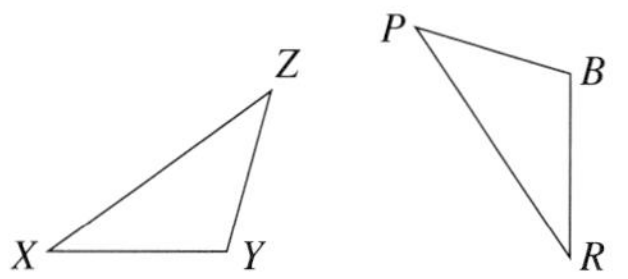

8. *Writing* $\triangle ABC \cong \triangle WPQ$. Explain how you can find the measure of an angle and of a side of $\triangle WPQ$. **See below.**

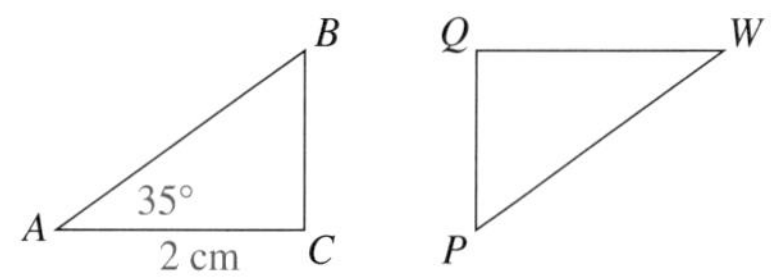

9. Complete in as many correct ways as you can: $\triangle ABC \cong$ ■ $\triangle DJK$, $\triangle DKJ$

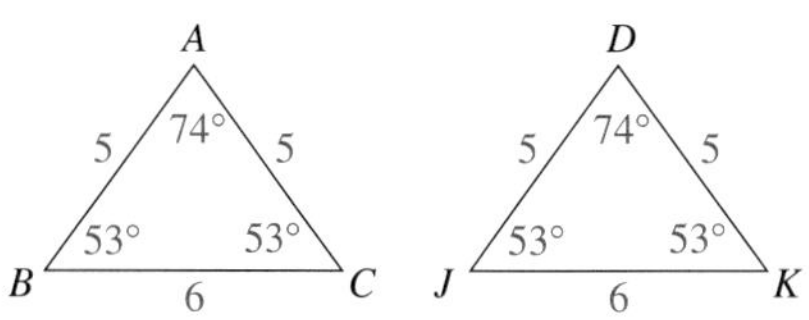

10. $\triangle RST \cong \triangle EFG$. Find as many angle measures and side lengths for $\triangle EFG$ as you can. $EF = 6$, $FG = 9$, $m\angle E = 67°$, $m\angle F = 75°$, $m\angle G = 38°$

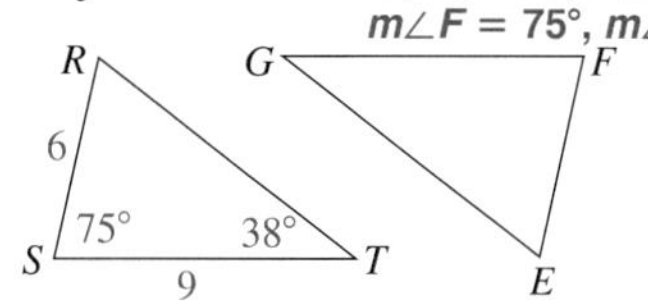

11. **Choose A, B, C, or D.** $\triangle RST$ and $\triangle XYZ$ are congruent equilateral triangles. Which angle or angles must be congruent to $\angle R$? **D**
   A. $\angle X$ only B. $\angle S$ and $\angle T$ C. $\angle X$, $\angle S$, and $\angle T$ D. $\angle S$, $\angle T$, $\angle X$, $\angle Y$, and $\angle Z$

8. **Since $\triangle ABC \cong \triangle WPQ$, $\angle A$ and $\angle W$ are congruent corresponding angles. Also, $\overline{AC}$ and $\overline{WQ}$ are congruent corresponding sides. Therefore, $m\angle W = 35°$ and $WQ = 2$ cm.**

Mixed Review

Write each fraction as a decimal. Use a bar to show repeating decimals. *(Lesson 4-9)*

12. $\frac{1}{2}$ 0.5 13. $\frac{4}{5}$ 0.8 14. $\frac{6}{8}$ 0.75 15. $\frac{1}{3}$ $0.\overline{3}$ 16. $\frac{33}{50}$ 0.66 17. $\frac{18}{12}$ 1.5

Write equations for Exercises 18 and 19. Then solve. *(Lesson 3-8)*

18. A number divided by 8 equals 9. $\frac{n}{8} = 9$; 72
19. Fifteen added to a number equals 45. $n + 15 = 45$; 30
20. *Choose a Strategy* Thieu worked 3 h per day on a jigsaw puzzle. It took him 13 h to complete the puzzle. If he started the puzzle on Saturday, on what day did he finish the puzzle? **Wednesday**

Extra Practice, Lesson 7-5, page 520

PRACTICE

Practice 7-5 *Congruent Triangles*

1. List the pairs of triangles that appear to be congruent. a and e, b and d

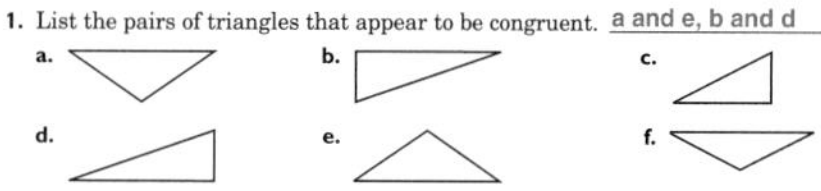

Complete. (Be sure that you name corresponding vertices in the same order.)

2. $\triangle ABC \cong$ $\triangle NLM$ 3. $\triangle ABC \cong$ $\triangle FED$ 4. $\triangle ABC \cong$ $\triangle RTS$

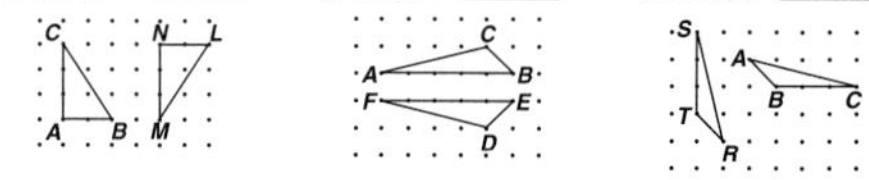

Write six congruences involving corresponding sides and angles for each pair of triangles.

5. $\triangle ABC \cong \triangle DEF$ 6. $\triangle JKL \cong \triangle MNO$ 7. $\triangle TUV \cong \triangle WXY$

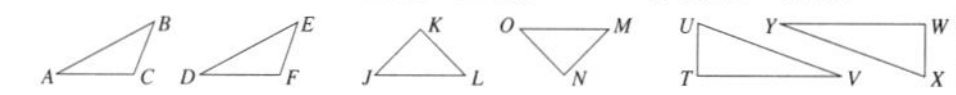

5. $\overline{AB} \cong \overline{DE}$, $\overline{BC} \cong \overline{EF}$; $\overline{AC} \cong \overline{DF}$, $\angle A \cong \angle D$; $\angle B \cong \angle E$, $\angle C \cong \angle F$
6. $\overline{JK} \cong \overline{MN}$, $\overline{KL} \cong \overline{NO}$; $\overline{JL} \cong \overline{MO}$, $\angle J \cong \angle M$; $\angle K \cong \angle N$, $\angle L \cong \angle O$
7. $\overline{TU} \cong \overline{WX}$, $\overline{TV} \cong \overline{WY}$; $\overline{UV} \cong \overline{XY}$, $\angle T \cong \angle W$; $\angle U \cong \angle X$, $\angle V \cong \angle Y$

Use the diagram at the right to complete each of the following.

8. a. $\angle ABC \cong$ $\angle FED$
   b. $\overline{AB} \cong$ $\overline{FE}$
   c. $\angle F \cong$ $\angle A$
9. a. $\triangle ABC \cong$ $\triangle FED$
   b. $\triangle BAC \cong$ $\triangle EFD$
   c. $\triangle CAB \cong$ $\triangle DFE$

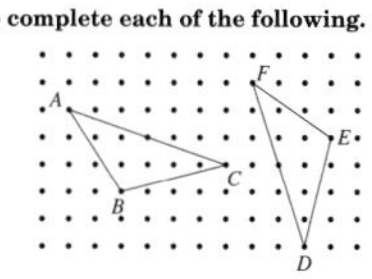

10. Circle A, B, C, or D. $\triangle MNO$ and $\triangle TRS$ are congruent isosceles right triangles. $\angle N$ and $\angle R$ are right angles. Which angle or angles must be congruent to $\angle M$?
    A. $\angle S$ only B. $\angle S$ and $\angle T$ only C. $\angle T$ only (D.) $\angle O$, $\angle S$, and $\angle T$

In copymaster and workbook formats

RETEACHING

Reteaching 7-5 *Congruent Triangles*

Congruent polygons have congruent sides and angles. These are called the *corresponding parts* of the congruent figures.

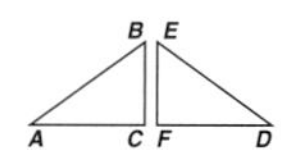

$\triangle ABC \cong \triangle DEF$

Corresponding Angles	Corresponding Sides
$\angle A \cong \angle D$	$\overline{BC} \cong \overline{EF}$
$\angle B \cong \angle E$	$\overline{CA} \cong \overline{FD}$
$\angle C \cong \angle F$	$\overline{AB} \cong \overline{DE}$

Complete.

1. $\triangle LMN \cong \triangle RPQ$

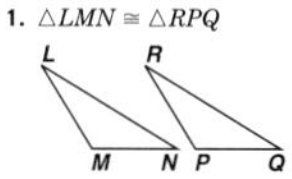

$\overline{MN} \cong \overline{PQ}$ $\angle M \cong \angle P$
$\overline{NL} \cong \overline{QR}$ $\angle L \cong \angle R$

2. $\triangle FGJ \cong \triangle YWX$

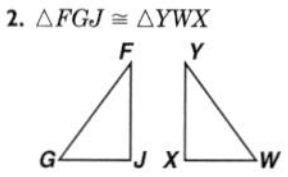

$\overline{JF} \cong \overline{XY}$ $\angle G \cong \angle W$
$\overline{FG} \cong \overline{YW}$ $\angle J \cong \angle X$

3. $\triangle ABC \cong \triangle DEF$ a. $\angle A \cong \angle D$ b. $\angle B \cong \angle E$ c. $\angle C \cong \angle F$ d. $\overline{AC} \cong \overline{DF}$ e. $\overline{BC} \cong \overline{EF}$ f. $\overline{AB} \cong \overline{DE}$

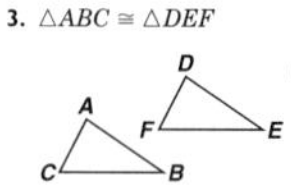

4. $\triangle GHI \cong \triangle TRS$ a. $\angle G \cong \angle T$ b. $\angle I \cong \angle S$ c. $\angle H \cong \angle R$ d. $\overline{HI} \cong \overline{RS}$ e. $\overline{GH} \cong \overline{TR}$ f. $\overline{GI} \cong \overline{TS}$

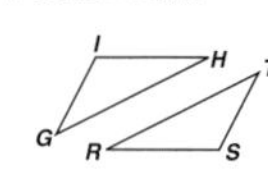

5. $\triangle JKL \cong \triangle MNO$ a. $\angle K \cong \angle N$ b. $\angle M \cong \angle J$ c. $\angle O \cong \angle L$ d. $\overline{NO} \cong \overline{KL}$ e. $\overline{JK} \cong \overline{MN}$ f. $\overline{OM} \cong \overline{LJ}$

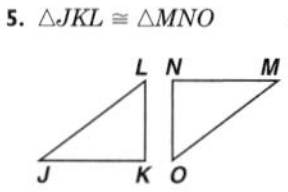

ENRICHMENT

Minds on Math Transparency

7-5

Points W, X, Y, and Z lie on the same line. Z is the point farthest to the left. If $XY = 5$, $XZ = 2$, and $XW = 6$, what is YW?

$YW = 1$

See *Solution Key* for worked-out answers.

7-6 Teaching Notes

1 Focus

CONNECTING TO PRIOR KNOWLEDGE Have students name all the geometric shapes they can recall that are not triangles. Draw the shapes they name on the board.

2 Teach

THINK AND DISCUSS

AEP AUDITORY LEARNING Question 1 Have students compare the name for each figure to a similar word. The word need not be in English. For example, *quadrilateral*, *quarter*, and the French number *quatre* all refer to four. *Octagon*, *octopus*, and the Spanish number *ocho* all refer to eight.

DIVERSITY Americans use road signs of different shapes to alert drivers to changes in road conditions. Have students who may have lived or traveled outside the United States share their knowledge of road signs from other countries.

KINESTHETIC LEARNING Question 5 Organize students into groups of 6–8. Give each student a length of string 2–5 ft long. Call out different shapes of polygons. Have each group of students form the shapes by holding the strings between them. Each student is a vertex of the polygon.

Lesson Planning Options

Prerequisite Skill

- finding congruent parts of polygons (7-5)

Vocabulary/Symbols

polygon, regular polygon, quadrilaterals, parallel, trapezoid, parallelogram, rectangle, rhombus, square, diagonals

Materials/Manipulatives

- dot paper
- scissors

Resources

Student Edition

Skills Handbook, p. 528
Extra Practice, p. 520
Glossary/Study Guide

Teaching Resources

Chapter Support File, Ch. 7
- Lesson Planner 7-6
- Practice 7-6, Reteaching 7-6
- Answer Masters 7-6

Teaching Aids Masters 1–3, 7–9, 19
Glossary, Spanish Resources

Transparencies

1, 7, 16, 17, 91, Minds on Math 7-6

Warm Up

Use mental math to find each product.

$180 \times 33\frac{1}{3}\% \times 2$ **120**

$240 \times 25\% \times 3$ **180**

7-6 Polygons and Quadrilaterals

What You'll Learn

1. To classify polygons and identify regular polygons
2. To work with special quadrilaterals

...And Why

Polygons and quadrilaterals are all around you, from architecture to signs.

Here's How

Look for questions that
- build understanding
- ✔ check understanding

THINK AND DISCUSS

1 Classifying Polygons

You name *polygons* by the number of sides.

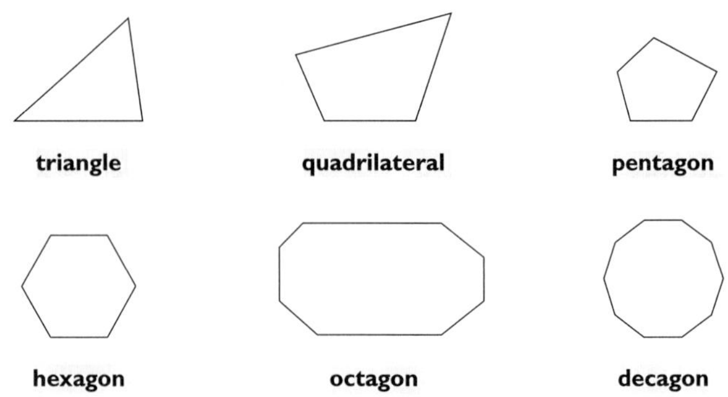

1. How many sides does a pentagon have? A hexagon? An octagon? A decagon? **5 sides, 6 sides, 8 sides, 10 sides**

2. What shape is the gazebo in this landscape designer's sketch? What is the shape of the flower beds? Of the path? **octagon, pentagon, rectangle**

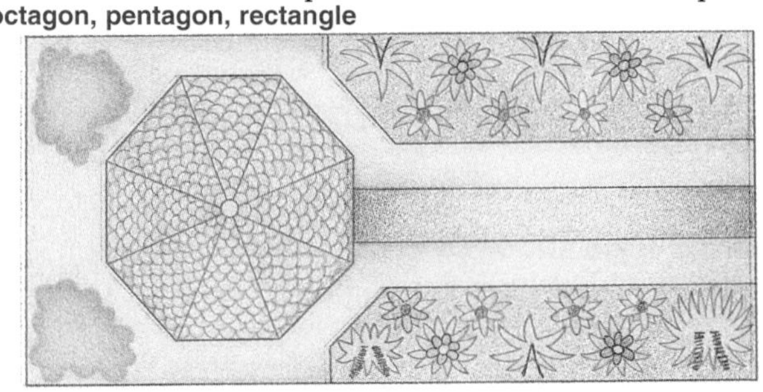

A **regular polygon** has all sides congruent and all angles congruent.

3. Which of the labeled polygons above appear to be regular? **hexagon, decagon**

4. What is another name for a regular triangle? **equilateral triangle**

Now you may assign Exercises 1–4, 9–11, 15.

EXTENSION Questions 3 and 4 Challenge students to draw regular polygons with 6, 7, 8, and 10 sides. Have students name the polygons. Ask: *What happens to the angles as you increase the number of sides?* **The angles become larger.**

TACTILE LEARNING Organize students in pairs. One student chooses a pattern block and the partner states all names of the shape.

■ ADDITIONAL EXAMPLE

FOR EXAMPLE

Draw a trapezoid that has at least one right angle. **Answers may vary. Sample:**

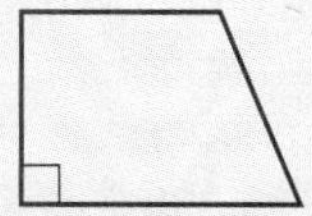

ERROR ALERT! Some students may need help to see how the special quadrilaterals are related. **Remediation:** Sketch and label a graphic display like the following for students to copy and keep as a reference.

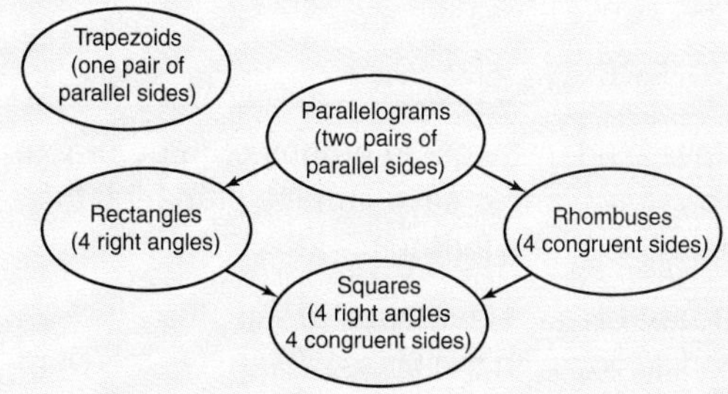

2 *Special Quadrilaterals*

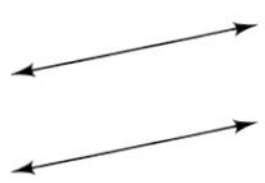

parallel lines

Some quadrilaterals have special names. Recall that two lines are **parallel** if they lie in the same plane (a flat surface) and do not intersect.

A **trapezoid** has exactly one pair of parallel sides.

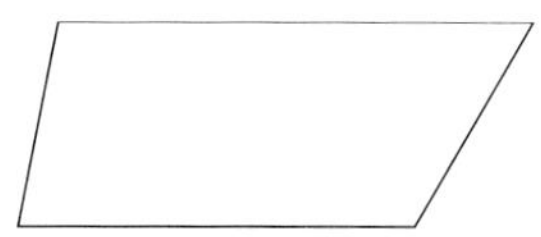

A **parallelogram** has both pairs of opposite sides parallel.

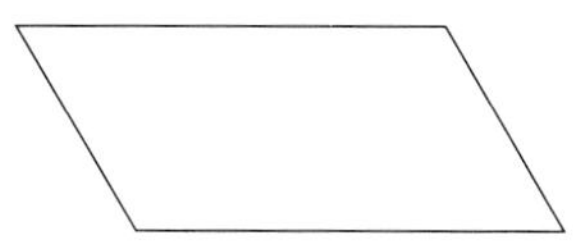

A **rectangle** is a parallelogram with four right angles.

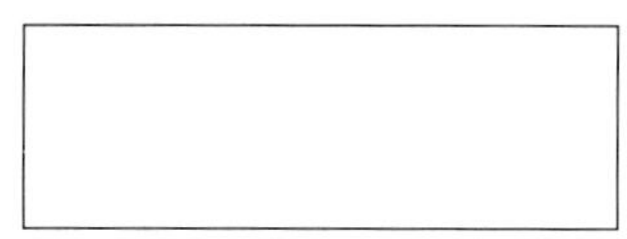

A **rhombus** is a parallelogram with four congruent sides.

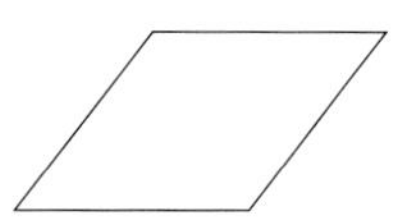

A **square** is a parallelogram with four right angles and four congruent sides.

5. What is another name for a regular quadrilateral? **square**

■ EXAMPLE

Draw each of the following figures on dot paper.

a. parallelogram *ABCD* that is not a rectangle or a rhombus

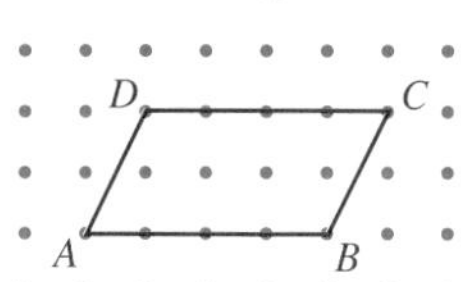

b. rhombus *EFGH* that is not a square

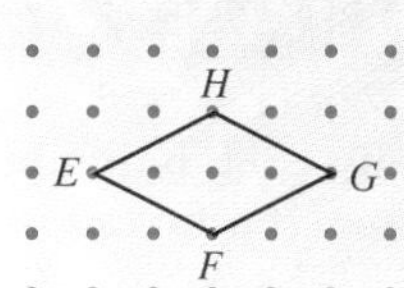

6. ✔*Try It Out* Use dot paper to draw a trapezoid. **See above left.**

7. *Think About It* Can a trapezoid have three right angles? Draw a diagram to support your answer. **See left.**

6.

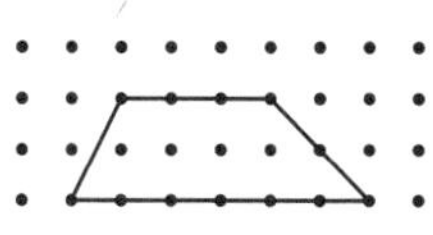

7. **No; a quadrilateral with three right angles will have both pairs of opposite sides parallel. So, it cannot be a trapezoid.**

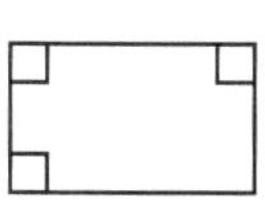

Technology Options

Prentice Hall Technology

Software for Learners
- Hot Page™ 2–6*
- Math Blaster® Mystery*
- Interactive Student Tutorial, Chapter 7*

Teaching Resource Software
- Computer Item Generator 7-6
- Resource Pro™ Chapter 7*

Internet • For related mathematics activities, visit the Prentice Hall site at www.phschool.com/math

**Available on CD-ROM only*

Assignment Options for Exercises On Your Own

To provide flexible scheduling, this lesson can be subdivided into parts.

1 **Core** 1–4, 9–11
Extension 15

2 **Core** 5–8, 12–14, 16–27, 29–33
Extension 28

Use Mixed Review to maintain skills.

TACTILE LEARNING Question 7 Have students use a geoboard to attempt to make a trapezoid with three right angles.

Work Together

Have students work in groups of three or four. You may want to save time by preparing the parallelograms for them.

Question 11 Have each group share its conclusion with the class. You may also want to have paper rectangles, squares, and rhombuses prepared for the students. Ask: *Do you think this conclusion is also true for trapezoids? Explain.* **No; the two triangles formed by cutting the diagonal of the trapezoid are not congruent.**

ASSESSMENT Have students work with a partner to make a chart of four special quadrilaterals: *parallelogram*, *rhombus*, *rectangle*, and *square*. Have students describe similarities and differences of the shapes. Display charts around the room for future reference.

3 Practice/Assess

EXERCISES *On Your Own*

Exercises 5–8 Point out that each figure has more than one name.

OPEN-ENDED Exercises 9–19 Explain that the figures do not have to be regular if the description does not include the term *regular.*

pages 310–312 On Your Own

9. 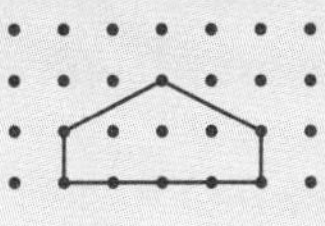

10. 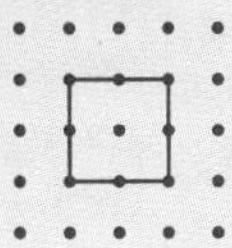

11. 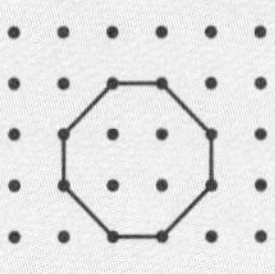

12. 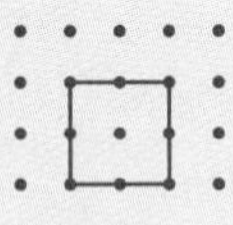

13. 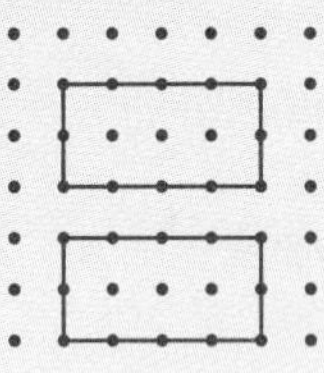

14. 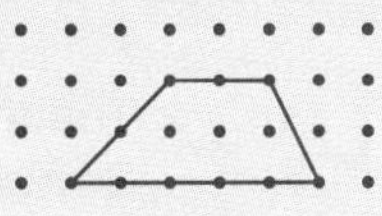

15. 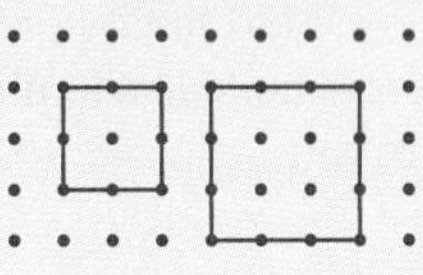

16. 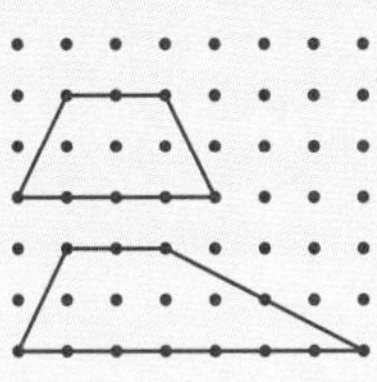

17. 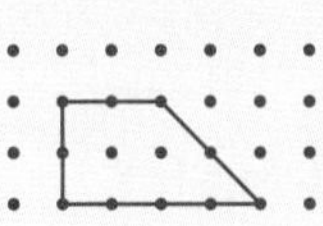

18. 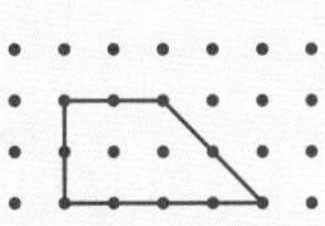

19. 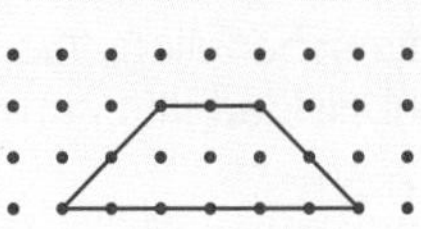

Every quadrilateral has two pairs of opposite sides and two pairs of opposite angles.

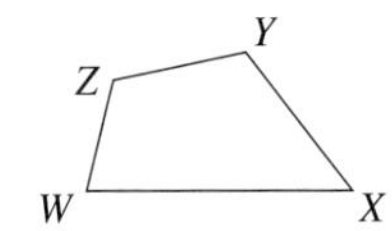

8. Name two pairs of opposite sides. **$\overline{ZY}$ and $\overline{WX}$, $\overline{ZW}$ and $\overline{YX}$**

9. Name two pairs of opposite angles. **$\angle Z$ and $\angle X$, $\angle Y$ and $\angle W$**

The **diagonals** of quadrilateral $ABCD$ are $\overline{AC}$ and $\overline{BD}$.

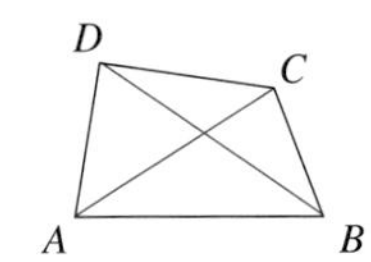

Work Together

Exploring Parallelograms

- Start with a parallelogram that is a different shape from those of the other members of your group.
- Draw one diagonal of your parallelogram.
- Cut out the parallelogram and then cut along the diagonal.

10. a. Are the two triangles that are formed congruent? Why or why not? **Yes; their sides and angles match.**

b. Were the opposite sides of your parallelogram congruent? Why or why not? **Yes; they are the same length.**

c. What have you shown about two opposite angles of your parallelogram? Suppose you had cut along the other diagonal. What do you think would have been the result? **They are congruent; same result.**

11. Compare your results with those of your group. What can you conclude about parallelograms? Do your conclusions also apply to rectangles, squares, and rhombuses? Why or why not?

11. Opposite sides and angles are congruent; yes; they are parallelograms.

Now you may assign Exercises 5–8, 12–14, 16–33.

EXERCISES *On Your Own*

Classify each polygon by the number of sides. Then state whether it appears to be a regular polygon.

1. 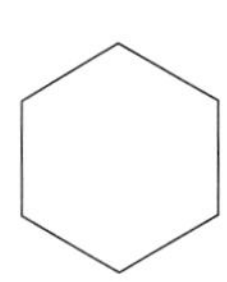

hexagon; regular

2. 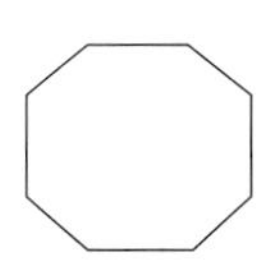

octagon; not regular

3. 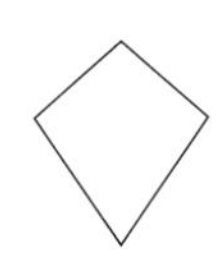

quadrilateral; not regular

4. 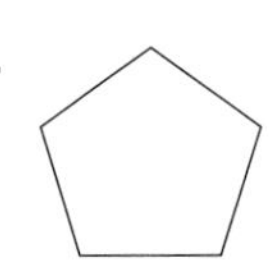

pentagon; regular

CONNECTION TO SOCIAL STUDIES
Exercise 20a You may want to discuss why only Australia would use this road sign. Have students name animal crossing signs they have seen in the United States.

REASONING Exercise 21 Have students refer to the charts they made for the Assessment.

WRITING Exercise 23 Write the following sentences on the board. Ask students to replace the blanks with words from the exercise.

- *All __ are __.*
- *Some __ are __.*
- *No __ are __.*

Exercises 29–33 Have students label the angles in their diagrams clockwise. Make sure they follow the order of the letters exactly as listed in the name of the polygon.

WRAP UP

IDENTIFYING THE BIG IDEA Ask students to name types of quadrilaterals and to describe similarities and differences.

JOURNAL Ask students to brainstorm a list of road signs and group them by shape. Have them think about what signs that are the same shape have in common.

Judging by appearance, write all the correct names for each quadrilateral. Then circle the best name.

7. polygon, quadrilateral, parallelogram, [rhombus]

5. 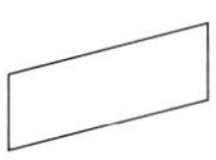
polygon, quadrilateral, [parallelogram]

6. 
polygon, quadrilateral, parallelogram, rectangle, rhombus, [square]

7. 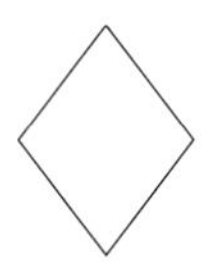

8. 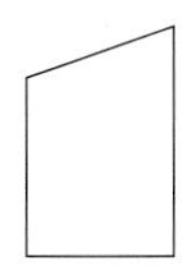
polygon, quadrilateral, [trapezoid]

Open-ended **Use dot paper to draw each of the following.**
9–19. See margin.

9. a pentagon
10. a regular quadrilateral
11. an octagon
12. a rhombus
13. two congruent rectangles
14. a trapezoid
15. two regular quadrilaterals that are not congruent
16. two noncongruent trapezoids that have a pair of congruent sides
17. a trapezoid with two right angles
18. a trapezoid with two congruent adjacent sides
19. a trapezoid with two congruent opposite sides

20b. polygon, quadrilateral, parallelogram, rectangle, rhombus, [square]

a. polygon, quadrilateral, parallelogram, [rectangle]

20. a. *Social Studies* Write all the names that can be used for the shape of the bottom Australian road sign. Circle the best name.
b. Write all the names that can be used for the shape of the top sign. Circle the best name.
See above right.

21. *Reasoning* Can a quadrilateral be both a rhombus and a rectangle? Explain.
Yes; a square is a rhombus and a rectangle.

22. **Choose A, B, C, or D.** Which statement or statements are false? C
I. Every trapezoid is a quadrilateral.
II. Every rectangle is a square.
III. Every parallelogram is a rhombus.
A. II only
B. III only
C. II and III
D. I, II, and III

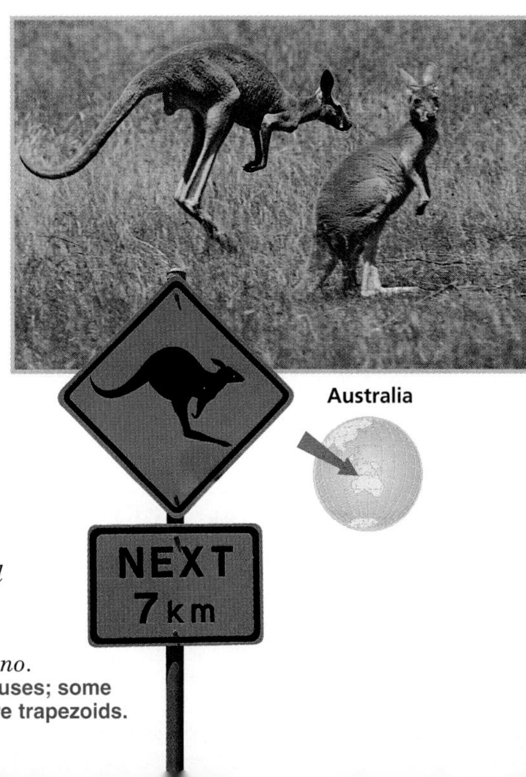

23. *Writing* Write a sentence that uses the word *all* and some of the following words: trapezoids, parallelograms, rectangles, rhombuses, squares. Repeat for the word *some* and then for the word *no*.
Answers may vary. Samples: All squares are rhombuses; some parallelograms are rectangles; no parallelograms are trapezoids.

PRACTICE

Practice 7-6 *Polygons and Quadrilaterals*

Classify each polygon by the number of sides. State whether it appears to be a regular polygon.

1. quadrilateral; no
2. octagon; no
3. pentagon; no
4. hexagon; yes

Judging by appearance, state all correct names for each quadrilateral. Then circle the best name.

5. parallelogram, (rectangle)
6. parallelogram, rectangle, rhombus, (square)
7. parallelogram, (rhombus)
8. (trapezoid)

Draw each of the following on the dot grid. Sample drawings given.

9. a rectangle that is not a square
10. a rhombus with two right angles
11. a trapezoid with no right angles

12. Draw a pair of quadrilaterals where the angles of the first quadrilateral are congruent to the angles of the second quadrilateral. No side of one quadrilateral is to be congruent to any side of the other quadrilateral. Sample:

In copymaster and workbook formats

RETEACHING

Reteaching 7-6 *Polygons and Quadrilaterals*

You name polygons by the number of sides. A **quadrilateral** is a polygon with four sides. The table shows the names and properties of some special quadrilaterals.

Special Quadrilaterals

Quadrilateral	Figure	Only 1 Pair of Parallel Sides	2 Pairs of Parallel Sides	All Sides Must be Congruent	Opposite Sides Are Congruent	All Angles Must Be Right Angles
Square			✓	✓	✓	✓
Rectangle			✓		✓	✓
Rhombus			✓	✓	✓	
Parallelogram			✓		✓	
Trapezoid		✓				

Look at the rhombus. It is also a parallelogram, but the name *rhombus* is best because it gives the most information about the figure.

Judging by appearence, write the best name for each quadrilateral.

1. rectangle
2. rhombus
3. trapezoid
4. parallelogram

Draw each of the following. Samples given.

5. a trapezoid with a right angle
6. a quadrilateral with opposite sides parallel and a right angle

Reteaching

ENRICHMENT

Minds on Math Transparency

7-6

I am a seven-digit number. My first 5 digits are 2, 1, 3, 5, and 8 in that order. I am divisible by 99. What are my last two digits?

2, 6

See *Solution Key* for worked-out answers.

312

PROJECT LINK Before students begin building their cubes, challenge them to predict how many toothpicks and raisins they will need by imagining the finished cube.

LESSON QUIZ

1. A regular polygon contains five congruent angles. What is the name of this shape? **pentagon**
2. Can you have a regular trapezoid? Explain. **No; a trapezoid cannot have all sides or angles congruent.**
3. What other names can you call a square? **Answers may vary. Sample: rectangle, rhombus, parallelogram, quadrilateral, polygon**

Judging by appearance, classify each quadrilateral. Then name the congruent sides and angles. 26. parallelogram; $\overline{EF} \cong \overline{HG}$, $\overline{FG} \cong \overline{EH}$, $\angle E \cong \angle G$, $\angle F \cong \angle H$

24. 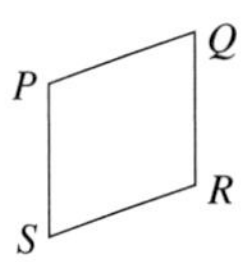

25. trapezoid 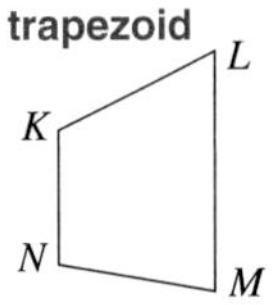

26. 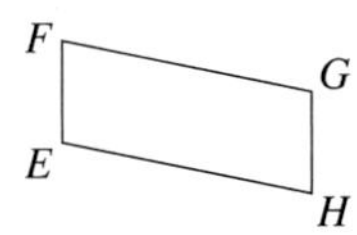

27. 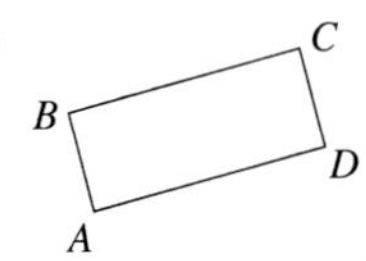

See margin p. 313.

24. rhombus; $\overline{PQ} \cong \overline{QR} \cong \overline{RS} \cong \overline{PS}$, $\angle P \cong \angle R$, $\angle Q \cong \angle S$

28. a. Draw a quadrilateral with exactly one pair of opposite angles that are congruent.
    b. Draw a quadrilateral with exactly one pair of opposite sides that are congruent.

a. 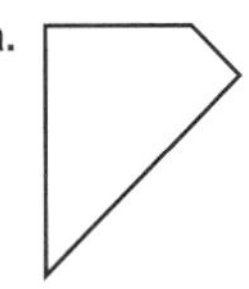 b. 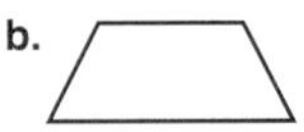

List all additional side lengths and angle measures you can find for each quadrilateral. (*Hint:* Draw a diagram.)

29. parallelogram $ABCD$, $AB = 6$ cm, $m\angle A = 65°$ **$m\angle C = 65°$, $DC = 6$ cm**
30. square $EFGH$, $EF = 3$ m **$m\angle E = 90°$, $m\angle F = 90°$, $m\angle G = 90°$, $\angle H = 90°$, $FG = 3$ m, $GH = 3$ m, $EH = 3$ m**
31. rhombus $WXYZ$, $WX = 4$ cm **$XY = 4$ cm, $YZ = 4$ cm, $WZ = 4$ cm**
32. rectangle $JKLN$, $KL = 5$ in. **$m\angle J = 90°$, $m\angle K = 90°$, $m\angle L = 90°$, $m\angle N = 90°$, $JN = 5$ in.**
33. trapezoid $PQRS$, $QR = 10$ cm, $m\angle Q = 65°$ **No additional measures can be found.**

JOURNAL Describe how polygons are used for the shapes of common road signs.

Mixed Review

Estimate each answer. (*Lesson 5-1*) 34–38. Answers may vary. Samples are given.

34. $12\frac{1}{2} - 5\frac{2}{3}$ **7**
35. $16\frac{1}{2} \div 4\frac{3}{4}$ **4**
36. $\frac{1}{2} + \frac{5}{12}$ **1**
37. $3\frac{7}{12} \cdot 2\frac{2}{5}$ **8**
38. $\frac{7}{12} - \frac{3}{10}$ **0**

State whether each number is prime or composite. If composite, write its prime factorization. (*Lesson 4-5*)

39. 15 **composite; 3 · 5**
40. 29 **prime**
41. 333 **composite; 3 · 3 · 37**
42. 6,453 **composite; 3 · 3 · 3 · 239**
43. 146 **composite; 2 · 73**
44. 31 **prime**

CHAPTER PROJECT

PROJECT LINK: CREATING

Use toothpicks and raisins to build a cube. How many of each are needed? Use additional toothpicks to strengthen the cube. Describe how you did it.

Check students' work for construction and reasoning; 12 toothpicks; 6 toothpicks.

Extra Practice, Lesson 7-6, page 520

In Lesson 7-6, students learned how to classify polygons and quadrilaterals. This toolbox shows students how to use a computer and geometry software to investigate the angles of polygons.

ERROR ALERT! Students may have trouble following the steps used in the geometry software. **Remediation:** Have students compare results with a partner after completing each step. If their results differ, students can repeat the steps again to discover where they made a mistake.

ASSESSMENT Exercise 7 Have students compare their findings in small groups. Challenge students to use their findings to write a general rule about the relationship between the number of sides of a figure and the number of triangles they can form by drawing all the diagonals from the vertex. Have students share their rules with the class.

MATH TOOLBOX TECHNOLOGY

Sum of the Measures of the Angles of a Polygon

After Lesson 7-6

You can use a computer and geometry software to investigate the angles of polygons. We shall consider only convex polygons.

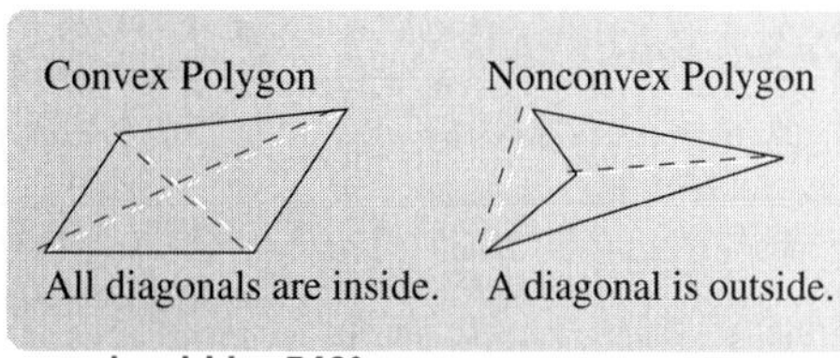

Draw a pentagon like the one shown.

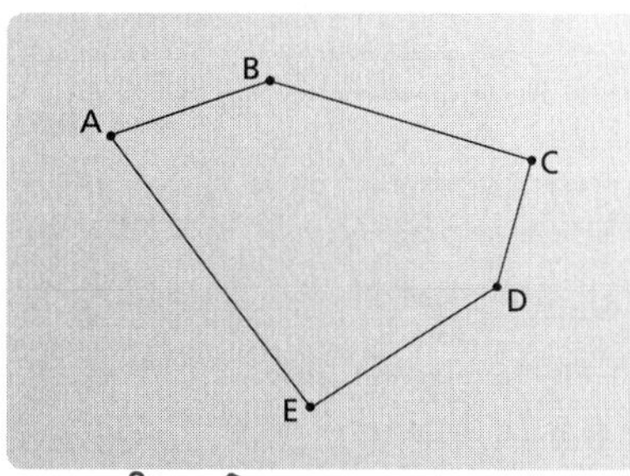

1. a. Use the computer program to measure each angle. Find the sum of the measures. **The sum should be 540°.**
   b. Change the pentagon's shape, but keep it convex. Find the sum of the angle measures. **540°**
   c. *Draw a Conclusion* What is the sum of the measures of the angles of a pentagon? **540°**
2. a. Sketch a pentagon and divide it into triangles by drawing all the diagonals from one vertex.
   b. Multiply the number of triangles you drew by the sum of the angle measures of a triangle. **540°**

2a.

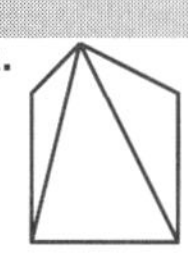

3. What relationship do you find between your answers to Questions 1(c) and 2(b)? **The answers are the same.**
4. a. Sketch a hexagon. Divide the hexagon into triangles by drawing all the diagonals from one vertex.
   b. Multiply the number of triangles you drew by 180°. **720°**

4a. Answers may vary. Sample:

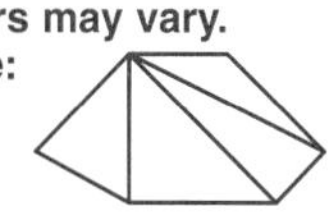

5. Draw a hexagon using a computer. Measure the angles and find their sum. Change the shape of your hexagon. What do you notice about the sum of the angle measures? **It is always 720°.**
6. Tell how many sides each polygon has and the number of triangles that you can form by drawing all the diagonals from one vertex.
   a. quadrilateral **4 sides; 2 triangles**
   b. pentagon **5 sides; 3 triangles**
   c. hexagon **6 sides; 4 triangles**
   d. octagon **8 sides; 6 triangles**
7. *Writing* What is the relationship between the number of sides of a figure and the number of triangles you can form? **The number of triangles that can be formed from one vertex is 2 less than the number of sides of the polygon.**
8. What is the sum of the measures of the angles of a 12-sided polygon? **1,800°**

Materials/Manipulatives

- geometry software

Resources

Teaching Aids Masters 3, 7, 8

Transparencies

16, 17

pages 310–312 On Your Own

27. rectangle; $\overline{AB} \cong \overline{DC}$, $\overline{BC} \cong \overline{AD}$, $\angle A \cong \angle B \cong \angle C \cong \angle D$

7-7 Teaching Notes

1 Focus

CONNECTING TO PRIOR KNOWLEDGE Ask students to brainstorm a list of objects that are circular or partially circular. Then ask students which of their vocabulary terms describe circles.

2 Teach

THINK AND DISCUSS

Make sure students understand that a circle is not a polygon. A polygon is made up of segments and a circle has no segments.

ERROR ALERT! Students often confuse the terms *radius* and *diameter.* **Remediation:** Invite students to think of mnemonics to tell the two terms apart. For example, the word *diameter* is longer than the word *radius,* so the diameter is longer than the radius.

ASSESSMENT Check students' understanding of the terms introduced by asking questions such as the following:

- *Can a radius also be a chord? Explain.* **No. A radius has only one endpoint on the circle; a chord has both endpoints on the circle.**
- *What is the name for the sides of a central angle?* **radii**

Lesson Planning Options

Prerequisite Skill

- naming line segments and polygons (precourse)

Vocabulary/Symbols

circle, center, radius, diameter, central angle, chord, arc, semicircle, endpoints, compass, inscribed polygon

Materials/Manipulatives

- compass
- protractor

Resources

Student Edition

Skills Handbook, p. 528
Extra Practice, p. 520
Glossary/Study Guide

Teaching Resources

Chapter Support File, Ch. 7
- Lesson Planner 7-7
- Practice 7-7, Reteaching 7-7
- Alternative Activity 7-7
- Answer Masters 7-7

Teaching Aids Masters 3, 10
Glossary, Spanish Resources

Transparencies
8, Minds on Math 7-7

Warm Up

Find the number of apples, if birds pecked at $\frac{1}{4}$ of the apples and only 15 apples were pecked. **60**

7-7 Circles

What You'll Learn

1. To identify parts of circles
2. To work with inscribed quadrilaterals

...And Why

Circles are important parts of some three-dimensional figures and are used to present statistics in circle graphs.

Here's How

Look for questions that
- build understanding
- ✓ check understanding

THINK AND DISCUSS

1 *Parts of a Circle*

A **circle** is the set of points in a plane that are all the same distance from a given point, called the *center.* You name a circle by its center. Circle O is shown at the right.

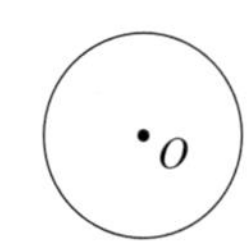

A **radius** is a segment that has one endpoint at the center and the other endpoint on the circle.

$\overline{OB}$ is a radius of circle O.

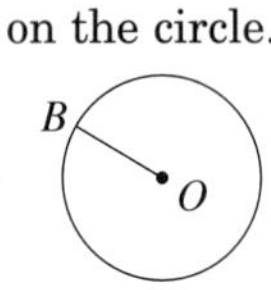

A **diameter** is a segment that passes through the center of a circle and has both endpoints on the circle.

$\overline{AC}$ is a diameter of circle O.

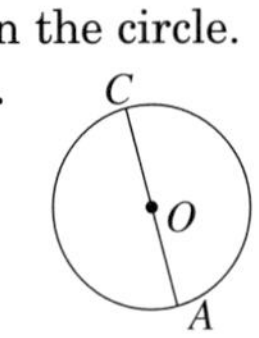

A **central angle** is an angle with its vertex at the center of a circle.

$\angle AOB$ is a central angle of circle O.

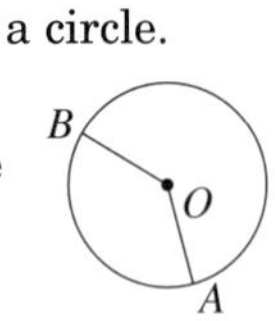

A **chord** is a segment that has both endpoints on the circle.

$\overline{AD}$ is a chord of circle O.

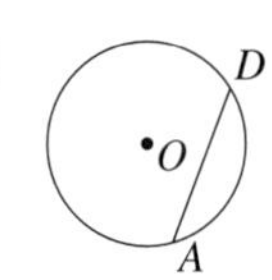

QUICKreview

Radii is the plural of radius.

EXAMPLE 1

Name all the radii, diameters, and chords shown for circle O.

The radii are $\overline{OA}$, $\overline{OB}$, $\overline{OC}$, and $\overline{OD}$.

The diameter is $\overline{AC}$.

The chords are $\overline{AB}$, $\overline{BC}$, $\overline{CD}$, $\overline{DA}$, and $\overline{AC}$.

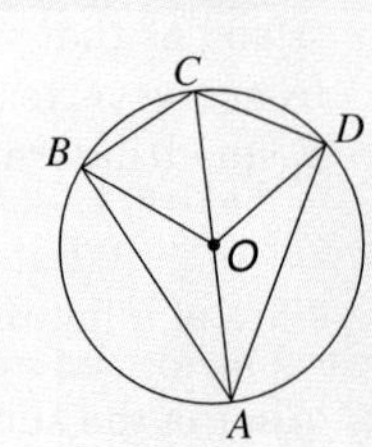

- *What is the name for a chord that passes through the center of a circle?* **diameter**

AEP The Spanish verb for *write* is *escribir.* Some students may remember the term *inscribed* as one figure written *inside* another.

Question 5 Ask students: *△COB and △COD appear to be equilateral. Can you conclude that they are?*
No; you do not know if $\overline{BC} \cong \overline{DC}$

ADDITIONAL EXAMPLES

FOR EXAMPLE 1

Name all the radii, diameters, and chords shown in circle *T.*

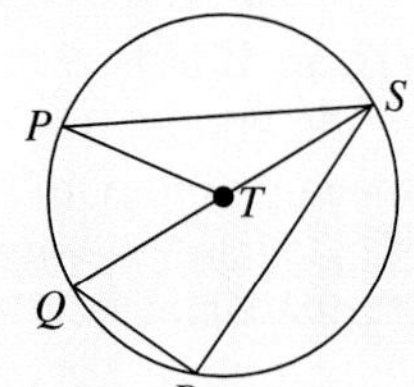

radii: $\overline{TP}$, $\overline{TQ}$, $\overline{TS}$; diameter: $\overline{QS}$; chords: $\overline{PS}$, $\overline{QR}$, $\overline{QS}$, $\overline{RS}$

FOR EXAMPLE 2

Name the polygon inscribed in circle *T.*
△QRS

Work Together

TACTILE LEARNING Question 12 Have students use a compass to create circles. Students can then use rulers to draw quadrilaterals inside the circles. Have students estimate to measure the angles.

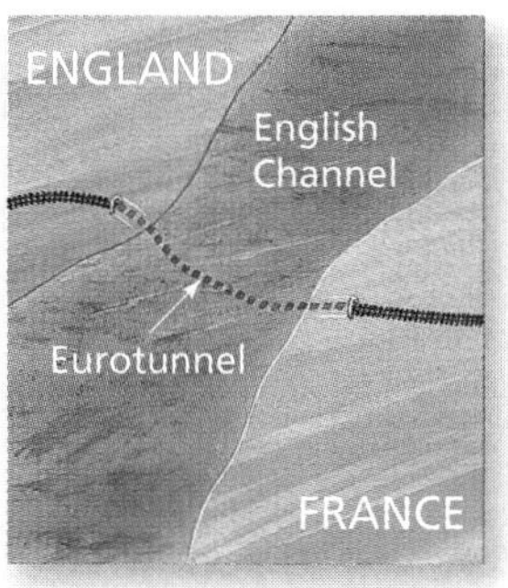

ENGINEERING Circles were important in the design and construction of the Eurotunnel, which is usually called the Chunnel. The 30-mi long tunnel allows you to travel from one country to another in 35 min.

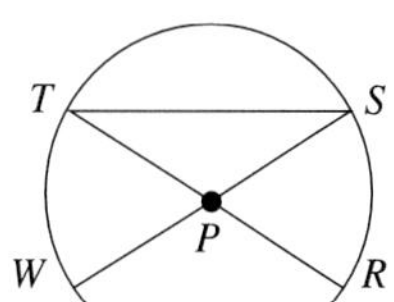

1. ✔ *Try It Out* Name all the radii, diameters, and chords shown in circle *P.* **radii: $\overline{PT}$, $\overline{PS}$, $\overline{PR}$, $\overline{PW}$; diameters: $\overline{RT}$, $\overline{SW}$; chords: $\overline{RT}$, $\overline{SW}$, $\overline{ST}$**
2. *Think About It* Can a radius also be a chord? Explain. **See margin p. 316.**
3. Must a diameter also be a chord? Explain. **Yes; a diameter must be a chord because its two endpoints are on the circle.**
4. How do the lengths of a radius and a diameter compare? **The length of a radius is half the length of the diameter.**
5. Name the isosceles triangles in the diagram for Example 1. How do you know they are isosceles? **△*AOB*, △*BOC*, △*COD*, △*AOD*; two sides are radii which are congruent.**
6. a. Name four *non-overlapping* central angles of circle *O* in Example 1. **∠*AOB*, ∠*BOC*, ∠*COD*, ∠*AOD***
   b. What is the sum of the measures of the four non-overlapping central angles? Explain. **360°; m∠*AOB* + m∠*BOC* = 180° and m∠*COD* + m∠*AOD* = 180°.**

An **arc** is part of a circle. A **semicircle** is half a circle.

arc semicircle

You use three letters to name a semicircle. The first and third letters name the *endpoints* of the semicircle. One semicircle in Example 1 is $\overset{\frown}{ADC}$ (read "arc *ADC*"). You use two letters to name an arc shorter than a semicircle.

7. a. ✔ *Try It Out* Name another semicircle in Example 1. **$\overset{\frown}{ABC}$**
   b. Why do you need to use three letters to name a semicircle? **You need to know which points are between the endpoints.**
8. ✔ *Try It Out* $\overset{\frown}{AB}$ is one arc of circle *O* in Example 1. Name the other arcs that are shorter than a semicircle. **$\overset{\frown}{BC}$, $\overset{\frown}{CD}$, $\overset{\frown}{AD}$, $\overset{\frown}{BD}$**

Technology Options

Prentice Hall Technology

Software for Learners
- Math Blaster® Mystery*
- Interactive Student Tutorial, Chapter 7*

Teaching Resource Software
- Computer Item Generator 7-7
- Resource Pro™ Chapter 7*

Internet • For related mathematics activities, visit the Prentice Hall site at www.phschool.com/math

**Available on CD-ROM only*

Assignment Options for Exercises On Your Own

To provide flexible scheduling, this lesson can be subdivided into parts.

1 **Core** 1–8
Extension 9

2 **Core** 10–13
Extension 14

Use Mixed Review to maintain skills.

3 Practice

EXERCISES. *On Your Own*

Exercises 1–8 Make sure students understand that *several* means more than one, but it can also mean more than two. Encourage students to find all parts possible for each exercise.

OPEN-ENDED Exercise 10 Suggest students read all three parts of the question before drawing their design. They may wish to keep their designs simple to make them easier to describe.

WRITING Exercise 10b Have students describe where the endpoint of each chord is. Suggest that they use the numbers on the face of a clock to locate the vertices. **Answers may vary. Sample: There is a chord from 12 o'clock to 5 o'clock.** Assure students they do not have to write perfect instructions the first time. Explain that 10c gives them a chance to test their description and rewrite it if necessary.

REASONING and AUDITORY LEARNING Exercise 12 Have partners take turns reading aloud each description. One student reads the description, the other draws the figure. Then they look at the figure together and read the description again to check.

pages 314–316 Think and Discuss

2. **No; both endpoints of a chord are on the circle and only one endpoint of a radius is on the circle.**

9. 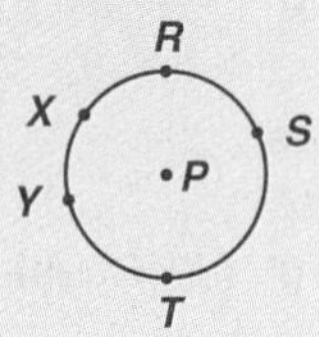

A **compass** is a geometric tool used to draw circles and arcs.

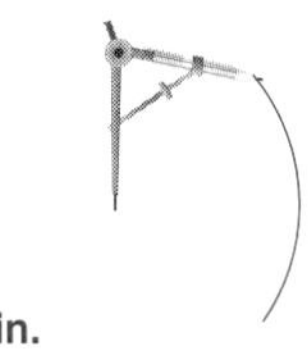

9. Use a compass to draw and label a circle P. Label a semicircle as $\overset{\frown}{RST}$ and a shorter arc as $\overset{\frown}{XY}$. **See margin.**

Now you may assign Exercises 1–9.

To draw a circle or an arc with a SAFE-T-COMPASS®, use the center hole of the white dial as the center.

2 *Inscribed Polygons*

You call a polygon whose sides are chords of a circle an **inscribed polygon.**

EXAMPLE 2

Name the polygons inscribed in circle P.

The inscribed polygons are $\triangle RST$ and $\triangle STW$.

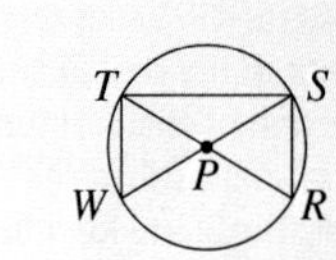

10. ✔ *Try It Out* Name the polygons that are inscribed in circle O. ***ABCD*, △*ABC*, △*ADC***

11. What is true of all the vertices of an inscribed polygon? **They lie on the circle.**

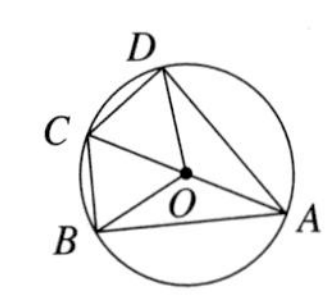

Work Together — *Exploring Inscribed Quadrilaterals*

Work in a group. Inscribe several quadrilaterals in circles. **The sum of the measures of each pair of opposite angles is 180°.**

12. Measure the angles of the quadrilaterals. Make a conjecture about the sum of the measures of the opposite angles of an inscribed quadrilateral.

Now you may assign Exercises 10–14.

EXERCISES *On Your Own*

Name each of the following for circle *O*.

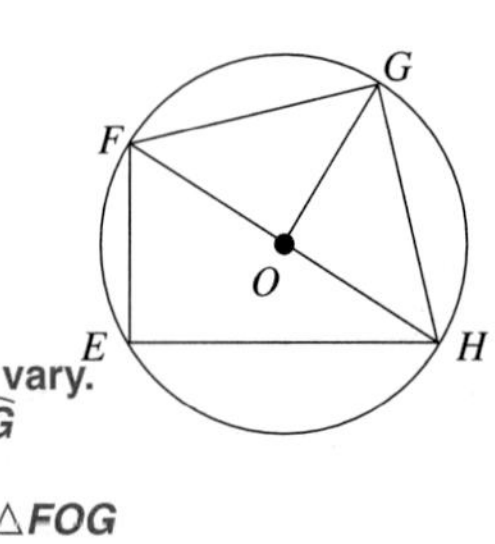

1. two or more chords **Answers may vary. Samples: *FH*, and *FG***
2. three radii **$\overline{OF}$, $\overline{OG}$, $\overline{OH}$**
3. a diameter **$\overline{FH}$**
4. several central angles **∠*FOH*, ∠*FOG*, ∠*GOH***
5. two semicircles **$\overset{\frown}{FEH}$, $\overset{\frown}{FGH}$**
6. several arcs **Answers may vary. Samples: $\overset{\frown}{EF}$, $\overset{\frown}{EFG}$, $\overset{\frown}{EFH}$, $\overset{\frown}{FG}$**
7. the longest chord shown **$\overline{FH}$**
8. an isosceles triangle **Answers may vary. Sample: △*FOG***

WRAP UP

IDENTIFYING THE BIG IDEA Ask students to identify the parts of a *circle* and define each part. Then ask them how to recognize the sides of a polygon *inscribed* in a circle.

LESSON QUIZ

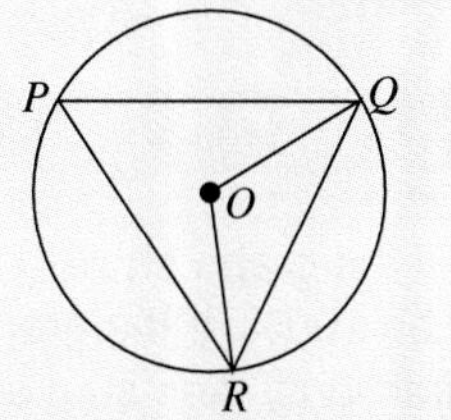

1. Name the radii, diameters, and chords shown in circle *O*. **radii: $\overline{OQ}$, $\overline{OR}$; diameters: none; chords: $\overline{PR}$, $\overline{PQ}$, $\overline{QR}$**
2. Name the polygon inscribed in circle *O*. **$\triangle PQR$**

9. Name all the radii, diameters, and chords shown in the figure at the right. **radii: $\overline{OE}$, $\overline{OF}$, $\overline{OG}$, $\overline{OH}$; diameters: $\overline{EG}$, $\overline{FH}$; chords: $\overline{EG}$, $\overline{FH}$, $\overline{FG}$**

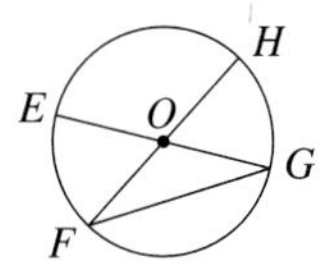

10. a. *Open-ended* Draw a circular design that includes an inscribed quadrilateral. **a–c. Check students' work.**
    b. *Writing* Describe your design so someone could draw it without looking at your drawing.
    c. Ask a family member or friend to use your description to draw your design. Rewrite the description if necessary.

11. **Choose A, B, C, or D.** Which of the following is *not* an inscribed polygon? **D**

A. B. C. D.

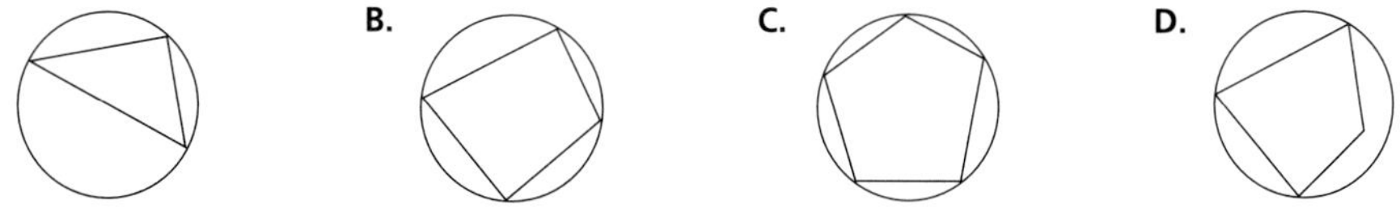

Reasoning **Draw several different diagrams that fit each description. Then make a conjecture.**
12–13. Check students' work for diagrams.

12. an inscribed quadrilateral whose vertices are the endpoints of two diameters **The quadrilateral is a rectangle.**
13. an inscribed triangle that has a diameter as one of its sides **The triangle is a right triangle.**
14. Do the following to inscribe a regular hexagon in a circle.
    - Use a compass to draw a circle.
    - Keeping the compass set to the same width, put the tip on the circle and make a small arc that intersects the circle.
    - Move the tip of the compass to the intersection. Make another small arc. Continue around the circle.
    - Join each pair of consecutive arcs.

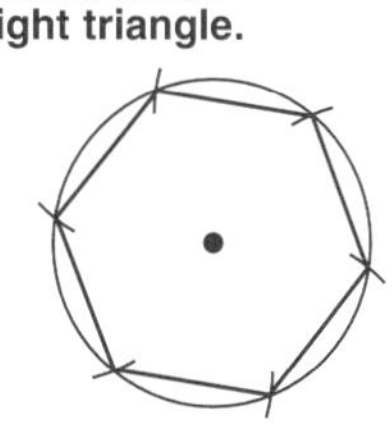

Mixed Review

Solve each equation. (Lesson 5-4)

15. $p - \frac{4}{7} = 5\frac{1}{14}$ **$5\frac{9}{14}$**
16. $3\frac{1}{2} = x - 1\frac{3}{4}$ **$5\frac{1}{4}$**
17. $t = 12\frac{9}{10} - 10\frac{2}{3}$ **$2\frac{7}{30}$**
18. $\frac{1}{2} = w - 4\frac{5}{12}$ **$4\frac{11}{12}$**

Find each missing number. (Lesson 4-2)

19. $\frac{15}{50} = \frac{3}{■}$ **10**
20. $\frac{4}{■} = \frac{20}{35}$ **7**
21. $\frac{18}{32} = \frac{■}{16}$ **9**
22. $\frac{■}{40} = \frac{4}{5}$ **32**
23. $\frac{10}{25} = \frac{2}{■}$ **5**
24. *Shopping* A \$39.95 sweater and a \$19.65 skirt were on sale for 40% off. What is the total cost for the sweater and skirt? (Lesson 6-9) **\$35.76**

Extra Practice, Lesson 7-7, page 520

PRACTICE

Practice 7-7 Circles

Name each of the following for circle *O*. Answers may vary. Samples are given.

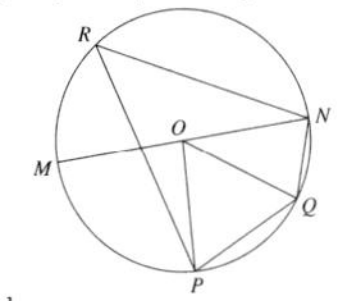

1. two chords $\overline{RN}$, $\overline{PQ}$
2. three radii $\overline{OM}$, $\overline{OP}$, $\overline{OQ}$
3. a diameter $\overline{MN}$
4. a central angle $\angle MOP$
5. a semicircle $\overset{\frown}{MRN}$
6. two arcs $\overset{\frown}{MR}$, $\overset{\frown}{NQ}$
7. the longest chord $\overline{MN}$
8. an inscribed quadrilateral $RPQN$

Circle A, B, C, or D.

9. Which of the following is not an inscribed polygon?
A. (B.) C. D.

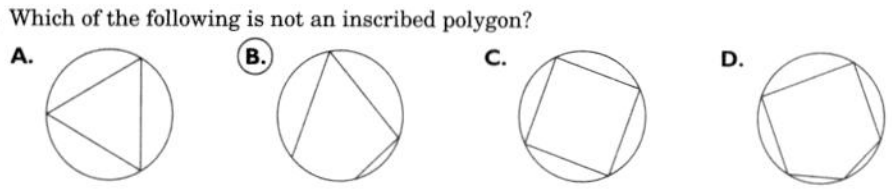

10. Which of the following shows an inscribed triangle that has a diameter as one of its sides?
(A.) B. C. D.

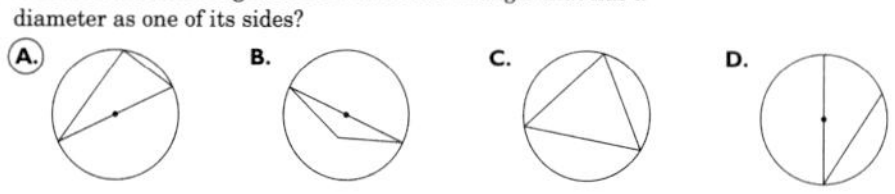

11. Which of the following polygons can be inscribed in a circle? There may be more than one choice. Make a sketch of each of the polygons that can be inscribed.
(A.) Square (B.) Rectangle C. Parallelogram that is not a rectangle D. Rhombus that is not a square

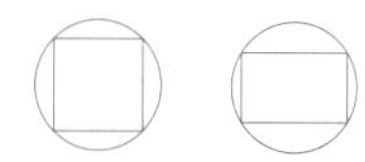

Practice

In copymaster and workbook formats

RETEACHING

Reteaching 7-7 Circles

A **circle** is the set of points in a plane that are all the same distance from a point, called the *center*. This circle is called circle *A*.

$\overline{AB}$ is a **radius** of circle *A*. It is a segment that has one endpoint on the circle and the other at the center. $\overline{AC}$ and $\overline{AD}$ are also *radii* of circle *A*.

$\overline{DC}$ is a **diameter** of circle *A*. It is a segment that passes through the center of the circle and has both endpoints on the circle.

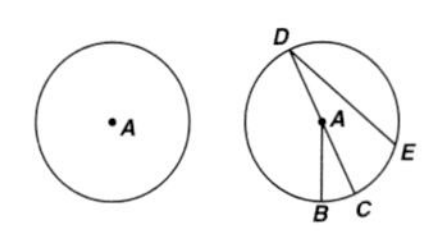

$\overline{DE}$ is a chord of circle *A*. A **chord** is a segment that has both endpoints on the circle.

$\angle DAB$ is a **central angle** of circle *A*. It is an angle with its vertex at the center of the circle.

$\overset{\frown}{DB}$ is an arc of circle *A*. An **arc** is part of a circle.

$\overset{\frown}{DEC}$ is a semicircle. A **semicircle** is an arc that is half a circle.

Name each of the following shown for circle *P*.

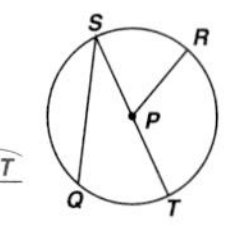

1. all radii $\overline{PR}$, $\overline{SP}$, $\overline{PT}$
2. all chords $\overline{SQ}$, $\overline{ST}$
3. 3 arcs Answers may vary. Samples: $\overset{\frown}{SQ}$, $\overset{\frown}{RT}$, $\overset{\frown}{SQT}$

Name each of the following shown for circle *M*.
Answers may vary. Samples are given.

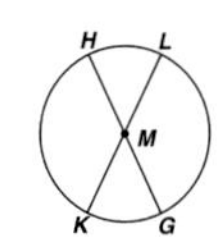

4. all diameters $\overline{LK}$, $\overline{HG}$
5. 3 central angles $\angle HML$, $\angle HMK$, $\angle KMG$
6. all chords $\overline{LK}$, $\overline{HG}$
7. 2 semicircles $\overset{\frown}{KHL}$, $\overset{\frown}{KGL}$
8. two radii $\overline{ML}$, $\overline{MK}$

ENRICHMENT

Minds on Math Transparency

7-7

Angie and Tim drew different angles. The measure of Angie's angle is 2 more than 3 times the measure of Tim's angle. Angie's angle is 26° larger than a right angle. What is the measure of Tim's angle?

38°

See *Solution Key* for worked-out answers.

7-8 Teaching Notes

1 Focus

CONNECTING TO PRIOR KNOWLEDGE Ask students if they know what a *pie chart* is. Show examples from newspapers or magazines. Ask students: *What do you think the size of each pie slice represents?* **Answers may vary. Sample: A larger slice represents a larger number.**

2 Teach

THINK AND DISCUSS

Tell students if the graph shows percents, their totals should be 100%. If the graph shows decimals or fractions, their sum should be 1.

ASSESSMENT Question 5a After students have completed this question, ask: *Will you always represent 41% using a sector with the same central angle? Explain.* **Yes, 41% of 360° is about 148°.**

DIVERSITY Physically challenged students can use graphing software to draw circle graphs, instead of using a compass.

Example Suggest students check their calculations by adding the measures of all the central angles. The sum should be close to 360°, but could vary by about 2 degrees because of rounding, not because of a calculation mistake.

Lesson Planning Options

Prerequisite Skills
- adding decimals (2-3)
- using proportions to find percents (6-7)
- measuring angles (7-2)

Vocabulary/Symbols
circle graphs, sectors

Materials/Manipulatives
- protractor
- compass

Resources

Student Edition

Skills Handbook, pp. 530, 531
Extra Practice, p. 520
Glossary/Study Guide

Teaching Resources

Chapter Support File, Ch. 7
- Lesson Planner 7-8
- Practice 7-8, Reteaching 7-8
- Answer Masters 7-8

Teaching Aids Masters 3, 10
Glossary, Spanish Resources

Transparencies

15, 43, 44, Minds on Math 7-8

Warm Up

Draw an example of each kind of angle and describe its properties.
acute angle A **$0° < m\angle A < 90°$**
right angle R **$m\angle R = 90°$**
obtuse angle O **$90° < m\angle O < 180°$**
Check students' drawings.

DATA ANALYSIS Connection

7-8 Circle Graphs

What You'll Learn
1. To analyze circle graphs
2. To construct circle graphs

...And Why
A circle graph is an effective way to present certain types of data.

Here's How
Look for questions that
- build understanding
- ✔ check understanding

THINK AND DISCUSS

1 Reading Circle Graphs

Circle graphs present data as percents or fractions of a total. The total must be 100% or 1.

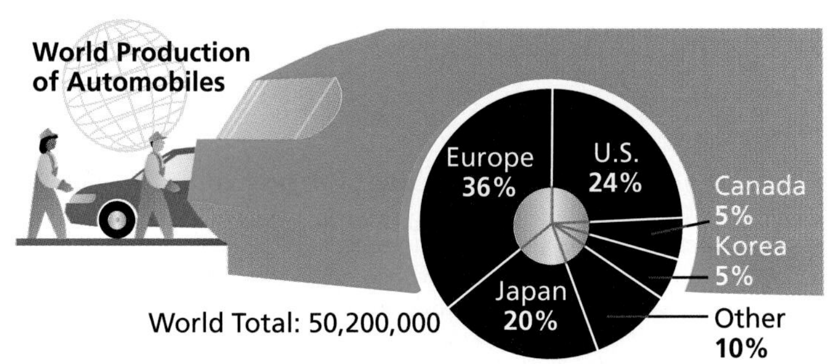

1. ✔ *Try It Out* Use the graph above. Where were the most automobiles produced? **Europe**
2. Canada's production was what fraction of Japan's production? **$\frac{1}{4}$**
3. *Predict* About how many automobiles were produced in the United States? in Japan? **12,048,000 automobiles; 10,040,000 automobiles**
4. *Number Sense* What is the sum of the percents in the graph? **100%**

Now you may assign Exercises 1–4.

2 Making Circle Graphs

A circle graph is divided into sectors. Each sector is determined by a central angle.

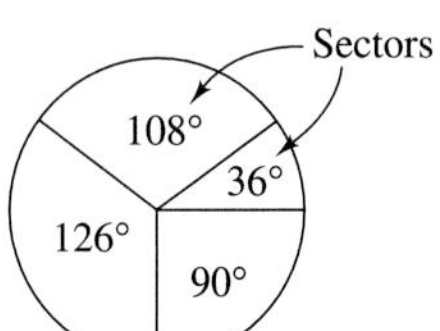

5. a. What is the sum of the measures of the central angles in the circle at the right? **360°**
   b. What percent of the circular region is each sector? **10%, 25%, 35%, 30%**

ADDITIONAL EXAMPLE

FOR EXAMPLE

Of 30 students, 5 go to band practice after school, 8 play basketball, 10 go to jobs, and 7 go to the library. Draw a circle graph for the data.

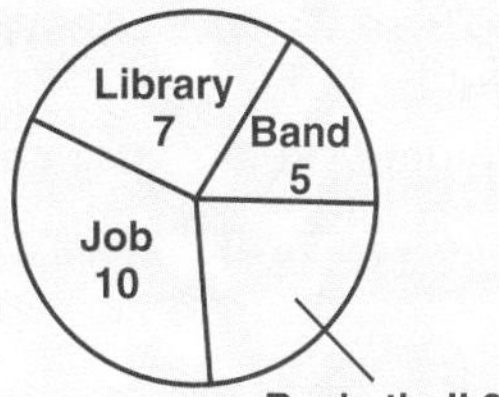

VISUAL LEARNING Draw a circle graph on the board. Divide the graph into one half, then quarters, eighths, and sixteenths. Shade one of each type of sector a different color. Then write 50%, 25%, 12.5%, and 6.25% in random order. Have students match the percents with the correct sector.

ERROR ALERT! When drawing a circle graph, students may draw each sector so that the measure of the central angle is the same as the value of the percent. **Remediation:** Remind students that a circle contains 360°. This represents 100%. Therefore, 1% of the data represented corresponds to an angle of 3.6° in the circle graph. The central angle of each sector should have a measure between 3 and 4 times the percent value it represents.

EXAMPLE *Real-World Problem Solving*

Population Statistics The table below shows the number of people in the United States who have at least one grandchild under the age of 18. Draw a circle graph for the data.

Number of Grandparents

Age	People (Millions)
44 and less	3.6
45-54	10.3
55-64	15.0
65 and more	18.2

First add to find the total number.

$$3.6 + 10.3 + 15.0 + 18.2 = 47.1 \text{ (million)}$$

For each central angle, set up a proportion to find the measure. Use a calculator to solve.

$\frac{3.6}{47.1} = \frac{a}{360°}$ $\frac{10.3}{47.1} = \frac{b}{360°}$ $\frac{15.0}{47.1} = \frac{c}{360°}$ $\frac{18.2}{47.1} = \frac{d}{360°}$

$a \approx 27.5°$ $b \approx 78.7°$ $c \approx 114.6°$ $d \approx 139.1°$

Use a compass to draw a circle. Draw the central angles with a protractor.

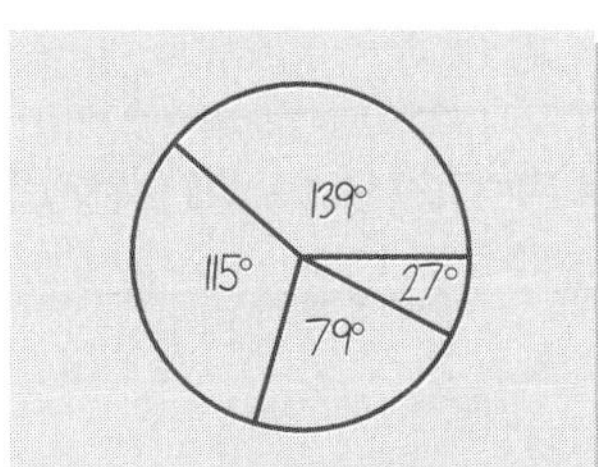

Label each sector. Add any necessary information.

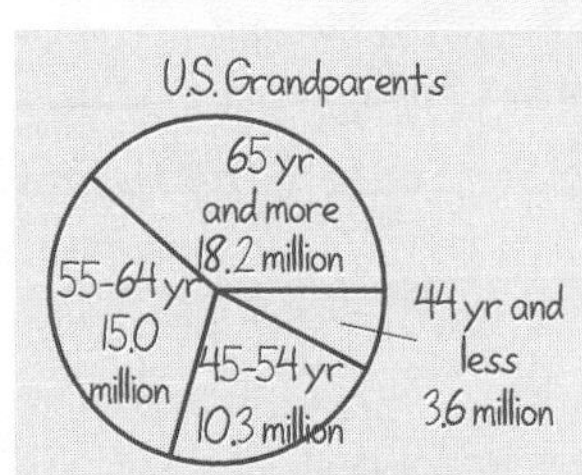

6. a. ✔ *Try It Out* Draw a circle graph to show the ways apples are used. **See left.**
   b. Did you have to calculate the measure of each central angle? Why or why not? **No; the table shows only two different percents.**

Uses of Apples

Use	Percent
Juice	41
Fresh	41
Applesauce	9
Other	9

a.

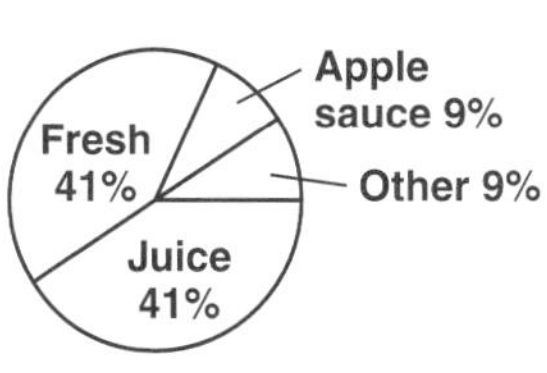

Now you may assign Exercises 5–18.

Technology Options

Prentice Hall Technology

Software for Learners
- Hot Page™ 9–12*
- Math Blaster® Mystery*
- Interactive Student Tutorial, Chapter 7*

Teaching Resource Software
- Computer Item Generator 7-8
- Resource Pro™ Chapter 7*

Internet • For related mathematics activities, visit the Prentice Hall site at www.phschool.com/math

**Available on CD-ROM only*

Assignment Options for Exercises On Your Own

To provide flexible scheduling, this lesson can be subdivided into parts.

1 **Core** 1–3
Extension 4

2 **Core** 5–15, 18
Extension 16, 17

Use Mixed Review to maintain skills.

3 Practice/Assess

EXERCISES *On Your Own*

CONNECTION TO ECOLOGY Exercise 2 Ask students to discuss the consequences of half the traffic being made up of vehicles carrying only one person. **Answers may vary. Sample answer: More traffic leads to more air pollution.**

CONNECTION TO NUMBER SENSE
Exercises 5–7 Tell students that there is more than one way to find the missing measures for each graph.

Exercise 8 If you have block scheduling or extended class periods, have students work in small groups to collect.

Exercises 9–14 Challenge students to find a shorter method for finding the measure of the central angle when you know the percent of the circle graph. **Multiply the percent by 3.6.**

RESEARCH Exercise 16 Encourage students to find the measure of the central angle using proportions, and then check with a protractor.

REASONING Exercise 17c Have students give reasons for the changes they suggest. Ask students: *Are some changes easier to make than others? Explain.* **Answers may vary. Sample: Yes; it is easier to change the amount spent on clothing and food than to change where you live.**

pages 320–322 On Your Own

1a. **Answers may vary. Sample: No; you can use the percents to determine the number of states if you need to since there are 50 states.**

8. **In the first survey, many people may have chosen more than one feature. The results of the second survey can be shown in a circle graph because the sum of the percents is 100%.**

18.
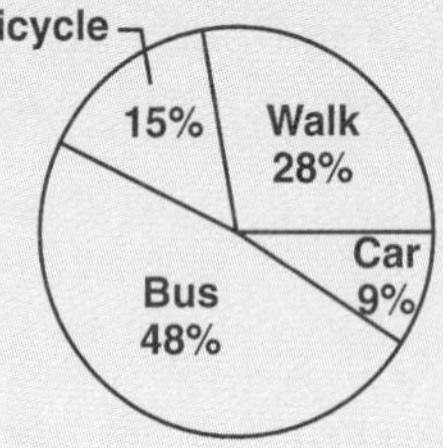

EXERCISES *On Your Own*

1. The age for obtaining a driver's license without a driver's education course varies by state. The circle graph shows the percent of states requiring the indicated minimum ages.
   a. The graph does not tell the total number of states. Do you think the total should be part of the graph? Explain. **See margin.**
   b. What is the most common minimum age for obtaining a license without a driver's education course? How many states require this age? **18 yr; 23 states**

Minimum Driving Ages
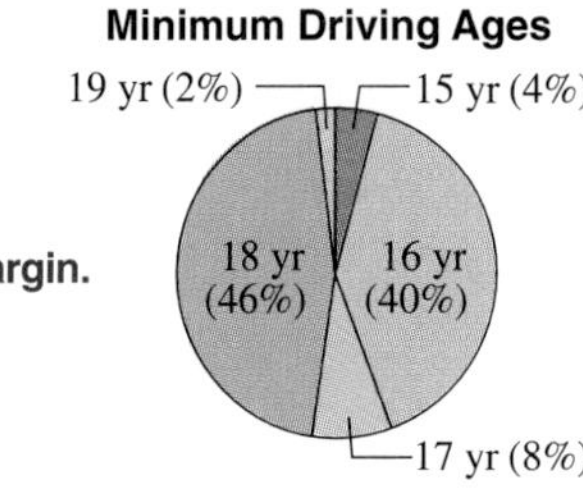

Use the graph at the right for Exercises 2 and 3. In the graph, the angle measure for the portion of the graph that represents 4 people in a vehicle is 20°.

Number of People in Vehicles
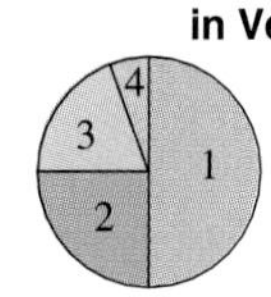

Each digit indicates the number of people in one vehicle.

Total Vehicles: 536

2. What fraction of the circle represents the given number of people in a vehicle?
   a. 1 person $\frac{1}{2}$ b. 2 people $\frac{1}{4}$ c. 3 people $\frac{7}{36}$ d. 4 people $\frac{1}{18}$
3. How many vehicles contained 4 people? Why must you round your answer? **30 vehicles; you can have only a whole number of vehicles.**
4. **Choose A, B, C, or D.** Which circle graph shows 25%, 5%, 40%, and 30%? **C**

A.
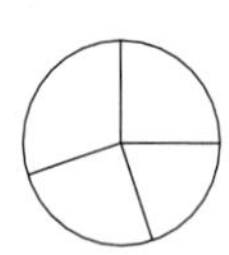
B.
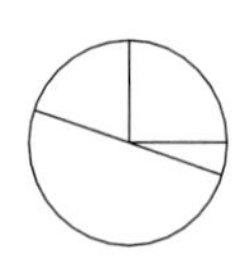
C.
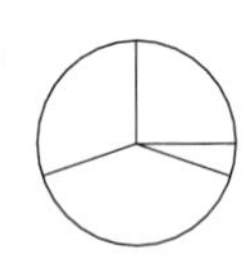
D.
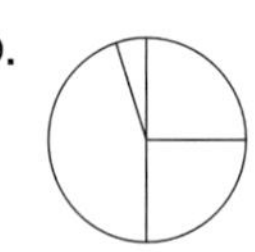

Number Sense **Find the missing measures in each graph.**

5.
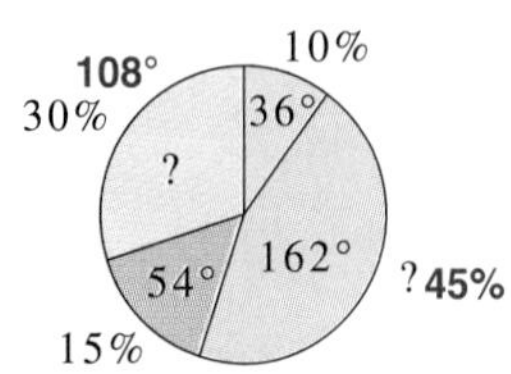

6.
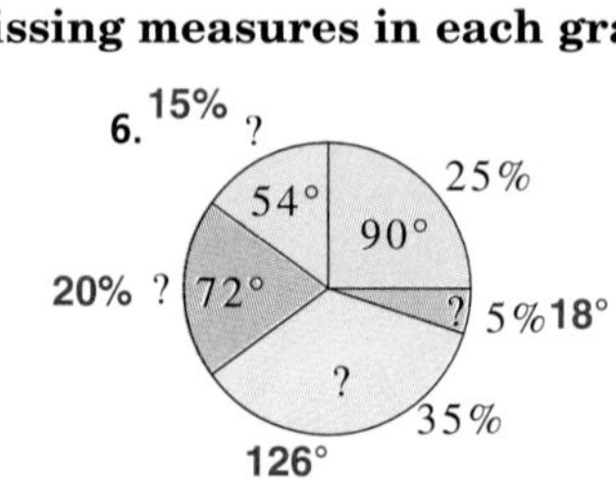

7.
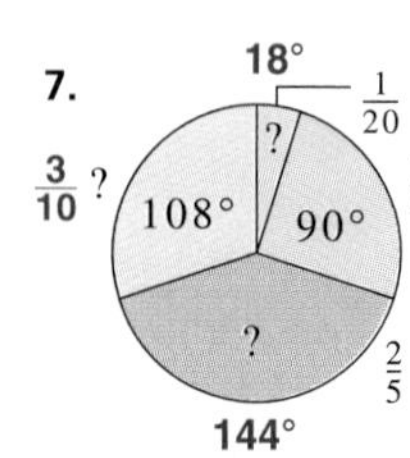

8. *Writing* Suppose you take two surveys asking people what they consider important safety features on a car. In one, people can give more than one safety feature. In the other, they give only the safety feature they consider most important. Which survey results can you show in a circle graph? Why? **See margin.**

EXTENSION Exercise 18 Have students collect data on how their classmates get to school and draw a circle graph to represent the data.

WRAP UP

IDENTIFYING THE BIG IDEA Ask students: *How do you construct a circle graph? Why are circle graphs useful?*

PROJECT LINK Have students recall their research on building design. Ask students to make notes concerning types of materials used for construction. Have students conjecture why builders might select one type of material over another.

LESSON QUIZ

1. The graph shows how one class of 36 students spent their recess. About how many students spent their recess eating a snack? 5

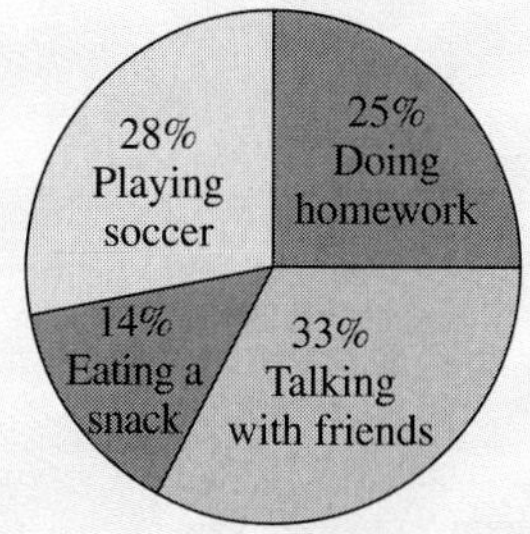

Find the measure of the central angle that you would draw to represent each percent in a circle graph. Round to the nearest degree.

9. 25% 90° 10. 28% 101° 11. 30% 108° 12. 11% 40° 13. 12.5% 45° 14. 14.5% 52°

15. a. The data below show the percent of shoppers who prefer to shop on a specific day of the week. Use the data to draw a circle graph.

Day	Percent	Day	Percent
Monday	4	Friday	17
Tuesday	5	Saturday	29
Wednesday	12	Sunday	7
Thursday	13	No preference	13

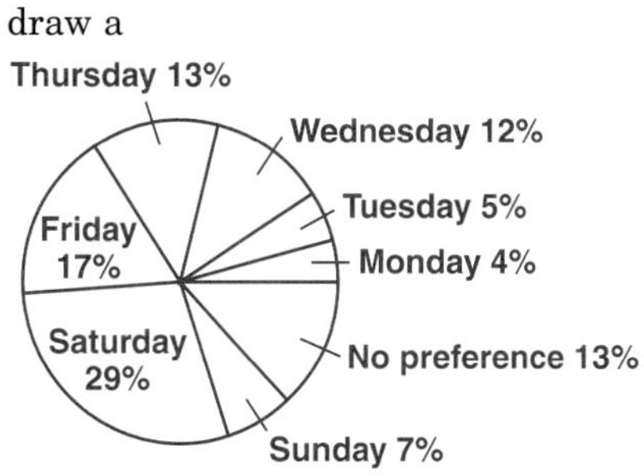

b. If 1,200 people were interviewed for the survey, how many people gave each response? **Monday: 48, Tuesday: 60, Wednesday: 144, Thursday: 156, Friday: 204, Saturday: 348, Sunday: 84, No preference: 156**

16. a. *Research* Find a circle graph in a newspaper or magazine. Use the data in the graph to find the measure of each central angle. **a–b. Check students' work.**

b. Use a protractor to measure the central angles in the graph. Was the graph accurately made? Justify your answer.

17. The Miller family wants to buy a new car. Mr. Miller made a graph of how the family spends their monthly income of $2,400.

a. What percent of the budget is car expenses? $12\frac{1}{2}$%

b. Mr. Miller estimates that payments on a new car will increase their monthly car expenses to $480. What percent of their monthly budget will car expenses be if the Millers buy a new car? **20%**

c. *Reasoning* What changes do you think the Miller family should make in their budget so that they can buy a new car? Make a circle graph that shows the changes you suggest. **Check students' work.**

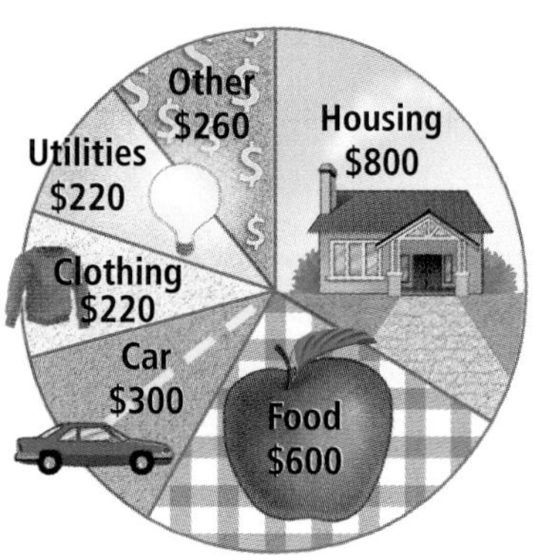

18. Use the data about how a group of students get to school to draw a circle graph. **See margin p. 320.**

Transportation Mode	Walk	Bicycle	Bus	Car
Number of Students	252	135	432	81

CHECKPOINT 2

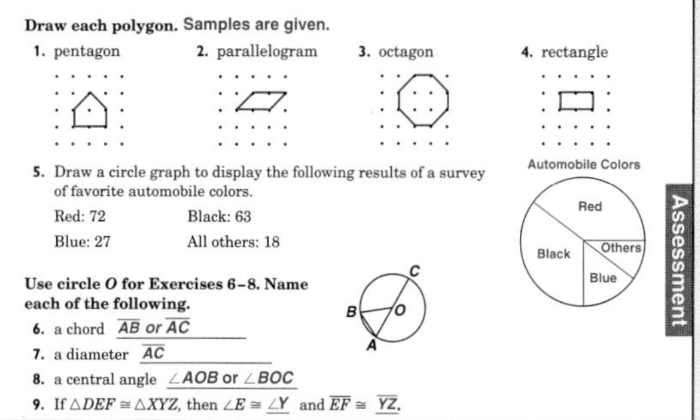

Checkpoint 2 *Lessons 7-4 through 7-8*

Draw each polygon. Samples are given.

1. pentagon 2. parallelogram 3. octagon 4. rectangle

5. Draw a circle graph to display the following results of a survey of favorite automobile colors.

Red: 72 Black: 63
Blue: 27 All others: 18

Use circle *O* for Exercises 6–8. Name each of the following.

6. a chord $\overline{AB}$ or $\overline{AC}$
7. a diameter $\overline{AC}$
8. a central angle ∠AOB or ∠BOC
9. If △DEF ≅ △XYZ, then ∠E ≅ ∠Y and $\overline{EF}$ ≅ $\overline{YZ}$.

Assessment

page 322 Checkpoint 2

1.
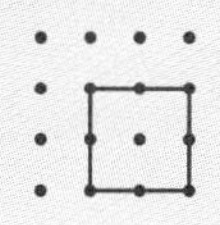
2.
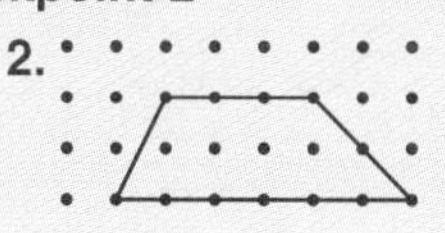
3.
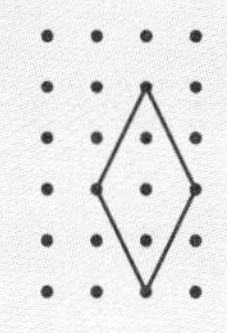
4.
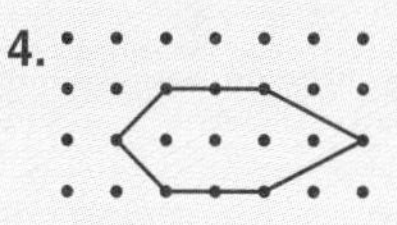
5.
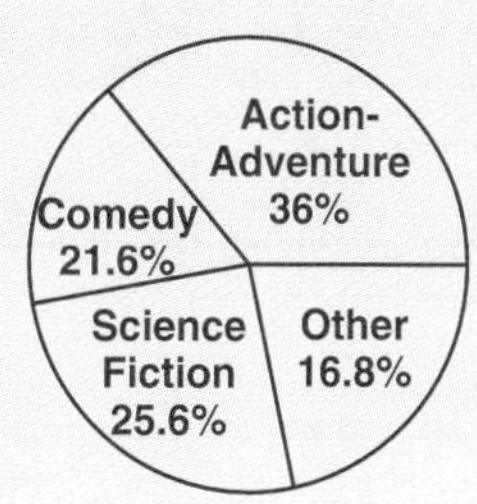

PRACTICE

Practice 7-8 Circle Graphs

Use the data in Exercises 1, 2, and 3 to make circle graphs.

1. The data show the total number of space vehicles that either successfully reached or exceeded orbit around Earth.

Years	Number of Successful Space Launches
1957–1959	21
1960–1969	854
1970–1979	1,162
1980–1988	1,056

Source: *World Almanac and Book of Records*

Successful Space Launches 1957–1988

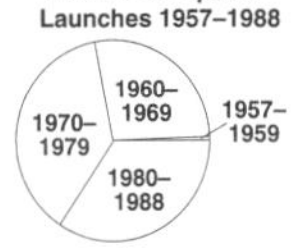

2. The data represent the percent of private schools in the United States that have an annual tuition in each of the given ranges.

Annual Tuition	% of Private Schools
Less than \$500	13
\$500–\$1,000	28
\$1,001–\$1,500	26
\$1,501–\$2,500	15
More than \$2,500	18

Source: *National Center for Education Statistics, U.S. Dept. of Education*

Tuition Categories for Private Schools

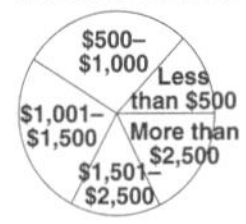

3. The data represent a poll taken in a seventh-grade class.

Favorite Color for a Car	Number of 7th-Graders
Red	14
Blue	9
White	3
Green	1

Car Color Preference of Seventh-Grade Class

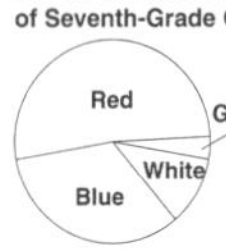

In copymaster and workbook formats

RETEACHING

Reteaching 7-8 Circle Graphs

The class took a survey of what time students usually go to sleep. The results are shown in the table. Use them to make a circle graph.

To make a circle graph:

① Find the total number of students.

② Use a proportion to find the measure of each central angle. Round to the nearest degree.

③ Use a compass. Draw a circle. Use a protractor. Draw the central angles. Label each sector.

Time Students Go to Sleep	Number of Students	② Central Angle Measure
Before 9 P.M.	2	$\frac{2}{28} = \frac{a}{360°}$ $a \approx 26°$
9 P.M.–10 P.M.	3	$\frac{3}{28} = \frac{b}{360°}$ $b \approx 39°$
10 P.M.–11 P.M.	9	$\frac{9}{28} = \frac{c}{360°}$ $c \approx 116°$
After 11 P.M.	14	$\frac{14}{28} = \frac{d}{360°}$ $d \approx 180°$
① Total	28	

Time Students Go to Sleep

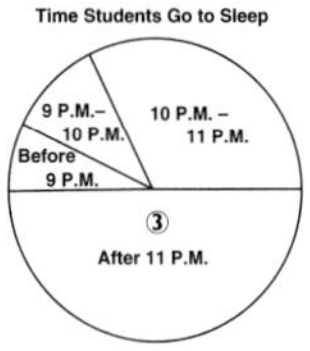

The central angle measures add to 361° because of rounding, but the difference does not show in the graph.

Complete the table. Draw a circle graph of the data.

Tuesday's Music CD Sales

Type of Music	Number of CDs Sold	Central Angle Measure
Country	10	75°
Rock	8	60°
Jazz	16	120°
Rap	14	105°
Total	48	

Tuesday's Music CD Sales

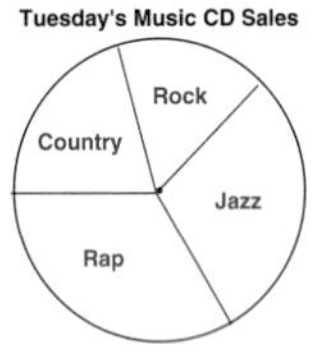

Reteaching

ENRICHMENT

Minds on Math Transparency

7-8

Use 3 segments to divide the equilateral triangle below into 4 congruent triangles.

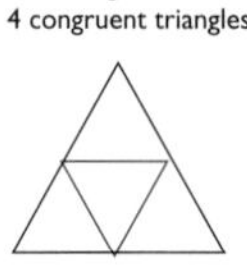

See *Solution Key* for worked-out answers.

2. A class of 72 students voted for a class president. 18 students voted for Maria, 24 students voted for Chan, and 6 students voted for Sara. The rest voted for James. Construct a circle graph to show the student votes.

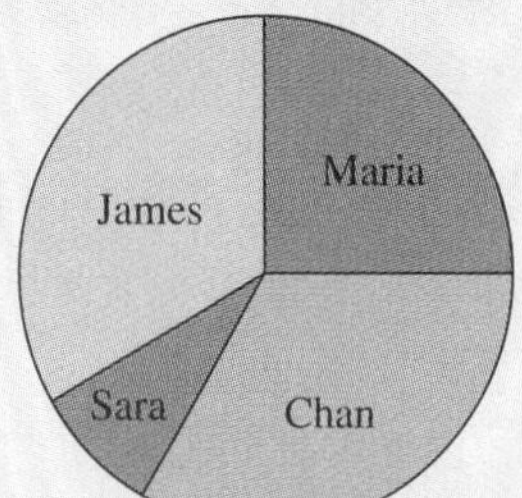

Mixed Review

Write each number as a percent. Round to the nearest tenth of a percent where necessary. *(Lesson 6-7)*

19. 0.07 **7%** **20.** 3.5 **350%** **21.** $\frac{3}{8}$ **37.5%** **22.** $\frac{9}{20}$ **45%** **23.** 0.099 **9.9%** **24.** $\frac{40}{125}$ **32%**

Find each sum or difference. *(Lessons 5-2, 5-3)*

25. $\frac{2}{3} + \frac{3}{8}$ $1\frac{1}{24}$ **26.** $4\frac{1}{6} + 6\frac{2}{9}$ $10\frac{7}{18}$ **27.** $7\frac{3}{4} + \frac{11}{16}$ $8\frac{7}{16}$ **28.** $\frac{7}{8} - \frac{1}{4}$ $\frac{5}{8}$ **29.** $9\frac{7}{10} - 4\frac{3}{5}$ $5\frac{1}{10}$ **30.** $7\frac{1}{8} - 3\frac{1}{6}$ $3\frac{23}{24}$

31. *Raffle Tickets* Melinda bought 9 more tickets than Lorissa. Together they bought 17. How many did each buy? *(Lessons 3-6, 3-8)* **Lorissa, 4 tickets; Melinda, 13 tickets**

CHAPTER PROJECT

PROJECT LINK: MEASURING

Sketch a design of a tower that is at least 4 in. tall. How many toothpicks are needed? Build the tower using glue instead of raisins. Test it by gently placing a baseball on it. If your tower starts to buckle, reinforce it. **Check students' work.**

✓ CHECKPOINT 2

Lessons 7-4 through 7-8

Use dot or graph paper to draw each polygon. **1–4. See margin p. 321.**

1. a square
2. a trapezoid
3. a rhombus
4. a hexagon

5. Draw a circle graph to display the following results of a survey of favorite types of movies. **See margin p. 321.**

   Action-Adventure: 45 Comedy: 27 Science Fiction: 32 Other: 21

6. *Open-ended* Draw, label, and identify a circle, four radii, two diameters, an inscribed quadrilateral, and five chords. **Check students' work.**

7. **Choose A, B, or C.** Which triangle is *not* congruent to $\triangle XYZ$? **C**

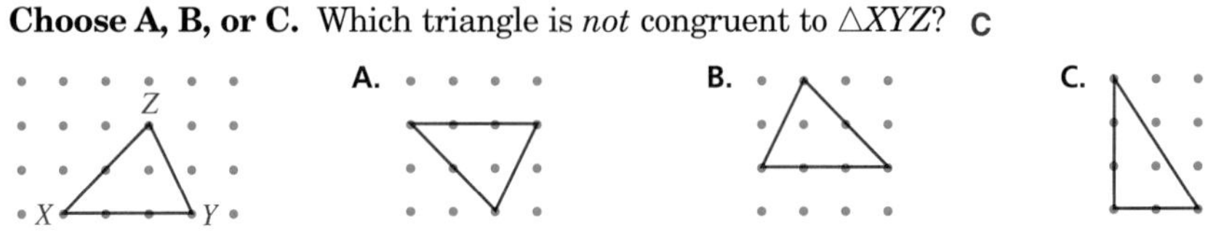

7-9 Teaching Notes

1 Focus

CONNECTING TO PRIOR KNOWLEDGE Have students explain in their own words what they use a compass for. Ask volunteers to explain or demonstrate how they used a compass in earlier lessons.

2 Teach

Work Together

Questions 1 and 2 Assure students that though their individual drawings may vary, the relationships are the same.

THINK AND DISCUSS

KINESTHETIC LEARNING Have students work in groups to find the midpoint of a segment and one of its bisectors. Give each group a piece of string and a yardstick. Two students can find the midpoint of the string by putting the two ends together, and mark the midpoint at the fold with a red pen. Students open the string to its full length and tape it to the floor. Then use a yardstick as a bisector touching the string at the marked midpoint.

ERROR ALERT! Example 1 Students may assume that a bisector of a segment must be perpendicular. This is not true. A bisector may pass through the midpoint at any angle.

7-9 Constructing Bisectors

What You'll Learn

1. To construct the perpendicular bisector of a segment
2. To construct the bisector of an angle

...And Why

Constructions made with only a straightedge and compass have been an important part of geometry since the time of the ancient Greeks.

Here's How

Look for questions that
- build understanding
- ✔ check understanding

Work Together — *Folding Bisectors*

Work with a partner. Draw a segment, $\overline{AB}$, on tracing paper. Fold the paper so that point A lies on point B. Unfold the paper and label the intersection of $\overline{AB}$ and the fold line as point M.

1. ***Analyze*** Compare your result with your partner's.
   a. What is the relationship between $\overline{AM}$ and $\overline{MB}$?
   b. What kind of angles does the fold line make with $\overline{AB}$?
   a. $\overline{AM} \cong \overline{MB}$ b. right angles

Draw an angle, $\angle CDE$, on tracing paper. Fold the paper so that $\overrightarrow{DC}$ lies on $\overrightarrow{DE}$. Unfold the paper. Label any point of the fold line inside $\angle CDE$ as point F. Draw $\overrightarrow{DF}$.

2. ***Analyze*** Compare your result with your partner's. What is the relationship between $\angle CDF$ and $\angle FDE$?
   $\angle CDF \cong \angle FDE$

THINK AND DISCUSS

1 Segment Bisectors

The **midpoint** of a segment is the point that divides a segment into two congruent segments. A **segment bisector** is a line (or segment or ray) that goes through the midpoint of the segment.

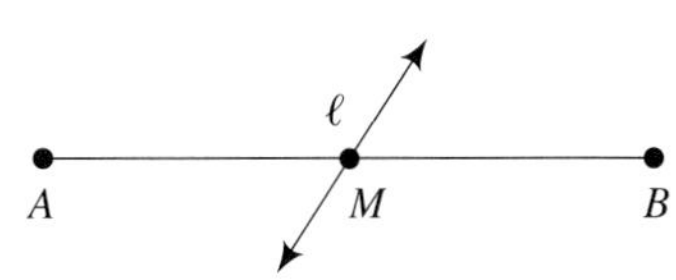

$\overline{AM} \cong \overline{MB}$
M is the midpoint of $\overline{AB}$.
Line ℓ is a segment bisector of $\overline{AB}$.

Perpendicular lines are lines that intersect to form right angles. A line that is perpendicular to a segment at its midpoint is the **perpendicular bisector** of the segment.

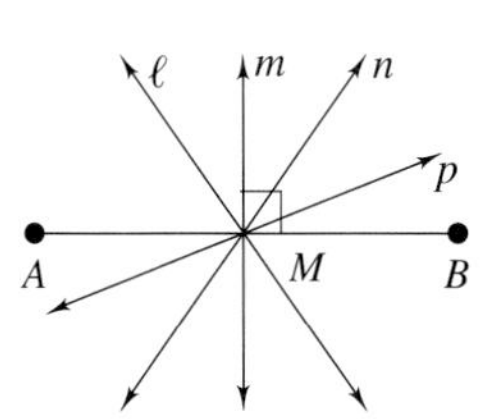

3. In the figure at the left, if M is the midpoint of $\overline{AB}$, which of the segment bisectors is the perpendicular bisector of $\overline{AB}$?
   line m
4. ***Reasoning*** How many bisectors does a segment have?
   infinitely many

Lesson Planning Options

Prerequisite Skill
- drawing with a compass (7-7)

Vocabulary/Symbols
midpoint, segment bisector, perpendicular lines, perpendicular bisector, bisector

Materials/Manipulatives
- straightedge
- compass
- tracing paper
- graph paper

Resources

Student Edition

Skills Handbook, p. 531
Extra Practice, p. 520
Glossary/Study Guide

Teaching Resources

Chapter Support File, Ch. 7
- Lesson Planner 7-9
- Practice 7-9, Reteaching 7-9
- Answer Masters 7-9

Teaching Aids Master 3
Glossary, Spanish Resources

Transparencies
Minds on Math 7-9

Warm Up

Use a calculator to write these fractions to the nearest tenth of a percent.

$\frac{65}{255}$ **25.5%** $\frac{42}{52}$ **80.8%**

Remediation: Have students work in pairs. Direct one student in each pair to hold taut a 20-cm piece of string. Have one student measure to the midpoint at 10 cm, and mark it with a colored dot. The partner uses a ruler to model bisecting the midpoint. Have students discuss why it is possible to find an infinite number of bisectors.

ADDITIONAL EXAMPLES

FOR EXAMPLE 1

Draw $\overline{GH}$ exactly 2 in. long. Construct the perpendicular bisector of $\overline{GH}$, passing through point J. Use a ruler to check that $\overline{GJ}$ and $\overline{JH}$ are both 1 in. long.

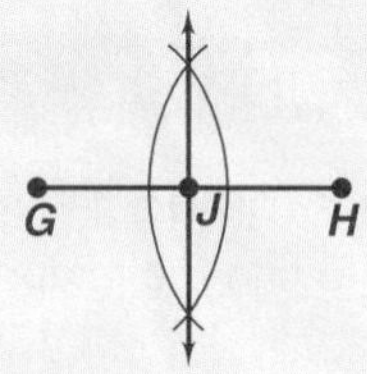

FOR EXAMPLE 2

Draw $\angle C$ with a measure of 50°. Construct the bisector of $\angle C$.

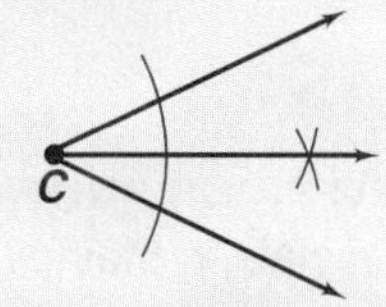

DIVERSITY Have physically challenged students work with a partner. The student can discuss the steps as the partner does the constructions.

Technology Options

Prentice Hall Technology

Software for Learners
- Math Blaster® Mystery*
- Interactive Student Tutorial, Chapter 7*

Teaching Resource Software
- Computer Item Generator 7-9
- Resource Pro™ Chapter 7*

Internet • For related mathematics activities, visit the Prentice Hall site at www.phschool.com/math

**Available on CD-ROM only*

Assignment Options for Exercises On Your Own

To provide flexible scheduling, this lesson can be subdivided into parts.

1 **Core** 1–7, 11
Extension 10

2 **Core** 8, 9, 12–14
Extension 15

Use Mixed Review to maintain skills.

5. Point Z is the midpoint of $\overline{XY}$. **19 mm; 19 mm**
   a. If $\overline{XY}$ is 38 mm long, what is the length of $\overline{XY}$? of $\overline{ZY}$?
   b. If $\overline{XZ}$ is $\frac{3}{4}$ in. long, what is the length of $\overline{ZY}$? of $\overline{XY}$?
   $\frac{3}{4}$ in.; $1\frac{1}{2}$ in.

You can use a compass and *straightedge* (an unmarked ruler) to construct the perpendicular bisector of a given segment.

HISTORY This 1482 edition of Euclid's *Elements of Geometry* was the first math book printed on a printing press.

Source: Wellesley College Library, Special Collections

EXAMPLE 1

Use a compass and straightedge to construct the perpendicular bisector of $\overline{AB}$.

Step 1

Open the compass to more than half the length of $\overline{AB}$. Put the tip of the compass at A and draw an arc intersecting $\overline{AB}$.

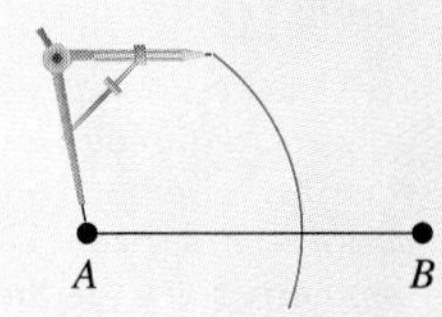

Step 2

Keeping the compass open to the same width, put the tip at B and draw another arc intersecting $\overline{AB}$. Label the points of intersection of the arcs as C and D.

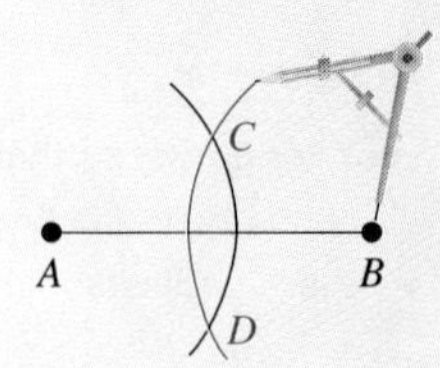

Step 3

Draw $\overleftrightarrow{CD}$. Label the intersection of $\overline{AB}$ and $\overleftrightarrow{CD}$ as point M.

$\overleftrightarrow{CD}$ is the perpendicular bisector of $\overline{AB}$. Point M is the midpoint of $\overline{AB}$.

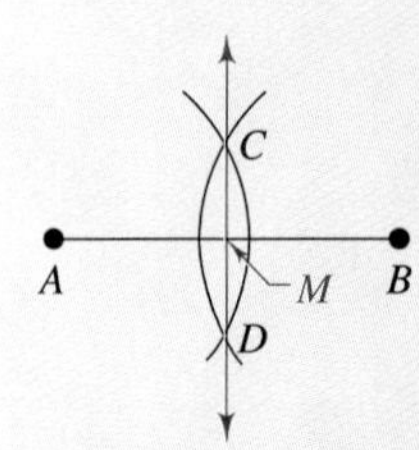

6.

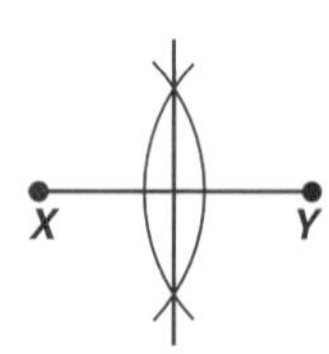

7a. No, a segment has only one midpoint and at that point there is only one line perpendicular to the segment.

6. ✔ *Try It Out* Draw $\overline{XY}$. Construct the perpendicular bisector of $\overline{XY}$.

7. a. *Think About It* Could you construct a different perpendicular bisector of $\overline{XY}$ in Question 6? Explain.
   b. How many perpendicular bisectors does a segment have?
   one

Now you may assign Exercises 1–7, 10–11.

ASSESSMENT Tell students: *Ray RT bisects ∠QRS and m∠QRT = 45°. Then ask: What is m∠TRS? m∠QRS? Describe ∠QRS.* **45°; 90°; right angle**

3 Practice/Assess

EXERCISES *On Your Own*

WRITING Exercise 14 Have students draw and label several examples of each type of bisector. Ask students to explain when there can be more than one bisector.

WRAP UP

IDENTIFYING THE BIG IDEA Ask: *How do you construct the perpendicular bisector of a segment? How do you bisect an angle?*

PORTFOLIO Share with students the criteria you will use to assess their work in portfolios, as well as how you plan to use the results. Students should understand how the rubrics are used to assess their work, how each piece in the portfolio counts, and how the scores they get in their portfolios will affect their overall evaluation.

2 Angle Bisectors

The **bisector** of an angle is the ray that divides the angle into two congruent angles.

EXAMPLE 2

Use a compass and straightedge to construct the angle bisector of ∠*P*.

Step 1

Put the tip of the compass at *P* and draw an arc that intersects the sides of ∠*P*. Label the points of intersection as *S* and *T*.

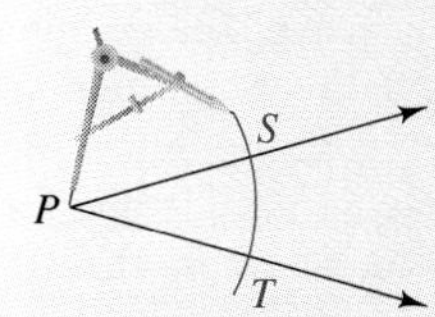

Step 2

With the compass tip at *S* and then at *T*, and with the same compass opening, draw intersecting arcs. Label the point where they intersect as *X*.

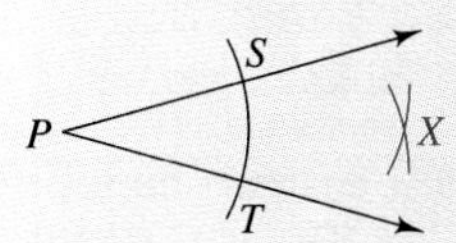

Step 3

Draw $\overrightarrow{PX}$.

$\overrightarrow{PX}$ is the bisector of ∠*SPT*.

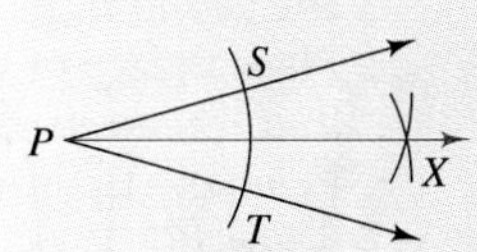

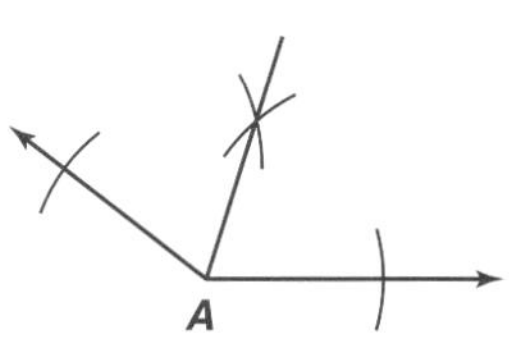

8. ✔ *Try It Out* Draw an obtuse angle. Construct its bisector.

Now you may assign Exercises 8–9, 12–15.

EXERCISES *On Your Own*

Point *B* is the midpoint of $\overline{AC}$. Complete.

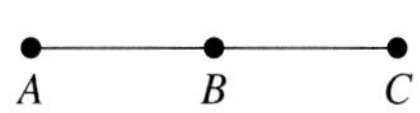

1. $AB = 4$ in., $AC =$ ■ **8 in.**
2. $AC = 9$ cm, $AB =$ ■ **4.5 cm**
3. $BC = 5$ ft, $AB =$ ■ **5 ft**
4. $AB = 17$ mm, $AC =$ ■ **34 mm**
5. $AC = 3$ in., $BC =$ ■ **$1\frac{1}{2}$ in.**
6. $BC = 75$ cm, $AC =$ ■ **150 cm**
7. Draw a segment. Then construct its perpendicular bisector.
8. Draw an acute angle. Then construct its angle bisector.
9. The bisector of ∠*JKL* is $\overrightarrow{KN}$. If the measure of ∠*JKN* is 66°, what is the measure of ∠*JKL*? **132°**

7.

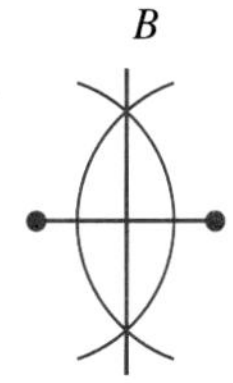

8.

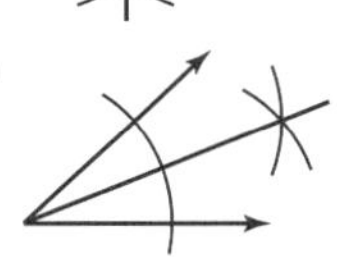

page 325–326 On Your Own

11.

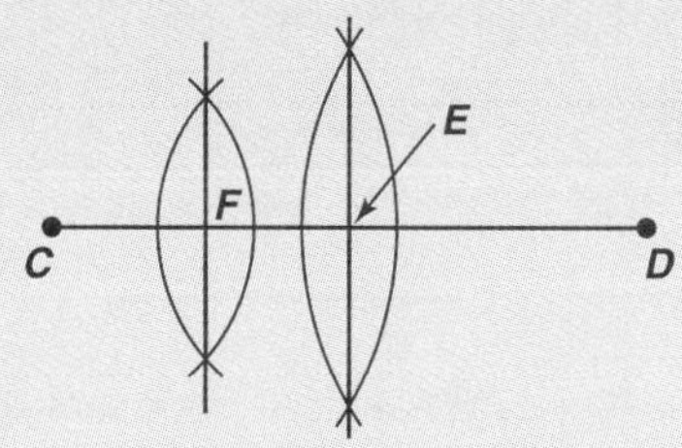

12.

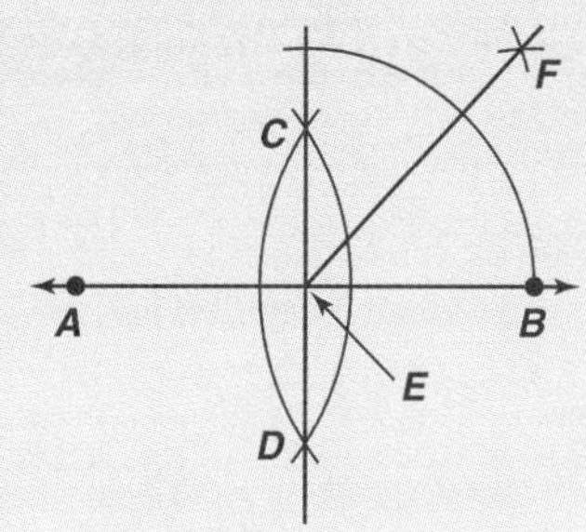

a. **∠AEC, ∠AED, ∠BEC, and ∠BED are all 90° angles.**

b. **∠CEF and ∠BEF are 45° angles.**

13.

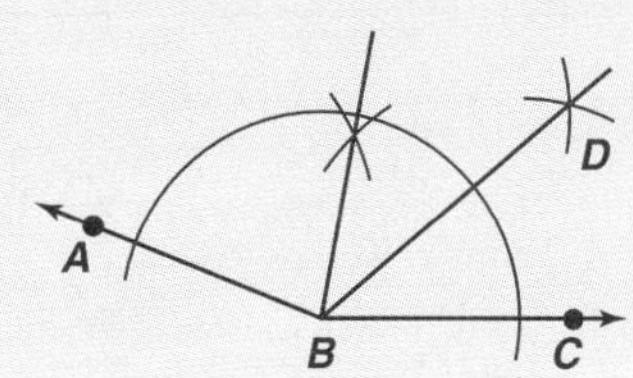

a. **m∠CBD = $\frac{1}{4}$ m∠ABC**

b. **m∠ABD = $\frac{3}{4}$ m∠ABC**

pages 325–326 On Your Own

15a–d.

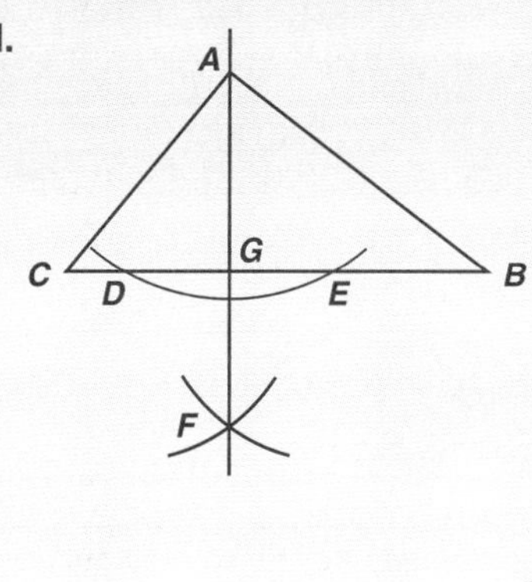

PRACTICE

Practice 7-9 *Constructing Bisectors*

Construct the perpendicular bisector of each segment. See students' constructions.

1.

2.

Construct the bisector of each angle. See students' constructions.

3.

4.

5. Construct a segment with measure $\frac{3}{4}$ that of $\overline{AB}$. See students' constructions.

6. Construct an angle with measure $\frac{1}{4}$ times that of $\angle MNO$. See students' constructions.

7. Draw an obtuse angle, $\angle RST$. Then construct and label its bisector $\overrightarrow{SV}$. See students' constructions.

8. Draw an acute angle, $\angle MAT$. Then construct and label its bisector $\overrightarrow{AH}$. See students' constructions.

9. **Circle A, B, C, or D.** $\overline{AD}$ bisects $\overline{BC}$ but does not bisect $\angle A$. Which of the following must be true?
   I. $\triangle ABD \cong \triangle ACD$ II. $\overline{AB} \cong \overline{AC}$
   III. $\angle BDA \cong \angle CDA$ IV. $\overline{BD} \cong \overline{CD}$
   A. I and IV B. I, II, IV
   C. I and II (D.) IV

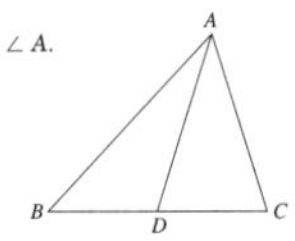

10. Each square represents one acre of a farm. Draw 11 sections of fence along the dotted lines shown, so that four fields are formed, each containing four acres of land.

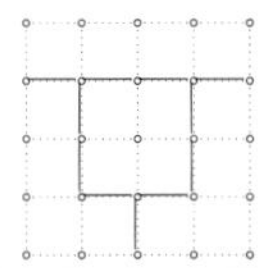

Practice

In copymaster and workbook formats

RETEACHING

Reteaching 7-9 *Constructing Bisectors*

To bisect $\overline{AB}$:

① Open the compass more than half the length of $\overline{AB}$. With the compass tip on A, draw an arc.

② Without changing the opening, move the compass tip to B. Draw another arc.

③ Draw $\overleftrightarrow{CD}$ through the intersections of the arcs. $\overleftrightarrow{CD}$ is the bisector of $\overline{AB}$. Point M is the midpoint of $\overline{AB}$.

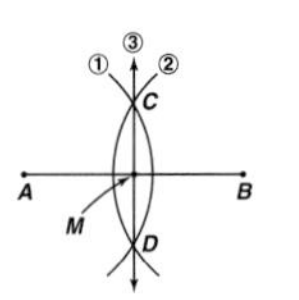

To bisect $\angle ABC$:

① Place the compass point on vertex B. Draw an arc intersecting the sides of the angle at points P and M.

② Place the compass tip on point M. Draw an arc in the interior of the angle. Keep the opening the same and place the compass tip on point P. Draw a second arc intersecting the first at point Q.

③ Draw $\overrightarrow{BQ}$. $\overrightarrow{BQ}$ is the bisector of $\angle ABC$.

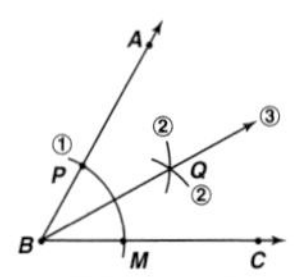

Complete each construction to bisect the figure.

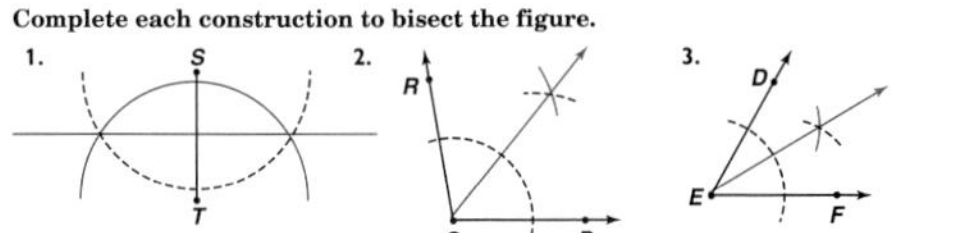

1. Bisect $\overline{ST}$. 2. Bisect $\angle RQP$. 3. Bisect $\angle DEF$.

Bisect each figure.

4. 5. 6.

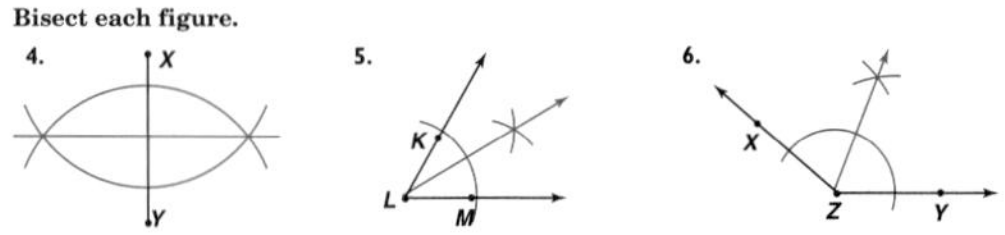

ENRICHMENT

Minds on Math Transparency

7-9

How would you divide the figure below into two congruent parts?

See *Solution Key* for worked-out answers.

LESSON QUIZ

1. Draw $\overline{EK}$ exactly 3.5 in. long. Construct the perpendicular bisector of $\overline{EK}$, passing through point L. Use a ruler to check that $\overline{EL}$ and $\overline{LK}$ are both 1.75 in. long.

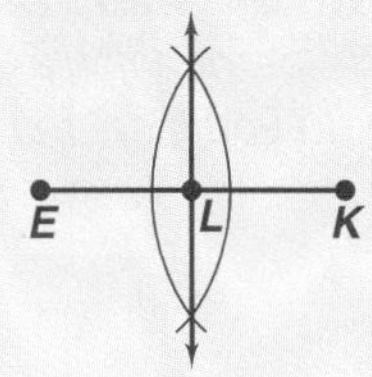

2. Draw $\angle Z$ with a measure of 75°. Construct the bisector of $\angle Z$.

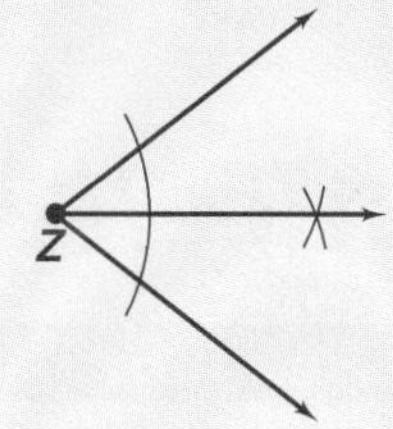

10. Point A is the midpoint of $\overline{XY}$. Point Y is the midpoint of $\overline{XZ}$. Point Z is the midpoint of $\overline{AB}$. If $\overline{XA}$ is 2 cm long, how long is $\overline{XB}$? (*Hint:* Draw a diagram.) **14 cm**

11. Draw $\overline{CD}$ at least 3 in. long. Then construct and label the following. **See margin p. 325 for diagram.**
    a. a segment half as long as $\overline{CD}$ **$\overline{CE}$ and $\overline{ED}$ are half as long as $\overline{CD}$.**
    b. a segment one fourth as long as $\overline{CD}$ **$\overline{CF}$ and $\overline{FE}$ are $\frac{1}{4}$ as long as $\overline{CD}$.**

12. a. Construct a 90° angle.
    b. Construct a 45° angle.
    a–b. See margin p. 325.

13. Draw an obtuse angle, $\angle ABC$. Then construct and label the following two angles.
    a. an angle one fourth the measure of $\angle ABC$
    b. an angle three fourths the measure of $\angle ABC$
    a–b. See margin p. 325.

14. *Writing* How are a segment bisector and an angle bisector alike? **They divide a figure into two congruent parts that measure $\frac{1}{2}$ the original figure.**

15. Construct an altitude of a triangle by following these steps.
    a. Draw a triangle about 2 in. high that is shaped like the one at the right.
    b. Place the tip of your compass on point A and draw an arc that intersects $\overline{BC}$ in two points. Label the points D and E.
    c. Place the tip of your compass on point D and draw an arc below $\overline{BC}$. Do the same from point E keeping the same compass setting.
    d. Label the intersection of the two arcs F. Draw $\overleftrightarrow{AF}$. Label the intersection of $\overleftrightarrow{AF}$ and $\overline{BC}$ as G. $\overline{AG}$ is an altitude of $\triangle ABC$.
    a–d. See margin p. 325.

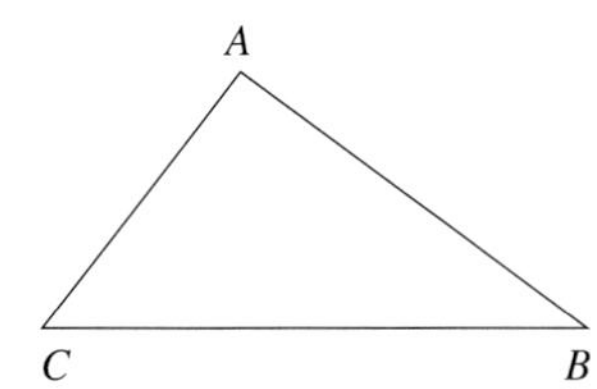

PORTFOLIO

Select one or two items from your work for this chapter. Consider:
- cooperative work
- work that shows the most surprising thing you learned
- part of your project

Explain why you included each selection.

Mixed Review

Draw figures on 10 × 10 squares of graph paper to represent each of the following percents. (Lesson 6-6)

16. 150% 17. 98% 18. 310% 19. 75% 20. 27%

16–17. See margin p. 327. 18. See back of book. 19–20. See margin p. 328.

21. *Entertainment* Terick listens to the radio for two and a half hours every day after school. How many hours does he listen to the radio each week? (Lesson 5-5) **$12\frac{1}{2}$ h**

Extra Practice, Lesson 7-9, page 520

MATH TOOLBOX

ı Lesson 7-9, you learned to construct isectors of segments and angles. In this ɔolbox you will learn to construct congruent ıngles and parallel lines.

ERROR ALERT! Question 3b Students sometimes place the tip of the compass back at point *B*. **Remediation:** Have students use highlighters, markers, colored pencils, or crayons to mark corresponding parts with the same colors. For example, have students mark points *D*, *A*, and *C* with three different colors. When their matching points are constructed, students should mark each with the matching color.

ASSESSMENT Group students in pairs. Each student uses a straightedge to draw an angle on a sheet of typing paper. The partners trade angles and contract new congruent angles. Then students construct parallel lines. To check the lines, they may put notebook paper behind their paper and see if the lines on the paper are parallel to the ones they drew.

EXPLORATION

ATH OLBOX

Constructing Congruent Angles and Parallel Lines

After Lesson 7-9

You can use a compass and straightedge to construct an angle congruent to a given angle. **1–5. Check students' work.**

1. Draw an angle like $\angle A$ at the right. Also draw ray ℓ with endpoint B.

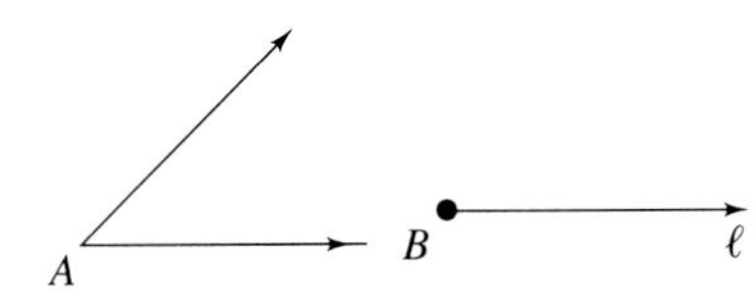

2. a. Place the tip of the compass at A. Make an arc that intersects the sides of $\angle A$. Label the points of intersection as C and D.
   b. With the same compass opening, place the tip of the compass at B and draw an arc that intersects ℓ at E.

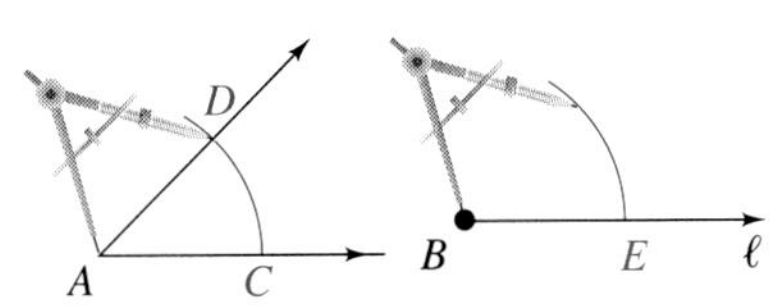

3. a. Change the compass opening to the length from C to D.
   b. Using this compass opening, place the tip of the compass at E. Draw an arc to determine point F.

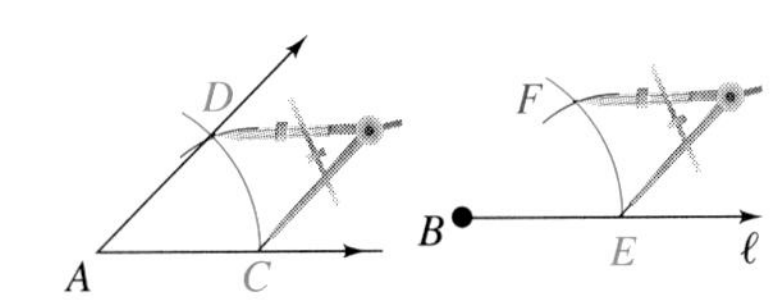

4. Draw $\overrightarrow{BF}$. $\angle DAC \cong \angle FBE$.

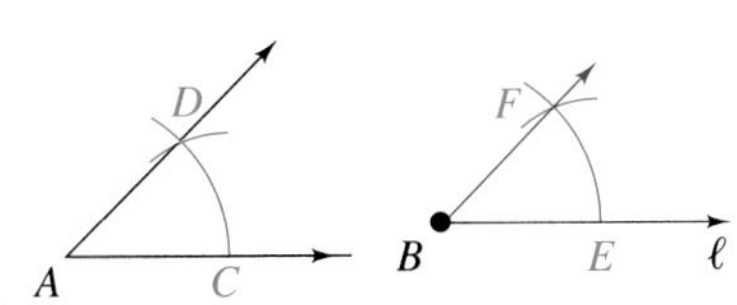

When a line intersects two parallel lines, congruent angles are formed. In the diagram at the right $\angle 1 \cong \angle 2$. Now you can apply your ability to construct congruent angles to construct parallel lines.

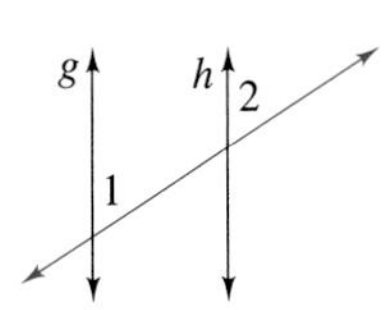

Line *g* is parallel to line *h*.

5. a. To construct a line parallel to m, first draw line n that intersects m at A as shown at the right. Then label point B on n.
   b. Follow the instructions for Questions 2 and 3 above to copy $\angle 1$ at B.
   c. Draw $\overleftrightarrow{BF}$. $\overleftrightarrow{BF}$ is parallel to m.

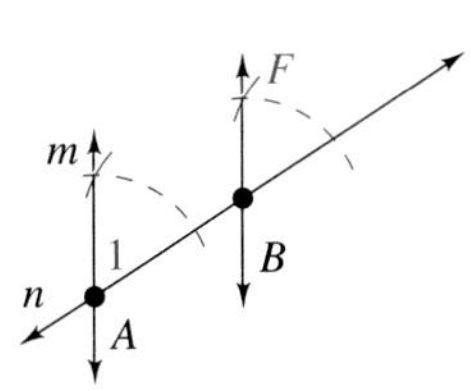

page 326 Mixed Review

16.

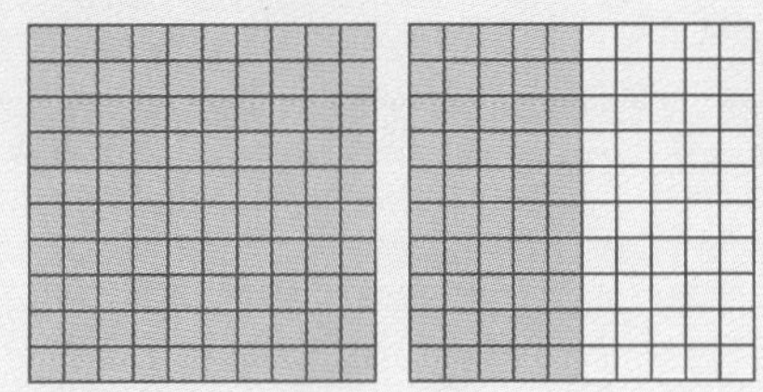

17.

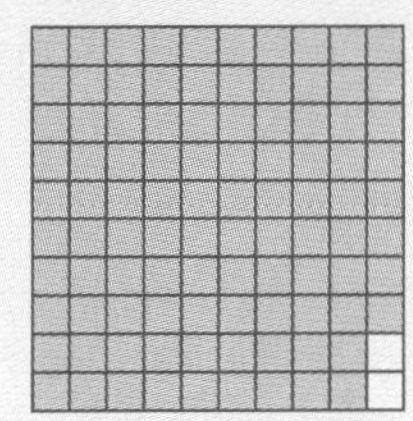

18.

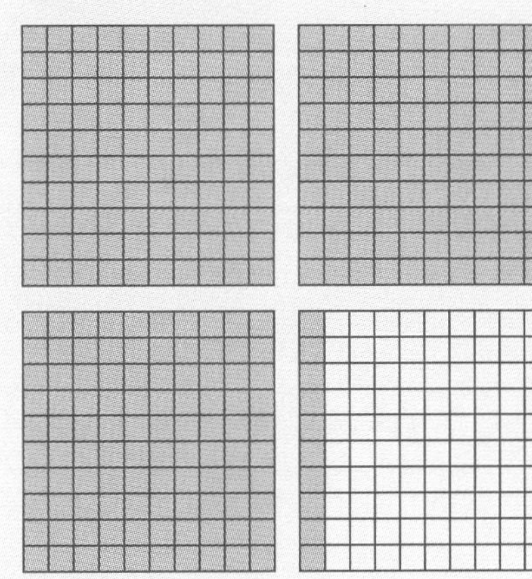

page 326 Mixed Review

19.

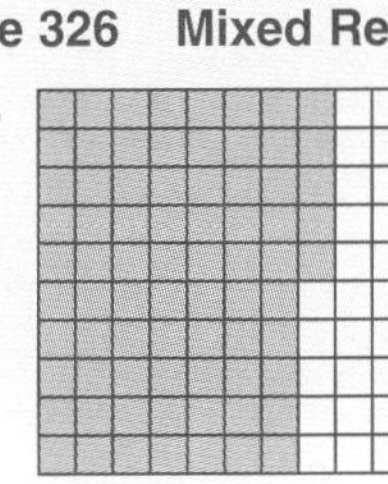

20.

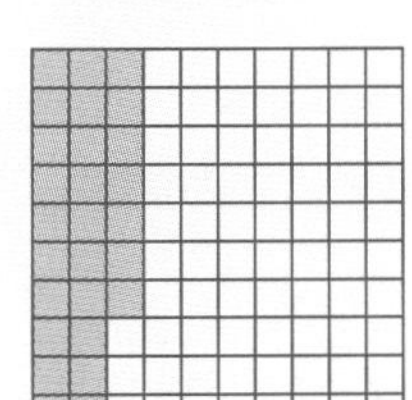

PROBLEM SOLVING PRACTICE ★★

This page provides problems for students to solve using their knowledge of similar figures, solving equations, simplifying expressions, ratios, and percents. Allow students to use any method they find helpful.

Exercise 1 Have students explain the reasons for their answers.

Exercise 5 Encourage students to write the ratio in simplest form for each choice before selecting an answer.

Exercises 6 and 7 If students choose *Not Here* as their answer for either exercise, ask students to supply the correct answer.

PROBLEM SOLVING PRACTICE ★★★★★

Read each question and choose the best answer.

1. Which best represents a pair of similar figures? B

A. 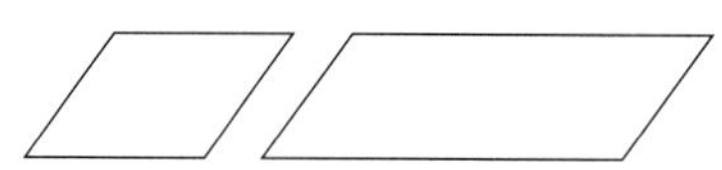

B. 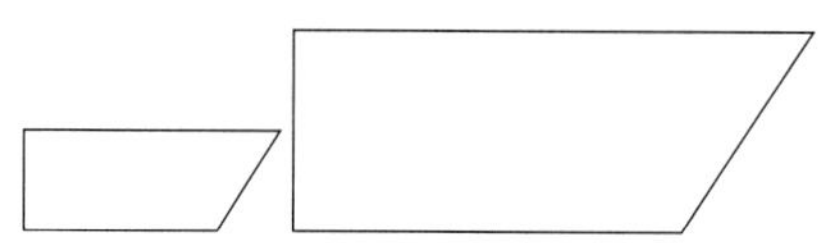

C. 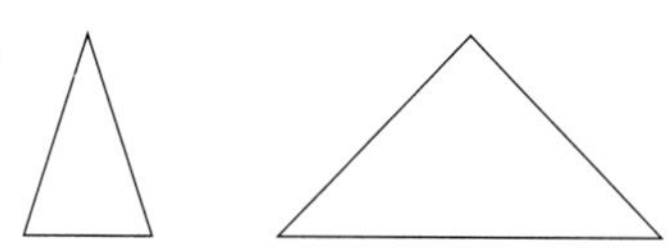

D. 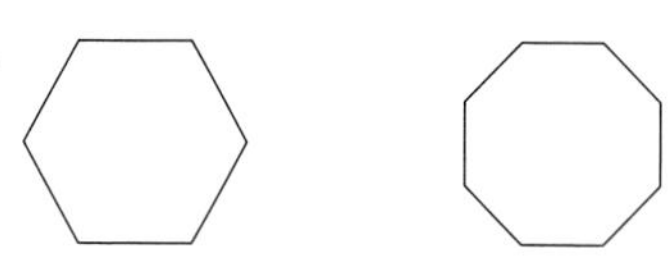

2. If $15c = 40$, what is the value of c? H

F. $2\frac{1}{3}$
G. $2\frac{1}{2}$
H. $2\frac{2}{3}$
J. 3

3. During registration, 40% of the 500 students at Grove Middle School chose to take a foreign language. What fraction of the students are taking foreign language? C

A. $\frac{3}{10}$
B. $\frac{1}{3}$
C. $\frac{2}{5}$
D. $\frac{3}{5}$

4. Which expression is equivalent to $2\frac{1}{5} \times 1\frac{1}{8} + 3\frac{1}{4}$? J

F. $2\frac{1}{5} \times (1\frac{1}{8} + 3\frac{1}{4})$
G. $1\frac{1}{8} \times 3\frac{1}{4} \times 2\frac{1}{5}$
H. $2\frac{1}{5} \times 3\frac{1}{4} + 1\frac{1}{8}$
J. $3\frac{1}{4} + 2\frac{1}{5} \times 1\frac{1}{8}$

5. If the ratio of dogs to cats at a pet store is exactly 4 to 1, then the pet store could have— C

A. 15 dogs and 3 cats
B. 18 dogs and 3 cats
C. 20 dogs and 5 cats
D. 12 cats and 4 dogs

Please note that items 6 and 7 have *five* answer choices.

6. A Fahrenheit temperature can be converted to a Celsius temperature by using the formula

$$C = \frac{5}{9}(F - 32),$$

where C is the Celsius temperature and F is the Fahrenheit temperature. The temperature on a summer day reached 104 degrees Fahrenheit. What is this temperature in degrees Celsius? K

F. 32 degrees Celsius
G. 140 degrees Celsius
H. 72 degrees Celsius
J. 76 degrees Celsius
K. Not Here

7. For an art project, a class is going to create a mural that contains an enlargement of this smaller drawing. If the building in the mural is 60 in. tall, what is its width? A

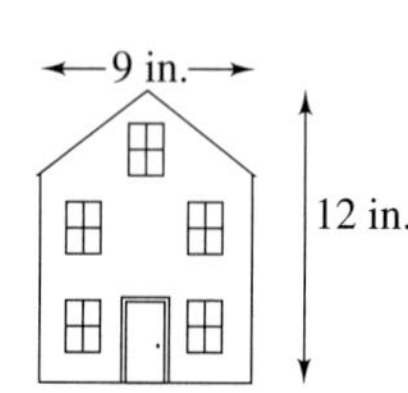

A. 45 in.
B. 48 in.
C. 57 in.
D. 72 in.
E. Not Here

FINISHING THE CHAPTER PROJECT

PROJECT DAY You may wish to plan a project day on which students share their completed projects. Encourage students to explain their process as well as their product.

PROJECT NOTEBOOK Ask students to review their project work and bring their notebooks up to date.

Have students review their methods for designing, building, testing, and improving their towers for the project.

SCORING RUBRIC

3 You provide several sample pictures showing the use of triangles in construction. You draw and describe how you strengthened your toothpick-and-raisin constructions. You sketch and build a tower that is at least four inches tall and can support a baseball. Your explanations, drawings, and construction are neat and clean.

2 You provide a picture showing triangles in construction. You explain how you strengthened your toothpick-and-raisin constructions, and you build a tower that is at least four inches tall and can support a baseball.

1 You build a tower but you don't provide any evidence that you tested toothpick-and-raisin constructions beforehand.

0 Your preliminary tests and your tower are incomplete or missing.

FINISHING THE CHAPTER PROJECT

CHAPTER PROJECT

Raisin' the Roof

Build a Tower The Project Link questions on pages 295, 304, 312, and 322 should help you complete your project. Here is a checklist to help you gather together the parts of your project.

- ✔ pictures of structures built using triangles
- ✔ your description of how to strengthen a square
- ✔ your description of how to strengthen a cube
- ✔ your sketch for the design of a tower
- ✔ your completed tower

Try to make your tower attractive as well as strong. Demonstrate to the class that your tower will support a baseball.

Reflect and Revise
Show your tower to a friend, and discuss its design. Demonstrate its strength. Can you use fewer toothpicks without losing strength? If necessary, revise the design.

Internet Connection

Web Extension
Prentice Hall's Internet site contains information you might find helpful as you complete your project. Visit www.phschool.com/mgm2/ch7 for some links and ideas related to construction and architecture.

Materials/Manipulatives

- toothpick towers
- baseball

STUDENT SELF-ASSESSMENT SURVEY

Chapter 7 Student Self-Assessment

1. Now that you have finished this chapter, think about what you have learned about geometry. Check each topic that you feel confident you understand.
   - ______ continue visual patterns (7-1)
   - ______ work with complementary, supplementary, vertical, and adjacent angles (7-2)
   - ______ classify triangles by sides and by angles (7-3)
   - ______ work with the measures of the angles of a triangle (7-3)
   - ______ solve problems by drawing a diagram (7-4)
   - ______ work with congruent triangles (7-5)
   - ______ work with polygons, including special quadrilaterals (7-6)
   - ______ identify parts of circles and work with inscribed quadrilaterals (7-7)
   - ______ analyze and construct circle graphs (7-8)
   - ______ construct perpendicular bisectors of segments and angles (7-9)
2. Before the Chapter Assessment, I need to review ______
3. a. Check one. In general, I thought this chapter was ___ a snap ___ easy ___ average ___ hard ___ a monster
   b. Why do you feel this way? ______
4. In this chapter, I did my best work on ______
5. In this chapter, I had trouble with ______
6. Check each one that applies. Now that I've spent some time studying geometric figures, I think they are ___ important ___ boring ___ useful ___ fun ___ a waste of time ___ confusing ___ tricky ___ interesting
7. One place outside the classroom where people use geometry is ______
8. In this chapter, you drew diagrams to help you solve problems. Did you find this strategy helpful? Explain. ______

Assessment

Vocabulary/Symbols

adjacent angles, angle, arc, bisector, center, central angle, chord, circle, circle graphs, compass, complementary, congruent (≅), congruent polygons, corresponding parts, diagonals, diameter, endpoints, inscribed polygon, midpoint, parallel, parallelogram, perpendicular bisector, perpendicular lines, polygon, quadrilaterals, radius, rectangle, regular polygon, rhombus, sectors, segment bisector, semicircle, square, straightedge, supplementary, trapezoid, vertex, vertical angles

Materials/Manipulatives

- protractor
- straight edge
- compass
- dot paper

Resources

Student Edition

Extra Practice, p. 520
Glossary/Study Guide

Teaching Resources

Chapter Support file, Ch. 7
- Student Self-Assessment Survey, Glossary, Spanish Resources

Tools for Studying Smarter

WRAP UP

ASSESSMENT **Exercise 1** Have students draw the next two figures for the pattern. Then exchange drawings with a partner to check their work.

Exercise 4 Challenge students to name *all* pairs of adjacent angles in the figure. Then compare with a partner to make sure their list is complete.

Exercise 8 Suggest students draw a triangle and try various measurements before answering.

ASSESSMENT **Exercises 11–13** Students choose a figure and write a description of its essential characteristics. **Answers may vary. Sample answer: trapezoid; exactly four sides, only two sides parallel**

7 WRAP UP

Exploring Patterns 7-1

1. Draw the next figure for the pattern at the right.

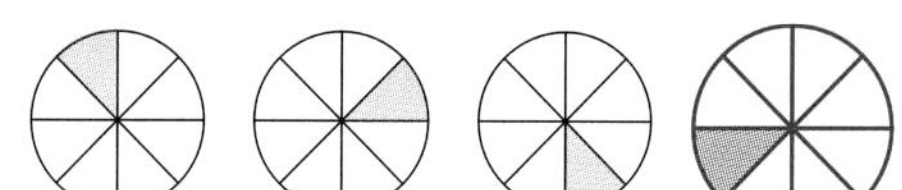

Angles and Triangles 7-2, 7-3, 7-5

An **angle** is made up of two rays with a common endpoint. You can classify angles according to their measures.

You can classify triangles by the number of congruent sides or by the measures of the angles. The sum of the measures of the angles of a triangle is 180°.

The corresponding angles and sides of **congruent triangles** are congruent.

Name a pair of angles in the figure at the right for each of the following.

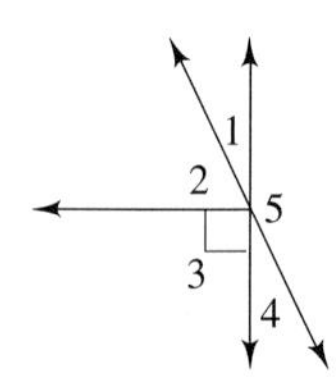

2. vertical angles **∠1, ∠4**
3. complementary angles **∠1, ∠2**
4. adjacent angles **Answers may vary. Sample: ∠2, ∠3**
5. supplementary angles **Answers may vary. Sample: ∠1, ∠5**
6. If $m\angle D = 67°$, what is the measure of a complementary angle? Of a supplementary angle? **23°; 113°**

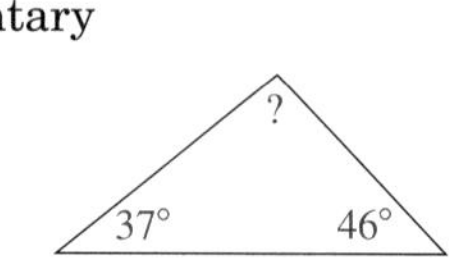

7. a. Find the missing angle measure. **97°**
   b. Classify the triangle by its angles. **obtuse**
8. **Choose A, B, C, or D.** In $\triangle DEF$, the measure of $\angle D$ is twice the measure of $\angle E$. Which words might describe $\triangle DEF$? **D**
   I. acute II. obtuse III. right
   A. I or II B. I or III C. II or III D. I, II, or III
9. $\triangle UVW \cong \triangle YXZ$. Write six congruence statements involving corresponding angles and sides.
   $\overline{UV} \cong \overline{YX}$, $\overline{VW} \cong \overline{XZ}$, $\overline{UW} \cong \overline{YZ}$, $\angle U \cong \angle Y$, $\angle V \cong \angle X$, $\angle W \cong \angle Z$

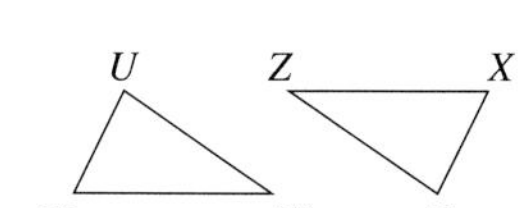

10. Is it reasonable to use the measure of the largest angle of a triangle to classify the triangle by its angle measures? Explain. **Yes, if the largest angle is obtuse, the triangle is obtuse. If the largest angle is a right angle, the triangle is a right triangle. If the largest angle is acute, the triangle is acute.**

WRITING Exercise 19 Ask students to make a rough sketch of their circle graphs.

ASSESSMENT Exercises 20 and 21 Students can check their constructions by measuring the angles with a protractor and the segments with a ruler.

Remind students that the new mathematical terms in this chapter are defined in the Glossary/Study Guide in the back of the book.

CHAPTER ASSESSMENT • FORM A

Chapter 7 Assessment • Form A

Answers

1. Draw the next figure for the pattern below.

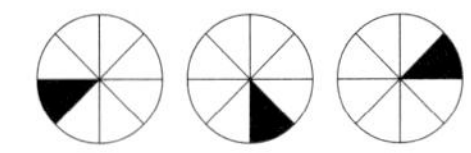

1. 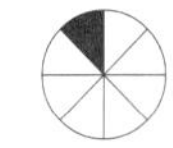

2. If the measure of an angle is 70°, what is the measure of its supplementary angle? — 2. 110°

3. What type of angle measures greater than 90° and less than 180°? — 3. obtuse

4. Name one pair of vertical angles in this figure. — 4. ∠1 and ∠3 or ∠2 and ∠4

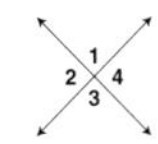

5. ∠X and ∠Y are complementary. If $m\angle X = 23°$, what is $m\angle Y$? — 5. 67°

6. What is the measure of each angle in a right isosceles triangle? — 6. 45°, 45°, 90°

7. In △ABC, $m\angle A = 30°$ and $m\angle B = 75°$. What is the measure of ∠C? — 7. 75°

8. Measure the sides of △DEF and then classify it. — 8. equilateral

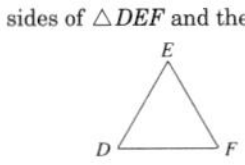

9. Name the congruent sides of △DEF above. — 9. $\overline{DE}$, $\overline{EF}$, $\overline{FD}$

10. △ABC ≅ △ZYX. Find the measure of $\overline{AB}$. — 10. 4

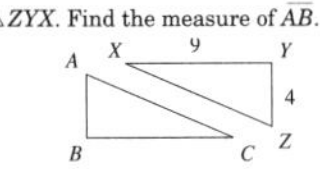

Assessment

Problem Solving Strategies

Diagrams help you see the relationships described in a problem.

11. △ABC is an isosceles triangle. If $m\angle A = 32°$, find the possible measures of the other two angles of the triangle.
32° and 116°, 74° and 74°

Polygons and Circles — 7-6, 7-7, 7-8

All sides and all angles of a **regular polygon** are congruent.

Trapezoids, parallelograms, rhombuses, rectangles, and **squares** are special **quadrilaterals.**

A **circle** is the set of points in a plane that are all the same distance from a point called the *center*. **Circle graphs** present data as percents or fractions of a total.

12. 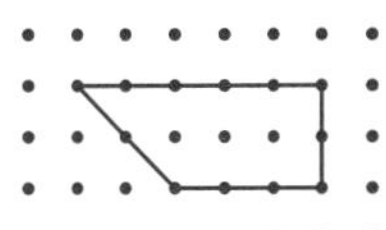

13. 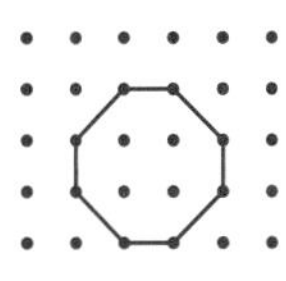

Use dot or graph paper to draw each of the following.
12–14. Answers may vary. See right for samples.

12. a trapezoid 13. an octagon 14. a nonregular rhombus

Name each of the following for circle *O*.
15–16, 18. Answers may vary. Samples are given.

15. two chords
$\overline{BC}$, $\overline{AC}$

16. a central angle
∠AOB

17. all semicircles
$\widehat{ABC}$, $\widehat{ADC}$

18. an inscribed triangle
△ADC

19. an inscribed quadrilateral
ABCD

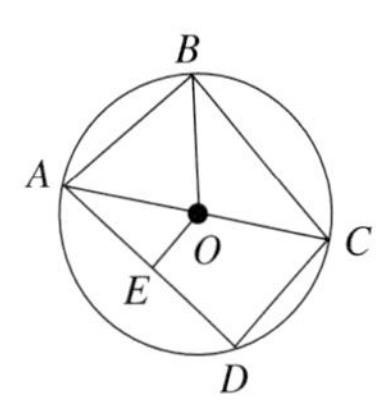

20. *Writing* Describe how you would make a circle graph of this data about the percent of licensed drivers in each age group.
Multiply 360° by each of the percents to find the measure of the central angles.

14. 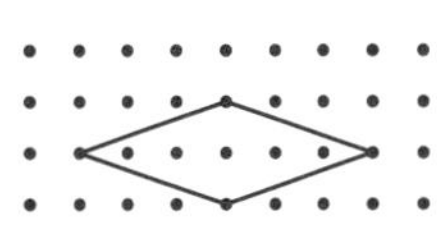

Who Drives

Age Group	19 and under	20–24	25–49	50–69	79 and over
Percent	6	10	54	22	8

CHAPTER ASSESSMENT • FORM A

Chapter 7 Assessment • Form A (continued)

11. What is the measure of the central angle that represents 40% in a circle graph? — 11. 144°

12. Name the quadrilaterals that each have four congruent sides. — 12. square, rhombus

13. Name four central angles of circle *E*. — 13. ∠AEB, ∠BEC, ∠AEC, ∠BED, ∠CED, ∠DEA

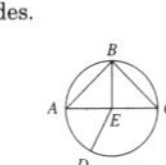

14. Which arcs are semicircles of circle *E* above? — 14. $\widehat{ABC}$, $\widehat{ADC}$

15. Point *X* is the midpoint of $\overline{AD}$. Which of the following *must* be true? — 15. D

A. $\overline{AB} \cong \overline{CD}$
B. $\overline{BX}$ is the perpendicular bisector of $\overline{AD}$.
C. $\overline{BX} \cong \overline{CX}$
D. $\overline{AX} \cong \overline{DX}$

16. Which has more sides, an octagon or a hexagon? How many more? — 16. octagon; 2

Choose A, B, C, or D.

17. △LMN and △RST are congruent right triangles. $m\angle M = 90°$ and $m\angle S = 90°$. Which angles must be congruent to ∠T? — 17. A

A. ∠N only B. ∠N, ∠L, and ∠R
C. ∠M and ∠S D. ∠L and ∠R

Choose a Strategy

18. From her house Nancy rode her bicycle 1 mi north. Then she rode 1 mi east, 1 mi south, 1 mi east, 1 mi south, and 2 mi west. How far away is Nancy from her house? — 18. 1 mi

Writing

19. How are a parallelogram and a trapezoid alike? different?
Both have one pair of opposite sides parallel; a parallelogram has a second pair parallel, a trapezoid doesn't.

Constructions — 7-9

You can use a compass and straightedge to construct an **angle bisector** or the **perpendicular bisector** of a segment.

Draw a large triangle *LMN* with an obtuse ∠*L*. 21–22. See back of book.

21. Construct the bisector of ∠L. 22. Construct the perpendicular bisector of $\overline{MN}$.

CHAPTER ASSESSMENT • FORM B

Chapter 7 Assessment • Form B

Choose the best answer. Circle A, B, C, or D.

1. Which is the next figure for the pattern?

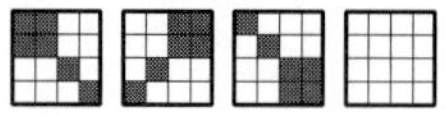

(A.) B. C. D.

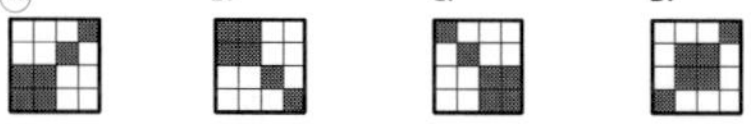

2. If the measure of an angle is 57°, what is the measure of its supplementary angle?

A. 57° B. 33° (C.) 123° D. 180°

3. What type of angle measures greater than 0° and less than 90°?

A. obtuse (B.) acute C. right D. straight

4. Which of the pairs of angles are vertical angles?

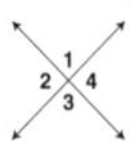

A. ∠1 and ∠2 B. ∠1 and ∠4 C. ∠3 and ∠4 (D.) ∠4 and ∠2

5. ∠R and ∠S are complementary. If $m\angle R = 85°$, what is the measure of ∠S?

A. 90° B. 180° (C.) 5° D. 95°

6. What are the measures of the angles of an equilateral triangle?

A. 45°, 45°, 90° B. 30°, 60°, 90° C. 50°, 50°, 50° (D.) 60°, 60°, 60°

7. In △XYZ, $m\angle X = 65°$ and $m\angle Z = 45°$. What is the measure of ∠Y?

(A.) 70° B. 65° C. 45° D. 10°

8. Classify △RST by its angles.

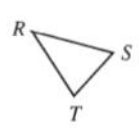

A. obtuse (B.) acute C. equilateral D. right

9. What is the measure of the central angle that you would draw to represent 30% in a circle graph?

A. 30° B. 60° (C.) 108° D. 120°

Assessment

CHAPTER ASSESSMENT • FORM B

Chapter 7 Assessment • Form B (continued)

10. △ABC ≅ △DEF. Find the measure of $\overline{DE}$.

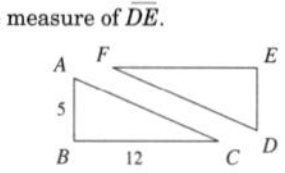

A. 3 (B.) 5 C. 4 D. 6

11. △LMN and △PQR are congruent right isosceles triangles. $m\angle Q = 90°$. Which sides must be congruent to $\overline{LM}$?

A. $\overline{LN}$ and $\overline{PR}$ B. $\overline{LN}$, $\overline{PR}$, and $\overline{QR}$ C. $\overline{MN}$ and $\overline{LN}$ (D.) $\overline{MN}$, $\overline{PQ}$, and $\overline{QR}$

12. Which two quadrilaterals must have congruent angles?

(A.) rectangle, square B. parallelogram, rectangle
C. square, rhombus D. parallelogram, rhombus

13. Name a central angle of circle D.

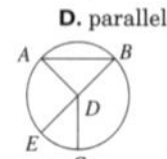

A. ∠DAB B. ∠ABD
(C.) ∠ADC D. ∠DBA

14. Which arc is a semicircle of the circle in Exercise 13?

A. $\widehat{ABC}$ B. $\widehat{AB}$ C. $\widehat{BAC}$ (D.) $\widehat{BCE}$

15. Point Y is the midpoint of $\overline{CD}$. Which of the following must be true?

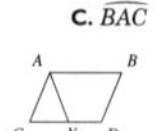

A. $\overline{AB} \cong \overline{AC}$ B. $\overline{AC} \cong \overline{AY}$ (C.) $\overline{CY} \cong \overline{YD}$ D. $\overline{AC} \cong \overline{AY} \cong \overline{BD}$

16. If you construct a perpendicular bisector of a segment and then bisect one of the angles, what sizes of angles will show in your diagram

A. 45° only B. 90° only
C. 45° and 90° only (D.) 45°, 90°, and 135°

17. Which list has the polygons in order according to their numbers of sides?

A. hexagon, octagon, pentagon B. square, triangle, quadrilateral
(C.) trapezoid, hexagon, decagon D. triangle, decagon, pentagon

Teaching Resources

Chapter Support File, Ch. 7, and Spanish Resources

Teacher's Edition

See pp. 286C–D for Assessment Options.

Teaching Resource Software

- Computer Item Generator, Ch. 7

ASSESSMENT

ENHANCED MULTIPLE CHOICE QUESTIONS are more complex than traditional multiple choice questions, which assess only one skill. Enhanced multiple choice questions assess the processes that students use, as well as the end results. They are written so that students can use more than one strategy to solve the problem. Using multiple strategies is encouraged by the National Council of Teachers of Mathematics (NCTM). **Exercise 2** is an enhanced multiple choice question.

WRITING EXERCISES allow students to describe more fully their thinking and understanding of the concepts they've learned. **Exercise 7** is a writing exercise.

Exercise 9 Remind students to write the vertices in the triangle congruence statement in corresponding order. Also, they must write the vertices in the six congruences in corresponding order.

7 ASSESSMENT

1. Draw two figures that continue this pattern. **See back of book.**

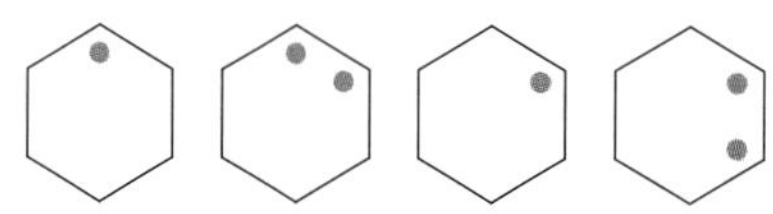

2. **Choose A, B, C, or D.** ∠1 and ∠2 are acute vertical angles. ∠1 and ∠3 are adjacent supplementary angles. What must be true? **D**

   I. ∠1 is obtuse.
   II. ∠2 and ∠3 are complementary.
   III. $m\angle 1 = m\angle 3$
   IV. ∠2 and ∠3 are supplementary.

   A. I only B. I and II
   C. III and IV D. IV only

3. Two angles of a triangle are complementary. Describe the triangle. **It is a right triangle.**

4. a. The measures of two angles of a triangle are 54° and 26°. What is the measure of the third angle? **100°**
   b. Classify the triangle by its angles. **obtuse**

5. Describe the error that was made in constructing the perpendicular bisector of $\overline{AB}$. **The radius of the arc with center A does not equal the radius of the arc with center B.**

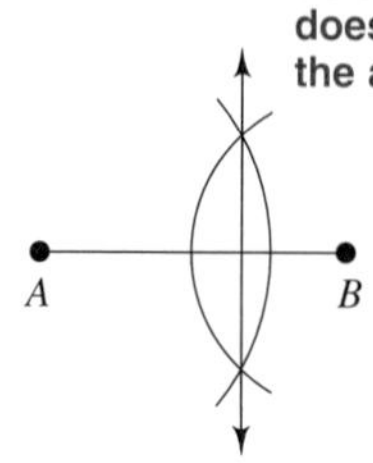

6. Construct a 45° angle. **See back of book.**

7. *Writing* Write a definition for *square* that uses the word *rhombus*. **A square is a rhombus with four right angles.**

8. From home, Belinda walked half way to the playground. She continued on for $\frac{1}{4}$ mi and was then $\frac{5}{8}$ mi from home. How far is it from her home to the playground? **$\frac{3}{4}$ mi**

9. △ABC ≅ △ZYX. Write six congruences involving corresponding sides and angles. **$\overline{AB} \cong \overline{ZY}$, $\overline{BC} \cong \overline{YX}$, $\overline{AC} \cong \overline{ZX}$, ∠A ≅ ∠Z, ∠B ≅ ∠Y, ∠C ≅ ∠X**

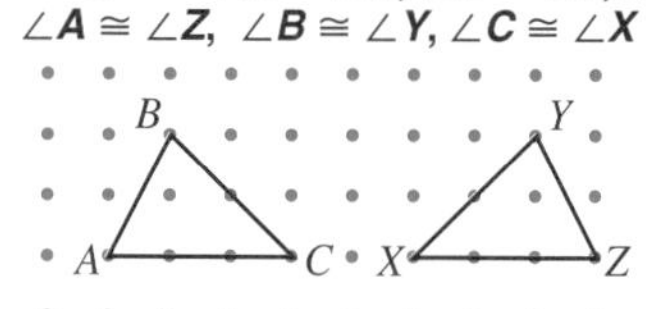

10. △ABC ≅ △EBD. Find as many angle measures and side lengths as you can. **See back of book.**

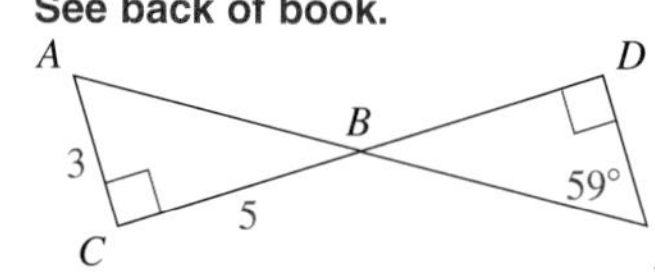

11. Name each of the following for circle O.
    a. a central angle
    b. three radii
    c. a chord that is not a diameter **$\overline{BC}$**
    d. two semicircles

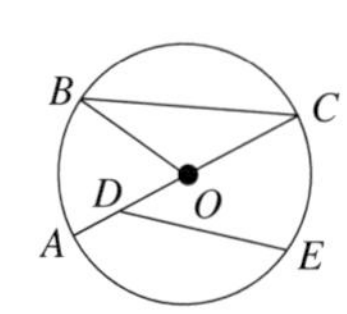

11a. Answers may vary. Samples: ∠AOB, ∠BOC
b. $\overline{OA}$, $\overline{OB}$, $\overline{OC}$ d. $\widehat{ABC}$, $\widehat{AEC}$

12. Students earned the following amounts of money to pay the transportation costs of a class trip. Make a circle graph for the data. **See back of book.**

Fund Raiser	Money
Car wash	$150
Paper drive	$75
Book sale	$225
Food stand	$378

CUMULATIVE REVIEW

Item	Review Topic	Ch
1	Divisibility rules	6
2, 5, 6, 7, 11	Geometric concepts	7
3	Interpreting data	1
4	Estimating perimeter	Precourse

Item	Review Topic	Ch
8, 13	Mean, median, and mode	1
9	Decimal operations	2
10	Solving equations	3
12	Evaluating expressions	3

7 CUMULATIVE REVIEW

Choose the best answer.

1. In which set of numbers is 9 a factor of all the numbers? B
   A. 36, 18, 21 B. 108, 252, 45
   C. 98, 81, 450 D. 120, 180, 267

2. $\angle 1$ and $\angle 2$ are complementary and the measure of $\angle 1$ is four times the measure of $\angle 2$. What is the measure of $\angle 2$? A
   A. 18° B. 36° C. 72° D. 144°

3. Which kind of graph would best show the change in population of the United States from 1930 to 1990? A
   A. line graph
   B. bar graph
   C. line plot
   D. stem-and-leaf plot

4. Find the *best* estimate for the perimeter of the shaded region. B

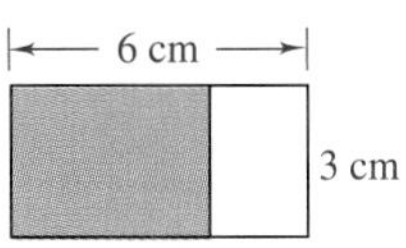

   A. 8 cm B. 14 cm
   C. 12 cm D. 18 cm

5. Which figure continues the pattern? C

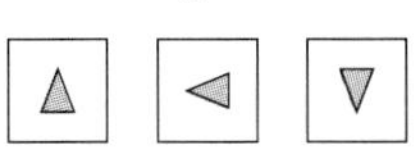

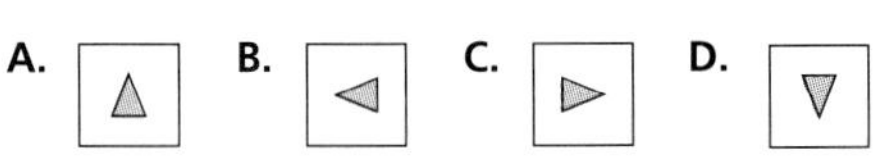

6. Two angles of a triangle each measure 36°. Which classification is correct? C
   A. acute triangle B. right triangle
   C. obtuse triangle D. scalene triangle

7. In parallelogram $ABCD$, the length of side $\overline{AB}$ is 9. The measure of $\angle A$ is 40°. Which measure *cannot* be found? A
   A. length of $\overline{BC}$ B. length of $\overline{CD}$
   C. $m\angle C$ D. $m\angle D$

8. The mean of six numbers is 9. Five of the numbers are 4, 7, 9, 10, and 11. What is the sixth number? D
   A. 6 B. 9 C. 12 D. 13

9. Miki bought 4.4 lb of apples at \$1.09/lb, 3.8 lb of pears at \$1.29/lb, and two melons for \$1.69 each. How much did she spend? A
   A. \$13.08 B. \$11.39
   C. \$12.16 D. \$13.20

10. What is the solution of the equation $\frac{x}{4} + 8 = -1$? B
    A. 28 B. −36 C. −9 D. −28

11. What is the name of this figure? D

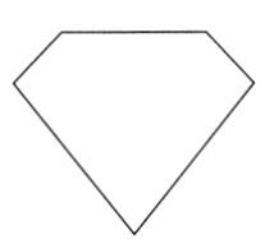

    A. hexagon
    B. regular polygon
    C. octagon
    D. pentagon

12. Which expression has the least value? C
    A. $|12 - 10|$ B. $|10 - 12|$
    C. $|10| - |12|$ D. $|12| - |10|$

13. Find the mean of the data in the stem-and-leaf plot. A
    A. 4.1
    B. 41
    C. 47
    D. 4.7

7	5
5	0 3
4	7
2	8
1	6 8

1|6 means 1.6

CUMULATIVE REVIEW

Chapter 7 Cumulative Review

Choose the best answer. Circle A, B, C, or D.

1. Compare. −14 × 10 ▒ −28 + (−102)
   (A) < B. >
   C. ≥ D. =

2. What is the value of 5 × 6 − 7 × 3?
   A. −15 (B) 9
   C. 51 D. 69

3. What is $\frac{19}{25}$ written as a decimal?
   A. 0.91 B. 0.1925
   C. 0.25 (D) 0.76

4. John has $4\frac{1}{2}$ lb of halibut. He wants each person to get a 6-oz serving. How many people can he feed?
   A. 6 people (B) 12 people
   C. 27 people D. 75 people

5. What is the value of 1^{20}?
   (A) 1 B. 5
   C. 10 D. 20

6. What is the range of the data given below?
   13.4, 24.2, 33.0, 11.5, 21.0, 35.9, 40.2
   A. 22.5 B. 26.8
   C. 27.0 (D) 28.7

7. Which fraction is equivalent to $\frac{8}{12}$?
   A. $\frac{2}{6}$ (B) $\frac{10}{15}$
   C. $\frac{3}{4}$ D. $\frac{16}{20}$

8. Solve $-3m - 1 = -25$.
   A. −24 B. −8
   C. 3 (D) 8

9. Complete. 153 in. = ____ ft
   A. 4.25 (B) 12.75
   C. 51 D. 459

10. Last month the flower was $11\frac{1}{4}$ in. tall. This month it is $50\frac{7}{8}$ in. tall. How many inches has the flower grown in the month?
    A. $31\frac{3}{4}$ in. (B) $39\frac{5}{8}$ in.
    C. $62\frac{1}{8}$ in. D. not here

11. What is $\frac{24}{5}$ as a mixed number?
    A. $2\frac{4}{5}$ B. $4\frac{2}{5}$
    (C) $4\frac{4}{5}$ D. $5\frac{1}{5}$

12. What is the prime factorization for 210?
    (A) 2 × 3 × 5 × 7 B. 5 × 6 × 7
    C. 2 × 7 × 15 D. 2 × 5 × 21

Assessment

CUMULATIVE REVIEW

Chapter 7 Cumulative Review (continued)

13. According to the graph, during which month is the difference in average temperatures for the two cities the greatest?

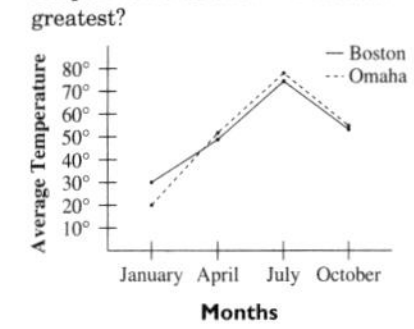

    (A) January B. April
    C. July D. October

14. ΔFGH has angle measures of 78° and 54°. What is the measure of the third angle?
    A. 12° B. 36°
    (C) 48° D. 96°

15. A scale on a map is 1.5 in. : 200 mi. The map distance from Miami to Chicago is 9 in. What is the actual distance between the cities?
    A. 600 mi (B) 1,200 mi
    C. 1,800 mi D. 2,700 mi

16. Which one of the following is a regular quadrilateral?
    A. trapezoid B. triangle
    (C) square D. pentagon

17. The mean of five numbers is 20. Four of the numbers are 24, 19, 25, and 22. What is the fifth number?
    A. 18 (B) 10
    C. 21 D. 24

18. According to the graph, how many families have more than two cars?

Number of Cars Owned by Families

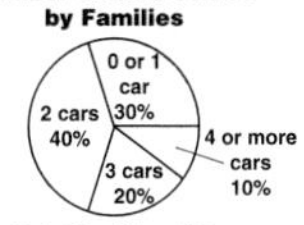

Total Families: 150

    A. 15 families (B) 45 families
    C. 60 families D. 105 families

19. What is the median of the data shown in the stem-and-leaf plot below?

0	3 4 6
1	0 5 5 7
2	1 1 6 8 9
3	2

0 | 3 means 3

    A. 5 B. 7
    C. 15 (D) 17

20. Find the value of n in $\frac{32}{n} = \frac{4}{9}$ that makes the proportion true.
    A. 4 B. 8
    C. 36 (D) 72

21. What is 60% of 60?
    (A) 36 B. 60
    C. 100 D. 360

22. A computer costs \$2,800 on sale. The original price was \$3,500. Find the percent of change.
    (A) 20% decrease
    B. 20% increase
    C. 25% decrease
    D. 25% increase

Resources

Teaching Resources

Chapter Support File, Ch. 7
- Cumulative Review

Teacher's Edition

See pp. 286C–D for Assessment Options.

8 Geometry and Measurement

Chapter Overview

To accommodate flexible scheduling, most lessons are divided into parts. Assignment Options are given in the Teacher's Edition for each lesson.

Pages	Lesson	NCTM	Contents
336–339	**Lesson 8-1** Estimating Length and Area	2, 4, 5, 7, 9, 12, 13	Part 1 Estimating Length Part 2 Estimating Area **Key term:** area
340–343	**Lesson 8-2** Area of Parallelograms	1, 2, 3, 5, 7, 12	**Key term:** height **Journal** **Project Link**
344–348	**Lesson 8-3** Area of Triangles and Trapezoids	1, 2, 3, 4, 5, 7, 9, 12, 13	Part 1 Area of Triangles Part 2 Area of Trapezoids
364–367	**Lesson 8-7** Technology: Applying the Pythagorean Theorem	2, 3, 4, 12, 13	**Alternative Activity** 8-7
368–371	**Lesson 8-8** Three-Dimensional Figures	3, 4, 9, 12	Part 1 Identifying Prisms Part 2 Other Three-Dimensional Figures **Key terms:** three-dimensional figures, faces, prisms, bases, edge, cube, pyramid
373–376	**Lesson 8-9** Surface Area of Prisms and Cylinders	1, 2, 3, 4, 8, 9, 12	Part 1 Finding the Surface Area of Prisms Part 2 Finding the Surface Area of Cylinders **Key terms:** net, surface area **Alternative Activity** 8-9 **Project Link**

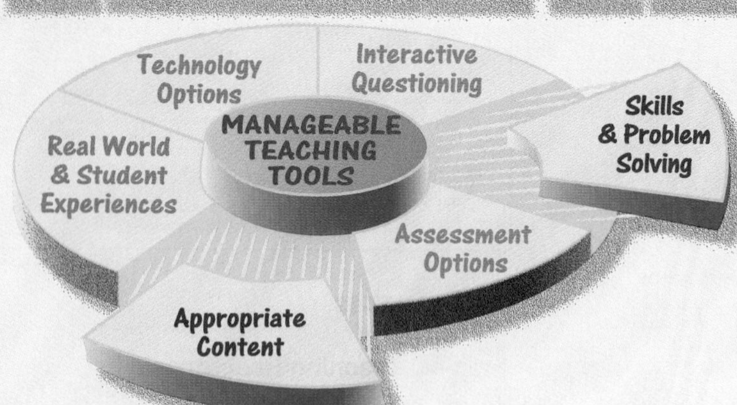

Pacing Options

This chart suggests pacing only for the core lessons and their parts. It is provided merely as a possible guide. It will help you determine how much time you have in your schedule to cover other features, such as the Chapter Project, Math Toolboxes, Wrap Up, and Assessment.

	1 Class Period	1 Class Period	1 Class Period	1
Traditional (40–45 min class periods)	8–1 (1) 8–1 (2)	8–2	8–3 (1)	
Block Scheduling (90 min class periods)	8–1 (1) 8–1 (2) 8–2	8–2 8–3 (1) 8–3 (2)	8–4 (1) 8–4 (2) 8–5 (1) 8–5 (2)	8–6 (1)

CHAPTER PROJECT

Shape Up and Ship Out

Goal: Analyze arrangements of shapes and design boxes for shipping cylinders

THEME: SHIPPING/ PACKAGING

NCTM STANDARDS

1 Problem Solving
2 Communication
3 Reasoning
4 Mathematical Connections
5 Number and Number Relationships
6 Number Systems and Number Theory
7 Computation and Estimation
8 Patterns and Functions
9 Algebra
10 Statistics
11 Probability
12 Geometry
13 Measurement

Pages	Lesson
Pages 349–353	**Lesson 8-4 Algebra: Circumference and Area of Circles**
NCTM 1, 2, 4, 5, 7, 12	Part 1 Circumference of a Circle Part 2 Area of a Circle **Key terms:** circumference, pi (π) **Checkpoint 1**
Pages 354–357	**Lesson 8-5 Algebra: Exploring Square Roots**
NCTM 1, 2, 3, 4, 5, 6, 7, 8	Part 1 Finding Square Roots of Perfect Squares Part 2 Estimating Square Roots **Key terms:** perfect square, square root ($\sqrt{\ }$) **Project Link** **Journal** **Math at Work**
Pages 359–363	**Lesson 8-6 Algebra: Exploring the Pythagorean Theorem**
NCTM 1, 3, 4, 5, 6, 8, 9, 12	Part 1 Using the Pythagorean Theorem Part 2 Determining Right Triangles **Key terms:** legs, hypotenuse, Pythagorean theorem
Pages 377–380	**Lesson 8-10 Volume of Rectangular Prisms and Cylinders**
NCTM 1, 2, 3, 7, 12	Part 1 Finding the Volume of Prisms Part 2 Finding the Volume of a Cylinder **Key terms:** volume, cubic unit **Alternative Activity** 8-10 **Checkpoint 2**
Pages 381–383	**Lesson 8-11 Problem Solving Strategy**
NCTM 1, 2, 4, 5, 7	**Guess and Test** **Key term:** Guess and Test **Project Link**

Optional Materials and Manipulatives

ruler (8-1, 8-4)
string (8-1, 8-4)
scissors (8-3)
centimeter graph paper (8-3, 8-6, 8-9)
3 different-sized cans (8-4)
square tiles (8-5)
graph paper (8-8)
Optional calculator use is integrated throughout the course.

ss od	1 Class Period	1 Class Period	1 Class Period	1 Class Period	1 Class Period	1 Class Period	1 Class Period	1 Class Period	1 Class Period	1 Class Period
-4 2	8–5 1 8–5 2	8–6 1	8–6 2	8–7	8–8 1 8–8 2	8–9 1	8–9 2	8–10 1 8–10 2	8–11	
-8 2	8–9 1 8–9 2	8–10 1 8–10 2 8–11								

Meeting Individual Needs

Accommodating Diverse Learning Styles

In your Teacher's Edition, you will find suggestions as to how you can help students complete mathematical tasks in Chapter 8 by meeting individual needs and supporting various learning styles. Here are some examples:

VISUAL LEARNING
coloring squares to visualize the Pythagorean theorem *(p. 359)*

TACTILE LEARNING
cutting out parallelograms to create rectangles *(p. 340)*

AUDITORY LEARNING
listening to and classifying customary and metric units *(p. 336)*

KINESTHETIC LEARNING
making trapezoids using yardsticks *(p. 346)*

EARLY FINISHERS
Performance-Based Project, MathBlaster® Mystery, Interdisciplinary Units

GIFTED AND TALENTED
researching mathematicians *(p. 344)*

DIVERSITY listening to music from different musical instruments *(p. 347)*

ACQUIRING ENGLISH PROFICIENCY (AEP)
relating area to area rugs *(p. 338)*

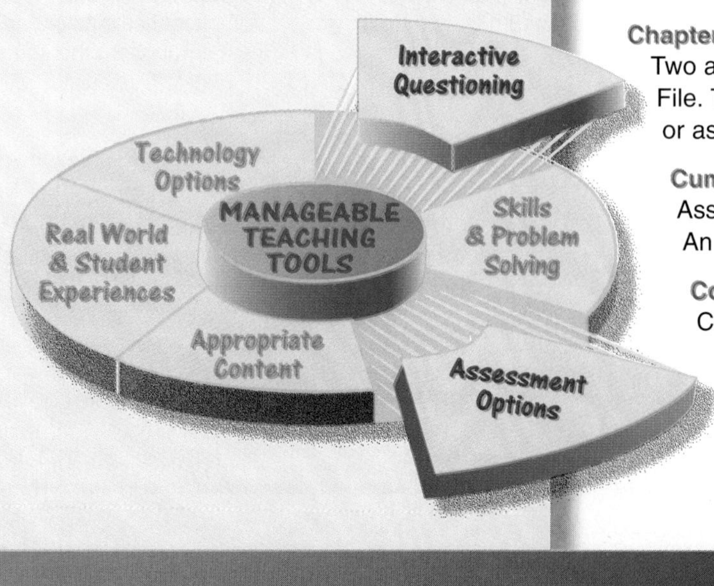

Assessing Progress

A broad range of assessment tools are available to reach a variety of learners.

INFORMAL ASSESSMENT

Informal assessments provide day-to-day feedback to help give you a picture of conceptual understanding and skill development.

ONGOING ASSESSMENT is built into lesson instruction and the Teaching Notes of the Teacher's Edition.

In the Teacher's Edition
Lesson Quiz for every lesson

In the Student Edition
On Your Own, Mixed Review, Journal, Portfolio, Project Link, Chapter Wrap Up

Look for **Interactive Questions** within lessons that

- **BUILD UNDERSTANDING** with labels such as **Analyze, Reasoning, Estimation, Writing, and Summarize**
- ✔ **CHECK UNDERSTANDING** with the **Try It Out** label.

FORMAL ASSESSMENT

Formal assessment can occur before and after the chapter, as well as at natural breaking points in the chapter.

Checkpoints
Two forms of each self-assessment Checkpoints are available: one in the Student Edition and another in the Chapter Support File in the Teaching Resources box.

- Mid-Chapter Checkpoint 1, page 353
- End-of-Chapter Checkpoint 2, page 380

Chapter 8 Assessment, page 388.
Two alternative forms are available in the Chapter Support File. They may be used after a chapter has been completed, or as a pre-test and post-test comparison.

Cumulative Review, page 389.
Assesses skills and concepts in Chapters 1–8. An alternative form is available in Chapter Support File.

Computer Item Generator for Chapter 8
Customized tests can be generated for each lesson and for mid-chapter and end-of-chapter assessments, and for pre- and post-test comparisons of achievement.

PERFORMANCE-BASED ASSESSMENT

CHAPTER PROJECT The Chapter Project in the student edition provides a real-world connection to the math context of the chapter. The Teacher's Edition contains a scoring rubric.

A Performance Assessment with a scoring rubric can be found in the Chapter Support File in the Teaching Resources box.

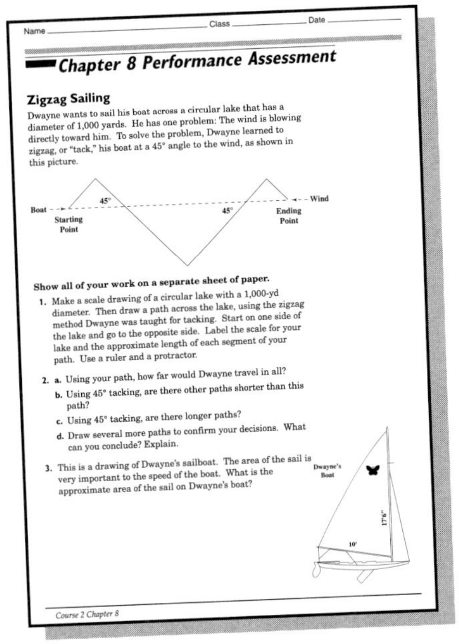
Name ______ Class ______ Date ______

Chapter 8 Performance Assessment

Zigzag Sailing

Dwayne wants to sail his boat across a circular lake that has a diameter of 1,000 yards. He has one problem: The wind is blowing directly toward him. To solve the problem, Dwayne learned to zigzag, or "tack," his boat at a 45° angle to the wind, as shown in this picture.

Show all of your work on a separate sheet of paper.

1. Make a scale drawing of a circular lake with a 1,000-yd diameter. Then draw a path across the lake, using the zigzag method Dwayne was taught for tacking. Start on one side of the lake and go to the opposite side. Label the scale for your lake and the approximate length of each segment of your path. Use a ruler and a protractor.
2. a. Using your path, how far would Dwayne travel in all?
   b. Using 45° tacking, are there other paths shorter than this path?
   c. Using 45° tacking, are there longer paths?
   d. Draw several more paths to confirm your decisions. What can you conclude? Explain.
3. This is a drawing of Dwayne's sailboat. The area of the sail is very important to the speed of the boat. What is the approximate area of the sail on Dwayne's boat?

Course 2 Chapter 8

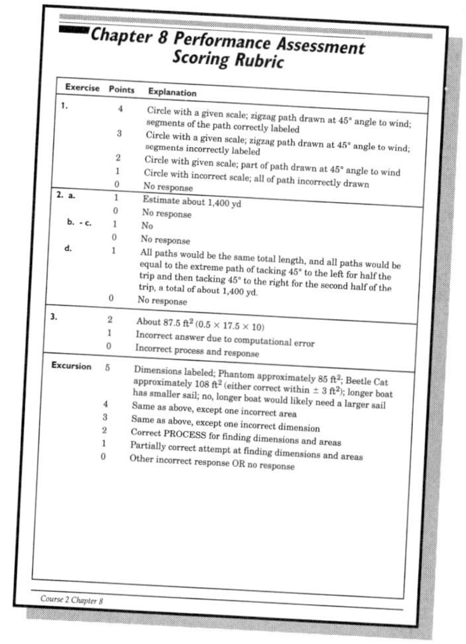
Chapter 8 Performance Assessment Scoring Rubric

Exercise	Points	Explanation
1.	4	Circle with a given scale; zigzag path drawn at 45° angle to wind; segments of the path correctly labeled
	3	Circle with a given scale; zigzag path drawn at 45° angle to wind; segments incorrectly labeled
	2	Circle with given scale; part of path drawn at 45° angle to wind
	1	Circle with incorrect scale; all of path incorrectly drawn
	0	No response
2. a.	1	Estimate about 1,400 yd
	0	No response
b. - c.	1	No
	0	No response
d.	1	All paths would be the same total length, and all paths would be equal to the extreme path of tacking 45° to the left for half the trip and then tacking 45° to the right for the second half of the trip, a total of about 1,400 yd.
	0	No response
3.	2	About 87.5 ft^2 (0.5 × 17.5 × 10)
	1	Incorrect answer due to computational error
	0	Incorrect process and response
Excursion	5	Dimensions labeled; Phantom approximately 85 ft^2; Beetle Cat approximately 108 ft^2 (either correct within ± 3 ft^2); longer boat has smaller sail; no, longer boat would likely need a larger sail
	4	Same as above, except one incorrect area
	3	Same as above, except one incorrect dimension
	2	Correct PROCESS for finding dimensions and areas
	1	Partially correct attempt at finding dimensions and areas
	0	Other incorrect response OR no response

Course 2 Chapter 8

Correlation to Standardized Tests

Lesson		STANDARDIZED TEST ITEMS					
		CAT5	Terra Nova	ITBS, Form M	MAT7	SAT9	Local Test
8-1	Estimating Length and Area	CA18	19, 22, 23, 43	CE43	CP17	PS35–36	
8-2	Area of Parallelograms	CA24, 42		CE22	CP24	PS33	
8-3	Area of Triangles and Trapezoids						
8-4	Algebra: Circumference and Area of Circles						
8-5	Algebra: Exploring Square Roots						
8-6	Algebra: Exploring the Pythagorean Theorem						
8-7	Technology: Applying the Pythagorean Theorem						
8-8	Three-Dimensional Figures		18, 44		CP22		
8-9	Surface Area of Prisms and Cylinders			CE16			
8-10	Volume of Rectangular Prisms and Cylinders				CP26		
8-11	Problem Solving Strategy: Guess and Test				CP11		

CA: Concepts and Applications
PS: Problem Solving
PR: Math Procedures
CP: Concepts and Problem Solving
MC: Math Computation
PD: Problem Solving and Data Interpretation
CE: Concepts and Estimation

See page 2D for the level of each test referenced.

MAKING CONNECTIONS

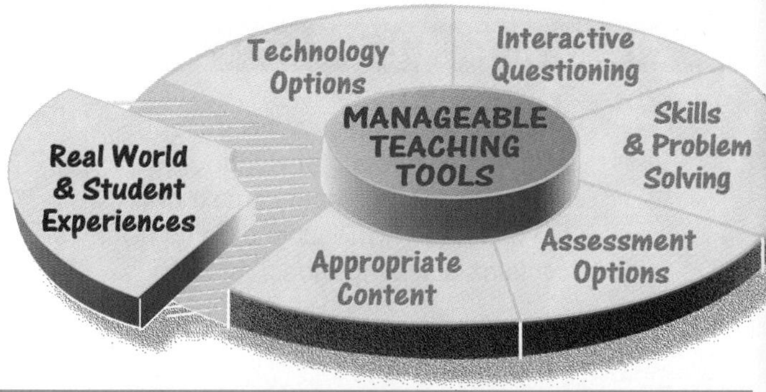

TEAM TEACHING WITH PRENTICE HALL MATERIALS

MIDDLE GRADES MATH INTERDISCIPLINARY UNITS	INTERDISCIPLINARY EXPLORATIONS	PRENTICE HALL SCIENCE L Life Science E Earth Science P Physical Science
• **The Arts: Activity 9**	• ***Riddles of the Pharaohs:*** **pp. 14, 15, 22, & 23**	**P Sec. 1-4 Tools of Measurement** **Sec. 2-3 Volume and Density**

Lesson	Interdisciplinary Connections	Real World Connections	Math Integration
8-1	Geography	Amusement Parks	Algebra Geometry Measurement
8-2	Geometry	Surveying	Geometry
8-3	Music	Cooking	Algebra Geometry Measurement
8-4	Social Studies Sports	Entertainment	Algebra Geometry
8-5	Agriculture	Gardening	Algebra
8-6	History Carpentry	Construction Camping Home Repair	Algebra Geometry
8-7	Sports Architecture History	Water Parks Aviation Home Repair Hobbies	Geometry Measurement
8-8	Drafting	Photography Architecture	Algebra Geometry
8-9	Geometry	Construction	Algebra Geometry
8-10	Geometry	Waterfalls	Geometry
8-11	Science Geography	Jobs Pets	Data Analysis

School to Home

MATERIALS:
one each of penny, nickel, dime, quarter
metric ruler
tape measure
five circular objects
standard ruler
scissors tape
paper pencil

English version is in the Chapter Support File. Spanish version is in the Spanish Resources.

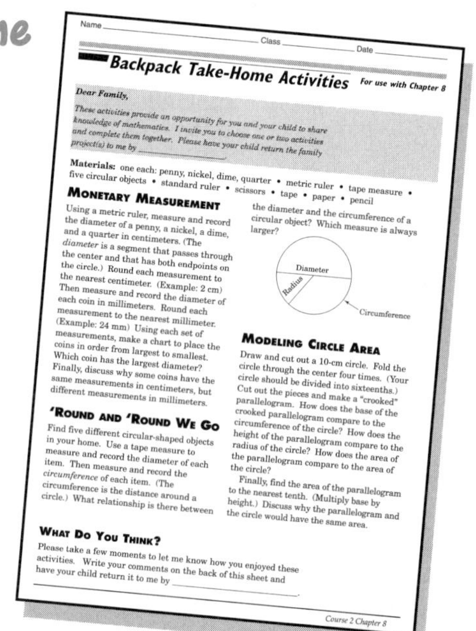
Name ______ Class ______ Date ______

Backpack Take-Home Activities *For use with Chapter 8*

Dear Family,

These activities provide an opportunity for you and your child to share knowledge of mathematics. I invite you to choose one or two activities and complete them together. Please have your child return the family project(s) to me by ______.

Materials: one each: penny, nickel, dime, quarter • metric ruler • tape measure • five circular objects • standard ruler • scissors • tape • paper • pencil

MONETARY MEASUREMENT

Using a metric ruler, measure and record the diameter of a penny, a nickel, a dime, and a quarter in centimeters. (The *diameter* is a segment that passes through the center and that has both endpoints on the circle.) Round each measurement to the nearest centimeter. (Example: 2 cm) Then measure and record the diameter of each coin in millimeters. Round each measurement to the nearest millimeter. (Example: 24 mm) Using each set of measurements, make a chart to place the coins in order from largest to smallest. Which coin has the largest diameter? Finally, discuss why some coins have the same measurements in centimeters, but different measurements in millimeters.

'ROUND AND 'ROUND WE GO

Find five different circular-shaped objects in your home. Use a tape measure to measure and record the diameter of each item. Then measure and record the *circumference* of each item. (The circumference is the distance around a circle.) What relationship is there between the diameter and the circumference of a circular object? Which measure is always larger?

Diameter
Radius
Circumference

MODELING CIRCLE AREA

Draw and cut out a 10-cm circle. Fold the circle through the center four times. (Your circle should be divided into sixteenths.) Cut out the pieces and make a "crooked" parallelogram. How does the base of the crooked parallelogram compare to the circumference of the circle? How does the height of the parallelogram compare to the radius of the circle? How does the area of the parallelogram compare to the area of the circle?

Finally, find the area of the parallelogram to the nearest tenth. (Multiply base by height.) Discuss why the parallelogram and the circle would have the same area.

WHAT DO YOU THINK?

Please take a few moments to let me know how you enjoyed these activities. Write your comments on the back of this sheet and have your child return it to me by ______.

Course 2 Chapter 8

Using Technology to Enhance Instruction

For the Student

Multimedia Math Hot Pages™
This interactive software and video package on CD-ROM integrates solid math content through a variety of media.
- Hot Page™ 2-9
- Hot Page™ 5-1
- Hot Page™ 5-4
- Hot Page™ 5-9

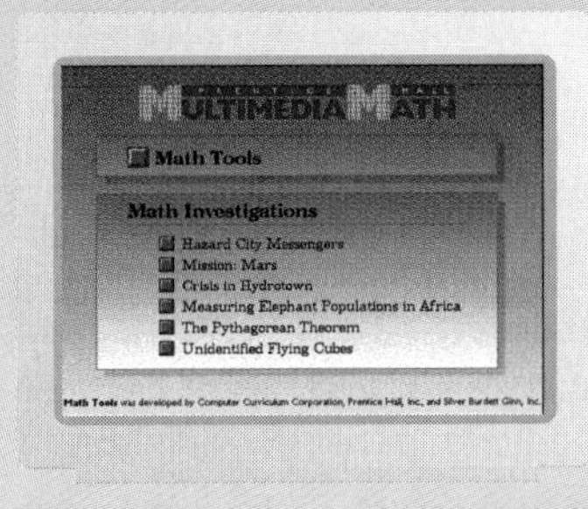

Multimedia Math Investigations
These in-depth interactive activities on CD-ROM develop real-world applications of mathematics. They allow students the opportunity to reinforce key concepts.
- The Pythagorean Theorem
- Unidentified Flying Cubes

MathBlaster® Mystery

This award-winning, interactive software program on CD-ROM can be used to maintain skills or to accommodate early finishers.
- Level: Earn 4 coins; Pay 4 coins
- Mission Mode (all lessons)
- Kitchen Comparisons (8-2)
- Number Guesser (8-1, 8-11)
- Equation Maker (8-4, 8-6, 8-7, 8-10)
- Word Problems (8-3, 8-8, 8-9, Problem Solving Practice)

Math Tools/Math Labs
This software, available on CD-ROM, includes on-screen Math Lab activities. Students use linkable, interactive tools to explore math concepts.
- Math Lab: Area of Triangles and Trapezoids (8-3)

Interactive Student Tutorial
Available on CD-ROM, this test preparation program contains self-tests with questions in standardized test format. Software includes electronic versions of the text lessons and an on-line glossary.

Internet Connection

For Students
Support for the Chapter Project
A career-oriented link for Math at Work feature

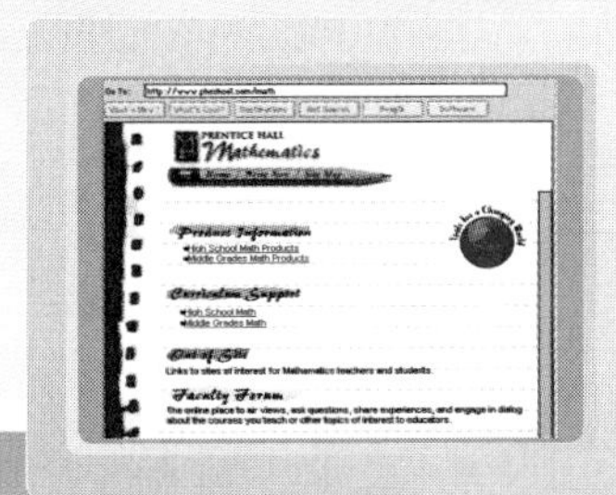

www.phschool.com/math

For teachers
Curriculum Support
Product Information
Regional Support Information

For the Teacher

Computer Item Generator with Standardized Test Practice
This software generates customized practice sheets and tests. It also generates unlimited practice sheets for the standardized tests listed on page 334D.

Resource Pro™ with Planning Express™
Available on CD-ROM, this software can be used to customize and plan lessons. It contains over 1,700 resource pages.

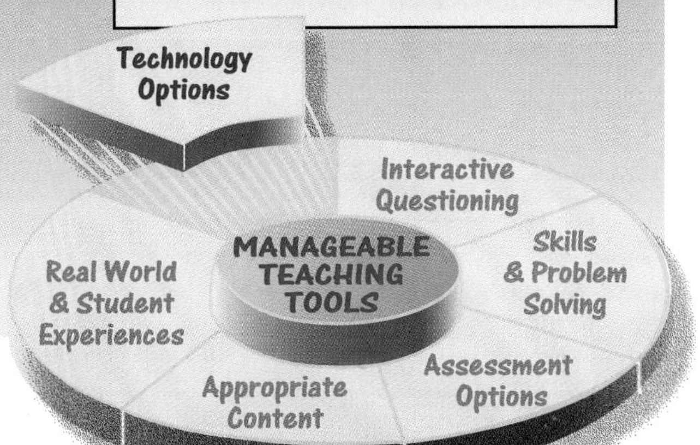

CHAPTER 8

Geometry and Measurement

CONNECTING TO PRIOR LEARNING Ask students to describe packaging they have observed while shopping. Ask students: *What makes a good package design?* **Answers may vary. Sample: packages that contain the most product while using the least amount of material**

CULTURAL CONNECTIONS Point out to students that a factory in their town or region may ship its product as far away as China or Japan. Discuss with students the concerns a business would have about the design of a package when it has to travel so far. **Answers may vary. Sample: light weight, durability**

INTERDISCIPLINARY CONNECTIONS Ask students: *How might a geographer use area to describe a country or region?* **Answers may vary. Sample: A geographer might describe a certain area as a percent of the total area of the country.**

ABOUT THE PROJECT The Chapter Project has students use their knowledge of geometry and measurement to design a box in which to ship cylindrical containers.

Internet • For information and activities related to the Chapter Project, visit the Prentice Hall site at www.phschool.com/mgm2/ch8

WHAT YOU WILL LEARN IN THIS CHAPTER

- How to use area formulas
- How to model and find the surface area and volume of prisms and cylinders
- How to apply the Pythagorean theore

LAUNCHING THE CHAPTER PROJECT

Ask students:

- *Name some products that are packaged as cylinders.*
- *How do you think cylinders would best fit in a box?*
- *How can you test the best designs for a package?*

PROJECT NOTEBOOK Encourage students to keep all project-related materials in a separate folder or notebook.

TRACKING THE PROJECT You may wish to have students read Finishing the Chapter Project on page 385 to help them get an overview of the project. Set benchmark deadlines for students to show you their work in progress.

CHAPTER PROJECT

THEME: Packaging

SHAPE UP AND SHIP OUT

Space is money! So before cargo is prepared for shipment in large containers, like those shown on a wharf in Houston, it is packaged in smaller containers, based on its size and shape.

Cans of tuna are examples of items you buy in cylindrical containers. Would you pack two cylinders side-by-side or one above the other? One arrangement wastes cardboard! But which one?

Design Boxes for Shipping Cylinders For the chapter project, you will design boxes to hold cylindrical items. Your final product will be a model of a box that holds six cylinders.

Next steps to help you complete the project:

p. 343 **Project Link:** *Analyzing*
p. 357 **Project Link:** *Drawing*
p. 376 **Project Link:** *Writing*
p. 383 **Project Link:** *Calculating*
p. 385 *Finishing the Project*

- How to solve problems by guessing an answer and testing the guess

SCORING RUBRIC

3 You provide nine drawings of box designs: one for a single cylinder, two for two cylinders, and three each for four and six cylinders. For the two-, four-, and six-cylinder designs you methodically and accurately calculate the surface areas to determine which boxes require the least amount of cardboard. Your completed project includes explanations of your work and a model of your best six-cylinder design.

2 You provide at least seven of the required designs, and most of your surface area calculations are both easy to follow and accurate. You complete a model of your best six-cylinder design.

1 You only complete a few box designs with accompanying surface area calculations. Your work is either inaccurate or sloppy.

0 You do not complete a majority of the box designs or surface area calculations.

8-1 Teaching Notes

1 Focus

CONNECTING TO PRIOR KNOWLEDGE Have students guess your height. Pass around a roll of string. Have each student cut the length of string they think would match your height. Then have students compare their strings to your height. See whose length of string is the most accurate.

2 Teach

Work Together

DIVERSITY Some students might not want to call attention to their feet. An alternative might be to use the measurement of their arm from the elbow to the fingertips.

THINK AND DISCUSS

AUDITORY LEARNING Have students write *customary* and *metric* on their papers. Read aloud customary and metric units. Have students write the unit in the appropriate column as they hear it.

Question 6 Help students choose reasonable units by asking: *What happens if the unit of measure is larger than your*

Lesson Planning Options

Prerequisite Skills

- visualizing metric and customary units of length (precourse)

Vocabulary/Symbols

area

Materials/Manipulatives

- ruler
- string

Resources

Student Edition

Skills Handbook, p. 528
Extra Practice, p. 521
Glossary/Study Guide

Teaching Resources

Chapter Support File, Ch. 8
- Lesson Planner 8-1
- Practice 8-1, Reteaching 8-1
- Answer Masters 8-1

Teaching Aids Masters 1–3, 19
Glossary, Spanish Resources

Transparencies

1, 7, 92, Minds on Math 8-1

Warm Up

Rudy works 4 days each week for 8 hours per day. He earns \$5.80 per hour. How much does he earn in a week? **\$185.60**

8-1 Estimating Length and Area

What You'll Learn

1. To estimate lengths and perimeters
2. To estimate areas

...And Why

Sometimes an estimate of length or area is all you need.

Here's How

Look for questions that
- build understanding
- ✔ check understanding

5. The average length; some measurements may overestimate and some may underestimate the actual length, so the average length would be more accurate.

Work Together

Measuring Length

1. *Data Collection* Walk the length of your classroom heel-to-toe. Count the number of steps.
   1–4. Check students' work.
2. Measure your foot and determine the length of the room.
3. How close were the lengths found by members of your group? What accounts for the differences in the lengths?
4. Average the lengths found by the members of your group.
5. Which estimate do you think is the more accurate, the individual measurements or the average? Explain.
   See below left.

THINK AND DISCUSS

1 *Estimating Length*

Measurements must include a unit in order to make sense. A height of 12 for a building is meaningless. However, if you know that a building is 12 in. tall, you know that the building is just a model.

EXAMPLE 1

What unit of measure would you use to estimate the width of a lake?

You might use meters or feet. For a large lake, you might use kilometers or miles.

Note that there is a table of metric measures and U.S. customary measures on page 525.

6a–c. Answers may vary. Samples are given.

6. ✔ *Try It Out* What unit of measure would you use to estimate each of the following?
   a. the wingspread of a butterfly **inches, centimeters, millimeters**
   b. the perimeter of a picture frame **inches, centimeters**
   c. the perimeter of an amusement park **yards, miles, meters, kilometers**

QUICKreview

Perimeter is the distance around an object or figure.

object? **Answers may vary. Sample: You have to use fractions or decimals.** Then ask: *What if the unit is very tiny compared to the object?* **Answers may vary. Sample: You may lose count.**

ADDITIONAL EXAMPLES

FOR EXAMPLE 1

What unit of measure would you use to estimate the length of a computer keyboard? **Answers may vary. Sample: in., cm**

FOR EXAMPLE 2

Each square below represents 50 cm^2. Estimate the area of the figure. **250 cm^2**

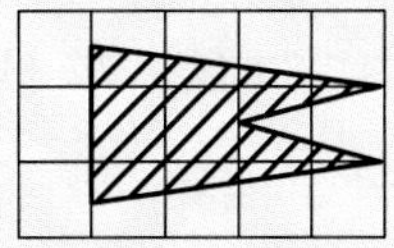

ERROR ALERT! Question 8a Students may not know which squares to count as 1, $\frac{1}{2}$, or 0. **Remediation:** Have students trace the squares not completely filled. Have them draw a line through the middle. This will help them visualize whether the shaded part is closer to 1, $\frac{1}{2}$, or 0.

ASSESSMENT Have students work with a partner to draw a picture of a pond on a piece of graph paper. Pairs label what each square unit represents, and estimate the area. Then have them trade with another pair of partners to check the areas of their drawings.

WHAT? Lake Superior is the largest body of fresh water in the world.

a–b. See margin p. 338.

7. a. How could you use a piece of string to estimate the perimeter of the puzzle piece at the right?

b. Estimate the perimeter.

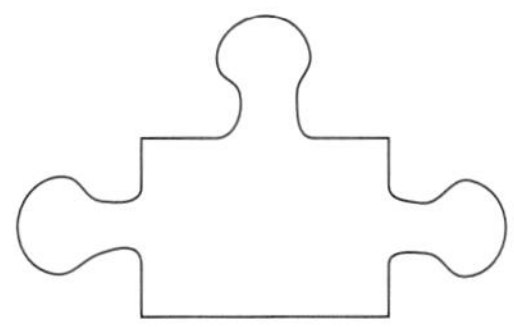

Now you may assign Exercises 1–6, 14.

2 *Estimating Area*

When you find the number of square units inside a figure, you are finding the **area** of the figure.

EXAMPLE 2 *Real-World Problem Solving*

Geography Each square below represents 900 mi^2. Estimate the area of Lake Superior.

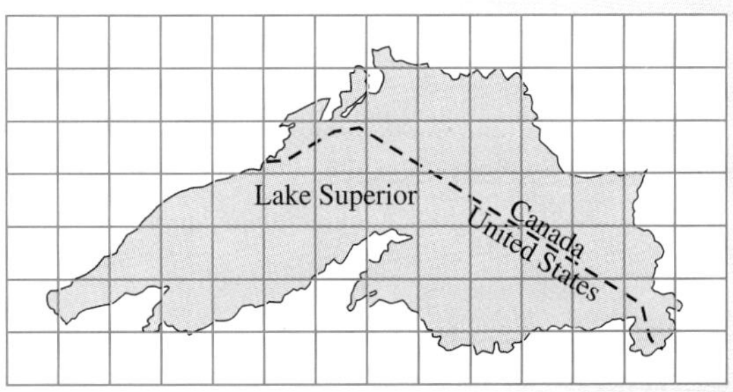

Count the number of squares that are filled or almost filled. Count the number of squares that are about half-filled.

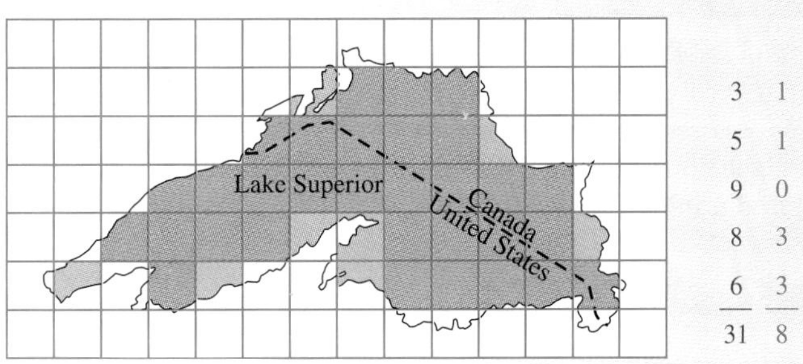

Estimate the number of squares filled: $31 + \frac{1}{2}(8)$, or 35.
Multiply 35 by 900 mi^2. The area is about 31,500 mi^2.

Lake Superior

Technology Options

Prentice Hall Technology

Software for Learners
- Hot Page™ 5–1*
- Math Blaster® Mystery*
- Interactive Student Tutorial, Chapter 8*

Teaching Resource Software
- Computer Item Generator 8-1
- Resource Pro Chapter 8*

Internet • For related mathematics activities, visit the Prentice Hall site at www.phschool.com/math

**Available on CD-ROM only*

Assignment Options for Exercises On Your Own

To provide flexible scheduling, this lesson can be subdivided into parts.

1 **Core** 1–6
Extension 14

2 **Core** 7–9, 12–13
Extension 10, 11

Use Mixed Review to maintain skills.

EXERCISES *On Your Own*

AEP **Exercises 7 and 8** Remind students that you always represent area in *square* units. Relate *area* to an area rug that covers square floor tiles.

ESTIMATION **Exercise 9** Students' estimates may vary, but they should be close to the actual perimeter and area. If a student is having difficulty, suggest he or she trace the figure on graph paper. Then the student labels each square 0, $\frac{1}{2}$, or 1.

Exercise 10c Suggest that students divide mentally using compatible numbers.

CONNECTING TO THE STUDENTS' WORLD
Exercise 14 If you have block scheduling or extended class periods, have students draw a map of a room in their home or the school library. Then have them write a plan to rearrange the furniture in that room. Have them pace to estimate lengths and widths of furniture and walls. Have them use their estimated measurements to explain why their plan would or would not work.

WRAP UP

IDENTIFYING THE BIG IDEA Have students explain the methods they can use to estimate length and area.

pages 336–338 Think and Discuss

7a. Wrap the string around the outer edge of the puzzle piece, marking the length on the string. Then measure the length of the marked piece.

b. Estimates may vary slightly. Sample: 14 cm or $5\frac{1}{2}$ in.

8. ✔ *Try It Out* Each square below is 1 cm by 1 cm.
   a. Estimate the area of the figure. **about 10 cm^2**
   b. Suppose the figure is a map of a lake. Each square represents 25 km^2. Estimate the area of the lake. **about 250 km^2**

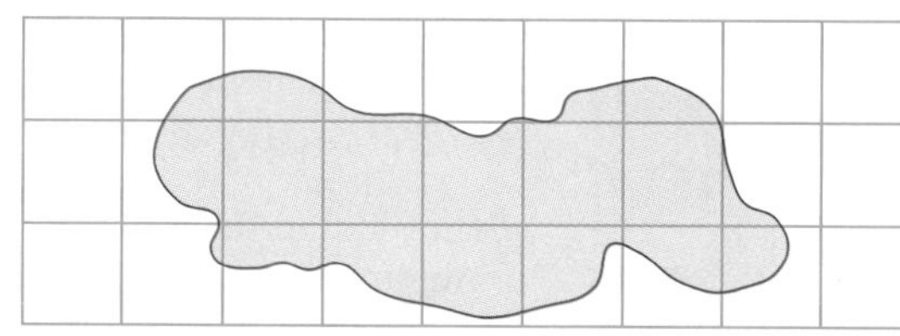

Now you may assign Exercises 7–13.

EXERCISES *On Your Own*

Estimate each length in inches. 1 in.

1. ______________ **about 2 in.**

2. ______________ **about 3 in.**

Estimate each length in centimeters. 1 cm

3. ______________ **about 5 cm**

4. ______________ **about 7 cm**

Choose the unit of measure listed that you would use to estimate the given length or area.

5. the height of a telephone pole: mm, cm, m, km **m**

6. the perimeter of a picture frame: in., ft, yd, mi **in.**

7. the area of a swimming pool: $in.^2$, yd^2, ft^2, mi^2 **ft^2 or yd^2**

8. the area of a soccer field: mm^2, cm^2, m^2, km^2 **m^2**

9. Each square below is 1 cm by 1 cm. Estimate the perimeter and area of the figure below. **Answers may vary. Sample: 30 cm; 13 cm^2**

LESSON QUIZ

Choose the unit of measure listed that you would use to estimate the given length or area.

1. the perimeter of a piece of notebook paper: in., ft, yd, mi **in.**
2. the area of a living room: mm^2, cm^2, m^2, km^2 **m^2**

Trace the figure for Question 7 on 1-cm graph paper.

3. Estimate the area of the figure. **about 5 cm^2**

Use the article at the right for Exercises 10 and 11.

Oldest Park Inspires

Tivoli Gardens in Copenhagen, Denmark, founded in 1833, is the world's oldest amusement park. The park covers about 20 acres and has 29 restaurants and 25 attractions.

The park features animated scenes from Hans Christian Andersen's fairy tales. After his visit there in the 1950s, Walt Disney began his plans for Disneyland.

10. a. An acre contains 43,560 ft^2. Estimate the number of square feet in Tivoli Gardens. **about 870,000 ft^2**
    b. The area of a football field is 57,600 ft^2. Does a football field have more area or less area than an acre? **more area**
    c. About how many football fields are equal to the area of Tivoli Gardens? **about 15 football fields**
11. Disneyland covers about 180 acres. About how many times larger than Tivoli Gardens is Disneyland? **about 9 times**

Each square below represents 25 mi^2. Estimate the area of each region. **12–13. Answers may vary. Samples are given.**

12. 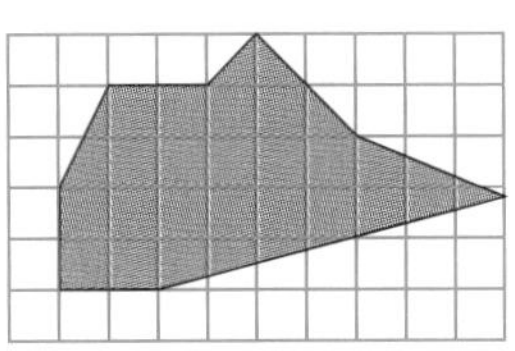 **625 mi^2**

13. 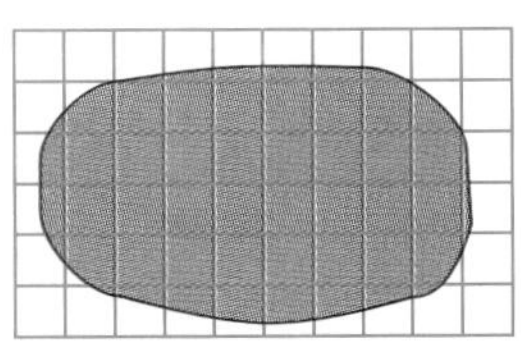 **900 mi^2**

14. a. Measure the length of your *pace* (the distance you cover when you take a normal walking step). **14a–b. Check students' work.**
    b. Use your pace to estimate the length and width of a room in your home. Then estimate the perimeter of the room.
    c. *Writing* Which would be more accurate, measuring the length of your room using your pace or the heel-to-toe method you used in the Work Together. Why? **Answers may vary. Sample: Heel-to-toe; your pace may vary from step to step, but the length of your foot does not change.**

Mixed Review

Solve each equation. *(Lesson 5-9)*

15. $4m = 416$ **104**
16. $\frac{72}{3} = 8n$ **3**
17. $\frac{p}{4} = \frac{325}{600}$ **$\frac{13}{6}$, or $2\frac{1}{6}$**
18. $\frac{-81}{3} = \frac{q}{9}$ **−243**
19. $\frac{s}{2} = 5\frac{7}{8}$ **$11\frac{3}{4}$**

20. Four test scores are 87, 80, 77, and 83. A fifth score makes the mean 82. Find the mode. *(Lesson 1-4)* **83**

Extra Practice, Lesson 8-1, page 521

PRACTICE

Practice 8-1 *Estimating Length and Area*

Estimate each length in inches.

1. 2 in.
2. 5 in.
3. 6 in.
4. 4 in.

Estimate each length in centimeters.

5. 7 cm
6. 9 cm
7. 12 cm
8. 10 cm

Suppose each square below is 1 cm by 1 cm. Estimate the area of each figure. Answers will vary. Samples given.

9. 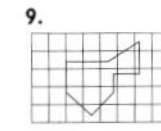 about 7cm^2
10. 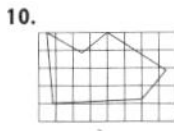 about 19 cm^2
11. 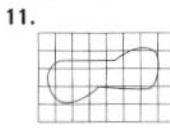 about 10 cm^2
12. 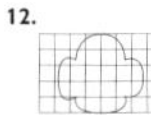 about 18 cm^2

Circle A, B, C, or D. Which unit of measure would you use to measure the given length or area?

13. the height of a tree
A. mm B. cm **(C.)** m D. km

14. the perimeter of the cover of a book
(A.) in. B. ft C. yd D. mi

15. the area of an ocean
A. ft^2 B. yd^2 C. $in.^2$ **(D.)** mi^2

Practice

In copymaster and workbook formats

RETEACHING

Reteaching 8-1 *Estimating Length and Area*

To estimate the length of a line segment in inches, use the part of your index finger between the knuckles. To estimate in centimeters, use the width of your finger nail.

Estimate the length in inches. 1 in.
The line segment is about 2 in. long.

Estimate the length in centimeters. 1 cm
The line segment is about 6 cm long.

To estimate the area of a figure, estimate the number of square units contained in the figure.

Each square unit represents 1 ft^2. Estimate the area.
12 whole squares
partial squares ≈ 2 whole squares
12 + 2 = 14
The area is about 14 ft^2.

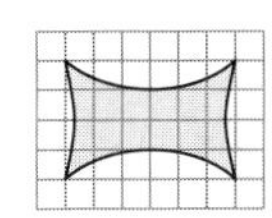

Estimate each length in inches. Answers may vary.

1. 3 in.
2. 1 in.

Estimate each length in centimeters. Answers may vary.

3. 5 cm
4. 3 cm
5. 7 cm
6. 2 cm

Each square below represents 10 mi^2. Estimate the area of each region. Answers may vary.

7. 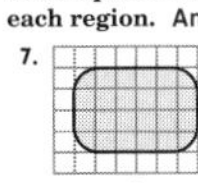 220 mi^2
8. 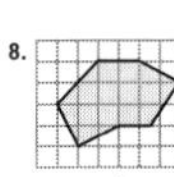 140 mi^2

ENRICHMENT

Minds on Math Transparency

8-1

Jena, Sally, Jack, and Gary have seats next to each other at a play. Jack sits next to Sally but not next to Gary. Gary is not sitting next to Jena. Who is sitting next to Jena?

Jack

See *Solution Key* for worked-out answers.

8-2 Teaching Notes

1 Focus

CONNECTING TO PRIOR KNOWLEDGE
Write the expression $l \times w$ for the class. Ask students: *Evaluate the expression for $l = 5$, and $w = 3$.* **15** Then ask students: *What do the variables l and w usually represent in geometry?* **length and width** Review with students how to find the area of a rectangle.

2 Teach

THINK AND DISCUSS

TACTILE LEARNING Have students draw several parallelograms on graph paper and cut them out. Then have them follow the steps in Questions 1 and 2 to create rectangles. Have students also create a parallelogram on a geoboard and create a rectangle with the same area using a different color band.

AEP VISUAL LEARNING Question 3a
Students might need help with the terms *base* and *height*. Have them cut two strips of paper and tape them together to make an upside-down *T*. Have them label the horizontal strip *base* and the vertical strip *height*.

Example To help students remember to write square units on the area, remind them that cm $\times$ cm $=$ cm^2. Then show them how the units are multiplied by writing:

$$47.5 \text{ cm} \cdot 18.2 \text{ cm} = 864.5 \text{ cm}^2$$

(cm × cm = cm²)

Lesson Planning Options

Prerequisite Skills
- exploring perpendicular segments (precourse)
- evaluating expressions (3-1)

Vocabulary/Symbols
height

Resources

Student Edition

Skills Handbook, p. 541
Extra Practice, p. 521
Glossary/Study Guide

Teaching Resources

Chapter Support File, Ch. 8
- Lesson Planner 8-2
- Practice 8-2, Reteaching 8-2
- Answer Masters 8-2

Teaching Aids Masters 1–3, 8, 9, 19
Glossary, Spanish Resources

Transparencies
1, 7, 15, 17, Minds on Math 8-2

Warm Up

Marques spent \$2.50 on a rubber snake. He spent \$.25 less than that on a yo-yo. He bought a slice of pizza for \$1.50 and juice for half that price. How much money did Marques have left if he started out with a \$10 bill? **\$3.00**

8-2 Area of Parallelograms

What You'll Learn

▼ To find the area and perimeter of parallelograms

...And Why

Area of a parallelogram is related to the areas of rectangles, squares, triangles, and trapezoids.

Here's How

Look for questions that
- build understanding
- ✔ check understanding

THINK AND DISCUSS

You can use what you know about the area of a rectangle (a special parallelogram) to find the area of *any* parallelogram.

1. *Spatial Reasoning* What figures are formed by the perpendicular segment drawn as shown at the right? **trapezoid, triangle**

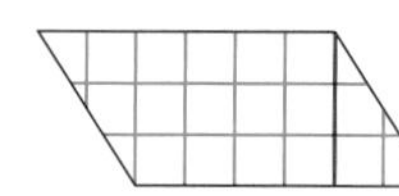

2. a. If you cut along the perpendicular segment and rearrange the two figures as shown, you will form a rectangle. What is its area? **18 square units**

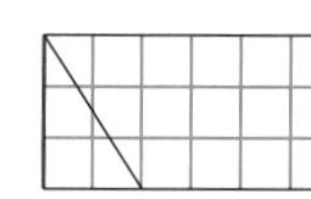

   b. What is the area of the original parallelogram? Why? **18 square units; the area of each piece does not change when you move the pieces.**

3. a. How many units long are the *base* b and the *height* h of the parallelogram?

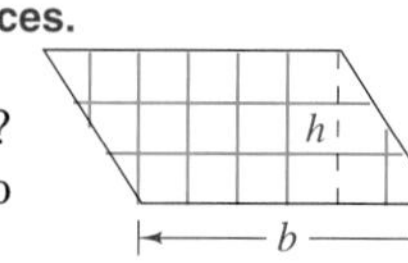

   b. *Explain* How are b and h related to the length and width of the rectangle that was formed? $b = \ell$, $h = w$

3a. b = 6 units; h = 3 units

The formula for the area of a parallelogram follows from the formula for the area of a rectangle.

AREA OF A PARALLELOGRAM

The area of a parallelogram is the product of any base and the corresponding height.

$$A = bh$$

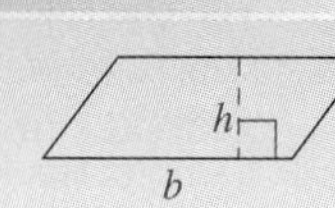

EXAMPLE

Find the area of the parallelogram.

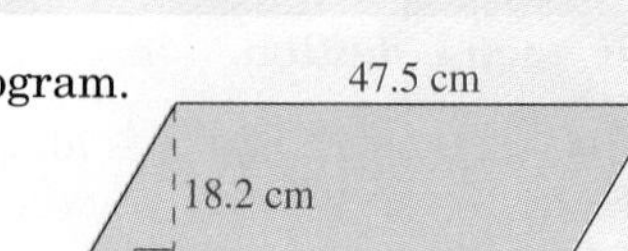

Use $A = bh$ to find the area.

$A = 47.5 \cdot 18.2$
$= 864.5$

The area is 864.5 cm^2.

ERROR ALERT! Question 5a Students might use the slanted side as the height. **Remediation:** Inform students that the height is perpendicular to the base. Have them place a corner of the paper at the intersection of the height and base to check for a right angle.

■ ADDITIONAL EXAMPLE

Find the area of the parallelogram.
223.56 in.^{2}

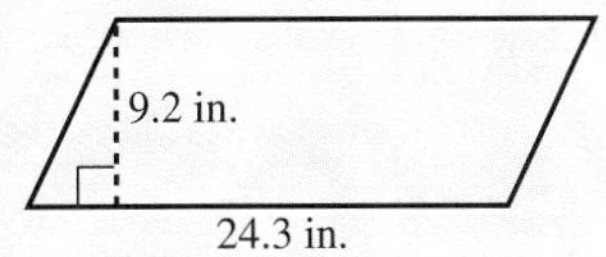

Work Together

EXTENSION Question 8 Ask:

- *Write the ratio of the length of the first triangle to the length of each of the other three rectangles.* $\frac{1}{2}, \frac{1}{3}, \frac{1}{4}$
- *Write the ratio of the perimeter of the first triangle to the perimeter of each of the other three rectangles.* $\frac{1}{2}, \frac{1}{3}, \frac{1}{4}$
  Compare these to the ratios of the lengths.
  They are the same.

4. Suppose you want to find the perimeter of the parallelogram in the Example. What information do you need?
   the length of each side
5. **a.** ✔ *Try It Out* Find the area of the parallelogram. **80 m^2**
   b. Find the perimeter of the parallelogram. **44 m**

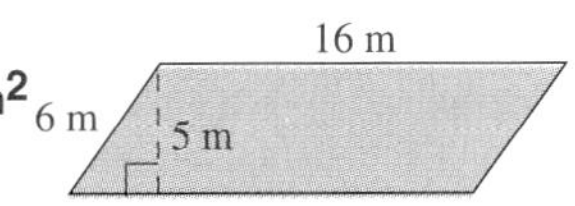

6. *Estimation* The shape of the state of Tennessee is approximately a parallelogram. Find the area of the parallelogram to estimate the area of Tennessee. **41,800 mi^2**

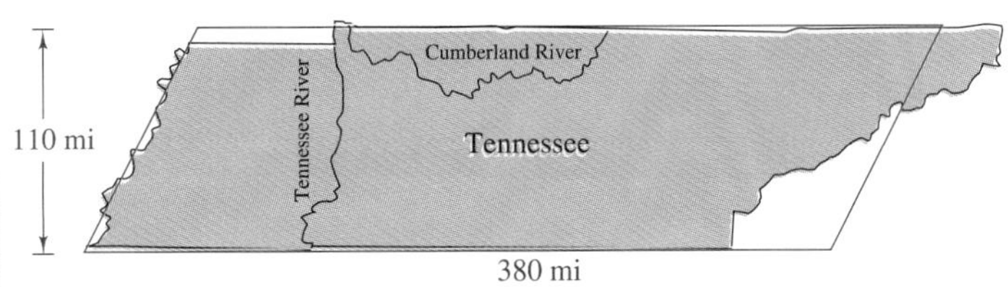

WHO? Surveyors are one of the many skilled workers involved in making a map. They measure distance, direction, and difference in elevation between points on Earth's surface.

Work Together

Exploring Similar Rectangles

If you double the dimensions of a rectangle, you get a rectangle similar to the original one. What do you think happens to the perimeter and area of a rectangle when you double each dimension?

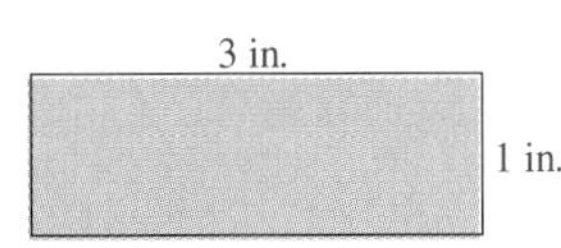

8.

ℓ	w	P	A
3 in.	1 in.	8 in.	3 in.^{2}
6 in.	2 in.	16 in.	12 in.^{2}
9 in.	3 in.	24 in.	27 in.^{2}
12 in.	4 in.	32 in.	48 in.^{2}

7. Find the perimeter and area of the rectangle shown.
   8 in.; 3 in.^{2}
8. Copy and complete the table by finding the perimeter and area of rectangles with the dimensions shown.
   See above right.

ℓ	w	P	A
3 in.	1 in.	■	■
6 in.	2 in.	■	■
9 in.	3 in.	■	■
12 in.	4 in.	■	■

9. *Number Sense* What happens to the perimeter of a rectangle when you double, triple, or quadruple the dimensions?
   The perimeter is doubled, tripled, or quadrupled.
10. *Number Sense* What happens to the area of a rectangle when you double, triple, or quadruple the dimensions?
    The area is multiplied by 4, 9, or 16.

Now you may assign Exercises 1–19.

Technology Options

Prentice Hall Technology

Software for Learners
- Math Blaster® Mystery*
- Interactive Student Tutorial, Chapter 8*

Teaching Resource Software
- Computer Item Generator 8-2
- Resource Pro Chapter 8*

Internet • For related mathematics activities, visit the Prentice Hall site at www.phschool.com/math

**Available on CD-ROM only*

Assignment Options for Exercises On Your Own

Core 1–12, 14–17
Extension 13, 18–19

Use Mixed Review to maintain skills.

- *Write the ratio of the area of the first rectangle to the area of each of the other three rectangles.* $\frac{1}{4}, \frac{1}{9}, \frac{1}{16}$ *Compare these to the ratios of the lengths.* **They are squares of the ratios of the lengths.**

ASSESSMENT Have students draw a rectangle and a parallelogram, each with an area of 30 cm^2. Have them use graph paper or draw their own squares. **Answers may vary. Sample: Rectangle may have dimensions of 1 cm × 30 cm, 2 cm × 15 cm, 3 cm × 10 cm, or 5 cm 6 cm; parallelogram should have base and height matching one of the dimensions given.**

3 Practice/Assess

EXERCISES *On Your Own*

MENTAL MATH Exercises 4–9 Ask students to solve at least two problems mentally. Have volunteers point out exercises for which they can use mental math. You may want to limit the number of calculator exercises.

MENTAL MATH Exercise 10 Ask students what the formulas for perimeter and area of a square have in common. ***s*** Then help students see they must first find *s* before finding the area.

REASONING Exercise 13a The following equations may help the students see a pattern: $2l \times 2w = 4A$; $3l \times 3w = 9A$; $4l \times 4w = 16A$. Then ask students: $nl \times nw =$ ■? $\mathbf{n^2A}$

pages 342–343 On Your Own

14. **The area is doubled; you cannot tell how much the perimeter is increased. For a 3-cm by 4-cm rectangle, the area is 12 cm^2, and the perimeter is 14 cm. If the 4-cm side is doubled, the new area is 24 cm^2, and the perimeter is 22 cm. If the 3 cm side is doubled, the new area is also 24 cm^2, but the new perimeter is 20 cm.**

16a. **7,300 yd^2**

b. **Find the area of each parallelogram. Find the mean of the areas.**

EXERCISES *On Your Own*

Find the area of a parallelogram with base length *b* and height *h*.

1. $b = 7$ ft, $h = 10$ ft **70 ft^2**
2. $b = 12$ in., $h = 7$ in. **84 $in.^2$**
3. $b = 8$ cm, $h = 0.5$ cm **4 cm^2**

Choose **Use a calculator, pencil and paper, or mental math to find the area and perimeter of each parallelogram.**

4. square **25 $in.^2$; 20 in.**

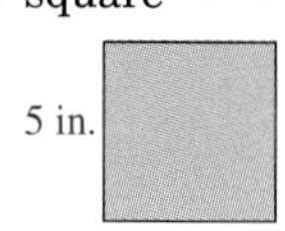

5. rectangle **120 ft^2; 52 ft**

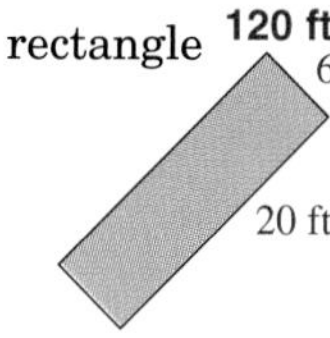

6. **80 cm^2; 40 cm**

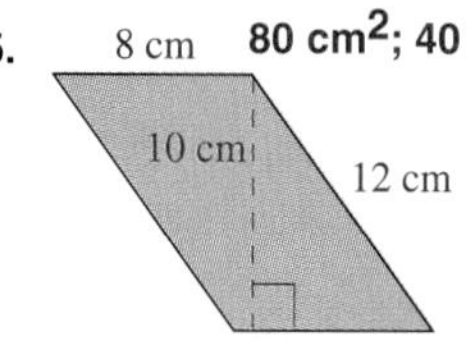

7.

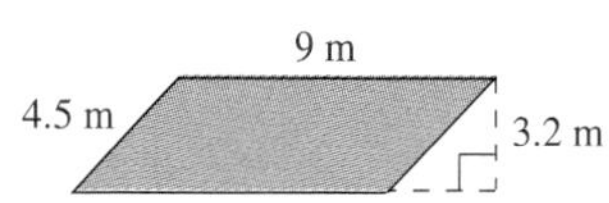

28.8 m^2; 27 m

8.

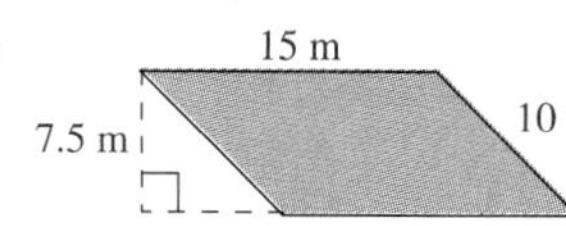

112.5 m^2; 50 m

9.

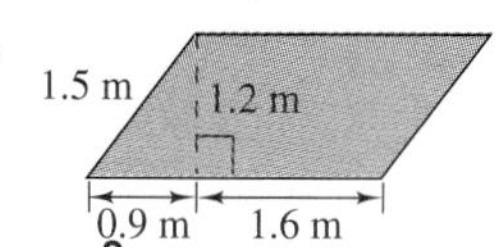

3 m^2; 8 m

10. *Mental Math* The perimeter of a square is 28 in. What is the area? **49 $in.^2$**

11. Find the area of a parallelogram with base length 3 m and height 50 cm. **1.5 m^2, or 15,000 cm^2**

12. *Design* You can use parallelograms to make a design that gives the illusion of being three-dimensional. Do all of the parallelograms in this design have the same area? Why or why not? **Yes; all the parallelograms have the same size and shape.**

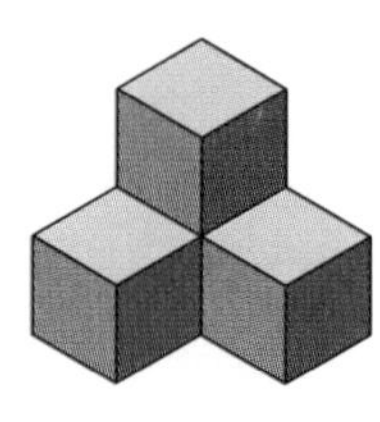

13. a. *Reasoning* What happens to the area of the rectangle in the Work Together activity if you multiply the dimensions by n? **You multiply the area by n^2.**
    b. What happens to the perimeter of the rectangle if you multiply the dimensions by n? **You multiply the perimeter by n.**

14. The length of a rectangle is doubled and the width remains the same. What, if anything, can you say about the new area? About the new perimeter? Explain using examples. **See margin.**

15. The area of a certain rectangle is 20 $in.^2$. The perimeter is 21 in. If you double the length and width, what will be the area and perimeter of the new rectangle? **80 $in.^2$; 42 in.**

JOURNAL
Some parallelograms are rectangles. Explain why the formula $A = bh$ is the same as $A = \ell w$ for these special parallelograms.

WRITING Exercise 18 Encourage students to find the areas of both figures before writing their answers.

WRAP UP

IDENTIFYING THE BIG IDEA Have students explain how they find the perimeter and area of parallelograms.

JOURNAL Have students use perpendicular lines as part of their explanation.

PROJECT LINK Discuss with students why the width and height of the box must be at least equal to the diameter and height of the cylinder.

LESSON QUIZ

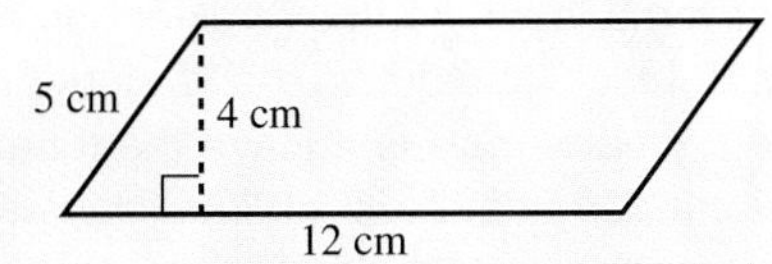

1. Find the area. **48 cm²**
2. Find the perimeter. **34 cm**

16. a. Estimate the area of the pond.
    b. *Writing* Explain how you estimated the area.

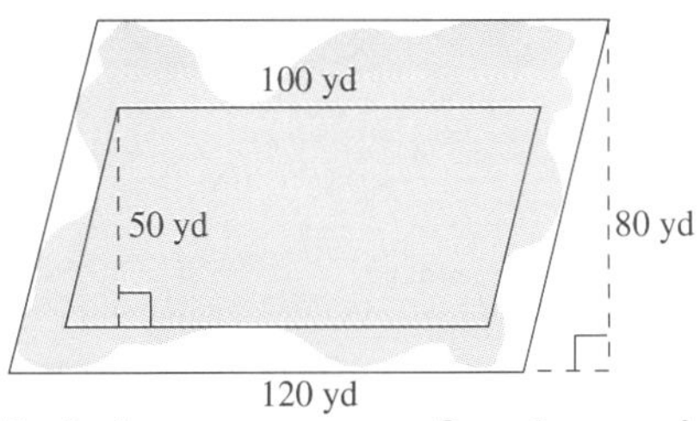

16a–b. Answers may vary. Samples are given. See margin p. 342.

17. Find the area and perimeter of the figure.

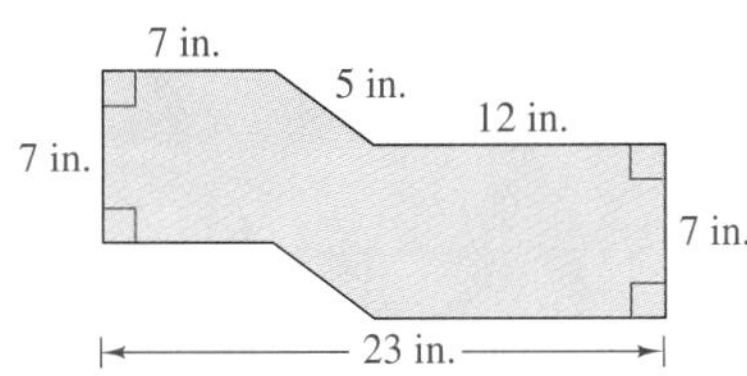

161 in.²; 62 in.

18. *Writing* Why is the area of the rectangle at the right greater than the area of the parallelogram even though they have the same perimeter?

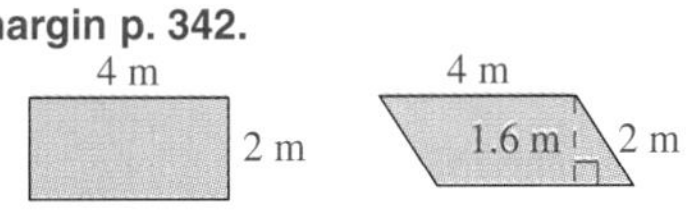

The height of the rectangle is greater than the height of the parallelogram, and they have the same base.

19. The area of a rectangle is 120 cm^2. The width of the rectangle is 8 cm. What is the perimeter of the rectangle? **46 cm**

Mixed Review

Find the value of each expression. *(Lessons 3-3, 3-4)*

20. $120 + 43 - 95$ **68**
21. $28 - 9 + 35 + 14$ **68**
22. $37 + (-89)$ **−52**
23. $(-5)^2 + 6(2 - 4)$ **13**

Find the percent of change. State whether the change is an increase or a decrease. Round to the nearest percent. *(Lesson 6-11)*

24. old: $3.95; new: $4.55 **about 15% increase**
25. old: $180; new: $150 **about 17% decrease**
26. old: $32.50; new: $44 **about 35% increase**
27. *Choose a Strategy* Whitney picked up twice as many books from the library as Lorena, who took 3 more than Amira. If Amira checked out 4 fewer books than Dominic, and he took 5 books, how many books did each person check out? **Whitney: 8 books; Lorena: 4 books; Amira: 1 book; Dominic: 5 books**

CHAPTER PROJECT

PROJECT LINK: ANALYZING

Choose an everyday item that is packaged in a cylinder. It is your job to design a rectangular box for shipping one such cylinder. Decide on the length, width, and height of the box. Remember, don't waste any cardboard. **Check students' work.**

PRACTICE

Practice 8-2 Area of Parallelograms

Choose a calculator, pencil and paper, or mental math to find the perimeter and area of each parallelogram.

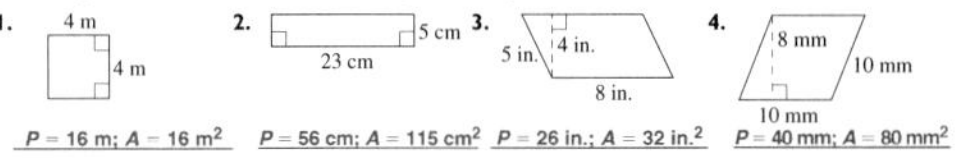

1. $P = 16$ m; $A = 16 \text{ m}^2$
2. $P = 56$ cm; $A = 115 \text{ cm}^2$
3. $P = 26$ in.; $A = 32 \text{ in.}^2$
4. $P = 40$ mm; $A = 80 \text{ mm}^2$

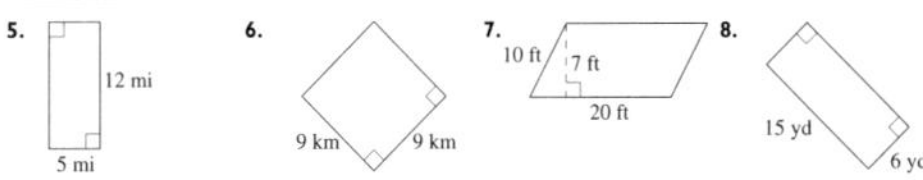

5. $P = 34$ mi; $A = 60 \text{ mi}^2$
6. $P = 36$ km; $A = 81 \text{ km}^2$
7. $P = 60$ ft; $A = 140 \text{ ft}^2$
8. $P = 42$ yd; $A = 90 \text{ yd}^2$

Find the area of each parallelogram.

9. rectangle: $l = 16$ mm, $w = 12$ mm — 192 mm^2
10. parallelogram: $b = 23$ km, $h = 14$ km — 322 km^2
11. square: $s = 27$ ft — 729 ft^2
12. rectangle: $l = 65$ mi, $w = 48$ mi — $3{,}120 \text{ mi}^2$
13. parallelogram: $b = 19$ in., $h = 15$ in. — 285 in.^2
14. square: $s = 42$ m — $1{,}764 \text{ m}^2$
15. The perimeter of a square is 60 ft. What is the area? — 225 ft^2
16. The area of a rectangle is 320 m^2. The width of the rectangle is 16 m. What is the perimeter of the rectangle? — 72 m

Solve.

17. The area of a certain rectangle is 288 yd^2. The perimeter is 68 yd. If you double the length and width, what will be the area and perimeter of the new rectangle? — $A = 1{,}152 \text{ yd}^2$; $P = 136$ yd
18. If you have 36 ft of fencing, what are the areas of the different rectangles you could enclose with the fencing? Consider only whole-number dimensions. — 17 ft^2, 32 ft^2, 45 ft^2, 56 ft^2, 65 ft^2, 72 ft^2, 77 ft^2, 80 ft^2, 81 ft^2

In copymaster and workbook formats

RETEACHING

Reteaching 8-2 Area of Parallelograms

You can use the area of a rectangle to find the area of a parallelogram.

- Draw a perpendicular segment from one vertex to the opposite side to form a triangle.
- Move the triangle to the right side of the parallelogram to form a rectangle.
- Find the area of the rectangle.
  $A = \text{length} \times \text{width} = \text{base} \times \text{height} = bh$

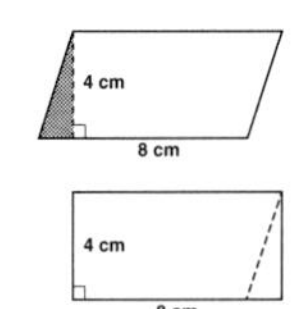

The parallelogram has the same base, height, and area as the rectangle.

$$A = bh = 8 \cdot 4 = 32 \text{ cm}^2$$

Find the area of each parallelogram.

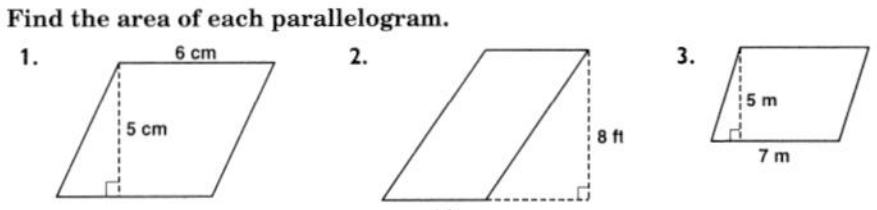

1. 30 cm^2
2. 32 ft^2
3. 35 m^2

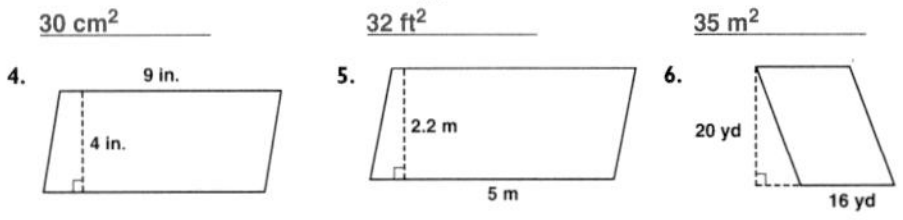

4. 36 in.^2
5. 11 m^2
6. 320 yd^2

Find the area of a parallelogram with base length *b* and height *h*.

7. $b = 7$ in., $h = 4$ in. — 28 in.^2
8. $b = 9$ m, $h = 1.5$ m — 13.5 m^2
9. $b = 12.5$ cm, $h = 2$ cm — 25 cm^2

Reteaching

ENRICHMENT

Minds on Math Transparency

8-2

One of the players on the Jenks High School football team tells his friend that all of the numbers on their jerseys are prime numbers less than 100. What is the greatest number of players that can be on the team?

25 players

See *Solution Key* for worked-out answers.

8-3 Teaching Notes

1 Focus

CONNECTING TO PRIOR KNOWLEDGE
Ask students to name types of quadrilaterals that have two pairs of parallel sides. **square, rectangle, parallelogram, rhombus** Then have students draw an example of one quadrilateral. Ask: *What shapes are formed when you draw one diagonal?* **triangles**

2 Teach

Work Together

EXTENSION This Work Together activity enables students to see how mathematicians discover formulas. If you have extended class periods or block scheduling, have students research a mathematician. Have them name at least one formula the mathematician discovered, and write a short summary about how he or she discovered it.

ERROR ALERT! Question 2 Students may not make the connection that the area of each triangle is one half the area of the parallelogram. **Remediation:** Ask students:

- *How many triangles formed the parallelogram?* **2**
- *Write an equation to represent this.* $2t = p$
- Solve for t. $t = \frac{p}{2}$ or $t = \frac{1}{2}p$

Lesson Planning Options

Prerequisite Skills

- adding decimals (2-3)
- multiplying decimals (2-5)
- using order of operations (2-8)
- multiplying fractions (5-5)

Materials/Manipulatives

- scissors
- calculator
- centimeter graph paper

Resources

Student Edition

Skills Handbook, p. 535
Extra Practice, p. 521
Glossary/Study Guide

Teaching Resources

Chapter Support File, Ch. 8
- Lesson Planner 8-3
- Practice 8-3, Reteaching 8-3
- Answer Masters 8-3

Teaching Aids Masters 2, 9
Glossary, Spanish Resources

Transparencies

1, 15, Minds on Math 8-3

Warm Up

How much more is half of 10,000 than 4,987? **13**

8-3 Area of Triangles and Trapezoids

What You'll Learn

1. To find the area of triangles
2. To find the area of trapezoids

...And Why

You will be able to find the area not only of triangles and trapezoids, but also of more complicated figures.

Here's How

Look for questions that
- build understanding
- ✔ check understanding

Work Together

Finding the Area of a Triangle

Step 1 Use centimeter graph paper to draw two congruent triangles.

Step 2 Cut out both triangles. Put them together to form a parallelogram.

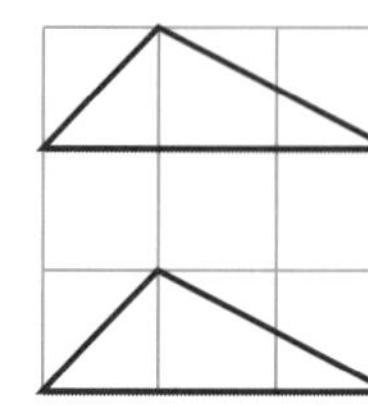

Sample

1. What is the area of the parallelogram? **Check students' work.**
2. What is the area of each triangle? Explain your answer. **See below left.**

2. Check students' work for areas. The area of each triangle should be half the area of the parallelogram in Question 1; the triangles are congruent and the area of the parallelogram is the sum of the area of the triangles.

THINK AND DISCUSS

1 *Area of Triangles*

Any side of a triangle can be considered the *base* of the triangle, with length b. The *height* h is the length of the perpendicular segment from the opposite vertex to the line containing the base.

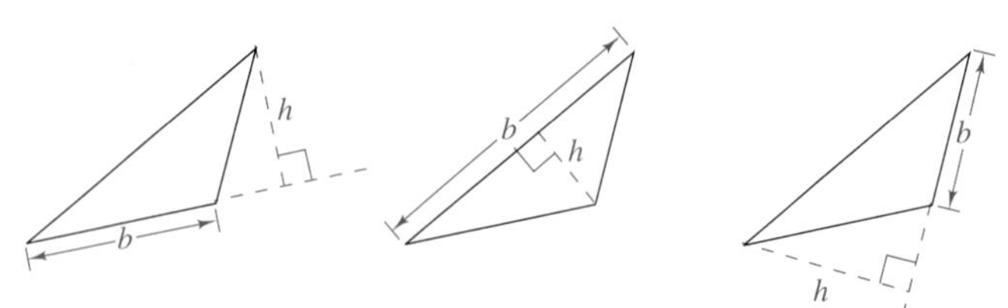

As you discovered in the Work Together activity, the formula for the area of a triangle follows from the area of a parallelogram.

AREA OF TRIANGLE

The area of a triangle is half the product of any base and the corresponding height.

$$A = \frac{1}{2}bh$$

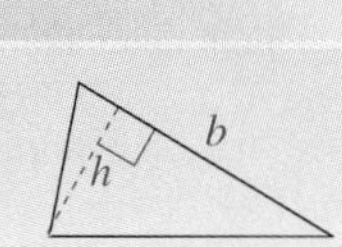

THINK AND DISCUSS

Example 1 Remind students that multiplication is associative. They can simplify by finding $(\frac{1}{2} \cdot 6) \cdot 5$ or $\frac{1}{2} \cdot (6 \cdot 5)$.

MENTAL MATH Question 4 Point out that the base and height must form a 90° angle. In a right triangle, the base and height are the legs of the triangle.

■ ADDITIONAL EXAMPLES

FOR EXAMPLE 1

Find the area and perimeter of the triangle.
$A = 17.5 \text{ ft}^2$; $P = 21.5$ ft

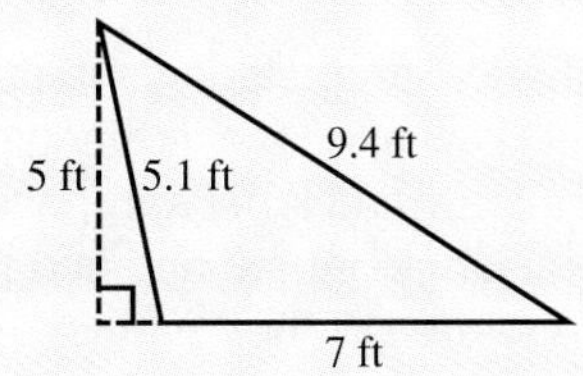

FOR EXAMPLE 2

Find the area of the trapezoid.
$A = 48 \text{ cm}^2$

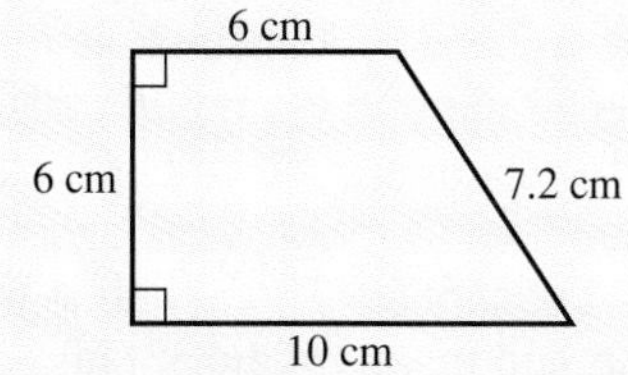

Question 6d Ask students: *How much of the parallelogram is one trapezoid?* $\frac{1}{2}$

■ EXAMPLE 1

Find the area and perimeter of the triangle.

Use $A = \frac{1}{2}bh$ to find the area.

$A = \frac{1}{2} \cdot 6 \cdot 5 = 15$

Add the lengths of the sides to find the perimeter P.

$P = 6.4 + 6 + 5.4 = 17.8$

The area is 15 cm². The perimeter is 17.8 cm.

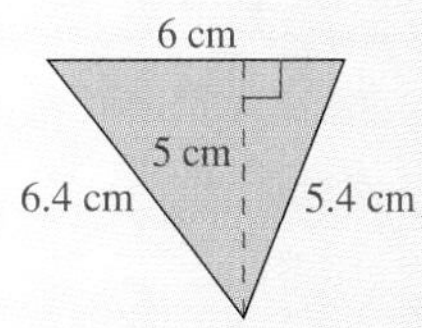

3. The perimeter is the sum of lengths of the sides, and 5 cm is not a length of a side.

3. *Look Back* Why is 5 cm not included in finding the perimeter in Example 1?

4. Find the area and the perimeter of the triangle at the right. **6 ft²; 12 ft**

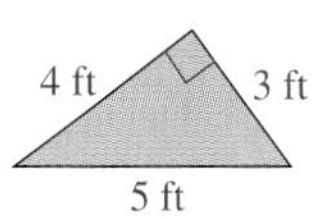

5a. Sample: Double the area. Then divide the result by the height.

5. a. *Go a Step Further* The area of a triangle is 16 in.². The height of the triangle is 2 in. How would you find the length of the base of the triangle?
   b. Find the length of the base. **16 in.**

Now you may assign Exercises 1–6, 11–12.

2 *Area of Trapezoids*

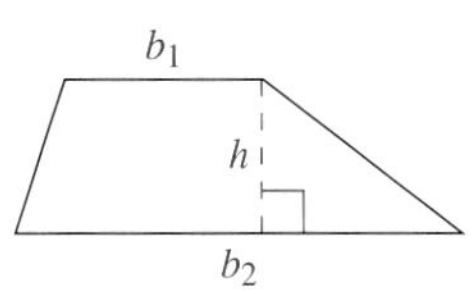

The two parallel sides of a trapezoid are the *bases* of the trapezoid, with lengths b_1 and b_2. The *height* h is the length of a perpendicular segment connecting the bases.

6. a. *Modeling* Suppose you put a trapezoid and a copy of the trapezoid together to form a parallelogram. What will be the length of a base of the parallelogram?
   the sum of the 2 bases of the trapezoid or $b_1 + b_2$

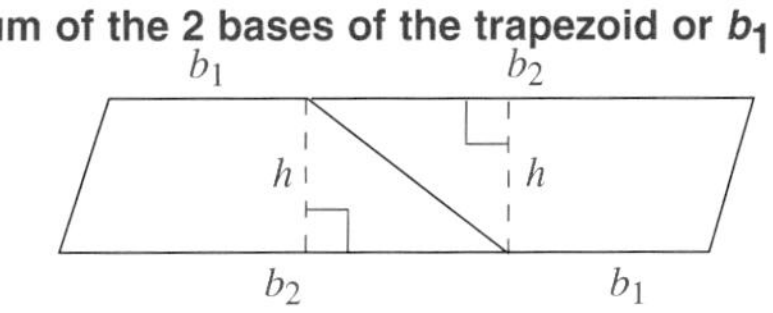

   the same as the height of the trapezoid or h
   b. What will be the height of the parallelogram?
   c. What is an expression for the area of the parallelogram?
   d. What is an expression for the area of the trapezoid?
   c. $h(b_1 + b_2)$ d. $\frac{1}{2}h(b_1 + b_2)$

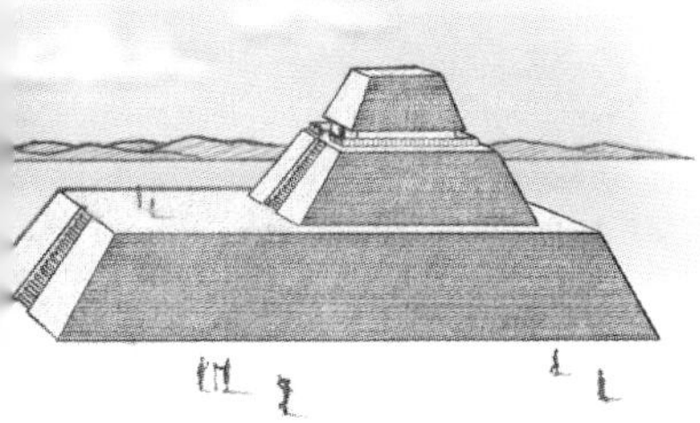

This temple mound was built near the Mississippi River by a Native American culture that thrived from 700 to 1700 A.D.

Technology Options

Prentice Hall Technology

Software for Learners
- Math Lab: Area of Triangles and Trapezoids
- Math Blaster® Mystery*
- Interactive Student Tutorial, Chapter 8*

Teaching Resource Software
- Computer Item Generator 8-3
- Resource Pro Chapter 8*

Internet • For related mathematics activities, visit the Prentice Hall site at www.phschool.com/math

**Available on CD-ROM only*

Assignment Options for Exercises On Your Own

To provide flexible scheduling, this lesson can be subdivided into parts.

1 **Core** 1–6
Extension 11, 12

2 **Core** 7–10, 13–19, 21–26
Extension 20, 27

Use Mixed Review to maintain skills.

KINESTHETIC LEARNING Example 2 Have students work in groups of five. Label five yardsticks A, B, C, D, and E. Describe a trapezoid using inches. For example, the bases A and B are 36 in. and 30 in.; the height C is 12 in.; and the non-parallel sides D and E are 15 in. and 18 in. Have students work on the floor to make a trapezoid to match the description. Then change the description and make the height and one nonparallel side the same length.

ERROR ALERT! Question 7a Students may think the bases are always the top and bottom sides. **Remediation:** Remind students that the bases have to be *parallel.* Have students trace the trapezoid and turn the copy around in all directions.

ASSESSMENT Group students in pairs. Have one student draw and label a triangle. Have one student draw and label a trapezoid. Partners exchange papers and find the perimeter and area of their partner's figure.

TACTILE LEARNING Give each student a tangram. Have students find the area of each of the seven pieces using a ruler and the formulas. Have them check their answers with a partner and discuss shortcuts and patterns such as the area of two small triangles equals the area of the square or the parallelogram.

The formula for the area of a trapezoid follows from the formula for the area of a parallelogram.

AREA OF A TRAPEZOID

The area of a trapezoid is half the product of the height and the sum of the lengths of the bases.

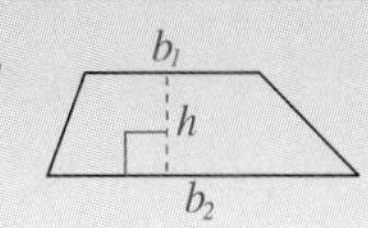

$$A = \frac{1}{2}h(b_1 + b_2)$$

EXAMPLE 2

Find the area of the trapezoid at the right.

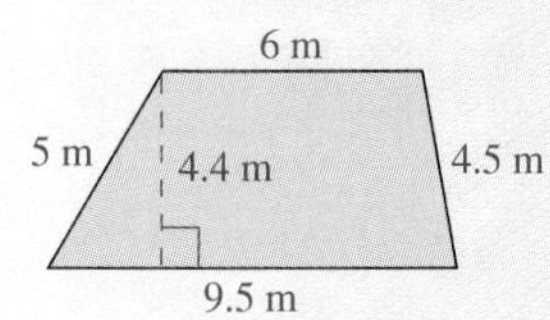

Use $A = \frac{1}{2}h(b_1 + b_2)$ to find the area.

$A = \frac{1}{2}(4.4)(6 + 9.5)$ ← Substitute.

1 ÷ 2 × 4.4 × (6 + 9.5) = 34.1

The area is 34.1 m^2.

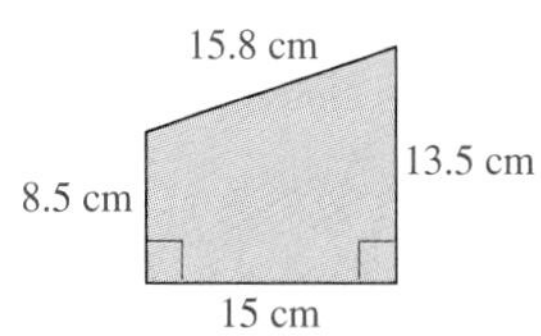

7. a. What are the lengths of the bases of the trapezoid at the left? What is the height? **8.5 cm, 13.5 cm; 15 cm**
   b. *✔ Try It Out* Find the area. **165 cm²**
   c. Find the perimeter. **52.8 cm**

Now you may assign Exercises 7–10, 13–27

EXERCISES *On Your Own*

Find the area of a triangle with base length b and height h.

1. $b = 15$ ft, $h = 10$ ft **75 ft²**
2. $b = 16$ cm, $h = 9$ cm **72 cm²**
3. $b = 5$ m, $h = 11$ m **27.5 m²**
4. $b = 7$ in., $h = 20$ in. **70 in.²**
5. $b = 5.2$ mm, $h = 9.6$ mm **24.96 mm²**
6. $b = 2$ m, $h = 150$ cm **1.5 m², or 15,000 cm²**

Find the area of a trapezoid with base lengths b_1 and b_2 and height h.

7. $b_1 = 3$ m, $b_2 = 7$ m, $h = 3$ m **15 m²**
8. $b_1 = 11$ in., $b_2 = 16$ in., $h = 9$ in. **121.5 in.²**
9. $b_1 = 5.6$ cm, $b_2 = 8.5$ cm, $h = 6$ cm **42.3 cm²**
10. $b_1 = 3\frac{1}{2}$ ft, $b_2 = 2\frac{1}{4}$ ft, $h = 2$ ft **$5\frac{3}{4}$ ft²**

3 Practice/Assess

EXERCISES *On Your Own*

Exercises 1–6 Have students write the formula before finding the area of each triangle.

REASONING Exercise 12 Have students first compare the heights of each shaded triangle. Then have them compare the bases before writing their explanations.

OPEN-ENDED Exercise 20b Students may find it helpful to write the equation $3 = \frac{1}{2} \cdot 1(b^1 + b^2)$, and then solve for $(b^1 + b^2)$. $(b^1 + b^2) = 6$

WRITING Exercise 20c Ask students: *What must the sum of the bases be in order to satisfy the equation?* 6

CONNECTION TO ALGEBRA Exercise 21 Have students draw a trapezoid. Label the height 6 cm, the short base *x*, and the long base 3*x*. Then point out that students can use the equation for the area of a trapezoid to solve for *x*. Remind them to find both bases.

DIVERSITY Exercise 26 Some students may not know what a dulcimer sounds like. If you have block scheduling or extended class periods, have students bring in tapes or CDs of different types of musical instruments. Have students identify the different shapes used in forming the instruments.

RESEARCH Exercise 27 Students may find a map of the United States in an atlas, a geography textbook, or an encyclopedia.

11. Choose A, B, C, or D. What is the area of the shaded region in the rectangle? **D**

A. 12 cm^2 **B.** 32 cm^2 **C.** 8 cm^2 **D.** 20 cm^2

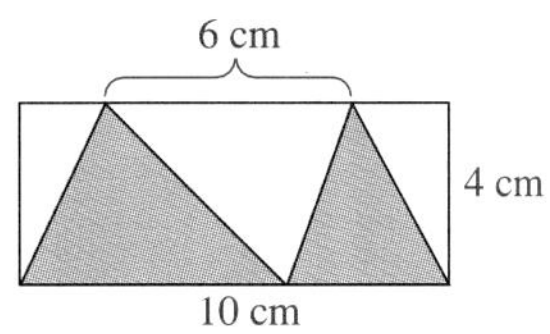

12. *Reasoning* How do you think that the areas of the two shaded regions compare? Explain. **The areas are the same; the regions have the same heights and bases with equal lengths.**

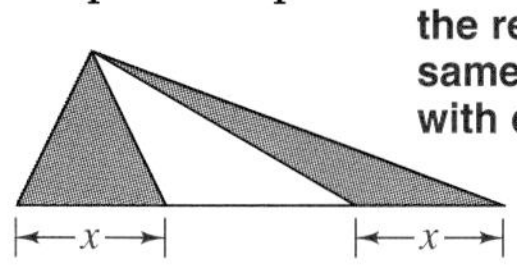

13. The area of the trapezoid is 90 ft^2. What is the height? **5 ft**

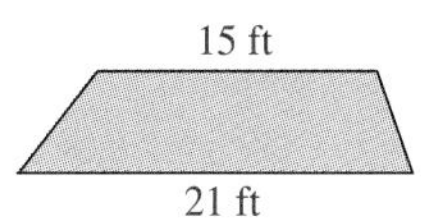

Choose **Use a calculator, paper and pencil, or mental math to find the area and perimeter of each triangle or trapezoid.**

14.

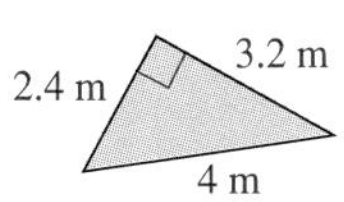

3.84 m^2; 9.6 m

15.

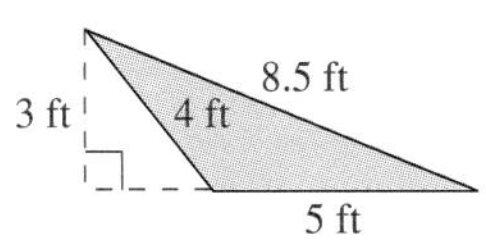

7.5 ft^2; 17.5 ft

16.

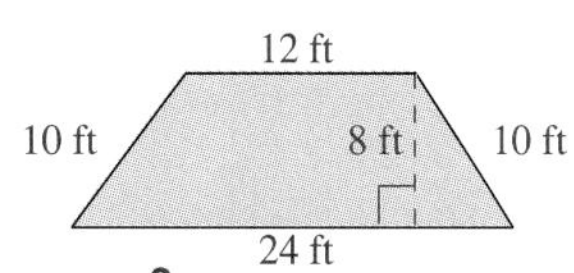

144 ft^2; 56 ft

17.

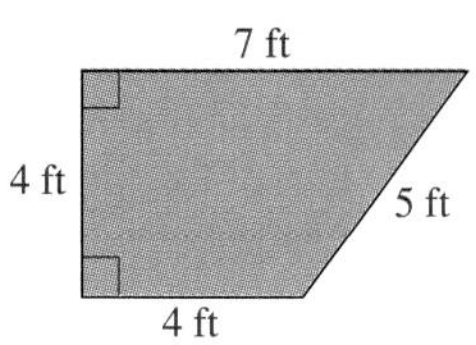

22 ft^2; 20 ft

18.

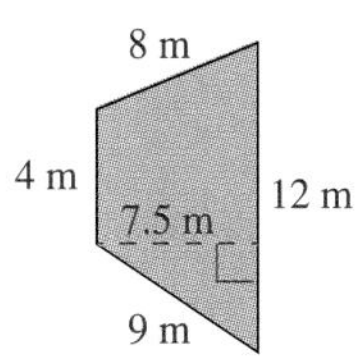

60 m^2; 33 m

19.

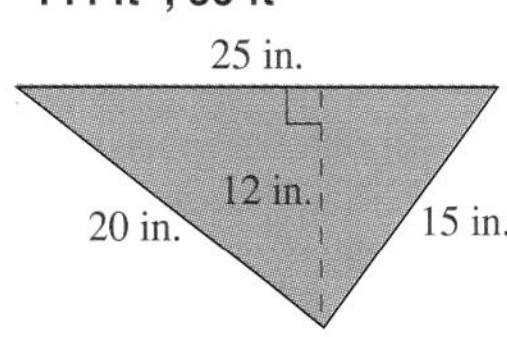

150 $in.^2$; 60 in.

20. a. *Open-ended* Use graph paper to draw a trapezoid that has an area of 3 square units and a height of 1 unit. **Answers may vary. The trapezoid should have bases whose sum is 6 cm.**

b. What are the whole-number possibilities for the lengths of the bases if a trapezoid has an area of 3 square units and a height of 1 unit? **1 and 5, 2 and 4**

c. *Writing* Explain how you found the different lengths in part (b). **The sum of bases is twice the area divided by height, or 6 cm. The pair 3 cm and 3 cm forms a parallelogram.**

21. *Algebra* One base of a trapezoid is three times as long as the other. The height is 6 cm. The area of the trapezoid is 48 cm^2. Write an equation to find the length of the bases. Solve your equation. **$\frac{1}{2} \cdot 6(b + 3b) = 48$; 12 cm, 4 cm**

pages 346–348 On Your Own

27a. Answers may vary. Samples: Alabama, Arizona, Arkansas, Indiana, Mississippi, Missouri, Montana, Nevada, North Dakota, Vermont

b. Answers may vary. For samples in part (a): Alabama—51,600 mi^2; Arizona—113,900 mi^2; Arkansas—53,100 mi^2; Indiana—36,300 mi^2; Mississippi—47,400 mi^2; Missouri—69,500 mi^2; Montana—147,100 mi^2; Nevada—110,500 mi^2; North Dakota—70,700 mi^2; Vermont—9,600 mi^2

PRACTICE

Practice 8-3 *Area of Triangles and Trapezoids*

Choose a calculator, paper and pencil, or mental math to find the area and perimeter of each figure.

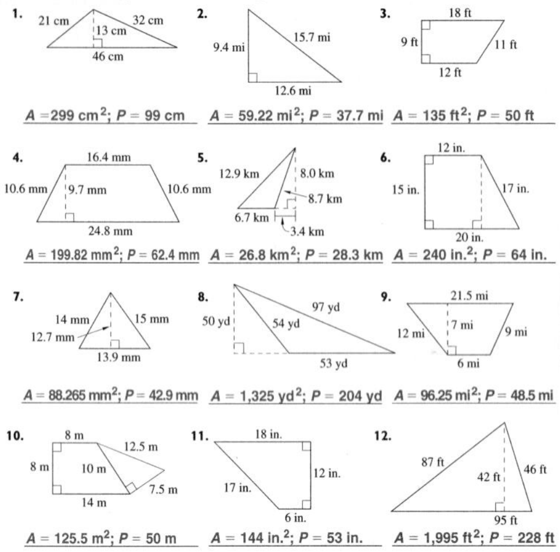

1. $A = 299\ cm^2$; $P = 99$ cm
2. $A = 59.22\ mi^2$; $P = 37.7$ mi
3. $A = 135\ ft^2$; $P = 50$ ft
4. $A = 199.82\ mm^2$; $P = 62.4$ mm
5. $A = 26.8\ km^2$; $P = 28.3$ km
6. $A = 240\ in.^2$; $P = 64$ in.
7. $A = 88.265\ mm^2$; $P = 42.9$ mm
8. $A = 1{,}325\ yd^2$; $P = 204$ yd
9. $A = 96.25\ mi^2$; $P = 48.5$ mi
10. $A = 125.5\ m^2$; $P = 50$ m
11. $A = 144\ in.^2$; $P = 53$ in.
12. $A = 1{,}995\ ft^2$; $P = 228$ ft

Solve.

13. The area of a triangle is 6 square units. Both the height and the length of the base are whole numbers. What are the possible lengths and heights? 1, 12; 2, 6; 3, 4
14. A trapezoid has an area of 4 square units, and a height of 1 unit. What are the possible whole-number lengths for the bases? 1, 7; 2, 6; 3, 5; 4, 4

In copymaster and workbook formats

RETEACHING

Reteaching 8-3 *Area of Triangles and Trapezoids*

You can use the area of a parallelogram to find the area of a triangle and the area of a trapezoid.

Triangle
Two identical triangles, together as shown, form a parallelogram. Each triangle has half the area of the parallelogram.

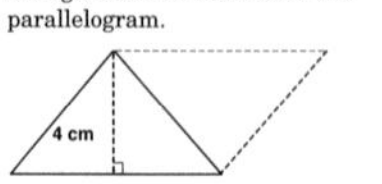

Area of parallelogram: $A = bh$

Area of triangle: $A = \frac{1}{2}bh$

$= \frac{1}{2} \cdot 7 \cdot 4$

$= 14\ cm^2$

Trapezoid
Two identical trapezoids, together as shown, form a parallelogram. The trapezoid has half the area of the parallelogram.

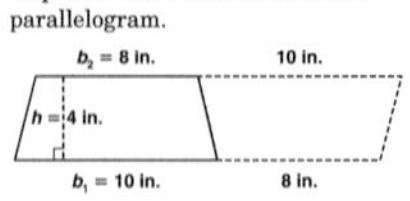

Area of parallelogram: $A = (b_1 + b_2)h$

Area of trapezoid: $A = \frac{1}{2}h(b_1 + b_2)$

$= \frac{1}{2} \cdot 4 \cdot (10 + 8)$

$= 2 \cdot 18 = 36\ in.^2$

Find the area of each figure.

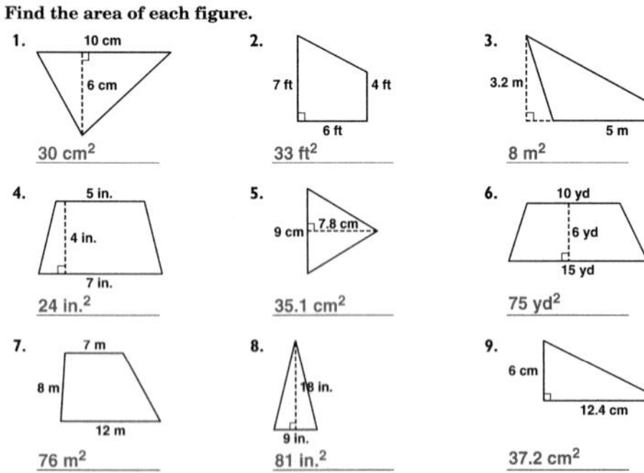

1. $30\ cm^2$
2. $33\ ft^2$
3. $8\ m^2$
4. $24\ in.^2$
5. $35.1\ cm^2$
6. $75\ yd^2$
7. $76\ m^2$
8. $81\ in.^2$
9. $37.2\ cm^2$

ENRICHMENT

Minds on Math Transparency

8-3

The students in Miss Kirk's dance class stand evenly spaced in a circle. The students count off by 1s. The student who counts a 6 is directly across from the student who counts 19. How many students are in Miss Kirk's class?

26 students

See *Solution Key* for worked-out answers.

WRAP UP

IDENTIFYING THE BIG IDEA Have students explain the similarities and differences in the formulas for the area of a triangle and a trapezoid.

LESSON QUIZ

Find the area of each figure.

1. triangle: $b = 25$ ft, $h = 12$ ft
150 ft²

2. trapezoid: $b_1 = 4$ cm, $b_2 = 11$ cm, and $h = 18$ cm **135 cm²**

3.

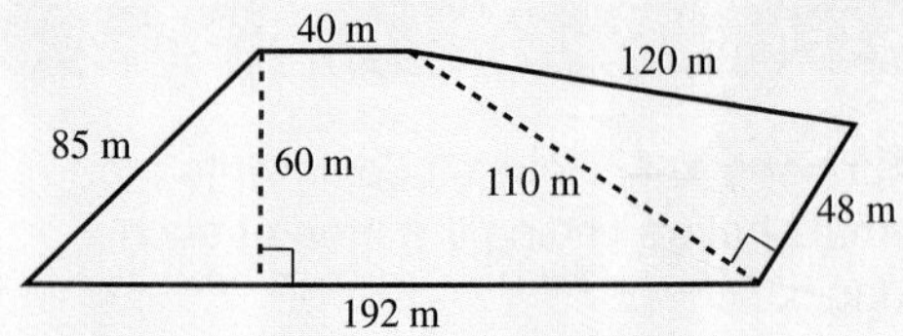

9,600 m²

Find the area and perimeter of each figure.

22. **13,000 yd²; 520 yd**

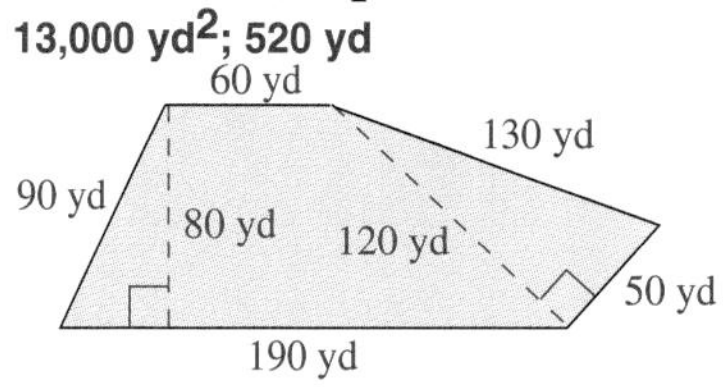

23. **35.5 m²; 23.8 m**

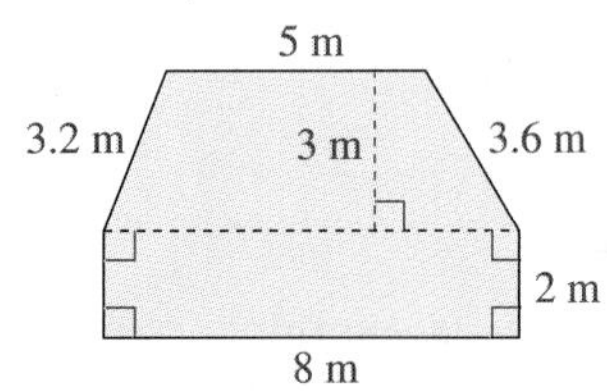

24.

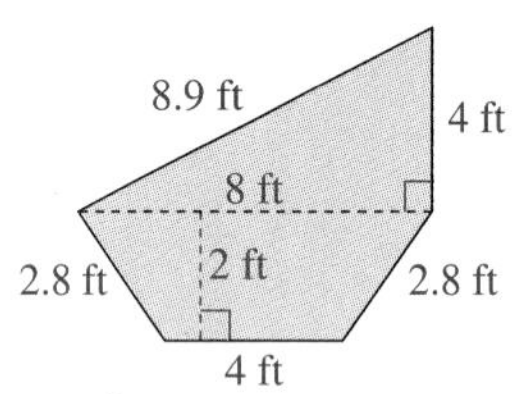

28 ft²; 22.5 ft

25.

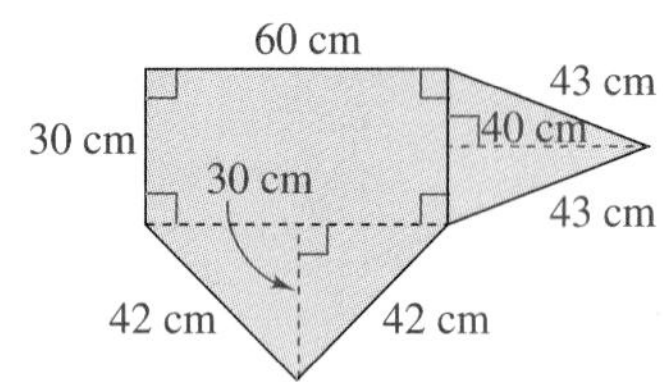

3,300 cm²; 260 cm

26. *Music* The hammer dulcimer at the right is a trapezoid. The top edge is 17 in. long, while the bottom edge is 39 in. long. The distance from the top edge to the bottom edge is 16 in. What is the area of the top of the dulcimer? **448 in.²**

27. a. *Research* Use a map of the United States to name at least three states that resemble trapezoids.
b. *Open-ended* Use the scale on the map to estimate the area of each of the three states.
a–b. See margin, p. 347.

Mixed Review

Classify each angle as acute, right, obtuse, or straight. *(Lesson 7-2)*

28. $m\angle A = 84°$ **acute**
29. $m\angle C = 179°$ **obtuse**
30. $m\angle B = 91°$ **obtuse**
31. $m\angle P = 18°$ **acute**
32. $m\angle Q = 63°$ **acute**

Find each sum or difference. *(Lessons 5-2, 5-3)*

33. $\frac{1}{10} + \frac{3}{4}$ **$\frac{17}{20}$**
34. $\frac{7}{9} - \frac{1}{3}$ **$\frac{4}{9}$**
35. $2 - \frac{3}{5}$ **$1\frac{2}{5}$**
36. $5\frac{1}{2} + 3\frac{7}{8}$ **$9\frac{3}{8}$**
37. $\frac{3}{10} - \frac{3}{15}$ **$\frac{1}{10}$**

38. *Cooking* Ms. Williams baked cookies for a bake sale. She sold 50% of them in the morning and $\frac{2}{3}$ of what was left in the afternoon. She had 4 cookies left. How many did she have at the beginning of the sale? *(Lesson 6-7)* **24 cookies**

8-4 Teaching Notes

1 Focus

CONNECTING TO PRIOR KNOWLEDGE
Draw a circle for the class. Have volunteers draw and label the center point, a radius, and a diameter. Ask: *How can you find the diameter when you know the radius?* **Multiply the radius by 2.** Ask: *How can you find the radius when you know the diameter?* **Divide the diameter by 2.**

2 Teach

Work Together

Question 1 Ask: *Is any segment joining two points on a circle a diameter?* **no** *Why or why not?* **The segment must go through the center.** Suggest students measure the diameter of each can twice. Then use the average of the measurements.

AEP Students may confuse *diameter* and *radius*. Give students this memory device: *The word diameter is longer than the word radius; a diameter is longer than a radius.*

THINK AND DISCUSS

Ask: *How is the circumference of a circle similar to the perimeter of a polygon?* **both measure the distance around a figure**

ALGEBRA Connection

8-4 Circumference and Area of Circles

What You'll Learn

1. To find the circumference of a circle
2. To find the area of a circle

...And Why

Circles are all around you, from dinner plates to circus rings.

Here's How

Look for questions that
- build understanding
- ✔ check understanding

Work Together

Finding the Ratio $\frac{C}{d}$ for a Circle

Use three cans that have bases of different sizes.

1. Measure the diameter d of a base of each can. Use string to measure the distance C around a base of each can. Record your results in a table. **Check students' work.**
2. Use a calculator to find the quotient $\frac{C}{d}$ for each can. Round each quotient to the nearest tenth. **Check students' work. Quotients should range from 3.1 to 3.2.**
3. *Draw a Conclusion* What seems to be true about each quotient $\frac{C}{d}$? **Each quotient is about 3.1.**

THINK AND DISCUSS

1 Circumference of a Circle

Circumference is the distance around a circle. The ratio of every circle's circumference C to its diameter d is always the same, a number that is close to 3.14. Mathematicians use the symbol π, read as "pi," for this ratio. So, $\pi = \frac{C}{d}$.
If you multiply both sides of the equation $\pi = \frac{C}{d}$ by d, you get a formula for the circumference of a circle.

CIRCUMFERENCE OF A CIRCLE

The circumference of a circle is π times the diameter.

$$C = \pi d = 2\pi r$$

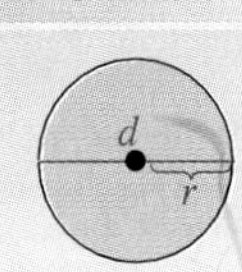

Many calculators have a π key.

4. *Calculator* Press the π key on your calculator. What is the result? **3.141592654**

Lesson Planning Options

Prerequisite Skills
- multiplying decimals (2-5)
- evaluating expression (3-1)
- multiplying fractions (5-5)

Vocabulary/Symbols
circumference, pi (π)

Materials/Manipulatives
- string
- 3 different-sized cans
- calculator
- ruler

Resources

Student Edition
Skills Handbook, p. 541
Extra Practice, p. 521
Glossary/Study Guide

Teaching Resources
Chapter Support File, Ch. 8
- Lesson Planner 8-4
- Practice 8-4, Reteaching 8-4
- Answer Masters 8-4

Teaching Aids Masters 1–3, 10, 19
Glossary, Spanish Resources

Transparencies
1, 7, 15, 17, Minds on Math 8-4

Warm Up
Karen placed 56 bottles into boxes that each hold 6 bottles. How many boxes did she use? **10**

TACTILE LEARNING To demonstrate the circumference of a circle, give students circular objects. They roll their objects one revolution, and mark the spots where the object started and stopped. Then measure the distance between the marks. This approximates the circumference.

ADDITIONAL EXAMPLES

FOR EXAMPLE 1

A pizza has a diameter of 18 in. What is the circumference? **about 56.5 in.**

FOR EXAMPLE 2

The diameter of a circle is 25 mm. Find the area of the circle to the nearest unit. **about 491 mm^2**

EXTENSION If you have block scheduling or extended class periods, have students research the discovery of π. Have them research the number of places to which π has been carried out.

Example 1 Point out that circumference is measured, like perimeter, in linear units. Linear units are a measure of distance, not of region or area.

Technology Options

Prentice Hall Technology

Software for Learners

- Hot Page™ 5–4*
- Math Blaster® Mystery*
- Interactive Student Tutorial, Chapter 8*

Teaching Resource Software

- Computer Item Generator 8-4
- Resource Pro Chapter 8*

Internet • For related mathematics activities, visit the Prentice Hall site at www.phschool.com/math

**Available on CD-ROM only*

Assignment Options for Exercises On Your Own

To provide flexible scheduling, this lesson can be subdivided into parts.

1 **Core** 1–5, 22–26
Extension 27

2 **Core** 6–21, 28
Extension 29

Use Mixed Review to maintain skills.

Approximations such as 3.14 and $\frac{22}{7}$ are often used for π.

EXAMPLE 1 *Real-World Problem Solving*

Entertainment A standard circus ring has a diameter of 13 m. What is the circumference?

Use $C = \pi d$ to find the circumference.

[π] [×] 13 [=] 40.8407045 ← Use a calculator.

The circumference is about 40.8 m.

WHERE? Circus acts go back thousands of years. The modern circus developed in England during the 1700s and soon spread to America. Russia's Moscow Circus is shown at the right.

5. a. *Go a Step Further* The circumference of a circle is about 50 cm. How would you find the diameter? **Divide the circumference by π.**
   b. *Calculator* Find the diameter to the nearest unit. **16 cm**
   c. Is your answer reasonable? Explain. **Yes; 16 × 3 = 48, which is close to 50.**

Now you may assign Exercises 1–5, 22–27.

2 *Area of a Circle*

6. *Estimation* For each circle below, do the following:
   - Find the radius r.
   - Estimate the area A.
   - Use a calculator to find the ratio $\frac{A}{r^2}$.

a.

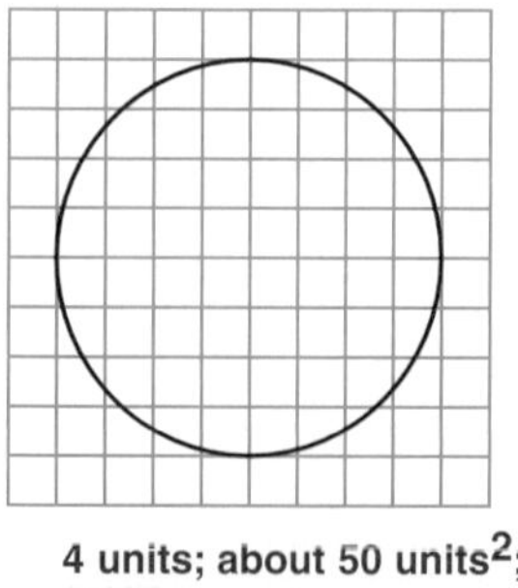

4 units; about 50 units^2; 3.125

b.

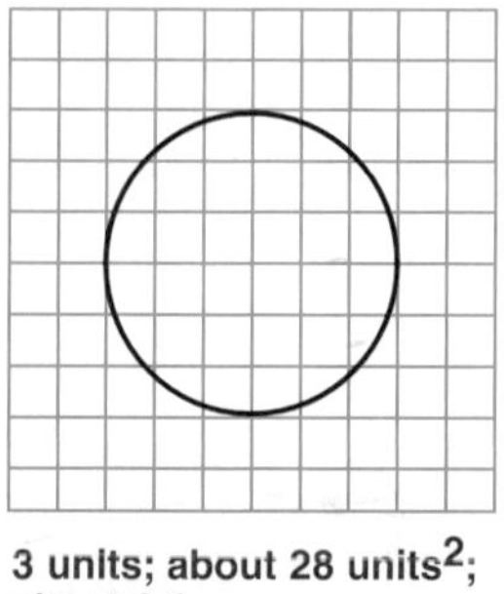

3 units; about 28 units^2; about 3.1

ESTIMATION **Question 6** Have students describe how they will estimate the area. **Answers may vary. Sample: Count the shaded and almost-shaded squares as 1. Count the half-shaded squares as $\frac{1}{2}$. Count the squares barely shaded as 0.**

ERROR ALERT! **Example 2** Some students may multiply π times the radius and then square the *product.* **Remediation:** Have students write $\pi \times 7.5^2$ as $\pi \times 7.5 \times 7.5$. Then they can multiply the three numbers in any order.

ASSESSMENT Assign groups of three. Have each student draw a circle. They should include a diameter or a radius labeled with a measurement of their choice. Have them exchange circles and find the circumference. Then exchange circles again and find the area. Have students check the circumference and the area of their own circles.

3 Practice/Assess

EXERCISES *On Your Own*

Exercises 1–5 Remind students to find the diameter first for each exercise that gives the radius. Have them write the formula $C = \pi d$, and show the value they used for d. Remind students to use the π button on the calculator, because using 3.14 may give a slightly different answer.

Did you find that in each case the quotient was a little more than 3? In fact, the quotient is equal to π!

$$\frac{A}{r^2} = \pi$$

If you multiply both sides of the equation $\frac{A}{r^2} = \pi$ by r^2, you get the following formula.

AREA OF A CIRCLE

The area of a circle is the product of π and the square of the radius.

$$A = \pi r^2$$

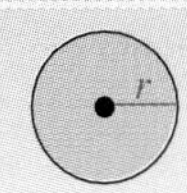

7. ***Explain*** How would you find the area of a circle if you know its diameter? **Divide the diameter by 2. Then square the quotient and multiply by π.**

■ **EXAMPLE 2**

The diameter of a circle is 25 cm. Find the area of the circle to the nearest unit.

Use $A = \pi r^2$ to find the area.

$r = 25 \div 2 = 12.5$ ← First divide the diameter by 2 to find r.

[π] [×] 12.5 [x^2] [=] 490.8738521

The area is about 491 cm^2.

8. ✔ ***Try It Out*** The diameter of the inside of a basketball hoop is 18 in. What is the area enclosed by a basketball hoop? Round to the nearest tenth. **about 254.5 $in.^2$**

9. ***Explain*** How would you find the area of a circle if you know its circumference?
Now you may assign Exercises 6–21, 28–29.

9. Divide the circumference by π and then by 2 to find the radius. Use the formula $A = \pi r^2$ to find the area.

EXERCISES *On Your Own*

Calculator **Find the circumference of each circle to the nearest unit.**

1.
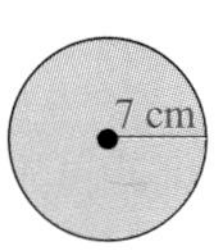

44 cm

2.
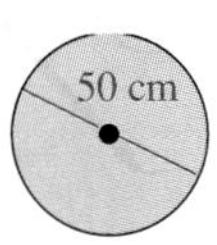

157 cm

3.
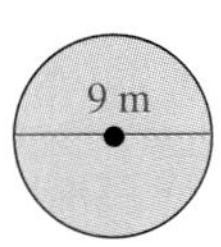

28 m

4.
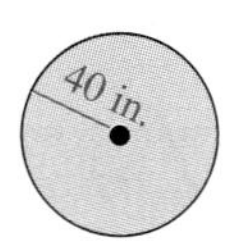

251 in.

5.
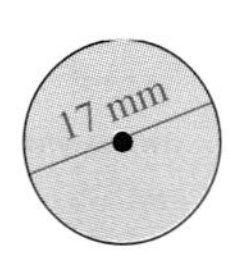

53 mm

Exercises 6–10 Have students write $r = \frac{d}{2}$ for each exercise that gives the diameter. Remind them that the formula is for the *radius.*

MENTAL MATH Exercises 11–14 Some students may need to write the formulas for area and circumference on their papers. They can still do the computations mentally.

WRITING Exercise 15c Explain to students that π is a nonterminating decimal that does not repeat. Ask students to consider which student used the closer approximation for π.

CONNECTION TO SPORTS Exercise 27 Ask students why they are asked to find the *perimeter* instead of the *circumference.* **Answers may vary. Sample: The whole shape is not a circle.** Also note that a rectangle separates the two halves of the circle.

Exercise 29 Have students write an equation similar to the following:
A(big circle) − 4[A(small circle)] = A(shaded region).

Exercises 30–32 Some students may choose to solve the percent problems with proportions. Others may want to write algebraic equations.

Exercises 33–36 Encourage students to check their solutions using substitution.

CHECKPOINT 1

Checkpoint 1 *Lessons 8-1 through 8-4*

Find the area and perimeter of each figure.

1. (square, 2.5 cm by 2.5 cm) A = 6.25 cm² P = 10 cm
2. (triangle, sides 15 cm, 14 cm, 13 cm, height 12 cm) A = 84 cm² P = 42 cm
3. (trapezoid, 12 m, 10 m, 9 m, 20 m) A = 144 m² P = 51 m

4. **Circle A, B, C, or D.** The diameter of a large circle at the right is 8 in. The diameter of each small circle is 2 in. What is the area of the shaded region? Use 3.14 for π.

Ⓐ 40.82 in.² **B.** 59.66 in.² **C.** 163.28 in.² **D.** 628 in.

5. Choose the unit you would use to estimate the area of a baseball field: ft², mi, ft, yd², mi². yd²

pages 351–352 On Your Own

15c. 99 m²; using the π key gives a more accurate area than using 3.14, so Kenny's answer is closer to the actual area of the circle.

Calculator **Find the area of each circle to the nearest unit.**

6. 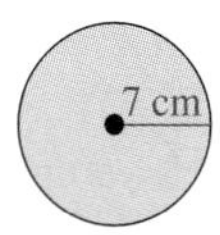

154 cm²

7. 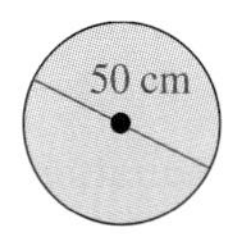

1,963 cm²

8. 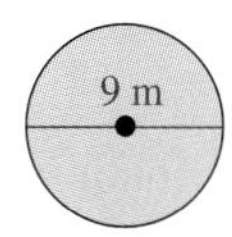

64 m²

9. 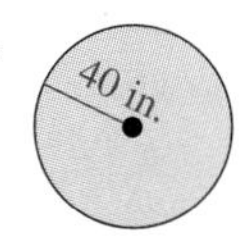

5,027 in.²

10. 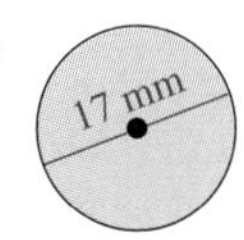

227 mm²

Mental Math **Use 3 for π to estimate the circumference and area of each circle.**

11. $d = 2$ cm 6 cm; 3 cm²
12. $r = 10$ ft 60 ft; 300 ft²
13. $r = 6$ in. 36 in.; 108 in.²
14. $d = 4$ m 12 m; 12 m²

15. a. *Calculator* Use the π key to find the area of this circle to the nearest hundredth. 98.52 m²

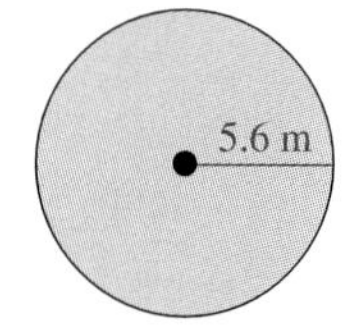

b. *Calculator* Find the area of the circle to the nearest hundredth, using 3.14 for π. 98.47 m²

c. *Writing* Kenny said that the area of the circle is about 99 m². Lynn said that the area is about 98 m². Which answer would you give for the area? Explain. 99 m²; using the π key gives a more accurate area than using 3.14, so Kenny's answer is closer to the actual area of the circle.

16. **Choose A, B, C, or D.** If you double the radius of a circle, what happens to the area? D

A. It remains the same.
B. It is doubled.
C. It is tripled.
D. It is quadrupled.

Use $\frac{22}{7}$ for π to find the circumference and area of a circle with the given radius or diameter.

17. $r = 14$ ft 88 ft; 616 ft²
18. $d = 9$ cm $28\frac{2}{7}$ cm; $63\frac{9}{14}$ cm²
19. $r = 3\frac{1}{2}$ yd 22 yd; $38\frac{1}{2}$ yd²
20. $d = 7$ in. 22 in.; $38\frac{1}{2}$ in.²
21. $r = 11$ mm $69\frac{1}{7}$ mm; $380\frac{2}{7}$ mm²

Given the circumference of a circle, find the radius to the nearest tenth.

22. $C = 58$ m 9.2 m
23. $C = 41$ ft 6.5 ft
24. $C = 35$ in. 5.6 in.
25. $C = 93$ mm 14.8 mm
26. $C = 12$ cm 1.9 cm

27. *Sports* The track shown has two lanes separated by a dashed white line. Each lane is 1 m wide.

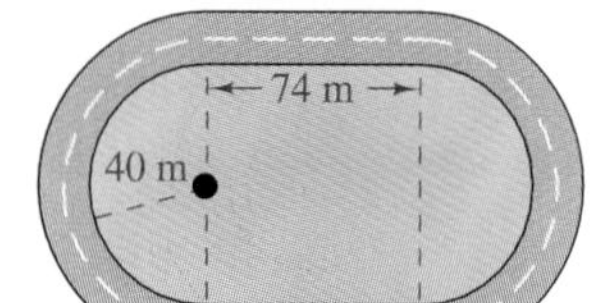

a. What is the difference between the inside perimeter and the outside perimeter of the inner lane? How does that compare to the difference between the perimeters of the outer lane? About 6.3 m; the differences are the same.

b. The runner in the inner lane is to run once around the track. Where should the runner in the outer lane start if both runners are to run equal distances? Explain. About 6.3 m forward; the outer lane is 6.3 m longer.

WRAP UP

IDENTIFYING THE BIG IDEA Have students explain how to find the circumference and area of a circle. Also, have them tell what pi (π) represents.

LESSON QUIZ

Find the circumference of each circle to the nearest unit.

1. radius = 9 yd **57 yd**
2. diameter = 40 cm **126 cm**

Find the area of each circle to the nearest unit.

3. radius = 8.5 m **227 m²**
4. diameter = 32 cm **804 cm²**

28. *Social Studies* Tipis of the Sioux and Cheyenne tribes were often over 12 ft tall. The circular base had a diameter of about 15 ft. What was the area of a base? Round to the nearest unit. **177 ft²**
29. The diameter of the large circle shown below is 3.6 cm. The diameter of each of the small circles is 0.9 cm. Find the area of the shaded region to the nearest tenth. **7.6 cm²**

Mixed Review

Find each answer. *(Lessons 6-9, 6-10)*

30. What is 40% of 360? **144**
31. 45 is what percent of 360? **12.5%**
32. 36 is 12% of what number? **300**

Solve each equation. *(Lesson 3-9)*

33. $13 + 3x = 7$ **−2**
34. $16 + 2y = 9$ **−3.5**
35. $1.1a + 2 = 7.5$ **5**
36. $\frac{1}{2}b - 16 = 10$ **52**

✓ CHECKPOINT 1 — *Lessons 8-1 through 8-4*

1. Choose the unit you would use to estimate the area of your classroom: in., ft, mi, in.², ft², mi². **ft²**

Find the area and perimeter of each figure.

2. triangle

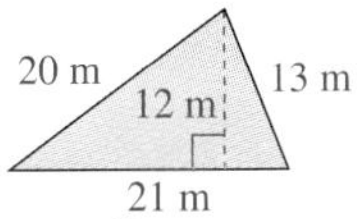

126 m²; 54 m

3. parallelogram

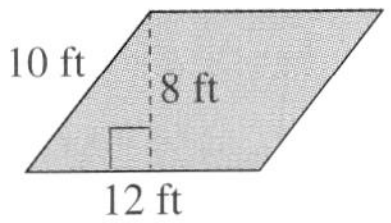

96 ft²; 44 ft

4. triangle

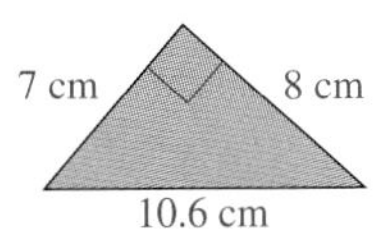

28 cm²; 25.6 cm

5. trapezoid

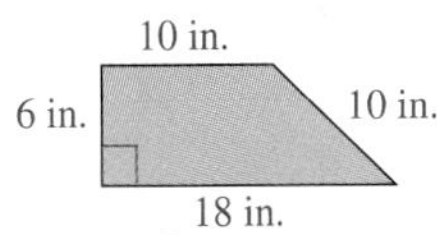

84 in.²; 44 in.

6. *Calculator* The radius of a circle is 75 cm. Find the circumference and area to the nearest unit. **471 cm; 17,671 cm²**

PRACTICE

Practice 8-4 Circumference and Area of Circles

Find the circumference and area of each circle to the nearest tenth.

1. 3 in. — $C \approx 9.4$ in.; $A \approx 7.1$ in.²
2. 2 m — $C \approx 12.6$ m; $A \approx 12.6$ m²
3. 7 ft — $C \approx 22.0$ ft; $A \approx 38.5$ ft²
4. 6 km — $C \approx 37.7$ km; $A \approx 113.1$ km²
5. 8 mi — $C \approx 25.1$ mi; $A \approx 50.3$ mi²
6. 15 in. — $C \approx 94.2$ in.; $A \approx 706.9$ in.²
7. 4.6 cm — $C \approx 14.6$ cm; $A \approx 16.6$ cm²
8. 9.3 mm — $C \approx 58.4$ mm; $A \approx 271.7$ mm²
9. 47 km — $C \approx 147.7$ km; $A \approx 1{,}734.9$ km²
10. 15.6 m — $C \approx 98.0$ m; $A \approx 764.5$ m²
11. 17 yd — $C \approx 53.4$ yd; $A \approx 227.0$ yd²
12. 8.4 m — $C \approx 52.8$ m; $A \approx 221.7$ m²

Given the circumference of a circle, find the radius to the nearest tenth.

13. $C = 80$ km — 12.7 km
14. $C = 92$ ft — 14.6 ft
15. $C = 420$ in. — 66.8 in.
16. $C = 700$ km — 111.4 km
17. The radius of the large circle is 8 in. The radius of each of the smaller circles is 1 in. Find the area of the shaded region to the nearest unit. 192 in.²

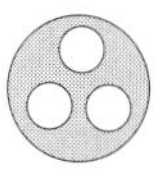

In copymaster and workbook formats

RETEACHING

Reteaching 8-4 Circumference and Area of Circles

The **circumference** of a circle is the distance around it. To find the circumference of a circle with radius r and diameter d, use either the formula $C = 2\pi r$ or $C = \pi d$. Use 3.14 for π.

8 cm

$d = 8$ cm
$C = \pi d$
$\approx 3.14 \cdot 8$
≈ 25.12 cm

To the nearest centimeter, the circumference is 25 cm.

6 ft

$r = 6$ ft
$C = 2\pi r$
$\approx 2 \cdot 3.14 \cdot 6$
≈ 37.68 ft

To the nearest foot, the circumference is 38 ft.

8 cm

To find the area of a circle, use $A = \pi r^2$.
The diameter of the circle is 8 cm, so the radius is 4 cm.
$C = \pi r^2$
$\approx 3.14 \cdot 4 \cdot 4$
≈ 50.24 cm²
To the nearest square centimeter, the area is 50 cm².

Find the circumference and area of each circle to the nearest unit.

1. 7 cm — 44 cm; 154 cm²
2. 2 in. — 13 in.; 13 in.²
3. 10 m — 31 m; 79 m²
4. 2 cm — 6 cm; 3 cm²
5. 3 ft — 19 ft; 28 ft²
6. 8 yd — 50 yd; 201 yd²

Reteaching

ENRICHMENT

Minds on Math Transparency

8-4

What is the total number of triangles in the figure?

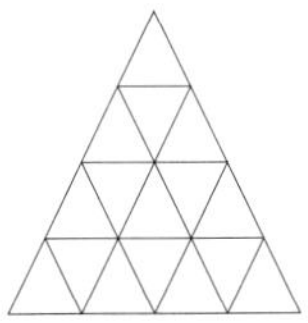

27 triangles

See *Solution Key* for worked-out answers.

8-5 Teaching Notes

1 Focus

CONNECTING TO PRIOR KNOWLEDGE Ask students to complete the following:

$4 \cdot 4 = \blacksquare$ 16
$9 \cdot 9 = \blacksquare$ 81
$25 \div 5 = \blacksquare$ 5
$49 \div 7 = \blacksquare$ 7

Ask: *What do these statements have in common?* **Answers may vary. Sample: One number appears twice in each statement.**

2 Teach

Work Together

Students may find it helpful to write *length of sides* above the variable *n* in their chart. Likewise, they may want to write *area of square* above n^2.

THINK AND DISCUSS

VISUAL LEARNING Example 1 Give each student a piece of graph paper. Demonstrate $\sqrt{16}$ by having students draw a square made up of exactly 16 units. Then ask: *What is the length of each side of the square?* **4 units**

REASONING Question 5c Show students a number line with 0 in the middle and integers labeled on both sides of 0. Ask:

- *What type of numbers do you write to the left of 0?* **negative integers**

Lesson Planning Options

Prerequisite Skills

- using exponents (4-4)

Vocabulary/Symbols

perfect square, square root ($\sqrt{}$)

Materials/Manipulatives

- square tiles

Resources

Student Edition

Skills Handbook, p. 541
Extra Practice, p. 521
Glossary/Study Guide

Teaching Resources

Chapter Support File, Ch. 8
- Lesson Planner 8-5
- Practice 8-5, Reteaching 8-5
- Answer Masters 8-5

Teaching Aids Masters 1, 2, 27
Glossary, Spanish Resources

Transparencies

1, 14, 15, Minds on Math 8-5

Warm Up

Evaluate each algebraic expression.

$c + 5 \cdot 2$ for $c = 7$ 17
$20 - 8 \div p$ for $p = 2$ 16

ALGEBRA Connection

8-5 Exploring Square Roots

What You'll Learn

1. To find perfect squares and square roots of perfect squares
2. To estimate square roots

...And Why

You will be able to find the length of a side of a square whose area is a perfect square.

Here's How

Look for questions that
- build understanding
- ✔ check understanding

Work Together

Investigating Square Numbers

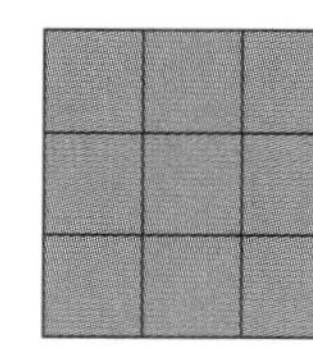

Look at the diagram at the right. If you form a square with 3 tiles on each side, you will use 9 tiles. This shows that $3^2 = 9$.

1. Use square tiles to form squares with 1, 2, . . . , 12 tiles on each side.
   Check students' work.
2. Make a table that shows the number of tiles needed for each square. Label the columns of the table n for side lengths and n^2 for number of tiles.
3. Extend your table for side lengths 13 through 20.
   2–3. **See margin p. 356.**

THINK AND DISCUSS

1 *Finding Square Roots of Perfect Squares*

A number like 9 that is the square of an integer is a **perfect square.** The inverse of squaring a number is finding its **square root.** Because $3^2 = 9$, the (positive) square root of 9 is 3.

■ **EXAMPLE 1** *Real-World Problem Solving*

Gardening If the area of a square garden is 16 ft^2, what is the length of each side of the garden?

$A = s^2$ ← Use the formula for the area of a square.
$16 = s^2$ ← Substitute 16 for the area.
$4 = s$ ← Find the square root of each side.

The length of each side of the garden is 4 ft.

- *What is the result when you multiply two negative integers?* **a positive integer**

ADDITIONAL EXAMPLES

FOR EXAMPLE 1

If the area of a square parking lot is 36 m^2, what is the length of each side of the parking lot? **6 m**

FOR EXAMPLE 2

Find two consecutive whole numbers that $\sqrt{55}$ is between. **7 and 8**

ERROR ALERT! Students may divide by 2 instead of finding the square root. **Remediation:** Have students check a square root by multiplying the answer times itself.

ASSESSMENT Write the numbers 10, 36, 55, 64, and 100. Have students write an equation, draw a picture, or model with tiles to show whether each number is a perfect square. If the number is a square, have them find the square root.

3 Practice/Assess

EXERCISES *On Your Own*

WRITING Exercise 25 Suggest students compare their work for Exercises 6 and 24.

OPEN-ENDED Exercise 48 Suggest students work backward by first finding the squares of 9 and 10.

The symbol $\sqrt{\ }$ is used to indicate nonnegative square roots.

4. ✔ *Try It Out* What is $\sqrt{4}$? **2**

5. a. What is 7^2? **49**
   b. What is $\sqrt{49}$? **7**
   c. *Reasoning* What other number, besides 7, can you square to get 49? **−7**

Every nonnegative number has two square roots. *Note*: In this book when we talk about *the* square root, we will mean the nonnegative square root.

You can use what you know about the perfect squares to find the square roots of some larger perfect squares.

6. *Patterns* Find each perfect square.
   a. 20^2 **400** b. 30^2 **900** c. 40^2 **1,600** d. 50^2 **2,500** e. 60^2 **3,600**

7. a. How are 6^2 and 60^2 related? **60^2 is 100 times greater than 6^2.**
   b. How are $\sqrt{6^2}$ and $\sqrt{60^2}$ related?
   c. What is $\sqrt{900}$? How is it related to $\sqrt{9}$?
   d. *Number Sense* Why does $\sqrt{90}$ not fit in the pattern with $\sqrt{9}$ and $\sqrt{900}$? **90 is not a perfect square.**

7b. $\sqrt{60^2}$ is 10 times $\sqrt{6^2}$.
c. 30; $\sqrt{900}$ is 10 times $\sqrt{9}$.

Now you may assign Exercises 1–37.

2 *Estimating Square Roots*

When a number is not a perfect square, you can estimate its square root.

EXAMPLE 2

Estimation Find two consecutive whole numbers that $\sqrt{33}$ is between.

The consecutive perfect squares that 33 is between are 25 and 36.

$$\sqrt{25} < \sqrt{33} < \sqrt{36}$$
$$5 < \sqrt{33} < 6$$

$\sqrt{33}$ is between 5 and 6.

8. ✔ *Try It Out* Find two consecutive whole numbers that each square root is between.
   a. $\sqrt{50}$ **7 and 8** b. $\sqrt{88}$ **9 and 10** c. $\sqrt{150}$ **12 and 13** d. $\sqrt{340}$ **18 and 19**

Now you may assign Exercises 38–49.

Technology Options

Prentice Hall Technology

Software for Learners
- Math Blaster® Mystery*
- Interactive Student Tutorial, Chapter 8*

Teaching Resource Software
- Computer Item Generator 8-5
- Resource Pro Chapter 8*

Internet • For related mathematics activities, visit the Prentice Hall site at www.phschool.com/math

**Available on CD-ROM only*

Assignment Options for Exercises On Your Own

To provide flexible scheduling, this lesson can be subdivided into parts.

1 **Core** 1–36
Extension 37

2 **Core** 38–48
Extension 49

Use Mixed Review to maintain skills.

CONNECTION TO GEOMETRY Exercise 49 Remind students of the formulas for area and perimeter of a square: $A = s^2$; $P = 4s$.

WRAP UP

IDENTIFYING THE BIG IDEA Have students explain how square roots relate to squares. Also, have students explain how multiplication can help them check a square root.

JOURNAL Have students consider that if they square every whole number, the results will not cover every number you can find on a number line.

PROJECT LINK Have students exchange their package sketches with a partner to estimate which box uses less cardboard.

Math at Work

If you have block scheduling or extended class periods, organize the class into groups of four. Have each group decide if they will work with crops, livestock, or both. Assign them $500 to make a weekly budget that will include supplies, insurance, and payroll. Have each group share their budget with the class.

page 354 Work Together

2–3.

n	n^2	n	n^2
1	1	11	121
2	4	12	144
3	9	13	169
4	16	14	196
5	25	15	225
6	36	16	256
7	49	17	289
8	64	18	324
9	81	19	361
10	100	20	400

pages 356–357 On Your Own

25. To find the square of a number, you multiply the number by itself. To find the square root of a number, you look for a number whose square is the original number.

EXERCISES *On Your Own*

Find each of the following. Use mental math as much as possible.

1. 8^2 64
2. 13^2 169
3. 15^2 225
4. 18^2 324
5. 90^2 8,100
6. 100^2 10,000
7. 14^2 196
8. 16^2 256
9. 17^2 289
10. 20^2 400
11. $\sqrt{64}$ 8
12. $\sqrt{169}$ 13
13. $\sqrt{81}$ 9
14. $\sqrt{36}$ 6
15. $\sqrt{144}$ 12
16. $\sqrt{25}$ 5
17. $\sqrt{100}$ 10
18. $\sqrt{196}$ 14
19. $\sqrt{16}$ 4
20. $\sqrt{289}$ 17
21. $\sqrt{256}$ 16
22. $\sqrt{2{,}500}$ 50
23. $\sqrt{4{,}900}$ 70
24. $\sqrt{10{,}000}$ 100

25. *Writing* Describe the difference between finding the square of a number and finding the square root of a number. See margin.

Find the length of a side of a square with the given area.

26. 64 cm^2 8 cm
27. 121 km^2 11 km
28. 225 mm^2 15 mm
29. 169 ft^2 13 ft
30. 1,600 m^2 40 m
31. 900 $in.^2$ 30 in.
32. 289 mi^2 17 mi
33. 400 cm^2 20 cm
34. 196 mm^2 14 mm
35. 8,100 ft^2 90 ft

36. **Choose A, B, C, or D.** Which figure has an area twice the area of the figure at the right? B

A.

B.
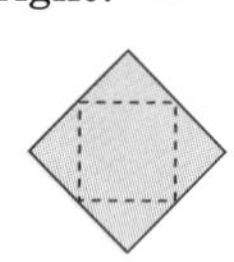

C.
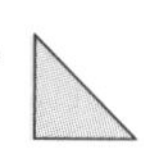

D.
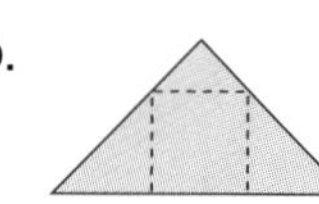

37. a. Find $\frac{1}{2} \times \frac{1}{2}$. $\frac{1}{4}$
    b. What is the square root of $\frac{1}{4}$? $\frac{1}{2}$
    c. What is the square root of $\frac{4}{9}$? $\frac{2}{3}$

Estimation **Find two consecutive whole numbers that each square root is between.**

38. $\sqrt{95}$ 9 and 10
39. $\sqrt{61}$ 7 and 8
40. $\sqrt{42}$ 6 and 7
41. $\sqrt{125}$ 11 and 12
42. $\sqrt{200}$ 14 and 15
43. $\sqrt{38}$ 6 and 7
44. $\sqrt{119}$ 10 and 11
45. $\sqrt{220}$ 14 and 15
46. $\sqrt{175}$ 13 and 14
47. $\sqrt{390}$ 19 and 20

48. *Open-ended* Write two whole numbers whose square roots are between 9 and 10. Answers may vary. Use any two whole numbers between 81 and 100.

JOURNAL Why does every whole number not have a square root that is a whole number?

LESSON QUIZ

Find each of the following.

1. 19^2 361
2. $\sqrt{484}$ 22

Find two consecutive whole numbers that each square root is between.

3. $\sqrt{87}$ 9 and 10
4. $\sqrt{235}$ 15 and 16

49. *Gardening* The area of a square garden is 170 ft^2. Estimate the perimeter of the garden. **Estimates may vary slightly. Sample: 52 ft**

Mixed Review

Solve each proportion. *(Lesson 6-3)*

50. $\frac{13}{x} = \frac{39}{60}$ 20 51. $\frac{4}{9} = \frac{7}{y}$ 15.75 52. $\frac{2}{3} = \frac{n}{12}$ 8 53. $\frac{x}{8} = \frac{6}{15}$ 3.2 54. $\frac{18}{25} = \frac{y}{100}$ 72

55. $\overrightarrow{QS}$ bisects $\angle PQR$. The measure of $\angle PQR$ is 102°. Find the measure of $\angle SQR$. *(Lesson 7-9)* **51°**

56. *Choose a Strategy* Jeshaun stopped at a rung one half of the way up a ladder. After climbing four more rungs, he was three fourths of the way up the ladder. How many rungs are there? **16 rungs**

CHAPTER PROJECT

PROJECT LINK: DRAWING

Use the cylinders you chose in the Project Link on page 343. Sketch two ways that you could package two of the cylinders in rectangular boxes. Label the dimensions of both boxes. Estimate which box uses less cardboard. **Check students' work.**

Math at Work

FARM OPERATOR

Today's farm operator usually has a bachelor's degree in agriculture. A farm operator manages and trains farm workers who work with crops and livestock. Factors that influence a farm operator's job include weather, changes in prices of farm products, and federal farm programs. Farm operators use math and accounting skills to manage inventory and control budgets.

Internet Connection

Visit this Web site for current information on farming: http://www.agriculture.com

Extra Practice, Lesson 8-5, page 521

PRACTICE

Practice 8-5 *Exploring Square Roots*

Find each of the following. Use mental math as much as possible.

1. 6^2 36	2. 1^2 1	3. $\sqrt{64}$ 8	4. 4^2 16
5. $\sqrt{81}$ 9	6. 5^2 25	7. $\sqrt{100}$ 10	8. 2^2 4
9. $\sqrt{144}$ 12	10. 3^2 9	11. 9^2 81	12. $\sqrt{121}$ 11
13. $\sqrt{1}$ 1	14. $\sqrt{36}$ 6	15. 13^2 169	16. 7^2 49
17. 14^2 196	18. $\sqrt{169}$ 13	19. 15^2 225	20. $\sqrt{25}$ 5
21. 16^2 256	22. 10^2 100	23. $\sqrt{16}$ 4	24. $\sqrt{256}$ 16
25. $\sqrt{9}$ 3	26. 12^2 144	27. $\sqrt{196}$ 14	28. 8^2 64
29. $\sqrt{49}$ 7	30. $\sqrt{225}$ 15	31. 11^2 121	32. $\sqrt{4}$ 2

Find the length of a side of a square with the given area.

33. 64 km^2 8 km	34. 81 m^2 9 m	35. 121 ft^2 11 ft	36. 4 mi^2 2 mi
37. 225 $in.^2$ 15 in.	38. 196 yd^2 14 yd	39. 169 cm^2 13 cm	40. 144 mm^2 12 mm

Solve.

41. The square of a certain number is the same as three times the number. What is the number? 0 or 3

42. The area of a square lawn is 196 yd^2. What is the perimeter of the lawn? 56 yd

Find two consecutive whole numbers that each square root is between.

43. $\sqrt{80}$ 8, 9	44. $\sqrt{56}$ 7, 8	45. $\sqrt{130}$ 11, 12	46. $\sqrt{150}$ 12, 13
47. $\sqrt{70}$ 8, 9	48. $\sqrt{190}$ 13, 14	49. $\sqrt{204}$ 14, 15	50. $\sqrt{159}$ 12, 13

Practice

In copymaster and workbook formats

RETEACHING

Reteaching 8-5 *Exploring Square Roots*

The number 25 is a **perfect square.**

It is the square of the whole number 5. $5^2 = 25$

5 is the **square root** of 25. $5 = \sqrt{25}$

You can find the length of a side of a square by finding the square root of the area.

$s^2 = A = 225$

$s = \sqrt{A} = \sqrt{225} = 15$

The length of each side is 15 in.

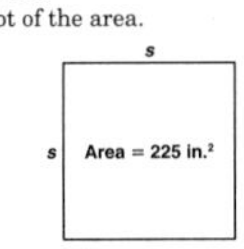

You can use patterns to find the square roots of some larger numbers.

$9^2 = 81 \rightarrow 90^2 = 8{,}100$

$9 = \sqrt{81} \rightarrow 90 = \sqrt{8{,}100}$

Find each of the following.

1. 11^2 121	2. 7^2 49	3. 70^2 4,900
4. 17^2 289	5. $\sqrt{144}$ 12	6. $\sqrt{36}$ 6
7. $\sqrt{100}$ 10	8. $\sqrt{2{,}500}$ 50	9. 80^2 6,400
10. $\sqrt{324}$ 18	11. 13^2 169	12. $\sqrt{400}$ 20

Find the length of a side of a square with the given area.

13. $A = 49\ cm^2$ Side $= \sqrt{49} =$ 7 cm	14. $A = 81\ in.^2$ Side $= \sqrt{81} =$ 9 in.	15. $A = 144\ cm^2$ Side $= \sqrt{144} =$ 12 cm
16. $A = 625\ in.^2$ 25 in.	17. $A = 676\ ft^2$ 26 ft	18. $A = 3{,}600\ yd^2$ 60 yd
19. $A = 256\ m^2$ 16 m	20. $A = 900\ mi^2$ 30 mi	21. $A = 10{,}000\ mm^2$ 100 mm
22. $A = 2{,}500\ cm^2$ 50 cm	23. $A = 289\ in.^2$ 17 in.	24. $A = 169\ ft^2$ 13 ft

ENRICHMENT

Minds on Math Transparency

8-5

There are fewer sixth-grade students than seventh-grade students in the Rice School District. The ninth grade has more students than either the eighth grade or the seventh grade. The number of students in the fifth grade is less than the number in the sixth grade. Which grade has the most students?

ninth grade

See *Solution Key* for worked-out answers.

PROBLEM SOLVING PRACTICE ★★

This page provides a variety of problems for students to solve using their knowledge of area, percents, expressions, multiplying and dividing mixed numbers, similarity, and writing equations. Allow students to use any method they find helpful.

Exercise 5 Suggest students find the amount of ribbon they would need for 1 puppet before finding the amount of ribbon for 14 puppets.

Exercises 7 and 8 Students may want to draw diagrams to help them solve the problems.

PROBLEM SOLVING PRACTICE ★★★★★

Choose the best answer.

1. Kevin's yard measures 60 feet by 40 feet. Kevin will plant bushes and flowers at the front of his yard. He will plant grass in the rest of his yard.

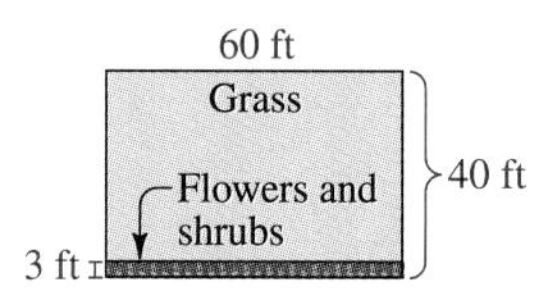

How many square feet will Kevin plant with grass? B

A. 180 ft^2 B. 2,220 ft^2
C. 2,400 ft^2 D. 2,580 ft^2

2. On Wednesday, $\frac{3}{5}$ of the students at school bought a hot lunch. What percent of the students bought a hot lunch? G

F. 65% G. 60% H. 40% J. 20%

3. A beauty parlor charges $15 for a haircut and $10 for styling hair. If c represents the number of customers who have their hair cut and styled, then the money the beauty parlor will make is represented by this expression.

$$15c + 10c$$

How much money will the beauty parlor make if 12 customers have their hair both cut and styled? B

A. $350 B. $300 C. $180 D. $120

4. The price of a coat is $114 before sales tax. The sales tax is 7%. To find the tax on the coat, multiply $114 by — H

F. 7.0 G. 0.7 H. 0.07 J. 0.007

5. The instructions for making puppets require $1\frac{1}{3}$ feet of ribbon for 4 puppets. How many feet of ribbon will be needed to make 14 puppets? A

A. $4\frac{2}{3}$ ft B. $5\frac{1}{3}$ ft
C. $18\frac{2}{3}$ ft D. 56 ft

6. $\triangle QRS$ and $\triangle TUV$ are similar. What is the value of x? H

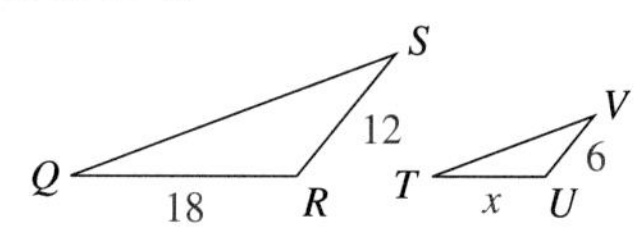

F. 4 G. 8 H. 9 J. 12

Please note that items 7–9 have *five* answer choices.

7. The top of a large birthday cake is 10 in. wide and 18 in. long. "Happy Birthday!" is written in a rectangular section that is 5 in. by 6 in. Which number sentence could be used to find d, the amount of space left for decorations? A

A. $d = (18 \times 10) - (5 \times 6)$
B. $d = (18 + 10) - (5 + 6)$
C. $d = 18 \times 10 \times 5 \times 6$
D. $d = (18 - 6) + (10 - 5)$
E. $d = \frac{18}{6} \times \frac{10}{5}$

8. The diameter of the top of a jar of pickles is 3 in. What is the area of the top of the jar to the nearest hundredth? Use 3.14 for π. J

F. 28.26 in.^{2} G. 14.13 in.^{2}
H. 9.12 in.^{2} J. 7.07 in.^{2}
K. Not Here

9. Which fraction equals 3.4? D

A. $\frac{22}{7}$ B. $\frac{15}{4}$ C. $\frac{23}{6}$ D. $\frac{17}{5}$ E. $\frac{10}{3}$

8-6 Teaching Notes

1 Focus

CONNECTING TO PRIOR KNOWLEDGE
Draw a right triangle. Label the two legs *base* and *height*. Ask: *What has to be true about the base and height of a triangle?* **They have to form a right, or 90°, angle.** Ask: *How can you make sure the angle is 90°?* **measure with a protractor**

2 Teach

Work Together

VISUAL LEARNING Have students color the squares that they form on each side of a triangle so that they can get a stronger visual picture.

REASONING Question 3 Have students write an equation that compares the areas of the squares for each triangle.
9 + 16 = 25; 64 + 225 = 289

THINK AND DISCUSS

AEP Mention that the second part of the word *hypotenuse* comes from the Greek word meaning "stretch." Have students tack a rubber band on a wall near the corner of the room. Stretch the rubber band across the corner and tack it to the other wall. The stretched rubber band represents a hypotenuse.

ALGEBRA Connection

8-6 Exploring the Pythagorean Theorem

What You'll Learn

1. To use the Pythagorean theorem
2. To determine whether a triangle is a right triangle

...And Why

When you know the lengths of two sides of a right triangle, you can find the length of the third side.

Here's How

Look for questions that
- build understanding
- ✔ check understanding

Work Together — *Building Squares on Right Triangles*

Work with a partner to investigate a right triangle.

Step 1 Use centimeter graph paper to draw a right triangle with the right angle included between sides that are 3 cm and 4 cm long.

Step 2 Draw squares that have the horizontal and vertical sides of the right triangle as sides.

Step 3 Use another piece of the graph paper to make a square on the side opposite the right angle, as shown below.

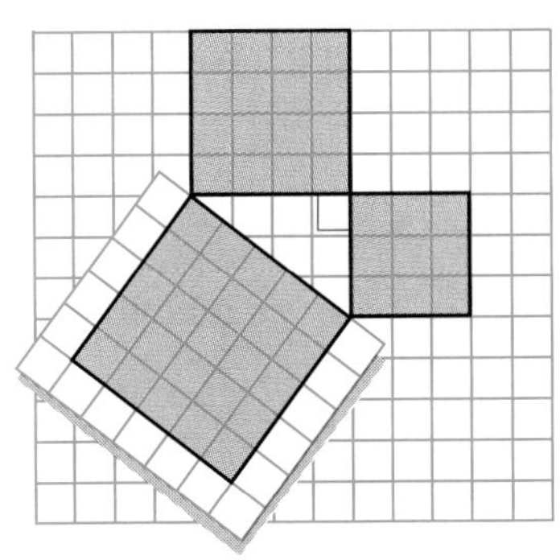

1. a. What is the length of each side of the square made on the side opposite the right angle? **5 cm**
   b. What is the area of each of the three squares?
   9 cm^2, 16 cm^2, 25 cm^2
2. *Modeling* Draw a right triangle on centimeter graph paper with the right angle included between sides that are 8 cm and 15 cm long. Repeat Steps 2 and 3 above.
   a. What is the length of each side of the square made on the side opposite the right angle? **17 cm**
   b. What is the area of each of the three squares?
   64 cm^2, 225 cm^2, 289 cm^2
3. *Reasoning* Look for a pattern. What seems to be the relationship of the areas of the smaller two squares and the third square built on the sides of a right triangle?
   The area of the square opposite the right angle is equal to the sum of the areas of the other two squares.

Lesson Planning Options

Prerequisite Skills
- finding squares and square roots (8-5)

Vocabulary/Symbols
legs, hypotenuse, Pythagorean theorem

Materials/Manipulatives
- centimeter graph paper

Resources

Student Edition

Skills Handbook, p. 530
Extra Practice, p. 521
Glossary/Study Guide

Teaching Resources

Chapter Support File, Ch. 8
- Lesson Planner 8-6
- Practice 8-6, Reteaching 8-6
- Answer Masters 8-6

Teaching Aids Masters 1, 2, 9, 19, 27
Glossary, Spanish Resources

Transparencies
1, 7, 14, 15, 93, Minds on Math 8-6

Warm Up

Which word best completes the statement: *sometimes*, *always*, or *never?*
If the product of two factors is zero, both factors are ■ zero. **sometimes**

KINESTHETIC LEARNING Example 1 Have students form the legs of the triangle by marking the starting place and taking 9 heel-to-toe steps. Turn 90°, then take 12 more heel-to-toe steps. Mark the finish point. To check the hypotenuse, have students walk 15 heel-to-toe steps to see if they end up where they started.

Question 4 Point out that students can substitute the sides into the Pythagorean theorem in either order.

ADDITIONAL EXAMPLES

FOR EXAMPLE 1

Find the hypotenuse of a triangle with legs 20 in. and 21 in. **29 in.**

FOR EXAMPLE 2

A ladder 25 ft long covers a horizontal distance of 15 ft. What is the vertical rise of the ladder? **20 ft**

FOR EXAMPLE 3

Is a triangle with sides of length 11 cm, 13 cm, and 17 cm a right triangle? Explain. **No; $11^2 + 13^2$ does not equal 17^2.**

ERROR ALERT! Example 2 Students might substitute *a* or *b* with the value for the hypotenuse. **Remediation:** Have students copy the triangle and label the legs and hypotenuse.

REASONING Question 6 Have students look at all the examples in this lesson. Ask: *Which side is always the longest?* **hypotenuse**

Technology Options

Prentice Hall Technology

Software for Learners

- Math Blaster® Mystery*
- Interactive Student Tutorial, Chapter 8*

Teaching Resource Software

- Computer Item Generator 8-6
- Resource Pro Chapter 8*

Internet • For related mathematics activities, visit the Prentice Hall site at www.phschool.com/math

**Available on CD-ROM only*

Assignment Options for Exercises On Your Own

To provide flexible scheduling, this lesson can be subdivided into parts.

1 **Core** 1–7
Extension 8

2 **Core** 10–20
Extension 9

Use Mixed Review to maintain skills.

WHO? Pythagoras was a Greek mathematician born about 500 B.C. His work was so important that the relationship involving the lengths of the sides of a right triangle was named for him.

THINK AND DISCUSS

1 *Using the Pythagorean Theorem*

The two shorter sides of a right triangle are the **legs.** The side opposite the right angle is the **hypotenuse.**

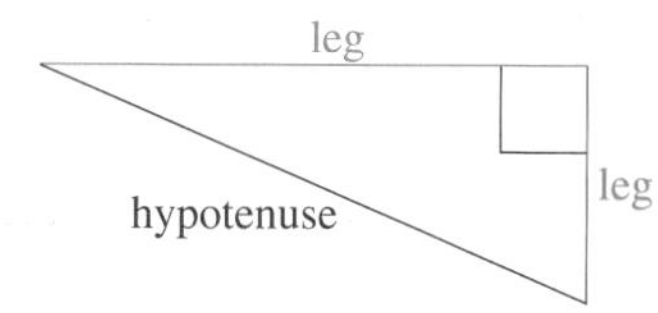

PYTHAGOREAN THEOREM

In any right triangle, the sum of the squares of the lengths a and b of the legs is equal to the square of the length c of the hypotenuse.

$$a^2 + b^2 = c^2$$

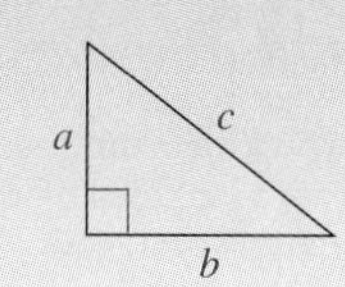

If you know the lengths of two sides of a right triangle, you can use the Pythagorean theorem to find the length of the third side.

EXAMPLE 1

Find the length of the hypotenuse of the figure at the right.

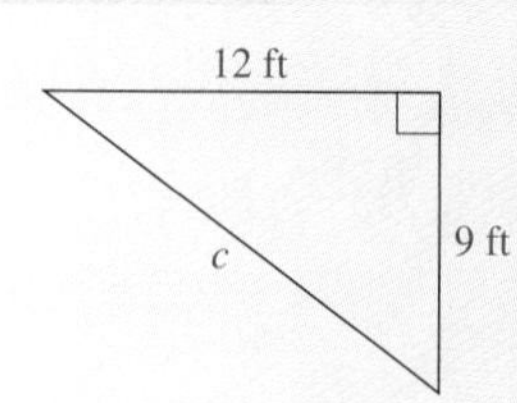

$$a^2 + b^2 = c^2$$
$$9^2 + 12^2 = c^2 \quad \leftarrow \text{Substitute.}$$
$$81 + 144 = c^2$$
$$225 = c^2$$
$$\sqrt{225} = c \quad \leftarrow \text{Find the value of } c.$$
$$15 = c$$

The length of the hypotenuse is 15 ft.

4. ✓ *Try It Out* Find the hypotenuse of each figure below.

a.

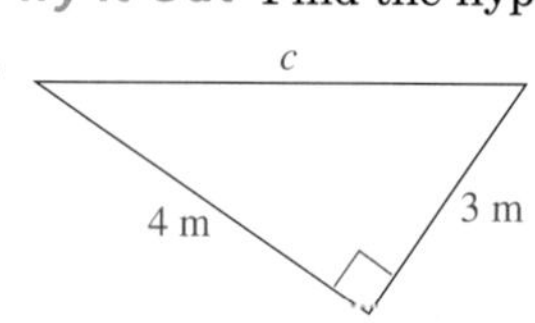

b.

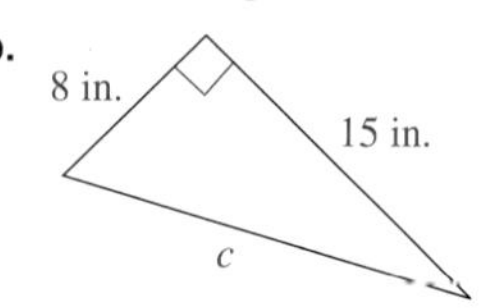

5 m **17 in.**

CONNECTION TO GEOMETRY Example 3 The converse of the Pythagorean theorem states: If the sum of the squares of a and b is equal to the square of c, then the triangle is a right triangle.

Question 7b Point out that each side of the Pythagorean theorem equation must be equal for the triangle to be a right triangle.

If you have block scheduling or extended class periods, have students cut out at least five pictures that contain right triangles from a magazine or newspaper. Have them measure the legs and hypotenuse of each right triangle.

ASSESSMENT Describe the following two triangles. Have students determine whether the triangles are right triangles.

- legs: 5 cm and 7 cm; hypotenuse: 8 cm **no**
- legs: 16 cm and 30 cm; hypotenuse: 34 cm **yes**

3 Practice/Assess

EXERCISES *On Your Own*

Exercise 6 Point out that since the sides are the two longest, the missing side must be a leg.

Exercise 8 Have students note that the diameter of the circle is also the hypotenuse of the right triangle.

■ **EXAMPLE 2** *Relating to the Real World*

Construction A wheelchair ramp 626 cm long covers a horizontal distance of 624 cm. What is the vertical rise of the ramp?

Draw a diagram.

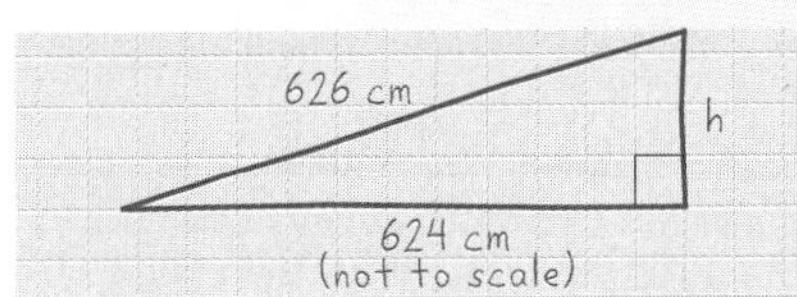

Use the Pythagorean theorem.

$$a^2 + b^2 = c^2$$
$$624^2 + b^2 = 626^2 \quad \leftarrow \text{Substitute.}$$
$$b^2 = 626^2 - 624^2 \quad \leftarrow \text{Solve for } b^2.$$
$$b^2 = 391{,}876 - 389{,}376$$
$$b^2 = 2{,}500$$
$$b = \sqrt{2{,}500} = 50 \quad \leftarrow \text{50 is the square root of 2,500.}$$

The vertical rise is 50 cm.

5. ✔ *Try It Out* One leg of a right triangle is 40 in. long. The hypotenuse is 41 in. long. What is the length of the other leg? **9 in.**

6. *Reasoning* The sides of a right triangle are 30 in., 50 in., and 40 in. long. Which is the length of the hypotenuse? How do you know? **50 in.; hypotenuse is the longest side.**

Now you may assign Exercises 1–8.

2 *Determining Right Triangles*

If the lengths a, b, and c of the sides of a triangle satisfy the equation $a^2 + b^2 = c^2$, then the triangle is a right triangle.

■ **EXAMPLE 3**

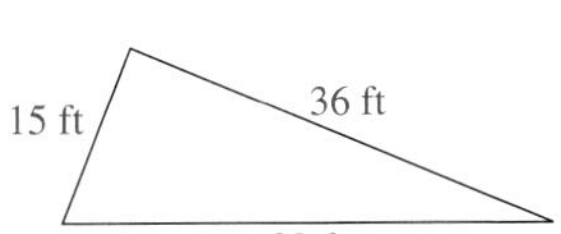

Is the triangle at the left a right triangle? Explain.

$$a^2 + b^2 \stackrel{?}{=} c^2$$
$$15^2 + 36^2 \stackrel{?}{=} 39^2 \quad \leftarrow \text{The longest side is 39 ft long. Substitute 39 for } c.$$
$$225 + 1{,}296 \stackrel{?}{=} 1{,}521$$
$$1{,}521 = 1{,}521 \checkmark$$

The lengths of the sides satisfy the equation $a^2 + b^2 = c^2$. The triangle is a right triangle.

DIVERSITY Exercise 9 Some students may have had experience looking at property. Have them share their knowledge of property lines.

WRITING Exercise 9b Point out that students will divide the twelve equal parts into a Pythagorean triple.

Exercises 13–18 Have students write the three lengths. Then have them circle the longest side and label it *H* for hypotenuse.

EXTENSION Exercise 20 Have students sketch parts of fences from their homes or neighborhoods. Have them make a list of all geometric shapes they see.

Exercise 21 Remind students that a circle graph contains percents. The sum of the percents in the circle graph must equal 100%.

Exercise 23 Have students make a list of important information such as: *Cary went to work on Saturday.* Then they should deduce information such as: *This means she is not a teacher.*

WRAP UP

IDENTIFYING THE BIG IDEA Have students state the Pythagorean theorem. Students explain how to use it to prove a triangle is a right triangle and to find the length of a missing side.

page 363 Mixed Review

21. Favorite Pets

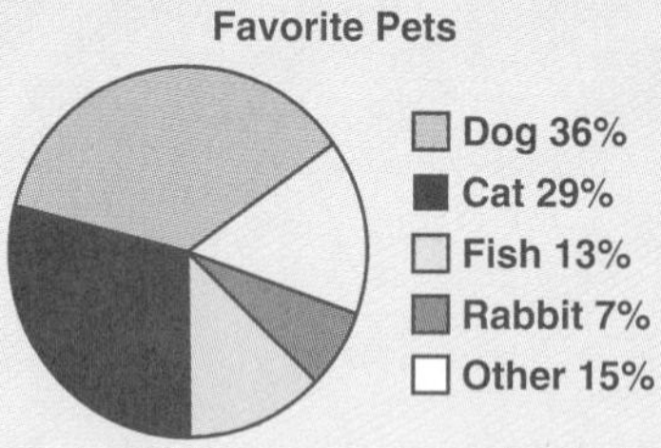

7a. yes; $15^2 + 20^2 = 25^2$

7. a. ✔ *Try It Out* Is a triangle with sides of length 15 cm, 20 cm, and 25 cm a right triangle? Why or why not?
   b. Is a triangle with sides of length 3 ft, 5 ft, and 6 ft a right triangle? Why or why not? no; $3^2 + 5^2 \neq 6^2$

Now you may assign Exercises 9–20.

EXERCISES *On Your Own*

Find the missing side length.

1.
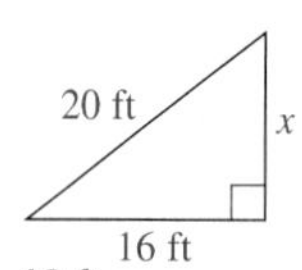

12 ft

2.
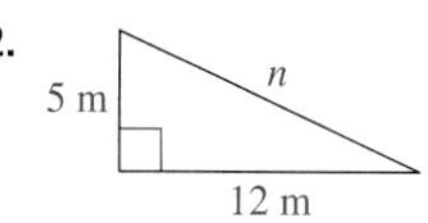

13 m

3.
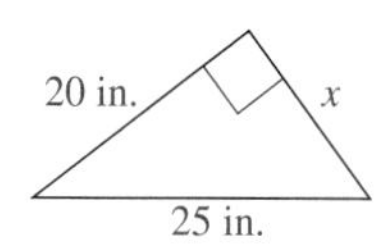

15 in.

4.
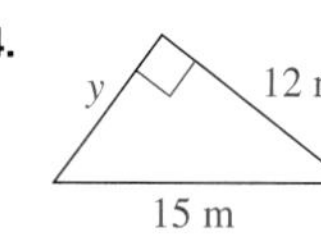

9 m

5. The hypotenuse of a right triangle is 37 ft long. One leg is 35 ft long. What is the length of the other leg? 12 ft

6. The two longest sides of a right triangle are 60 m and 61 m long. What is the length of the third side? 11 m

7. *Camping* A large tent has an adjustable center pole. A rope 26 ft long connects the top of the pole to a peg 24 ft from the bottom of the pole. What is the height of the pole? 10 ft

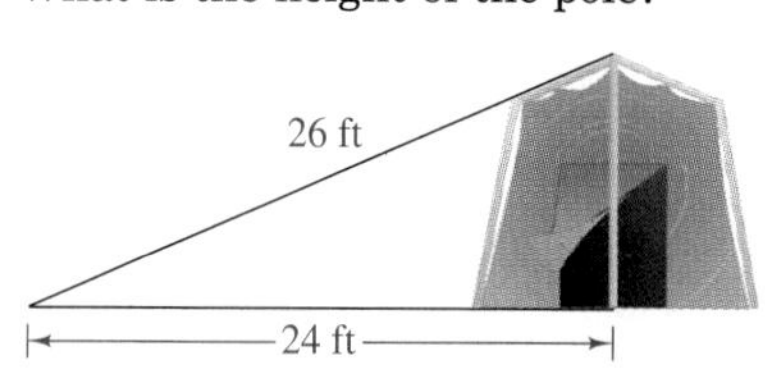

8. a. $\overline{AC}$ is the diameter of circle *O*. Find $\overline{AC}$. 20 m
   b. Find the circumference and area of the circle. 62.8 m; 314.2 m^2

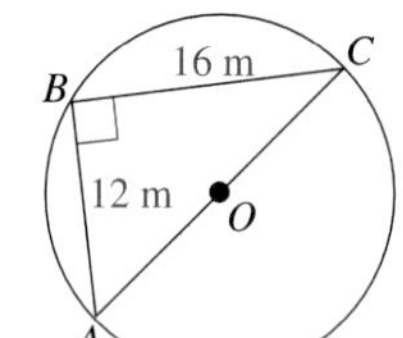

9a.

9. *History* The ancient Egyptians used a knotted rope to help them relocate property lines after the annual flooding of the Nile River. They divided a rope into 12 equal parts by tying knots. Then they used the rope to form a right triangle. The right angle helped them re-establish the square corners of boundary lines.
   a. Draw a sketch to show how the knotted rope could be used to form a right triangle. See above right.
   b. *Writing* Explain why the triangle must be a right triangle. The lengths of the sides are 3, 4, and 5, and $3^2 + 4^2 = 5^2$. So the sides must form a right triangle.

LESSON QUIZ

Find the missing side length.

1. leg: 9 m; hypotenuse: 15 m **12 m**
2. leg: 15 mm; leg: 36 mm **39 mm**

The lengths of the sides of a triangle are given. Is each triangle a right triangle?

3. 12 in., 19 in., 21 in. **no**
4. 70 m, 42 m, 56 m **yes**

Determine whether each triangle is a right triangle. Explain your answer.

10. 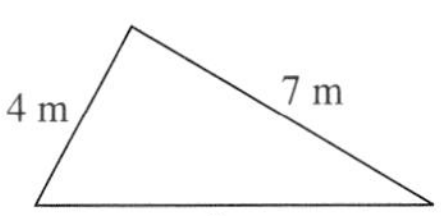

no; $4^2 + 7^2 \neq 8^2$

11. 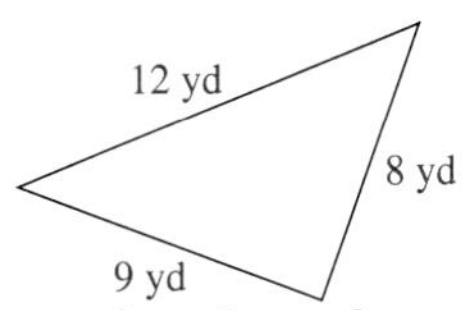

no; $8^2 + 9^2 \neq 12^2$

12. 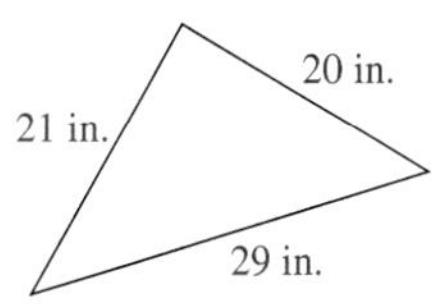

yes; $20^2 + 21^2 = 29^2$

The lengths of the sides of a triangle are given. Is the triangle a right triangle? Explain your answer.

13. 15 in., 18 in., 24 in. **no; $15^2 + 18^2 \neq 24^2$**
14. 10 m, 8 m, 13 m **no; $10^2 + 8^2 \neq 13^2$**
15. 28 mm, 53 mm, 45 mm **yes; $28^2 + 45^2 = 53^2$**
16. 12 yd, 13 yd, 20 yd **no; $12^2 + 13^2 \neq 20^2$**
17. 16 ft, 30 ft, 34 ft **yes; $16^2 + 30^2 = 34^2$**
18. 42 cm, 56 cm, 70 cm **yes; $42^2 + 56^2 = 70^2$**
19. *Home Repair* What is the height at which the ladder touches the side of the house? **12 ft**

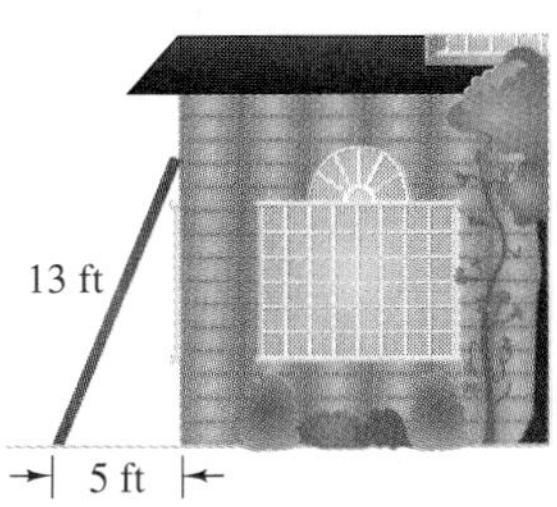

20. *Carpentry* The rectangular section of wood fencing shown below is reinforced with a piece of wood nailed across the diagonal of the rectangle. What is the length of the diagonal? **10 ft**

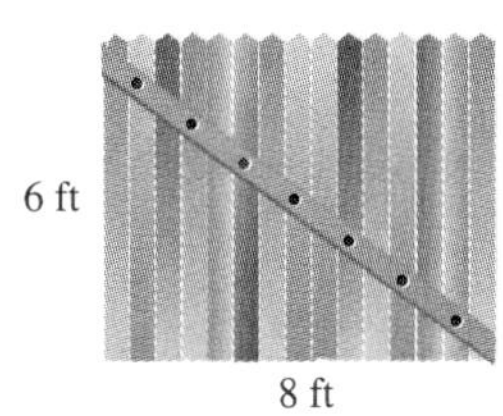

Mixed Review

The table shows the results of a survey in which seventh graders named their favorite pet. *(Lesson 7-8)*

Pet	Number of Students
Dog	26
Cat	21
Fish	9
Rabbit	5
Other	11

21. Make a circle graph to show this information. **See margin p. 362.**
22. What percent of the students do not prefer dogs as pets? **64%**
23. *Choose a Strategy* Elicia, Michelle, and Cary are an engineer, a teacher, and a salesperson. Elicia and the engineer drove Cary to her company's main office on Saturday. Who is the teacher? **Elicia**

PRACTICE

Practice 8-6 Exploring the Pythagorean Theorem

Find the missing side length.

1. 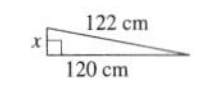

$x = 22$ cm

2. 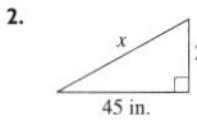

$x = 51$ in.

3. 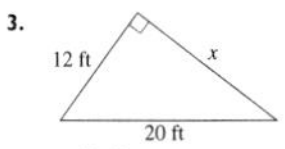

$x = 16$ ft

4. 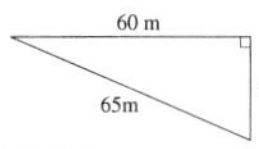

$x = 25$ m

5. 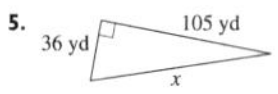

$x = 111$ yd

6. 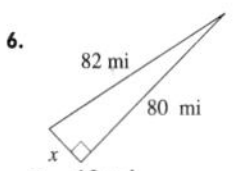

$x = 18$ mi

Determine whether each triangle is a right triangle. Explain your answer.

7. 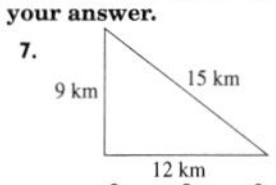

yes; $9^2 + 12^2 = 15^2$

8. 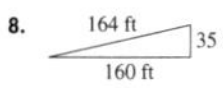

no; $35^2 + 160^2 \neq 164^2$

9. 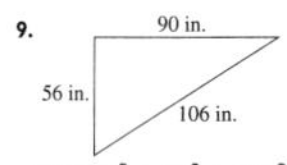

yes; $56^2 + 90^2 = 106^2$

10. 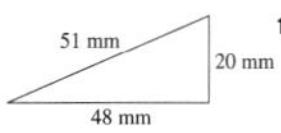

no; $20^2 + 48^2 \neq 51^2$

11. 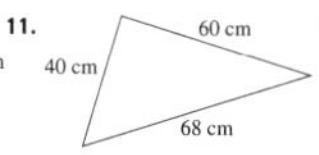

no; $40^2 + 60^2 \neq 68^2$

12. 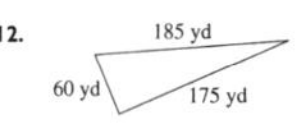

yes; $60^2 + 175^2 = 185^2$

13. A guy wire runs from the top of a tower to the ground, where the wire is anchored 11 ft from the tower. If the guy wire is 61 ft long, how tall is the tower? 60 ft
14. The base of a ladder is placed 6 ft from the bottom of the house. The ladder reaches 8 ft up the house. How long is the ladder? 10 ft
15. Ishmael owns a triangular piece of land. The sides of the land measure 6 mi by 8 mi by 9 mi. Is the land a right triangle? no
16. A park along a river is in the shape of a triangle. The lengths of the sides of the park are 330 yd by 1,800 yd by 1,830 yd. Does the park form a right triangle? yes

In copymaster and workbook formats

RETEACHING

Reteaching 8-6 Exploring the Pythagorean Theorem

Pythagorean Theorem

$a^2 + b^2 = c^2$

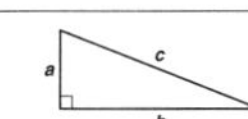

If you know the lengths of two sides of a right triangle, you can find the length of the third side.

Find the length of a.

$$a^2 + b^2 = c^2$$
$$a^2 + 12^2 = 13^2$$
$$a^2 + 144 = 169$$
$$a^2 = 169 - 144$$
$$a^2 = 25$$
$$a = 5$$

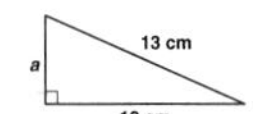

If $a^2 + b^2 = c^2$, then the triangle is a right triangle.

Is this triangle a right triangle?

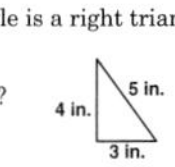

$3^2 + 4^2 = 9 + 16 = 25 = 5^2$
Yes, the triangle is a right triangle.

Find the missing side length.

1. 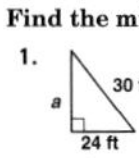

18 ft

2. 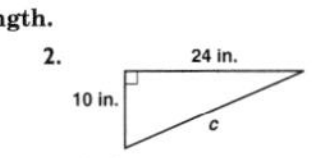

26 in.

3. 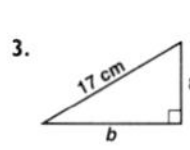

15 cm

Determine whether each triangle is a right triangle. Show why.

4. 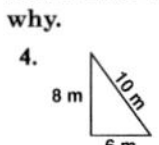

yes; $6^2 + 8^2 = 10^2$

5. 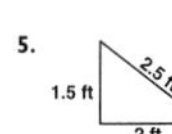

yes; $1.5^2 + 2^2 = 2.5^2$

6. 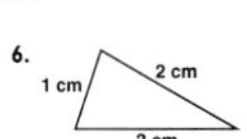

no; $1^2 + 2^2 \neq 2^2$

Reteaching

ENRICHMENT

Minds on Math Transparency

8-6

Tia's softball uniform number has 2 digits and is a multiple of 2, 4, 8, and 9. What is Tia's number?

72

See *Solution Key* for worked-out answers.

8-7 Teaching Notes

1 Focus

CONNECTING TO PRIOR KNOWLEDGE Organize students into three groups. Write $a^2 + b^2 = c^2$ for the class. Ask: *How do you find the length of the side of a right triangle if you know the length of two sides?* **Substitute the known lengths and then solve for the unknown variable.**

2 Teach

THINK AND DISCUSS

Question 1a Have a discussion with students about the real-world applications of the Pythagorean theorem. Help students understand that many times a triangle is not obvious, but they can visualize the sides of a triangle and then draw a picture.

Question 2 Have students use a calculator to check the value of *x* by finding x^2. Ask: *How close is x^2 to 130?* **129.96 is very close to 130.**

REASONING **Question 3a** Remind students that a perfect square has two whole number square roots.

AUDITORY LEARNING Read aloud the lengths of the sides of a right triangle. Have students draw the triangle and label the sides.

Lesson Planning Options

Prerequisite Skills

- rounding decimals (2-1)
- exploring Pythagorean theorem (8-6)

Materials/Manipulatives

- calculator

Resources

Student Edition

Skills Handbook, p. 529
Extra Practice, p. 521
Glossary/Study Guide

Teaching Resources

Chapter Support File, Ch. 8
- Lesson Planner 8-7
- Practice 8-7, Reteaching 8-7
- Alternative Activity 8-7
- Answer Masters 8-7

Glossary, Spanish Resources

Transparencies

15, 93, Minds on Math 8-7

Warm Up

A theater has 25 seats in the first row. Each of the following rows has two more seats than the row before it. How many seats are in the 15-row theater? **585**

TECHNOLOGY

8-7 Applying the Pythagorean Theorem

What You'll Learn

▼ To use a calculator to apply the Pythagorean theorem

...And Why

You can use a calculator to find lengths that are not square roots of perfect squares.

Here's How

Look for questions that
- build understanding
- ✔ check understanding

THINK AND DISCUSS

The water splashes around you as you rocket down the longest slide at the water park. As soon as you reach the bottom, you're up and set to go again.

Suppose you know that a slide starts 9 m above the water and covers 7 m horizontally. You want to find the length of the slide.

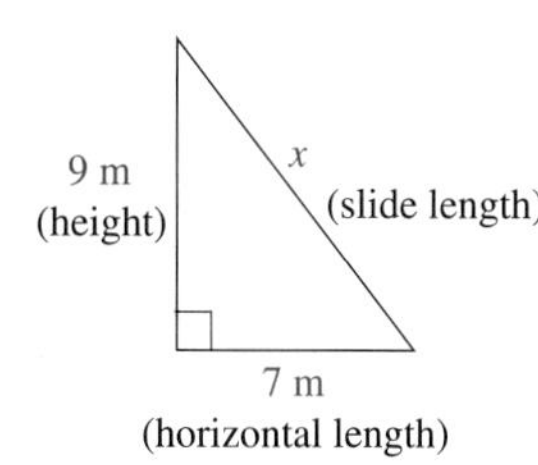

1. a. Use the Pythagorean theorem to write an equation involving the lengths of the sides of the triangle. $7^2 + 9^2 = x^2$
   b. Solve the equation for x^2. **130 m²**
   c. Is x^2 a perfect square? Explain. **No; 130 is not a square of a whole number.**

You can use the square root key on your calculator to find the square root of any nonnegative number.

2. *Calculator* Use your calculator to find the value of *x* in the figure above. Round the result to the nearest tenth of a meter. **11.4 m**

3. a. *Reasoning* How could you use your calculator to determine whether a number is a perfect square?
   b. Is 18,769 a perfect square? Why or why not?
   c. Is 7,925 a perfect square? Why or why not? **No; $\sqrt{7{,}925}$ is not a whole number.**

3a. Use the square root key to find whether the square root is a whole number.
b. Yes; 18,769 is a square of 137.

Then read aloud two of the three sides of a right triangle. Have students draw the triangle and label the sides.

ERROR ALERT! Example Students might think 900 m is the hypotenuse because it is the largest number given. **Remediation:** Remind students that all measurements must be in the same unit. Convert 1 km to 1,000 m. Also tell students to carefully draw a diagram of the problem. A jet airplane taking off would not form a horizontal or vertical line.

ADDITIONAL EXAMPLE

FOR EXAMPLE

The Wetlands Company must measure the distance from *A* to *B* across a swamp. To avoid crossing the swamp, the company measured 523 m west from *A*, then 1,150 m north to *B* to create the legs of a right triangle. What is the distance from *A* to *B*? **about 1,263 m**

ASSESSMENT Have students draw a right triangle and label two sides. Then have them exchange with a partner and find the length of the unknown side. Students can check their partners' work.

EXERCISES *On Your Own*

Exercises 1–12 Have students summarize the steps for finding the missing side. **Answers may vary. Sample:**

- **When you know the length of two legs, find the *sum* of the squares of the lengths. Then find the square root of the sum.**

EXAMPLE *Real-World Problem Solving*

Aviation A jet airplane takes off in a straight path. When it has traveled 1 km, it has covered a horizontal distance of 900 m. To the nearest meter, what is the height of the jet at that point?

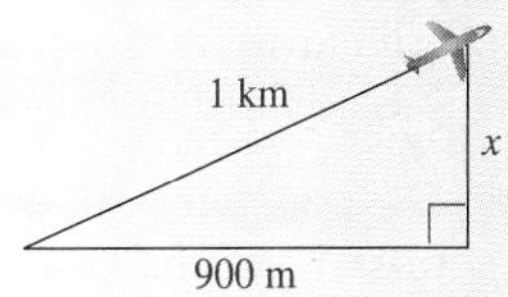

Need Help? For practice converting metric units, see Skills Handbook page 541.

Use the Pythagorean theorem.

$1{,}000^2 = 900^2 + x^2$ ← 1 km = 1,000 m

$1{,}000^2 - 900^2 = x^2$

1000 [x^2] [−] 900 [x^2] [=] [√] 435.8898944

The jet is about 436 m high.

4. a. ✔ *Try It Out* The legs of a right triangle are 80 cm and 1.5 m long. What is the length of the hypotenuse? **1.7 m**

b. The leg of a right triangle is 80 cm long. The length of the hypotenuse is 1.5 m. What is the length of the other leg?

b. about 126.9 cm or about 1.269 m

Now you may assign Exercises 1–24.

EXERCISES *On Your Own*

Find the missing side length to the nearest tenth.

1. **19.7 cm**

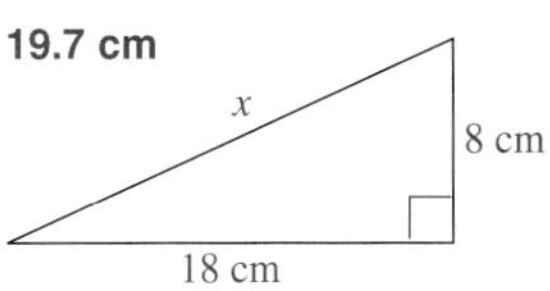

2. **11.2 m**

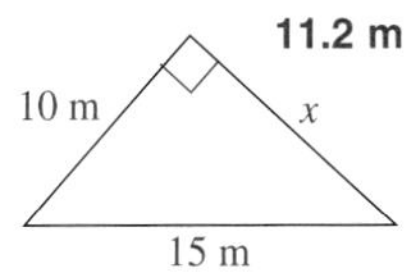

3. **13.2 cm**

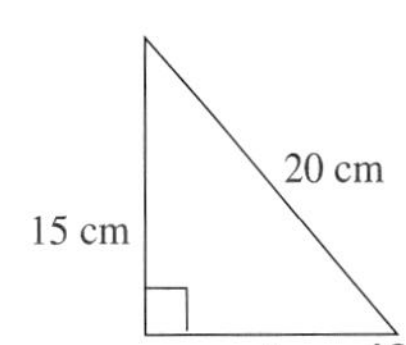

4. **13.0 m**

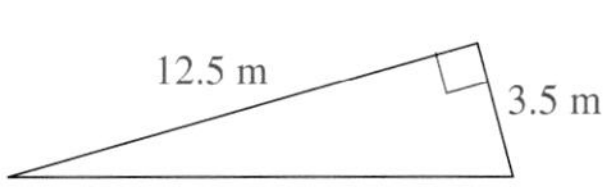

5. **6.8 cm**

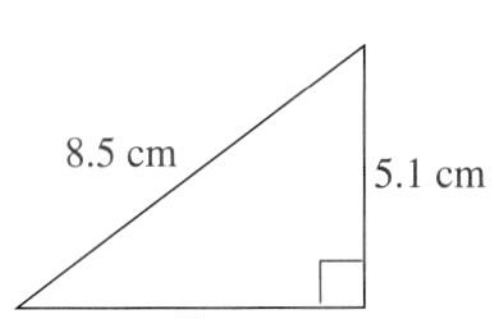

6. **1.6 km or 1,612.5 m**

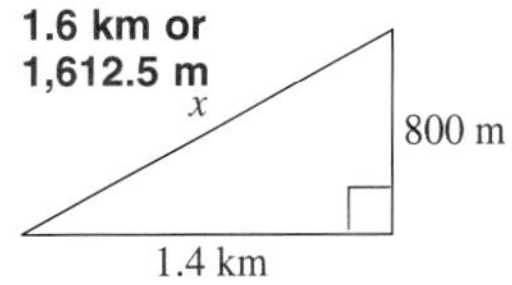

The lengths of two sides of a right triangle are given. Find the length of the third side to the nearest tenth of a unit.

7. legs: 8 m and 11 m **13.6 m**
8. legs: 10 cm and 14 cm **17.2 cm**
9. leg: 25 in.; hypotenuse: 35 in. **24.5 in.**
10. legs: 6 m and 15 m **16.2 m**
11. legs: 12 ft and 20 ft **23.3 ft**
12. leg: 18 yd; hypotenuse: 28 yd **21.4 yd**

Technology Options

Prentice Hall Technology

Software for Learners

- Math Blaster® Mystery*
- Interactive Student Tutorial, Chapter 8*

Teaching Resource Software

- Computer Item Generator 8-7
- Resource Pro Chapter 8*

Internet • For related mathematics activities, visit the Prentice Hall site at www.phschool.com/math

**Available on CD-ROM only*

Assignment Options for Exercises On Your Own

Core 1–17, 19–21

Extension 18, 22–24

Use Mixed Review to maintain skills.

- **When you know the length of the hypotenuse and of a leg, find the *difference* of the squares of the hypotenuse and leg. Then find the square root of the difference.**

WRITING Exercise 13b Students may need to review *rhombus.*

DIVERSITY Exercise 16 Some students may not have any experience with ladders. Have students that are familiar with ladders make a model out of toothpicks and demonstrate this exercise for the class.

Exercise 19 Have students write *leg, leg,* and *hypotenuse* on their diagrams. Then have them find clues that indicate values for each side of the triangle.

ALTERNATE METHOD Exercises 22–24 Students will use the Pythagorean theorem to find the missing side of the right triangle and then the area of the triangle to the nearest tenth. Tell students their answer will be less accurate if they round the measure of the missing leg before calculating the area than if they only round the area at the end. Have students discuss why this is true.

CONNECTION TO ARCHITECTURE
Exercises 35 and 36 Remind students how to set up a proportion for a scale drawing.
$\frac{\text{scale (in.)}}{\text{actual (ft)}}: \frac{1.5}{1} = \frac{21}{n}; \frac{1.5}{1} = \frac{24}{n}.$

WRAP UP

IDENTIFYING THE BIG IDEA Have students explain how to use a calculator to apply the Pythagorean theorem.

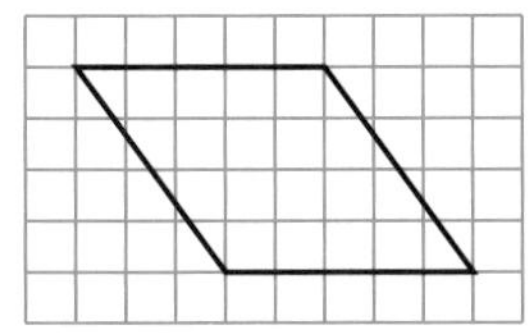

13. a. Find the perimeter and area of this quadrilateral.
    b. ***Writing*** Which of the following is the best name for this quadrilateral: square, parallelogram, rhombus, trapezoid? Explain your choice. **See right.**

a. 20 units; 20 square units

13b. Rhombus; a quadrilateral with 4 congruent sides is a rhombus. The angles are not right angles, so it is not a square.

14. A rectangular park is 600 m long and 300 m wide. Tomi walked diagonally across the park from corner to corner. How far did he walk, to the nearest meter? **671 m**

15. A support wire is attached to the top of a 60-m tower. It meets the ground 25 m from the base of the tower. How long is the support wire? **65 m**

16. ***Home Repair*** A ladder is 6 m long. How much farther up a wall does it reach when the foot of the ladder is 2 m from the wall than when it is 3 m from the wall? Give the answer to the nearest tenth of a meter. **0.5 m**

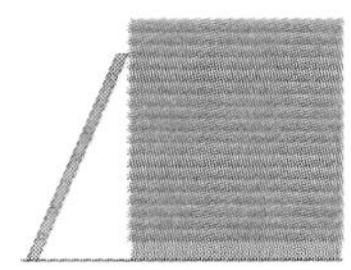

17. ***Reasoning*** The length of two sides of a right triangle are 9 cm and 14 cm. What are the two possible lengths for the third side? Round to the nearest tenth. **10.7 cm, 16.6 cm**

18. The area of $\triangle RSW$ is 216 cm^2.
    The area of $\triangle TSW$ is 540 cm^2. **a. 18 cm; 45 cm**
    a. Find the lengths of $\overline{RW}$ and $\overline{WT}$.
    b. Find the lengths of $\overline{RS}$ and $\overline{ST}$.
    c. Find the perimeter of $\triangle RST$. **144 cm**

b. 30 cm; 51 cm

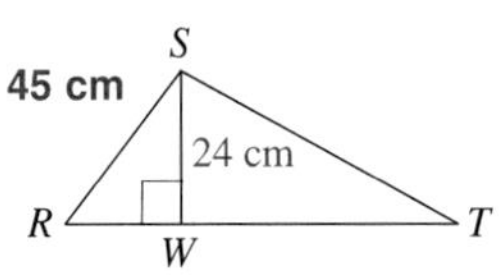

THE TILTING TOWER

Building began on the bell tower at Pisa, Italy, in 1173. Shortly after that, the builders realized the tower was beginning to lean. They tried to fix the problem, but the tower has continued to tilt even more over the centuries.

The tower leans because the foundation lies on a mixture of sand, clay, and water.

The tower now tilts southward about 5.5° from vertical. That means that a point 150 ft up the south side of the tower is about $149\frac{1}{4}$ ft above the ground.

19. If someone dropped a weight from 150 ft up the south side of the Leaning Tower of Pisa, about how far would it land from the base of the tower? **about 15 ft**

LESSON QUIZ

The lengths of two sides of a right triangle are given. Find the length of the third side to the nearest tenth of a unit.

1. legs: 9 cm and 14 cm **16.6 cm**
2. legs: 15 in. and 19 in. **24.2 in.**
3. leg: 8 mm; hypotenuse: 18 mm **16.1 mm**
4. leg: 20 ft; hypotenuse: 23 ft **leg: 11.4 ft**

20. a. *Hobbies* If the area of a chessboard is 144 in.^{2}, what is the length of a side of the chessboard? **12 in.**

b. What is the length of a diagonal of the chessboard? **about 17 in.**

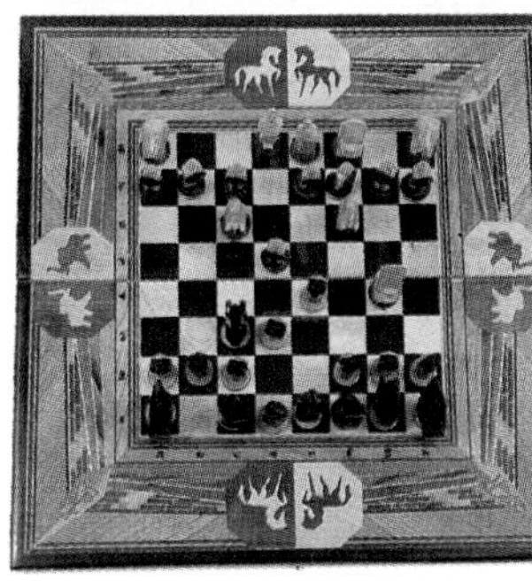

21. *Sports* A softball diamond is a square 60 ft by 60 ft. A baseball diamond is a square 90 ft by 90 ft.

a. How far is it from home plate to second base on a softball diamond? (*Hint:* Draw a diagram.) **about 85 ft**

b. How far is it from home plate to second base on a baseball diamond? **about 127 ft**

c. A baseball right fielder catches a fly ball on the first base line, 30 ft beyond first base. If he throws it to second base, how far does he throw the ball? **about 95 ft**

d. A baseball right fielder catches a fly ball on the first base line, 30 ft beyond first base. If he throws it to third base, how far does he throw the ball? **150 ft**

Find the area of each triangle to the nearest tenth.

22.

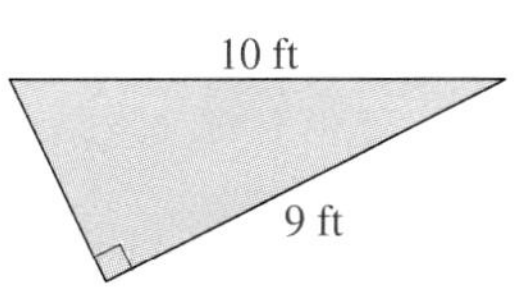

19.6 ft^2

23.

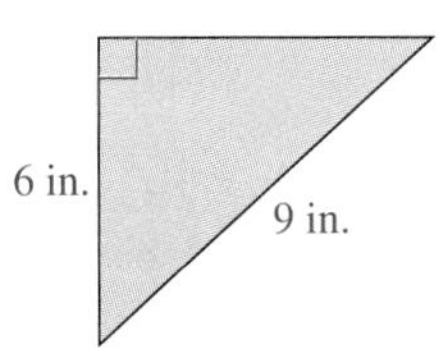

20.1 in.^{2}

24.

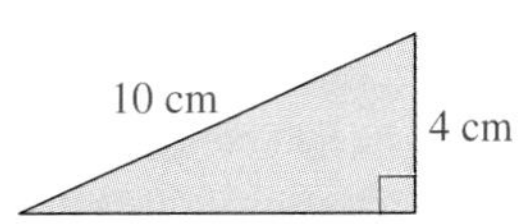

18.3 cm^2

Mixed Review

Write the prime factorization of each number. *(Lesson 4-5)*

25. 28 **$2^2 \cdot 7$** **26.** 57 **$3 \cdot 19$** **27.** 72 **$2^3 \cdot 3^2$** **28.** 108 **$2^2 \cdot 3^3$** **29.** 156 **$2^2 \cdot 3 \cdot 13$** **30.** 200 **$2^3 \cdot 5^2$**

Compare using <, >, or =. *(Lesson 2-1)*

31. 1.72 ■ 1.7 **>** **32.** 10.1 ■ 100.0 **<** **33.** 0.02 ■ 0.0002 **>** **34.** 6.211 ■ 6.21 **>**

Architecture **A floor plan has the scale 1.5 in. : 1 ft.** *(Lesson 6-5)*

35. What are the actual dimensions of a room that measures 21 in. × 24 in. on the floor plan? **14 ft × 16 ft**

36. What are the floor plan dimensions of a room measuring 12 ft × 15 ft? **18 in. × 22.5 in.**

PRACTICE

Practice 8-7 Applying the Pythagorean Theorem

The lengths of two sides of a right triangle are given. Find the length of the third side to the nearest tenth of a unit.

1. legs: 5 ft and 12 ft **13.0 ft**
2. legs: 13 cm and 9 cm **15.8 cm**
3. leg: 7 m; hypotenuse: 14 m **12.1 m**
4. legs: 17 ft and 6 ft **18.0 ft**
5. legs: 11 cm and 21 cm **23.7 cm**
6. leg: 15 m; hypotenuse: 20 m **13.2 m**

Find the missing side length to the nearest tenth.

7. (x; 9 cm; 12 cm) **x = 15 cm**
8. (15 in.; x; 25 in.) **x = 29.2 in.**
9. (32 cm; x; 47 cm) **x = 34.4 cm**
10. (16 m; 28 m; x) **x = 23.0 m**
11. (21 ft; 45 ft; x) **x = 39.8 ft**
12. (6 mi; 14 mi; x) **x = 12.6 mi**
13. (x; 32 yd; 49 yd) **x = 58.5 yd**
14. (x; 50 m; 28 m) **x = 41.4 m**
15. (x; 17 km; 24 km) **x = 29.4 km**

Solve.

16. A playground is 50 yd by 50 yd. Amy walked across the playground from one corner to the opposite corner. How far did she walk? **70.7 yd**
17. A 70-ft ladder is mounted 10 ft above the ground on a fire truck. The bottom of the ladder is 40 ft from the wall of a building. The top of the ladder is touching the building. How high off the ground is the top of the ladder? **67.4 ft**

Practice

In copymaster and workbook formats

RETEACHING

Reteaching 8-7 Applying the Pythagorean Theorem

The Pythagorean Theorem and a calculator can help you solve problems.

The sides of a picture frame are 12 in. and 18 in. Find the length of the diagonal.

Use $c^2 = a^2 + b^2$
$= 12^2 + 18^2$
$= 468$
$= \sqrt{468}$

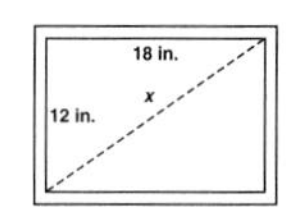

Use your calculator to find the square root of 468.

468 [√x] 21.63330765

To the nearest tenth, the diagonal is 21.6 in.

Use a calculator to find the missing side length to the nearest tenth.

1. (6 cm; 9 cm; x) **6.7 cm**
2. (7 m; 3 m; x) **7.6 m**
3. (5.8 cm; 4.1 cm; x) **4.1 cm**
4. (8 m; x; 5 m) **9.4 m**
5. (x; 6.2 cm; 7.5 cm) **4.2 cm**
6. (x; 8 in.; 15 in.) **12.7 in.**
7. A ladder leans against a wall 6 feet above the ground. The base of the ladder is 3 feet from the wall. How long is the ladder? **6.7 ft**
8. A small rectangular tray measures 16 cm by 18 cm. How long is the diagonal? **24.1 cm**
9. One side of a rectangular nature preserve is 6 mi. A diagonal path through the preserve is 12 mi. How long is the other side? **10.4 mi**
10. A string of flags is attached to a 4.8 m pole. The string meets the ground 5.6 m from the base of the pole. How long is the string? **7.4 m**

ENRICHMENT

Minds on Math Transparency

8-7

If Lori gives Cameron 5 cookies, he will have 3 times as many cookies as Lori. If Cameron gives Lori 5 cookies, they will have the same number of cookies. How many cookies do they each have?

Lori has 15 cookies and Cameron has 25 cookies.

See *Solution Key* for worked-out answers.

8-8 Teaching Notes

1 Focus

CONNECTING TO PRIOR KNOWLEDGE Draw a rectangle. Ask:

- *Name the dimensions of the rectangle.* **length and width**
- *How many dimensions is this?* **two**

Draw the segments necessary to make the rectangle appear as a rectangular prism. Ask:

- *Now, how many dimensions does the figure have?* **three**

2 Teach

THINK AND DISCUSS

DIVERSITY Have students bring pictures of famous buildings of the world to class. Have the class name the geometric figures they see.

VISUAL LEARNING **Question 2** Have students look at each prism and complete the following checklist.

- *Are all the surfaces faces?*
- *Are all the faces polygons?*
- *Are there two bases?*
- *What types of polygons are the bases?*

Lesson Planning Options

Prerequisite Skills

- identifying polygons (7-6)

Vocabulary/Symbols

three-dimensional figures, faces, prisms, bases, edge, cube, pyramid

Materials/Manipulatives

- graph paper

Resources

Student Edition

Skills Handbook, p. 528
Extra Practice, p. 521
Glossary/Study Guide

Teaching Resources

Chapter Support File, Ch. 8
- Lesson Planner 8-8
- Practice 8-8, Reteaching 8-8
- Answer Masters 8-8

Teaching Aids Masters 1, 2, 11–17
Glossary, Spanish Resources

Transparencies

1, Minds on Math 8-8

Warm Up

Use your classmates as subjects and estimate these percents.
About what percent have curly hair?
About what percent are girls?
About what percent are twins?
Answers may vary.

8-8 Three-Dimensional Figures

What You'll Learn

1. To identify prisms
2. To identify other three-dimensional figures

...And Why

Architects use many different three-dimensional shapes in buildings.

Here's How

Look for questions that
- build understanding
- ✔ check understanding

THINK AND DISCUSS

1 *Identifying Prisms*

What geometric figures do you see in the entrance to the Louvre in Paris, France? In the Jomo Kenyatta Conference Center in Nairobi, Kenya? Figures that do not lie in a plane, such as these buildings, are *three-dimensional figures.*

Louvre

Jomo Kenyatta Conference Center

Some three-dimensional figures have only flat surfaces. The flat surfaces, called **faces,** are shaped like polygons.

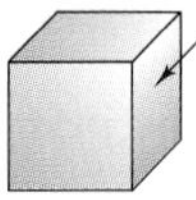

1. *Draw a Conclusion* Which building has faces? **the Louvre**

Prisms are three-dimensional figures with two parallel and congruent polygonal faces, called **bases.** The other faces are rectangles. A prism is named for the shape of its bases.

■ **EXAMPLE 1**

Give the best name for the prism.

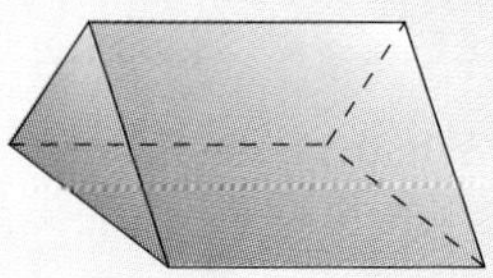

The only parallel and congruent faces are triangular. The figure is a triangular prism.

Question 3 Remind students that the term side is appropriate only for two-dimensional figures.

Question 4 Ask: *What shape is the base of a cube?* **square**

■ **ADDITIONAL EXAMPLES**

FOR EXAMPLE 1

Give the best name for the prism.
rectangular prism

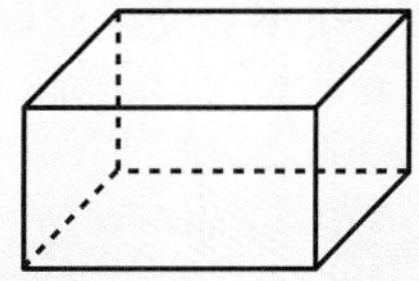

FOR EXAMPLE 2

Draw a pentagonal prism. **Check students' work.**

VISUAL LEARNING Question 5 Have students look at each pyramid and complete the following checklist:

- *Are all the surfaces faces?*
- *Are all the faces triangles?*
- *Is there one base?*
- *What type of polygon is the base?*

AEP Have small groups of students each create a poster that illustrates the figures from this lesson. Have four columns on the poster: *two-dimensional figures*, *prisms*, *pyramids*,

Notice in Example 1 that the bases of a prism are not necessarily at the "top" and "bottom."

2. ✔ *Try It Out* Match each prism with one of the following names: rectangular prism, pentagonal prism, hexagonal prism.

a. 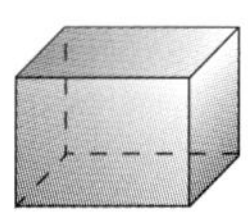 b. 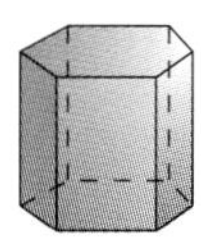 c. 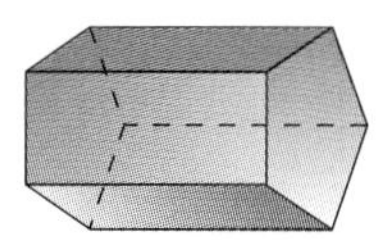

rectangular prism **hexagonal prism** **pentagonal prism**

3. *Analyze* Each segment formed by the intersection of two faces is an *edge*. Why are some of the edges of the prisms in Question 2 dashed? **The dashed edges are hidden from view by the prism.**

4. *Think About It* A *cube* is a rectangular prism whose faces are squares. Are the edges of a cube congruent? Explain. **See below left.**

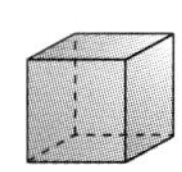

Now you may assign Exercises 1–3, 9–11, 14.

2 *Other Three-Dimensional Figures*

A **pyramid** is a three-dimensional figure with only one base. The base is a polygon and the other faces are triangles. A pyramid is named for the shape of its base.

5. *Visual Thinking* Match each pyramid with one of the following names: triangular pyramid, rectangular pyramid, pentagonal pyramid, hexagonal pyramid.

a. 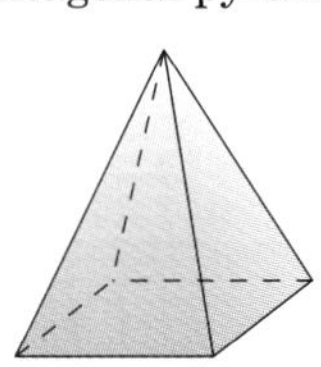 b. 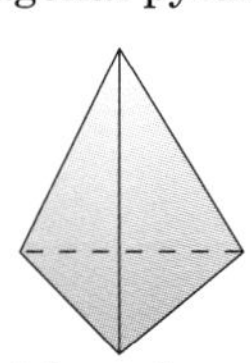 c. 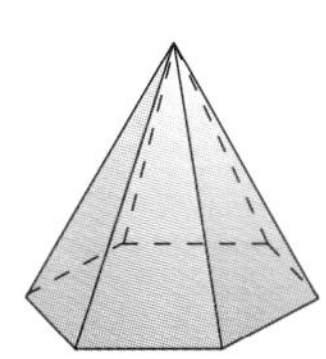

rectangular pyramid **triangular pyramid** **hexagonal pyramid**

6. *Think About It* Which of the three-dimensional figures below have bases? Describe the bases. **cylinder, cone; circles**

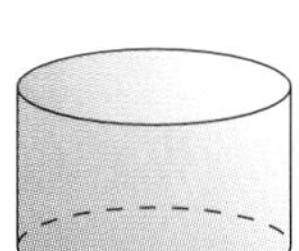
cylinder

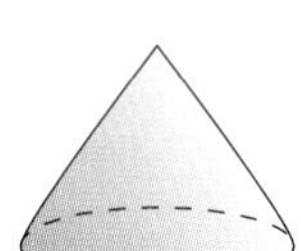
cone

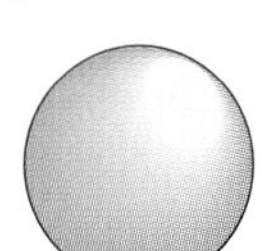
sphere

WHO? Architect I. M. Pei designed the glass and steel entrance of the Louvre, the French national art museum.

4. Yes; the faces of a cube are congruent squares, so the sides of all the squares are congruent to each other. Each edge is a side of two faces. So all the edges are congruent.

Technology Options

Prentice Hall Technology

Software for Learners

- Hot Page™ 2–9*
- Math Blaster® Mystery*
- Interactive Student Tutorial, Chapter 8*

Teaching Resource Software

- Computer Item Generator 8-8
- Resource Pro Chapter 8*

Internet • For related mathematics activities, visit the Prentice Hall site at www.phschool.com/math

**Available on CD-ROM only*

Assignment Options for Exercises On Your Own

To provide flexible scheduling, this lesson can be subdivided into parts.

1 **Core** 1–3, 9, 14
Extension 10, 11

2 **Core** 4–8, 12, 13, 15–23
Extension 24, 25

Use Mixed Review to maintain skills.

and *other three-dimensional figures.* Encourage students to color code the figures.

ERROR ALERT! Students may confuse *prism* and *pyramid.* **Remediation:** Have students ask themselves:

- *Can the figure stand on both of its bases?* **If yes, it is a prism.**
- *Do all the faces come to a point?* **If yes, it is a pyramid.**

ASSESSMENT Have students work in groups of four. Assign a three-dimensional figure from this lesson to each group. Students draw the figure on a card and write its name on another card. Then mix the cards and lay them face down. Play a memory game to match the pictures and names. Each player picks two cards. If the cards match, the player keeps the cards and picks two more. If not, another player picks two cards.

3 Practice/Assess

EXERCISES *On Your Own*

TACTILE LEARNING Exercises 9–11 Have students use their index fingers to trace the appropriate edges as a volunteer reads each exercise aloud.

EXTENSION Exercises 20–22 Have students create their figures on a computer or build them with objects.

7. 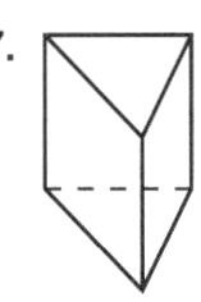

You can use graph paper to draw three-dimensional figures.

■ **EXAMPLE 2**

Draw a hexagonal prism.

Step 1	**Step 2**	**Step 3**
Draw a hexagon.	Draw a second hexagon.	Connect the vertices.

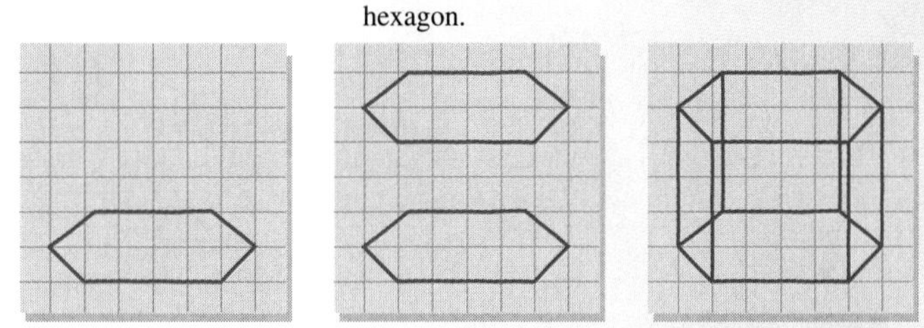

7. ✔ *Try It Out* Draw a triangular prism on graph paper.

Now you may assign Exercises 4–8, 12, 13, 15–25.

EXERCISES *On Your Own*

Visual Thinking **Give the best name for each figure.**

1. 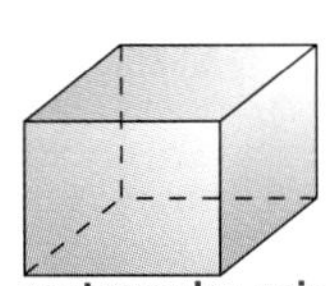
rectangular prism

2. 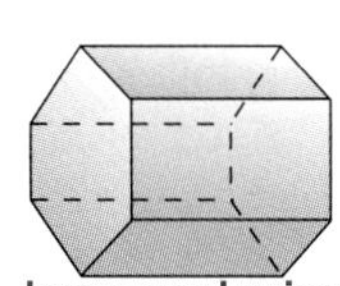
hexagonal prism

3. 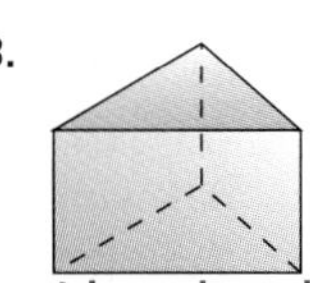
triangular prism

4. 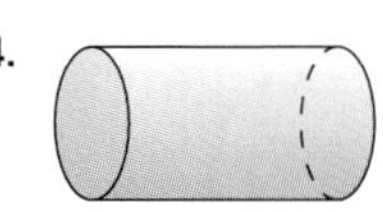
cylinder

5. 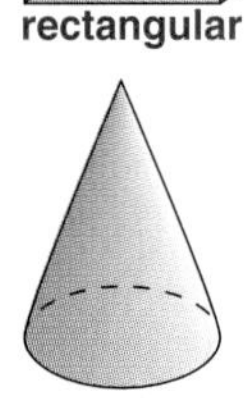
cone

6. 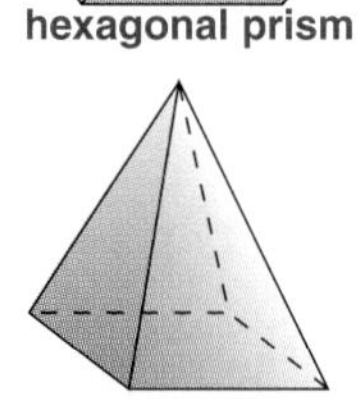
rectangular pyramid

7. 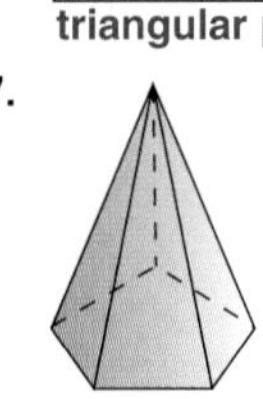
pentagonal pyramid

8. 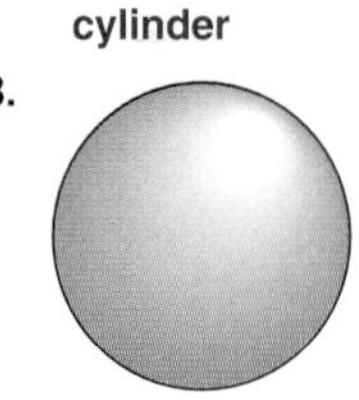
sphere

Use the rectangular prism at the right.

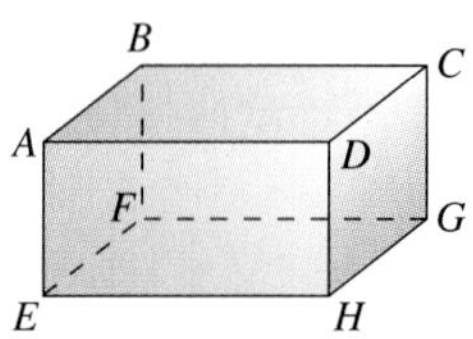

9. Name the four edges that intersect $\overline{AB}$.
$\overline{AD}$, $\overline{AE}$, $\overline{BC}$, $\overline{BF}$
10. Name the three edges that are parallel to $\overline{AB}$.
$\overline{CD}$, $\overline{EF}$, $\overline{HG}$
11. Name the four edges that are *not* parallel to $\overline{AB}$ and do *not* intersect $\overline{AB}$. $\overline{CG}$, $\overline{DH}$, $\overline{EH}$, $\overline{FG}$

Exercise 24 Because of the word *every*, students need to think of only one exception to make the answer false.

WRAP UP

IDENTIFYING THE BIG IDEA Have students describe the three-dimensional figures they studied in this lesson. Then have them name real-life examples.

LESSON QUIZ

Give the best name for each figure.

1. 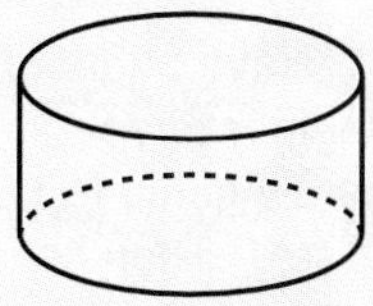
cylinder

2. 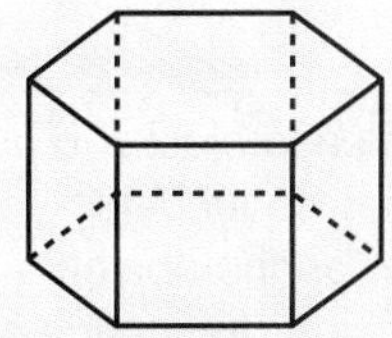
hexagonal prism

Use graph paper to draw each figure.

3. Triangular prism **Check students' work.**
4. Rectangular pyramid **Check students' work.**

Architecture **Name some three-dimensional figures in each photograph on page 368.**

12. the Louvre
rectangular pyramid

13. the Jomo Kenyatta Conference Center
cone and cylinder

Architecture **Name the three-dimensional figures in each photograph.**

14. 
14. pentagonal prism

15. 
15. cylinders and rectangular prisms

16. 
16. rectangular pyramid

Drafting **Use graph paper to draw each figure.**

17. a rectangular prism
18. a rectangular pyramid
19. a triangular prism

17. 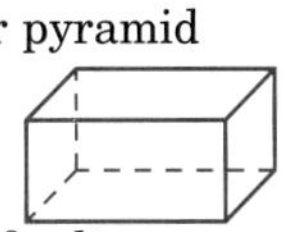
18. 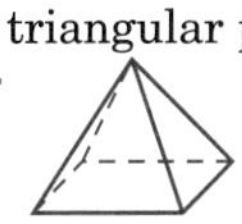
19. 

Sketch each three-dimensional figure.
20–22. Check students' work for diagrams.

20. a television set
21. a container of salt
22. a tipi

23. How are a cylinder and a cone alike? How are they different?
They both have circular bases. A cylinder has two bases, and a cone has only one.

Analyze **Classify as *true* or *false*. Explain.**

24. Every rectangular prism is a cube.
24. False; only if all the faces of a rectangular prism are square can it be a cube.

25. Some pyramids are prisms.
25. False; pyramids have only one base and prisms have two.

Mixed Review

Solve. *(Lesson 3-6)*

26. $4 + x = -6$ −10
27. $x - 8 = 5$ 13
28. $10 = y - (-2)$ 8
29. $h + (-3) = -5$ −2

Order from least to greatest. *(Lesson 4-3)*

30. $\frac{3}{8}, \frac{2}{12}, \frac{2}{3}$ $\frac{2}{12}, \frac{3}{8}, \frac{2}{3}$
31. $\frac{5}{9}, \frac{7}{12}, \frac{43}{81}$ 31. $\frac{43}{81}, \frac{5}{9}, \frac{7}{12}$
32. $\frac{11}{24}, \frac{17}{42}, \frac{12}{36}$ 32. $\frac{12}{36}, \frac{17}{42}, \frac{11}{24}$
33. $\frac{4}{6}, \frac{10}{18}, \frac{18}{24}$ 33. $\frac{10}{18}, \frac{4}{6}, \frac{18}{24}$
34. $\frac{25}{27}, \frac{5}{7}, \frac{2}{5}$ 34. $\frac{2}{5}, \frac{5}{7}, \frac{25}{27}$

35. *Photography* April must enlarge a 3 in. by 5 in. photograph so it is 185% of the original size. What will be the dimensions of the enlarged photograph? *(Lesson 6-9)* 5.55 in. by 9.25 in.

Extra Practice, Lesson 8-8, page 521

PRACTICE

Practice 8-8 Three-Dimensional Figures

Give the best name for each three-dimensional figure. Describe the base.

1. triangular prism; triangle
2. cylinder; circle
3. hexagonal pyramid; hexagon

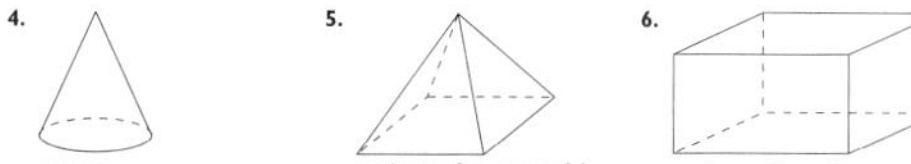

4. cone; circle
5. rectangular pyramid; rectangle or square
6. rectangular prism; rectangle

Use the figure at the right for Exercises 7–8. Answers may vary. Sample answers shown.

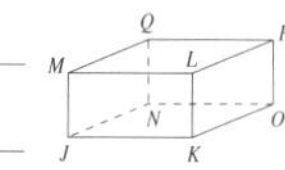

7. Name three pairs of parallel edges.
$\overline{MQ}$ and $\overline{LP}$, $\overline{JM}$ and $\overline{NQ}$, $\overline{NO}$ and $\overline{JK}$

8. Name four edges that intersect $\overline{ML}$.
$\overline{MQ}$, $\overline{MJ}$, $\overline{LP}$, $\overline{LK}$

Draw each figure named. Answers may vary. Samples given.

9. a triangular pyramid
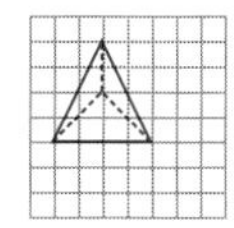

10. a square prism
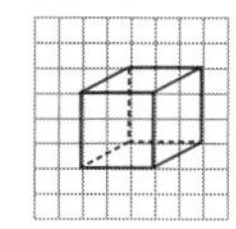

In copymaster and workbook formats

RETEACHING

Reteaching 8-8 Three-Dimensional Figures

A **prism** is a three-dimensional figure with two parallel and congruent polygonal **bases.** It is named by the shape of a base.

Rectangular prism The bases are rectangles.
Triangular prism The bases are triangles.
Hexagonal prism The bases are hexagons.

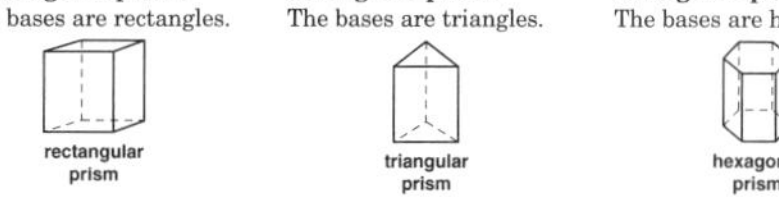

A **pyramid** is a three-dimensional figure with only one base.

Triangular pyramid The base is a triangle.

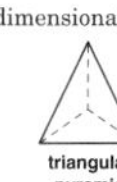

Square pyramid The base is a square.

The **cylinder, cone,** and **sphere** are also three-dimensional figures.

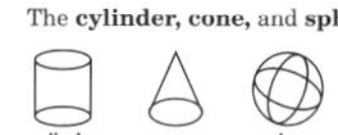

Give the best name for each figure.

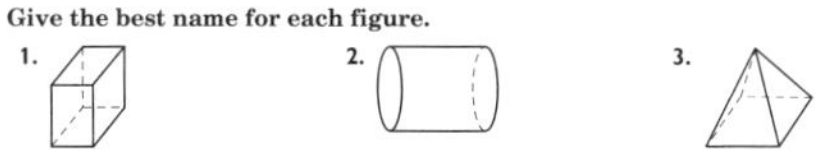

1. rectangular prism
2. cylinder
3. square pyramid

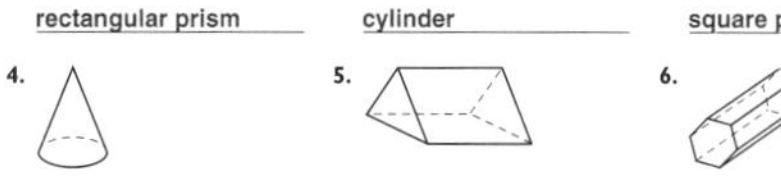

4. cone
5. triangular prism
6. hexagonal prism

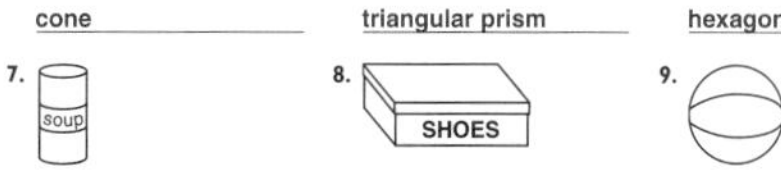

7. cylinder
8. rectangular prism
9. sphere

Reteaching

ENRICHMENT

Minds on Math Transparency

8-8

Find the length x of the side of the triangle below.

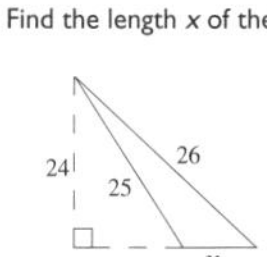

3

See *Solution Key* for worked-out answers.

In Lesson 8-8, students learn to identify prisms and other three-dimensional figures. This toolbox allows students to explore the three views of an object.

ERROR ALERT! Students may have trouble imagining a three-dimensional object from a two-dimensional view. **Remediation:** Have students use blocks to model the example with a partner. Then look at the arrangement from the top, front, and side. Suggest students close one eye so that the view they get is as flat as possible.

ASSESSMENT Exercise 1 Have partners each use blocks to build another three-dimensional object that has the same top view as the object in Exercise 1. Then have partners draw each other's top view. They can repeat the process to build objects that have the same front view and the same side view.

ADDITIONAL PROBLEM

Stack one more block on the middle column of blocks in Exercise 3. Draw the top, front, and side view of the new figure.

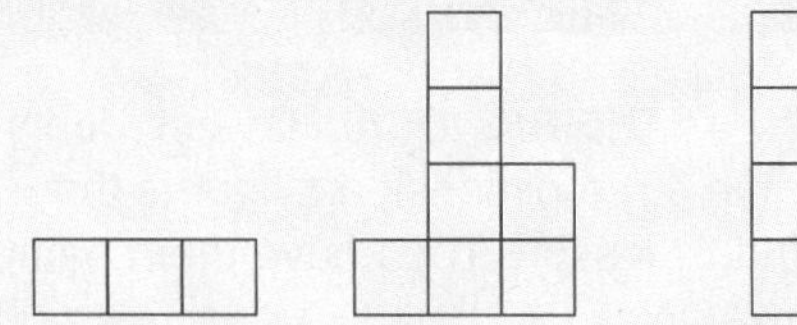

Top Front Side

Resources

Teaching Resources

Teaching Aids Master 18

Transparencies

6

page 372 Math Toolbox

1.

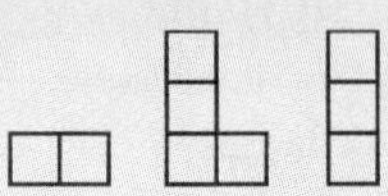

Top Front Right

2.

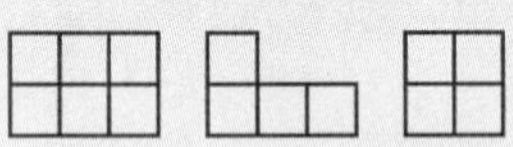

Top Front Right

3.

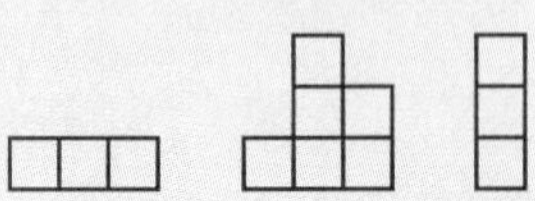

Top Front Right

4.

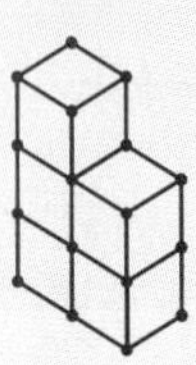

5.

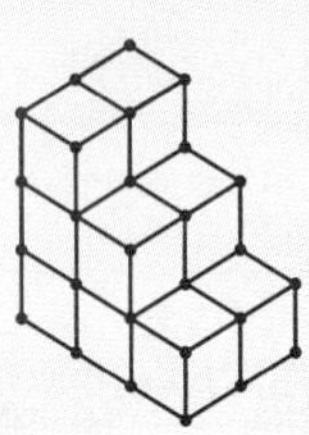

MATH TOOLBOX EXPLORATION

Three Views of an Object

After Lesson 8-8

Three-dimensional objects can be drawn to show that they have length, width, and height, as in the drawing at the right. You can also make drawings that show only one view of the blocks.

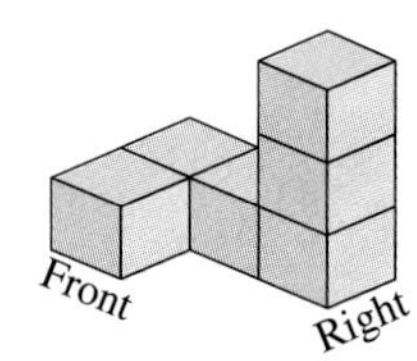

■ EXAMPLE

a. Make a drawing of the six blocks shown above. Draw them as if you are looking down on the blocks. This is called a *top view*.

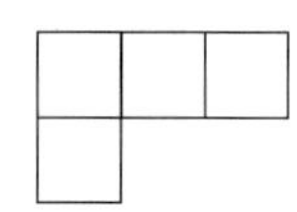

b. Make a drawing of the *front view* of the blocks.

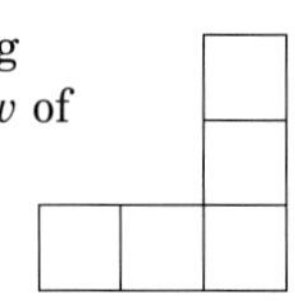

c. Make a drawing of the *right side view* of the blocks.

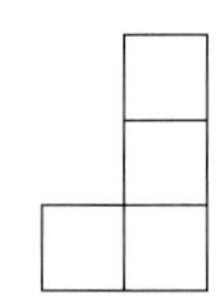

1–3. See margin.

Draw the top, front, and right side views of each figure.

1.

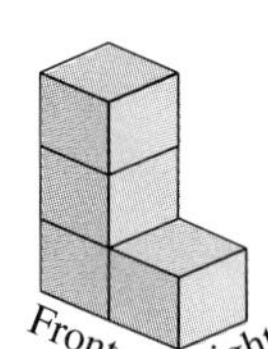

2.

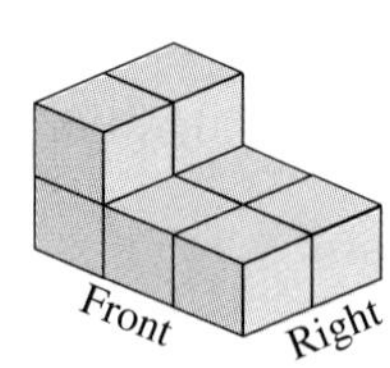

3.

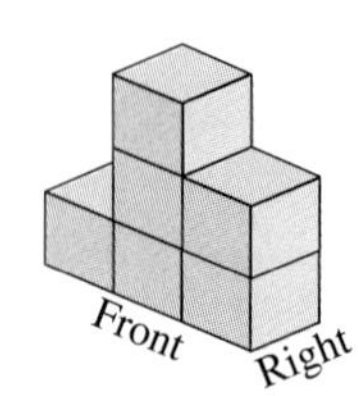

4–5. See margin.

Use the top, front, and side views to draw each figure.

4. Top Front Right

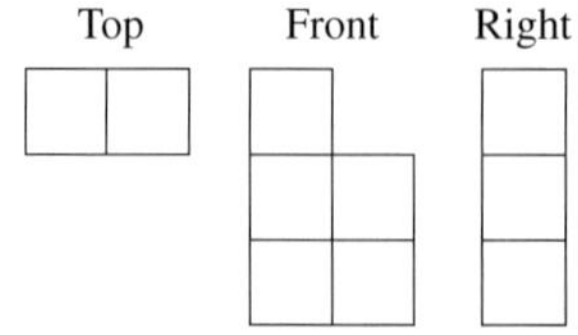

5. Top Front Right

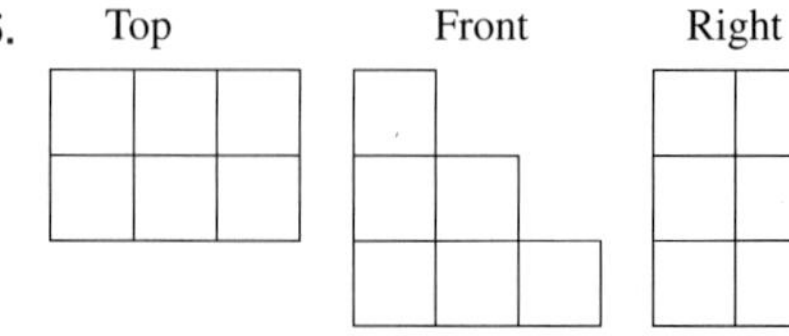

6. *Writing* Describe a solid you can build with blocks that has the same front, side, and top views.
A cube; the front, right, and top views of a cube are congruent squares.

1 Focus

CONNECTING TO PRIOR KNOWLEDGE Tell students you want to cover a box with the least amount of paper possible. Have students explain how to do this. **Answers may vary. Sample: Measure each face. Cut a piece of paper the same size as each face. Glue or tape the paper to each face of the box.**

2 Teach

THINK AND DISCUSS

AEP Most students think of a *net* as a fishing net or a hairnet. Use these references to help them understand the mathematical meaning. Tell students: *You lay out a fishing net over an area, and a hair net covers an area.*

TACTILE LEARNING Question 1 Have students work in pairs to trace and cut out each possible net. Then have one student fold the paper along the fold lines while the other student tapes it in place. Ask: *How do you know pattern B is not a net for a rectangular solid?* **Pattern B has two edges on the same side.**

Question 2 Students can find the surface area by counting the squares on the graph paper or by finding the sum of the areas of the rectangles.

8-9 Surface Area of Prisms and Cylinders

What You'll Learn

1. To find the surface area of prisms
2. To find the surface area of cylinders

...And Why

The surface area of prisms and cylinders determines the amount of material needed to cover their surfaces.

Here's How

Look for questions that
- build understanding
- ✔ check understanding

3a–b. Answers may vary. Samples:

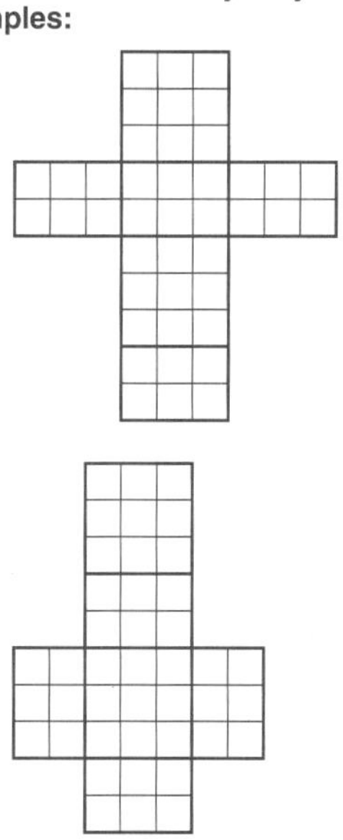

THINK AND DISCUSS

1 *Finding the Surface Area of Prisms*

The centimeter graph paper covering a rectangular prism has been cut along the edges and folded flat.

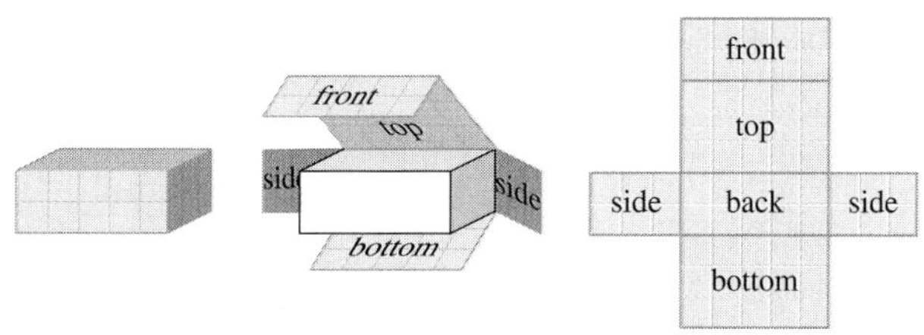

A pattern that can be folded to cover a solid figure is called a **net** for that figure.

1. **Choose A, B, or C.** Which pattern is *not* a net for the rectangular solid above? **B**

A. B. C.

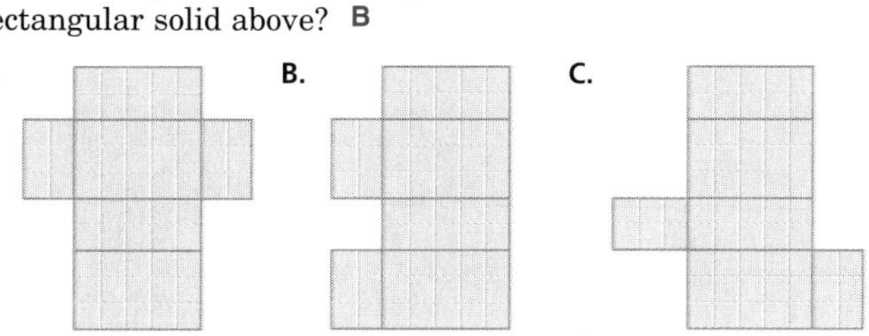

The **surface area** of a prism is the sum of the areas of its faces. So, the surface area of a rectangular prism equals the sum of the areas of the six rectangles that make up its net.

2. What is the surface area of the rectangular prism above? **62 cm^2**
3. a. *Modeling* This rectangular prism has been covered with inch graph paper. Draw a net for the prism.
   b. Draw a different net for the prism.
   c. Find the surface area of the prism. **42 in.^{2}**

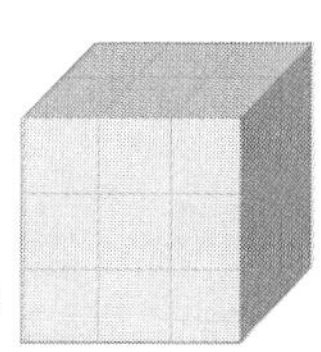

a–b. Answers may vary. See left for samples.

Lesson Planning Options

Prerequisite Skills
- finding area of circles (8-4)
- finding area of rectangles (8-2)
- finding area of triangles (8-3)

Vocabulary/Symbols
net, surface area

Materials/Manipulatives
- centimeter graph paper

Resources

Student Edition

Skills Handbook, p. 530
Extra Practice, p. 521
Glossary/Study Guide

Teaching Resources

Chapter Support File, Ch. 8
- Lesson Planner 8-9
- Practice 8-9, Reteaching 8-9
- Alternative Activity 8-9
- Answer Masters 8-9

Teaching Aids Masters 1, 2, 11, 14–17
Glossary, Spanish Resources

Transparencies
1, 15, Minds on Math 8-9

Warm Up

What number is 42,625 less than the sum of 62,345 and 51,284? **71,004**

ERROR ALERT! Question 3c Students may count only the one-inch squares on the faces shown in the drawing. **Remediation:** Tell students to count the one-inch squares in the drawing and on their net. Compare the amounts. Ask: *If you count only the squares in the drawing, have you counted all the squares?* **no** Remind students to check for "hidden faces" when counting squares to determine the area of a figure.

Question 4 Have students make a list of all rectangles of their net. **two 8 in. by 6 in. rectangles; two 8 in. by 2 in. rectangles; two 6 in. by 2 in. rectangles**

■ ADDITIONAL EXAMPLES

FOR EXAMPLE 1

Find the surface area of this triangular prism. **540 in.²**

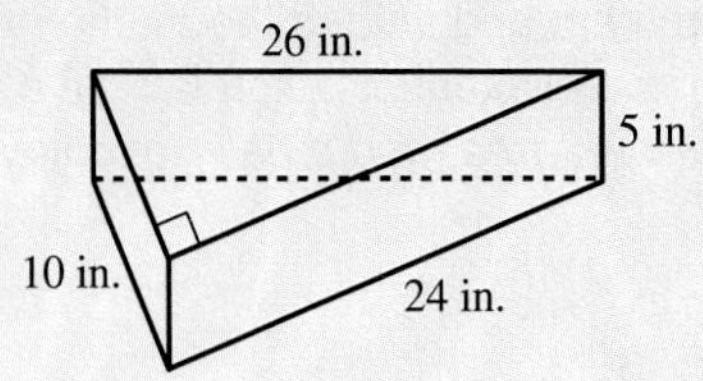

FOR EXAMPLE 2

Find the surface area of a can of soup with a radius of 8 cm and a height of 11 cm. **955 cm²**

AUDITORY LEARNING Example 1 Have a volunteer describe each face of the triangular prism while other students point to the appropriate face. Encourage the volunteer to give a description such as: *The 4 cm by 9 cm rectangle is on the left side.*

Technology Options

Prentice Hall Technology

Software for Learners
- Math Blaster® Mystery*
- Interactive Student Tutorial, Chapter 8*

Teaching Resource Software
- Computer Item Generator 8-9
- Resource Pro Chapter 8*

Internet • For related mathematics activities, visit the Prentice Hall site at www.phschool.com/math

**Available on CD-ROM only*

Assignment Options for Exercises On Your Own

To provide flexible scheduling, this lesson can be subdivided into parts.

1 Core 1–6
Extension 7

2 Core 8–12
Extension 13

Use Mixed Review to maintain skills.

4.

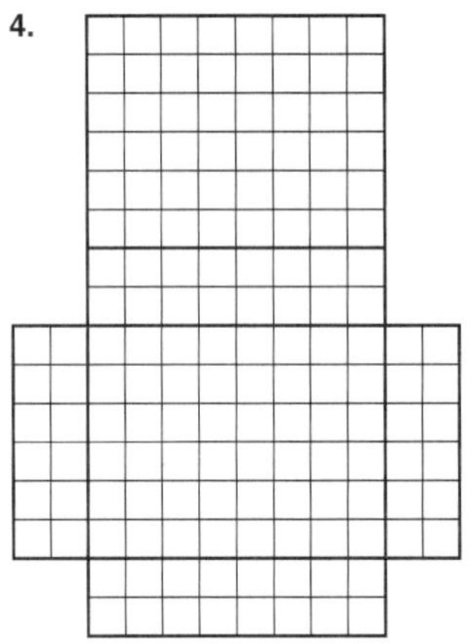

4. ✔ *Try It Out* A rectangular prism is 8 in. by 6 in. by 2 in. Draw a net and find the surface area. **152 in.²**

Nets can be used to find the surface of any prism.

■ EXAMPLE 1

Find the surface area of this triangular prism.

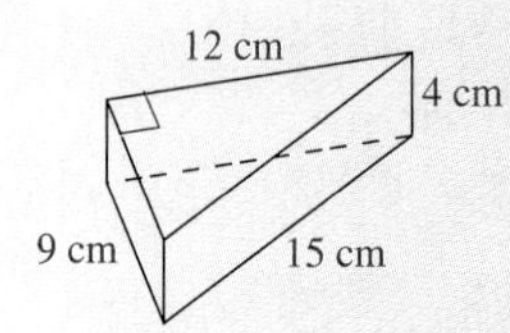

Draw a net for the prism.

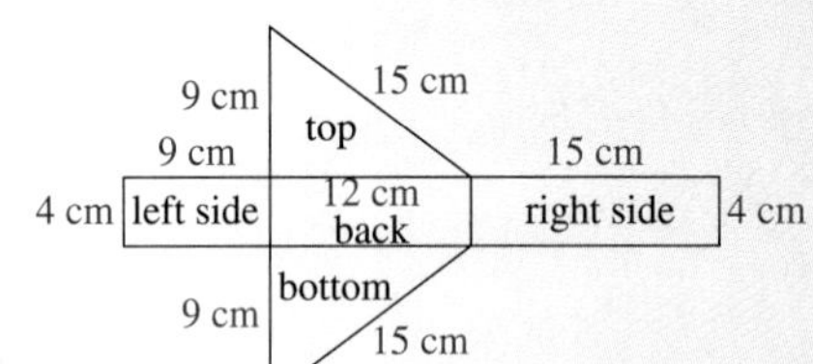

Find the total area of the five faces.

$$\underset{\text{left side}}{4(9)} + \underset{\text{back}}{4(12)} + \underset{\text{right side}}{4(15)} + \underset{\text{top}}{\tfrac{1}{2}(12)(9)} + \underset{\text{bottom}}{\tfrac{1}{2}(12)(9)} = 252$$

The surface area of the triangular prism is 252 in.².

5. ✔ *Try It Out* Suppose a triangular prism has the same base as in Example 1, but its height is 8 cm instead of 4 cm. Draw a net. Then find the surface area. **396 cm²**

Now you may assign Exercises 1–7.

2 *Finding the Surface Area of Cylinders*

When you cut the paper covering a cylinder along the edges and fold it flat, you get two circles and a rectangle.

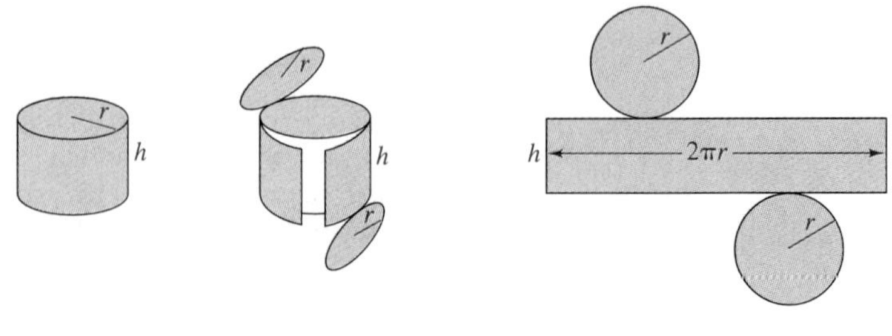

Question 5 Have students copy the equation from Example 1. Then have them replace each 9 with an 8.

Example 2 Point out that the base of the rectangle is equal to the circumference of the circle. So, the area of the rectangle is $(b)h$ or $(2\pi r)h$.

ASSESSMENT Name a figure and have students describe how to find its surface area. For example: *triangular prism;* sum of the areas of three rectangles and the areas of two triangles.

TACTILE LEARNING Give pairs of students some clay and a set of geometric solids. Have students press the sides of the geometric solids into the clay. Have them roll a cylinder in the clay to create a rectangle. This will reinforce the fact that the curved part of the cylinder is a rectangle.

3 Practice/Assess

EXERCISES *On Your Own*

Exercise 1 Students might find it helpful to match each face of a rectangular prism model to each part of the net.

Exercise 12 Point out that students will use the formula $(\pi d)(h)$ for the area of the rectangle.

You can use a net of a cylinder to find its surface area.

■ **EXAMPLE 2** *Real-World Problem Solving*

Find the surface area of the roller on the steamroller.

Draw a net for the roller.

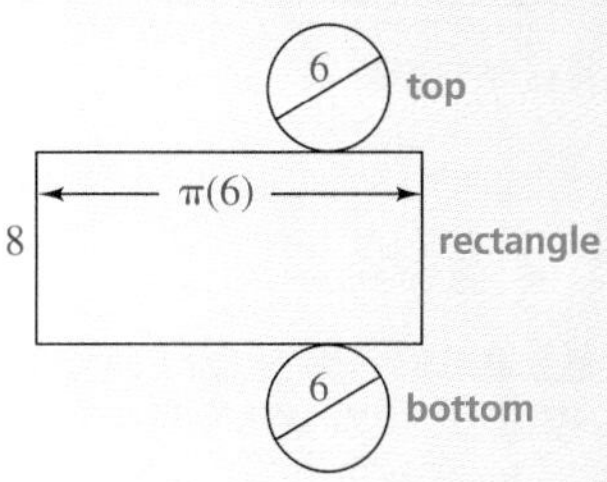

Radius = 3 ft

Area of one circle = $\pi r^2 = \pi(3)^2 = \pi(9) \approx 28.27$

Area of rectangle = $(2\pi r)h = 2\pi(3)(8) = 48\pi \approx 150.80$

top bottom rectangle

Surface area ≈ $28.27 + 28.27 + 150.80 = 207.34$

The surface area of the roller is about 207 ft^2.

6. ✔ *Try It Out* Find the surface area of a cylinder with base radius 5 cm and height 2 cm. Round to the nearest unit. **220 cm^2**

Now you may assign Exercises 8–13.

EXERCISES *On Your Own*

1. **Choose A, B, or C.** Which pattern is a net for the rectangular prism at the right? **B**

A.

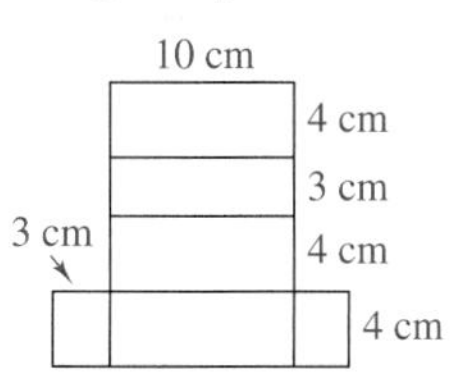

B.

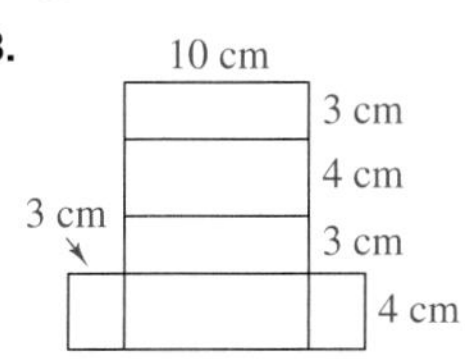

C.

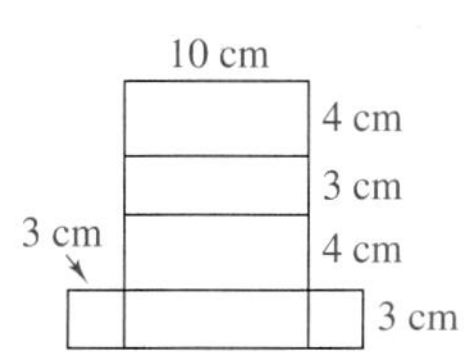

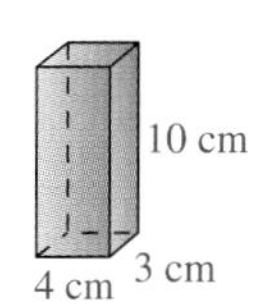

2. Find the surface area of the prism shown in Exercise 1. **164 cm^2**

Draw a net for each prism. Then find the surface area.

3–5. Nets may vary. See margin for sample diagrams.

3.

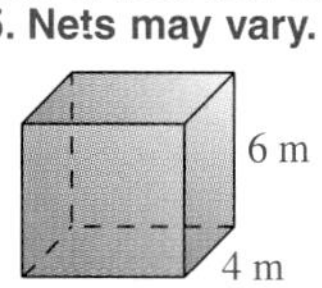

188 m^2

4.

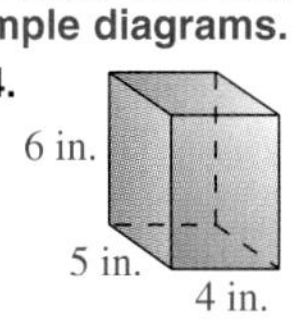

148 $in.^2$

5.

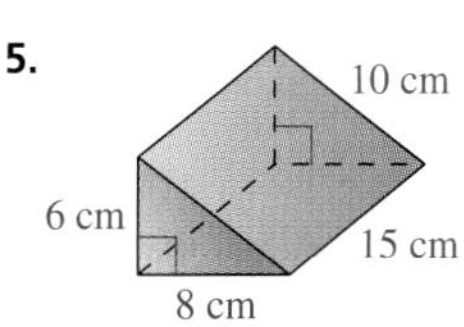

408 cm^2

pages 375–376 On Your Own

3.

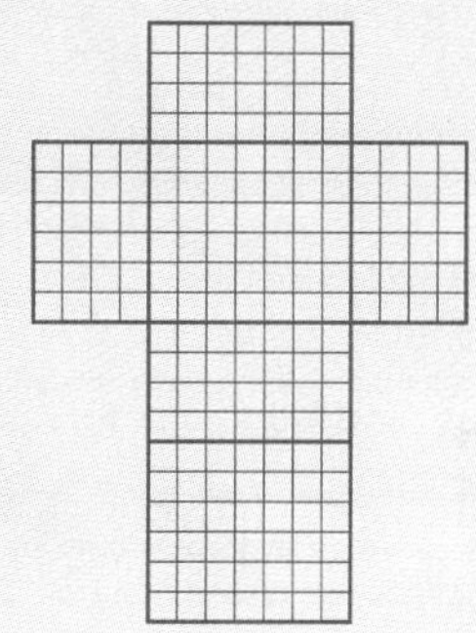

4.

5.

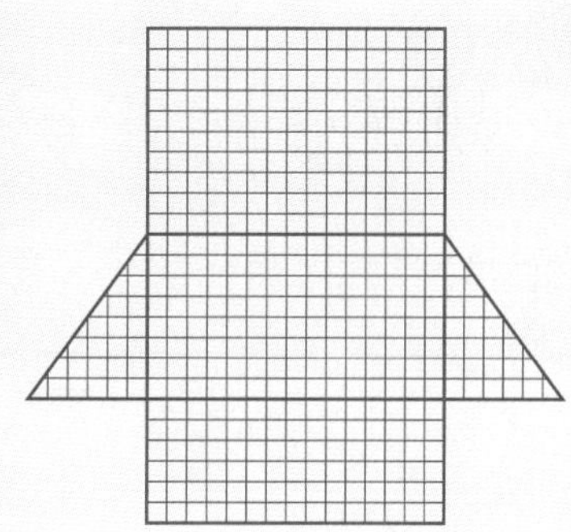

PRACTICE

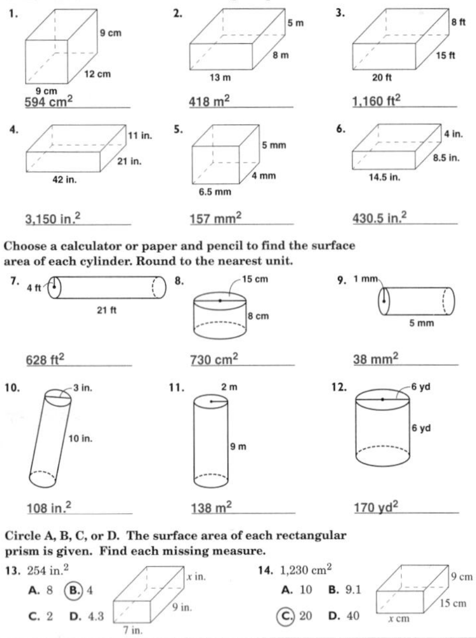
Practice 8-9 *Surface Area of Prisms and Cylinders*

Choose a calculator, paper and pencil, or mental math to find the surface area of each rectangular prism.

Choose a calculator or paper and pencil to find the surface area of each cylinder. Round to the nearest unit.

Circle A, B, C, or D. The surface area of each rectangular prism is given. Find each missing measure.

Practice

In copymaster and workbook formats

RETEACHING

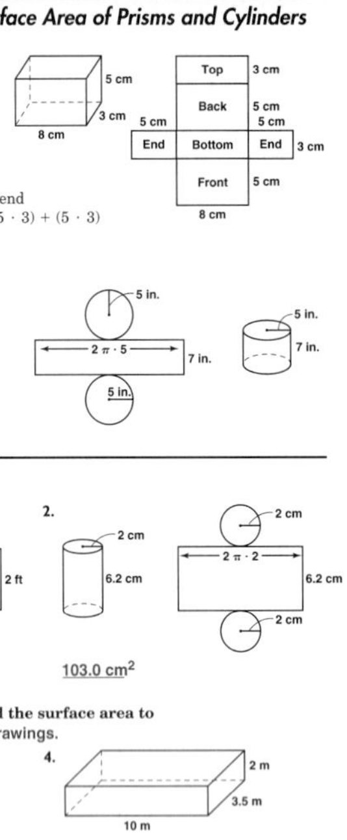
Reteaching 8-9 *Surface Area of Prisms and Cylinders*

The **surface area** of a prism is the sum of the areas of its faces. You can use a **net**, or pattern, for the prism to help you find its surface area.

- Add the areas of all the surfaces.

Surface Area
= front + back + top + bottom + end + end
= (8 · 5) + (8 · 5) + (8 · 3) + (8 · 3) + (5 · 3) + (5 · 3)
= 40 + 40 + 24 + 24 + 15 + 15
= 158 cm²

- To find the surface area of a cylinder, add the area of the rectangle and the areas of the bases. Use $\pi = 3.14$.

Surface Area
= top + bottom + side (rectangle)
= (π · 5 · 5) + (π · 5 · 5) + (2π · 5 · 7)
= (25π) + (25π) + (70π)
= (120π) ≈ 376.8 in.²

Use the net to find the surface area.

Draw a net for each figure. Then find the surface area to the nearest tenth. Check students' drawings.

ENRICHMENT

Minds on Math Transparency

8-9

The lengths of the sides of a right triangle are consecutive whole numbers. What is the area of the triangle?

6 square units

See *Solution Key* for worked-out answers.

WRAP UP

IDENTIFYING THE BIG IDEA Have students explain how to find the surface area of a prism and a cylinder. Also have them explain how to use a net to find the surface area.

PROJECT LINK This activity will help students see that a taller box does not necessarily have a greater surface area than a shorter box.

LESSON QUIZ

Find the surface area for each three-dimensional figure.

1. rectangular prism: 12 in. by 8 in. by 9 in. **552 in.²**
2. triangular prism: base 3 mm; height 4 mm; hypotenuse 5 mm; prism height 2 mm **36 mm²**
3. cylinder: radius 6 cm; height 10 cm **about 602.19 cm²**

6. Draw two different nets for a rectangular prism 3 units by 4 units by 7 units. **Answers may vary. See back of book for samples.**

7. *Open-ended* Draw a net for a prism that has a surface area of 80 cm². **Check students' work.**

8. Which of these patterns is a net for a cylinder? **C**

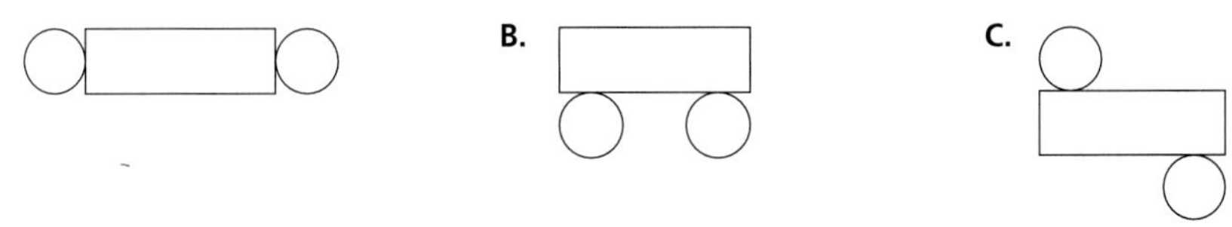

Draw a net for each cylinder. Then find its surface area. Round to the nearest unit. **See back of book for diagrams.**

9. **848 m²**

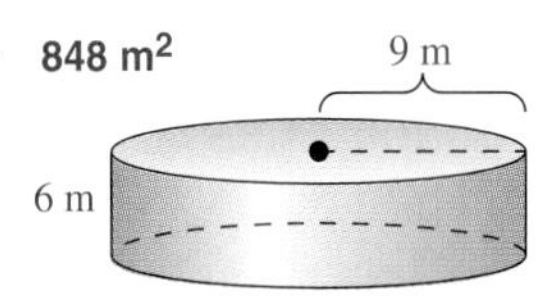

10.

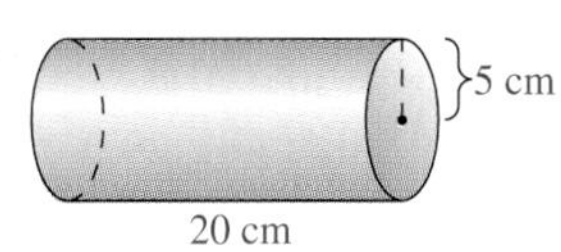

785 cm²

11.

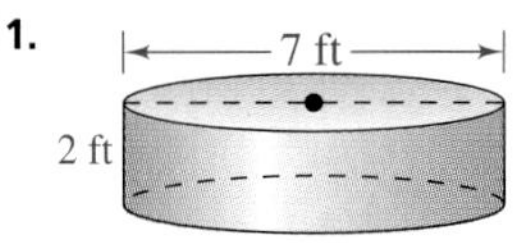

121 ft²

12. The interior of a cylindrical water tank needs resurfacing. Its diameter is 60 ft and its height is 35 ft. What is the area of the interior to the nearest unit? **12,252 ft²**

13. *Reasoning* Which has the greater effect on the surface area of a cylinder: doubling the base radius or doubling the height? Explain using examples. **See back of book.**

Mixed Review

Which unit is best for measuring each of the following? *(Lesson 8-1)*

14. the perimeter of your desk: in., ft, yd, mi **in.**
15. the area of the gym floor: cm², m², km² **m²**

Estimate each answer. *(Lessons 2-3, 2-5, 2-6)* **16–19. Answers may vary. Samples are given.**

16. 25.5986 × 3.598 **100**
17. 12.3 ÷ 4.3 **3**
18. 21.6 + 7.8 **30**
19. 39.7 − 5.24 **35**

20. *Choose a Strategy* A club has 100 members. Each of the 5 officers gets 6 other members to help them decorate for a party. What percent of the club members do the decorating? **35%**

CHAPTER PROJECT

PROJECT LINK: WRITING

Describe at least three different ways you can pack four of your cylinders in rectangular boxes. Which box has the least surface area? Calculate the surface area of the box.

Check students' work.

1 Focus

CONNECTING TO PRIOR KNOWLEDGE
Display several rectangular prisms and cylinders that appear to be about the same size. Ask students which figure they think would hold the most uncooked rice. Fill each figure with rice and compare the amounts to check their guesses.

2 Teach

THINK AND DISCUSS

DIVERSITY Some students may think of volume only as an amount of liquid. They may have trouble thinking of volume in terms of cubic units. Explain that you use two different measuring cups in cooking—one for dry ingredients and one for liquids.

Question 1c It may help students to imagine six bases one-unit high stacked on top of each other.

Example 1 Point out that volume is expressed in cubic units, or units^3. Ask: *Why do you think the volume is 120 cm^3 instead of 120 cm^2 or 120 cm?* **Answers may vary. Sample: The unit cm is multiplied together three times.**

8-10 Volume of Rectangular Prisms and Cylinders

What You'll Learn

1. To find the volume of a prism
2. To find the volume of a cylinder

...And Why

The volume of prisms and cylinders determines the amount of material needed to fill them.

Here's How

Look for questions that
- build understanding
- ✔ check understanding

THINK AND DISCUSS

1 *Finding the Volume of Prisms*

The **volume** of a three-dimensional figure is the number of cubic units needed to fill the space inside the figure. A **cubic unit** is a cube whose edges are one unit long.

a cubic centimeter
(1 cm^3)

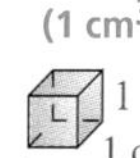

■ **EXAMPLE 1**

Find the volume of the rectangular prism.

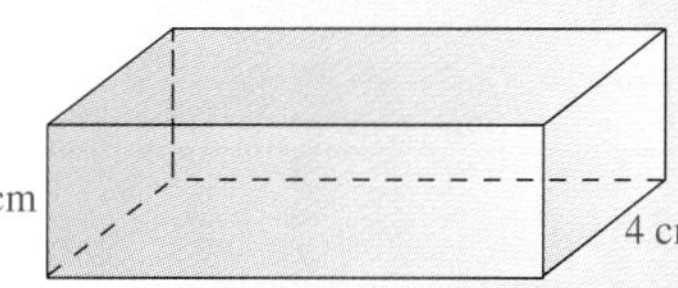

There are
$10 \cdot 4 = 40$ cubes
in the bottom layer.

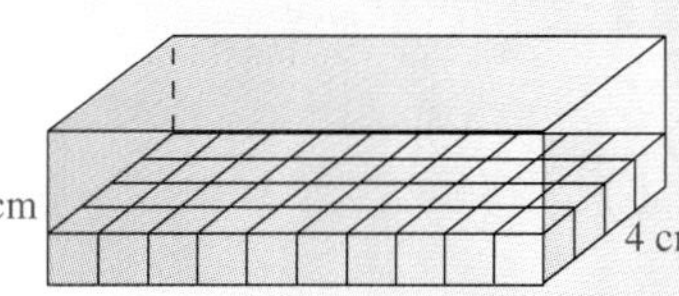

Three layers of cubes fit in the prism.
$40 \cdot 3 = 120$

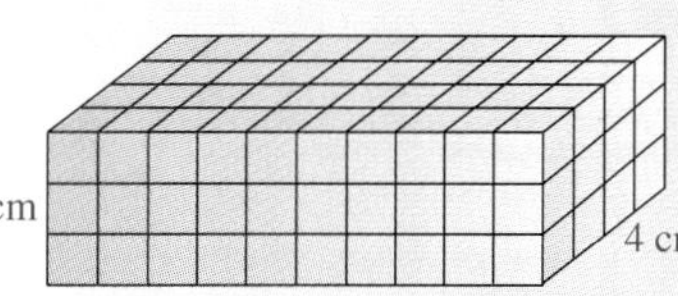

The volume is 120 cm^3.

1. a. *Analyze* Find the area of the bottom of the prism at the right. **12 in.^{2}**
   b. How many unit cubes one inch on an edge would fit in the bottom layer? **12 cubes**
   c. Find the volume of the prism. **72 in.^{3}**

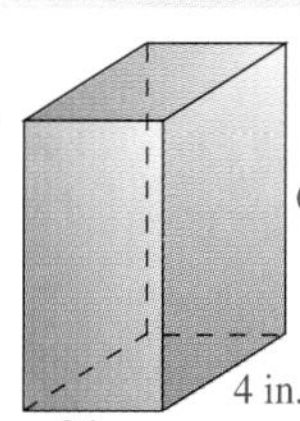

Lesson Planning Options

Prerequisite Skills
- finding area of rectangles, triangles, circles (8-2 to 8-4)

Vocabulary/Symbols
volume, cubic unit

Materials/Manipulatives
- calculator

Resources

Student Edition
Skills Handbook, p. 541
Extra Practice, p. 521
Glossary/Study Guide

Teaching Resources
Chapter Support File, Ch. 8
- Lesson Planner 8-10
- Practice 8-10, Reteaching 8-10
- Alternative Activity 8-10
- Answer Masters 8-10

Teaching Aids Masters 1, 2, 11, 16
Glossary, Spanish Resources

Transparencies
1, 15, Minds on Math 8-10

Warm Up
Write the word expression for 85,250,003,620. **eighty-five billion, two hundred fifty million, three thousand, six hundred twenty**

VISUAL LEARNING Show students a $10 \times 10 \times 10$ cube made of place-value blocks. Ask: *What is the volume of this cube?* **1,000 units³**

■ **ADDITIONAL EXAMPLES**

FOR EXAMPLE 1

Find the volume of a rectangular prism with a length of 12 m, a width of 8 m, and a height of 10 m. **960 m³**

FOR EXAMPLE 2

A cylinder is 9.3 cm high and has a base radius of 3.6 cm. Estimate the volume. **Answers may vary. Sample: 360 cm³** Then use a calculator to find the volume. **378.7 cm³**

ERROR ALERT! Example 2 Students may multiply π and r and then square. **Remediation:** Have students write $V = \pi \cdot r \cdot r \cdot h$. Then have them substitute the values into the formula and multiply.

ASSESSMENT Ask:

- *What measurements do you need to find the volume of a rectangular prism?* **l, w, and h**
- *What measurements do you need to find the volume of a cylinder?* **r and h**
- *What operation is used to find volume?* **multiplication**
- *How is the answer expressed?* **in cubic units (units³)**

Technology Options

Prentice Hall Technology

Software for Learners

- Hot Page™ 5–9*
- Math Blaster® Mystery*
- Interactive Student Tutorial, Chapter 8*

Teaching Resource Software

- Computer Item Generator 8-10
- Resource Pro Chapter 8*

Internet • For related mathematics activities, visit the Prentice Hall site at www.phschool.com/math

**Available on CD-ROM only*

Assignment Options for Exercises On Your Own

To provide flexible scheduling, this lesson can be subdivided into parts.

1 **Core** 1–7, 12
Extension 15

2 **Core** 8–11, 13
Extension 14

Use Mixed Review to maintain skills.

WHERE? In one second approximately 212,000 ft³ of water flows over Niagara Falls. If you made a cube to hold that amount of water, the edges of the cube would need to be about 59.6 ft long.

You can calculate the volume V of a rectangular prism by multiplying the area of a base B by the height h.

VOLUME OF A RECTANGULAR PRISM

$V = \text{area of base} \times \text{height}$
$= Bh$
$= \ell wh$

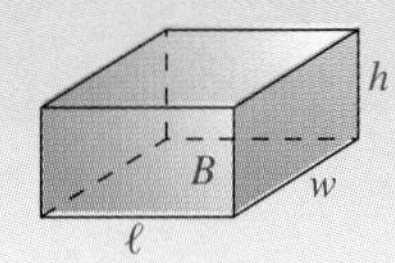

2. ✔ *Try It Out* The length of each edge of a cube is 7 m. What is the volume of the cube? **343 m³**

Now you may assign Exercises 1–7, 12, 15.

2 *Finding the Volume of a Cylinder*

You can calculate the volume of a cylinder in much the same way as you calculate the volume of a prism.

VOLUME OF A CYLINDER

$V = \text{area of base} \times \text{height}$
$= Bh$
$= (\pi r^2)h$

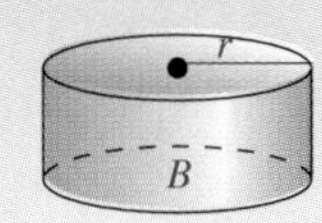

■ **EXAMPLE 2**

A cylinder is 8.2 m high and has a base radius of 2.1 m. Estimate the volume. Then use a calculator to find the volume.

Use $V = \pi r^2 h$. Use 3 to estimate π.

Estimate: $V \approx 3 \cdot 2 \cdot 2 \cdot 8 = 96$ m³

π × 2.1 x² × 8.2 = 113.6062735 ← Use a calculator.

The volume is about 113.6 m³.

1,125 cm³; about 1,085.7 cm³

3. ✔ *Try It Out* The base radius of a cylinder is 4.8 cm. The height is 15 cm. Estimate the volume. Then use a calculator to find the volume. Round to the nearest tenth.

Niagara Falls

Now you may assign Exercises 8–11, 13, 14.

Then have students discuss their answers with a partner.

3 Practice/Assess

EXERCISES *On Your Own*

Exercises 1–3 Point out multiplication is associative, so the *l*, *w*, and *h* can be multiplied in any order.

Exercise 6 Ask: *What three steps are necessary for this exercise?* **Find the volume of 3 gal. Find the volume of the container. Compare the volumes.**

REASONING Exercise 14b Suggest students draw a circle within a square and compare the areas.

WRITING Exercise 15b Remind students the formula for the volume of a rectangular prism is also the area of its base times its height.

WRAP UP

IDENTIFYING THE BIG IDEA Have students define *volume* and explain how to find the volume of a rectangular prism and a cylinder.

CHECKPOINT 2

Checkpoint 2 *Lessons 8-5 through 8-10*

Find the missing side length to the nearest tenth.

1. 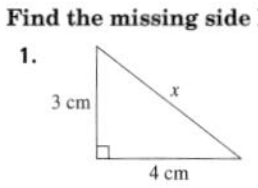

5 cm

2. 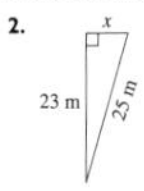

9.8 m

3. 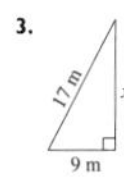

14.4 m

Find the surface area and volume of each rectangular prism.

4. length = 7 m, width = 4 m, height = 3 m; *SA* = 122 m²; *V* = 84 m³
5. length = 9 cm, width = 3 cm, height = 2 cm; *SA* = 102 cm²; *V* = 54 cm³
6. length = 6 m, width = 15 m, height = 4 m; *SA* = 348 m²; *V* = 360 m³
7. Find the surface area and volume of a cylinder with a radius of 3.5 cm and a height of 7 cm. 230.8 cm²; 269.4 cm³

EXERCISES *On Your Own*

Choose **Use a calculator, paper and pencil, or mental math to find the volume of each rectangular prism.**

1. 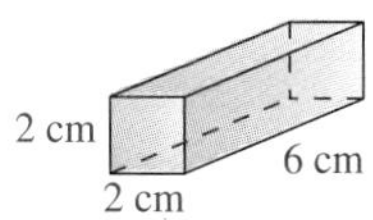

24 cm³

2. 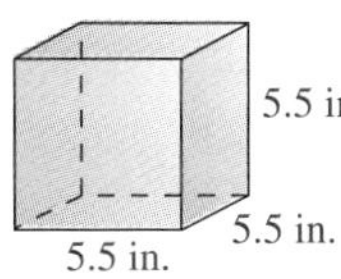

166.375 in.³

3. 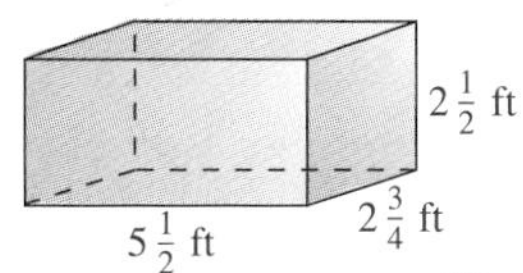

$37\frac{13}{16}$ ft³

4. **Choose A, B, C, or D.** Which expression represents the volume of the rectangular prism at the right? **D**

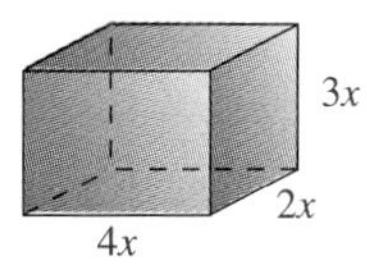

A. $9x$ B. $24x$ C. $24x^2$ D. $24x^3$

5. Find the volume of a rectangular prism with length 11 ft, width 5 ft, and height 2 yd. **330 ft³**

6. A gallon of milk occupies 231 in.³ of space. Can a container 15 in. by 6 in. by 8 in. hold 3 gallons? Why or why not?
Yes; 3 gal occupy 693 in.³ and the capacity of the container is 720 in.³.

7. a. The volume of a rectangular prism is 60 m³. Find all possible whole number triples that could be the dimensions of the prism. For example, 2 m, 3 m, 10 m is a possible triple.
   b. *Writing* Explain how you solved the problem in part (a).
   Answers may vary. Sample: Made an organized list.

7a. 1 m, 1 m, 60 m; 1 m, 2 m, 30 m; 1 m, 3 m, 20 m; 1 m, 4 m, 15 m; 1 m, 5 m, 12 m; 1 m, 6 m, 10 m; 2 m, 2 m, 15 m; 2 m, 3 m, 10 m; 2 m, 5 m, 6 m; 3 m, 4 m, 5 m

Find the volume of each cylinder. Round to nearest tenth.

8. 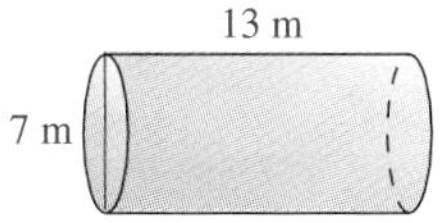

about 500.3 m³

9. 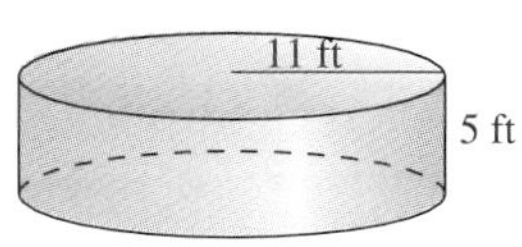

about 1,900.7 ft³

10. 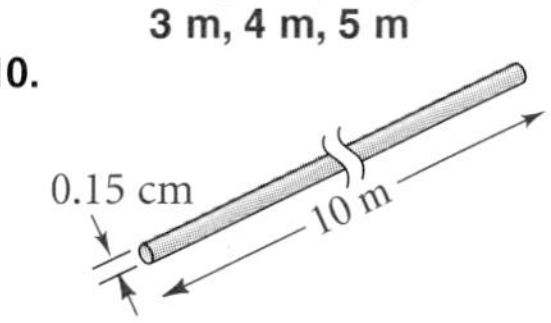

about 17.7 cm³

11. Find the volume of a cylinder with a base radius of 2 cm and a height of 4 cm to the nearest unit. **50 cm³**

Mental Math **Estimate each volume.**

12. 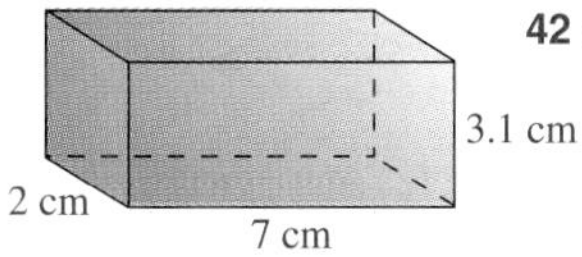

42 cm³

13. 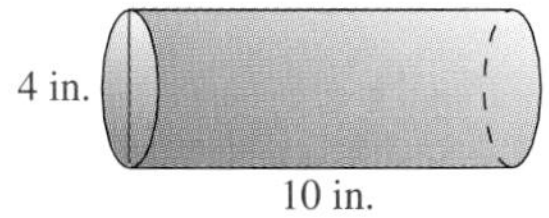

120 in.³

PRACTICE

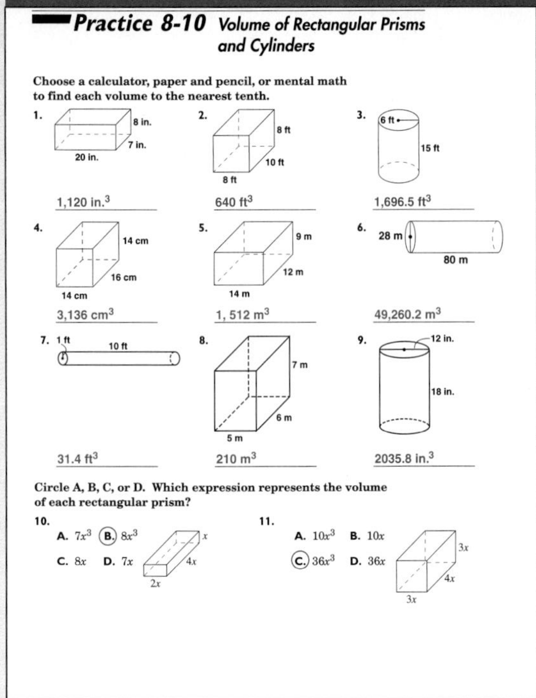
Practice 8-10 *Volume of Rectangular Prisms and Cylinders*

Choose a calculator, paper and pencil, or mental math to find each volume to the nearest tenth.

1. 1,120 in.^{3}
2. 640 ft^3
3. 1,696.5 ft^3
4. 3,136 cm^3
5. 1, 512 m^3
6. 49,260.2 m^3
7. 31.4 ft^3
8. 210 m^3
9. 2035.8 in.^{3}

Circle A, B, C, or D. Which expression represents the volume of each rectangular prism?

10. A. $7x^3$ (B.) $8x^3$ C. $8x$ D. $7x$
11. A. $10x^3$ B. $10x$ (C.) $36x^3$ D. $36x$

In copymaster and workbook formats

RETEACHING

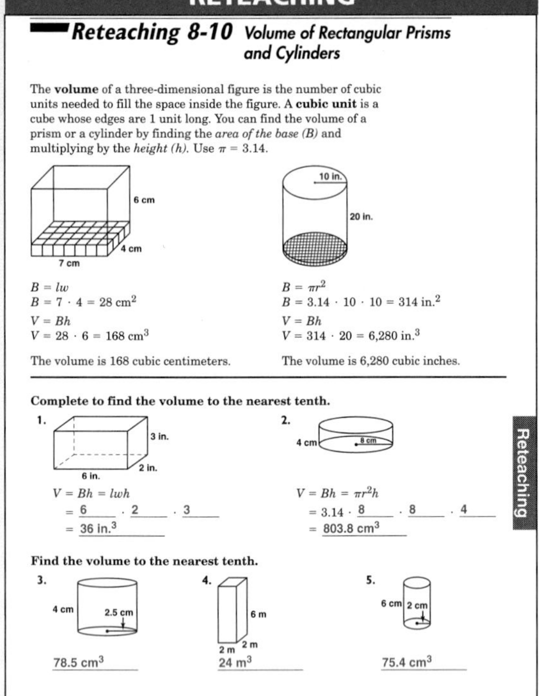
Reteaching 8-10 *Volume of Rectangular Prisms and Cylinders*

The **volume** of a three-dimensional figure is the number of cubic units needed to fill the space inside the figure. A **cubic unit** is a cube whose edges are 1 unit long. You can find the volume of a prism or a cylinder by finding the *area of the base (B)* and multiplying by the *height (h)*. Use $\pi = 3.14$.

$B = lw$	$B = \pi r^2$
$B = 7 \cdot 4 = 28$ cm^2	$B = 3.14 \cdot 10 \cdot 10 = 314$ in.^{2}
$V = Bh$	$V = Bh$
$V = 28 \cdot 6 = 168$ cm^3	$V = 314 \cdot 20 = 6{,}280$ in.^{3}
The volume is 168 cubic centimeters.	The volume is 6,280 cubic inches.

Complete to find the volume to the nearest tenth.

1. $V = Bh = lwh$
   $= 6 \cdot 2 \cdot 3$
   $= 36$ in.^{3}
2. $V = Bh = \pi r^2 h$
   $= 3.14 \cdot 8 \cdot 8 \cdot 4$
   $= 803.8$ cm^3

Find the volume to the nearest tenth.

3. 78.5 cm^3
4. 24 m^3
5. 75.4 cm^3

ENRICHMENT

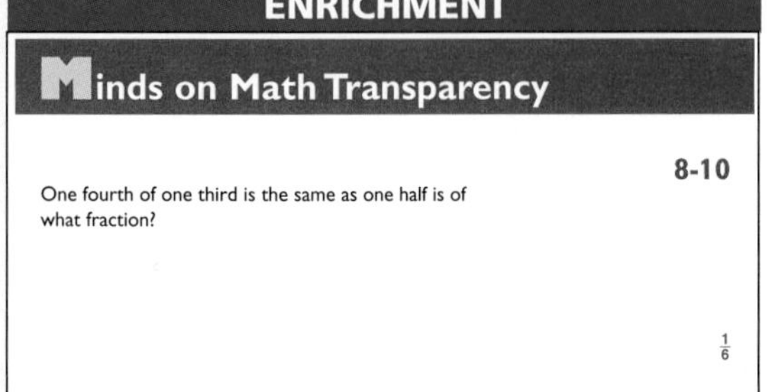
Minds on Math Transparency

8-10

One fourth of one third is the same as one half is of what fraction?

$\frac{1}{6}$

See *Solution Key* for worked-out answers.

380

LESSON QUIZ

1. Find the volume of a rectangular prism with a length of 5.9 mm, a width of 8.2 mm, and a height of 7.5 mm. **362.85 mm^3**
2. Find the volume of a cylinder that is 7.4 ft high and has a radius of 3.2 ft. **238 ft^3**

14a. The volume of the cube is about 35 cm^3 greater than the volume of the cylinder.

14. a. A cylinder has a base diameter and height of 5.5 cm. A cube has edges 5.5 cm long. Compare the volumes.

b. ***Reasoning*** What accounts for the difference in the volumes? **The cylinder fits completely inside the cube.**

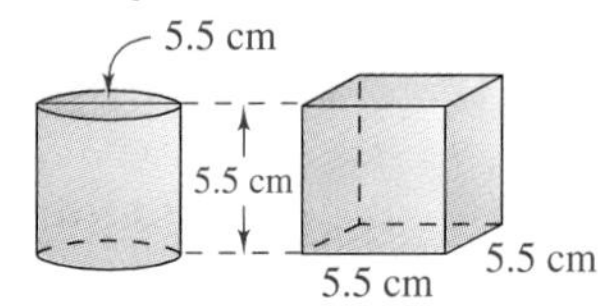

15. a. The triangular prism at the right was formed by cutting a rectangular prism in half. Find the volume of the rectangular prism and of the triangular prism. **24 in.^{3}; 12 in.^{3}**

b. ***Writing*** Show that the volume of this triangular prism equals the area of its base times its height.

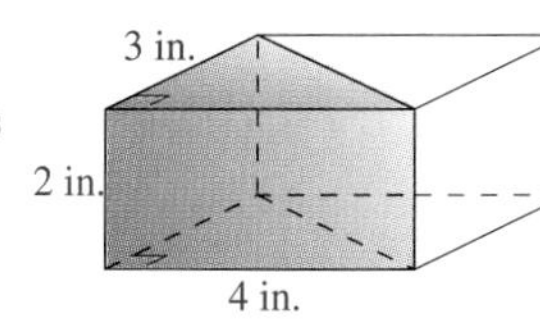

15b. The area of the triangular base is 6 in.^{2}. The height is 2 in. So, 6 in.^{2} × 2 in. = 12 in.^{3}.

Mixed Review

Write the unit rate for each situation. *(Lesson 6-2)*

16. 18 mi in 3 h **6 mi/h**
17. \$32.00 for 8 CDs **\$4.00 for 1 CD**
18. 12 lb in 5 wk **2.4 lb/wk**
19. 4 c for 3 loaves **$1\frac{1}{3}$ c per loaf**

Write each decimal as a fraction in simplest form. *(Lesson 4-9)*

20. 1.25 **$1\frac{1}{4}$**
21. 0.00215 **$\frac{43}{20{,}000}$**
22. 5.55 **$5\frac{11}{20}$**
23. 0.429 **$\frac{429}{1{,}000}$**
24. 8.95 **$8\frac{19}{20}$**
25. 0.003 **$\frac{3}{1{,}000}$**

26. ***Choose a Strategy*** Diego can mow Mrs. Jones' lawn twice as fast as Peter. Jody can mow the same lawn in 45 min. How long does it take Diego to mow the lawn? What do you need to know to solve the problem? **not enough information to solve the problem; how fast Peter mows the lawn**

✓ CHECKPOINT 2

Lessons 8-5 through 8-10

Find the length of the third side of each right triangle. Round to the nearest tenth if necessary.

1. legs: 9 ft and 12 ft **15 ft**
2. leg: 5 cm; hypotenuse: 25 cm **24.5 cm**
3. legs: both 6 in. **8.5 in.**

Draw and label a figure for each description. Find the surface area and the volume of each. Use 3.14 for π.
4–5. Check students' work for diagrams.

4. a rectangular prism with dimensions 6 ft, 10 ft, and 5 ft **280 ft^2; 300 ft^3**
5. a cylinder with radius 8 m and height 20 m **1,406.72 m^2; 4,019.2 m^3**
6. **Choose A, B, C, or D.** A cylinder has a radius of 1 ft and a height of 3 ft. If you double the radius, the volume is __?__. **C**

A. doubled B. tripled C. quadrupled D. unchanged

Extra Practice, Lesson 8-10, page 521

8-11 Teaching Notes

1 Focus

CONNECTING TO PRIOR KNOWLEDGE
Have students discuss strategies they have used to work a jigsaw puzzle. Ask: *What pieces do you usually try first?* **Answers may vary. Sample: pieces that look like they will fit** *What do you do if a piece does not fit?* **Sample: Try another.**

2 Teach

THINK AND DISCUSS

DIVERSITY Some students may become frustrated if they do not guess an answer right away. Remind them the purpose of the lesson is to practice the process. Encourage every attempt to use the procedure.

KINESTHETIC LEARNING Hide an object in the room. Give several clues as to its whereabouts. Have students guess until they find the object.

ERROR ALERT! Question 5 Students may not use their first guess to make a second guess. **Remediation:** Have students make a list of possible questions they can ask as they test each guess. **Answers may vary. Sample: Should my next guess be higher or lower? How close should my second guess be to my first guess?**

PROBLEM SOLVING STRATEGY

READ PLAN LOOK BACK SOLVE

8-11 Guess and Test

Problem Solving Strategies

- Draw a Diagram
- ✔ Guess and Test
- Look for a Pattern
- Make a Model
- Make a Table
- Simulate a Problem
- Solve a Simpler Problem
- Too Much or Too Little Information
- Use Logical Reasoning
- Use Multiple Strategies
- Work Backward
- Write an Equation

THINK AND DISCUSS

Sometimes the best way to solve a problem is to make a guess and then test your guess. Using what you learn from testing your guess, you make another guess and test it. You repeat this process until you are able to solve the problem.

SAMPLE PROBLEM

> At a pet store, Alani decided on the number and kinds of fish she would like to have. The salesperson helped her figure that those fish would need an aquarium with a capacity of 10,648 cm^3. She wants a cubic aquarium. What should be the length of each edge of the cube?

READ
Read for understanding. Summarize the problem.

1. Think about the information you are given and what you are asked to find.
   a. What type of three-dimensional figure is involved? **cube**
   b. What dimensions are important in the figure? **length, width, and height which are all equal**

PLAN
Decide on a strategy.

Guess and Test is a good strategy to use here. You can guess the length of each edge of the cube. Then test your guess by using a calculator to multiply the dimensions. If the test reveals that you guessed too high or too low, you can make a better guess and try again. A table can help you organize your guesses and the results.

SOLVE
Try the strategy.

2. Suppose you start with a guess of 30 cm.
   a. Find the volume of the cube. **27,000 cm^3**
   b. Is the volume too high or too low? **too high**

3. a. What number would you use for your next guess for the length of each edge? Why?
   b. What will be the volume of the cube with this edge length? Make a table like the one below to record your guesses.

Length of Each Edge	Volume	Too High or Too Low?
30 cm	■	■
■	■	■

3a. Answers may vary. Sample: 20 cm; it is less than 30 cm and easy to work with.
b. Answers may vary. Sample: 8,000 cm^3; check students' work for tables.

Lesson Planning Options

Prerequisite Skills
- finding volume (8-10)

Vocabulary/Symbols
Guess and Test

Resources

Student Edition
Skills Handbook, p. 530
Extra Practice, p. 521
Glossary/Study Guide

Teaching Resources
Chapter Support File, Ch. 8
- Lesson Planner 8-11
- Practice 8-11, Reteaching 8-11
- Answer Masters 8-11

Glossary, Spanish Resources

Transparencies
15, Minds on Math 8-11

Warm Up

Palindromes are numbers, words, or sentences that read the same forward and backward, such as *mom*, 4224, and 145.541. For each of the following numbers, find another number that when added gives a palindrome as a sum.
436.148 25.7
Answers may vary. Sample: 0.486 gives 436.634; 24.35 gives 50.05.

ADDITIONAL PROBLEM

The volume of a cube is 17,576 mm^3. What is the length of each edge of the cube? **26 mm**

ASSESSMENT Pair students. Have them organize their guesses in a list or table. Ask: *You have $1.19 in pennies, nickels, and dimes. How many of each coin do you have?* **Answers may vary. Sample: 4 pennies, 7 nickels, 8 dimes** Have them discuss various solutions.

3 Practice/Assess

EXERCISES *On Your Own*

Exercise 9 Allow students to use the tile as a border for a rectangle.

CONNECTION TO SCIENCE Exercise 11 Mass is the amount of matter in an object.

WRAP UP

IDENTIFYING THE BIG IDEA Have students explain how to use Guess and Test to solve problems and give examples of when they would use the strategy.

PORTFOLIO Share with students the criteria you will use to assess their work in portfolios, as well as how you plan to use the results. Students should understand how the rubrics are used to assess their work, how

Technology Options

Prentice Hall Technology

Software for Learners
- Math Blaster® Mystery*
- Interactive Student Tutorial, Chapter 8*

Teaching Resource Software
- Computer Item Generator 8-11
- Resource Pro Chapter 8*

Internet • For related mathematics activities, visit the Prentice Hall site at www.phschool.com/math

**Available on CD-ROM only*

Assignment Options for Exercises On Your Own

Core 1–7, 9–12
Extension 8

Use Mixed Review to maintain skills.

Continue your guesses if necessary and add them to your table.

4. What length of each edge of the cube will give a volume of 10,648 cm^3? **22 cm**

LOOK BACK
Think about how you solved the problem.

5. Explain how the results of previous guesses helped you to make the next guess. **Each result narrows the range for the next guess.**

Now you may assign Exercises 1–12.

EXERCISES *On Your Own*

Solve using the Guess and Test strategy.

1. What are two whole numbers whose product is 147 and whose quotient is 3? **7, 21**

2. The volume of a rectangular prism is 2,058 cm^3. The length of the prism is three times the width. The height is twice the width. Find the width, length, and height of the prism. **7 cm; 21 cm; 14 cm**

Solve if possible. If not, tell what information is needed. Show all your work.

3. Find the next two numbers in the pattern below.
100, 25, 50, 12.5, 25, ■, ■ **6.25, 12.5**

4. *Jobs* After selling food during a soccer game, the cashier at the concession stand has some $1 bills, $5 bills, and $10 bills. She has 13 bills worth a total of $69. How many $1 bills, $5 bills, and $10 bills does she have? **4 $1 bills; 5 $5 bills; 4 $10 bills**

5. Adam and Pablo each made a purchase at the bookstore. Adam bought 1 pencil and 2 pens for 86¢. Pablo bought 2 pencils and 1 pen for 67¢. How much does 1 pencil cost? **16¢**

6. The width of a rectangle is 4 cm less than the length of the rectangle. The area of the rectangle is 96 cm^2. Find the length and width of the rectangle. **12 cm; 8 cm**

7. Mr. Quarles has cartons that measure 3 ft × 2 ft × 6 in. He wishes to store them in a 15 ft × 9 ft × 24 ft space. He can only stack the cartons on top of each other, not inside one another. How many cartons can he store? **1,080 cartons**

each piece in the portfolio counts, and how the scores they get in their portfolios will affect their overall evaluation.

PROJECT LINK Suggest students clearly label the measurements on each box. Have them organize the surface area and volume of each box in a table.

LESSON QUIZ

1. What are two whole numbers whose product is 128 and whose quotient is 8? **32 and 4**
2. Joe has 19 bills worth a total of $87. How many $1 bills, $5 bills, and $10 bills does he have? **seven $1 bills, eight $5 bills, and four $10 bills**

8. a. Which is the longest segment shown in the rectangular prism at the right? $\overline{AG}$
   b. What measurements do you need to use to find x? To find y? **21 in., 28 in.; 12 in., x**
   c. Find x and then find y. **35 in.; 37 in.**

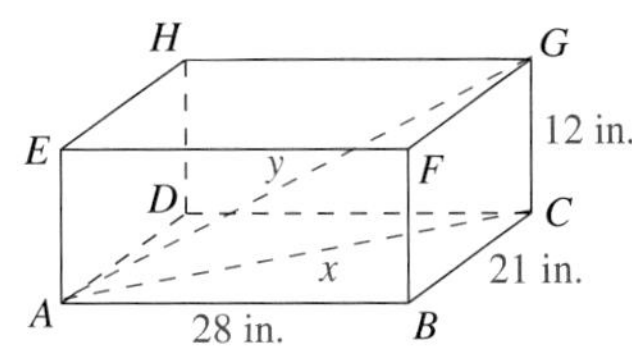

9. Suppose you have 12 square tiles that measure 1 in. by 1 in. What are the dimensions of the rectangle you can make that has the greatest perimeter? The least perimeter? **1 in. by 12 in.; 3 in. by 4 in.**
10. The sum of the digits of a certain two-digit number equals the square root of the number. What is the number? **81**
11. *Science* The mass of 8 cm^3 of aluminum is 22 g. The mass of the same volume of gold is 154.4 g. Name two sets of dimensions that could give an 8 cm^3 rectangular prism. **Answers may vary. Samples: 1 cm × 1 cm × 8 cm, 1 cm × 2 cm × 4 cm, 2 cm × 2 cm × 2 cm**
12. a. Use a calculator to find the following products.
    15 · 15   25 · 25   35 · 35   45 · 45 **225, 625, 1225, 2025**
    b. *Writing* Look for patterns in part (a). Describe any patterns that you find. **See above right.**
    c. Use the patterns you found to write each of the following products without multiplying the given numbers.
    55 · 55   65 · 65   75 · 75   85 · 85
    3,025; 4,225; 5,625; 7,225

12b. Answers may vary. Samples: The last two digits of each product are 25. The digit in the hundreds place is even. The products increase in a sequence 400, 600, 800, ...

PORTFOLIO
Select one or two items from your work for this chapter. Consider:
- drawings or models that you have made
- work you found challenging
- part of your project

Explain why you have included each selection.

Mixed Review

Estimation **Find two consecutive whole numbers that each square root is between.** *(Lesson 8-5)*

13. $\sqrt{95}$ **9 and 10**
14. $\sqrt{117}$ **10 and 11**
15. $\sqrt{59}$ **7 and 8**
16. $\sqrt{160}$ **12 and 13**
17. $\sqrt{75}$ **8 and 9**
18. $\sqrt{200}$ **14 and 15**
19. *Geography* The actual distance from San Francisco to Mexico City is about 1,890 mi. What is the map distance if the scale of the map is 2 in. : 420 mi? *(Lesson 6-5)* **9 in.**

CHAPTER PROJECT

PROJECT LINK: CALCULATING

Give at least three ways you can pack six of your cylinders in rectangular boxes. Find the surface area and volume of each box. Build a model of the box that uses the least cardboard.

Check students' work.

PRACTICE

Practice 8-11 Problem-Solving Strategy: Guess and Test

Solve using the Guess and Test strategy.

1. The volume of a cube is 79,507 $in.^3$. What is the length of each edge of the cube? **43 in.**
2. What are two whole numbers whose product is 294 and whose quotient is 6? **42 and 7**
3. Tickets for a concert sold for $8 for floor seats and $6 for balcony seats. For one performance, 400 tickets were sold, bringing in $2,888. How many of each ticket were sold? **156 of the $6 tickets, 244 of the $8 tickets**
4. Aaron bought 6 books and 2 notebooks for $46.86. Erin bought 2 books and 6 notebooks for $27.78. How much does one book cost? **$7.05**

Solve if possible. If not, tell what information is needed.

5. Find the volume of a rectangular prism. The width is half the length. The height is twice the length. **not possible to solve; need to know the length**
6. Sal raises pigs and chickens. She has 420 creatures, with a total of 1,240 legs. How many pigs does Sal raise? **200 pigs**
7. The width of a rectangle is 6 in. less than the length. The area of the rectangle is 135 $in.^2$. Find the length and width. **l = 15 in., w = 9 in.**
8. A cube is filled with water that has a volume of 4,096 cm^3. What is the length of each edge of the cube? **16 cm**
9. Tom is 26 years older than Paul. The product of their ages is 560. How old is Paul? **14 years old**

Practice

In copymaster and workbook formats

RETEACHING

Reteaching 8-11 Problem-Solving Strategy: Guess and Test

The length and width of a rectangular prism are equal and the height is 2 times that amount. If the volume of the prism is 3,456 m^3, what are the dimensions of the rectangle?

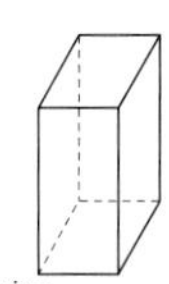

Read What is the volume of the prism? What do you know about the dimensions? *The volume is 3,456 m^3. The length and width are the same. The height is 2 times that dimension.*

Plan You can use a guess and test strategy and the prism volume formula. Guess the length, then find the width and height. Multiply to find volume, then check.

Solve
① Start with a guess of 10 for the length. The width would be 10 and the height 20. Volume of 2,000 is not enough.
② Try 15 for the length. The width would be 15 and the height 30. Volume of 6,750 is too much.
③ Try 12 m. A length of 12 m gives the correct volume.

Length	Width	Height	Volume
① 10	10	20	2,000
② 15	15	30	6,750
③ 12	12	24	3,456

Look Back The guesses of 10 and 15 helped you make the next guess of 12.

Complete the table to solve using the guess and test strategy.

1. The volume of a cube is 2,744 $in.^3$. Find the length of each edge of the cube. **14 in.**

Edge	Volume	Solution?
10	1,000	Too small
15	3,375	Too large
14	2,744	Solution

Solve using the guess and test strategy.

2. The product of two numbers is 2,250. Their difference is 5. What are the two numbers? **45, 50**
3. The width of a rectangle is twice the length. The area of the rectangle is 648 ft^2. How wide is the rectangle? **36 ft**
4. Kevin opened a book. The product of the 2 page numbers was 7,832. What are the page numbers? **88, 89**
5. The base of a triangle is 8 cm and the area is 36 cm^2. What is the height? **9 cm**

ENRICHMENT

Minds on Math Transparency

8-11

The diagonal of a rectangle has length $\sqrt{40}$ m. The area of the rectangle is 12 m^2. What is the perimeter of the rectangle?

16 m

See *Solution Key* for worked-out answers.

In Lesson 8-11, students learn how to use Guess and Test to solve problems, such as finding the length of the edges of a cube. This toolbox allows students to explore number patterns using unit cubes.

ERROR ALERT! Students may have trouble imagining the formation of the various cubes. **Remediation:** Have students use blocks or diagrams to model the first few arrangements.

Students should then begin to concentrate on the number pattern that emerges from the data.

ASSESSMENT Exercises 2–4 Have students compare tables with a partner. Partners should agree on their results. Partners can discuss the pattern in the tables and agree on a description of the pattern. Students can then use their descriptions to answer Exercise 4 individually.

■ ADDITIONAL PROBLEM

What would be the total number of unit cubes in a large cube that had 12 units on a side?
$12^3 = 1,728$

Materials/Manipulatives

- unit cubes

Resources

Teaching Resources

Teaching Aids Masters 1, 2, 14

Transparencies
6

page 384 Math Toolbox

3. **The number of cubes with zero sides painted is a cubed number; the number of cubes with 1 side painted is a product of 6 and a square number; the number of cubes with 2 sides painted is a multiple of 12; the number of cubes with 3 sides painted is always 8.**

MATH TOOLBOX EXPLORATION

Exploring Cubes

After Lesson 8-11

You can explore number patterns using unit cubes.

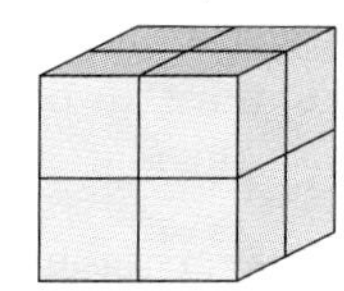

1. *Visual Thinking* Suppose you use unit cubes to make a larger cube. You paint the outside of a cube formed with two unit cubes on an edge.
   a. How many unit cubes are used to form the larger cube? **8 unit cubes**
   b. How many sides of each unit cube are painted? **3 sides**

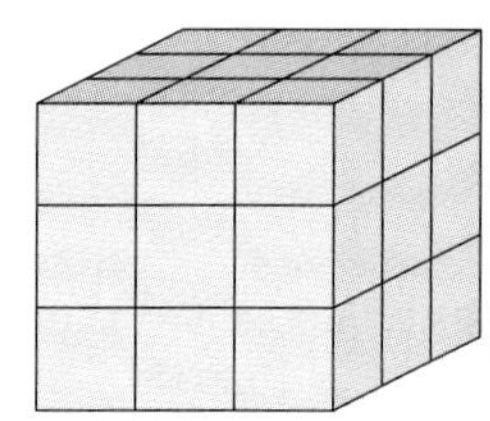

2. Make a chart like the one below for cubes formed by the given number of unit cubes on an edge.

Number of Unit Cubes on an Edge	Total Number of Unit Cubes	Total Number Expressed as a Power	Number of Unit Cubes with Given Number of Sides Painted			
			0	1	2	3
2	8	2^3	0	0	0	8
3	27	3^3	1	6	12	8
4	64	4^3	8	24	24	8
5	125	5^3	27	54	36	8
6	216	6^3	64	96	48	8
7	343	7^3	125	150	60	8

3. *Patterns* Describe the number pattern you see in each of the last four columns of your table. **See margin.**

4. Use the number patterns you found for Question 3. Extend the table for 8 number cubes on an edge.
   512; 8^3; 216; 216; 72; 8

5. a. *Predict* What would be the total number of unit cubes in a cube that had 10 unit cubes on an edge? **1,000 unit cubes**
   b. If there are 15 unit cubes on one edge of a cube, how many unit cubes will have no sides painted? One side? Two sides? Three sides? **2,197 cubes; 1,014 cubes; 156 cubes; 8 cubes**
   c. *Reasoning* If 144 unit cubes have two sides painted, how many unit cubes are on one edge of the cube? **14 unit cubes**

6. *Writing* Can you tell the number of unit cubes on one edge of a cube if you know that eight unit cubes have three sides painted? Explain. **No; all cubes made of more than one unit cube per side will have 8 unit cubes with three sides painted.**

FINISHING THE CHAPTER PROJECT

PROJECT DAY You may wish to plan a project day on which students share their completed projects. Encourage students to explain their process as well as their product.

PROJECT NOTEBOOK Ask students to review their project work and bring their notebooks up to date.

Have students review their methods for calculating the dimensions of the cylinder and the boxes, and for making the model of their box for the project.

SCORING RUBRIC

3 You provide nine drawings of box designs: one for a single cylinder, two for two cylinders, and three each for four and six cylinders. For the two-, four-, and six-cylinder designs you methodically and accurately calculate the surface areas to determine which boxes require the least amount of cardboard. Your completed project includes explanations of your work and a model of your best six-cylinder design.

2 You provide at least seven of the required designs, and most of your surface area calculations are both easy to follow and accurate. You complete a model of your best six-cylinder design.

1 You only complete a few box designs with accompanying surface area calculations. Your work is either inaccurate or sloppy.

0 You do not complete a majority of the box designs or surface area calculations.

Finishing the Chapter Project

CHAPTER PROJECT

SHAPE UP AND SHIP OUT

Design Boxes for Shipping Cylinders The Project Link questions on pages 343, 357, 376, and 383 should help you complete your project. Here is a checklist to help you gather together the parts of your project.

- ✔ the dimensions of your cylinder
- ✔ the dimensions of rectangular boxes that hold one, two, four, and six cylinders using the least cardboard
- ✔ a model of the box that holds six cylinders

Your job calls for boxing shipments of cylinders. You don't want to waste cardboard, so design the boxes wisely! Remember, there can be lots of different ways to pack the cylinders, so pick the best arrangement for the six cylinders.

Reflect and Revise

Show your model to a friend. See if your friend agrees that you have thought of the best arrangement of six cylinders. If necessary, improve on your model.

Web Extension

Internet Connection

Prentice Hall's Internet site contains information you might find helpful as you complete your project. Visit www.phschool.com/mgm2/ch8 for some links and ideas related to containers, surface area, and volume.

STUDENT SELF-ASSESSMENT SURVEY

Chapter 8 Student Self-Assessment Survey

1. Now that you have finished this chapter, think about what you have learned about geometry and measurement. Check each topic that you feel confident you understand.
   ____ estimate length, perimeter, and area (8-1)
   ____ find the area and perimeter of parallelograms (8-2)
   ____ find the area of triangles and trapezoids (8-3)
   ____ find the circumference and area of circles (8-4)
   ____ find perfect squares and square roots of perfect squares (8-5)
   ____ estimate square roots (8-5)
   ____ use the Pythagorean theorem (8-6)
   ____ identify right triangles (8-6)
   ____ use a calculator to apply the Pythagorean theorem (8-7)
   ____ identify three-dimensional figures (8-8)
   ____ find the surface area of cylinders and prisms (8-9)
   ____ find the volume of prisms and cylinders (8-10)
   ____ use the *Guess and Test* strategy to solve problems (8-11)
2. Before the Chapter Assessment, I need to review ____________
3. a. Check one. In general, I thought this chapter was
   ____ a snap ____ easy ____ average ____ hard ____ a monster
   b. Why do you feel this way? ____________
4. In this chapter, I did my best work on ____________
5. In this chapter, I had trouble with ____________
6. Check each one that applies. Now that I've spent some time working with the measurement of geometric figures, I think this kind of measurement is
   ____ important ____ boring ____ useful ____ fun
   ____ a waste of time ____ confusing ____ tricky ____ interesting
7. Describe how your calculator helped you in this chapter. ____________

Assessment

Vocabulary/Symbols

area, bases, circumference, cube, cubic unit, edge, faces, Guess and Test, height, hypotenuse, legs, net, perfect square, pi (π), prisms, pyramid, Phythagorean theorem, square root ($\sqrt{\ }$), surface area, three-dimensional figures, volume

Materials/Manipulatives

- calculator
- graph paper

Resources

Student Edition

Extra Practice, p. 521
Glossary/Study Guide

Teaching Resources

Chapter Support File, Ch. 8
- Student Self-Assessment Survey

Glossary, Spanish Resources
Tools for Studying Smarter

WRAP UP

ASSESSMENT **Exercise 1** Have students describe the difference between linear units, and square units. Then have them give examples of when to use each of the units in the exercise. **Answers may vary. Sample: length of a piece of paper: in.; area of a city: mi^2**

Exercises 2–5 Remind students of the formulas for finding area and perimeter. Students can write the formulas on their papers to use for reference.

Exercises 6–9 Clarify for students whether they are to use 3.14 or the π button on their calculator for π.

ASSESSMENT **Exercises 10–15** Have students exchange papers with a partner. Partners can check Exercises 10 and 11 by finding the square root of the given answer. Then they can check Exercises 12–15 by finding the square of the given answer.

8 WRAP UP

Area — 8-1, 8-2, 8-3

Area is the number of square units inside a figure. Area is measured in square units such as square inches (in.^{2}), square meters (m^2), and square feet (ft^2).

1. Choose the unit you would use to estimate the area of a wall of a room: in., ft, mi, in.^{2}, ft^2, mi^2 **ft^2**

Find the perimeter and area of each parallelogram, triangle, or trapezoid.

2. 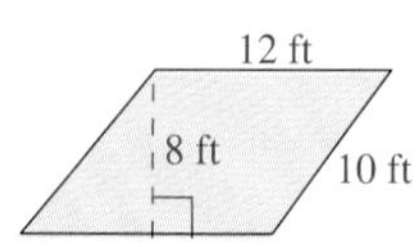

44 ft; 96 ft^2

3. 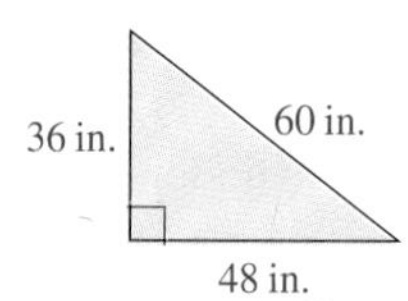

144 in.; 864 in.^{2}

4. 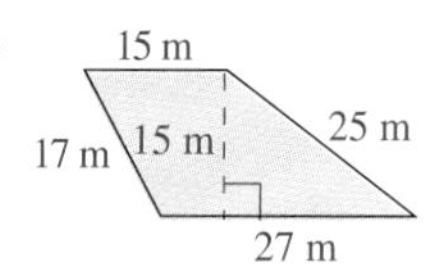

84 m; 315 m^2

5. 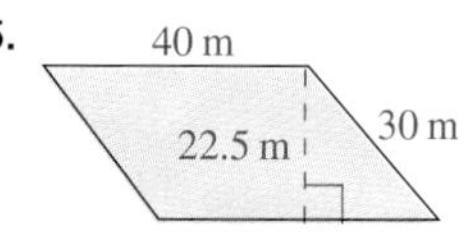

140 m; 900 m^2

Circumference and Area of Circles — 8-4

Circumference is the distance around a circle. The ratio of the circumference to the diameter of any circle is represented by π, which is close to the values 3.14 and $\frac{22}{7}$.

Calculator **Find the circumference and area of each circle to the nearest unit.**

6. 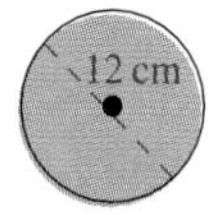

38 cm; 113 cm^2

7. 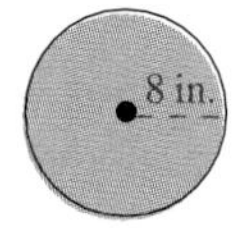

50 in.; 201 in.^{2}

8. 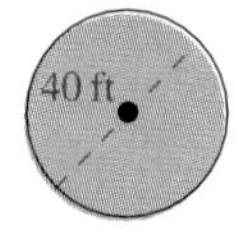

126 ft; 1,257 ft^2

9. 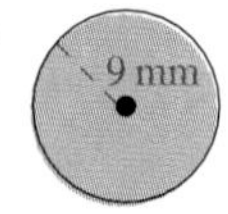

57 mm; 254 mm^2

Square Roots and the Pythagorean Theorem — 8-5, 8-6, 8-7

A **perfect square** is a square of an integer. The opposite of squaring a number is finding its **square root.**

The **Pythagorean theorem** states that in any right triangle the sum of the squares of the lengths a and b of the legs is equal to the square of the length c of the hypotenuse.

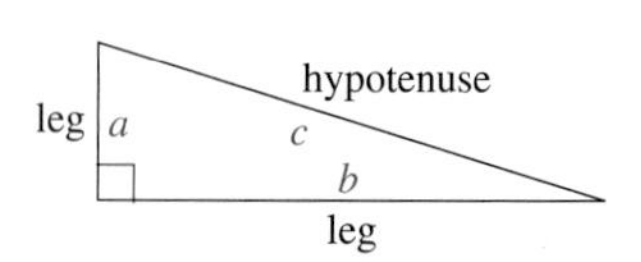

$$a^2 + b^2 = c^2$$

Exercises 17–20 Remind students to write the Pythagorean theorem on their papers so they can refer to it as they work on the problems.

Exercise 23 Have students write a description of how Guess and Test helps them solve the problem.

Remind students that the new mathematical terms in this chapter are defined in the Glossary/Study Guide in the back of the textbook.

Mental Math **Find each of the following.**

10. 11^2 **121** 11. 7^2 **49** 12. $\sqrt{16}$ **4** 13. $\sqrt{64}$ **8** 14. $\sqrt{144}$ **12** 15. $\sqrt{400}$ **20**

16. *Estimation* Find two consecutive whole numbers that $\sqrt{87}$ lies between. **9 and 10**

17. **Choose A, B, C, or D.** Which of the following could *not* be the lengths of sides of a right triangle? **B**
A. 3 m, 4 m, 5 m B. 2 cm, 2 cm, 4 cm C. 51 in., 85 in., 68 in. D. 16 ft, 20 ft, 12 ft

The lengths of two sides of a right triangle are given. Find the length of the third side. Round to the nearest tenth if necessary.

18. leg: 12 mm; hypotenuse: 15 mm **9 mm**
19. legs: both 1 m **1.4 m**
20. leg: 8 in.; hypotenuse: 14 in. **11.5 in.**

Surface Area and Volume of Three-Dimensional Figures 8-8, 8-9, 8-10

The **surface area** of a prism is the sum of the areas of the faces.

The **volume** of a three-dimensional figure is the number of cubic units needed to fill the space inside the figure.

22a.

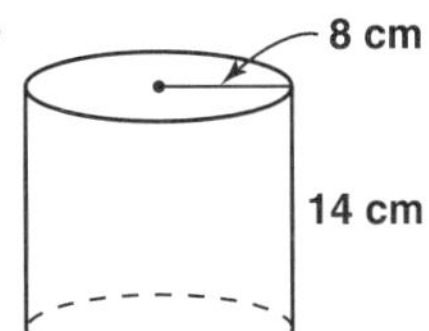

22c.

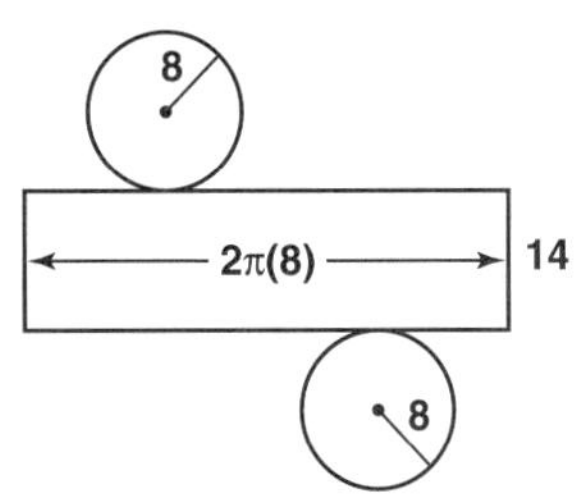

21. The dimensions of a rectangular prism are 7 ft, 5 ft, and 3 ft. **a, c. See back of book.**
a. Sketch the rectangular prism.
b. Find the volume of the rectangular prism. **105 ft^3**
c. Draw a net for the rectangular prism.
d. Find the surface area of the rectangular prism. **142 ft^2**

22. A cylinder is 14 cm high and has a base radius of 8 cm.
a. Sketch the cylinder. **See above right.**
b. Find the volume of the cylinder to the nearest tenth.
c. Draw a net for the cylinder. **See right.**
d. Find the surface area of the cylinder to the nearest tenth.
b. 2,814.9 cm^3 **d. 1,105.8 cm^2**

Problem Solving Strategies 8-11

You can use the problem-solving strategy *Guess and Test* to solve many problems.

23. The volume of a rectangular prism is 24 m^3. The surface area is 52 m^2. Find the whole number dimensions of the prism. **2 m, 3 m, 4 m**

CHAPTER ASSESSMENT • FORM A

Chapter 8 Assessment • Form A

Answers

1. **Choose A, B, C, or D.** Which unit of measure would you use to measure the size of a circus tent? — 1. B
A. cm^2 B. m^2 C. km^2 D. mm^2
2. Find the area of a circle with a radius of 10 m. Use 3.14 for π. — 2. 314 m^2
3. The area of a rectangle is 96 in.^{2}. The length is 12 in. What is the perimeter? — 3. 40 in.
4. Find the area of a parallelogram with $b = 5.1$ m and $h = 4$ m. — 4. 20.4 m^2
5. Which has the larger area, a triangle with $b = 5$ and $h = 20$ or a rectangle with $l = 8$ and $w = 10$? — 5. rectangle
6. The area of a trapezoid is 100 ft^2, with $b_1 = 6$ ft and $b_2 = 4$ ft. What is the height? — 6. 20 ft
7. The radius of a circle is 3 cm. Will the area be greater than or less than 27 cm^2? — 7. greater
8. The circumference of a circle is about 60 in. What is the diameter to the nearest tenth of an inch? — 8. 19.1 in.
9. Find 14^2. — 9. 196
10. Find the length of a side of a square with area 169 ft^2. — 10. 13 ft
11. One leg of a right triangle is 36 in. long. The hypotenuse is 45 in. long. What is the length of the other leg? — 11. 27 in.
12. A triangle has sides of 18, 20, and 32. Is the triangle a right triangle? — 12. no
13. Find the length, to the nearest tenth, of the hypotenuse of a right triangle if one leg is 8 m and the other leg is 18 m. — 13. 19.7 m

Assessment

CHAPTER ASSESSMENT • FORM A

Chapter 8 Assessment • Form A (continued)

14. Find the surface area of a box that measures 16 in. by 12 in. by 12 in. — 14. 1,056 in.^{2}
15. If the box in Exercise 14 were cut from one piece of cardboard as shown, what must be the dimensions of the cardboard? — 15. 56 in. by 44 in.

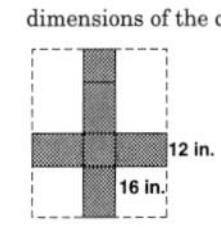

16. What is the volume of the box in Exercise 14? — 16. 2,304 in.^{3} or $1\frac{1}{3}$ ft^3
17. A cylinder is 7 m high and has a base radius of 1 m. What is the volume to the nearest m^3? — 17. 22 m^3
18. A roll of 12-in. paper towels has a cardboard core with a 2-in. diameter. How many square inches of cardboard are used to make this core? — 18. 75.4 in.^{2}

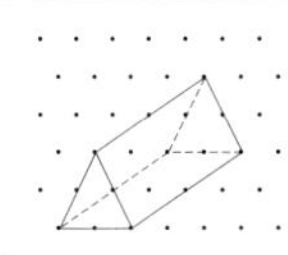

19. Draw a triangular prism using the dot grid. — 19.

Choose a Strategy

20. What are two whole numbers whose product is 108 and whose quotient is 3? — 20. 18, 6

Writing

21. Alfredo wants to put new shingles on his roof. One side of his roof measures 25 ft by 60 ft. Roofing shingles are sold in squares. Each square covers 100 ft^2 and costs $16.95. Explain (no calculations needed) how you would find the cost of putting new shingles on the roof.

First, find the area of the roof. Then find how many squares are needed.
Last, multiply the number of squares by the cost per square.

CHAPTER ASSESSMENT • FORM B

Chapter 8 Assessment • Form B

Choose the best answer. Circle A, B, C, or D.

1. Which unit would you use to measure the width of a rubber band?
   (A) mm B. cm C. m D. km
2. Which unit would you use to measure the cover of a book?
   (A) $in.^2$ B. ft^2 C. yd^2 D. mi^2
3. The area of a rectangle is 56 $in.^2$. The length is 7 in. What is the perimeter?
   A. 15 in. (B) 30 in. C. 56 in. D. 224 in.
4. Find the area of a parallelogram with $b = 15.7$ cm and $h = 11$ cm.
   A. 17.27 cm^2 B. 26.7 cm^2 C. 165 cm^2 (D) 172.7 cm^2
5. Which figure has the largest area?
   A. a triangle with $b = 5, h = 8$ B. a rectangle with $l = 5, w = 8$
   C. a parallelogram with $b = 5, h = 8$ (D) a trapezoid with $b_1 = 5, b_2 = 8$, and $h = 8$
6. The height of a trapezoid is 8 cm, with $b_1 = 10$ cm and $b_2 = 3$ cm. What is the area?
   A. 21 cm^2 B. 27 cm^2 (C) 52 cm^2 D. 104 cm^2
7. The radius of a circle is 5 mm. Which statement best describes the area?
   A. The area is less than 75 mm^2. (B) The area is greater than 75 mm^2.
   C. The area is exactly 75 mm^2. D. The area can't be determined.
8. The circumference of a circle is about 100 cm. What is the diameter to the nearest tenth of a centimeter?
   A. 3.18 cm B. 15.9 cm (C) 31.8 cm D. 318.3 cm
9. Find 15^2.
   A. 144 B. 169 C. 196 (D) 225
10. What is the length of a side of a square with area 1.96 m^2?
    A. 1.2 m B. 1.3 m (C) 1.4 m D. 1.5 m
11. One leg of a right triangle is 12 ft long. The hypotenuse is 13 ft long. What is the length of the other leg?
    A. 1 ft (B) 5 ft C. 17.7 ft D. 25 ft

Assessment

CHAPTER ASSESSMENT • FORM B

Chapter 8 Assessment • Form B (continued)

12. Which of the following could *not* be the lengths of sides of a right triangle?
    A. 6, 8, 10 B. 8, 15, 17 C. 9, 12, 15 (D) 8, 10, 12
13. What is the surface area of a box that measures 8 in. by 10 in. by 10 in.?
    A. 260 $in.^2$ B. 420 $in.^2$ C. 460 $in.^2$ (D) 520 $in.^2$
14. If the box in Exercise 13 were cut from one piece of cardboard as shown, what must be the dimensions of the cardboard?
    A. 30 in. by 20 in. (B) 36 in. by 26 in.
    C. 28 in. by 26 in. D. 26 in. by 18 in.

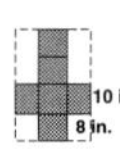

15. What is the volume of the box in Exercise 13?
    (A) 800 $in.^3$ B. 180 $in.^3$ C. 108 $in.^3$ D. 80 $in.^3$
16. A cylinder is 9 mm high and has a base radius of 1 mm. What is the volume to the nearest mm^3?
    A. 9 mm^3 B. 12 mm^3 C. 27 mm^3 (D) 28 mm^3
17. Toya is putting carpet in her living room. The room measures 5 yd by 6 yd. If the carpet she wants to buy costs $12/$yd^2$, how much will her new carpet cost?
    A. $300 B. $264 (C) $360 D. $432
18. What are two whole numbers whose product is 126 and whose sum is 25?
    A. 5, 20 (B) 7, 18 C. 10, 15 D. 6, 21
19. To the nearest tenth, what is the length of the hypotenuse of a right triangle whose legs are 9 in. and 14 in.?
    A. 4.8 in. B. 6.8 in. (C) 16.6 in. D. 23.0 in.
20. Which figure is a pentagonal prism?

(A)
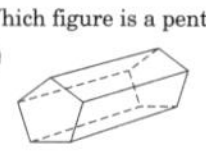
B.
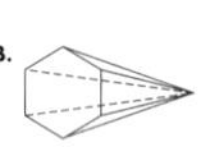
C.
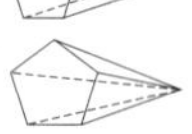
D.
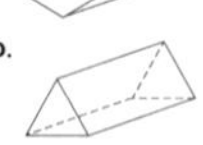

Teaching Resources

Chapter Support File, Ch. 8, and Spanish Resources

Teacher's Edition

See pp. 334C–D for Assessment Options.

Teaching Resource Software

- Computer Item Generator, Ch. 8

ASSESSMENT

ENHANCED MULTIPLE CHOICE QUESTIONS are more complex than traditional multiple choice questions, which assess only one skill. Enhanced multiple choice questions assess the processes that students use, as well as the end result. They are written so that students can use more than one strategy to solve the problem. Using multiple strategies is encouraged by the National Council of Teachers of Mathematics (NCTM).

Exercises 10 and 14 are enhanced multiple choice questions.

WRITING EXERCISES allow students to describe more fully their thinking and understanding of the concepts they've learned. **Exercise 8** is a writing exercise.

8 ASSESSMENT

1. Choose the unit you would use to estimate the length of an automobile: mm, cm, m, km, mm^2, cm^2, m^2, km^2 **m**
2. Find the area of a parallelogram with base length 14 m and height 9 m. **126 m^2**
3. Find the area of a triangle with base length 12 cm and height 10 cm. **60 cm^2**
4. Find the area and perimeter of the trapezoid. **3.75 cm^2; 9.61 cm**

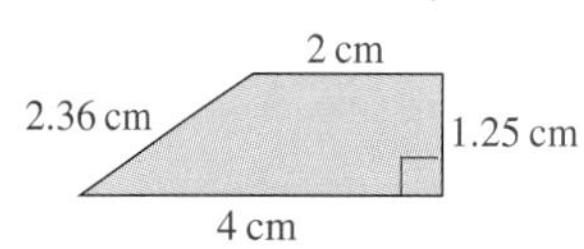

5. The area of a piece of land shaped like a rectangle is 114 yd^2. One dimension is 19 yd. Find the perimeter. **50 yd**
6. *Calculator* The diameter of a circle is 21 cm. Find the circumference and area of the circle to the nearest unit. **66 cm; 346 cm^2**
7. *Mental Math* Find each of the following.
   a. 8^2 **64** b. 10^2 **100** c. $\sqrt{25}$ **5** d. $\sqrt{81}$ **9**
8. *Writing* Explain what a perfect square is. **A perfect square is a number whose square root is a whole number.**
9. Find x. **8 ft**

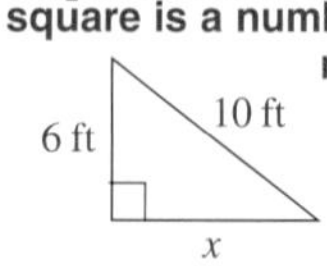

10. **Choose A, B, C, or D.** Suppose you want to estimate the number of bricks you could store in a shed. Which must you know about the shed? **D**
    A. perimeter B. area
    C. surface area D. volume
11. *Calculator* Find the missing side length to the nearest tenth. **8.7 m**

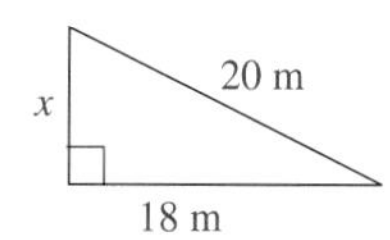

12. A rectangular garden is 40 m long and 30 m wide. Find the length of a diagonal walkway across the garden. **50 m**
13. Give the best name for each shape.

a.
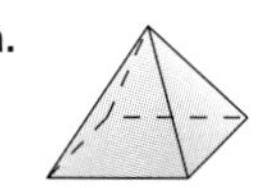
rectangular pyramid

b.
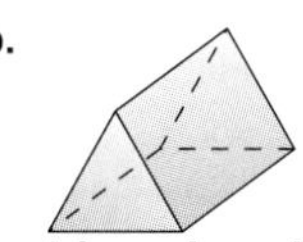
triangular prism

c.
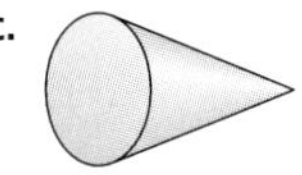
cone

d.
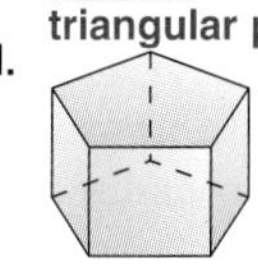
pentagonal prism

14. **Choose A, B, C, or D.** The surface area of a cube is 150 cm^2. Find the volume. **C**
    A. 15 cm^3 B. 30 cm^3
    C. 125 cm^3 D. 150 cm^3
15. Rectangular prism A has dimensions 10 cm, 2 cm, and 3 cm. Rectangular prism B has dimensions 5 cm, 2 cm, and 6 cm. Use $<$, $>$, or $=$ to compare the volumes of A and B. **volume A = volume B**
16. *Estimation* The base radius of a cylinder is 9.7 cm. The height is 20 cm. To make a quick mental estimate of the volume, what would you use for a value of π? What is your estimate? **3; 6,000 cm^3**
17. A cylinder-shaped tank is 12 ft long. It has a base diameter of 18 ft. Find the volume of the tank to the nearest unit. **3,054 ft^3**

CUMULATIVE REVIEW

Item	Review Topic	Ch
1	Exponents	4
2, 7, 8	Area, perimeter, and volume	8
3	Similarity	6
4, 11	Pythagorean theorem	8

Item	Review Topic	Ch
5, 6, 10	Simplifying expressions	3
9	Writing equations	3

8 CUMULATIVE REVIEW

Choose the best answer.

1. Which number has the greatest value? A
   A. 2^5 B. 3^3
   C. 5^2 D. 20^1

2. Rectangle $ABCD$ is 3 ft × 4 ft. What is the area and the perimeter of $ABCD$? B
   A. $A = 12\text{ ft}^2, P = 12\text{ ft}$
   B. $A = 12\text{ ft}^2, P = 14\text{ ft}$
   C. $A = 6\text{ ft}^2, P = 12\text{ ft}$
   D. $A = 12\text{ ft}^2, P = 7\text{ ft}$

3. The rectangles are similar. Which proportion could *not* be used to find the value of x? B

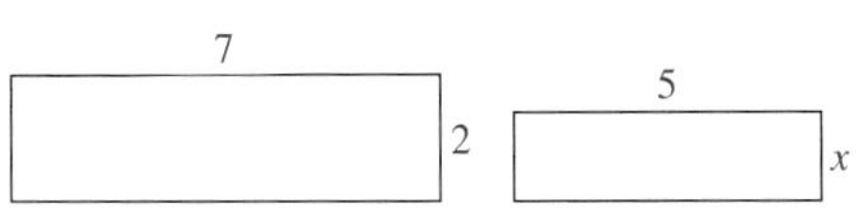

   A. $\frac{7}{5} = \frac{2}{x}$ B. $\frac{x}{2} = \frac{7}{5}$
   C. $\frac{x}{5} = \frac{2}{7}$ D. $\frac{2}{7} = \frac{x}{5}$

4. Which of the following could *not* be the sides of a right triangle? C
   A. 8, 15, 17 B. 10, 24, 26
   C. 15, 35, 40 D. 12, 16, 20

5. Which expression equals 8.23? A
   A. $6.584 \div 0.8$
   B. $74.34 \div 9$
   C. $1{,}152.2 \div 14$
   D. $57.61 \div 7.1$

6. Which expression does *not* equal -12? C
   A. $-3 \cdot 4$
   B. $-10 - 2$
   C. $-48 \div (-3)$
   D. $-16 - (-4)$

7. Which expression could you use to find the area of the cylinder's base? B
   A. $(2 \cdot \pi \cdot 5)$
   B. $(\pi \cdot 2.5 \cdot 2.5)$
   C. $(\pi \cdot 5 \cdot 5)$
   D. $(2 \cdot \pi \cdot 2.5 \cdot 6)$

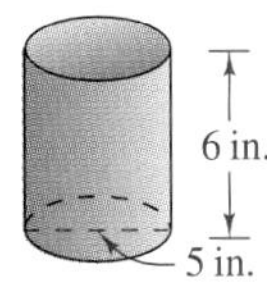

8. Which container has the greatest volume? D

A.
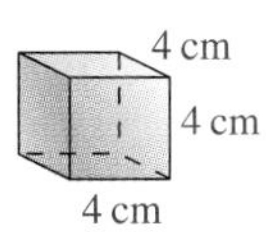

B.
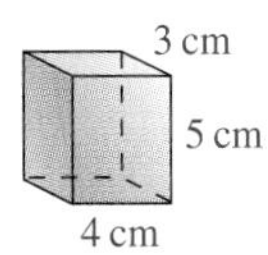

C.
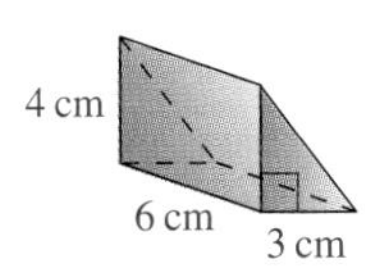

D.
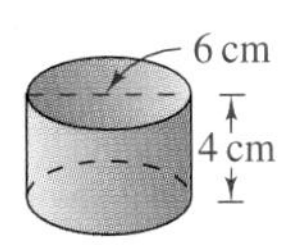

9. Which equation could you use to represent the following problem: Five more than half of the people (p) on the bus were students (s)? A
   A. $\frac{p}{2} + 5 = s$
   B. $(p - 5) \div 2 = s$
   C. $\frac{p}{2} - 5 = s$
   D. $(p - 5) \div 2 = s$

10. Which expression does *not* have the same value as the other expressions? C
   A. $\sqrt{144}$
   B. $\sqrt{36} + \sqrt{36}$
   C. $\sqrt{4} + \sqrt{64}$
   D. $\sqrt{81} + \sqrt{9}$

11. What is the value of x to the nearest tenth? B
   A. 17.0 B. 12.7
   C. 7.0 D. 8.5

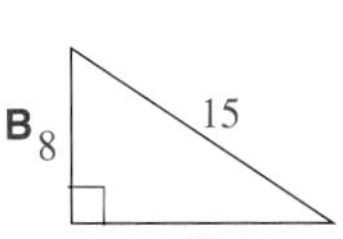

CUMULATIVE REVIEW

Chapter 8 Cumulative Review

Choose the best answer. Circle A, B, C, or D.

1. What is 3.9256 rounded to the nearest hundredth?
   A. 3.9 B. 3.92
   (C) 3.93 D. 3.927

2. Find $3\frac{3}{4} \times 4$.
   A. $7\frac{3}{4}$ B. 12
   C. $12\frac{3}{4}$ (D) 15

3. Find the sum mentally.
   $5.4 + 4.3 + 0.7 + 1.6$
   A. 10 B. 11
   C. 11.5 (D) 12

4. How many inches are there in 2 yd 2 ft 5 in.?
   A. 53 in. (B) 101 in.
   C. 149 in. D. not here

5. Find the sum $2\frac{1}{3} + 1\frac{1}{4}$.
   A. $1\frac{7}{12}$ B. $3\frac{1}{12}$
   C. $3\frac{2}{7}$ (D) $3\frac{7}{12}$

6. Which variable expression means "a number decreased by 7"?
   A. $7n$ B. $7 - n$
   (C) $n - 7$ D. $\frac{n}{7}$

7. Which measure is that of an obtuse angle?
   A. 14° B. 54°
   C. 84° (D) 94°

8. A floor plan has a scale 2 cm : 3 m. What is the actual length of a room measuring 30 cm on the floor plan?
   A. 5 m B. 20 m
   (C) 45 m D. 90 m

9. The measures of two angles of a triangle are 94° and 16°. What is the measure of the third angle?
   A. 60° (B) 70°
   C. 140° D. not here

10. Out of 240 marbles, 180 marbles are red. What percent of the marbles are red?
   A. 18% B. 25%
   C. 42% (D) 75%

11. A photograph is 8 in. by 10 in. Sally must enlarge it so its sides are 125% of the original. What will the enlarged photograph measure?
   A. 6.4 in. by 8 in.
   (B) 10 in. by 12.5 in.
   C. 16 in. by 20 in.
   D. 64 in. by 100 in.

12. What percent is $\frac{3}{5}$?
   A. 30% B. 35%
   (C) 60% D. 75%

Assessment

CUMULATIVE REVIEW

Chapter 8 Cumulative Review (continued)

13. A triangle has two angles that measure 28°. What type of triangle is it?
   (A) isosceles B. right
   C. acute D. equilateral

14. After buying boots, Yan had \$23.45. Which equation could you use to find out how much money Yan had to start with if the boots cost \$29.55?
   A. $x + 23.45 = 29.55$
   B. $x + 29.55 = 23.45$
   (C) $x - 29.55 = 23.45$
   D. $29.55 - 23.45 = x$

15. Solve $\frac{r}{-9} = 36$.
   A. −4 B. 27
   C. 45 (D) −324

16. Which unit would you use to estimate the amount of shelf space a box of tissues will occupy?
   A. mm^2 (B) cm^2
   C. m^2 D. km^2

17. Find the area of the triangle below.

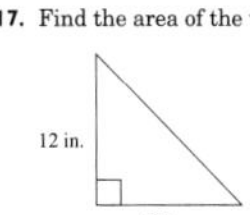

   A. 144 in.^2 B. 96 in.^2
   (C) 72 in.^2 D. 24 in.^2

18. Find the area of the trapezoid below.

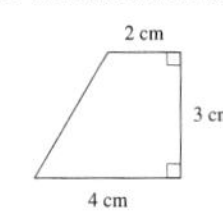

   (A) 9 cm^2 B. 12 cm^2
   C. 18 cm^2 D. 24 cm^2

19. The volume of a cube is 216 cm^3. Find the value of x.

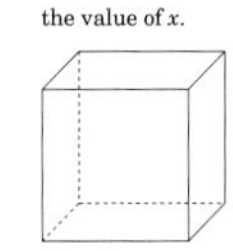

   A. 3 cm B. 4 cm
   C. 5 cm (D) 6 cm

20. What are two integers whose product is −28 and whose sum is −3?
   A. −14, 2 B. 14, −2
   (C) −7, 4 D. 7, −4

21. How many square yards of carpeting are needed to carpet a room 4 yd by 5.5 yd?
   A. 9.5 yd^2 B. 11 yd^2
   C. 19 yd^2 (D) 22 yd^2

22. Solve $4y + 12 = 0$.
   A. 0 (B) −3
   C. −8 D. −48

Resources

Teaching Resources

Chapter Support File, Ch. 8
- Cumulative Review

Teacher's Edition

See pp. 334C–D for Assessment Options.

9 Using Probability

Chapter Overview

To accommodate flexible scheduling, most lessons are divided into parts. Assignment Options are given in the Teacher's Edition for each lesson.

Pages	Lesson	Content
Pages 392–396 NCTM 1, 2, 3, 4, 9, 10, 11	**Lesson 9-1** **Data Analysis: Experimental Probability**	Part 1 Finding Experimental Probability Part 2 Simulating Events **Key terms:** probability, event, experimental probability **Alternative Activity** 9-1
Pages 398–400 NCTM 1, 3, 10, 11	**Lesson 9-2** **Problem Solving Strategy**	**Simulate a Problem** **Key term:** trial
Pages 401–405 NCTM 1, 3, 4, 5, 10, 11	**Lesson 9-3** **Theoretical Probability and Proportional Reasoning**	Part 1 Finding Theoretical Probability Part 2 Finding the Probability of a Complement **Key terms:** outcomes, theoretical probability, complement **Alternative Activity** 9-3 **Journal** ▼ **Project Link**
Pages 419–422 NCTM 1, 2, 10, 11, 12	**Lesson 9-7** **Combinations**	**Key term:** combination ▼ **Project Link** ☑ **Checkpoint 2** **Math at Work**
Pages 424–426 NCTM 1, 2, 3, 4, 5, 7, 10	**Lesson 9-8** **Data Analysis: Estimating Population Size**	**Key terms:** capture/recapture

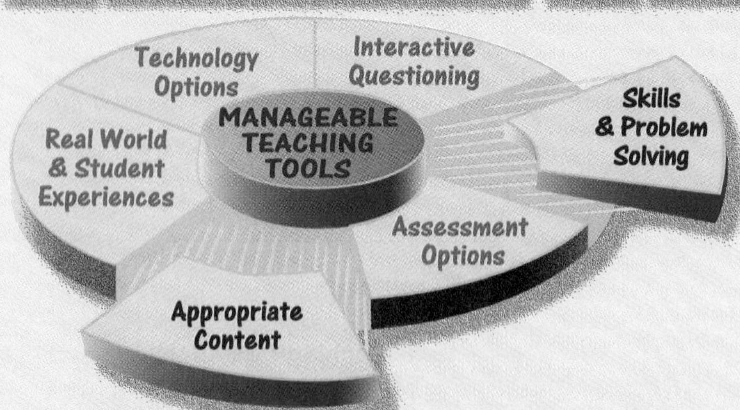

Pacing Options

This chart suggests pacing only for the core lessons and their parts. It is provided merely as a possible guide. It will help you determine how much time you have in your schedule to cover other features, such as the Chapter Project, Math Toolboxes, Wrap Up, and Assessment.

	1 Class Period	1 Class Period	1 Class Period	1 F
Traditional (40–45 min class periods)	9–1 ▼1	9–1 ▼2	9–2	
Block Scheduling (90 min class periods)	9–1 ▼1 9–1 ▼2	9–2 9–3 ▼1	9–3 ▼2 9–4 ▼1 9–4 ▼2	9-

CHAPTER PROJECT

Let the Buyer Beware

Goal: Design number cubes and use probability to create a carnival game.

THEME: LOGIC

NCTM STANDARDS

1 Problem Solving
2 Communication
3 Reasoning
4 Mathematical Connections
5 Number and Number Relationships
6 Number Systems and Number Theory
7 Computation and Estimation
8 Patterns and Functions
9 Algebra
10 Statistics
11 Probability
12 Geometry
13 Measurement

Pages	Lesson
Pages 407–411	**Lesson 9-4 Sample Spaces**
NCTM 1, 2, 3, 4, 10, 11, 12, 13	Part 1 Finding a Sample Space Part 2 Using the Counting Principle **Key terms:** sample space, counting principle **Journal** **Checkpoint 1**
Pages 412–415	**Lesson 9-5 Independent and Dependent Events**
NCTM 1, 2, 3, 4, 5, 9, 10, 11, 12	Part 1 Finding Probability of Independent Events Part 2 Finding Probability of Dependent Events **Key terms:** independent, dependent **Alternative Activity** 9-5 **Project Link**
Pages 416–418	**Lesson 9-6 Permutations**
NCTM 2, 3, 4, 5, 10, 11, 12	**Key term:** permutation

Optional Materials and Manipulatives

coins for tossing (9-1)
standard number cubes (9-1, 9-2, 9-3)
square tiles (9-8)

markers (9-8)
bag (9-8)

Optional calculator use is integrated throughout the course.

ss od	1 Class Period	1 Class Period	1 Class Period	1 Class Period	1 Class Period	1 Class Period	1 Class Period	1 Class Period	1 Class Period	1 Class Period
	9–4 1 9–4 2	9–5 1	9–5 2	9–6	9–7	9–7	9–8	9–8		
–6	9–7	9–8								

Meeting Individual Needs

Accommodating Diverse Learning Styles

In your Teacher's Edition, you will find suggestions as to how you can help students complete mathematical tasks in Chapter 9 by meeting individual needs and supporting various learning styles. Here are some examples:

VISUAL LEARNING
drawing spinners *(p. 404)*

TACTILE LEARNING
modeling probability using bags of counters *(p. 398)*

AUDITORY LEARNING
saying the complements of events *(p. 402)*

KINESTHETIC LEARNING
modeling outcomes with handshakes *(p. 407)*

EARLY FINISHERS
Performance-Based Project, MathBlaster® Mystery, Interdisciplinary Units

GIFTED AND TALENTED
planning how to pack the most number of outfits for a trip *(p. 409)*

DIVERSITY discussing different meanings of fair *(p. 403)*

ACQUIRING ENGLISH PROFICIENCY (AEP)
writing definitions of probability terms *(p. 392)*

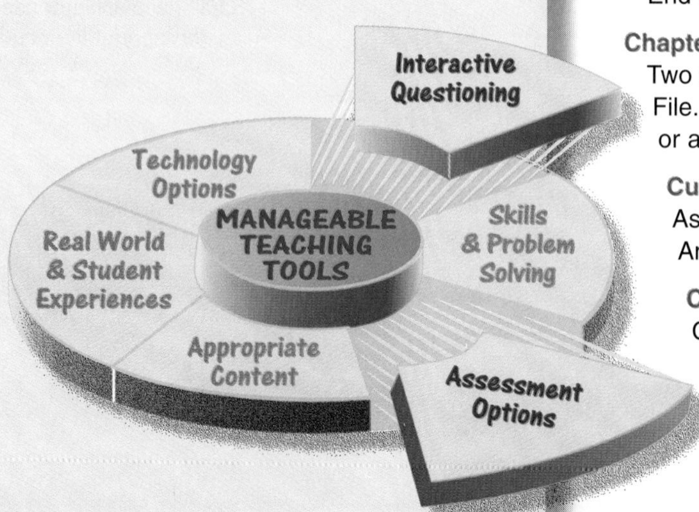

Assessing Progress

A broad range of assessment tools are available to reach a variety of learners.

INFORMAL ASSESSMENT

Informal assessments provide day-to-day feedback to help give you a picture of conceptual understanding and skill development.

ONGOING ASSESSMENT is built into lesson instruction and the Teaching Notes of the Teacher's Edition.

In the Teacher's Edition
Lesson Quiz for every lesson

In the Student Edition
On Your Own, Mixed Review, Journal, Portfolio, Project Link, Chapter Wrap Up

Look for **Interactive Questions** within lessons that

- **BUILD UNDERSTANDING** with labels such as **Analyze, Reasoning, Estimation, Writing, and Summarize**
- ✔ **CHECK UNDERSTANDING** with the **Try It Out** label.

FORMAL ASSESSMENT

Formal assessment can occur before and after the chapter, as well as at natural breaking points in the chapter.

Checkpoints
Two forms of each self-assessment Checkpoints are available: one in the Student Edition and another in the Chapter Support File in the Teaching Resources box.

- Mid-Chapter Checkpoint 1, page 411
- End-of-Chapter Checkpoint 2, page 422

Chapter 9 Assessment, page 430.
Two alternative forms are available in the Chapter Support File. They may be used after a chapter has been completed, or as a pre-test and post-test comparison.

Cumulative Review, page 431.
Assesses skills and concepts in Chapters 1–9. An alternative form is available in Chapter Support File.

Computer Item Generator for Chapter 9
Customized tests can be generated for each lesson and for mid-chapter and end-of-chapter assessments, and for pre- and post-test comparisons of achievement.

PERFORMANCE-BASED ASSESSMENT

CHAPTER PROJECT

The Chapter Project in the student edition provides a real-world connection to the math context of the chapter. The Teacher's Edition contains a scoring rubric.

A Performance Assessment with a scoring rubric can be found in the Chapter Support File in the Teaching Resources box.

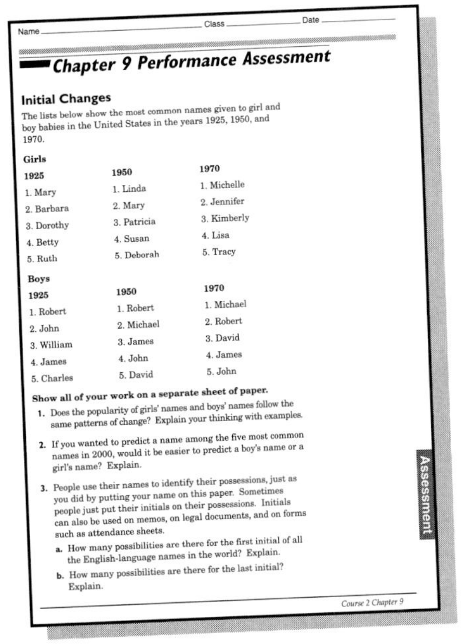

Name ______ Class ______ Date ______

Chapter 9 Performance Assessment

Initial Changes

The lists below show the most common names given to girl and boy babies in the United States in the years 1925, 1950, and 1970.

Girls

1925	1950	1970
1. Mary	1. Linda	1. Michelle
2. Barbara	2. Mary	2. Jennifer
3. Dorothy	3. Patricia	3. Kimberly
4. Betty	4. Susan	4. Lisa
5. Ruth	5. Deborah	5. Tracy

Boys

1925	1950	1970
1. Robert	1. Robert	1. Michael
2. John	2. Michael	2. Robert
3. William	3. James	3. David
4. James	4. John	4. James
5. Charles	5. David	5. John

Show all of your work on a separate sheet of paper.

1. Does the popularity of girls' names and boys' names follow the same patterns of change? Explain your thinking with examples.
2. If you wanted to predict a name among the five most common names in 2000, would it be easier to predict a boy's name or a girl's name? Explain.
3. People use their names to identify their possessions, just as you did by putting your name on this paper. Sometimes people just put their initials on their possessions. Initials can also be used on memos, on legal documents, and on forms such as attendance sheets.
   a. How many possibilities are there for the first initial of all the English-language names in the world? Explain.
   b. How many possibilities are there for the last initial? Explain.

Assessment

Course 2 Chapter 9

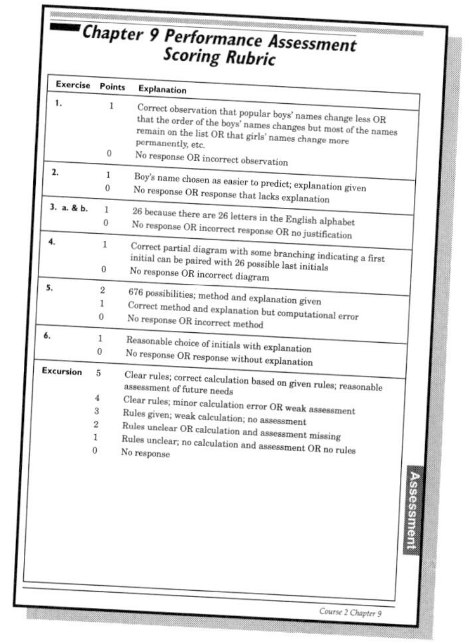

Chapter 9 Performance Assessment Scoring Rubric

Exercise	Points	Explanation
1.	1	Correct observation that popular boys' names change less OR that the order of the boys' names changes but most of the names remain on the list OR that girls' names change more permanently, etc.
	0	No response OR incorrect observation
2.	1	Boy's name chosen as easier to predict; explanation given
	0	No response OR response that lacks explanation
3. a. & b.	1	26 because there are 26 letters in the English alphabet
	0	No response OR incorrect response OR no justification
4.	1	Correct partial diagram with some branching indicating a first initial can be paired with 26 possible last initials
	0	No response OR incorrect diagram
5.	2	676 possibilities; method and explanation given
	1	Correct method and explanation but computational error
	0	No response OR incorrect method
6.	1	Reasonable choice of initials with explanation
	0	No response OR response without explanation
Excursion	5	Clear rules; correct calculation based on given rules; reasonable assessment of future needs
	4	Clear rules; minor calculation error OR weak assessment
	3	Rules given; weak calculation; no assessment
	2	Rules unclear OR calculation and assessment missing
	1	Rules unclear; no calculation and assessment OR no rules
	0	No response

Assessment

Course 2 Chapter 9

Correlation to Standardized Tests

Lesson		STANDARDIZED TEST ITEMS					
		CAT5	Terra Nova	ITBS, Form M	MAT7	SAT9	Local Test
9-1	Data Analysis: Experimental Probability						
9-2	Problem Solving Strategy: Simulate a Problem						
9-3	Theoretical Probability and Proportional Reasoning	CA28	17	CE12	CP41	PS15	
9-4	Sample Spaces						
9-5	Independent and Dependent Events					PS16	
9-6	Permutations						
9-7	Combinations					PS17	
9-8	Data Analysis: Using Data to Make Predictions						

CA: Concepts and Applications
PS: Problem Solving
PR: Math Procedures
CP: Concepts and Problem Solving
MC: Math Computation
PD: Problem Solving and Data Interpretation
CE: Concepts and Estimation

See page 2D for the level of each test referenced.

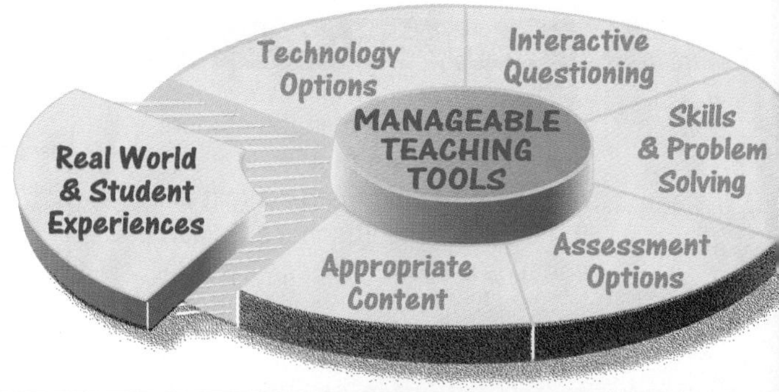

MAKING CONNECTIONS

TEAM TEACHING WITH PRENTICE HALL MATERIALS

MIDDLE GRADES MATH INTERDISCIPLINARY UNITS	*INTERDISCIPLINARY EXPLORATIONS*	*PRENTICE HALL SCIENCE* L Life Science E Earth Science P Physical Science
• **The Environment: Activity 3** • **The Arts: Activities 2 & 12**	• ***Sleuth's Supper* p. 41**	**P Lab p. 290 Half-Life of a Sugar Cube**

Lesson	Interdisciplinary Connections	Real World Connections	Math Integration
9-1	Science Sports Language	Manufacturing Real Estate	Algebra Statistics Probability
9-2	Library	Cereal Box Prizes Fundraisers Comic Strips Sales	Statistics Probability
9-3	Biology	Weather	Statistics Probability
9-4	Education	Food Service Fashion Entertainment Environment	Statistics Probability Geometry Measurement
9-5	Theater Arts	Games	Algebra Statistics Probability Geometry
9-6	Geometry	Business	Probability Statistics Geometry
9-7	Music	Clothing Field Day	Statistics Probability Geometry
9-8	Biology Ecology	Wildlife Management Shopping	Statistics

School to Home

MATERIALS:
newspaper
pennies
books
self-stick labels
shorts or sweaters
skirts or pants
paper
pencil

English version is in the Chapter Support File. Spanish version is in the Spanish Resources.

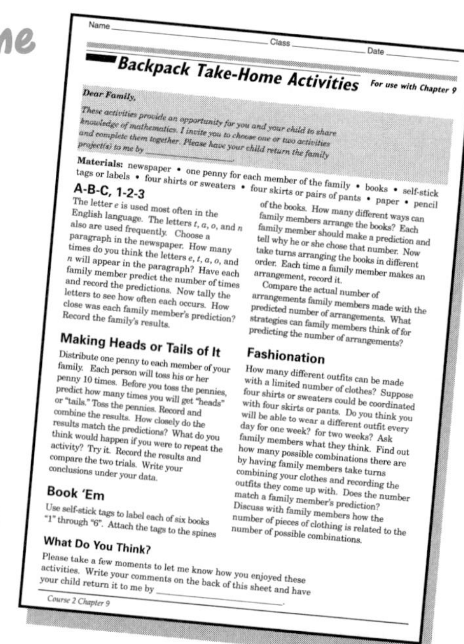
Name ______ Class ______ Date ______

Backpack Take-Home Activities *For use with Chapter 9*

Dear Family,

These activities provide an opportunity for you and your child to share knowledge of mathematics. I invite you to choose one or two activities and complete them together. Please have your child return the family project(s) to me by ______.

Materials: newspaper • one penny for each member of the family • books • self-stick tags or labels • four shirts or sweaters • four skirts or pairs of pants • paper • pencil

A-B-C, 1-2-3

The letter *e* is used most often in the English language. The letters *t*, *a*, *o*, and *n* also are used frequently. Choose a paragraph in the newspaper. How many times do you think the letters *e*, *t*, *a*, *o*, and *n* will appear in the paragraph? Have each family member predict the number of times and record the predictions. Now tally the letters to see how often each occurs. How close was each family member's prediction? Record the family's results.

Making Heads or Tails of It

Distribute one penny to each member of your family. Each person will toss his or her penny 10 times. Before you toss the pennies, predict how many times you will get "heads" or "tails." Toss the pennies. Record and combine the results. How closely do the results match the predictions? What do you think would happen if you were to repeat the activity? Try it. Record the results and compare the two trials. Write your conclusions under your data.

Book 'Em

Use self-stick tags to label each of six books "1" through "6". Attach the tags to the spines of the books. How many different ways can family members arrange the books? Each family member should make a prediction and tell why he or she chose that number. Now take turns arranging the books in different order. Each time a family member makes an arrangement, record it.

Compare the actual number of arrangements family members made with the predicted number of arrangements. What strategies can family members think of for predicting the number of arrangements?

Fashionation

How many different outfits can be made with a limited number of clothes? Suppose four shirts or sweaters could be coordinated with four skirts or pants. Do you think you will be able to wear a different outfit every day for one week? for two weeks? Ask family members what they think. Find out how many possible combinations there are by having family members take turns combining your clothes and recording the outfits they come up with. Does the number match a family member's prediction? Discuss with family members how the number of pieces of clothing is related to the number of possible combinations.

What Do You Think?

Please take a few moments to let me know how you enjoyed these activities. Write your comments on the back of this sheet and have your child return it to me by ______.

Course 2 Chapter 9

Using Technology to Enhance Instruction

For the Student

Multimedia Math Hot Pages™
This interactive software and video package on CD-ROM integrates solid math content through a variety of media.

- Hot Page™ 10-1
- Hot Page™ 10-5
- Hot Page™ 10-8

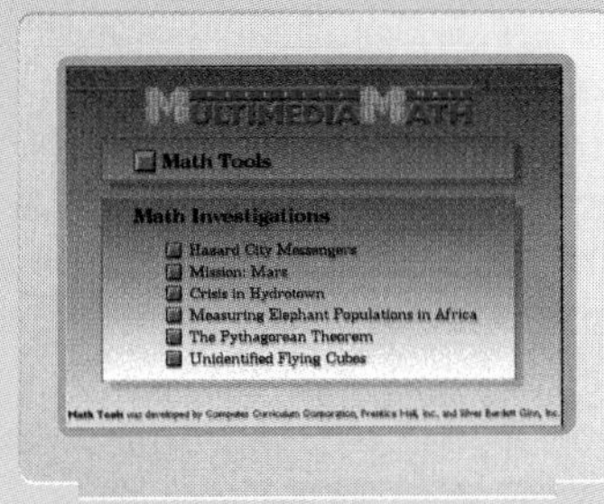

Multimedia Math Investigations
These in-depth interactive activities on CD-ROM develop real-world applications of mathematics. They allow students the opportunity to reinforce key concepts.

- Measuring Elephant Population in Africa
- Hazard City Messengers

MathBlaster® Mystery

This award-winning, interactive software program on CD-ROM can be used to maintain skills or to accommodate early finishers.

- Level: Earn 4 coins; Pay 4 coins
- Mission Mode (all lessons)
- Kitchen Comparisons (9-4, 9-6)
- Number Guesser (9-3, 9-7)
- Equation Maker (9-1, 9-5)
- Word Problems (9-2, 9-8, Problem Solving Practice)

Math Tools/Math Labs
This software, available on CD-ROM, includes on-screen Math Lab activities. Students use linkable, interactive tools to explore math concepts.

- Math Lab: Experimental Probability and Simulations (9-1)

Interactive Student Tutorial
Available on CD-ROM, this test preparation program contains self-tests with questions in standardized test format. Software includes electronic versions of the text lessons and an on-line glossary.

Internet Connection

For Students
Support for the Chapter Project
A career-oriented link for Math at Work feature

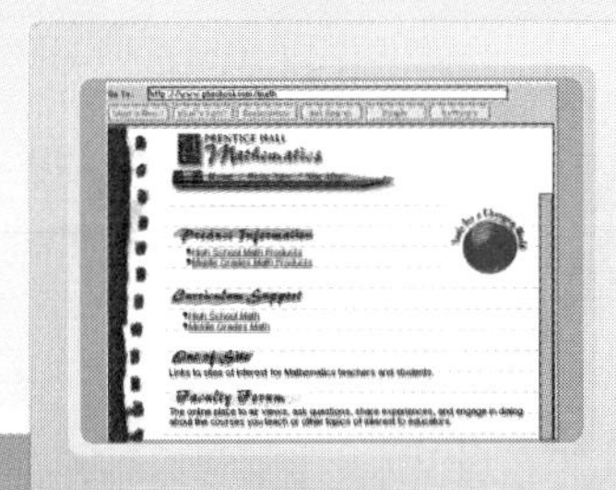

www.phschool.com/math

For teachers
Curriculum Support
Product Information
Regional Support Information

For the Teacher

Computer Item Generator with Standardized Test Practice
This software generates customized practice sheets and tests. It also generates unlimited practice sheets for the standardized tests listed on page 390D.

Resource Pro™ with Planning Express™
Available on CD-ROM, this software can be used to customize and plan lessons. It contains over 1,700 resource pages.

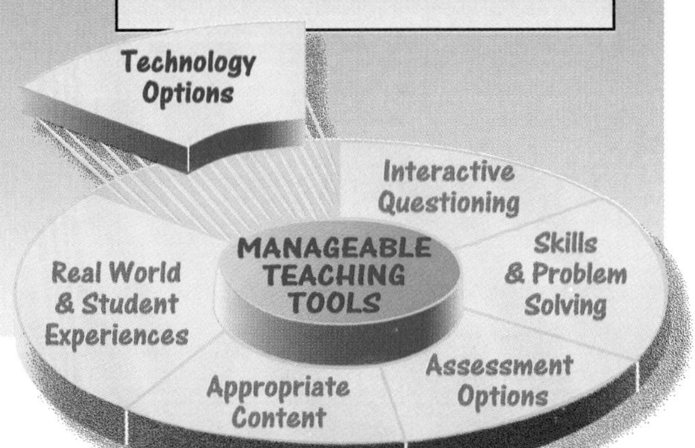

CHAPTER 9

USING PROBABILITY

CONNECTING TO PRIOR LEARNING Ask students if they have ever calculated their chances of winning a game before playing. Discuss with students their methods for calculating the odds. **Answers may vary. Sample: comparing the number of possible results that win with the possible results that lose**

CULTURAL CONNECTIONS Point out to students that the U.S. Constitution proposes that every citizen should have equal opportunity to succeed. Discuss with students laws or organizations that help foster equal opportunity in the U.S. **Answers may vary. Sample: laws giving each citizen the right to vote**

INTERDISCIPLINARY CONNECTIONS Ask students: *How do weather forecasters and stock-market analysts attempt to predict future events?* **Answers may vary. Sample: They look at current trends and conditions and apply them to future situations.**

ABOUT THE PROJECT The Chapter Project allows students to use probability to design a game using three simple number cubes.

Internet • For information and activities related to the Chapter Project, visit the Prentice Hall site at www.phschool.com/mgm2/ch9

WHAT YOU WILL LEARN IN THIS CHAPTER

- How to use probabilities to make predictions
- How to find the probability of independent and dependent events
- How to find permutations and combinations

LAUNCHING THE CHAPTER PROJECT

Ask students:

- *What games have you played that involved chance?*
- *How did chance affect the outcome of the game?*
- *How might you use chance to design your own game?*

PROJECT NOTEBOOK Encourage students to keep all project-related materials in a separate folder or notebook.

TRACKING THE PROJECT You may wish to have students read Finishing the Chapter Project on page 427 to help them get an overview of the project. Set benchmark deadlines for students to show you their work in progress.

- How to solve problems by doing a simulation

CHAPTER PROJECT

THEME: LOGIC

Everybody Wins

Remember the game "Rock, Paper, Scissors"? It is an unusual game because paper wins over rock, rock wins over scissors, and scissors win over paper. You can use mathematics to create and investigate a situation with similar characteristics.

Make Three Number Cubes For this chapter project, you will design three number cubes A, B, and C, which have a surprising property: A usually beats B, B usually beats C, and C usually beats A. Your final product will be to construct your cubes.

Steps to help you complete the project:

p. 405 Project Link: *Analyzing*
p. 415 Project Link: *Calculating*
p. 421 Project Link: *Designing*
p. 427 *Finishing the Chapter Project*

SCORING RUBRIC

3 You design and construct three cubes (A, B, and C) so that A beats B, B beats C, and C beats A. You provide sample spaces for the cubes in the Project Link on page 415 as well as for each of the three pairs of cubes that you designed. Your work also includes either explanations or experimental data showing that your cubes work as predicted.

2 You construct three cubes, and your sample spaces for each pair of cubes show correctly that these cubes satisfy the requirements of the project.

1 You build cubes but either your sample spaces are incorrect or your cubes don't behave as required by the project description.

0 You do not build the cubes, or you fail to use sample spaces or explanations to prove that your cubes behave as they should.

9-1 Teaching Notes

1 Focus

CONNECTING TO PRIOR KNOWLEDGE
Have students recall playing games with a number cube. Ask: *What numbers are there on a number cube?* **Answers may vary. Sample: usually 1, 2, 3, 4, 5, 6** Have students brainstorm games they have played that used number cubes. Ask:

- *About how often did you roll a 6?* **Answers may vary.**
- *Did you have a better chance of rolling a 3 than a 6?* **Answers may vary. Sample: no**

2 Teach

THINK AND DISCUSS

AEP Have students make sentences with the words *probably*, *event*, and *experiment*. Then have them compare their sentences with the definitions of *probability*, *event*, and *experimental probability*.

VISUAL LEARNING Example 1 Have students draw a rectangle made of 50 squares. Have them label 20 squares with *H* for *heads*. Ask: *What should you label the other squares?* **T for tails** Ask: *What is the experimental probability that the result is tails?* $\frac{3}{5}$

Lesson Planning Options

Prerequisite Skills
- writing ratios (6-1)
- expressing ratios as decimals and percents (6-7)

Vocabulary/Symbols
probability, event, experimental probability

Materials/Manipulatives
- coins for tossing
- standard number cube

Resources

Student Edition

Skills Handbook, p. 533
Extra Practice, p. 522
Glossary/Study Guide

Teaching Resources

Chapter Support File, Ch. 9
- Lesson Planner 9-1
- Practice 9-1, Reteaching 9-1
- Alternative Activity 9-1
- Answer Masters 9-1

Teaching Aids Master 10
Glossary, Spanish Resources

Transparencies
15, 17, Minds on Math 9-1

Warm Up
A prism has 7 faces and 10 vertices. How many edges does it have? **15**

DATA ANALYSIS Connection

9-1 Experimental Probability

What You'll Learn
1. To find the experimental probability of an event
2. To use simulations to find experimental probability

...And Why
Manufacturers use probability to predict the number of defective items.

Here's How
Look for questions that
- build understanding
- ✓ check understanding

THINK AND DISCUSS

1 Finding Experimental Probability

Suppose you play a game that includes tossing a coin and rolling a number cube. These are the results of eight turns.

Coin	heads	heads	tails	heads	tails	heads	tails	heads
Cube	2	5	1	2	3	2	3	5

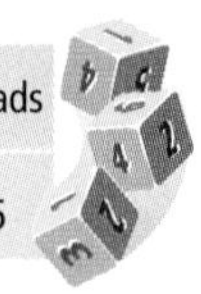

Probability measures how likely it is that an event occurs. One or more results of an experiment make an **event.** In the game described above, "heads and a 2" is an example of an event.

For **experimental probability,** you collect data through observations or experiments. To find the experimental probability of the event "heads and a 2," use this ratio.

$$P(\text{event}) = \frac{\text{number of times an event occurs}}{\text{total number of experiments}}$$

$$P(\text{heads and a 2}) = \frac{\text{number of times "heads and a 2" occurs}}{\text{total number of experiments}} = \frac{3}{8}$$

QUICKreview

To simplify a fraction, divide the numerator and denominator by the same nonzero number.
$\frac{20}{50} = \frac{20 \div 10}{50 \div 10} = \frac{2}{5}$

■ **EXAMPLE 1**

Suppose you toss a coin 50 times. You get heads 20 times. Find the experimental probability that you get heads.

$P(\text{heads}) = \frac{20}{50}$ ← number of heads / number of tosses

$= \frac{2}{5}$ ← Simplify the fraction.

The probability that the result is heads is $\frac{2}{5}$.

1. a. ✓ *Try It Out* Suppose you toss a coin 60 times, and you get tails 25 times. Find the experimental probability of tails. $\frac{5}{12}$
   b. Suppose you plan to toss the same coin 10 more times. About how many times would you expect to get tails? **4 times**

ERROR ALERT! Example 2 Some students may write 0.03 as 0.03%. **Remediation:** Tell students that the decimal "sign" always moves two places closer to the percent "sign" so they can speak "sign" language together.

ADDITIONAL EXAMPLES

FOR EXAMPLE 1

Suppose you toss a coin 80 times. You get heads 50 times. Find the experimental probability that you get heads. $\frac{5}{8}$

FOR EXAMPLE 2

An employee of the Marvelous Music Company checked 600 cassette tapes for quality. He found 42 defective tapes. What is the experimental probability a cassette tape is defective? $\frac{42}{600} = \frac{7}{100} = 0.07 = 7\%$

FOR EXAMPLE 3

Use the same simulation to determine what the likelihood is that the last two children are boys. $\frac{7}{20} = 35\%$

REASONING Question 5 Have students demonstrate different tossing techniques.

REASONING Question 6 If you have block scheduling or extended class periods, have groups of five students each conduct a simulation for Example 3. Have groups compare their results.

Stress to students that a *simulation* provides a controllable environment to gather experimental data. Sometimes it is not possible to gather such data in the real world.

You can write a probability as a fraction, decimal, or percent.

EXAMPLE 2 *Real-World Problem Solving*

Manufacturing An employee of the Great Toys Manufacturing Company checked 400 toy cars. He found 12 defective cars. What is the experimental probability a toy car is defective?

$P(\text{defective toy car}) = \frac{12}{400}$ ← number of times "defective car" occurs / ← total number of cars checked

$= \frac{3}{100} = 0.03 = 3\%$

The probability of a defective toy car is $\frac{3}{100}$, or 0.03, or 3%.

2. *Predict* How many defective toy cars would you predict in 1,250 toy cars? **about 38 toy cars**

3. ✔ *Try It Out* Madison High School ordered 64 new soccer balls. The students found leaks in 5 of the balls. Write the experimental probability of finding a leaky soccer ball as a percent. **about 7.8%**

Now you may assign Exercises 1–16.

2 *Simulating Events*

You can simulate situations in order to find probabilities.

EXAMPLE 3 *Real-World Problem Solving*

Science In a family of three children, what is the likelihood that the first two children are girls?

Simulate the situation by tossing three coins at the same time. Let "heads" represent a girl and "tails" represent a boy. The results of twenty tosses are at the left.

$P(\text{first two children girls}) = \frac{6}{20} = 30\%$

Using the data from this simulation, there is a 30% probability that the first two children are girls.

4. a. ✔ *Try It Out* Use the data in Example 3. What is the probability of all boys in a family of three children? **$\frac{1}{5}$ or 20%**
   b. About how many families would you predict have all boys in 200 families of three children? **40 families**

5. *Reasoning* Is it reasonable to expect that every simulation of 20 tosses will give exactly the same results as those in Example 3? Explain. **No; each simulation of 20 tosses will have somewhat different results.**

Technology Options

Prentice Hall Technology

Software for Learners
- Math Lab: Experimental Probability and Simulations
- Math Blaster® Mystery*
- Interactive Student Tutorial, Chapter 9*

Teaching Resource Software
- Computer Item Generator 9-1
- Resource Pro™ Chapter 9*

Internet • For related mathematics activities, visit the Prentice Hall site at www.phschool.com/math

**Available on CD-ROM only*

Assignment Options for Exercises On Your Own

To provide flexible scheduling, this lesson can be split into parts.

1 **Core** 1–12, 14–16
Extension 13

2 **Core** 17–21, 23
Extension 22, 24

Use Mixed Review to maintain skills.

Make sure students understand the difference between experimental probability based on real-world data and experimental probability based on simulations.

Work Together

Have students abbreviate with *M* for *male* and *F* for *female*. Suppose you write *MMMF* for the first set of tosses and *MFMM* for the fifth set of tosses. Ask:

- *How are the tosses the same?* **Both show three kittens are male.**
- *How are they different?* **the order**
- *Does the order matter?* **no**

ASSESSMENT Assign partners. Have students find the probability that two out of five students have an even house number. They should use five coins to simulate the house numbers. After 20 coin tosses, have each group share their probability with the class as a fraction, a decimal, and a percent. If there is time, poll the class to see how many students actually have an even house number.

3 Practice/Assess

EXERCISES *On Your Own*

Exercises 1–6 Ask: *Is this data collected through observations or experiment?* **observation**

Exercises 7–12 Remind students to write the probability as a fraction first. Point out that the denominator will be the same for each exercise.

6. *Reasoning* Which results do you think will more accurately reflect families with three children, the simulation in Example 3 or a simulation done 1,000 times? Explain. **1,000 times; a larger sample is more likely to give a more accurate prediction.**

Work Together

Conducting a Simulation

Work with a partner. Find the probability that three kittens in a litter of four kittens are male. Use four coins to simulate a litter.

7. Conduct the simulation. Find the probability that three kittens are male based on twenty tosses of the coins.

7–8. Check students' work.

8. Combine your results with the other groups in your class. Using all the results, what is the probability?

Now you may assign Exercises 17–24.

EXERCISES *On Your Own*

Suppose you collect data on the color of shirts worn by the students in your class. Eight wore green, five wore red, three wore white, and ten wore blue. Write each probability as a fraction in simplest form.

1. P(green) $\frac{4}{13}$
2. P(red) $\frac{5}{26}$
3. P(white) $\frac{3}{26}$
4. P(blue) $\frac{5}{13}$
5. P(purple) **0**
6. P(blue or white) $\frac{1}{2}$

Data Analysis **Use the data in the line plot at the right. Write each probability as a percent.**

7. P(Sunday) **12%**
8. P(Monday) **24%**
9. P(Tuesday) **20%**
10. P(Friday) **8%**
11. P(weekday) **72%**
12. P(weekend) **28%**

Students' Birthdays

	X					
	X	X				
	X	X				X
X	X	X		X		X
X	X	X	X	X	X	X
X	X	X	X	X	X	X
Su	M	Tu	W	Th	F	Sa

13. a. *Manufacturing* The quality control engineer of Top Notch Tool Company found flaws in 8 of 60 wrenches. Find the probability that a wrench is defective. **$13.\overline{3}$%**
    b. Which is the most effective way of writing the probability, as a fraction, a decimal, or a percent? Explain. **Check students' work.**
    c. *Predict* Suppose the company produces 2,400 wrenches a day. How many will *not* have flaws? **2,080 wrenches**

14. *Science* The probability that a male is colorblind is 8%. Suppose you interview 1,000 males. About how many will be colorblind? Will you get exactly this number? Explain. **80 males; no; probability only predicts the outcome that is *likely* to occur.**

CONNECTION TO SCIENCE Exercise 14 Remind students to write a proportion to solve. For example: $\frac{8}{100} = \frac{n}{1{,}000}$.

Exercises 17–19 Ask students: *How many possible results can you get when rolling a number cube?* **6** *tossing a coin?* **2** *choosing cards numbered 1 through 6?* **6**

Exercise 21 Suggest students write 40% as a fraction and simplify. For example: $40\% = \frac{40}{100} = \frac{2}{5}$.

OPEN-ENDED Exercise 24 Remind students that probabilities that can be simulated must have a limited number of results. For example, whether a child is a boy or a girl has two results. There can be various numbers of children in a family so this would not be suited to a simulation.

WRAP UP

IDENTIFYING THE BIG IDEA Have students explain how to use *simulation* to find the *experimental probability* of an event.

15. *Sports* Suppose you attempt 16 free throws in a basketball game. Your results are at the right.
   a. Find the probability of making a free throw. **$\frac{1}{2}$ or 50%**
   b. *Predict* Suppose in the next game you attempt twelve free throws. How many do you expect to make? **6 free throws**
   c. *Reasoning* Can you expect to make the same number of baskets every time you attempt 12 free throws? Explain. **No; probability cannot predict exact outcomes.**

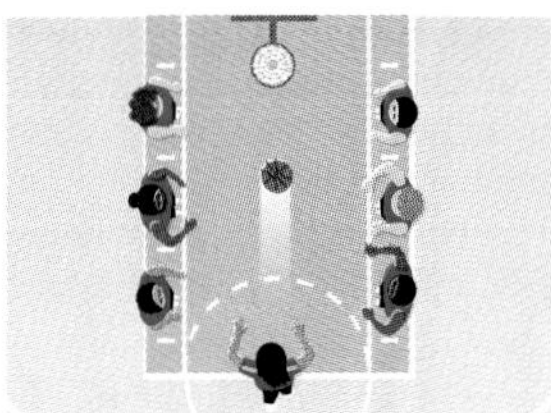

Results of Free Throw Attempts

0 = miss 1 = make

0	0	1	1	1	0	1	0
0	1	0	1	1	0	0	1

16. *Data Collection* Roll a number cube 50 times. Keep a record of how many times each number occurs.
   a. Find the probability for each number.
   b. Is the probability the same for each number?
   a–b. Check students' work.

Match each situation in Exercises 17–19 with an appropriate simulation. Justify your choice.

17. The Golden Hen Egg Company packs eggs in groups of six per carton. The probability that an egg is cracked is $\frac{1}{6}$. How likely is it that an egg carton will have two broken eggs? **A**

18. To win a carnival game, you must guess two numbers. Each number is less than 7. What is the probability that you guess the numbers? **C**

19. Joshua guesses the answers on six true/false quiz questions. How likely is he to guess two correct answers? **B**

A. Roll six number cubes 30 times.

B. Toss six coins 10 times.

C. Choose a card from each of two groups of cards numbered 1 to 6. Repeat 40 times.

20. *Data Collection* "Spin Your Age" is a carnival game. To play, you spin a wheel numbered 0–9. To win, you must spin the two digits of your age in order. **a–c. Check students' work.**
   a. To simulate the situation, write each digit from 0 to 9, using one slip of paper for each number. Put the slips in a bag. Make a second set of numbered slips, and put them in another bag. Randomly select a slip from each bag, and write down the digits in the order you look at them. Return the slips to their bags and select two more. Collect 100 pieces of data.
   b. Find the probability you select your age.
   c. *Reasoning* Would you play "Spin Your Age" at a carnival? Why or why not?

PRACTICE

Practice 9-1 Experimental Probability

Suppose you observe the color of socks worn by students in your class. Twelve have white, four have black, three have blue, and one has red. Write each probability as a fraction in simplest form.

1. P(white) $\frac{3}{5}$
2. P(red) $\frac{1}{20}$
3. P(blue) $\frac{3}{20}$
4. P(black) $\frac{1}{5}$
5. P(yellow) 0
6. P(black or red) $\frac{1}{4}$

Use the data in the table at the right for Exercises 7–12. Write each probability as a percent.

Favorite Snack Survey Results

Snack	Number of Students
Fruit	8
Candy	2
Pretzels	3
Chips	7
Cookies	5

7. P(fruit) 32%
8. P(candy) 8%
9. P(pretzels) 12%
10. P(cookies) 20%
11. P(not fruit) 68%
12. P(candy or chips) 36%
13. Do an experiment to find the probability that a word chosen randomly in a book is the word *the*. How many words did you look at to find P(the)? What is P(the)? Answers may vary.
14. **Circle A, B, C, or D.** Suppose each of the following are the results of tossing a coin. Which result suggests an experimental probability of 60% for heads?
    - A. head, tail, tail, tail, head
    - B. head, head, tail, head,head
    - C. tail, tail, head, head, tail
    - (D.) head, tail, head, tail, head

Solve.

15. The probability that a twelve-year-old is taller than 60 inches is 25%. Suppose you measure 300 twelve-year-old boys. About how many do you think will be taller than 60 inches? about 75 boys
16. a. A quality control inspector found flaws in 13 out of 150 sweaters. Find the probability that a sweater has a flaw. Round to the nearest tenth of a percent. 8.7%
    b. Suppose the company produces 500 sweaters a day. How many will not have flaws? 457 sweaters

In copymaster and workbook formats

RETEACHING

Reteaching 9-1 Experimental Probability

Probability measures how likely it is that an event will occur. For an **experimental probability,** you collect data through observations or experiments and use the data to state the probability.

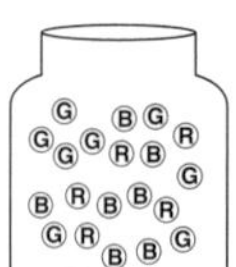

The jar contains red, green, and blue chips. You shake the jar, draw a chip, note its color, and then put it back. You do this 20 times with these results: 7 blue chips, 5 red chips, and 8 green chips. The experimental probability of drawing a green chip is

$P(\text{green chip}) = \frac{\text{number of times "green chips" occur}}{\text{total number of experiments}}$

$P(\text{green chip}) = \frac{8}{20} = \frac{2}{5} = 0.4 = 40\%$

The probability of drawing a green chip is $\frac{2}{5}$, or 0.4, or 40%.

Use the 20 draws above to complete each exercise.

1. What is the experimental probability of drawing a red chip? Write the probability as a fraction.
   $P(\text{red chip}) = \frac{5}{20} = \frac{1}{4}$
2. What is the experimental probability of drawing a blue chip? Write the probability as a percent.
   $P(\text{blue chip}) = \frac{7}{20} =$ 35%

Suppose you have a bag with 30 chips: 12 red, 8 white, and 10 blue. You shake the jar, draw a chip, note its color, and then put it back. You do this 30 times with these results: 10 blue chips, 12 red chips, and 8 white chips. Write each probability as fraction in simplest form.

3. P(red) $\frac{2}{5}$
4. P(white) $\frac{4}{15}$
5. P(blue) $\frac{1}{3}$

Suppose you surveyed the students in your class on their favorite ice cream flavors. Six chose vanilla, 10 chose chocolate, 1 chose bubble gum, and 3 chose cookie dough. Write each probability as a fraction in simplest form.

6. P(bubble gum) $\frac{1}{20}$
7. P(vanilla) $\frac{3}{10}$
8. P(chocolate) $\frac{1}{2}$
9. P(cookie dough) $\frac{3}{20}$

ENRICHMENT

Minds on Math Transparency

9-1

A class of 22 students wants to break into small groups of different sizes. No two groups can have the same number of students. What is the greatest number of groups they could form? What are the sizes of these groups?

6 groups; groups of 1, 2, 3, 4, 5, 7 students

See *Solution Key* for worked-out answers.

LESSON QUIZ

Suppose you collect data on the hair color of your teachers. Four have brown hair, two have black hair, one has blonde hair, and one has red hair.

1. Write P(black) as a fraction in simplest form. $\frac{1}{4}$
2. Write P(brown) as a decimal. **0.5**
3. Write P(blonde) as a percent. **12.5%**

21. **Choose A, B, C, or D.** Suppose each of the following are the results of tossing a coin. Which result has the probability of 40% heads? **B**
    - A. heads, heads, tails, tails, heads
    - B. tails, heads, heads, tails, tails
    - C. tails, heads, tails, tails, tails
    - D. heads, tails, heads, heads, heads
22. a. *Language* Find the probability that a randomly selected word in this book contains the letter e. **Check students' work.**
    b. *Writing* How many words did you sample to find $P(e)$? If you looked at twice as many words, would your results be different? Explain. **Numbers may vary; yes; experimental probability does not predict exact outcomes.**
23. There are 15 boys and 15 girls in a group of 30 students. Five are selected at random.
    a. *Reasoning* Would you prefer to toss one coin five times or five coins once to simulate the situation? Explain.
    b. Simulate the situation 20 times. Record your results.
    c. Use your results from part (b). What is the probability that three of the five are boys? What is the probability that all five are girls? **b–c. Check students' work.**

23a. Answers may vary. Sample: No preference; each simulation reasonably represents the situation.

24. *Open-ended* Give an example of a probability that you can find by conducting a simulation. Describe the simulation. **See margin p. 397.**

Mixed Review

Find the area of each triangle. *(Lesson 8-3)*

25.
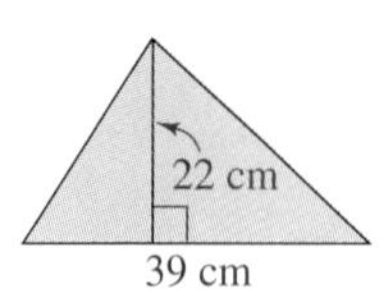

429 cm²

26.
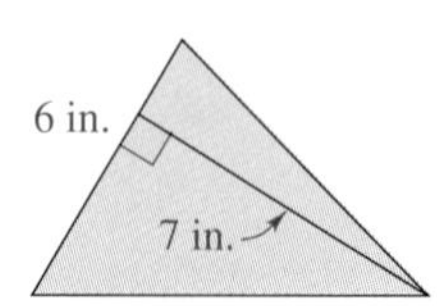

21 in.²

27.
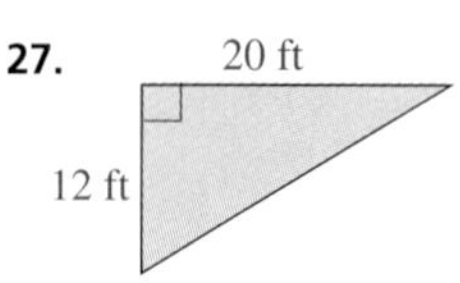

120 ft²

28.
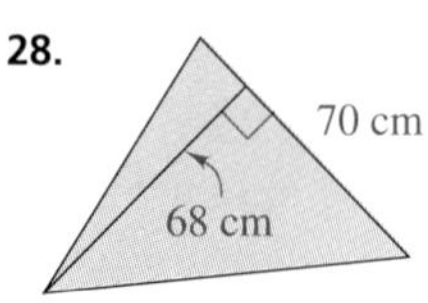

2,380 cm²

Evaluate for $x = 2$. *(Lesson 4-4)*

29. $5x^2 - 2x$ **16**
30. $x^3 + 5x$ **18**
31. $3x^2 \div x$ **6**
32. $-4x(-2x)^2$ **−128**
33. $-16x^2 - 5$ **−69**
34. *Real Estate* An agent sells a property for $140,000. The broker's commission is 6%. The agent receives 60% of the broker's commission. How much does the agent receive? *(Lesson 6-10)* **$5,040**

Extra Practice, Lesson 9-1, page 522

MATH TOOLBOX

In Lesson 9-1, students learn how to find the experimental probability of an event using simulation. This toolbox shows students how to use a random number table to simulate situations.

ERROR ALERT! Students may not understand that zero is considered an even digit. **Remediation:** Have students list the digits from 0–9. Then have them circle all of the odd digits. Explain that the remaining digits are even, and that includes the digit zero.

ASSESSMENT Exercise 1 Pair students and have each pair brainstorm ways in which to use the information in the Example to solve the problem. Have partners write their strategies and compare strategies with another pair of students.

ADDITIONAL PROBLEM

Use the information in the Example to find the probability that exactly one out of four bulbs will grow. **$\frac{1}{5}$ or 20%**

MATH TOOLBOX

TECHNOLOGY

Using Random Numbers

After Lesson 9-1

You can use a *random number table* to simulate some situations. Some calculators and computer programs can generate random number tables.

To generate a random number table in a spreadsheet, follow these steps.

Step 1 Set the number format to four digits.

Step 2 Use the formula RAND()*10,000. This will create groups of 4 digits in each cell of a spreadsheet. (*Note:* Each time you generate a random number table, you will get a different group of digits.)

	A	B	C	D
1	2660	1927	7807	0912
2	8879	6235	5897	8068
3	8121	4646	8368	1613
4	0821	8911	3022	0307
5	9393	5403	4930	4898

EXAMPLE

Suppose a rare lily bulb has a 50% chance of growing. You plant four bulbs. What is the probability that all four will grow?

Use the random number table. Let all the even digits represent "grow" and all the odd digits represent "does *not* grow."

The probability of four bulbs growing is $\frac{3}{20}$ or 15%.

2660	1927	7807	0912
8879	6235	5897	8068
8121	4646	8368	1613
0821	8911	3022	0307
9393	5403	4930	4898

Any group with 4 even digits represents "four bulbs grow."

Choose **Use the random number table above or generate your own to simulate each problem.**

1. Use the information in the Example. Find the probability that exactly three out of four bulbs will grow. **$\frac{1}{5}$ or 20%**

2. a. Suppose there is a 30% probability of being stopped by a red light at each of four stop lights. What is the probability of at least two red lights? Let 0, 1, and 2 represent red lights. **$\frac{9}{20}$ or 45%**
   b. *Reasoning* Suppose there is a 60% chance of a red light at each stop light. How many numbers would you use to represent getting a red light? Justify your answer. **6; 6 digits out of 10 is 60%.**

3. *Writing* Write a probability problem you could solve using a random number table. Solve your problem. **Check students' work.**

pages 394–396 On Your Own

24. Sample: A laundry hamper is filled with white, black, blue, green, red, purple socks. Find the probability that the first two socks pulled out of the hamper are a matching pair. Use a pair of number cubes with each number representing a color. Roll both cubes 25 times. Find the number of matching pairs.

9-2 Teaching Notes

1 Focus

CONNECTING TO PRIOR KNOWLEDGE Ask students to describe situations for which you must create an imitation or simulation. **Answers may vary. Sample: pilot or astronaut training, animal settings in zoos, crash testing vehicles to check for seat belt safety** Point out that this type of simulation involves finding an easy-to-operate model for a given problem. The model must have the same mathematical characteristics as the original problem.

2 Teach

THINK AND DISCUSS

DIVERSITY and CONNECTION TO SCIENCE Some students may be familiar with the different dinosaur names, but not know what each looks like. Bring models or a book about dinosaurs to class to help these students become familiar with them.

TACTILE LEARNING Question 2 Have students make two bags of objects. Let bag A have 1 black, 1 blue, and 1 white object. Let bag B have 3 black, 1 blue, and 1 white object. Ask: *Suppose you choose an object from a bag. From which bag will you have an equally likely chance of choosing a black object?* **bag A** *Why?* **Bag A has the same number of each color.**

Lesson Planning Options

Prerequisite Skills

- finding mean (1-4)

Vocabulary/Symbols

trial

Materials/Manipulatives

- standard number cubes

Resources

Student Edition

Skills Handbook, p. 528
Extra Practice, p. 522
Glossary/Study Guide

Teaching Resources

Chapter Support File, Ch. 9
- Lesson Planner 9-2
- Practice 9-2, Reteaching 9-2
- Answer Masters 9-2

Teaching Aids Master 10
Glossary, Spanish Resources

Transparencies

17, Minds on Math 9-2

Warm Up

Draw 6 nonlinear points. How many different segments can you draw connecting the points. **15**

PROBLEM SOLVING STRATEGY

READ PLAN SOLVE LOOK BACK

9-2 Simulate a Problem

Problem Solving Strategies

Draw a Diagram
Guess and Test
Look for a Pattern
Make a Model
Make a Table
✔ Simulate a Problem
Solve a Simpler Problem
Too Much or Too Little Information
Use Logical Reasoning
Use Multiple Strategies
Work Backward
Write an Equation

THINK AND DISCUSS

You can use simulations to act out some real-world situations. First develop a model. Then conduct experiments.

SAMPLE PROBLEM

Kayley Karl wants to collect the six different model dinosaurs being given as prizes in boxes of Crispy Crunchy cereal. Each box of cereal contains one model, and there is an equally likely chance of any one of the prizes being in any one box. Kayley has enough money to buy 20 boxes. Is she likely to get all six prizes in those 20 boxes?

READ

Read for understanding. Summarize the problem.

Think about the problem.

1. a. What is the least number of boxes of cereal Kayley may need to buy to collect all six dinosaurs? **6 boxes**
   b. After buying 20 boxes of cereal, what is the least number of types of dinosaurs that she could have collected? **1 type**
   c. Guess the number of boxes you think she may need to buy. **Check students' work.**
2. *Reasoning* Why is it important to know that there is an equally likely chance of a prize being in any one box?

2. Answers may vary. Sample: If one type is less common than the others, then the probability would be hard to predict.

PLAN

Decide on a strategy.

Kayley can simulate the problem to estimate how many boxes she will need to buy to get all six dinosaurs.

3. Suppose Kayley uses a standard number cube to simulate the problem. Rolling a 1 means Kayley gets a brontosaurus model. Rolling a 2 means Kayley gets a stegosaurus, and so on. How many different numbers will Kayley have to roll to receive the six different dinosaur models? **6 numbers**

ASSESSMENT Random devices include number cubes, coins, spinners, and random numbers. Ask students: *How do you determine which random device to use?* **Choose the device with the same number of choices as in the real situation.** *How do you know when a trial is finished?* **when you get all the possible responses**

ADDITIONAL PROBLEM

Mrs. Callen is awarding students in her class a coupon for each completed homework assignment. She has marked the coupons with one of these letters: F, I, V, or E. Students have an equally likely chance of receiving any of the letters on a coupon. Mrs. Callen will add five extra-credit points to the next test grade of any student who spells the word FIVE with coupons. Fawn earns ten coupons.

a. What is the least number of coupons Fawn must earn to spell the word FIVE? **4**

b. What random device could you use to simulate the problem? **a spinner**

c. Conduct a trial. How many times did you have to spin to complete the trial? **Check students' work.**

3 Practice/Assess

EXERCISES *On Your Own*

Exercises 1–2 Have students solve each exercse using the simulation they described.

One *trial* for a simulation is completed when you get all possible responses once. You may get some responses more than once.

4. Kayley simulated the problem by rolling a number cube. The tally she made during the first trial is at the right.

a. How many times did she have to roll the number cube to get all six numbers? **14 times**

b. According to this trial, how many boxes of cereal would Kayley have to buy to get all six model dinosaurs? **14 boxes**

Rolls of a Number Cube

Number	Roll
1	||
2	||||
3	|
4	||
5	||
6	|||
Total	■

SOLVE
Try the strategy.

Simulate the problem by rolling a number cube.
a–b. Check students' work.

5. a. Roll a number cube as many times as necessary to receive all six dinosaurs. Keep a tally of your results.

b. Conduct 10 trials. Find the mean of the number of boxes Kayley would need to buy.

LOOK BACK
Think about how you solved the problem.

6. How close was your guess in Question 1(c) to the mean number of boxes you found in Question 5(b)?
6–7. Check students' work.

7. The more trials you have the better your estimate is. Find the mean number of boxes Kayley needs to buy based on the results of the trials for your class.

8. a. *Reasoning* Do you think Kayley is likely to get all six prizes if she buys 20 boxes of cereal? Explain.

b. Do you know for sure that Kayley will have all six prizes after she buys 20 boxes of cereal? **no**

8a. Answers may vary. Sample: Yes; 20 is much greater than the simulated mean number of boxes she needs.

Now you may assign Exercises 1–7.

EXERCISES *On Your Own*

Describe a simulation you could use to solve each problem.

1. A restaurant gives away a model car with each purchase. You are equally likely to get any of three different cars. Estimate the number of purchases you would need to make to get all the cars. **Check students' work. Sample strategy: Use a standard number cube. Each model corresponds to 2 different numbers on the number cube.**

Technology Options

Prentice Hall Technology

Software for Learners
- Hot Page™ 10–5*
- Math Blaster® Mystery*
- Interactive Student Tutorial, Chapter 9*

Teaching Resource Software
- Computer Item Generator 9-2
- Resource Pro™ Chapter 9*

Internet • For related mathematics activities, visit the Prentice Hall site at www.phschool.com/math

**Available on CD-ROM only*

Assignment Options for Exercises On Your Own

Core 1, 2, 4–7
Extension 3

Use Mixed Review to maintain skills.

PRACTICE

Practice 9-2 *Problem-Solving Strategy: Simulate a Problem*

Describe a simulation you could use to solve each problem.

1. A grocery store is running a contest. Every time you enter the store, you receive a card with the letter W, I, N, E, or R. You have an equally likely chance of receiving any one card. To win a prize, you must spell WINNER by collecting the cards. How many times will you have to enter the store to win a prize?
   Sample: Use a number cube with one number for W, I, E, and R, and two numbers for N.

2. A sugarless-gum company wraps its product in a piece of paper with one of the digits 1 to 6 on the paper. When you collect wrappers that contain all 6 digits, you win a prize. Use a number cube to help you decide how many pieces of gum you will need to buy in order to get all 6 digits.
   Sample: Roll a number cube as many times as necessary to get all 6 digits.

Use any strategy to solve each problem. Show your work.

3. In 1960, the submarine *Triton* traveled 36,014 miles journeying around the world. If the trip took 76 days, how many miles did the Triton average each day?
   Answers may vary. Sample: about 474 mi/d

4. After working for a company for a year, Melanie received a 10% raise in her salary. Later, the entire company took a 10% cut in pay because of budget difficulties. If Melanie started working at $2,000 a month, what would she now be receiving?
   $1,980/month

5. At the mall on Saturday, Suki bought a pair of blue jeans for $15.55 and some books for $8.53. For lunch she spent $1.50 on juice and $3.25 on a sandwich. When she left the mall she had $5.27 left. How much money did Suki take to the mall?
   $34.10

6. Mari plans to make a doll's quilt with 16 squares. Half of the squares will be solid red. The rest of the squares will be half calico print and half white. If each square is 9 inches on a side, how many square feet of each type of fabric will she need?
   $4\frac{1}{2}$ ft² of red, $2\frac{1}{4}$ ft² of calico, $2\frac{1}{4}$ ft² of white

Practice

In copymaster and workbook formats

RETEACHING

Reteaching 9-2 *Problem-Solving Strategy: Simulate a Problem*

When you use simulation to solve a problem, you must first develop a model. Then, conduct experiments to generate data.

You and a friend are equally skilled at playing checkers. Estimate how many games you will have to play until one of you wins 6 games.

Read What do you want to find? *You want to find out how many games of checkers you can expect to play until one of you wins six games.*

Plan Instead of actually playing the games, develop a simulation. You can toss a coin to see who wins each game. Heads means you win. Tails means your friend wins. Keep track of your results.

Solve Show the results of the simulation in a table. You tossed the coin 10 times before either 6 heads or 6 tails appeared. So you estimate that you would have to play 10 games before one of you would win 6 games.

Tosses of a Coin

Result	Number
Heads	𝍸 /
Tails	////

Look Back Do you think you would get the same results if you repeated the simulation?

Describe a simulation you could use to solve each problem. **Check students' answers.**

1. There is one of four symbols on the inner wrapper of energy bars. The symbols are equally distributed among the wrappers. If you collect all four symbols, you get a free bar. Estimate how many bars you need to purchase to win a free bar.
   Sample: Use a spinner divided into four parts, one for each symbol.

2. A bakery puts a saying in each cookie. There are 36 different sayings, and there is an equally likely chance that any one of them will be inside any cookie. Estimate how many cookies Mary would have to buy to collect all 36 sayings.
   Sample: Roll two number cubes, letting each of the 36 combinations represent a different saying.

3. A bank gives away one of six baseball cards each time you make a deposit. There is an equal chance of getting any one of the cards. Estimate how many deposits you will have to make to get all six cards.
   Sample: Toss a number cube.

4. Your 10 pairs of socks are in the dryer. Each pair of socks is a different color. Estimate how many socks you will have to pull out without looking to get two the same color.
   Sample: Use two sets of number cards 1–10 and draw them from a bag.

Reteaching

ENRICHMENT

Minds on Math Transparency

9-2

Henry used $\frac{1}{2}$ of his flour to make blueberry muffins and $\frac{1}{2}$ of the remaining flour to make bran muffins. He has $1\frac{1}{2}$ c of flour left. How much flour did he start with?

6 cups

See *Solution Key* for worked-out answers.

WRAP UP

IDENTIFYING THE BIG IDEA Have students explain why using a *simulation* is a helpful problem-solving technique. Have them summarize the steps necessary to complete a simulation.

LESSON QUIZ

Refer to the Additional Problem on page 399.

1. Conduct 5 trials. Find the mean number of coupons Fawn will need to earn. **Answers may vary. Sample: 7**
2. Is Fawn likely to receive five bonus points on her next test? Explain. **Answers may vary. Sample: Yes; the mean number of coupons needed in the simulation was less than ten.**

---

2. Suppose you are given a matching quiz in a language you do not know. There are six questions and six answers. Find the average number of guesses you need to make to get a match.
   2. Check students' work. Sample strategy: Make two piles with cards with numbers 1–6 in each. Then pull 1 card from each pile. Repeat until the piles are empty. Repeat the process 20 times. Find the average number of matching pairs.

Use any strategy to solve each problem. Show your work.

3. The Booster Club hired a rock band for a fund-raiser. The club guaranteed the band a fee of $1,500 plus $4.50 for each ticket sold. There are 1,132 seats in the auditorium. What is the greatest possible amount of money the band can earn?
   $6,594
4. The largest window in the world is in Paris, France, at the Palace of Industry and Technology. The window measures 715.2 ft wide by 164 ft high. How many square yards of glass are in this window?
   about 13,032.5 yd²
5. The longest-lived comic strip is "The Katzenjammer Kids." It was created by Rudolph Dirks and first published in the *New York Journal* on December 12, 1897. Use today's date to calculate the age of this comic strip.
   Check students' work.

6. There are five different letters under the bottle caps for Sparky Juice: J, U, I, C and E. To win a prize, you must collect all five caps to spell JUICE. Estimate the number of juice bottles you will need to buy to win a prize. **Check students' work. Sample strategy: Let 2 different digits represent each letter. Use a random number table.**
7. *Writing* During a sale a store manager reduces a sweater's price by 30%. After the sale, the manager increases the price of the sweater by 30%. Is the price before and after the sale the same? Explain.
   No; the discount is 30% of a greater amount than the mark up.

Mixed Review

Geometry **Find the circumference and area of each circle with diameter d or radius r. Round to the nearest hundredth.** *(Lesson 8-4)*

8. $r = 5$ cm **31.42 cm; 78.54 cm²**
9. $d = 8$ in. **25.13 in.; 50.27 in.²**
10. $r = 22$ cm **138.23 cm; 1,520.53 cm²**
11. $d = 18$ ft **56.55 ft; 254.47 ft²**
12. $r = 38$ yd **238.76 yd; 4,534.46 yd²**

Express as unit rates. *(Lesson 6-2)*

13. 560 words typed in 8 min **70 words/min**
14. 450.5 km driven in 9 h **50 km/h**
15. $68 earned in 8 h **$8.50/h**

16. *Library* The public library charges $.50 for the first day a book is overdue and $.25 for each day after that. What is the charge for a book that is 10 days overdue? *(Lesson 2-5)* **$2.75**

9-3 Teaching Notes

1 Focus

CONNECTING TO PRIOR KNOWLEDGE Draw a circle. Divide it into eight sections and number each section 1–8. Ask: *What fraction of the sections contains the number 4?* $\frac{1}{8}$ Add an arrow to the circle, making it a spinner. Then ask students: *Do you think there is a relationship between the fraction of sections containing a 4 and the probability of spinning a 4?* **Answers may vary. Sample: Yes; each section has the same chance of the spinner landing on it. The probability of spinning 4 is $\frac{1}{8}$.**

2 Teach

THINK AND DISCUSS

Example 1 Ask: *How is the denominator of a theoretical probability different from the denominator of an experimental probability?* **The denominator of a theoretical probability is the total number of *outcomes*. The denominator of an experimental probability is the total number of *experiments*.**

ERROR ALERT! Question 2a Students may think there are five numbers that are less than 5. **Remediation:** Have students make a list of the possible outcomes of rolling a number cube. Then have them circle the numbers that are less than 5 and count the favorable outcomes.

9-3 Theoretical Probability and Proportional Reasoning

What You'll Learn

1. To find the theoretical probability of an event
2. To find the probability of a complement

...And Why

You can use theoretical probability to determine when games are fair.

Here's How

Look for questions that
- build understanding
- ✔ check understanding

THINK AND DISCUSS

1 *Finding Theoretical Probability*

In Lesson 9-1, you found the experimental probability of "heads and a 2" by tossing a coin and rolling a number cube. Another way to find probability is to list the possible results, or **outcomes.**

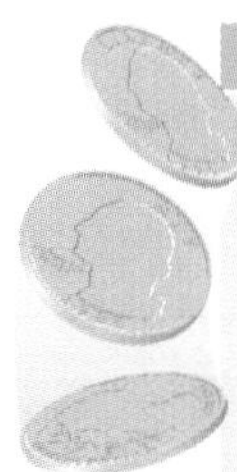

Coin	Cube	Coin	Cube
heads	1	tails	1
heads	2	tails	2
heads	3	tails	3
heads	4	tails	4
heads	5	tails	5
heads	6	tails	6

All of the outcomes are *equally likely*. Therefore, you can use the formula below to find the **theoretical probability** of "heads and a 2."

$$P(\text{event}) = \frac{\text{number of favorable outcomes}}{\text{number of possible outcomes}}$$

$$P(\text{heads and a 2}) = \frac{\text{number of outcomes with heads and a 2}}{\text{number of possible outcomes}} = \frac{1}{12}$$

■ **EXAMPLE 1**

A letter is selected at random from the letters A, E, I, O, and U. Find the theoretical probability that the letter is an E.

There are five possible outcomes. The event E has one favorable outcome.

$$P(\text{E}) = \frac{1}{5} \begin{array}{l} \leftarrow \text{number of favorable outcomes} \\ \leftarrow \text{number of possible outcomes} \end{array}$$

The probability of selecting an E is $\frac{1}{5}$.

1. ✔ *Try It Out* Use the letters E, X, A, M, P, L, and E. Suppose you select one letter at random.
   a. How many possible outcomes are there? **7 outcomes**
   b. How many outcomes are there for the event E? **2 outcomes**
   c. Find the probability of selecting an E. **$\frac{2}{7}$ or 28.6%**

Lesson Planning Options

Prerequisite Skills
- writing ratios (6-1)
- expressing percents as decimals (6-7)

Vocabulary/Symbols
outcomes, theoretical probability, complement, equally likely, fair

Materials/Manipulatives
- standard number cubes

Resources

Student Edition

Skills Handbook, p. 532
Extra Practice, p. 522
Glossary/Study Guide

Teaching Resources

Chapter Support File, Ch. 9
- Lesson Planner 9-3
- Practice 9-3, Reteaching 9-3
- Alternative Activity 9-3
- Answer Masters 9-3

Teaching Aids Master 10
Glossary, Spanish Resources

Transparencies
15, 17, 94, Minds on Math 9-3

Warm Up

Write 0.125 as a fraction. $\frac{1}{8}$

OPEN-ENDED Question 3 Point out that a certain event has a probability of 1. Ask: *What are different ways of representing 1?* **100%, $\frac{6}{6}$**

OPEN-ENDED Question 4 Point out that an impossible event has a probability of 0. Ask: *What are different ways of representing 0?* **0%, $\frac{0}{6}$**

■ ADDITIONAL EXAMPLES

FOR EXAMPLE 1

Select a letter at random from the group of letters O, U, T, C, O, M, E, S. Find the theoretical probability that the letter is an O. **$\frac{2}{8} = \frac{1}{4}$**

FOR EXAMPLE 2

Find the probability of rolling a number greater than 4 using a standard number cube. **$\frac{2}{6} = \frac{1}{3}$**

FOR EXAMPLE 3

Suppose there is a 65.5% chance it will rain today. Find P(no rain). **34.5%**

AEP Example 3 Point out the difference between *complement* and *compliment.* You may want to relate the *i* to "*I* can receive a compl*i*ment."

AUDITORY LEARNING Example 3 Have students write or say the complement of each event.

- *even numbers* **odd numbers**

Technology Options

Prentice Hall Technology

Software for Learners

- Hot Page™ 10–1*
- Math Blaster® Mystery*
- Interactive Student Tutorial, Chapter 9*

Teaching Resource Software

- Computer Item Generator 9-3
- Resource Pro™ Chapter 9*

Internet • For related mathematics activities, visit the Prentice Hall site at www.phschool.com/math

**Available on CD-ROM only*

Assignment Options for Exercises On Your Own

To provide flexible scheduling, this lesson can be split into parts.

1 Core 1–25, 41
Extension 34, 43

2 Core 26–29, 35–40,42
Extension 30–33

Use Mixed Review to maintain skills.

An event can be a combination of several outcomes.

■ EXAMPLE 2

Find the probability of rolling an even number using a standard number cube.

The event of an even number has three outcomes: 2, 4, and 6.

$$P(\text{even}) = \frac{3}{6} \quad \begin{array}{l}\leftarrow \text{number of favorable outcomes} \\ \leftarrow \text{number of possible outcomes}\end{array}$$

$$= \frac{1}{2}$$

The probability of rolling an even number is $\frac{1}{2}$.

2. ✔*Try It Out* Find the probability of each event using a standard number cube.
   a. P(number less than 5) **$\frac{2}{3}$** b. P(multiple of 3) **$\frac{1}{3}$**

All probabilities range from 0 to 1.

0	0.5	1
impossible event	equally likely or unlikely	certain event

3. *Open-ended* Give an example of a certain event.
4. *Open-ended* Give an example of an impossible event.

3. Answers may vary. Sample: You roll a number less than 10 on a standard number cube.
4. Answers may vary. Sample: You roll a 7 on a standard number cube.

Now you may assign Exercises 1–25, 34, 41, 43.

2 *Finding the Probability of a Complement*

The event *no rain* is the **complement** of the event *rain*. The probability of an event plus its complement equals 1, or 100%.

■ EXAMPLE 3 *Real-World Problem Solving*

Science In the United States, there is a 2.3% chance that a child is a twin. Find P(not a twin).

2.3% = 0.023 ← **Write the percent as a decimal.**

total probability	−	P(twin)	=	P(not a twin)
1	−	0.023	=	0.977 or 97.7%

There is a 97.7% chance that a child is not a twin.

5. a. ✔*Try It Out* When rolling a number cube, what is $P(6)$? What is P(not 6)? **$\frac{1}{6}$; $\frac{5}{6}$**
   b. What is P(1, 2, 3, 4, or 5)? **$\frac{5}{6}$**

- *vowels* consonants
- *not 1–4 on a number cube* 1–4

ERROR ALERT! Question 5a When asked to find the probability of numerical outcomes, students may use the given number as the numerator. For example, they may write *P*(6) as $\frac{6}{6}$. **Remediation:** Tell students: List all of the possible outcomes. 1, 2, 3, 4, 5, 6 Then ask: *How many times does the favorable outcome, 6, appear in your list?* 1 time

Work Together

DIVERSITY Students may have different ideas of the meaning of *fair*. Point out that fair does not mean that everyone scores the same number of points. It means everyone has an equally likely chance of scoring. We design a game to help students understand the mathematical meaning of *fair* which is based on probability.

3 Practice/Assess

EXERCISES *On Your Own*

ASSESSMENT Exercises 1–4 Assign partners. Have students make a chart comparing the similarities and differences between experimental probability and theoretical probability. Then have students use their charts to help explain their answer choices for Exercises 1–4.

Work Together *Investigating Fair Games*

Work with a partner. A game is *fair* if all the players are equally likely to win. Play the following game.

- Take turns rolling two standard number cubes. Find the product of the two numbers. If the product is even, Player A scores a point. If the product is odd, Player B scores a point.
- After 15 rolls each, the player with more points wins.

Product Chart

	1	2	3	4	5	6
1	1	2	3	■	■	■
2	2	4	■	■	■	■
3	■	■	■	■	■	■
4	■	■	■	■	■	■
5	■	■	■	■	■	■
6	■	■	■	■	■	■

6. Play the game twice. Based on your results, do you think the game is fair? Explain. **No; an even product occurs more often than an odd product.**
7. a. Copy and complete the product chart at the left.
   b. What is the total number of even products? What is the total number of odd products? **27 products; 9 products**
   c. Find *P*(even) and *P*(odd). $\frac{3}{4}, \frac{1}{4}$

7a. See margin.

8. Create a game using two number cubes. Make sure the game is fair. **See margin.**

Now you may assign Exercises 26–33, 35–40, 42.

EXERCISES *On Your Own*

Reasoning **For each of the following, decide whether the probability is *theoretical* or *experimental*. Explain.**

1. The letters C, I, R, C, L, and E are written on cards and put in a hat. One letter is selected at random. The probability of selecting a C is $\frac{2}{6}$ or $\frac{1}{3}$. **theoretical probability**
2. A coin is tossed 100 times. Fifty-two outcomes are heads. The probability of heads is $\frac{52}{100}$ or $\frac{13}{25}$. **experimental probability**
3. A number cube is rolled 60 times. Twelve outcomes are the number 3. The probability of a 3 is $\frac{12}{60}$ or $\frac{1}{5}$. **experimental probability**
4. There are 20 students in a class, 8 boys and 12 girls. The probability of selecting a girl's name from a basket containing all of the students' names is $\frac{12}{20}$ or $\frac{3}{5}$. **theoretical probability**

Find each probability for one roll of a standard number cube.

5. *P*(4) $\frac{1}{6}$
6. *P*(multiple of 2) $\frac{1}{2}$
7. *P*(number less than 3) $\frac{1}{3}$
8. *P*(1 or 2) $\frac{1}{3}$
9. *P*(number less than 7) 1
10. *P*(7) 0

page 403 Work Together

7a.

	1	2	3	4	5	6
1	1	2	3	4	5	6
2	2	4	6	8	10	12
3	3	6	9	12	15	18
4	4	8	12	16	20	24
5	5	10	15	20	25	30
6	6	12	18	24	30	36

8. **Answers may vary. Sample: Use the sums. Player A scores a point if the sum is even. Player B scores a point if the sum is odd. Each player's probability of scoring is $\frac{1}{2}$.**

REASONING and VISUAL LEARNING Exercise 34 Have students draw a spinner divided into fourths. Have students shade $\frac{1}{4}$ red, and $\frac{3}{4}$ green.

WRITING Exercise 41 Have students consider factors such as size.

OPEN-ENDED Exercise 42 Encourage students to be careful when defining complements. Ask: *Are P(sunny day) and P(rainy day) complements? Why?* **No, it could be cloudy or snowing.**

WRAP UP

IDENTIFYING THE BIG IDEA Have students explain how to find the *theoretical probability* of an event. Then have them explain the *complement* of an event. Ask them to give an example of two events that are complements.

JOURNAL Students may want to include the following vocabulary: *equally likely, event, simulate, random device, outcome, favorable outcome.*

PROJECT LINK Students will be better able to compare the two cubes if they write their probabilities as decimals or percents.

page 403–405 On Your Own

42. Sample: There is an 80% chance your flight will arrive on time. What is the probability that the flight will *not* arrive on time?

Project Link. $\frac{2}{3}$; 1; A; when A rolls a 4, it beats B. When A rolls a 1, it loses. A is more likely to roll a 4 than a 1.

Use the spinner at the right. Write each probability as a fraction, a decimal, and a percent.

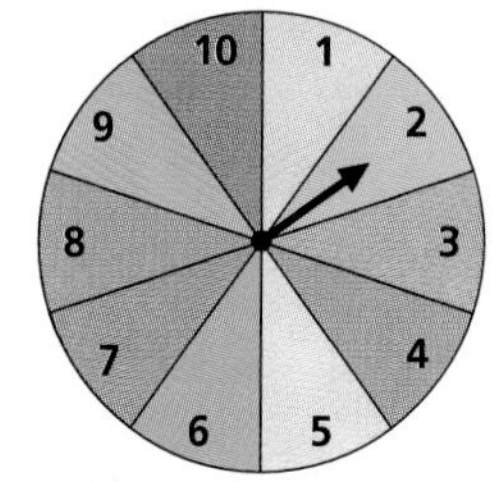

11. $P(5)$ **$\frac{1}{10}$; 0.1; 10%**
12. $P(\text{odd})$ **$\frac{1}{2}$; 0.5; 50%**
13. $P(\text{number less than } 11)$ **1; 1; 100%**
14. $P(\text{multiple of } 3)$ **$\frac{3}{10}$; 0.3; 30%**
15. $P(\text{number greater than } 6)$ **$\frac{2}{5}$; 0.4; 40%**
16. $P(\text{multiple of } 4)$ **$\frac{1}{5}$; 0.2; 20%**

A box contains cards numbered from 1 to 100. Suppose you pull a card at random. Express each probability as a percent.

17. $P(1)$ **1%**
18. $P(\text{multiple of } 10)$ **10%**
19. $P(\text{number less than } 12)$ **11%**
20. $P(\text{prime number})$ **25%**
21. $P(\text{even number})$ **50%**
22. $P(\text{factor of } 100)$ **9%**
23. $P(\text{multiple of } 15)$ **6%**
24. $P(\text{factor of } 51)$ **4%**
25. $P(\text{number greater than } 65)$ **35%**

Use the spinner at the right to find each probability.

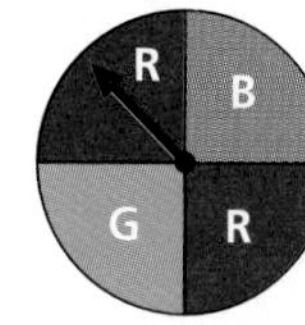

26. $P(\text{not green})$ **$\frac{3}{4}$**
27. $P(\text{red or blue})$ **$\frac{3}{4}$**
28. $P(\text{white})$ **0**

29. Your teacher selects one student at random from your class.
   a. What is the probability that you are selected?
   b. What is the probability that a girl is *not* selected?
   c. Find $P(\text{girl or boy is selected})$. **1**
   a–b. Check students' work.

30. a. Suppose $P(E) = 0.3$. Find $P(\text{not } E)$. **0.7**
   b. Suppose $P(\text{not } E) = 65\%$. Find $P(E)$. **35%**

Suppose you draw a marble at random from the bag.

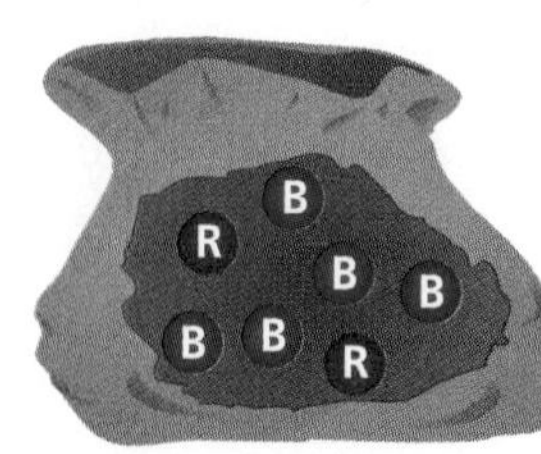

31. Find each probability.
   a. $P(\text{red})$ **$\frac{2}{7}$**
   b. $P(\text{blue})$ **$\frac{5}{7}$**
   c. $P(\text{red}) + P(\text{blue})$ **1**
   d. $P(\text{red or blue})$ **1**

32. Complete: $P(\text{not red}) = P(\_\_?\_\_)$, and $P(\text{not blue}) = P(\_\_?\_\_)$. **blue; red**

33. a. You add six yellow marbles to the bag. What is $P(\text{yellow})$? **$\frac{6}{13}$**
   b. What is the complement of the event "yellow"? **"red or blue"**

34. *Reasoning* A bag contains an unknown number of marbles. You know $P(\text{red}) = \frac{1}{4}$ and $P(\text{green}) = \frac{3}{4}$.
   a. Are all the marbles either red or green? How do you know? **Yes; *P*(green) is the complement of *P*(red).**
   b. How many marbles of each color might be in the bag? Is your answer the only possibility? Explain.
   Answers may vary. Sample: 25 red and 75 green; no; any numbers are possible as long as the number of green is 3 times the number of red.

LESSON QUIZ

A box contains cards numbered from 1 to 50. Suppose you pull a card at random. Find each probability.

1. P(odd number) $\frac{1}{2}$
2. P(number less than 29) $\frac{14}{25}$
3. P(factor of 50) $\frac{3}{25}$
4. P(not a factor of 50) $\frac{22}{25}$

Use the letters C, O, M, P, L, E, M, E, N, and T. Find each probability.

35. P(not a consonant) 0.3 **36.** P(not a vowel) 0.7 **37.** P(not E) 0.8

38. P(not T) 0.9 **39.** P(not Z) 1 **40.** P(not E or M) 0.6

41. *Writing* Suppose you have 3 nickels, 3 dimes, and 3 quarters in your pocket. Are you equally likely to select a dime as a quarter from your pocket? Explain.
Answers may vary. Sample: No; the coins are different in size.

42. *Open-ended* Make up a probability problem in which you find the probability of the complement of an event.
See margin p. 404.

43. **Choose A, B, C, or D.** The forecast for tomorrow is an 80% chance of rain. Which conclusion is most appropriate? D

- **A.** 80% of the region will receive rain.
- **B.** It will rain on 8 of the next 10 days.
- **C.** It will rain for 9.6 h of the next 24 h.
- **D.** On similar days in the past, 8 out of 10 have had rain.

JOURNAL
Describe the difference between experimental and theoretical probability.

Mixed Review

Geometry **Find the measure of the central angle that would represent each percent in a circle graph.** *(Lesson 7-8)*

44. 40% 144° **45.** 15% 54° **46.** 5% 18° **47.** 9.5% 34.2° **48.** 34% 122.4° **49.** 49% 176.4°

Find each difference. *(Lessons 2-3, 5-2)*

50. $1 - \frac{5}{6}$ $\frac{1}{6}$ **51.** $1 - 0.52$ 0.48 **52.** $1 - \frac{5}{12}$ $\frac{7}{12}$ **53.** $1 - 0.39$ 0.61 **54.** $1 - \frac{2}{7}$ $\frac{5}{7}$ **55.** $1 - 0.937$ 0.063

56. *Choose a Strategy* A gas tank holds 18 gallons. The tank is one-quarter full. How many gallons will it take to fill it? 13.5 gal

CHAPTER PROJECT

PROJECT LINK: ANALYZING

Suppose you have two number cubes, A and B. Cube A has two 1s and four 4s, and Cube B has six 3s. What is the probability of rolling a 4 on Cube A? What is the probability of rolling a 3 on Cube B? Suppose both number cubes are rolled. Which cube will usually beat the other by having a higher number? Why? See margin p. 404.

PRACTICE

Practice 9-3 Theoretical Probability and Proportional Reasoning

A spinner numbered 1 through 10 is spun. Each outcome is equally likely. Write each probability as a fraction, decimal, and percent.

1. P(9) $\frac{1}{10}$; 0.1; 10%
2. P(even) $\frac{1}{2}$; 0.5; 50%
3. P(number greater than 0) 1; 1.0; 100%
4. P(multiple of 4) $\frac{1}{5}$; 0.2; 20%

There are eight blue marbles, nine orange marbles, and six yellow marbles in a bag. It is equally likely that any marble is drawn from the bag.

5. Find the probability of drawing a blue marble. $\frac{8}{23}$ or 34.8%
6. Find the probability of drawing a yellow marble. $\frac{6}{23}$ or 26.1%
7. What marble could you add or remove so that the probability of drawing a blue marble is $\frac{1}{3}$? Add a marble that is not blue.

Suppose you have a box that contains 12 slips of paper as shown. Each slip of paper is equally likely to be drawn. Find the probability of each event.

red	blue	yellow	blue
yellow	red	blue	red
red	red	red	yellow

8. P(red) $\frac{1}{2}$
9. P(blue) $\frac{1}{4}$
10. P(yellow) $\frac{1}{4}$
11. P(red) + P(blue) $\frac{3}{4}$
12. P(red) + P(yellow) $\frac{3}{4}$
13. P(blue) + P(yellow) $\frac{1}{2}$
14. P(red or blue) $\frac{3}{4}$
15. P(red or yellow) $\frac{3}{4}$
16. P(blue or yellow) $\frac{1}{2}$
17. P(not red) $\frac{1}{2}$
18. P(not blue) $\frac{3}{4}$
19. P(not yellow) $\frac{3}{4}$

In a raffle, there will be 3 prizes for every 1,000 tickets sold.

20. What is the probability of winning? $\frac{3}{1,000}$, 0.3%, 0.003
21. What is the probability of not winning? $\frac{997}{1,000}$, 99.7%, 0.997

In copymaster and workbook formats

RETEACHING

Reteaching 9-3 Theoretical Probability and Proportional Reasoning

To find a **theoretical probability,** first list all possible **outcomes.** Then use the formula:

$$P(\text{event}) = \frac{\text{number of favorable outcomes}}{\text{total number of outcomes}}.$$

A letter is selected at random from the letters of the word FLORIDA. What is the probability that the letter is an A?

- There are 7 letters (possible outcomes).
- There is 1 A, which represents a favorable outcome.

$$P(\text{A}) = \frac{\text{number of favorable outcomes}}{\text{total number of outcomes}} = \frac{1}{7}$$

The probability that the letter is an A is $\frac{1}{7}$.

Selecting a letter other than A is called *not* A and is the **complement** of the event A. The probabilities of an event and its complement add to 1, or 100%.

What is the probability of the event *not* A?

$$P(\text{A}) + P(\textit{not } \text{A}) = 1$$

$$\frac{1}{7} + P(\textit{not } \text{A}) = 1$$

$$P(\textit{not } \text{A}) = 1 - \frac{1}{7} = \frac{6}{7}$$

The probability of the event *not* A (selecting F, L, O, R, I, or D) is $\frac{6}{7}$.

Use the spinner. Write each probability as a fraction. Then write it as a decimal and a percent.

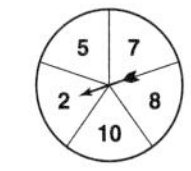

1. P(5) $\frac{\text{number of favorable outcomes}}{\text{total number of outcomes}} = \frac{1}{5}$ 0.2; 20%
2. P(odd number) $\frac{\text{number of favorable outcomes}}{\text{total number of outcomes}} = \frac{2}{5}$ 0.4; 40%

A box contains cards numbered from 1 to 10. Write each probability as a fraction, a decimal, and a percent.

3. P(even number) $\frac{1}{2}$, 0.5, 50%
4. P(number less than 4) $\frac{3}{10}$, 0.3, 30%
5. P(not 5) $\frac{9}{10}$, 0.9, 90%

Use the letters M, A, T, H, E, M, A, T, I, C, and S. Find each probability.

6. P(M) $\frac{2}{11}$
7. P(not vowel) $\frac{7}{11}$
8. P(not E) $\frac{10}{11}$

A number is selected at random from the numbers 1 to 50. Find each probability.

9. P(multiple of 3) $\frac{8}{25}$
10. P(a factor of 50) $\frac{3}{25}$
11. P(not factor of 50) $\frac{22}{25}$

ENRICHMENT

Minds on Math Transparency

9-3

Shauna is half as old as Tatum. In twelve years, Shauna will be $\frac{5}{8}$ as old as Tatum. How old is Tatum now?

36 years old

See *Solution Key* for worked-out answers.

MATH TOOLBOX

In Lesson 9-3, students learn how to find the theoretical probability of an event and to find the probability of a complement. This toolbox allows students to explore outcomes using odds.

ERROR ALERT! Students may confuse the word *to*, used in a statement of odds, with the word *in*, used in a statement of probability. **Remediation:** Point out that odds is a comparison of favorable *to* unfavorable outcomes. Probability is the chance of one thing happening *in* a total number of possibilities. Tell students that *odds* of rolling an even number on a six-sided number cube are 3 *to* 3, while the probability of rolling an even number is 3 *in* 6.

ASSESSMENT **Exercise 1** Have students discuss their reasoning with a partner. Ask partners to write a plan for how to use the odds *in favor* of spinning an 11 to find the odds *against* spinning an 11. **Set the number of unfavorable outcomes above the number of favorable outcomes.**

■ **ADDITIONAL PROBLEM**

What are the odds of a coin landing heads up after landing tails up 5 times in a row? **1 to 1; past experience does not affect the odds.**

Resources

Transparencies
15

MATH TOOLBOX EXPLORATION

Odds

After Lesson 9-3

You can compare favorable outcomes to unfavorable outcomes using *odds*.

To calculate odds, you need to know how many of each type of outcome are possible.

$$\text{odds in favor of an event} = \frac{\text{number of favorable outcomes}}{\text{number of unfavorable outcomes}}$$

■ **EXAMPLE**

Use the spinner at the right. What are the odds in favor of spinning an 11?

There is one favorable outcome. There are 19 unfavorable outcomes.

$$\text{Odds} = \frac{\text{number of favorable outcomes}}{\text{number of unfavorable outcomes}} = \frac{1}{19}.$$

The odds in favor of spinning an 11 are 1 to 19.

1. *Reasoning* What are the odds *against* spinning an 11 on the spinner in the Example? **19 to 1**

2. a. In the Example, what is the sum of the number of favorable and unfavorable outcomes? **20**
   b. Use your answer to part (a) to find the probability of spinning an 11. $\frac{1}{20}$

Calculate the odds for and against each event.

3. Spin a spinner lettered A–Z; the spinner lands on the first letter of your name. **1 to 25; 25 to 1**

4. Roll a standard number cube; the number is a multiple of 3. **2 to 4; 4 to 2**

5. You buy a raffle ticket to win a computer. One of 200 tickets will be drawn from a box to determine the winner.
   a. Find the odds that you win. **1 to 199**
   b. Find the probability that you win. $\frac{1}{200}$ **or 0.5%**

6. *Writing* You are given a choice of two medical treatments, A and B. The odds in favor of recovery are 5 to 4 for A and 4 to 3 for B. Which treatment would you choose? Explain.
   ***B*; the probability of recovery is $\frac{5}{9}$ for *A* and $\frac{4}{7}$ for *B*. $\frac{5}{9} < \frac{4}{7}$**

9-4 Teaching Notes

1 Focus

CONNECTING TO PRIOR KNOWLEDGE Have students make a multiplication table for the numbers 1 to 6. Ask students to explain how to determine which product goes in each cell. Then have students complete a factor tree for the number 36. Discuss how both factor trees and tables help to organize information.

2 Teach

THINK AND DISCUSS

AEP The phrase *sample space* is the same as *the set of all possible outcomes.* Use both phrases until students fully understand the concept.

KINESTHETIC LEARNING Example 1 Form two groups of six students. Have each member of Group 1 shake hands with each member of Group 2. Have students keep track of how many handshakes take place.

Question 2 Review how to find *theoretical probability*. Remind students to write their answers in simplest form.

ERROR ALERT! Question 5 Students may not notice that the outcomes HTT, THT, and TTH are all favorable. **Remediation:** Point out to students that *P*(one head and two tails) does not specify the order of the coins.

9-4 Sample Spaces

What You'll Learn

1. To find a sample space
2. To use the counting principle

...And Why

You can find probabilities once you know the number of possible outcomes.

Here's How

Look for questions that
- build understanding
- ✔ check understanding

THINK AND DISCUSS

1 *Finding a Sample Space*

You win a million dollars—if you choose the right two letters from A, B, C, D, E. What are the possibilities?

A, B   A, C   A, D   A, E   B, C   B, D   B, E   C, D   C, E   D, E

This list shows the **sample space,** the set of all possible outcomes.

1. Give the sample space for each situation. How many possible outcomes are there?
   a. You toss a coin. heads, tails; 2 outcomes
   b. You spin the spinner once. See below.
   c. You toss a coin and spin the spinner once. Hr, Hg, Hb, Tr, Tg, Tb; 6 outcomes

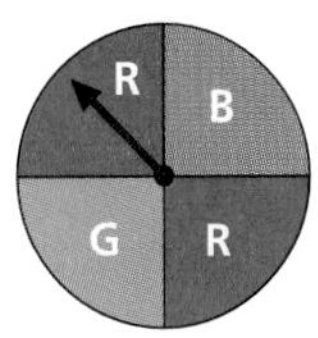

You can make a table to find a sample space.

1b. red, green, blue; 3 outcomes

EXAMPLE 1

Make a table to find the sample space for rolling two number cubes. Write the outcomes as ordered pairs.

	1	2	3	4	5	6
1	(1, 1)	(2, 1)	(3, 1)	(4, 1)	(5, 1)	(6, 1)
2	(1, 2)	(2, 2)	(3, 2)	(4, 2)	(5, 2)	(6, 2)
3	(1, 3)	(2, 3)	(3, 3)	(4, 3)	(5, 3)	(6, 3)
4	(1, 4)	(2, 4)	(3, 4)	(4, 4)	(5, 4)	(6, 4)
5	(1, 5)	(2, 5)	(3, 5)	(4, 5)	(5, 5)	(6, 5)
6	(1, 6)	(2, 6)	(3, 6)	(4, 6)	(5, 6)	(6, 6)

There are 36 possible outcomes.

2. *Think About It* What is the probability of rolling "doubles" (the same number on both number cubes)? $\frac{1}{6}$

3. a. ✔ *Try It Out* Give the sample space for tossing two coins.
   b. Find the probability of tossing two heads. $\frac{1}{4}$
   a. HH, HT, TH, TT

Lesson Planning Options

Prerequisite Skills

- determining outcomes (9-3)
- finding theoretical probability (9-3)
- multiplying whole numbers (precourse)

Vocabulary/Symbols

sample space, counting principle

Resources

Student Edition

Skills Handbook, p. 530
Extra Practice, p. 522
Glossary/Study Guide

Teaching Resources

Chapter Support File, Ch. 9
- Lesson Planner 9-4
- Practice 9-4, Reteaching 9-4
- Answer Masters 9-4

Teaching Aids Master 10
Glossary, Spanish Resources

Transparencies
15, 17, 94, Minds on Math 9-4

Warm Up

Rewrite each sentence using symbols.

The product of 2 and 4 is 8.
$2 \times 4 = 8$

The difference between 7 and $\frac{1}{2}$ is $6\frac{1}{2}$.
$7 - \frac{1}{2} = 6\frac{1}{2}$

ADDITIONAL EXAMPLES

FOR EXAMPLE 1

Make a table to find the sample space for tossing one coin and rolling one number cube. Write the outcomes as ordered pairs.

	1	2	3	4	5	6
H	(H, 1)	(H, 2)	(H, 3)	(H, 4)	(H, 5)	(H, 6)
T	(T, 1)	(T, 2)	(T, 3)	(T, 4)	(T, 5)	(T, 6)

There are 12 possible outcomes.

FOR EXAMPLE 2

You toss two coins and spin a number from 1–3. What is the sample space? **There are 12 possible outcomes: HH1, HH2, HH3, HT1, HT2, HT3, TH1, TH2, TH3, TT1, TT2, TT3**

FOR EXAMPLE 3

Leon owns six pairs of pants and nine shirts. How many different outfits does Leon have in his closet? **There are 54 different outfits that Leon can wear.**

3 Practice/Assess

EXERCISES *On Your Own*

Remind students to allow enough space for tree diagrams.

ASSESSMENT Exercises 1 and 2 Have students use all three methods. They can make a list, a table, and a tree diagram to show all the outcomes in the sample space. Have them tell which method they prefer and why.

Technology Options

Prentice Hall Technology

Software for Learners
- Math Blaster® Mystery*
- Interactive Student Tutorial, Chapter 9*

Teaching Resource Software
- Computer Item Generator 9-4
- Resource Pro™ Chapter 9*

Internet • For related mathematics activities, visit the Prentice Hall site at www.phschool.com/math

**Available on CD-ROM only*

Assignment Options for Exercises On Your Own

To provide flexible scheduling, this lesson can be split into parts.

1 **Core** 1–6, 15–17
Extension 19

2 **Core** 7–14, 20, 21
Extension 18

Use Mixed Review to maintain skills.

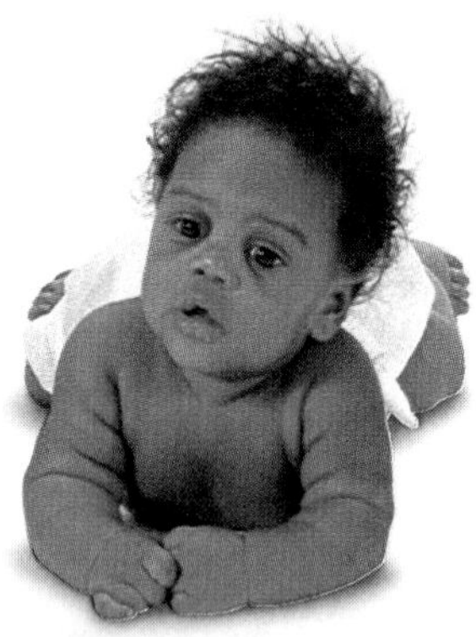

WHEN? In 1995, there were 3,848,000 children under the age of one in the United States. In this age group, *P*(girl) is 0.488 and *P*(boy) is 0.512.

Source: *Statistical Abstract*

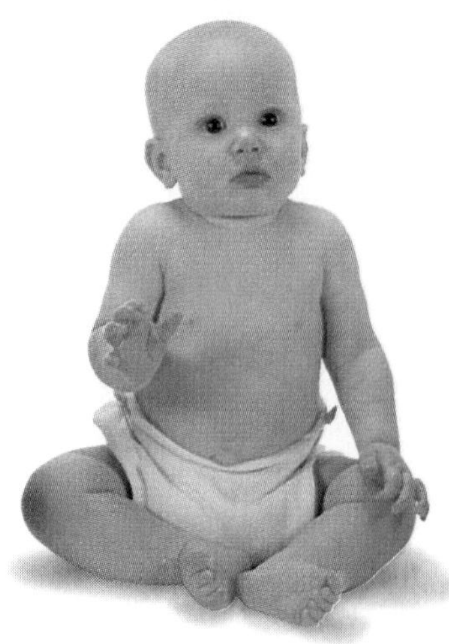

Another way to show a sample space is by using a tree diagram.

EXAMPLE 2

You toss three coins. What is the sample space?

Make a tree diagram in which you consider the outcomes one coin at a time.

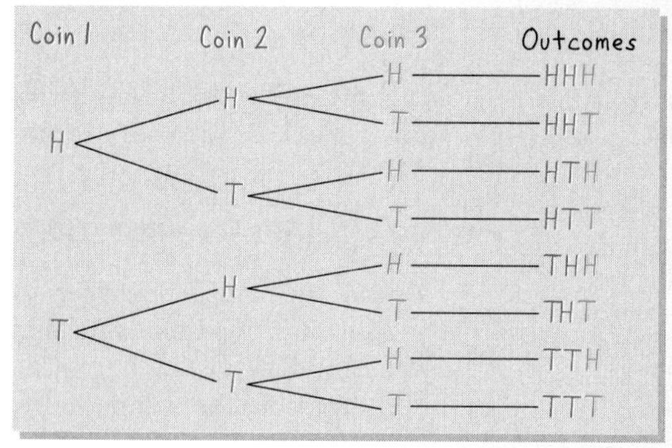

There are eight possible outcomes: HHH, HHT, HTH, HTT, THH, THT, TTH, and TTT.

4. Use the tree diagram in Example 2.
   a. Find *P*(at least two heads). $\frac{1}{2}$ b. Find *P*(exactly two heads). $\frac{3}{8}$
5. *Error Alert* Sarah used the tree diagram in Example 2 to find that *P*(one head and two tails) = $\frac{1}{8}$. What is her error? **She counted HTT, but not THT and TTH.**
6. a. *✔Try It Out* Four coins are tossed. Draw a tree diagram to show the sample space. **See margin p. 409.**
   b. Find *P*(three heads and one tail). $\frac{1}{4}$

Now you may assign Exercises 1–6, 15–17, 19.

2 Using the Counting Principle

When you have many outcomes, you can use the **counting principle** to find the number of outcomes.

THE COUNTING PRINCIPLE

If there are m ways of making one choice and n ways of making a second choice, then there are $m \times n$ ways of making the first choice followed by the second.

CONNECTING TO THE STUDENTS' WORLD
Exercise 5 Have students find out how many science, language, math, and social studies teachers there are for the next grade. Then have them find the possible outcomes for the four teachers they will have.

EXTENSION and CONNECTION TO TRAVEL
Exercise 6 If you have extended class periods or block scheduling, have students plan what to pack for a trip if they can choose 12 items. They may choose clothing items such as shirts, pants, shorts, skirts, jackets, or blouses. They can have more than one color of each item. Outfits can consist of either two or three items. Have them choose a destination city and research its climate. Students should pack for the weather. Have students cut out pictures of their clothing items from a catalogue or magazine. Then have them display their items on a poster, along with a list of all the different outfits they can create from 12 items.

Exercises 7–14 Group students in pairs. Have each student choose a different method to find the number of outcomes. They then compare answers with their partner.

REASONING Exercise 18 Have students find the total number of possible outcomes.

EXAMPLE 3 *Real-World Problem Solving*

Food Service To order a Deli-Button sandwich, a customer chooses one bread and one meat. Use the menu at the left. How many different sandwiches are available at the Deli-Button?

Bread		**Meat**	
number of choices	×	number of choices	
5	×	6	= 30

There are 30 different sandwiches available.

7. *Reasoning* Why is it helpful to use the counting principle instead of a tree diagram to solve this problem? **Answers may vary. Sample: The counting principle is faster and takes up less space.**
8. *Try It Out* The manager of the Deli-Button decides to add chicken to the list of meat choices. How many different sandwiches are now available? **35 sandwiches**
9. *Think About It* What information does a tree diagram or a table give you that the counting principle does not? **See margin.**

Now you may assign Exercises 7–14, 18, 20–21.

EXERCISES *On Your Own*

Choose **Make a list, a table, or a tree diagram to show all the outcomes in the sample space.** **1–4. Representations may vary. Samples are given.**

1. tossing a coin and spinning a number from 1 to 4 **H1, H2, H3, H4, T1, T2, T3, T4**
2. rolling a standard number cube and tossing a coin **1H, 1T, 2H, 2T, 3H, 3T, 4H, 4T, 5H, 5T, 6H, 6T**
3. choosing from two colors of shirts and three colors of pants **s1p1, s1p2, s1p3, s2p1, s2p2, s2p3**
4. choosing from two sets of letters, A, B, C, D and X, Y, Z **AX, AY, AZ, BX, BY, BZ, CX, CY, CZ, DX, DY, DZ**
5. *Education* Cuong is taking art and music. There are 4 art teachers and 3 music teachers. How many possible outcomes are there for the two teachers Cuong will have? **12 outcomes**
6. *Fashion* Ardell has four shirts (white, blue, green, and tan) and four pairs of socks in the same colors.
   a. How many different shirt–socks outfits does Ardell have? **16 outfits**
   b. Suppose he grabs a shirt and a pair of socks without looking. What is the probability that they will *not* be the same color? $\frac{3}{4}$

pages 407–409 Think and Discuss

6a.

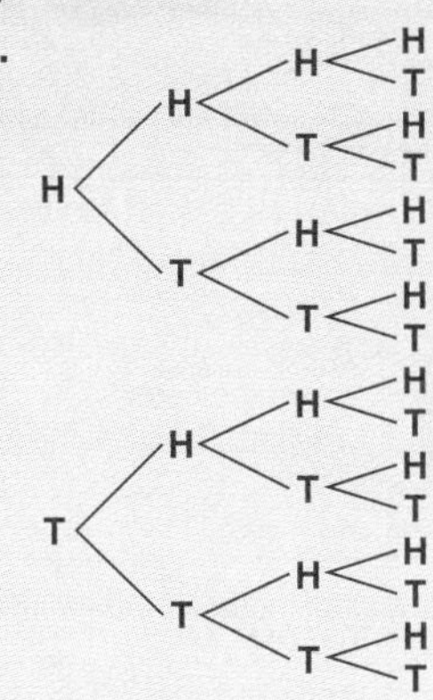

9. You can find the number of favorable or unfavorable outcomes.

WRITING Exercise 20 Encourage students to use an example in their explanation. They may find it helpful to use one of the situations in Exercises 7–14.

EXERCISE 21 Ask students: *Can one person hold two or three positions in the Student Council?* **no** Help students see that when someone is selected, they are no longer eligible for the next position.

Exercises 22–27 Remind students to narrow their choices by trial and error. For example, $10 \cdot 10 = 100$ and $20 \cdot 20 = 400$, so $\sqrt{225}$ must be between 10 and 20.

CONNECTION TO GEOMETRY Exercises 28–30 Recall mnemonic devices students may have used for *acute* and *obtuse*. For example, *acute* angle: $< 90°$ (a *cute* little angle); obtuse: $> 90°$ (*o* is for *obese* or fat angle).

WRAP UP

IDENTIFYING THE BIG IDEA Have students explain how *tables, tree diagrams*, and the *counting principle* are used to determine the outcomes in a sample space.

JOURNAL Have students look over the examples and exercises. This may clarify the different uses of a table, a tree diagram, or the counting principle.

CHECKPOINT 1

Checkpoint 1 *Lessons 9-1 through 9-4*

Use the cards at the right for Exercises 1–3. Write each probability as a fraction, a decimal, and a percent. A P E B E

1. P(E) $\frac{2}{5}$, 0.40, 40%
2. P(not A) $\frac{4}{5}$, 0.80, 80%
3. P(a vowel) $\frac{3}{5}$, 0.60, 60%

4. Ryan is buying a coat. He must decide if he wants a short coat or a long coat and whether the color should be blue, brown, beige, or black. How many choices does he have? 8 choices

5. Simulate the problem. Describe your simulation: A true/false test has 5 questions. How likely are you to get at least 3 answers right if you guess every answer?
Sample: Toss 5 coins several times. Each time, record whether there are at least 3 heads (right guesses).
$P(\text{at least 3 right}) = \frac{\text{number of times with at least 3 heads}}{\text{total number of tosses}}$

pages 409–410 On Your Own

16. lemonade popcorn

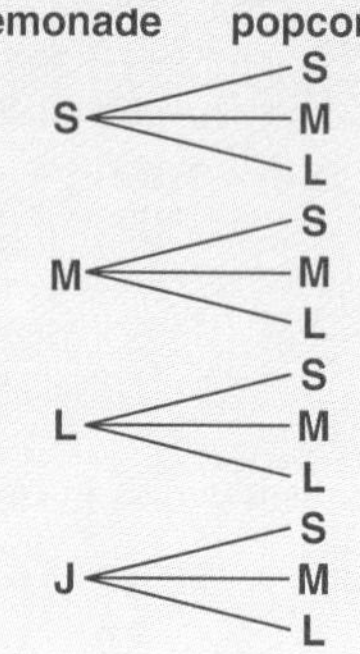

Find the number of outcomes for each situation.

7. Toss five coins. **32**
8. Roll three number cubes. **216**
9. Pick one of 7 boys and one of 12 girls. **84**
10. Toss two coins and roll a number cube. **24**
11. Choose three letters from A, B, C, and D. Use each letter only once. **24**
12. Roll two number cubes and spin a two-part spinner. **72**
13. Choose one letter from A to J and roll a number cube. **60**
14. Pick a day of the week and a number 1 to 31. **217**

Entertainment **Use the information at the right for Exercises 15–19.**

15. List all the possible beverage orders. **See below.**
16. You order lemonade and popcorn at the City Movie Theater. Draw a tree diagram to show the sample space. **See margin.**
17. How many possible orders are there for popcorn and a beverage? **24 orders**
18. *Reasoning* The theater manager used the counting principle to find that P(small popcorn, medium lemonade) $= \frac{1}{24}$. Do you agree? Explain. **Yes; (S popcorn, M lemonade) is 1 of 24**
19. Suppose the popcorn choices are plain, buttered, and cheese. Find P(medium plain popcorn, medium fruit punch). $\frac{1}{72}$
20. *Writing* Explain how to use the counting principle to find the number of outcomes in a sample space. **Find the number of outcomes for each choice. Then multiply the numbers.**
21. Seven people are eligible for three different positions on the student council. Their names are placed in a bag.
    a. How many people are eligible for the first position? **7 people**
    b. How many people are eligible for the second position once the first has been selected? The third position once the first two have been selected? **6 people; 5 people**
    c. Use the counting principle to find the number of ways three people out of seven can be selected for the three positions. **210 ways**

JOURNAL
Explain when you would use a table, a tree diagram, or the counting principle to show a sample space.

15. S punch, M punch, L punch, J punch, S lemonade, M lemonade, L lemonade, J lemonade

LESSON QUIZ

Find the number of outcomes for each situation.

1. Toss a coin six times. 64
2. Pick one of four girls and one of ten boys. 40
3. Roll a number cube twice and spin a four-part spinner. 144

Mixed Review

Find the square root. *(Lesson 8-5)*

22. 225 15 **23.** 8,100 90 **24.** 676 26 **25.** 289 17 **26.** 625 25 **27.** 196 14

Geometry **Classify each angle as acute, right, or obtuse.** *(Lesson 7-2)*

28. $m\angle A = 90°$ right **29.** $m\angle B = 122°$ obtuse **30.** $m\angle C = 74°$ acute

31. Environment Approximately 107 million aluminum cans are made on an average day. Of these, about 50% are recycled. *(Lessons 5-8, 6-7)*

a. To the nearest million, how many aluminum cans are recycled each day? 54 million cans

b. One aluminum can weighs about 0.5 oz. How many pounds of aluminum are recycled each day? about 1.7 million lb

✓ CHECKPOINT 1

Lessons 9-1 through 9-4

Use the spinner at the right. Write each probability as a fraction, a decimal, and a percent.

1. P(not 4) $\frac{4}{5}$; 0.8; 80%
2. P(2 or 3) $\frac{2}{5}$; 0.4; 40%
3. P(prime number) $\frac{3}{5}$; 0.6; 60%
4. P(6) 0; 0; 0%
5. P(5) $\frac{1}{5}$; 0.2; 20%
6. P(whole number) 1; 1; 100%
7. **Choose A, B, C, or D.** Use the wheel from Exercises 1–6. Which probability is *not* the same as the others? D

   A. P(even number) B. P(3 or 5)

   C. P(factor of 3) D. P(multiple of 1)

8. a. A teacher uses a seating chart for students. Rows are numbered 1 through 6, and columns are lettered A through D. One possible seat for a student is 3A. Make a table to display the sample space for the seats.

   b. Use the counting principle to find the number of seats. Does your answer agree with the total in your table? 24 seats; yes

a.

	A	B	C	D
1	1A	1B	1C	1D
2	2A	2B	2C	2D
3	3A	3B	3C	3D
4	4A	4B	4C	4D
5	5A	5B	5C	5D
6	6A	6B	6C	6D

9. Simulate the problem. A true/false quiz has 10 questions. How likely are you to get at least seven answers right if you guess every answer? Check students' work. Sample strategy: Use 10 coins. Heads are correct, tails are wrong.

Extra Practice, Lesson 9-4, page 522

PRACTICE

Practice 9-4 Sample Spaces

Solve the problem.

1. A theater uses a letter to show which row a seat is in, and a number to show the column the seat is in. If there are eight rows and ten columns, make a table to show the sample space for the seats.

	1	2	3	4	5	6	7	8	9	10
A	A1	A2	A3	A4	A5	A6	A7	A8	A9	A10
B	B1	B2	B3	B4	B5	B6	B7	B8	B9	B10
C	C1	C2	C3	C4	C5	C6	C7	C8	C9	C10
D	D1	D2	D3	D4	D5	D6	D7	D8	D9	D10
E	E1	E2	E3	E4	E5	E6	E7	E8	E9	E10
F	F1	F2	F3	F4	F5	F6	F7	F8	F9	F10
G	G1	G2	G3	G4	G5	G6	G7	G8	G9	G10
H	H1	H2	H3	H4	H5	H6	H7	H8	H9	H10

A coin is tossed three times.

2. a. Draw a tree diagram that shows all the possible outcomes of how the coin will land.

   b. Find the probability that the coin will land heads up all three times or tails up all three times. $\frac{1}{4}$

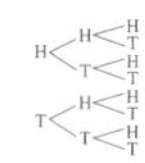

3. A pizza company makes pizza in three different sizes, small, medium, and large. There are four possible toppings, pepperoni, sausage, green pepper, and mushroom. How many different kinds of pizza with one topping are available? 12 kinds

Susan, Joanne, and Diane are triplets. Susan has red, blue, green, and yellow sweaters. Joanne has green, red, purple, and white sweaters. Diane's sweaters are red, blue, purple, and mauve. Each girl has only one sweater of each color, and will pick a sweater to wear at random. Find each probability.

4. P(each girl chooses a different color) $\frac{21}{32}$
5. P(each girl chooses the same color) $\frac{1}{64}$
6. P(two girls choose the same color, and the third chooses a different color) $\frac{21}{64}$
7. P(each girl chooses a red sweater) $\frac{1}{64}$

Practice

In copymaster and workbook formats

RETEACHING

Reteaching 9-4 Sample Spaces

The set of all possible outcomes of an experiment is called the **sample space.**

You can sometimes use a tree diagram or a table to show the sample space for an experiment. This tree diagram below on the right shows the sample space for spinning the spinner and tossing a coin.

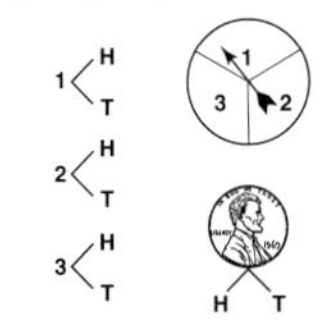

There are 6 possible outcomes: 1H, 1T, 2H, 2T, 3H, 3T

You can use the **counting principle** to find the number of possible outcomes: If there are m ways of making one choice and n ways of making a second choice, then there are $m \times n$ ways of making the first choice followed by the second.

Evelyn and Kara are planning to go skating or to a movie. Afterward they want to go out for pizza, tacos, or cheeseburgers. How many possible choices do they have?

- There are *two choices* for an activity and *three choices* for food.
- First choices × Second choices
  2 × 3 = 6

There are 6 possible choices.

Complete the tree diagram to show the sample space.

1. Roll a number cube and toss a coin.

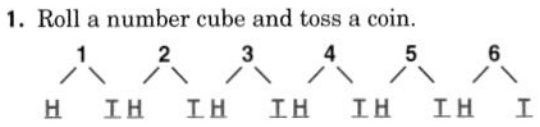

Number of outcomes 12

2. Choose the letter m or n and then choose a vowel.

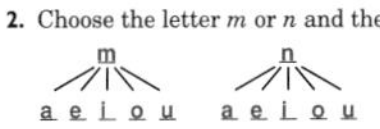

Number of outcomes 10

Find the number of possibilities.

3. 4 kinds of yogurt and 8 toppings 32
4. 6 shirts and 9 pairs of slacks 54
5. 3 types of sandwiches and 3 flavors of juice 9
6. 4 types of bread and 6 different sandwich spreads 24

Reteaching

ENRICHMENT

Minds on Math Transparency

9-4

I am a percent. The sum of my digits is 15. I have three digits and a decimal point. I am less than 100%. I am equal to a fraction in simplest form. The fraction in simplest form has a denominator that is a multiple of 4 and less than 10. What percent am I?

37.5%

See *Solution Key* for worked-out answers.

9-5 Teaching Notes

1 Focus

CONNECTING TO PRIOR KNOWLEDGE
Place a group of eight objects in front of the class. Have a student take away one object. Then have another student take away a second object. Continue this process. Ask students to explain how the group changes after each item is chosen. **There is one less item for the group.**

2 Teach

Work Together

VISUAL LEARNING **Question 1c** Have students sketch two bags. Have them label the first bag *first draw* and show the contents of the original bag. Have them label the next bag *second draw* and show its contents as missing one red marble. Have them write the probability of drawing a red marble underneath each picture.

ERROR ALERT! and TACTILE LEARNING
When finding the probability of dependent events, students may not realize that the sample space changes for the second event. **Remediation:** Model the bag of marbles using colored tiles. Have a student draw a tile without replacing it. Then have students count the remaining outcomes. Encourage students to consider whether an object has been replaced before finding the probability.

Lesson Planning Options

Prerequisite Skills

- multiplying fractions (5-5)
- finding theoretical probability (9-3)

Vocabulary/Symbols

independent, dependent

Resources

Student Edition
Skills Handbook, p. 530
Extra Practice, p. 522
Glossary/Study Guide

Teaching Resources
Chapter Support File, Ch. 9
- Lesson Planner 9-5
- Practice 9-5, Reteaching 9-5
- Alternative Activity 9-5
- Answer Masters 9-5

Teaching Aids Master 10
Glossary, Spanish Resources

Transparencies
15, 17, 94, Minds on Math 9-5

Warm Up

Pearl magazine has 16 pages. $3\frac{1}{2}$ pages are poems and $7\frac{1}{2}$ are short stories. How many pages are not poems or stories? **5 pages**

9-5 Independent and Dependent Events

What You'll Learn

1. To find the probability of independent events
2. To find the probability of dependent events

...And Why

You can make predictions about winning multiple-part games.

Here's How

Look for questions that
- build understanding
- ✔ check understanding

Work Together

Exploring Multiple Events

Work in pairs. Suppose you have a bag of marbles like the one at the right, and you draw a marble at random.

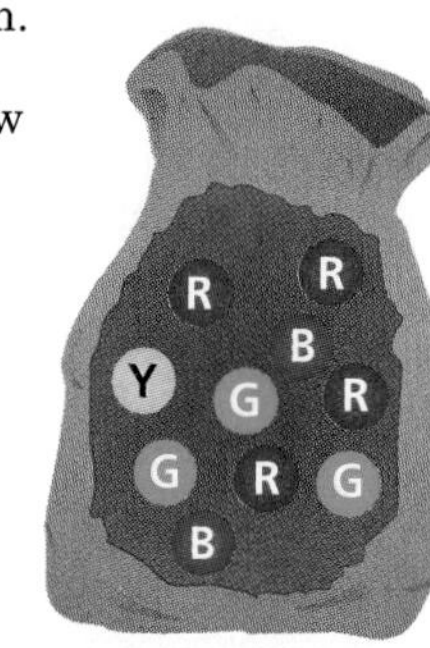

1. a. What is the probability that you draw a red marble? $\frac{2}{5}$
   b. Suppose you drop the first marble back in the bag. Find P(red) for the second draw. $\frac{2}{5}$
   c. Suppose that you draw a red marble and do not replace it. Describe the sample space for the second draw. What is P(red) on your second draw? **The sample space has only 9 outcomes, 3 of which are red; $\frac{1}{3}$.**

THINK AND DISCUSS

1 Finding Probability of Independent Events

Two events are **independent** if the outcome of one event does not affect the outcome of a second event.

PROBABILITY OF INDEPENDENT EVENTS

If A and B are independent events,
$$P(A \text{ and } B) = P(A) \times P(B).$$

EXAMPLE 1 *Real-World Problem Solving*

Games "Spin Your Initials" uses a wheel lettered A–Z. Suppose you spin it twice. Find P(B and Z).

The two events are independent.

$$P(\text{B and Z}) = P(\text{B}) \times P(\text{Z})$$ ← Selecting B is the first event. Selecting Z is the second event.
$$= \frac{1}{26} \times \frac{1}{26}$$ ← Substitute.
$$= \frac{1}{676}$$ ← Multlply.

The probability is $\frac{1}{676}$.

WHAT? The chances of a fair coin landing heads up 50 times in a row are very low. If one million coins were tossed 10 times/min for 40 h/wk, then 50 consecutive heads would happen about once every 9 centuries.

THINK AND DISCUSS

Example 1 Ask: *How is finding the probability of independent events similar to the counting principle?* **Answers may vary. Sample: Both involve multiplication.** Then ask: *How are they different?* **Answers may vary. Sample: Probability is expressed as a fraction, while the counting principal expresses outcomes as whole numbers.**

ADDITIONAL EXAMPLES

FOR EXAMPLE 1

A wheel is numbered 1–20. Suppose you spin it twice. Find *P*(11 and even). $\frac{1}{40}$

FOR EXAMPLE 2

You draw two cards from a bucket that contains cards numbered 1–20. To win, the cards must be 5 and 15. Find *P*(5, then 15) if the first card is not replaced. $\frac{1}{380}$

Be sure students understand that when you write (*B* and *Z*) or (*C*, then *M*) that the events happen in order. For example, *B* is selected first, and *Z* is selected second.

AEP Example 2 Have students write mnemonic sentences that will help them remember *dependent*. For example, "In a *de*pendent probability problem, the number of outcomes *de*creases."

2. Sample: The school cafeteria will serve pizza on Friday; it will rain on Sunday.

2. *Open-ended* Describe two events that are independent.

3. ✓ *Try It Out* Two number cubes are rolled. Find *P*(6 and 6). $\frac{1}{36}$

Now you may assign Exercises 1–14.

2 *Finding Probability of Dependent Events*

Two events are **dependent** if the outcome of the first event affects the outcome of a second event. In the Work Together, when the first marble is not returned to the bag before the second marble is drawn, the events (red, then red) are dependent.

PROBABILITY OF DEPENDENT EVENTS

If *A* and *B* are dependent events, then

$$P(A, \text{ then } B) = P(A) \times P(B \text{ after } A).$$

EXAMPLE 2 *Real-World Problem Solving*

Games To play "Draw Your Initials," you draw a card from a bucket that contains cards lettered A–Z. Without replacing the first card, you draw a second one. Find the probability of winning if your initials are C and M.

The two events are dependent.

$$P(\text{C, then M}) = P(\text{C}) \times P(\text{M after C}) \quad \leftarrow \text{Use the formula.}$$
$$= \frac{1}{26} \times \frac{1}{25} \quad \leftarrow \text{Substitute.}$$
$$= \frac{1}{650} \quad \leftarrow \text{Multiply.}$$

The probability of winning is $\frac{1}{650}$.

4. *Reasoning* Explain why the probability of selecting M second is $\frac{1}{25}$. **After you choose 1 card, there are only 25 cards left in the bucket.**
5. *Analyze* You remove a flower from a flower arrangement. Then you remove another flower without replacing the first. Why are these events dependent? **After you remove 1 flower, there is 1 less flower in the arrangement.**
6. ✓ *Try It Out* Suppose the names of all the students in your class are in a basket. Your teacher draws one name, then draws a second name without replacing the first. Choose two students in your class. Find *P*(one student, then the other). **Check students' work.**
7. *Open-ended* Describe two dependent events.

7. Sample: It will be cloudy tomorrow; it will rain tomorrow.

Now you may assign Exercises 15–27.

Technology Options

Prentice Hall Technology

Software for Learners
- Math Blaster® Mystery*
- Interactive Student Tutorial, Chapter 9*

Teaching Resource Software
- Computer Item Generator 9-5
- Resource Pro™ Chapter 9*

Internet • For related mathematics activities, visit the Prentice Hall site at www.phschool.com/math

**Available on CD-ROM only*

Assignment Options for Exercises On Your Own

To provide flexible scheduling, this lesson can be split into parts.

1 **Core** 1–12, 14
Extension 13

2 **Core** 15, 16, 18–26
Extension 17, 27

Use Mixed Review to maintain skills.

ASSESSMENT Organize students into groups of four. Give each group a coin, a bag of marbles, a blank number cube, a stack of cards, and a blank spinner. Then have students create one independent and one dependent probability problem. Have them present their problems to the class. Ask students: *Which of these materials can be used only for independent situations?* **number cube, coin, and spinner**

3 Practice/Assess

EXERCISES *On Your Own*

CONNECTION TO LANGUAGE ARTS
Exercises 7–12 Review with students the definitions of *consonant* and *vowel.*

Exercises 17a Ask students: *Should the teacher replace the first name? Explain.* **No; she wants to have two different announcers.**

WRITING Exercise 17c Students may consider it fair to ensure that there is one girl and one boy. However, remind them that there are more boys than girls in the class.

Exercise 27b Point out that the number 1 will branch out only to the numbers 2 and 3.

WRAP UP

IDENTIFYING THE BIG IDEA Have students describe an *independent event* and a *dependent event.* Then have them explain how

pages 414–415 On Your Own

13. No; the probability does not double. The probability is $\frac{1}{8} \cdot \frac{1}{8} = \frac{1}{64}$.

17c. No; each girl has $\frac{1}{5}$ chance of being selected. Each boy has $\frac{1}{7}$ chance of being selected.

27a.
1 — 1, 2, 3
2 — 1, 2, 3
3 — 1, 2, 3

b.
1 — 2, 3
2 — 1, 3
3 — 1, 2

EXERCISES *On Your Own*

You roll one number cube twice. Find each probability.

1. P(1 and odd) $\frac{1}{12}$
2. P(3 and even) $\frac{1}{12}$
3. P(odd and even) $\frac{1}{4}$
4. P(6 and 4) $\frac{1}{36}$
5. P(5 and 5) $\frac{1}{36}$
6. P(6 and 7) 0

You draw a letter from the group at the right, then replace it. Then you draw a second letter. Find each probability.

7. P(A and B) $\frac{1}{64}$
8. P(G and vowel) $\frac{3}{64}$
9. P(consonant and A) $\frac{5}{64}$
10. P(vowel and vowel) $\frac{9}{64}$
11. P(red and Z) $\frac{3}{64}$
12. P(consonant and blue) $\frac{25}{64}$
13. *Reasoning* For the cards at the right, is it reasonable to find P(two Zs) by multiplying 2 times $\frac{1}{8}$? Explain. **See margin.**

You draw two marbles from the bag at the right.

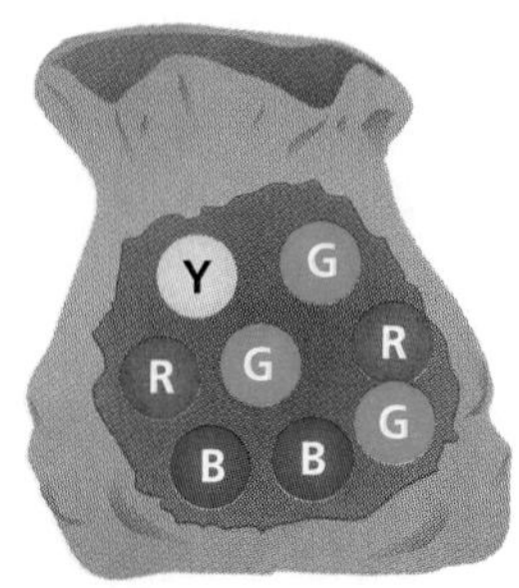

14. Suppose you replace the first marble before drawing the second one. What is P(two green marbles)? $\frac{9}{64}$
15. Suppose you do *not* replace the first marble before drawing the second one. What is P(two green marbles)? $\frac{3}{28}$
16. **Choose A, B, C, or D.** Suppose you do *not* replace the first marble before drawing the second. Find P(yellow, then red). **C**
    A. $\frac{1}{8}$ B. $\frac{1}{14}$ C. $\frac{1}{28}$ D. $\frac{1}{32}$
17. *Theater Arts* Five girls and seven boys want to be the two announcers for a variety show. To be fair, a teacher put the names of the twelve students in a hat and drew two.
    a. Find P(boy, then boy). $\frac{7}{22}$ b. Find P(girl, then girl). $\frac{5}{33}$
    c. *Writing* One of the girls suggests separate hats for the girls' names and the boys' names. Is this a better method? Explain. **See margin.**
18. A box contains the letters M I S S I S S I P P I. What is the probability of selecting an S first and a P second, if:
    a. the first letter *is not* replaced? $\frac{4}{55}$ b. the first letter *is* replaced? $\frac{8}{121}$

to find the probability of an independent event and the probability of a dependent event.

PROJECT LINK Make sure students count each of the sides on cube A and cube B as a different outcome. There are 36 possible outcomes.

LESSON QUIZ

1. You roll one number cube twice. Find P(2 and even). $\frac{1}{12}$

2. You draw a card from a stack of 10 cards numbered 1–10. You do not replace it. Then you draw a second card. Find P(5, then 9). $\frac{1}{90}$

Are the two events *independent* or *dependent*?

19. You toss a nickel, then you toss a dime. independent
20. You draw a card, then you draw another. dependent
21. You grab a sock from the dryer, then grab another sock from the dryer. dependent
22. You open this math book to a page, close it, then open it again. independent

A box contains cards with the numbers 1–20. You draw two cards. Find each probability.

23. P(7 and 2) if the first card is replaced $\frac{1}{400}$
24. P(7, then 7) if the first card is not replaced 0
25. P(7, then 2) if the first card is not replaced $\frac{1}{380}$
26. P(multiple of 3 and multiple of 7) if the first card is replaced $\frac{3}{100}$
27. Suppose you have cards with the numbers 1, 2, and 3.
    a. Make a tree diagram showing the sample space for selecting a card, replacing it, then selecting a second card.
    b. Make a tree diagram for selecting a card, *not* replacing it, then selecting a second card. a–b. See margin p. 414.
    c. Find the probability of the independent events of selecting 1 on the first draw and 2 on the second draw. $\frac{1}{9}$

Mixed Review

Geometry **Two legs of a right triangle are given. Find the hypotenuse to the nearest tenth of a unit.** *(Lesson 8-7)*

28. 12 ft, 25 ft 27.7 ft
29. 15 yd, 24 yd 28.3 yd
30. 4 mm, 6 mm 7.2 mm
31. 5 cm, 8 cm 9.4 cm
32. 14 m, 18 m 22.8 m

Solve each equation. *(Lesson 5-9)*

33. $\frac{3}{4}b = 21$ 28
34. $\frac{1}{2}x = 4.5$ 9
35. $28q = 36$ $1\frac{2}{7}$
36. $5y = \frac{15}{7}$ $\frac{3}{7}$
37. $8z = \frac{1}{2}$ $\frac{1}{16}$

38. ***Choose a Strategy*** Start with a number, subtract 7, then divide by 13. The result is 21. What was the original number? 280

CHAPTER PROJECT

PROJECT LINK: CALCULATING

Show a sample space of all the possible outcomes for Cubes A and B from the project link on page 405. What is the probability that A beats B when each cube is rolled once?

1 3, 1 3, 4 3, 4 3, 4 3, 4 3; $\frac{2}{3}$

Extra Practice, Lesson 9-5, page 522

PRACTICE

Practice 9-5 Independent and Dependent Events

Each letter in the word MASSACHUSETTS is written on a card. You are equally likely to get any card.

1. What is the probability of selecting two Ss if the first card is replaced before selecting the second card? $\frac{16}{169}$
2. What is the probability of selecting two Ss if the first card is not replaced before selecting the second card? $\frac{12}{156} = \frac{1}{13}$

You roll a fair number cube. What is the probability of each of the events?

3. P(3, then 5) $\frac{1}{36}$
4. P(2, then 2) $\frac{1}{36}$
5. P(5, then 4, then 6) $\frac{1}{216}$
6. P(6, then 0) 0
7. P(9, then 4) 0
8. P(2, then 1, then 5) $\frac{1}{216}$

Four girls and eight boys are running for president or vice president of the Student Council.

9. Find the probability that two boys are elected. $\frac{14}{33}$
10. Find the probability that two girls are elected. $\frac{1}{11}$
11. Find the probability that the president is a boy and the vice president is a girl. $\frac{8}{33}$
12. Find the probability that the president is a girl and the vice president is a boy. $\frac{8}{33}$

The box contains ten balls, numbered 1 through 10. Marisha reaches in without looking and draws a ball. Then Penney draws a ball without looking. Find each probability.

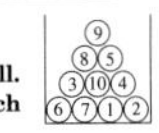

13. P(the sum of the numbers is even) $\frac{4}{9}$
14. P(the sum of the numbers is odd) $\frac{5}{9}$
15. P(the sum of the numbers is 7) $\frac{1}{15}$
16. P(the sum of the numbers is 20) 0
17. P(the sum of the numbers is prime) $\frac{2}{5}$
18. P(the sum of the numbers is greater than 8) $\frac{11}{15}$

In copymaster and workbook formats

RETEACHING

Reteaching 9-5 Independent and Dependent Events

If you toss a coin and roll a number cube, the events are **independent.** The outcome of one event does not affect the outcome of the second event.

Find the probability of tossing a head (H) and rolling an even number (E).

Find P(H and E).
H and E are independent.

① Find P(H):
$P(\text{H}) = \frac{1 \text{ head}}{2 \text{ sides}} = \frac{1}{2}$.

② Find P(E):
$P(\text{E}) = \frac{3 \text{ evens}}{6 \text{ faces}} = \frac{1}{2}$.

③ $P(\text{H and E}) = P(\text{H}) \times P(\text{E}) = \frac{1}{2} \times \frac{1}{2} = \frac{1}{4}$

If the outcome of the first event affects the outcome of the second event, the events are **dependent.**

A bag contains 3 blue and 3 red marbles. Draw a marble, then draw a second marble without replacing the first marble. Find the probability of drawing 2 blue marbles.

① Find P(blue).
$P(\text{blue}) = \frac{3 \text{ blue}}{6 \text{ marbles}} = \frac{1}{2}$

② Find P(blue after blue).
$P(\text{blue after blue}) = \frac{2 \text{ blue}}{5 \text{ marbles}} = \frac{2}{5}$

③ Find P(blue, then blue)
P(blue, then blue)
$= P(\text{blue}) \times P(\text{blue after blue})$
$= \frac{1}{2} \times \frac{2}{5} = \frac{1}{5}$

Use the bag of marbles shown for Exercises 1-6. You draw a marble, then replace it and draw again. Find each probability.

1. P(blue and red) $\frac{6}{25}$
2. P(2 reds) $\frac{9}{25}$
3. P(2 blues) $\frac{4}{25}$

You draw two marbles without replacing the first marble. Find each probability.

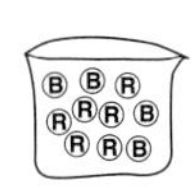

4. P(blue and red) $\frac{4}{15}$
5. P(2 reds) $\frac{1}{3}$
6. P(2 blues) $\frac{2}{15}$

You draw two letters from a box containing the letters M, I, S, S, O, U, R, and I.

7. Suppose you do not replace the first letter before drawing the second. What is P(M and I)? $\frac{1}{28}$
8. Suppose you replace the first letter before drawing the second. What is P(M and I)? $\frac{1}{32}$

ENRICHMENT

Minds on Math Transparency

9-5

What is the relationship between the radius of each circle and the sides of the rectangle?

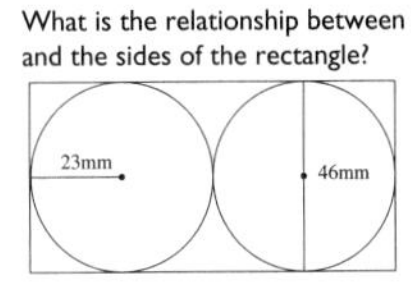

The radius is $\frac{1}{2}$ the width and $\frac{1}{4}$ the length.

See *Solution Key* for worked-out answers.

9-6 Teaching Notes

1 Focus

CONNECTING TO PRIOR KNOWLEDGE Have students consider this situation: Sara, Alex, and Mike want to think of all the ways they can arrange themselves in one car on a roller coaster ride. Draw a tree diagram or make a list to find the number of arrangements. **6** Ask: *Is the arrangement Sara-Alex-Mike the same as Mike-Alex-Sara? Why or why not?* **No; Sara is first in one arrangement, but Mike is first in the other.**

2 Teach

Work Together

DIVERSITY and ALTERNATIVE METHOD Some students may be intimidated by the short amount of time. Pairs could work together for five minutes to find four-letter words. The pair with the greatest number of words wins.

THINK AND DISCUSS

TACTILE LEARNING Question 2 Have students write the letters S, T, O, and P on index cards so that they can easily move the letters to form the arrangements.

REASONING Question 3 Suggest that students recall the definition of *dependent events* from Lesson 9-5.

ERROR ALERT! Example 2 Students may try to continue the pattern 5 × 4 × 3 to include

Lesson Planning Options

Prerequisite Skills

- multiplying whole numbers (4-6)

Vocabulary/Symbols

permutation

Resources

Student Edition

Skills Handbook, p. 530
Extra Practice, p. 522
Glossary/Study Guide

Teaching Resources

Chapter Support File, Ch. 9
- Lesson Planner 9-6
- Practice 9-6, Reteaching 9-6
- Answer Masters 9-6

Teaching Aids Master 2
Glossary, Spanish Resources

Transparencies
15, Minds on Math 9-6

Warm Up

A car salesperson has to be at a meeting in Chicago at 8:00 A.M. One train leaves at 3:30 A.M. and takes 3 h 40 min to reach Chicago. A second train leaves at 5:30 A.M. and takes half the time of the other train to reach Chicago. When should the salesperson leave if it takes 50 min in Chicago to drive to the meeting? **3:30 A.M.**

9-6 Permutations

What You'll Learn

▼ To find permutations

...And Why

You can find all the arrangements of items in a group.

Here's How

Look for questions that
- build understanding
- ✔ check understanding

Work Together

Exploring Arrangements

Play the game STOP with your group. You have one minute in which to write as many words as possible that use all four letters in the word STOP. A word counts only if it is in a dictionary. The player who has the greatest number of words wins.

1. What strategies did you use to find every possible arrangement of the four letters? **Check students' work.**

2a. Check students' work.

2. Make an organized list of all arrangements of the letters.
   a. How many of these arrangements are in your list?
   b. How many of these arrangements are real words? **6 words: STOP, SPOT, POST, POTS, TOPS, OPTS**

THINK AND DISCUSS

An arrangement in which order is important is a **permutation.** The permutation STOP is different from the permutation POTS because the order of the letters is different.

■ EXAMPLE 1

Use the counting principle to find the number of arrangements of the letters S, T, O, and P.

first letter		second letter		third letter		fourth letter	
4	×	3	×	2	×	1	= 24

There are 24 different arrangements.

QUICKreview

To use the counting principle, multiply by the number of choices for each decision.

3. *Reasoning* Why are there 4 choices for the first letter but only 3 choices for the second letter? **Answers may vary. Sample: After choosing the 1st letter, there are only 3 left to choose from.**
4. a. ✔ *Try It Out* Use the four letters S, T, O, and P. Make an organized list of all the three-letter permutations.
   b. *Go a Step Further* What do you notice about the number of permutations when you use all 4 items and when you use 3 of 4 items? Explain why this makes sense.

a–b. See back of book.

× 2 × 1. **Remediation:** Ask students: *How many events are in the question?* **3 events, choosing each letter in the permutation** Then have students draw three blanks on their papers to be filled with the number of possible outcomes for each event.

■ **ADDITIONAL EXAMPLES**

FOR EXAMPLE 1

Use the counting principle to find the number of arrangements of the letters G, R, O, U, and P. **120**

FOR EXAMPLE 2

Use the counting principle to find the number of two-letter permutations of the six letters S, Q, U, A, R, and E. **30**

ASSESSMENT Write the letters M, O, N, K, E, and Y. Then ask students to:

- *Find the number of arrangements of the letters.* **720**
- *Find the number of three-letter permutations.* **120**

3 Practice/Assess

EXERCISES *On Your Own*

EXTENSION Exercise 13 Have students find out how many area codes are currently in use.

■ **EXAMPLE 2**

Use the counting principle to find the number of three-letter permutations of the five letters S, L, I, D, and E.

first letter		second letter		third letter	
5	×	4	×	3	= 60

There are 60 three-letter permutations of the five letters.

5. ✔ *Try It Out* Use the counting principle to find the number of two-letter permutations of the letters S, T, O, and P. To check your work, make an organized list of all possible arrangements. **12 permutations; check students' work.**

Now you may assign Exercises 1–18.

EXERCISES *On Your Own*

Use the counting principle to find the number of permutations for each group of letters. Use all the letters.

1. W, O, R, L, D **120 permutations**
2. H, U, M, A, N, I, T, Y **40,320 permutations**
3. P, I, C, K, L, E **720 permutations**

Find the number of two-letter permutations of each group.

4. C, A, T **6 permutations**
5. P, A, C, K **12 permutations**
6. I, N, C, L, U, D, E **42 permutations**
7. D, E, P, A, R, T **30 permutations**

Find the number of four-letter permutations of each group.

8. R, E, P, S **24 permutations**
9. Q, I, E, R, T, Y, U **840 permutations**
10. G, D, X, Z, C **120 permutations**
11. A, E, I, O, U, Y **360 permutations**

COUNTING AREA CODES

THREE-DIGIT AREA CODES were first developed in 1947. At that time the first digit could not be 0 or 1 because 0 and 1 were used for contacting telephone operators. The second digit was always 0 or 1 to indicate a long distance phone call.

In the 1990s, new technology was developed so that the second digit could be any digit. The new area codes were put into use in 1995.

12. How many different area codes were available in 1947? **160 area codes**
13. How many area codes were available in 1995? **800 area codes**

Technology Options

Prentice Hall Technology

Software for Learners
- Math Blaster® Mystery*
- Interactive Student Tutorial, Chapter 9*

Teaching Resource Software
- Computer Item Generator 9-6
- Resource Pro™ Chapter 9*

Internet • For related mathematics activities, visit the Prentice Hall site at www.phschool.com/math

**Available on CD-ROM only*

Assignment Options for Exercises On Your Own

Core 1–11, 14, 16
Extension 12, 13, 15, 17, 18

Use Mixed Review to maintain skills.

PRACTICE

Practice 9-6 Permutations

Start with the letters in the word STEP.

1. Make an organized list of all the possible four-letter permutations of the letters.

STEP	STPE	SETP	SEPT	SPET	SPTE
TEPS	TESP	TSEP	TSPE	TPES	TPSE
EPTS	EPST	ESPT	ESTP	ETSP	ETPS
PEST	PETS	PTES	PTSE	PSET	PSTE

2. How many of the permutations form real words? 3

Use the counting principle to find the number of permutations for each group of letters. Use all the letters.

3. C, H, A, I, R 120
4. L, I, G, H, T, S 720
5. C, O, M, P, U, T, E, R 40,320

Find the number of three-letter permutations of each group.

6. A, P, Q, M 24
7. L, S, U, V, R, 60
8. M, B, T, O, D, K 120

Solve.

9. Suppose that first, second, and third place winners of a contest are to be selected from eight students who entered. In how many ways can the winners be chosen? 336
10. Antonio has nine different sweatshirts that he can wear for his job doing yard work. He has three pairs of jeans and two pairs of sweatpants. How many different outfits can Antonio wear for the yard work? 45
11. Ramona has a combination lock for her bicycle. She knows the numbers are 20, 41, and 6, but she can't remember the order. How many different arrangements are possible? 6 arrangements
12. Travis is planting 5 rose bushes along a fence. Each rose bush has a different flower color: red, yellow, pink, peach, and white. If he wants to plant 3 rose bushes in between white and yellow rose bushes, in how many ways can he plant the 5 rose bushes? 12 ways

Practice

In copymaster and workbook formats

RETEACHING

Reteaching 9-6 Permutations

You can arrange the letters A, B, and C in different ways: ABC, ACB, and so on. An arrangement in which order is important is a **permutation.**

How many ways can the three blocks be arranged in a line?

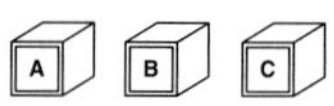

① List the ways.

② Count the number of arrangements.

ABC ACB
BAC BCA
CAB CBA

There are 6 possible arrangements.

You can use the counting principle as a shortcut.

choices for 1st block		choices for 2nd block		choice for 3rd block	
3	×	2	×	1	= 6

Complete to find the number of permutations for each.

1. In how many ways can you arrange 4 different books on a shelf? $4 \times$ 3 $\times$ 2 $\times 1 =$ 24
2. In how many ways can the first, second, and third prizes be awarded to 10 contestants? 10 $\times$ 9 $\times$ 8 $=$ 720

Find the number of permutations for each.

3. In how many different ways can the letters in BIRD be arranged if you use all four letters? 24
4. How many different ways can you frame two of five pictures in different frames? 20
5. How many different seating arrangements are possible for a row of five chairs, choosing from six people? 720
6. A basket contains five different pieces of fruit. If three people each choose one piece, in how many different ways can they make their choices? 60

Find the number of two-letter permutations for each group.

7. R, I, B 6
8. H, E, L, P 12
9. R, A, M, B, L, E 30
10. C, A, N, D, L, E, S 42

Find the number of three-letter permutations for each group.

11. T, A, B 6
12. R, A, D, I, O 60
13. T, O, P, S 24
14. W, A, L, R, U, S 120

Reteaching

ENRICHMENT

Minds on Math Transparency

9-6

Kahlil, Juan, Waylon, and Ricki all bought identical T-shirts. Kahlil paid 10% more than Juan. Juan paid one fourth of what Waylon paid. Ricki paid 50% less than Waylon. Who paid the most? Who paid the least?

Waylon paid the most. Juan paid the least.

See *Solution Key* for worked-out answers.

Wrap Up

IDENTIFYING THE BIG IDEA Have students explain how to find the number of *permutations* of five letters. Have them explain how to find the number of three-letter permutations of five letters.

LESSON QUIZ

1. Find the number of permutations of the letters A, B, C, and D. **24**
2. Find the number of four-letter permutations of the letters S, T, W, X, Y, and Z. **360**

14. A club of 10 students chooses officers. One student will be president and another student will be vice president. How many different outcomes are possible? **90 outcomes**
15. The combination to open your lock has three numbers: 10, 45, and 6. You cannot remember the order of the numbers.
    a. List all the possible arrangements of the numbers. **See below.**
    b. You decide to try different arrangements. If you are as unlucky as possible, how many will you have to try before you open the lock? **b. 6 arrangements**

15a. 6, 10, 45; 6, 45, 10; 10, 6, 45; 10, 45, 6; 45, 6, 10; 45, 10, 6

16. *Writing* Explain how to find the number of permutations of all the letters C, H, E, M, I, S, T, R, Y. Then explain how to find the number of permutations of five of the letters. **Multiply $9 \times 8 \times 7 \times 6 \times 5 \times 4 \times 3 \times 2 \times 1$; multiply $9 \times 8 \times 7 \times 6 \times 5$.**
17. Suppose you scramble the letters P, E, T, and S.
    a. Make an organized list of the sample space. **See back of book.**
    b. How many of the groups form real words? What are they? **4 words; PETS, PEST, SEPT, STEP**
    c. Find the probability that a real word is formed when the letters P, E, T, and S are scrambled. $\frac{1}{6}$
18. Dan, Eugene, Fran, and Gabi are in line for movie tickets.
    a. Make a list to show the sample space. **See back of book.**
    b. What is the probability that they line up boy-girl-boy-girl? $\frac{1}{6}$
    c. What is the probability that they line up girl-girl-boy-boy? $\frac{1}{6}$

Mixed Review

Geometry **Classify each polygon by the number of sides. Judging by appearance, state whether it appears to be a regular polygon.** *(Lesson 7-6)*

19. 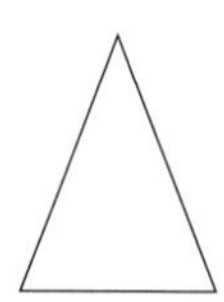 triangle; no

20. 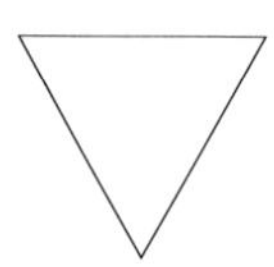 triangle; yes

21.  quadrilateral; yes

22. 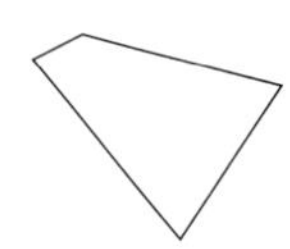 quadrilateral; no

Find each sum or difference. *(Lesson 5-3)*

23. $6\frac{1}{2} + 5\frac{2}{3}$ $12\frac{1}{6}$
24. $12\frac{1}{8} + 4\frac{3}{4}$ $16\frac{7}{8}$
25. $9\frac{2}{5} - 8\frac{5}{6}$ $\frac{17}{30}$
26. $17\frac{2}{9} - 6\frac{5}{12}$ $10\frac{29}{36}$
27. $12\frac{3}{5} + 14\frac{7}{12}$ $27\frac{11}{60}$
28. *Business* A can of frozen juice is in the shape of a cylinder. It has a radius of 1.5 in. and is 6 in. high. Find the amount of paper necessary to make a label for the can. *(Lessons 8-9)* **56.55 in.^{2}**

Extra Practice, Lesson 9-6, page 522

9-7 Teaching Notes

1 Focus

CONNECTING TO PRIOR KNOWLEDGE Have students recall the last time they ordered a combination meal from a fast-food restaurant. Ask: *Is a hamburger, french fries, and drink meal the same as a french fries, drink, and hamburger meal?* **yes** *Did the order in which you received the meal change the price of the meal?* **no** Have students think of other arrangements in which the order does not matter. **Answers may vary. Sample: lunchroom meal; choosing of basketball team**

2 Teach

THINK AND DISCUSS

Have students compare this Example to Exercise 6a in Lesson 9–4. Ask: *How are the problems different?* **In Exercise 6, you choose one item from each of two different groups. In this Example, you choose two items from the same group.** Then ask: *How are the problems the same?* **Both involve clothing and choices.**

DIVERSITY Students with dyslexia or other visual impairments may have difficulty reading arrangements of single letters. Instead of listing the letters (b, g), write complete words (blue, green), or use colored markers or chalk.

9-7 Combinations

What You'll Learn

▼ To find combinations

...And Why

You can use combinations to find the number of arrangements when order does not matter.

Here's How

Look for questions that
- build understanding
- ✔ check understanding

THINK AND DISCUSS

In some arrangements, order does not matter. For example, suppose you choose LeVar, Ramon, and May to be on a committee. That is the same as choosing Ramon, May, and LeVar or May, LeVar, and Ramon. An arrangement in which order does *not* matter is a **combination.**

■ **EXAMPLE 1** *Real-World Problem Solving*

Clothing Suppose you are packing for a hiking trip. You are choosing two T-shirts from the list at the right. In how many ways can you choose them?

T-shirts

Color	Letter
blue	b
yellow	y
green	g
red	r
purple	p

Let the letters represent the five T-shirts. List all the possible arrangements.

(b, y) (b, g) (b, r) (b, p) (y, b) (y, g) (y, r) (y, p),
(g, b) (g, y) (g, r) (g, p) (r, b) (r, y) (r, g) (r, p),
(p, b), (p, y), (p, g), (p, r)

Cross out the duplicate arrangements.

(b, y) (b, g) (b, r) (b, p) ~~(y, b)~~ (y, g) (y, r) (y, p),
~~(g, b)~~ ~~(g, y)~~ (g, r) (g, p) ~~(r, b)~~ ~~(r, y)~~ ~~(r, g)~~ (r, p),
~~(p, b)~~, ~~(p, y)~~, ~~(p, g)~~, ~~(p, r)~~

(y, b) is the same group as (b, y), so keep only one.

You have 10 different choices.

Another way to find combinations is to make an organized list.

(b, y)	(b, g)	(b, r)	(b, p)
	(y, g)	(y, r)	(y, p)
		(g, r)	(g, p)
			(r, p)

1. *Think About It* Describe the organization of the list above. **See back of book.**

2. ✔ *Try It Out* In how many ways can a camp counselor choose a relay team of three swimmers from a group of five? **10 ways**

Lesson Planning Options

Prerequisite Skills
- listing outcomes (9-4)

Vocabulary/Symbols

combination

Resources

Student Edition

Skills Handbook, p. 528
Extra Practice, p. 522
Glossary/Study Guide

Teaching Resources

Chapter Support File, Ch. 9
- Lesson Planner 9-7
- Practice 9-7, Reteaching 9-7
- Answer Masters 9-7

Teaching Aids Master 2
Glossary, Spanish Resources

Transparencies

15, Minds on Math 9-7

Warm Up

Find the difference between $\frac{3}{12}$ and $\frac{1}{8}$. $\frac{3}{24} = \frac{1}{8}$

ERROR ALERT! Question 1 Students may count the same combination twice. **Remediation:** Have students write each letter in a different color. Then make sure no two combinations have the same two colors.

■ **ADDITIONAL EXAMPLE**

Seven students showed up after school to help the librarian. He needed only two students. In how many ways can the librarian choose two students from the seven that showed up? **21**

AUDITORY LEARNING Divide the class into two teams and post the letters A, B, C, and D. Have students take turns naming two-letter combinations such as (A, B). If students name a combination that has been already named, such as (B, A), the opposing team earns a point. Students should listen carefully to hear if anyone repeats previous combinations. The game is over when all of the combinations have been named.

ASSESSMENT Have each student write and label two situations: one permutation and one combination. Collect the situations and randomly read them aloud. Ask different students whether each situation is a permutation or a combination. Have them support their answers. Continue until everyone has answered.

Technology Options

Prentice Hall Technology

Software for Learners

- Math Blaster® Mystery*
- Interactive Student Tutorial, Chapter 9*

Teaching Resource Software

- Computer Item Generator 9-7
- Resource Pro™ Chapter 9*

Internet • For related mathematics activities, visit the Prentice Hall site at www.phschool.com/math

**Available on CD-ROM only*

Assignment Options for Exercises On Your Own

Core 1–13, 15, 16, 18–22
Extension 14, 17

Use Mixed Review to maintain skills.

a. 60 permutations
b. 10 combinations

3. Use the letters A, B, C, D, and E.
   a. Find the number of three-letter permutations.
   b. Find the number of three-letter combinations.
   c. *Reasoning* Which is greater, the number of permutations or the number of combinations? Explain. **Permutations; each combination includes several permutations.**

Now you may assign Exercises 1–22.

EXERCISES *On Your Own*

Find the number of combinations.

1. Choose 2 people from 3. **3**
2. Choose 3 people from 5. **10**
3. Choose 2 people from 6. **15**

Use the letters B, E, O, P, R, W. Make a list of all the combinations.

4. 2 vowels **EO**
5. 3 consonants **BPR, BPW, BRW, PRW**
6. any 3 letters **See margin p. 421.**
7. 1 consonant and 1 vowel **BE, BO, PE, PO, RE, RO, WE, WO**
8. any 4 letters **See margin p. 421.**
9. any 5 letters **See above.**

9. BEOPW, BEOPR, BEORW, BEPRW, BOPRW, EOPRW

Use the poster for Exercises 10–14. Find the number of combinations for each situation.

10. participate in 2 track events **6 combinations**
11. participate in 1 game, 1 track event, and 1 field event **24 combinations**
12. participate in 2 field events **3 combinations**
13. participate in 2 track events and 2 field events **18 combinations**
14. *Open-ended* Write a combination problem from the information on the poster. Solve your problem. **Check students' work.**
15. Twelve students volunteer to help organize a class trip. Two of them are assigned to collect money for the trip. In how many ways can these two students be chosen? **66 ways**
16. *Music* Suppose you have five different CDs to play. Your CD player can hold three CDs. How many different sets of three CDs can you select? **10 sets**
17. *Writing* Use your own words and an example to explain the difference between a permutation and a combination. **A combination is a way of selecting a number of items from a list in any order. A permutation is a way of selecting a number of items from a list in a specific order. For example, there are 3 combinations of 2 letters from A, B, C–AB, AC, BC. There are 6 permutations of the same letters–AB, BA, AC, CA, BC, CB.**

3 Practice/Assess

EXERCISES *On Your Own*

Exercise 3 Students may find it helpful to let different letters represent each of the six people. Suggest that they list the combinations.

OPEN-ENDED **Exercise 14** Encourage students to choose events they would enjoy. Because answers will vary, have them exchange work with a partner to check their answers.

WRITING **Exercise 17** Students may have difficulty beginning. Have them compare their work for Lesson 9-6 Exercise 3 and Lesson 9-7 Exercise 8.

WRAP UP

IDENTIFYING THE BIG IDEA Have students explain how to find combinations. Then have them explain the difference between a combination and a permutation by giving examples of each.

PROJECT LINK Students may have a hard time believing this is possible. Suggest that they start with cubes A and B given in the Project Link on page 405. Then suggest that they may want to design a cube with four low numbers and two high numbers.

18. **Choose A, B, C, or D.** Andrea plans to buy a bicycle, a helmet, a water bottle, and a lock. Today she will buy some of the accessories. How many different sets of two accessories can she select? A

A. 3 B. 5 C. 4 D. 7

Tell whether each of the following is a permutation or a combination problem. Explain your choice.

19. You select three books from a bookshelf that holds eight books. How many different sets of books could you choose? Combination; the order in the set is not important.
20. You select three books to read over summer vacation. In how many different orders can you read the books? Permutation; the order is important.
21. Four students stand beside each other for a photograph. How many different orders are possible? Permutation; the order in the photograph is important.
22. A committee of four people is chosen from your class. How many different committees may be chosen? Combination; the order in the committee is not important.

Mixed Review

Complete. *(Lesson 5-8)*

23. 12,000 lb = ■ T 6
24. 2.5 gal = ■ fl oz 320
25. 3 qt 1 pt = ■ c 14
26. 15 in. = ■ ft $1\frac{1}{4}$

Write a proportion and solve. *(Lessons 6-9, 6-10)*

27. 54 is 40% of what number? 135
28. 99 is what percent of 150? 66%
29. What number is 65% of 200? 130
30. What number is 15.5% of 45? 6.975

31. *Geometry* A rectangle has a perimeter of 48 m. Make a list of all of the possible dimensions that are whole meter units. Which dimensions give you the greatest area? *(Lesson 8-2)* 1 m by 23 m, 2 m by 22 m, 3 m by 21 m, 4 m by 20 m, 5 m by 19 m, 6 m by 18 m, 7 m by 17 m, 8 m by 16 m, 9 m by 15 m, 10 m by 14 m, 11 m by 13 m, 12 m by 12 m; 12 × 12 gives the greatest area.

CHAPTER PROJECT

PROJECT LINK: DESIGNING

Construct three cardboard number cubes A, B, and C. Design your cubes so that A usually beats B, B usually beats C, and C usually beats A. Use sample spaces to support your work.

Check students' work. Sample: A (3, 3, 3, 4, 4, 4), B (2, 2, 2, 2, 6, 6), C (1, 1, 5, 5, 5, 5)

CHECKPOINT 2

Checkpoint 2

Lessons 9-5 through 9-7

Use the letters P, E, A, R, and S. Find the number of permutations and the number of combinations.

1. 2 vowels 2, 1
2. any 3 letters 60, 10
3. 1 vowel and 1 consonant 12, 6
4. Five students get into a line for lunch. How many different arrangements of these students could there be in this line? 120 arrangements
5. **Circle A, B, C, or D.** A bowl contains 3 red marbles, 4 green marbles, and 5 blue marbles. What is the probability of selecting two red marbles if the first marble is not replaced before selecting the second marble?

A. $\frac{1}{8}$ (B.) $\frac{1}{22}$ C. $\frac{1}{24}$ D. $\frac{3}{44}$

Assessment

pages 420–421 On Your Own

6. BEO, BEP, BER, BEW, BOP, BOR, BOW, BPR, BPW, BRW, EOP, EOR, EOW, EPR, EPW, ERW, OPR, OPW, ORW, PRW
8. BEOP, BEOR, BEOW, BEPR, BEPW, BERW, BOPR, BOPW, BORW, BPRW, EOPR, EOPW, EORW, EPRW, OPRW

PRACTICE

Practice 9-7 Combinations

Find the number of combinations.

1. Choose 3 people from 4. 24
2. Choose 4 people from 6. 360

Use the numbers 3, 5, 8, 10, 12, 15, 20. Make a list of all the combinations. Answers may vary.

3. 2 even numbers 8, 10; 8, 12; 8, 20; 10, 12; 10, 20; 12, 20
4. 3 odd numbers 3, 5, 15
5. 1 even, 1 odd 8, 3; 8, 5; 8, 15; 10, 3; 10, 5; 10, 15; 12, 3; 12, 5; 12, 15; 20, 3; 20, 5; 20, 15
6. any 2 numbers 3, 5; 3, 8; 3, 10; 3, 12; 3, 15; 3, 20; 5, 8; 5, 10; 5, 12; 5, 15; 5, 20; 8, 10; 8, 12; 8, 15; 8, 20; 10, 12; 10, 15; 10, 20; 12, 15; 12, 20; 15, 20
7. You just bought five new books to read. You want to take two of them with you on vacation. In how many ways can you choose two books to take? 10 ways

Charmayne is organizing a track meet. There are 4 runners in her class. Each runner must compete one-on-one against each of the other runners in her class.

8. How many races must Charmayne schedule? 6 races
9. Must Charmayne schedule permutations or combinations? combinations

A committee for the end-of-year party is composed of four eighth graders and three seventh graders. A three-member subcommittee is formed.

10. How many different combinations of eighth graders could there be if there are three eighth graders on the subcommittee? 4 combinations of eighth graders
11. How many different combinations of seventh graders could there be if the subcommittee consists of three seventh graders? 1 combination of seventh graders
12. Find the probability that all 3 members on the subcommittee are eighth graders. $\frac{4}{35}$
13. Find the probability that all 3 members on the subcommittee are seventh graders. $\frac{1}{35}$

In copymaster and workbook formats

RETEACHING

Reteaching 9-7 Combinations

An arrangement in which order does *not* matter is a **combination.** For example, if you pair Raiz and Carla to play tennis, it is the same as if you pair Carla and Raiz.

How many groups of 2 letters can you form from A, B, C, and D?

① Make an organized list.

② Eliminate any duplicates.

③ List the combinations.

① AB AC AD
BA BC BD
② CA CB CD
DA DB DC

AB, AC, AD, BC, BD, CD

There are 6 possible combinations.

Use the letters C, O, M, P, U, T, E, R for Exercises 1–4.

1. How many combinations of 2 vowels are there? Show an organized list with no duplicates. 3 combinations: EO, EU, OU (Organizations may vary.)
2. How many combinations of 3 consonants are there? Show an organized list with no duplicates. 10 combinations: CMP, CMT, CMR, MPT, MPR, PTR, PTC, TRC, TRM (Organizations may vary.)
3. If you use C, O, M, P, U, T, E, R, S instead of C, O, M, P, U, T, E, R, how many combinations of 2 vowels are there? 3 combinations
4. If you use C, O, M, P, U, T, E, R, S instead of C, O, M, P, U, T, E, R, how many combinations of 3 consonants are there? 20 combinations

Find the number of combinations.

5. In how many ways can Robin pick 2 different kinds of muffins from a choice of wheat, raisin, blueberry, banana, garlic, and plain? 15 ways
6. Sara has 24 tapes. In how many different ways can she take 2 tapes to school? 276 ways
7. Augusto has purple, green, black, red, and blue T-shirts. In how many ways can he choose 3 for his vacation? 10 ways
8. Abdul selects three light filters from a box of ten different filters. How many different sets could he choose? 120 sets

ENRICHMENT

Minds on Math Transparency

9-7

We are three different unit fractions that add to 1. What unit fractions are we?

$\frac{1}{2}$, $\frac{1}{3}$, and $\frac{1}{6}$

See *Solution Key* for worked-out answers.

Math at Work

If you have block scheduling or extended class periods, have groups of students make a lesson plan. Have each group choose a lesson from this chapter. Have them decide how they would teach this lesson to the class. Give them a sample of one of your lesson plans to use as a guide.

LESSON QUIZ

1. Find the number of combinations of choosing 3 people from 6. **20**
2. Use the letters C, D, S, T, and U. Make a list of the combinations of any two letters. **(C, D), (C, S), (C, T), (C, U), (D, S), (D, T), (D, U), (S, T), (S, U), (T, U)**

✓ CHECKPOINT 2

Lessons 9-5 through 9-7

The letters M A T H E M A T I C S are written on cards.

1. Find the probability of selecting a vowel, replacing it, then selecting another vowel. $\frac{16}{121}$
2. Find the probability of selecting an A, then a T, if the first letter *is not* replaced before selecting the second one. $\frac{2}{55}$
3. Find the probability of selecting any two vowels, if the first letter *is not* replaced before selecting the second one. $\frac{6}{55}$

Use the numbers 1, 2, 3, 4, 5, and 6. Find the number of permutations and the number of combinations.

4. two odd numbers 6; 3
5. three even numbers 6; 1
6. all multiples of 3 2; 1
7. all numbers less than 5 24; 1
8. any two numbers 30; 15
9. any four numbers 360; 15
10. You decide to pin the pictures of six friends in a row on a bulletin board. In how many ways can you arrange the pictures? **720 ways**
11. *Calculator* Find the number of ways to arrange nine books on a shelf. **362,880 ways**

Math at Work

TEACHER

In addition to traditional classroom responsibilities, teachers plan lessons, supervise after-school activities, and meet with parents. Today's teachers use mathematics skills to help their students solve problems, understand concepts, and develop critical-thinking skills. Telecommunications technology is now opening a whole new world for teachers and students alike.

Internet Connection: Find out more about working as a teacher at the Web site for the National Education Association: http://www.nea.org/

Extra Practice, Lesson 9-7, page 522

PROBLEM SOLVING PRACTICE ★★

This page provides problems for students to solve using their knowledge of congruence, probability, multiplying and dividing decimals, making geometric constructions, proportion, volume, and making predictions. Allow students to use any method they find helpful.

Exercise 3 Students may want to draw a diagram to help them answer the question.

Exercises 5 and 7 If students choose "E. Not Here" for either exercise, have them find the correct answer.

PROBLEM SOLVING PRACTICE ★★★★★

Read each question and choose the best answer.

1. $\triangle XYZ \cong \triangle MON$. Which statement is *not necessarily* true? A

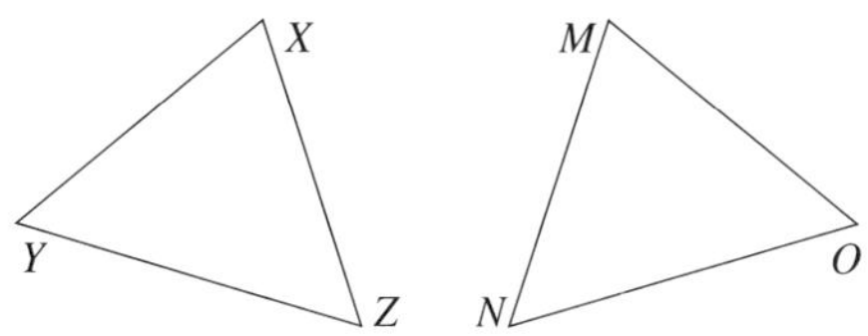

A. $\overline{YX} \cong \overline{NO}$ B. $m\angle N = m\angle Z$
C. $\angle Y \cong \angle O$ D. $\overline{MN} \cong \overline{XZ}$

2. A game uses a spinner that is divided into 10 equal sections that are labeled with the following numbers: 2, 4, 5, 5, 8, 10, 10, 11, 12, and 15. What is the probability of spinning an even number? H

F. $\frac{2}{5}$ G. $\frac{4}{5}$ H. $\frac{3}{5}$ J. $\frac{1}{10}$

3. Cans of peas are sold 3 for \$.75. How much will 6 cans of peas cost? B

A. \$1.80 B. \$1.50 C. \$1.35 D. \$.90

4. This drawing shows how to — G

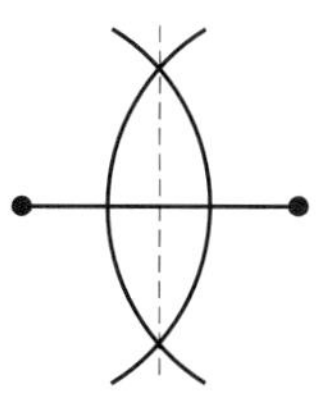

F. construct a line segment congruent to a given line segment
G. construct the perpendicular bisector of a line segment
H. construct complementary angles
J. bisect an angle

Please note that items 5–8 have *five* answer choices.

5. Latisha and her sister are standing next to each other. Latisha is 6 feet tall and casts an 8-foot shadow. How long is the shadow cast by Latisha's younger sister? D

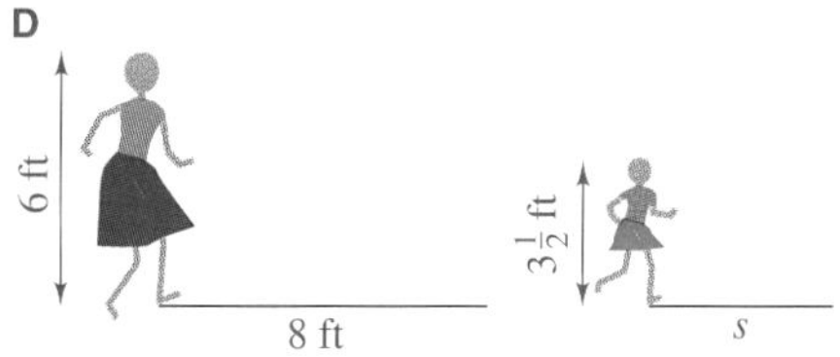

A. 28 ft B. $16\frac{5}{8}$ ft C. $10\frac{1}{2}$ ft
D. $4\frac{2}{3}$ ft E. Not Here

6. A storage chest is a rectangular prism 4.5 feet long, 1.5 feet wide, and 2 feet tall. What is the volume of the chest? H

F. 15.75 ft^3 G. 12 ft^3 H. 13.5 ft^3
J. 8 ft^3 K. 6.75 ft^3

7. Cards with the letters A through H are placed in a bag. Ken selects a card from the bag at random. He doesn't put the card back. Then he chooses a second card. What is the probability that both of the cards will be vowels? E

A. $\frac{1}{16}$ B. $\frac{1}{14}$ C. $\frac{10}{56}$
D. $\frac{5}{16}$ E. Not Here

8. In a survey about pets, 30 out of 80 students questioned said that their families owned a dog. If 500 were surveyed, what is a good prediction for the number of students whose families own a dog? J

F. 20 G. 50 H. 100
J. 200 K. 320

9-8 Teaching Notes

1 Focus

CONNECTING TO PRIOR KNOWLEDGE Have students recall using probability to make predictions in Lesson 9-1. Ask: *In a family of three children, the probability that all three children are girls is $\frac{3}{20}$. Suppose there are 200 families with three children, how many would you predict have all girls?* $\frac{3 \times 10}{20 \times 10} = \frac{30}{200}$**; 30 families**

2 Teach

THINK AND DISCUSS

ERROR ALERT! Students may place the data in the proportion incorrectly. For example, they may confuse marked deer with counted marked deer. **Remediation** Point out that both ratios contain $\frac{\text{marked deer}}{\text{total deer}}$. The ratio on the left is *counted*, and the ratio on the right is *actual*. The numerator and denominator on the left should be smaller than those on the right.

KINESTHETIC LEARNING **Question 1** Set up a large proportion frame on the floor with masking tape—two fraction bars with an equals sign between them. Take eight index cards and label them: *marked sea otters counted, total sea otters counted, number of marked sea otters, estimate of sea otter population, 12, 42, 20,* and *x*. Give the first four cards to students and have them arrange

Lesson Planning Options

Prerequisite Skills

- writing ratios (6-1)
- solving proportions (6-3)

Vocabulary/Symbols

capture/recapture

Materials/Manipulatives

- calculator
- markers
- square tiles
- bag

Resources

Student Edition

Skills Handbook, p. 534
Extra Practice, p. 522
Glossary/Study Guide

Teaching Resources

Chapter Support File, Ch. 9
- Lesson Planner 9-8
- Practice 9-8, Reteaching 9-8
- Answer Masters 9-8

Glossary, Spanish Resources

Transparencies

15, 95, Minds on Math 9-8

Warm Up

Draw several different shaped quadrilaterals. Use a red crayon or pencil to connect the midpoints of the sides of each figure. Write a sentence explaining in what way the red figures are alike. **They are all parallelograms.**

9-8 Estimating Population Size

What You'll Learn

▼ To estimate the size of a population using the capture/recapture method

...And Why

Park rangers can estimate the size of animal populations.

Here's How

Look for questions that
- build understanding
- ✔ check understanding

THINK AND DISCUSS

From 1979 to 1986, the Montana Department of Fish, Wildlife, and Parks monitored the mule deer population in the mountains near Bozeman. They used the *capture/recapture* method to estimate the number of deer each winter.

Researchers placed a visible collar on a number of deer to "mark" them. Later, the researchers flew over an area and counted the number of marked deer and the total number of deer they saw. They used the proportion below to estimate the deer population.

$$\frac{\text{marked deer counted}}{\text{total deer counted}} = \frac{\text{number of marked deer}}{\text{estimate of deer population}}$$

■ **EXAMPLE** *Real-World Problem Solving*

Biology Suppose researchers knew that there were 55 marked deer in an area. On a flight over the area, they counted 48 marked deer and a total of 638 deer. Estimate the deer population.

$$\frac{\text{marked deer counted}}{\text{total deer counted}} = \frac{\text{number of marked deer}}{\text{estimate of deer population}}$$

$\frac{48}{638} = \frac{55}{x}$ ← Write a proportion.

$48x = 55 \cdot 638$ ← Write cross products.

$48x = 35{,}090$ ← Multiply.

$\frac{48x}{48} = \frac{35{,}090}{48}$ ← Divide each side by 48.

35,090 ÷ 48 = 731.0416667 ← Use a calculator.

$x \approx 731$ ← Round to the nearest integer.

There are about 731 deer in the area.

1. ✔ *Try It Out* There are 20 marked sea otters in one coastal region. In one survey, marine biologists counted 42 sea otters, of which 12 were marked. About how many sea otters are in the area? **about 70 sea otters**

themselves in the proportion frame to represent the proportion needed to solve the problem. Give the last four cards to four more students. Have them find the place in the proportion where their number or variable belongs and replace the person already there.

■ ADDITIONAL EXAMPLE

FOR EXAMPLE

There are 30 marked beavers. In a survey, you counted 58 beavers, 16 of which were marked. About how many beavers are in the area? 109

Work Together

ASSESSMENT Have students work in pairs to create a capture/recapture problem. Have both students solve the problem separately. Then have them exchange papers and summarize each step of their partner's work. Have them compare their work to the Example.

3 Practice/Assess

EXERCISES *On Your Own*

WRITING **Exercise 11b** Have students consider the following questions: *Are you likely to see all of the marked deer?* **no** *If you counted a high percent of the marked deer, what does this imply about your total count?* **You probably counted a high percent of the total population.**

Work Together

Using Capture/Recapture

Work in a group to use the capture/recapture method.

a–f. Check students' work.

2. a. Place some square tiles in a bag without counting them.
   b. Decide how many tiles to mark. Remove them from the bag and mark each tile with an X. Then replace the marked tiles in the bag and shake it.
   c. Take a sample from the bag. Record the number of marked tiles in the sample. Record the total number of tiles in the sample.
   d. Write and solve a proportion to estimate the number of tiles in the bag.
   e. *Reasoning* Do you think the number of tiles you decided to mark affects your estimate of the total number of tiles? Explain.
   f. Count the actual number of tiles. How close was your estimate?

On Your Own

1. **about 1,823 deer**
2. **about 2,010 deer**
3. **about 2,273 deer**
4. **about 2,048 deer**
5. **about 2,110 deer**
6. **about 2,535 deer**
7. **about 1,822 deer**
8. **about 2,081 deer**
9. **about 2,345 deer**

Now you may assign Exercises 1–13.

EXERCISES *On Your Own*

Use a proportion to estimate the total number of deer for each year.

	Date	Total Deer Counted	Marked Deer Counted	Total Marked Deer
1.	3/79	1,173	65	101
2.	3/80	1,017	42	83
3.	3/81	1,212	32	60
4.	3/82	1,707	30	36
5.	3/83	1,612	68	89
6.	3/84	1,590	37	59
7.	3/85	1,417	42	54
8.	3/86	1,608	85	110
9.	3/87	1,469	52	83

Technology Options

Prentice Hall Technology

Software for Learners

- Hot Page™ 10–8*
- Math Blaster® Mystery*
- Interactive Student Tutorial, Chapter 9*

Teaching Resource Software

- Computer Item Generator 9-8
- Resource Pro™ Chapter 9*

Internet • For related mathematics activities, visit the Prentice Hall site at www.phschool.com/math

**Available on CD-ROM only*

Assignment Options for Exercises On Your Own

Core 1–9, 12, 13
Extension 10, 11

Use Mixed Review to maintain skills.

PRACTICE

Practice 9-8 *Using Data to Make Predictions*

Workers at a state park caught, tagged, and set free the species shown at the right. Later that same year, the workers caught the number of animals shown in the table below, and counted the tagged animals. Estimate the park population of each species.

Tagged Animals	
Bears	12
Squirrels	50
Raccoons	23
Rabbits	42
Trout	46
Owls	24
Foxes	14
Skunks	21

	Caught	Counted Tagged	Estimated Population
1. Bears	30	9	40
2. Squirrels	1,102	28	1,968
3. Raccoons	412	10	948
4. Rabbits	210	2	4,410
5. Trout	318	25	585
6. Owls	117	10	281
7. Foxes	54	9	84
8. Skunks	45	6	158

Imagine that you are working in a National Park. One season, you tag 100 animals. Estimate the total population for each of the following samples.

9. 23 out of 100 animals are tagged
   435 animals
10. 12 out of 75 animals are tagged
   625 animals
11. 8 out of 116 animals are tagged
   1,450 animals
12. 5 out of 63 animals are tagged
   1,260 animals
13. 4 out of 83 animals are tagged
   2,075 animals
14. 3 out of 121 animals are tagged
   4,033 animals
15. 83 out of 125 animals are tagged
   151 animals
16. 7 out of 165 animals are tagged
   2,357 animals

Practice

In copymaster and workbook formats

RETEACHING

Reteaching 9-8 *Using Data to Make Predictions*

Researchers tagged 100 fish in a pond and then released them back into the pond. Later they captured 60 fish and found that 3 were tagged. Estimate the number of fish in the pond.

① Write a proportion of tagged fish to total fish $\frac{\text{tagged fish (pond)}}{\text{total fish (pond)}} = \frac{\text{tagged fish (sample)}}{\text{total fish (sample)}}$

$\frac{100}{n} = \frac{3}{60}$

② Write cross products. $3n = 6{,}000$

③ Solve. $n = 2{,}000$

There are about 2,000 fish in the pond.

Complete to estimate the number of deer in the woods.

1. One year researchers tagged 80 deer. They later captured 15 deer and found 5 were tagged. Estimate the number of deer in the woods.
   $\frac{80}{n} = \frac{5}{15}$
   $5n = 15 \cdot$ 80
   $n =$ 240
   There are about 240 deer.
2. Two years later, researchers tagged 45 deer. They later captured 20 and found 3 were tagged. Estimate the number of deer in the woods then.
   $\frac{45}{n} = \frac{3}{20}$
   $3n =$ 20 · 45
   $n =$ 300
   There are about 300 deer.

Solve.

3. In another project, researchers caught and tagged 85 sea lions in a bay. Later they caught and released 50 sea lions. Of those, 9 had tags. Estimate the sea lion population in the bay.
   about 472 sea lions
4. Other researchers caught and tagged 5 spotted owls. Later they caught 7 owls. Of those, 4 were tagged. Estimate the number of spotted owls in that forest.
   about 9 owls
5. An ecology class helped researchers determine the rabbit population in a nature preserve. One weekend, the students captured, tagged, and set free 32 rabbits. A month later, they captured 27 rabbits including 16 with tags. Estimate the number of rabbits in the nature preserve.
   about 54 rabbits
6. Another ecology class helped researchers determine the pigeon population in a city park. In one day, the students captured, banded, and released 200 pigeons. Two weeks later, of the 24 pigeons they captured, 3 had bands. Estimate the pigeon population in the park.
   about 1,600 pigeons

Reteaching

ENRICHMENT

Minds on Math Transparency

9-8

In April, 20% of the customers at Auto World bought blue cars. Of those customers, 15% chose gray interiors. What percent of the customers at Auto World did not choose a blue car with a gray interior?

97%

See *Solution Key* for worked-out answers.

WRAP UP

IDENTIFYING THE BIG IDEA Have students explain how to use proportions to estimate populations with the capture/recapture method.

PORTFOLIO Share with students the criteria you use to assess their work in portfolios, as well as how you plan to use the results. Students should understand how the rubrics are used to assess their work, how each piece in the portfolio counts, and how the scores they get in their portfolios affect their overall evaluation.

LESSON QUIZ

Use a proportion to estimate the total number of each kind of fish in the lake.

1. Total catfish counted: 205
   Marked catfish counted: 45
   Total marked catfish: 162 **738**
2. Total bass counted: 192
   Marked bass counted: 32
   Total marked bass: 85 **510**

10. *Analyze* Use your answers to Exercises 1–9 on page 425. Describe how the deer population changed over time. **Answers may vary. Sample: For every 3 years the population of deer increases for the first 2 years, then declines for 1 year.**
11. Some researchers calculate the ratio of marked deer counted to the number of marked deer.
    a. Calculate this ratio for each year from 1979 to 1987. Write each ratio as a decimal rounded to the nearest thousandth. **0.644, 0.506, 0.533, 0.833, 0.764, 0.627, 0.778, 0.773, 0.627**
    b. *Writing* Explain how counting a high percent of the marked deer might affect the estimate of the deer population. **Answers may vary. Sample: You could end up with too great an estimate of the deer population.**
12. In a study of catfish in Beaver Lake, the state extension service caught, tagged, and set free 124 catfish. A few weeks later they caught and set free 140 catfish. Thirty-five had tags. Estimate the number of catfish in the lake. **496 catfish**
13. a. An ecology class is helping the local conservation society determine the squirrel population in a city park. In early October, the students and society members captured, tagged, and set free 68 squirrels. Three weeks later, of 84 squirrels captured, 16 had tags. Estimate the number of squirrels in the park. **357 squirrels**
    b. *Reasoning* Suppose some squirrels lost their tags. How would this affect your estimate of the squirrel population? **The estimate would be too low.**

> **PORTFOLIO**
> For your portfolio, choose one or two items from your work for this chapter. Here are some possibilities:
> - a journal entry
> - corrected work
> - part of your project
>
> Explain why you have included each selection.

Mixed Review

14. *Geometry* $\triangle PQR \cong \triangle XYZ$. Find the angle measures and side lengths of $\triangle XYZ$. (Lesson 7-5)
    $m\angle X = 34$, $m\angle Y = 90$, $m\angle Z = 56$; $XY = 9$, $YZ = 6$, $XZ \approx 10.8$

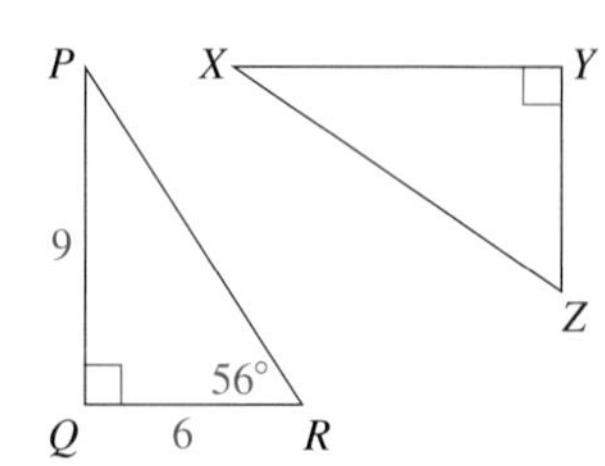

Write each decimal as a fraction in simplest form. (Lesson 4-9)

15. 0.096 $\frac{12}{125}$
16. 0.875 $\frac{7}{8}$
17. 0.26 $\frac{13}{50}$
18. 1.85 $1\frac{17}{20}$
19. 8.5 $8\frac{1}{2}$
20. 6.04 $6\frac{1}{25}$
21. 0.18 $\frac{9}{50}$
22. 0.05 $\frac{1}{20}$

23. *Shopping* A \$75 dollar coat is on sale for \$52.50. What percent of the regular price is the sale price? (Lesson 6-7) **70%**
24. *Choose a Strategy* The manager of a cafeteria ordered three times as many plain bagels as onion bagels. He ordered the same number of onion and garlic bagels. He ordered 285 bagels in all. How many of each kind of bagel did he order? **171 plain, 57 onion, and 57 garlic bagels**

Extra Practice, Lesson 9-8, page 522

FINISHING THE CHAPTER PROJECT

PROJECT DAY You may wish to plan a project day on which students share their completed projects. Encourage students to explain their process as well as their product.

PROJECT NOTEBOOK Ask students to review their project work and bring their notebooks up to date.

Have students review their methods for designing, making, and demonstrating their three number cubes for the project.

SCORING RUBRIC

3 You design and construct three cubes (A, B, and C) so that A beats B, B beats C, and C beats A. You provide sample spaces for the cubes in the Project Link on page 415 as well as for each of the three pairs of cubes that you designed. Your work also includes either explanations or experimental data showing that your cubes work as predicted.

2 You construct three cubes, and your sample spaces for each pair of cubes show correctly that these cubes satisfy the requirements of the project.

1 You build cubes but either your sample spaces are incorrect or your cubes don't behave as required by the project description.

0 You do not build the cubes, or you fail to use sample spaces or explanations to prove that your cubes behave as they should.

FINISHING THE CHAPTER PROJECT

CHAPTER PROJECT

Everybody Wins

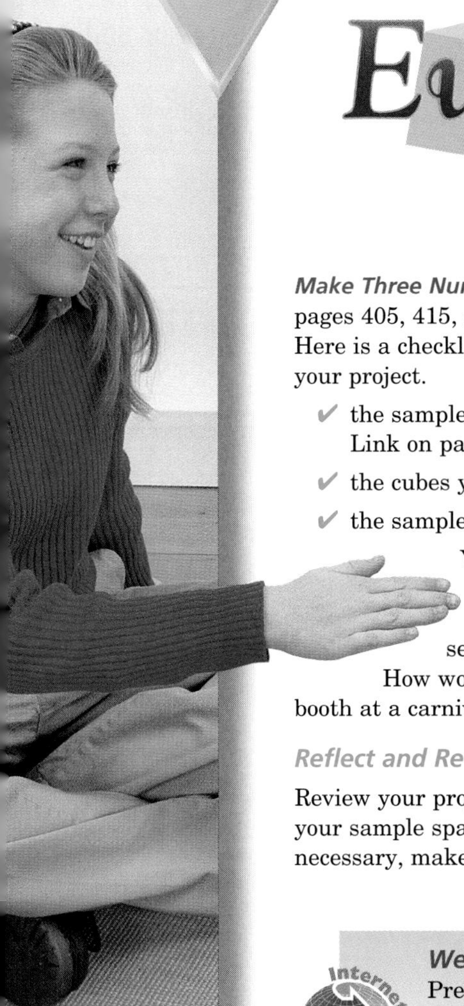

Make Three Number cubes The Project Link questions on pages 405, 415, and 421 should help you complete your project. Here is a checklist to help you gather together the parts of your project.

- ✔ the sample space for Cubes A and B from the Project Link on page 415
- ✔ the cubes you designed
- ✔ the sample spaces for each pair of cubes

Your number cubes should have the property that A usually beats B and B usually beats C, yet C usually beats A. Roll your cubes several times to verify they have this property. How would you use them if you were in charge of a booth at a carnival?

Reflect and Revise

Review your project with a friend or someone at home. Are your sample spaces clear? Are your calculations correct? If necessary, make revisions in the design of your cubes.

Web Extension

Prentice Hall's Internet site contains information you might find helpful as you complete your project. Visit www.phschool.com/mgm2/ch9 for some links and ideas related to probability.

STUDENT SELF-ASSESSMENT SURVEY

Chapter 9 Student Self-Assessment Survey

1. Now that you have finished this chapter, think about what you have learned about probability. Check each topic that you feel confident you understand.
   - ______ find the experimental probability of an event (9-1)
   - ______ use simulations to find experimental probability (9-1)
   - ______ use simulation to solve a problem (9-2)
   - ______ find the theoretical probability of an event (9-3)
   - ______ find the probability of a complement (9-3)
   - ______ find a sample space (9-4)
   - ______ use the counting principle (9-4)
   - ______ find the probability of independent and dependent events (9-5)
   - ______ find permutations (9-6)
   - ______ find combinations (9-7)
   - ______ use the capture/recapture method to estimate population (9-8)
2. Before the Chapter Assessment, I need to review ______________________
3. **a.** Check one. In general, I thought this chapter was

   ____ a snap ____ easy ____ average ____ hard ____ a monster

   b. Why do you feel this way? ______________________
4. In this chapter, I did my best work on ______________________
5. In this chapter, I had trouble with ______________________
6. Check each one that applies. Now that I've spent some time studying probability, I think it is

   ____ important ____ boring ____ useful ____ fun

   ____ a waste of time ____ confusing ____ tricky ____ interesting
7. What is a situation in your everyday life in which it is helpful to know something about probability? Explain. ______________________
8. Did you like working with simulations? ________ Explain. ______________________

Vocabulary/Symbols

capture/recapture, combination, complement, counting principle, dependent, equally likely, event, experimental probability, fair, independent, outcomes, permutation, probability, sample space, theoretical probability, trial

Resources

Student Edition

Extra Practice, p. 522

Glossary/Study Guide

Teaching Resources

Chapter Support File, Ch. 9

- Student Self-Assessment Survey

Glossary, Spanish Resources

Tools for Studying Smarter

WRAP UP

Exercises 1–7 Encourage students to show their formulas for finding the probability or complement for these exercises.

ASSESSMENT **Exercise 8** Students work with partners. Each pair writes all the possible dinner combinations on a piece of paper. Each pair compares lists with another pair.

Exercise 9 Remind students that student council members cannot hold more than one office.

Exercises 13 and 14 Have students state whether the situation is a permutation or a combination before answering the question.

WRITING **Exercise 15** Remind students that a simulation is an experiment that models the situation in the problem. Have the class offer suggestions for the simulation, and write the suggestions on the board. Have each student

9 WRAP UP

Probability 9-1, 9-3

You can find the **experimental probability** of an event using this formula.

$$P(\text{event}) = \frac{\text{number of times an event occurs}}{\text{total number of experiments}}$$

You can find the **theoretical probability** of an event using this formula.

$$P(\text{event}) = \frac{\text{number of favorable outcomes}}{\text{number of possible outcomes}}$$

The sum of the probability of an event and the probability of its **complement** is 1.

A card is drawn at random. Find each probability.

T	R	U	M	P	E	T

1. selecting a P $\frac{1}{7}$
2. selecting a T $\frac{2}{7}$
3. not selecting a P $\frac{6}{7}$

Use the cards above to find the complement of each event.

4. selecting a T $\frac{5}{7}$
5. selecting an E $\frac{6}{7}$
6. selecting a consonant $\frac{2}{7}$

7. **a.** *Games* You draw 10 marbles from a bag that contains 60 marbles. Three are blue, four red, one yellow, and two green. Find P(blue), P(red), P(yellow), P(green). $\frac{3}{10}, \frac{2}{5}, \frac{1}{10}, \frac{1}{5}$
   b. Based on your answers to part (a), predict the number of marbles of each color in the bag. 18 blue, 24 red, 6 yellow, and 12 green marbles

Sample Space and the Counting Principle 9-4

The **sample space** is the set of all possible outcomes of an event. You can use the **counting principle** to find the number of outcomes for an event with more than one step by multiplying the number of outcomes for each step.

8. **a.** At the China Panda, if you order the Family Dinner, you choose one appetizer, one soup, and one main dish from the menu at the right. Use a tree diagram to find the sample space of all the possible dinners. See back of book.
   b. Use the counting principle to find the number of possible dinners. 12 dinners

Appetizers	Soups
Egg Rolls	Won-ton
Fried Won-tons	Sizzling Rice

Main Dishes
Almond Chicken
Sweet & Sour Pork
Beef with Broccoli

9. Use the counting principle. Find the number of ways the offices of president, secretary, and treasurer can be filled from the 12-member student council. 1,320 ways

perform one of the simpler suggestions, such as tossing a coin five times. Record their results, and find the mean for the class.

Remind students that the new mathematical terms in this chapter are defined in the Glossary/Study Guide in the back of the textbook.

Independent and Dependent Events 9-5

Two events are **independent** if the outcome of the first event *does not* affect the outcome of the second event.

You can find the probability of two independent events using this formula.

$$P(A \text{ and } B) = P(A) \times P(B).$$

Two events are **dependent** if the outcome of the first event *does* affect the outcome of the second event.

You can find the probability of two dependent events using this formula.

$$P(A, \text{ then } B) = P(A) \times P(B \text{ after } A)$$

Classify each pair of events as *independent* or *dependent*.

10. You select a card from a set of cards. Without returning the card you select a second card. dependent

11. You roll a standard number cube once. Then you roll it again. independent

12. **Choose A, B, C, or D.** A jar contains 5 blue, 3 red, and 2 green marbles. What is the probability of choosing a red marble and then another red marble when the first marble is *not* replaced? B

A. $\frac{1}{5}$ B. $\frac{1}{15}$ C. $\frac{3}{10}$ D. $\frac{3}{100}$

Permutations and Combinations 9-6, 9-7

A **permutation** is an arrangement of a set of objects where order is important. A **combination** is an arrangement of objects where order does not matter.

13. Five students compete on a relay team. Only four of them can race at a time. How many different teams are possible? 5 teams

14. Four students are selected for a relay team. In how many ways can they line up for the race? 24 ways

Problem Solving Strategies and Estimating Population Size 9-2, 9-8

You can simulate some problems by tossing a coin or rolling a number cube. To estimate population size, you can use the *capture/recapture* method.

15. *Writing* In a basketball game, Charlie usually makes one out of two baskets. Describe a simulation to find the probability that he will make four out of five baskets. Answers may vary. Sample: Toss 5 coins. Count the number of heads. Repeat 25 times.

16. *Biology* Researchers marked 22 lions in an area. They make an aerial count of 68 lions, 16 of which are marked. Estimate the lion population. about 94 lions

CHAPTER ASSESSMENT • FORM A

Chapter 9 Assessment • Form A

Use the spinner below to answer Exercises 1–5.

Answers

1. What is P(△) for the spinner? Write your answer as a fraction, a decimal, and a percent.

1. $\frac{3}{8}$; 0.375; 37.5%

2. Which event is least likely, the spinner stopping on △, □, or ⬠?

2. stopping on ⬠

3. What is the probability of the spinner *not* stopping on ⬠? Write your answer as a fraction, a decimal, and a percent.

3. $\frac{6}{8}$ or $\frac{3}{4}$; 0.75; 75%

4. Find P(△ or ⬠). Write your answer as a fraction, a decimal, and a percent.

4. $\frac{5}{8}$; 0.625; 62.5%

5. What is the complement of P(⬠ or △)?

5. 0.375

6. Suppose you use another spinner that also includes a hexagon. The square is spun 12 times The triangle is spun 14 times. The pentagon is spun 6 times, and the hexagon is spun 10 times. Write P(□) as a fraction in simplest form.

6. $\frac{2}{7}$

7. A coin is tossed three times. List the sample space.

7. HHH, HHT, HTH, THH, TTH, THT, HTT, TTT

8. You have 6 pairs of socks in your drawer, 3 pairs blue and 3 pairs black. Without looking in the drawer, the first sock you pull out is blue. It is not returned. What is the probability that the second sock you pull out will be blue?

8. $\frac{5}{11}$

9. Two number cubes are rolled. What is the probability that each shows a 4?

9. $\frac{1}{36}$

10. How many two-letter permutations can be made from the letters L, M, N, O, and P?

10. 20 permutations

11. How many three-letter combinations can be made from the letters in the word BLACK?

11. 10 combinations

12. Researchers marked 36 pike in a pond. Then they counted 20 pike, 12 of which were marked. Estimate the pike population.

12. 60 pike

Assessment

CHAPTER ASSESSMENT • FORM A

Chapter 9 Assessment • Form A (continued)

Use the information below for Exercises 13 and 14.

A restaurant offers the following choices for breakfast:
Eggs: scrambled, fried, or poached
Meat: bacon, sausage, or ham
Toast: wheat, white, rye, or pumpernickel

13. How many different breakfast combinations are possible if one item is selected from each list of eggs, meat, and toast choices?

13. 36 combinations

14. The Super Breakfast allows you to select two items from the meat list. How many breakfast combinations are possible if you select one each of the eggs and toast choices and two different meat choices?

14. 36 combinations

Choose A, B, C, or D.

15. Which of the following are considered independent events?

A. You select one card from a deck. Without putting the card back, you select another card.
B. You roll a number cube. If you get a 6, you roll again.
C. You toss a coin and write down the result. You toss the coin again and write down the result.
D. You draw a red marble from a bag of red, green, and blue marbles. Then you draw another marble from the bag without putting the first marble back in the bag.

15. C

Choose a Strategy

16. Roy is trying to collect all nine baseball cards of the All Star team. Each package of cards he can buy has one card of a member of the team. The cards are equally distributed among all the packages. How could you use a simulation to estimate the number of packages of cards Roy will need to buy to get all nine cards?

16. Answers may vary. Sample: Make a spinner with the numbers 1 to 9. Then spin until each of the numbers comes up at least once. Count the number of spins.

Writing

17. You randomly pick a number from 1 to 10, and then you must pick a different number from 1 to 10. Explain why these two events are dependent. The outcome of the second pick is dependent on the outcome of the first pick.

CHAPTER ASSESSMENT • FORM B

Chapter 9 Assessment • Form B

Choose the best answer. Circle A, B, C, or D.
Use the spinner for Exercises 1–6.

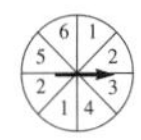

1. What is $P(2)$?
   Ⓐ $\frac{1}{4}$ B. $\frac{1}{5}$ C. $\frac{1}{6}$ D. $\frac{1}{8}$
2. What is P(a number less than 4)?
   A. $\frac{3}{8}$ B. $\frac{1}{2}$ Ⓒ $\frac{5}{8}$ D. $\frac{7}{8}$
3. Which events have the same probability?
   Ⓐ 1 and 2 B. 1 and 3 C. 1 and 4 D. 1 and 5
4. What is the probability of the spinner *not* stopping on 1?
   A. 0.25 B. 0.5 Ⓒ 0.75 D. 1
5. What is P(even)?
   A. 12.5% B. 25% C. 37.5% Ⓓ 50%
6. What is the complement of the event: 1 or 2?
   A. 3 B. 1 and 2
   Ⓒ 3, 4, 5, or 6 D. odd
7. A coin is tossed four times. How many outcomes are there in the sample space?
   A. 4 outcomes B. 8 outcomes Ⓒ 16 outcomes D. 32 outcomes
8. Paula's two-year-old daughter has 2 pairs of shoes, 4 shirts, 3 pairs of pants, and 5 pairs of socks. In how many different outfits can Paula dress her daughter?
   A. 14 outfits B. 40 outfits C. 60 outfits Ⓓ 120 outfits
9. If the five pairs of socks are different colors, in how many ways can Paula's daughter choose 2 socks of different colors to wear?
   A. 14 ways Ⓑ 10 ways C. 8 ways D. 5 ways
10. Researchers marked 48 geese in an area. Then they made an aerial count of 16, 12 of which were marked. Estimate the goose population.
    A. 4 B. 36 Ⓒ 64 D. 128

Assessment

CHAPTER ASSESSMENT • FORM B

Chapter 9 Assessment • Form B (continued)

11. Which of the following are considered dependent events?
    A. You roll a number cube and get a 5. You roll it again and get a 3.
    B. You roll two number cubes and get a 4 on each cube.
    Ⓒ You roll a number cube. If you get a 1, you roll again.
    D. You roll two number cubes. The total on the two cubes is 7.
12. Three number cubes are rolled. What is the probability that each cube shows a 6?
    A. $\frac{1}{6}$ B. $\frac{1}{36}$ Ⓒ $\frac{1}{216}$ D. $\frac{1}{1,296}$
13. You have 15 marbles in a bag. Three are red, five are white, and seven are black. On the first draw you get a black marble. If it is not replaced, what is the probability that the second marble you draw is also black?
    A. $\frac{1}{6}$ Ⓑ $\frac{3}{7}$ C. $\frac{2}{3}$ D. $\frac{1}{7}$
14. How many three-letter permutations can be made from the letters in the word ORANGE?
    A. 6 B. 12 C. 60 Ⓓ 120
15. How many four-letter combinations can be made from the letters A, B, C, D, and E?
    Ⓐ 5 B. 8 C. 12 D. 16
16. Five coins were used to simulate a litter of 5 puppies. The five coins were tossed 10 times with the results shown. What is the probability that exactly 3 puppies are male as suggested by the simulation if heads means male and tails means female?

HTHTT	TTHTH
HHHTT	HHHHT
TTTTH	HTTHH
TTHTT	HTTTT
HHTTH	TTHHH

    A. $\frac{1}{10}$ B. $\frac{1}{5}$ Ⓒ $\frac{2}{5}$ D. $\frac{3}{10}$

Choose a Strategy

17. There is a miniature animal in each box of tea bags. There are 4 different animals in all. Describe a simulation from which you could estimate how many months it will take to collect all 4 if you buy one box of tea each month?
    Sample: Make a spinner with the numbers 1 to 4. Then spin until each of the numbers occurs at least once. Count the number of spins. This is one estimate of how many months you will need to buy tea.

Teaching Resources

Chapter Support File, Ch. 9, and Spanish Resources

Teacher's Edition

See pp. 390C–D for Assessment Options.

Teaching Resource Software

- Computer Item Generator, Ch. 9

ASSESSMENT

Exercise 1 Remind students to write their fractions in simplest form.

WRITING EXERCISES allow students to describe more fully their thinking and understanding of the concepts they've learned. **Exercise 9** is a writing exercise.

ENHANCED MULTIPLE CHOICE QUESTIONS are more complex than traditional multiple choice questions, which assess only one skill. Enhanced multiple choice questions assess the processes that students use, as well as the end results. They are written so that students can use more than one strategy to solve the problem. Using multiple strategies is encouraged by the National Council of Teachers of Mathematics (NCTM). **Exercise 10** is an enhanced multiple choice question.

9 ASSESSMENT

1. Use the data at the right. Write each probability as a fraction, a decimal, and a percent.

Marker Color	Number Drawn
purple	6
green	2
white	3
black	5

   a. P(purple)
   b. P(green)
   c. P(orange) 0; 0; 0%
   a. $\frac{3}{8}$; 0.375; 37.5% b. $\frac{1}{8}$; 0.125; 12.5%
2. Factory workers test 80 batteries. Four batteries are defective. Find the probability that a battery from the factory is defective. Write the probability as a percent. 5%
3. There are six open containers arranged as shown. A ball is tossed and falls into one of the containers. Find the probability of each event.

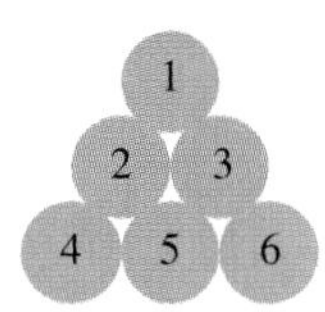

   a. $P(4)$ $\frac{1}{6}$ b. P(even number) $\frac{1}{2}$
   c. P(a number greater than 4) $\frac{1}{3}$
4. Suppose you have a bag that contains 6 blue, 3 red, 2 green, and 1 white marble. All marbles are equally likely to be drawn from the bag. Find each probability.
   a. P(blue) $\frac{1}{2}$ b. P(white) $\frac{1}{12}$
   c. P(blue or white) $\frac{7}{12}$ d. P(red or blue) $\frac{3}{4}$
   e. P(blue, then white when blue is not replaced) $\frac{1}{22}$
5. The letters of the word HALLOWEEN are written on a set of cards. You are equally likely to get any card. What is the probability of selecting an L, then a W? The first card is *not* replaced before selecting the second card. $\frac{1}{36}$
6. Suppose that the probability that you make a basket each time you shoot is 0.2. What is the probability that you will *not* make a basket? 0.8
7. Javier is buying a new car. He has a choice of 3 models, 8 colors, and 2 interiors. How many different car choices does he have? 48 choices
8. a. Find the number of two-letter permutations of the letters A, B, C. 8a. 6 permutations
   b. Find the number of two-letter combinations of the letters A, B, C. 3 combinations
9. *Writing* Fifty students chosen at random were asked what kind of pizza crust they liked best. Fifteen preferred thick crust. There are 940 students in the school. What would you do to estimate the number of students in the school who prefer thick crust? See below.
10. **Choose A, B, C, or D.** You are equally likely to get one of four prizes when you buy Good Morning cereal. You want to find out how many boxes of cereal you should buy to get all four prizes. Which of the following is *not* a true statement? B
    A. You can simulate buying the cereal by using a spinner divided into four equal sections. One trial ends when the spinner has stopped in each of the sections at least once. Average the results of several trials.
    B. The result of the simulation is the exact number of boxes you will need to buy.
    C. The more trials you have, the better your results.
    D. A possible answer is 4 boxes.

9. Find the ratio of the number who preferred thick crust to the number chosen. Then multiply by the total number of students.

Cumulative Review

Item	Review Topic	Ch
1	Unit rates	6
2, 8	Fractions	5
3, 9, 10	Geometry and measurement	8
4, 7	Probability	9
5	Similarity	6
6	Percents	6
11	Exponents	4
12	Classifying angles	7

9 Cumulative Review

Choose the best answer.

1. Which jar of peanut butter is the best buy? B
   A. an 18-oz jar for $1.69
   B. a 30-oz jar for $2.59
   C. a 32-oz jar for $2.89
   D. a 24-oz jar for $2.09

2. Sarah bought a remnant of fabric $5\frac{1}{8}$ yards long to make pennants for the school fair. How many pennants can she make if $\frac{3}{4}$ yd is needed for each pennant? B
   A. 5 B. 6 C. 7 D. 8

3. *Estimation* If the area of the shaded region is 4 in.^{2}, what is the best estimate for the area of the unshaded region? C
   A. 4 in.^{2}
   B. 8 in.^{2}
   C. 12 in.^{2}
   D. 16 in.^{2}

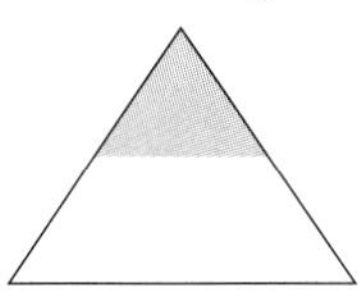

4. Which event does *not* have a 50% theoretical probability of occurring? D
   A. getting heads on one toss of a coin
   B. drawing a red marble from a bag that has 3 red, 2 blue, and 1 yellow marble
   C. rolling a number cube and getting an even number
   D. rolling a number cube and getting either a 5 or a 6

5. Rectangle $ABCD$ and rectangle $AXYZ$ are similar. How long is $\overline{XY}$? C
   A. 2.5 cm
   B. 2 cm
   C. 1.6 cm
   D. 1.5 cm

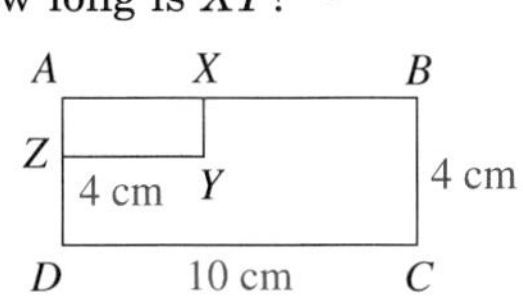

6. Which one does *not* equal the others? B
   A. 4% of 3,000 B. 40% of 30
   C. 40% of 300 D. 30% of 400

7. If the two spinners are each spun once, what is the probability that the sum of the numbers spun is 10? B
   A. 0 B. $\frac{1}{4}$ C. $\frac{1}{2}$ D. 1

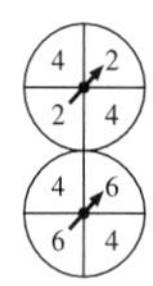

8. The least common denominator of three fractions is 42. Two of the fractions are $\frac{5}{3}$ and $\frac{6}{7}$. Which fraction could be the third one? D
   A. $\frac{10}{21}$ B. $\frac{1}{35}$ C. $\frac{17}{284}$ D. $\frac{9}{14}$

9. What is the volume of a rectangular prism that has dimensions 1 in., 2 in., and 3 in.? C
   A. 27 in.^{3} B. 18 in.^{3}
   C. 6 in.^{3} D. 12 in.^{3}

10. A circle has circumference 56.52 ft. What is its area? Use 3.14 for π. A
    A. 254.34 ft^2 B. 56.52 ft^2
    C. 28.26 ft^2 D. 1,017.36 ft^2

11. What is 64 written in exponential form? D
    A. 2^6 B. 4^3 C. 8^2
    D. All of the above are correct.

12. In the diagram at the right, which two angles are adjacent angles? A
    A. $\angle EOD$, $\angle DOC$ B. $\angle BOC$, $\angle BOD$
    C. $\angle AOE$, $\angle BOC$ D. $\angle AOB$, $\angle EOD$

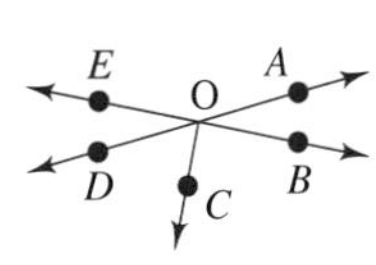

CUMULATIVE REVIEW

Chapter 9 Cumulative Review

Choose the best answer. Circle A, B, C, or D.

1. What is the area of the trapezoid below?

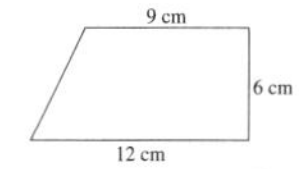

   A. 36 cm^2 (B.) 63 cm^2
   C. 64 cm^2 D. 126 cm^2

2. What is the length of the side of a square with area 2.25 m^2?
   A. 15 m (B.) 1.5 m
   C. 0.15 m D. 0.015 m

3. A triangle has sides measuring 5 cm, 7 cm, and 13 cm. Which formula could you use to find out whether the triangle is a right triangle?
   A. $A = \frac{1}{2}bh$
   B. $C = r^2$
   (C.) $a^2 + b^2 = c^2$
   D. $P = s_1 + s_2 + s_3$

4. In $\triangle ABC$ below, $\overline{BD}$ is the perpendicular bisector of $\overline{AC}$. The height is 8 in. and the base is 12 in. What are the lengths of $\overline{AB}$ and $\overline{BC}$?

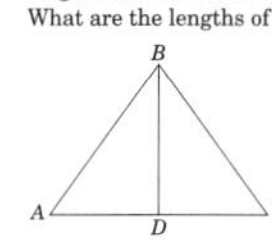

   A. 8 in. B. 9 in.
   (C.) 10 in. D. 12 in.

5. Margaret wants to paint a rectangular toy box that is 2 ft wide by 1.5 ft high by 4 ft long. One quart of paint will cover 100 ft^2. How many quarts of paint will she need to buy if she puts two coats on both the inside and outside of the toy box?
   A. 1 qt (B.) 2 qt
   C. 3 qt D. 4 qt

6. Which is between 5 and 6?
   A. $5\frac{1}{2} + 2\frac{1}{4}$ B. $4\frac{3}{5} + 2\frac{3}{4}$
   C. $11\frac{2}{3} - 6\frac{7}{8}$ (D.) $9\frac{1}{3} - 3\frac{4}{5}$

7. Solve $x - \frac{3}{4} = 9\frac{1}{2}$.
   (A.) $10\frac{1}{4}$ B. 10
   C. $9\frac{3}{4}$ D. $8\frac{3}{4}$

8. The length of a room is 12 ft 4 in. The width is 15 ft 6 in. What is the area of the room in square feet?
   A. $17\frac{5}{6}$ ft^2 B. 180 ft^2
   C. $180\frac{1}{6}$ ft^2 (D.) $191\frac{1}{6}$ ft^2

9. Solve $\frac{5}{6}t = 9$.
   A. $7\frac{1}{2}$ B. 9
   C. 10 (D.) $10\frac{4}{5}$

10. A bicycle is on sale at $\frac{1}{3}$ off the original price of $276. What is the sale price of the bike?
    A. $83 B. $92
    (C.) $184 D. $201

Assessment

CUMULATIVE REVIEW

Chapter 9 Cumulative Review (continued)

11. In the figure below, what is the ratio of the shaded area to the unshaded area?

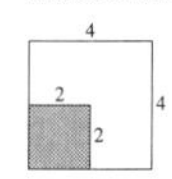

    A. $\frac{1}{4}$ (B.) $\frac{1}{3}$
    C. $\frac{3}{4}$ D. $\frac{4}{5}$

12. Jan earned $125 last week. If she worked 5 h each day, Monday through Friday, how much did she make per hour?
    A. $25 (B.) $5
    C. $4.25 D. $3.57

13. The trapezoids are similar. What is the length of $\overline{CD}$?

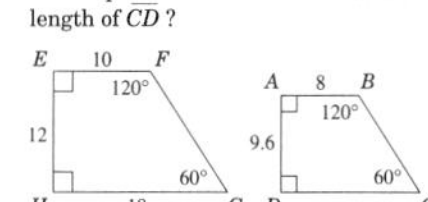

    A. 12 B. 22
    (C.) 14.4 D. 12.4

14. Which proportion will help you find 36% of 290?
    A. $\frac{36}{290} = \frac{n}{100}$ B. $\frac{290}{36} = \frac{n}{100}$
    (C.) $\frac{n}{290} = \frac{36}{100}$ D. $\frac{100}{290} = \frac{n}{36}$

15. Ragan made $5.25 per hour before he received a raise of $.50 per hour. What percent increase is this, rounded to the nearest tenth of a percent?
    A. 10.5% B. 10%
    (C.) 9.5% D. 9%

16. Two angles in a triangle measure 38° and 56°. What type of angle is the third angle?
    A. right B. straight
    C. obtuse (D.) acute

17. A bag contains red, blue, white, and yellow chips. You draw a chip, replace it, and draw another. How many possible outcomes are there?
    A. 4 B. 10
    C. 12 (D.) 16

18. You draw out a second chip from the bag of chips in Exercise 17 above without replacing the first chip. What can you say about the two events?
    (A.) They are dependent.
    B. They are equally likely.
    C. They are independent.
    D. They are unlikely.

19. You know that there are 3 red chips, 4 blue chips, 6 white chips, and 5 yellow chips in a bag. What is the probability that the first two chips you draw are both red if you do not replace the first chip?
    A. $\frac{2}{9}$ B. $\frac{5}{35}$
    C. $\frac{1}{54}$ (D.) $\frac{1}{51}$

Choose a Strategy

20. If you start with a number, add 6, multiply by 2, and then subtract 7, the result is 9. What was the original number?
    A. 5 (B.) 2
    C. 3 D. 4

Resources

Teaching Resources

Chapter Support File, Ch. 9
- Cumulative Review

Teacher's Edition

See pp. 390C–D for Assessment Options.

10 Algebra: Patterns and Functions

Chapter Overview

To accommodate flexible scheduling, most lessons are divided into parts. Assignment Options are given in the Teacher's Edition for each lesson.

Pages 434–437	**Lesson 10-1** **Number Patterns**
NCTM **2, 3, 4, 6, 8, 12**	**Part 1** Arithmetic Sequences **Part 2** Geometric and Other Sequences **Key terms:** sequence, term, arithmetic sequence, geometric sequence

Pages 438–440	**Lesson 10-2** **Measurement: Scientific Notation**
NCTM **2, 3, 4, 5, 8, 13**	**Part 1** Scientific Notation **Part 2** Standard Form **Key terms:** scientific notation, standard form **Project Link**

Pages 442–445	**Lesson 10-3** **Problem Solving Strategy**
NCTM **1, 5, 7, 9, 10, 11, 12**	**Solve a Simpler Problem** **Math at Work** **Checkpoint 1**

Pages 459–463	**Lesson 10-7** **Data Analysis: Interpreting Graphs**
NCTM **1, 3, 4, 5, 7, 13**	**Part 1** Describing Graphs **Part 2** Drawing Graphs **Alternative Activity** 10-7 **Project Link**

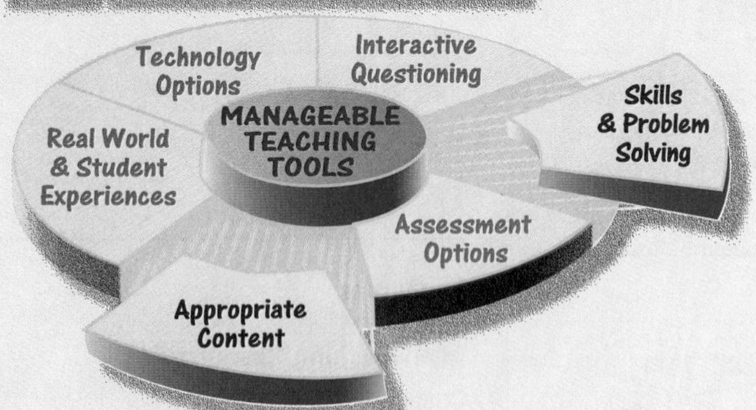

Pacing Options

This chart suggests pacing only for the core lessons and their parts. It is provided merely as a possible guide. It will help you determine how much time you have in your schedule to cover other features, such as the Chapter Project, Math Toolboxes, Wrap Up, and Assessment.

	1 Class Period	1 Class Period	1 Class Period	1
Traditional (40–45 min class periods)	10–1 (1) 10–1 (2)	10–2 (1) 10–2 (2)	10–3	
Block Scheduling (90 min class periods)	10-1 (1) 10-1 (2) 10-2 (1) 10-2 (2)	10–3 10–4 (1)	10–4 (2) 10–5 (1) 10–5 (2)	1(

CHAPTER PROJECT

THEME: SCIENCE

Happy Landings

Goal: Measuring how fast water drains from a container and graphing the data

NCTM STANDARDS

1 Problem Solving	6 Number Systems and Number Theory	10 Statistics
2 Communication	7 Computation and Estimation	11 Probability
3 Reasoning	8 Patterns and Functions	12 Geometry
4 Mathematical Connections	9 Algebra	13 Measurement
5 Number and Number Relationships		

Pages	Lesson	Pages	Lesson	Pages	Lesson
Pages 446–449	**Lesson 10-4 Technology: Simple and Compound Interest**	**Pages 450–453**	**Lesson 10-5 Using Tables, Rules, and Graphs**	**Pages 454–457**	**Lesson 10-6 Function Rules**
NCTM 1, 2, 3, 4, 5, 7, 8, 12	**Part 1** Simple Interest **Part 2** Compound Interest **Key terms:** simple interest, principle, balance, compound interest **Alternative Activity** 10-4 **Journal**	**NCTM 1, 4, 5, 8, 9, 12, 13**	**Part 1** Using Tables and Rules **Part 2** Graphing Functions **Key term:** function **Alternative Activity** 10-5 **Project Link**	**NCTM 1, 2, 4, 5, 8**	**Part 1** Making Tables **Part 2** Looking for Patterns **Journal** **Checkpoint 2**

Optional Materials and Manipulatives

pattern blocks (10-1)
graph paper (10-1, 10-5, 10-7)
spreadsheet software (10-4)

computer (10-4)
watch with second hand (10-5)
coin (10-7)

Optional calculator use is integrated throughout the course.

ass od	1 Class Period	1 Class Period	1 Class Period	1 Class Period	1 Class Period	1 Class Period	1 Class Period	1 Class Period	1 Class Period	1 Class Period
10–5 1	10–5 2	10–6 1	10–6 2 10–7 1	10–7 2						
10–7 2										

Meeting Individual Needs

Accommodating Diverse Learning Styles

In your Teacher's Edition, you will find suggestions as to how you can help students complete mathematical tasks in Chapter 10 by meeting individual needs and supporting various learning styles. Here are some examples:

VISUAL LEARNING
visualizing problems by using colored highlighters *(p. 442)*

TACTILE LEARNING
using play money to simulate a problem *(p. 447)*

AUDITORY LEARNING
counting places aloud as they move decimal points *(p. 438)*

KINESTHETIC LEARNING
making patterns on tiled floors with counters *(p. 434)*

EARLY FINISHERS
Performance-Based Project, MathBlaster® Mystery, Interdisciplinary Units

GIFTED AND TALENTED
exploring integer sequences on-line *(p. 436)*

DIVERSITY experimenting with a balance scale *(p. 444)*

ACQUIRING ENGLISH PROFICIENCY (AEP)
understanding the different ways to refer to numbers with exponents *(p. 438)*

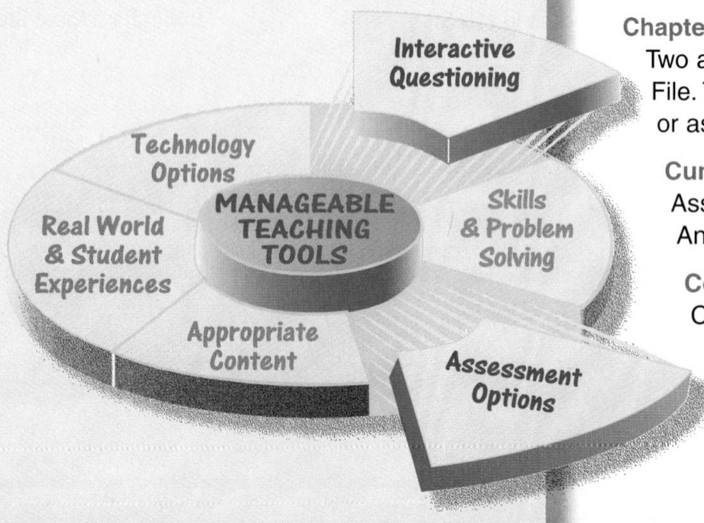

Assessing Progress

A broad range of assessment tools are available to reach a variety of learners.

INFORMAL ASSESSMENT

Informal assessments provide day-to-day feedback to help give you a picture of conceptual understanding and skill development.

ONGOING ASSESSMENT is built into lesson instruction and the Teaching Notes of the Teacher's Edition.

In the Teacher's Edition
Lesson Quiz for every lesson

In the Student Edition
On Your Own, Mixed Review, Journal, Portfolio, Project Link, Chapter Wrap Up

Look for **Interactive Questions** within lessons that

- **BUILD UNDERSTANDING** with labels such as **Analyze, Reasoning, Estimation, Writing, and Summarize**
- ✔ **CHECK UNDERSTANDING** with the **Try It Out** label.

FORMAL ASSESSMENT

Formal assessment can occur before and after the chapter, as well as at natural breaking points in the chapter.

Checkpoints
Two forms of each self-assessment Checkpoints are available: one in the Student Edition and another in the Chapter Support File in the Teaching Resources box.

- Mid-Chapter Checkpoint 1, page 445
- End-of-Chapter Checkpoint 2, page 457

Chapter 10 Assessment, page 468.
Two alternative forms are available in the Chapter Support File. They may be used after a chapter has been completed, or as a pre-test and post-test comparison.

Cumulative Review, page 469.
Assesses skills and concepts in Chapters 1–10. An alternative form is available in Chapter Support File.

Computer Item Generator for Chapter 10
Customized tests can be generated for each lesson and for mid-chapter and end-of-chapter assessments, and for pre- and post-test comparisons of achievement.

PERFORMANCE-BASED ASSESSMENT

CHAPTER PROJECT The Chapter Project in the student edition provides a real-world connection to the math context of the chapter. The Teacher's Edition contains a scoring rubric.

A Performance Assessment with a scoring rubric can be found in the Chapter Support File in the Teaching Resources box.

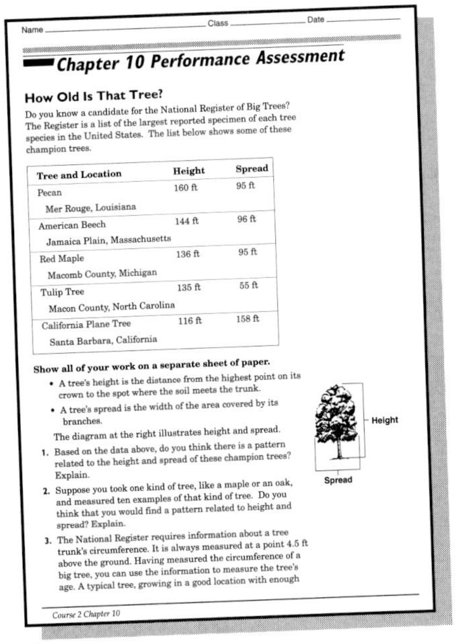

Name ______ Class ______ Date ______

Chapter 10 Performance Assessment

How Old Is That Tree?

Do you know a candidate for the National Register of Big Trees? The Register is a list of the largest reported specimen of each tree species in the United States. The list below shows some of these champion trees.

Tree and Location	Height	Spread
Pecan Mer Rouge, Louisiana	160 ft	95 ft
American Beech Jamaica Plain, Massachusetts	144 ft	96 ft
Red Maple Macomb County, Michigan	136 ft	95 ft
Tulip Tree Macon County, North Carolina	135 ft	55 ft
California Plane Tree Santa Barbara, California	116 ft	158 ft

Show all of your work on a separate sheet of paper.

- A tree's height is the distance from the highest point on its crown to the spot where the soil meets the trunk.
- A tree's spread is the width of the area covered by its branches.

The diagram at the right illustrates height and spread.

1. Based on the data above, do you think there is a pattern related to the height and spread of these champion trees? Explain.
2. Suppose you took one kind of tree, like a maple or an oak, and measured ten examples of that kind of tree. Do you think that you would find a pattern related to height and spread? Explain.
3. The National Register requires information about a tree trunk's circumference. It is always measured at a point 4.5 ft above the ground. Having measured the circumference of a big tree, you can use the information to measure the tree's age. A typical tree, growing in a good location with enough

Course 2 Chapter 10

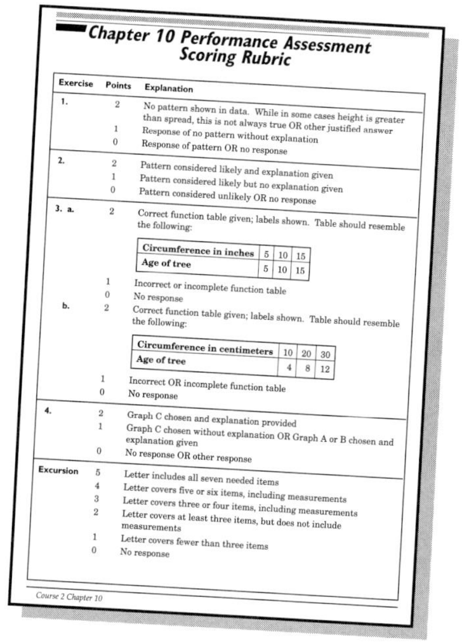

Chapter 10 Performance Assessment Scoring Rubric

Exercise	Points	Explanation
1.	2	No pattern shown in data. While in some cases height is greater than spread, this is not always true OR other justified answer
	1	Response of no pattern without explanation
	0	Response of pattern OR no response
2.	2	Pattern considered likely and explanation given
	1	Pattern considered likely but no explanation given
	0	Pattern considered unlikely OR no response
3. a.	2	Correct function table given; labels shown. Table should resemble the following: Circumference in inches: 5, 10, 15; Age of tree: 5, 10, 15
	1	Incorrect or incomplete function table
	0	No response
b.	2	Correct function table given; labels shown. Table should resemble the following: Circumference in centimeters: 10, 20, 30; Age of tree: 4, 8, 12
	1	Incorrect OR incomplete function table
	0	No response
4.	2	Graph C chosen and explanation provided
	1	Graph C chosen without explanation OR Graph A or B chosen and explanation given
	0	No response OR other response
Excursion	5	Letter includes all seven needed items
	4	Letter covers five or six items, including measurements
	3	Letter covers three or four items, including measurements
	2	Letter covers at least three items, but does not include measurements
	1	Letter covers fewer than three items
	0	No response

Course 2 Chapter 10

Correlation to Standardized Tests

		STANDARDIZED TEST ITEMS					
Lesson		CAT5	Terra Nova	ITBS, Form M	MAT7	SAT9	Local Test
10-1	Number Patterns	CA31	15, 35, 48				
10-2	Measurement: Scientific Notion						
10-3	Problem Solving Strategy: Solve a Simpler Problem						
10-4	Technology: Simple and Compound Interest						
10-5	Using Tables, Rules, and Graphs						
10-6	Function Rules	CA38					
10-7	Data Analysis: Interpreting Graphs						

CA: Concepts and Applications PR: Math Procedures MC: Math Computation CE: Concepts and Estimation
PS: Problem Solving CP: Concepts and Problem Solving PD: Problem Solving and Data Interpretation

See page 2D for the level of each test referenced.

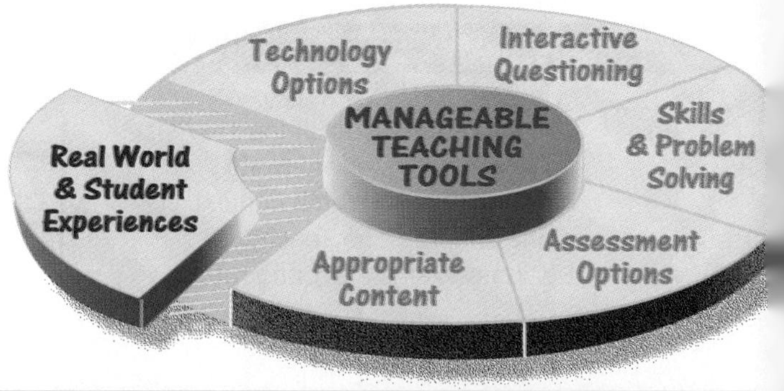

MAKING CONNECTIONS

TEAM TEACHING WITH PRENTICE HALL MATERIALS

INTERDISCIPLINARY EXPLORATIONS	PRENTICE HALL SCIENCE **L** Life Science **E** Earth Science **P** Physical Science
• ***The Power of Patterns*** **pp. 30 & 31**	**P Sec. 12–2 Measuring Motion**

Lesson	Interdisciplinary Connections	Real World Connections	Math Integration
10-1	Business Biology	Flowers Number Theory	Geometry
10-2	Science	Astronomy Hot Air Balloons	Measurement
10-3	Sports Business	City Planning	Algebra Statistics Geometry
10-4	Finance	Investing Banking Technology	Algebra Geometry
10-5	Sports	Scuba Diving Cars Data Collection Jobs	Algebra Geometry Measurement
10-6	Finance	Libraries Money	Algebra Geometry
10-7	Sports	Population Bicycling Driving	Measurement

School to Home

MATERIALS:
graph paper
newspaper
paper
pencil

English version is in the Chapter Support File. Spanish version is in the Spanish Resources.

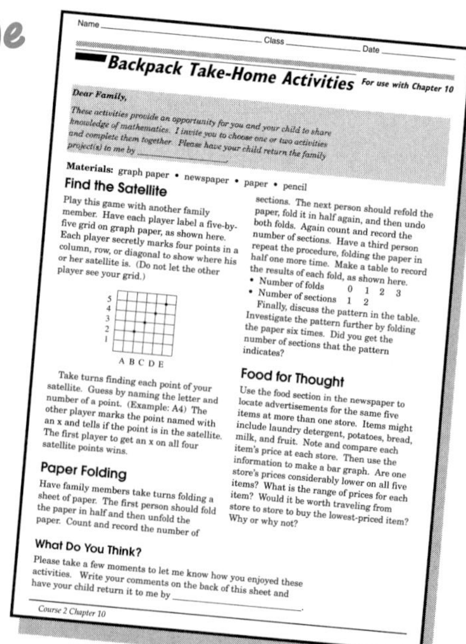

Name ______ Class ______ Date ______

Backpack Take-Home Activities *For use with Chapter 10*

Dear Family,

These activities provide an opportunity for you and your child to share knowledge of mathematics. I invite you to choose one or two activities and complete them together. Please have your child return the family project(s) to me by ______.

Materials: graph paper • newspaper • paper • pencil

Find the Satellite

Play this game with another family member. Have each player label a five-by-five grid on graph paper, as shown here. Each player secretly marks four points in a column, row, or diagonal to show where his or her satellite is. (Do not let the other player see your grid.)

Take turns finding each point of your satellite. Guess by naming the letter and number of a point. (Example: A4) The other player marks the point named with an x and tells if the point is in the satellite. The first player to get an x on all four satellite points wins.

Paper Folding

Have family members take turns folding a sheet of paper. The first person should fold the paper in half and then unfold the paper. Count and record the number of sections. The next person should refold the paper, fold it in half again, and then undo both folds. Again count and record the number of sections. Have a third person repeat the procedure, folding the paper in half one more time. Make a table to record the results of each fold, as shown here.

- Number of folds 0 1 2 3
- Number of sections 1 2

Finally, discuss the pattern in the table. Investigate the pattern further by folding the paper six times. Did you get the number of sections that the pattern indicates?

Food for Thought

Use the food section in the newspaper to locate advertisements for the same five items at more than one store. Items might include laundry detergent, potatoes, bread, milk, and fruit. Note and compare each item's price at each store. Then use the information to make a bar graph. Are one store's prices considerably lower on all five items? What is the range of prices for each item? Would it be worth traveling from store to store to buy the lowest-priced item? Why or why not?

What Do You Think?

Please take a few moments to let me know how you enjoyed these activities. Write your comments on the back of this sheet and have your child return it to me by ______.

Course 2 Chapter 10

Using Technology to Enhance Instruction

For the Student

Multimedia Math Hot Pages™

This interactive software and video package on CD-ROM integrates solid math content through a variety of media.

- Hot Page™ 6-1
- Hot Page™ 6-2
- Hot Page™ 6-3

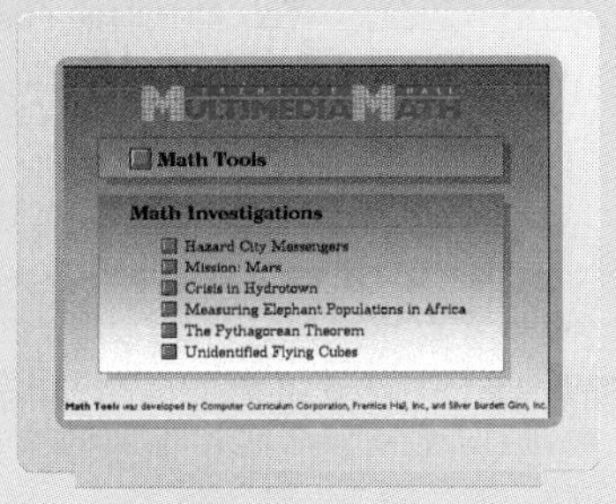

Multimedia Math Investigations

These in-depth interactive activities on CD-ROM develop real-world applications of mathematics. They allow students the opportunity to reinforce key concepts.

- Unidentified Flying Cubes

MathBlaster® Mystery

This award-winning, interactive software program on CD-ROM can be used to maintain skills or to accommodate early finishers.

- Level: Earn 4 coins; Pay 4 coins
- Mission Mode (all lessons)
- Kitchen Comparisons (10-6)
- Number Guesser (10-1)
- Equation Maker (10-2, 10-4)
- Word Problems (10-3, 10-5, 10-7, Problem Solving Practice)

Math Tools/Math Labs

This software, available on CD-ROM, includes on-screen Math Lab activities. Students use linkable, interactive tools to explore math concepts.

Interactive Student Tutorial

Available on CD-ROM, this test preparation program contains self-tests with questions in standardized test format. Software includes electronic versions of the text lessons and an on-line glossary.

Internet Connection

For Students

Support for the Chapter Project

A career-oriented link for Math at Work feature

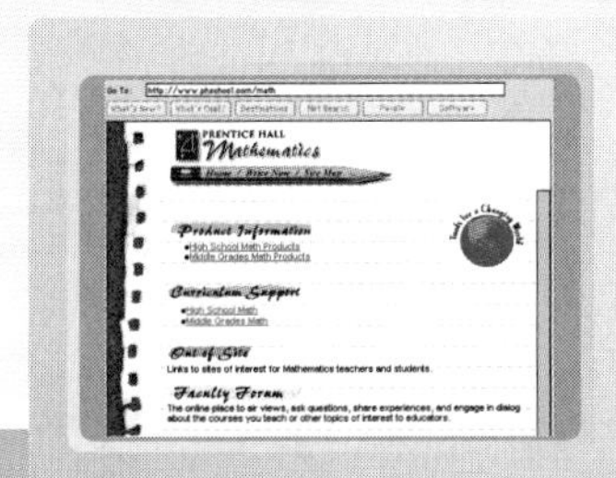

www.phschool.com/math

For teachers

Curriculum Support

Product Information

Regional Support Information

For the Teacher

Computer Item Generator with Standardized Test Practice

This software generates customized practice sheets and tests. It also generates unlimited practice sheets for the standardized tests listed on page 432D.

Resource Pro™ with Planning Express™

Available on CD-ROM, this software can be used to customize and plan lessons. It contains over 1,700 resource pages.

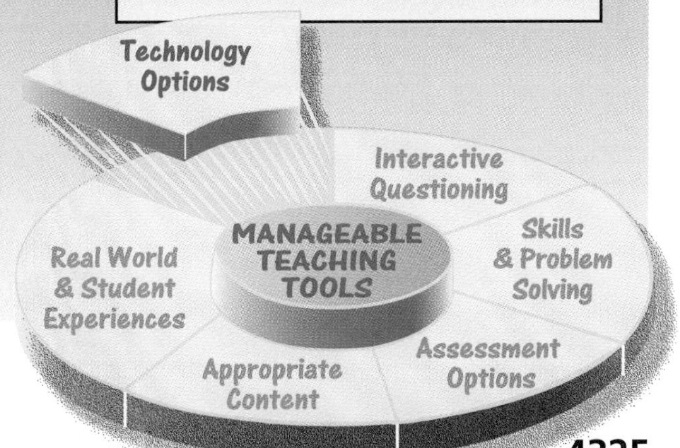

CHAPTER 10 ALGEBRA: PATTERNS AND FUNCTIONS

CONNECTING TO PRIOR LEARNING Ask students to name natural patterns that occur with the changing of the seasons. **Answers may vary. Sample: Temperatures rise in the summer and fall in the winter; winter days are shorter than summer days.** Discuss with students how the patterns might look displayed in a graph. Allow students to explore ideas on the chalkboard or overhead.

CULTURAL CONNECTIONS Many games we play are based on patterns. Tell students that the country of India is the source of the pattern-based games of chess and Parcheesi™.

INTERDISCIPLINARY CONNECTIONS Ask students: *How can a statistician use patterns to make general statements about a population based on a small sample?* **The statistician can apply the ratios found in the sample to the population as a whole.**

ABOUT THE PROJECT The Chapter Project has students use patterns to graph data on the loss of water from a container with a hole.

Internet • For information and activities related to the Chapter Project, visit the Prentice Hall site at www.phschool.com/mgm2/ch10

WHAT YOU WILL LEARN IN THIS CHAPTER
- How to use patterns to find sequences
- How to write numbers in scientific notation
- How to graph functions and write function rules

LAUNCHING THE CHAPTER PROJECT

Ask students:

- *What types of graphs have you used? How have you used the graphs?*
- *How do graphs show data?*
- *What important characteristics make a graph accurate and easy to read?*

PROJECT NOTEBOOK Encourage students to keep all project-related materials in a separate folder or notebook.

TRACKING THE PROJECT You may wish to have students read Finishing the Chapter Project on page 465 to help them get an overview of the project. Set benchmark deadlines for students to show you their work in progress.

CHAPTER PROJECT

THEME: SCIENCE

happy landings

Imagine this—you have just opened your parachute and you are floating through the air. Exciting, huh? How long it takes you to come to the ground can be predicted because the change in height versus time occurs in a predictable pattern. Many other things change in a predictable pattern, for instance, the height of a burning candle and the growth of money in a bank account.

Graphing Data For the chapter project, you will find how fast a container of water will empty if there is a hole in it. Your final project will be a graph of the data you collect.

Steps to help you complete the project:

p. 440 Project Link: *Measuring*
p. 453 Project Link: *Collecting Data*
p. 463 Project Link: *Graphing*
p. 465 *Finishing the Chapter Project*

- How to use simpler problems to solve more complex problems

SCORING RUBRIC

3 Your graph is clearly labeled and accurately reflects the water level across time. Your explanations are clear and concise. You include the data from your experiment.

2 Your graph is complete, and you explain your thinking and your observations clearly.

1 Your data, your graph, and your explanations are incomplete or do not provide a clear picture of your work.

0 You omit important parts of the project.

433

10-1 Teaching Notes

1 Focus

CONNECTING TO PRIOR KNOWLEDGE
Ask students:

- *What is a dozen?* **12 items**
- *Find the number of items in 1, 2, 3, 4, and 5 dozen. Describe the pattern.* **12, 24, 36, 48, 60; adding 12**

2 Teach

Work Together

Ask students to find the patterns by discussion, in addition to pattern blocks. Ask students to describe the pattern.

THINK AND DISCUSS

AEP Have students use a thesaurus or dictionary to look up the term *sequence*. Have students write definitions or synonyms in English and in their own first language.

KINESTHETIC LEARNING **Example 1** If your school has long hallways with square tiles, take students to a section of hall that is at least 50 tiles long. Have students start on one end of the hall and place counters on tiles 6, 13, 20, and 27. Continue placing chips on every seventh tile down the length of the hall.

Lesson Planning Options

Prerequisite Skills

- finding patterns (precourse)

Vocabulary/Symbols

sequence, term, arithmetic sequence, geometric sequence

Materials/Manipulatives

- pattern blocks
- graph paper

Resources

Student Edition

Skills Handbook, p. 530
Extra Practice, p. 523
Glossary/Study Guide

Teaching Resources

Chapter Support File, Ch. 10
- Lesson Planner 10-1
- Practice 10-1, Reteaching 10-1
- Answer Masters 10-1

Teaching Aids Masters 1, 2, 8, 19
Glossary, Spanish Resources

Transparencies
1, 7, 15, Minds on Math 10-1

Warm Up

Round to the nearest whole number and to the nearest tenth.
4.07 **4; 4.1**
0.708 **1; 0.7**
364.825 **365; 364.8**

10-1 Number Patterns

What You'll Learn

1. To identify and continue arithmetic sequences
2. To identify and continue geometric and other sequences

...And Why

A sunflower is just one place where you can see number patterns in nature.

Here's How

Look for questions that
- build understanding
- ✔ check understanding

Work Together

Exploring Patterns

Work with a partner to find a number pattern.
a. See back of book.

1. a. Use pattern blocks to make the next two figures in the pattern at the right.
   b. How many blocks do you add to each figure to make the next figure in the pattern? **6 blocks**
   c. Copy and complete the table.

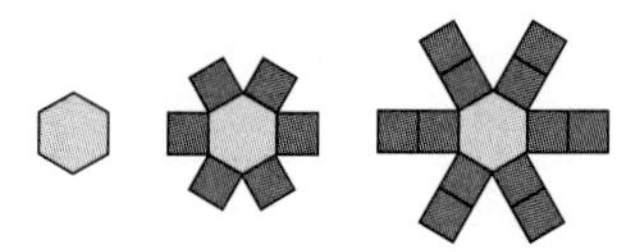

Figure 1 Figure 2 Figure 3

Figure	1	2	3	4	5	6	7	8
Total Blocks in Figure	■	■	■	■	■	■	■	■

1 7 13 19 25 31 37 43

THINK AND DISCUSS

1 Arithmetic Sequences

A **sequence** is a set of numbers that follow a pattern. In the Work Together, the list of numbers that tell the total blocks in a figure is a sequence. Each number in a sequence is a **term.**

You find each term of an **arithmetic sequence** by adding the same number to the preceding term. The three dots ". . . " in a sequence indicate that the pattern continues.

How? You pronounce arithmetic sequence as ar ith MEH tik SEE kwens.

EXAMPLE 1

a. Write a rule to describe the sequence 6, 13, 20, 27, ...

$6 \xrightarrow{+7} 13 \xrightarrow{+7} 20 \xrightarrow{+7} 27$

The rule is *Start with 6 and add 7 repeatedly.*

b. Find the next three terms in the sequence.

$27 + 7 = 34 \longrightarrow 34 + 7 = 41 \longrightarrow 41 + 7 = 48$

The next three terms are 34, 41, and 48.

REASONING Question 2a Remind students that adding a negative number is the same as subtracting a positive number.

ADDITIONAL EXAMPLES

FOR EXAMPLE 1

Write a rule to describe the sequence 100, 93, 86, 79, . . . **Start with 100 and add −7 repeatedly.**

FOR EXAMPLE 2

Write a rule to describe the sequence 2, 8, 32, 128, . . . **Start with 2 and multiply by 4 repeatedly.**

FOR EXAMPLE 3

Is 0, 2, 6, 12, . . . arithmetic, geometric, or neither? **neither**

Example 2 Point out to students that if a geometric sequence is decreasing, the multiplier is a fraction.

ERROR ALERT! Example 3 Students may think that this sequence is arithmetic because you add to find each term in the sequence. **Remediation:** Stress that in an arithmetic sequence, you add the same number repeatedly for each term in the sequence. For a geometric sequence, you multiply by the same number.

2. a. *Reasoning* What is added to each term to find the next term in the sequence 35, 29, 23, 17, . . . ? **−6**
   b. Write a rule for the sequence. Find the next three terms.

b. Start with 35 and add −6 repeatedly; 11, 5, −1.

Now you may assign Exercises 1–10.

2 *Geometric and Other Sequences*

In a **geometric sequence,** you multiply the preceding term by the same number repeatedly.

EXAMPLE 2

a. Write a rule to describe the sequence 1, 3, 9, 27, ...

1 → 3 → 9 → 27 (×3, ×3, ×3)

The rule is *Start with 1 and multiply by 3 repeatedly.*

b. Find the next three terms in the sequence.

$27 \times 3 = 81 \longrightarrow 81 \times 3 = 243 \longrightarrow 243 \times 3 = 729$

The next three terms are 81, 243, and 729.

3. *Try It Out* Write a rule for the sequence 800, 400, 200, 100, ... Then find the next three terms.
   Start with 800 and multiply by $\frac{1}{2}$ repeatedly; 50, 25, $12\frac{1}{2}$

Some sequences are neither arithmetic nor geometric.

EXAMPLE 3

Is 1, 2, 6, 24, . . . arithmetic, geometric, or neither? Explain.

1 → 2 → 6 → 24 (×2, ×3, ×4)

The sequence is neither arithmetic nor geometric because you do not add or multiply by the same number.

4. *Try It Out* Is each sequence arithmetic, geometric, or neither?
   a. 1, 3, 6, 10, . . . **neither**
   b. 2, 3, 6, 11, . . . **neither**
   c. 3, 6, 12, 24, . . . **geometric**
5. A sequence that often occurs in nature is the *Fibonnaci sequence,* which is 1, 1, 2, 3, 5, 8, . . .
   a. Is it arithmetic, geometric, or neither? **neither**
   b. *Try It Out* Find the next three terms of the sequence. **13, 21, 34**

The sunflower is an example of the Fibonacci sequence. The number of seed pods in each ring equals the sum of the pods in the two preceding rings.

Now you may assign Exercises 11–28.

Technology Options

Prentice Hall Technology

Software for Learners
- Hot Page™ 6–1*
- Math Blaster® Mystery*
- Interactive Student Tutorial, Chapter 10*

Teaching Resource Software
- Computer Item Generator 10-1
- Resource Pro™ Chapter 10*

Internet • For related mathematics activities, visit the Prentice Hall site at www.phschool.com/math

**Available on CD-ROM only*

Assignment Options for Exercises On Your Own

To provide flexible scheduling, this lesson can be split into parts.

1 **Core** 1–9
Extension 10

2 **Core** 11–26
Extension 27, 28

Use Mixed Review to maintain skills.

ASSESSMENT Have students write the first four terms of three original sequences: one arithmetic, one geometric, and one neither. Then have them exchange their sequences with a partner and try to find the next two in each term. Encourage students to share their sequences with the class.

EXTENSION Students can explore an online encyclopedia of integer sequences. The encyclopedia claims to contain over 28,000 different sequences! Visit this Web site at: http://www.research.att.com/~njas/sequence

3 Practice/Assess

EXERCISES *On Your Own*

REASONING **Exercise 10** Challenge students to find one arithmetic rule and one geometric rule.

WRITING **Exercise 28** Encourage students to write a rule for each type of sequence.

pages 436–437 On Your Own

1. Start with 5 and add 5 repeatedly; 25, 30, 35.
2. Start with 3 and add 4 repeatedly; 19, 23, 27.
3. Start with 34 and add −5 repeatedly; 14, 9, 4.
4. Start with 25 and add −4 repeatedly; 9, 5, 1.
5. Start with 63 and add −9 repeatedly; 27, 18, 9.
6. Start with −8 and add 7 repeatedly; 20, 27, 34.

11. Start with 1 and multiply by 2 repeatedly; 16, 32, 64.
12. Start with 2 and multiply by 3 repeatedly; 162; 486; 1,458.
13. Start with 600 and multiply by $\frac{1}{2}$ repeatedly; $37\frac{1}{2}$, $18\frac{3}{4}$, $9\frac{3}{8}$.
14. Start with 0.1 and multiply by 3 repeatedly; 8.1, 24.3, 72.9.
15. Start with $\frac{1}{4}$ and multiply by $\frac{1}{3}$ repeatedly; $\frac{1}{324}$, $\frac{1}{972}$, $\frac{1}{2,916}$.
16. Start with 0.5 and multiply by 3 repeatedly; 40.5, 121.5, 364.5.

25a. row 4: 1 2 3 4 3 2 1; row 5: 1 2 3 4 5 4 3 2 1; row 6: 1 2 3 4 5 6 5 4 3 2 1; row 7: 1 2 3 4 5 6 7 6 5 4 3 2 1

c. The sum of the numbers in each row is the square of the row number.

EXERCISES *On Your Own*

Write a rule for each arithmetic sequence. Then find the next three terms. 1–6. See margin.

1. 5, 10, 15, 20, . . .
2. 3, 7, 11, 15, . . .
3. 34, 29, 24, 19, . . .
4. 25, 21, 17, 13, . . .
5. 63, 54, 45, 36, . . .
6. −8, −1, 6, 13, . . .

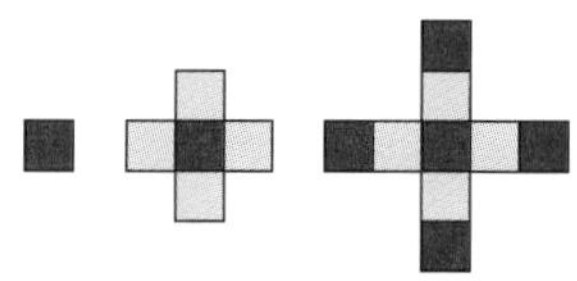

7. Use the pattern at the right. 17 red tiles
  a. How many red tiles would be in the ninth figure?
  b. How many yellow tiles would be in the ninth figure? 16 yellow tiles

8. *Business* Suppose an employer starts employees at \$6/h and raises the wage \$.50/h every six months. What kind of sequence is this? Write a rule to describe the sequence. Arithmetic; start with 6 and add 0.5 repeatedly.

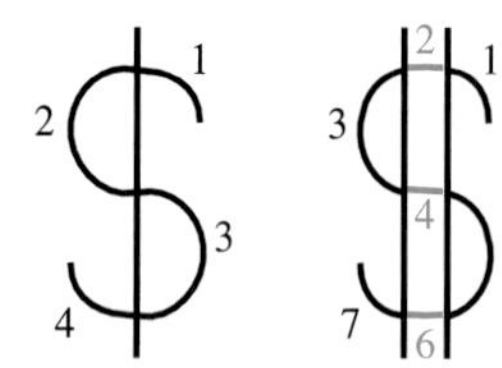

9. Many people draw a dollar sign as an S-shape with one line through it. The line divides the S into four parts, as shown at the right. Other people draw two lines, dividing the S into seven parts. Suppose you drew the S with 15 vertical lines through it. Into how many parts would the S be divided? 46 parts

10. *Reasoning* What is the rule for an arithmetic sequence whose terms are all 37? Start with 37 and add 0 repeatedly.

Write a rule for each geometric sequence. Then find the next three terms. 11–16. See margin.

11. 1, 2, 4, 8, . . .
12. 2, 6, 18, 54, . . .
13. 600, 300, 150, 75, . . .
14. 0.1, 0.3, 0.9, 2.7, . . .
15. $\frac{1}{4}, \frac{1}{12}, \frac{1}{36}, \frac{1}{108}, \ldots$
16. 0.5, 1.5, 4.5, 13.5, . . .

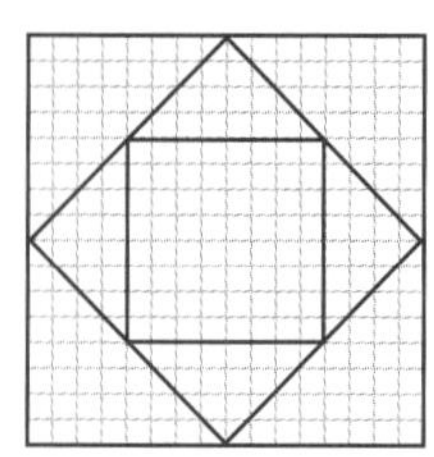

17. *Geometry* Draw a 16 × 16 square on graph paper.
  a. Find its area. 256 $units^2$
  b. Join the midpoints of the sides of the square. Find the area of the inner square. 128 $units^2$
  c. Join the midpoints of the sides of the inner square. Find the area of the innermost square. 64 $units^2$
  d. What would be the area of the innermost square in the sixth figure in this sequence? 8 $units^2$

18. **Choose A, B, C, or D.** What are the next two numbers in the sequence 1, 64, 2, 32, 4, 16, . . . ? C
  A. 16, 8 **B.** 8, 16 **C.** 8, 8 **D.** 32, 64

WRAP UP

IDENTIFYING THE BIG IDEA Ask students: *How do you know if a sequence is arithmetic? geometric? Neither?*

LESSON QUIZ

Identify whether each sequence is arithmetic, geometric, or neither. Give the next two terms in each sequence.

1. 2, 6, 18, 54, . . . **geometric; 162, 486**

2. 5, 6, 8, 11, . . . **neither; 15, 20**

3. 42, 37, 32, 27, . . . **arithmetic; 22, 17**

Identify each sequence as arithmetic, geometric, or neither. Then find the next three terms.

19. 2, 5, 10, 17, 26, . . . neither; 37, 50, 65
20. 0.2, 0.4, 0.6, 0.8, . . . arithmetic; 1.0, 1.2, 1.4
21. 1, 4, 9, 16, 25, . . . neither; 36, 49, 64
22. 7, 14, 28, 56, . . . geometric; 112, 224, 448
23. 1, 2, 4, 7, 11, . . . neither; 16, 22, 29
24. 300, 60, 12, 2.4, . . . geometric; 0.48, 0.096, 0.0192

25. A pattern of numbers is shown at the right. a. See margin p. 436.

row 1	1
row 2	1 2 1
row 3	1 2 3 2 1

a. List the numbers in rows 4, 5, 6, and 7. b. 1, 4, 9, 16, 25, 36, 49
b. Find the sum of the numbers in each of the first 7 rows.
c. Write a rule to find the sum of the numbers in each row. See margin p. 436.
d. Predict the sum of the numbers in the twentieth row. 400

26a. Start with 2 and multiply by 2 repeatedly.

26. a. Write a rule for the geometric sequence 2, 4, 8, 16, ...
b. Write a rule for the geometric sequence −2, 4, −8, 16, ...
c. Find the next three terms of each sequence. 32, 64, 128; −32, 64; −128

26b. Start with −2 and multiply by −2 repeatedly.

27. *Biology* A female bee has two biological parents, a female and a male. A male bee has one biological parent, a female. See back of book for diagram; 2; 3; 5; 8; 13; 21; 34
a. Make a "family tree" showing seven generations of ancestors of a female bee. Find the number of ancestors in each of the seven generations.
b. The numbers of ancestors form a number sequence. Is the sequence arithmetic, geometric, or neither? neither

28. *Writing* Is the sequence 1, 1, 1, . . . arithmetic, geometric, both, or neither? Explain. Both; the rule for the arithmetic sequence is "Start with 1 and add 0 repeatedly;" the rule for the geometric sequence is "Start with 1 and multiply by 1 repeatedly."

Mixed Review

Solve. *(Lesson 3-6)*

29. $4 + x = -6$ −10 **30.** $x - 8 = 5$ 13 **31.** $10 = y - (-2)$ 8 **32.** $h + (-3) = -5$ −2

Classify each angle as acute, right, obtuse, or straight. *(Lesson 7-2)*

33. $m\angle A = 100°$ obtuse **34.** $m\angle B = 76°$ acute **35.** $m\angle C = 26°$ acute **36.** $m\angle D = 179°$ obtuse

37. A party store sells paper plates at \$3.45 for 300 and paper cups at \$2.94 for 50. At the supermarket, the same plates cost \$1.98 for 200, and cups are \$1.45 for 30. *(Lesson 6-2)*
a. Find the unit price for each item at each store. \$0.0115 per plate, \$0.0588 per cup; \$0.0099 per plate, about \$0.048 per cup
b. Which store has a better buy for plates and for cups? The supermarket has a better buy on each item.

PRACTICE

Practice 10-1 Number Patterns

Identify each sequence as arithmetic, geometric, or neither. Write a rule to describe each arithmetic and geometric sequence.

1. 2, 6, 18, 54, . . . geometric: start with 2 and multiply by 3 repeatedly
2. 5, −10, 20, −40, . . . geometric: start with 5 and multiply by −2 repeatedly
3. 3, 5, 7, 9, . . . arithmetic: start with 3 and add 2 repeatedly
4. 5, 6, 8, 11, 15, . . . neither
5. 1, 2, 6, 24, . . . neither
6. 17, 16, 15, 14, . . . arithmetic: start with 17 and add −1 repeatedly
7. 50, −50, 50, −50, . . . geometric: start with 50 and multiply by −1 repeatedly
8. 1, 2, 4, 5, 10, 11, 22, . . . neither

Circle A, B, C, or D. Find the next three numbers in each sequence.

9. 15, −14, 13, −12, . . .
A. −8, 11, −14 B. −10, 17, −21 C. −11, 10, −9 (D.) 11, −10, 9
10. 243, 81, 27, . . .
(A.) 9, 3, 1 B. 9, 27, 81 C. 27, 81, 243 D. 9, 3, 0
11. 5, 12, 26, . . .
A. 52, 104, 208 B. 33, 40, 47 (C.) 54, 110, 222 D. 40, 54, 68
12. 2, 5, 9, 14, . . .
A. 19, 24, 29 (B.) 20, 27, 35 C. 17, 20, 23 D. 20, 26, 32

Write the first five terms in the sequence described by the rule. Identify the sequence as arithmetic, geometric, or neither.

13. Start with 2 and multiply by −3 repeatedly. 2, −6, 18, −54, 162; geometric
14. Start with 27 and add −9 repeatedly. 27, 18, 9, 0, −9; arithmetic
15. Start with 18 and multiply by 0.1, then by 0.2, then by 0.3, and so on. 18, 1.8, 0.36, 0.108, 0.0432; neither

Practice

In copymaster and workbook formats

RETEACHING

Reteaching 10-1 Number Patterns

A set of numbers that follows a pattern form a **sequence.** The numbers 2, 4, 6, 8, . . . form a sequence. The three dots ". . ." tell you that the pattern continues. The numbers 2, 4, 6, 8, and so on are the **terms** of the sequence.

Arithmetic Sequence

Add the same number to each term to get the next term. In the sequence 2, 4, 6, 8, . . . , you add 2 to each term to get the next term.

Write a rule to describe this sequence, and find the next three terms.
5, 10, 15, 20, . . .

5 10 15 20 (+5 +5 +5)

Rule: *Start with 5 and add 5 repeatedly.*
To find the next three terms, add 5.
20 + 5 = 25
25 + 5 = 30
30 + 5 = 35
The next three terms are 25, 30, and 35.

Geometric Sequence

Multiply each term by the same number to get the next term. In the sequence 1, 4, 16, 64, . . . , you multiply each term by 4 to get the next term.

Write a rule to describe this sequence, and find the next three terms.
2, 4, 8, 16, . . .

2 4 8 16 (×2 ×2 ×2)

Start with 2 and multiply by 2 repeatedly.
For the next three terms, multiply by 2.
16 × 2 = 32
32 × 2 = 64
64 × 2 = 128
The next three terms are 32, 64, and 128.

Write a rule for each arithmetic sequence. Then find the next three terms.

1. 4, 7, 10, 13, . . . Start with 4 and add 3 repeatedly. 16, 19, 22
2. 2, 4, 6, 8, . . . Start with 2 and add 2 repeatedly. 10, 12, 14
3. 20, 35, 50, . . . Start with 20 and add 15 repeatedly. 65, 80, 95

Write a rule for each geometric sequence. Then find the next three terms.

4. 5, 25, 125, 625, . . . Start with 5 and multiply by 5 repeatedly. 3,125; 15,625; 78,125
5. 7, 49, 343, 2,401, . . . Start with 7 and multiply by 7 repeatedly. 16,807; 117,649; 823,543
6. 0.3, 0.9, 2.7, 8.1, . . . Start with 0.3 and multiply by 3 repeatedly. 24.3, 72.9, 218.7

ENRICHMENT

Minds on Math Transparency

10-1

Misty is sharing some cookies with three of her friends. She gives half of the cookies plus half a cookie to Lisa. She then gives half of the cookies left plus half a cookie to Laura. Finally she gives half of what is left and half a cookie to Lani. Misty says that she has given away all of her cookies without cutting, breaking, or dividing any of the cookies. How many cookies did Misty have at the beginning?

7 cookies

See *Solution Key* for worked-out answers.

10-2 Teaching Notes

1 Focus

CONNECTING TO PRIOR KNOWLEDGE Ask students: *How many digits are in the numeral for one billion?* **13 digits** Tell students that a centillion is the number 1 followed by 600 zeros. Have students brainstorm ways to write this number without writing 601 digits.

2 Teach

THINK AND DISCUSS

AEP Question 1 Students may have trouble understanding the various ways we read decimals aloud. Point out that for all the powers, we use ordinal numbers such as ten to the *first power* or *second power*. We may leave off the word *power*. But for the powers of 2 and 3, we can also say *squared* or *cubed*. For example, ten *squared* or ten *cubed*.

AUDITORY LEARNING Question 3 Suggest students count each place aloud as they move the decimal point.

ERROR ALERT! Question 3 Students may find the exponent by counting the zeros or all the digits rather than the number of places the decimal point moved. **Remediation:** Have students cover the left-most digit with one finger and count the remaining digits.

Lesson Planning Options

Prerequisite Skills

- multiplying powers of 10 (precourse)

Vocabulary/Symbols

scientific notation, standard form

Resources

Student Edition

Skills Handbook, p. 538
Extra Practice, p. 523
Glossary/Study Guide

Teaching Resources

Chapter Support File, Ch. 10
- Lesson Planner 10-2
- Practice 10-2, Reteaching 10-2
- Answer Masters 10-2

Glossary, Spanish Resources

Transparencies

15, Minds on Math 10-2

Warm Up

Match each expression in Column 1 with an equivalent expression in column 2.

Column 1	Column 2
1. 50% of 250	**a.** 250
2. 100% of 250	**b.** 2.5
3. 1% of 250	**c.** 25
4. 10% of 250	**d.** 125

1d, 2a, 3b, 4c

MEASUREMENT Connection

10-2 Scientific Notation

What You'll Learn

1. To write numbers in scientific notation
2. To write numbers in standard form

...And Why

Astronomers use scientific notation to express great distances.

Here's How

Look for questions that
- build understanding
- ✔ check understanding

Need Help? For practice with powers of 10, see Skills Handbook page 538.

THINK AND DISCUSS

1 Scientific Notation

The seventh of Jupiter's moons, Ganymede, orbits Jupiter 1,070,000 km from the planet. **Scientific notation** is a shorthand method for writing very large numbers like this. A number in scientific notation is written as the product of two factors.

$$1{,}070{,}000 = 1.07 \times 10^6$$

The first factor is greater than or equal to one, but less than 10. The second factor is a power of 10.

b. In each statement the power of 10 is equal to the number of 10s being multiplied and to the number of zeros in the product.

1. a. Copy and complete each statement.
   $10^1 = 10$
   $10^2 = 10 \times 10 = \blacksquare$ **100**
   $10^3 = 10 \times 10 \times 10 = \blacksquare$ **1,000**
   $10^4 = 10 \times 10 \times 10 \times 10 = \blacksquare$ **10,000**
   b. *Patterns* What patterns do you see in part (a)?
   c. Write 100,000,000 using a power of 10. **10^8**

EXAMPLE 1 *Real-World Problem Solving*

Astronomy The moon orbits Earth at a distance of 384,400 km. Write this number in scientific notation.

384,400. ← Move the decimal point to get a factor greater than 1 but less than 10.

5 places

3.844×10^5 ← The decimal point moved 5 places to the left. Use this number as the exponent of 10.

The moon orbits Earth at 3.844×10^5 km.

2. The first factor must be greater than or equal to 1 but less than 10.

2. *Explain* Why is the scientific notation for 1,070,000 *not* 107×10^4?

3a. 3.96×10^8 b. 4.3×10^7 c. 2.7×10^9

3. ✔ *Try It Out* Write each number in scientific notation.
   a. 396,000,000 b. 43,000,000 c. 2,700,000,000

Now you may assign Exercises 1–17.

■ **ADDITIONAL EXAMPLES**

FOR EXAMPLE 1

Write the number 54,280,000 in scientific notation. **5.428×10^7**

FOR EXAMPLE 2

Write the number 2.36×10^4 in standard form. **23,600**

ASSESSMENT **Questions 3 and 4** Without looking at the book, have students write their answers for Question 3 in standard form. Then have them write their answer for Question 4 in scientific notation. Their new answers should match the given questions in the book.

3 Practice/Assess

EXERCISES *On Your Own*

WRITING **Exercise 13** Remind students to write clear, concise directions. Then have them trade with a partner to check.

REASONING **Exercise 30c** Ask students to find two more scales—one reasonable and one unreasonable. **Answers may vary. Sample: reasonable–1mm: 2,000,00 mi; unreasonable–200,000 mm :1 mi.**

2 *Standard Form*

You can change a number from scientific notation to **standard form** by multiplying the two factors.

■ **EXAMPLE 2** *Real-World Problem Solving*

Astronomy The mean distance from Earth to the sun is about 1.5×10^8 km. Write this number in standard form.

$10^8 = 100{,}000{,}000$

$1.5 \times 10^8 = 150{,}000{,}000.$

Multiplying by 100,000,000 moves the decimal point **8** places to the right.

The mean distance is about 150,000,000 km.

WHAT? The distance from Earth to the sun varies between 1.47×10^8 km and 1.52×10^8 km.

Source: *Atlas of the Solar System*

4. ✓ *Try It Out* Write 5.6×10^6 in standard form. **5,600,000**

Now you may assign Exercises 18–30.

EXERCISES *On Your Own*

Write each number in scientific notation.

1. 7,500 **7.5×10^3**
2. 75 million **7.5×10^7**
3. 125 **1.25×10^2**
4. 3,400,000 **3.4×10^6**
5. 102 thousand **1.02×10^5**
6. 61,300,000 **6.13×10^7**
7. 490 billion **4.9×10^{11}**
8. 44,000 **4.4×10^4**
9. There are about 350,000 different kinds of plants on Earth. **3.5×10^5**
10. The Folsom Dam in California holds 326 billion gallons of water in a reservoir. **3.26×10^{11}**
11. A light-year is how far light travels in one year. This distance is 5,880 trillion miles. **5.88×10^{15}**
12. The tallest mountain in our solar system is on Mars. Olympus Mons is 78,000 ft tall. **7.8×10^4**
13. *Writing* Explain how you find the power of 10 to write 725,000,000 in scientific notation. **Answers may vary. Sample: Count the number of digits. Then subtract 1.**

Explain why each number is *not* in scientific notation.

14. 35.4×10^6 **14. The first factor must be greater than or equal to 1 but less than 10.**
15. 8×2^{10} **15. The second factor must be a power of 10.**
16. 0.387×10^7 **16. The first factor must be greater than or equal to 1 but less than 10.**
17. 75.5×10^7 **17. The first factor must be greater than or equal to 1 but less than 10.**

Write each number in standard form.

18. 8.6×10^7 **86,000,000**
19. 5×10^{11} **500,000,000,000**
20. 7.02×10^1 **70.2**
21. 8.3×10^5 **830,000**
22. 2.25×10^3 **2,250**
23. 9.3×10^6 **9,300,000**
24. 3.02×10^4 **30,200**
25. 6.678×10^2 **667.8**

Technology Options

Prentice Hall Technology

Software for Learners
- Hot Page™ 6–2*
- Math Blaster® Mystery*
- Interactive Student Tutorial, Chapter 10*

Teaching Resource Software
- Computer Item Generator 10-2
- Resource Pro™ Chapter 10*

Internet • For related mathematics activities, visit the Prentice Hall site at www.phschool.com/math

**Available on CD-ROM only*

Assignment Options for Exercises On Your Own

To provide flexible scheduling, this lesson can be split into parts.

1 **Core** 1–12, 14–17
Extension 13

2 **Core** 18–29
Extension 30

Use Mixed Review to maintain skills.

PRACTICE

Practice 10-2 *Scientific Notation*

Write each number in scientific notation.

1. 73,000,000 7.3×10^7
2. 4,300 4.3×10^3
3. 510 5.1×10^2
4. 56,870 5.687×10^4
5. 68,900 6.89×10^4
6. 98,000,000,000 9.8×10^{10}
7. 4,890,000 4.89×10^6
8. 38 3.8×10^1
9. 120,000 1.2×10^5
10. 543,000 5.43×10^5
11. 27 2.7×10^1
12. 54,000 5.4×10^4

Write each number in standard form.

13. 5.7×10^6 5,700,000
14. 2.45×10^8 245,000,000
15. 4.706×10^{11} 470,600,000,000
16. 8×10^1 80
17. 7.2×10^3 7,200
18. 1.63×10^{12} 1,630,000,000,000
19. 8.03×10^{14} 803,000,000,000,000
20. 3.26×10^4 32,600
21. 5.179×10^5 517,900

Write each number in scientific notation.

22. One type of roundworm can lay 200,000 eggs each day. 2×10^5
23. The nose of a German shepherd dog has about 220 million cells that are used in picking out smells. 2.2×10^8
24. In a given day, a total of 15,000 tons of potatoes are consumed by the people of Britain. 1.5×10^4
25. A computer microchip can perform about 400,000 operations each second. 4×10^5
26. The brain contains about 100 trillion nerve connections. 1×10^{14}
27. During an average life span, the human heart will beat about 2,800,000,000 times. 2.8×10^9
28. The volume of the Grand Coulee Dam is about 10.6 million cubic yards. 1.06×10^7
29. A second has been defined as the time it takes for an atom of a particular metal to vibrate 9,192,631,770 times. 9.19263177×10^9

In copymaster and workbook formats

RETEACHING

Reteaching 10-2 *Scientific Notation*

Scientific notation is an efficient way to write very large numbers. A number is written as the product of a number between 1 and 10 and a power of 10.

Write 4,000,000,000 in scientific notation.

① Count the number of places that you need to move the decimal point to the left to get a factor between 1 and 10.

4,000,000,000 → 4.000 000 000 (9 places)

② Use the number of places as the exponent of 10.

$4{,}000{,}000{,}000 = 4 \times 10^9$

To change a number from scientific notation to **standard form,** undo the steps at the left.

Write 3.5×10^8 in standard form.

① Note the exponent of 10. (Here it is 8.)

② Move the decimal point to the right the number of places that is equal to the exponent.

3.5×10^8 → 350,000,000 (8 places)

$3.5 \times 10^8 = 350{,}000{,}000$

Write each number in scientific notation.

1. 3,500
   Move the decimal point 3 places to the left.
   $3{,}500 = 3.5 \times 10^3$
2. 1,400,000
   Move the decimal point 6 places to the left.
   $1{,}400{,}000 = 1.4 \times 10^6$
3. 93,000,000 9.3×10^7
4. 1,200,000 1.2×10^6
5. 17,000 1.7×10^4
6. 750,000 7.5×10^5
7. 2,400 2.4×10^3
8. 6,532,000 6.532×10^6
9. 560,000,000,000 5.6×10^{11}
10. 34,800,000 3.48×10^7

Write each number in standard form.

11. 2.58×10^3 2,580
12. 8×10^6 8,000,000
13. 4.816×10^5 481,600
14. 8.11×10^2 811
15. 1.85×10^7 18,500,000
16. 3.7509×10^3 3,750.9
17. 8.003×10^1 80.03
18. 5.66×10^9 5,660,000,000
19. 4.23×10^2 423
20. 9.992×10^{10} 99,920,000,000

Reteaching

ENRICHMENT

Minds on Math Transparency

10-2

I am a mixed number less than 10. When I am divided by 4, the result is the same as when 4 is subtracted from me. What mixed number am I?

$5\frac{1}{3}$

See *Solution Key* for worked-out answers.

WRAP UP

IDENTIFYING THE BIG IDEA Ask: *How do you write numbers in scientific notation?*

PROJECT LINK Encourage students to bring plastic containers of unusual shapes as well as the standard plastic soda bottle. They may be able to find a plastic pumpkin or piggy bank. Explore the effect unusual shapes have on the rate at which water drips through the hole.

LESSON QUIZ

Write each number in scientific notation.

1. 21,000 **2.1×10^4**
2. 132,400,000 **1.324×10^8**

Write each number in standard form.

3. 5.02×10^7 **50,200,000**
4. 1.2×10^3 **1,200**

Write each number in standard form.

26. The first balloon to carry passengers weighed 1.6×10^3 lb. **1,600 lb**
27. There are about 2×10^{13} red blood cells in a 125-lb person. **20,000,000,000,000 cells**
28. In 2001, the world population will be about 6.128×10^9. **6,128,000,000 people**
29. A CD-ROM can store about 6×10^8 bytes of information. **600,000,000 bytes**
30. Suppose a science museum plans to make a model of the solar system. The distance from the sun to Mercury is about 3.6×10^7 mi. The distance from the sun to Pluto is about 3.7×10^9 mi. **36,000,000 mi; 3,700,000,000 mi**
    a. Write each number in standard form.
    b. About how much greater is the distance from the sun to Pluto than the sun to Mercury? **100 times**
    c. Is using 1 mm : 1,000,000 mi as a scale for this model reasonable? Explain. **Yes; the model would take 3.7 meters to model the distance from the sun to Mercury and would fit in the museum.**

WHAT? The first balloons were flown by the Montgolfier brothers, Joseph and Etienne, in France in 1783.

Mixed Review

Find the number of two-letter permutations and combinations of each set. *(Lessons 9-6, 9-7)*

31. B, D, E, Y **12 permutations; 6 combinations**
32. E, M, O, R, S **20 permutations; 10 combinations**
33. K, O, L **6 permutations; 3 combinations**
34. A, E, I, R, V, Z **30 permutations; 15 combinations**

Find the percent of change. State whether the change is an increase or decrease. *(Lesson 6-11)*

35. old: \$35; new: \$70 **100% increase**
36. old: \$275; new: \$150 **45% decrease**
37. old: \$9.80; new: \$10 **about 2% increase**
38. Find two whole numbers whose sum is 23 and whose product is 132. *(Lessons 3-6, 3-7)* **11 and 12**

CHAPTER PROJECT

PROJECT LINK: MEASURING

Select a plastic container for the project. Measure the height of the water level when the container is full. If you put a hole in the bottom, do you think the level will drop at a steady rate? Explain. **Check students' work.**

Extra Practice, Lesson 10-2, page 523

MATH TOOLBOX

In Lesson 10-2, students learn how to represent large numbers in scientific notation and in standard form. This toolbox shows students how to use scientific notation and negative exponents to represent very small numbers.

ERROR ALERT! Students may confuse the negative sign of an exponent with a negative whole number. **Remediation:** Point out that the negative sign in the exponent refers only to the direction the decimal point moves when rewriting a number in scientific notation. If they move the decimal point to the right, the exponent is negative.

ASSESSMENT **Exercises 1–5** Have students meet with a partner. Partners can take turns telling each other how to change the numbers in scientific notation back to the numbers in standard form for each exercise. Students should agree on the steps taken for each conversion.

ADDITIONAL PROBLEMS

1. Write 0.00027 in scientific notation.
   2.7×10^{-4}
2. Write 3.14×10^{-3} in standard form.
   0.00314

Resources

Transparencies 15

MATH TOOLBOX EXPLORATION

Scientific Notation with Negative Exponents

After Lesson 10-2

Scientists also use scientific notation to write very small numbers. Remember that a number in scientific notation has two factors, one greater than or equal to 1 and less than 10, and the other a power of 10.

EXAMPLE 1

Write 0.0084 in scientific notation.

0.0084 ← Move the decimal point to get a factor greater than 1 but less than 10.

3 places

8.4×10^{-3} ← The decimal point moved 3 places to the right so the exponent of 10 is –3.

In scientific notation, 0.0084 is 8.4×10^{-3}.

EXAMPLE 2

Write 3.52×10^{-5} in standard form.

$10^{-5} = 0.00001$

$3.52 \times 10^{-5} = 0.0000352$

Multiplying by 0.00001 moves the decimal point 5 places to the left.

The standard form of 3.52×10^{-5} is 0.0000352.

8. Answers may vary. Sample: To find the exponent of 10, count the number of digits in 4,500,000, then subtract 1. Count the number of zeros before the first non-zero digit in 0.0000045, then add 1. Since the number is less than 1, the exponent will be negative.

Write each number in scientific notation.

1. 0.0008 8×10^{-4}
2. 0.0037 3.7×10^{-3}
3. 0.00000691 6.91×10^{-6}
4. 0.00000307 3.07×10^{-6}
5. 0.005006 5.006×10^{-3}

Write each number in standard form.

6. The width of a hair is about 3×10^{-7} in. 0.0000003
7. A flea weighs 4.9×10^{-3} g. 0.0049
8. *Writing* Explain how to write the numbers 4,500,000 and 0.0000045 in scientific notation. See above.

10-3 Teaching Notes

1 Focus

CONNECTING TO PRIOR KNOWLEDGE Ask students: *Have you ever felt overwhelmed by a math problem and thought you might never be able to solve it?* Then ask: *Describe strategies you used to solve the problem.* **Answers may vary. Sample: break it into parts, use simpler numbers**

2 Teach

THINK AND DISCUSS

KINESTHETIC LEARNING Write *open* and *closed* on opposite sides of 20 index cards. Line them up on the floor or on a long desk. Have 20 students act out the problem to help them develop a clearer sense of what happens in the problem.

ERROR ALERT! Students may feel overwhelmed by the complexity of this problem and rush through it. This may cause careless mistakes. **Remediation:** Urge students not to get discouraged. Keep them focused on breaking the problem down into a simpler problem by stressing strategy over finding a solution.

VISUAL LEARNING **Question 7** Suggest that students use two different colored highlighters to mark open and closed lockers in their table. The colors may help them see the patterns.

Lesson Planning Options

Prerequisite Skills

- listing factors (7-4)
- calculating multiples (precourse)

Resources

Student Edition

Skills Handbook, p. 528
Extra Practice, p. 523
Glossary/Study Guide

Teaching Resources

Chapter Support File, Ch. 10
- Lesson Planner 10-3
- Practice 10-3, Reteaching 10-3
- Answer Masters 10-3

Glossary, Spanish Resources

Transparencies
Minds on Math 10-3

Warm Up

Use estimation to draw a circle graph. Twenty percent of the students surveyed always prefer a salad. Thirty percent always prefer a hamburger. The rest prefer a hamburger sometimes and a salad sometimes. **Check students' graphs. The graphs should show 20% (72°) salad, 30% (108°) hamburger, and 50% (180°) salad or hamburger.**

PROBLEM SOLVING STRATEGY

READ PLAN SOLVE LOOK BACK

10-3 Solve a Simpler Problem

Problem Solving Strategies

Draw a Diagram
Guess and Test
Look for a Pattern
Make a Model
Make a Table
Simulate a Problem
✓ Solve a Simpler Problem
Too Much or Too Little Information
Use Logical Reasoning
Use Multiple Strategies
Work Backward
Write an Equation

THINK AND DISCUSS

When a problem seems to have an overwhelming number of steps, try to solve a similar but simpler problem.

SAMPLE PROBLEM

A school has 1,000 students and 1,000 lockers. The lockers are numbered from 1 to 1,000. The students enter the building one at a time.

- The first student opens all the lockers.
- The second student begins with the second locker and closes all the lockers with even numbers.
- The third student begins with the third locker and changes—either by opening closed doors or closing open doors—all lockers with numbers that are multiples of 3.
- The fourth student begins with the fourth locker and changes all lockers with numbers that are multiples of 4.

Repeat this pattern until all the students walk past all the lockers. After the last student has gone by the lockers, which lockers are open?

READ
Read for understanding. Summarize the problem.

Think about the information you are given.

1. Which lockers are open *after* the second student closes all the lockers with even numbers? **all the lockers with odd numbers**
2. Will any other student change the door to locker 3 after the third student makes changes? **no**
3. Make a prediction. Do you think the twelfth locker will be open or closed after the twelfth student has passed it? **closed**

PLAN
Decide on a strategy.

Solve a simpler problem with 20 lockers and 20 students. Then look for a pattern to help you solve the original problem.

ASSESSMENT Question 8 Have pairs work together to write an explanation of how to tell whether a locker is open or closed.

Question 9a Stress that the question asks for the *number* of factors, not what the factors are.

■ ADDITIONAL PROBLEM

Ten people meet. Each person shakes hands with every other person. How many handshakes occur? Explain how you solved the problem. **45; Answers may vary. Sample: Solve the problem for 2, 3, 4, and 5 people. Then you see the pattern: as the number of people increases by 1, the number of handshakes increases by 1 fewer than the number of people.**

3 Practice/Assess

EXERCISES *On Your Own*

Exercise 3 Clarify that students are counting digits, *not* numbers. Remind students that the number 248 contains 3 digits. Suggest students think about how many 1-digit, 2-digit, and 3-digit numbers they write.

EXTENSION and CONNECTION TO BUSINESS Exercise 6 If you have block scheduling or extended class periods, have students imagine they are the contractor responsible for ordering house numbers. Have students create an order form listing the total of each digit required to number all the houses on Main Street. Explain that house numbers cost $.85 per digit. Ask: *What is the total cost of the order?* **The contractor must**

SOLVE
Try the strategy.

4. Copy and complete the table below. "O" means open and "C" means closed. **See margin p. 444.**

Student Number	Locker Number								
	1	2	3	4	5	6	7	8	9
1	O	O	O	O	O	O	O	O	O
2	O	C	O	C	O	C	O	C	O
3	O	C	C	C	O	O	O	C	C
4									
5									
6									

5. Which lockers did student number 3 change? **lockers 3, 6, and 9**
6. a. Which students open or close the door to locker 6?
   b. These numbers are factors of what number? **6**
   6a. students 1, 2, 3, and 6
7. Extend your table to include 20 students and 20 lockers.
   a. Which of the first 20 lockers are open after 20 students pass through? **1, 4, 9, 16**
   b. What is the pattern of the numbers of the lockers left open? **The numbers of the lockers left open are squares of whole numbers.**
8. Tell whether each of the following lockers is open or closed after the last student passes through the building.
   a. 24 **closed** b. 25 **open** c. 49 **open** d. 1,000 **closed**

7. See back of book for table.
9a. Numbers may vary. Sample: Closed—12, 15, 24 have even number of factors; open—9, 25, 49 have odd number of factors.
9b. A door was opened or closed for each factor its number has.

LOOK BACK
Think about how you solved the problem.

9. a. Choose three closed and three open doors. How many factors do the numbers of the closed doors have? The open doors? **a–b. See above left.**
   b. Look at your table. How does the number of factors relate to the number of times a door was opened or closed?

Now you may assign Exercises 1–8.

EXERCISES *On Your Own*

Solve using a simpler problem.

1. You schedule the games for your basketball league's tournament. If a team loses a game, it is eliminated. There are 32 teams. How many games do you need to schedule to determine the league champion? **31 games**

Technology Options

Prentice Hall Technology

Software for Learners
- Math Blaster® Mystery*
- Interactive Student Tutorial, Chapter 10*

Teaching Resource Software
- Computer Item Generator 10-3
- Resource Pro™ Chapter 10*

Internet • For related mathematics activities, visit the Prentice Hall site at www.phschool.com/math

**Available on CD-ROM only*

Assignment Options for Exercises On Your Own

Core 1–7
Extension 8

Use Mixed Review to maintain skills.

order the following amount of each digit: twenty-four 0's, seventy-five 1's, thirty-four 2's, thirty-four 3's, twenty-five 4's, twenty-four each of 5's, 6's, 7's, 8's, and 9's. A total of 312 digits costs $265.20.

DIVERSITY Exercise 8 Some students may not understand how a balance scale works. If possible, borrow a scale and weights from a science teacher to demonstrate. You may need to show students how to add weights to both sides to get the scale to balance. For example: To measure a 4-oz object by using a 5-oz weight, place a 1-oz weight on the side of the scale holding the object.

WRAP UP

IDENTIFYING THE BIG IDEA Ask: *How does solving a simpler problem help you solve a more complicated problem?*

Math at Work

If you have extended class periods or block scheduling, have students draw a picture inspired by something they have learned in math class. Give them markers and paints to draw with. Have different students present their drawings to the class and have everyone try to figure out how the picture relates to math class. Consider posting the drawing on a bulletin board.

CHECKPOINT 1

Checkpoint 1

Lessons 10-1 through 10-3

Identify each sequence as arithmetic, geometric, or neither. Then find the next three terms.

1. 0.6, 1.8, 5.4, 16.2, . . . geometric; 48.6, 145.8, 437.4
2. 25, 18, 11, 4, . . . arithmetic; −3, −10, −17
3. 7, 8, 10, 13, . . . neither; 17, 22, 28

Write each number in scientific notation or standard form.

4. 370,000,000 3.7×10^8
5. 6.0×10^5 600,000
6. 6.2×10^4 62,000
7. **Choose A, B, C, or D.** How many diagonals can you draw in a regular 8-sided figure?
   A. 8 (B.) 20 C. 26 D. not here

pages 442–443 Think and Discuss

4.

	1	2	3	4	5	6	7	8	9
1	O	O	O	O	O	O	O	O	O
2	O	C	O	C	O	C	O	C	O
3	O	C	C	C	O	O	O	C	C
4	O	C	C	O	O	O	O	O	C
5	O	C	C	O	C	O	O	O	C
6	O	C	C	O	C	C	O	O	C

page 445 Checkpoint 1

1. Arithmetic; start with 3 and add 3 repeatedly; 15, 18, 21.
2. Arithmetic; start with 53 and add −8 repeatedly; 21, 13, 5.
3. Geometric; start with 3 and multiply by 2 repeatedly; 48, 96, 192.
4. Arithmetic; start with 4 and add 7 repeatedly; 39, 46, 53.
5. Neither; start with 87 and subtract 10, then subtract 11, then subtract 12 and continue the subtraction pattern; 41, 27, 12.
6. Geometric; start with 0.5 and multiply by 3 repeatedly; 40.5, 121.5, 364.5.

2. *Geometry* How many diagonals can you draw in a regular 8-sided figure? **20 diagonals**

Use any strategy to solve each problem. Show your work.

3. Suppose you are numbering 248 tickets for the class play by hand. How many digits do you have to write? **636 digits**
4. In this section of the city of Gridville, the streets are either one-way going east or one-way going south. A section of the city is shown at the right. How many possible routes are there from point A to point B? **10 routes**

5. *Geometry* The measure of the first of three angles of a triangle is three times the measure of the second angle. The measure of the third angle is twice the measure of the second angle. What is the measure of each angle? **90°, 30°, 60°**
6. The houses on Main Street are numbered from 1 to 140. How many house numbers contain the digit 6 at least once? **23 numbers**
7. You have three 29-cent stamps and two 23-cent stamps. How many different amounts of postage do you have? **11 amounts**
8. A fruit seller has three weights that can be used to weigh any whole number of pounds from 1 lb to 13 lb on a balance scale. What are the weights? **1 lb, 3 lb, and 9 lb**

Mixed Review

Find each product. *(Lesson 5-5)*

9. $3 \cdot 4\frac{5}{8}$ $13\frac{7}{8}$
10. $2\frac{1}{2} \cdot 3\frac{3}{4}$ $9\frac{3}{8}$
11. $\frac{4}{5} \cdot 2\frac{3}{4}$ $2\frac{1}{5}$
12. $4\frac{1}{3} \cdot 7\frac{1}{5}$ $31\frac{1}{5}$
13. $3\frac{2}{5} \cdot 2\frac{5}{6}$ $9\frac{19}{30}$

Find the volume of each rectangular prism. *(Lesson 8-10)*

14. $\ell = 6$ m, $w = 3.5$ m, $h = 7$ m **147 m³**
15. $\ell = 3$ ft, $w = 2$ ft, $h = 9$ ft **54 ft³**
16. Suppose it takes 18 min to cut a board into 6 pieces. How long would it take to cut the board into 8 pieces? *(Lesson 6-3)* **25 min 12 sec**
17. *Choose a Strategy* Darcy has $1.35 in dimes and quarters. How many different combinations of coins might she have? **3 combinations**

LESSON QUIZ

You are planting petunias around the cafeteria. You want to plant a purple petunia after every two white petunias. You want to begin and end with a purple petunia and have room for 121 plants.

1. How many purple petunias will you need? 41
2. How many white petunias? 80

✓ CHECKPOINT 1

Lessons 10-1 through 10-3

Identify each sequence as arithmetic, geometric, or neither. Write a rule for each sequence. Then find the next three terms. 1–6. See margin p. 444.

1. 3, 6, 9, 12, . . .
2. 53, 45, 37, 29, . . .
3. 3, 6, 12, 24, . . .
4. 4, 11, 18, 25, 32, . . .
5. 87, 77, 66, 54, . . .
6. 0.5, 1.5, 4.5, 13.5, . . .

Write each number in scientific notation.

7. 738,000,000 7.38×10^8
8. 29 thousand 2.9×10^4
9. 78.6×10^5 7.86×10^6
10. 1,807,000 1.807×10^6

Write each number in standard form.

11. 8.06×10^5 806,000
12. 1.74×10^3 1,740
13. 8.3×10^9 8,300,000,000
14. 1.008×10^7 10,080,000
15. **Choose A, B, C, or D.** What is 9 trillion in scientific notation? D

    A. 9×10^9 B. 9×10^{10} C. 9×10^{11} D. 9×10^{12}
16. a. The figures at the right show the first three *pentagonal numbers*. How many dots will be on each side of the fourth figure? Include the endpoints. 4

    b. What is the tenth pentagonal number? 145

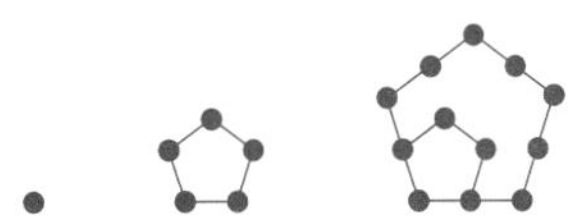

Math at Work

ARTIST

Artists use a variety of materials such as oils, watercolors, plaster, clay, or even computers to create images. Graphic artists work for businesses. Fine artists display their works in galleries or museums. Artists use angles and lines when they draw in perspective, an important skill for any aspiring artist.

Internet Connection: Visit this Web site for more information: http://www.yahoo.com/Arts/Artists/

PRACTICE

Practice 10-3 *Problem-Solving Strategy: Solve a Simpler Problem*

Solve using a simpler problem.

1. A school's gym lockers are numbered from 1 to 125. How many locker numbers contain the digit 4? 22 lockers
2. How many diagonals can you draw in an 8-sided regular polygon? 20 diagonals
3. Sixty-four players signed up for a tennis tournament. A player is eliminated upon losing a match. How many matches must be scheduled to determine the tournament champion? 63 games
4. Study the dot patterns. How many dots will the 12th pattern have? 144 dots

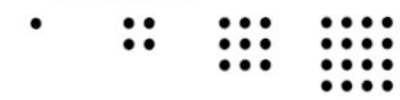

Choose any strategy to solve each problem.

5. Andy, Bryan, and Samantha are friends. One is an architect, another is a teacher, and another is a baker. The architect, who lives next door to Bryan, took Samantha to lunch today. Before lunch, Samantha bought bread from the baker. Who is the baker? Bryan
6. Study the dot patterns. Draw the next four patterns.

7. The sum of three children's ages is 21 and the product of their ages is 336. How old are the children? 6, 7, and 8 years old

Solve or tell what information is needed to solve.

8. Al saves $4 each week. He has $64 already saved for a special bike. He also received $20 for his birthday. How many more weeks does he need to save before he can buy the bike? The cost of the bike is needed.

In copymaster and workbook formats

RETEACHING

Reteaching 10-3 *Problem-Solving Strategy: Solve a Simpler Problem*

If a problem has large numbers or many steps, try to solve a similar, but simpler, problem.

A rope is long enough to be cut into 56 jump ropes. How many cuts are needed?

Read	What are you asked to find? *You need to find how many cuts to make in a rope to create 56 jump ropes.*
Plan	Try solving a similar problem, but with simpler numbers. A rope is long enough to be cut into 2 jump ropes. ⟶ 1 cut is needed. A rope is long enough to be cut into 3 jump ropes. ⟶ 2 cuts are needed. A rope is long enough to be cut into 4 jump ropes. ⟶ 3 cuts are needed.
Solve	What pattern do you see? *The number of cuts is 1 less than the number of pieces. So, it would take 56 − 1, or 55, cuts to create 56 jump ropes.*
Look Back	How could you check your answer? *Try solving the problem another way. You can draw a diagram.*

Solve using a simpler problem.

1. Into how many pieces can you cut a sheet of plywood with 24 cuts? 25 pieces
2. How many diagonals can you draw in a 12-sided regular polygon? 54 diagonals
3. You are hand-numbering the pages of a report. If there are 476 numbered pages, how many digits will you write? 1,320 digits
4. In a basketball tournament, each of 8 teams plays 1 game against each of the other teams. How many games will be played? 28 games
5. A basketball team scores 60 points in its first game, 62 points in its second, 64 in its third, and 66 in its fourth. At this rate, how many points will the team score in its sixteenth game? 90 points
6. Ms. Owens is ordering jars of paint for her art class. She needs 25 jars, one for each student. Her class uses one jar each week, and she replaces each jar. How many jars should she order to last a 16-week period? 40 jars

ENRICHMENT

Minds on Math Transparency

10-3

I am a polygon. When either one of my two diagonals are drawn, I am divided into 2 congruent triangles. What kind of polygon must I be?

a parallelogram

See *Solution Key* for worked-out answers.

10-4 Teaching Notes

1 Focus

CONNECTING TO PRIOR KNOWLEDGE Ask students who have a bank account to tell the class about interest. If there are no students with an account, explain how bank accounts work. Define the terms *balance, interest,* and *interest rate.*

2 Teach

THINK AND DISCUSS

DIVERSITY Some students may be suspicious of banks or believe bank accounts are only for wealthy people. Help students recognize the benefits of bank accounts.

CONNECTION TO TECHNOLOGY Discuss the use of computers in banking. Banks use computers to keep track of the amount of money in each account, to calculate interest, and to transfer funds between accounts or between banks.

AEP Question 1 Make sure students understand the difference between *interest rate* and *amount of interest.*

REASONING Question 2 Students can assume they did not deposit more money into the account.

Lesson Planning Options

Prerequisite Skills

- expressing percents as decimals (6-7)
- multiplying decimals (2-5)
- exponents and order of operations (4-4)

Vocabulary/Symbols

simple interest, principle, balance, compound interest

Materials/Manipulatives

- computer
- calculator
- spreadsheet software

Resources

Student Edition

Skills Handbook, p. 535
Extra Practice, p. 523
Glossary/Study Guide

Teaching Resources

Chapter Support File, Ch. 10
- Lesson Planner 10-4
- Practice 10-4, Reteaching 10-4
- Alternative Activity 10-4
- Answer Masters 10-4

Glossary, Spanish Resources

Transparencies

15, Minds on Math 10-4

Warm Up

Find the value of n.

$\frac{18}{15} = \frac{n}{5}$ $n = 6$

$\frac{1.5}{4.5} = \frac{n}{2.7}$ $n = 0.9$

10-4 Simple and Compound Interest

What You'll Learn

1. To find simple interest
2. To find compound interest

...And Why

When you invest money or borrow money, you earn or pay interest.

Here's How

Look for questions that
- build understanding
- ✔ check understanding

THINK AND DISCUSS

1 *Simple Interest*

Money may not grow on trees, but it can grow in a bank! A bank pays you interest on your deposit because they use your money to earn more money.

Simple interest is interest paid only on your original deposit, or **principal.** To calculate simple interest, you can use the formula $I = p \cdot r \cdot t$, where I is the interest,
p is the principal,
r is the interest rate per year,
and t is the time in years.

The **balance** of an account is the principal plus the interest earned.

■ **EXAMPLE 1**

Find the simple interest earned on $200 invested at 4% annual interest for three years.

$I = p \cdot r \cdot t$
$I = 200 \cdot 0.04 \cdot 3$ ← Substitute. Use 0.04 for 4%.
$= 24$

The account earns $24 in interest for three years.

1. ✔ *Try It Out* Suppose you borrow $2,500 to buy a car. The annual interest rate is 8%. Find the amount of simple interest that you will pay for one year. **$200**

2. a. *Reasoning* You deposit $150 into an account at the beginning of the year. The balance in the account at the beginning of the next year is $156.75. How much interest did your money earn? **$6.75**
   b. What was the interest rate? **4.5%**

Now you may assign Exercises 1–8.

ADDITIONAL EXAMPLES

FOR EXAMPLE 1

Find the simple interest earned on $500 invested at 3% annual interest for four years. **$60**

FOR EXAMPLES 2 AND 3

You deposit $500 in a bank paying 3% interest compounded annually. Make a spreadsheet or use the formula to find out how much money will be in the account after 4 years. **$562.75**

TACTILE LEARNING Example 2 Have students use play money to simulate the activity shown in the first few lines of the spreadsheet.

Example 2 Remind students to round all interest amounts to the nearest cent.

ASSESSMENT Example 2 Ask: *Why does the bank pay more interest in each successive year?* **After the first year, the bank pays interest on both the deposit and the interest previously earned.**

ALTERNATIVE METHOD Example 2 If students are not using computers, they can draw tables and use calculators to find the amounts.

ERROR ALERT! Example 3 Students may multiply 1,000(1.05) first. **Remediation:** Review the order of operations. Remind students to find the power before multiplying.

2 *Compound Interest*

Finding simple interest is the first step in computing compound interest. **Compound interest** is interest paid on both the principal and the interest earned in previous interest periods.

You can use a spreadsheet to calculate compound interest.

EXAMPLE 2 *Real-World Problem Solving*

Banking Suppose someone put $1,000 in the bank for you the day you started first grade. The interest rate is 5% compounded annually. How much will be in the account after seven years?

Make a spreadsheet.

	A	B	C	D	E
1	Year	Start of Year	Rate	Interest	Balance at End of Year
2	1st	$1,000.00	0.05	$50.00	$1,050.00
3	2nd	$1,050.00	0.05	$52.50	$1,102.50
4	3rd	$1,102.50	0.05	$55.13	$1,157.63
5	4th	$1,157.63	0.05	$57.88	$1,215.51
6	5th	$1,215.51	0.05	$60.78	$1,276.28
7	6th	$1,276.28	0.05	$63.81	$1,340.10
8	7th	$1,340.10	0.05	$67.00	$1,407.10

The account has $1,407.10 at the end of seven years.

3a. **The balance at the end of the 1st year is the same as the balance at the beginning of the 2nd year.**

4a. **$1,503.63**

3. a. Why is the amount in cell B3 the same as that in cell E2?
   b. How was the amount in cell E2 calculated? **Add the amounts in B2 and D2.**
4. a. *✔Try It Out* Suppose the annual interest on $1,000 principal is 6%. What is the balance after seven years?
   b. How much more interest was earned with 6% annual interest rather than 5% annual interest after seven years? **$96.53**

At the end of a year, the balance in Example 2 is 105% of the amount at the start of the year. 105% is the same as 1 + 0.05. This sum is part of the following formula to find a balance with compound interest.

$B = p(1 + r)^t$, where B is the balance in the account,
p is the principal,
r is the annual interest rate,
and t is the time in years.

Technology Options

Prentice Hall Technology

Software for Learners
- Math Lab 44
- Math Blaster® Mystery*
- Interactive Student Tutorial, Chapter 10*

Teaching Resource Software
- Computer Item Generator 10-4
- Resource Pro™ Chapter 10*

Internet • For related mathematics activities, visit the Prentice Hall site at www.phschool.com/math

**Available on CD-ROM only*

Assignment Options for Exercises On Your Own

To provide flexible scheduling, this lesson can be split into parts.

1 **Core** 1–7 **Extension** 8

2 **Core** 9–16 **Extension** 17

Use Mixed Review to maintain skills.

Work Together

Question 7 Have students work in groups of three. Suggest students first guess which change most increases the balance. Then suggest each of the three students calculates the result of a different change.

3 Practice/Assess

EXERCISES *On Your Own*

EXTENSION Exercise 7 Challenge interested students to find out the difference between credit cards and debit cards. Have them make a list of the advantages and disadvantages of each to share with the class.

WRITING Exercise 16 Encourage students to calculate the account balances for each of the two situations before they begin writing.

RESEARCH Exercise 17a Students may find that banks offer different interest rates, depending on the minimum account balance. You may want to set a minimum account balance of $100.

OPEN-ENDED Exercise 17b Students may enjoy experimenting with large amounts, such as a million dollars.

Consider the problem in Example 2 once again.

EXAMPLE 3 *Real-World Problem Solving*

Banking Suppose you deposit $1,000 in a bank account paying 5% annual interest. Use the formula to find your balance after 7 years.

$B = p(1 + r)^t$
$= 1{,}000(1 + 0.05)^7$ ← Substitute. Use 0.05 for 5%.
$= 1{,}000(1.05)^7$ ← Evaluate within the parentheses.
$= 1{,}000(1.407100423)$ ← Use a calculator to find $(1.05)^7$.
$\approx 1{,}407.10$ ← Multiply. Round to the nearest cent.

There is $1,407.10 in the account after seven years.

5. ✔ *Try It Out* You deposit $1,000 for 21 years. The bank pays 5% interest compounded annually. What is your balance? **$2,785.96**

Work Together *Investigating Compound Interest*

Work in a group to investigate compound interest.

6. Suppose you invest $2,000 for 5 years. Your interest rate is 4% compounded annually. What will your balance be? **$2,433.31**

7. *Technology* For the account in Question 6, predict which of the three changes below would increase the balance the most. Then calculate each balance to check your prediction.
   a. doubling the starting amount from $2,000 to $4,000
   b. doubling the interest rate to 8% annual interest **$2,938.66**
   c. doubling the time from 5 years to 10 years **$2,960.49**

a. Doubling the starting amount will increase the ending balance the most; $4,866.61.

Now you may assign Exercises 9–17.

EXERCISES *On Your Own*

Choose **Use a calculator or pencil and paper to find the simple interest earned by each account.**

1. $500 principal
   4% annual interest rate
   3 years
   $60
2. $2,000 principal
   6.5% annual interest rate
   7 years
   $910
3. $1,400 principal
   5.5% annual interest rate
   11 years
   $847
4. $900 principal
   6% annual interest rate
   5 years
   $270
5. $1,900 principal
   4.5% annual interest rate
   10 years
   $855
6. $3,500 principal
   7% annual interest rate
   9 years
   $2,205

WRAP UP

IDENTIFYING THE BIG IDEA Ask students: *What is simple interest? What is compound interest?*

JOURNAL Students can provide examples to illustrate the differences in types of interest. Ask students which type they would prefer to receive and why.

LESSON QUIZ

You open a bank account with $100 and leave the money for 5 years. Find the balance for each interest rate to the nearest cent.

1. 3% simple interest **$115.00**
2. 3% interest compounded annually **$115.93**
3. 6% simple interest **$130.00**
4. 6% interest compounded annually **$133.82**

7. When you use a credit card and leave a balance, you owe interest. If you leave a $500 balance for a year on a card with 18% simple interest, how much will you owe after one year?
$590
8. You invest $2,000 in an account earning simple interest. The balance after 8 years is $2,720. What was the interest rate?
4.5%

Choose **Use a spreadsheet or a calculator to find the balance of each account earning compound interest.**

9. $500 principal, 4% annual interest rate, 3 years — **$562.43**
10. $1,200 principal, 5.5% annual interest rate, 9 years — **$1,942.91**
11. $1,400 principal, 6.5% annual interest rate, 8 years — **$2,316.99**
12. $1,800 principal, 6% annual interest rate, 11 years — **$3,416.94**
13. $900 principal, 5% annual interest rate, 14 years — **$1,781.94**
14. $1,500 principal, 4.7% annual interest rate, 6 years — **$1,975.93**

15. **Choose A, B, C, or D.** Which expression would you use to find the balance of $200 invested for 6 years at 5% interest compounded annually? **B**

A. $200 \cdot 0.05 \cdot 6$ B. $200(1 + 0.05)^6$ C. $200 \cdot 0.06 \cdot 5$ D. $200(1 + 0.06)^5$

16. *Writing* Which would you prefer, $2,000 at 6% interest compounded annually for 5 years or $2,000 at 5% interest compounded annually for 6 years? Explain your choice.
5% for 6 yr; the choice gives you 1 more year to earn interest on interest you have already earned.
17. a. *Research* Find the interest rate of savings accounts at three banks.
b. *Open-ended* Decide on an amount as the principal. Using interest that compounds annually, calculate the balance after four years at each bank.

17a–b. Check students' work.

> JOURNAL
> Explain the difference between simple and compound interest.

Mixed Review

Solve. *(Lesson 3-7)*

18. $w \div 13 = 5$ **65**
19. $-8z = 56$ **−7**
20. $27 = -3x$ **−9**
21. $16 = t \div (-4)$ **−64**
22. $5y = -20$ **−4**

Determine whether the given sides form a right triangle. *(Lesson 7-3)*

23. 3, 4, 5 **yes**
24. 12, 13, 17 **no**
25. 6, 5, 2 **no**
26. 6, 8, 10 **yes**
27. 20, 15, 12 **no**
28. 3, 8, 12 **no**

29. The length of a rectangle is twice the width. The area is 32 cm^2. Find the dimensions of the rectangle. *(Lesson 8-2)*
8 cm long and 4 cm wide

Extra Practice, Lesson 10-4, page 523

PRACTICE

Practice 10-4 *Simple and Compound Interest*

Choose a calculator or pencil and paper to find the simple interest earned by each account.

1. $700 principal, 3% interest rate, 2 years — $42
2. $950 principal, 8% interest rate, 5 years — $380
3. $5,000 principal, 6.5% interest rate, 3 years — $975

Choose a spreadsheet or calculator to find the balance of each account earning compound interest.

4. $800 principal, 6% interest rate, 9 years — $1,351.58
5. $5,200 principal, 5% interest rate, 4 years — $6,320.63
6. $3,500 principal, 4.5% interest rate, 10 years — $5,435.39

Circle A, B, C, or D. Which expression yields the greatest amount?

7. A. $400(1 + .06)^3$ B. $400(1 + .07)^3$ C. $400(1 + .08)^3$ (D.) $400(1 + .09)^3$
8. (A.) $500(1 + .06)^2$ B. $450(1 + .07)^2$ C. $250(1 + .06)^3$ D. $200(1 + .07)^3$
9. A. $100(1 + .06)^2$ B. $100(1 + .05)^2$ (C.) $100(1 + .005)^{24}$ D. $100(1 + .006)^{18}$
10. A. $200(1 + .06)^{10}$ B. $200(1 + .006)^{120}$ C. $200(1 + .05)^{15}$ (D.) $200(1 + .006)^{150}$

Choose a calculator or a computer. Use exponents. Answers may vary due to rounding.

11. You deposit $600. The account pays 5% interest compounded annually. How much money is in the account at the end of 4 years?
$729.30
12. You deposit $2,000 in an account that pays 6% interest compounded annually. How much money is in the account at the end of 12 years?
$4,024.39
13. You invest $5,000 in an account earning simple interest. The balance after 6 years is $6,200. What is the interest rate?
4%

In copymaster and workbook formats

RETEACHING

Reteaching 10-4 *Simple and Compound Interest*

When you deposit money in a bank, the bank pays interest. **Simple interest** is interest paid only on the amount you deposited, or the **principal. Compound interest** is interest paid on both the principal and any interest earned in previous interest periods.

Simple Interest

To find simple interest, use this formula.

Interest = principal · rate · time in years
$I = p \cdot r \cdot t$

Find the simple interest on $1,800 invested at 5% annual interest for 3 years.

$I = p \cdot r \cdot t$
$= 1{,}800 \cdot 0.05 \cdot 3$ ← **Use 0.05 for 5%.**
$= 270$

The interest is $270. (The balance will be $1,800 + $270, or $2,070.)

Compound Interest

To find compound interest, use this formula.

Balance = principal · (1 + rate)$^{\text{time in years}}$
$B = p(1 + r)^t$

You put $1,800 in the bank. The interest rate is 5% compounded annually. How much will be in the account after 3 years?

$B = p(1 + r)^t$
$= 1{,}800(1 + 0.05)^3$ ← **Use 0.05 for 5%.**
= 1,800 [×] 1.05 [y^x] 3
$\approx 2{,}083.73$

The balance is $2,083.73.

Use a calculator or pencil and paper to find the simple interest earned by each account.

1. $800 principal, 4% interest rate, 5 years
$I = p \cdot r \cdot t$
= 800 · 0.04 · 5
= $160
2. $1,200 principal, 5.5% interest rate, 25 years
$I = p \cdot r \cdot t$
= 1,200 · 0.055 · 25
= $1,650
3. $800 principal, 3% interest, 4 years — $96
4. $1,900 principal, 4.5% interest, 20 years — $1,710
5. $20,000 principal, 3.5% interest, 15 years — $10,500

Use a spreadsheet or calculator to find the balance of each account earning compound interest.

6. $600 principal, 6% interest rate, 3 years
$B = p(1 + r)^t$
$= 600(1 + 0.06)^3$
= $714.61
7. $9,000 principal, 5% interest rate, 4 years
$B = p(1 + r)^t$
$= 9{,}000(1 + 0.05)^4$
= $10,939.56

Reteaching

ENRICHMENT

Minds on Math Transparency

10-4

Jacalyn asked her friends to guess the number of buttons in a jar. Three of her friends guessed 495, 514, and 537. One of the guesses was off by 8, another by 15, and another by 27. How many buttons were in the jar?

522 buttons

See *Solution Key* for worked-out answers.

10-5 Teaching Notes

1 Focus

CONNECTING TO PRIOR KNOWLEDGE On the board, write the numbers 1–10 in one column and the *even* numbers 2–20 in the next column. Label the columns *Number of Bicycles* and *Number of Wheels.* Show students how the numbers correspond. Now ask students to brainstorm other ways they could title the columns, for example, *Number of People* and *Number of Shoes.*

2 Teach

THINK AND DISCUSS

MENTAL MATH Question 1 Help students realize that *50 mi/h* tells them the distance the car travels each hour.

AEP Some students may think the function machine is a real mechanical device. Explain that this is an imaginary machine to illustrate a mathematical definition. The drawing could be almost any shape.

Question 4 Students can use Guess-and-Check if they miss the pattern.

Question 6 Point out that the rule is more useful than the table because 3.5 h is not in the table.

Lesson Planning Options

Prerequisite Skills

- evaluating expressions (3-1)
- drawing line graphs (1-2)

Vocabulary/Symbols

function

Materials/Manipulatives

- graph paper
- watch with second hand

Resources

Student Edition

Skills Handbook, p. 530
Extra Practice, p. 523
Glossary/Study Guide

Teaching Resources

Chapter Support File, Ch. 10
- Lesson Planner 10-5
- Practice 10-5, Reteaching 10-5
- Alternative Activity 10-5
- Answer Masters 10-5

Teaching Aids Masters 1, 2, 4
Glossary, Spanish Resources

Transparencies
1, 2, 15, 96, Minds on Math 10-5

Warm Up

Lauralee pitched 12 innings. Maureen pitched $3\frac{2}{3}$ fewer innings. How many innings did Maureen pitch?
$8\frac{1}{3}$

10-5 Using Tables, Rules, and Graphs

What You'll Learn

1. To represent functions with tables and rules
2. To graph functions

...And Why

You can use functions to describe many real-world relationships, such as time and distance.

Here's How

Look for questions that
- build understanding
- ✔ check understanding

THINK AND DISCUSS

1 Using Tables and Rules

Suppose your family is planning a sight-seeing vacation by car. You expect to drive at an average speed of 50 mi/h.

1. *Mental Math* How many miles will you drive in 1 h? 2 h? **50 mi; 100 mi**
2. *Reasoning* How many hours will it take to drive 200 mi? **4 h**

You can represent the relationship between the time you drive and the distance you drive using a function machine like the one at the right. You say that the distance is a **function** of time, since each input value (time) has exactly one output value (distance).

Input (time in hours)

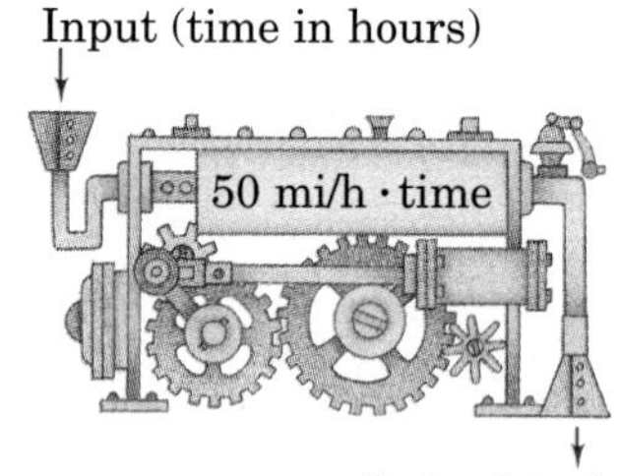

Output (mi)

3. When the input is 3, what is the output? **150**
4. If the output is 300, what is the input? **6**

You can represent functions using a table or a rule.

EXAMPLE 1 *Real-World Problem Solving*

a. Make a table to represent the relationship between the time and distance you drive.

Input (hours)	1	2	3	4
Output (miles)	50	100	150	200

b. Write a rule to represent the relationship between the time and distance you drive.

distance = 50 · time

$d = 50t$ ← Variables represent the input (t) and output (d).

ERROR ALERT! Example 2 Students may think that a graph must have the same scale for both axes. **Remediation:** Assure students that the scales may differ. Point out that if the *x*-axis and *y*-axis had the same scale, the graph would be too large to fit on one page.

ADDITIONAL EXAMPLES

FOR EXAMPLE 1

Suppose you can bicycle about 10 mi/h. Write a rule to represent the relationship between the time and distance you bicycle. $d = 10t$

FOR EXAMPLE 2

Graph the input and output data from the table in For Example 1. Draw a line through the points on your graph.

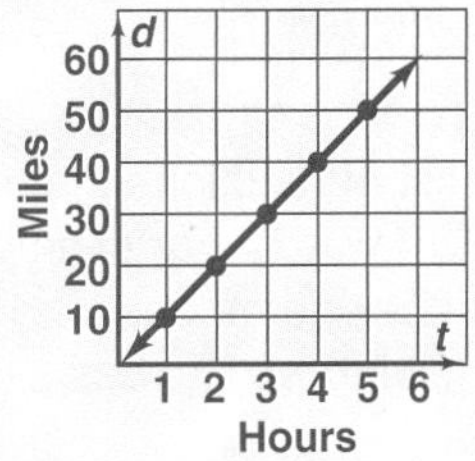

Work Together

DIVERSITY Question 9 Students who have asthma or other breathing problems may feel self-conscious as volunteers. Use volunteers who seem comfortable having their breathing observed for data. Assign the remaining students as partners.

VISUAL LEARNING Question 10b Provide students with colored markers or pencils so that they can easily see the points and lines they are graphing.

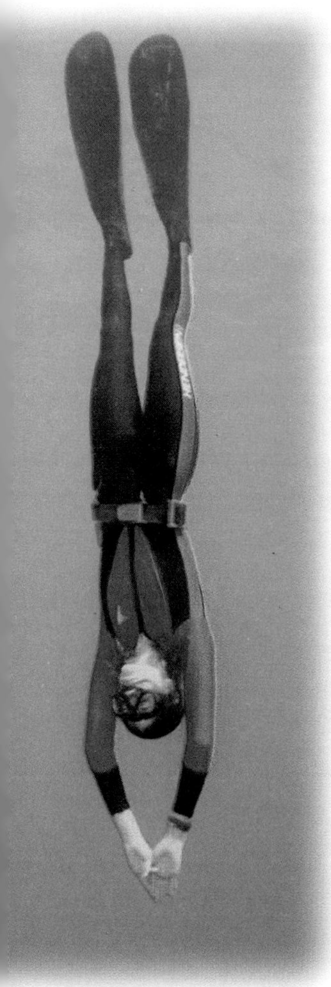

5. *Look Back* What kind of sequence is the number pattern you see in the output row of the table in Example 1? **arithmetic**

6. *Try It Out* Use the rule to find the miles you drive in 3.5 h. **175 mi**

Now you may assign Exercises 1–10.

2 *Graphing Functions*

You can make a graph to represent a function.

EXAMPLE 2

Graph the input and output data from the table in Example 1. Draw a line through the points on your graph.

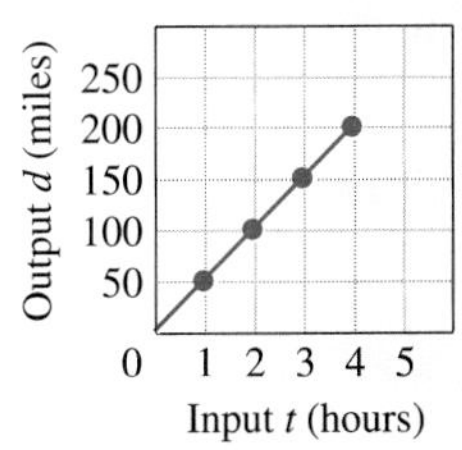

7. *Predict* Use the graph to predict the miles traveled in 5 h. **250 mi**

8. *Try It Out* Make a table of values for the function rule output = 3 · input. Then graph the data. **See back of book.**

Work Together *Investigating Functions*

Work with a partner to investigate a function.

9. a. *Data Collection* Count the number of times you or your partner breathes in one minute. Record the result.
   b. Repeat the experiment four times. Then find the mean of your results.

9–10. Check students' work.

10. a. Use your mean number of breaths per minute. Copy and complete this table.

Input *t* (minutes)	1	2	3	4	5	6
Output *b* (number of breaths)	■	■	■	■	■	■

   b. Graph the data in your table.
   c. Write a rule for the function.

Now you may assign Exercises 11–18.

WHAT? Most people can hold their breath for about 1 min. Experienced skin divers can hold their breath for about $2\frac{1}{2}$ min. A beaver can stay under water for about 15 min.

Source: *Encyclopedia Britannica*

Technology Options

Prentice Hall Technology

Software for Learners
- Math Blaster® Mystery*
- Interactive Student Tutorial, Chapter 10*

Teaching Resource Software
- Computer Item Generator 10-5
- Resource Pro™ Chapter 10*

Internet • For related mathematics activities, visit the Prentice Hall site at www.phschool.com/math

**Available on CD-ROM only*

Assignment Options for Exercises On Your Own

To provide flexible scheduling, this lesson can be split into parts.

1 **Core** 1–9
Extension 10

2 **Core** 11–17
Extension 18

Use Mixed Review to maintain skills.

3 Practice/Assess

EXERCISES ***On Your Own***

OPEN-ENDED Exercise 10 Remind students of the bicycle and wheels table in Connecting to Prior Knowledge. For Questions 8 and 9 suggest they try to think of things that come in multiples of 2 such as pant legs, shoes, or ears.

EXTENSION Exercise 18 Help students create graphs for each of these situations. Tell them if any vertical line will go through more than one point on their graph, then the graph is not a function. Have them check their work with the vertical line test.

CONNECTION TO SPORTS Invite students to brainstorm a list of functions that relate to sports they play or watch. For example, the score in a basketball game could be written as $s = 2b + f$ where b = baskets and f = free throws.

WRAP UP

IDENTIFYING THE BIG IDEA Ask: *What are some ways you can represent functions?*

PROJECT LINK Urge students to make the hole using a pin. If the hole is too large, the water will empty too quickly to measure. Students can use rulers to measure the height of the water level.

pages 452–453 On Your Own

4. Answers may vary. Sample: you can use a table when you only have a few values or when you cannot state the rule; you can use the rule when you have many values.

5a.

Input	Output
−5	22
−4	14
−3	8
−2	4
−1	2
0	2
1	4
2	8
3	14
4	22
5	32

6.

Input	Output
1	5
2	10
3	15
4	20
5	25

7.

Input	Output
1	4
2	5
3	6
4	7
5	8

8.

Input	Output
1	3
2	5
3	7
4	9
5	11

9.

Input	Output
1	0.5
2	1
3	1.5
4	2
5	2.5

11c.

Input	Output
1	40
2	80
3	120
4	160

15d. Sample:

Input p	Output c
\$1.25	\$3.75
\$3.40	\$1.60
\$4.65	\$.35

16a.

Input s	Output A
1	1
2	4
3	9
4	16

b.

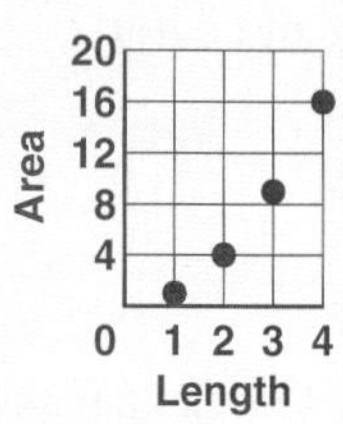

EXERCISES ***On Your Own***

Write a function rule for each table of values.

1. $s = 6.5h$

Hours Worked	Salary
1	\$6.50
2	\$13.00
3	\$19.50
4	\$26.00

2. $p = 11.99n$

Number of CDs	Price Paid
1	\$11.99
2	\$23.98
3	\$35.97
4	\$47.96

3. $h = 2w + 1$

Weeks	Plant Height
1	3 in.
2	5 in.
3	7 in.
4	9 in.

4. *Writing* Explain when you would use a table to represent a function, and when you would use a rule. **See margin.**

5. *Algebra* Use the function machine at the right.
   a. Make an input/output table for input values from −5 to 5. **a. See margin.**
   b. What two inputs result in an output of 22? **−5 and 4**

Input

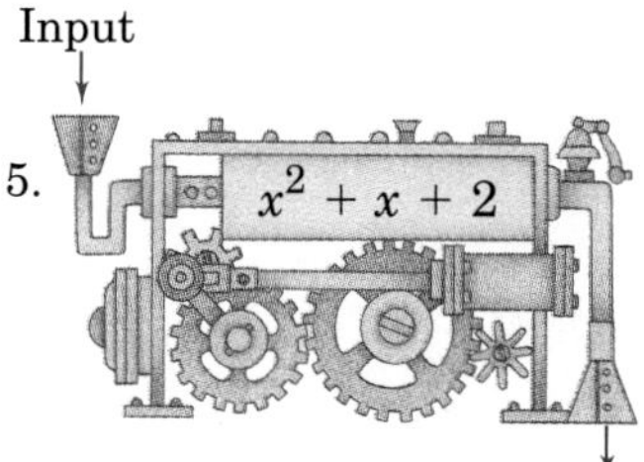

Output

Make a table of values for each function rule. Use input values of 1, 2, 3, 4, and 5. **6–9. See margin.**

6. Output = 5 · Input
7. Output = Input + 3
8. Output = 2 · Input + 1
9. Output = Input ÷ 2

10. *Open-ended* Describe a situation for each rule in Exercises 6–9.

10. Samples: Each poster costs \$5; a fair charges \$3 admission and \$1 for each ride; a book club credits you 1 bonus point for signing up and 2 bonus points for each book you buy; there are 2 bus stops for every mile on a bus route.

11. *Cars* The graph at the right shows the relationship between distance and time for a car driven at a constant speed.
    a. What is the speed? Explain. **40 mi/h**
    b. Use the graph to find the number of hours it takes to drive 120 miles. **3**
    c. Make a table for the function. Use input (time) for 1, 2, 3, and 4 hours. **See margin.**
    d. Write a rule to represent the function. **$d = 40t$**

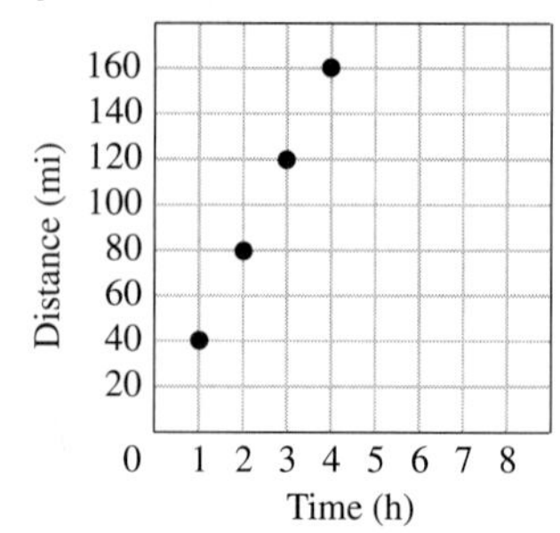

Match the graph with the rule.

12. **C**

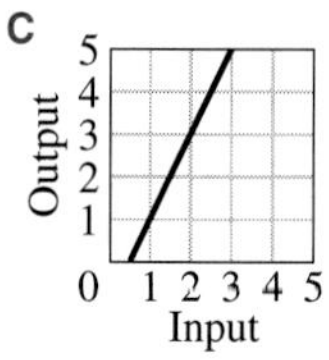

13. **A**

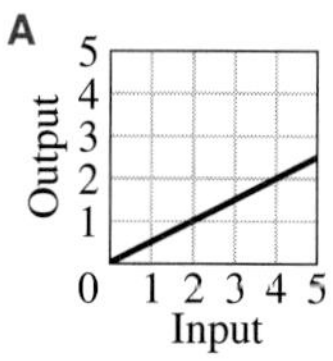

14. **B**

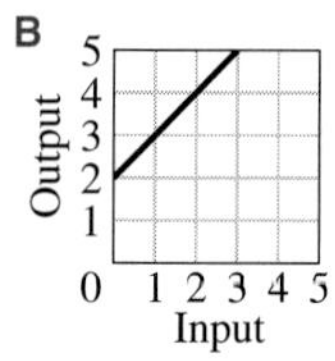

A. Output = $\frac{1}{2}$ · Input
B. Output = Input + 2
C. Output = 2 · Input − 1

LESSON QUIZ

Riding horses wear iron horseshoes to protect their hoofs—one shoe per hoof.

1. Make a table representing the number of horseshoes needed for 3–8 horses.

Horses	3	4	5	6	7	8
Shoes	12	16	20	24	28	32

2. Represent this function with a rule.
   $s = 4h$

3. Graph this function.

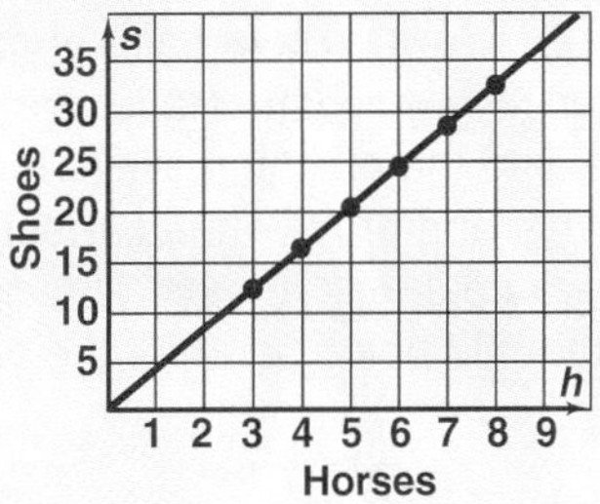

15. a. Copy and complete the function table at the right.
    b. Use the data from your table to make a graph.
    c. Write a rule for the function. $c = 5 - p$
    d. List three more input/output pairs for the function.
    15a–b. See back of book. d. See margin p. 452.

Change from a $5.00 Purchase

Input p (cost)	Output c (change)
$ .50	■
$1.00	■
$1.50	■
. . .	. . .
$5.00	■

16. *Geometry* The formula $A = s^2$ is a function rule. It shows that the area of a square is a function of the length of a side.
    a. Using the rule, make a table for the area of a square with sides of length 1, 2, 3, and 4. a–b. See margin.
    b. Use the data from your table to graph the function.
    c. Describe what your graph looks like.
    Answers may vary. Sample: The graph rises faster as you move away from 0.
17. a. *Jobs* Use the function machine at the right. Suppose you work six hours (input). What are your wages (output)? $21
    b. Make a table of five inputs and outputs for this machine.
    c. Make a graph of the function using the data in your table.
    17 b–c. See back of book.

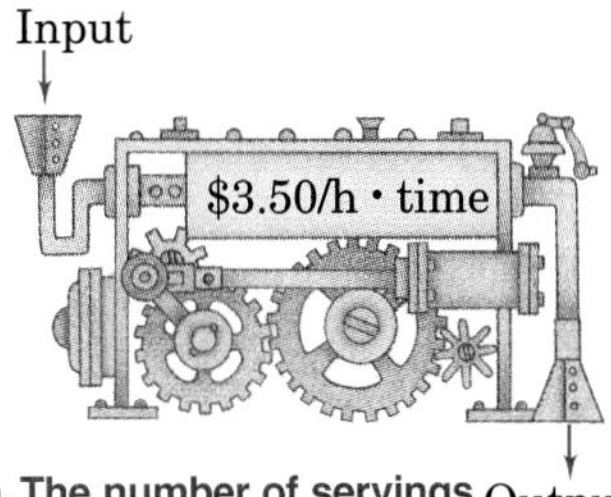

18. A function has only one output for each input. Explain if each situation represents a function.
    a. Input: the number of pounds a turkey weighs
       Output: the number of $\frac{1}{3}$-lb servings of turkey
       It is a function. The number of servings depends on the weight of the turkey.
    b. Input: the number of days in a month
       Output: the number of holidays in the month
       It is not a function. The number of days in a month does not determine the number of holidays.

Mixed Review

Find the value of each expression. *(Lessons 2-5, 2-6)*

19. 95.26×110 10,478.6
20. 0.23×8.45 1.9435
21. $4\overline{)1.988}$ 0.497
22. $0.384 \div 9.6$ 0.04
23. $19.563 \div 6$ 3.2605

Compare. Use <, >, or =. *(Lesson 4-3)*

24. $\frac{7}{9}$ ■ $\frac{3}{4}$ >
25. $\frac{5}{14}$ ■ $\frac{2}{6}$ >
26. $\frac{7}{30}$ ■ $\frac{1}{3}$ <
27. $\frac{8}{24}$ ■ $\frac{2}{6}$ =
28. $\frac{11}{49}$ ■ $\frac{12}{42}$ <

29. Suppose that January 1 is a Monday. What are the dates of the other Mondays in January? *(Lesson 10-1)* January 8, 15, 22, 29

CHAPTER PROJECT

PROJECT LINK: COLLECTING DATA

Put a small hole in the bottom of the container. Measure the height of the water level every 30 seconds. How long does it take to empty? Use your data to make a table of the height of the water level at each time. Check students' work.

PRACTICE

Practice 10-5 *Using Tables, Rules, and Graphs*

The graph at the right shows the relationship between distance and time for a car driven at a constant speed.

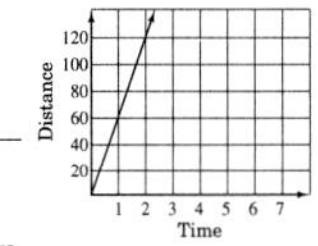

1. What is the speed? 60 mi/h
2. Is this a function relationship? yes
3. If this is a function, write a rule to represent it. $d = 60t$
4. Make a table for the function, listing six input/output pairs.

Answers will vary. Sample:

Input	Output
1	60
2	120
3	180
4	240
5	300
6	360

5. The function machine at the right shows your hourly wages. What are your wages if you work 5 h? $25.75
6. Write a rule for the function. $w = 5.15h$
7. For the function machine at the right, what input would give an output of $15.45? 3

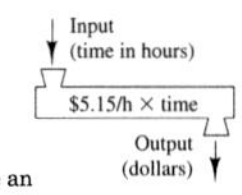

A car travels at a constant speed of 55 mi/h. Complete the table to show the time and distance the car would travel.

	Time (h)	Distance (mi)
8.	1	55
9.	1.75	96.25
10.	2.5	137.5
11.	3.25	178.75

Circle A, B, C, or D. Which value could *not* be an output for the given function if only whole numbers are used as inputs?

12. $3x + 8$
    (A.) 6 B. 14 C. 11 D. 8
13. $2x - 1$
    A. 3 B. 21 (C.) 8 D. 11

Practice

In copymaster and workbook formats

RETEACHING

Reteaching 10-5 *Using Tables, Rules, and Graphs*

If you ride a bicycle at 12 mi/h, the distance you ride is a **function** of time. For each input value (time), there is exactly one output value (distance).

- You can represent the relationship between time and distance with a table.

Input (hours)	1	2	3	4
Output (miles)	12	24	36	48

- You can represent the relationship, or function, with a rule.

  output = 12 · input
  distance = 12 · time

- You can represent the relationship, or function, with a graph.

① Graph the points from the table. (1, 12), (2, 24), (3, 36), (4, 48)

② Draw a line through the points.

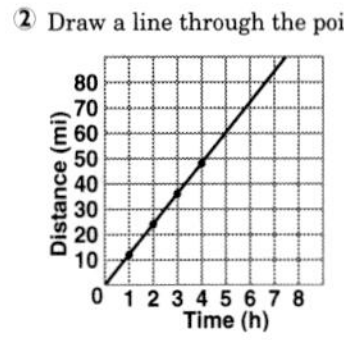

Write an input-output function rule for each table of values.

1.

Input	Output
3	6
4	8
5	10
6	12

Output = 2 · input

2.

Input	Output
1	3
2	4
3	5
4	6

Output = input + 2

3.

Input	Output
1	45
2	90
3	135
4	180

Output = 45 · input

Complete the table of values. Then make a graph for the rule.

4. Output = 3 · Input

Input	Output
1	3
2	6
3	9
4	12

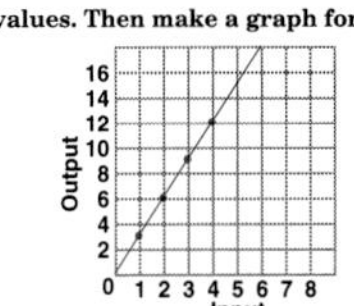

ENRICHMENT

Minds on Math Transparency

10-5

There are a total of 12 cards of four colors in a box. The probability of drawing a green card is the same as the probability of drawing a yellow card. The probability of drawing a red card is $\frac{1}{4}$. The probability of drawing a blue card is $\frac{1}{12}$. How many green cards are in the box?

4 green cards

See *Solution Key* for worked-out answers.

10-6 Teaching Notes

1 Focus

CONNECTING TO PRIOR KNOWLEDGE Ask students: *Name several ways in which you can represent a function.* **table, rule, graph** Then ask them to explain which way they prefer. **Answers may vary. Sample: graphs, because they give you a visual picture of the function**

2 Teach

Work Together

TACTILE LEARNING Have pairs of students create a function machine. Have one student input chips into the machine. Have the partner think of a rule and provide the correct number of chips as output. Ask the first student to describe the rule being used for the function.

THINK AND DISCUSS

Make sure students understand that the function rule must work for every row in the table.

AEP Cognates of the term *notation* exist in other languages, including Spanish (*notación*) and Italian (*annotazione*). Invite students to suggest definitions or synonyms for notation in English or in their own first language.

Lesson Planning Options

Prerequisite Skills

- using function tables and rules (10-5)

Resources

Student Edition

Skills Handbook, p. 530
Extra Practice, p. 523
Glossary/Study Guide

Teaching Resources

Chapter Support File, Ch. 10
- Lesson Planner 10-6
- Practice 10-6, Reteaching 10-6
- Answer Masters 10-6

Glossary, Spanish Resources

Transparencies

15, 97, Minds on Math 10-6

Warm Up

Multiply. Express the answers in lowest terms.

$3 \times \frac{5}{6}$ $\frac{5}{2}$ or $2\frac{1}{2}$

$\frac{3}{4} \times \frac{12}{15}$ $\frac{3}{5}$

$\frac{7}{10} \times \frac{2}{21}$ $\frac{1}{15}$

10-6 Function Rules

What You'll Learn

1. To make a table given a function rule
2. To find a function rule given a table

...And Why

Different views of functions are useful in different situations.

Here's How

Look for questions that
- build understanding
- ✓ check understanding

Work Together

Viewing Functions

Use the function table below. Consider these three rules.

Input	Output
1	2
2	3
3	4
4	5

I. Output = 2 × Input
II. Output = Input + 1
III. Output = 2 × Input − 1

1. a. *Analyze* Which rule(s) describes the relationship between the first input and output? **I and II**
   b. Which rule(s) describes the relationship between the input and output when the input is 2? **II and III**
   c. Which rule(s) describes the relationship between the input and output in all of the rows? **II**

2. Use the variable n to represent any input in the table. Write a variable expression to represent the related output. $n + 1$

THINK AND DISCUSS

1 *Making Tables*

Input	Output
1	4
2	5
3	6
4	7

Here are two ways you can describe the relationship of the values in the table at the left.

Each output is three greater than the input

Output = Input + 3

Another way to state the rule is using function notation.

Input

$$f(n) = n + 3$$

Output   Rule for Function

You read the function rule above as "f of n equals n plus three."

AUDITORY LEARNING Have students practice saying aloud the words "*f of n*" when they see the function notation *f*(*n*).

ERROR ALERT! Students may read *f*(*n*) as f times n. **Remediation:** Emphasize that *f*(*n*) is a single symbol and not a product. Remind students to say "*f* of *n*" to themselves whenever they see this notation.

Example 1 Ask: *What does f(2) mean?* **the value of the function when the input is 2**

ADDITIONAL EXAMPLES

FOR EXAMPLE 1

Use the function rule in Example 1. Find *f*(−1). **8**

FOR EXAMPLE 2

Write a rule for the function represented by the table. **Answers may vary. Sample: $f(n) = 4n - 2$**

n	*f*(*n*)
0	−2
1	2
2	6
3	10
4	14

You also use function notation to find input/output pairs.

EXAMPLE 1

Use the function rule $f(n) = -3n + 5$. Find $f(0)$, $f(1)$, $f(2)$, and $f(3)$. Then make a table for the function.

Use the expression $-3n + 5$. Replace *n* with 0, 1, 2, and 3.

$f(0) = -3(0) + 5 = 5$

$f(1) = -3(1) + 5 = 2$

$f(2) = -3(2) + 5 = -1$

$f(3) = -3(3) + 5 = -4$

Put the inputs and outputs in a table.

n	$f(n) = -3n + 5$
0	5
1	2
2	−1
3	−4

3. ✓ *Try It Out* Use the function rule in Example 1. Find *f*(4). **−7**

Now you may assign Exercises 1–16.

2 *Looking for Patterns*

When you have a function table, you can find a function rule by looking for patterns.

EXAMPLE 2

Write a rule for each function represented by a table below.

a.

n	*f*(*n*)
0	0
1	−4
2	−8
3	−12

+1, +1, +1 (inputs); −4, −4, −4 (outputs)

When $n = 0$, $f(n) = 0$. Each number in the second column is $n \cdot (-4)$.

The function rule is $f(n) = n \cdot (-4)$, or $f(n) = -4n$.

b.

n	*f*(*n*)
0	2
1	5
2	8
3	11

+1, +1, +1 (inputs); +3, +3, +3 (outputs)

When $n = 0$, $f(n) = 2$. Then as inputs increase by 1, outputs increase by 3.

The function rule is $f(n) = 3n + 2$.

WHAT? Fractals, like the one pictured below, are created using a feedback process. This means that an output is used for the next input. For example, suppose you used $n = 0.8$ as the first value for *n* in $f(n) = n^2$. The output is 0.64. You would use the output 0.64 as the second input value for *n*.

Source: *The Beauty of Fractals*

Technology Options

Prentice Hall Technology

Software for Learners
- Hot Page™ 6–6*
- Math Blaster® Mystery*
- Interactive Student Tutorial, Chapter 10*

Teaching Resource Software
- Computer Item Generator 10-6
- Resource Pro™ Chapter 10*

Internet • For related mathematics activities, visit the Prentice Hall site at www.phschool.com/math

**Available on CD-ROM only*

Assignment Options for Exercises On Your Own

To provide flexible scheduling, this lesson can be split into parts.

1 **Core** 1–15
Extension 16

2 **Core** 17–25
Extension 26

Use Mixed Review to maintain skills.

EXTENSION and CONNECTION TO TECHNOLOGY Encourage interested students to find out about fractals. If you have extended class periods or block scheduling, consider having someone demonstrate fractal software. Allow students to create, print, and color their own designs.

ASSESSMENT Have students create a function rule and use their rule to make a table for $f(1)$, $f(2)$, $f(3)$, and $f(4)$. Then have students exchange tables with a partner. The partner looks for a pattern in the table. Each partner writes a rule for the function using function notation.

3 Practice/Assess

EXERCISES *On Your Own*

Exercise 16 Ask: *How would the rule change if the book can be overdue for 2 days without a fine?* **$f(n) = 0.05(n - 2)$**

WRITING Exercise 25 Point out that there may be more than one correct rule for each table.

WRAP UP

IDENTIFYING THE BIG IDEA Ask: *What is a function rule? How do you find a function rule from a table?*

JOURNAL Tell students to describe briefly each method. Suggest that they use the same function for their examples of each method.

CHECKPOINT 2

Checkpoint 2

Lessons 10-4 through 10-6

1. Complete the table of values for $f(n) = 1 + n$. Then make a graph.

n	$f(n)$
1	2
2	3
3	4
4	5

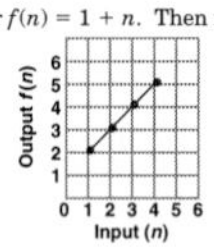

Write a rule for the function represented by each table.

2.

n	$f(n)$
1	5
2	10
3	15
4	20

$f(n) = 5n$

3.

n	$f(n)$
1	−3
2	−2
3	−1
4	0

$f(n) = n - 4$

4.

n	$f(n)$
1	3
2	5
3	7
4	9

$f(n) = 2n + 1$

5. What is the simple interest earned on \$700 invested at 5% annual interest for 2 years? \$70

Assessment

pages 456–457 On Your Own

7.

n	$f(n)$
0	2
1	3
2	4
3	5

8.

n	$f(n)$
0	12
1	10
2	8
3	6

9.

n	$f(n)$
0	0
1	4
2	8
3	12

10.

n	$f(n)$
0	0
1	0.5
2	1
3	1.5

11.

n	$f(n)$
0	9
1	8
2	7
3	6

12.

n	$f(n)$
0	0
1	−3
2	−6
3	−9

13.

n	$f(n)$
0	1
1	3
2	5
3	7

14.

n	$f(n)$
0	1
1	2
2	5
3	10

15a.

n	$f(n)$
1	3
2	4
3	5
4	6
5	7
6	8

n	0	1	2	3
$f(n)$	1	5	9	13

4. **a.** What is $f(n)$ when $n = 0$? How much do the outputs increase when the inputs increase by 1? **1; 4**
   b. ✔ *Try It Out* Write a rule for the function represented by the table. **$f(n) = 4n + 1$**

Now you may assign Exercises 17–26.

EXERCISES *On Your Own*

Use the function rule $f(n) = 2n + 7$. Find each output.

1. $f(3)$ **13**
2. $f(0)$ **7**
3. $f(-1)$ **5**
4. $f(-4)$ **−1**
5. $f(0.5)$ **8**
6. $f\left(\frac{1}{4}\right)$ **$7\frac{1}{2}$**

Make a table for the function represented by each rule. Find $f(0)$, $f(1)$, $f(2)$, and $f(3)$. **7–14. See margin.**

7. $f(n) = n + 2$
8. $f(n) = 12 - 2n$
9. $f(n) = 4n$
10. $f(n) = n \div 2$
11. $f(n) = 9 - n$
12. $f(n) = -3n$
13. $f(n) = 2n + 1$
14. $f(n) = n^2 + 1$

15. **a.** Make a table of input/output pairs for the graph at the right. **See margin.**
    b. Use your table to write a rule for the function. **$f(n) = n + 2$**

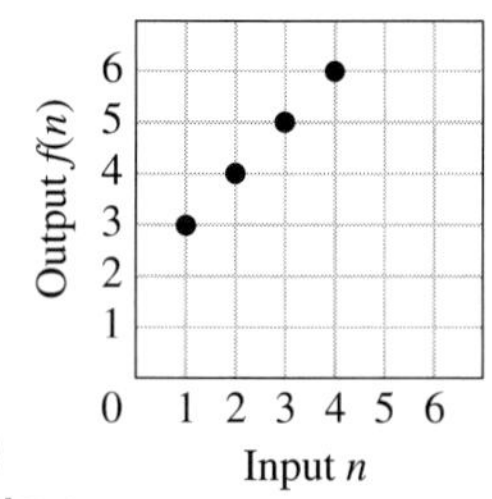

16. You pay \$.05 for each day a library book is overdue. A rule that describes this is $f(n) = 0.05n$, where n represents the number of days overdue.
    a. What is the charge for a book that is nine days overdue? **\$.45**
    b. A book has a fine of \$1.05. How many days is it overdue? **21 days**

Write a rule for the function represented by each table.

17.

n	$f(n)$
0	0
1	5
2	10
3	15

$f(n) = 5n$

18.

n	$f(n)$
0	4
1	5
2	6
3	7

$f(n) = n + 4$

19.

n	$f(n)$
0	−6
1	−5
2	−4
3	−3

$f(n) = n - 6$

20.

n	$f(n)$
0	−2
1	0
2	2
3	4

$f(n) = 2n - 2$

21.

n	$f(n)$
0	0
1	−8
2	−16
3	−24

$f(n) = -8n$

22.

n	$f(n)$
0	5
1	8
2	11
3	14

$f(n) = 3n + 5$

23.

n	$f(n)$
0	5
1	9
2	13
3	17

$f(n) = 4n + 5$

24.

n	$f(n)$
0	1
1	−8
2	−17
3	−26

$f(n) = -9n + 1$

LESSON QUIZ

1. Make a table for the function represented by: $f(n) = 3n - 4$.
Find $f(0)$, $f(1)$, $f(2)$, and $f(3)$.

n	$f(n)$
0	−4
1	−1
2	2
3	5

2. Write a rule for the function represented by the table. **Answers may vary. Sample: $f(n) = 2n + 4$**

n	$f(n)$
0	4
1	6
2	8
3	10

25. *Writing* Explain how you found the rule you wrote for one of the tables in Exercises 17–24. **See below.**

26. *Money* Suppose you put \$.50 in your piggy bank on July 1, \$1.00 on July 2, \$1.50 on July 3, and so on. Use n to represent the date in July. Write a function rule for the amount you put in the piggy bank on any date in July.
$f(n) = 0.5n$

JOURNAL
Summarize the methods that you can use to represent a function. Include an example of each.

Mixed Review

Write each number as a percent. *(Lesson 6-7)*

27. 0.455 **45.5%**
28. $\frac{7}{8}$ **87.5%**
29. 9.25 **925%**
30. $\frac{209}{400}$ **52.25%**
31. $6\frac{1}{2}$ **650%**
32. 2 **200%**

Find the circumference and area of each circle. Round your answers to the nearest tenth. *(Lesson 8-4)*

33. $r = 1.75$ ft **11.0 ft; 9.6 ft^2**
34. $d = 17$ yd **53.4 yd; 227.0 yd^2**
35. $r = 1.5$ m **9.4 m; 7.1 m^2**
36. $d = 9.5$ km **29.8 km; 70.9 km^2**
37. $r = 1$ in. **6.3 in.; 3.1 in.^{2}**

38. The three sides of a right triangle are 6 in., 8 in., and 10 in. What is the area of the triangle? *(Lesson 8-3)* **24 in.^{2}**

25. Answers may vary. Sample: Find the differences between successive values of $f(n)$. This is the number being multiplied by n. Then add $f(0)$.

✓ CHECKPOINT 2

Lessons 10-4 through 10-6

Make a table of values for each function. Then graph the function. **1–4. See back of book.**

1. $f(n) = 3n$
2. $f(n) = 2n - 4$
3. $f(n) = 8 - n$
4. $f(n) = n + 7$

Write a rule for the function represented by each table.

5.

n	$f(n)$
0	0
1	−12
2	−24
3	−36

$f(n) = -12n$

6.

n	$f(n)$
0	4
1	3
2	2
3	1

$f(n) = 4 - n$

7.

n	$f(n)$
0	1
1	4
2	7
3	10

$f(n) = 3n + 1$

8.

n	$f(n)$
0	0
1	7
2	14
3	21

$f(n) = 7n$

9. *Writing* You invest \$600 for three years. The interest rate is 4% compounded annually. Explain how to find your balance.
4% is 0.04 of the balance. So the balance at the beginning of each year is multiplied by (1 + 0.04) by the end of the year. Multiply the initial balance \$600 by 1.04 for each of the 3 years to get $600 \cdot 1.04^3$.

PRACTICE

Practice 10-6 Function Rules

Find $f(1)$, $f(2)$, $f(3)$, and $f(4)$ for the function represented by each rule.

1. $f(n) = 2n$ **2; 4; 6; 8**
2. $f(n) = n + 4$ **5; 6; 7; 8**
3. $f(n) = n^2 - 1$ **0; 3; 8; 15**
4. $f(n) = -2n$ **−2; −4; −6; −8**
5. $f(n) = 3n + 1$ **4; 7; 10; 13**
6. $f(n) = 8 - 3n$ **5; 2; −1; −4**
7. $f(n) = 6 + 4n$ **10; 14; 18; 22**
8. $f(n) = n - 5$ **−4; −3; −2; −1**
9. $f(n) = 2n + 7$ **9; 11; 13; 15**
10. $f(n) = -5n + 6$ **1; −4; −9; −14**
11. $f(n) = 3n + 9$ **12; 15; 18; 21**
12. $f(n) = \frac{n}{2}$ **$\frac{1}{2}$; 1; $\frac{3}{2}$; 2**

Write a rule for the function represented by each table.

13.

n	$f(n)$
1	6
2	7
3	8
4	9

$f(n) = n + 5$

14.

n	$f(n)$
1	4
2	8
3	12
4	16

$f(n) = 4n$

15.

n	$f(n)$
1	−6
2	−9
3	−12
4	−15

$f(n) = -3n - 3$

16.

n	$f(n)$
1	5
2	7
3	9
4	11

$f(n) = 2n + 3$

17.

n	$f(n)$
1	4
2	7
3	10
4	13

$f(n) = 3n + 1$

18.

n	$f(n)$
1	−1
2	−3
3	−5
4	−7

$f(n) = -2n + 1$

Circle A, B, C, or D. If input values must be given in whole numbers, which function would *not* produce the given number as an output?

19. 9
A. $f(n) = n^2$
B. $f(n) = \frac{2}{3}n - 1$
(C.) $f(n) = n^2 - 1$
D. $f(n) = 2n + 1$

20. −1
A. $f(n) = n - 1$
(B.) $f(n) = n^2$
C. $f(n) = n^2 - 1$
D. $f(n) = 2n - 7$

In copymaster and workbook formats

RETEACHING

Reteaching 10-6 Function Rules

The function table shows the relationship between input and output. A function rule is:

output = 4 × input.

Input	Output
1	4
2	8
3	12

You can also state the rule using *function notation.*

$f(n) = 4n$ ← **Read $f(n) = 4n$ as "f of n equals four times n."**
($f(n)$: output; $4n$: input)

You can use the function rule $f(n) = 2n + 3$ to find $f(0)$, $f(1)$, $f(2)$, and $f(3)$. Replace n with 0, 1, 2, and 3.

n	$f(n) = 2n + 3$
0	$f(0) = 2(0) + 3 = 3$
1	$f(1) = 2(1) + 3 = 5$
2	$f(2) = 2(2) + 3 = 7$
3	$f(3) = 2(3) + 3 = 9$

Use the function rule $f(n) = 5n - 2$. Find each output.

1. $f(3)$
$f(n) = 5n - 2$
$= 5$ **(3)** $- 2$
$=$ **13**

2. $f(0)$
$f(n) = 5n - 2$
$= 5$ **(0)** $- 2$
$=$ **−2**

3. $f(2)$
$f(n) = 5n - 2$
$= 5$ **(2)** $-$ **2**
$=$ **8**

4. $f(\frac{3}{5})$
$f(n) = 5n - 2$
$= 5$ **$\left(\frac{3}{5}\right)$** $-$ **2**
$=$ **1**

Make a table for the function represented by each rule. Find $f(0)$, $f(1)$, $f(2)$, and $f(3)$.

5. $f(n) = 10n$

n	$f(n)$
0	0
1	10
2	20
3	30

6. $f(n) = n - 4$

n	$f(n)$
0	−4
1	−3
2	−2
3	−1

7. $f(n) = 2n + 4$

n	$f(n)$
0	4
1	6
2	8
3	10

8. $f(n) = 3n - 1$

n	$f(n)$
0	−1
1	2
2	5
3	8

Reteaching

ENRICHMENT

Minds on Math Transparency

10-6

I am a four-digit number. All of my digits are different, and none is a zero. The last digit is twice the first digit. The second digit is 3 less than the third digit. The sum of the first digit and the last digit is equal to the third digit. What number am I?

2,364

See *Solution Key* for worked-out answers.

Extra Practice, Lesson 10-6, page 523

In Lesson 10-6, students learn how to write tables and rules and to represent functions. This toolbox shows students how to use a graphing calculator to find the graph of a function and make a table of values.

ERROR ALERT! Students may get a graph with more than one line. **Remediation:** Tell students to clear any previous information in the [Y=] window before inputting another function.

ASSESSMENT Exercise 1 Assign partners. Partners should agree on the same range and then follow the steps to graph the function. Partners compare results to make sure their calculator displays are the same.

ADDITIONAL PROBLEM

Use a graphing calculator to graph $f(x) = 3x$ and make a table of values. **Check students' work.**

Materials/Manipulatives

- graphing calculator

page 458 Math Toolbox

1–3. Students' graphs may vary from these calculator screens.

1.

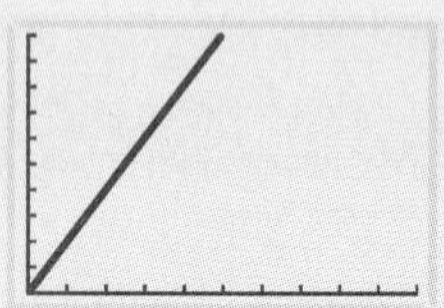

X	Y1
0	0
1	2
2	4
3	6
4	8
5	10
6	12
X=	

2.

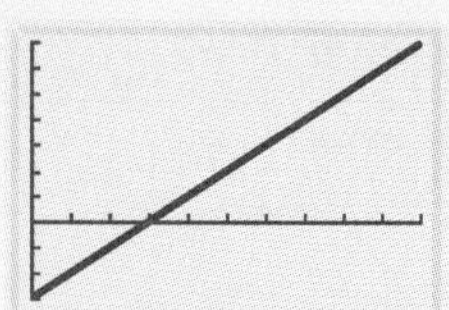

X	Y1
0	−3
1	−2
2	−1
3	0
4	1
5	2
6	3
X=	

3.

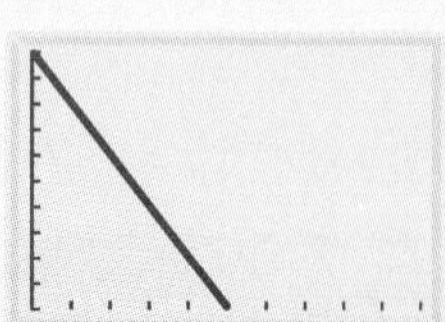

X	Y1
0	13
1	11
2	9
3	7
4	5
5	3
6	1
X=	

458

MATH TOOLBOX TECHNOLOGY

Three Views of a Function

After Lesson 10-6

When you input a function in a graphing calculator, you can view the graph of the function or a table of values.

EXAMPLE

Graph $f(x) = 9 - x$ and make a table of values.

Step 1 Use WINDOW to set the range.

WINDOW FORMAT
Xmin = 0
Xmax = 10
Xscl = 1
Ymin = 0
Ymax = 10
Yscl = 1

Step 2 Use Y= to enter the function.

Y1 = 9–X
Y2 =
Y3 =
Y4 =
Y5 =
Y6 =
Y7 =
Y8 =

Step 3 Use the GRAPH feature to view the graph.

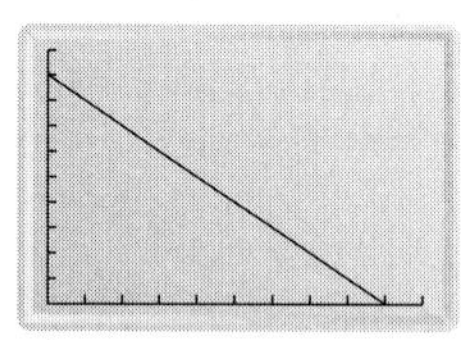

Step 4 Use the TABLE feature to make a table of values.

X	Y1
0	9
1	8
2	7
3	6
4	5
5	4
6	3
X=0	

Step 5 Sketch the graph and copy the table of values.

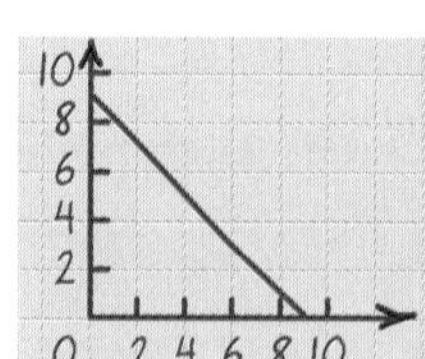

x	y
0	9
1	8
2	7
3	6
4	5
5	4

Use a graphing calculator to graph each function and make a table of values. Sketch the graph and copy the table of values. 1–3. See margin. 4–8. See back of book.

1. $f(x) = 2x$
2. $f(x) = x - 3$
3. $f(x) = 13 - 2x$
4. $f(x) = x + 1$
5. $f(x) = 3x - 4$
6. $f(x) = 0.5x + 6$
7. $f(x) = 7$
8. $f(x) = x^2 - 8x + 16$

10-7 Teaching Notes

1 Focus

CONNECTING TO PRIOR KNOWLEDGE Ask students: *Where have you seen graphs outside of school?* **Answers may vary. Sample: in newspapers** Ask: *What makes a good graph?* **Sample: colored lines**

2 Teach

THINK AND DISCUSS

AUDITORY LEARNING **Example 1** Describe what is happening for each stage of the graph. Explain what happens at each point the graph changes direction.

ERROR ALERT! **Example 1** Students may interpret the horizontal line as horizontal movement. **Remediation:** Tell students to first choose three points on the horizontal line. Then determine what each point represents. Finally, have students describe the similarities and differences between the points.

ASSESSMENT **Example 2** Have students work with a partner to write an answer to the following question: *What does a horizontal line mean on this graph? Explain.* **Tedrick is not moving. His distance from home is staying the same while time is increasing.**

DATA ANALYSIS Connection

10-7 Interpreting Graphs

What You'll Learn

1. To write a description for a graph
2. To sketch a graph from a description

...And Why

You can use graphs to analyze events.

Here's How

Look for questions that
- build understanding
- ✔ check understanding

THINK AND DISCUSS

1 Describing Graphs

In some situations, a visual description such as a graph can be more helpful than a verbal description.

■ **EXAMPLE 1** *Real-World Problem Solving*

A trip to the supermarket combines riding your bike with time spent shopping. The graph at the right relates time and your distance from home. Describe what the graph shows.

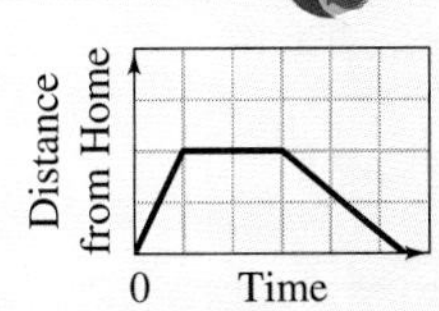

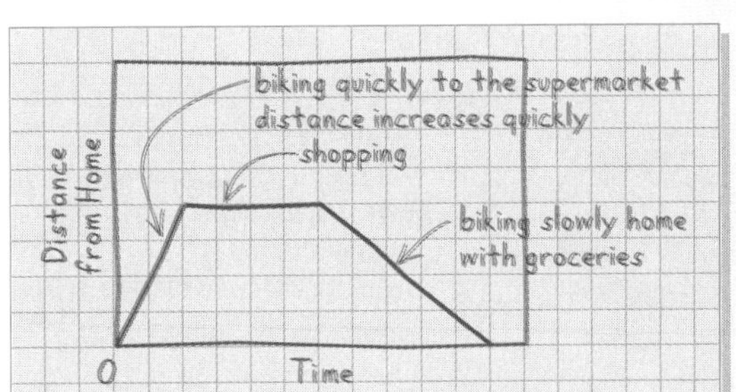

1. ✔ *Try It Out* Suppose you live six blocks from school. The graphs show your walk home on a sunny and a rainy day. Describe what each graph shows.

a.

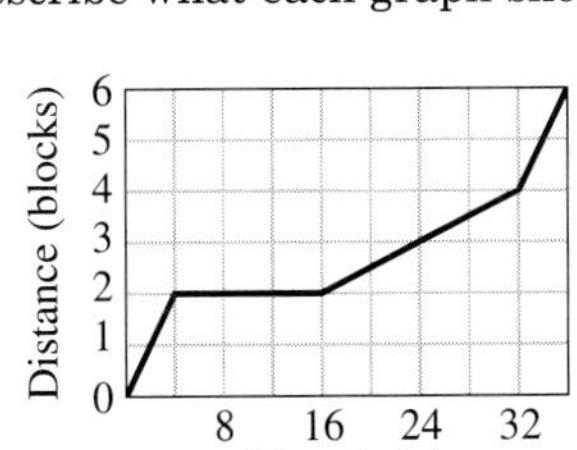

b.

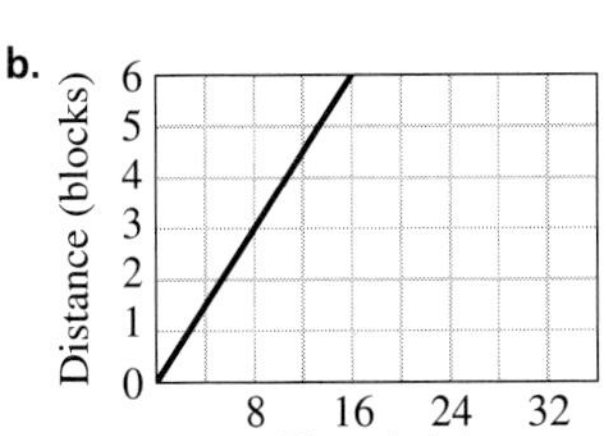

a. **You walk fast for 4 min, then stop for 12 min. Then you walk slowly for 16 min before rushing the last 4 min.**

b. **You walk at a constant speed for 16 min.**

Now you may assign Exercises 1–4.

Lesson Planning Options

Prerequisite Skills
- drawing line graphs (1-2)

Materials/Manipulatives
- coin
- graph paper

Resources

Student Edition

Skills Handbook, p. 533
Extra Practice, p. 523
Glossary/Study Guide

Teaching Resources

Chapter Support File, Ch. 10
- Lesson Planner 10-7
- Practice 10-7, Reteaching 10-7
- Alternative Activity 10-7
- Answer Masters 10-7

Teaching Aids Masters 1, 2
Glossary, Spanish Resources

Transparencies

1, 15, Minds on Math 10-7

Warm Up

Renée practices her clarinet for 20 min on Wednesday, 30 min on Thursday, 35 min on Friday, and 60 min on both Saturday and Sunday. What operations would you use to find the average time she practiced each day? **addition and division**

ADDITIONAL EXAMPLES

FOR EXAMPLE 1

Describe how this graph might be different if you bought only one item at the supermarket. **Answers may vary. Sample: The horizontal section would be shorter.**

FOR EXAMPLE 2

Erin misses the bus home from school so she begins to walk. One third of the way home, she gets a ride from her neighbor. Sketch a graph to show the distance Erin traveled. Label each section. **Answers may vary. Sample:**

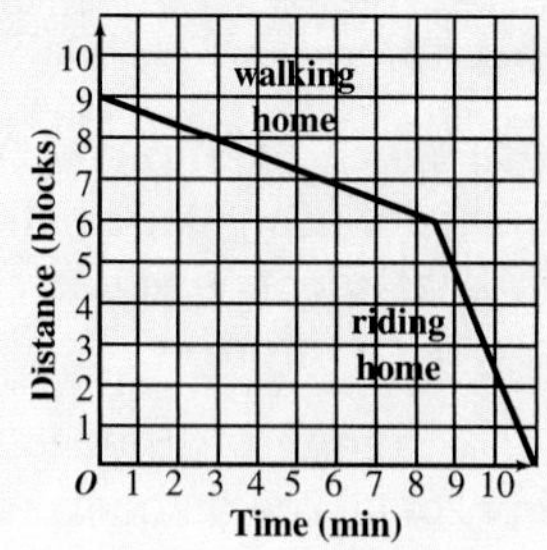

Question 3 Tell students to sketch the graphs using curves rather than straight lines.

KINESTHETIC LEARNING Have students work in small groups. Sketch a graph that compares the number of paces to distance for one member of the group who started walking from a fixed spot in the classroom.

Technology Options

Prentice Hall Technology

Software for Learners

- Math Blaster® Mystery*
- Interactive Student Tutorial, Chapter 10*

Teaching Resource Software

- Computer Item Generator 10-7
- Resource Pro™ Chapter 10*

Internet • For related mathematics activities, visit the Prentice Hall site at www.phschool.com/math

**Available on CD-ROM only*

Assignment Options for Exercises On Your Own

To provide flexible scheduling, this lesson can be split into parts.

1 **Core** 1–3
Extension 4

2 **Core** 5–12, 14, 15
Extension 13

Use Mixed Review to maintain skills.

2 *Drawing Graphs*

You can sketch a graph to describe real-world situations.

EXAMPLE 2 *Real-World Problem Solving*

2b. In Example 2, the distance never decreases. In part (a), the distance decreases to 0 as Tedrick rides the bus home.

3.

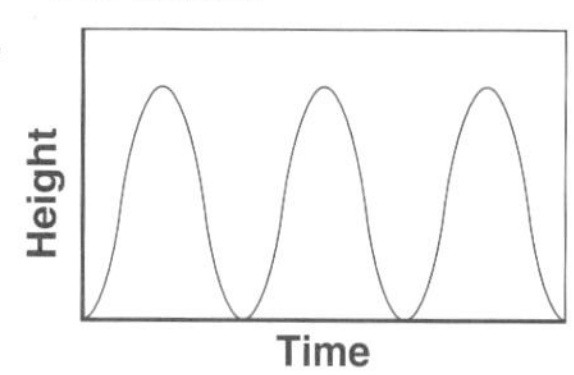

Tedrick's mother drove him part of the way to school. After he got out of the car, he waited for a friend. Then they walked the rest of the way to school. Tedrick took a bus home. Sketch a graph to show the distance Tedrick traveled. Label each section.

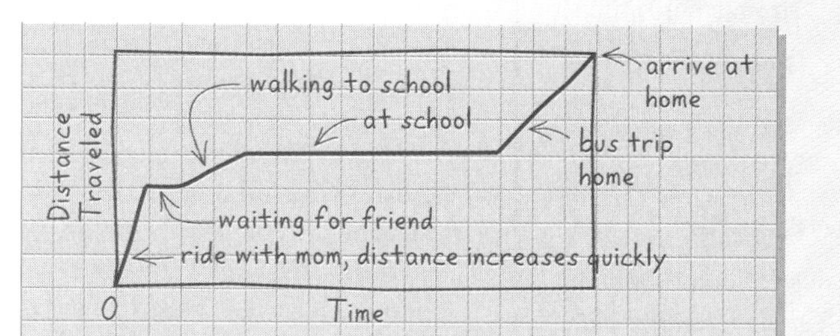

2. a. *Try It Out* Sketch a graph of the situation in Example 2, but use "Distance from Home" instead of "Distance Traveled" for one axis. See margin p. 461.
   b. How is your graph different from the one in Example 2? See above left.

3. *Go a Step Further* Make a graph that represents the height above the ground of one car on a Ferris wheel during three turns of the wheel. You can use a coin to simulate the Ferris wheel as it turns. See above left for sample.

Now you may assign Exercises 5–15.

EXERCISES *On Your Own*

Match each graph with its situation. Explain your choices.

1. 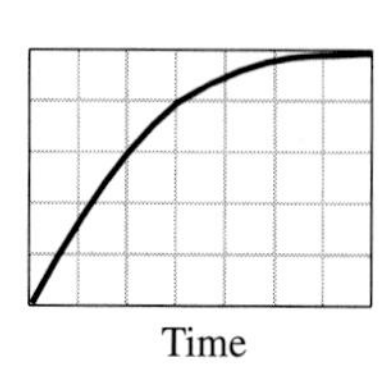

C

2. 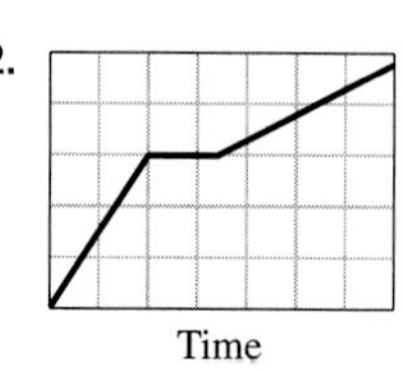

A

3. 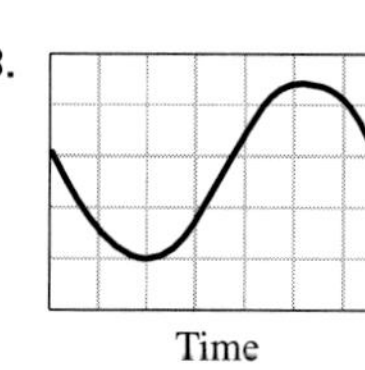

B

A. distance in a hurdles race, falling over a hurdle

B. air temperature in the 24-h period starting from midnight

C. height of a person from birth to age 20

VISUAL LEARNING If you have block scheduling or extended class periods, have students make a graph of the distance you are from the door. The horizontal axis records the number of paces. The vertical axis records the distance from the door. Start at the door and begin moving, counting your paces aloud as you walk. Take some steps forward, backward, and some in place. Vary the length of your stride. Have students compare their finished graph with their partner's.

3 Practice/Assess

EXERCISES *On Your Own*

REASONING **Exercise 9** Ask a volunteer to describe *cruise control.*

ESTIMATION **Exercise 10** Ask students: *Why doesn't the height of the ball begin at zero?* **The person throwing the ball was standing.**

DIVERSITY and EXTENSION **Exercise 11** Have each student pick a country and find the population of their country last year. Ask them to use graphs to approximate the population of the world last year. Have them find what portion of the world's people live in their country. Have students compare their numbers.

OPEN-ENDED **Exercise 14** Have students carefully label their axes. They may graph the distance from home, from school, or distance traveled.

4. Lee, Paulo, and Mary each walked six blocks from school to the library. The graphs at the right show the time and distance for each person's walk.
   a. Who walked fastest? Slowest? Explain how you know. See right.
   b. How is the steepness of the line related to the speed? The faster the speed, the steeper the line.

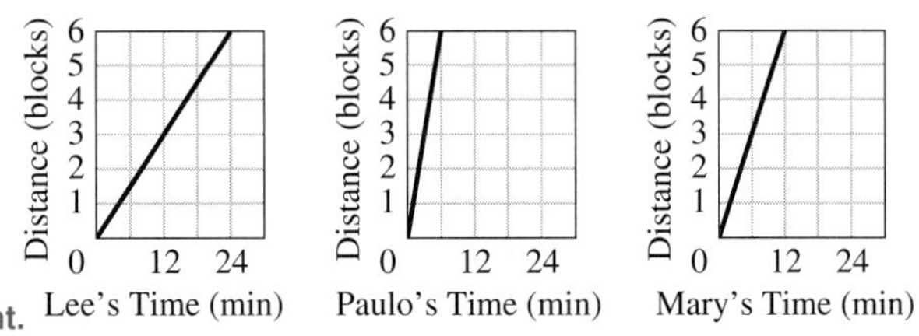

4a. Paulo; Lee; Paulo took the least time to walk 6 blocks. Lee took the longest.

Sketch a graph for each situation. Label each section and your axes. 5–7. See margin.

5. You run the first three blocks from the library to your house, then walk the remaining five blocks.
6. You ride your bike slowly up a steep hill, then quickly down the other side.
7. You climb a jungle gym, then slide down the slide.
8. Suppose you are steadily pouring sand into the container at the right. Which graph below better shows the relationship of the height of the sand with the amount you have poured? Why?

A.
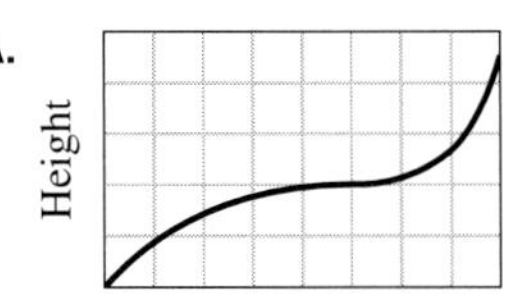

B.
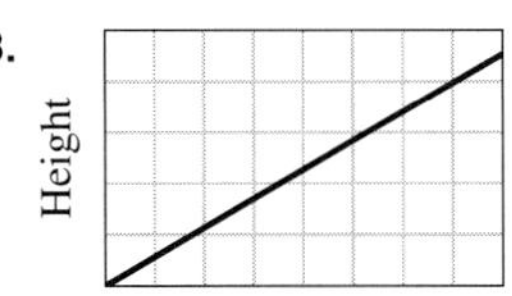

A; the width of the container changes so the height does not increase at a constant rate.

9. *Reasoning* A driver sets a car's cruise control to 50 mi/h. Which graph shows the speed of the car? Which graph shows the distance traveled? Explain your reasoning. See margin p. 462.

A.
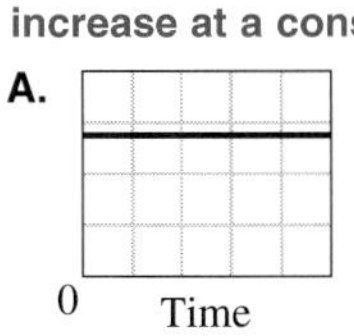

B.
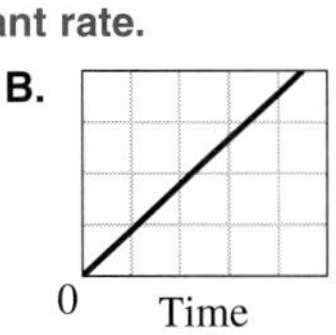

10. *Estimation* The graph at the right shows what happens when a ball is thrown into the air.
    a. What is the greatest height that the ball reaches? 35 ft
    b. How long does it take for the ball to hit the ground? about $2\frac{3}{4}$ s
    c. Why are there two times when the height of the ball is 20 ft? What are the times?
    d. When the time is 0, why is the height of the ball *not* 0? The ball is thrown, so it starts above the ground.

c. The ball reaches 20 ft on its way up and then on the way down; about $\frac{2}{5}$s, about $2\frac{1}{3}$s.

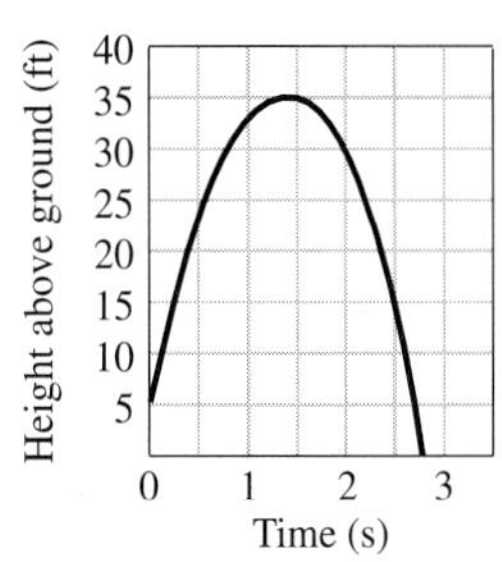

pages 459–460 Think and Discuss

2a.

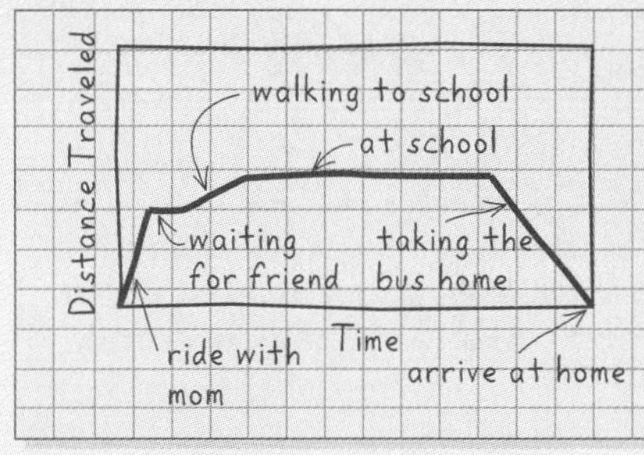

pages 460–463 On Your Own

5.

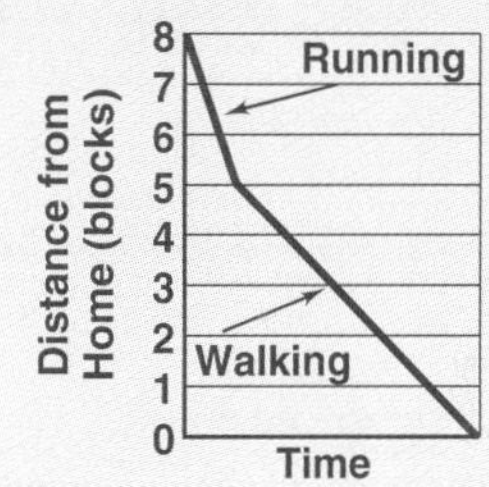

6.

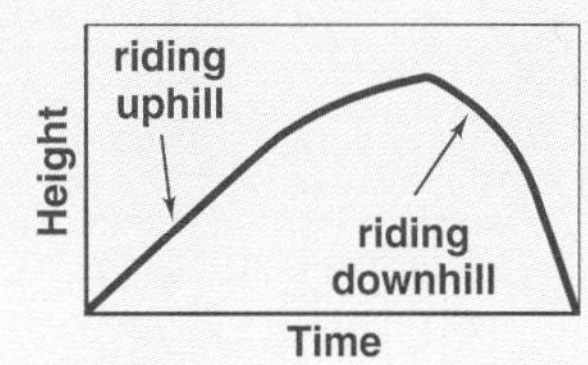

7.

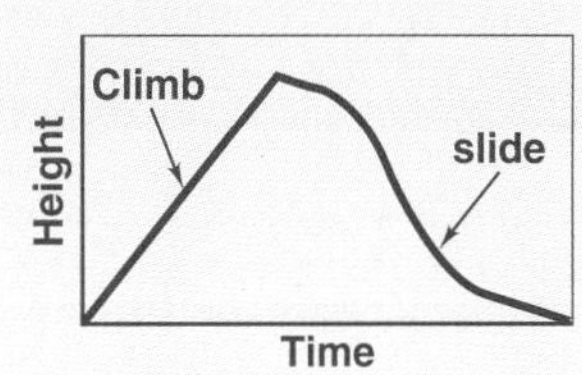

WRITING Exercise 15 Suggest that students first study the graph. They can see when the water is decreasing and increasing before thinking of a situation that would cause a similar change in volume.

WRAP UP

IDENTIFYING THE BIG IDEA Ask students: *What can you learn about a situation by looking at a graph of distance and time? How do you sketch a distance-time graph from a description?*

PROJECT LINK Have students compare their graphs to those of students who used containers of different shapes.

PORTFOLIO Share with students the criteria you will use to assess their work in portfolios, as well as how you plan to use the results. Students should understand how the rubrics are used to assess their work, how each piece in the portfolio counts, and how the scores they get in their portfolios will affect their overall evaluation.

LESSON QUIZ

1. This graph shows Nancy taking a roundtrip walk from home. Describe what the graph shows.

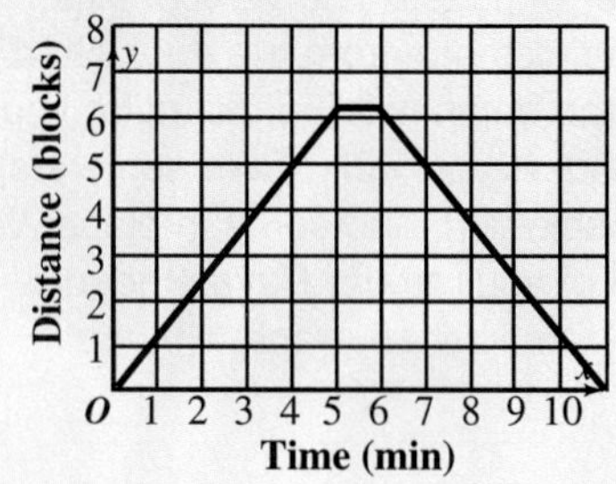

pages 460–463 On Your Own

9. A; B; graph A shows speed because it shows a quantity that is not changing with time. The quantity in graph B increases at a constant rate.

11a. The population grows very slowly in the beginning, then a little faster from about 1400 to about 1800, then very fast in the end.

The Population EXPLOSION

From A.D. 1 to A.D. 1650, the world population grew by 300 million. This translates to an average of just 180,000 people per year, or about 21 people per hour. In contrast, today nine babies are born every two seconds, but only three people die. This means that the population is growing by about 10,800 people per hour, 259,200 per day, 1.8 million per week, 7.2 million per month, and 86.4 million per year. By the year 2000, the population will increase 94 million per year, and by 2020 that number will be 98 million per year.

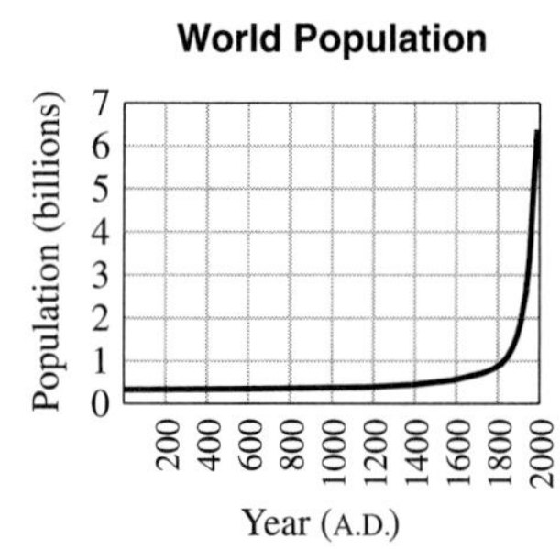

11. a. Explain how the graph at the right illustrates the numbers mentioned in the article. **See margin.**
    b. At what time in history would you say that the rate of population growth began a dramatic increase? **about 1800**

12. *Sports* The graph at the right shows the results of a 50-m race. In this race Edwin had a 15-m head start over Carl.
    a. Who won the race? **Edwin**
    b. By how many seconds did he win? **1 s**
    c. Predict what might happen in another race between Edwin and Carl if Edwin does not have a head start. **Carl would win.**

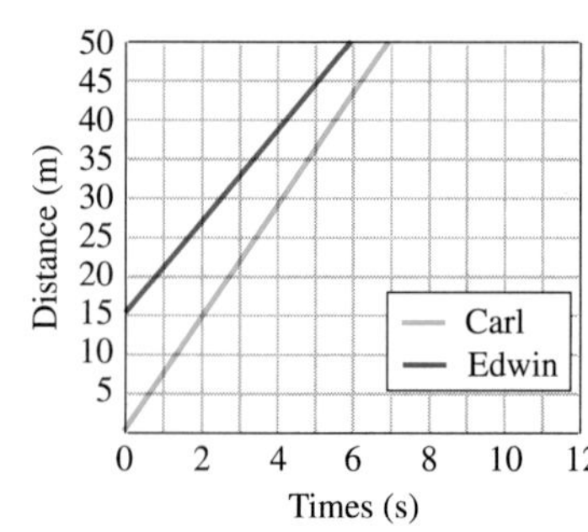

13. *Reasoning* Fares for Sunshine Taxi fares are $.90 for the first 0.2 mi and $.40 for each additional 0.2 mi or less. Carmen and Brian graphed the taxi fares. Which graph would you use to find the cost of a 0.5 mi trip? Explain your choice. **Carmen's graph; the cost of a ride stays the same for each 0.2 mi.**

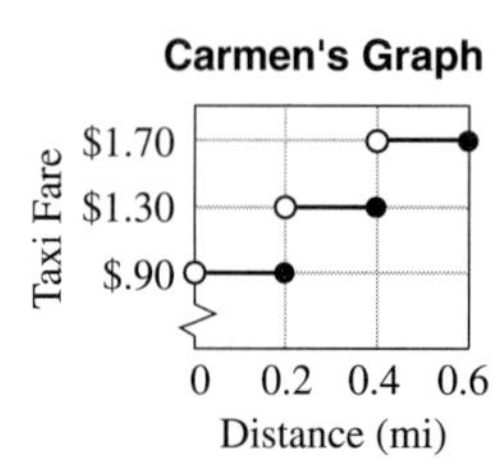

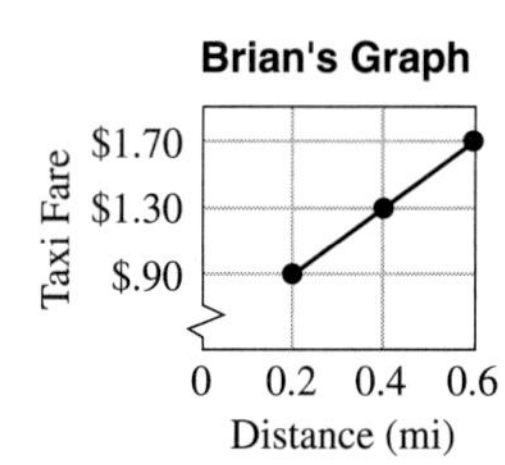

Answers may vary. Sample: Nancy walked for 5 min. Then she rested for a minute before returning home at the same speed.

2. After 5 min, Nancy remembered she was late for a meeting. She ran home. Draw the new graph. **Answers may vary. Sample:**

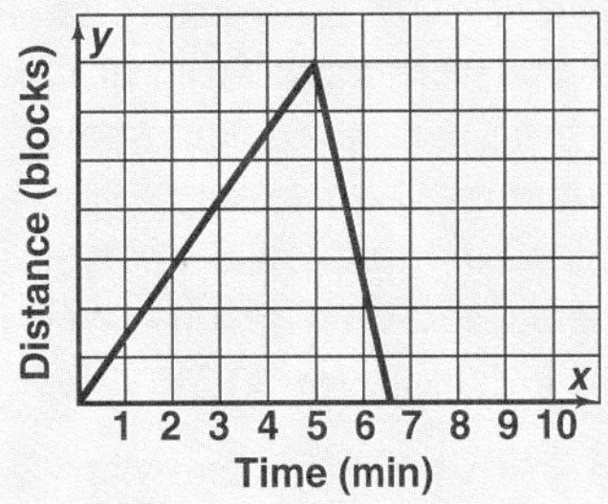

14. *Open-ended* Sketch a graph that represents your trip home from school yesterday. **Check students' work.**

15. *Writing* Describe a situation that the graph below might represent. **Sample: The bathtub tap is open for 8 min. You shut it off and bathe for 8 min. The tub then drains in 12 min.**

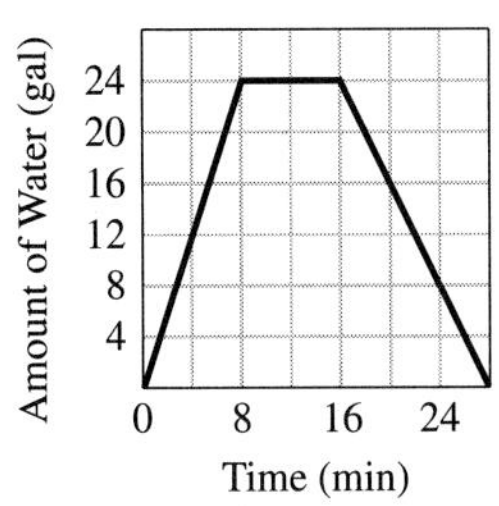

PORTFOLIO

Select one or two items from your work for this chapter. Consider:

- a journal entry
- corrected work
- work that you found challenging

Explain why you have included each selection.

Mixed Review

Complete. *(Lesson 5-8)*

16. ■ kg = 157 g **0.157** **17.** 8 c = ■ pt **4** **18.** 50 in. = ■ ft $4\frac{1}{6}$ **19.** 9 lb = ■ oz **144** **20.** $2\frac{1}{4}$ m = ■ cm **225**

Make a stem-and-leaf plot. *(Lesson 1-5)* **21–22. See below.**

21. 34 46 50 48 53 33 20 44 48 45 34 **22.** 9.6 9.2 7.3 8.1 7.4 8.1 7.8 7.5 8.5 9.6

23. A florist can create an arrangement in 14 min. An order arrives for 124 arrangements for a large banquet. How long will it take the florist to make the arrangements, to the nearest hour? *(Lesson 6-2)* **29 h**

24. The six members of the Estrella family walked a total of 60 mi in 5 days. What is the average number of miles each family member walked each day? *(Lesson 3-5)* **12 mi**

21.

Stem	Leaf
2	0
3	3 4 4
4	4 5 6 8 8
5	0 3

5 | 0 means 50

22.

Stem	Leaf
7	3 4 5 8
8	1 1 5
9	2 6 6

9 | 2 means 9.2

CHAPTER PROJECT

PROJECT LINK: GRAPHING

Make a graph of your table from the Project Link on page 453. Label the horizontal axis "Time" and the vertical axis "Water Level." Begin with time zero when the container is full, and end when the water level is zero. Connect the points and give your graph a title. Explain how the graph reflects the shape of your container.

Check students' work.

PRACTICE

Practice 10-7 *Interpreting Graphs*

Graphs I through VI represent one of the six situations described below. Match each graph with the appropriate situation.

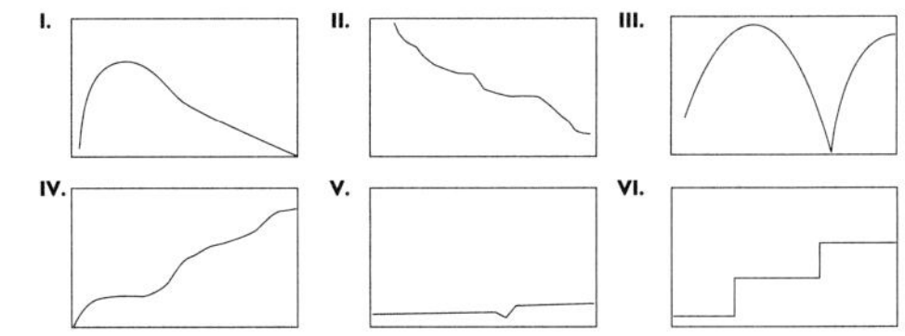

1. temperature as the weather changes from rainy to snowy II
2. number of fish caught per hour on a bad fishing day V
3. total rainfall during a rainy day IV
4. speed of a car starting from a stop sign and then approaching a stoplight I
5. height of a cricket as it jumps III
6. total amount of money spent over time during a trip to the mall VI

Sketch a graph to represent each situation. Graphs may vary.

7. The speed of a runner in a 1-mi race.
8. The height above ground of the air valve on a tire of a bicycle ridden on flat ground. (You can model this using a coin.)

In copymaster and workbook formats

RETEACHING

Reteaching 10-7 *Interpreting Graphs*

You can describe a situation shown by a graph.

- An airplane ascends to its cruising altitude of 20,000 ft in 20 min. After 50 min it begins its descent into Atlanta. The descent takes 15 min.

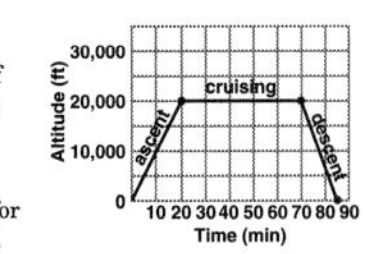

The graph at the right shows time and altitude for the airplane trip. Each part of the trip is labeled.

You can sketch a graph to describe a situation.

- When Ahmad goes out for a run, he walks for a few minutes to warm up, runs for a while, jogs in place while he waits for a light to change, and then walks the rest of the way to cool down.

The graph at the right shows the distance Ahmad travels and each type of movement.

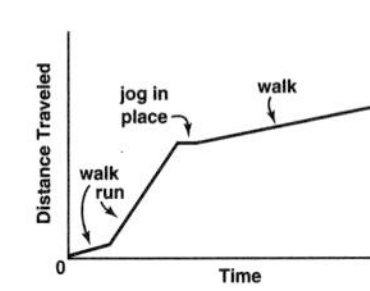

Match each graph with its situation.

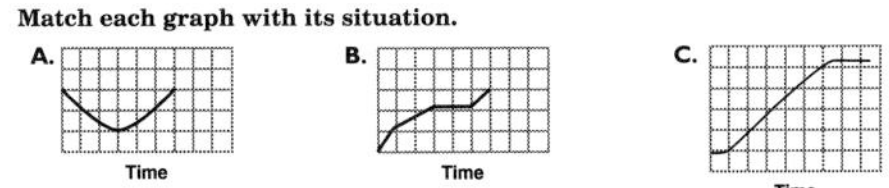

1. A car travels 10 mph for 5 min, 50 mph for 27 min, and then is stopped for 10 min. C
2. Total rainfall over a 24-hour period B
3. Water level in a bay A

Sketch a graph for the situation. Include labels. Answers may vary.

4. You walk to a park, visit with a friend for few minutes, and then jog home.
5. You climb up a ladder, then climb down the ladder.

ENRICHMENT

Minds on Math Transparency

10-7

Write the numbers 1 through 10 in the rectangles so that the numbers along any of the sides total 18.

2	10	6
3		7
8		1
5	9	4

Answers may vary. Sample answer is shown.

See *Solution Key* for worked-out answers.

PROBLEM SOLVING PRACTICE ★★

This page provides problems for students to solve using their knowledge of geometric constructions, number lines, permutations, scientific notation, probability, circumference, area, and proportions. Allow students to use any method they find helpful.

COOPERATIVE GROUPS Exercise 1
Students can work together in groups of four to determine the construction shown. Have each student draw an example of one of the constructions in the answer choices. The group should agree on which construction matches the one shown in the question.

USING MANIPULATIVES Exercise 3
Students can use colored blocks or counters to model the possible orders.

PROBLEM SOLVING PRACTICE ★★★★★

Read each question and choose the best answer.

1. This drawing shows how to— C

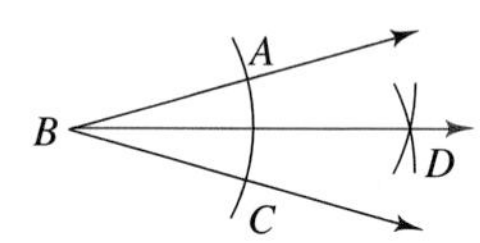

A. construct a right angle
B. construct an angle
C. construct an angle bisector
D. construct complementary angles

2. One ride at an amusement park requires that passengers be at least 40 inches tall. Which number line shows the range of heights for people who can go on this ride? F

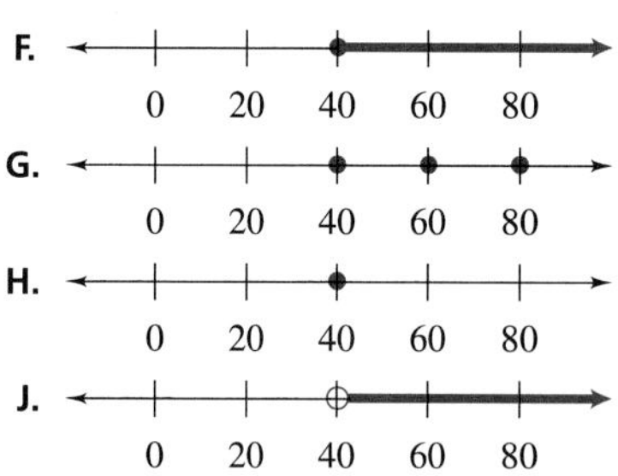

3. Anoki, Moy, Carmisha, and Ellen run the 100-m dash. In how many different orders could the four runners finish the race? D

A. 4 B. 12 C. 16 D. 24

4. The farthest distance that Earth is from the sun is 9.45×10^7 miles. This distance is— G

F. 945,000,000 miles
G. 94,500,000 miles
H. 9,450,000 miles
J. 945,000 miles

5. Ears of corn are sold 3 for \$.45. How much will 10 ears of corn cost? B

A. \$1.80 B. \$1.50 C. \$1.35 D. \$.90

6. The winner of a contest will be chosen by drawing a name out of a bag without looking. The bag holds the names of 4 sixth graders, 5 seventh graders, and 6 eighth graders. What is the probability that the winner will *not* be in the seventh grade? F

F. $\frac{2}{3}$ G. $\frac{3}{5}$ H. $\frac{1}{3}$ J. $\frac{4}{15}$

Please note that items 7–9 have *five* answer choices.

7. The outside edge of a circular window measures 88 in. What is the diameter of the window? Use $\frac{22}{7}$ for π. D

A. 12 in. B. 14 in. C. 21 in.
D. 28 in. E. 56 in.

8. A large box will be used to hold school supplies. All of the sides of the box will be decorated except the top and the bottom. The box is 15 in. long, 7 in. wide, and 5 in. tall. How many square inches of paper are needed to decorate the box? G

F. 110 $in.^2$ G. 220 $in.^2$ H. 280 $in.^2$
J. 360 $in.^2$ K. Not Here

9. A survey of 125 customers showed that 35 customers were extremely happy with the Super Speedy bicycle manufactured by the Roadster Company. If 1,000 customers have purchased the Super Speedy bicycle, what is a good prediction for the number of customers who are extremely happy with the bicycle? D

A. 70 B. 105 C. 210
D. 280 E. 560

FINISHING THE CHAPTER PROJECT

PROJECT DAY You may wish to plan a project day on which students share their completed projects. Encourage students to explain their process as well as their product.

PROJECT NOTEBOOK Ask students to review their project work and bring their notebooks up to date.

Have students review their methods for taking and recording their measurements, analyzing the data, and graphing the results for the project.

SCORING RUBRIC

3 Your graph is clearly labeled and accurately reflects the water level across time. Your explanations are clear and concise. You include the data from your experiment.

2 Your graph is complete, and you explain your thinking and your observations clearly.

1 Your data, your graph, and your explanations are incomplete or do not provide a clear picture of your work.

0 You omit important parts of the project.

FINISHING THE CHAPTER PROJECT

CHAPTER PROJECT

happy *landings*

Graphing Data The Project Link questions on pages 440, 453, and 463 should help you to complete your project. Here is a checklist to help you gather together the parts of your project.

- ✓ the container
- ✓ the table of the height of water level at different times
- ✓ the graph of your data
- ✓ the explanation of how your graph reflects the shape of your container

Your graph should be large, clear, and neat. Did the container empty at a steady rate? Be prepared to explain how the graph helps you answer this question.

Reflect and Revise

Review your project with a friend or someone at home. Is your table complete? Is your graph accurate? Is your explanation clear? If necessary, make changes to improve your project.

Web Extension

Prentice Hall's Internet site contains information you might find helpful as you complete your project. Visit www.phschool.com/mgm2/ch10 for some links and ideas related to science.

STUDENT SELF-ASSESSMENT SURVEY

Chapter 10 Student Self-Assessment Survey

1. Now that you have finished this chapter, think about what you have learned about patterns and functions. Check each topic that you feel confident you understand.
   - ____ continue arithmetic, geometric, and other sequences (10-1)
   - ____ write numbers in scientific notation and standard form (10-2)
   - ____ solve problems by solving a simpler problem (10-3)
   - ____ find simple and compound interest (10-4)
   - ____ represent functions with tables and rules (10-5)
   - ____ graph functions (10-5)
   - ____ make a table given a function rule (10-6)
   - ____ find a function rule given a table (10-6)
   - ____ write a description for a graph (10-7)
   - ____ sketch a graph from a description (10-7)
2. Before the Chapter Assessment, I need to review ____
3. a. Check one. In general, I thought this chapter was ____ a snap ____ easy ____ average ____ hard ____ a monster
   b. Why do you feel this way? ____
4. In this chapter, I did my best work on ____
5. In this chapter, I had trouble with ____
6. Check each one that applies. Now that I've spent some time studying number patterns and functions, I think they are ____ important ____ boring ____ useful ____ fun ____ a waste of time ____ confusing ____ tricky ____ interesting
7. List some situations in which people use spreadsheets in their jobs. ____
8. Did you use a graphing calculator to graph a function and make a table of values? ____ List two situations in which people use functions or graphs in their jobs. ____

Assessment

Vocabulary/Symbols

arithmetic sequence, balance, compound interest, function, geometric sequence, principle, scientific notation, sequence, simple interest, standard form

Resources

Student Edition

Extra Practice, p. 523

Glossary/Study Guide

Materials/Manipulatives

- calculator
- graph paper

Teaching Resources

Chapter Support File, Ch. 10
- Student Self-Assessment Survey

Glossary, Spanish Resources

Tools for Studying Smarter

WRAP UP

ASSESSMENT Exercise 5 Have students use their rule to check their answers for Exercises 1–3. You cannot express Exercise 4 with a rule. Then have them find the 8th term of all four sequences. 35; 0.375; 6,561; −29

ASSESSMENT Exercises 7–10 When students have finished these exercises, have them write their answers in standard form.

Exercises 13–15 Have students begin work on each exercise by writing the appropriate formula. Then students can rewrite the formula substituting the data from each exercise.

Exercise 18 Students may want to display their answers in a table.

WRITING Exercise 19 Encourage students to include their reasoning for selecting their situation.

10 WRAP UP

Number Patterns — 10-1

A **sequence** is a set of numbers arranged according to some pattern. Each number in a sequence is a **term.**

You find each term of an **arithmetic sequence** by adding the same number to the preceding term.

You find each term of a **geometric sequence** by multiplying the preceding term by the same number.

Identify each sequence as arithmetic, geometric, or neither. Then find the next three terms of each sequence.

1. 7, 11, 15, 19, . . . arithmetic; 23, 27, 31
2. 48, 24, 12, 6, . . . geometric; 3, $\frac{3}{2}$, $\frac{3}{4}$
3. 3, 9, 27, 81, . . . geometric; 243; 729; 2,187
4. 20, 16, 11, 5, . . . neither; −2, −10, −19
5. Write a rule for each sequence in Exercises 1–3. Start with 7 and add 4 repeatedly; start with 48 and multiply by $\frac{1}{2}$ repeatedly; start with 3 and multiply by 3.
6. **Choose A, B, C, or D.** What is the seventh term of the sequence 1, 3, 7, 15, . . .? A

   A. 127 B. 99 C. 64 D. 101

Scientific Notation — 10-2

A number in **scientific notation** is the product of two factors. The first factor is greater than or equal to 1 and less than 10. The second factor is a power of 10. Multiply the two factors to write the number in **standard form.**

Write each number using scientific notation.

7. 1,524,000,000 1.524×10^9
8. 250,000 2.5×10^5
9. 383 million 3.83×10^8
10. 87,600 8.76×10^4
11. The population of the United States in 1990 was about 2.49×10^8. Write this number in standard form. 249,000,000

Problem Solving Strategies — 10-3

Sometimes you can solve a problem by solving a simpler problem.

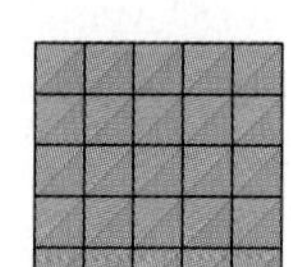

12. You have a game that uses the board at the right. How many triangles with sides on the gridlines are on the board? 110 triangles

Remind students that the new mathematical terms in this chapter are defined in the Glossary/Study Guide in the back of the book.

Simple and Compound Interest — 10-4

Simple interest is earned only on the beginning **principal.** You use the formula $I = p \cdot r \cdot t$ to find the interest earned.

Compound interest is earned on the principal and any interest already earned. You use the formula $B = p(1 + r)^t$ to find the **balance** of an account.

13. You deposit $1,500 in an account earning 6% simple interest. How much interest is earned after 5 years? $450

14. You leave a $600 balance for a year on a credit card charging 20% simple interest. How much will you owe after one year? $720

15. You deposit $1,500 in an account that pays 5% interest compounded annually. What is the balance after 5 years? $1,914.42

Functions — 10-5, 10-6

You can represent a **function** using a table, a rule, or a graph.

16. a. Write a rule for the function represented by the table at the right. $f(n) = 2n + 2$
    b. Graph the function. See back of book.

n	$f(n)$
0	2
1	4
2	6
3	8

17. a. Make an input/output table for the graph at the right. a. See back of book.
    b. Write a rule for the function. $f(n) = \frac{1}{2}n + 3$

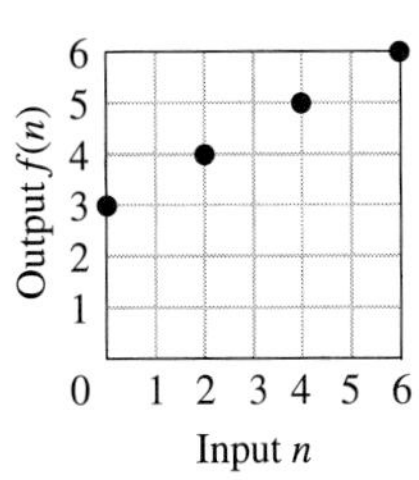

18. A rule for a function is $f(n) = 2n + 5$. Find $f(-1)$, $f(0)$, $f(1)$, and $f(2)$. 3; 5; 7; 9

Interpreting Graphs — 10-7

You can use graphs to represent real-world situations.

19. *Writing* Describe a situation that the graph at the right might represent. Sample: The Romano family drives to their grandparents' house for a holiday dinner, then drives home.

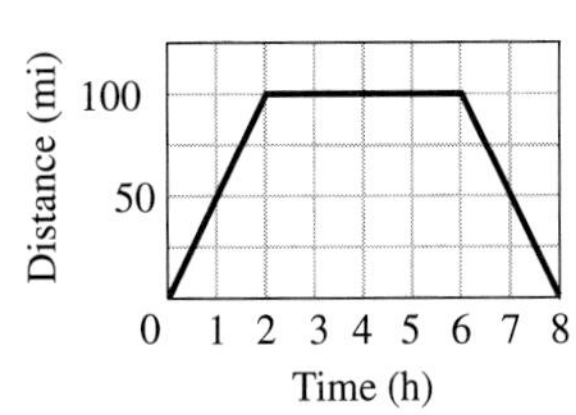

20. Tani walks at a rate of about 3 mi/h. She leaves home and walks for 3 h. She stops and spends 1 h eating lunch. Then she walks one more hour. Sketch a graph that represents the distance she has walked over the 5-h period. See back of book.

CHAPTER ASSESSMENT • FORM A

Chapter 10 Assessment • Form A

Answers

1. Find the next three terms in the sequence. 8, 14, 20, 26, . . . — 1. 32, 38, 44
2. Write a rule for the following pattern. 96, 84, 72, 60, . . . — 2. Start with 96 and subtract 12 repeatedly.
3. Find the next three terms in the sequence. 1, 4, 9, 16, . . . — 3. 25, 36, 49
4. Suppose you get an allowance starting at one penny a week. Each week thereafter, the amount you get doubles. What kind of sequence is this? — 4. geometric
5. Suppose your allowance starts at $.05 a week. Each week thereafter the amount doubles. During which week will your allowance be over $10? — 5. the 9th week
6. In 1991, the IRS collected over $1,086,000,000,000. Write this number in scientific notation. — 6. $\$1.086 \times 10^{12}$
7. Light waves are measured in angstroms. There are about 2.5×10^8 angstroms in one inch. Write this number in standard form. — 7. 250,000,000
8. Suppose you deposit $5,000 in a bank account that pays 4% interest compounded annually. How much will you have in your account at the end of 2 years? Use $B = p(1 + r)^t$. — 8. $5,408
9. The rule for a function is $f(n) = n^2 - 10$. Find $f(0)$, $f(1)$, and $f(2)$. — 9. −10, −9, −6
10. Write a rule for the function represented by the table at the right. — 10. $f(n) = 4n + 1$

n	$f(n)$
1	5
2	9
3	13
4	17

Assessment

CHAPTER ASSESSMENT • FORM A

Chapter 10 Assessment • Form A (continued)

The function table below shows distance in miles that Nikki plans to bike each day during a 10-week training program. Use the table for Exercises 11–13.

Week	1	2	3	4	5	6	7	8	9	10
Distance	1	3	5	7	9	11	13	■	■	■

11. What are the last three values in the table? — 11. 15, 17, 19
12. Make a graph of the function using the data. — 12.

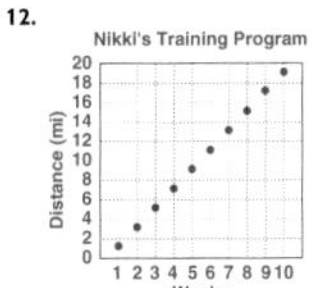

13. Write a rule for the table. — 13. Sample: $d = 2w - 1$

Choose A, B, C, or D.

14. Suppose you deposit n dollars in an account earning 6% simple interest each year. Which function rule describes the total amount of money you will have after 1 year? — 14. C
    A. $f(n) = 0.06n$ B. $f(n) = n(0.06)$
    C. $f(n) = 1.06n$ D. $f(n) = 6n$

Choose a Strategy

15. Divide the numbers one to four by eleven. Examine the pattern in the quotients. Predict what ten divided by eleven will be. — 15. $0.\overline{90}$ or 0.909090 . . .

Writing

16. The graph at the right shows the time and total distance Jerry walked from his house to the Pizza Barn and back to his house. Which part of the graph represents the time he spent walking? from 0 min to 20 min and from 50 min to 70 min

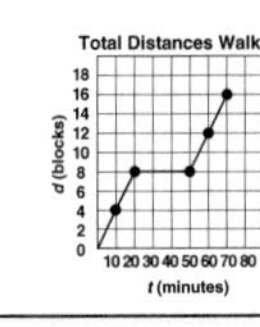

467

CHAPTER ASSESSMENT • FORM B

Chapter 10 Assessment • Form B

Choose the best answer. Circle A, B, C, or D.

1. Find the next three numbers in the sequence 243, 81, 27, 9, ...
   A. 3, 1, 1 B. 6, 3, 0 C. 3, 1, $\frac{1}{3}$ D. 6, 2, 1
2. Write a rule for the pattern 5, 20, 80, 320.
   A. Start with 320 and divide by 4 repeatedly.
   B. Start with 5 and divide by 4 repeatedly.
   C. Start with 5 and multiply by 5 repeatedly.
   D. Start with 5 and multiply by 4 repeatedly.
3. Find the next three terms in the sequence 4, 2, 1, 0.5, ...
   A. 0.15, 0.25, 0.35 B. 0.25, 0.125, 0.0625
   C. 0.1, 0.2, 0.4 D. 0, –0.5, –1
4. Suppose you save $1 the first week. Each week thereafter, you save $3 more than the amount you saved the week before. What kind of sequence is this?
   A. geometric B. arithmetic C. exponential D. none of these
5. If you save $2 the first week and double the amount you saved the week before, in which week will you add over $200 to your savings?
   A. sixth B. fourth C. fifth D. eighth
6. According to the *1993 Information Please Almanac*, there were over 5,400,000 cars produced in 1991. Write this number using scientific notation.
   A. 54×10^5 B. 5.4×10^6
   C. 5.4×10^4 D. 54×10^6
7. Extremely small lengths are measured in microns. There are 2.54×10^6 microns in an inch. Write this number in standard notation.
   A. 2,540,000 B. 2.5400000 C. 254,000,000 D. 254,000
8. Suppose you deposit $25,000 in a bank account that pays 4% interest compounded annually. How much will you have in your account at the end of one year? Use $B = p(1 + r)^t$.
   A. $31,000 B. $26,000 C. $29,000 D. $35,000
9. Divide the numbers ten to fourteen by nine. Examine the pattern in the quotients. What do you predict seventeen divided by nine will be?
   A. $1.\overline{6}$ B. $1.\overline{7}$ C. $1.\overline{8}$ D. $1.\overline{9}$

Assessment

CHAPTER ASSESSMENT • FORM B

Chapter 10 Assessment • Form B (continued)

This function table shows how many miles Marta plans to jog daily in a 10-wk training program. Use the table for Exercises 10–12.

Week (w)	1	2	3	4	5	6	7	8	9	10
Distance (d)	2	3	4	5	6	7	8	■	■	■

10. What are the last three values in the table?
    A. 7, 8, 9 B. 11, 10, 9 C. 8, 9, 10 D. 9, 10, 11
11. Which graph represents the data in the table?

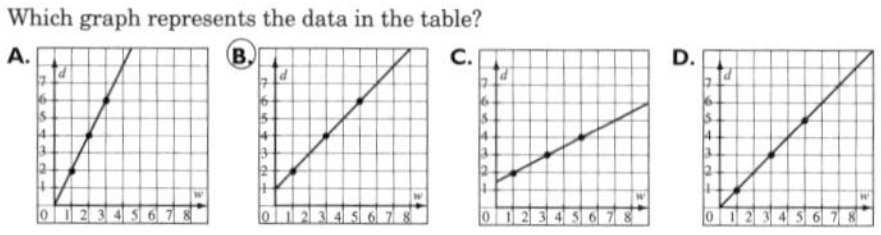

12. Which rule represents the data in the table?
    A. $d = 1 + w$ B. $d = 2 - w$ C. $d = 2w - 1$ D. $d = w^2 - 1$
13. The rule for a function is $f(n) = 5 - n^2$. Find $f(0)$, $f(1)$, and $f(2)$.
    A. 5, 4, 3 B. 5, 4, 1 C. 3, 2, 1 D. 0, 1, 2
14. What is the rule for the function represented by the table at the right?
    A. $f(n) = 5(n + 7)$ B. $f(n) = n + 7$
    C. $f(n) = 7n + 5$ D. $f(n) = 5n + 7$

n	$f(n)$
0	7
1	12
2	17
3	22

15. Which function rule describes the amount of money in your bank account after *one* year if you deposit $1,000 and the rate is r?
    A. $f(n) = \$1,000 + r$ B. $f(n) = \$1,000(1 + r)$
    C. $f(n) = \$1,000r$ D. $f(n) = \$1,000r^2$
16. The graph at the right shows the time and the distance for Sue's walk to the park and back to her house. Which part of the graph represents the time she spent at the park?
    A. from 0 min to 20 min B. from 10 min to 40 min
    C. from 20 min to 50 min D. from 50 min to 70 min

Total Distance Walked

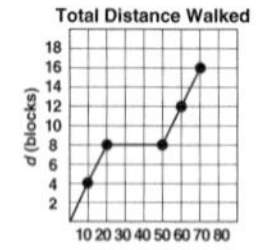

Teaching Resources

Chapter Support File, Ch. 10, and Spanish Resources

Teacher's Edition

See pp. 432C–D for Assessment Options.

Teaching Resource Software

- Computer Item Generator, Ch. 10

ASSESSMENT

ENHANCED MULTIPLE CHOICE QUESTIONS are more complex than traditional multiple choice questions, which assess only one skill. Enhanced multiple choice questions assess the processes that students use, as well as the end result. They are written so that students can use more than one strategy to solve the problem. Using multiple strategies is encouraged by the National Council of Teachers of Mathematics (NCTM). **Exercise 10** is an enhanced multiple choice question.

WRITING EXERCISES allow students to describe more fully their thinking and understanding of the concepts they've learned. **Exercise 11** is a writing exercise.

OPEN-ENDED PROBLEMS allow for more than one solution. Students must construct their own responses instead of choosing from possible answers. The student responses will help you determine the depth of their understanding and any possible areas of difficulty. **Exercise 14** is an open-ended problem.

10 ASSESSMENT

1. Identify each sequence as arithmetic, geometric, or neither. Then find the next three terms. **a–f. See back of book.**
   a. 1, 3, 9, 27, . . . b. 4, 9, 14, 19, . . .
   c. 3, 4, 6, 9, . . . d. 10, 8, 6, 4, . . .
   e. −1, 3, 7, 11, . . . f. 1.5, 3, 6, 12, . . .
2. Write rules for the arithmetic and geometric sequences in Exercise 1.
   See back of book. **3a. 1.75×10^8**
3. Write each number in scientific notation.
   a. 175,000,000 b. 600 **6×10^2**
   c. 9,600,000,000 **9.6×10^9** d. 22 million **2.2×10^7**
4. Write each number in standard form.
   a. 4×10^2 **400** b. 6.72×10^7 **67,200,000**
   c. 7.80×10^4 **78,000** d. 1.046×10^9 **1,046,000,000**
5. An amusement park costs $12/person. The park offers special rates for groups. Admission charges are $40 for four people, $49 for five, $57 for six, $64 for seven, and so on. How much does each member of a group of twelve save by getting a group rate? **$5**
6. Suppose you deposit $2,000 in an account that earns 6.5% simple interest each year. How much interest is earned after 10 years? **$1,300**
7. Suppose you deposit $1,000 in an account that earns 6% interest compounded annually. What is the balance in the account after four years? Use the formula $B = p(1 + r)^t$. **$1,262.48**
   8a–b. See back of book.
8. Make a table of the input/output pairs for each of the following.
   a. the cost of 1 to 5 books at $2.95 each
   b. the perimeter of a square with sides 5 in., 6 in., 7 in., 8 in., and 9 in. long
9. Find $f(-2)$, $f(0)$, and $f(5)$ for each function represented by a rule below.
   a. $f(n) = n - 5$ **−7; −5; 0** b. $f(n) = 9 + n$ **7; 9; 14**
   c. $f(n) = 2n + 1$ **−3; 1; 11** d. $f(n) = n^2 - 1$ **3; −1; 24**
10. **Choose A, B, C, or D.** Which is *not* an output for $f(n) = 2n^2 - 5$? **D**
    A. −3 B. 45 C. 27 D. −8
11. *Writing* Tori earns $4.50/h. How can she use a function to find her earnings for any number of hours she works?
    See back of book. **12c. $f(n) = -5n - 2$**
12. Write a function rule for each table.

a.

n	$f(n)$
0	0
1	3
2	6
3	9

$f(n) = 3n$

b.

n	$f(n)$
0	1
1	3
2	5
3	7

$f(n) = 2n + 1$

c.

n	$f(n)$
0	−2
1	−7
2	−12
3	−17

See above.

13. Use the graph for the questions below.

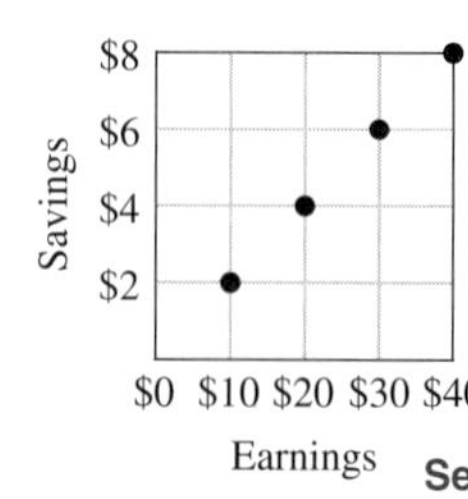

See back of book.
   a. Make a table of input/output pairs.
   b. Write a rule for the function. **$s = \frac{1}{5}e$**
   c. Find how much money is saved when $100 is earned. **$20**
14. Sketch a graph describing the height of a basketball as it is dribbled down the court and a basket is made. Label the sections of your graph. **See back of book.**

CUMULATIVE REVIEW

Item	Review Topic	Ch	Item	Review Topic	Ch
1	Scientific notation	10	8	Integers	3
2, 3, 5, 6	Expressions and equations	3	9	Displaying data	1
4, 7	Interpreting graphs	10	10	Classifying angles and triangles	7

10 CUMULATIVE REVIEW

Choose the best answer.

1. Which number is written in scientific notation? D
   A. 0.2×10^9 B. 9.14×2^5
   C. 10×10^8 D. 7.12×10^{11}

2. Which equation has the same solution as $2x + 7 = 9$? C
   A. $x + 3 = 2$ B. $3x = -2$
   C. $x - 3 = -2$ D. $x + 3 = -2$

3. The A-One Hotel charges \$88/day for two people in a room, plus \$7 for each additional person. Which equation could you use to find the cost c for n people to stay in a room one day? B
   A. $c = 88 + n(7)$
   B. $c = 88 + (n - 2)(7)$
   C. $c = (n + 2)(88 + 7)$
   D. $c = 88 + (n + 2)(7)$

4. What could the graph below represent? C

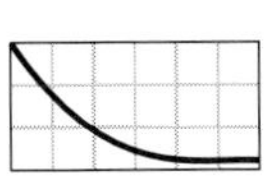

Time

   A. height of a ball t seconds after it is thrown upward
   B. temperature of an oven t minutes after it is turned on
   C. temperature of hot water while cooling for t minutes
   D. distance a car has traveled at 45 mi/h after t hours

5. Which expression has the greatest value? D
   A. $4^2 - 3$ B. $22 - |-5|$
   C. $(8 - 6)^2 + 10$ D. $11 - (-7)$

6. Florisa earns \$16/week. Which equation can you use to find how many weeks it will take her to earn \$400? B
   A. $16 + w = 400$ B. $16w = 400$
   C. $\frac{16}{w} = 400$ D. $\frac{16}{400} = w$

7. Find the median of the data in the stem-and-leaf plot. D

7	0 0 5 8
8	1 5 6 9 9
9	4

9 | 4 means 94

   A. 81.7 B. 89
   C. 85 D. 83

8. Find two numbers whose sum is 10 and whose product is −24. B
   A. −6 and 4 B. 12 and −2
   C. −8 and −3 D. 6 and −4

9. Which type of graph would best display the following data on the number of viewers (in millions) watching television during prime time? A
   Mon., 91.9 Tue., 89.8 Wed., 93.9
   Thu., 93.9 Fri., 78.0 Sat., 77.1
   Sun., 87.7
   A. line B. double line
   C. bar D. double bar

10. An obtuse triangle has one angle whose measure is 30°. What is the measure of the other acute angle? A
   A. any measure between 0° and 60°
   B. any measure less than 90°
   C. any measure between 30° and 60°
   D. any measure between 60° and 90°

CUMULATIVE REVIEW

Chapter 10 Cumulative Review

Choose the best answer. Circle A, B, C, or D.

1. A shirt, originally priced at \$40, is marked down to \$26. What is the percent of decrease?
   (A) 35% B. 54%
   C. 65% D. not here

2. What is the volume of a cylinder with a base area of 24 m^2 and a height of 6 m?
   A. 36 m^3 B. 48 m^3
   C. 72 m^3 (D) 144 m^3

3. Find the circumference of a circle with a radius of 4 ft. Use 3.14 for π.
   A. 6.28 ft B. 12.56 ft
   (C) 25.12 ft D. 31.4 ft

4. Which lengths could be side lengths of a right triangle?
   A. 6, 6, 5 B. 8, 9, 10
   C. 7, 7, 7 (D) 5, 12, 13

5. Chris is buying a new bicycle. He has a choice of 4 models, 6 colors, and 3 seats. How many different bicycle choices does he have?
   A. 13 B. 24
   C. 36 (D) 72

6. There are 10 red, 12 blue, 14 green, and 4 yellow marbles in a bag. You pick one marble without looking. Find P (blue or yellow).
   (A) $\frac{2}{5}$ B. $\frac{3}{10}$
   C. $\frac{1}{10}$ D. $\frac{1}{20}$

7. What type of relationship is shown by a negative trend?
   A. an increase in both sets of values
   B. a decrease in both sets of values
   C. neither an increase nor a decrease
   (D) an increase in one set of values and a decrease in the other

8. Suppose a stem-and-leaf plot is to be made for the following data. Which set of values would be used for the stems?
   10, 7, 10, 15, 21, 5, 32, 18, 26
   A. 1, 2, 3
   (B) 0, 1, 2, 3
   C. 5, 10, 15, 20, 25, 30, 35
   D. 10, 20, 30

9. Find the mean, median, and mode for the data in Exercise 8.
   A. 20, 21, 10 (B) 16, 15, 10
   C. 15, 21, 5 D. 27, 21, 10

10. Which number has the same value as $|-13|$?
   A. $-|-13|$ B. $-|13|$
   (C) 13 D. −13

11. Order −5, 6, 0, −2, and 1 from least to greatest.
   A. 0, 1, −2, −5, 6 B. 6, 1, 0, −2, −5
   C. −2, −5, 0, 1, 6 (D) −5, −2, 0, 1, 6

12. Which choice is equivalent to the sum of −43 and 18?
   (A) 18 + (−43) B. −43 + (−18)
   C. −18 + 43 D. 43 + (−18)

Assessment

CUMULATIVE REVIEW

Chapter 10 Cumulative Review (continued)

13. Write a numerical expression for "9 less than −12."
   A. 9 − 12 B. 12 − 9
   (C) −12 − 9 D. 9 + (−12)

14. What is the sign of the product of two integers with different signs?
   A. the sign of the smaller number
   (B) negative
   C. the sign of the larger number
   D. positive

15. Which number is the best estimate of $-210 \div 29$?
   A. −10 B. 9
   C. 8 (D) −7

16. Which equation is equivalent to $\frac{x}{6} - 12 = -6$?
   A. $\frac{x}{6} = 18$ B. $6x = 6$
   (C) $x = 36$ D. $x - 12 = 1$

17. Which rule could you use to find the next number in this sequence?
   −3, −1, 1, 3, 5, . . .
   A. add −1 B. subtract 2
   (C) add 2 D. subtract −2

18. The rule for one function is $f(n) = 2n - 4$. The rule for a second function is $f(n) = 4n - 2$. For which value of n are the output values opposites?
   (A) $n = 1$ B. $n = -1$
   C. $n = 2$ D. $n = -2$

19. Evaluate $(-1)^{45}$.
   A. −145 B. −45
   (C) −1 D. 1

20. A student graphed the distances traveled by a toy car after going down a ramp set at heights of 6 in., 12 in., and 18 in. Use the graph below to estimate the distance the toy car would travel if the height of the ramp were 2 ft.

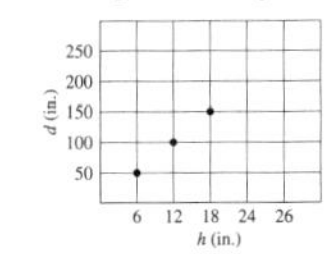

   A. 24 in. B. 50 in.
   C. 175 in. (D) 200 in.

21. What is the rule for the function represented by the table below?

n	$f(n)$
−1	−4
0	−1
1	2
2	5

   A. $f(n) = 3n + 1$
   B. $f(n) = -3n + 1$
   (C) $f(n) = 3n - 1$
   D. $f(n) = -3n - 1$

22. You deposit \$500 in your savings account. The bank pays 4% interest each year. Use the formula $B = p(1 + r)^t$ to find the amount of money in your account after 2 years.
   A. \$20.00 B. \$40.80
   C. \$520.00 (D) \$540.80

Resources

Teaching Resources

Chapter Support File, Ch. 10
• Cumulative Review

Teacher's Edition

See pp. 432C–D for Assessment Options.

11 Graphing in the Coordinate Plane

Chapter Overview

To accommodate flexible scheduling, most lessons are divided into parts. Assignment Options are given in the Teacher's Edition for each lesson.

Pages	Lesson
Pages 472–476	**Lesson 11-1 Graphing Points in Four Quadrants**
NCTM 1, 2, 4, 8, 9, 10, 11	Part 1 Graphing Points Part 2 Identifying Quadrants **Key terms:** coordinate plane, origin, ordered pair (*x, y*), quadrants **Math at Work**

Pages	Lesson
Pages 477–481	**Lesson 11-2 Graphing Linear Equations**
NCTM 1, 2, 3, 4, 5, 7, 8, 9, 12, 13	Part 1 Finding Ordered Pairs Part 2 Graphing a Linear Equation **Key terms:** solution, graph of an equation, linear equation **Alternative Activity** 11-2 **Journal** **Project Link**

Pages	Lesson
Pages 482–484	**Lesson 11-3 Data Analysis: Finding the Slope of a Line**
NCTM 2, 3, 4, 5, 7, 8, 10, 11	**Key term:** slope of a line

Pages	Lesson
Pages 499–503	**Lesson 11-7 Geometry: Symmetry and Reflections**
NCTM 2, 4, 8, 9, 12	Part 1 Identifying Lines of Symmetry Part 2 Graphing Reflections **Key terms:** symmetry, symmetrical, line of symmetry, reflection, line of reflection **Alternative Activity** 11-7 **Project Link** **Checkpoint 2**

Pages	Lesson
Pages 505–508	**Lesson 11-8 Geometry: Rotations**
NCTM 1, 2, 4, 12	Part 1 Identifying Rotational Symmetry Part 2 Rotating a Figure **Key terms:** rotation, center of rotation, rotational symmetry

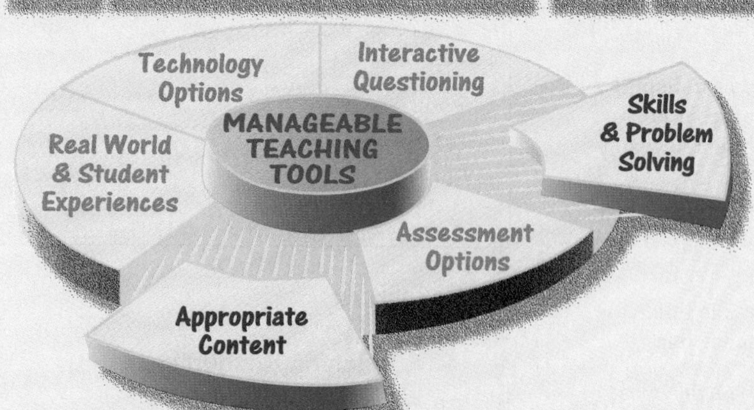

Pacing Options

This chart suggests pacing only for the core lessons and their parts. It is provided merely as a possible guide. It will help you determine how much time you have in your schedule to cover other features, such as the Chapter Project, Math Toolboxes, Wrap Up, and Assessment.

	1 Class Period	1 Class Period	1 Class Period	1 P
Traditional (40–45 min class periods)	11–1 (1) 11–1 (2)	11–2 (1) 11–2 (2)	11–3	11- (1)
Block Scheduling (90 min class periods)	11–1 (1) 11–1 (2) 11–2 (1) 11–2 (2)	11–3 11–4 (1) 11–4 (2)	11–5 11 6 (1) 11 6 (2)	11 (1)

CHAPTER PROJECT

People's Choice

Goal: Students analyze what sample size they need to make an accurate prediction

THEME: BUSINESS

NCTM STANDARDS

1 Problem Solving
2 Communication
3 Reasoning
4 Mathematical Connections
5 Number and Number Relationships
6 Number Systems and Number Theory
7 Computation and Estimation
8 Patterns and Functions
9 Algebra
10 Statistics
11 Probability
12 Geometry
13 Measurement

Pages	Lesson
Pages 486–489	**Lesson 11-4 Exploring Nonlinear Relationships**
NCTM 1, 2, 4, 8, 9, 12	Part 1 Graphing Parabolas Part 2 Graphing an Absolute Value Equation **Key term:** parabola **Journal** **Checkpoint 1**
Pages 490–492	**Lesson 11-5 Problem Solving Strategy**
NCTM 1, 4, 8, 9, 10, 11, 12	**Write an Equation** **Project Link**
Pages 494–498	**Lesson 11-6 Geometry: Translations**
NCTM 1, 2, 3, 4, 8, 12	Part 1 Graphing Translations Part 2 Writing a Rule for a Translation **Key terms:** transformations, translation, image, prime notation (*A*′), tessellation

Optional Materials and Manipulatives

graph paper (11-1, 11-2, 11-3, 11-4, 11-7)
colored paper (11-7)

scissors (11-7)

Optional calculator use is integrated throughout the course.

ass od	1 Class Period	1 Class Period	1 Class Period	1 Class Period	1 Class Period	1 Class Period	1 Class Period	1 Class Period	1 Class Period	1 Class Period
-5	11–6 1	11–6 2 11–7 1	11–7 2	11–8 1 11–8 2						
11–8 2										

MEETING INDIVIDUAL NEEDS

Accommodating Diverse Learning Styles

In your Teacher's Edition, you will find suggestions as to how you can help students complete mathematical tasks in Chapter 11 by meeting individual needs and supporting various learning styles. Here are some examples:

VISUAL LEARNING
using color to help students visualize translations
(p. 496)

TACTILE LEARNING
tracing paths on a graph using fingers or pencils
(p. 472)

AUDITORY LEARNING
reading coordinates like giving directions *(p. 473)*

KINESTHETIC LEARNING
using arms to model shapes of functions *(p. 486)*

EARLY FINISHERS
Performance-Based Project, MathBlaster® Mystery, Interdisciplinary Units

GIFTED AND TALENTED
writing and trading equations
(p. 480)

DIVERSITY using tracing paper to model rotations
(p. 505)

ACQUIRING ENGLISH PROFICIENCY (AEP)
using French and Spanish terms to help students understand *linear equation*
(p. 478)

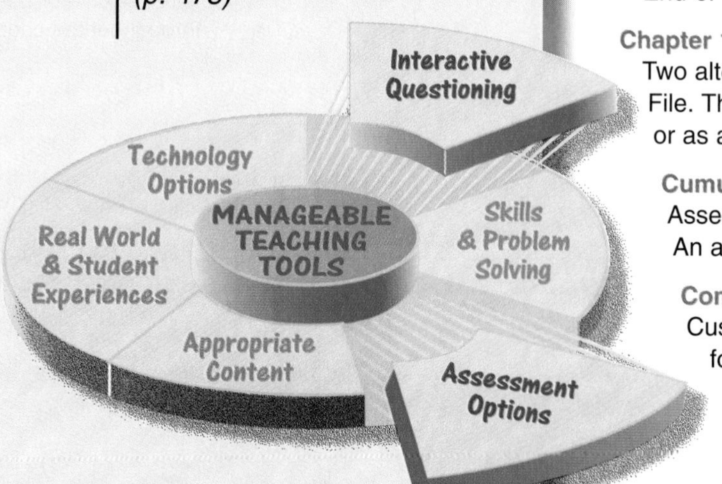

ASSESSING PROGRESS

A broad range of assessment tools are available to reach a variety of learners.

INFORMAL ASSESSMENT

Informal assessments provide day-to-day feedback to help give you a picture of conceptual understanding and skill development.

ONGOING ASSESSMENT is built into lesson instruction and the Teaching Notes of the Teacher's Edition.

In the Teacher's Edition
Lesson Quiz for every lesson

In the Student Edition
On Your Own, Mixed Review, Journal, Portfolio, Project Link, Chapter Wrap Up

Look for **Interactive Questions** within lessons that

- **BUILD UNDERSTANDING** with labels such as **Analyze, Reasoning, Estimation, Writing, and Summarize**
- ✔ **CHECK UNDERSTANDING** with the **Try It Out** label.

FORMAL ASSESSMENT

Formal assessment can occur before and after the chapter, as well as at natural breaking points in the chapter.

Checkpoints
Two forms of each self-assessment Checkpoints are available: one in the Student Edition and another in the Chapter Support File in the Teaching Resources box.

- Mid-Chapter Checkpoint 1, page 489
- End-of-Chapter Checkpoint 2, page 503

Chapter 11 Assessment, page 512
Two alternative forms are available in the Chapter Support File. They may be used after a chapter has been completed, or as a pre-test and post-test comparison.

Cumulative Review, page 513.
Assesses skills and concepts in Chapters 1–11.
An alternative form is available in Chapter Support File.

Computer Item Generator for Chapter 11
Customized tests can be generated for each lesson and for mid-chapter and end-of-chapter assessments, and for pre- and post-test comparisons of achievement.

PERFORMANCE-BASED ASSESSMENT

CHAPTER PROJECT

The Chapter Project in the student edition provides a real-world connection to the math context of the chapter. The Teacher's Edition contains a scoring rubric.

A Performance Assessment with a scoring rubric can be found in the Chapter Support File in the Teaching Resources box.

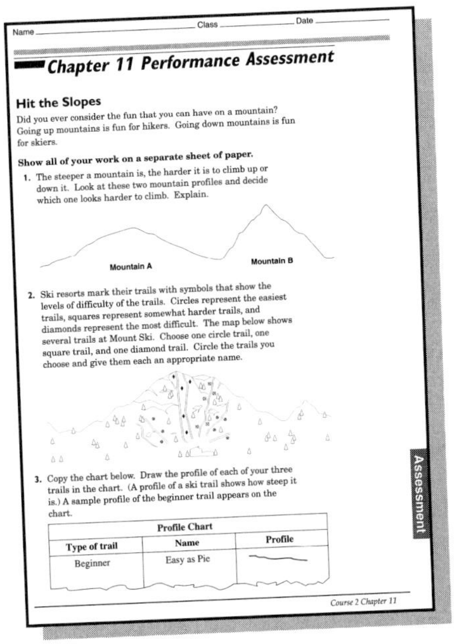
Name ______ Class ______ Date ______

Chapter 11 Performance Assessment

Hit the Slopes

Did you ever consider the fun that you can have on a mountain? Going up mountains is fun for hikers. Going down mountains is fun for skiers.

Show all of your work on a separate sheet of paper.

1. The steeper a mountain is, the harder it is to climb up or down it. Look at these two mountain profiles and decide which one looks harder to climb. Explain.

2. Ski resorts mark their trails with symbols that show the levels of difficulty of the trails. Circles represent the easiest trails, squares represent somewhat harder trails, and diamonds represent the most difficult. The map below shows several trails at Mount Ski. Choose one circle trail, one square trail, and one diamond trail. Circle the trails you choose and give them each an appropriate name.

3. Copy the chart below. Draw the profile of each of your three trails in the chart. (A profile of a ski trail shows how steep it is.) A sample profile of the beginner trail appears on the chart.

Profile Chart		
Type of trail	Name	Profile
Beginner	Easy as Pie	

Assessment

Course 2 Chapter 11

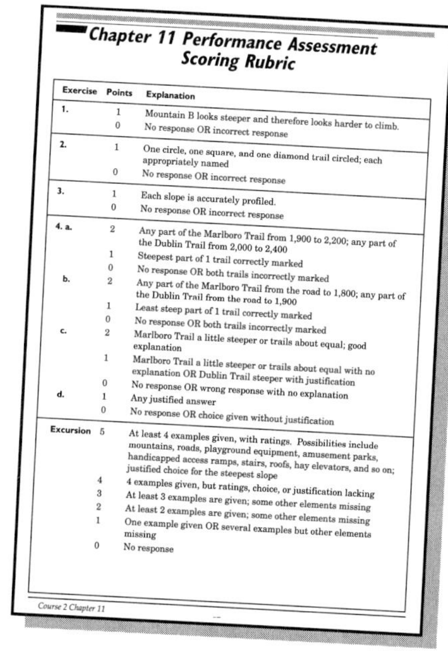
Chapter 11 Performance Assessment Scoring Rubric

Exercise	Points	Explanation
1.	1	Mountain B looks steeper and therefore looks harder to climb.
	0	No response OR incorrect response
2.	1	One circle, one square, and one diamond trail circled; each appropriately named
	0	No response OR incorrect response
3.	1	Each slope is accurately profiled.
	0	No response OR incorrect response
4. a.	2	Any part of the Marlboro Trail from 1,900 to 2,200; any part of the Dublin Trail from 2,000 to 2,400
	1	Steepest part of 1 trail correctly marked
	0	No response OR both trails incorrectly marked
b.	2	Any part of the Marlboro Trail from the road to 1,800; any part of the Dublin Trail from the road to 1,900
	1	Least steep part of 1 trail correctly marked
	0	No response OR both trails incorrectly marked
c.	2	Marlboro Trail a little steeper or trails about equal; good explanation
	1	Marlboro Trail a little steeper or trails about equal with no explanation OR Dublin Trail steeper with justification
	0	No response OR wrong response with no explanation
d.	1	Any justified answer
	0	No response OR choice given without justification
Excursion	5	At least 4 examples given, with ratings. Possibilities include mountains, roads, playground equipment, amusement parks, handicapped access ramps, stairs, roofs, hay elevators, and so on; justified choice for the steepest slope
	4	4 examples given, but ratings, choice, or justification lacking
	3	At least 3 examples are given; some other elements missing
	2	At least 2 examples are given; some other elements missing
	1	One example given OR several examples but other elements missing
	0	No response

Course 2 Chapter 11

Correlation to Standardized Tests

Lesson		STANDARDIZED TEST ITEMS					
		CAT5	Terra Nova	ITBS, Form M	MAT7	SAT9	Local Test
11-1	Graphing Points in Four Quadrants				CP25	PS29	
11-2	Graphing Linear Equations						
11-3	Data Analysis: Finding the Slope of a Line						
11-4	Exploring Nonlinear Relationships						
11-5	Problem Solving Strategy: Write an Equation						
11-6	Geometry: Translations		57				
11-7	Geometry: Symmetry and Reflections				CP23	PS30–31	
11-8	Geometry: Rotations						

CA: Concepts and Applications
PS: Problem Solving
PR: Math Procedures
CP: Concepts and Problem Solving
MC: Math Computation
PD: Problem Solving and Data Interpretation
CE: Concepts and Estimation

See page 2D for the level of each test referenced.

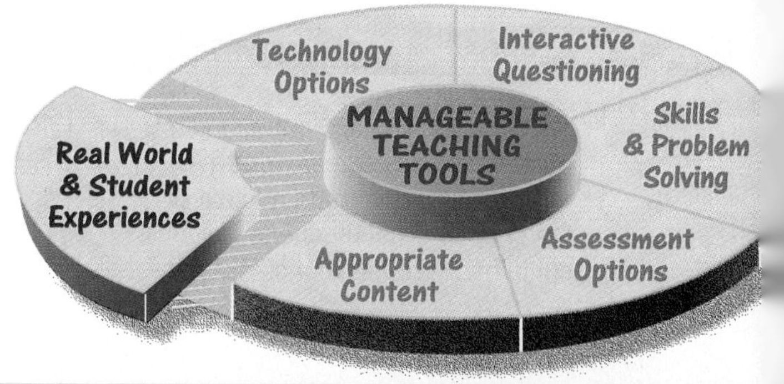

MAKING CONNECTIONS

TEAM TEACHING WITH PRENTICE HALL MATERIALS

MIDDLE GRADES MATH INTERDISCIPLINARY UNITS	*INTERDISCIPLINARY EXPLORATIONS*	PRENTICE HALL SCIENCE **L** Life Science **E** Earth Science **P** Physical Science
• **Health, Exercise, and Fitness: Activity 11** • **The Environment: Activity 7** • **Advancements in Industry: Activity 4**	• ***Riddles of the Pharaohs* p. 39**	**E Sec. 8-3 Mapping the Earth's Surface (longitude, latitude)**

Lesson	Interdisciplinary Connections	Real World Connections	Math Integration
11-1	History	Robotics Automotive Engineering	Statistics Probability Geometry
11-2	Ecology	Cooking Food Preparation Money	Algebra Geometry Measurement
11-3	Science	Cars	Statistics Probability Geometry
11-4	Physics	Working	Algebra Geometry
11-5	Architecture	Zoo Money Entertainment Fund-raising	Algebra Statistics Probability Geometry
11-6	Art	Fabric Design Aviation	Geometry
11-7	Photography Language Biology	Nature	Algebra Geometry
11-8	Engineering	Windmills Nature	Geometry

School to Home

MATERIALS:
paper
colored pencils, pens, or crayons
mirror
newspaper
magazines
scissors
tape
pencil

English version is in the Chapter Support File. Spanish version is in the Spanish Resources.

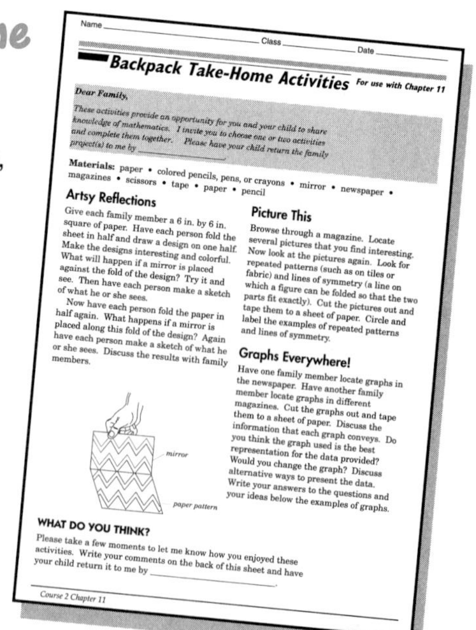
Name ______ Class ______ Date ______

Backpack Take-Home Activities *For use with Chapter 11*

Dear Family,

These activities provide an opportunity for you and your child to share knowledge of mathematics. I invite you to choose one or two activities and complete them together. Please have your child return the family project(s) to me by ______.

Materials: paper • colored pencils, pens, or crayons • mirror • newspaper • magazines • scissors • tape • paper • pencil

Artsy Reflections

Give each family member a 6 in. by 6 in. square of paper. Have each person fold the sheet in half and draw a design on one half. Make the designs interesting and colorful. What will happen if a mirror is placed against the fold of the design? Try it and see. Then have each person make a sketch of what he or she sees.

Now have each person fold the paper in half again. What happens if a mirror is placed along this fold of the design? Again have each person make a sketch of what he or she sees. Discuss the results with family members.

mirror
paper pattern

Picture This

Browse through a magazine. Locate several pictures that you find interesting. Now look at the pictures again. Look for repeated patterns (such as on tiles or fabric) and lines of symmetry (a line on which a figure can be folded so that the two parts fit exactly). Cut the pictures out and tape them to a sheet of paper. Circle and label the examples of repeated patterns and lines of symmetry.

Graphs Everywhere!

Have one family member locate graphs in the newspaper. Have another family member locate graphs in different magazines. Cut the graphs out and tape them to a sheet of paper. Discuss the information that each graph conveys. Do you think the graph used is the best representation for the data provided? Would you change the graph? Discuss alternative ways to present the data. Write your answers to the questions and your ideas below the examples of graphs.

WHAT DO YOU THINK?

Please take a few moments to let me know how you enjoyed these activities. Write your comments on the back of this sheet and have your child return it to me by ______.

Course 2 Chapter 11

Using Technology to Enhance Instruction

For the Student

Multimedia Math Hot Pages™

This interactive software and video package on CD-ROM integrates solid math content through a variety of media.

- Hot Page™ 11-3
- Hot Page™ 11-5
- Hot Page™ 11-10

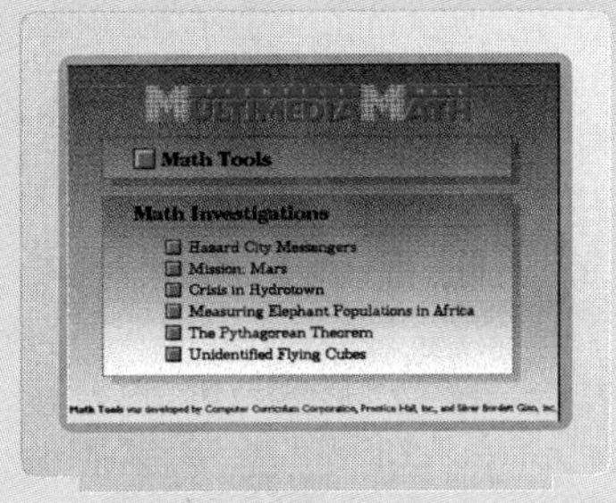

Multimedia Math Investigations

These in-depth interactive activities on CD-ROM develop real-world applications of mathematics. They allow students the opportunity to reinforce key concepts.

- Mission: Mars
- Measuring Elephant Populations in Africa

MathBlaster® Mystery

This award-winning, interactive software program on CD-ROM can be used to maintain skills or to accommodate early finishers.

- Level: Earn 4 coins; Pay 4 coins
- Mission Mode (all lessons)
- Kitchen Comparisons (11-4, 11-7)
- Number Guesser (11-6)
- Equation Maker (11-2, 11-3, 11-5)
- Word Problems (11-1, 11-8, Problem Solving Practice)

Math Tools/Math Labs

This software, available on CD-ROM, includes on-screen Math Lab activities. Students use linkable, interactive tools to explore math concepts.

- Math Lab: Graphing Equations (11-2)

Interactive Student Tutorial

Available on CD-ROM, this test preparation program contains self-tests with questions in standardized test format. Software includes electronic versions of the text lessons and an on-line glossary.

Internet Connection

For Students

Support for the Chapter Project

A career-oriented link for Math at Work feature

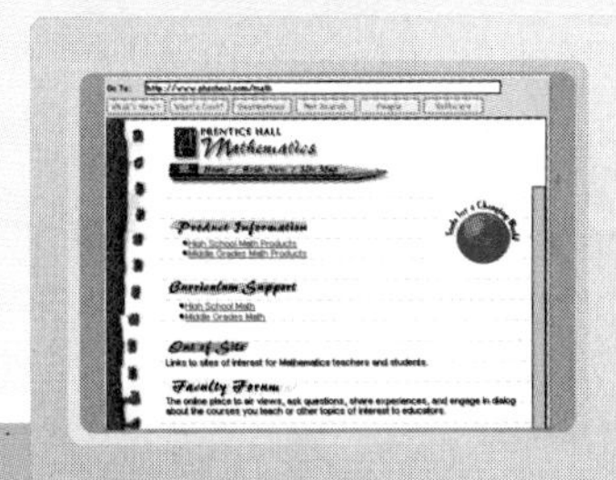

www.phschool.com/math

For teachers

Curriculum Support

Product Information

Regional Support Information

For the Teacher

Computer Item Generator with Standardized Test Practice

This software generates customized practice sheets and tests. It also generates unlimited practice sheets for the standardized tests listed on page 470D.

Resource Pro™ with Planning Express™

Available on CD-ROM, this software can be used to customize and plan lessons. It contains over 1,700 resource pages.

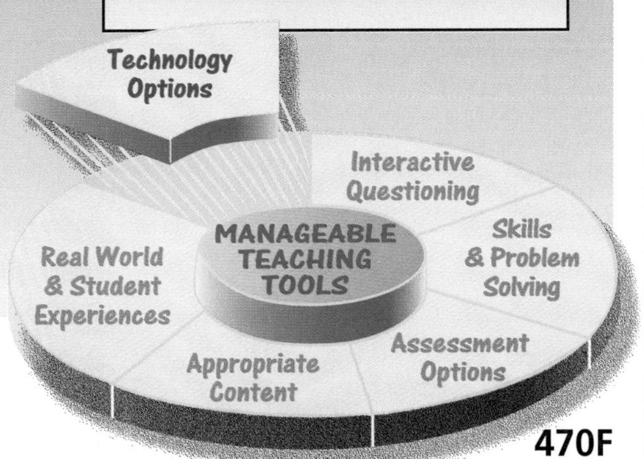

CHAPTER 11 GRAPHING IN THE COORDINATE PLANE

CONNECTING TO PRIOR LEARNING Ask students if they have ever read the results of a poll. Ask students: *What are polls used for?* **Answers may vary. Sample: to predict winners in elections** Discuss with students how they might use a poll at school.

CULTURAL CONNECTIONS Point out to students that running far behind an opponent in a poll before an election does not mean that your campaign has been futile. In the Reverend Jesse Jackson's bids to become president of the United States, he only captured a small percentage of the votes. But he did draw peoples' attention to the importance of African American voters and other minority voters.

INTERDISCIPLINARY CONNECTIONS Ask students: *If you were opening a small business, how might you use a poll of your prospective customers?* **Answers may vary. Sample: to stock the items people want**

ABOUT THE PROJECT The Chapter Project has students apply their knowledge of graphing in the coordinate plane to conduct a poll.

Internet • For information and activities related to the Chapter Project, visit the Prentice Hall site at www.phschool.com/mgm2/ch11

WHAT YOU WILL LEARN IN THIS CHAPTER

- How to graph points and lines in the coordinate plane
- How to find the slope of a line
- How to translate, reflect, and rotate figures

LAUNCHING THE CHAPTER PROJECT

Ask students:

- *Have you ever been included in a market survey?*
- *How can market surveys be used to help develop something new to sell?*
- *How might a survey be used to help make a product more successful?*

PROJECT NOTEBOOK Encourage students to keep all project-related materials in a separate folder or notebook.

TRACKING THE PROJECT You may wish to have students read Finishing the Chapter Project on page 509 to help them get an overview of the project. Set benchmark deadlines for students to show you their work in progress.

- How to solve problems by writing an equation

CHAPTER PROJECT

THEME: BUSINESS

People's choice

You're an advertising executive, and you want to know which of three television shows is the most popular. So you plan to conduct a poll of viewers.

But how many viewers do you survey? Polling is expensive, so you don't want to poll too many. Polling too few viewers might give you the wrong information. Here's your chance to explore the process!

Find a Sample Size Fill a container with three different kinds of beans. Use the beans to find the sample size that best predicts the percent of each kind of bean in the container.

Steps to help you complete the project:

p. 481 **Project Link:** ***Collecting Data***
p. 492 **Project Link:** ***Graphing***
p. 503 **Project Link:** ***Writing***
p. 509 ***Finishing the Chapter Project***

SCORING RUBRIC

3 For each of ten samples, you provide a table listing the number and percentage of each bean type in the sample. For each type of bean, you draw a graph of percent versus sample size. You write a paragraph describing how sample size affects the accuracy of the survey results. Your work is clear and provides convincing evidence to support the statements you make in your paragraph.

2 You collect data and calculate percentages accurately for at least seven sample sizes. You provide percentage versus sample size graphs for at least two of the bean types, and you write a brief conclusion to your investigation.

1 Your data, your graphs, and your conclusions are incomplete or do not provide a clear picture of your work or your findings.

0 You omit important parts of the project.

11-1 Teaching Notes

1 Focus

CONNECTING TO PRIOR KNOWLEDGE Tell students: *Write directions for a classmate explaining how to get from his or her desk to your desk using only the directions north, south, east, and west.* Then have volunteers read their directions out loud. Ask students: *Would the directions work for a different classmate?* **no** *Explain.* **They would not be starting from the same location.** Lead the class into a discussion about the point called the origin in a coordinate plane.

2 Teach

THINK AND DISCUSS

TACTILE LEARNING Have students trace the path from the origin to point *A*. Students always begin by tracing along the *x*-axis until they line up with the point. Then slide their finger or pencil straight up or down to reach the point.

ERROR ALERT! Example 1 Students may have difficulty remembering which is the *x*- and *y*-axis, and the order of the coordinates. **Remediation:** Encourage students to think alphabetically! The letter *x* comes before *y* in the alphabet. Likewise, you list the *x*-coordinate before the *y*-coordinate. Also, the word *horizontal* alphabetically comes before the word *vertical*. The *x*-axis is *horizontal* and the *y*-axis is vertical.

Lesson Planning Options

Prerequisite Skills

- using integers on a number line (precourse)

Vocabulary/Symbols

coordinate plane, origin, ordered pair (*x*, *y*), quadrants

Materials/Manipulatives

- graph paper

Resources

Student Edition

Skills Handbook, p. 528
Extra Practice, p. 524
Glossary/Study Guide

Teaching Resources

Chapter Support File, Ch. 11
- Lesson Planner 11-1
- Practice 11-1, Reteaching 11-1
- Answer Masters 11-1

Teaching Aids Master 4
Glossary, Spanish Resources

Transparencies

2, Minds on Math 11-1

Warm Up

Natasha plans to park her car for 5 h. The parking lot charges $1.50 for the first hour and $.90 for each additional hour, or $4.75 for the day. What is the better option for her? **Park for the day.**

11-1 Graphing Points in Four Quadrants

What You'll Learn

1. To graph points on the coordinate plane
2. To identify quadrants

...And Why

Computer programmers and robotics engineers use the coordinate plane to describe locations.

Here's How

Look for questions that
- build understanding
- ✔ check understanding

WHAT? To direct a robot/computer like this one, programmers use coordinates.

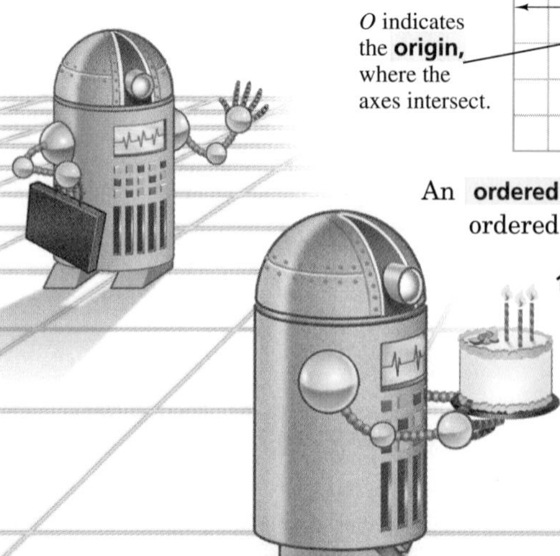

THINK AND DISCUSS

1 Graphing Points

René Descartes (1596–1650) was a French mathematician and philosopher. An old legend says that he looked up at the ceiling one day and noticed a fly crawling across it. Descartes began thinking about how to describe the exact position of the fly on the ceiling. His thoughts generated the *coordinate plane*.

A **coordinate plane** is formed by a horizontal number line called the x-axis and a vertical number line called the y-axis.

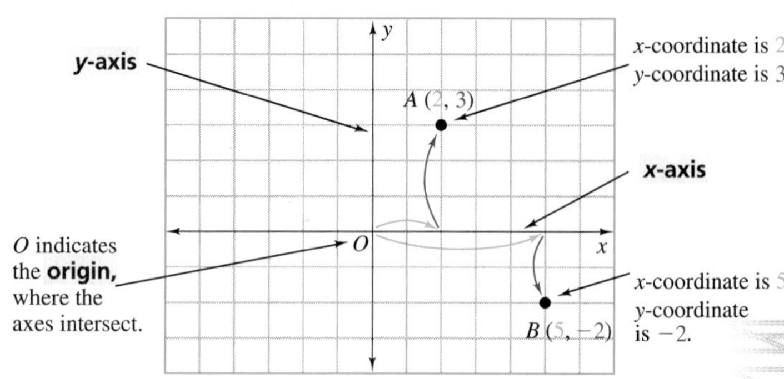

An **ordered pair** identifies the location of a point. The ordered pair (2, 3) identifies point A.

1. a. *Think About It* On the x-axis, which direction is positive? Negative? **right; left**
   b. On the y-axis, which direction is positive? Negative? **up; down**

ADDITIONAL EXAMPLES

FOR EXAMPLE 1

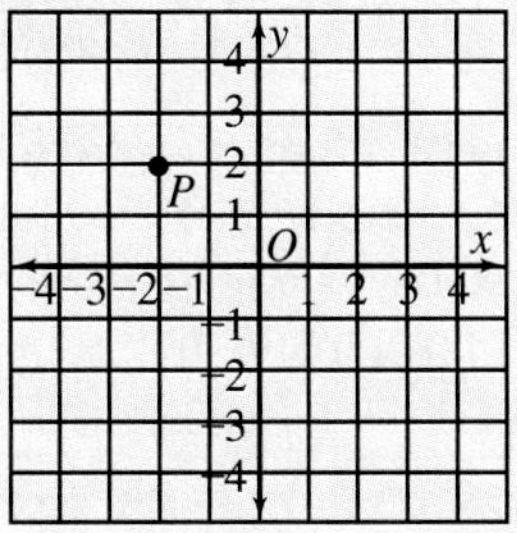

Write the coordinates for point *P*. **(−2, 2)**

FOR EXAMPLE 2

Graph point *Q* with coordinates (−2, 1).

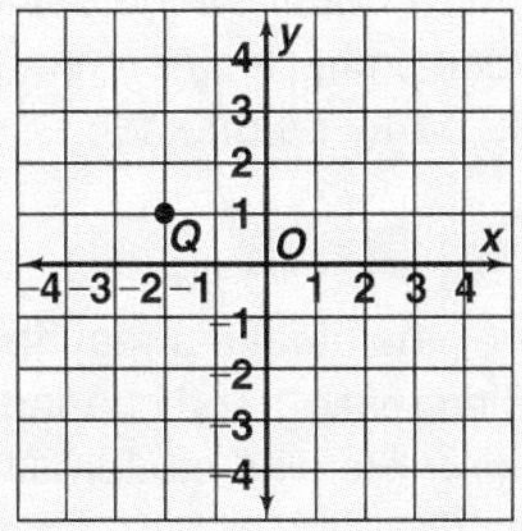

FOR EXAMPLE 3

In which quadrant would you find the point (3, −2)? **IV**

AUDITORY LEARNING **Example 2** Have students read the coordinates as if they were giving directions. For example: Read (3, −5) as *right three, down five,* or (0, 4) as *stay zero, up four.*

VISUAL LEARNING If students are having difficulty remembering to move sideways first when graphing coordinates, tell them to look at the ordered pair. The coordinates are

The *x*-coordinate of an ordered pair shows the position left or right of the origin. The *y*-coordinate shows the position up or down. You can use this information to write coordinates.

EXAMPLE 1

Write the coordinates for the fly on the coordinate plane at the right.

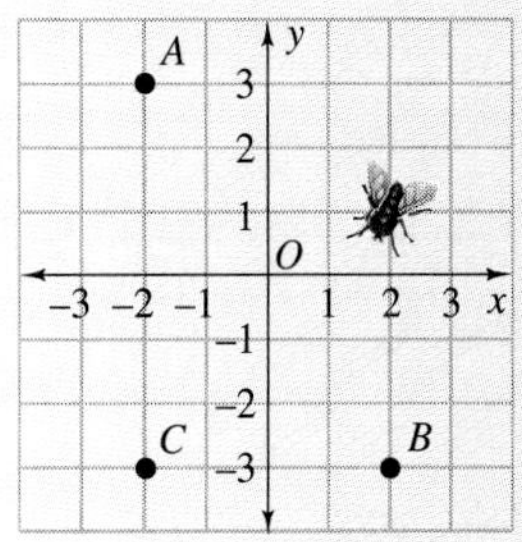

The fly is 2 units to the right of the *y*-axis. So the *x*-coordinate is 2.

The fly is 1 unit above the *x*-axis. So the *y*-coordinate is 1.

The ordered pair for the location of the fly is (2, 1).

2. ✔ *Try It Out* Use the graph in Example 1. What are the coordinates of points *A*, *B*, and *C*? **A(−2, 3); B(2, −3); C(−2, −3)**

3. *Go a Step Further* Find the coordinates of the origin. **(0, 0)**

You can use an ordered pair to graph a point on a plane.

EXAMPLE 2

Graph the point with coordinates (3,−5).

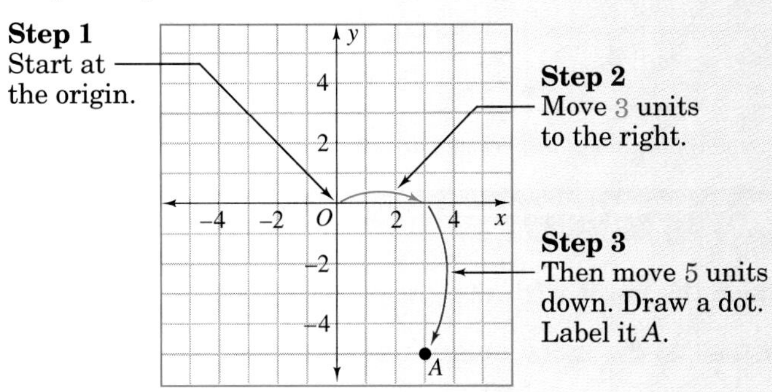

4a–c.

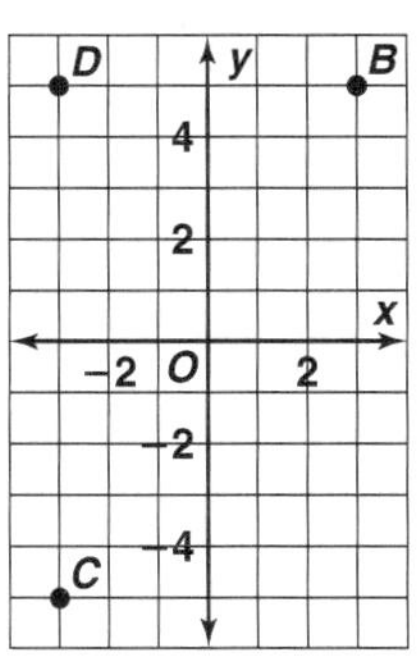

4. ✔ *Try It Out* Graph the points on the same plane.
   a. *B*(3, 5) b. *C*(−3, −5) c. *D*(−3, 5)
   a–c. See left.

5. a. Graph the points *G*(0, 4), *H*(−2, 0), *J*(0, −3) and *K*(5, 0). Tell on which axis each point lies.
   b. *Draw a Conclusion* On which axis does the point (*m*, 0) lie? On which axis does the point (0, *n*) lie? **x-axis; y-axis**

5a. Check students' work for graph; G: y-axis; H: x-axis; J: y-axis; K: x-axis.

Now you may assign Exercises 1–17, 29.

Technology Options

Prentice Hall Technology

Software for Learners
- Math Blaster® Mystery*
- Interactive Student Tutorial, Chapter 11*

Teaching Resource Software
- Computer Item Generator 11-1
- Resource Pro™ Chapter 11*

Internet • For related mathematics activities, visit the Prentice Hall site at www.phschool.com/math

**Available on CD-ROM only*

Assignment Options for Exercises On Your Own

To provide for flexible scheduling, this lesson can be split into parts..

1 **Core** 1–17
Extension 29

2 **Core** 18–28
Extension 30, 31

Use Mixed Review to maintain skills.

written be*side* each other so move *side*ways first.

VISUAL LEARNING Example 3 To help students remember how to number their quadrants, have them write a large letter *C*, for coordinate plane, on their graph paper. Begin in quadrant I and end in quadrant IV. Number the quadrants in the same direction as a pencil moves to write the letter *C*.

ASSESSMENT Have students graph one point in each quadrant. Then have them list the coordinates for their points on a separate sheet of paper. Students trade coordinates with a partner. They graph the points and observe in which quadrant the points are located. Students check by comparing their graph to their partner's original.

Work Together

DIVERSITY Some students may feel uncomfortable creating and sharing an original drawing. Remind students that the drawing does not have to form a picture. You may also suggest a simple drawing such as a block initial for either the first or last name.

3 Practice

EXERCISES *On Your Own*

Exercises 1–12 When they have finished, students should make sure they have used each point exactly one time. If they find they have used a point twice, they should check their work for errors.

CONNECTION TO PATTERNS Exercise 13 Have students write the coordinates to the left of each point before looking for a pattern.

2 *Identifying Quadrants*

The *x*- and *y*-axes divide the coordinate plane into four **quadrants.**

EXAMPLE 3

In which quadrant is the point (−4, −1) located?

Start at the origin (*O*). Move 4 units to the left and 1 unit down.

The point (−4, −1) is in the third quadrant.

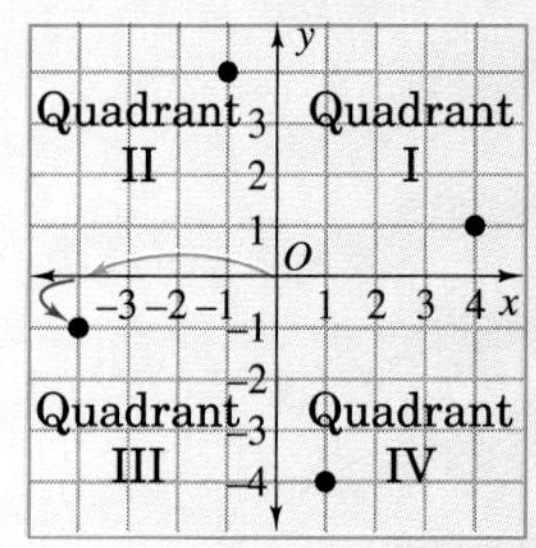

6. ✓*Try It Out* Identify the quadrant in which each point lies.
   a. (4, 5) **I** b. (−1, 7) **II** c. (10, −13) **IV**

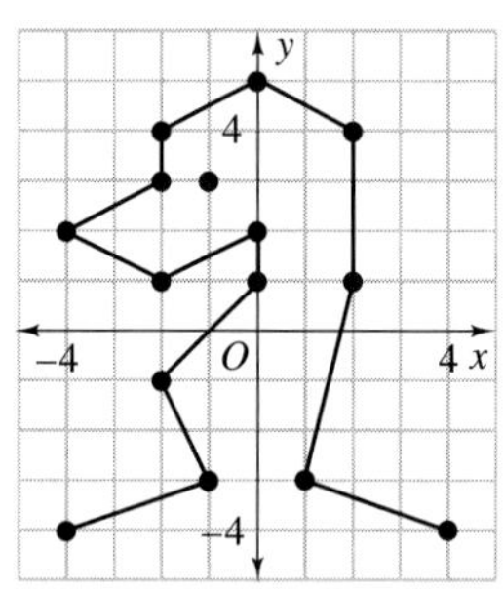

Work Together *Exploring the Coordinate Plane*

Work with a partner.

7. Make a dot-to-dot drawing (such as the one at the left). On a separate sheet of paper, write the coordinates of the dots in the order in which you connected them.

7–8. Check students' work.

8. Exchange lists of ordered pairs with your partner. Recreate your partner's drawing by graphing the coordinates.

Now you may assign Exercises 18–28, 30–31.

EXERCISES *On Your Own*

Name the point with the given coordinates.

1. (−5, 3) ***C*** 2. (4, 0) ***E*** 3. (−6, 2) ***F***
4. (5, −3) ***D*** 5. (0, 5) ***A*** 6. (6, 2) ***B***

Write the coordinates of each point.

7. *G* **(−3, −2)** 8. *K* **(−5, 6)** 9. *J* **(5, −4)**
10. *H* **(0, −3)** 11. *M* **(2, 6)** 12. *L* **(−2, 0)**

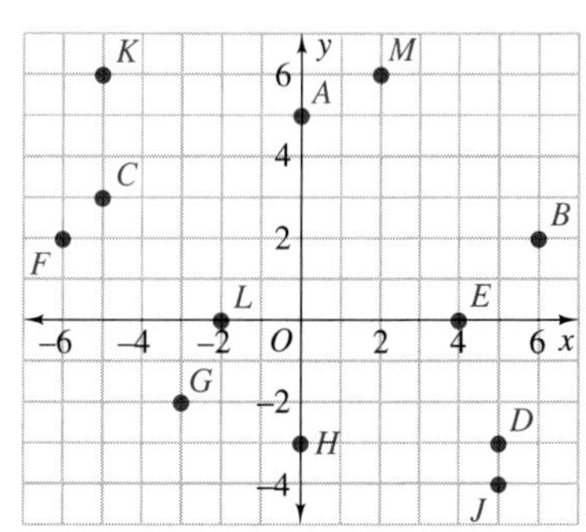

WRITING Exercise 15 Suggest students write as if they were giving directions to a friend. Have students trade papers to test their directions.

CONNECTION TO GEOMETRY Exercises 26–28 Have students review the definitions of *square, parallelogram,* and *trapezoid.*

OPEN-ENDED Exercise 29 Challenge students to find the path with the least number of moves.

WRAP UP

IDENTIFYING THE BIG IDEA Ask students to describe how to write the coordinates of a given point. Then have them explain how to graph points on the coordinate plane.

Math at Work

If you have block scheduling or extended class periods, have students act as engineers by testing toy cars for wind resistance. Have groups of four bring a light-weight plastic car. They can use a blow dryer as the wind tunnel and record how far back the wind pushed the vehicle. Encourage them to suggest ways to alter the car to make it more wind resistant.

---

13. a. *Patterns* Graph the points $(-3, -2)$, $(-3, 2)$, $(-3, -6)$, and $(-3, 6)$. **See margin.**

b. What do you notice about these four points? **b. All the points lie on a vertical line.**

c. Give the coordinates of two other points that fit the pattern. **Answers may vary. Answers are coordinates in the form $(-3, y)$.**

14a. Answers may vary. Answers are coordinates in the form $(x, -3)$.

14. a. A horizontal line is shown in red at the right. List the ordered pairs of 3 points that are on the line.

b. Which coordinate of an ordered pair stays the same for all points on the line? Which coordinate changes? **y-coordinate; x-coordinate**

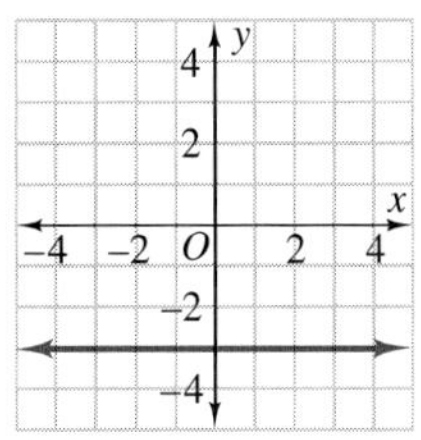

15. *Writing* Describe how to find the point $(5, -1)$ on a coordinate plane. **Starting from the origin, move 5 units right. Then move 1 unit down.**

16. Four of these points are the vertices of a square. Which one is not? **(4, −2)**
$(-1, -3)$ $(-1, 0)$ $(2, -3)$ $(4, -2)$ $(2, 0)$

17. Choose A, B, C, or D. Which of the following groups of ordered pairs are *not* the vertices of a rectangle? **B**

A. $(-4, 1)$, $(4, 1)$, $(-4, -1)$, and $(4, -1)$
B. $(-1, 0)$, $(-5, -3)$, $(-1, -4)$, and $(-5, 0)$
C. $(3, 6)$, $(6, 6)$, $(3, 9)$, and $(6, 9)$
D. $(-3, 8)$, $(3, 8)$, $(3, -8)$, and $(-3, -8)$

Identify the quadrant in which each point lies.

18. $(-3, 7)$ **II**
19. $(9, 5)$ **I**
20. $(6, -2)$ **IV**
21. $(-1, -9)$ **III**
22. $(3, -15)$ **IV**
23. $(-2{,}000, 12)$ **II**
24. $(-0.05, -0.39)$ **III**
25. $\left(\frac{17}{2}, \frac{3}{21}\right)$ **I**

Open-ended **Draw each quadrilateral on a coordinate grid such that each vertex is in a different quadrant. Label each vertex and identify which quadrant it is in.**

26. square
27. parallelogram
28. trapezoid

26–29. Check students' work.

29. *Open-ended* A robot arm must move the black peg in the diagram onto the white square, but the peg must be moved around—not over—the red walls. List the coordinates of the vertices of a path the robot arm might follow to move the peg.

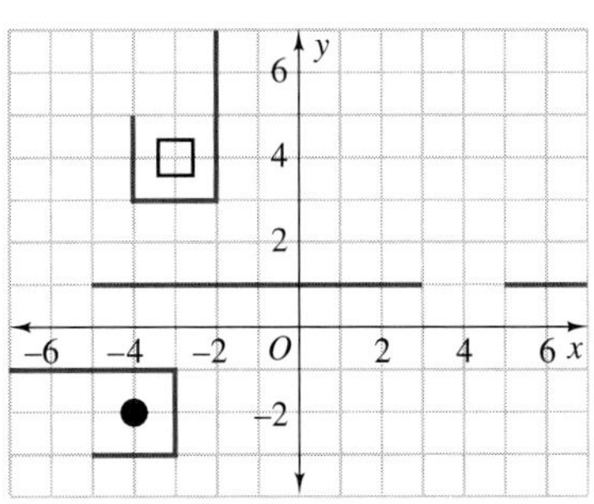

pages 474–476 On Your Own

13a.

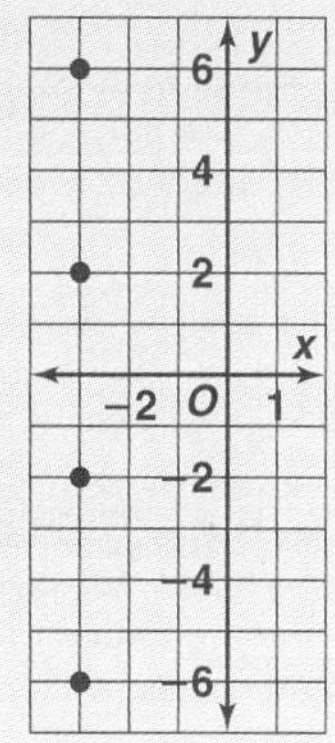

PRACTICE

Practice 11-1 *Graphing Points in Four Quadrants*

Name the point with the given coordinates.

1. (–2, 2) L
2. (8, 0) F
3. (4, –3) D
4. (–7, 3) B
5. (0, –5) I
6. (–8, –4) C

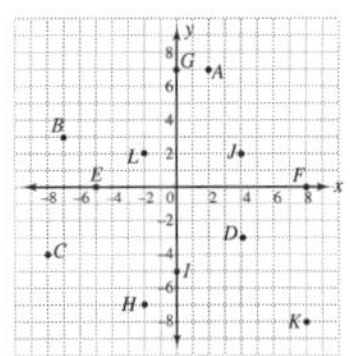

Write the coordinates of each point.

7. E (–5, 0)
8. A (2, 7)
9. H (–2, –7)
10. K (8, –8)
11. G (0, 7)
12. J (4, 2)

Identify the quadrant in which each point lies.

13. (–4, 3) II
14. (7, 21) I
15. (5, –8) IV
16. (–2, –7) III

In each drawing, a robot arm must move the black peg onto the white square, but the peg must be moved around—not over—the solid walls. List the coordinates of the vertices of a path the robot arm might follow to move the peg.
Sample answers are given.

17.

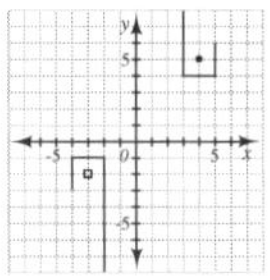

(4, 5), (4, 8), (6, 8), (6, 0), (–5, 0), (–5, –4), (–3, –4), (–3, –2)

18.

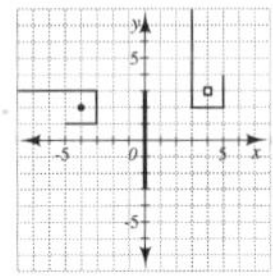

(–4, 2), (–6, 2), (–6, –5), (6, –5), (6, 5), (4, 5), (4, 3)

19. **Circle A, B, C, or D.** Which of the following groups of ordered pairs are *not* the vertices of a square?

A. (3, 0), (0, 3), (–3, 0), (0, –3)
B. (0, 0), (4, 0), (4, 4), (0, 4)
Ⓒ (3, 3), (–3, 3), (5, –5), (–5, 5)
D. (6, 6), (–6, 6), (–6, –6), (6, –6)

In copymaster and workbook formats

RETEACHING

Reteaching 11-1 *Graphing Points in Four Quadrants*

The intersection of a horizontal number line and a vertical number line forms the **coordinate plane.** The coordinate plane below shows point *A* for the **ordered pair** (3, – 4).

To graph point *A* with **coordinates** (3, – 4):
① Start at the origin, *O*. Move 3 units to the right.
② Move 4 units down for – 4. Draw point *A*.

To write the coordinates for point *B*:
① From the origin, move 2 units left to – 2.
② Move 3 units up to *B* at (– 2, 3).

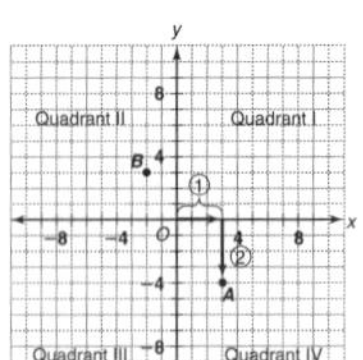

The axes form four **quadrants** in the coordinate plane.
- The point (3, – 4) is located in quadrant IV.
- Point *B* is located in quadrant II.

Name the point with the given coordinates.

1. (8, 0) A
2. (8, – 8) E
3. (1, 4) C
4. (– 7, – 4) F
5. (– 5, 6) H
6. (– 2, 0) B
7. (6, – 5) R
8. (– 5, – 3) T

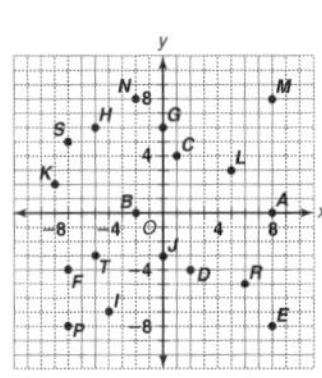

Write the coordinates of each point.

9. *D* (2, – 4)
10. *G* (0, 6)
11. *I* (– 4, – 7)
12. *J* (0, – 3)
13. *K* (– 8, 2)
14. *L* (5, 3)
15. *M* (8, 8)
16. *S* (– 7, 5)

Identify the quadrant in which each point lies.

17. *F* III
18. *C* I
19. *D* IV
20. *H* II
21. *N* II
22. *P* III
23. *S* II
24. *R* IV

ENRICHMENT

Minds on Math Transparency

11-1

Judy listed a fifth number with the set of data 3, 6, 7, 10. The number she included made the mean of the five numbers equal to their median. What numbers could Judy have included with the data?

4, 6.5, 9

See *Solution Key* for worked-out answers.

LESSON QUIZ

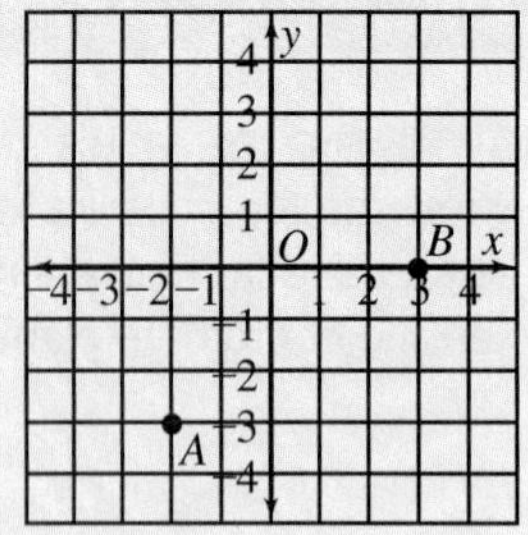

1. Write the coordinates of point *A*. (−2, −3)
2. Write the coordinates of point *B*. (3, 0)
3. Graph the point *C*(−6, 2). Check students' work.
4. Identify the quadrant in which the point (−4, −1) lies. III

30. The robot arm at the right is moving the computer chip from the point (−2, 5) to a point three units up and seven units to the right. In which quadrant will the chip be placed? I

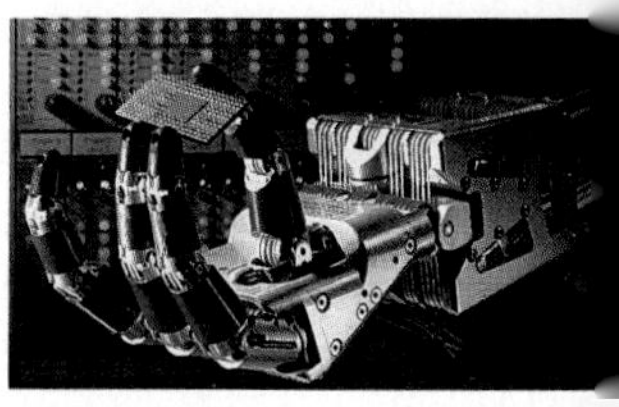

31. *Analyze* For each quadrant, identify the signs of the *x*- and *y*-coordinates of an ordered pair in the quadrant.
I: (+, +); II: (−, +); III: (−, −); IV: (+, −)

Mixed Review

32. Find the number of two-letter permutations for the group of letters M, A, R, S. *(Lesson 9-6)* 12

Choose **Use a calculator or pencil and paper to find the simple interest earned by each account.** *(Lesson 10-4)*

33. $3,000 principal
4.5% annual interest rate
2 years
$270

34. $1,500 principal
5.25% annual interest rate
5 years
$393.75

35. $3,150 principal
6% annual interest rate
4 years
$756

36. *Choose a Strategy* Carla used her baby-sitting money and $15 she received on her birthday to go shopping. She bought film for $12.49, a flash for $29, and batteries for $2.99. She had $3.91 left. How much money did Carla earn baby-sitting?
$33.39

Math at Work

AUTOMOTIVE ENGINEER

Automotive engineers design, develop, test, and produce all kinds of vehicles. They also test and evaluate a design's cost, reliability, and safety.

An automotive engineer has many opportunities to use math skills. Engineers apply problem-solving skills to determine causes of breakdowns and to test for quality. And they use computer-aided design systems to create the cars of the future!

Internet Connection

Vist the Web site www.sqe.org to find out more about automotive engineering.

Extra Practice, Lesson 11-1, page 524

11-2 Teaching Notes

1 Focus

CONNECTING TO PRIOR KNOWLEDGE
Have a volunteer draw a coordinate plane for the class. Have students graph the points (−4, −2), (−2, −1), (6, 3) and (0, 0) on the coordinate plane. Ask students: *Do you notice a pattern in these points?* **They all lie in a straight line.** Then ask: *Can you name any other points that will fit this pattern?* **Answers may vary. Sample: (2, 1), (4, 2)**

2 Teach

THINK AND DISCUSS

Encourage students to imagine multiple solutions by using the following phrase: *The value of y depends on the value of x.* This will help students understand that the amount of rope needed to hang the tire swing *depends* on how far below the branch you want the tire to hang.

ALTERNATIVE METHOD Example 1 Remind students of the tables they made for functions in Lesson 10-6. Explain that y can be written as a function of x. The equation $y = x + 5$ is the same as $f(x) = x + 5$. Then have students make a function table showing x as the input and y as the output.

MENTAL MATH Question 4 Encourage students to use both positive and negative integers for x.

11-2 Graphing Linear Equations

What You'll Learn

1. To find ordered pairs that are solutions of equations in two variables
2. To graph a linear equation

...And Why

You can use linear equations to model business situations.

Here's How

Look for questions that
- build understanding
- ✔ check understanding

THINK AND DISCUSS

1 *Finding Ordered Pairs*

Ronelle Moore makes tire swings for local day-care centers. Each swing requires enough rope to reach the tree branch plus another 5 ft for tying the rope around the tire and the branch.

1. *Mental Math* Suppose you want a swing to hang 8 ft below the branch. How much rope do you need? **13 ft**

2. *Reasoning* Suppose you have 17 ft of rope. How far below the branch will the swing hang? **12 ft**

Ronelle let x represent the distance the swing hangs below a branch and y represent the length of rope. She wrote the equation $y = x + 5$, which is an equation in two variables. Any ordered pair that makes the equation true is a **solution** of the equation.

■ **EXAMPLE 1** ***Real-World Problem Solving***

Find three solutions of Ronelle's equation $y = x + 5$ and explain what one solution represents.

Choose three values for x. Then make a table.

x	$x + 5$	y	(x, y)
8	8 + 5	13	(8, 13)
10	10 + 5	15	(10, 15)
12	12 + 5	17	(12, 17)

The ordered pairs (8, 13), (10, 15), and (12, 17) are solutions of the equation $y = x + 5$.

The solution (8, 13) means that Ronelle needs 13 ft of rope to make a swing that will hang 8 ft from a branch.

Lesson Planning Options

Prerequisite Skills
- evaluating expressions (3-1)

Vocabulary/Symbols
solution, graph of an equation, linear equation

Materials/Manipulatives
- graph paper

Resources

Student Edition
Skills Handbook, p. 530
Extra Practice, p. 524
Glossary/Study Guide

Teaching Resources
Chapter Support File, Ch. 11
- Lesson Planner 11-2
- Practice 11-2, Reteaching 11-2
- Alternative Activity 11-2
- Answer Masters 11-2

Teaching Aids Master 4
Glossary, Spanish Resources

Transparencies
2, 15, 98, Minds on Math 11-2

Warm Up

Identify the data needed: At a fund raiser, \$5 was collected from each parent and \$1 was collected from each child. How much money was raised? **how many parents and children**

■ ADDITIONAL EXAMPLES

FOR EXAMPLE 1

Find three solutions of the equation $y = x - 4$. **Answers may vary. Sample: (−1, −5), (0, −4), (1, −3)**

FOR EXAMPLE 2

Tell whether (−2, 0) is a solution of $y = x + 2$. **yes**

FOR EXAMPLE 3

Graph the equation $y = x - 2$. Is it a linear equation? **yes**

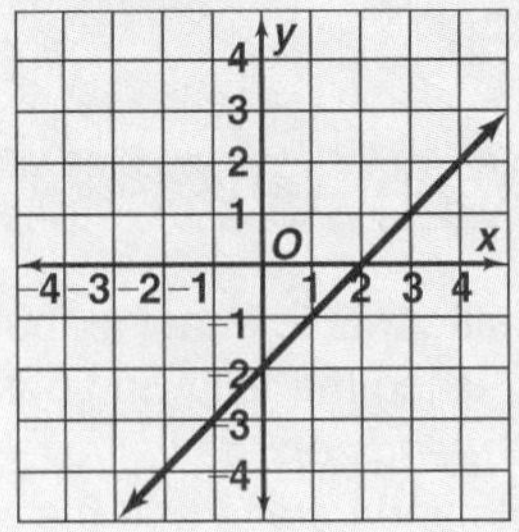

VISUAL LEARNING Example 2 Students may need to visually separate the left side of the equation from the right. Have them underline the original equations. Then they can draw a vertical line through the equal sign and extending far below it.

AEP Example 3 The phrase *linear equation* refers to an equation whose solutions lie on a *line*. The word *line* in Spanish is *linéa*, and in French it is *ligne*.

Technology Options

Prentice Hall Technology

Software for Learners

- Math Lab: Graphing Equations
- Math Blaster® Mystery*
- Interactive Student Tutorial, Chapter 11*

Teaching Resource Software

- Computer Item Generator 11-2
- Resource Pro™ Chapter 11*

Internet • For related mathematics activities, visit the Prentice Hall site at www.phschool.com/math

**Available on CD-ROM only*

Assignment Options for Exercises On Your Own

To provide for flexible scheduling, this lesson can be split into parts.

1 **Core** 1–16
Extension 17

2 **Core** 18–36
Extension 37

Use Mixed Review to maintain skills.

3. Find one other solution of the equation in Example 1.
Answers may vary. Answers are coordinates in the form (x, $x + 5$).
4. ✔ *Try It Out* Find three solutions of $y = 2x$.
Answers may vary. Answers are coordinates in the form (x, $2x$).

■ EXAMPLE 2

Tell whether each ordered pair is a solution of $y = x + 5$.

a. (40, 45)

$y = x + 5$
$45 \stackrel{?}{=} 40 + 5$ ← Substitute for x and y in the equation.
$45 = 45$ ✔ yes

b. (21, 27)

$y = x + 5$
$27 \stackrel{?}{=} 21 + 5$
$27 \neq 26$ no

5. ✔ *Try It Out* Is (10, 15) a solution of $y = 2x - 7$? Explain.
no; $15 \neq 2(10) - 7$
6. **Choose A, B, C, or D.** Which ordered pair is *not* a solution of the equation $y = 3x - 1$? **B**

A. (4, 11) **B.** (7, 22) **C.** $(\frac{1}{3}, 0)$ **D.** (−2, −7)

Now you may assign Exercises 1–17.

2 *Graphing a Linear Equation*

The **graph of an equation** is the graph of all the points whose coordinates are solutions of the equation. An equation is a **linear equation** if all its solutions lie on a line.

■ EXAMPLE 3

Graph the equation $y = x + 1$. Is it a linear equation?

Choose values for x. Then make a table of values.

x	$x + 1$	y	(x, y)
0	0 + 1	1	(0, 1)
−2	−2 + 1	−1	(−2, −1)
3	3 + 1	4	(3, 4)
1	1 + 1	2	(1, 2)
−4	−4 + 1	−3	(−4, −3)

Graph the points. Then draw a line through the points.

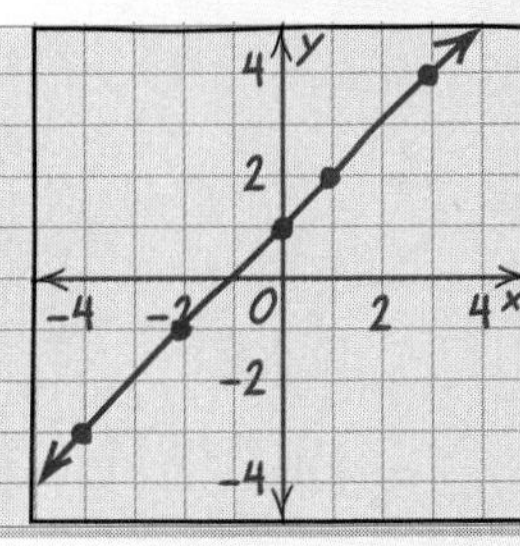

Since the solutions lie on a line, $y = x + 1$ is a linear equation.

7. *Look Back* Use the graph from Example 3 to find two more solutions of the equation $y = x + 1$.
Answers may vary. Sample: (−1, 0), (2, 3)

KINESTHETIC LEARNING and ERROR ALERT! Question 8 Students may not plot enough points to ensure the equation is linear. **Remediation:** Demonstrate that any two points can be connected by a straight line. Randomly pick two students and have them hold a string to demonstrate a line. Repeat with other pairs of students. Explain to students that they should always plot at least three points to graph a function. Suggest that if three plotted points do not line up, they should check by plotting a fourth point.

3 Practice

EXERCISES *On Your Own*

ASSESSMENT Exercises 1 and 2 Have partners work together to graph their solutions for each exercise on the same piece of graph paper. All of their solutions should lie on the same line.

OPEN-ENDED Exercises 1–5 Students may be uncertain about how to choose the values for *x*. Suggest they choose a negative integer, a positive integer, and zero.

Exercises 11–16 Have students first make a table to graph each line. Then have students look to see which points lie on which lines. Have students check their answers by substituting the coordinates into the linear equations chosen for each point.

Exercises 18–20 Students may find it helpful to locate a unique point on each line. Then substitute the coordinates for *x* and *y* in each equation.

8. ✔ *Try It Out* Graph the equation $y = 2x$. Is this equation a linear equation? **yes**

Now you may assign Exercises 18–37.

EXERCISES *On Your Own*

Open-ended **Find three solutions of each equation.** **1–5. Answers may vary. Answers are coordinates in the form given.**

1. $y = x - 2$ **(x, x − 2)**
2. $y = 5x$ **(x, 5x)**
3. $y = 3x + 1$ **(x, 3x + 1)**
4. $y = -2x + 4$ **(x, −2x + 4)**
5. $y = x + 9$ **(x, x + 9)**

Tell whether each ordered pair is a solution of $y = x + 12$. Explain how you know.

6. $(-12, 24)$ **no; 24 ≠ (−12) + 12**
7. $(12, 24)$ **yes; 24 = (12) + 12**
8. $(0, -12)$ **no; −12 ≠ (0) + 12**
9. $(-12, 0)$ **yes; 0 = (−12) + 12**
10. $(-24, -12)$ **yes; −12 = (−24) + 12**

On which of the following lines does each point lie?
(*Hint*: A point may lie on more than one line.)

11. $(-2, -1)$ **C**
12. $(-6, 0)$ **A, B**
13. $(-3, -3)$ **B, C**
14. $(0, -6)$ **B**
15. $(0, 0)$ **none**
16. $(3, 9)$ **A, C**

A. $y = x + 6$
B. $y = -x - 6$
C. $y = 2x + 3$

17. *Error Analysis* LaVonna said that $(-1, -5)$ is a solution of $y = -3x - 2$. Explain why her answer is incorrect.
If you substitute −1 for x and −5 for y, the equality is not true.

Match each equation with a line on the graph below.

18. $y = x - 3$ **line r**
19. $y = 2x$ **line q**
20. $y = -x$ **line p**

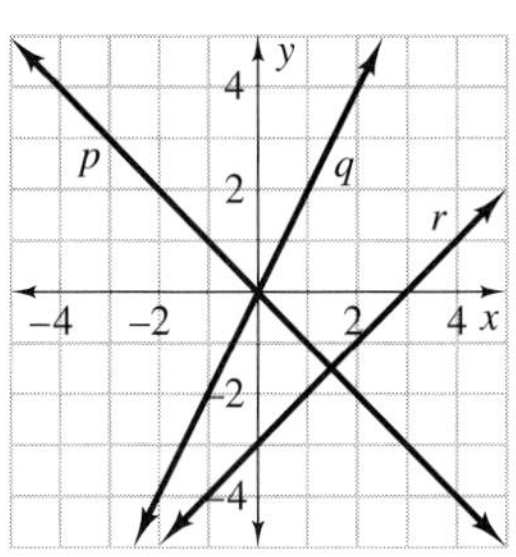

21b.

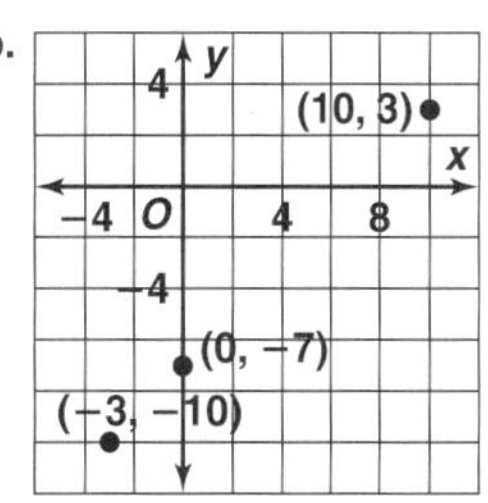

21a.

x	x − 7	y	(x, y)
0	0 − 7	−7	(0, −7)
−3	−3 − 7	−10	(−3, −10)
10	10 − 7	3	(10, 3)

21. a. Copy and complete the table at the right to find three solutions of $y = x - 7$.
    b. Graph the ordered pairs on a coordinate plane. **See above right.**
    c. Is this a linear equation? Explain how you know. **Yes; the solutions lie on one line.**

x	*x* − 7	*y*	(*x*, *y*)
0	■	■	■
−3	■	■	■
10	■	■	■

CONNECTION TO GEOMETRY Exercise 22 Remind students that the arrows on the ends of the lines mean that the lines go on forever in both directions.

MENTAL MATH Exercise 23 Have students use their knowledge of integers to eliminate some choices. To pass through the second quadrant, the x-coordinate must be negative when the y-coordinate is positive. This eliminates answer choices B and D since for these equations coordinates will either be both positive or both negative.

EXTENSION Exercise 24 Have students write an equation for which point P is a solution. Have students trade equations with a partner and graph to verify.

REASONING Exercise 34 Ask students: *Can you make popcorn for −5 minutes?* **no** Then ask: *What are some values that cannot be expressed with negative numbers.* **Answers may vary. Sample: length, width, weight**

CONNECTION TO GEOMETRY Exercise 37 Ask volunteers to sketch examples of *perpendicular* and *parallel lines* for the class.

WRAP UP

IDENTIFYING THE BIG IDEA Ask students to explain how to find solutions for equations with two variables, and how to tell from a graph whether the equation is linear.

JOURNAL Students may find it helpful to look over their work for Exercises 6–10 before beginning to write.

pages 479–481 On Your Own

26.
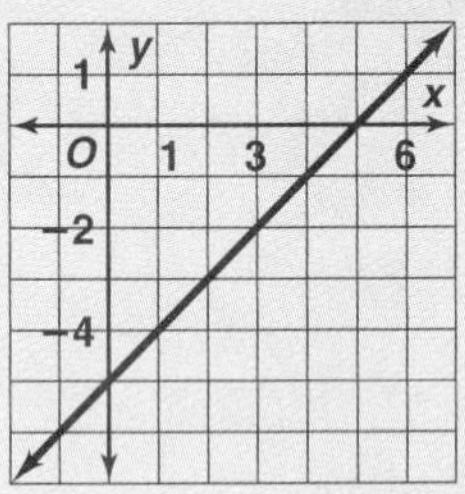

27.
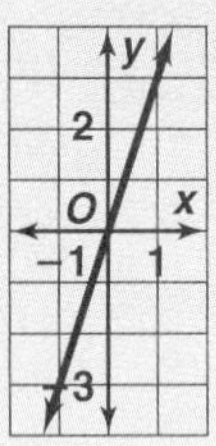

28.
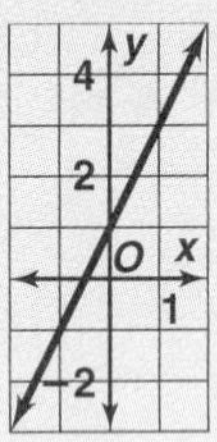

29.
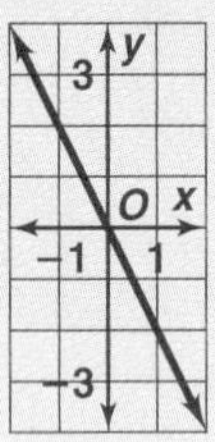

30.
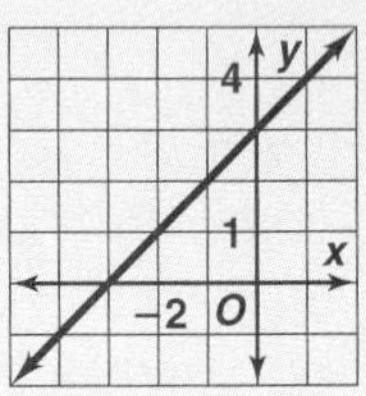

31.
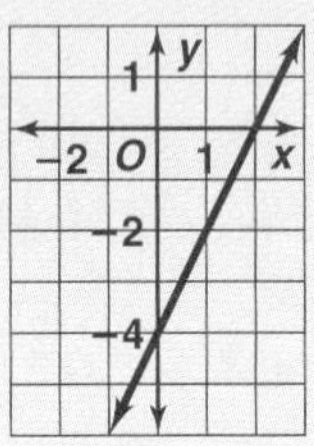

32.
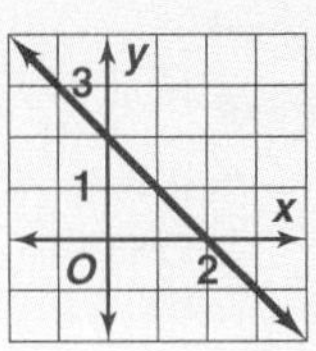

33.
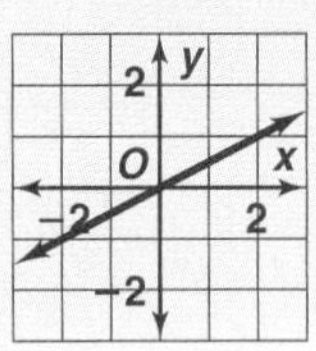

36a.
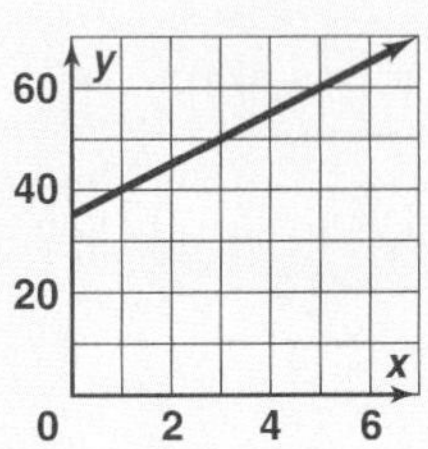

37a.
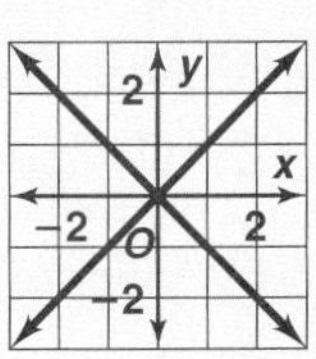

22. *Reasoning* How many solutions does a linear equation have? Explain your reasoning. **An infinite number; for any x-value you can find a corresponding y-value which makes the equality true. There is an infinite number of possible x-values.**

23. **Choose A, B, C, or D.** The graph of which equation passes through the second quadrant? **C**

A. $y = x - 5$ **B.** $y = 2x$ **C.** $y = x + 3$ **D.** $y = x$

Use the graph at the right for Exercises 24 and 25.

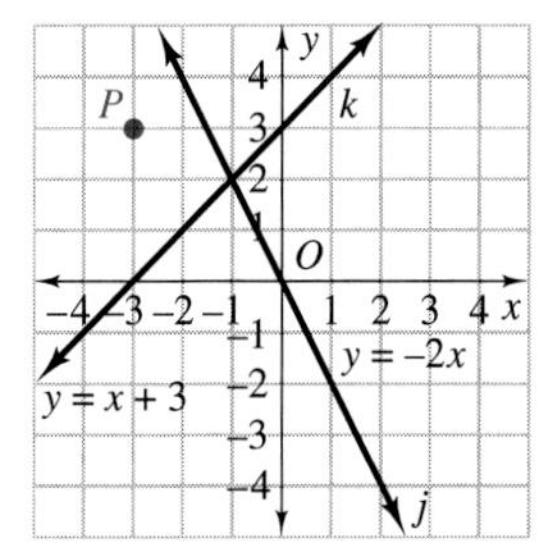

24. *Reasoning* Substitute the x- and y-coordinates for point P into the equation for line j to show that this ordered pair is *not* a solution of the equation. **$(3) \neq -2(-3)$**

25. What are the coordinates of the point that is a solution of the equations of both lines j and k? **(−1, 2)**

Graph each equation on a coordinate plane. **26–33. See margin.**

26. $y = x - 5$
27. $y = 3x$
28. $y = 2x + 1$
29. $y = -2x$
30. $y = x + 3$
31. $y = 2x - 4$
32. $y = -x + 2$
33. $y = \frac{1}{2}x$

CUSHIONS of CORN

The Popcorn Institute reports that sales of popcorn have increased recently. One reason is that many companies now use popcorn instead of Styrofoam to cushion packages.

Environmentally friendly popcorn is easy to produce. A hot-air popper about the size of a microwave oven can make about $\frac{1}{2}$ pound of popcorn in 1 minute, or about 30 pounds in 1 hour.

34. a. *Food Preparation* Let x represent the number of minutes the popper is on and let y represent the popper's output in pounds. Then the equation $y = \frac{1}{2}x$ describes the relationship between x and y. Make a table for the equation. Find three solutions.

a. Answers may vary. Sample:

x	2	4	6
y	1	2	3

b. Graph the points from your table. Draw the line that represents the equation.

b.
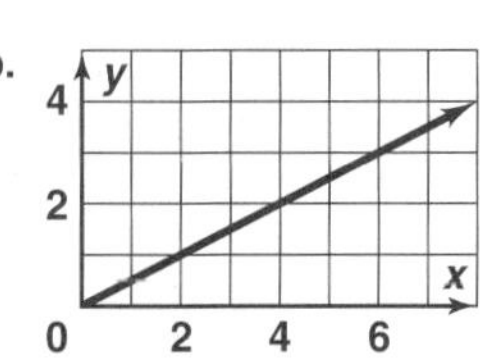

c. *Reasoning* Does it make sense to extend the line into the third quadrant? Why or why not?
No; neither time nor the amount of popcorn can be negative.

PROJECT LINK You may want to use a coffee scoop or teaspoon to help students select their samples. Each sample then can be one scoop larger than the previous one.

LESSON QUIZ

1. Find three solutions of $y = -3x$. **Answers may vary. Sample: (−1, 3), (0, 0), (1, −3)**
2. Tell whether (−2, 5) is a solution of $y = x - 7$. **no**
3. Graph the equation $y = x - 1$. Is it a linear equation? **yes**

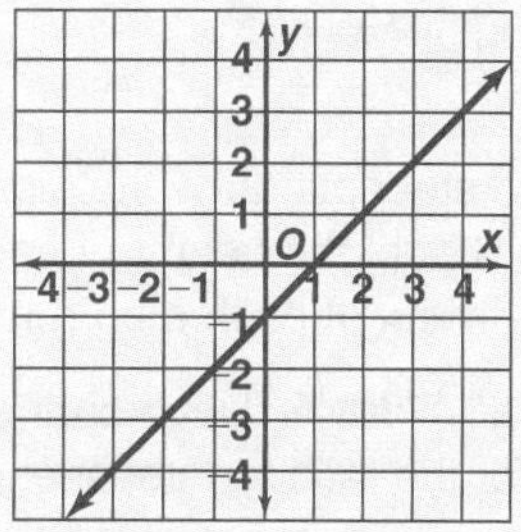

35. *Writing* When you graph the equation of a line, you could use any two points. Explain why graphing a third point is a good idea. **The third point serves as a check that you graphed the first two points correctly.**

36. *Money* Adin had $35 saved at the beginning of the year. He planned to save $5 each week. He modeled his savings plan with the equation $y = 5x + 35$.
   a. Graph the equation. **See margin p. 480.**
   b. How many weeks will it take him to save $60? **5 weeks**

37a. See margin p. 480.

37. a. Graph the equations $y = x$ and $y = -x$ on the same axes.
   b. Find the ordered pair that is a solution of both equations.
   c. *Geometry* Do these lines appear to be perpendicular or parallel?
   b. (0, 0) c. perpendicular

JOURNAL
Explain how you can determine if an ordered pair is a solution of a linear equation.

Mixed Review

Write a function rule for each table of values. *(Lesson 10-5)*

38.

Hours	Salary
0	$0.00
1	$5.25
2	$10.50
3	$15.75

f(x) = 5.25x

39.

Hours	Service Cost
0	$35
1	$60
2	$85
3	$110

f(x) = 25x + 35

40.

Weeks	Plant Height
1	42 mm
2	84 mm
3	126 mm
4	168 mm

f(x) = 42x

Use the Pythagorean theorem to determine if a triangle with the given side lengths is a right triangle. *(Lesson 8-7)*

41. 4 cm, 5 cm, 7 cm **no**
42. 12 ft, 16 ft, 20 ft **yes**
43. 20 m, 21 m, 29 m **yes**
44. 7 in., 8 in., 12 in. **no**

45. *Cooking* Larry is making a casserole for dinner. For every 2 onions, his recipe requires 3 tomatoes. How many onions should Larry use when he has 15 tomatoes? *(Lesson 6-3)* **10 onions**

CHAPTER PROJECT

PROJECT LINK: COLLECTING DATA

Sample the beans in the container ten times. Make each sample larger than the previous one. Remember to mix the sampled beans back into the container each time. Keep track of the size of each sample and the percent of each type of bean.

Check students' work.

Extra Practice, Lesson 11-2, page 524

PRACTICE

Practice 11-2 *Graphing Linear Equations*

Tell whether each ordered pair is a solution of $y = x - 4$.

1. (0, −4) **yes**
2. (5, −1) **no**
3. (−3, −7) **yes**
4. (−7, −3) **no**

On which of the following lines does each point lie? (A point may lie on more than one line.)

I. $y = x + 5$
II. $y = -x + 7$
III. $y = 2x - 1$

5. (0, 5) **I**
6. (1, 6) **I, II**
7. $\frac{8}{3}, \frac{13}{3}$ **II, III**
8. (0, −1) **III**
9. (4, 9) **I**
10. (4, 3) **II**
11. (−2, −5) **III**
12. (−8, 15) **II**

Graph each equation on a coordinate plane.

13. $y = 3x - 1$

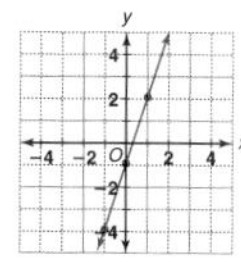

14. $y = -2x + 1$

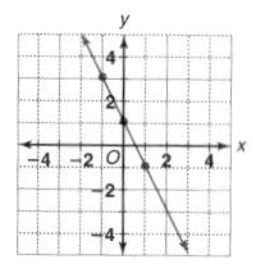

15. $y = 2x - 4$

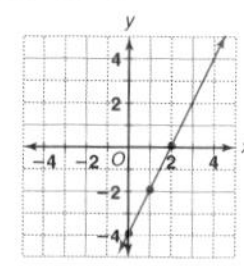

16. **Circle A, B, C, or D.** The graph of which equation passes through the fourth quadrant?
   A. $y = x + 1$ **(B.)** $y = -x$ C. $y = x$ D. $y = 2x$

17. Use the graph at the right to determine the coordinates of the point that is a solution of the equations of lines p and q. **(−1, 1)**

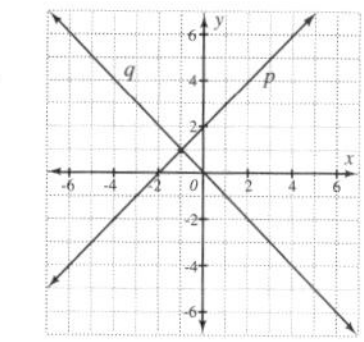

Practice

In copymaster and workbook formats

RETEACHING

Reteaching 11-2 *Graphing Linear Equations*

The **solutions** of $y = x + 3$ are the (x, y) pairs that make the equation true.

The solutions can be listed in a table.

x	$x + 3$	y	(x, y)
0	0 + 3	3	(0, 3)
1	1 + 3	4	(1, 4)
−2	−2 + 3	1	(−2, 1)

The solutions can be graphed in the coordinate plane, as shown.

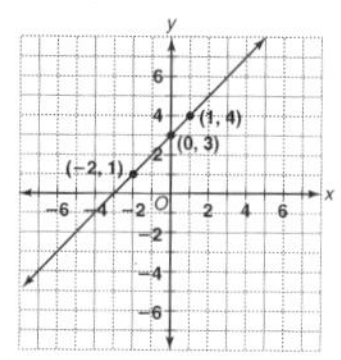

If all the solutions lie on a line, the equation is a **linear equation** and the line is its **graph.**

$y = x + 3$ is a linear equation.

Complete each table.

1. $y = x - 4$

x	$x - 4$	y	(x, y)
2	2 − 4	−2	(2, −2)
4	4 − 4	0	(4, 0)
6	6 − 4	2	(6, 2)

2. $y = 3x$

x	$3x$	y	(x, y)
−1	3(−1)	−3	(−1, −3)
0	3(0)	0	(0, 0)
3	3(3)	9	(3, 9)

3. $y = -x + 1$

x	$-x + 1$	y	(x, y)
0	0 + 1	1	(0, 1)
2	−2 + 1	−1	(2, −1)
−3	−(−3) + 1	4	(−3, 4)

Graph each equation on a coordinate plane.

4. $y = x - 5$

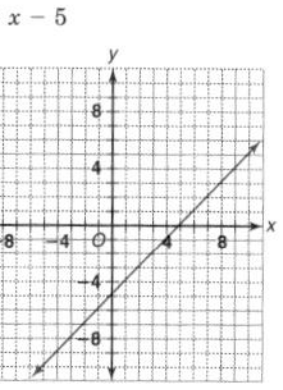

5. $y = 3x - 4$

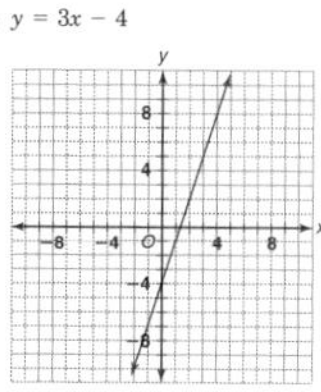

Reteaching

ENRICHMENT

Minds on Math Transparency

11-2

Kerri, Cassi, and Sam run laps every day after school. Kerri runs $\frac{1}{3}$ of a lap per minute, Cassi runs $\frac{1}{5}$ of a lap per minute, and Sam runs $\frac{1}{6}$ of a lap per minute. They start running at the same place and agree to continue running until they reach the starting point at the same time. How many laps do they each run?

Kerri runs 10 laps, Cassi runs 6 laps, and Sam runs 5 laps.

See *Solution Key* for worked-out answers.

11-3 Teaching Notes

1 Focus

CONNECTING TO PRIOR KNOWLEDGE
Graph points $A(2, 0)$ and $B(-3, 2)$. Draw line AB. Ask: *Imagine yourself walking on the line from left to right. Are you walking uphill or downhill?* **downhill**

2 Teach

Work Together

AEP Have students draw the side view of a set of stairs. Label the height of each step rise and the width of each step run.

AUDITORY LEARNING Have partners create a mnemonic for the ratio for steepness. Example: The sun *rises* before the jogger begins to *run*.

THINK AND DISCUSS

ERROR ALERT! Students may forget to write the negative sign for a downward slope. **Remediation:** Have students write the sign for each direction of rise and run. Down and left are negative, up and right are positive. Then refer to the drawing to check.

Lesson Planning Options

Prerequisite Skills

- graphing points on a coordinate plane (11-1)
- simplifying fraction (4-6)

Vocabulary/Symbols

slope of a line

Materials/Manipulatives

- graph paper

Resources

Student Edition

Skills Handbook, p. 528
Extra Practice, p. 524
Glossary/Study Guide

Teaching Resources

Chapter Support File, Ch. 11
- Lesson Planner 11-3
- Practice 11-3, Reteaching 11-3
- Answer Masters 11-3

Teaching Aids Master 4
Glossary, Spanish Resources

Transparencies
2, 15, Minds on Math 11-3

Warm Up

Find the missing numbers in the pattern 7, 22, 37, 52, n, 82, r. **67, 97**

DATA ANALYSIS Connection

11-3 Finding the Slope of a Line

What You'll Learn

▼ To calculate the slope of a line

...And Why

You can use the slope of a line to describe real-world relationships.

Here's How

Look for questions that
- build understanding
- ✔ check understanding

Going from left to right, the rise in the first graph is always positive. The rise in the right graph is always negative.

Work Together

Exploring Slope

Work with a partner. Notice the rise and run of the stair steps. You can use rise and run to describe the steepness of a line.

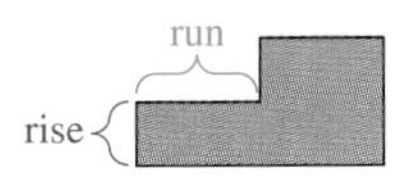

1. Use the ratio $\frac{\text{rise}}{\text{run}}$ to express the steepness of the graph of each line.

a. $\frac{1}{2}$

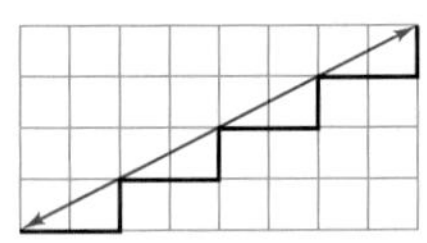

b. $-\frac{2}{3}$

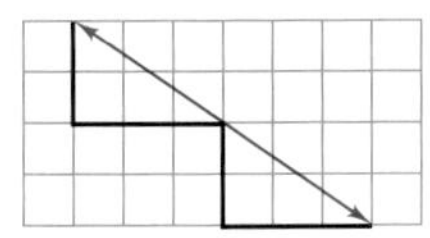

2. *Reasoning* Going from left to right, the graph on the left goes upward. The one on the right goes downward. How can you indicate this when describing the steepness of these lines?

THINK AND DISCUSS

Slope describes the steepness of the graph of a line.

$$\textbf{slope of a line} = \frac{\text{rise}}{\text{run}}$$

■ EXAMPLE 1

Find the slope of each line.

a.

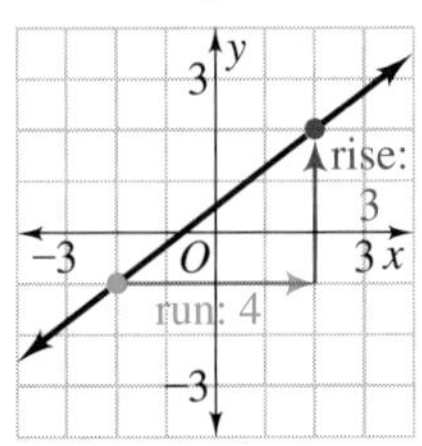

$$\text{slope} = \frac{\text{rise}}{\text{run}} = \frac{3}{4}$$

The slope is $\frac{3}{4}$.

b.

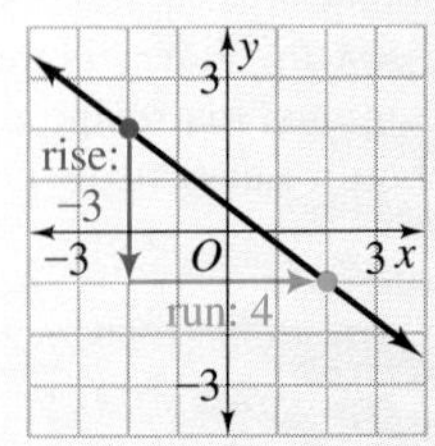

$$\text{slope} = \frac{\text{rise}}{\text{run}} = \frac{-3}{4} = -\frac{3}{4}$$

The slope is $-\frac{3}{4}$.

■ **ADDITIONAL EXAMPLES**

FOR EXAMPLE 1

Find the slope of each line. **line *a*: $-\frac{2}{3}$; line *b*: $\frac{2}{1} = 2$**

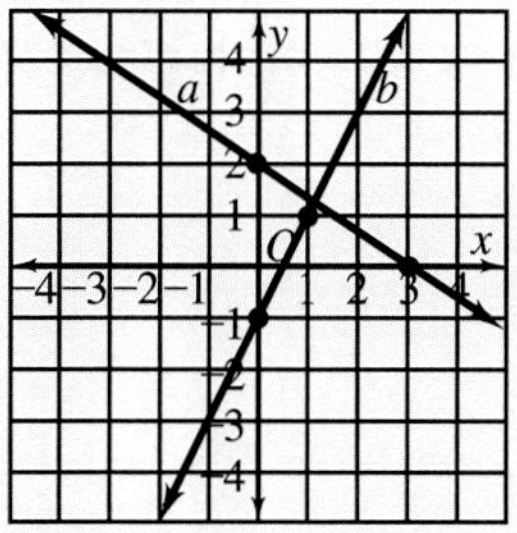

FOR EXAMPLE 2

The graph shows the relationship between number of tickets sold and dollars earned. Find the slope of the line. How does the amount of money earned change in relation to the number of tickets sold? **$\frac{5}{1}$; money earned increases $5 for every 1 ticket sold.**

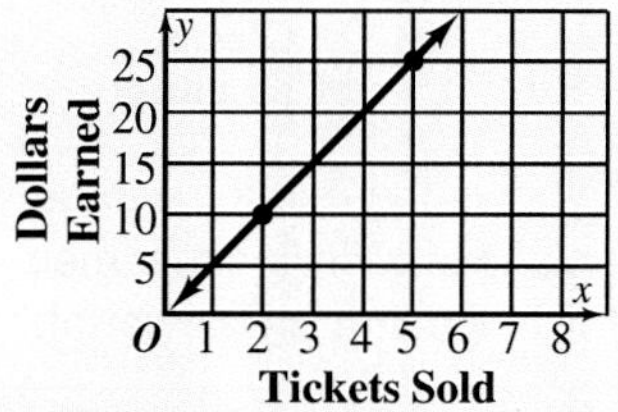

3 Practice

EXERCISES *On Your Own*

ASSESSMENT Exercises 1–3 Have students draw each exercise. Then label arrows indicating the rise and run.

WRAP UP

IDENTIFYING THE BIG IDEA Ask students to describe how to use *rise* and *run* to find the *slope of a line.*

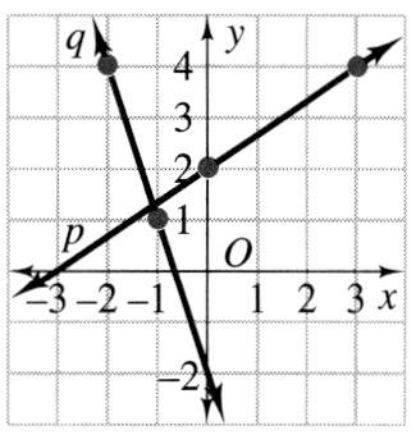

3. ✔ *Try It Out* Find the slope of line *q* and line *p*. **$\frac{-3}{1}$, or -3; $\frac{2}{3}$**

4. *Look Back* Use the graphs and slopes of the lines in Example 1 and in Question 2 to answer the questions below.
   a. Does a line that goes upward from left to right have *positive* or *negative* slope? **positive**
   b. Does a line that goes downward from left to right have *positive* or *negative* slope? **negative**

The slope of a line tells you how fast one variable is changing in relation to the other variable.

■ **EXAMPLE 2** *Real-World Problem Solving*

Science The graph shows the relationship between the time a candle burns and the candle's height. Find the slope of the line. How does the candle's height change in relation to the time it has been burning?

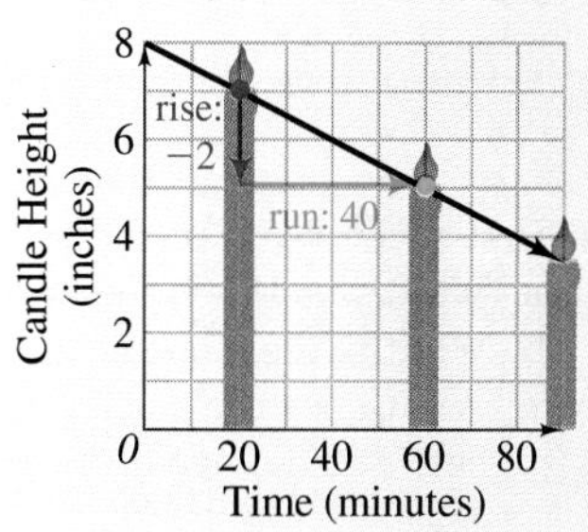

slope of the line $= \frac{-2}{40} = -\frac{1}{20}$

The candle gets 1 in. shorter every 20 min.

5. a. *Look Back* Could you find the slope by starting at (60, 5) and going to (20, 7)? What would be the rise and the run? **yes; 2; −40**
   b. Does this affect the value of the slope? **No; $\frac{-2}{40}$ simplifies to $-\frac{1}{20}$.**

Now you may assign Exercises 1–12.

EXERCISES *On Your Own*

Find the slope of each line.

1. $\frac{1}{2}$

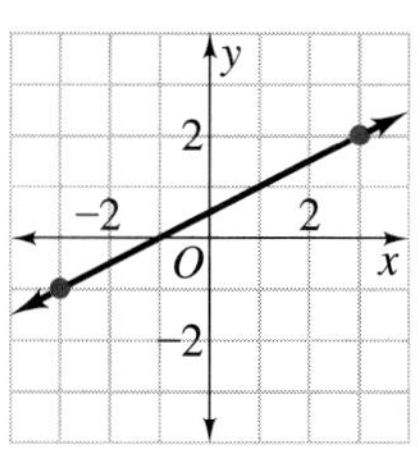

2. -1

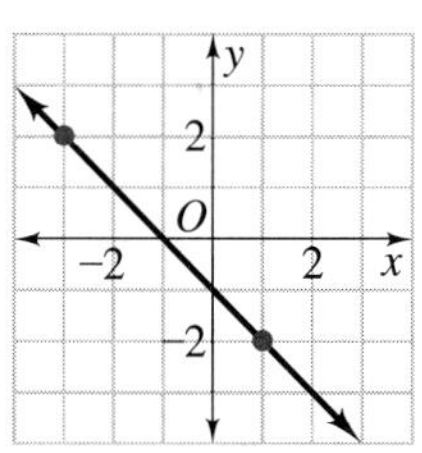

3. $-\frac{1}{3}$

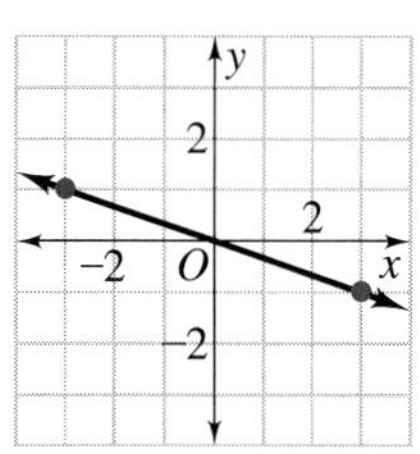

Technology Options

Prentice Hall Technology

Software for Learners
- Hot Page™ 11–3*
- Math Blaster® Mystery*
- Interactive Student Tutorial, Chapter 11*

Teaching Resource Software
- Computer Item Generator 11-3
- Resource Pro™ Chapter 11*

Internet • For related mathematics activities, visit the Prentice Hall site at www.phschool.com/math

*Available on CD-ROM only

Assignment Options for Exercises On Your Own

Core 1–11
Extension 12

Use Mixed Review to maintain skills.

PRACTICE

Practice 11-3 *Finding the Slope of a Line*

Find the slope of each line.

1. $\frac{1}{2}$ 2. 2 3. $-\frac{3}{4}$

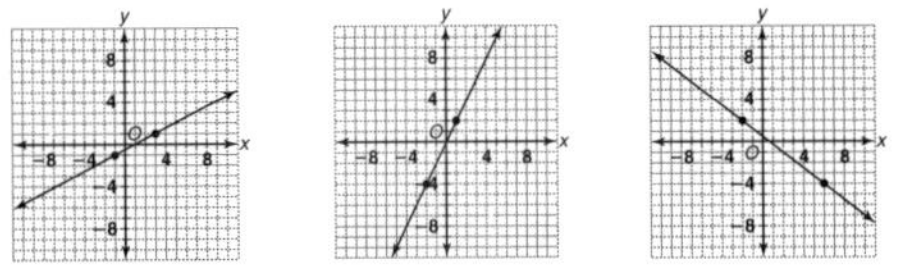

Use the coordinate plane provided to graph the given points. Determine the slope of the line through the points.

4. (−4, 6), (8, 4) $-\frac{1}{6}$ 5. (−1, 3), (4, 6) $\frac{3}{5}$ 6. (−2, 3), (4, −6) $-\frac{3}{2}$

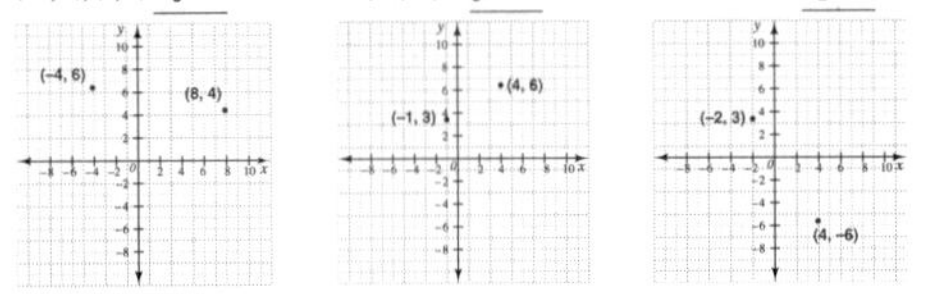

7. Which slope would it be easiest to push a heavy cart up, $\frac{1}{2}$, $\frac{1}{6}$, 3, or 5? $\frac{1}{6}$

8. Which slope would probably give you the greatest speed down a hill when you are skiing, $\frac{1}{8}$, $\frac{1}{4}$, 1, or 2? 2

9. Which slope would be the most dangerous for a roofer trying to repair a roof, $\frac{1}{16}$, $\frac{1}{10}$, $\frac{1}{2}$, or $\frac{3}{2}$? $\frac{3}{2}$

10. Which of the slopes from Exercise 9 would be the easiest for the roofer? $\frac{1}{16}$

In copymaster and workbook formats

RETEACHING

Reteaching 11-3 *Finding the Slope of a Line*

The steepness of a line is measured by its **slope.** To find the slope of a line, follow these steps.

① Pick any two points on the line. Find the *rise,* or vertical change. Here, the rise is −4.

② Find the *run,* or horizontal change. Here, the run is 2.

③ Find the ratio of rise to run.

$$\text{slope} = \frac{\text{rise}}{\text{run}} = \frac{-4}{2} = -2$$

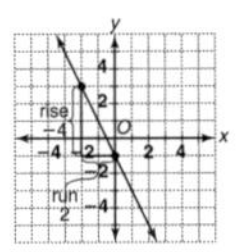

Sometimes the two points are given, such as (2, 3) and (4, 6). Graph both points. Draw their line. Then determine the slope.

$$\text{slope} = \frac{\text{rise}}{\text{run}} = \frac{3}{2}$$

The slope of the line through (2, 3) and (4, 6) is $\frac{3}{2}$.

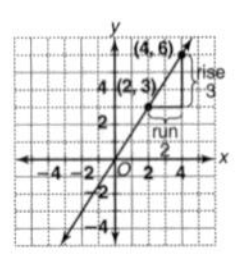

Complete to find the slope of each line.

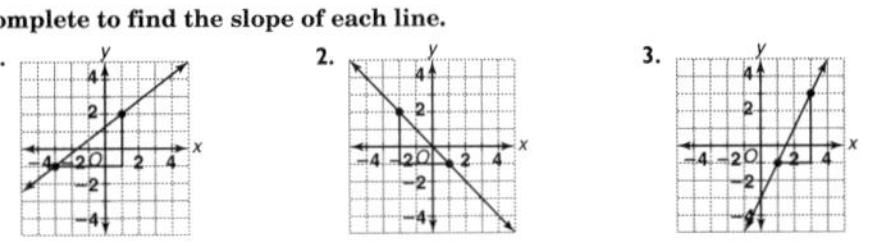

1. slope $= \frac{\text{rise}}{\text{run}} = \frac{3}{4}$ 2. slope $= \frac{\text{rise}}{\text{run}} = -1$ 3. slope $= \frac{\text{rise}}{\text{run}} = 2$

Graph the given points. Find the slope of the line through the points.

4. (3, 5), (2, 2) 3 5. (1, −1), (−1, 1) −1 6. (1, −2), (2, 0) 2

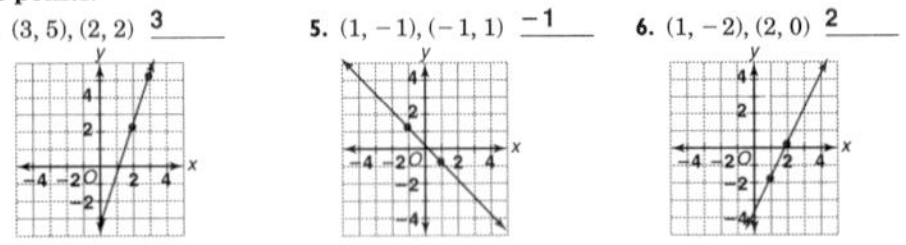

ENRICHMENT

Minds on Math Transparency

11-3

One year, there were exactly 4 Tuesdays and 4 Saturdays in October. On what day did October 1 fall that year?

Wednesday

See *Solution Key* for worked-out answers.

LESSON QUIZ

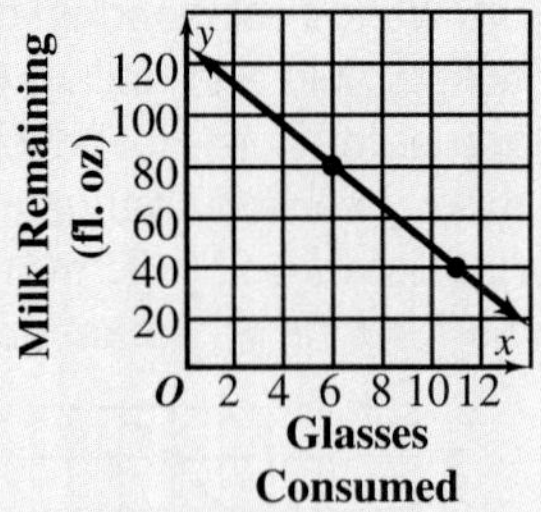

The graph shows the relationship between the number of glasses of milk consumed and the amount of milk left in a gallon carton.

1. Find the slope of the line. $-\frac{8}{1}$
2. What does the slope tell you about the relationship between the amount of milk in a carton and the number of glasses of milk consumed? **The milk decreases by 8 fl oz with each glass consumed.**

For each exercise, graph the given points. Find the slope of the line through the points.

4. (4, 8), (5, 10) **2** 5. (2, 2), (1, 1) **1** 6. (4, −1), (−4, 1) $-\frac{1}{4}$ 7. (2, 7), (3, −1) **−8**

8. a. Use the graph at the right to name two points on line *j* and two points on line *k*. **on line *j* (−2, 2) and (−1, 0); on line *k* (0, 0) and (−3, −2)**
   b. Find the slope of lines *j* and *k*. **−2; $\frac{2}{3}$**
   c. Which line has a negative slope? **line *j***

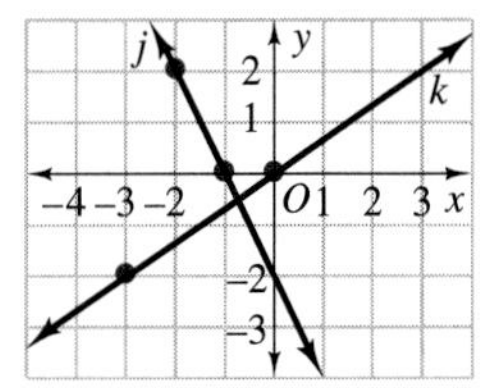

9. *Error Analysis* Suppose Kenji found the slope of a line through the points (4, 2) and (5, −1) to be 3. His friend Kelton found the slope to be −3. Who is correct? What mistake was made? **Kelton; Kenji thought the rise was positive.**

10. *Writing* Describe how to find the slope of a line. **See back of book.**

11. *Cars* The graph at the right shows the value of a car for the first seven years of ownership.
    a. What was the value of the car when it was new? **$12,000**
    b. What is the slope of the graph? **−1**
    c. What does the slope tell you about the relationship between the age of the car and its value? **The car loses $1,000 in value each year.**

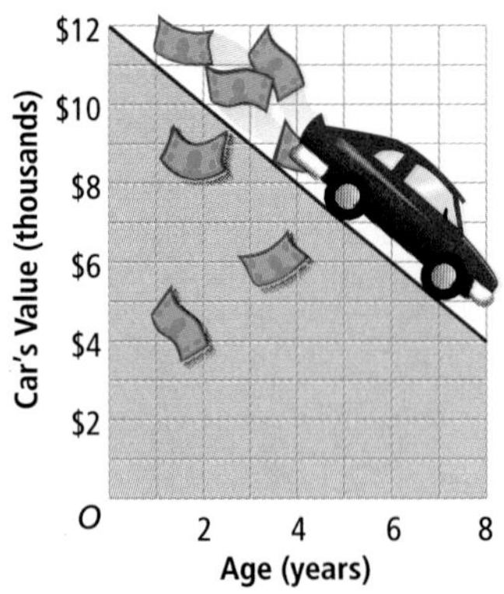

12. a. Graph a line through the points (0, 4) and (3, −3). Find the slope of the line. **a–b. See back of book for graphs.**
    b. Graph a line through the points (1, 5) and (4, −2). Find the slope of the line. **a. $-\frac{7}{3}$ b. $-\frac{7}{3}$**
    c. *Geometry* What do you notice about the slopes? Look at the lines. What seems to be true about the two lines? **The slopes are the same; the lines are parallel.**

23.

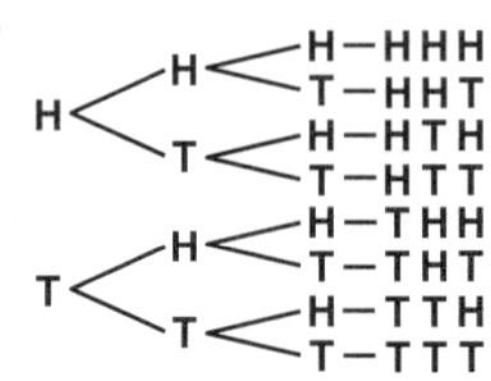

Mixed Review

Identify each number sequence as an arithmetic sequence, geometric sequence, or neither. Then find the next three terms. (Lesson 10-1)

13. 4, 9, 14, 19, . . . **arithmetic; 24, 29, 34**
14. 6, 12, 24, 48, . . . **geometric; 96, 192, 384**
15. 6, 13, 20, 27, . . . **arithmetic; 34, 41, 48**
16. 5, 7, 10, 14, . . . **neither; 19, 25, 32**

Identify the quadrant in which each point lies. (Lesson 11-1)

17. (−3, 2) **II** 18. (1, −8) **IV** 19. (5, 11) **I** 20. (−12, −7) **III** 21. $\left(-\frac{6}{7}, \frac{2}{3}\right)$ **II** 22. (0.16, −0.3) **IV**

23. Make a tree diagram to show the outcomes for tossing three coins. (Lesson 9-4) **See above right.**

MATH TOOLBOX

In Lesson 11-3, students learn how to calculate the slope of a line. This toolbox allows students to explore slope using a graphing calculator.

ERROR ALERT! Students may think the line $y = x$ has no slope. **Remediation:** Ask students:

- *How many x's are in 3x?* **3**
- *How many x's are in 1x?* **1**
- *Is 1x the same as x?* **yes**

ASSESSMENT **Exercise 3d** Group students in pairs. Have partners compare their answers and reasons. Partners should agree on the correct answer and the reason the answer is correct. Students can compare their answers again after Exercise 4b.

ADDITIONAL PROBLEM

Write the equation of a line that is steeper than $y = \frac{1}{4}x$. **Answers may vary. Sample:** $y = \frac{1}{3}x$. Verify that your line is steeper by graphing your equation and $y = \frac{1}{4}x$. **Check students' work.**

MATH TOOLBOX TECHNOLOGY

Exploring Slope

After Lesson 11-3

There is a relationship between the slope of a line and its equation. At the right is the graph of the equation $y = -\frac{3}{5}x$.

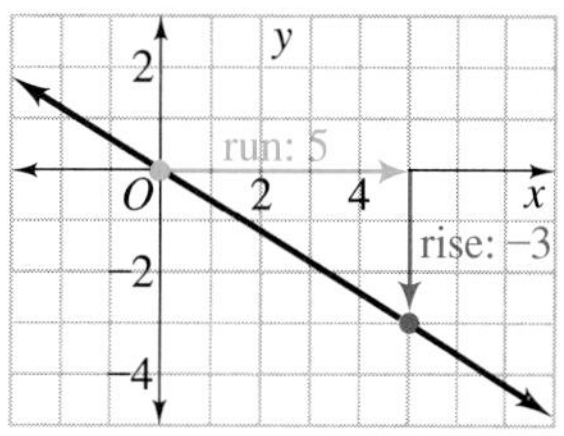

1. a. What is the slope of the line? $-\frac{3}{5}$
   b. How does the equation for the graph express the slope of the line? **The value that multiplies x has the same value as the slope.**
2. What is the slope of each line?
   a. $y = \frac{2}{3}x$ $\frac{2}{3}$ b. $y = -4x$ -4 c. $y = \frac{7}{2}x$ $\frac{7}{2}$

You can explore the effect slope has on a line using a graphing calculator. **3c. For lines with positive slopes, the greater the value of the slope, the steeper the graph of the line.**

3. a. Use the window values at the right. Graph the equations $y = x$, $y = 3x$, and $y = 4x$. **See right.**
   b. Which line is steepest? Which line is the least steep? **b. $y = 4x$; $y = x$**
   c. How does the value of the slope affect the steepness of the line? **See above.**
   d. *Predict* Describe where you would expect the graph of $y = 5x$ to be. Check your prediction. **closer to the y-axis**

WINDOW FORMAT
Xmin=−10
Xmax=10
Xscl=1
Ymin=−10
Ymax=10
Yscl=1

3a.

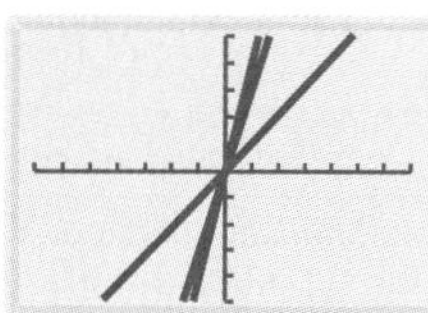

4. a. Graph the lines $y = x$, $y = \frac{1}{3}x$, and $y = \frac{1}{4}x$. **See right.**
   b. *Analyze* What happens to the steepness of the graph as the value of the slope gets closer to zero? **The graph becomes less steep.**
5. *Open-ended* Write the equation of a line that is less steep than $y = \frac{1}{4}x$. Verify that your line is less steep by graphing your equation and $y = \frac{1}{4}x$. **Answers may vary. Slope will be between 0 and $\frac{1}{4}$.**
6. *Writing* Explain how you can determine which of two lines with positive slope is steeper without graphing them. **The line with the greater slope is steeper.**

4a.

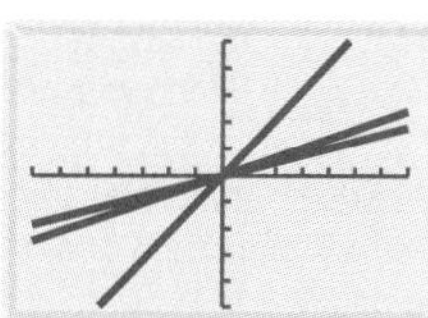

7. a. Graph the line $y = -x$. **See right.**
   b. Through what quadrants does the graph of this line pass? **II and IV**
   c. Graph the lines $y = -3x$ and $y = -4x$. Are these lines steeper than $y = -x$? **yes**
   d. *Open-ended* Write the equation of a line steeper than $y = -7x$ that passes through the same quadrants as $y = -7x$. **Answers may vary. Answers will show the slope < −7.**

7a.

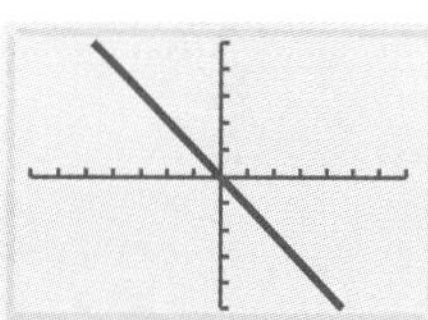

Materials/Manipulatives

- graphing calculator

11-4 Teaching Notes

1 Focus

CONNECTING TO PRIOR KNOWLEDGE Ask students to answer the following questions:

- *Find f(−2) and f(2) for each function.*
  $f(n) = n^2$ $f(-2) = 4$; $f(2) = 4$
  $f(n) = |n|$ $f(-2) = 2$; $f(2) = 2$
- *What do the two functions have in common?* **Answers may vary. Sample: They both have positive outputs.**
- *What are the differences between the functions?* **Answers may vary. Sample: One squares *n*, and the other finds *n*'s distance from zero on a number line.**

2 Teach

THINK AND DISCUSS

AEP *Parabola* has cognates in several languages. For example, the Spanish word for parabola is *parábola*. The French word is *parabole*.

KINESTHETIC LEARNING Have students use their arms to model the basic shapes of the functions. Read the following in random order: *$y = x^2$, $y = |x|$, parabola, absolute value.* Have students raise their arms in the appropriate U or a V shape.

ERROR ALERT! Question 1 Students may multiply the coefficient before finding the square. **Remediation:** Remind students that the Order of Operations requires them to simplify the exponents first.

Lesson Planning Options

Prerequisite Skills
- working with exponents (4-4)
- finding absolute value (3-2)

Vocabulary/Symbols
parabola

Materials/Manipulatives
- graph paper

Resources

Student Edition

Skills Handbook, p. 528
Extra Practice, p. 524
Glossary/Study Guide

Teaching Resources

Chapter Support File, Ch. 11
- Lesson Planner 11-4
- Practice 11-4, Reteaching 11-4
- Answer Masters 11-4

Teaching Aids Master 4
Glossary, Spanish Resources

Transparencies
2, 15, Minds on Math 11-4

Warm Up
Write three decimals that are between three hundred forty-five thousandths and four tenths.
Answers may vary. Sample: 0.35, 0.36, 0.39

11-4 Exploring Nonlinear Relationships

What You'll Learn

1. To draw graphs of parabolas
2. To draw graphs of absolute value functions

...And Why

Nonlinear equations are models for many applications such as the path of a thrown object.

Here's How

Look for questions that
- build understanding
- ✔ check understanding

THINK AND DISCUSS

1 Graphing Parabolas

Not all equations in two variables have graphs that are straight lines (linear). The nonlinear graph of $y = x^2$ is a curve called a *parabola*. A parabola is U-shaped.

EXAMPLE 1

Make a table of values for the equation $y = x^2$. Graph the ordered pairs and draw a smooth curve through them.

x	x^2	y	(x, y)
−3	$(-3)^2$	9	(−3, 9)
−2	$(-2)^2$	4	(−2, 4)
−1	$(-1)^2$	1	(−1, 1)
0	$(0)^2$	0	(0, 0)
1	$(1)^2$	1	(1, 1)
2	$(2)^2$	4	(2, 4)
3	$(3)^2$	9	(3, 9)

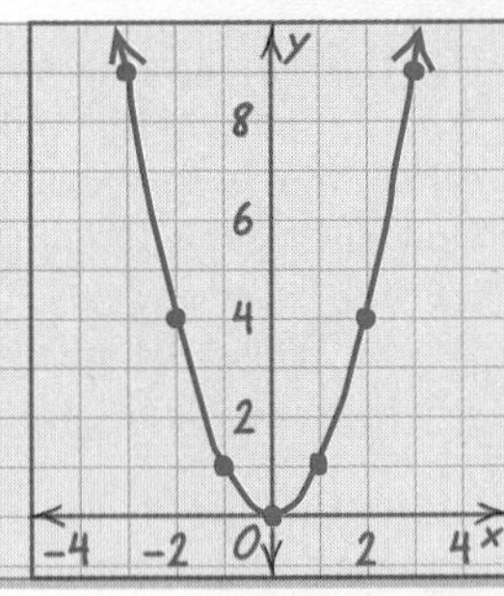

1a. Answers may vary. Sample:

x	−3	−2	−1	0	1	2	3
y	18	8	2	0	2	8	18

c. Each half of the graph of $y = 2x^2$ is steeper.

1. a. ✔ *Try It Out* Make a table of values for the equation $y = 2x^2$. Include both positive and negative values for x.
   b. Graph the ordered pairs. Draw a smooth curve through the points. **See back of book.**
   c. *Think About It* How does the parabola that is the graph of $y = 2x^2$ differ from the graph of $y = x^2$?

WHAT? When you throw or kick a ball, the path that the ball follows is in the shape of a parabola.

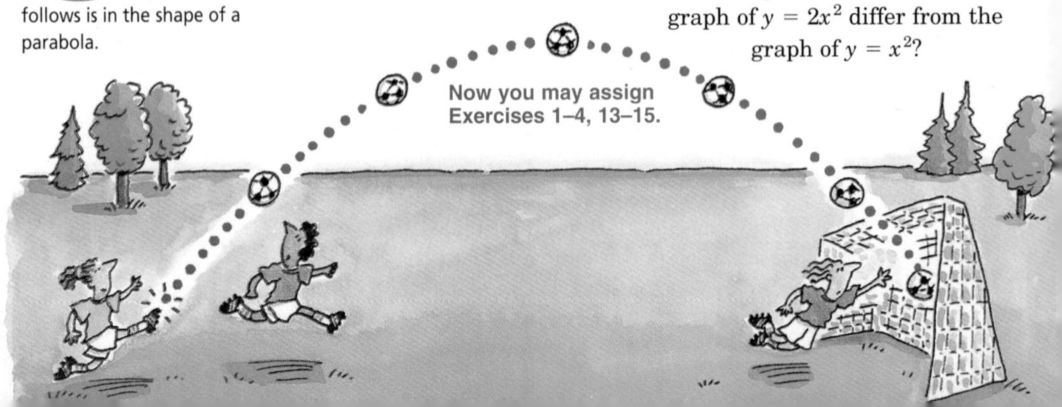

Now you may assign Exercises 1–4, 13–15.

ADDITIONAL EXAMPLES

FOR EXAMPLE 1

Make a table of values for the equation $y = x^2 + 2$. Graph the ordered pairs and draw a smooth curve between them.

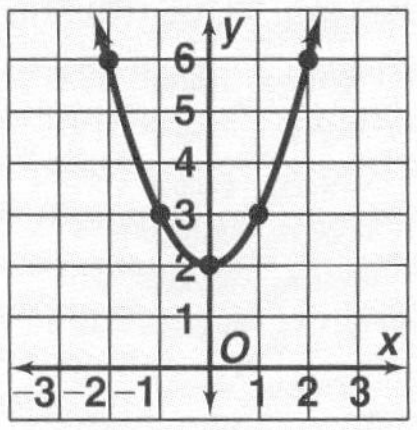

FOR EXAMPLE 2

Make a table of values for the equation $y = |x| - 2$. Graph the ordered pairs. Join the points.

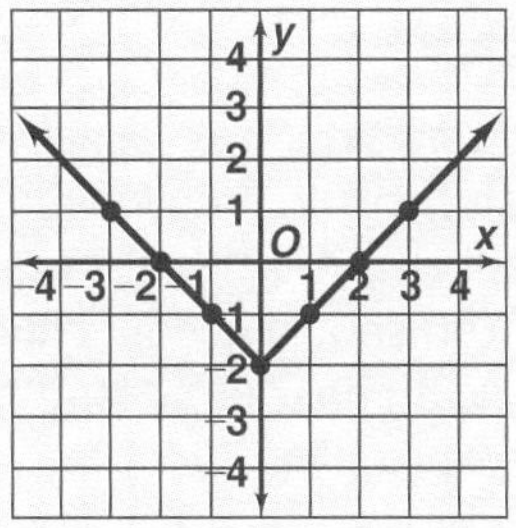

REASONING Question 3 Suggest students consider the possible values for *y* in both the graph and the quadrants described.

ASSESSMENT Questions 1 and 4 Have students compare their graphs for Questions 1 and 4. Then have them use their graphs to create a list of the similarities and differences between the graphs of parabolas and the graphs of absolute value equations.

2 *Graphing an Absolute Value Equation*

The equation $y = |x|$ is an absolute value equation in two variables. The graphs of absolute value equations are V-shaped.

EXAMPLE 2

Make a table of values for the equation $y = |x|$. Graph the ordered pairs. Connect the points.

x	$\lvert x\rvert$	y	(x, y)
-3	|-3|	3	(-3, 3)
-2	|-2|	2	(-2, 2)
-1	|-1|	1	(-1, 1)
0	|0|	0	(0, 0)
1	|1|	1	(1, 1)
2	|2|	2	(2, 2)
3	|3|	3	(3, 3)

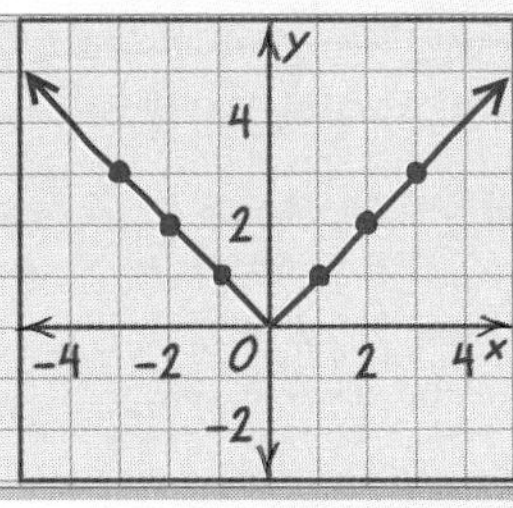

2f. yes; $\frac{1}{2} = \left|-\frac{1}{2}\right|$

3. No; no; absolute value cannot be negative, so points on the graph cannot have a negative *y*-coordinate.

4. Tables may vary. Sample:

x	−3	−2	−1	0	1	2	3
y	6	4	2	0	2	4	6

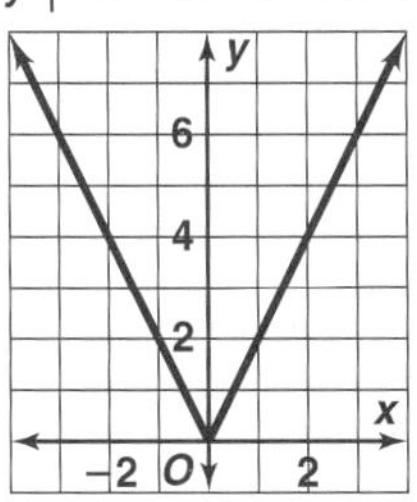

a. yes; $4 = |4|$ b. yes; $4 = |-4|$ c. no; $-4 \neq |4|$

2. Which of the following points are on the graph of $y = |x|$?
   a. $(4, 4)$ b. $(-4, 4)$ c. $(4, -4)$
   d. $(-4, -4)$ e. $\left(\frac{1}{2}, \frac{1}{2}\right)$ yes; $\frac{1}{2} = \left|\frac{1}{2}\right|$ f. $\left(-\frac{1}{2}, \frac{1}{2}\right)$ See left.
   d. no; $-4 \neq |-4|$
3. *Reasoning* Will the graph of $y = |x|$ ever have points in quadrant III? In quadrant IV? Justify your answer.
   See above left.
4. ✔ *Try It Out* Make a table of values for the equation $y = 2|x|$. Graph the equation. See left.

Now you may assign Exercises 5–12, 16–20.

EXERCISES *On Your Own*

Make a table of values. Then graph each parabola.

1. $y = \frac{1}{2}x^2$
2. $y = 3x^2$
3. $y = x^2 - 4$
4. $y = x^2 + 4$

1–8. Tables may vary. See back of book for sample tables and graphs.

Make a table of values. Then graph each absolute value equation.

5. $y = 3|x|$
6. $y = \frac{1}{2}|x|$
7. $y = |x| + 1$
8. $y = |x| - 1$

What is the shape of the graph of each equation?

9. $y = 5x^2$ parabola
10. $y = 5x - 2$ line
11. $y = 10|x|$ V-shape
12. $y = -\frac{1}{10}x + 7$ line

Technology Options

Prentice Hall Technology

Software for Learners
- Hot Page™ 11–5*
- Math Blaster® Mystery*
- Interactive Student Tutorial, Chapter 11*

Teaching Resource Software
- Computer Item Generator 11-4
- Resource Pro™ Chapter 11*

Internet • For related mathematics activities, visit the Prentice Hall site at www.phschool.com/math

**Available on CD-ROM only*

Assignment Options for Exercises On Your Own

To provide flexible scheduling, this lesson can be split into parts.

1 **Core** 1–4, 13, 14
Extension 15

2 **Core** 5–12, 17–20
Extension 16

Use Mixed Review to maintain skills.

VISUAL LEARNING and ERROR ALERT! Students may confuse when a graph is to be U-shaped with when it is to be V-shaped.
Remediation: Display a poster that shows:
If *x* is sq**U**ared, the graph is **U**-shaped.
For absolute **V**alue, the graph is **V**-shaped.

3 Practice

EXERCISES *On Your Own*

CONNECTION TO PHYSICS Exercise 13 If you have block scheduling or extended class periods, have students experiment by dropping two objects of different weights that have the same shape. Then to provide different air resistance, have students drop two objects of the same weight that have different shapes.

EXTENSION and WRITING Exercise 14 To encourage students to practice reasoning, you may want to give students a third option of $y = 4x$. You should accept either Option 2 or Option 3 as an answer as long as students give a valid explanation.

WRAP UP

IDENTIFYING THE BIG IDEA Have students describe how to graph *parabolas* and *absolute value equations.*

JOURNAL Some students may benefit from comparing two actual equations. Ask: *How is the graph of $y = 2|x|$ like the graph of $y = 2x$?*

CHECKPOINT 1

Checkpoint 1 — Lessons 11-1 through 11-4

1. **Circle A, B, C, or D.** Which of the following ordered pairs describes a point in the third quadrant?
   A. (−4, 3) B. (5, −2) ⓒ (−3, −2) D. (3, 2)
2. a. Graph $y = 2x + 1$.
   b. What is the slope? 2

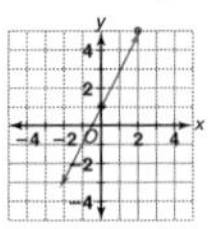

3. a. Make a table of values for $y = x^2 + 2$.
   Check students' tables. Sample:

x	y
0	2
1	3
2	6
−1	3
−2	6

   b. Graph the equation.

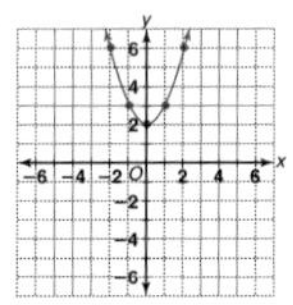

pages 487–489 On Your Own

14. Option 2; the *y*-value (pay) increases more rapidly.

15a. Answers may vary. Sample:

x	−3	−2	−1	0	1	2	3
y	−9	−4	−1	0	−1	−4	−9

b.

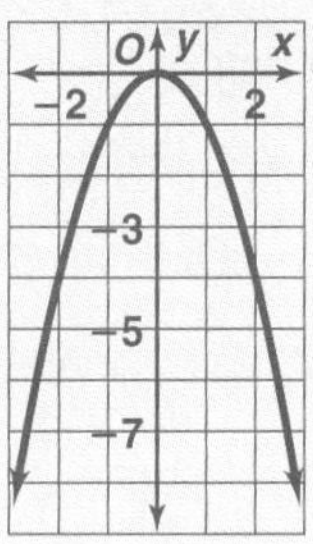

20c. The graph of $y = -|x|$ is a reflection of the graph of $y = |x|$ in the *x*-axis.

d. No; since the absolute value of a number is never negative, no point on the graph has a positive y-value.

13. *Physics* When an object (with little air resistance) is dropped, you can use the equation $d = 16t^2$ to find the distance in feet the object has dropped in t seconds.
    a. Suppose a ball is dropped from the top of a tall tower. How far has it dropped after 1 second? 2 seconds? 3 seconds?
    b. *The Tower of the Americas* in San Antonio, Texas, is 650 ft tall. About how many seconds will it take an object dropped from the tower to hit the ground?

13a. 16 ft; 64 ft; 144 ft b. about 6.4 s

14. *Writing* Suppose you were paid by the hour for stuffing pillows. Which of the equations below would you prefer to use to calculate your salary? Explain. See margin.

Salary Options	
Option 1	$y = x$
Option 2	$y = x^2$
(x = hours worked; y = dollars earned)	

15. a. Make a table of values for $y = -x^2$. Use at least 7 values for x, some positive and some negative. Include 0.
    b. Draw a graph of the equation. a–b. See margin.
    c. How is this parabola different from the others you have seen? The graph of $y = -x^2$ is a reflection of the graph of $y = x^2$ in the *x*-axis.
16. a. *Geometry* What kind of angle is formed when you graph $y = |x|$? 90°
    b. What kind of angle is the graph of $y = 2|x|$? acute
    c. *Reasoning* Describe the absolute value equations whose graphs are obtuse angles. The number that multiplies |*x*| is between −1 and 1.

Match each graph with an equation. (*Hint*: Substitute values for x into the equations to find coordinates of points.)

17. A

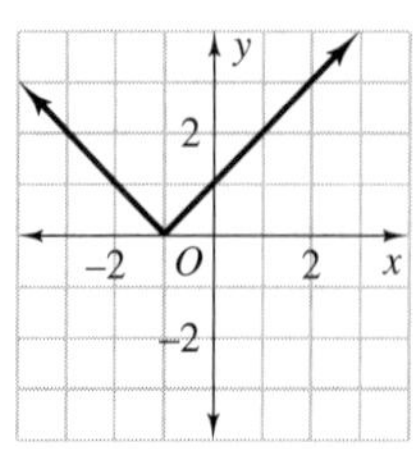

18. D

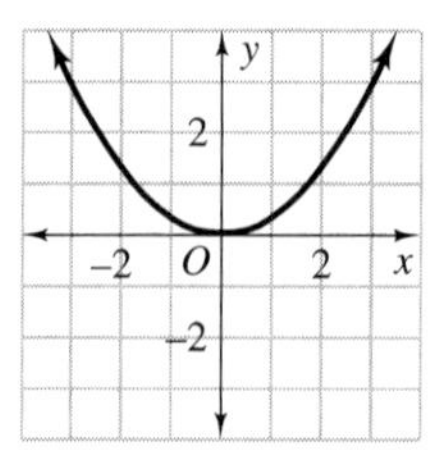

19. F

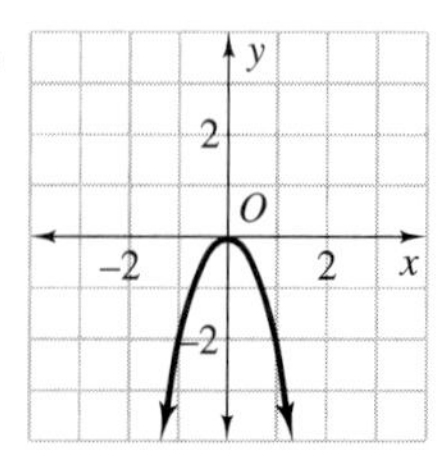

A. $y = |x + 1|$
B. $y = |x| - 1$
C. $y = \frac{1}{2}x^2$
D. $y = \frac{1}{3}x^2$
E. $y = x^2 - 8$
F. $y = -2x^2$

LESSON QUIZ

Make a table of values. Then graph each equation.

1. $y = x^2 + 3$

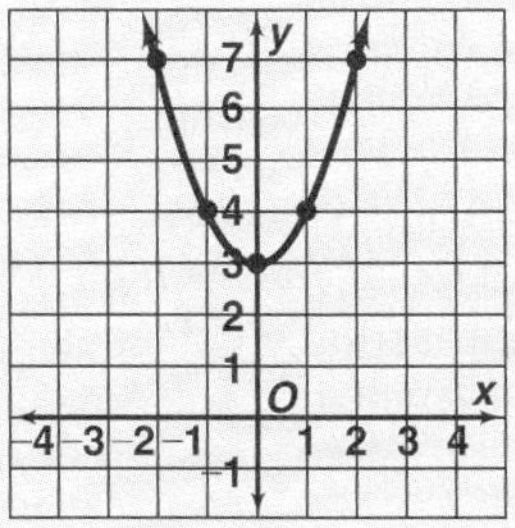

2. $y = 5|x|$

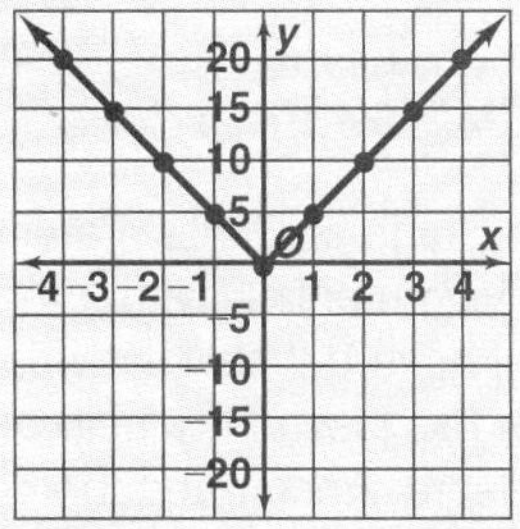

20. a. Make a table of values for $y = -|x|$. Use at least 7 values for x, some positive and some negative. Include 0.
b. Graph the ordered pairs and connect them.
c. How is this graph different from the graph of other absolute value equations you have seen? c–d. See margin p. 488.
d. Will the graph of $y = -|x|$ ever have points in quadrants I and II? Why or why not?

a–b. Answers may vary. See back of book for samples.

JOURNAL

How is the graph of an absolute value equation like the graph of a linear equation? How is it different?

Mixed Review

Suppose you have cards numbered consecutively from 1 through 25. A card is drawn and is *not* replaced. What is the probability of each of the events? *(Lesson 9-5)*

21. P(4 and 5) $\frac{1}{600}$
22. P(two even numbers) $\frac{132}{600}$ or $\frac{11}{50}$
23. P(odd and even) $\frac{156}{600}$ or $\frac{13}{50}$

Tell whether each ordered pair is a solution of $y = 2x - 3$. Explain how you know. *(Lesson 11-2)*

24. $(-2, -1)$ no; $-1 \neq 2(-2) - 3$
25. $(4, 5)$ yes; $5 = 2(4) - 3$
26. $(-3, -3)$ no; $-3 \neq 2(-3) - 3$
27. $(0, -5)$ no; $-5 \neq 2(0) - 3$
28. $(2, 1)$ yes; $1 = 2(2) - 3$
29. $(3, 9)$ no; $9 \neq 2(3) - 3$

30. *Working* This week, Lena worked $2\frac{1}{3}$ times the 15 hours she worked last week. How many hours did she work? *(Lesson 5-9)* 35 h

✓ CHECKPOINT 1 — Lessons 11-1 through 11-4

Name the point with the given coordinates.

1. $(-4, 1)$ *B*
2. $(3, -3)$ *D*
3. $(0, 2)$ *G*

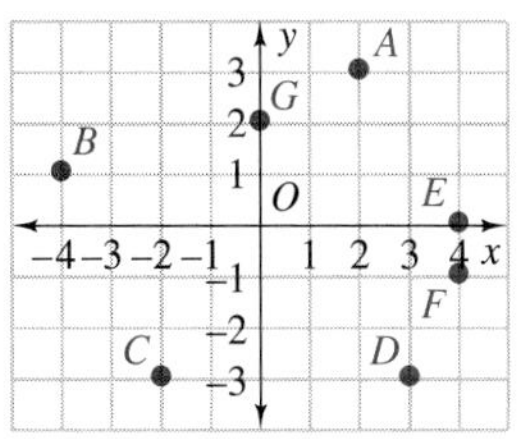

Name the coordinates of each point.

4. F (4, −1)
5. C (−2, −3)
6. A (2, 3)
7. E (4, 0)

8. **Choose A, B, or C.** The graph of which equation passes through the first quadrant? C

A. $y = -\frac{2}{3}x - 1$
B. $y = -x$
C. $y = 4 + x$

9. a. Make a table of values and graph $y = x - 2$.
b. What is the slope of the line? 1

9a. Answers may vary. Sample:

x	−3	−2	−1	0	1	2	3
y	−5	−4	−3	−2	−1	0	1

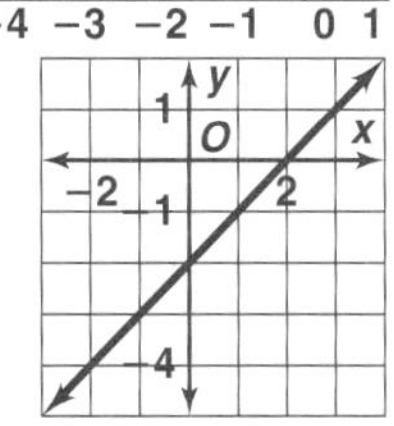

10. a. Make a table of values for $y = x^2 - 5$.
b. Graph the equation. See back of book.

10a. Answers may vary. Sample:

x	−4	−2	0	2	4
y	11	−1	−5	−1	11

PRACTICE

Practice 11-4 Exploring Nonlinear Relationships

Match each graph with an equation.

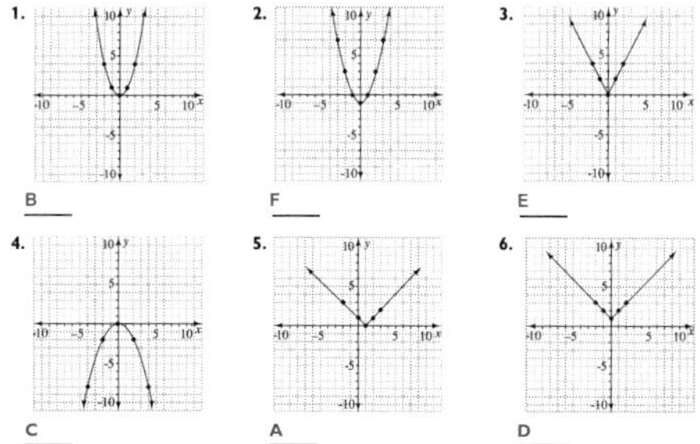

1. B 2. F 3. E 4. C 5. A 6. D

A. $y = |x - 1|$
B. $y = x^2$
C. $y = -\frac{1}{2}x^2$
D. $y = |x| + 1$
E. $y = |2x|$
F. $y = x^2 - 1$

7. a. Complete the table below for the equation $y = x^2 + 2$.

x	−3	−2	−1	0	1	2	3
y	11	6	3	2	3	6	11

b. Graph the ordered pairs and connect the points as smoothly as possible.
c. Describe how this graph is different from the graph of $y = x^2$.
same shape, but 2 units higher

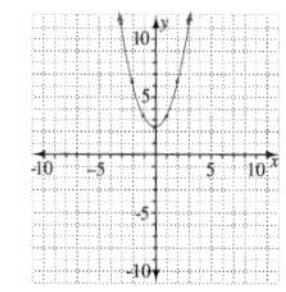

In copymaster and workbook formats

RETEACHING

Reteaching 11-4 Exploring Nonlinear Relationships

The graph of $y = x^2 - 1$ is a U-shaped curve called a **parabola.** To graph a parabola:

① Make a table of values.

x	$x^2 - 1$	y	(x, y)
−2	$(-2)^2 - 1$	3	(−2, 3)
−1	$(-1)^2 - 1$	0	(−1, 0)
0	$0^2 - 1$	−1	(0, −1)
1	$1^2 - 1$	0	(1, 0)
2	$2^2 - 1$	3	(2, 3)

② Graph the points.

③ Draw the U shape.

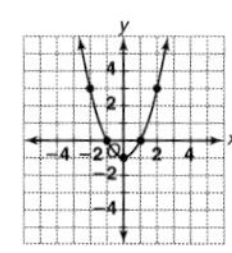

The graph of $y = 2|x|$ is called an absolute value equation. Its graph is V-shaped. To graph the equation:

① Make a table of values.

x	$2\|x\|$	y	(x, y)
−2	2 · 2	4	(−2, 4)
−1	2 · 1	2	(−1, 2)
0	2 · 0	0	(0, 0)
1	2 · 1	2	(1, 2)
2	2 · 2	4	(2, 4)

② Graph the points.

③ Draw the V shape.

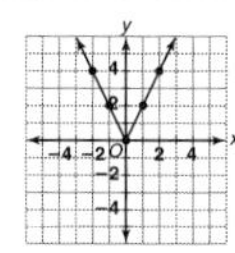

Complete the table of values. Then graph each equation.

1. $y = x^2 - 2$

x	y
−2	2
−1	−1
0	−2
1	−1
2	2

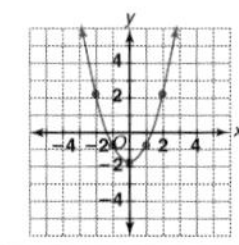

2. $y = 2x^2 - 3$

x	y
−2	5
−1	−1
0	−3
1	−1
2	5

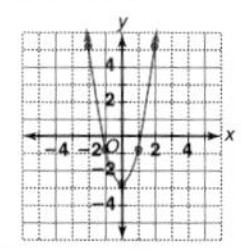

3. $y = \frac{1}{2}|x| + 1$

x	y
−4	3
−2	2
0	1
2	2
4	3

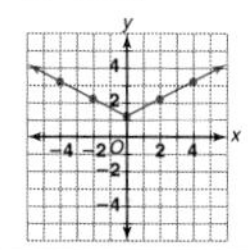

ENRICHMENT

Minds on Math Transparency

11-4

Gregory arranged the numbers 2, 3, 4, and 5, one plus sign, and one equals sign into a true equation. What was Gregory's equation?

Answers may vary. Sample: $3^2 = 4 + 5$

See *Solution Key* for worked-out answers.

11-5 Teaching Notes

1 Focus

CONNECTING TO PRIOR KNOWLEDGE Ask students: *Name some real-life situations in which you use equations.* **Answers may vary. Sample: finding compound interest, converting temperatures from degrees Celsius to degrees Fahrenheit**

2 Teach

THINK AND DISCUSS

DIVERSITY Some students prefer to do their problem solving mentally rather than writing an equation. Assure them that writing the equations in this lesson will help prepare them for algebra. Encourage them to use their mental math skills to check the solutions to their equations.

ERROR ALERT! Students may set up the equations accurately but make mistakes in their solutions. **Remediation:** Review the steps for solving two-step equations found on page 131. Have students make sure their answers are reasonable and check their solutions.

TACTILE LEARNING **Question 1** Give students manipulatives such as counters or blocks to represent the ostriches and elephants.

Lesson Planning Options

Prerequisite Skills

- writing variable expressions (3-1)
- solving equations (3-9)

Resources

Student Edition

Skills Handbook, p. 533
Extra Practice, p. 524
Glossary/Study Guide

Teaching Resources

Chapter Support File, Ch. 11
- Lesson Planner 11-5
- Practice 11-5, Reteaching 11-5
- Answer Masters 11-5

Glossary, Spanish Resources

Transparencies
Minds on Math 11-5

Warm Up

The lumber yard has sheets of paneling that are $3\frac{3}{4}$ ft wide. Dutch bought one sheet that was $5\frac{1}{2}$ ft long and another that was $4\frac{1}{5}$ ft long. What was the total area of the two sheets? **$36\frac{3}{8}$ ft^2**

PROBLEM SOLVING STRATEGY

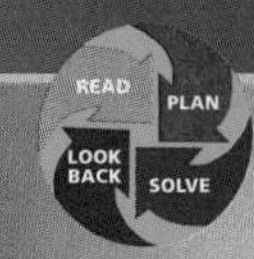

11-5 Write an Equation

Problem Solving Strategies

- Draw a Diagram
- Guess and Test
- Look for a Pattern
- Make a Model
- Make a Table
- Simulate a Problem
- Solve a Simpler Problem
- Too Much or Too Little Information
- Use Logical Reasoning
- Use Multiple Strategies
- Work Backward
- ✔ Write an Equation

Sometimes you can write an equation to solve a problem.

SAMPLE PROBLEM

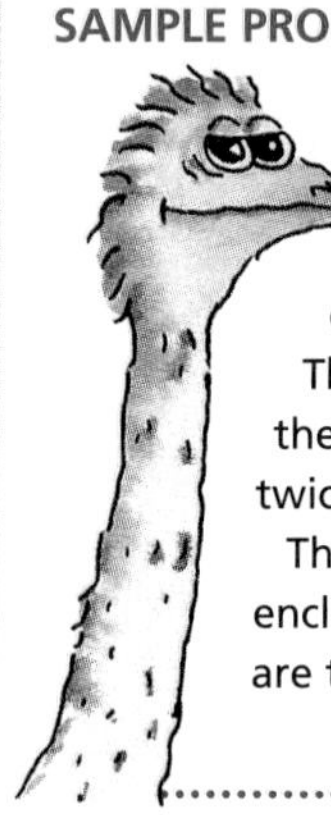

There is an enclosure at the city zoo that contains both ostriches and elephants. The number of ostriches in the enclosure is 17 more than twice the number of elephants. There are 29 ostriches in the enclosure. How many elephants are there?

READ
Read for understanding. Summarize the problem.

1. Think about the information and what you are asked to find.
   a. What information are you given about the ostriches? **See below.**
   b. What do you need to find? **the number of elephants**

PLAN
Decide on a strategy.

Since you are given the relationship between the numbers, an equation may help solve the problem.

Let e represent the number of elephants. A number sentence that relates the number of ostriches and the number of elephants is

$$\text{number of ostriches} = 17 + 2e.$$

Since there are 29 ostriches, you can write

$$29 = 17 + 2e.$$

SOLVE
Try the strategy.

You can solve the equation for e.

$$29 = 17 + 2e$$
$$29 - 17 = 17 - 17 + 2e \quad \leftarrow \text{Subtract 17 from each side.}$$
$$12 = 2e \quad \leftarrow \text{Simplify.}$$
$$\frac{12}{2} = \frac{2e}{2} \quad \leftarrow \text{Divide each side by 2.}$$
$$6 = e \quad \leftarrow \text{Simplify.}$$

2. How many elephants are there? **6 elephants**

1a. There are 29 ostriches. The number ostriches is 17 more than twice the number of elephants.

ADDITIONAL PROBLEM

Lindsey has been saving her allowance to go to the movies. She has saved $3 more than twice the cost of a movie. Lindsey has saved $12. How much does it cost to see a movie? **$4.50**

3 Practice

EXERCISES *On Your Own*

ASSESSMENT Exercises 1 and 2 Have students write the equations they will use to solve the first two exercises. Then have them compare their equations with a partner before solving.

CONNECTION TO RATIOS Exercise 4 Point out to students that the club sold $\frac{3}{4}$ of their tickets. Ask: *What fraction of the tickets do they have left?* $\frac{1}{4}$

CONNECTION TO GEOMETRY Exercise 9 You may need to remind students of the formulas for the area of a square ($A = s^2$) and the area of a triangle ($A = \frac{1}{2}bh$).

WRAP UP

IDENTIFYING THE BIG IDEA Ask students: *What are two basic questions to ask before*

LOOK BACK
Think about how you solved the problem.

Another advantage of using an equation to solve a problem is that if any aspect of the problem changes, only a small adjustment needs to be made to the equation.

3. Suppose there were 33 ostriches in the enclosure, not 29.
   a. How would the original equation change? **a. 29 would change to 33.**
   b. Write and solve the new equation. **b. $33 = 17 + 2e$; 8 elephants**
4. Suppose the number of ostriches was 11 more than twice the number of elephants instead of 17 more.
   a. How would the original equation change? **4a. 17 would change to 11.**
   b. Write and solve the new equation. **$29 = 11 + 2e$; 9 elephants**

Now you may assign Exercises 1–10.

EXERCISES *On Your Own*

Write and solve an equation for each problem.

1. *Money* A pair of boots costs $5 more than twice the cost of a pair of shoes. The boots cost $42.90. How much do the shoes cost? **$42.9 = 5 + 2x$; $18.95**
2. *Geometry* The perimeter of a rectangle is 64 cm. The length is 20 cm. Find the width. **$2(20) + 2w = 64$; 12 cm**
3. *Entertainment* Daheem and Judy read mystery novels. Judy has read 3 less than 5 times as many as Daheem. She has read 17 mysteries. How many has Daheem read? **$17 = 5D - 3$; 4 mystery novels**
4. *Fund-raising* The booster club sold $\frac{3}{4}$ of their raffle tickets. They had 175 tickets left. How many tickets were printed? **See right.**
5. A piggy bank contains $4.30 in dimes and quarters. The bank has $2.80 in dimes. How many quarters does the bank contain? (*Hint*: Let n be the number of quarters. Since each quarter has a value of $.25, the value of n quarters is $0.25n$.) **$2.8 + 0.25n = 4.3$; 6 quarters**

4. $x - \frac{3}{4}x = 175$; 700 tickets

Use any strategy to solve each problem.

6. *Money* With the $5.75 in her pocket, Tia decided to treat herself to lunch. How much can she spend on lunch so she still has enough to leave a 15% tip for the waitress? **$5.00**
7. Paloma, Jasper, and Holly are each less than 45 years old. The mode of their ages is 35. The range is 14. What is the mean of their ages? What is the median of their ages? **$30\frac{1}{3}$ yr; 35 yr**

Technology Options

Prentice Hall Technology

Software for Learners
- Math Blaster® Mystery*
- Interactive Student Tutorial, Chapter 11*

Teaching Resource Software
- Computer Item Generator 11-5
- Resource Pro™ Chapter 11*

Internet • For related mathematics activities, visit the Prentice Hall site at www.phschool.com/math

**Available on CD-ROM only*

Assignment Options for Exercises On Your Own

Core 1–8, 10
Extension 9

Use Mixed Review to maintain skills.

PRACTICE

Practice 11-5 *Problem-Solving Stategy: Write an Equation*

Write an equation to solve each problem. Show your work. Samples are given.

1. In a pet store the number of dogs is 12 more than three times the number of cats. If the pet store has 21 dogs, how many cats does it have?
   $3c + 12 = 21$; 3 cats
2. In the pet store the number of birds is 10 less than twice the number of rabbits. If the pet store has 56 birds, how many rabbits does it have?
   $2r - 10 = 56$; 33 rabbits
3. A sweater cost $12 more than a shirt. Together they cost $46. What was the price of the shirt?
   $2y + 12 = 46$; $17
4. The perimeter of a rectangle is 84 cm. The length is twice the width. Find the length and width.
   $4w + 2w = 84$; $w = 14$ cm, $l = 28$ cm
5. Mark and Melinda collect baseball caps. Mark has 7 more than Melinda. Together, they have 115 caps. How many baseball caps does each of them have?
   $2a + 7 = 115$; Mark 61; Melinda 54

Use any strategy to solve each problem.

6. Lydia sold $\frac{4}{5}$ of her candles to raise money for the band. She has 8 candles left. How many candles did Lydia start with?
   40 candles
7. A coin purse contains quarters, dimes, and nickels. There are the same number of dimes as nickels and half as many quarters as dimes. The coins are worth $1.65. How many of each coin are in the coin purse?
   3 quarters, 6 dimes, 6 nickels
8. The sum of two numbers is 20. The greater number is 4 more than the lesser number. What are the two numbers?
   8 and 12
9. A garage charged Mr. Tilton $48 in parts and $36/h in labor. How many hours did the garage spend on Mr. Tilton's car if the total bill was $156?
   3 h

In copymaster and workbook formats

RETEACHING

Reteaching 11-5 *Problem-Solving Strategy: Write an Equation*

The cost for a car and driver on a car ferry is $15. Each additional passenger is $2. If Brett pays a toll of $21, how many additional passengers does he have?

Read What information are you given? *You know the cost for the car and driver, and the cost for each passenger.* What are you asked to find? *You want to find the number of additional passengers.*

Plan You are given a relationship between numbers. So, an equation may help solve the problem. The toll is $15 for the car and driver plus $2 for each passenger ($p$).

$15 + 2p = \text{toll}$

$15 + 2p = 21$

Solve Solve the equation for p.

$15 + 2p = 21$

$15 - 15 + 2p = 21 - 15$ ← **Subtract 15.**

$2p = 6$ ← **Simplify.**

$\frac{2p}{2} = \frac{6}{2}$ ← **Divide by 2.**

$p = 3$ ← **Simplify.**

There are 3 passengers.

Look Back $15 for car + $2 × 3 additional passengers = $21.

Write and solve an equation for each problem. Equations may vary.

1. Mia is 8 years older than Kenji. Mia is 26 years old. How old is Kenji?
   $K + 8 = 26$; 18 years old
2. The perimeter of a rectangle is 100 in. The width is 18 in. Find the length.
   $36 + 2l = 100$; 32 in.
3. A jacket costs $28 more than twice the cost of a pair of slacks. If the jacket costs $152, how much do the slacks cost?
   $(s \cdot 2) + 28 = 152$; $62
4. Jennifer has $22.75 in her bank. She saves quarters and half dollars. She has $10.50 in half dollars. How many quarters does she have?
   $(22.75 - 10.50) \div 0.25 = q$; 49 quarters
5. One number is 6 less than another number. Their sum is 20. Find the greater number.
   $(x + 6) + x = 20$; 13
6. Sari has 11 more markers than Sam. Together they have 61 markers. How many does Sam have?
   $(s + 11) + s = 61$; 25 markers

ENRICHMENT

Minds on Math Transparency

11-5

A survey of 40 shoppers found that 12 liked Crunchy Cereal and 23 liked Wheat Bran Cereal. Twice as many disliked both brands as liked both brands. How many shoppers liked both brands?

5 shoppers

See *Solution Key* for worked-out answers.

writing the equation to solve a problem? **What do I know? What do I need to find?**

PROJECT LINK Encourage students to consider the size of their largest sample before choosing intervals for the *x*-axis. For example: If their largest sample was 40 beans, they may want to use intervals of 5 rather than 2.

LESSON QUIZ

1. The perimeter of a rectangle is 58 m. The width is 8 m. Find the length. **21 m**
2. When doing homework, Terrence spent 5 min less than 2 times the number of minutes he spent talking on the phone. He spent 55 min on homework. How much time did he spend talking on the phone? **30 min**

8. *Architecture* JoAnne's kitchen measures 11 ft by $13\frac{1}{2}$ ft. She wants to tile the floor using square ceramic tiles that are 6 in. on each side. How many tiles does she need? **594 tiles**

9. *Geometry* The area of the square at the right is 64 square units. Point C is the midpoint of $\overline{AD}$. Point B is the midpoint of $\overline{AC}$. What fraction of the square is shaded? $\frac{1}{8}$

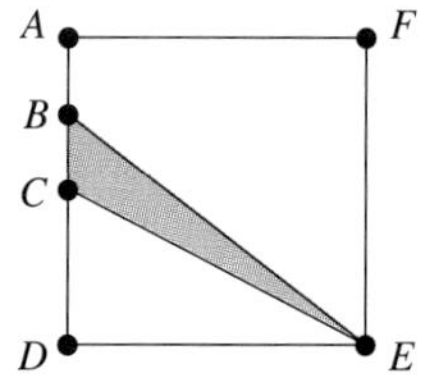

10. A worm is at the bottom of a 40-m hole. It can crawl upward at the rate of 4 m in one day, but at night it slips back 3 m. How long will it take the worm to crawl out of the hole? **37 days and 36 nights**

Mixed Review

Suppose you flip a coin 1,000 times and get 548 heads. *(Lessons 9-1, 9-3)*

11. What is the experimental probability of getting heads? Tails? **See right.**
12. What is the theoretical probability of getting heads? $\frac{1}{2}$

11. $\frac{548}{1{,}000}$, or $\frac{137}{250}$; $\frac{452}{1{,}000}$, or $\frac{113}{250}$

Calculator **Use the formula $B = p(1 + r)^t$ to find the balance of each account earning compound interest. Recall that B is the balance, p is the principal, r is the annual interest rate, and t is the time in years.** *(Lesson 10-4)*

13. $4,000 principal
    4.5% annual interest rate
    1 year **$4,180**
14. $12,500 principal
    5.25% annual interest rate
    5 years **$16,144.35**
15. $3,870 principal
    6% annual interest rate
    4 years **$4,885.79**

16. Sketch a graph of your height above ground as you swing four times on a swing. Include labels. *(Lesson 10-7)* **Check students' work.**

17. *Choose a Strategy* The water at Limestone Cove is 5 ft deep. Every $\frac{1}{4}$ mile out to sea, the water is 3 ft deeper. How deep is the water $\frac{1}{2}$ mi from Limestone Cove? **11 ft**

CHAPTER PROJECT

PROJECT LINK: GRAPHING

For each type of bean, make a graph relating the different sample sizes to the percents you found in each sample. Put *sample size* on the *x*-axis and *percent* on the *y*-axis. Use your graphs to decide the smallest sample size you need to predict the percent of each kind of bean in the jar.

Check students' work.

MATH TOOLBOX

In Examples 1 and 2 of Lesson 11-6, students learn how to graph translations. This toolbox allows students to review slides, flips, and turns before using the terms *translation*, *reflection*, and *rotation.*

TACTILE LEARNING and ERROR ALERT! Students may have trouble keeping the terms *slide, flip,* and *turn* clear in their minds.

Remediation: Have students model the transformations by moving a geometric tile along a sheet of dot paper. Students can trace the tile and then trace the result after the transformation.

ASSESSMENT Exercise 1 Have a volunteer stand at the front of the class. Ask the volunteer to strike a pose with both feet on the ground. Ask another volunteer to model whatever command you give. Your choices for commands are *slide* and *flip.* Other students determine if the second volunteer moved to the correct position. Repeat.

ADDITIONAL PROBLEM

Draw a simple geometric figure on graph paper. On the same piece of graph paper, draw a slide, a flip, and a turn of the original figure. **Check students' work.**

MATH TOOLBOX SKILLS REVIEW

Slides, Flips, and Turns

Before Lesson 11-6

There are many transformations you can do with geometric figures. Three of these are *slides, flips,* and *turns.*

A *slide* moves a figure so that every point moves the same direction and the same distance.

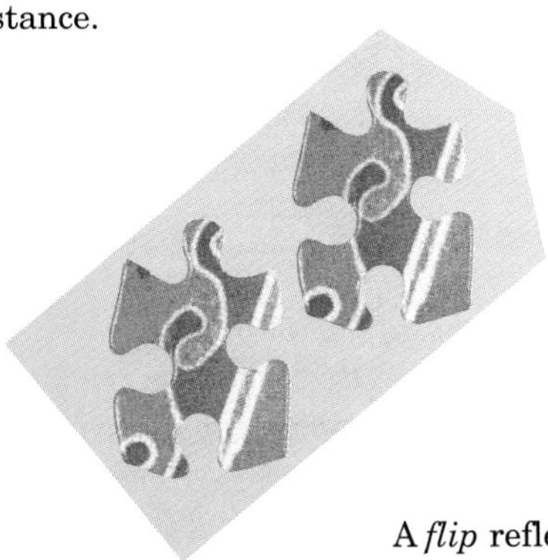

A *turn* rotates a figure around a point.

A *flip* reflects a figure over a line.

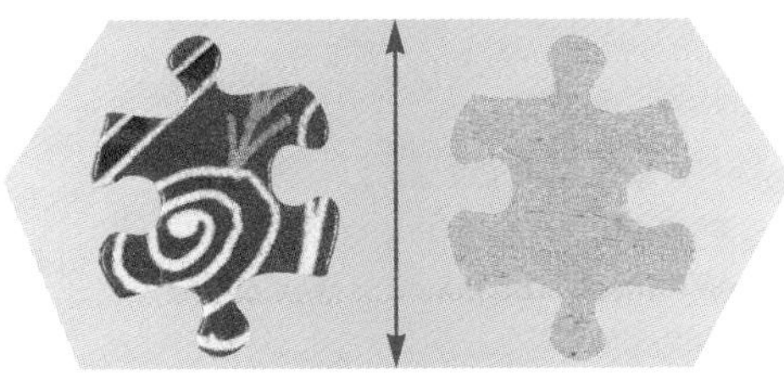

Describe each transformation from the black figure to the red figure as a *slide*, *flip*, or *turn*.

1. turn

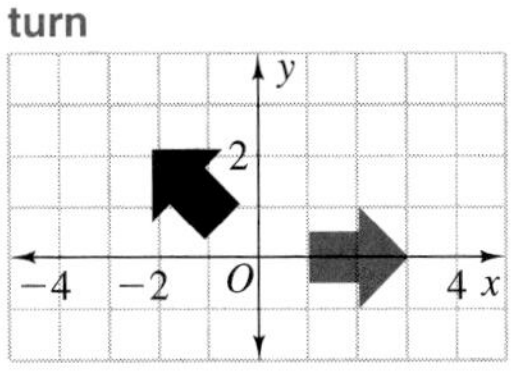

2. slide

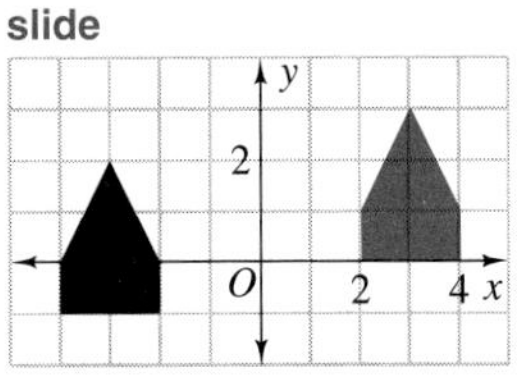

3. flip

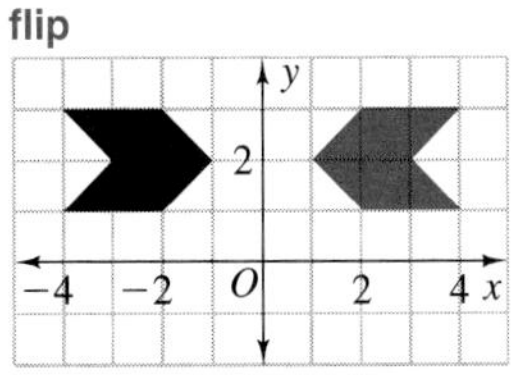

4. If you flip a figure over two parallel lines, the resulting image is the same as after a slide.

4. *Writing* Describe how two flips can have the same effect as a slide. Include a drawing to illustrate your example. **Check students' work for drawing.**

Resources

Teaching Resources

Teaching Aids Master 4

Transparencies

2

11-6 Teaching Notes

1 Focus

CONNECTING TO PRIOR KNOWLEDGE
Have students think of different types of printed fabric they have seen. Ask them: *Name some fabric patterns that have repeating shapes?* **Answers may vary. Sample: polka dots, plaids, houndstooth check**

2 Teach

THINK AND DISCUSS

AEP Students may confuse the words *transformation* and *translation.* Show students that a translation is one kind of transformation, using a Venn diagram. The diagram previews the different kinds of transformations that students will study in the next few lessons.

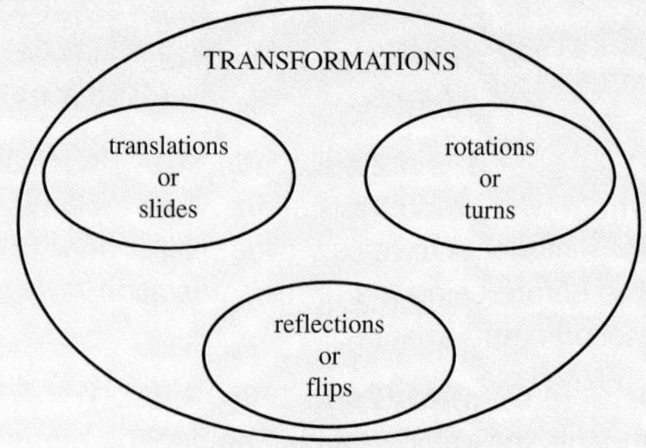

Lesson Planning Options

Prerequisite Skills
- graphing on a coordinate plane (11-1)

Vocabulary/Symbols
transformations, translation, image, prime notation (A′), tessellation

Materials/Manipulatives
- graph paper

Resources

Student Edition
Skills Handbook, p. 528
Extra Practice, p. 524
Glossary/Study Guide

Teaching Resources
Chapter Support File, Ch. 11
- Lesson Planner 11-6
- Practice 11-6, Reteaching 11-6
- Answer Masters 11-6

Teaching Aids Master 4
Glossary, Spanish Resources

Transparencies
2, 15, 99, Minds on Math 11-6

Warm Up

Find the product in lowest terms.
$13\frac{1}{2} \times 8\frac{1}{3}$ $112\frac{1}{2}$

GEOMETRY Connection

11-6 Translations

What You'll Learn
- 1 To graph translations
- 2 To write a rule for a translation

...And Why
Fabric designers and artists use translations to create repeating designs.

Here's How
Look for questions that
- build understanding
- ✔ check understanding

THINK AND DISCUSS

1 *Graphing Translations*

Movements of figures on a plane are **transformations.** A transformation can be a slide, a flip, or a turn. The pattern in the tie is created by sliding a single, purple shape into new positions on the fabric. Another name for a slide is a **translation.**

1. *Patterns* Describe the other figure that has been translated on the tie.
Answers may vary. Sample: a gray kite

The figure you get after a translation is the **image** of the original. You use *prime notation* (A') to identify an image point.

■ **EXAMPLE 1**

Translate point $F(4, 1)$ up 2 units. What are the coordinates of the image F'?

The coordinates of F' are $(4, 3)$.

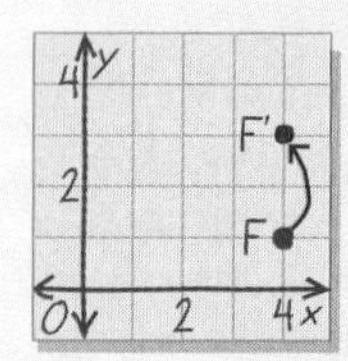

2. ✔ *Try It Out* Point G has coordinates $(-4, 1)$. Graph it and its image G' after a translation three units to the left.

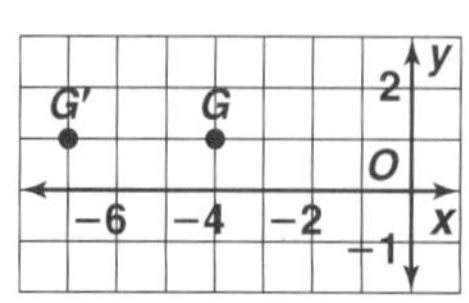

To show a translation, you can use arrow notation. For the translation of F to F' in Example 1, you can write $F(4, 1) \rightarrow F'(4, 3)$.

3. Use the points you graphed in Question 2. Write the translation of G to G' using arrow notation.
$G(-4, 1) \rightarrow G'(-7, 1)$

CONNECTING TO THE STUDENTS' WORLD

Ask students: *Is anyone wearing clothing with a repeated pattern? Is this repeated pattern a translation?* You might bring fabric samples of translations to class in case none of the students' clothing has a pattern that repeats.

ADDITIONAL EXAMPLES

FOR EXAMPLE 1

Translate point $J(2, -4)$ right 3 units. What are the coordinates of the image J'?

$J'(5, -4)$

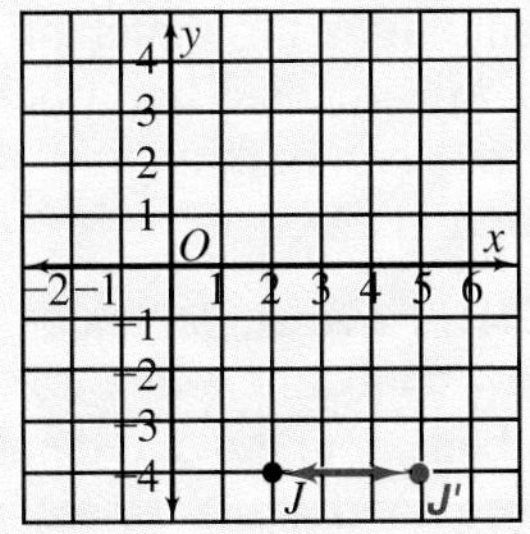

FOR EXAMPLE 2

To make a tie, the designer could have translated figure *WXYZ*. Draw its image after a translation one unit to the left, and two units up. Use prime notation to label the image.

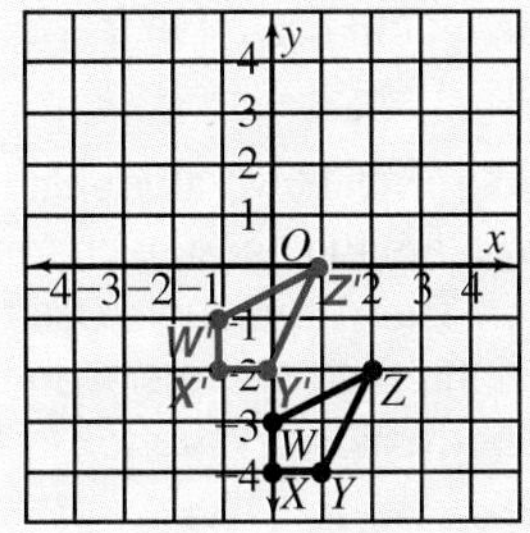

To translate a geometric figure, first translate the vertices of the figure. Then connect the new points to form the translated image of the original figure.

EXAMPLE 2 *Real-World Problem Solving*

Fabric Design To make the tie design on page 494, the designer translated figure *ABCD*. Draw its image after a translation four units to the right and one unit down. Use prime notation to label the image.

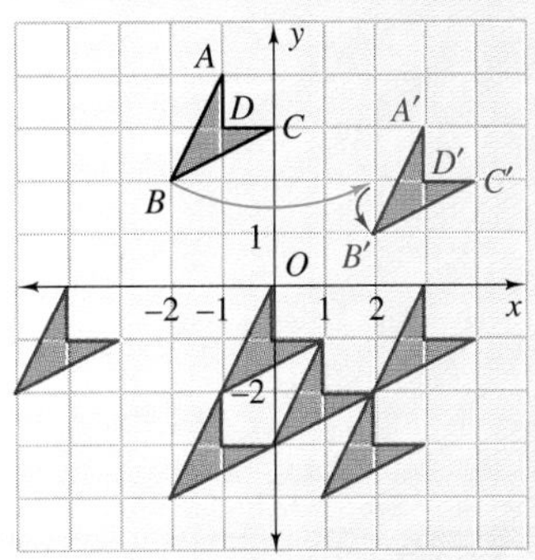

4a. $A(-1, 4)$, $B(-2, 2)$, $C(0, 3)$, $D(-1, 3)$; $A'(3, 3)$, $B'(2, 1)$, $C'(4, 2)$, $D'(3, 2)$

5a.

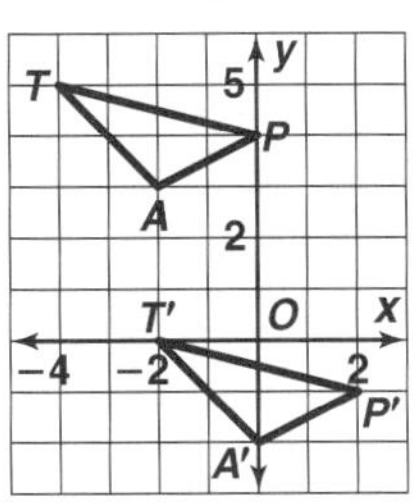

4. a. *Look Back* What are the coordinates of points A, B, C, and D? What are the coordinates of their images, points A', B', C', D'? **See left.**

   b. Use arrow notation to describe the translation of point A to point A'; point B to point B'; point C to point C'; point D to point D'. **$A(-1, 4) \to A'(3, 3)$, $B(-2, 2) \to B'(2, 1)$, $C(0, 3) \to C'(4, 2)$, $D(-1, 3) \to D'(3, 2)$**

5. a. *Try It Out* Graph $\triangle PAT$ with vertices $P(0, 4)$, $A(-2, 3)$, and $T(-4, 5)$. Then graph its image $P'A'T'$ after a translation two units right and five units down. **See left.**

   b. Complete:
   $P(0, 4), A(-2, 3), T(-4, 5) \to P'(■, ■), A'(■, ■), T'(■, ■)$
   2 −1   0 −2   −2 0

Now you may assign Exercises 1–15.

2 *Writing a Rule for a Translation*

To find the coordinates of a translated image, you can add or subtract the amount of movement from the coordinates of the original figure.

6. *Think About It* Suppose you translate a point to the left two units and up one unit. Would you add or subtract to find the x-coordinate of the image? Would you add or subtract to find the y-coordinate of the image? **subtract 2; add 1**

Technology Options

Prentice Hall Skills

Software for Learners
- Math Blaster® Mystery*
- Interactive Student Tutorial, Chapter 11*

Teaching Resource Software
- Computer Item Generator 11-6
- Resource Pro™ Chapter 11*

Internet • For related mathematics activities, visit the Prentice Hall site at www.phschool.com/math

**Available on CD-ROM only*

Assignment Options for Exercises On Your Own

To provide flexible scheduling, this lesson can be split into parts.

1 **Core** 1–8, 10–15
Extension 9

2 **Core** 16–23
Extension 24

Use Mixed Review to maintain skills.

FOR EXAMPLE 3

Write a rule for the translation of *WXYZ* as shown in Additional Example 2. Use arrow notation. $(x, y) \rightarrow (x - 1, y + 2)$

VISUAL LEARNING Have students use colored pencils or markers to shade each vertex a different color. Then have them use the same color to trace the path of translation from each vertex to its corresponding vertex in the image.

ERROR ALERT! **Example 3** Students may count the unit changes between vertices that do not correspond. **Remediation:** Have students mark the matching corresponding vertices. Then trace the path of translation. Each path should have the same length and slope.

ASSESSMENT Have students use graph paper to draw an example of a translation. Then have them write the coordinates of the original vertices and a rule describing the translation. Have partners trade coordinates and rules. Partners check the rule by using it with the original coordinates to find the vertices of the image. The image vertices should match those in the initial drawing.

Work Together

EXTENSION and CONNECTION TO ART If you have block scheduling or extended class periods, have students research the Dutch artist M.C. Escher. Then have students embellish their Work Together project to create an Escher-style drawing.

pages 497–498 On Your Own

4.

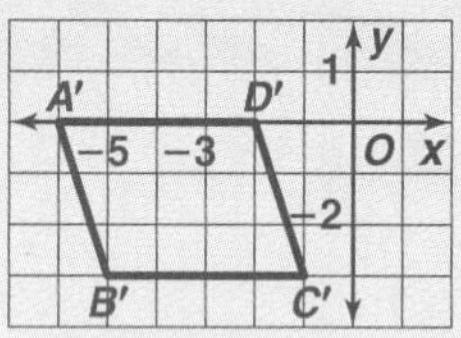

$A'(-6, 0)$, $B'(-5, -3)$, $C'(-1, -3)$, $D'(-2, 0)$

5.

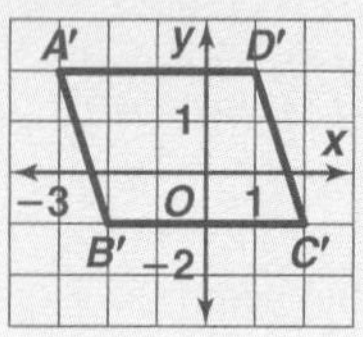

$A'(-3, 2)$, $B'(-2, -1)$, $C'(2, -1)$, $D'(1, 2)$

6.

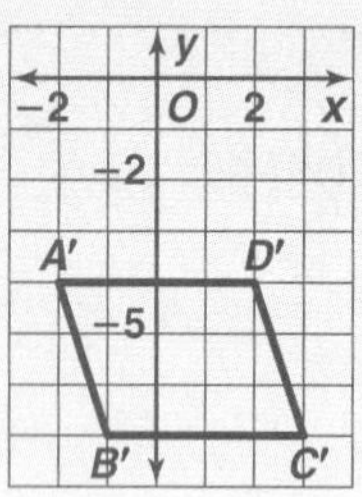

$A'(-2, -4)$, $B'(-1, -7)$, $C'(3, -7)$, $D'(2, -4)$

■ **EXAMPLE 3**

Write a rule for the translation of $\triangle MNP$. Use arrow notation.

The horizontal change from N to N' is 4 units to the right, so $x \rightarrow x + 4$.

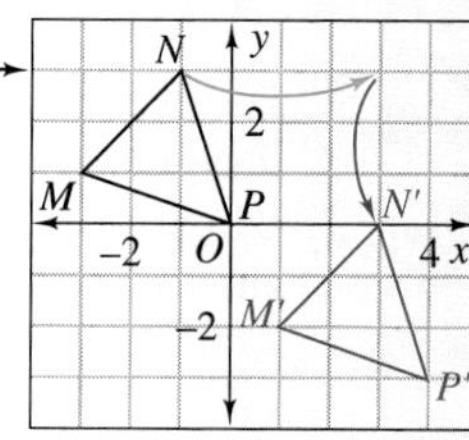

The vertical change from N to N' is 3 units down, so $y \rightarrow y - 3$.

The rule for the translation is $(x, y) \rightarrow (x + 4, y - 3)$.

7. ✔ *Try It Out* Suppose a figure is translated to the right 2 units and up 6 units. Complete the general rule to show how to find the image: $(x, y) \rightarrow (x + ■, y + ■)$. 2 6

WHO? The Dutch artist M.C. Escher (1898–1972) used translations to create tessellations. Many art and math books include examples of his work.

Work Together

Exploring Tessellations

Art A *tessellation* is a repeating pattern of figures that has no gaps or overlaps, like the pattern in the tie. The pattern at the right shows how you can create a design for fabric or wrapping paper.

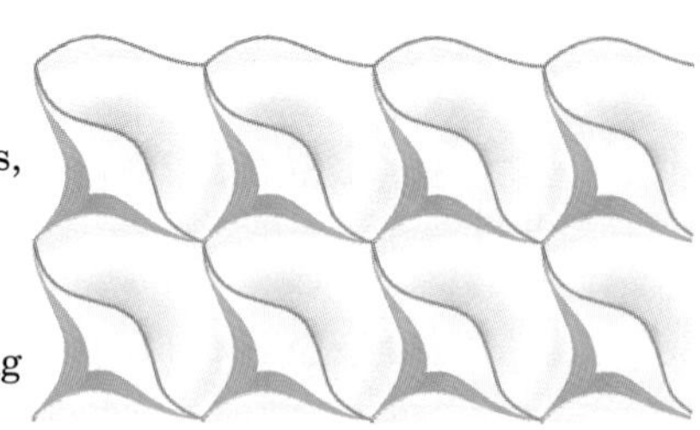

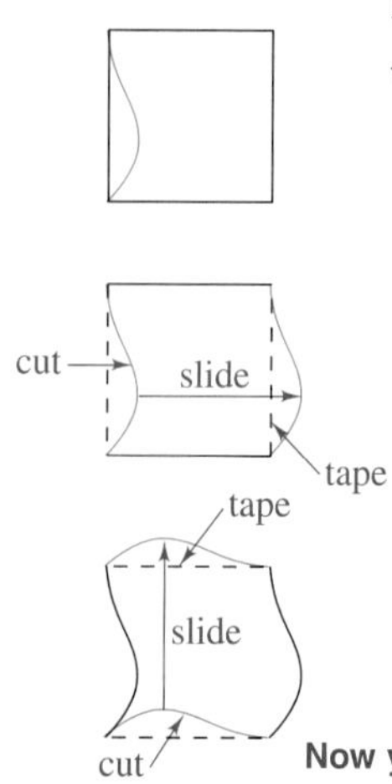

Work with a partner. Start with a cardboard cutout of a square.

8a–c. Check students' work.

8. **a.** As shown at the left, draw a curve from one vertex of the square to a neighboring vertex.

   b. Cut along the curve you drew in part (a). Slide the cut-out piece to the opposite side of the square. Tape the flat edge of the cut-out piece to that side of the square.

   c. Repeat the process using the other two sides of the square.

9a–b. Check students' work.

9. **a.** Trace around your figure on a piece of paper. Carefully translate the figure so that the edges touch. Continue tracing until you have covered a large area of the paper.

   b. Congratulations! You've created a tessellation! Now decorate your tessellation to create a work of art.

Now you may assign Exercises 16–24.

3 Practice

EXERCISES *On Your Own*

Exercises 4–6 To avoid confusion, have students graph the images for each exercise on a separate coordinate grid.

REASONING Exercise 9 Encourage students to graph the triangle before finding the coordinates of S' and T'. However, some students may prefer the challenge of writing a rule for the translation by using the coordinates for point R and R'.

EXTENSION Exercises 18–23 Have students use prime notation to label the images. Then ask students: *Why is it helpful to describe a translation by stating the horizontal change first, and then the vertical change?* **This lists the changes in the same order they effect the *x*- and *y*-coordinates.**

WRITING and CONNECTION TO GEOMETRY Exercise 24 Point out to students that they use the word *transformation* rather than translation. Have students review the definitions of *similar* and *congruent figures* and encourage them to use the definitions in their justifications.

WRAP UP

IDENTIFYING THE BIG IDEA Ask students to explain how to graph *translations.* Then have them describe how to write a rule for a *translation.*

EXERCISES *On Your Own*

Use the graph at the right for Exercises 1 and 2.

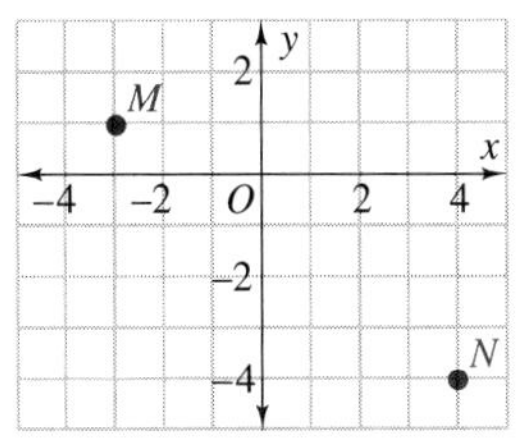

1. Give the coordinates of point M after it is translated right 5 units. **(2, 1)**
2. Give the coordinates of point N after it is translated up 4 units. **(4, 0)**
3. Suppose $P(3, 4) \rightarrow P'(-2, -3)$. What is the horizontal change? What is the vertical change? **5 units left; 7 units down**

For Exercises 4–6, use graph paper to graph each image of figure *ABCD*. Name the coordinates of A', B', C', and D'.

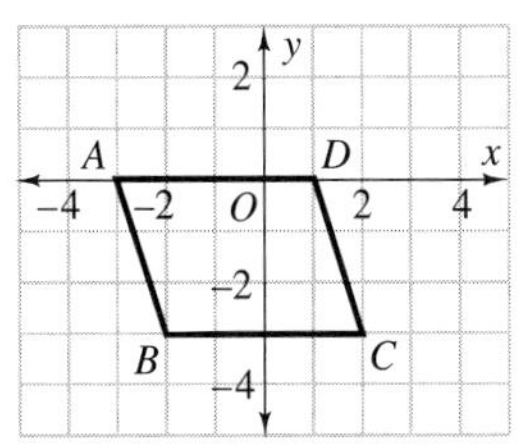

4–6. See margin p. 496.

4. left 3 units 5. up 2 units 6. right 1 unit, down 4 units

7. The vertices of $\triangle DEF$ are $D(-1, 2)$, $E(-1, -1)$, and $F(2, -1)$.
   a. Graph the triangle. **a–b. See margin.**
   b. Graph its translation right 2 units and down 1 unit.
   c. Write the coordinates of $\triangle D'E'F'$. **$D'(1, 1)$, $E'(1, -2)$, $F'(4, -2)$**

8. **Choose A, B, or C.** On the graph at the right, which shape is a translation of $\triangle XYZ$? **A**

   A. $\triangle ABC$ B. $\triangle JKL$ C. $\triangle PQR$

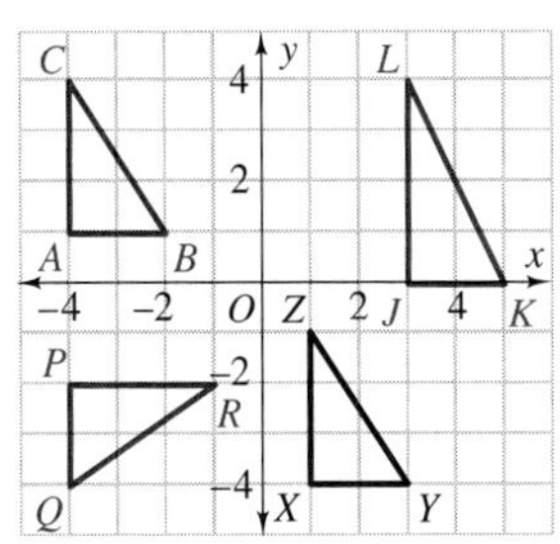

9. *Reasoning* $\triangle RST$ has coordinates $R(2, -5)$, $S(1, 1)$, $T(-3, -1)$. Point $R(2, -5) \rightarrow R'(5, -7)$. If $\triangle RST$ is translated to $\triangle R'S'T'$, give the coordinates of S' and T'. **$S'(4, -1)$, $T'(0, -3)$**

Find the horizontal change and the vertical change for each translation.

10. $P(4, 6) \rightarrow P'(0, 8)$ **left 4 units, up 2 units**
11. $A(-1, 3) \rightarrow A'(2, 4)$ **right 3 units, up 1 unit**
12. $F(2, -2) \rightarrow F'(1, -7)$ **left 1 unit, down 5 units**
13. $M(0, -1) \rightarrow M'(2, -4)$ **right 2 units, down 3 units**

14. *Aviation* Three airplanes are flying in a triangular formation. In 1 min, airplane P moves as shown in the graph at the right. The planes remain in formation as they fly.
    a. Give the original coordinates and the new coordinates of each airplane.
    b. How far in each direction did the airplanes move? **b. right 4 units and up 3 units**

    a. $P(-2, 1) \rightarrow P'(2, 4)$, $L(-5, 1) \rightarrow L'(-1, 4)$, $N(-2, -2) \rightarrow N'(2, 1)$

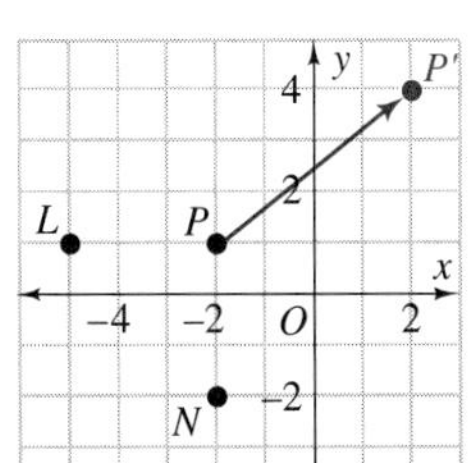

7a–b.

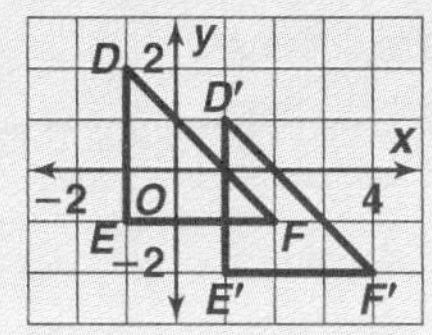

24a–c.

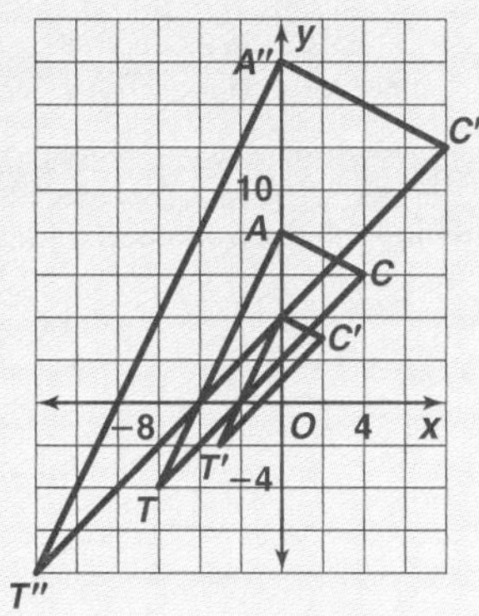

d. The original triangle and its images are the same shape but not the same size. They are not congruent, but they are similar.

29b.

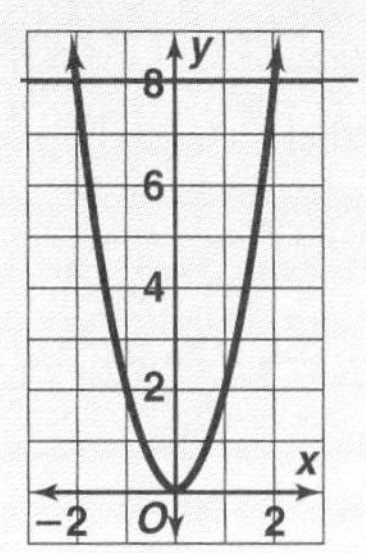

PRACTICE

Practice 11-6 *Translations*

Use the graph at the right for Exercises 1–4.

1. Give the coordinates of point *A* after it has been translated down 3 units. (2, 2)
2. Give the coordinates of point *B* after it has been translated left 3 units. (–4, –4)
3. Suppose *M*(–7, 3) → *M*′(4, –1). What is the horizontal change? the vertical change? 11; – 4
4. What are the coordinates of point *N* after it is translated right 8 units and up 5 units? (1, 3)

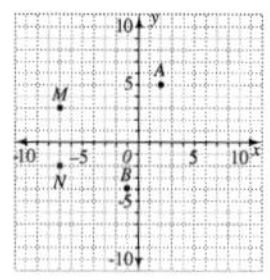

Graph figure *ABCD* and its image after each translation. Name the coordinates of *A*′, *B*′, *C*′, and *D*′.

5. *A* (2, 1), *B* (4, 5), *C* (7, 4), *D* (5, –1); right 2 units
6. *A* (2, 1), *B* (4, 5), *C* (7, 4), *D* (5, –1); down 1 unit, left 2 units

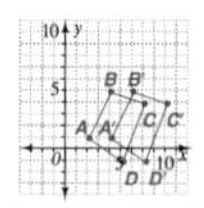

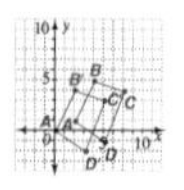

A′(4, 1), *B*′(6, 5), *C*′(9, 4), *D*′(7, –1) *A*′(0, 0), *B*′(2, 4), *C*′(5, 3), *D*′(3, –2)

Write the rule for the translation shown in each graph.

7.

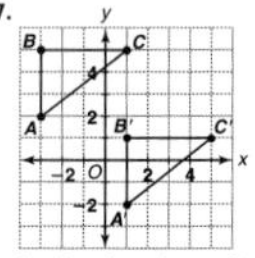

(x, y) → (x + 4, y – 4)

8.

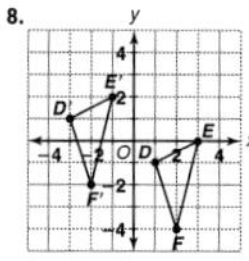

(x, y) → (x – 4, y + 2)

Practice

In copymaster and workbook formats

RETEACHING

Reteaching 11-6 *Translations*

Movements of figures on a plane are called **transformations.** A translation, or slide, moves all points the same distance and direction.

The translation (x, y) → (x + 4, y – 1) moves *each* point to the right 4 units and down 1 unit.

A(–3, 1) moves to (–3 + 4, 1 – 1), where point *A*′(1, 0) is its **image.**

The square *ABCD* moves to its image square *A*′*B*′*C*′*D*′.

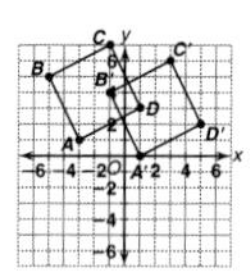

Complete the following for the figure above.

1. *B*(–5, 5) → *B*′(–1, 4)
2. *C*(–1, 7) → *C*′(3, 6)
3. *D*(1, 3) → *D*′(5, 2)

Graph the image of figure *PRST* after each translation.

4. right 2 units
5. left 2 units, down 2 units
6. right 1 unit, up 3 units

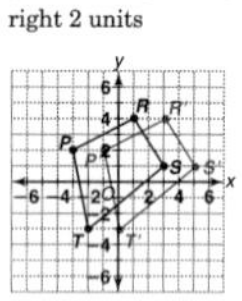

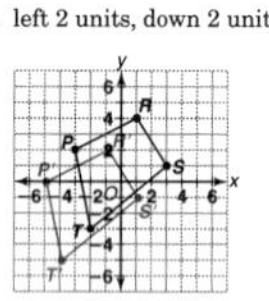

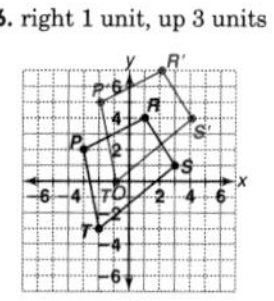

Complete the rule for each translation.

7. right 3 units, up 1 unit (x, y) → (x + 3, y + 1)
8. left 4 units, up 5 units (x, y) → (x – 4, y + 5)
9. left 1 unit, down 9 units (x, y) → (x – 1, y – 9)

Write the rule for each translation.

10. left 1 unit, down 3 units (x, y) → (x – 1, y – 3)
11. right 1 unit, up 2 units (x, y) → (x + 1, y + 2)
12. left 3 units, up 2 units (x, y) → (x – 3, y + 2)

Reteaching

ENRICHMENT

Minds on Math Transparency

11-6

In the first 3 games of this basketball season, Trisha made 12 of her first 30 shots. In her next game, she took 10 shots and raised her season average to 50%. How many of the 10 shots did she make?

8 shots

See *Solution Key* for worked-out answers.

LESSON QUIZ

Graph the figure with its image. Then write a rule to describe the translation.

1. Point *K*(–1, 4); right 2 units, down 3 units
(x, y) → (x + 2, y – 3)

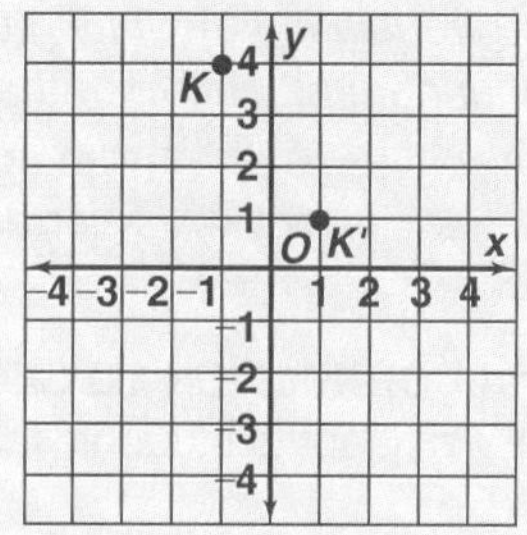

2. △*CDE*: *C*(2, 3), *D*(–1, –1), *E*(3, –1); left 2 units, up 2 units
(x, y) → (x – 2, y + 2)

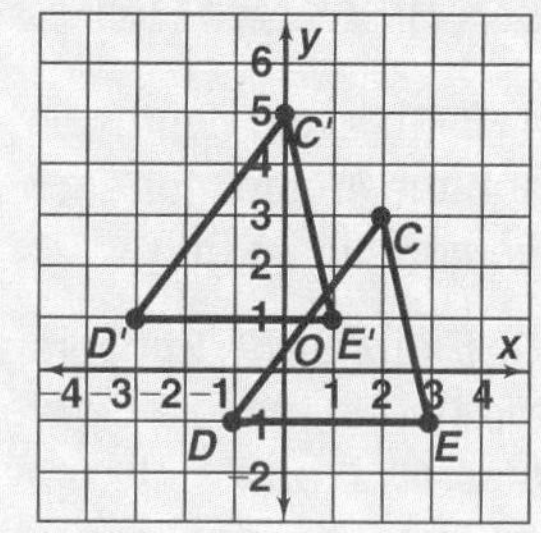

15. Suppose you translated a figure to the left 2 units and up 1 unit. Complete the general rule to show how to find the image: (*x*, *y*) → (*x* – ■, *y* + ■).
2 1

Write the rule for the translation shown in each graph.

16.

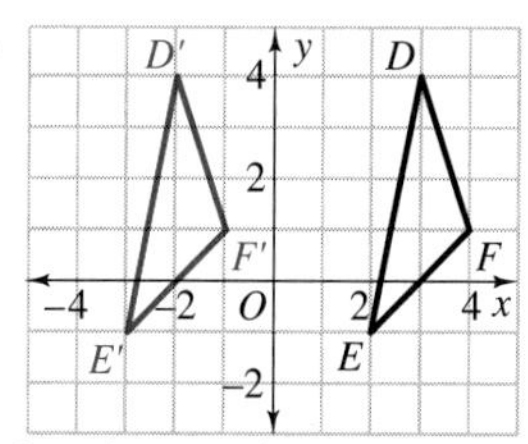

(x, y) → (x – 5, y)

17.

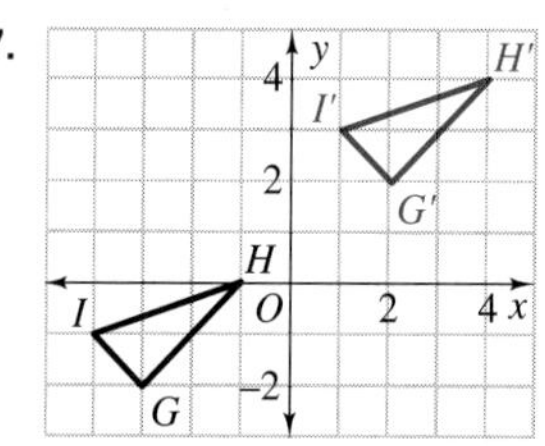

(x, y) → (x + 5, y + 4)

Graph the point and its translated image. Then write a rule to describe the translation.

18. *M*(3, 5); right 3 units, down 1 unit
(x, y) → (x + 3, y – 1)
19. *T*(–1, 6); right 4 units, up 2 units
(x, y) → (x + 4, y + 2)
20. *H*(4, 0); left 1 unit, up 4 units
(x, y) → (x – 1, y + 4)
21. *C*(–2, –5); right 5 units, down 2 units
(x, y) → (x + 5, y – 2)
22. *W*(3, –1); left 1 unit, up 5 units
(x, y) → (x – 1, y + 5)
23. *B*(0, 6); left 3 units, down 4 units
(x, y) → (x – 3, y – 4)
24. a. *Geometry* Graph △*CAT* with vertices *C*(4, 6), *A*(0, 8), and *T*(–6, –4). a–c. See margin p. 497 for graphs.
b. Graph the image of △*CAT* after the transformation $(x, y) \to \left(\frac{1}{2}x, \frac{1}{2}y\right)$. Write the coordinates of the image. *C*′(2, 3), *A*′(0, 4), *T*′(–3, –2)
c. Graph the image of △*CAT* after the transformation (*x*, *y*) → (2*x*, 2*y*). Write the coordinates of the image. *C*″(8, 12), *A*″(0, 16), *T*″(–12, –8)
d. *Writing* Look at △*CAT* and its images. Are the triangles congruent? Are they similar? Justify your reasoning. See margin.

Mixed Review

Write each number in standard form. *(Lesson 10-2)*

25. 4.31×10^5 431,000
26. 5.36×10^6 5,360,000
27. 8.596×10^3 8,596
28. 2.001×10^8 200,100,000

29. a. Make a table of values for the equation $y = 2x^2$.
b. Graph the equation. *(Lesson 11-4)* See margin p. 497.

29a.

x	–2	–1	0	1	2
y	8	2	0	2	8

30. *Choose a Strategy* Pilar recycled 6 fewer than 5 times the number of boxes of newspaper that Alice recycled. Pilar recycled 34 boxes. How many boxes did Alice recycle? 8 boxes

11-7 Teaching Notes

1 Focus

CONNECTING TO PRIOR KNOWLEDGE Ask students to describe what happens to an image when you reflect it in a mirror. **Answers may vary. Sample: The right side of the object appears to be on the left; letters appear flipped.**

2 Teach

THINK AND DISCUSS

Question 2 Be sure to check students' handwriting. The way individuals write their letters may affect the symmetry.

DIVERSITY Students with dyslexia may have difficulty with symmetry and reflections. Have students trace their figures on paper and fold or use mirrors to test for symmetry.

ERROR ALERT! Students may think an object is symmetrical if they can divide it into two congruent halves. For example, students may think N, S, and Z are symmetrical. **Remediation:** Show students if they fold a figure along the line of symmetry, the two halves should line up exactly. Have students try this with the letters M and N. The folded halves of letter N do not line up. N is not symmetrical.

GEOMETRY Connection

11-7 Symmetry and Reflections

What You'll Learn

- 1 To identify lines of symmetry
- 2 To graph reflections

...And Why

Reflections occur in art, architecture, and nature.

Here's How

Look for questions that
- build understanding
- ✔ check understanding

THINK AND DISCUSS

1 *Identifying Lines of Symmetry*

When water vapor freezes, it becomes a snowflake. Scientists think that each snowflake is one of a kind. Every snowflake has *symmetry*.

A figure is **symmetrical** when one side is a mirror image of the other side. The red line drawn through the snowflake is a **line of symmetry.**

1. Some objects have more than one line of symmetry. How many lines of symmetry do you see in the snowflake? **There are 6 lines of symmetry.**

EXAMPLE 1 *Real-World Problem Solving*

Photography Identify the lines of symmetry in each photograph.

a. 

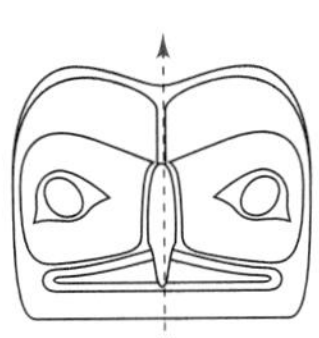

The mask has one line of symmetry.

b. 

The flower has five lines of symmetry.

2. ✔ *Try It Out* Name four capital letters of the alphabet that have a line of symmetry. Write the letters and show the line of symmetry.

Answers may vary. Sample:

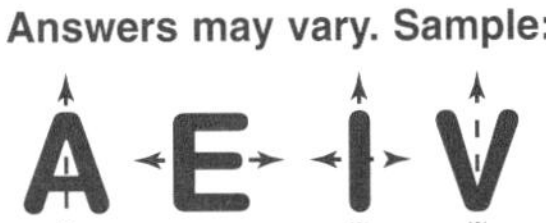

Now you may assign Exercises 1–10.

Lesson Planning Options

Prerequisite Skills
- graphing on a coordinate plane (11-1)

Vocabulary/Symbols
symmetry, symmetrical, line of symmetry, reflection, line of reflection

Materials/Manipulatives
- graph paper
- colored paper
- scissors

Resources

Student Edition

Skills Handbook, p. 528
Extra Practice, p. 524
Glossary/Study Guide

Teaching Resources

Chapter Support File, Ch. 11
- Lesson Planner 11-7
- Practice 11-7, Reteaching 11-7
- Alternative Activity 11-7
- Answer Masters 11-7

Teaching Aids Master 4
Glossary, Spanish Resources

Transparencies
2, 15, 99, Minds on Math 11-7

Warm Up

Order the following from least to greatest: $\frac{2}{3}$, 0.65, $\frac{5}{8}$, $\frac{3}{5}$, 0.58. **0.58, $\frac{3}{5}$, $\frac{5}{8}$, 0.65, $\frac{2}{3}$**

■ ADDITIONAL EXAMPLES

FOR EXAMPLE 1

Identify the lines of symmetry in a square.

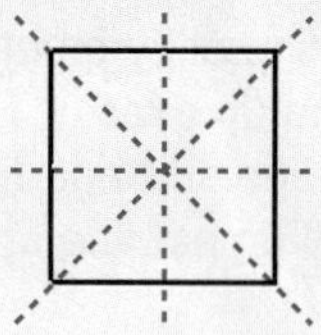

FOR EXAMPLE 2

Draw the image of $\triangle XYZ$. Use the x-axis as the line of reflection. Use arrow notation to describe the image and its reflection. $X(3, 1), Y(4, 5), Z(5, 2) \rightarrow X'(3, -1), Y'(4, -5), Z'(5, -2)$.

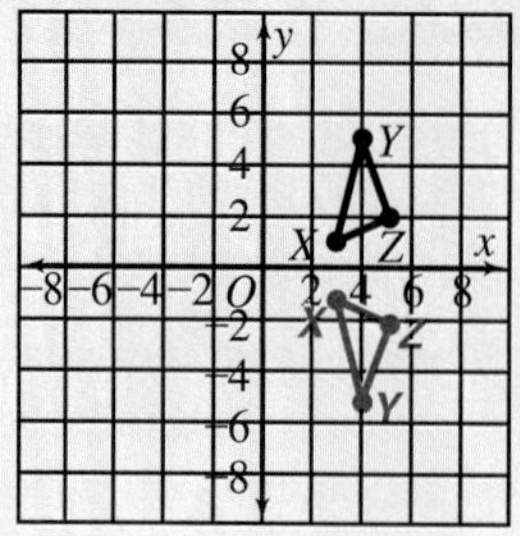

TACTILE LEARNING Have students write the letter A on a piece of paper and fold the paper vertically so that a line of symmetry passes through the point at the top of A. Students then open the paper and lay it flat on their desk. Have students place both index fingers at the top of A. Then slowly trace down each side of A. Have students note that both fingers are directly across from each other and the same distance from the folded line of symmetry at all times. Repeat the activity with the letter N. Have students note that their fingers are the same distance from the line of

Technology Options

Prentice Hall Technology

Software for Learners
- Math Blaster® Mystery*
- Interactive Student Tutorial, Chapter 11*

Teaching Resource Software
- Computer Item Generator 11-7
- Resource Pro™ Chapter 11*

Internet • For related mathematics activities, visit the Prentice Hall site at www.phschool.com/math

**Available on CD-ROM only*

Assignment Options for Exercises On Your Own

To provide for flexible scheduling, this lesson can be split into parts.

1 Core 1–9
Extension 10

2 Core 11–19, 21–26
Extension 20, 27

Use Mixed Review to maintain skills.

2 *Graphing Reflections*

A **reflection,** or flip, is a transformation you can use to create symmetry on the coordinate plane. The line you reflect a figure across is called the **line of reflection.**

■ EXAMPLE 2

Draw the reflected image of $\triangle ABC$. Use the y-axis as the line of reflection. Use arrow notation to describe the original triangle and its reflection.

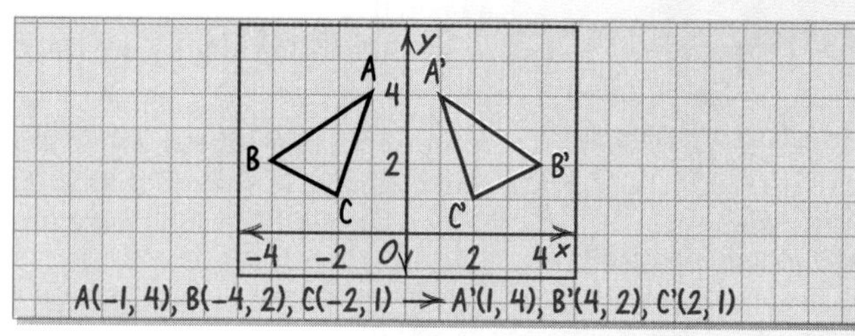

3. The y-coordinates are the same.

3. a. *Look Back* What do you notice about the y-coordinate of each vertex of $\triangle ABC$ and its reflected image?

4a. See margin p. 501 for diagram; $(x, y) \rightarrow (x, -y)$.

4. a. ✔ *Try It Out* Draw $\triangle ABC$ from Example 2 on graph paper. Reflect $\triangle ABC$ across the x-axis. Use arrow notation to describe $\triangle ABC$ and its reflected image.
   b. What do you notice about the y-coordinate of each vertex of $\triangle ABC$ and its reflected image? **The y-coordinate of the image is the opposite of the y-coordinate of the original figure.**

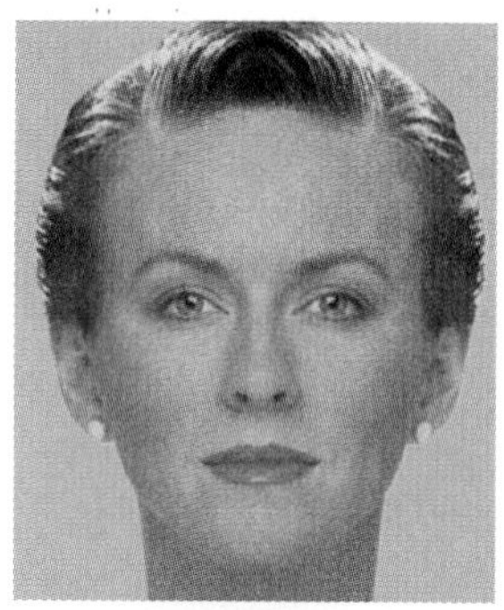

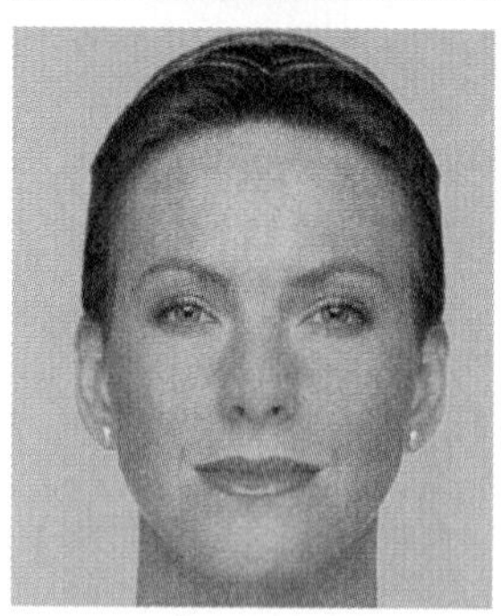

A person's face is not perfectly symmetrical. These photographs are of the same woman. The top one is the right side of the woman's face and its reflection. The bottom is the left side and its reflection.

Work Together *Exploring Symmetry*

Work with a partner. Fold a rectangular piece of paper into sixths by first folding into thirds and then folding in half as shown at the right.

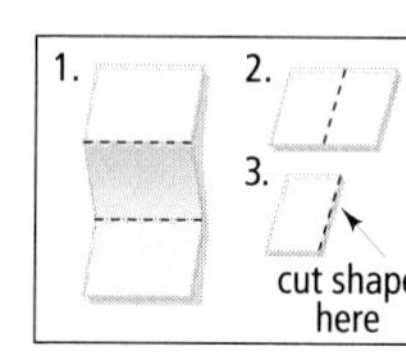

Use scissors to cut a heart shape into the folded paper. Do not cut the edges of the paper.

5. Mark the line or lines of symmetry on paper. **Check students' work.**
6. a. What transformations relate the middle and bottom figures to the top figure? **a–b. See margin p. 501.**
   b. Repeat this activity by folding a rectangular piece of paper into eighths instead of sixths. How does this affect the cut-out figures?

Now you may assign Exercises 11–27.

symmetry, but they are not directly across from each other.

EXTENSION Example 2 Ask students: *Use the diagonal line y = x as the line of reflection. What do you notice about the x- and y-coordinates of each vertex of △ABC and its image?* **The coordinates are reversed: $A(-1, 4) \rightarrow A'(4, -1)$.**

KINESTHETIC LEARNING Have two students show reflection. One student moves his or her arms and head. The other student models the reflection. Have them stand as if on the sides of a 90° angle so they are half facing the class and half facing each other. This allows the class to see the symmetry and to see how to create it.

ASSESSMENT Pair students. Have each student draw four figures–one with no lines of symmetry, one with one line of symmetry, one with two lines of symmetry, and one with more than two lines of symmetry. Ask them not to mark the lines of symmetry. Have partners trade drawings to draw the lines of symmetry.

TACTILE LEARNING Have students use rubbings to draw reflections. Have them draw the original figure with a very soft lead pencil. Then have them fold along the line of reflection, and firmly rub the outside of the paper. The reflected image will transfer to the opposite quadrant if the figure is dark enough.

Work Together

Students can avoid cutting a fold or an edge of the paper by cutting into the middle of the folded paper. Have students unfold their paper before drawing the lines of symmetry.

EXERCISES *On Your Own*

Trace each figure and draw the line(s) of symmetry. If there are no lines of symmetry, write *none*.

1. 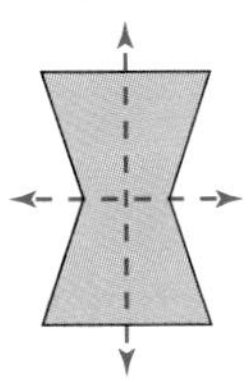

2. 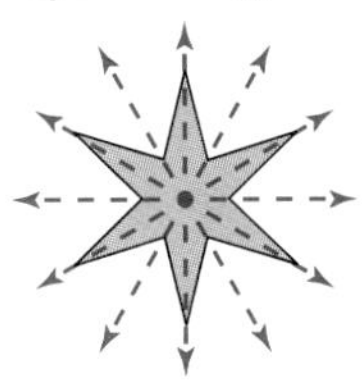

3. none 

4. 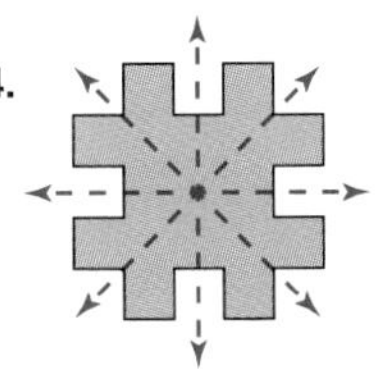

5. 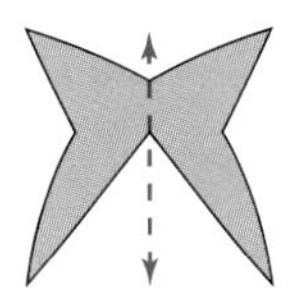

Nature **Describe the line(s) of symmetry for each figure.**

6. 
One line of symmetry down the center of the body of the butterfly.

7. 
Three lines of symmetry, one down the center of each petal.

8. 
Five lines of symmetry, one each bisecting an angle of the five-pointed star formed by the seeds of the apple.

9. *Open-ended* Name two items in your classroom that have a line of symmetry. Explain your choice.
Answers may vary. Samples: window, wall

10. *Research* Photocopy or cut out a picture in a magazine that has symmetry. Draw the line(s) of symmetry.
Check students' work.

Use the graph at the right for Exercises 11–13.

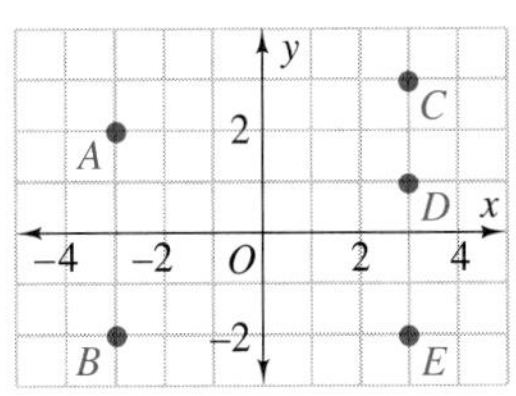

11. For which two points is the x-axis the line of reflection? A, B

12. For which two points is the y-axis the line of reflection? B, E

13. Point C is *not* a reflection of Point E over the x-axis. Why?
It is not the same distance from the x-axis.

Graph each point and its reflection. Write the coordinates of each reflected point.

14. $(3, 8)$ across the x-axis
$(3, -8)$

15. $(-5, 7)$ across the y-axis
$(5, 7)$

16. $(-3, -6)$ across the x-axis
$(-3, 6)$

$\triangle A'B'C'$ is a reflection of $\triangle ABC$ over the y-axis. Complete each statement.

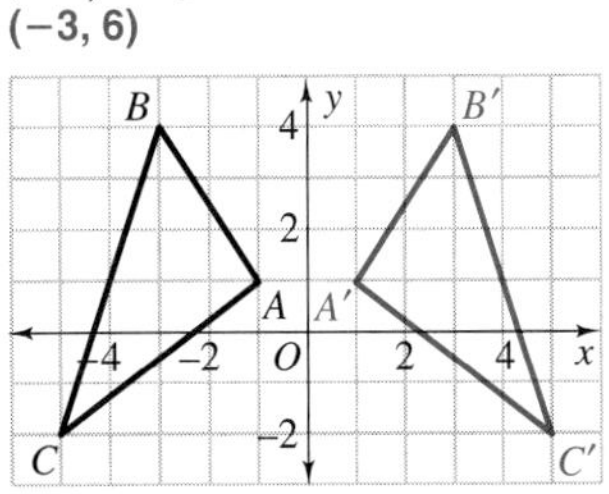

17. $A(-1, 1) \rightarrow A'(■, ■)$ $(1, 1)$

18. $B(-3, 4) \rightarrow B'(■, ■)$ $(3, 4)$

19. $C(-5, -2) \rightarrow C'(■, ■)$ $(5, -2)$

pages 499–500 Think and Discuss

4a. 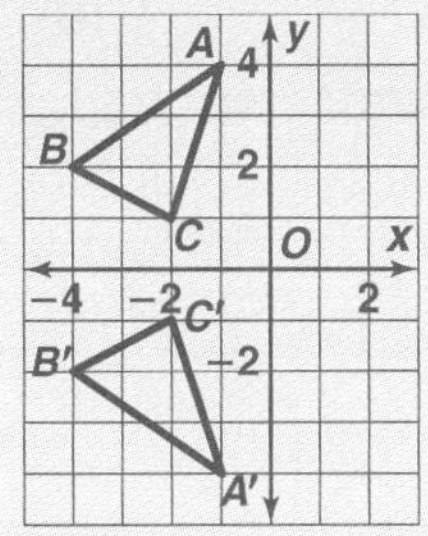

page 500 Work Together

6a. The middle figure is a reflection of the top figure. The bottom figure is a translation of the top figure.

b. Answers may vary. Sample: There are 4 images. A repeating pattern of 2 hearts reflecting each other.

pages 501–502 On Your Own

20a–d. 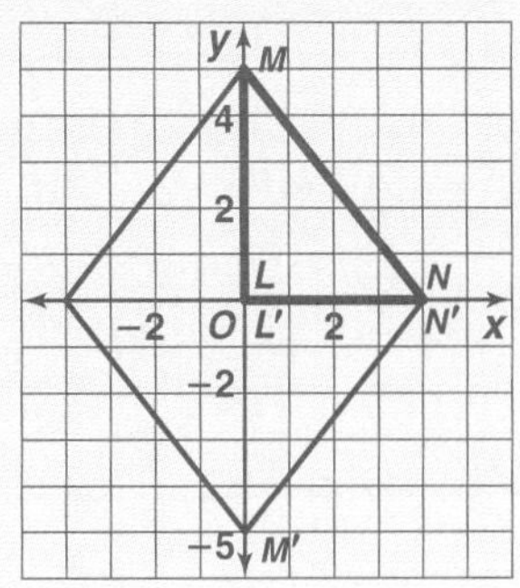

21. The image of a translation has the same orientation as the original figure, and the distance between any point and its image is the same. The image of a reflection faces in the opposite direction, and the farther away a point is from the line of reflection, the greater the distance between the point and its image.

3 Practice

EXERCISES *On Your Own*

Exercises 1–5 Students may need to trace with their fingers to determine symmetry.

Exercise 9 Challenge students to find items with only one line of symmetry, then only two lines of symmetry.

RESEARCH Exercise 10 If students do not have magazines or newspapers available, suggest they trace a picture from another textbook.

Exercises 11–13 Remind students that reflections are the same distance from the line of reflection.

Exercises 14–16 Students may draw these points on the same graph if they clearly label the points.

CONNECTION TO GEOMETRY Exercise 20 Encourage students to give the most specific name for the figure. Ask: *What is special about this quadrilateral?* **Answers may vary. Sample: Opposite sides are parallel; all four sides are equal.**

WRITING Exercise 21 Have students work with a partner to generate a list of similarities and differences before writing their explanations.

WRAP UP

IDENTIFYING THE BIG IDEA Ask students: *How can you identify lines of symmetry?* Then ask: *How can you recognize and graph reflections?*

CHECKPOINT 2

Checkpoint 2 *Lessons 11-5 through 11-7*

1. At a bake sale, Ms. Snow's class sells muffins for $.50 each. Ingredients for the muffins cost $5.
   a. Write an equation to find how many muffins must be sold to make a profit of $25. Answers may vary. Sample: $25 = 0.50n - 5$
   b. How many muffins must be sold to make a profit? 60 muffins
2. Describe the translation of point $A(-1, 4)$ to $A'(6, 2)$. right 7, down 2
3. Draw the line(s) of symmetry.

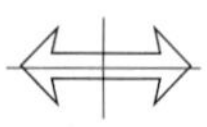

pages 501–502 On Your Own

26a–b.

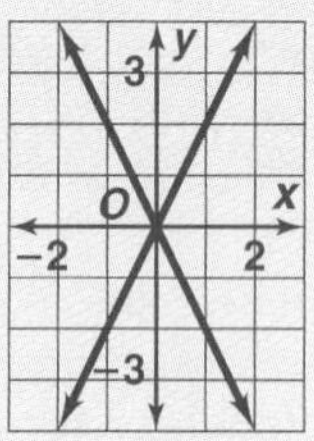

page 503 Checkpoint 2

1.

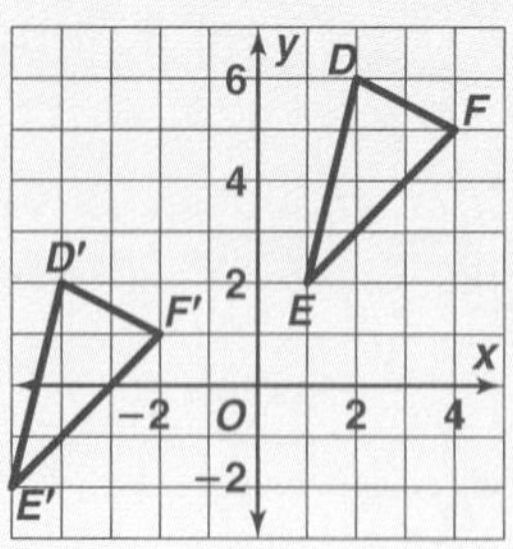

2.

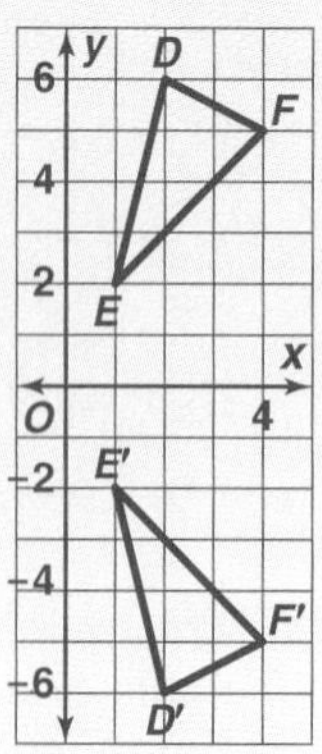

20. a. *Geometry* The vertices of $\triangle LMN$ are $L(0, 0)$, $M(0, 5)$, and $N(4, 0)$. Graph $\triangle LMN$ on a coordinate plane. **a–d. See margin p. 501 for diagram.**
    b. Graph the reflection of $\triangle LMN$ over the x-axis.
    c. Use $\triangle LMN$ and its image. Reflect both triangles over the y-axis.
    d. Outline the perimeter of the figure formed by the four triangles. What type of polygon is formed? **rhombus**

21. *Writing* Explain the difference between a translation and a reflection. Use examples. **See margin.**

Tell whether the graph shows a reflection or a translation. Name the line of reflection or describe the translation.

22.

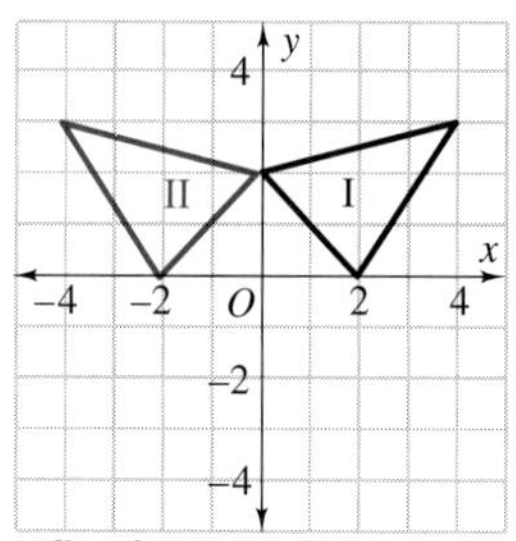

reflection; y-axis

23.

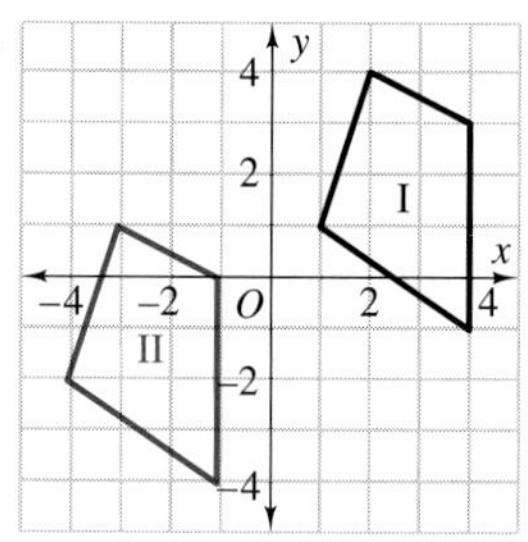

translation; $(x, y) \rightarrow (x + 5, y + 3)$

24.

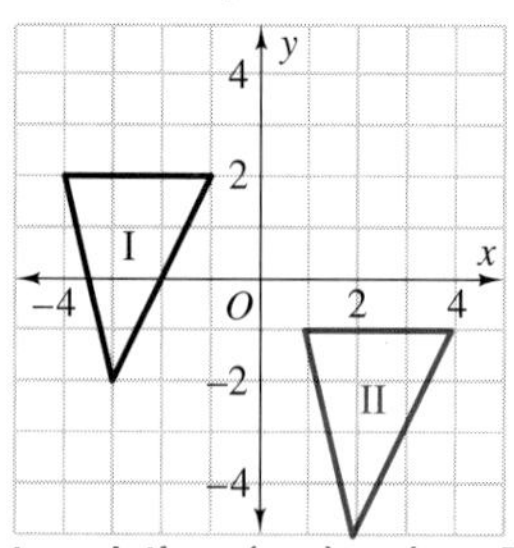

translation: $(x, y) \rightarrow (x + 5, y - 3)$

25.

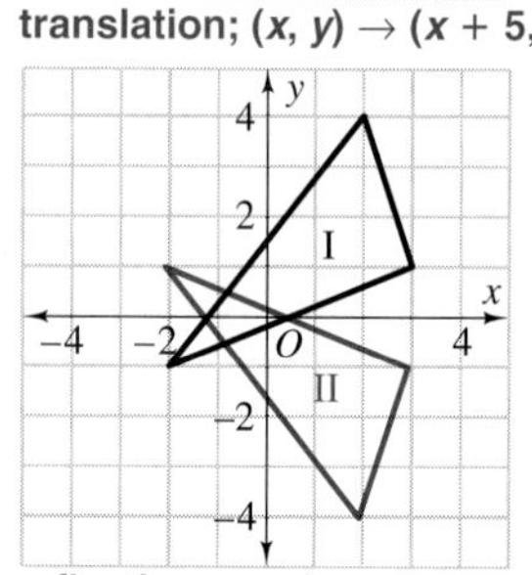

reflection; x-axis

26. a. Graph the line $y = -2x$. **a–b. See margin.**
    b. Draw the reflection of this line across the y-axis.

27. a. *Language* Some of the following words have a line of symmetry. Trace the words that show symmetry. Draw the lines of symmetry.

    BIKE CODE BOY MOM FOOD HIKE EXIT

    b. *Open-ended* Find another word that has a line of symmetry. **Check students' work.**

Artist Scott Kim uses reflections in the creation of his calligraphy.

PROJECT LINK Ask: *What might make it difficult to ask everyone's opinion?* Answers may vary. Sample: Not everyone is available to interview. It's expensive.

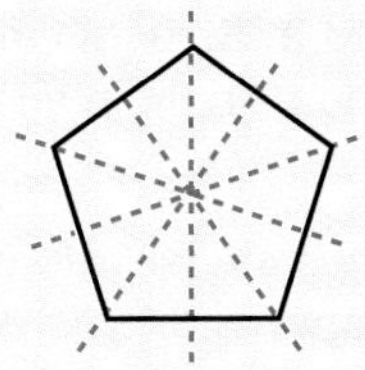

LESSON QUIZ

1. Draw the lines of symmetry of a regular pentagon.

2. $\triangle ABC$ has vertices at $A(1, 4)$, $B(4, 3)$, and $C(3, 1)$. Find the vertices of $\triangle ABC$'s reflection over the y-axis.
 $A'(-1, 4)$; $B'(-4, 3)$; $C'(-3, 1)$

PRACTICE

Practice 11-7 *Symmetry and Reflections*

Use the graph at the right for Exercises 1–3.

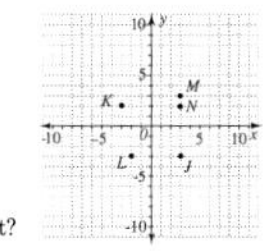

1. For which two points is the *x*-axis a line of reflection? M, J
2. For which two points is the y-axis a line of reflection? K, N
3. Points *L* and *J* are not reflections across the *y*-axis. Why not? Sample: They are not the same distance from the y-axis.

$\triangle A'B'C'$ is a reflection of $\triangle ABC$ across the *x*-axis. Draw $\triangle A'B'C'$ and complete each statement.

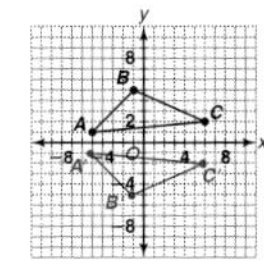

4. $A(-4, 1) \rightarrow A'(■, ■)$ −4, −1
5. $B(-1, 5) \rightarrow B'(■, ■)$ −1, −5
6. $C(6, 2) \rightarrow C'(■, ■)$ 6, −2

Draw the lines of symmetry of each figure. If there are none, write *none*.

7. 8. 9. 10.

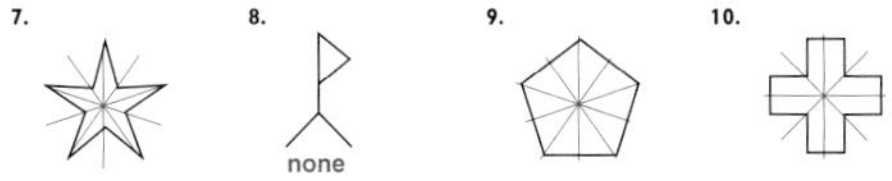

Use the graph at the right. Graph the image point for each reflection. Name the coordinates of the image point.

11. (−3, 4) across the *y*-axis (3, 4)
12. (−4, −2) across the *x*-axis (−4, 2)

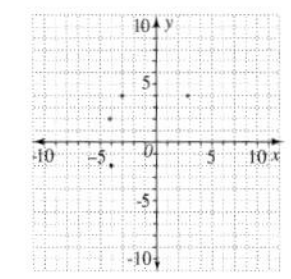

In copymaster and workbook formats

Mixed Review

Make a table for the function represented by each rule. Find $f(0)$, $f(1)$, $f(2)$, and $f(3)$. *(Lesson 10-6)* 28–30. See below.

28. $f(n) = 2n^2 - 1$ 29. $f(n) = 3n + 32$ 30. $f(n) = -5n + 4$ 31. $f(n) = 6 - n$

31.

x	0	1	2	3
f(x)	6	5	4	3

Write *always, sometimes,* or *never*. *(Lesson 7-7)*

32. A chord is ■ a radius. never
33. A diameter is ■ a chord. always
34. A chord is ■ a diameter. sometimes

35. *Biology* Researchers tagged 1,250 black bears in an area of Canada. The researchers made an aerial count of 120 black bears, of which 75 were tagged. Estimate the black bear population. *(Lesson 9-8)* 2,000 black bears

28.

x	0	1	2	3
f(x)	−1	1	7	17

29.

x	0	1	2	3
f(x)	32	35	38	41

30.

x	0	1	2	3
f(x)	4	−1	−6	−11

CHAPTER PROJECT

PROJECT LINK: WRITING

Connect your findings about sample sizes to a real situation. Do you need to survey everyone who watches television to get an idea about which shows are most popular? Explain.

No; a random sample survey will give a reasonable estimate.

RETEACHING

Reteaching 11-7 *Symmetry and Reflections*

Symmetry

A figure is **symmetrical** if one side is a mirror image of the other. The line that divides a figure into two identical parts is called a **line of symmetry.**

The figure below has 2 lines of symmetry.

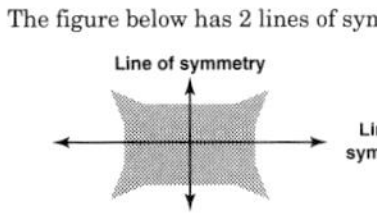

You can trace the figure and fold it along either line to see that the two halves match.

Reflections

A **reflection** is a transformation that creates a mirror image. $\triangle A'B'C'$ is the mirror image of $\triangle ABC$ across the *x*-axis. The *x*-axis is the **line of reflection.**

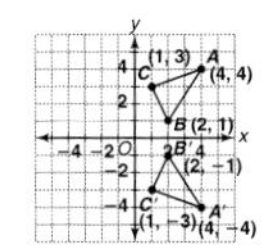

- When you reflect across the *x*-axis, the *x*-coordinates change sign.
- When you reflect across the y-axis, the y-coordinates change sign.
- When you reflect across a line of symmetry, the image is the figure itself.

Draw the line(s) of symmetry. If there are no lines of symmetry, write *none*.

1. 2. 3.

$\triangle ABC$ is shown. Draw $\triangle A'B'C'$ so it is a reflection of $\triangle ABC$ over the specified axis. Then complete each statement.

4. over the *x*-axis
 $A(-4, 4) \rightarrow A'$ (−4, −4)
 $B(-2, 0) \rightarrow B'$ (−2, 0)
 $C(0, 2) \rightarrow C'$ (0, −2)

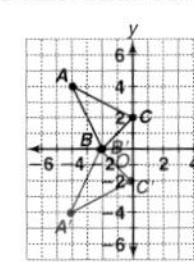

5. over the *y*-axis
 $A(-4, 4) \rightarrow A'$ (4, 4)
 $B(-2, 0) \rightarrow B'$ (2, 0)
 $C(0, 2) \rightarrow C'$ (0, 2)

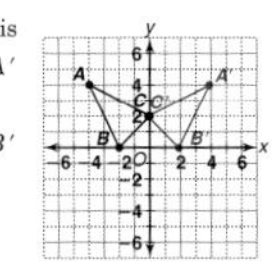

✓ CHECKPOINT 2

Lessons 11-5 through 11-7

For Exercises 1–2, $\triangle DEF$ has vertices $D(2, 6)$, $E(1, 2)$, and $F(4, 5)$.

1. Graph $\triangle DEF$ and its image after a translation 6 units left and 4 units down. See margin p. 502.
2. Graph $\triangle DEF$ and its image after a reflection across the *x*-axis. See back of book.
3. *Writing* Do a line and its image after a translation have the same slope? Explain. Yes; the rise and run do not change when you translate a line, so the slope does not change.
4. *Open-ended* Draw two figures. Be sure the first figure has one line of symmetry, the second has two lines of symmetry. Check students' work.
5. Samantha delivers pizzas for Alfonso's Pizza. Alfonso pays Samantha \$2 for each pizza she delivers.
 a. Samantha uses \$10 worth of gas each week. Write an equation to find Samantha's weekly profit. $y = 2p - 10$
 b. How many pizzas must Samantha deliver to make a profit of \$70 in a week? 40 pizzas

ENRICHMENT

Minds on Math Transparency

11-7

Shauna and Tatum are making marshmallow treats for camp. Their recipe calls for a total of 160 ounces of marshmallows. Marshmallows come in 16-ounce, 24-ounce, and 36-ounce bags. How many different combinations of bags could they use so that they would not have any left over?

7 combinations of 16-oz, 24-oz, 36-oz bags as follows: (10, 0, 0), (7, 2, 0), (4, 4, 0), (4, 1, 2), (1, 6, 0), (1, 3, 2), (1, 0, 4).

See *Solution Key* for worked-out answers.

Extra Practice, Lesson 11-7, page 524

PROBLEM SOLVING PRACTICE ★★

This page provides problems for students to solve using their knowledge of scientific notation, combinations and permutations, symmetry, percents, linear equations, proportions, and probability. Allow students to use any method they find helpful.

Exercises 1 and 5 Review with students what the exponent means in a number written in scientific notation.

Exercises 2 and 3 Students may want to draw diagrams to help them find the correct answers.

Exercise 4 Direct students to write the words on a sheet of paper and try to draw a line of symmetry for each.

Exercise 8 To help students find the correct equation, they can write the slope and *y*-intercept for the line separately before looking at the answer choices.

PROBLEM SOLVING PRACTICE ★★★★★

Choose the best answer.

1. The approximate weight of the largest blue whale ever measured was 160,000 kilograms. This weight expressed in scientific notation is — D

   A. 1.6×10^6 kg B. 0.16×10^6 kg
   C. 16×10^4 kg D. 1.6×10^5 kg

2. David is planting a row of 5 rosebushes in his garden. Each bush has a different color rose. In how many ways could David plant the rosebushes? J

   F. 10 G. 25 H. 60 J. 120

3. For a social studies project, students will prepare a presentation about the culture of two different countries. If students have six countries to choose from, how many different groups of two countries can be chosen? C

   A. 69 B. 30 C. 15 D. 12

4. Which word has a line of symmetry? H

   F. BOOT G. TIE
   H. HIKE J. BACK

5. The number of visitors in one year to the Grand Canyon National Park were 4.4×10^6. The number of visitors is — B

   A. 440,000 B. 4,400,000
   C. 44,000,000 D. 440,000,000

6. The Outdoor Store had a sale. All clothing was sold for 30% off the marked price. Esteban bought a jacket marked \$58.90 and a pair of jeans marked \$29.95. Estimate the total amount he spent. G

   F. \$30 G. \$60 H. \$90 J. \$120

7. Which ordered pair is *not* a solution to the linear equation $y = 2x + 5$? C

   A. (2, 9) B. (5, 15)
   C. (3, 12) D. (4, 13)

Please note that items 8–10 have *five* answer choices.

8. Which linear equation is graphed? H

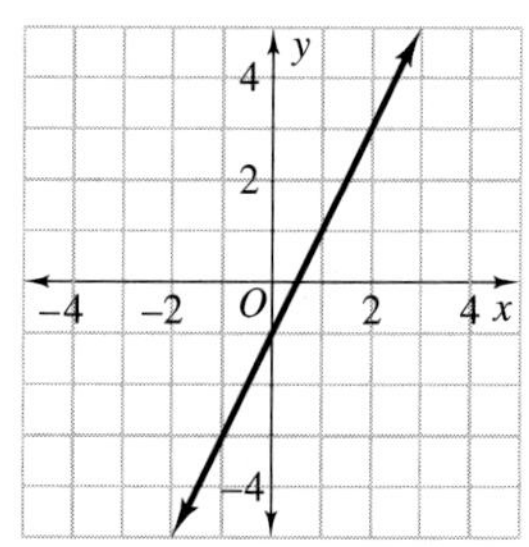

   F. $y = -2x - 1$ G. $y = 2x + 1$
   H. $y = 2x - 1$ J. $y = -2x + 1$
   K. $y = \frac{1}{2}x - 1$

9. For a party of 50 people, 29 people chose chicken for their main course. For a banquet of 300 people, what is a good prediction for the number of people who would choose chicken as their main course? C

   A. 89 B. 145 C. 174
   D. 203 E. 205

10. Lupe picked a letter out of a bag 50 times and replaced it each time. She drew the letter *A* 20 times, the letter *B* 10 times, the letter *C* 15 times, and the letter *D* 5 times. If there are 10 letters in the bag, how many letters would you expect to have the letter *C*? J

   F. 6 G. 5 H. 4
   J. 3 K. 2

11-8 Teaching Notes

1 Focus

CONNECTING TO PRIOR KNOWLEDGE Most students understand the general meaning of the word rotate. Ask students: *Give examples of things that rotate.* **Answers may vary. Sample: hands of a clock, tires, blades of a fan, players' positions on a volley ball team**

2 Teach

THINK AND DISCUSS

ERROR ALERT! Example 1 Students may assume symmetrical figures have rotational symmetry. **Remediation:** Have students work with the following letters of the alphabet. Begin with A and T. Point out that the images rotated 180° will not fit exactly on top of the original figure. Any figure can be rotated, but it may not have rotational symmetry.

Question 3 If you have block scheduling or extended class periods, challenge students to find the capital letters of the alphabet that have *both* symmetry, and rotational symmetry. **H, I, O, X**

DIVERSITY and ALTERNATIVE METHOD and VISUAL LEARNING Example 2 Visualizing relationships after movement may be difficult for some students. Give them tracing paper. Have them trace the figures then model the rotation by holding their pencil tip on point *O* and turning their drawing. Have them sketch the rotation on their assignment paper.

GEOMETRY Connection

11-8 Rotations

What You'll Learn

1. To identify figures that have rotational symmetry
2. To rotate a figure about a point

...And Why

Many artistic designs use rotational symmetry.

Here's How

Look for questions that
- build understanding
- ✔ check understanding

THINK AND DISCUSS

1 *Identifying Rotational Symmetry*

The blades of this windmill revolve counterclockwise. One full turn brings the blade at position *A* back to its original position.

1. How much of a turn brings the blade at position A to the A′ position? The A′′ position? The A′′′ position? **90°; 180°; 270°**

A **rotation** is a transformation that turns a figure about a fixed point (*O*). Point *O* is the **center of rotation.** In this book, all rotations are counterclockwise.

A figure has **rotational symmetry** when an image after a rotation of 180° or less fits exactly on top of the original figure. In the photo, windmill blades show 90° rotational symmetry because after a turn of 90° the blades look like they did before the turn. They also have 180° symmetry.

■ **EXAMPLE 1** *Real-World Problem Solving*

Nature Does the flower at the right have rotational symmetry?

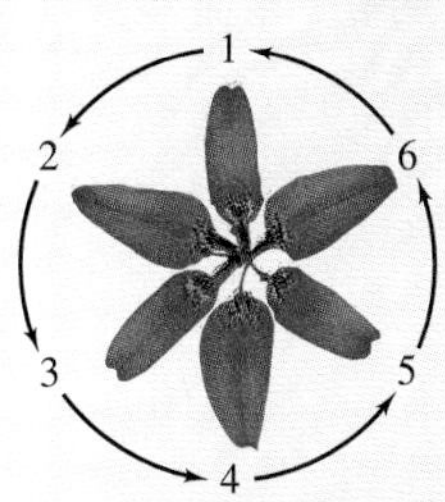

To determine if the flower has rotational symmetry, rotate petal 1 to the position of each of the other petals.

Since the flower looks the same at each position, the flower has rotational symmetry.

Lesson Planning Options

Prerequisite Skills

- measuring angles (7-2)
- graphing on a coordinate plane (11-1)

Vocabulary/Symbols

rotation, center of rotation, rotational symmetry

Resources

Student Edition

Skills Handbook, p. 528
Extra Practice, p. 524
Glossary/Study Guide

Teaching Resources

Chapter Support File, Ch. 11
- Lesson Planner 11-8
- Practice 11-8, Reteaching 11-8
- Answer Masters 11-8

Teaching Aids Master 4
Glossary, Spanish Resources

Transparencies

2, 3, 15, 99, Minds on Math 11-8

Warm Up

Use two of the given digits to make the equation true. 2, 3, 4

$8 \div \frac{\blacksquare}{\blacksquare} = 10\frac{2}{3}$ $\frac{3}{4}$

■ ADDITIONAL EXAMPLES

FOR EXAMPLE 1

Does this figure have rotational symmetry? Explain. **Yes, it looks the same after a quarter turn.**

FOR EXAMPLE 2

Draw the image of $\triangle ABC$ after a rotation of 90˚ about *B*.

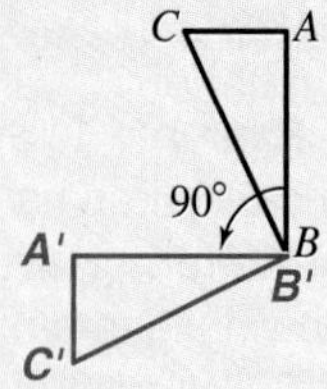

ASSESSMENT Have students choose a nonsymmetrical letter of the alphabet, and use it to illustrate a rotation of either 90˚, 180˚, or 270˚. Ask students to exchange drawings and identify the degree of rotation.

3 Practice

EXERCISES *On Your Own*

Exercises 1–7 Suggest students include the degree of rotation in their answer explanations.

Technology Options

Prentice Hall Technology

Software for Learners

- Hot Page™ 11–10*
- Math Blaster® Mystery*
- Interactive Student Tutorial, Chapter 11*

Teaching Resource Software

- Computer Item Generator 11-8
- Resource Pro™ Chapter 11*

Internet • For related mathematics activities, visit the Prentice Hall site at www.phschool.com/math

**Available on CD-ROM only*

Assignment Options for Exercises On Your Own

To provide for flexible scheduling, this lesson can be split into parts.

1 **Core** 1–8, 13
Extension 14

2 **Core** 9–12, 15–19
Extension 20

Use Mixed Review to maintain skills.

506

2. a. ✔ *Try It Out* Does star *A* at the right have rotational symmetry? How do you know?

b. Does star *B* have rotational symmetry? Explain.

a. Yes; the image of star *A* after 72° rotation fits exactly on top of the original figure.
b. No; you cannot rotate star *B* 180° or less so that the image fits on top of the original figure.

3. *Think About It* Name a capital letter in the alphabet that has rotational symmetry. Name one that does not have rotational symmetry. **Answers may vary. Letters with symmetry: H, I, N, O, S, X, Z; remaining letters have no rotational symmetry.**

Now you may assign Exercises 1–8, 13, 14.

2 *Rotating a Figure*

In the figure below, $\triangle TRO$, has been rotated 90° around point *O*. The center of rotation is point *O*. The image of $\triangle TRO$ is $\triangle T'R'O'$.

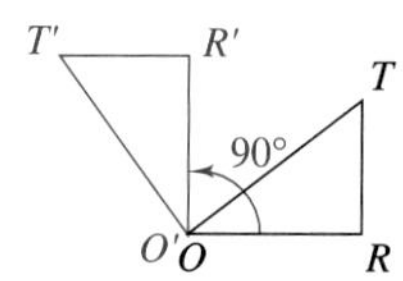

■ EXAMPLE 2

Draw the image of $\triangle TRO$ after a rotation of:

a. 180° about *O*.
b. 270° about *O*.

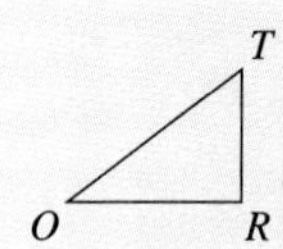

a.

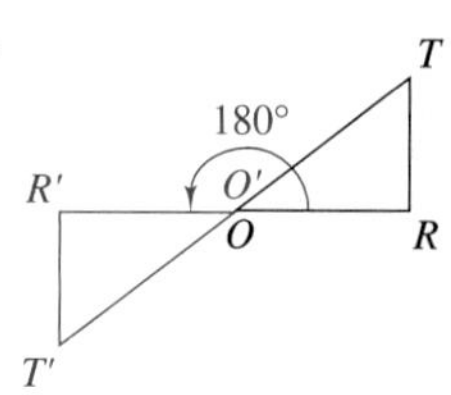

b.

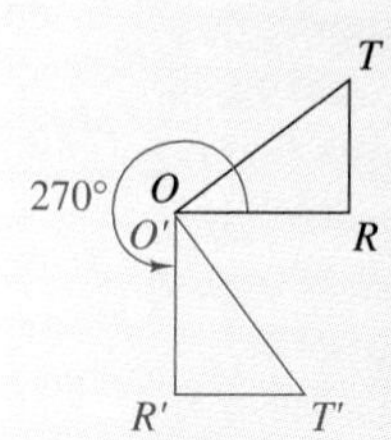

4. a. ✔ *Try It Out* In the square at the right, what rotation will move point *A* to the position held by point *B*? What rotation will move *A* to *C*? What rotation will move *A* to *D*? **90°; 180°; 270**

b. Does the square have rotational symmetry? **Yes; the image of the square under a 180° or a 90° rotation fits exactly on top of the original figure.**

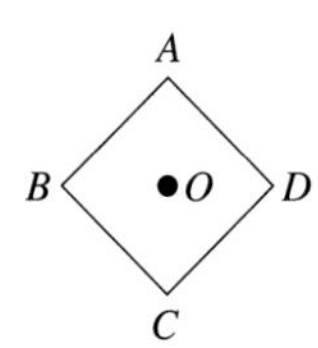

Now you may assign Exercises 9–12, 15–20.

WRITING Exercise 8 Have students include a drawing with their description.

Exercises 9–12 Some students may have difficulty rotating a whole figure. Have them rotate one segment or curve and then draw the rest of the shape.

CONNECTION TO ENGINEERING
Exercise 14 Challenge a student interested in engineering to research why a rotary gasoline engine's rotor is triangular. Ask the student to share the information with the class.

Exercises 15–19 Point out the figure is purposefully not symmetrical so there is only one answer.

WRAP UP

IDENTIFYING THE BIG IDEA Ask students to explain how to recognize rotational symmetry and how to draw the image of a figure after a rotation.

PORTFOLIO Share with students the criteria you use to assess their work in portfolios, as well as how you plan to use the results. Students should understand how the rubrics are used to assess their work, how each piece in the portfolio counts, and how the scores they get in their portfolios affect their overall evaluation.

EXERCISES *On Your Own*

Which figures below have rotational symmetry? Explain.

1. 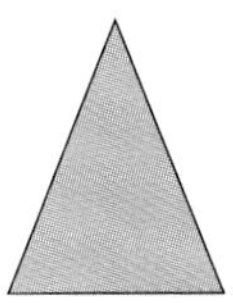

2. 

3. 

4. 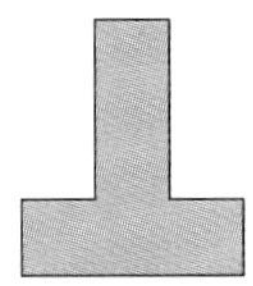

5. 

6. 

7. 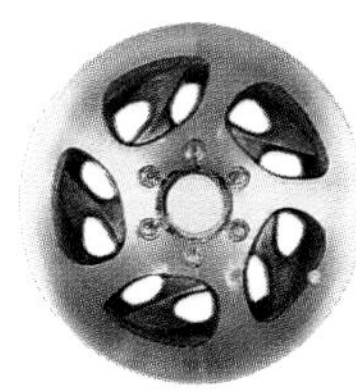

1–8. See margin.

8. *Writing* Describe an object in your classroom that has rotational symmetry. Explain how it shows rotational symmetry.

Trace and shade each figure in Exercises 9–12. Draw the image of each figure after a rotation of 90°, 180°, and 270° about point *O*. **9–12. See back of book.**

9. 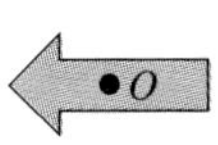

10. 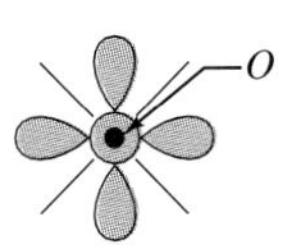

11. 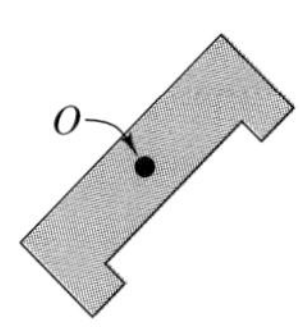

12. 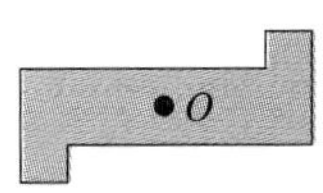

13. Which figures in Exercises 9–12 have rotational symmetry? **See margin.**

14. *Engineering* In a rotary gasoline engine, a "triangular" rotor moves in a specially shaped chamber. The three tips of the rotor always touch the walls of the chamber. This divides the chamber into three parts which change in volume as the rotor rotates. Does the rotor have rotational symmetry? Explain.
Yes; you can fit the image on top of the original figure after rotating the figure 120°.

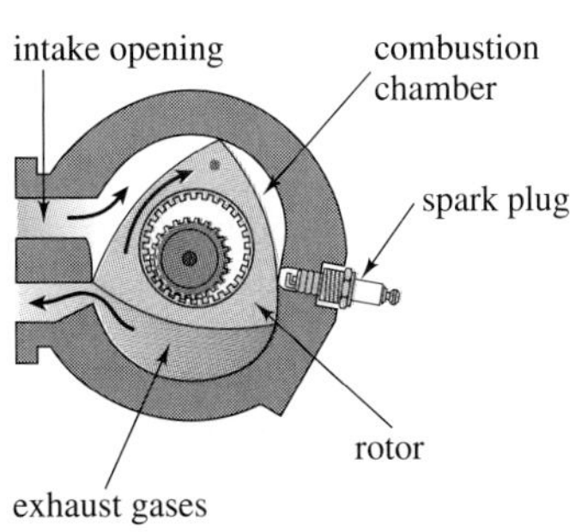

pages 507–508 On Your Own

1. **No; you cannot rotate the figure 180° or less so that the image fits on top of the original figure.**
2. **Yes; the image after 180° rotation fits exactly on top of the original figure.**
3. **Yes; the image after 180° or 90° rotation fits exactly on top of the original figure.**
4. **No; you cannot rotate the figure 180° or less so that the image fits on top of the original figure.**
5. **No; you cannot rotate the figure 180° or less so that the image fits on top of the original figure.**
6. **Yes; the image after 60°, 120°, or 180° rotation fits exactly on top of the original figure.**
7. **Yes; the image after 72° rotation fits exactly on top of the original figure.**
8. **Answers may vary. Sample: ceiling tile; if you rotate a tile 180°, it will fit in the same space.**
13. **The figures in exercises 10 and 12 have rotational symmetry because each can be fit exactly on top of itself after a rotation of 180° or less.**

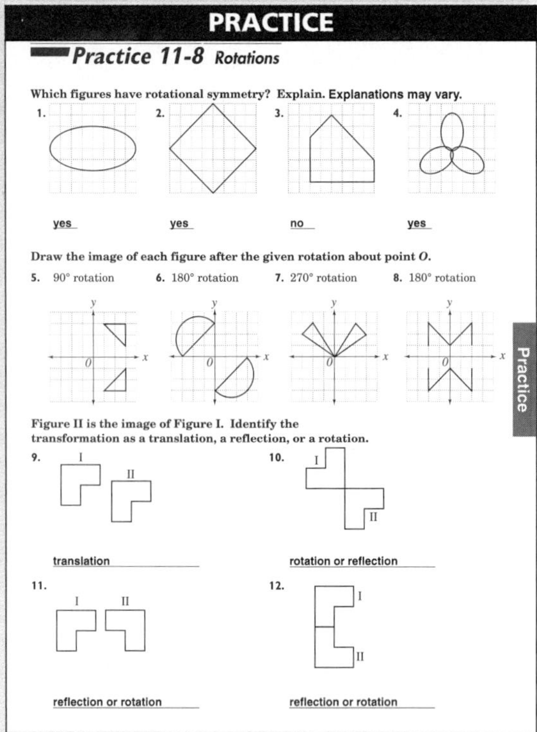

PRACTICE

Practice 11-8 Rotations

Which figures have rotational symmetry? Explain. Explanations may vary.

1. yes 2. yes 3. no 4. yes

Draw the image of each figure after the given rotation about point *O*.

5. 90° rotation 6. 180° rotation 7. 270° rotation 8. 180° rotation

Figure II is the image of Figure I. Identify the transformation as a translation, a reflection, or a rotation.

9. translation
10. rotation or reflection
11. reflection or rotation
12. reflection or rotation

In copymaster and workbook formats

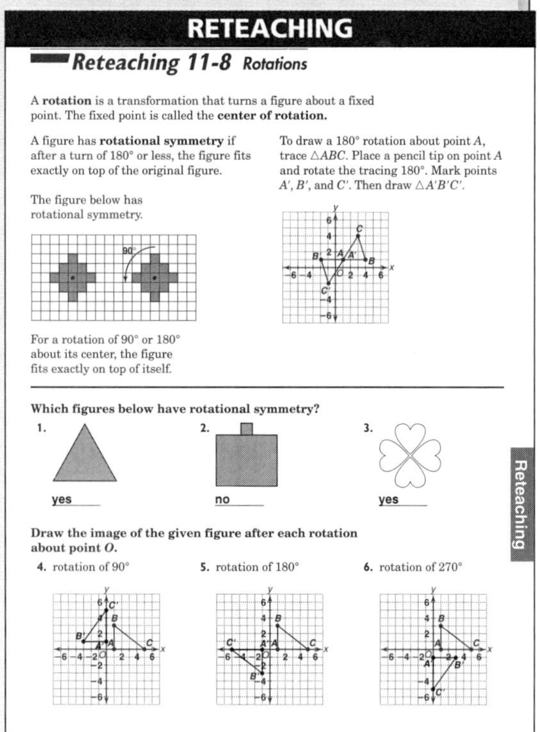

RETEACHING

Reteaching 11-8 Rotations

A **rotation** is a transformation that turns a figure about a fixed point. The fixed point is called the **center of rotation.**

A figure has **rotational symmetry** if after a turn of 180° or less, the figure fits exactly on top of the original figure.

The figure below has rotational symmetry.

For a rotation of 90° or 180° about its center, the figure fits exactly on top of itself.

To draw a 180° rotation about point *A*, trace △*ABC*. Place a pencil tip on point *A* and rotate the tracing 180°. Mark points *A′*, *B′*, and *C′*. Then draw △*A′B′C′*.

Which figures below have rotational symmetry?

1. yes 2. no 3. yes

Draw the image of the given figure after each rotation about point *O*.

4. rotation of 90° 5. rotation of 180° 6. rotation of 270°

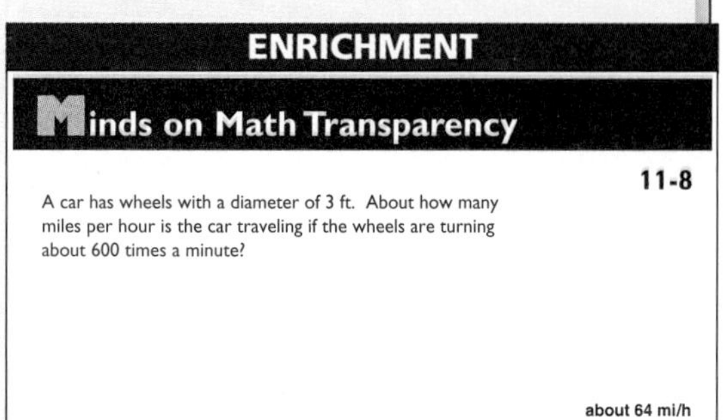

ENRICHMENT

Minds on Math Transparency

11-8

A car has wheels with a diameter of 3 ft. About how many miles per hour is the car traveling if the wheels are turning about 600 times a minute?

about 64 mi/h

See *Solution Key* for worked-out answers.

LESSON QUIZ

1. Which of the following math symbols have rotational symmetry? **b and c**

   a. > b. ÷ c. %

2. On graph paper, draw triangle △*XYZ* with vertices at *X*(0, 0), *Y*(3, 4), and *Z*(0, 4). Then draw the three images formed by rotating the triangle 90°, 180°, and 270° about point *X*.

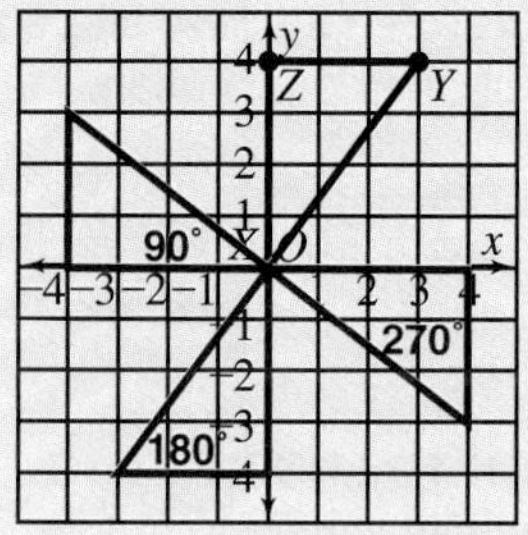

Figure II is the image of Figure I. Identify each transformation as a translation, a reflection, or a rotation.

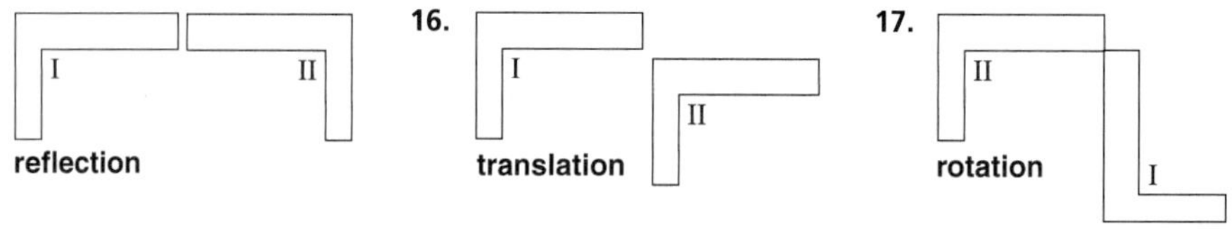

15. reflection
16. translation
17. rotation
18. reflection
19. rotation

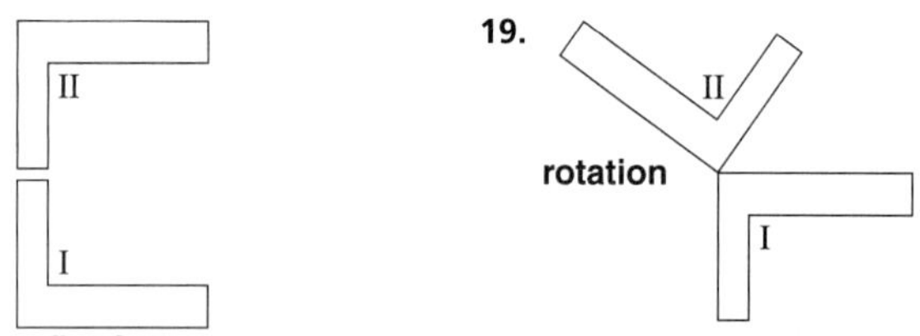

20. a. On graph paper, draw rectangle *ABCD* with vertices at *A*(0, 0), *B*(0, 2), *C*(4, 2), and *D*(4, 0). **b. (2, 1)**
    b. What are the coordinates of the center of the rectangle?
    c. Draw three images formed by rotating the rectangle 90°, 180°, and 270° about its center.
    d. Draw three images formed by rotating the rectangle 90°, 180°, and 270° about the origin.
    a; c–d. See margin p. 509.

PORTFOLIO
Select one or two items from your work for this chapter. Consider:
- cooperative work
- work you found challenging
- part of your project

Explain why you have included each selection.

Mixed Review

Calculator **Find the length of the third side of each right triangle to the nearest unit.** *(Lesson 8-6)*

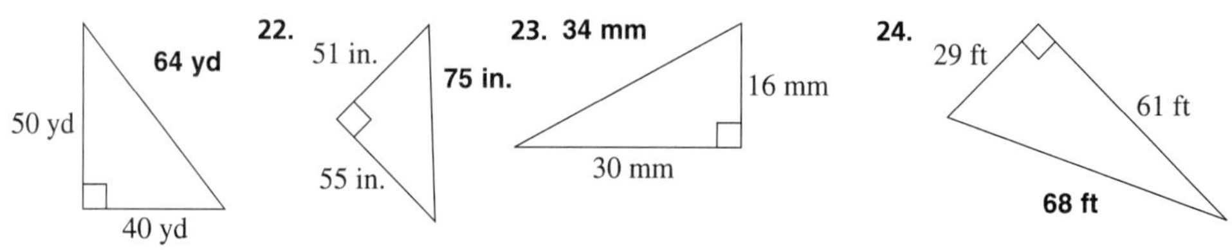

21. **64 yd** (50 yd, 40 yd)
22. **75 in.** (51 in., 55 in.)
23. **34 mm** (16 mm, 30 mm)
24. **68 ft** (29 ft, 61 ft)

25. The ratio of vowels to consonants in the word *bear* is 2 : 2. List ten more animal names, then write a ratio for each that compares the vowels to consonants. *(Lesson 9-1)* **Check students' work.**

26. *Choose a Strategy* At a museum, each adult pays $3 and each student pays $2. A group of 20 people paid a total of $44. How many are adults and how many are students? **4 adults, 16 students**

FINISHING THE CHAPTER PROJECT

PROJECT DAY You may wish to plan a project day on which students share their completed projects. Encourage students to explain their process as well as their product.

PROJECT NOTEBOOK Ask students to review their project work and bring their notebooks up to date.

SCORING RUBRIC

3 For each of ten samples, you provide a table listing the number and percentage of each bean type in the sample. For each type of bean, you draw a graph of percent versus sample size. You write a paragraph describing how sample size affects the accuracy of the survey results. Your work is clear and provides convincing evidence to support the statements you make in your paragraph.

2 You collect data and calculate percentages accurately for at least seven sample sizes. You provide percentage versus sample size graphs for at least two of the bean types, and you write a brief conclusion to your investigation.

1 Your data, your graphs, and your conclusions are incomplete or do not provide a clear picture of your work or your findings.

0 You omit important parts of the project.

Finishing the Chapter Project

CHAPTER PROJECT

People's choice

Find a Sample Size The Project Link questions on pages 481, 492, and 503 should help you complete your project. Here is a checklist to help you gather together the parts of your project.

- ✔ the table of data from all ten samples
- ✔ a graph for each sample
- ✔ a paragraph about sampling

Plan a presentation to show your results. Explain the connection between the size of a sample and how accurately that sample represents the container of beans.

Reflect and Revise

Show your graphs to a friend or family member, and practice your presentation. If necessary, make revisions that make your ideas more forceful or your graphs more clear.

Web Extension

Prentice Hall's Internet site contains information you might find helpful as you complete your project. Visit www.phschool.com/mgm2/ch11 for some links and ideas related to sampling.

pages 507–508 On Your Own

20a.

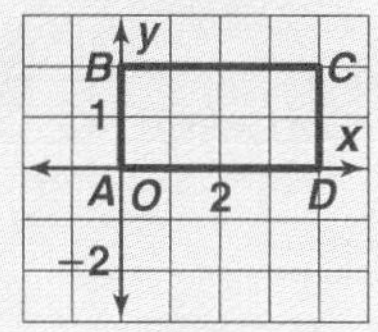

c.

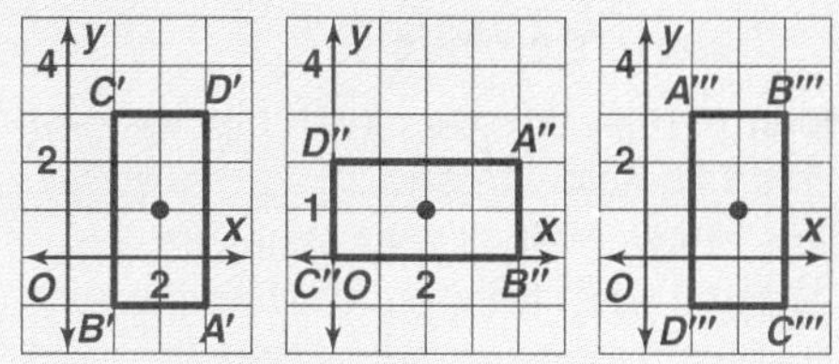

d.

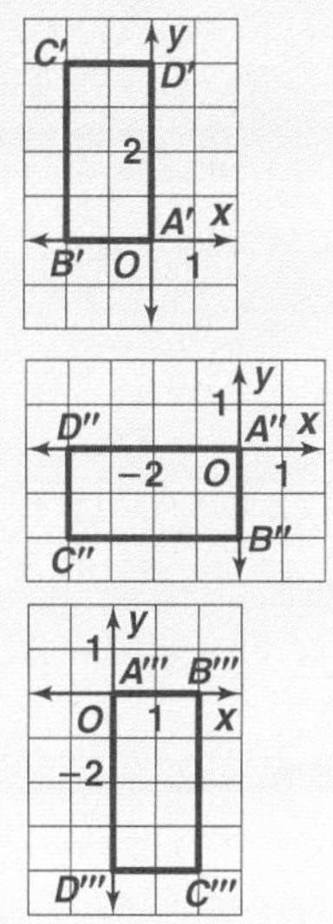

STUDENT SELF-ASSESSMENT SURVEY

Chapter 11 Student Self-Assessment Survey

1. Now that you have finished this chapter, think about what you have learned about graphing in the coordinate plane. Check each topic that you feel confident you understand.
   - ______ graph points on the coordinate plane (11-1)
   - ______ identify quadrants (11-1)
   - ______ find solutions of equations in two variables (11-2)
   - ______ graph linear equations (11-2)
   - ______ calculate the slope of a line (11-3)
   - ______ draw graphs of parabolas (11-4)
   - ______ draw graphs of absolute value functions (11-4)
   - ______ write equations to solve problems (11-5)
   - ______ graph translations and write rules for them (11-6)
   - ______ identify lines of symmetry (11-7)
   - ______ graph reflections (11-7)
   - ______ identify figures that have rotational symmetry (11-8)
   - ______ rotate figures about a point (11-8)
2. Before the Chapter Assessment, I need to review ______
3. a. Check one. In general, I thought this chapter was
   ____ a snap ____ easy ____ average ____ hard ____ a monster
   b. Why do you feel this way? ______
4. In this chapter, I did my best work on ______
5. In this chapter, I had trouble with ______
6. List three situations outside the classroom in which people could use coordinate graphs. ______
7. When you work with translations and rotations, it helps to imagine moving objects in space. Do you find this easy or hard? ______ Explain. ______

Vocabulary/Symbols

center of rotation, coordinate plane, graph of an equation, image, line of reflection, line of symmetry, linear equation, ordered pair (*x, y*), parabola, prime notation (*A*′), quadrant, reflection, rotation, rotational symmetry, slope of a line, solution, symmetrical, symmetry, tessellation, transformations, translation

Materials/Manipulatives

- dot paper

Resources

Student Edition

Extra Practice, p. 524
Glossary/Study Guide

Teaching Resources

Chapter Support File, Ch. 11
- Student Self-Assessment Survey

Glossary, Spanish Resources
Tools for Studying Smarter

WRAP UP

Exercises 1 and 2 Remind students which coordinate in the ordered pair is *x* and which is *y*. As an example, have a volunteer plot the points (4, 2) and (2, 4) for the class before they begin to work on the exercises.

Exercise 5 Encourage students to follow a number of steps to eliminate the incorrect choices. Students can first determine whether the slope is positive or negative. Then they can check the ratio of rise over run.

ASSESSMENT **Exercises 6-9** Have students work in groups of two or three. First have group members graph the lines individually. Group members exchange graphs and calculate the slope by counting. Then students compare slopes to make sure everyone has the same slope. If the slopes are different, have students compare graphs and counting.

WRITING **Exercise 10b** Encourage students to include diagrams with their written responses. Students can refer to their diagrams for support in their answers.

11 WRAP UP

The Coordinate Plane and Graphing Linear Equations 11-1, 11-2

The **coordinate plane** is formed by a horizontal number line called the ***x*-axis** and a vertical number line called the ***y*-axis.** Every point on the plane is described by an *ordered pair* of numbers (*x*, *y*) called **coordinates.** An equation is linear if its solutions lie on a straight line.

Use the graph for Exercises 1 and 2.

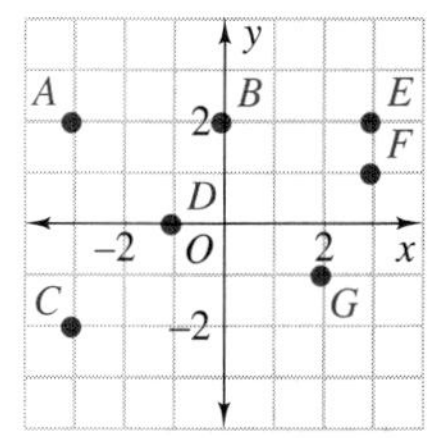

1. Name the point with the given coordinates.
   a. $(-3, 2)$ **A** b. $(2, -1)$ **G** c. $(3, 1)$ **F**
2. Write the coordinates of each point.
   a. *B* **(0, 2)** b. *C* **(−3, −2)** c. *D* **(−1, 0)**
3. Tell whether each ordered pair is a solution of $y = 3x - 5$.
   a. $(5, 10)$ b. $(-2, -1)$ c. $(1, -2)$
   yes; (10) = 3(5) − 5 b. no; (−1) ≠ 3(−2) − 5 c. yes; (−2) = 3(1) − 5
4. a. Find four solutions of the equation $y = x + 4$.
   b. Graph the ordered pairs on a coordinate plane. **See back of book.**
   a. Answers may vary. Samples: (−2, 2), (−1, 3), (0, 4), (2, 6)

Finding the Slope of a Line 11-3

The **slope** of a line is the ratio $\frac{rise}{run}$.

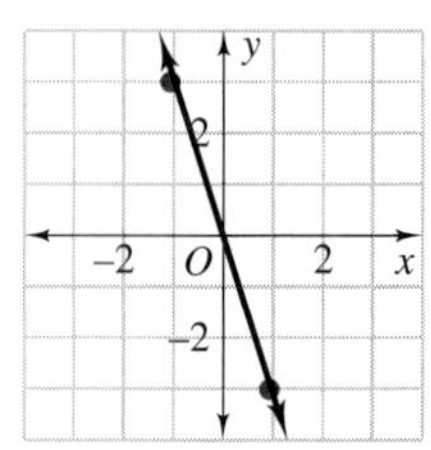

5. **Choose A, B, C or D.** What is the slope of the line graphed at the right? **B**
   A. $\frac{3}{1}$ B. $\frac{-3}{1}$ C. $\frac{1}{3}$ D. $\frac{-1}{3}$

Graph each set of points and find the slope of the line through the points. **6–9. See back of book for graphs.**

6. $(-2, 6), (4, 3)$ $-\frac{1}{2}$
7. $(-3, 2), (-1, 5)$ $\frac{3}{2}$
8. $(0, 5), (9, 8)$ $\frac{1}{3}$
9. $(6, 2), (-3, 4)$ $-\frac{2}{9}$

Exploring Nonlinear Relationships 11-4

The graph of a parabola is U-shaped. The graph of an absolute value function is V-shaped.

Remind students that the new mathematical terms in this chapter are defined in the Glossary/Study Guide in the back of the book.

10. a. Graph $(-2, 0)$, $(0, -4)$, $(2, 0)$, and $(-4, 12)$. See back of book.
b. *Writing* Explain whether $y = x^2 - 4$ or $y = |2x| - 4$ is a better model for the data. $y = x^2 - 4$; all four points lie on its graph.

11. Which equation has the greatest value for y when $x = 3$? When $x = 12$? I; II

I. $y = |3x + 5|$ II. $y = x^2 - 6$ III. $y = -2x^2 + 26$

Problem Solving Strategies 11-5

Some problems describe relationships between numbers. You can write an equation to find a solution.

12. The school band made a profit of \$352 on their spring concert. They sold 116 tickets and spent \$25 on photocopying. How much did each ticket cost? \$3.25

Geometric Transformations and Symmentry 11-6, 11-7, 11-8

You can move a figure in three ways. You can slide it, flip it, or turn it. The names for these *transformations* are **translations, reflections,** and **rotations.**

A figure has a **line of symmetry** when one side is a mirror image of the other side.

13. On graph paper, draw $\triangle SUN$ and its image after the translation $(x, y) \longrightarrow (x + 3, y - 4)$.

13.
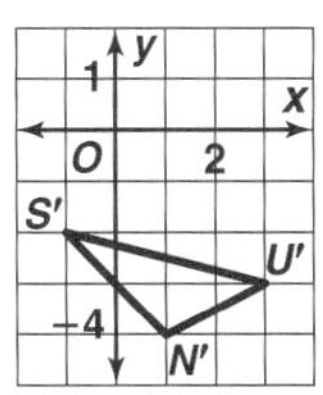

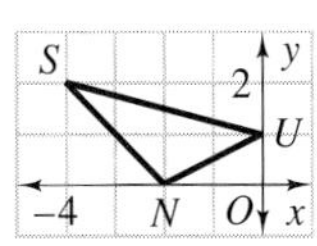

14. *Open-ended* Draw an everyday object that has at least two lines of symmetry. Show the lines of symmetry.
Check students' work.

Figure II is the image of Figure I. Is the transformation a *translation*, a *reflection*, or a *rotation*?

15.
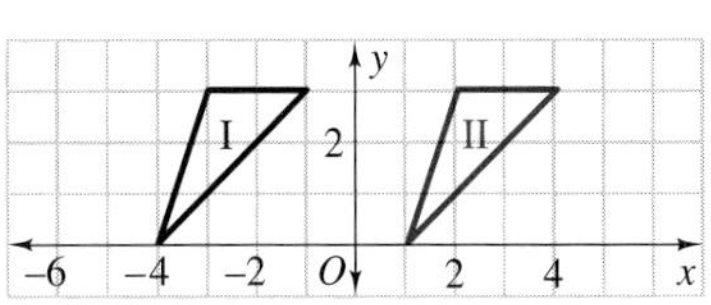

translation

16.
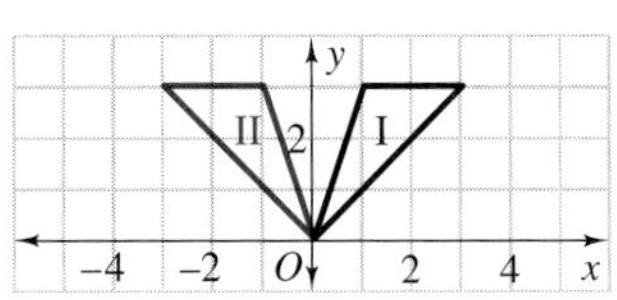

reflection

17.
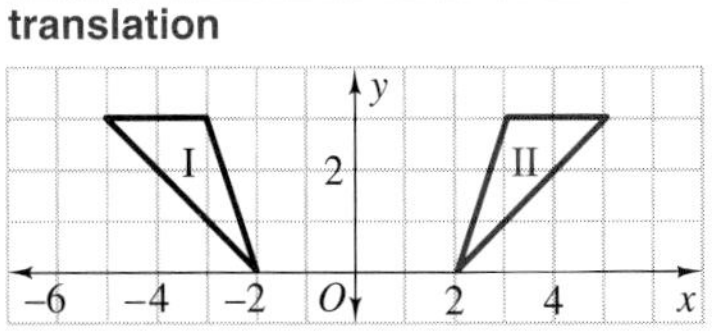

reflection

18.
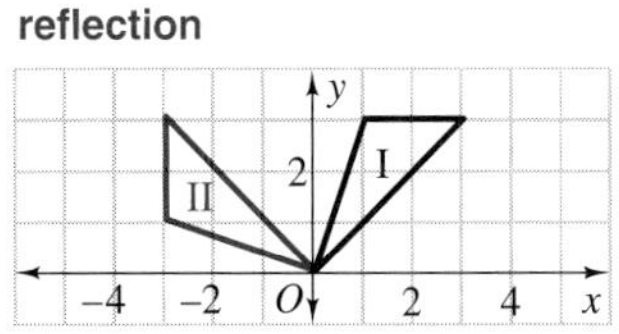

rotation

CHAPTER ASSESSMENT • FORM A

Chapter 11 Assessment • Form A

Use the coordinate plane below to answer Exercises 1–2. **Answers**

1. What are the coordinates of the point needed to form a square?

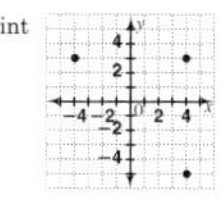

1. (–4, –5)

2. In which quadrant of the coordinate plane is point $(-5, -2)$ located?
2. quadrant III

3. Is the ordered pair $(0, 0)$ a solution to the equation $y = 6 - x$?
3. no

4. Graph $y = -2x + 1$.
4.
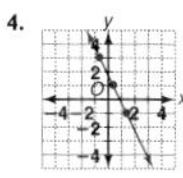

5. Point $N(x, y)$ is translated left 3 units and up 4 units. Write a rule to describe the translation.
5. $(x, y) \rightarrow (x - 3, y + 4)$

6. Which line is steeper, $y = 3x + 4$ or $y = \frac{3}{4}x + 4$?
6. $y = 3x + 4$

7. Suppose it costs \$25 to make some planters. Each planter is sold for \$35. Write an equation that shows what the profit will be for 10 planters. Solve the equation.
7. $P = (35 \times 10) - 25$; \$325

8. Make a table of values for $y = |x| + 2$. Then graph the equation.

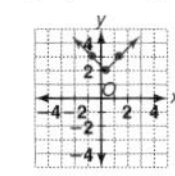

8. Sample table:

x	$\lvert x\rvert + 2$	y	(x, y)
−1	$\lvert -1\rvert + 2$	3	(−1, 3)
0	$\lvert 0\rvert + 2$	2	(0, 2)
1	$\lvert 1\rvert + 2$	3	(1, 3)

Assessment

CHAPTER ASSESSMENT • FORM A

Chapter 11 Assessment • Form A (continued)

9. Graph the equation $y = \frac{1}{4}x^2$.
9.
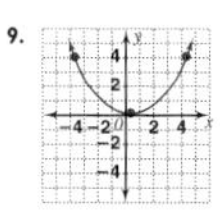

10. Suppose point $A(-2, 6)$ is translated to the right two units and down 6 units. What are the coordinates of A'?
10. (0, 0)

11. What are the coordinates of the image point when $(-4, -2)$ is reflected across the y-axis?
11. (4, −2)

12. Draw the image of the figure after a counterclockwise rotation of 90° about the point shown.

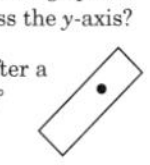

12.
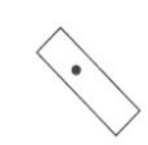

13. **Choose A, B, C, or D.** Which of the following does *not* have the same slope as the other three?
13. B

A. $y = -\frac{2}{3}x + 6$
B. $2y = -3x + 18$
C. the line containing $(-9, 6)$ and $(-6, 4)$
D. $y = 10 - \frac{2}{3}x$

Choose a Strategy

14. The perimeter of a rectangle is 72 in. The length is 6 in. longer than twice the width. Find the length and width of the rectangle.
14. $w = 10$ in.; $l = 26$ in.

Writing

15. Use what you know about rotational symmetry to explain why we could say, "All figures have 360° rotational symmetry."

Answers may vary. Sample: A figure that has been rotated 360° is back in its starting position.

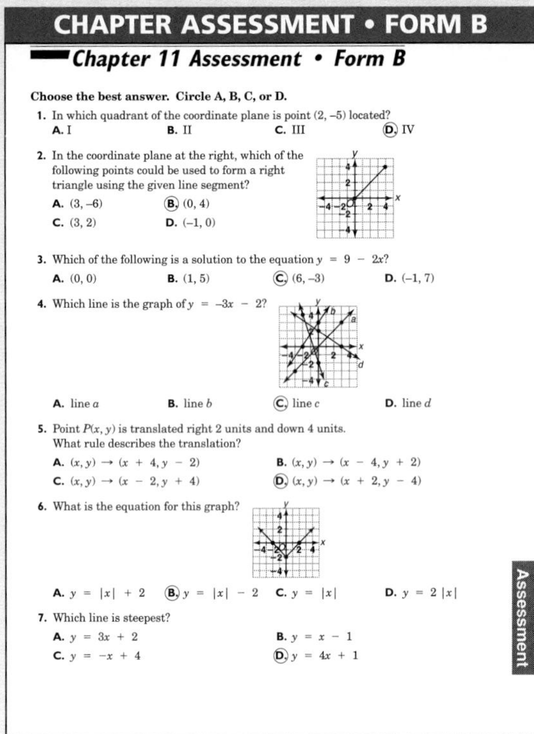

CHAPTER ASSESSMENT • FORM B

Chapter 11 Assessment • Form B

Choose the best answer. Circle A, B, C, or D.

1. In which quadrant of the coordinate plane is point (2, –5) located?
   A. I B. II C. III (D.) IV
2. In the coordinate plane at the right, which of the following points could be used to form a right triangle using the given line segment?
   A. (3, –6) (B.) (0, 4) C. (3, 2) D. (–1, 0)
3. Which of the following is a solution to the equation $y = 9 - 2x$?
   A. (0, 0) B. (1, 5) (C.) (6, –3) D. (–1, 7)
4. Which line is the graph of $y = -3x - 2$?
   A. line *a* B. line *b* (C.) line *c* D. line *d*
5. Point $P(x, y)$ is translated right 2 units and down 4 units. What rule describes the translation?
   A. $(x, y) \rightarrow (x + 4, y - 2)$ B. $(x, y) \rightarrow (x - 4, y + 2)$
   C. $(x, y) \rightarrow (x - 2, y + 4)$ (D.) $(x, y) \rightarrow (x + 2, y - 4)$
6. What is the equation for this graph?
   A. $y = |x| + 2$ (B.) $y = |x| - 2$ C. $y = |x|$ D. $y = 2|x|$
7. Which line is steepest?
   A. $y = 3x + 2$ B. $y = x - 1$
   C. $y = -x + 4$ (D.) $y = 4x + 1$

Assessment

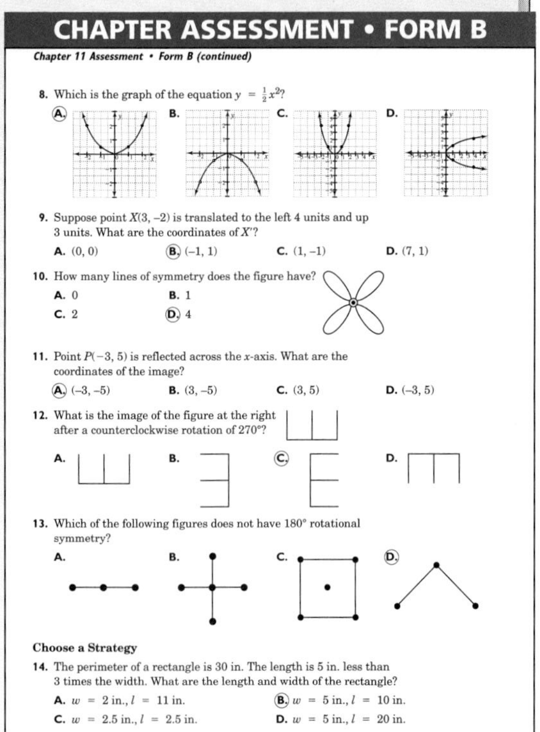

CHAPTER ASSESSMENT • FORM B

Chapter 11 Assessment • Form B (continued)

8. Which is the graph of the equation $y = \frac{1}{2}x^2$?
   (A.) B. C. D.
9. Suppose point $X(3, -2)$ is translated to the left 4 units and up 3 units. What are the coordinates of X'?
   A. (0, 0) (B.) (–1, 1) C. (1, –1) D. (7, 1)
10. How many lines of symmetry does the figure have?
    A. 0 B. 1 C. 2 (D.) 4
11. Point $P(-3, 5)$ is reflected across the *x*-axis. What are the coordinates of the image?
    (A.) (–3, –5) B. (3, –5) C. (3, 5) D. (–3, 5)
12. What is the image of the figure at the right after a counterclockwise rotation of 270°?
    A. B. (C.) D.
13. Which of the following figures does not have 180° rotational symmetry?
    A. B. C. (D.)

Choose a Strategy

14. The perimeter of a rectangle is 30 in. The length is 5 in. less than 3 times the width. What are the length and width of the rectangle?
    A. w = 2 in., l = 11 in. (B.) w = 5 in., l = 10 in.
    C. w = 2.5 in., l = 2.5 in. D. w = 5 in., l = 20 in.

Teaching Resources

Chapter Support File, Ch. 11, and Spanish Resources

Teacher's Edition

See pp. 470C–D for Assessment Options.

Teaching Resource Software

- Computer Item Generator, Ch. 11

ASSESSMENT

ENHANCED MULTIPLE CHOICE QUESTIONS are more complex than traditional multiple choice questions, which assess only one skill. Enhanced multiple choice questions assess the processes that students use, as well as the end results. They are written so that students can use more than one strategy to solve the problem. Using multiple strategies is encouraged by the National Council of Teachers of Mathematics (NCTM). **Exercise 5** is an enhanced multiple choice question.

WRITING EXERCISES allow students to describe more fully their thinking and understanding of the concepts they've learned. **Exercise 13** is a writing exercise.

11 ASSESSMENT

a. point *D* b. point *A*

1. Name the point with the given coordinates.
   a. (1, 4)
   b. (–2, –1)
   c. (3, –2)
   d. (–3, 2)

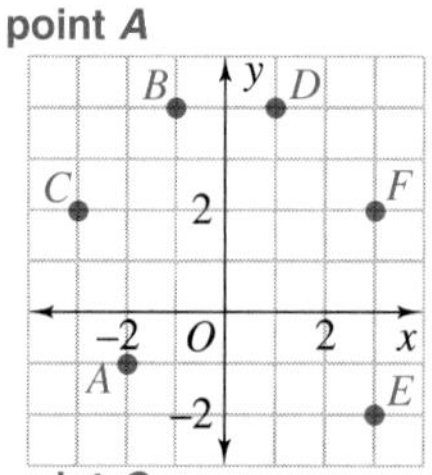

c. point *E* d. point *C*

2. Identify the quadrant in which each point lies.
   a. (–3, 3) II b. (–9, 4) II
   c. (5, –12) IV d. (1, 11) I

3a. no; $(-5) \neq -2(3) + 5$ b. yes; $(5) = -2(0) + 5$

3. Determine whether each ordered pair is a solution of the equation $y = -2x + 5$.
   a. (3, –5) b. (0, 5)
   c. (4, –3) d. (2.5, 0)

c. yes; $(-3) = -2(4) + 5$ d. yes; $(0) = -2(2.5) + 5$

4. Graph each pair of points. Determine the slope of the line through the points.
   a. $E(7, 1)$, $F(-3, 3)$ $-\frac{1}{5}$
   b. $G(-2, 6)$, $H(0, 0)$ -3
   c. $L(-4, 0)$, $M(0, 2)$ $\frac{1}{2}$
   d. $S(8, 5)$, $T(1, -1)$ $\frac{6}{7}$

5. **Choose A, B, C, or D.** Which set of ordered pairs does *not* describe the vertices of a parallelogram? A
   A. (2, 4), (3,4), (2, –1), (–3, –1)
   B. (0, 5), (5, 5), (0, 0), (–5, 0)
   C. (4, 3), (6, –2), (1, –2), (–1, 3)
   D. (5, –1), (–3, –1), (2, 5), (10, 5)

6. Quadrant III

6. In which quadrant(s) are both coordinates of a point negative?

7a. line *q* b. line *r*

7. Match each equation with its graph.
   a. $y = -x + 2$
   b. $y = x + 2$
   c. $y = 2$
   d. $x = 2$

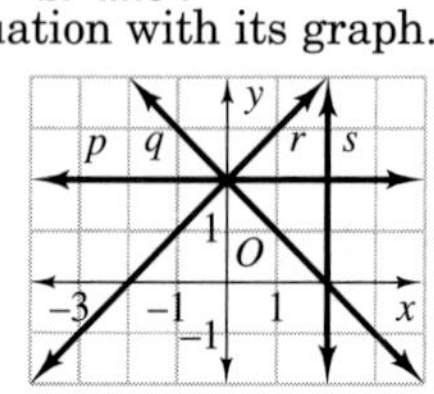

c. line *p*
d. line *s*

8. Graph each equation.
   a. $y = x - 3$ a–b. See back of book.
   b. $y = 3x + 1$

9. Find four solutions of each equation. Then graph each equation.
   a. $y = x^2$ a–b. See back of book.
   b. $y = |x|$

10. a. Graph $\triangle ABC$ with vertices $A(1, 3)$, $B(5, 8)$, and $C(7, 1)$. Then connect the vertices in order.
    b. Graph the image of $\triangle ABC$ after a reflection over the *x*-axis.
    c. Graph the image of $\triangle ABC$ after a translation 12 units left and 10 units down. a–c. See back of book.

11. Draw the image of the triangle after a rotation of 90°, 180°, and 270° about point *O*. See back of book.

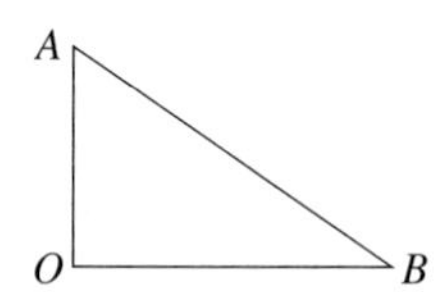

12. See back of book for table and graph.

12. Make a table and graph the equation $y = \frac{1}{2}x + 4$. Use the graph to find the slope of the line. $\frac{1}{2}$

13. *Writing* Give an example of a rotation, a reflection, and a translation you might see in the real world. See below.

14. Inez paid $185 for car repairs. The garage charged $65 for parts and $30 per hour for the mechanic's labor. Write and solve an equation to find the number of hours the mechanic worked on her car. 4 h

13. Answers may vary. Samples: a rotating faucet handle; a butterfly; ties on railroad tracks

CUMULATIVE REVIEW

Item	Review Topic	Ch
1	Functions	10
2, 9	Probability	9
3, 8	Linear equations	11
4, 5, 7	Percents and proportions	6

Item	Review Topic	Ch
6	Number patterns	10
10	Translations	11
11	Scientific notation	10
12	Expressions	3

11 CUMULATIVE REVIEW

Choose the best answer.

1. Which rule best describes the function in the table? **D**

n	$f(n)$
0	0
1	1
2	4
3	9

A. $f(n) = n + 2$
B. $f(n) = n$
C. $f(n) = 2n$
D. $f(n) = n^2$

2. How many two-letter permutations of the letters C, A, R contain the letter R? **C**

A. 2 B. 3 C. 4 D. 6

3. Which situation is described by the linear equation $P = 7.5x - 150$? **A**

A. A bus company's profit if x people buy tickets for a trip at $7.50 each, but it costs $150 to run the bus.
B. The total price of renting a restaurant for a party if the restaurant charges $150 plus $7.50 per person, and x people attend.
C. The price of a home video game machine if it costs $150, but you have x coupons, each of which says, "deduct $7.50."
D. The total profit made by putting on a concert if the profit is $7.50 per person and x people more than 150 attend.

4. A muffin recipe uses $2\frac{1}{4}$ c of flour and makes 12 muffins. How many muffins can you make with 6 c of flour? **C**

A. 24 B. 30 C. 32 D. 45

5. What percent of the letters of the alphabet are vowels? **B**

A. about 15% B. about 21%
C. about 30% D. about 33%

6. What is the ones digit of 7^{23}? **A**

A. 3 B. 5 C. 7 D. 9

7. What is the best estimate for the percent of the figure that is shaded? **B**

A. 10% B. 25%
C. 60% D. 75%

8. For which linear equation is $(-3, 0.5)$ *not* a solution? **D**

A. $x - 2y = -4$
B. $4y = 3x + 11$
C. $x = -6y$
D. $-x + 6y = 0$

9. What is the probability of spinning red or blue on the spinner? **B**

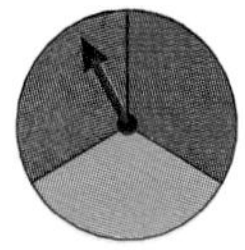

A. $P(\text{red}) - P(\text{blue})$
B. $P(\text{red}) + P(\text{blue})$
C. $P(\text{blue}) - P(\text{red})$
D. $P(\text{red}) \times P(\text{blue})$

10. Which translation takes $\triangle ABC$ to $\triangle A'B'C'$? **D**

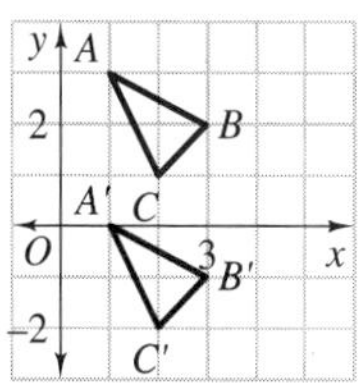

A. $(x, y) \longrightarrow (x - 3, y)$
B. $(x, y) \longrightarrow (x + 3, y)$
C. $(x, y) \longrightarrow (x, y + 3)$
D. $(x, y) \longrightarrow (x, y - 3)$

11. Write the numbers 0.361×10^7, 4.22×10^7, and 13.5×10^6 in order from least to greatest. **C**

A. $13.5 \times 10^6, 0.361 \times 10^7, 4.22 \times 10^7$
B. $4.22 \times 10^7, 13.5 \times 10^6, 0.361 \times 10^7$
C. $0.361 \times 10^7, 13.5 \times 10^6, 4.22 \times 10^7$
D. $13.5 \times 10^6, 4.22 \times 10^7, 0.361 \times 10^7$

12. Which expression has the greatest value?

C A. $\frac{3}{4}(8)$ B. $2 \cdot 3.3$ C. 2^3 D. $\frac{2}{3} \cdot \frac{6}{5}$

CUMULATIVE REVIEW

Chapter 11 Cumulative Review

Choose the best answer. Circle A, B, C, or D.

1. What is the next term in this pattern? 500, 250, 125, . . .

A. 100 B. 75
(C) 62.5 D. 50

2. What is 1.47×10^8 written in standard notation?

A. 14,700,000 **(B)** 147,000,000
C. 1,470,000,000 D. 14,700,000,000

3. Use the formula $B = p(1 + r)^t$ to find the amount of money in your savings account after ten years if you deposited $100 at an interest rate of 5% compounded annually.

A. $111.01 B. $112.74
C. $150.00 **(D)** $162.89

4. Find the circumference of a circle with a diameter of 10 cm. Use 3.14 for π.

A. 15.7 cm **(B)** 31.4 cm
C. 78.5 cm D. 314 cm

5. Which of the situations below could this graph describe?

(A) distance traveled on a train
B. height of a baseball after a pitch
C. weight of a person on a diet
D. amount of money after paying bills

6. What is the approximate unit price of a lemon if a bag of 15 lemons costs $2?

A. $.075 **(B)** $.13
C. $.15 D. $.30

7. A map of a city has a scale of 2 in. : $\frac{1}{2}$ mi. The distance on the map from the school to your house is $5\frac{1}{2}$ in. What is the actual distance from the school to your house?

A. $13\frac{3}{4}$ mi B. 11 mi
C. $5\frac{1}{2}$ mi **(D)** $1\frac{3}{8}$ mi

8. How far apart are the 12 posts used to fence in a region with a perimeter of 96 ft if they are at equal intervals?

A. 12 ft B. 10 ft
(C) 8 ft D. 6 ft

9. Which proportion will help you find 36% of 90?

A. $\frac{90}{36} = \frac{n}{100}$ **(B)** $\frac{n}{90} = \frac{36}{100}$
C. $\frac{90}{100} = \frac{36}{n}$ D. $\frac{100}{n} = \frac{36}{90}$

10. The sale price of a TV is $279. This is 80% of the original price. What was the original price?

A. $55.80 B. $286.74
(C) $348.75 D. $400

11. What is the probability of getting a 4 or a 6 when you roll a number cube?

A. $\frac{2}{3}$ B. $\frac{1}{2}$
(C) $\frac{1}{3}$ D. $\frac{3}{4}$

Assessment

CUMULATIVE REVIEW

Chapter 11 Cumulative Review (continued)

12. You roll a number cube. If you get a 6, you roll again. Which statement best describes these events?

A. They are equally likely.
(B) They are dependent.
C. They are not probable.
D. They are complementary.

13. How many permutations of the letters L, M, N, and O are there?

A. 4 permutations
B. 6 permutations
C. 12 permutations
(D) 24 permutations

14. How many different pairs of players can be made from the 8 members in the chess club?

A. 8 pairs B. 16 pairs
(C) 28 pairs D. 56 pairs

15. What is $P(\text{red})$ for this spinner?

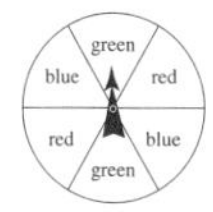

A. $\frac{1}{6}$ **(B)** $\frac{1}{3}$
C. $\frac{2}{3}$ D. 1

16. In which quadrant is the point $A(3, -1)$ located?

A. I B. II
C. III **(D)** IV

17. What is the slope of the line shown?

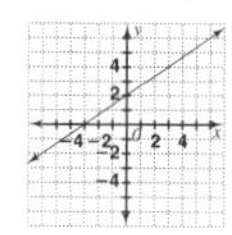

A. $\frac{3}{2}$ **(B)** $\frac{2}{3}$
C. $-\frac{3}{2}$ D. 3

18. Which equation is a linear equation?

(A) $y = 3x + 4$ B. $y = x^3 + 2$
C. $y = x^2 - 3$ D. $y = |x - 1|$

19. Jay has two more quarters than dimes in his pocket. He has a total of 20 dimes and quarters. Which equation could you use to find how many of each coin Jay has?

A. $x + 2 = 20$
B. $20 - x = 2x$
(C) $x + (x + 2) = 20$
D. $\frac{20}{2} = x$

20. What are the coordinates of the image of point $D(-2, 3)$ after reflecting D across the x-axis?

A. (3, –2) **(B)** (–2, –3)
C. (2, 3) D. (–3, 2)

21. A right triangle has legs of 12 ft and 16 ft. Find the longest side of the triangle. Use the Pythagorean theorem.

(A) 20 ft B. 28 ft
C. 400 ft D. not here

Resources

Teaching Resources

Chapter Support File, Ch. 11
- Cumulative Review

Teacher's Edition

See pp. 470C–D for Assessment Options.

End-of-Course Skills Assessment

A broad range of assessment tools are available to reach a variety of learners. Options for Formal and Informal Assessment appear on the **Assessing Progress** pages that precede each chapter.

Computer Item Generator

With the Computer Item Generator, you can customize assessment and create customized practice worksheets.

Standardized Test Preparation

You may wish to take advantage of the Standardized Test Preparation component that is available on the Computer Item Generator and the Resource Pro™ CD-ROM. With this component, you can generate tests to help students prepare for these standardized tests:

CAT5 California Achievement Test, 5th Edition
ITBS Iowa Test of Basic Skills, Form M
MAT7 Metropolitan Achievement Test, 7th Edition
SAT9 Stanford Achievement Test, 9th Edition
Terra Nova Comprehensive Test of Basic Skills, 5th Edition

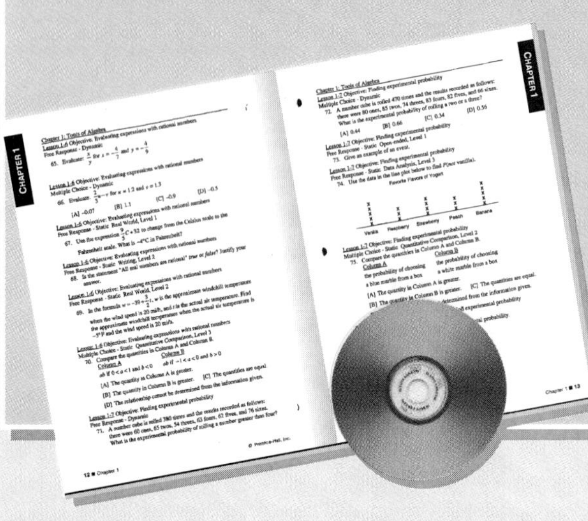

End-of-Course Assessment

The End-of-Course Assessment is available in the *Cumulative Assessment* booklet in the Teaching Resources.

Structure The End-of-Course Assessment is a four-page, multiple choice test. The test assesses student progress on the skills and concepts covered in Chapters 1–11 of *Prentice Hall Middle Grades Math* Course 2. The test contains 3–5 test items from each chapter.

Scoring Usually, 75% correct should demonstrate that the student has sufficient mastery of the content to be considered successful in this program. However, you may wish to set your own criteria.

Progress and Remediation Chart To assist you in assessing the skill level of your students, a Progress and Remediation Chart appears with the End-of-Course Assessment. This chart identifies the skills and concepts assessed, student achievement on the assessment, and suggests where remediation, if necessary, is found within the *Prentice Hall Middle Grades Math* program.

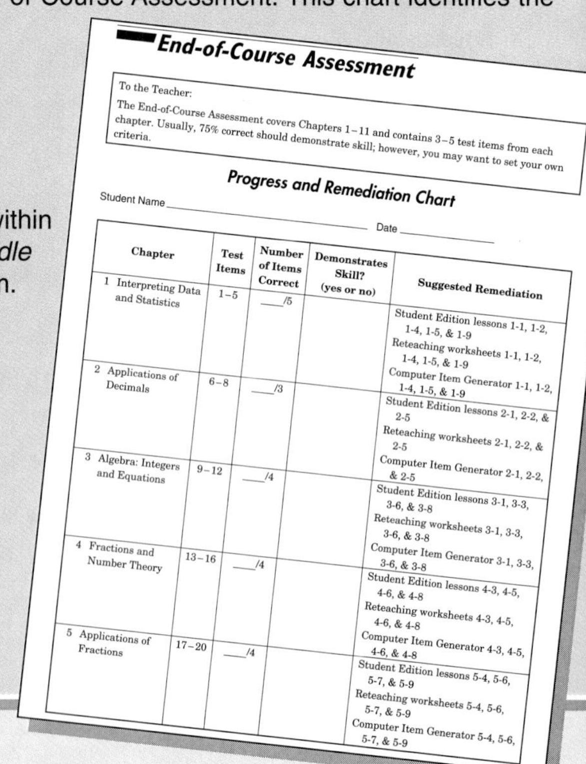

End-of-Course Assessment

To the Teacher:

The End-of-Course Assessment covers Chapters 1–11 and contains 3–5 test items from each chapter. Usually, 75% correct should demonstrate skill; however, you may want to set your own criteria.

Progress and Remediation Chart

Student Name ______________ Date ________

Chapter	Test Items	Number of Items Correct	Demonstrates Skill? (yes or no)	Suggested Remediation
1 Interpreting Data and Statistics	1–5	____/5		Student Edition lessons 1-1, 1-2, 1-4, 1-5, & 1-9 Reteaching worksheets 1-1, 1-2, 1-4, 1-5, & 1-9 Computer Item Generator 1-1, 1-2, 1-4, 1-5, & 1-9
2 Applications of Decimals	6–8	____/3		Student Edition lessons 2-1, 2-2, & 2-5 Reteaching worksheets 2-1, 2-2, & 2-5 Computer Item Generator 2-1, 2-2, & 2-5
3 Algebra: Integers and Equations	9–12	____/4		Student Edition lessons 3-1, 3-3, 3-6, & 3-8 Reteaching worksheets 3-1, 3-3, 3-6, & 3-8 Computer Item Generator 3-1, 3-3, 3-6, & 3-8
4 Fractions and Number Theory	13–16	____/4		Student Edition lessons 4-3, 4-5, 4-6, & 4-8 Reteaching worksheets 4-3, 4-5, 4-6, & 4-8 Computer Item Generator 4-3, 4-5, 4-6, & 4-8
5 Applications of Fractions	17–20	____/4		Student Edition lessons 5-4, 5-6, 5-7, & 5-9 Reteaching worksheets 5-4, 5-6, 5-7, & 5-9 Computer Item Generator 5-4, 5-6, 5-7, & 5-9

End-of-Course Assessment

Choose the best answer. Circle A, B, C, or D.

1. The graph shows the distribution of grades on a math test. According to the graph, how many students scored above 70 on the test?

Grades on a Math Test

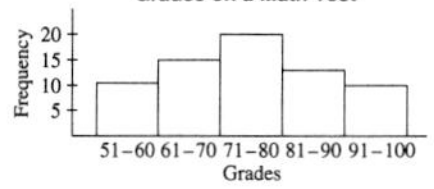

- **A.** between 20 and 25
- **(B)** between 40 and 45
- **C.** between 55 and 60
- **D.** between 65 and 70

2. This graph shows the number of students in grades 7–10 who play an instrument. How many more students in grade 10 than in grade 9 play an instrument?

Number of Students Who Play an Instrument

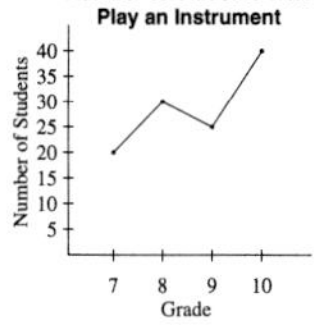

- **A.** 5 **B.** 10
- **(C)** 15 **D.** 20

3. In Exercise 2, what is the range of students who play an instrument?

- **(A)** 20 **B.** 27.75
- **C.** 28.75 **D.** 40

4. One of the values in a set of data appears to be an outlier. Which of the following is always affected by an outlier?

- **(A)** mean only
- **B.** median only
- **C.** mode only
- **D.** mean and median

5. The scatter plot shows the relationship between height and weight for a group of students. What can you conclude about the relationship?

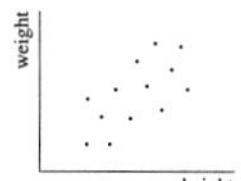

- **A.** There is no trend.
- **B.** The trend is negative.
- **(C)** The trend is positive.
- **D.** There is not enough information.

6. Which of the following is *not* true?

- **A.** $0.6703 > 0.6073$
- **B.** $0.0673 < 0.6073$
- **C.** $0.6730 = 0.673$
- **(D)** $0.6073 > 0.6703$

7. Round to estimate.
$3.79 + 2.99 + 1.07$

- **A.** 6 **B.** 7
- **(C)** 8 **D.** 9

End-of-Course Assessment (continued)

8. Find the product.
2.6×0.04

- **A.** 65 **B.** 6.5
- **C.** 1.04 **(D)** 0.104

9. Evaluate $a + 3b$ for $a = 7$ and $b = 8$.

- **A.** 10 **B.** 15
- **(C)** 31 **D.** 45

10. Which of the following is *not* equivalent to -1?

- **A.** $-9 + 8$ **B.** $-|6 - 7|$
- **C.** $-3 - (-2)$ **(D)** $4 - (-3)$

11. Solve $-10 = x + 2$.

- **(A)** -12 **B.** -8
- **C.** 8 **D.** 12

12. Which sentence is represented by $3p = -27$?

- **A.** Twenty-seven less than a number equals three.
- **B.** Three times negative twenty-seven equals a number.
- **(C)** Negative twenty-seven is three times a number.
- **D.** The product of three and a number is twenty-seven.

13. Which of the following statements is true?

- **(A)** $\frac{2}{3} < \frac{3}{4}$ **B.** $\frac{4}{5} > \frac{6}{7}$
- **C.** $2\frac{5}{8} > 2\frac{3}{4}$ **D.** $1\frac{4}{9} > 1\frac{7}{10}$

14. What is the prime factorization of 612?

- **(A)** $2^2 \cdot 3^2 \cdot 17$ **B.** $2^2 \cdot 3 \cdot 51$
- **C.** $4 \cdot 9 \cdot 17$ **D.** $2 \cdot 9 \cdot 34$

15. Which of the following is $\frac{108}{144}$ in simplest form?

- **A.** $\frac{54}{72}$ **B.** $\frac{27}{36}$
- **C.** $\frac{9}{12}$ **(D)** $\frac{3}{4}$

16. Which of the following is equivalent to $9\frac{2}{9}$?

- **A.** $\frac{18}{9}$ **B.** $\frac{81}{9}$
- **(C)** $\frac{83}{9}$ **D.** $\frac{162}{9}$

17. Solve the equation $x + \frac{3}{4} = \frac{5}{6}$.

- **(A)** $\frac{1}{12}$ **B.** $1\frac{7}{12}$
- **C.** $\frac{1}{6}$ **D.** $3\frac{1}{6}$

18. How many $2\frac{1}{4}$-ft boards can be cut from a $13\frac{1}{2}$-ft board?

- **A.** 5 boards **(B)** 6 boards
- **C.** 7 boards **D.** 8 boards

19. If you start with a number, add 7, then divide by 10, the result is $\frac{3}{4}$. What was the original number?

- **A.** $\frac{1}{4}$ **B.** $\frac{1}{3}$
- **(C)** $\frac{1}{2}$ **D.** 1

20. At a clearance sale a TV is marked $\frac{1}{3}$ off. The original price was $399.90. What is the sale price?

- **A.** $113.30 **(B)** $266.60
- **C.** $283.20 **D.** $300.00

End-of-Course Assessment (continued)

21. A house is 60 ft long and 45 ft wide. Which of the following does *not* represent the ratio of the width to the length?

- **A.** 0.75 **B.** 3 : 4
- **(C)** 4 to 3 **D.** $\frac{3}{4}$

22. Solve $\frac{15}{n} = \frac{50}{16}$.

- **A.** 53.3 **B.** 46.875
- **C.** 16.0 **(D)** 4.8

23. Which proportion will help you find 23% of 129?

- **(A)** $\frac{23}{100} = \frac{n}{129}$ **B.** $\frac{100}{129} = \frac{n}{23}$
- **C.** $\frac{n}{100} = \frac{129}{23}$ **D.** $\frac{23}{n} = \frac{129}{100}$

24. A year's subscription to a magazine was $27.00 last year. This year the same subscription costs $30.00. What is the percent of change rounded to the nearest whole percent?

- **A.** 1% **B.** 10%
- **(C)** 11% **D.** 15%

25. What is the measure of $\angle DBE$?

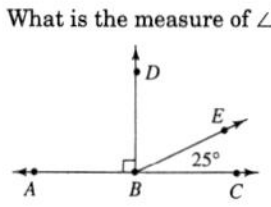

- **A.** 155° **B.** 90°
- **(C)** 65° **D.** 25°

26. Which of the following is true of parallelogram *LMNO*?

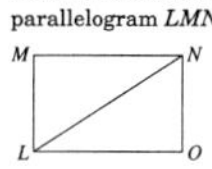

- **A.** $\angle LNM \cong \angle LMN$
- **B.** $\angle LNM \cong \angle LNO$
- **(C)** $\angle LNM \cong \angle NLO$
- **D.** $\angle LNM \cong \angle LON$

27. $\overrightarrow{WY}$ is the bisector of $\angle XWZ$. $\overrightarrow{WY}$ is the perpendicular bisector of $\overline{XZ}$. Which of the following must be true?

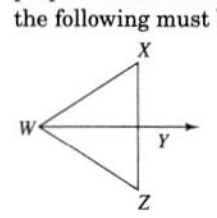

- **(A)** $\overline{WX} \cong \overline{WZ}$
- **B.** $\overline{WX} \cong \overline{XZ}$
- **C.** $\overline{WY} \cong \overline{WZ}$
- **D.** $\angle XWZ \cong \angle WXZ$

28. Find the area of a parallelogram with base length 14 in. and height 9 in.

- **A.** 23 in.^{2} **B.** 63 in.^{2}
- **(C)** 126 in.^{2} **D.** 136 in.^{2}

29. Which of the following is closest to the area of this triangle?

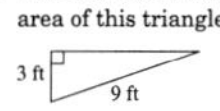

- **A.** 5 ft^2 **B.** 8.5 ft^2
- **(C)** 12.7 ft^2 **D.** 27 ft^2

End-of-Course Assessment (continued)

30. What is the surface area of a wooden crate that measures 4 ft by 3 ft by 5 ft?

- **A.** 47 ft^2 **B.** 60 ft^2
- **(C)** 94 ft^2 **D.** 120 ft^2

31. Find *P*(number less than 5) for one roll of a standard number cube.

- **A.** $\frac{1}{3}$ **(B)** $\frac{2}{3}$
- **C.** $\frac{1}{6}$ **D.** $\frac{5}{6}$

32. You roll a number cube twice. Find *P*(2, then odd).

- **(A)** $\frac{1}{12}$ **B.** $\frac{1}{6}$
- **C.** $\frac{1}{2}$ **D.** $\frac{2}{3}$

33. How many permutations of the letters in the word BIRD are possible?

- **A.** 4 permutations
- **B.** 10 permutations
- **C.** 16 permutations
- **(D)** 24 permutations

34. What is the next fraction in this sequence? $\frac{1}{3}, \frac{2}{9}, \frac{3}{27}, \frac{4}{81}, \ldots$

- **A.** $\frac{5}{240}$ **(B)** $\frac{5}{243}$
- **C.** $\frac{5}{324}$ **D.** $\frac{5}{729}$

35. What is 21,900,000,000 in scientific notation?

- **A.** 21.9×10^9 **(B)** 2.19×10^{10}
- **C.** 219×10^8 **D.** $2{,}190 \times 10^7$

36. You deposit $200 in a bank account that pays $.04 for every dollar in the account each year. Using the formula $B = p(1 + r)^t$, about how much will you have in the account after 10 years?

- **A.** $208 **(B)** $296
- **C.** $800 **D.** $2,080

37. One taxi cab company charges $1 for the first quarter mile and $.35 for each additional quarter mile. Which function rule represents this relationship?

- **A.** $C = 1.35m$
- **B.** $C = m + 1.35m$
- **C.** $C = 0.35m$
- **(D)** $C = 1 + 0.35(m - 1)$

38. The rule for a function is $f(n) = -5n^2 + 1$. What is $f(-2)$?

- **A.** 21 **B.** -9
- **(C)** -19 **D.** -20

39. Which of the following is *not* on the graph of $y = 5 - 2x$?

- **A.** (0, 5) **(B)** (−1, −7)
- **C.** (2, 1) **D.** (2.5, 0)

40. What is the slope of the line through the points (0, 4) and (−1, 2)?

- **A.** −2 **B.** −6
- **(C)** 2 **D.** 6

41. Point *A*(−3, 0) is translated left 3 units. What are the coordinates of the image point A'?

- **(A)** (−6, 0) **B.** (0, 0)
- **C.** (−3, 3) **D.** (−3,−3)

Extra Practice

CHAPTER 1

8.

4	0 4 8
5	1 5 7 7
6	0 0 4
7	2 3 7
8	0 2

4 | 0 means 40

12a. Answers may vary. Sample: The line graph shows a steady increase from 1989 to 1992, and a sudden increase in 1993.

b. Misleading; the title claims the graph to represent PC purchases while the graph shows households with PC's.

CHAPTER 1

Extra Practice

■ LESSON 1-1

The stem-and-leaf plot shows daily high temperatures on Mt. Washington, NH, during three weeks in January.

0	1 2 3 3 4 4 5 7
1	0 0 1 1 1 5 6
2	0 2 8 8
3	1 1

2 | 0 means 20

1. Create a frequency table for the data. Check students' work.
2. Create a line plot for the data. Check students' work.
3. How many days was the temperature above 10 degrees? 11

■ LESSONS 1-2, 1-3

Exercises 4–7 refer to the graph at the right.

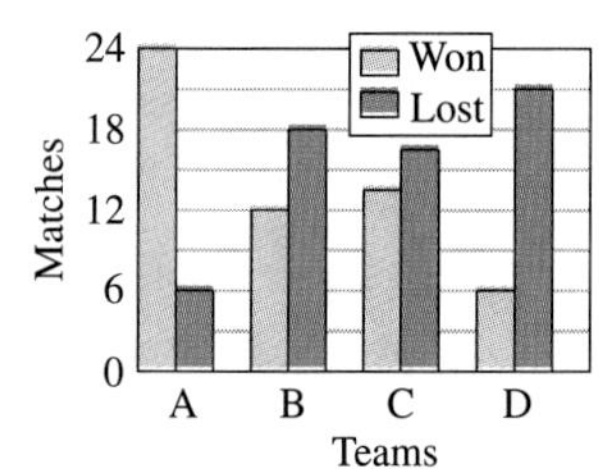

4. Which team has won the most matches? A
5. Which team has won the fewest matches? D
6. Which team has won almost the same number of matches as they lost? C
7. About how many more matches has Team A won than Team D? 18

■ LESSONS 1-4, 1-5

The data set at the right shows the number of stories of some tall buildings in the United States.

Number of Stories				
73	44	57	64	48
60	55	51	77	40
80	72	60	82	57

8. Display the data in a stem-and-leaf plot. See margin.
9. Find the mean, median, and mode of the data. 61.33; 60; 60
10. Find the range of the data. 42

■ LESSON 1-7

11. *Open-ended* Write a fair and a biased survey question. Check students' work.

■ LESSONS 1-8, 1-9

12. *Writing* The graph at the right shows the growth of personal computer purchases for home use.
    a. Describe the data as presented in the graph.
    b. Is the graph misleading or fair? Justify your answer.

12a–b. See margin.

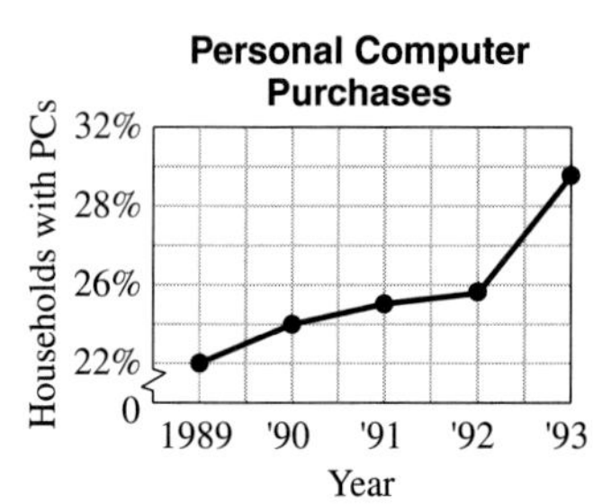

13. The data in the table below represent the heights and weights of some 7-year-olds.

Height	40 in.	39 in.	42 in.	45 in.	48 in.	43 in.	41 in.
Weight	56 lb	52 lb	62 lb	75 lb	72 lb	67 lb	62 lb

a. Make a scatter plot of the data. Check students' work.
b. Describe any trend you see in the data. In general, the weight increases with height.

CHAPTER 2 **Extra Practice**

Order from least to greatest. ■ LESSON 2-1

1. 0.092, 0.095, 0.102, 0.099
   0.092, 0.095, 0.099, 0.102
2. 1.01, 1.12, 1.02, 1.101
   1.01, 1.02, 1.101, 1.12
3. 0.55, 0.505, 0.52, 0.56
   0.505, 0.52, 0.55, 0.56
4. 4.301, 4.29, 4.30, 4.297, 3.40
   3.40, 4.29, 4.297, 4.3, 4.301
5. 0.708, 0.712, 0.699, 0.7
   0.699, 0.7, 0.708, 0.712
6. 10.1, 10.01, 11.01, 11.101
   10.01, 10.1, 11.01, 11.101

Compare. Use <, >, or =.

7. 0.101 ■ 0.10 >
8. 15.55 ■ 15.555 <
9. 1.16 ■ 1.160 =
10. 29.08 ■ 29.10 <
11. 10.4 ■ 1.04 >
12. 6.049 ■ 6.40 <
13. 37.02 ■ 37.2 <
14. 8.721 ■ 8.712 >

Estimation **Use any method to estimate.** ■ LESSON 2-2

15. 2.7236 − 0.6512 2
16. 1.2 + 2.4 + 0.86 4.5
17. \$34.50 − \$10.80 + \$2.10 \$27
18. 0.054 + 0.901 + 0.62 1.5
19. \$18.95 × 3.5 \$60
20. \$32.13 ÷ 6.15 \$5

Find each sum or difference. ■ LESSON 2-3

21. 5.87 + 2.41 8.28
22. 9.31 − 4.08 5.23
23. 7.2 + 1.907 9.107
24. 4.86 − 2.161 2.699
25. 11.46 − 10.64 0.82
26. 2.1 + 3.62 + 1.003 6.723
27. 10 − 5.98 4.02
28. 12.3 + 118.42 130.72

Find each product. ■ LESSON 2-5

29. 2.9 × 1.7 4.93
30. 3.5 × 4.4 15.4
31. 5.01 · 3.2 16.032
32. 0.56 × 8.21 4.5976
33. 6.09 × 1.3 7.917
34. 0.09 · 0.35 0.315
35. 4.17 · 7.1 29.607
36. 10.05 × 0.9 9.045

Choose **Use a calculator or paper and pencil to find each answer. Use a bar to show repeating decimals.** ■ LESSONS 2-6, 2-7

37. 3.2 ÷ 1.2 $2.\overline{6}$
38. 6.3 ÷ 2.1 3
39. 9.4 ÷ 3 $3.1\overline{3}$
40. 30.6 ÷ 3.6 8.5
41. 44.856 ÷ 7.12 6.3
42. 127 ÷ 2.4 $52.91\overline{6}$
43. 37 ÷ 11.1 $3.\overline{3}$
44. 3.64 ÷ 9.1 0.4

Find the value of each expression. ■ LESSON 2-8

45. 2(8 − 4.5) 7
46. 24 − (3 + 1.9) 19.1
47. 3.14(2.1 + 7.5) 30.144
48. 3(6.1 + 0.461) 19.683
49. (18 − 2.4)(0.7) 10.92
50. 8.3 · 6.9 − 4.7 52.57
51. (5.3 − 0.9) ÷ 1.1 4
52. 2.7 · (3.1 − 0.7) 6.48

CHAPTER 3 Extra Practice

Write a variable expression for each word phrase. ■ LESSON 3-1

1. the difference of a number and 3 $x - 3$
2. 17 increased by a number $17 + n$
3. 5 less than twice a number $2x - 5$
4. 6 more than a number divided by 2 $\frac{x}{2} + 6$
5. Copy and complete the table at the right. Substitute the value indicated on the left for the variable in the expression at the top of each column. Then evaluate.

	$3(x - 1)$	$3x - 1$	$3x + 1$
$x = 5$	■ 12	■ 14	■ 16
$x = 2$	■ 3	■ 5	■ 7

Write *true* or *false*. ■ LESSON 3-2

6. $|5| > |-5|$ F
7. $|6| < |8|$ T
8. $|-3| \leq |-2|$ F
9. $|10| = |-10|$ T

Order each group of numbers from least to greatest.

10. $-10, 8, 9, 0, -5, 3$
    $-10, -5, 0, 3, 8, 9$
11. $|-8|, -1, 3, |10|, -11$
    $-11, -1, 3, |-8|, |10|$
12. $|12|, |-3|, 22, -14, |5|, 0$
    $-14, 0, |-3|, |5|, |12|, 22$

Write the integer represented by each model. ■ LESSONS 3-3, 3-4, 3-5

13. 6
14. 5
15. 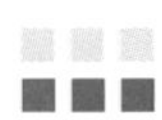 0
16.  −2

Simplify each expression.

17. $-110 + 5 - (-5)$
    -100
18. $3(-6 \div 3)$
    -6
19. $(-3)(-2)(-1)$
    -6
20. $2(-2) - 4$
    -8
21. $|-9| + 8 - (-1)$
    18
22. $-7 + |12 - 8|$
    -3
23. $4 + 11 - (-13)$
    28
24. $-14 \div (-7) + (-2)$
    0

Solve. ■ LESSONS 3-6, 3-7

25. $t - 3 = -10$ -7
26. $7 + x = -7$ -14
27. $\frac{m}{5} = -15$ -75
28. $-7y = -42$ 6
29. $-4a = 12$ -3
30. $\frac{x}{2} = -8$ -16
31. $-2x = -4$ 2
32. $\frac{y}{-6} = 3$ -18

Write an equation. Then solve. ■ LESSON 3-8

33. Fifty-one is three times what number?
    $51 = 3x,\ x = 17$
34. What number increased by eight is 35?
    $x + 8 = 35,\ x = 27$

Solve. ■ LESSON 3-9

35. $\frac{r}{-6} + 4 = -3$
    42
36. $12m + 24 = 0$
    -2
37. $3x + 1 = -11$
    -4
38. $\frac{k}{-3} - 2 = -20$
    54

CHAPTER 4 **Extra Practice**

Write a fraction for the part of each model that is shaded. ■ LESSON 4-1

1. 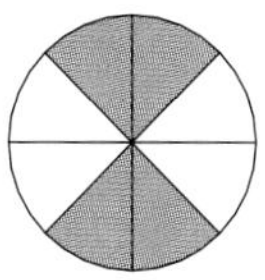 $\frac{4}{8}$ or $\frac{1}{2}$

2. 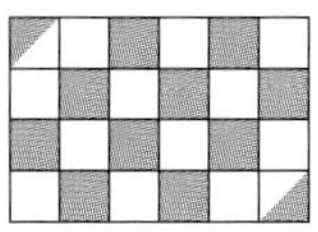 $\frac{11}{24}$

3. 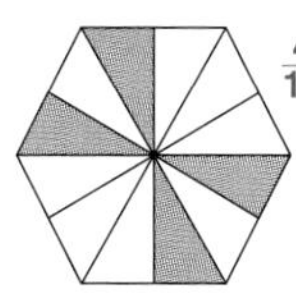 $\frac{4}{12}$ or $\frac{1}{3}$

4. 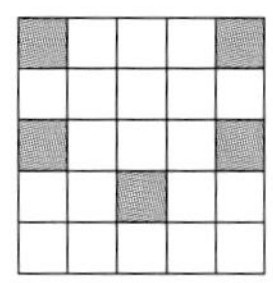 $\frac{5}{25}$ or $\frac{1}{5}$

Write two fractions equivalent to each fraction. Then write each fraction in simplest form. 5–16. Check students' work for equivalent fractions. ■ LESSONS 4-2, 4-6

5. $\frac{21}{24}$ $\frac{7}{8}$ 6. $\frac{65}{100}$ $\frac{13}{20}$ 7. $\frac{6}{9}$ $\frac{2}{3}$ 8. $\frac{40}{80}$ $\frac{1}{2}$ 9. $\frac{12}{36}$ $\frac{1}{3}$ 10. $\frac{18}{54}$ $\frac{1}{3}$

11. $\frac{15}{75}$ $\frac{1}{5}$ 12. $\frac{16}{36}$ $\frac{4}{9}$ 13. $\frac{110}{225}$ $\frac{22}{45}$ 14. $\frac{72}{108}$ $\frac{2}{3}$ 15. $\frac{45}{315}$ $\frac{1}{7}$ 16. $\frac{54}{96}$ $\frac{9}{16}$

Compare. Use <, >, or =. ■ LESSON 4-3

17. $\frac{1}{4}$ ■ $\frac{2}{9}$ $>$ 18. $\frac{3}{7}$ ■ $\frac{1}{2}$ $<$ 19. $\frac{2}{5}$ ■ $\frac{4}{10}$ $=$ 20. $\frac{5}{6}$ ■ $\frac{7}{8}$ $<$ 21. $\frac{3}{5}$ ■ $\frac{2}{3}$ $<$

Choose **Use a calculator, paper and pencil, or mental math to find the value of each expression.** ■ LESSON 4-4

22. 100^1 100 23. 5^3 125 24. 3^5 243 25. 15^2 225 26. 8^4 4,096 27. 4^3 64

Use prime factorization to find the GCF of each pair of numbers. ■ LESSON 4-5

28. 35, 49 7 29. 11, 12 1 30. 28, 40 4 31. 17, 34 17 32. 16, 26 2 33. 10, 30 10

Write each mixed number as an improper fraction. ■ LESSON 4-8

34. $7\frac{7}{8}$ $\frac{63}{8}$ 35. $3\frac{5}{7}$ $\frac{26}{7}$ 36. $3\frac{1}{4}$ $\frac{13}{4}$ 37. $4\frac{2}{5}$ $\frac{22}{5}$ 38. $10\frac{1}{6}$ $\frac{61}{6}$ 39. $2\frac{2}{5}$ $\frac{12}{5}$

Write each improper fraction as a mixed number.

40. $\frac{45}{8}$ $5\frac{5}{8}$ 41. $\frac{24}{5}$ $4\frac{4}{5}$ 42. $\frac{33}{8}$ $4\frac{1}{8}$ 43. $\frac{29}{4}$ $7\frac{1}{4}$ 44. $\frac{35}{6}$ $5\frac{5}{6}$ 45. $\frac{56}{9}$ $6\frac{2}{9}$

Write each fraction as a decimal. Write each decimal as a fraction. Use a bar to show repeating decimals. ■ LESSON 4-9

46. $\frac{4}{5}$ 0.8 47. 0.365 $\frac{73}{200}$ 48. $\frac{7}{8}$ 0.875 49. 0.42 $\frac{21}{50}$ 50. $\frac{9}{11}$ $0.\overline{81}$ 51. 0.7 $\frac{7}{10}$

52. $\frac{76}{15}$ $5.0\overline{6}$ 53. $\frac{136}{12}$ $11.\overline{3}$ 54. $\frac{76}{4}$ 19 55. $\frac{13}{4}$ 3.25 56. $\frac{28}{8}$ 3.5 57. $\frac{100}{6}$ $16.\overline{6}$

CHAPTER 5

Extra Practice

Estimate each sum, difference, product, or quotient. ■ LESSON 5-1

1. $\frac{2}{5} + \frac{7}{9}$ 1
2. $15\frac{1}{5} - 5\frac{4}{7}$ 10
3. $\frac{3}{5} - \frac{1}{8}$ $\frac{1}{2}$
4. $99\frac{9}{10} + \frac{1}{5}$ 100
5. $7\frac{4}{5} \div 1\frac{2}{3}$ 4
6. $9\frac{2}{3} \cdot 4\frac{2}{3}$ 50
7. $6\frac{1}{8} \cdot 12\frac{2}{3}$ 78
8. $62\frac{1}{2} \div 8\frac{3}{4}$ 7
9. $10\frac{3}{4} \div 5\frac{1}{5}$ 2
10. $71\frac{1}{5} \div 5\frac{2}{3}$ 12

Find each sum or difference. Write the answer in simplest form. ■ LESSON 5-2

11. $\frac{2}{3} + \frac{2}{3}$ $\frac{4}{3}$
12. $\frac{7}{10} - \frac{3}{10}$ $\frac{2}{5}$
13. $\frac{2}{5} + \frac{1}{3}$ $\frac{11}{15}$
14. $\frac{1}{4} + \frac{3}{8}$ $\frac{5}{8}$
15. $\frac{2}{3} - \frac{1}{6}$ $\frac{1}{2}$
16. $\frac{7}{12} - \frac{1}{4}$ $\frac{1}{3}$
17. $\frac{2}{3} - \frac{3}{8}$ $\frac{7}{24}$
18. $\frac{1}{3} + \frac{3}{4}$ $\frac{13}{12}$
19. $\frac{3}{4} + \frac{3}{10}$ $\frac{21}{20}$
20. $\frac{1}{6} + \frac{3}{4}$ $\frac{11}{12}$

Find each sum or difference. Write the answer in simplest form. ■ LESSON 5-3

21. $4\frac{3}{8} + 2\frac{5}{8}$ 7
22. $5\frac{2}{5} - 1\frac{4}{5}$ $3\frac{3}{5}$
23. $2\frac{2}{3} + 3\frac{1}{4}$ $5\frac{11}{12}$
24. $4\frac{1}{2} - 2\frac{3}{4}$ $1\frac{3}{4}$
25. $7\frac{3}{8} - 1\frac{3}{4}$ $5\frac{5}{8}$
26. $8\frac{3}{4} + 2\frac{5}{8}$ $11\frac{3}{8}$
27. $11 - 3\frac{1}{8}$ $7\frac{7}{8}$
28. $2\frac{1}{6} + 3\frac{3}{8}$ $5\frac{13}{24}$
29. $10\frac{2}{3} - 4\frac{1}{2}$ $6\frac{1}{6}$
30. $7\frac{2}{5} + 3\frac{1}{4}$ $10\frac{13}{20}$

Find each product. Write the answer in simplest form. ■ LESSON 5-5

31. $\frac{3}{8} \cdot \frac{2}{5}$ $\frac{3}{20}$
32. $\frac{1}{4}$ of $\frac{4}{5}$ $\frac{1}{5}$
33. $\frac{3}{10} \cdot \frac{5}{6}$ $\frac{1}{4}$
34. $\frac{2}{5} \cdot 40$ 16
35. $\frac{5}{6}$ of 30 25
36. $4\frac{2}{5} \cdot 2\frac{1}{2}$ 11
37. $2\frac{3}{4} \cdot 1\frac{1}{2}$ $4\frac{1}{8}$
38. $3\frac{2}{3} \cdot 4\frac{3}{5}$ $16\frac{13}{15}$
39. $3 \cdot 5\frac{3}{8}$ $16\frac{1}{8}$
40. $2\frac{7}{8} \cdot \frac{4}{5}$ $2\frac{3}{10}$

Find each quotient. Write the answer in simplest form. ■ LESSON 5-6

41. $\frac{3}{5} \div \frac{1}{5}$ 3
42. $4 \div \frac{1}{4}$ 16
43. $\frac{4}{5} \div \frac{4}{5}$ 1
44. $9 \div \frac{3}{4}$ 12
45. $\frac{5}{6} \div \frac{3}{8}$ $2\frac{2}{9}$
46. $2\frac{1}{5} \div \frac{5}{6}$ $2\frac{16}{25}$
47. $2\frac{3}{8} \div 1\frac{1}{4}$ $1\frac{9}{10}$
48. $\frac{3}{4} \div 6$ $\frac{1}{8}$
49. $3\frac{2}{3} \div 2\frac{1}{2}$ $1\frac{7}{15}$
50. $\frac{3}{4} \div 4\frac{1}{8}$ $\frac{2}{11}$

Complete. ■ LESSON 5-8

51. $\frac{3}{4}$ gal = ■ c 12
52. 4,500 lb = ■ T 2.25
53. $\frac{3}{8}$ mi = ■ yd 660
54. $12\frac{2}{3}$ lb = ■ oz $202\frac{2}{3}$
55. $6\frac{1}{8}$ T = ■ lb 12,250
56. 2 yd 1 ft = ■ yd $2\frac{1}{3}$
57. ■ gal = 18 pt $2\frac{1}{4}$
58. 2 lb 2 oz = ■ lb $2\frac{1}{8}$

Solve each equation. ■ LESSONS 5-4, 5-9

59. $j + \frac{1}{4} = \frac{5}{8}$ $\frac{3}{8}$
60. $1\frac{1}{3} + m = 2\frac{5}{6}$ $1\frac{1}{2}$
61. $\frac{2}{7} = y - \frac{1}{2}$ $\frac{11}{14}$
62. $\frac{4}{5} = t + \frac{3}{10}$ $\frac{1}{2}$
63. $38 = \frac{1}{4}b$ 152
64. $164t = 16$ $\frac{4}{41}$
65. $121 = 11c$ 11
66. $\frac{n}{3} = 18$ 54

APTER 6

Extra Practice

Write each ratio in two other ways. **LESSON 6-1**

1. $\frac{2}{3}$ $2:3$, 2 to 3
2. $3:5$ $\frac{3}{5}$, 3 to 5
3. 4 to 7 $4:7$, $\frac{4}{7}$
4. 17 to 3 $\frac{17}{3}$, $17:3$
5. $\frac{25}{50}$ $25:50$, 25 to 50
6. $66:99$ 66 to 99, $\frac{66}{99}$

Find each unit rate. Then determine the better buy. **LESSON 6-2**

7. 32 oz for \$2.29 48 oz
   48 oz for \$3.19
8. 3 yd for \$12.48 5 yd
   5 yd for \$20.30
9. 2 lb for \$4.17 10 lb
   10 lb for \$20.80

Find the value of *n* in each proportion. **LESSON 6-3**

10. $\frac{12}{n} = \frac{3}{5}$ 20
11. $\frac{n}{12} = \frac{4}{16}$ 3
12. $\frac{7}{8} = \frac{n}{4}$ 3.5
13. $\frac{7}{10} = \frac{14}{n}$ 20
14. $\frac{7}{n} = \frac{17.5}{5}$ 2
15. $\frac{15}{3} = \frac{n}{5}$ 25
16. $\frac{17}{3} = \frac{51}{n}$ 9
17. $\frac{18}{n} = \frac{3}{4}$ 24
18. $\frac{65}{n} = \frac{5}{1}$ 13
19. $\frac{n}{2} = \frac{5}{20}$ $\frac{1}{2}$ or 0.5

Find the missing lengths in each pair of similar figures. **LESSON 6-4**

20. 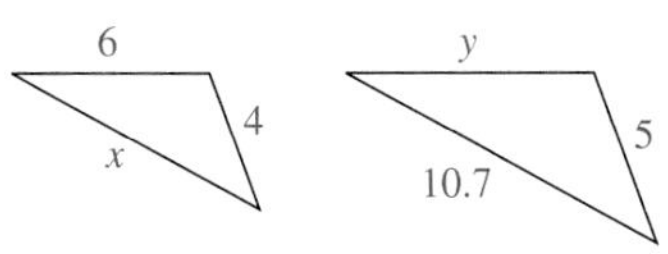

$x = 8.56$, $y = 7.5$

21. 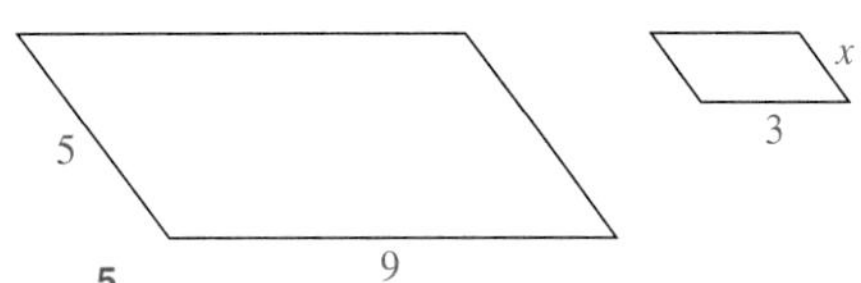

$x = \frac{5}{3}$

22. *Architecture* The scale on an architectural drawing is 0.5 in. : 15 ft. If the dimensions of a room in the drawing are 0.75 in. by 1.2 in., how big is the actual room? 22.5 ft × 36 ft **LESSON 6-5**

Write each fraction or decimal as a percent. Write each percent as a fraction in simplest form and as a decimal. **LESSONS 6-6, 6-7**

23. $\frac{5}{6}$ 83%
24. 37.5% $\frac{3}{8}$, 0.375
25. $\frac{11}{5}$ 220%
26. 87.5% $\frac{7}{8}$, 0.875
27. 64% $\frac{16}{25}$, 0.64
28. 0.12 12%
29. 27.3 2,730%
30. 225% $\frac{9}{4}$, 2.25
31. 0.000975 0.0975%
32. 1% $\frac{1}{100}$, 0.01
33. 0.1 10%
34. $\frac{3}{2}$ 150%

Write a proportion and solve. **LESSONS 6-9, 6-10**

35–40. Check students' work for proportions.

35. 54 is 40% of what number? 135
36. What is 5% of 48? 2.4
37. What percent of 200 is 120? 60%
38. What percent of 150 is 27? 18%
39. Find 25% of 130. 32.5
40. 8 is 40% of what number? 20

Find each percent of change. State whether the change is an *increase* or a *decrease*. **LESSON 6-11**

41. 25 to 40 60% increase
42. 95 to 45 about 52% decrease
43. 108 to 110 about 2% increase
44. 50 to 95 90% increase
45. 125 to 75 40% decrease

CHAPTER 7

Extra Practice

1. Draw the next figure in the pattern. ■ **Lesson 7-1**

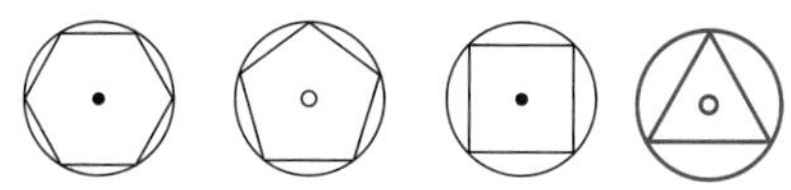

Match each description with a figure. ■ **Lesson 7-2**

2. vertical angles c

3. supplementary angles d

4. complementary angles a

5. nonadjacent angles b

a.

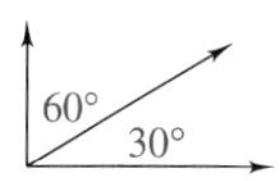

b.

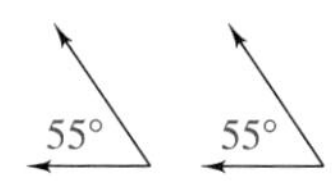

c.

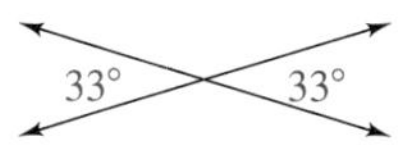

d.

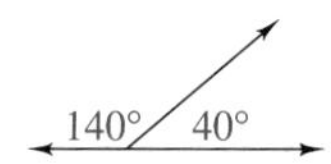

Find each missing angle measure. Then classify each triangle by its angles. ■ **Lesson 7-3**

6.

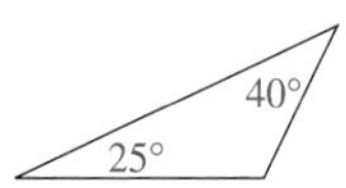

115°; obtuse triangle

7.

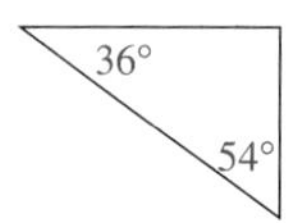

90°; right triangle

8.

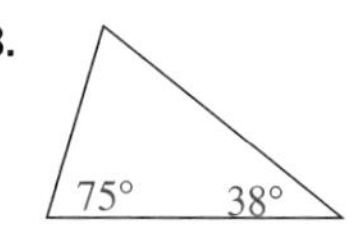

67°; acute triangle

9. $\triangle ABD \cong \triangle CED$. Which of the following are true? ■ **Lesson 7-5**

a. $\overline{AB} \cong \overline{CE}$ T **b.** $\overline{AD} \cong \overline{ED}$ F **c.** $\angle A \cong \angle C$ T

d. $\angle BDA$ and $\angle EDC$ are congruent angles. T **e.** $\overline{BD} \cong \overline{EC}$ F

Judging by appearance, classify each figure. Then name the congruent sides and angles. ■ **Lesson 7-6**

10.

parallelogram

11.

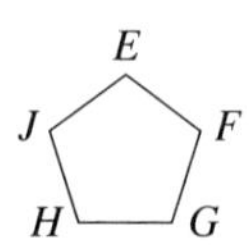

regular pentagon

12.

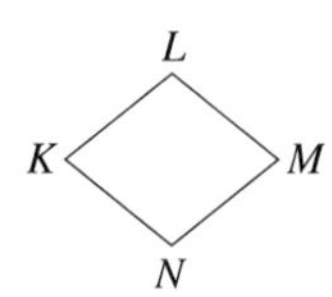

rhombus

13.

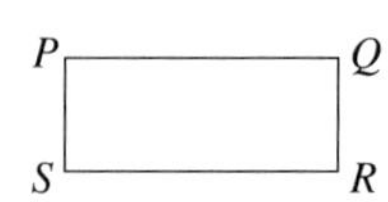

rectangle

14. Draw a circle O. Draw, label, and identify a diameter, a chord, a radius, and an arc that is not a semicircle. ■ **Lesson 7-7**
Check students' work.

15. In a survey of 500 people, 86 of them preferred Brand A. Find the measure of the central angle that you would draw to represent Brand A in a circle graph. 61.92° ■ **Lesson 7-8**

16. Draw an obtuse angle. Then construct its bisector. ■ **Lesson 7-9**
Check students' work.

CHAPTER 8

Extra Practice

1. Each square represents 100 ft^2. Estimate the perimeter and area of the figure. **180 ft, 1,400 ft^2**

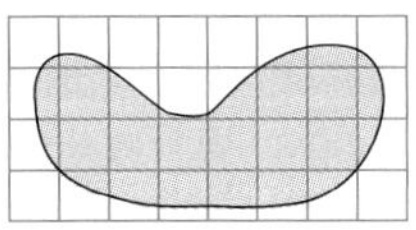

■ LESSON 8-1

Find the area and perimeter of each figure. ■ LESSONS 8-2, 8-3

2. **10 cm^2, 14 cm**

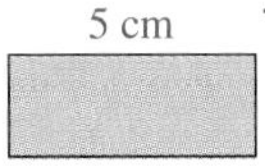

3. **40 m^2, 30 m**

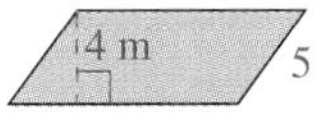

4. **240 ft^2, 66 ft**

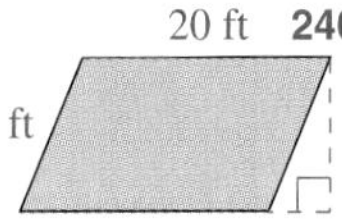

5.

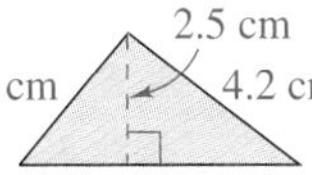

6.875 cm^2, 13 cm

6.

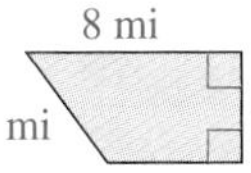

26 mi^2, 22 mi

7.

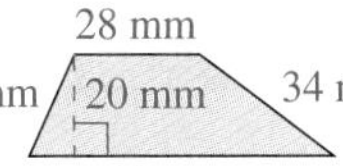

900 mm^2, 146 mm

8. The diameter of a circle is 40 cm. Find its circumference and area to the nearest unit. **125.7 cm, 1,257.1 cm^2** ■ LESSON 8-4

Find each square root. ■ LESSON 8-5

9. $\sqrt{1}$ **1**
10. $\sqrt{4}$ **2**
11. $\sqrt{49}$ **7**
12. $\sqrt{81}$ **9**
13. $\sqrt{900}$ **30**
14. $\sqrt{3,600}$ **60**

Find each missing side length. ■ LESSON 8-6

15. **8 m**

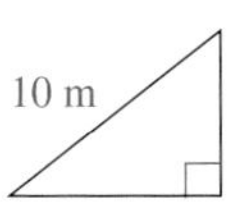

16. **13 yd**

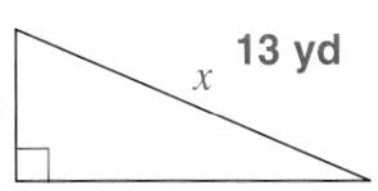

17. **8 cm**

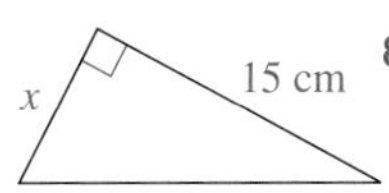

18. The lengths of the legs of a right triangle are 9 m and 14 m. How long is the third side to the nearest tenth of a unit? **16.6 m** ■ LESSON 8-7

Give the best name for each figure. Then find its surface area. Round to the nearest whole number if necessary. ■ LESSONS 8-8, 8-9

19.

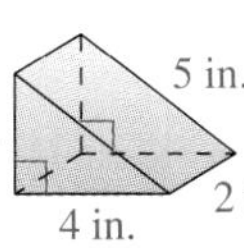

triangular prism, 36 $in.^2$

20.

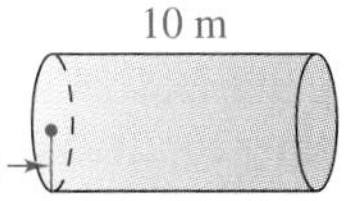

cylinder, 471 m^2

21.

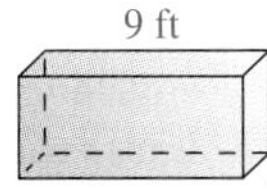

rectangular prism, 202 ft^2

22. Find the volumes of the figures in Exercises 20 and 21. **785 m^3, 180 ft^3** ■ LESSON 8-10

CHAPTER 9 Extra Practice

1. A quality control engineer at a factory inspected 300 glow sticks for quality. She found 15 defective glow sticks. ■ LESSON 9-1
   a. What is the probability that a glow stick is defective? $\frac{15}{300}$
   b. The factory can produce 1,400 glow sticks in one shift. Predict how many glow sticks will be defective. 70

Find each probability for one roll of a number cube. ■ LESSON 9-3

2. $P(3 \text{ or } 4)$ $\frac{2}{6}$ or $\frac{1}{3}$
3. $P(\text{not } 3)$ $\frac{5}{6}$
4. $P(5)$ $\frac{1}{6}$
5. $P(1 \text{ or } 7)$ $\frac{1}{6}$
6. $P(\text{not } 3 \text{ or } 4)$ $\frac{4}{6}$ or $\frac{2}{3}$

7. a. Toss two coins and spin a spinner with three congruent sections colored red, white, and blue. Draw a tree diagram to find the sample space. Check students' work. ■ LESSON 9-4
   b. Find $P(2 \text{ heads and blue})$ and $P(\text{at least 1 tails and red})$. $\frac{1}{12}$, $\frac{3}{12}$ or $\frac{1}{4}$

Events *A* and *B* are independent. Find *P*(*A* and *B*). ■ LESSON 9-5

8. $P(A) = \frac{1}{5}, P(B) = \frac{3}{4}$ $\frac{3}{20}$
9. $P(A) = \frac{1}{6}, P(B) = \frac{5}{6}$ $\frac{5}{36}$
10. $P(A) = 1, P(B) = 0$ 0

A bag contains 6 green marbles, 8 blue marbles, and 3 red marbles. Find *P*(*B*) after *A* has happened.

11. *A*: Draw a green marble. Keep it. *B*: Draw a red marble. $\frac{3}{16}$
12. *A*: Draw a blue marble. Replace it. *B*: Draw a red marble. $\frac{3}{17}$
13. *A*: Draw a red marble. Keep it. *B*: Draw a red marble. $\frac{2}{16}$
14. A box contains the letters S T A T I S T I C S. Suppose you select two letters, one after the other without replacement. Find $P(\text{S, then T})$. $\frac{9}{90}$ or $\frac{1}{10}$

State whether the situation is a *permutation* or a *combination*. Then answer the question. ■ LESSONS 9-6, 9-7

15. In how many ways can a committee of 2 be chosen from a club of 5 members? combination; 10 ways
16. In how many ways can a president and a treasurer be selected from a club of 5 members? permutation; 20 ways
17. Members of an environmental group marked 25 sea gulls in a nesting area. Later that summer they counted 500 gulls, 19 of which were marked. Estimate the sea gull population. 658 ■ LESSON 9-8

CHAPTER 10

25.

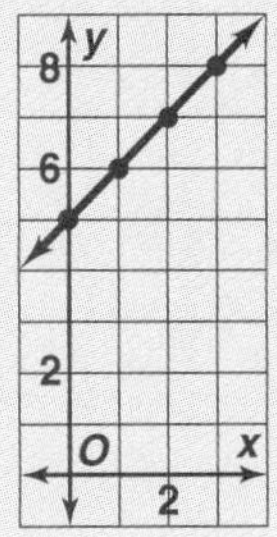

26.

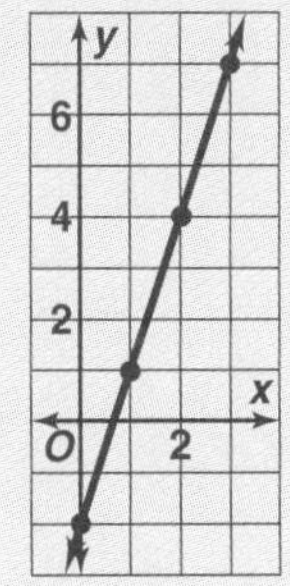

27.

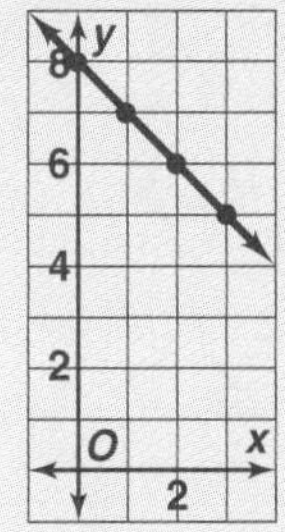

28.

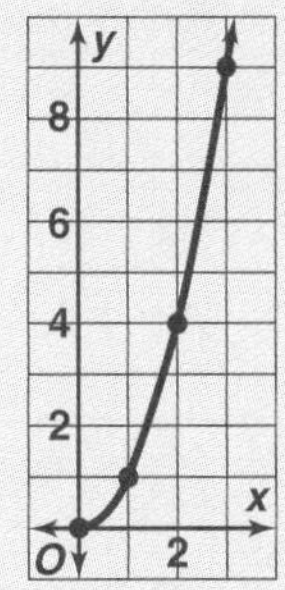

CHAPTER 10 **Extra Practice**

Identify each sequence as *arithmetic, geometric,* or *neither.* Then find the next three terms in the sequence. ■ LESSON 10-1

1. 7, 10, 13, 16, . . . arithmetic; 19, 22, 25
2. 800, 400, 200, 100, . . . geometric; 50, 25, 12.5
3. 50, 25, 48, 24, . . . neither; 46, 23, 44
4. 1, 2, 5, 6, 9, . . . neither; 10, 13, 14
5. 18.1, 17.5, 16.9, 16.3, . . . arithmetic; 15.7, 15.1, 14.5
6. 2, 3, 4.5, 6.75, . . . geometric; 10.125, 15.1875, 22.78125

Write each number in scientific notation. ■ LESSON 10-2

7. 70,000 7×10^4
8. 2,654,000 2.654×10^6
9. 610,000 6.1×10^5
10. 250 2.5×10^2
11. 2,200 2.2×10^3
12. 20,000,000 2×10^7

Write each number in standard form.

13. 7.03×10^4 70,300
14. 1.02×10^2 102
15. 2.56×10^7 25,600,000
16. 2.8×10^5 280,000
17. 8.2901×10^3 8,290.1

Choose **Use a calculator or pencil and paper to find the balance of each account earning compound interest. Use the formula $B = p(1 + r)^t$.** ■ LESSON 10-4

18. \$1,000 principal
    5% annual interest rate
    4 years \$1,215.51
19. \$700 principal
    4% annual interest rate
    12 years \$1,120.72
20. 1,500 principal
    5.5% annual interest rate
    7 years \$2,182.02

Write a function rule for each table of values. ■ LESSONS 10-5, 10-6

21.

n	f(n)
0	0
1	6
2	12
3	18

$f(n) = 6n$

22.

n	f(n)
0	−2
1	−1
2	0
3	1

$f(n) = n - 2$

23.

n	f(n)
0	1
1	4
2	7
3	10

$f(n) = 3n + 1$

24.

n	f(n)
0	10
1	8
2	6
3	4

$f(n) = 10 - 2n$

Find $f(0)$, $f(1)$, $f(2)$, and $f(3)$ for each function rule. Make a table of values, then graph the function. 25–28 See margin for graph.

25. $f(n) = n + 5$ 5, 6, 7, 8
26. $f(n) = 3n - 2$ −2, 1, 4, 7
27. $f(n) = 8 - n$ 8, 7, 6, 5
28. $f(n) = n^2$ 0, 1, 4, 9

29. On her trip to the library, Arlene walked two blocks to the bus stop in five minutes. She rode the bus for 15 min. The bus stopped three times, for one minute each time. Sketch a graph to represent Arlene's trip. Check students' work. ■ LESSON 10-7

17.

x	y
−2	7
−1	4
0	3
1	4
2	7

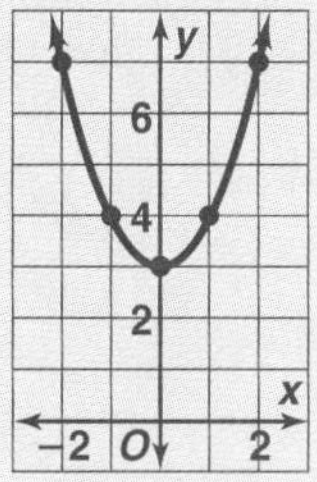

18.

x	y
−2	0
−1	3
0	−4
1	−3
2	0

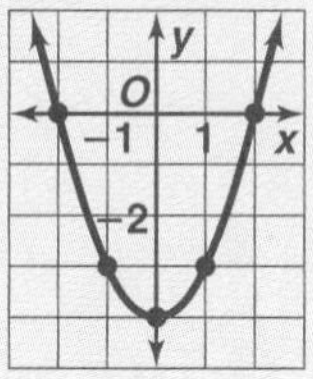

19.

x	y
−2	4
−1	2
0	0
1	2
2	4

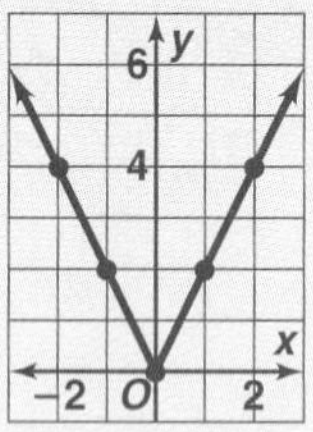

20.

x	y
−3	2
−2	1
−1	0
0	1
1	2
2	3

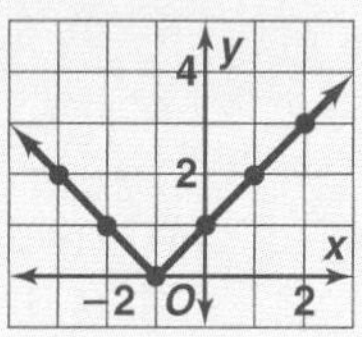

23a–b.

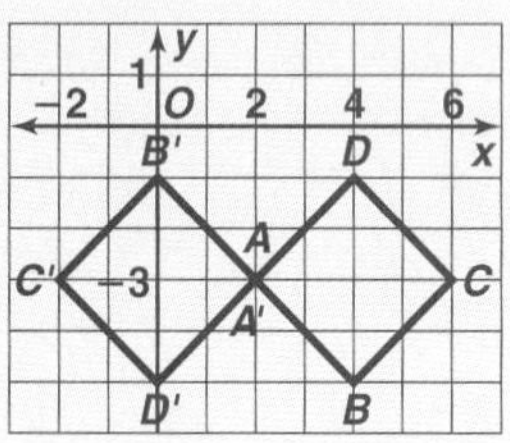

CHAPTER 11

Extra Practice

Use the graph at the right for Exercises 1–12. ■ LESSONS 11-1, 11-3

Name the point with the given coordinates.

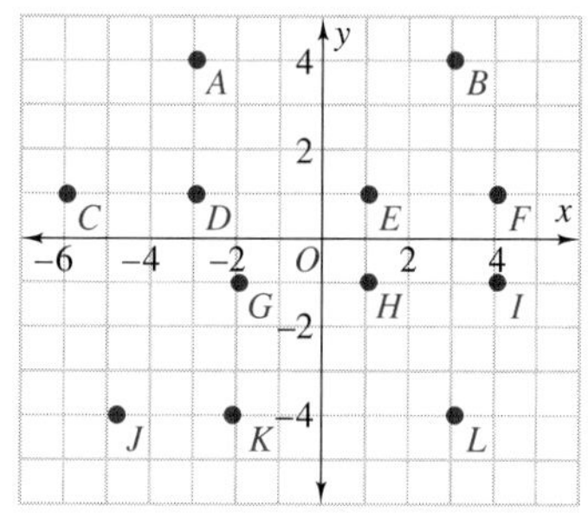

1. (−2, −1) G
2. (1, 1) E
3. (3, −4) L

Write the coordinates of each point.

4. A (−3, 4)
5. I (4, −1)
6. J (−5, −4)
7. C (−6, 1)
8. F (4, 1)
9. B (3, 4)

Find the slope of the line through the points.

10. A and E $-\frac{3}{4}$
11. G and E $\frac{2}{3}$
12. B and F −3

Tell whether each ordered pair is a solution of $y = x + 18$. Explain how you know. ■ LESSON 11-2

13. (2, 20) yes; 2 + 18 = 20
14. (22, 4) no; 22 + 18 ≠ 4
15. (36, −18) no; 36 + 18 ≠ −18
16. (−20, −2) yes; −20 + 18 = −2

Make a table of values. Then graph each function. ■ LESSON 11-4

17–20. See margin.

17. $y = x^2 + 3$
18. $y = x^2 - 4$
19. $y = 2|x|$
20. $y = |x + 1|$

Use the graph above right to answer Exercises 21 and 22. ■ LESSONS 11-6, 11-7

21. *Writing* Write a rule for the translation of the triangle formed by points C, A, and D to the triangle formed by points J, G, and K. Move △CAD 1 place to the right and 5 places down.

22. Is the triangle formed by points E, B, and F a reflection, a rotation, or a translation of the triangle formed by points H, L, and I? Explain. reflection

23a–b. See margin.

23. a. Graph the square $ABCD$ with vertices $A(2, -3)$, $B(4, -5)$, $C(6, -3)$, and $D(4, -1)$. Then connect the vertices in order. ■ LESSON 11-8
    b. Draw the image of square $ABCD$ after a rotation of 180° about point A.
    c. Write the coordinates of the vertices of the image of square $ABCD$. (2, −3), (0, −1), (−2, −3), (0, −5)

Tables

Tables

TABLE 1 *Measures*

Metric

Length

10 millimeters (mm) = 1 centimeter (cm)

100 cm = 1 meter (m)

1,000 m = 1 kilometer (km)

Area

100 square millimeters (mm^2) = 1 square centimeter (cm^2)

10,000 cm^2 = 1 square meter (m^2)

Volume

1,000 cubic millimeters (mm^3) = 1 cubic centimeter (cm^3)

1,000,000 cm^3 = 1 cubic meter (m^3)

Mass

1,000 milligrams (mg) = 1 gram (g)

1,000 g = 1 kilogram (kg)

Liquid Capacity

1,000 milliliters (mL) = 1 liter (L)

United States Customary

Length

12 inches (in.) = 1 foot (ft)

3 feet = 1 yard (yd)

36 in. = 1 yd

5,280 ft = 1 mile (mi)

1,760 yd = 1 mi

Area

144 square inches ($in.^2$) = 1 square foot (ft^2)

9 ft^2 = 1 square yard (yd^2)

4,840 yd^2 = 1 acre

Volume

1,728 cubic inches ($in.^3$) = 1 cubic foot (ft^3)

27 ft^3 = 1 cubic yard (yd^3)

Weight

16 ounces (oz) = 1 pound (lb)

2,000 lb = 1 ton (T)

Liquid Capacity

8 fluid ounces (fl oz) = 1 cup (c)

2 c = 1 pint (pt)

2 pt = 1 quart (qt)

4 qt = 1 gallon (gal)

Time

1 minute (min) = 60 seconds (s)

1 hour (h) = 60 min

1 day (da) = 24 h

1 year (yr) = 365 da

525

TABLE 2 *Formulas*

Circumference of a circle

$C = \pi d$ or $C = 2\pi r$

Area

parallelogram:	$A = bh$
rectangle:	$A = bh$
trapezoid:	$A = \frac{1}{2}h(b_1 + b_2)$
triangle:	$A = \frac{1}{2}bh$
circle:	$A = \pi r^2$

Volume

cylinder:	$V = \pi r^2 h$
rectangular prism:	$V = lwh$

TABLE 3 *Symbols*

$>$	is greater than
$<$	is less than
$\geq$	is greater than or equal to
$\leq$	is less than or equal to
$=$	is equal to
$\neq$	is not equal to
$^\circ$	degrees
%	percent
$f(n)$	f of n
$a : b$	ratio of a to b, $\frac{a}{b}$
$\lvert -5 \rvert$	absolute value of negative 5
$P(E)$	probability of an event E
π	pi
$\perp$	is perpendicular to
$\cong$	is congruent to
$\sim$	is similar to
$\approx$	is approximately equal to
$\overline{AB}$	segment AB
$\overrightarrow{AB}$	ray AB
$\overleftrightarrow{AB}$	line AB
$\triangle ABC$	triangle ABC
$\angle ABC$	angle ABC
$m\angle ABC$	measure of angle ABC
AB	length of segment AB
$\overset{\frown}{AB}$	arc AB

Tables

TABLE 4 *Squares and Square Roots*

N	N^2	$\sqrt{N}$	*N*	N^2	$\sqrt{N}$
1	1	1	51	2,601	7.141
2	4	1.414	52	2,704	7.211
3	9	1.732	53	2,809	7.280
4	16	2	54	2,916	7.348
5	25	2.236	55	3,025	7.416
6	36	2.449	56	3,136	7.483
7	49	2.646	57	3,249	7.550
8	64	2.828	58	3,364	7.616
9	81	3	59	3,481	7.681
10	100	3.162	60	3,600	7.746
11	121	3.317	61	3,721	7.810
12	144	3.464	62	3,844	7.874
13	169	3.606	63	3,969	7.937
14	196	3.742	64	4,096	8
15	225	3.873	65	4,225	8.062
16	256	4	66	4,356	8.124
17	289	4.123	67	4,489	8.185
18	324	4.243	68	4,624	8.246
19	361	4.359	69	4,761	8.307
20	400	4.472	70	4,900	8.367
21	441	4.583	71	5,041	8.426
22	484	4.690	72	5,184	8.485
23	529	4.796	73	5,329	8.544
24	576	4.899	74	5,476	8.602
25	625	5	75	5,625	8.660
26	676	5.099	76	5,776	8.718
27	729	5.196	77	5,929	8.775
28	784	5.292	78	6,084	8.832
29	841	5.385	79	6,241	8.888
30	900	5.477	80	6,400	8.944
31	961	5.568	81	6,561	9
32	1,024	5.657	82	6,724	9.055
33	1,089	5.745	83	6,889	9.110
34	1,156	5.831	84	7,056	9.165
35	1,225	5.916	85	7,225	9.220
36	1,296	6	86	7,396	9.274
37	1,369	6.083	87	7,569	9.327
38	1,444	6.164	88	7,744	9.381
39	1,521	6.245	89	7,921	9.434
40	1,600	6.325	90	8,100	9.487
41	1,681	6.403	91	8,281	9.539
42	1,764	6.481	92	8,464	9.592
43	1,849	6.557	93	8,649	9.644
44	1,936	6.633	94	8,836	9.695
45	2,025	6.708	95	9,025	9.747
46	2,116	6.782	96	9,216	9.798
47	2,209	6.856	97	9,409	9.849
48	2,304	6.928	98	9,604	9.899
49	2,401	7	99	9,801	9.950
50	2,500	7.071	100	10,000	10

Skills Handbook

Comparing and Ordering Whole Numbers

The numbers on a number line are in order from least to greatest.

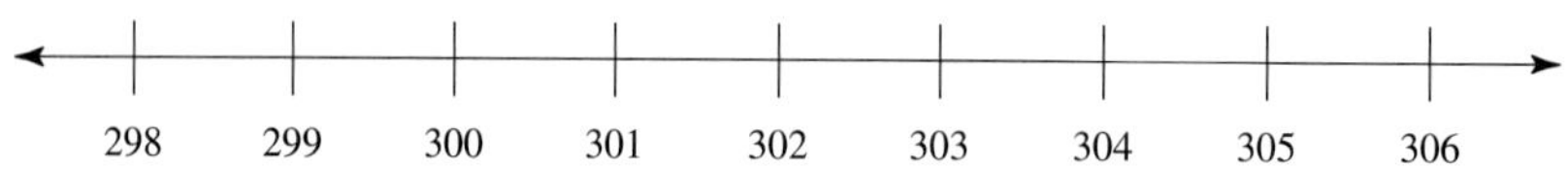

You can use a number line to compare whole numbers. Use the symbols > (is greater than) and < (is less than).

EXAMPLE 1

Use > or < to compare the numbers.

a. 303 ■ 299

303 is to the right of 299.

300 > 299

b. 301 ■ 305

301 is to the left of 305.

301 < 305

The value of a digit depends on its place in a number. Compare digits starting from the left.

EXAMPLE 2

Use > or < to compare the numbers.

a. 12,060,012,875 ■ 12,060,012,675

8 hundreds > 6 hundreds, so

12,060,012,875 > 12,060,012,675

b. 465,320 ■ 4,653,208

0 millions < 4 millions, so

465,320 < 4,653,208

EXERCISES *On Your Own*

Use > or < to compare the numbers.

1. 3,660 ■ 360 >
2. 74,328 ■ 74,238 >
3. 88,010 ■ 8,101 >
4. 87,524 ■ 9,879 >

5. 295,286 ■ 295,826 <
6. 829,631 ■ 842,832 <
7. 932,401 ■ 932,701 <
8. 60,000 ■ 500,009 <

9. 1,609,372,002 ■ 609,172,002 >
10. 45,248,315,150 ■ 45,283,718,150 <

Write the numbers from least to greatest.

11. 3,747; 3,474; 3,774; 3,347; 3,734
3,347; 3,474; 3,734; 3,747; 3,774

12. 70,903; 70,309; 73,909; 73,090
70,309; 70,903; 73,090; 73,909

13. 32,056,403; 302,056,403; 30,265,403; 30,256,403
30,256,403; 30,265,403; 32,056,403; 302,056,403

14. 884,172; 881,472; 887,142; 881,872
881,472; 881,872; 884,172; 887,142

Rounding Whole Numbers

You can use number lines to help you round numbers.

■ EXAMPLE 1

a. Round 7,510 to the nearest thousand.

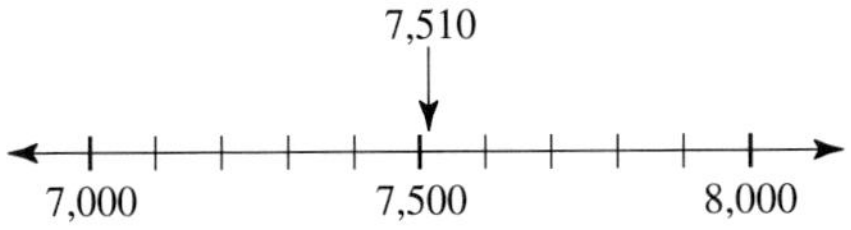

7,510 is between 7,000 and 8,000.
7,510 rounds to 8,000.

b. Round 237 to the nearest ten.

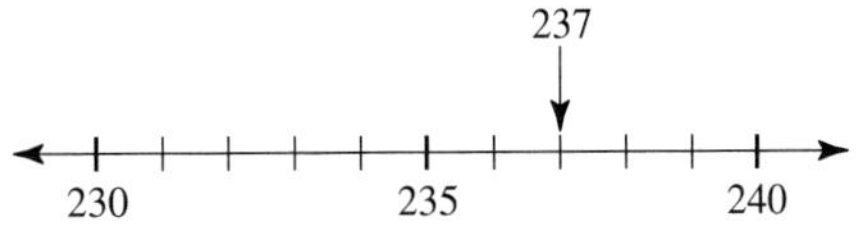

237 is between 230 and 240.
237 rounds to 240.

To round a number to a particular place, look at the digit to the right of that place. If the digit is less than 5, round down. If the digit is 5 or more, round up.

■ EXAMPLE 2

Round to the place of the underlined digit.

a. 3,463,280
The digit to the right of the 6 is 3, so 3,463,280 rounds down to 3,460,000.

b. 289,543
The digit to the right of the 9 is 5, so 289,543 rounds up to 290,000.

EXERCISES *On Your Own*

Round to the nearest ten.

1. 42 40 **2.** 89 90 **3.** 671 670 **4.** 3,482 3,480 **5.** 7,029 7,030 **6.** 661,423 661,420

Round to the nearest thousand.

7. 5,800 6,000 **8.** 3,100 3,000 **9.** 44,280 44,000 **10.** 9,936 10,000 **11.** 987 1,000 **12.** 313,591 314,000

13. 5,641 6,000 **14.** 37,896 38,000 **15.** 82,019 82,000 **16.** 808,155 808,000 **17.** 34,501 35,000 **18.** 650,828 651,000

Round to the place of the underlined digit.

19. 68,852 68,900 **20.** 451,006 500,000 **21.** 3,406,781 3,407,000 **22.** 28,512,030 29,000,000 **23.** 71,225,003 71,230,000

24. 96,359 96,400 **25.** 401,223 400,000 **26.** 8,902 9,000 **27.** 3,677 3,680 **28.** 2,551,750 2,551,800

29. 68,663 69,000 **30.** 701,803,229 702,000,000 **31.** 565,598 566,000 **32.** 32,810 32,800 **33.** 1,446,300 1,400,000

Skills Handbook

Skills Handbook

529

Multiplying Whole Numbers

When you multiply by a two-digit number, first multiply by the ones and then multiply by the tens. Add the products.

■ EXAMPLE 1

Multiply 62 × 704.

Step 1	Step 2	Step 3
$\begin{array}{r} 704 \\ \times\ 62 \\ \hline 1408 \end{array}$	$\begin{array}{r} 704 \\ \times\ 62 \\ \hline 1408 \\ 42240 \end{array}$	$\begin{array}{r} 704 \\ \times\ 62 \\ \hline 1\,408 \\ +\ 42\,240 \\ \hline 43{,}648 \end{array}$

■ EXAMPLE 2

Find each product.

a. 93 × 6	b. 25 × 48	c. 80 × 921
$\begin{array}{r} 93 \\ \times\ 6 \\ \hline 558 \end{array}$	$\begin{array}{r} 48 \\ \times\ 25 \\ \hline 240 \\ +\ 960 \\ \hline 1{,}200 \end{array}$	$\begin{array}{r} 921 \\ \times\ 80 \\ \hline 73{,}680 \end{array}$

EXERCISES *On Your Own*

Find each product.

1. 74 × 6 — 444
2. 35 × 9 — 315
3. 53 × 7 — 371
4. 80 × 8 — 640
5. 98 × 4 — 392
6. 65 × 8 — 520
7. 512 × 3 — 1,536
8. 407 × 9 — 3,663
9. 225 × 6 — 1,350
10. 340 × 5 — 1,700
11. 816 × 7 — 5,712
12. 603 × 3 — 1,809
13. 70 × 36 — 2,520
14. 41 × 55 — 2,255
15. 38 × 49 — 1,862
16. 601 × 87 — 52,287
17. 271 × 34 — 9,214
18. 450 × 67 — 30,150
19. 6 × 82 — 492
20. 405 × 5 — 2,025
21. 81 × 9 — 729
22. 3 × 274 — 822
23. 552 × 4 — 2,208
24. 60 × 84 — 5,040
25. 52 × 17 — 884
26. 31 × 90 — 2,790
27. 78 × 52 — 4,056
28. 43 × 66 — 2,838
29. 826 × 3 — 2,478
30. 702 × 4 — 2,808
31. 8 × 180 — 1,440
32. 6 × 339 — 2,034
33. 781 × 7 — 5,467

Dividing Whole Numbers

First estimate the quotient by rounding the divisor, the dividend, or both. When you divide, after you bring down a digit, you must write a digit in the quotient.

■ **EXAMPLE**

Find each quotient.

a. 741 ÷ 8

Estimate:

720 ÷ 8 ≈ 90

```
   92 R5
8)741
 -72
   21
 - 16
    5
```

b. 838 ÷ 43

Estimate:

800 ÷ 40 ≈ 20

```
    19 R21
43)838
  - 43
    408
  - 387
     21
```

c. 367 ÷ 9

Estimate:

360 ÷ 9 ≈ 40

```
   40 R7
9)367
- 360
    7
```

EXERCISES *On Your Own*

Divide.

15 R1	6 R5	12 R6	28	13 R3
1. 4)61	**2.** 8)53	**3.** 7)90)	**4.** 3)84	**5.** 6)81
78 R1	217 R2	80 R5	25 R6	103 R3
6. 6)469	**7.** 3)653	**8.** 8)645	**9.** 9)231	**10.** 4)415
7 R41	5 R13	7 R27	14 R12	3 R36
11. 60)461	**12.** 40)213	**13.** 70)517	**14.** 30)432	**15.** 80)276
6 R15	5 R21	3	3 R7	5 R28
16. 43)273	**17.** 52)281	**18.** 69)207	**19.** 38)121	**20.** 81)433
14 R52	18 R31	37 R12	17 R5	21 R30
21. 94)1,368	**22.** 62)1,147	**23.** 55)2,047	**24.** 85)1,450	**25.** 46)996
26. 94 ÷ 4	**27.** 66 ÷ 9	**28.** 90 ÷ 5	**29.** 69 ÷ 6	**30.** 58 ÷ 8
23 R2	7 R3	18	11 R3	7 R2
31. 323 ÷ 5	**32.** 849 ÷ 7	**33.** 404 ÷ 8	**34.** 934 ÷ 3	**35.** 619 ÷ 6
64 R3	121 R2	50 R4	311 R1	103 R1
36. 777 ÷ 50	**37.** 528 ÷ 20	**38.** 443 ÷ 70	**39.** 312 ÷ 40	**40.** 335 ÷ 60
15 R27	26 R8	6 R23	7 R32	5 R35
41. 382 ÷ 72	**42.** 580 ÷ 68	**43.** 279 ÷ 43	**44.** 232 ÷ 27	**45.** 331 ÷ 93
5 R22	8 R36	6 R21	8 R16	3 R52
46. 614 ÷ 35	**47.** 423 ÷ 28	**48.** 489 ÷ 15	**49.** 1,134 ÷ 51	**50.** 1,103 ÷ 26
17 R19	15 R3	32 R9	22 R12	42 R11

Skills Handbook

Place Value and Decimals

Each digit in a decimal has both a place and a value. The value of any place is one tenth the value of the place to its left. In the chart below, the digit 5 is in the hundredths place. So, its value is 5 hundredths.

thousands	hundreds	tens	ones	.	tenths	hundredths	thousandths	ten-thousandths	hundred-thousandths
2	8	3	6	.	7	5	0	1	4

■ EXAMPLE

a. In what place is the digit 8?
hundreds

b. What is the value of the digit 8?
8 hundred

EXERCISES *On Your Own*

Use the chart above. Write the place of each digit.

1. 3 tens
2. 4 hundred-thousandths
3. 6 ones
4. 7 tenths
5. 1
5. ten-thousandths
6. 0 thousandths

Use the chart above. Write the value of each digit.

7. 3 3 tens
8. 4
8. 4 hundred-thousandths
9. 6 6 ones
10. 7 7 tenths
11. 1
11. 1 ten-thousandths
12. 0
12. 0 thousandths

Write the value of the digit 6 in each number.

13. 0.162 6 hundredths
14. 0.016 6 thousandths
15. 13.672 6 tenths
16. 1,640.8 6 hundreds
17. 62.135 6 tens
18. 26.34 6 ones
19. 6,025.9 6 thousands
20. 0.6003 6 tenths
21. 2,450.65 6 tenths
22. 615.28 6 hundreds
23. 3.16125 6 hundredths
24. 1.20641 6 thousandths
25. 0.15361 6 ten-thousandths
26. 1.55736
26. 6 hundred-thousandths
27. 0.20516
27. 6 hundred-thousandths

Write the value of the underlined digit.

28. 24.0026 4 ones
29. 14.931 3 hundredths
30. 5.7894 9 thousandths
31. 0.87 8 tenths
32. 10.0563 3 ten-thousandths

Reading and Writing Decimals

A place value chart can help you read and write decimals. When there are no ones, write a zero before the decimal point.

billions	hundred millions	ten millions	millions	hundred thousands	ten thousands	thousands	hundreds	tens	ones	.	tenths	hundredths	thousandths	ten-thousandths	hundred-thousandths	millionths	Read
									0	.	0	7					7 hundredths
								2	3	.	0	1	4				23 and 14 thousandths
3	0	0	0	0	0	0	0	0	0	.	8						3 billion and 8 tenths
									5	.	0	0	0	1	0	2	5 and 102 millionths

■ **EXAMPLE**

a. Write thirteen ten-thousandths in numerals.

Ten-thousandths is 4 places after the decimal point. So, the decimal will have 4 places after the decimal point. The number is 0.0013.

b. Write 1.025 in words.

The digit 5 is in the thousandths place. So, 1.025 is one and twenty-five thousandths.

EXERCISES *On Your Own*

16. twenty-five and seven hundred-thousandths   17. fifteen hundred-thousandths

Write a number for the given words.

1. three hundredths 0.03
2. twenty-one millions 21,000,000
3. six and two hundredths 6.02
4. two billion and six tenths 2,000,000,000.6
5. two and five hundredths 2.05
6. five thousand twelve 5,012
7. seven millionths 0.000007
8. forty-one ten-thousandths 0.0041
9. eleven thousandths 0.011
10. one and twenty-five millionths 1.000025
11. three hundred four thousandths 0.304

Write each number in words. 14. twelve and sixty-nine millionths

12. five thousand seven hundred and four tenths   15. nine hundred and two hundredths

12. 5,700.4 **13.** 3,000,000.09 **14.** 12.000069 **15.** 900.02 **16.** 25.00007 **17.** 0.00015

13. three million and nine hundredths   16–17. See above.

Rounding Decimals

You can use number lines to help you round decimals.

■ EXAMPLE 1

a. Round 1.627 to the nearest tenth.

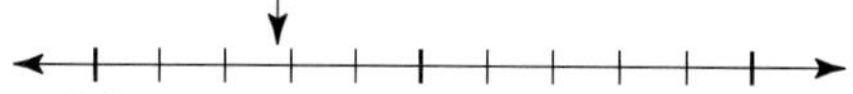

1.627 is between 1.6 and 1.7.
1.627 rounds to 1.6.

b. Round 0.248 to the nearest hundredth.

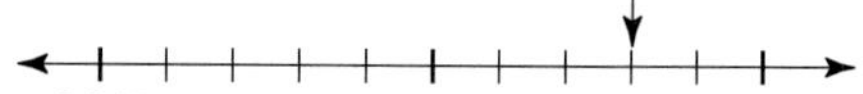

0.248 is between 0.24 and 0.25.
0.248 rounds to 0.25.

To round a number to a particular place, look at the digit to the right of that place. If the digit is less than 5, round down. If the digit is 5 or more, round up.

■ EXAMPLE 2

a. Round 2.4301 to the nearest whole number.

The digit to the right of 2 is 4, so 2.4301 rounds down to 2.

b. Round 0.0515 to the nearest thousandth.

The digit to the right of 1 is 5, so 0.0515 rounds up to 0.052.

EXERCISES *On Your Own*

Round to the nearest tenth.

1. 2.75 2.8	**2.** 3.816 3.8	**3.** 19.72 19.7	**4.** 401.1603 401.2	**5.** 499.491 499.5	**6.** 3.949 3.9
7. 4.67522 4.7	**8.** 20.397 20.4	**9.** 399.956 400.0	**10.** 129.98 130.0	**11.** 96.4045 96.4	**12.** 125.66047 125.7

Round to the nearest hundredth.

13. 31.723 31.72	**14.** 14.869 14.87	**15.** 1.78826 1.79	**16.** 0.1119 0.11	**17.** 736.941 736.94	**18.** 9.6057 9.61
19. 0.699 0.70	**20.** 4.231 4.23	**21.** 12.09531 12.10	**22.** 5.77125 5.77	**23.** 0.9195 0.92	**24.** 4.0033 4.00

Round to the nearest thousandth.

25. 0.4387 0.439	**26.** 0.0649 0.065	**27.** 3.4953 3.495	**28.** 8.07092 8.071	**29.** 0.6008 0.601	**30.** 6.0074 6.007

Round to the nearest whole number.

31. 3.942 4	**32.** 10.4 10	**33.** 79.52 80	**34.** 105.3002 105	**35.** 431.23 431	**36.** 0.4962 0

Multiplying Decimals

When you multiply with decimals, first multiply as if the factors were whole numbers. Then, count the decimal places in both factors to find how many places are needed in the product.

■ EXAMPLE 1

Multiply 2.5 × 1.8.

$$\begin{array}{r} 1.8 \\ \underline{\times\ 2.5} \\ 90 \\ \underline{+\ 360} \\ 4.50 \end{array}$$

1.8 ← one decimal place
× 2.5 ← one decimal place
4.50 ← two decimal places

■ EXAMPLE 2

Find each product.

a. 0.7 × 1.02

$$\begin{array}{r} 1.02 \\ \underline{\times\ 0.7} \\ 0.714 \end{array}$$

b. 0.03 × 407

$$\begin{array}{r} 407 \\ \underline{\times\ 0.03} \\ 12.21 \end{array}$$

c. 0.62 × 2.45

$$\begin{array}{r} 2.45 \\ \underline{\times\ 0.62} \\ 490 \\ \underline{+\ 14700} \\ 1.5190 \end{array}$$

d. 75 × 3.06

$$\begin{array}{r} 3.06 \\ \underline{\times\ 75} \\ 1530 \\ \underline{+\ 21420} \\ 229.50 \end{array}$$

EXERCISES *On Your Own*

Multiply.

1. 0.3 × 8 **2.4**
2. 5 × 0.06 **0.3**
3. 0.04 × 7 **0.28**
4. 6 × 0.8 **4.8**
5. 3.1 × 0.05 **0.155**
6. 14 × 0.2 **2.8**
7. 3.1 × 6 **18.6**
8. 0.05 × 43 **2.15**
9. 0.27 × 5 **1.35**
10. 72 × 0.6 **43.2**
11. 0.8 × 312 **249.6**
12. 4.56 × 7 **31.92**
13. 5 × 2.41 **12.05**
14. 704 × 0.3 **211.2**
15. 9 × 1.35 **12.15**
16. 1.2 × 0.3 **0.36**
17. 0.04 × 2.5 **0.1**
18. 6.6 × 0.3 **1.98**
19. 15.1 × 0.02 **0.302**
20. 0.8 × 31.3 **25.04**
21. 0.07 × 25.1 **1.757**
22. 42.2 × 0.9 **37.98**
23. 0.6 × 30.02 **18.012**
24. 0.05 × 11.8 **0.59**
25. 71.13 × 0.4 **28.452**
26. 48 × 2.1 **100.8**
27. 6.3 × 85 **535.5**
28. 0.42 × 98 **41.16**
29. 76 × 3.3 **250.8**
30. 0.77 × 51 **39.27**
31. 5.2 × 4.8 **24.96**
32. 0.12 × 6.1 **0.732**

Skills Handbook

Zeros in the Product

When you multiply with decimals, start at the right of the product to count the number of decimal places. Sometimes you need to write extra zeros to the left of a product before you can place the decimal point.

EXAMPLE 1

Multiply 0.03×0.51.

Step 1		Step 2	
0.51	←two decimal places→	0.51	
× 0.03	←two decimal places→	× 0.03	
1 53	←four decimal places→	0.01 53	← Put extra zeros to the left. Then place the decimal point.

EXAMPLE 2

Find each product.

a. 0.2×0.3

$$\begin{array}{r} 0.3 \\ \underline{\times\ 0.2} \\ 0.06 \end{array}$$

b. 0.5×0.04

$$\begin{array}{r} 0.04 \\ \underline{\times\ 0.5} \\ 0.020 \end{array}$$

c. 4×0.02

$$\begin{array}{r} 0.02 \\ \underline{\times\ \ \ 4} \\ 0.08 \end{array}$$

d. 0.02×0.45

$$\begin{array}{r} 0.45 \\ \underline{\times\ 0.02} \\ 0.0090 \end{array}$$

EXERCISES *On Your Own*

Multiply.

1. 0.1×0.6 0.06
2. 0.4×0.2 0.08
3. 0.05×0.06 0.003
4. 0.01×8 0.08
5. 0.7×0.02 0.014
6. 0.03×0.4 0.012
7. 0.03×0.9 0.027
8. 0.06×0.5 0.03
9. 0.2×0.02 0.004
10. 7×0.01 0.07
11. 0.05×0.05 0.0025
12. 0.6×0.06 0.036
13. 0.4×0.08 0.032
14. 0.07×0.05 0.0035
15. 0.03×0.03 0.0009
16. 0.09×0.05 0.0045
17. 0.5×0.08 0.04
18. 0.06×0.7 0.042
19. 0.07×0.01 0.0007
20. 0.16×0.2 0.032
21. 0.01×0.74 0.0074
22. 0.47×0.08 0.0376
23. 0.76×0.1 0.076
24. 0.19×0.3 0.057
25. 0.5×0.17 0.085
26. 0.31×0.08 0.0248
27. 0.14×0.05 0.007
28. 0.07×0.85 0.0595
29. 0.45×0.06 0.027
30. 0.4×0.23 0.092
31. 0.17×0.06 0.0102
32. 0.3×0.24 0.072
33. 0.67×0.09 0.0603
34. 0.08×0.39 0.0312
35. 0.3×0.27 0.081
36. 0.19×0.05 0.0095
37. 0.06×0.11 0.0066

Dividing a Decimal by a Whole Number

When you divide a decimal by a whole number, first divide as if the numbers were whole numbers. Then put a decimal point in the quotient directly above the decimal point in the dividend.

■ EXAMPLE 1

Divide 0.256 ÷ 8.

Step 1

$$\begin{array}{r} 32 \\ 8\overline{)0.256} \\ \underline{-\,24} \\ 16 \\ \underline{-\,16} \\ 0 \end{array}$$

Step 2

$$\begin{array}{r} 0.032 \\ 8\overline{)0.256} \\ \underline{-\,24} \\ 16 \\ \underline{-\,16} \\ 0 \end{array}$$

← Put extra zeros to the left. Then place the decimal point.

■ EXAMPLE 2

Find each quotient.

a. 12.6 ÷ 6

$$\begin{array}{r} 2.1 \\ 6\overline{)12.6} \\ \underline{-\,12} \\ 0\,6 \\ \underline{-\,6} \\ 0 \end{array}$$

b. 37.26 ÷ 81

$$\begin{array}{r} 0.46 \\ 81\overline{)37.26} \\ \underline{-\,32\,4} \\ 4\,86 \\ \underline{-\,4\,86} \\ 0 \end{array}$$

c. 0.666 ÷ 9

$$\begin{array}{r} 0.074 \\ 9\overline{)0.666} \\ \underline{-\,63} \\ 36 \\ \underline{-\,36} \\ 0 \end{array}$$

EXERCISES *On Your Own*

Divide.

1. $4\overline{)28.56}$ 7.14
2. $5\overline{)16.5}$ 3.3
3. $9\overline{)6.984}$ 0.776
4. $6\overline{)91.44}$ 15.24
5. $4\overline{)35.16}$ 8.79
6. $81\overline{)33.291}$ 0.411
7. $22\overline{)2.42}$ 0.11
8. $26\overline{)1723.8}$ 66.3
9. $83\overline{)15.272}$ 0.184
10. $39\overline{)26.91}$ 0.69
11. 22.2 ÷ 3 7.4
12. 1.2 ÷ 4 0.3
13. 4.65 ÷ 5 0.93
14. 7.11 ÷ 9 0.79
15. 17.52 ÷ 2 8.76
16. 10.53 ÷ 9 1.17
17. 14.49 ÷ 7 2.07
18. 37.14 ÷ 6 6.19
19. 0.0324 ÷ 9 0.0036
20. 0.1352 ÷ 8 0.0169
21. 0.0882 ÷ 6 0.0147
22. 0.8682 ÷ 6 0.1447
23. 79.599 ÷ 13 6.123
24. 45.918 ÷ 18 2.551
25. 59.7 ÷ 15 3.98
26. 74.664 ÷ 12 6.222
27. 12.342 ÷ 22 0.561
28. 29.792 ÷ 32 0.931
29. 22.568 ÷ 26 0.868
30. 11.340 ÷ 36 0.315

Skills Handbook

537

Powers of Ten

You can use shortcuts when multiplying and dividing by powers of ten.

When you multiply by	Move the decimal point
1,000	3 places to the right
100	2 places to the right
10	1 place to the right
0.1	1 place to the left
0.01	2 places to the left

When you divide by	Move the decimal point
1,000	3 places to the left
100	2 places to the left
10	1 place to the left
0.1	1 place to the right
0.01	2 places to the right

■ **EXAMPLE**

Multiply or divide.

a. 0.3 × 0.01

0.00.3 ← Move the decimal point 2 places to the left.

0.3 × 0.01 = 0.003

b. 0.18 ÷ 1,000

0.000.18 ← Move the decimal point 3 places to the left.

0.18 ÷ 1,000 = 0.00018

EXERCISES *On Your Own*

Multiply.

1. 3.2 × 0.01 0.032
2. 1,000 × 0.12 120
3. 0.7 × 0.1 0.07
4. 0.01 × 6.2 0.062
5. 0.09 × 100 9
6. 23.6 × 0.01 0.236
7. 5.2 × 10 52
8. 0.08 × 1,000 80
9. 100 × 0.05 5
10. 0.1 × 0.24 0.024
11. 18.03 × 0.1 1.803
12. 6.1 × 100 610

Divide.

13. 82.3 ÷ 0.1 823
14. 0.4 ÷ 1,000 0.0004
15. 5.02 ÷ 0.01 502
16. 16.5 ÷ 100 0.165
17. 236.7 ÷ 0.1 2,367
18. 45.28 ÷ 10 4.528
19. 0.9 ÷ 1,000 0.0009
20. 1.03 ÷ 0.01 103
21. 42.6 ÷ 0.1 426
22. 203.05 ÷ 0.01 20,305
23. 4.7 ÷ 10 0.47
24. 0.07 ÷ 100 0.0007

Multiply or divide.

25. 0.32 × 0.1 0.032
26. 0.03 ÷ 100 0.0003
27. 2.6 ÷ 0.1 26
28. 12.6 × 1,000 12,600
29. 0.8 ÷ 1,000 0.0008
30. 0.01 × 6.7 0.067
31. 100 × 0.15 15
32. 23.5 ÷ 10 2.35

Zeros in Decimal Division

When you are dividing by a decimal, sometimes you need to use extra zeros in the dividend, the quotient, or both.

■ EXAMPLE

Find each quotient.

a. $0.14 \div 0.04$

Multiply by 100.

$$\begin{array}{r} 3.5 \\ 0.04.\overline{)0.14.0} \\ -12 \\ \hline 2\,0 \\ -2\,0 \\ \hline 0 \end{array}$$

b. $0.00434 \div 0.07$

Multiply by 100.

$$\begin{array}{r} 0.062 \\ 0.07.\overline{)0.00.434} \\ -42 \\ \hline 14 \\ -14 \\ \hline 0 \end{array}$$

c. $0.045 \div 3.6$

Multiply by 10.

$$\begin{array}{r} 0.0125 \\ 3.6.\overline{)0.0.4500} \\ -36 \\ \hline 90 \\ -72 \\ \hline 180 \\ -180 \\ \hline 0 \end{array}$$

EXERCISES *On Your Own*

Divide.

1. $0.4\overline{)0.001}$ 0.0025
2. $0.05\overline{)0.0023}$ 0.046
3. $0.02\overline{)0.000162}$ 0.0081
4. $0.6\overline{)0.0015}$ 0.0025
5. $1.2\overline{)0.078}$ 0.065
6. $0.34\overline{)0.00119}$ 0.0035
7. $0.12\overline{)0.009}$ 0.075
8. $2.5\overline{)0.021}$ 0.0084
9. $0.0017 \div 0.02$ 0.085
10. $0.003 \div 0.6$ 0.005
11. $0.01099 \div 0.7$ 0.0157
12. $0.104 \div 0.05$ 2.08
13. $0.0945 \div 0.09$ 1.05
14. $0.00045 \div 0.3$ 0.0015
15. $0.052 \div 0.8$ 0.065
16. $0.142 \div 0.04$ 3.55
17. $0.034 \div 0.05$ 0.68
18. $0.0019 \div 0.2$ 0.0095
19. $0.9 \div 0.8$ 1.125
20. $0.000175 \div 0.07$ 0.0025
21. $0.0084 \div 1.4$ 0.006
22. $0.259 \div 3.5$ 0.074
23. $0.00468 \div 0.52$ 0.009
24. $0.00056 \div 0.16$ 0.0035
25. $0.0612 \div 7.2$ 0.0085
26. $0.17701 \div 3.1$ 0.0571
27. $0.00063 \div 0.18$ 0.0035
28. $0.011 \div 0.25$ 0.044
29. $0.3069 \div 9.3$ 0.033
30. $0.000924 \div 0.44$ 0.0021
31. $0.058023 \div 0.63$ 0.0921
32. $0.00123 \div 8.2$ 0.00015
33. $0.03225 \div 0.75$ 0.043
34. $0.006 \div 0.75$ 0.008
35. $0.73 \div 0.25$ 2.92
36. $0.68 \div 0.002$ 340
37. $0.398 \div 0.05$ 7.96
38. $0.0004 \div 0.002$ 0.2
39. $0.125 \div 0.005$ 25
40. $0.000096 \div 0.04$ 0.0024

Skills Handbook
539

Adding and Subtracting Fractions with Like Denominators

When you add or subtract fractions with the same denominator, first add or subtract the numerators. Write the answer over the denominator. If necessary, change the answer to simplest form.

■ EXAMPLE 1

Add or subtract. Write the answer in simplest form.

a. $\frac{5}{16} + \frac{3}{16}$

$$\begin{array}{r} \frac{5}{16} \\ +\ \frac{3}{16} \\ \hline \frac{8}{16} = \frac{1}{2} \end{array}$$

b. $\frac{7}{8} - \frac{1}{8}$

$$\begin{array}{r} \frac{7}{8} \\ -\ \frac{1}{8} \\ \hline \frac{6}{8} = \frac{3}{4} \end{array}$$

c. $\frac{3}{5} + \frac{2}{5}$

$\frac{3}{5} + \frac{2}{5} = \frac{5}{5} = 1$

To add or subtract mixed numbers, add or subtract the fractions first. Then add or subtract the whole numbers. If necessary, change the answer to simplest form.

■ EXAMPLE 2

Add or subtract. Write the answer in simplest form.

a. $2\frac{5}{8} + 3\frac{1}{8}$

$$\begin{array}{r} 2\frac{5}{8} \\ +\ 3\frac{1}{8} \\ \hline 5\frac{6}{8} = 5\frac{3}{4} \end{array}$$

b. $4\frac{3}{4} - 1\frac{1}{4}$

$$\begin{array}{r} 4\frac{3}{4} \\ -\ 1\frac{1}{4} \\ \hline 3\frac{2}{4} = 3\frac{1}{2} \end{array}$$

c. $5\frac{5}{6} + 2\frac{5}{6}$

$$\begin{aligned} 5\frac{5}{6} + 2\frac{5}{6} &= 7\frac{10}{6} \\ &= 7 + 1 + \frac{4}{6} \\ &= 8\frac{2}{3} \end{aligned}$$

EXERCISES *On Your Own*

Add or subtract. Write the answers in simplest form.

1. $\frac{2}{5} + \frac{2}{5}$ **$\frac{4}{5}$**
2. $\frac{2}{6} - \frac{1}{6}$ **$\frac{1}{6}$**
3. $\frac{2}{7} + \frac{2}{7}$ **$\frac{4}{7}$**
4. $9\frac{1}{3} - 8\frac{1}{3}$ **1**
5. $8\frac{6}{7} - 4\frac{2}{7}$ **$4\frac{4}{7}$**
6. $3\frac{1}{10} + 1\frac{3}{10}$ **$4\frac{2}{5}$**
7. $\frac{2}{8} + \frac{2}{8}$ **$\frac{1}{2}$**
8. $\frac{3}{6} - \frac{1}{6}$ **$\frac{1}{3}$**
9. $\frac{6}{8} - \frac{3}{8}$ **$\frac{3}{8}$**
10. $\frac{2}{9} + \frac{1}{9}$ **$\frac{1}{3}$**
11. $\frac{4}{5} - \frac{1}{5}$ **$\frac{3}{5}$**
12. $\frac{3}{4} + \frac{1}{4}$ **1**
13. $\frac{9}{10} - \frac{3}{10}$ **$\frac{3}{5}$**
14. $8\frac{7}{10} + 2\frac{3}{10}$ **11**
15. $1\frac{4}{5} + 3\frac{3}{5}$ **$5\frac{2}{5}$**
16. $2\frac{2}{9} + 3\frac{4}{9}$ **$5\frac{2}{3}$**
17. $3\frac{2}{5} + 8\frac{1}{5}$ **$11\frac{3}{5}$**
18. $8\frac{5}{8} - 3\frac{3}{8}$ **$5\frac{1}{4}$**
19. $1\frac{1}{12} + 5\frac{5}{12}$ **$6\frac{1}{2}$**
20. $9\frac{7}{10} - 2\frac{3}{10}$ **$7\frac{2}{5}$**
21. $9\frac{3}{4} + 1\frac{3}{4}$ **$11\frac{1}{2}$**

Metric Units of Length

The basic unit of length in the metric system is the meter. All the other units are based on the meter. In the chart below, each unit is 10 times the value of the unit to its left.

Unit	millimeter	centimeter	decimeter	meter	decameter	hectometer	kilometer
Symbol	mm	cm	dm	m	dam	hm	km
Value	0.001 m	0.01 m	0.1 m	1 m	10 m	100 m	1,000 m

To change a measure from one unit to another, start by using the chart to find the relationship between the two units.

■ EXAMPLE

Complete each equation.

a. 0.8 km = ■ m

1 km = 1,000 m

0.8 × 1,000 = 800 ← To change km to m, multiply by 1,000.

0.8 km = 800 m

b. 17.2 mm = ■ cm

1 mm = 0.1 cm

17.2 × 0.1 = 1.72 ← To change mm to cm, multiply by 0.1.

17.2 mm = 1.72 cm

c. ■ cm = 2.1 km

1 km = 100,000 cm

2.1 × 100,000 = 210,000 ← To change km to cm, multiply by 100,000.

210,000 cm = 2.1 km

d. ■ m = 5,200 cm

1 m = 0.01 cm

5,200 × 0.01 = 52 ← To change cm to m, multiply by 0.01.

52 m = 5,200 cm

EXERCISES *On Your Own*

Complete each equation.

1. 1 mm = ■ cm **0.1**
2. 1 m = ■ km **0.001**
3. 1 mm = ■ m **0.001**
4. 1 cm = ■ m **0.01**
5. 1.2 cm = ■ km **0.000012**
6. ■ km = 45,000 mm **0.045**
7. ■ m = 30 km **30,000**
8. 6.2 cm = ■ mm **62**
9. 3.3 km = ■ m **3,300**
10. 0.6 mm = ■ cm **0.06**
11. 72 cm = ■ m **0.72**
12. 180 m = ■ mm **180,000**
13. ■ cm = 13 km **1,300,000**
14. ■ m = 530 cm **5.3**
15. 4,900 mm = ■ m **4.9**
16. ■ cm = 24 m **2,400**
17. ■ km = 106,000 cm **1.06**
18. 259,000 mm = ■ m **259**
19. 1,200,000 mm = ■ km **1.2**

Skills Handbook
541

Metric Units of Capacity

The basic unit of capacity in the metric system is the liter. All the other units are based on the liter. In the chart below, each unit is 10 times the value of the unit to its left. Note that we use a capital L as the abbreviation for liters to avoid confusion with the number 1.

Unit	milliliter	centiliter	deciliter	liter	decaliter	hectoliter	kiloliter
Symbol	mL	cL	dL	L	daL	hL	kL
Value	0.001 L	0.01 L	0.1 L	1 L	10 L	100 L	1,000 L

To change a measure from one unit to another, start by using the chart to find the relationship between the two units.

■ **EXAMPLE**

Complete each equation.

a. 245 mL = ■ L

1 mL = 0.001 L

245 × 0.001 = 0.245 ← To change mL to L, multiply by 0.001.

245 mL = 0.245 L

b. ■ mL = 4.5 kL

1 kL = 1,000,000 mL

4.5 × 1,000,000 = 4,500,000 ← To change kL to mL, multiply by 1,000,000.

4,500,000 mL = 4.5 kL

EXERCISES *On Your Own*

Complete each equation.

1. 1 L = ■ mL 1,000

2. 1 mL = ■ kL 0.000001

3. 1 kL = ■ L 1,000

4. 1 kL = ■ mL 1,000,000

5. 200 L = ■ kL 0.2

6. 1.3 kL = ■ mL 1,300,000

7. ■ L = 30 kL 30,000

8. ■ kL = 5.2 L 0.0052

9. 180 mL = ■ L 0.18

10. ■ kL = 240 L 0.24

11. 0.6 mL = ■ L 0.0006

12. ■ kL = 106,000 L 106

13. 72 kL = ■ mL 72,000,000

14. ■ mL = 1.5 kL 1,500,000

15. ■ kL = 450,000 mL 0.45

16. 4,900 L = ■ kL 4.9

17. ■ kL = 200,000 mL 0.2

18. ■ L = 8 mL 0.008

19. 4.2 L = ■ mL 4,200

20. 57,000,000 mL = ■ L 57,000

21. 28,000 kL = ■ L 28,000,000

22. ■ mL = 9,000 L 9,000,000

23. 4,000 L = ■ mL 4,000,000

24. 870 L = ■ kL 0.87

Metric Units of Mass

The basic unit of mass in the metric system is the gram. All the other units are based on the gram. In the chart below, each unit is 10 times the value of the unit to its left.

Unit	milligram	centigram	decigram	gram	decagram	hectogram	kilogram
Symbol	mg	cg	dg	g	dag	hg	kg
Value	0.001 g	0.01 g	0.1 g	1 g	10 g	100 g	1,000 g

To change a measure from one unit to another, start by using the chart to find the relationship between the two units.

■ EXAMPLE

Complete each equation.

a. 2.3 kg = ■ g

1 kg = 1,000 g

2.3 × 1,000 = 2,300 ← To change kg to g, multiply by 1,000.

2.3 kg = 2,300 g

b. ■ g = 250 mg

1 mg = 0.001 g

250 × 0.001 = 0.25 ← To change mg to g, multiply by 0.001.

0.25 g = 250 mg

EXERCISES *On Your Own*

Complete each equation.

1. 1 mg = ■ g 0.001
2. 1 g = ■ kg 0.001
3. 1 mg = ■ kg 0.000001
4. 1 g = ■ mg 1,000
5. 1 kg = ■ g 1,000
6. 1 kg = ■ mg 1,000,000
7. ■ g = 8 mg 0.008
8. 1,500 mg = ■ kg 0.0015
9. ■ kg = 200,000 g 200
10. 72 g = ■ kg 0.072
11. ■ mg = 5.2 kg 5,200,000
12. 180 mg = ■ g 0.18
13. ■ mg = 3.7 g 3,700
14. 0.6 mg = ■ g 0.0006
15. 370 g = ■ kg 0.37
16. ■ kg = 300,000 mg 0.3
17. 900 g = ■ mg 900,000
18. ■ kg = 5.7 mg 0.0000057
19. 120 g = ■ kg 0.12
20. ■ kg = 440 g 0.44
21. ■ kg = 1,006,000 mg 1.006
22. 0.009 kg = ■ mg 9,000
23. 0.2 mg = ■ g 0.0002
24. 8.6 kg = ■ g 8,600
25. 800 g = ■ mg 800,000
26. 1.7 kg = ■ g 1,700
27. ■ mg = 6.2 kg 6,200,000

Glossary / Study Guide

Examples

A

Absolute value (p. 98) The absolute value of a number is its distance from zero on a number line.

-7 is 7 units from 0, so $|-7| = 7$.

Acute angle (p. 292) An acute angle is any angle that measures less than 90°.

$0° < m\angle 1 < 90°$

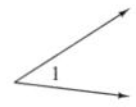

Acute triangle (p. 297) A triangle that contains all acute angles is an acute triangle.

Example: In the triangle, $\angle 1$, $\angle 2$, and $\angle 3$ are acute.

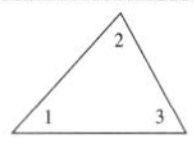

Addition Property of Equality (p. 120) If the same number is added to each side of an equation, the results are equal.

Since $\frac{20}{2} = 10$, $\frac{20}{2} + 3 = 10 + 3$.
If $a = b$, then $a + c = b + c$.

Adjacent angles (p. 292) Adjacent angles are two angles that share a vertex and one side but have no interior points in common.

Example: $\angle 1$ and $\angle 2$ are adjacent angles.

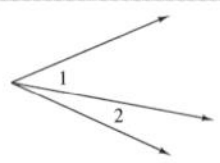

Angle (p. 291) An angle is made up of two rays with a common endpoint.

Example: $\angle 1$ is made up of $\overrightarrow{GP}$ and $\overrightarrow{GS}$ with common endpoint G.

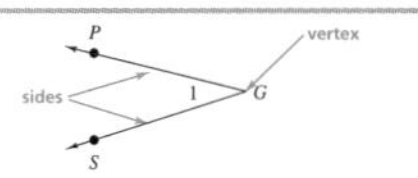

Angle bisector (p. 325) An angle bisector is the ray that divides the angle into two congruent angles.

Example: $\overrightarrow{DB}$ bisects $\angle ADC$ so $\angle 1 \cong \angle 2$.

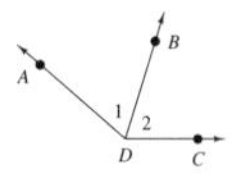

Arc (p. 315) An arc is part of a circle. A semicircle is an arc that is half of a circle.

Example: $\widehat{AB}$ is an arc of circle O. $\widehat{ABC}$ is a semicircle of circle O.

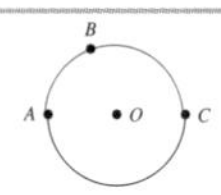

Examples

Area (p. 337) The number of square units inside a figure is the area.

Example: $\ell = 6$ ft, and $w = 4$ ft, so the area is 24 ft^2.

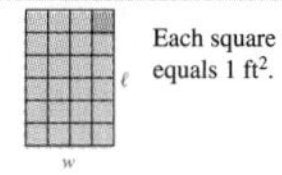

Arithmetic sequence (p. 434) In an arithmetic sequence, you add the same number to each term to find the next term.

The sequence 4, 10, 16, 22, 28, 34, . . . is an arithmetic sequence. You add 6 to each term to find the next term.

Associative Property of Addition (p. 60) Changing the grouping of the addends does not change the sum.

$(2 + 3) + 7 = 2 + (3 + 7)$
$(a + b) + c = a + (b + c)$

Associative Property of Multiplication (p. 68) Changing the grouping of the factors does not change the product.

$(3 \times 4) \times 5 = 3 \times (4 \times 5)$
$(a \times b) \times c = a \times (b \times c)$

B

Balance (p. 446) The balance of an account is the principal plus the interest earned.

You deposit $100 and earn $5 in interest. Your balance is $105.

Bar graph (p. 8) A bar graph compares amounts.

Example: This bar graph represents class sizes for grades 6, 7, and 8.

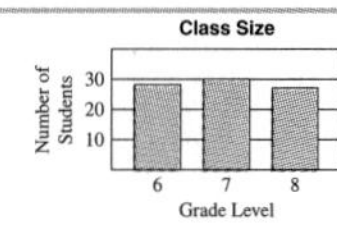

Base (p. 155) When a number is written in exponential form, the number that is used as a factor is the base.

$5^4 = 5 \times 5 \times 5 \times 5$
└base

Bases of two-dimensional figures (pp. 340, 344, 345)
See *Parallelogram, Triangle,* and *Trapezoid.*

Bases of three-dimensional figures (pp. 368, 369)
See *Cone, Cylinder, Prism,* and *Pyramid.*

Biased question (p. 31) A question is biased if it makes assumptions about the person being questioned or if it makes one answer seem better than another.

"Do you prefer good food or junk food?"

Examples

Box-and-whisker plot (p. 26) A box-and-whisker plot shows the distribution of data in each quartile, that is, in each quarter of the data.

Example: The box-and-whisker plot uses these data: 16 19 26 26 27 29 30 31 34 34 38 39 40

The lower quartile is 26. The median is 30. The upper quartile is 36.

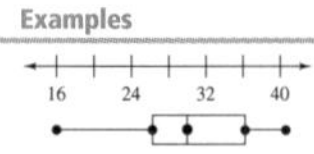

C

Capacity (p. 75) Capacity is a measure of the amount of space a liquid or dry ingredient occupies.

A juice bottle has a capacity of about 1 liter.

Central angle (p. 314) A central angle is an angle whose vertex is the center of a circle.

Example: $\angle AOB$ is a central angle of circle O.

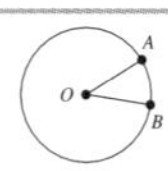

Chord (p. 314) A chord is a segment that has both endpoints on the circle.

Example: $\overline{CB}$ is a chord of circle O.

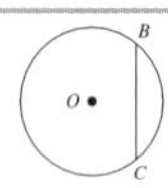

Circle (p. 314) A circle is the set of points in a plane that are all the same distance from a given point, called the center.

Circle O

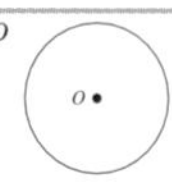

Circle graph (p. 318) A circle graph presents data as percents or fractions of a total. The total must be 100% or 1.

Example: This circle graph represents the types of plays William Shakespeare wrote.

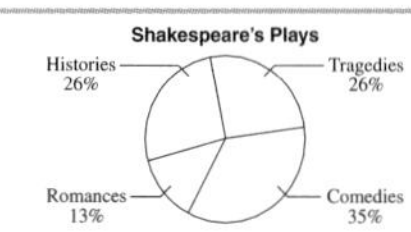

Circumference (p. 349) Circumference is the distance around a circle. You calculate the circumference of a circle by multiplying the diameter by pi, or π, ($C = \pi d$). Pi is approximately equal to 3.14.

Example: The circumference of a circle with a diameter of 10 cm is approximately 31.4 cm.

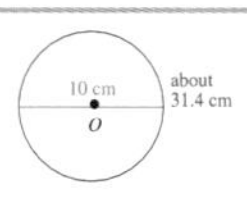

Examples

Combination (p. 419) An arrangement in which order does not matter is a combination.

You choose two vegetables from carrots, peas, and spinach. The possible combinations are carrots and peas, carrots and spinach, and peas and spinach.

Commutative Property of Addition (p. 60) Changing the order of the addends does not change the sum.

$3 + 1 = 1 + 3$
$a + b = b + a$

Commutative Property of Multiplication (p. 68) Changing the order of the factors does not change the product.

$6 \times 3 = 3 \times 6$
$ab = ba$

Compass (p. 316) A compass is a geometric tool you can use to draw circles and arcs.

Compatible numbers (p. 55) Compatible numbers are numbers close in value to the numbers you want to multiply or divide. Estimating products or quotients is easier when you use compatible numbers. Compatible numbers are easy to multiply or divide mentally.

Estimate $151 \div 14.6$.
$151 \approx 150$
$14.6 \approx 15$
$150 \div 15 = 10$
$151 \div 14.6 \approx 10$

Compensation (p. 63) A sum remains the same if you add a number to one addend and subtract it from another addend. A difference remains the same if you add the same number to both numbers or subtract the same number from both numbers.

$7 + 5 = (7 + 3) + (5 - 3)$
$22 - 8 = (22 + 2) - (8 + 2)$

Complement of an event (p. 402) The complement of an event is all the other possible events for that situation. The probability of an event plus the probability of its complement equals 1.

The event *no rain* is the complement of the event *rain.*

Complementary angles (p. 292) Two angles are complementary if the sum of their measures is 90°.

Example: $\angle BCA$ and $\angle CAB$ are complementary angles.

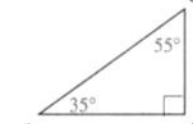

Composite number (p. 160) A whole number that has more than two factors is a composite number.

24 is a composite number that has 1, 2, 3, 4, 6, 8, 12, and 24 as factors.

Examples

Compound interest (p. 447) Compound interest is interest paid on both the principal and the interest earned in previous interest periods. To calculate compound interest, you can use the formula $B = p(1 + r)^t$, where B is the balance in the account, p is the principal, r is the annual interest rate, and t is the time in years that the account earns interest.

You deposit \$500 in an account earning 5% annual interest.

The balance after six years is $500(1 + 0.05)^6$ or \$670.05.

Cone (p. 369) A cone is a three-dimensional figure with one circular base and one vertex.

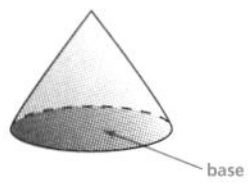

Congruent angles (p. 297) Congruent angles are angles that have the same measure.

$\angle B \cong \angle C$

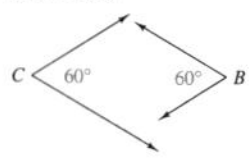

Congruent figures (p. 305) Figures that have the same size and shape are congruent. Congruent polygons have congruent corresponding sides and congruent corresponding angles.

Example: $\overline{AB} \cong \overline{QS}$, $\overline{CB} \cong \overline{RS}$, and $\overline{AC} \cong \overline{QR}$.
$\angle A \cong \angle Q$, $\angle C \cong \angle R$, and $\angle B \cong \angle S$.
$\triangle ABC \cong \triangle QSR$.

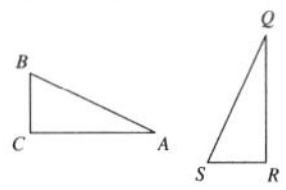

Congruent segments (p. 297) Congruent segments are segments that have the same length.

$\overline{AB} \cong \overline{WX}$

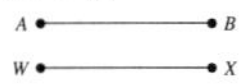

Coordinate plane (p. 472) A coordinate plane is formed by a horizontal number line called the x-axis and a vertical number line called the y-axis.

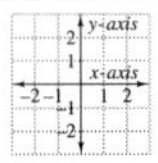

Coordinates (p. 473) Each point on the coordinate plane is identified by a unique ordered pair of numbers called coordinates. The first coordinate tells you how far from the origin to move along the x-axis. The second coordinate tells you how far from the origin to move along the y-axis.

Example: The ordered pair $(-2, 1)$ describes the point that is 2 units to the left of the y-axis and one unit above the x-axis.

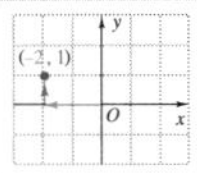

Examples

Corresponding angles of polygons (pp. 245, 305) The matching angles of similar or congruent figures are corresponding angles.

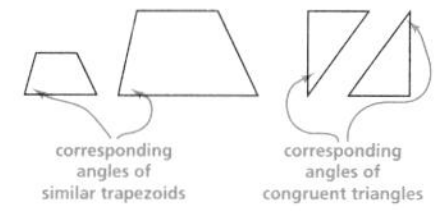

Corresponding sides of polygons (pp. 245, 305) The matching sides of similar or congruent figures are corresponding sides.

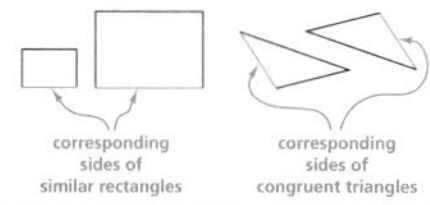

Counting principle (p. 408) If there are m ways of making one choice and n ways of making a second choice, then there are $m \times n$ ways of making the first choice followed by the second.

Toss a coin and roll a standard number cube. The total number of possible outcomes is $2 \times 6 = 12$.

Cross products (p. 241) In the proportion $\frac{a}{b} = \frac{c}{d}$, the cross products are ad and bc. Cross products of a proportion are equal.

In the proportion $\frac{2}{5} = \frac{10}{25}$, the cross products are 2(25) and 5(10).

Cube (p. 369) A cube is a rectangular prism whose faces are squares.

Cylinder (p. 369) A cylinder is a three-dimensional figure with two circular, parallel, and congruent bases.

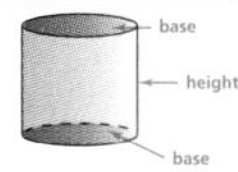

D

Dependent events (p. 413) Two events are dependent if the outcome of the first event affects the outcome of the second event.

Suppose you draw two marbles, one after the other, from a bag. If you do *not* replace the first marble before drawing the second marble, the events are dependent.

Diagonal (p. 310) A diagonal of a polygon is a segment that connects two vertices that are not next to each other.

Example: $\overline{BD}$ is a diagonal of quadrilateral $ABCD$.

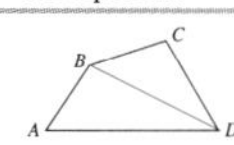

Examples

Diameter (p. 314) A diameter is a segment that passes through the center of a circle and has both endpoints on the circle.

Example: $\overline{RS}$ is a diameter of a circle O.

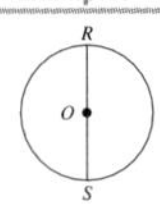

Distributive Property (p. 81) If a, b, and c are any numbers, then
$a(b + c) = ab + ac$ and $a(b - c) = ab - ac$.

$2(3 + \frac{1}{2}) = 2 \cdot 3 + 2 \cdot \frac{1}{2}$

$8(5 - 3) = 8(5) - 8(3)$

Divisible (p. 159) A number is divisible by another if the remainder is zero.

16 is divisible by 1, 2, 4, 8 and 16.

Division Property of Equality (p. 124) If both sides of an equation are divided by the same nonzero number, the results are equal.

Since $3(2) = 6$, $3(2) \div 2 = 6 \div 2$.

If $a = b$ and $c \neq 0$, then $\frac{a}{c} = \frac{b}{c}$.

Double bar graph (p. 12) A double bar graph compares quantities of two sets of data.

Example: This double bar graph shows class sizes for grades 6, 7, and 8 for both boys and girls.

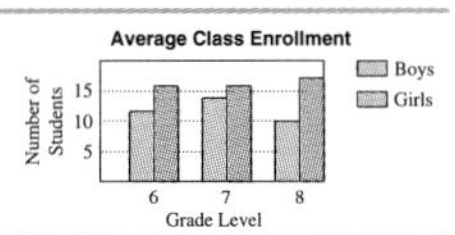

Double line graph (p. 12) A double line graph compares two sets of data over time.

Example: This double line graph represents seasonal air conditioner and snow blower sales (in thousands of dollars) for a large chain of department stores.

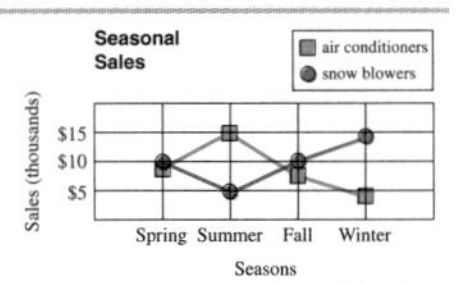

E

Edge (p. 369) An edge is a segment where two faces of a three-dimensional figure meet.

See *Three-dimensional figure.*

Equation (p. 118) A mathematical sentence that contains an equal sign, =, is an equation.

$27 \div 9 = 3$

$x + 10 = 8$

Equilateral triangle (p. 297) An equilateral triangle is a triangle with three congruent sides.

Example: $\overline{SL} \cong \overline{LW} \cong \overline{WS}$

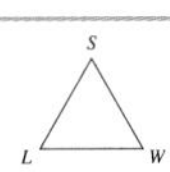

Examples

Equivalent decimals (p. 50) Decimals that name the same amount are equivalent decimals.

$0.6 = 0.60$

Equivalent fractions (p. 148) Fractions that are equal to each other are equivalent fractions.

$\frac{1}{2}$ and $\frac{25}{50}$ are equivalent fractions.

Evaluate an expression (p. 92) To evaluate an expression, replace each variable with a number. Then follow the order of operations.

To evaluate the expression $3x + 2$ for $x = 4$, substitute 4 for x.

$3x + 2 = 3(4) + 2 = 12 + 2 = 14$

Event (p. 392) An event is one or more results of an experiment.

In a game that includes tossing a coin and rolling a standard number cube, "heads and a 2" is an event.

Experimental probability (p. 392) You find the experimental probability of an event by repeating an experiment many times and using this ratio.

$$P(\text{event}) = \frac{\text{number of times an event happens}}{\text{number of times the experiment is done}}$$

Suppose a basketball player makes 19 baskets in 28 attempts. The experimental probability that she makes a basket is $\frac{19}{28} \approx 68\%$.

Exponent (p. 155) You can use an exponent to show repeated multiplication. An exponent tells you how many times a base is used as a factor.

exponent

$3^4 = 3 \times 3 \times 3 \times 3$

F

Face (p. 368) A flat surface on a three-dimensional figure is called a face.

See *Three-dimensional figure.*

Factor (p. 148) A factor is a whole number that divides another whole number with no remainder.

1, 2, 3, 4, 6, 9, 12, 18, and 36 are factors of 36.

Factor tree (p. 160) A factor tree is used to find a number's prime factors.

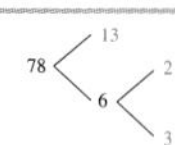

Fair game (p. 403) A game is fair if all players are equally likely to win.

Players A and B roll a number cube. Player A gets a point if the number is even; player B gets a point if the number is odd. This game is fair.

Glossary/Study Guide

Examples

Frequency table (p. 4) A frequency table lists items together with the number of times, or frequency, that they occur.

Example: This frequency table shows the number of household telephones for a class of students.

Household Telephones

Phones	Tally	Frequency
1	𝍸 |||	8
2	𝍸		6
3						4

Front-end estimation (p. 54) You can use front-end estimation to estimate a sum. First add the front-end digits. Then adjust by estimating the sum of the remaining digits. Add the two values.

Estimate \$3.49 + \$2.29.
$3 + 2 = 5$
$0.49 + 0.29 \approx 1$
$\$3.49 + \$2.29 \approx \$5 + \$1 = \$6$

Function (p. 450) A function is a relationship in which each input value has exactly one output value.

Earned income is a function of the number of hours worked (w). If you earn \$6/h, then your income is expressed by the function $f(w) = 6w$.

G

Geometric sequence (p. 435) In a geometric sequence, you multiply each term by the same number to find the next term.

The sequence 1, 3, 9, 27, 81, . . . is a geometric sequence. You multiply each term by 3 to find the next term.

Graph of an equation (p. 478) The graph of an equation in two variables is the graph of all the points whose coordinates are solutions of the equation.

Example: The coordinates of all of the points on the graph satisfy the equation $y = |x| - 1$.

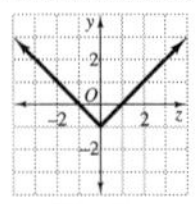

Greatest common factor (GCF) (p. 161) The greatest common factor of two or more numbers is the greatest number that is a factor of all the numbers.

The GCF of 12 and 30 is 6.

H

Height of two-dimensional figures (pp. 340, 344, 345) See *Parallelogram, Triangle,* and *Trapezoid.*

Height of three-dimensional figures (p. 378) See *Cylinder* and *Prism.*

Examples

Histogram (p. 5) A histogram is a special type of bar graph used to show frequency. The height of each bar gives the frequency of the data. Information on the horizontal axis is grouped into *intervals*.

Example: This histogram gives the frequency of board game purchases at a local toy store.

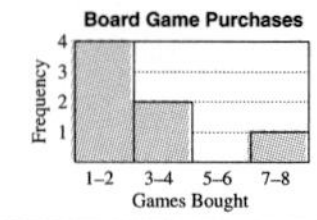

Hypotenuse (p. 360) The hypotenuse is the longest side of a right triangle. It is the side opposite the right angle.

Example: $\overline{AC}$ is the hypotenuse of $\triangle ABC$.

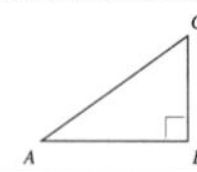

I

Identity Property of Addition (p. 60) The sum of zero and any number a is a.

$7 + 0 = 7$
$a + 0 = a$

Identity Property of Multiplication (p. 68) The product of one and any number a is a.

$5 \times 1 = 5$
$a(1) = a$

Image (p. 494) A point, line, or figure that has been transformed to a new set of coordinates is the image of the original point, line, or figure.

Example: $A'B'C'D'$ is the image of $ABCD$.

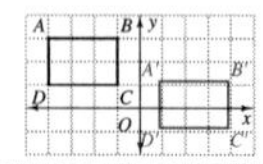

Improper fraction (p. 172) An improper fraction has a numerator that is greater than or equal to the denominator.

$\frac{24}{15}$ and $\frac{16}{16}$ are improper fractions.

Independent events (p. 412) Two events are independent if the outcome of one event does not affect the outcome of the other.

Suppose you draw two marbles, one after the other, from a bag. If you replace the first marble before drawing the second marble, the events are independent.

Inequality (p. 101) An inequality is a comparison of two expressions that uses one of the symbols $<$, $\leq$, $>$, or $\geq$.

$0 \leq 2$, $k > -3$, $10 < t$, $m + 2 \geq -5$

Integers (p. 98) Integers are the set of whole numbers and their opposites.

. . . −3, −2, −1, 0, 1, 2, 3, . . .

Inverse operations (p. 113) Operations that undo each other, such as addition and subtraction, are inverse operations.

$15 + 3 = 18$ and $18 - 3 = 15$

Glossary/Study Guide

Examples

Isosceles triangle (p. 297) An isosceles triangle is a triangle with at least two congruent sides.

$\overline{LM} \cong \overline{LB}$

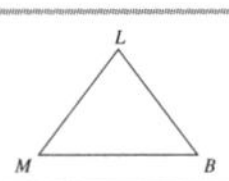

L

Least common denominator (LCD) (p. 152) The least common denominator of two or more fractions is the least common multiple of their denominators.

The least common denominator of $\frac{1}{5}$ and $\frac{2}{3}$ is 15.

Least common multiple (LCM) (p. 147) The least common multiple of two numbers is the least number that is a multiple of both.

The LCM of 10 and 6 is 30.

Legs of a right triangle (p. 360) The two shorter sides of a right triangle form a right angle and are the legs of the triangle.

Example: $\overline{AB}$ and $\overline{BC}$ are the legs of $\triangle ABC$.

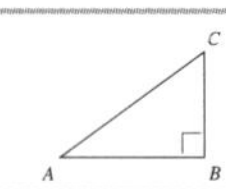

Line graph (p. 9) A line graph shows how an amount changes over time.

Example: This line graph shows the amount of time a student spends reading each night for a week.

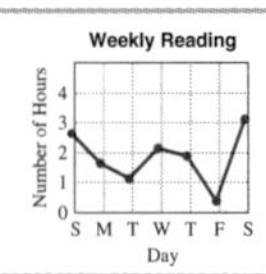

Line plot (p. 4) A line plot uses a number line to display data. An ✗ represents each data item.

Example: This line plot shows the number of pets owned by each of 12 students.

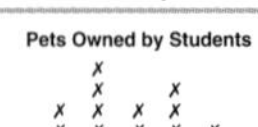

Line of reflection (p. 500) A line over which a figure is reflected

See *Reflection.*

Line of symmetry (p. 499) A line that divides a figure into mirror images

See *Symmetry.*

Linear equation (p. 478) An equation is a linear equation when the graph of all its solutions is a line.

Example: $y = \frac{1}{2}x + 3$ is a linear equation because the graph of its solutions is a line.

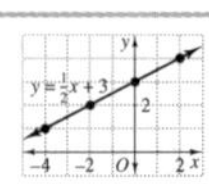

Examples

M

Mean (p. 17) The mean of a set of data is the sum of the data divided by the number of items in the set of data.

The mean temperature (°F) for the set of temperatures 44, 52, 48, 55, 61, 67 and 58 is

$\frac{44 + 52 + 48 + 55 + 61 + 67 + 58}{7} = 55°F$

Median (p. 17) The median is the middle number in a set of ordered data. If there is an even number of data items, the median is the mean of the two middle items.

Temperatures (°F) for one week arranged in numerical order are 44, 48, 52, 55, 58, 61, and 67. The median is 55 because it is the middle number in the set of data.

Midpoint (p. 323) The midpoint of a segment is the point that divides the segment into two congruent segments.

Example: $\overline{XM} \cong \overline{MY}$. M is the midpoint of $\overline{XY}$.

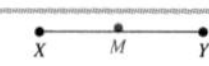

Mixed number (p. 172) A mixed number is the sum of a whole number and a fraction.

$3\frac{11}{16}$ is a mixed number.
$3\frac{11}{16} = 3 + \frac{11}{16}$

Mode (p. 18) The mode of a set of data is the data item that occurs most often.

The mode of the set of prices \$2.50, \$3.75, \$3.60, \$2.75, \$2.75, and \$3.70 is \$2.75.

Multiple (p. 147) A multiple of a number is the product of that number and a nonzero whole number.

Some multiples of 13 are 13, 26, 39, and 52.

Multiplication Property of Equality (p. 124) If each side of an equation is multiplied by the same number, the results are equal.

Since $\frac{12}{2} = 6$, $\frac{12}{2} \cdot 2 = 6 \cdot 2$.
If $a = b$, then $a \cdot c = b \cdot c$.

N

Net (p. 373) A pattern that can be folded to cover a solid figure is a net for the figure.

Example: These are nets for a cube.

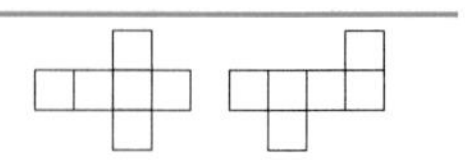

O

Obtuse angle (p. 292) An obtuse angle is any angle whose measure is greater than 90° and less than 180°.

Obtuse triangle (p. 297) A triangle that contains one obtuse angle is an obtuse triangle.

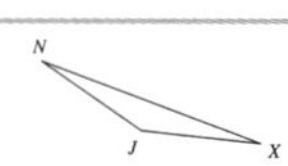

Glossary/Study Guide

Examples

Odds (p. 406) You can calculate the odds in favor of an event by using the ratio $\frac{\text{number of favorable outcomes}}{\text{number of unfavorable outcomes}}$.
Suppose you roll a standard number cube. The odds in favor of getting a 4 are $\frac{1}{5}$.

Opposites (p. 98) Numbers that are the same distance from zero on the number line but in opposite directions are opposites.
−17 and 17 are opposites.

Order of operations (pp. 80, 150)
1. Do all operations within grouping symbols.
2. Evaluate any term with exponents.
3. Multiply and divide in order from left to right.
4. Add and subtract in order from left to right.

$2^3(7 - 4) = 2^3 \cdot 3 = 8 \cdot 3 = 24$

Ordered pair (p. 472) An ordered pair is a pair of numbers that describe the location of a point on a coordinate plane. The first value is the x-coordinate and the second value is the y-coordinate.
Example: (−2, 1) is an ordered pair. The x-coordinate is −2; the y-coordinate is 1.

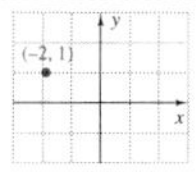

Origin (p. 472) The point of intersection of the x- and y-axes on a coordinate plane is the origin.
Example: The ordered pair that describes the origin is (0, 0).

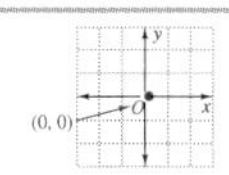

Outcomes (p. 401) Outcomes are the possible results or consequences of an action.
The outcomes of rolling a standard number cube are 1, 2, 3, 4, 5, and 6.

Outlier (p. 18) A data item that is far apart from the rest of the data is an outlier.
An outlier in the data set 6, 7, 9, 10, 11, 12, 14, and 52 is 52.

P

Parabola (p. 486) A parabola is a U-shaped graph of an equation like $y = x^2 - 2$.
Example: This parabola is the graph of the equation $y = x^2 - 2$.

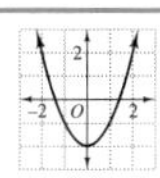

Parallel lines (p. 296) Parallel lines are lines in the same plane that do not intersect.
$\overleftrightarrow{EF}$ is parallel to $\overleftrightarrow{HI}$.

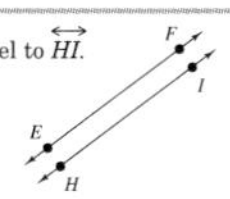

Examples

Parallelogram (p. 309) A parallelogram is a quadrilateral that has both pairs of opposite sides parallel.
Example: $\overline{KV}$ is parallel to $\overline{AD}$ and $\overline{AK}$ is parallel to $\overline{DV}$, so KVDA is a parallelogram.

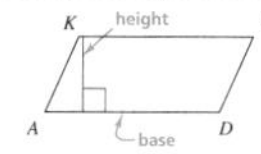

Percent (p. 256) A percent is a ratio that compares a number to 100. The symbol for percent is %.
$\frac{50}{100} = 50\%$

Percent of change (p. 276, 277) Percent of change is the percent something increases or decreases from its original measure or amount. You can find the percent of change by using this proportion.
$\frac{\text{amount of change}}{\text{original amount}} = \frac{\text{percent of change}}{100}$
The number of employees increased from 14 to 21.
$\frac{7}{14} = \frac{n}{100};\ n = 50$
The percent of increase is 50%.

Perfect square (p. 354) A perfect square is a number that is the square of an integer.
Since $25 = 5^2$, 25 is a perfect square.

Perimeter (p. 336) Perimeter is the distance around a figure.
Example: The perimeter of rectangle ABCD is 12 ft.

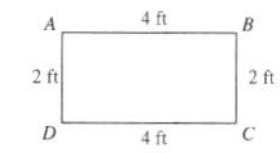

Permutation (p. 416) An arrangement in which order is important is a permutation.
There are six permutations of the letters W, A, and X: WAX, WXA, AXW, AWX, XWA, and XAW.

Perpendicular bisector (p. 323) A line that is perpendicular to a segment at its midpoint is the perpendicular bisector of the segment.
Example: $\overleftrightarrow{MK} \perp \overline{AB}$, $AM = MB$. $\overleftrightarrow{MK}$ is the perpendicular bisector of $\overline{AB}$.

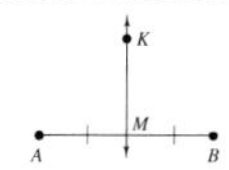

Perpendicular lines (p. 323) Perpendicular lines are lines that intersect to form right angles.
$\overleftrightarrow{DE} \perp \overleftrightarrow{RS}$

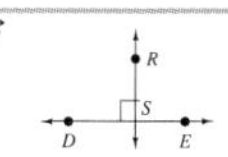

Pi (p. 349) Pi (π) is the ratio of the circumference to the diameter of a circle.

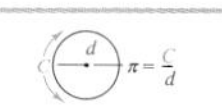

$\pi = \frac{C}{d}$

Examples

Polygon (p. 305) A polygon is a closed plane figure formed by three or more line segments that do not cross.

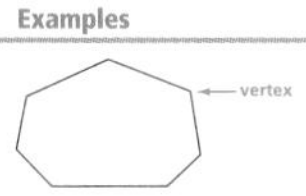

Population (p. 30) A population is a collection of objects or group of people about whom information is gathered.
A quality control inspector examines a sample of the population, which is the output of a factory.

Power (p. 155) A power is a number expressed using an exponent.
3^4, 5^2, and 2^{10} are powers.

Prime factorization (p. 160) To write the prime factorization of a composite number, write the number as a product of its prime factors.
The prime factorization of 12 is $2^2 \times 3$ or $2 \times 2 \times 3$.

Prime number (p. 160) A prime number has exactly two factors, 1 and the number itself.
13 is a prime number because its only factors are 1 and 13.

Principal (p. 446) Your original deposit in an account is your principal.
You deposit $500 in a savings account. Your principal is $500.

Prism (p. 368) A prism is a three-dimensional figure with two parallel and congruent polygonal faces called bases. A prism is named for the shape of its base.

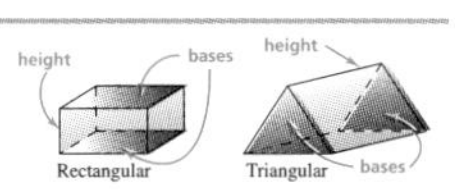

Probability (pp. 392, 401) Probability is used to describe how likely it is that an event will happen.
See Experimental Probability *and* Theoretical Probability.

Proportion (p. 241) A proportion is an equation stating that two ratios are equal.
$\frac{3}{12} = \frac{9}{36}$

Pyramid (p. 369) Pyramids are three-dimensional figures with only one base. The base is a polygon and the other faces are triangles. A pyramid is named for the shape of its base.

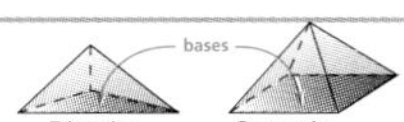

Pythagorean theorem (p. 360) In any right triangle, the sum of the squares of the lengths of the legs (a and b) is equal to the square of the length of the hypotenuse (c): $a^2 + b^2 = c^2$
Example: The right triangle at the right has legs 3 and 4 and hypotenuse 5: $3^2 + 4^2 = 5^2$

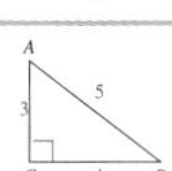

Examples

Q

Quadrant (p. 474) The x- and y-axes divide the coordinate plane into four regions, called quadrants.
Example: The quadrants are labeled I, II, III, and IV.

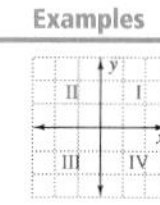

Quadrilateral (p. 308) A quadrilateral is a polygon with four sides.

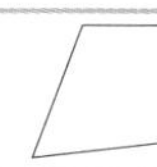

R

Radius (plural is radii) (p. 314) A radius is a segment that has one endpoint at the center and the other endpoint on the circle.
Example: $\overline{OA}$ is a radius of circle O.

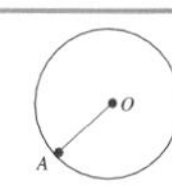

Random number table (p. 397) Some computers and calculators can generate lists of random numbers to use to simulate situations.

6032	4932	2767	4050
3014	5552	4917	1790
6074	8562	0968	8423
4191	8406	4426	4796
4095	2051	1096	2636

Random sample (p. 30) If each member of a population has an equal chance of being chosen for a sample, then the sample is a random sample.
For the population "customers at a mall," a random sample would be every 20th customer at each entrance for a 2-hour period.

Range (p. 23) The range of a set of numerical data is the difference between the greatest and least values of the set.
The range of the data 1, 3, 4, 2, 6, 1, 3 is 6 − 1 = 5.

Rate (p. 237) A rate is a ratio that compares two quantities measured in different units.
A student typed 1,100 words in 50 min. The student's typing rate is 1,100 words per 50 min, or 22 words/min.

Ratio (p. 232) A ratio is a comparison of two numbers by division.
You can write a ratio three ways:
72 to 100, 72 : 100, and $\frac{72}{100}$.

Reciprocal (p. 210) Two numbers are reciprocals if their product is 1. Dividing by a number is the same as multiplying by the reciprocal of that number.
The numbers 5 and $\frac{1}{5}$ are reciprocals because $5 \times \frac{1}{5} = 1$.

Rectangle (p. 309) A rectangle is a parallelogram with four right angles.

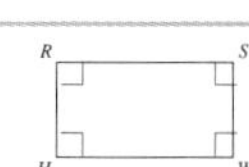

Examples

Reflection (p. 500) A reflection flips a figure over a line.
Example: $K'L'M'N'$ is a reflection of $KLMN$ over the y-axis.

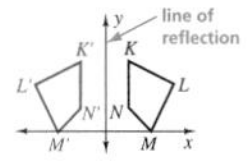

Regular polygon (p. 308) A regular polygon has all sides congruent and all angles congruent.
Example: $ABDFEC$ is a regular hexagon.

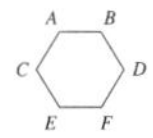

Repeating decimal (p. 76) A repeating decimal is a decimal in which a digit or a sequence of digits keeps repeating. Use a bar over a digit or digits to show that they repeat.

$0.8888\ldots = 0.\overline{8}$

Rhombus (p. 309) A rhombus is a parallelogram with four congruent sides.

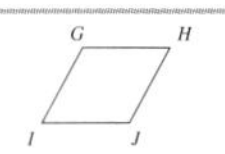

Right angle (p. 292) A right angle is an angle with a measure of 90°.

$m\angle D = 90°$

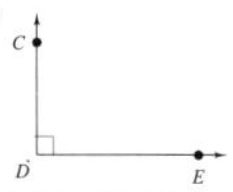

Right triangle (p. 297) A right triangle is a triangle with a right angle.
Example: $\triangle ABC$ is a right triangle because $\angle B$ is a right angle.

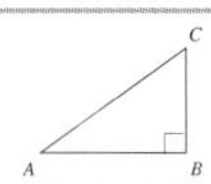

Rotation (p. 505) A rotation turns a figure about a fixed point, called the center of rotation.
Example: $\triangle RST$ has been rotated 180° about the origin (O) to $\triangle R'S'T'$.

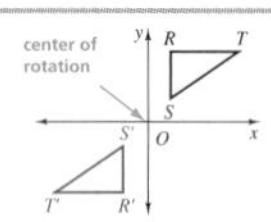

Rotational symmetry (p. 505) A figure has rotational symmetry when an image after a rotation of less than 180° fits exactly on the original figure.
Example: This figure has 60° rotational symmetry.

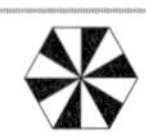

S

Examples

Sample (p. 30) A sample of a group is a subgroup selected from within the group.

Your English teacher might read one or two poems from the poems written by your class.

Sample space (p. 407) The set of all possible outcomes of a situation is called the sample space.

The sample space for tossing two coins is HH, HT, TH, TT.

Scale drawing (p. 251) A scale drawing is an enlarged or reduced drawing of an object that is proportional to the original object.

A map is a scale drawing.

Scalene triangle (p. 297) A scalene triangle is a triangle with no congruent sides.

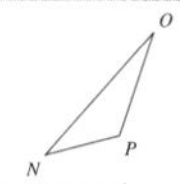

Scatter plot (p. 39) In a scatter plot two related sets of data are graphed as points.
Example: This scatter plot shows amounts spent by several companies on advertising (in dollars) versus product sales (in thousands of dollars).

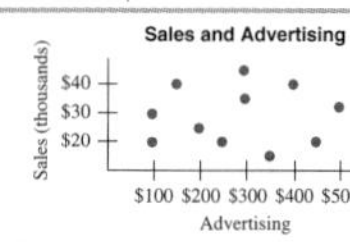

Scientific notation (p. 438) A number is expressed in scientific notation when it is written as the product of two factors. The first is a number greater than or equal to 1 and less than 10, and the second is a power of 10.

37,000,000 is written as 3.7×10^7 in scientific notation.

Segment bisector (p. 323) A segment bisector is a line (or segment or ray) that goes through the midpoint of a segment.
Example: $GM = MH$. $\overleftrightarrow{FD}$ is a bisector of $\overline{GH}$.

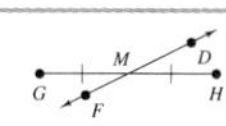

Semicircle (p. 315) A semicircle is half a circle.
Example: $\widehat{ABC}$ is a semicircle of circle O.

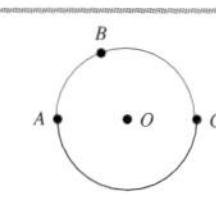

Sequence (p. 434) A sequence is a set of numbers that follow a pattern.

3, 6, 9, 12, 15, . . . is a sequence.

Sides of an angle (p. 291) The sides of an angle are its two rays.

See *Angle.*

Glossary/Study Guide

Examples

Similar figures (p. 245) In similar figures, corresponding angles are congruent and the ratios of the lengths of corresponding sides are equal.

$\triangle ABC \sim \triangle RTS$

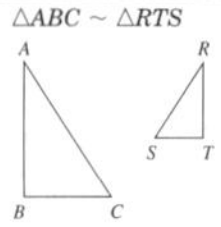

Simple interest (p. 446) Simple interest is paid only on the original deposit. Use the formula $I = prt$ where I is the simple interest, p is the principal, r is the annual interest rate, and t is the number of years that the account earns interest.

The simple interest earned on \$200 invested at 5% annual interest for three years is $\$200 \times 0.05 \times 6$ or \$30.

Simplest form of a fraction (p. 164) A fraction is in simplest form when the only common factor of the numerator and the denominator is 1.

$\frac{1}{3}$ is the simplest form of $\frac{27}{81}$.

Simulation (p. 393) A simulation is a model of a real-world situation.

A baseball team has an equal chance of winning or losing its next game. You can toss a coin to simulate the situation.

Slope (p. 482) Slope is a ratio that describes the steepness of a line.

Slope $= \frac{\text{rise}}{\text{run}}$

Example: The slope of the given line $= \frac{2}{4} = \frac{1}{2}$.

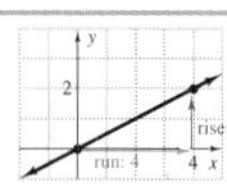

Solution (pp. 118, 477) Any value or values that make an equation true

4 is the solution of $x + 5 = 9$.

(8, 4) is a solution of $y = -1x + 12$ because $4 = -1(8) + 12$.

Sphere (p. 369) A sphere is the set of points in space that are the same distance from a given point called the center.

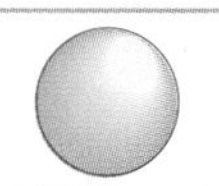

Spreadsheet (p. 12) A spreadsheet is a tool used for organizing and analyzing data. Spreadsheets are arranged in rows and columns. A cell is the box on a spreadsheet where a row and a column meet. The names of the row and column determine the name of the cell.
Example: In the spreadsheet shown, column C and row 2 meet at the shaded box, cell C2. The value in cell C2 is 2.75.

	A	B	C	D	E
1	0.50	0.70	0.60	0.50	2.30
2	1.50	0.50	2.75	2.50	7.25

Examples

Square (p. 309) A square is a parallelogram with four right angles and four congruent sides.

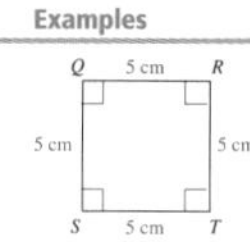

Square root (p. 354) The square root of a number is a number which when multiplied by itself equals the given number.

$\sqrt{9} = 3$ because $3^2 = 9$.

Standard form of a number (p. 439) When you multiply the factors of a number in scientific notation, the number is in standard form.

The standard form of 2.5×10^6 is 2,500,000.

Stem-and-leaf plot (p. 22) A stem-and-leaf plot displays data items in order. A leaf is a data item's last digit on the right. A stem represents the digits to the left of the leaf.
Example: This stem-and-leaf-plot displays recorded times in a race. The stem represents the number of seconds. The leaves represent tenths of a second.

stem	leaves
27	7
28	5 6 8
29	6 9
30	8

27 | 7 means 27.7

Straight angle (p. 292) An angle that measures 180° is a straight angle.

$m\angle TPL = 180°$

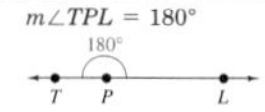

Subtraction Property of Equality (p. 120) If the same number is subtracted from each side of an equation, the results are equal.

Since $\frac{20}{2} = 10$, $\frac{20}{2} - 3 = 10 - 3$.
If $a = b$, then $a - c = b - c$.

Supplementary angles (p. 292) Two angles are supplementary if the sum of their measures is 180°.
Example: $\angle A$ and $\angle D$ are supplementary.

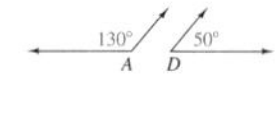

Surface area of a prism (p. 373) The surface area of a prism is the sum of the areas of the faces.
Example: $4 \times 12 \text{ in.}^2 + 2 \times 9 \text{ in.}^2 = 66 \text{ in.}^2$

Each square = 1 in.²

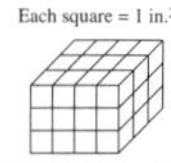

Symmetry (p. 499) A figure is symmetrical when one side of a figure is the mirror image of the other side.
Example: The left and right sides of the mask are mirror images of each other.

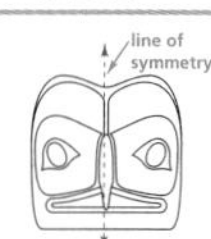

Glossary/Study Guide

T

Examples

Term (p. 434) Each number in a sequence is a term.

In the sequence 2, 4, 6, 8, . . ., the numbers 2, 4, 6, and 8 are terms.

Terminating decimal (p. 76) A terminating decimal is a decimal that stops, or terminates.

Both 0.6 and 0.7265 are terminating decimals.

Tessellation (p. 496) A tessellation is a repeated pattern of figures without gaps or overlaps.

Example: This tessellation consists of small and large squares.

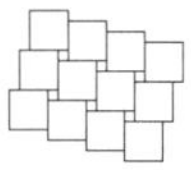

Theoretical probability (p. 401) You can compute the theoretical probability of an event using this formula.

$P(\text{event}) = \frac{\text{number of favorable outcomes}}{\text{number of possible outcomes}}$

Suppose you select a letter from the letters H, A, P, P, and Y. The theoretical probability of selecting a P is $\frac{2}{5}$.

Three-dimensional figure (p. 368) Figures, such as buildings, that do not lie in a plane are three-dimensional.

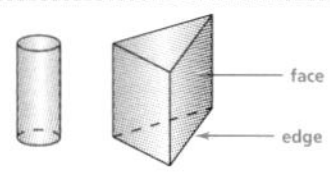

Transformation (p. 494) Movements of figures on a plane are transformations. A transformation can be a translation, reflection, or rotation.

Example: $K'L'M'N'$ is a reflection of $KLMN$.

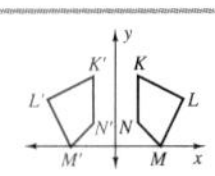

Translation (p. 494) A translation slides a figure.

Example: $ABCD$ has been translated to $A'B'C'D'$.

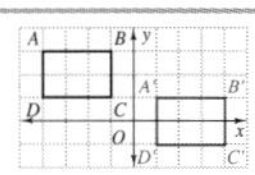

Transversal (p. 296) A transversal is a line that intersects two other coplanar lines in different points.

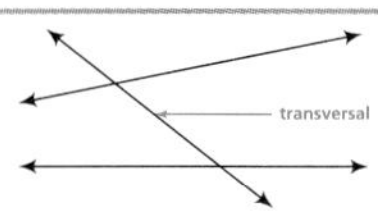

Trapezoid (p. 309) A trapezoid is a quadrilateral that has exactly one pair of parallel sides.

$\overline{UV}$ is parallel to $\overline{WY}$.

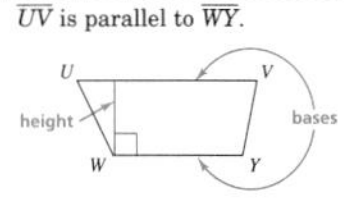

Examples

Tree diagram (p. 408) A tree diagram shows the total number of possible outcomes in a probability experiment.

Example: This tree diagram shows the possible outcomes of tossing two coins.

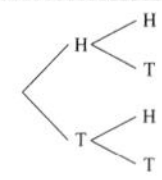

Trend (p. 40) Two sets of related data have a *positive trend* if, in general, as the values of one set of data increase, the values of the other set increase also. Two sets of related data have a *negative trend* if, in general, as the values of one set increase, the values of the other set decrease. Two sets of related data have little or *no trend* if the data show no relationship.

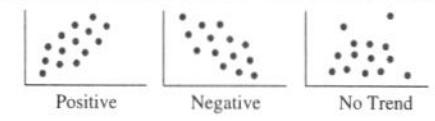

Triangle (p. 297) A triangle is a polygon with three sides.

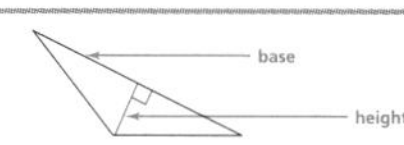

U

Unit price (p. 238) A unit price is the price per unit of an item.

$\frac{\$5.98}{10.2 \text{ fl oz}} = \$.59/\text{fl oz}$

Unit rate (p. 237) A unit rate is a rate that has a denominator of 1.

If you drive 165 mi in 3 h, your unit rate of travel is $\frac{55 \text{ mi}}{1 \text{ h}}$ or 55 mi/h.

V

Variable (p. 92) A variable is a symbol, usually a letter, that stands for a number.

x is a variable in the equation $9 - x = 3$.

Variable expression (p. 92) A variable expression is a group of numbers, variables, and operations.

$7 + x$, $2y - 4$, $\frac{3}{5}g$, $\frac{7}{k}$

Vertex of an angle (p. 291) The vertex of an angle is the common endpoint of its two rays.

See *Angle*.

Vertex of a polygon (p. 305) The vertex of a polygon is any point where two sides of a polygon meet.

See *Polygon*.

Volume (p. 377) The volume of a three-dimensional figure is the number of cubic units needed to fill the space inside the figure.

Example: The volume of the rectangular prism is 36 in.^{3}.

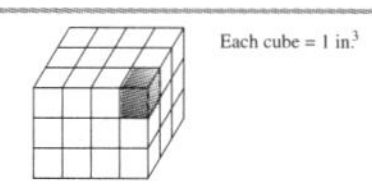

Glossary/Study Guide

W

Examples

Whole numbers (p. 98) The whole numbers are 0, 1, 2, 3, ...

4, 125, and 3,947 are whole numbers; −4, 17.5, and $2\frac{1}{2}$ are *not* whole numbers.

X

x-axis (p. 472) The x-axis is the horizontal number line that, together with the y-axis, forms the coordinate plane.

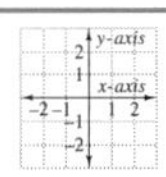

Y

y-axis (p. 472) The y-axis is the vertical number line that, together with the x-axis, forms the coordinate plane.

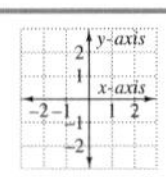

Z

Zero pair (p. 102) A positive tile and a negative tile make a zero pair.

Zero Property of Multiplication (p. 68) The product of zero and any number is a zero.

$6 \times 0 = 0$

$a \times 0 = 0$

Selected Answers

TOOLS FOR PROBLEM SOLVING

The Four-Step Approach — *page xxii*

ON YOUR OWN **1.** 3 small and 8 large tables or 11 small and 3 large tables **3.** 16 triangles **5.** troposphere, stratosphere, mesosphere, thermosphere

Using Strategies — *page xxv*

ON YOUR OWN **1.** Kim made $15, Petra made $32 **3.** 16 **5.** 3:55 A.M. **7.** 22,500

Working Together — *page xxvii*

ON YOUR OWN **1.** 75 different amounts **3.** 32 min **5.** at noon on March 7, if there is no leap year

Preparing for Standardized Tests — *page xxix*

ON YOUR OWN **1.** D **3.** E **5.** B

CHAPTER 1

Lesson 1-1 — *pages 4–7*

ON YOUR OWN

1. Tickets Sold

Number of Tickets	Frequency
45	2
46	4
47	0
48	2
49	1
50	3
51	2
52	0
53	1

3. Number of TVs per Household

TVs	Frequency
1	6
2	6
3	5
4	1

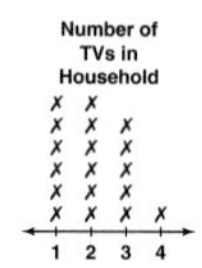

5a. 16 people **b.** 4 people **7.** 16 people **9a.** 12 people **b.** 4–5; 15 people **c.** 14 people **d.** 50 people

11.

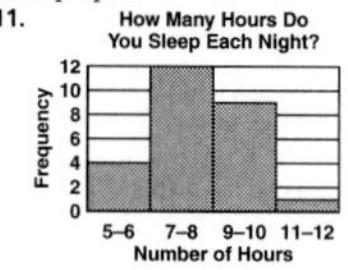

13a. What Time Do You Get Up?

Time	Frequency
5:30–5:59	2
6:00–6:29	5
6:30–6:59	1
7:00–7:29	3
7:30–7:59	3
8:00–8:29	2

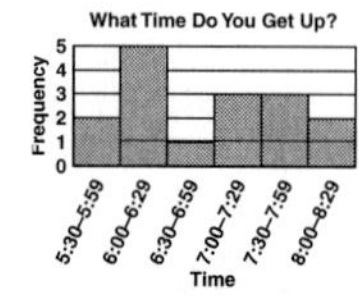

b. 6:00–6:29

MIXED REVIEW **15.** < **17.** > **19.** 310 **21.** 490

Lesson 1-2 — *pages 8–11*

ON YOUR OWN

1.

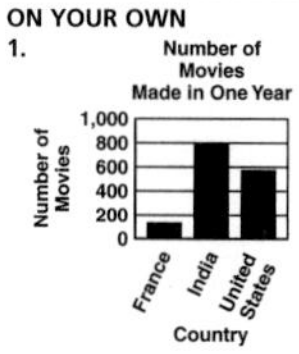

3. Los Angeles, Memphis, and Tokyo **5.** Memphis, Tokyo, Los Angeles, Kennedy, Frankfurt **7.** Bar graph; two quantities are being compared. **9.** The number of CD singles is rapidly increasing.

11a.

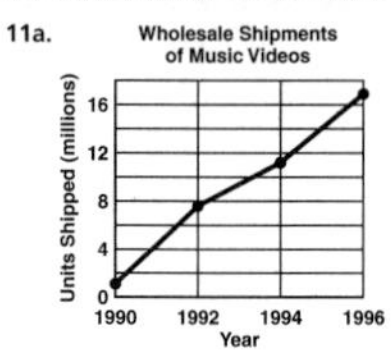

b. The number of music videos is increasing by about 5 million units every 2 years. **13.** B

MIXED REVIEW **15.** 32 students **17.** 13 **19.** 6 **21.** 56

Lesson 1-3 — *pages 12–15*

ON YOUR OWN **1.** 28 **3.** 9 calories **5a.** 1965 **7.** Corpus Christi, TX

9.

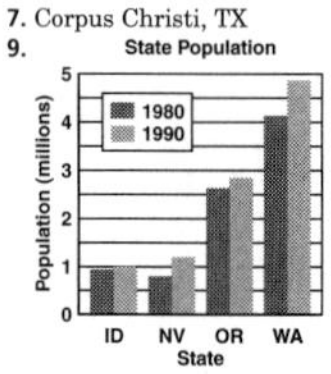

MIXED REVIEW **11a.** no

Toolbox — *page 16*

1. 15 **3.** 13 R1 **5.** 13 **7.** 217 R2 **9.** 25 R6 **11.** 6 R15 **13.** 3 **15.** 5 R28 **17.** 7 R3 **19.** 11 R2 **21.** 5 R22 **23.** 6 R21 **25.** 3 R52

Lesson 1-4 — *pages 17–21*

ON YOUR OWN **1.** 2; 2; 1 and 2 **3.** 63; 62; 62 **5.** 28.9; 28.5; 25 **7a.** Always **b.** No; people may give to charity in other ways than contributing their aluminum cans. **9a.** 21 students **b.** 10 students **11a.** 84; 81; 79 **b.** Yes; 102. **13.** C **15a.** 12.7 years **b.** 12 years; 12 and 15 years

Mixed Review **17.** Double bar graph; the graph compares two sets of quantities at one time. **19.** 800 **21.** 60 **23.** 27 and 3

CHECKPOINT

1.

Number	Frequency
1	2
2	2
3	2
4	2
5	3
6	1
7	2
8	2
9	1

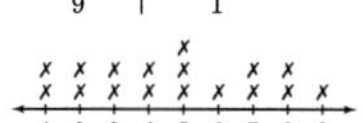

2. 120; 119; 117 **3.** 25; 25; 25

4.

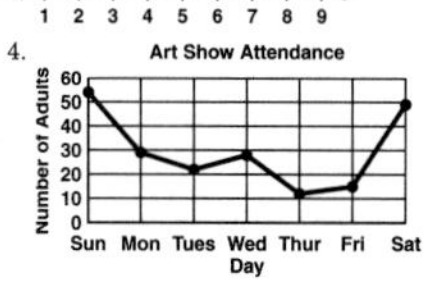

Use a line graph to show change over time.

Lesson 1-5 — *pages 22–25*

ON YOUR OWN

1.

1	3 3 4 4 4 4
2	3 4 5 5
3	6 9

2 | 3 means $2.3 million

3.

9	8 9
10	0 1 3 4 8 9
11	1 2 2 3 3 8

11 | 1 means 111°F

5. 12 **7.** 6 **9.** tenths **11.** 6

13. Count ten items up from 16 | 1 or down from 19 | 9. The median is 18.4.

15a.

3	5 8
4	2 2 7
5	0 5 7
6	
7	
8	2 8

8 | 2 means 82

b. 53

MIXED REVIEW **17.** 360 **19.** 1,200 **21.** = **23.** < **25.** 47

Toolbox — *page 26*

1. The data in the second quartile are closer together than in the third.

3.

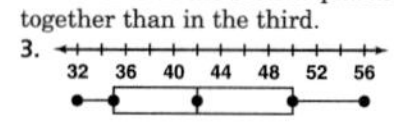

5.

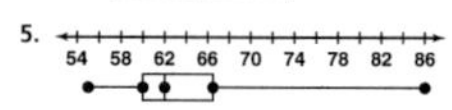

Lesson 1-6 — *pages 27–29*

ON YOUR OWN **1.** The locker marked "basketballs" has soccer balls. The locker marked "soccer balls" has footballs. **3.** 7 students **5.** 7 zebras

MIXED REVIEW **7.** 10 **9.** mode **11.** 192 **13.** 333

Lesson 1-7 — *pages 30–32*

ON YOUR OWN **1.** Survey bus drivers at the end of each shift. **3.** No; only teenagers from the nearby school are likely to be surveyed, and some of them you might ask more than once. **5.** Yes; each visitor has an equal chance of being surveyed. **7.** Biased; the terms "invigorating" and "couch potato" may influence responses. **9.** Fair; the question does not give preference to one answer or the other. **11.** Words are used to make one choice seem better than the other.

MIXED REVIEW **13.** 56; 50; 50; 99; the outlier significantly increases the mean.

Problem Solving Practice — *page 33*

1. D **3.** A **5.** B **7.** C

Lesson 1-8 — *pages 34–38*

ON YOUR OWN

1a.

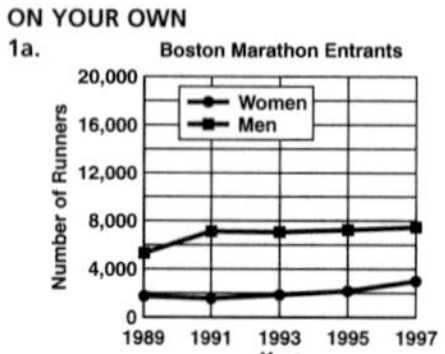

b.

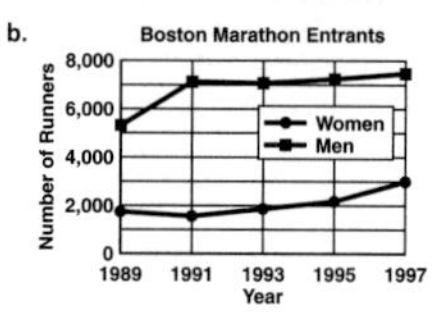

c. Second; the sponsors want to see an increasing number of participants. **5a.** mean **b.** mode **7.** The number of bald eagle pairs increased a lot from 1987 to 1995 **9.** about 2,500 pairs

MIXED REVIEW **11.** Biased; would you prefer to vacation in Florida or Maine? **13.** 300 **15.** 70 **17.** 2,000

CHECKPOINT **1.** Elsa carried the pink towel and a beach ball; Anna carried the blue towel and sandwiches; LaTonya carried the striped towel and iced tea. **2.** Mode; although the mode does not represent the data well, it is greater than the mean and the median.

3.

0	9
1	0 3 7
2	1 1 7

2 | 1 means 21

5. A

Lesson 1-9 — *pages 39–42*

ON YOUR OWN **1.** The moose population is generally increasing; there does not seem to be a pattern in the wolf population. **3.** None; there is no relationship between the number of children and the number of pets in a family. **5.** None; the number of governors a state has had depends on the age of the state, not its area. **7.** C; as temperature rises, more people go to the beach.

MIXED REVIEW

9.

1	5 9 9
2	2 4 5 7 7 9 9
3	0 4

1 | 5 means 15 students

11. No; the question shows no preference to either choice.

Wrap Up — pages 44–45

1.

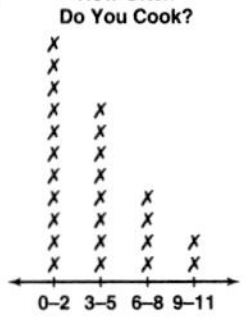

2a. 70.3 **b.** C4

3a.

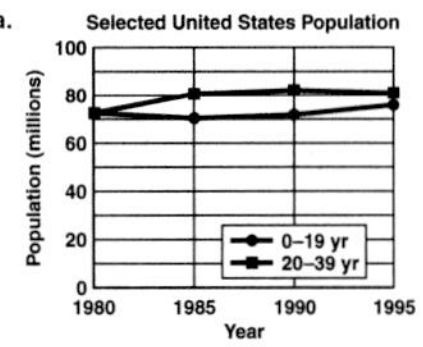

4a. 27.5; 25; 40 and 15 **b.** 75 is an outlier; it increases the mean. **c.** the mode 40

5.

0	0
1	0 5 5 5
2	0 5 5
3	0 5
4	0 0 0
5	
6	
7	5

4 | 0 means 40 min

6. Sam was the spider and brought apples; Katie was the fish and brought popcorn; Martin was the fox and brought cookies.

9a.

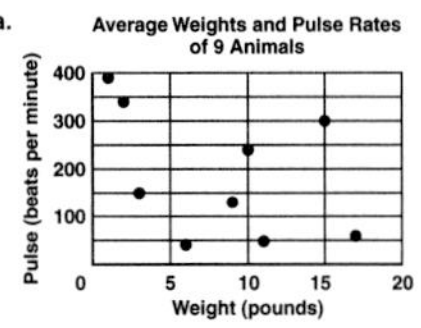

b. No; there is no clear trend in the data. **10.** B

Cumulative Review — page 47

1. A **3.** A **5.** B **7.** C **9.** A **11.** C

CHAPTER 2

Lesson 2-1 — pages 50–53

ON YOUR OWN **1a.** fifty-two hundredths or 0.52; thirty-six hundredths or 0.36; sixty-four hundredths or 0.64 **b.** $0.36 < 0.52 < 0.64$ **3.** 9.4, 9.42, 9.7 **5.** 0.29, 0.32, 0.38 **7.** 1.30, 1.6, 1.74 **9.** 5.42, 5.43, 5.51 **11.** John Olerud, Paul O'Neill, Alex Rodriguez, Edgar Martinez (1995), Edgar Martinez (1992), Julio Franco **17.** > **19.** > **21.** < **25.** No; the next digit is 4, so you round down. **27.** ten-thousandths; 5.1944 **29.** hundredths; 0.61 **31.** ones; 416 **33.** ten-thousandths; 15.6194

MIXED REVIEW **37.** 0.4; 0.4; 0.2 **39.** 231

Lesson 2-2 — pages 54–58

ON YOUR OWN **1.** \$11.50 **3.** \$18.50 **5.** \$3 **7.** 8 **9.** 8 **11a.** You missed the decimal point in 42.8. **15.** \$56 **17.** 8 boxes **19.** about \$2.80 **29a.** 2 in. **b.** 1.5 in. **31a.** 160 noodles **b.** Round 8,192 to 8,000. Round 59.29 to 50. Divide 8,000 by 50.

MIXED REVIEW **33.** 7.681, 7.6801, 7.618, 7.0681 **35.** 6,187 **37.** 244

Lesson 2-3 — pages 59–62

ON YOUR OWN **1.** 7.46 **3.** 5.26 **5.** 4.46 **7.** 2.212 **9.** 105.8 **11.** 0.0645 **13a.** 4 cm **15.** 29.66 m **17a.** \$1.75 **b.** \$8.75 **c.** \$8.25 **19.** identity **21.** associative **23.** 43.5; commutative, then associative **25.** 39.5; identity **27.** 11; identity **29.** 16.3; commutative, then associative **31.** 13.2; commutative, then associative

MIXED REVIEW **33.** biased **35.** 5 **37.** 12

CHECKPOINT **1.** = **2.** > **3.** > **4.** < **5a.** \$10.50 **b.** \$11 **6.** C **7.** 66.247 **8.** 24.6342 **9.** 5.1388

Toolbox — page 63

1. 2.3 **3.** 20.5 **5.** 11.6 **7.** 87.1 **9.** 27 **11.** 25 **13.** 4.8 **15.** 132 **17.** 203 **19.** 8.2

Lesson 2-4 — pages 64–66

On Your Own **1.** 1 yd **3.** You need to know the average speed with which the Coy family traveled.

5. \$28.50 **7.** James Johnson is writing; Emily Wong is interviewing; Marcia Brown is researching.

MIXED REVIEW **9.** 1 **11.** 9.5

13.

1	3 3 4 7
2	2

2 | 2 means 2.2

Lesson 2-5 — pages 67–70

ON YOUR OWN **1.** $1.2 \times 49 = 58.8$ **3.** $3.7 \times 6.4 = 23.68$ **5.** 0.24 **7.** 22,059 **9.** 0.065 **11.** 307.5 **13.** 3.915 **15.** 0.675 **19.** 4.2 mi **21a.** Multiply the numbers as whole numbers. Then place the decimal point before the three digits on the right. **b.** 196.875 ft^2 **23.** 25.5; identity **25.** 1; identity **27.** 6.5; associative **29.** 0 **31.** 21.5 **33.** B

MIXED REVIEW **35.** 0.619 **37.** 10.5 **39.** 60 packages

Problem Solving Practice — page 71

1. C **3.** C **5.** D **7.** C **9.** D

Lesson 2-6 — pages 72–74

ON YOUR OWN **1.** 7.4 **3.** 2.07 **5.** 6.123 **7.** 0.868 **9.** \$4.75 **11.** 4 **13.** 452 **15.** 74 **17.** 0.0035 **19.** 0.065 **21.** 2.5 **23a.** 4; 40; 400 **b.** For each place the decimal point moves to the left in the divisor, the quotient increases 10-fold. **25.** 2,367 **27.** 0.07 **29.** No; the quotient is about 17.5 mi/gal. **31.** No; $1 \div 10$ is not the same as $10 \div 1$.

MIXED REVIEW **33.** 18.043 **35.** 20.19

Toolbox — page 75

1. 0.09 **3.** 0.0006 **5.** 0.0012 **7.** 58,000 **9.** 8.5 **11.** 2,460,000 **13.** 3.09 **15.** 0.007

Lesson 2-7 — pages 76–79

ON YOUR OWN **1.** 0.75 **3.** 0.5 **5.** 0.5 **7.** 1 **9.** 0.375 **11.** $3.\overline{3}$ **13.** $0.\overline{285714}$ **15.** $5.\overline{45}$ **17.** $8.\overline{3}$ **19a.** Each successive divisor is one tenth of the one before it. **b.** 0.0001; 0.00001; 0.000001; 0.5; 5; 50; 500; 5,000; 50,000; 500,000; 5,000,000; 50,000,000 **21a.** 11, 12, 13, 14, 15, 18; 10, 16, 20 **b.** 17, 19; digits in the calculator display do not repeat, but fill all spaces. **23.** $223 \div 71$ **25.** No; the numbers in the pattern do not repeat in the same order.

MIXED REVIEW **27.** 2.78 **29.** 8.83 **31.** < **33.** < **35.** \$1.60

CHECKPOINT **1.** 49.2 **2.** 1.5 **3.** 21.84 **4.** 2.175 **5.** $1.558\overline{3}$ **6.** 58.71 **7.** $1.458\overline{3}$ **8.** 10.37 **9.** $2.\overline{648}$ **10.** 12.1584 **11.** $136.\overline{36}$ **12.** $3.8\overline{3}$ **14.** 63 students

Lesson 2-8 — pages 80–84

ON YOUR OWN **1.** 11 **3.** 3 **5.** 1 **7.** 12.5 **11.** × **13.** ÷ **15.** ÷ **17.** $4 + (4 \div 4) - 4 = 1$ **19.** $(4 + 4 + 4) \div 4 = 3$ **21.** $(4 + 4) \times 4 - 4 = 28$ **23a.** $20 \times (30 - 1.5)$ **b.** 570 $in.^2$ **25.** 3; 3 **27.** 7 **29.** 23.4 **31.** 18.2 **33.** $8 \times (3 + 1)$; $8 \times 3 + 8 \times 1$; 32 **35.** $5 \times (2 + 3)$; $5 \times 2 + 5 \times 3$; 25 **37.** \$3.56

MIXED REVIEW **39.** 1.3 **41.** 24.8 **43.** 8.875 **45.** 29 **47.** 42; 420; 4,200; 4,200,000

Wrap Up — pages 86–87

1. = **2.** > **3.** < **4.** > **5.** 17.85 **6.** 0.104 **7.** 110 **8.** 1.4 **9.** 5 **10.** 8.1947 **11.** 7; compatible numbers **12.** 6; front-end **13.** 51.5; rounding **14.** 63; rounding **15.** \$5; compatible numbers **16.** 1; rounding **17.** 5; front-end **18.** 160; rounding **19.** Use compatible numbers to estimate a quotient. **20.** 18.02 **21.** 3.97 **22.** 0.73 **23.** 17.14 **24.** 16.6 **25.** 2.44 **26.** 0.567 **27.** 0.115 **28.** 260.7569 m^2 **29.** You need to know the original price of the jeans. **30.** 5.5 **31.** 7.89 **32.** 3.425 **33.** 41.24645 **34.** 7.397 **35.** 2.84 **36.** C **37.** 1.96 **38.** $5.8\overline{6}$ **39.** $1.11\overline{3}$ **40.** $1.5\overline{90}$ **41.** 33 **42.** 0.396875 **43.** $0.4\overline{890}$ **44.** $5.255\overline{681}$

Cumulative Review — page 89

1. A **3.** D **5.** C **7.** E

CHAPTER 3

Lesson 3-1 — pages 92–96

ON YOUR OWN **1.** 23 **3.** 8 **5.** $\frac{3}{2}$ **7.** 0 **9.** 5

11.

	$t + 2$	$2t - 1$	$2(t - 1)$	$2(2t)$
$t = 1.7$	3.7	2.4	1.4	6.8
$t = 2.04$	4.04	3.08	2.08	8.16

13. 25.2 **15.** 0.2 **17.** 4 **19.** 5.8 **21.** 9.3 **23.** 6.9 **25a.** y **b.** 20,064 movies **27.** 14 **29.** 2 **31.** 54 **33.** 4 **35.** 35 **41.** $r + c$ **43.** $7t$ **45.** $x - 9$

51. p = number of pages in the directory, $440p$ **53a.** $599.4h$ **b.** 14,385.6 gallons of blood **55.** C

MIXED REVIEW **57.** 45 **59.** 50 **61.** 40 **63.** 62

Lesson 3-2 — pages 97–100

ON YOUR OWN **1.** 7 **3.** −2 **5.** C and D **7.** 83 **9.** −1,312 **11.** $|7|$ **13.** > **15.** < **17.** > **19.** =

25.

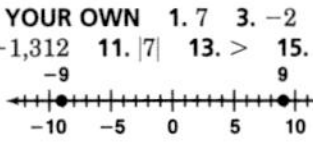

27.

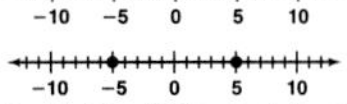

29. 11 **31.** 1 **33.** 7 **35.** 4 **37.** 4 **47.** 22; −43; the absolute value of −43 is 43. The absolute value of 22 is 22. $43 > 22$

MIXED REVIEW **49.** 37 **51.** 74 **53.** 562

Toolbox — page 101

1. −3 **3.** 0, 6

5.

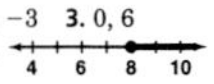

7.

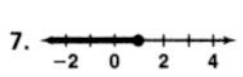

Lesson 3-3 — pages 102–105

ON YOUR OWN **1.** $-3 + 4$; 1 **3.** $3 + 6$; 9 **5.** 11 **7.** −6 **9.** 5 **11.** −9 **13.** −9 **15.** −3 **23.** 35 ft **25.** 9 **27.** −10 **29.** 2.6 **31.** −9.4 **33.** 12 **35.** −4 **37.** $-12 + 19 = 7$; 7°F **39.** 0 **41.** −6 **43.** 34 **45.** 38 **47.** 49

MIXED REVIEW

49.

24	3 4 8 9
25	0 3 7
26	2

26 | 2 means 2.62

51. > **53.** <

Lesson 3-4 — pages 106–110

ON YOUR OWN **1.** −2 **3.** −6 **5.** −6 **7.** 12 **9.** 16 **11.** −17 **13.** −3 **15.** 4 **17.** −104 **19.** 25 **21.** 0 **23.** 8 **25.** −219 **27.** −136 **29.** B **31.** $-9 + 6$; −3 **33.** $5 + 3$; 8 **35.** $1 + 9$; 10 **37a.** \$30 **b.** \$13 **c.** \$2.60 **39.** −6 **41.** 6 **43.** 0 **45.** 0 **47.** 14 **49.** 12 **51.** positive **53.** positive **67.** 218.95°C **69.** 234.334°C

MIXED REVIEW **73.** 11 **75.** −72 **77.** 2 **79.** 4.2 **81.** 56.2

CHECKPOINT **1a.** $6p$ **b.** 24; 60 **2.** $10a + 8t$ **3.** 20 **4.** 0 **5.** 3 **6.** 41.6 **7.** 4 **8.** −9 **9.** 4 **10.** −23 **11.** −9 **12.** 5 **13.** −3 **14.** −29 **15.** −5 **16.** 6

Toolbox — page 111

1. \$224.02, = D2 − C3; −\$15.38, = D3 − C4; \$106.62, = D4 + B5; \$51.97, = D5 − C6; \$401.97, = D6 + B7; \$238.17, = D7 − C8 **3.** Check in C9; the balance decreased.

Lesson 3-5 — pages 112–116

On Your Own **1.** negative **3.** negative **5.** positive **7.** 26 **9.** 30 **11.** −48 **13.** −72 **15.** −840 **17.** 6 min **27.** negative **29.** negative **31.** −3 **33.** −13 **35.** 8 **37.** 10 **39.** −9 **41.** $-21 \div 7 = -3$; $-21 \div (-3) = 7$ **53.** *D* **55.** *E* **57.** *B*

MIXED REVIEW **61.** 7 **63.** 5 **65.** −32 **67.** 25.6 **69.** 21.28 **71.** 24 ways

Problem Solving Practice — page 117

1. C **3.** D **5.** E **7.** B

Lesson 3-6 — pages 118–121

ON YOUR OWN **1.** $x + 2 = 1$; −1 **3.** $x + 4 = -3$; −7 **5.** 1 **7.** −5 **9.** 8 **11.** −5 **13.** −1 **15.** 4 **17.** −12 **19.** 0 **21.** 3 **23.** 10 **25.** 3 **27.** 16 **29.** 21 **31.** 17 **33.** −13 **35.** −12 **37.** 5 **39.** 4 **41.** 119 **43.** −9 **45a.** computer engineer; directory assistance operator **b.** $n - 17 = 5$ **c.** physician **47.** Add −15 to each side of the equation.

MIXED REVIEW **49.** −8 **51.** −30

Lesson 3-7 — pages 122–125

ON YOUR OWN **1.** $3x = -12$; −4 **3.** −4 **5.** −4 **7.** 2 **9.** −9 **11.** 28 **13.** −60 **15.** 28 **17.** 960 **19.** about 198 plays per year **21.** −3 **23.** −6 **25.** −55 **27.** −150 **29.** 2 **31.** −1 **33.** −56 **35.** 45 **37.** 416 **39.** −720 **41.** Susan divided 12 by −6; you find the solution by multiplying 12 by −6 to get −72. **43.** C

MIXED REVIEW **45.** identity property of multiplication **47.** commutative property of addition **49.** 77 **51.** 84 **53.** 12:44 P.M.

Lesson 3-8 — pages 126–129

ON YOUR OWN **1.** Sixty-seven is fifteen more than a number. **3.** Half a number is seventeen. **5.** Eighteen is a number divided by three. **7.** Negative fifty-five is five times a number.

9. $52 + x = 75$; 23 **11.** $5n = 45$; 9 **13.** $10x = 60$; 6 **15.** $-1n = 8$; −8 **17.** $7d = 72.5$; about 10 ft **19.** $4n = 52$; 13 **21.** $x + 12 = 61$; 49 **23.** $3 + n = -2$; −5 **25.** $13x = 91$; 7 **27.** 40 constellations **29.** 4 shelves

MIXED REVIEW **31.** eight hundred thirty-six thousand, one **33.** three hundred twelve million, two hundred ninety-one thousand, seven hundred forty-five **35.** twenty-five million, seven hundred eighty-five thousand, four hundred fifty-six **37.** 5.4 **39.** 3 **41a.** about \$2.50 **b.** Each book is about \$2.50. The total cost is about 3×2.50.

CHECKPOINT **1.** −42 **2.** 12 **3.** −5 **4.** −7 **5.** −54 **6.** 4 **7.** 72 **8.** 3 **9.** 53 **10.** −88 **11.** 48 **12.** −7 **13.** 64 **14.** 10 **15.** 18 **16.** −7 **17.** −42 **18.** −9 **19.** 21 **20.** −7 **21.** B **22.** $20 = 9 + n$; 11 **23.** $x - 6 = 15$; 21 **24.** $2n = 62$; 31 **25.** $\frac{x}{13} = 7$; 91

Lesson 3-9 — pages 130–133

ON YOUR OWN **1.** $3x - 2 = -5$; −1 **3.** $2x + 2 = 4$; 1 **5.** 12; $2 \times 12 - 6 = 18$ ✓ **7.** 2; $3 \times 2 - 2 = 4$ ✓ **9.** 2 **11.** 10 **13.** 4 **15.** 10 **17.** −3; $8(-3) - 8 = -32$ ✓ **19.** −3; $-9(-3) + 5 = 32$ ✓ **21.** 121; $\frac{121}{-11} + 1 = -10$ ✓ **23.** −14; $7(-14) - 6 = -104$ ✓ **25.** −3; $3(-3) - 6 = -15$ ✓ **27.** −3; $10(-3) + 3 = -27$ ✓ **29.** 3; $8 \times 3 - 1 = 23$ ✓ **31.** 35; $\frac{35}{-7} + 3 = -2$ ✓ **33.** [(] 12 [+/−] [+] 6 [)] [÷] 4 [=]; −1.5 **35.** [(] 10 [−] 5 [)] [×] 3 [=]; 15 **37.** E **39.** A **41.** G **43.** 4.4 h **45.** 3 extra nights **47.** $3n - 51 = 0$; 17 **49.** $\frac{n}{2} - 5 = -15$; −20

MIXED REVIEW **51.** 19 **53.** 26 **55.** 22

Lesson 3-10 — pages 134–136

ON YOUR OWN **1a.** 9 combinations **3.** 4 paperback and 2 hardcover books **5a.** Lundberg, Chester, Topson, Dornville **b.** 16.5 mi **9.** 42 ft **11.** 15th floor

MIXED REVIEW **13a.** about \$41,167; \$25,000; \$14,000 **b.** Mean; the gap between your salary and the mean is the greatest. **15.** 0.3, 0.36792, 0.368, 0.3681

Wrap Up — pages 138–139

1. 27 **2.** 43 **3.** 15 **4.** 11 **5.** 4 **6.** 1 **7.** $8 - n$ **8.** $6c$ **9.** $6 + 2n$ **10.** −9

11.

12a. 5 **b.** 2 **c.** 17 **13.** −6, −3, 0, 1, 7 **14.** < **15.** = **16.** < **17.** > **18.** > **19.** B **20.** $-4 + (-6)$; −10 **21.** $5 + (-4)$; 1 **22.** $-6 + 7$; 1 **23.** 3 **24.** −22 **25.** −5 **26.** 29 **27.** −3 **28.** −30 **29.** 84 **30.** −25 **31.** 2 **32.** −5 **34.** −6 **35.** 4 **36.** 35 **37.** −2 **38.** −9 **39.** −14 **40.** 3 **41.** 7 **42.** $4 + n = -7$; −11

43.

Large	Small
0 (\$0)	16 (\$20)
5 (\$8.75)	9 (\$11.25)
10 (\$17.50)	2 (\$2.50)

Cumulative Review — page 141

1. C **3.** D **5.** B **7.** D **9.** C **11.** C

CHAPTER 4

Lesson 4-1 — pages 144–146

ON YOUR OWN **1.** $\frac{1}{2}$ **3.** $\frac{3}{8}$ **7.** $\frac{5}{6}$ **9.** $1\frac{6}{10}$

MIXED REVIEW **11.** $2n - 4$ **13.** = **15.** > **17.** about 0.31 m

Lesson 4-2 — pages 147–151

ON YOUR OWN **1.** 1, 17 **3.** 1, 2, 4, 8, 16, 32 **5.** 1, 23 **7.** 7, 14, 21, 28, 35 **9.** 9, 18, 27, 36, 45 **11.** 18, 36, 54, 72, 90 **15.** 6 people **17.** 12 **19.** 40 **21.** 24 **23.** 10 **25.** 30 **27.** 48 **33a.** $\frac{5}{20}$ of the problems **b.** $\frac{1}{4}$ **35.** 20 **37.** 45 **39.** 1 **41.** 24 **43.** 63 **45.** 40 **47.** 40 **49.** 24 **51.** D

MIXED REVIEW **55.** 2 **57.** 30 **59.** 17.62 **61.** 43.49 **63.** 17.09

Lesson 4-3 — pages 152–154

ON YOUR OWN **1.** $\frac{3}{5} < \frac{4}{5}$ **3.** < **5.** < **7.** < **9.** > **11.** < **13.** < **15.** < **17.** > **23.** $\frac{2}{3}, \frac{3}{4}, \frac{5}{6}$ **25.** $\frac{4}{9}, \frac{1}{2}, \frac{2}{3}$ **27.** $\frac{1}{9}, \frac{1}{8}, \frac{1}{6}$ **29.** $\frac{3}{15}, \frac{3}{10}, \frac{3}{5}$ **31.** $\frac{1}{2}, \frac{3}{5}, \frac{2}{3}$ **33.** $\frac{3}{4}, \frac{4}{5}, \frac{5}{6}$ **35.** B **37.** C **39.** Cheese, since that was the pizza with the least amount of left-overs.

MIXED REVIEW **41.** 3 **43.** −13 **45.** −4 **47.** 3.4 **49.** 17.9 **51.** on the 27th day

Lesson 4-4 — pages 155–158

ON YOUR OWN **1.** 7^3 **3.** 0.3^5 **5.** $5 \times 5 \times 5$; 125 **7.** $0.2 \times 0.2 \times 0.2 \times 0.2$; 0.0016 **9.** $9 \times 9 \times 9 \times$

$9 \times 9 \times 9$; 531,441 **11.** $6 \times 6 \times 6 \times 6 \times 6$; 7,776 **13.** $8 \times 8 \times 8 \times 8$; 4,096 **15.** 0.6×0.6; 0.36 **17a.** 10, 100, 1,000, 10,000, 100,000; 2, 3, 4, 5 **b.** The number of zeros is the same as the exponent. **c.** 1,000,000,000,000 **19.** Answers may vary. Sample: 4^3, 6^2 **21.** C **23.** A **25.** 512 **27.** −2,401 **29.** −3,125 **31.** 256 **33.** 18 **35.** 66 **37.** 13 **39.** −64 **41.** 65 **43a.** (7 − 9); 4 **b.** 16

MIXED REVIEW **45.** −43 **47.** 1 **49.** > **51.** 1,750,000

Toolbox — page 159

1. 2, 3, 4, 9 **3.** 2, 3, 5, 10 **5.** 3, 5 **7.** 2, 3, 4, 8 **9.** 2, 3, 4, 8 **11.** 3, 9 **13.** 5 **15.** 2, 3, 4, 8, 9 **17.** 3, 5, 9 **19a.** 6

Lesson 4-5 — pages 160–163

ON YOUR OWN **1.** composite **3.** composite **5.** composite **7.** 2, 3, 5, 7, 11, 13, 17, 19, 23, 29, 31, 37, 41, 43, 47 **9.** 2^6 **11.** $3 \cdot 37$ **13.** $2^2 \cdot 13$ **15.** $2^2 \cdot 3 \cdot 11$ **17.** $2^2 \cdot 3 \cdot 5$ **19.** $5^2 \cdot 3$ **21.** $2n$ is composite unless $n = 1$. Since 2 is a factor of $2n$, it is not prime. **23.** 15 **25.** 25 **27.** 11 **29.** 2 **31.** 16 **33.** 7 **35a.** 6; GCF **b.** 72; LCM **37.** No

MIXED REVIEW **39.** 21 **41.** −45

CHECKPOINT **7.** D **8.** 75 **9.** 76 **10.** 36 **11.** 16 **12.** −125 **13.** −81 **14.** composite, composite; 3 **15.** composite, prime; 11 **16.** composite, prime; 3 **17.** composite, composite; 2 **18.** composite, composite; 9 **19.** prime, composite; 3

Lesson 4-6 — pages 164–167

ON YOUR OWN **1.** $\frac{3}{4}$ **3.** $\frac{5}{6}$ **5.** $\frac{11}{13}$ **7.** $\frac{4}{7}$ **9.** $\frac{3}{5}$ **11.** $\frac{3}{5}$ **13.** $\frac{9}{16}$ **15.** school $\frac{7}{24}$, delivering papers $\frac{1}{24}$, homework $\frac{1}{12}$, reading or talking on the phone $\frac{1}{8}$, sleep $\frac{1}{3}$ **17.** 21; $\frac{2}{3}$ **19.** 3; $\frac{4}{25}$ **21.** 15; $\frac{1}{7}$ **23.** 4; $\frac{7}{24}$ **25.** 12; $\frac{9}{10}$ **27.** 25; $\frac{5}{8}$ **29.** 5; $\frac{7}{19}$ **31.** 6; $\frac{3}{8}$ **33.** 17; $\frac{1}{3}$ **35.** B **37.** Asia $\frac{121}{200}$, Africa $\frac{16}{125}$, Europe $\frac{63}{500}$, Latin America $\frac{21}{250}$, North America $\frac{13}{250}$, Australia and New Zealand $\frac{1}{200}$

MIXED REVIEW **45.** 49 **47.** 31 **49.** 8 **51.** $3.\overline{6}$ **53.** $6.1\overline{6}$ **55.** in 60 months

Lesson 4-7 — pages 168–170

ON YOUR OWN **1a.** The sequence of ones digits repeats the pattern 7, 9, 3, 1. **b.** 7 **3.** −1 **5.** 15 combinations **7.** 8 school days **9.** 6 minutes **11.**

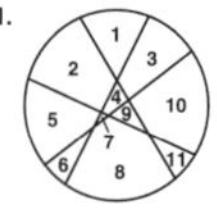

13. 13 strawberries

MIXED REVIEW **17.** 6 **19.** −1 **21.** \$9 **23.** 7

Problem Solving Practice — page 171

1. C **3.** A **5.** C **7.** D **9.** C

Lesson 4-8 — pages 172–175

ON YOUR OWN **1.** $\frac{19}{8}$ **3.** $\frac{13}{12}$ **5.** $\frac{10}{7}$ **7.** $\frac{17}{5}$ **9.** $\frac{17}{3}$ **11.** $\frac{22}{9}$ **13.** $\frac{39}{8}$ **15.** $\frac{59}{7}$ **17.** $\frac{43}{7}$ **21.** $2\frac{3}{8}$, $\frac{19}{8}$ **23.** $2\frac{5}{8}$, $\frac{21}{8}$ **25.** $5\frac{1}{3}$ **27.** $10\frac{1}{2}$ **29.** 4 **31.** 12 **33.** 6 **35.** $4\frac{1}{2}$ **37.** $4\frac{2}{5}$ **39.** $6\frac{3}{4}$ **41.** $4\frac{1}{2}$ **43.** 7 **45.** $3\frac{3}{4}$ h, $\frac{15}{4}$ h **47.** C **49.** $\frac{95}{2}$, $47\frac{1}{2}$

MIXED REVIEW **51.** 13 **53.** −24 **55.** 21 in.

CHECKPOINT **1.** $\frac{3}{4}$ **2.** $\frac{2}{3}$ **3.** $\frac{2}{3}$ **4.** $\frac{9}{10}$ **5.** $\frac{2}{9}$ **6.** $\frac{7}{10}$ **7.** $4\frac{5}{6}$ **8.** $16\frac{2}{5}$ **9.** $\frac{37}{9}$ **10.** $\frac{19}{10}$ **11.** $2\frac{3}{4}$ **12.** $\frac{17}{6}$ **14.** 42

Lesson 4-9 — pages 176–180

ON YOUR OWN **1.** 0.4 **3.** 0.15 **5.** $0.91\overline{6}$ **7.** 0.75 **9.** $0.41\overline{6}$ **11.** $0.1\overline{6}$ **13.** $0.\overline{75}$ **15.** 0.7 **17.** 0.9 **19a.** $\frac{3}{100}$ **b.** 0.03 **c.** $\frac{97}{100}$ **21.** C **25.** $\frac{3}{5}$ **27.** $\frac{33}{50}$ **29.** $3\frac{3}{4}$ **31.** $\frac{19}{100}$ **33.** $\frac{193}{200}$ **35.** $4\frac{61}{200}$ **37.** $\frac{13}{20}$ **39.** $1\frac{69}{100}$ **41.** $\frac{71}{125}$ **43.** $\frac{5}{9}$, 0.58, $\frac{7}{12}$, $\frac{2}{3}$, 0.67 **45.** $2\frac{63}{100}$, $\frac{263}{100}$

MIXED REVIEW **47.** $\frac{14}{5}$ **49.** $\frac{37}{12}$ **51.** $\frac{25}{11}$ **53.** 0.8 **55.** 10.2

Wrap Up — pages 182–183

1. $\frac{2}{5}$ **2.** $\frac{4}{7}$ **3.** $\frac{3}{4}$ **4.** $\frac{1}{4}$, $\frac{3}{8}$, $\frac{1}{2}$ **5.** $\frac{1}{6}$, $\frac{7}{12}$, $\frac{3}{4}$ **6.** $\frac{1}{3}$, $\frac{2}{5}$, $\frac{7}{15}$ **7.** $\frac{8}{20}$, $\frac{6}{10}$, $\frac{4}{5}$ **8.** $\frac{3}{4}$, $\frac{8}{10}$, $\frac{6}{7}$ **9.** $\frac{3}{5}$, $\frac{4}{6}$, $\frac{9}{12}$ **10.** B **11.** $2 \times 2 \times 2$; 8 **12.** $-(3 \times 3 \times 3 \times 3)$; −81 **13.** 6×6; 36 **14.** $0.2 \times 0.2 \times 0.2$; 0.008 **15.** 0.12×0.12; 0.0144 **16.** $-3 \times -3 \times -3 \times -3$; 81 **17.** prime; $1 \cdot 73$ **18.** composite; $2 \cdot 5 \cdot 11$ **19.** composite; $2 \cdot 2 \cdot 2 \cdot 2$ **20.** composite; $3 \cdot 29$ **21.** composite; $11 \cdot 11$ **22.** composite; $2 \cdot 2 \cdot 7$

23. $\frac{1}{2}$ **24.** $\frac{1}{4}$ **25.** $\frac{3}{4}$ **26.** $\frac{2}{5}$ **27.** $\frac{8}{9}$ **28.** $\frac{7}{12}$ $\frac{1}{12}$ **29.** 210 boxes **30.** $\frac{37}{8}$ **31.** $4\frac{3}{5}$ **32.** $\frac{52}{9}$ **33.** $\frac{11}{3}$ **34.** $1\frac{7}{8}$ **35.** $4\frac{2}{3}$ **37.** $\frac{1}{20}$ **38.** 0.75 **39.** $\frac{6}{25}$ **40.** 0.875 **41.** $2\frac{24}{25}$ **42.** $0.8\overline{3}$

CUMULATIVE REVIEW **1.** D **3.** C **5.** D **7.** D **9.** B **11.** C

CHAPTER 5

Lesson 5-1 — pages 188–191

ON YOUR OWN **1.** $\frac{1}{2}$ **3.** 5 **5.** 3 **7.** 5 **9.** 2 **11.** 2 tons **13.** $\frac{1}{2}$ ton **15.** 8 **17.** 3 **19.** 21 **21.** 9 **23.** 18 **27.** 2 **29.** 2 **31.** 25 **33.** 1 **35.** 60 **37.** $\frac{1}{2}$ **39.** 0 **41.** 1 **43.** No; $2\frac{3}{4}$ is almost 3, so the triple recipe will use almost 9 c of flour. **45.** C

MIXED REVIEW **47.** 0.91 **49.** 2,001 **51.** Positive trend; as people grow older, they grow taller. After you stop growing, the height remains the same. **53.** Positive trend; you are likely to get better income with greater experience.

Toolbox — page 192

1. $\frac{4}{5} - \frac{2}{5} = \frac{2}{5}$ **3.** $\frac{3}{4}$ **5.** $\frac{1}{5}$ **7.** $\frac{9}{10}$ **9.** $\frac{3}{10}$ **11.** $\frac{4}{3}$ **13.** $\frac{1}{2}$

Lesson 5-2 — pages 193–196

ON YOUR OWN **1.** $\frac{5}{7}$ **3.** $1\frac{1}{6}$ **5.** $1\frac{5}{8}$ **7.** $1\frac{3}{10}$ **9.** $1\frac{3}{4}$ **11a.** $\frac{7}{12}$ **b.** yes; $\frac{7}{12} > \frac{1}{2}$ **13.** No; $\frac{1}{2} + \frac{2}{3} + \frac{3}{4} = 1\frac{11}{12}$, so 2 c is enough. **15.** $\frac{3}{5}$ **17.** $\frac{1}{2}$ **19.** $\frac{5}{12}$ **21.** $\frac{1}{6}$ **23.** $\frac{5}{12}$ **25. a.** your friend; $\frac{2}{15}$ mi **b.** Subtraction; to find the difference of the distances, you subtract. **27.** $\frac{7}{12}$ **29.** $\frac{1}{12}$ **31.** $1\frac{7}{12}$ **33.** $\frac{3}{8}$ **35.** $\frac{5}{12}$ **37.** $1\frac{7}{20}$ **39.** $\frac{23}{40}$ **41.** $\frac{9}{20}$ mi **43.** positive; $\frac{2}{3} < \frac{5}{6}$ **45.** negative; $\frac{7}{8} > \frac{3}{4}$ **47a.** 7 [+] 8 [−] 3 [+] 5 [=] **b.** 0.275

MIXED REVIEW **49.** −7 **51.** −65 **53.** 37 **55.** 38

Lesson 5-3 — pages 197–199

ON YOUR OWN **1.** $8\frac{1}{5}$ **3.** $18\frac{5}{6}$ **5.** $11\frac{1}{3}$ **7.** $14\frac{8}{9}$ **9.** $21\frac{1}{8}$ **11.** $3\frac{3}{4}$ in.; $7\frac{1}{2}$ in. **13.** $4\frac{3}{5}$ **15.** $6\frac{1}{2}$ **17.** $7\frac{3}{8}$ **19.** $8\frac{4}{5}$ **21.** $5\frac{5}{6}$ **23.** $14\frac{7}{8}$ in. **25.** $2\frac{4}{5}$ **27.** $3\frac{5}{6}$ **29.** $7\frac{1}{12}$ **31.** $9\frac{1}{6}$ **33.** $8\frac{3}{8}$ **35.** $14\frac{2}{5}$ **37.** $13\frac{17}{20}$ **39.** $16\frac{3}{40}$ **41.** $6\frac{11}{15}$ **43.** $\frac{53}{60}$ **45.** $2\frac{7}{16}$ in. **47a.** [(] 4 [+] 1 [÷] 8 [)] [−] [(] 1 [+] 3 [÷] 4 [)] [=] **b.** 2.375

MIXED REVIEW **49.** $2^3 \times 13$ **51.** $2 \times 5 \times 7$ **53.** 0.4, 0.43, 0.431, 0.438 **55.** 75.09, 75.3, 75.98

Lesson 5-4 — pages 200–204

ON YOUR OWN **1.** $x - \frac{3}{4} = \frac{1}{12}$; $\frac{5}{6}$ **3.** $2\frac{3}{8}$ **5.** $\frac{7}{12}$ **7.** $d - 1\frac{3}{4} = 10\frac{1}{3}$; $12\frac{1}{12}$ ft **9.** $\frac{1}{8}$ **11.** $7\frac{1}{3}$ **13a.** $51\frac{1}{2} + h = 52\frac{1}{4}$ **b.** $\frac{3}{4}$ in. **15.** $1\frac{1}{24}$ **17.** $3\frac{5}{8}$ **19.** $2\frac{1}{8}$ **21.** $\frac{8}{9}$ **23.** 0 **25.** $7\frac{1}{3}$ **27.** $\frac{1}{2}$ **29.** 0 **31.** $3\frac{2}{9}$ **33.** $\frac{5}{9}$ **35.** $b + 3\frac{3}{4} = 5\frac{1}{4}$; $1\frac{1}{2}$ ft **37.** $\frac{1}{4} + r = \frac{2}{3}$; $\frac{5}{12}$ of trash

MIXED REVIEW **41.** 24 **43.** −13 **45.** 27

CHECKPOINT **1.** 1 **2.** $\frac{1}{2}$ **3.** 3 **4.** 24 **5.** 32 **6.** $1\frac{5}{8}$ **7.** $\frac{1}{24}$ **8.** $\frac{13}{24}$ **9.** $\frac{13}{18}$ **10.** $\frac{2}{3}$ **11.** $4\frac{1}{14}$ **12.** $4\frac{7}{15}$ **13.** $5\frac{7}{8}$ **14.** $5\frac{11}{15}$ **15.** $13\frac{1}{8}$ **16.** $\frac{1}{2} + \frac{1}{4} = \frac{3}{4}$ **17.** $\frac{1}{3} - \frac{1}{4} = \frac{1}{12}$ **18.** $\frac{1}{2} + \frac{2}{5} = \frac{9}{10}$ **19.** $1\frac{1}{8}$ **20.** $1\frac{7}{15}$ **21.** $1\frac{4}{5}$ **22.** $18\frac{7}{8}$ **23.** $\frac{1}{10}$ **24.** $\frac{5}{24}$ **25.** $7\frac{17}{20}$ **26.** $10\frac{2}{15}$

Lesson 5-5 — pages 205–209

ON YOUR OWN **1.** $\frac{3}{8} \cdot \frac{2}{3} = \frac{6}{24}$ **3.** $\frac{5}{6} \cdot \frac{3}{4} = \frac{15}{24}$ **5.** $\frac{3}{20}$ **7.** $\frac{5}{18}$ **9.** $\frac{7}{10}$ **11.** 4 **13.** $1\frac{1}{8}$ **15.** $\frac{4}{25}$ **17.** 15 **19.** $\frac{3}{8}$ **21.** 18 **23a.** 140,000,000 mi^2 **b.** 12,000,000 mi^2 **25.** $7\frac{1}{8}$ **27.** 18 **29.** $7\frac{1}{3}$ **31.** $\frac{4}{5}$ **33.** $\frac{2}{5}$ **35.** $3\frac{1}{8}$ **37.** $11\frac{5}{8}$ **39.** 1 **41.** $34\frac{2}{9}$ yd^2 **43.** [(] 1 [+] 1 [÷] 4 [)] [×] [(] 3 [+] 1 [÷] 5 [)] [=] **45.** $34\frac{1}{2}$ lb

MIXED REVIEW **47.** 76 **49.** 270 **51.** 400

Lesson 5-6 — pages 210–212

ON YOUR OWN **1.** $\frac{4}{3}$ **3.** 7 **5.** $\frac{6}{13}$ **7.** 16 **9.** 18 **11.** 3 **13.** 20 **15.** $\frac{1}{3}$ **17.** $1\frac{1}{4}$ **19.** $\frac{5}{8}$ **21.** 54 **25.** $\frac{1}{4}$ **27.** $3\frac{4}{5}$ **29.** $\frac{12}{23}$ **31.** $\frac{8}{49}$ **33.** $\frac{12}{23}$ **35.** $1\frac{1}{2}$ **37.** $1\frac{23}{27}$ **39.** 32 mi **41.** [(] 13 [+] 7 [÷] 8 [)] [÷] [(] 6 [+] 1 [÷] 6 [)] [=]; 2.25

MIXED REVIEW **43.** 0.375 **45.** $2.\overline{6}$ **47.** $0.291\overline{6}$ **49.** $\frac{5}{8}$ **51.** $2\frac{19}{50}$ **53.** $4\frac{61}{200}$

Toolbox — page 213

1. $17\frac{9}{10}$ **3.** $20\frac{1}{20}$ **5.** $3\frac{1}{46}$ **7.** $78\frac{7}{12}$ **9.** $382\frac{31}{32}$

Lesson 5-7 — pages 214–216

ON YOUR OWN **1a.** 6:15 P.M. **b.** 6:10 P.M. **3.** 14 **5a.** 132 tiles; 108 tiles **7.** \$9.60 **9.** 7th year **11.** \$59

MIXED REVIEW **13.** $1\frac{1}{8}$ **15.** $9\frac{5}{24}$ **17.** 44.8 **19.** 1.4 **21.** 3.2 **23a.** \$18.96 **b.** \$6.32

Problem Solving Practice — page 217

1. B **3.** B **5.** D **7.** A **9.** C

Lesson 5-8 — pages 218–221

ON YOUR OWN **1.** multiply **3.** multiply **5.** $4\frac{1}{2}$ **7.** $\frac{1}{4}$ **9.** $4\frac{1}{4}$ lb **11.** $2\frac{5}{8}$ **13.** $4\frac{1}{2}$ **15.** 32 **17.** $2\frac{1}{4}$ **19.** $5\frac{1}{3}$ **21.** $1\frac{2}{5}$ **23.** $\frac{7}{8}$ **25.** $3\frac{1}{2}$ **27.** Yes; 1 gal = 16 c, so 4 gal = 64 c. **31a.** about $6\frac{1}{4}$ mi **b.** about $\frac{3}{4}$ mi

MIXED REVIEW **33.** 41 **35.** 230 **37.** \$3.85

CHECKPOINT **1.** $\frac{1}{2}$ **2.** $\frac{3}{4}$ **3.** $\frac{1}{8}$ **4.** $26\frac{11}{14}$ **5.** 34 **6.** 7:05 A.M. **7.** $2\frac{1}{3}$ **8.** 136 **9.** $3\frac{3}{4}$ **10.** $7\frac{2}{3}$

Lesson 5-9 — pages 222–224

ON YOUR OWN **1.** 30 **3.** $18\frac{1}{2}$ **5.** $52\frac{1}{2}$ **7.** 8 mi/h **9.** $2\frac{1}{4}$ **11.** $2\frac{2}{3}$ **13.** $1\frac{7}{8}$ **15.** 3 **17.** 36 **19a.** Ed's; 49 is about 50, so the solution is $\frac{50}{20} = 2\frac{1}{2}$. **b.** Carl divided 20 by 50 instead of 50 by 20. **21.** $2\frac{2}{9}$ **23.** $\frac{1}{7}$ **25.** $4\frac{2}{7}$ **27.** 4 **29.** $\frac{1}{9}$ **31.** 4,290 **33.** 1,053 **41.** 13.7 times

MIXED REVIEW **45.** 17 **47.** 63 **49.** < **51.** = **53.** >

Wrap Up — pages 226–227

1. 1 **2.** 2 **3.** $\frac{1}{2}$ **4.** 30 **5.** 3 **6.** $1\frac{1}{5}$ **7.** $\frac{5}{8}$ **8.** $\frac{9}{10}$ **9.** $\frac{7}{16}$ **10.** $1\frac{5}{12}$ **11.** $3\frac{1}{12}$ **12.** $7\frac{2}{15}$ **13.** $15\frac{5}{12}$ **14.** $6\frac{11}{24}$ **15.** $\frac{7}{12}$ **16.** $1\frac{7}{8}$ **17.** $8\frac{1}{2}$ **18.** $1\frac{1}{10}$ **19.** $4\frac{19}{20}$ **20.** $1\frac{1}{10}$ **21.** $8\frac{7}{12}$ **22.** $7\frac{7}{12}$ **23.** $1\frac{9}{10}$ **24.** $\frac{3}{10}$ **25.** $\frac{1}{4}$ **26.** $\frac{9}{10}$ **27.** 9 **28.** $94\frac{23}{24}$ **29.** $\frac{1}{2}$ **30.** $\frac{1}{2}$ **31.** 6 **32.** $3\frac{3}{5}$ **33.** $\frac{5}{18}$ **34.** 6:00 A.M. **35.** \$39.76 **36.** $2\frac{1}{2}$ **37.** $3\frac{3}{8}$ **38.** 60 **39.** 28 **40.** $4\frac{2}{3}$ **41.** 7,500 **42.** $2\frac{1}{4}$ **43.** $6\frac{1}{2}$ **44.** 50 **45.** $\frac{1}{4}$ **46.** $3\frac{3}{5}$ **47.** $1\frac{1}{4}$ **48.** $3\frac{1}{2}$ **49.** 21 **50.** $6\frac{1}{2}$ **51.** $14\frac{1}{2}$ **52.** $\frac{5}{6}$ **53.** 4 **54.** $\frac{1}{5}s = 70$; 350 students

Cumulative Review — page 229

1. C **3.** D **5.** B **7.** B **9.** A **11.** D

CHAPTER 6

Lesson 6-1 — pages 232–236

ON YOUR OWN **1.** Sample: 1 : 4, 1 to 4, $\frac{1}{4}$ **3.** 12 to 4, $\frac{12}{4}$ **5.** 5 to 4, 5 : 4 **7.** 21 to 28, $\frac{21}{28}$ **9.** B **11a.** 23 : 19, 23 to 19, $\frac{23}{19}$ **b.** 19 : 42, 19 to 42, $\frac{19}{42}$ **13.** 0.9 **15.** 2.7 **17.** 0.5 **19a.** 225 : 3, 455 : 7 **b.** 75, 65 **27.** 5 : 2 **29.** $\frac{1}{50}$ **31.** 1 : 2 **33.** 25 to 1 **35a.** 8 : 4 **b.** 10 qt antifreeze, 5 qt water

MIXED REVIEW **37.** 650 ÷ 50 = 13 **39.** 23 + 23 + 23 = 69 **41.** 45 **43.** −54 **45.** \$28.50

Lesson 6-2 — pages 237–240

ON YOUR OWN **1.** 300 mi/h **3.** \$5.80/h **5.** 4.3 m/s **7.** \$3/yd **9.** \$3.29/gal **11.** \$2.50/m **13.** \$.95/oz **15.** \$.14/min **17.** \$.06/oz, \$.05/oz; 50 fl oz **19.** \$.04/oz, \$.05/oz; 48 fl oz **21.** \$.49/yd, \$.65/yd; 1 yd **23a.** 1 person/mi^2 **25a.** 10.35 m/s, 9.24 m/s, 7.90 m/s **27a.** 64-oz bottle **b.** 12-oz bottle

MIXED REVIEW **29.** 4.88 **31.** 21.46 **33.** 1.00 **35.**

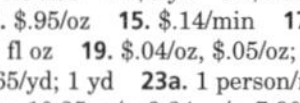

37.

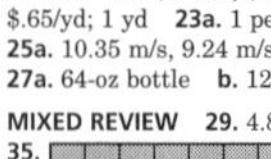

Lesson 6-3 — pages 241–244

ON YOUR OWN **1.** yes **3.** no **5.** yes **7.** $\frac{27}{18} = \frac{9}{6}$ **9.** no **11.** 25 **13.** 3 **15.** $1.\overline{3}$ **17.** 28 **19.** 15 **21.** 19.2 **23.** 30.25 **25a.** 6 h **27.** about 17,100,000 votes

MIXED REVIEW **31.** 5.1; 5 **33.** < **35.** = **37.** >

CHECKPOINT **7.** 152 **8.** 28 **9.** 12.5 **10.** 24 **11.** 5.3 **12.** 60 **13.** C **14.** 196 min

Lesson 6-4 — pages 245–249

ON YOUR OWN **1.** No; the sides are not proportional. **3.** Not similar; number of sides is different. **5.** Not similar; the ratios of the lengths of corresponding sides are not equal. **9.** 2.8 **11.** 24.7 **13.** 99 cm

MIXED REVIEW **15.** −14 **17.** −6 **19.** $\frac{11}{4}$ **21.** $\frac{13}{6}$ **23.** $\frac{25}{7}$

Toolbox — page 250

1. The triangle changes its shape and stays similar to $\triangle ABC$. **3a.** Each line passes through a vertex of $\triangle ABC$ and its image. **b.** Every line connecting a point and its image passes through D.

Lesson 6-5 — pages 251–254

ON YOUR OWN **1.** 60 km **3.** 3.75 km **5.** 6 km **7.** 1 in. **9.** $\frac{1}{4}$ in. **11.** 0.075 in. **13.** 1 in. : 1.2 mi **17a.** 4.7 in. **b.** 1 in. : 194.3 mi **19.** 3 in. **21.** 1 in. : 1,865 mi

MIXED REVIEW **23.** 40, 32 **25.** 80 **27.** \$1.45, \$1.65

Problem Solving Practice — page 255

1. B **3.** D **5.** B **7.** B **9.** B

Lesson 6-6 — pages 256–259

ON YOUR OWN **1.** 64% **3.** 45% **5.** 80% **7.** 10% **9.** 50% **11.** 100% **13.** about 25% **15.** about 25%

17.

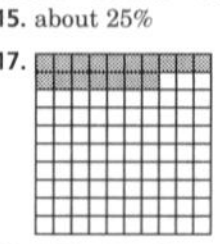

19.

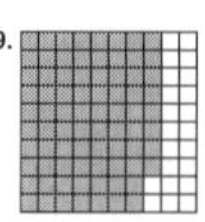

31. 60% **33.** 84% **35.** 35% **37.** 80% **39.** 30% **41.** 20% **43.** 87.5% **45.** 40% **47.** 14% **49.** 0.6% **51.** 176%

MIXED REVIEW **53.** $4\frac{8}{9}$ **55.** $36\frac{13}{20}$ **57.** −4 **59.** 0 **61.** 42 matches

Lesson 6-7 — pages 260–263

ON YOUR OWN **1.** $\frac{9}{20}$ **3.** $\frac{9}{5}$ **5.** $\frac{3}{50}$ **7.** $\frac{3}{40}$ **9.** $\frac{1}{1000}$ **11.** $\frac{17}{20}$ **13.** B **15.** 85% **17.** 62.5% **19.** 475% **21.** 101% **23.** 87.5% **25.** 60% **27.** 8% **29.** 83.3% **31.** No; 0.4% is 0.004, which is less than 0.4. **33.** 0.32 **35.** 0.88 **37.** 3.45 **39.** 0.03 **41.** 0.12 **43.** 0.0009 **45.** 50% **47.** 0.28% **49.** 0.33% **51.** 37.5% **53.** 98.7% **55.** 0.9% **57.** 1,000% **59.** 6,780% **61a.** $\frac{1}{10}$, 0.1; $\frac{3}{20}$, 0.15; $\frac{1}{25}$, 0.04; $\frac{1}{50}$, 0.02; $\frac{3}{100}$, 0.03 **b.** 25 servings

MIXED REVIEW **63.** 1,225 **65.** 3,250 **67.** 75 **69.** 6 **71.** −4.5 **73.** 2

Lesson 6-8 — pages 264–266

ON YOUR OWN **1a.** 10 **b.** 8 ft × 12 ft or 4 ft × 16 ft **3.** 91 **5.** 36 **7.** $1\frac{7}{8}$c **9a.** 1 3 5 7 9 11 **b.** 21; 45 **c.** 16; 100 **d.** The sum is the square of the row number. **11.** Alvin is the conductor, Breon is the banker, and Carl is the artist.

MIXED REVIEW **13.** $\frac{1}{6}$ **15.** $6\frac{3}{7}$ **17.** 6 **19.** 2 : 11, 2 to 11, $\frac{2}{11}$ **21a.** 2 **b.** 7

Lesson 6-9 — pages 267–270

ON YOUR OWN **1.** 5.4 **3.** 7 **5.** 180 **7.** 0.36 **9.** 21 **11.** 13.31 **13.** 63.7 **15.** 6.75 **17.** 2 **19.** 23.75 **21.** 4 **23.** 3.96 **25a.** $\frac{500}{100} \times 63{,}000$ **b.** 315,000 **27a.** 35 students; 23.3% **b.** French, 23.3%; German, 11.3%; Spanish, 45.3% **c.** French, 583; German, 283; Spanish, 1,133 **29.** D **31.** \$2.49 **33.** the calico fabric; \$.21 per yd

MIXED REVIEW **37.** $\frac{4}{5}$ **39.** $\frac{1}{20}$ **41.** $\frac{1}{7}$ **43.** $6\frac{1}{4}$ **45.** 44 **47.** \$48

CHECKPOINT **1.** 80% **2.** 0.4% **3.** $33\frac{1}{3}\%$ **4.** 56% **5.** 52% **6.** 20% **7.** 0.17, $\frac{17}{100}$ **8.** 0.29, $\frac{29}{100}$ **9.** 1.35, $1\frac{7}{20}$ **10.** 0.77, $\frac{77}{100}$ **11.** 0.98, $\frac{49}{50}$ **12.** 0.45, $\frac{9}{20}$ **13.** 16.82 **14.** 171% **15.** 14.4 **16.** 10, 6 **17.** 52.5 mi **18.** 35%

Lesson 6-10 — pages 271–274

ON YOUR OWN **1.** $\frac{n}{100} = \frac{12}{15}$; $n = 80$ **3.** $\frac{75}{100} = \frac{6}{n}$; $n = 8$ **5.** A **7.** 10% **9.** $33\frac{1}{3}\%$ **11.** 125% **13.** 40% **15.** 7% **17.** A **19.** $\frac{225}{100} = \frac{n}{48}$, 108 **21.** $\frac{80}{100} = \frac{15}{n}$, 18.75 **23.** $\frac{12}{100} = \frac{42}{n}$, 350 **25.** 459 students **27a.** 6.25% **b.** \$479.95

MIXED REVIEW **29.** $6\frac{3}{10}$ **31.** about 68,000,000 **33.** 4 mi

Toolbox — page 275

1. \$2.25 **3.** \$3.00

Lesson 6-11 — pages 276–280

ON YOUR OWN **1.** 25% **3.** 100% **5.** 133.3% **7.** 425% **9.** 4.2% **11.** 300% **13.** 25% **15.** 85.2% **17.** 44.5% **19.** 16.5% **21.** 2% **23.** 66.7% **25.** 37.5% **27.** 52% **29.** 40% **31.** 77.8% **33.** 35.7% **35.** 10% **37.** 41.8% **39.** 20.1% **41.** 10% decrease **43.** 13.2% increase **45.** 15.4% increase **47.** 30% decrease **49.** 23.6% increase **51.** 25.9% decrease **53.** 27.6% decrease **55.** 46.7% decrease

MIXED REVIEW **59.** 0 **61.** −7 **63.** 0.2 **65.** $0.1\overline{6}$ **67.** $0.\overline{6}$ **69.** \$2.35/lb

Wrap Up — pages 282–283

1. 44 : 101, 44 to 101, $\frac{44}{101}$ **2.** \$.28/oz, \$.31/oz; 10 oz box **3.** 12 **4.** 25 **5.** 3 **6.** 136 **7.** 4 **8a.** $\frac{5}{3} = \frac{n}{250{,}000}$; 416,667 board feet **b.** $\frac{3}{250{,}000} = \frac{8}{n}$; 666,667 board feet **9.** 45 **10.** 45, 36 **11.** 4,000 mi **12.** 0.75 in. **13.** 37.5% **14.** 0.018 **15.** $\frac{5}{8}$ **16.** $\frac{x}{100} = \frac{28}{40}$; 70% **17.** $\frac{38}{x} = \frac{80}{100}$; 47.5 **18.** $\frac{60}{100} = \frac{x}{420}$; 252 **19.** $\frac{80}{100} = \frac{x}{15}$; 12 **20.** $\frac{54}{x} = \frac{75}{100}$; 72 **21.** $\frac{36}{180} = \frac{x}{100}$; 20% **22.** \$300 **23.** D **24.** 17% decrease **25.** 20% increase **26.** 15% increase **28.** 32.5% decrease **29.** 31% decrease

Cumulative Review — page 285

1. D **3.** B **5.** C **7.** A **9.** C **11.** D **13.** C **15.** B

CHAPTER 7

Lesson 7-1 — pages 288–290

ON YOUR OWN **1a.**

b. 20 × 20 square array of dots **3.** C

MIXED REVIEW **7.** $\frac{2}{5}$ **9.** $\frac{3}{7}$ **11.** $\frac{4}{5}$ **13.** 9% increase **15.** 8% increase

Lesson 7-2 — pages 291–295

ON YOUR OWN **1.** acute **3.** right **5.** 50°; acute **7.** 130°; obtuse **9.** about 65° **11.**

13.

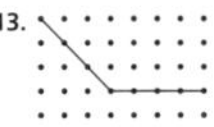

17. ∠*ABF*, ∠*FBC*, ∠*CBG*, ∠*ABG* **23.** 165°

25.

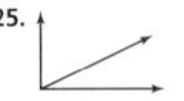

27. 75° **29.** reasonable **31.** 140° **33a.** mammoth **b.** elephant

MIXED REVIEW **35.** $\frac{1}{2}$ **37.** $\frac{22}{27}$ **39.** $\frac{2}{3}$

Toolbox — page 296

1. $m\angle 1 = 132°$, $m\angle 2 = 48°$, $m\angle 3 = 48°$, $m\angle 4 = 132°$, $m\angle 5 = 132°$, $m\angle 6 = 48°$, $m\angle 7 = 48°$, $m\angle 8 = 132°$ **3.** ∠2, ∠3, ∠6, ∠7 **5.** ∠3; ∠2, ∠4 **7.** ∠2, ∠3; ∠4 **9.** $m\angle 1 = 122°$, $m\angle 2 = 58°$, $m\angle 3 = 122°$

Lesson 7-3 — pages 297–301

ON YOUR OWN **1.** isosceles; $\overline{XY}$, $\overline{YZ}$ **3.** scalene **5.** right; ∠*Y* is right. **7.** obtuse; ∠*B* is obtuse. **9.** equilateral triangle **11.** 80° **13.** 44° **15.** 60° **17.** The two green triangles are scalene right triangles. The other triangles are acute isosceles triangles. **19a.** acute **b.** No; the angles of an equilateral triangle are congruent. **c.** No; two angles of an isosceles triangle are congruent. **d.** Yes; since it is not equilateral or isosceles, it must be scalene. **21.** 50°, 50° **23.** 59°, 62°

MIXED REVIEW **25.** 64 **27.** 49 **29.** 78,125 **31.** $1.\overline{6}$ **33.** $0.8\overline{3}$ **35.** 2.625

CHECKPOINT **1.**

2. acute **3.** obtuse **4.** right **5.** straight **6.** equilateral, acute **7.** isosceles, obtuse **8.** scalene, right

Lesson 7-4 — pages 302–304

ON YOUR OWN **1.** 8:36 A.M.; he walks one block in 4 min and has 3 blocks, or 12 min, to go at 8:24 A.M. **3a.** 84 toothpicks **b.** row 8

5. 225 tulip bulbs **7.** Rosa plays piano, Alberto plays drums, and Vernesha plays guitar. **9.** 6 angles; 3 obtuse angles **11.** 13 triangles

MIXED REVIEW **13.** $\frac{9}{2}$, or $4\frac{1}{2}$ **15.** $\frac{2}{3}$ **17.** 1 **19.** $2\frac{1}{2}$ **21.** bicycling

Lesson 7-5 — pages 305–307

ON YOUR OWN **1.** a and f, b and e, c and d **3.** △*FDE* **5a.** ∠*C* **b.** ∠*L* **c.** ∠*K* **d.** $\overline{CL}$ **e.** $\overline{LK}$ **f.** $\overline{CK}$ **7.** $\overline{XY} \cong \overline{RB}$, $\overline{YZ} \cong \overline{BP}$, $\overline{XZ} \cong \overline{RP}$, $\angle X \cong \angle R$, $\angle Y \cong \angle B$, $\angle Z \cong \angle P$ **9.** △*DJK*, △*DKJ* **11.** D

MIXED REVIEW **13.** 0.8 **15.** $0.\overline{3}$ **17.** 1.5 **19.** $n + 15 = 45$; 30

Lesson 7-6 — pages 308–312

ON YOUR OWN **1.** hexagon; regular **3.** quadrilateral; not regular **5.** polygon, quadrilateral, [parallelogram] **7.** polygon, quadrilateral, parallelogram, [rhombus]

9.

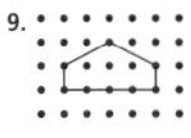

11.

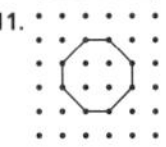

21. Yes; a square is a rhombus and a rectangle. **25.** trapezoid **27.** rectangle; $\overline{AB} \cong \overline{DC}$, $\overline{BC} \cong \overline{AD}$, $\angle A \cong \angle B \cong \angle C \cong \angle D$ **29.** $m\angle C = 65°$, $DC = 6$ cm **31.** $XY = 4$ cm, $YZ = 4$ cm, $WZ = 4$ cm **33.** No additional measures can be found.

MIXED REVIEW **39.** composite; 3 · 5 **41.** composite; 3 · 3 · 37 **43.** composite; 2 · 73

Toolbox — page 313

1a. The sum should be 540°. **b.** 540° **c.** 540° **5.** It is always 720°. **7.** The number of triangles that can be formed from one vertex is 2 less than the number of sides of the polygon.

Lesson 7-7 — pages 314–317

ON YOUR OWN **3.** $\overline{FH}$ **5.** $\widehat{FEH}$, $\widehat{FGH}$ **7.** $\overline{FH}$ **9.** radii: $\overline{OE}$, $\overline{OF}$, $\overline{OG}$, $\overline{OH}$; diameters: $\overline{EG}$, $\overline{FH}$; chords: $\overline{EG}$, $\overline{FH}$, $\overline{FG}$ **11.** D **13.** The triangle is right.

MIXED REVIEW **15.** $5\frac{9}{14}$ **17.** $2\frac{7}{30}$ **19.** 10 **21.** 9 **23.** 5

Lesson 7-8 — pages 318–322

ON YOUR OWN **1b.** 18 yr; 23 states **3.** 30 vehicles; you can have only a whole number of vehicles. **5.** 108°, 45% **7.** $\frac{3}{10}$, 18°, 144° **9.** 90° **11.** 108° **13.** 45° **15a.**

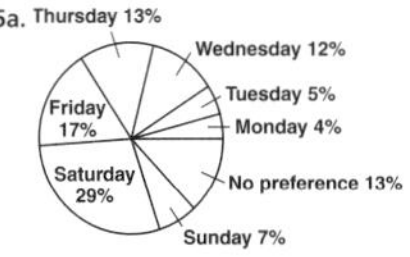

b. Monday: 48, Tuesday: 60, Wednesday: 144, Thursday: 156, Friday: 204, Saturday: 348, Sunday: 84, No preference: 156 **17a.** $12\frac{1}{2}$% **b.** 20%

MIXED REVIEW **19.** 7% **21.** 37.5% **23.** 9.9% **25.** $1\frac{1}{24}$ **27.** $8\frac{7}{16}$ **29.** $5\frac{1}{10}$ **31.** Lorissa, 4 tickets; Melinda, 13 tickets

CHECKPOINT

1.

2.

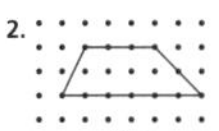

5.

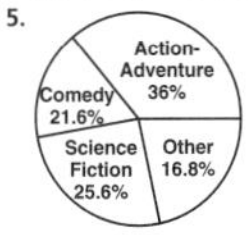

7. C

Lesson 7-9 — pages 323–326

ON YOUR OWN **1.** 8 in. **3.** 5 ft **5.** $1\frac{1}{2}$ in.

7.

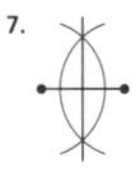

9. 132°

11.

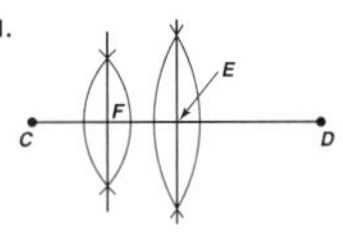

11a. $\overline{CE}$ and $\overline{ED}$ are half as long as $\overline{CD}$. **b.** $\overline{CF}$ and $\overline{FE}$ are $\frac{1}{4}$ as long as $\overline{CD}$.

13.

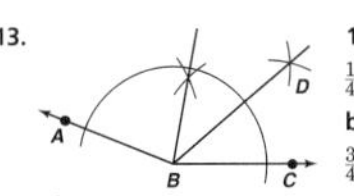

13a. $m\angle CBD = \frac{1}{4}m\angle ABC$ **b.** $m\angle ABD = \frac{3}{4}m\angle ABC$

15a–d.

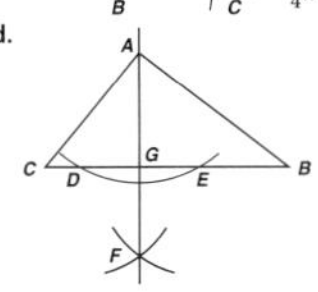

MIXED REVIEW

17.

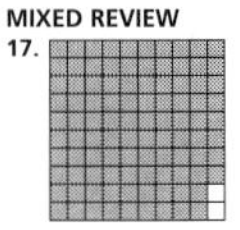

19.

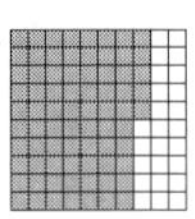

21. $12\frac{1}{2}$ h

Problem Solving Practice — page 328

1. B **3.** C **5.** C **7.** A

Wrap Up — pages 330–331

1.

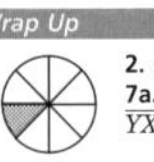

2. ∠1, ∠4 **3.** ∠1, ∠2 **6.** 23°; 113° **7a.** 97° **b.** obtuse **8.** D **9.** $\overline{UV} \cong \overline{YX}$, $\overline{VW} \cong \overline{XZ}$, $\overline{UW} \cong \overline{YZ}$, $\angle U \cong \angle Y$, $\angle V \cong \angle X$, $\angle W \cong \angle Z$ **10.** Yes; if the largest angle is obtuse, the triangle is obtuse. If the largest angle is a right angle, the triangle is a right triangle. If the largest angle is acute, the triangle is acute. **11.** 32° and 116°, 74° and 74° **17.** $\widehat{ABC}$, $\widehat{ADC}$ **19.** *ABCD* **21.**

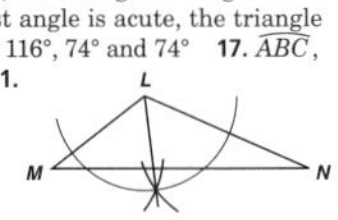

22.

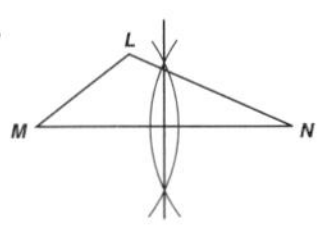

Cumulative Review — page 333

1. B **3.** A **5.** C **7.** A **9.** A **11.** D **13.** A

CHAPTER 8

Lesson 8-1 — pages 336–339

ON YOUR OWN **1.** about 2 in. **3.** about 5 cm **5.** m **7.** ft^2 or yd^2 **11.** about 9 times

MIXED REVIEW **15.** 104 **17.** $\frac{13}{6}$, or $2\frac{1}{6}$ **19.** $11\frac{3}{4}$

Lesson 8-2 — pages 340–343

ON YOUR OWN **1.** 70 ft^2 **3.** 4 cm^2 **5.** 120 ft^2; 52 ft **7.** 28.8 m^2; 27 m **9.** 3 m^2; 8 m **11.** 1.5 m^2, or 15,000 cm^2 **13a.** You multiply the area by n^2. **b.** You multiply the perimeter by n. **15.** 80 $in.^2$; 42 in. **17.** 161 $in.^2$; 62 in. **19.** 46 cm

MIXED REVIEW **21.** 68 **23.** 13 **25.** about 17% decrease **27.** Whitney: 8 books; Lorena: 4 books; Amira: 1 book; Dominic: 5 books

Lesson 8-3 — pages 344–348

ON YOUR OWN **1.** 75 ft^2 **3.** 27.5 m^2 **5.** 24.96 mm^2 **7.** 15 m^2 **9.** 42.3 cm^2 **11.** D **13.** 5 ft **15.** 7.5 ft^2; 17.5 ft **17.** 22 ft^2; 20 ft **19.** 150 $in.^2$; 60 in. **21.** $\frac{1}{2} \cdot 6(b + 3b) = 48$; 12 cm, 4 cm **23.** 35.5 m^2; 23.8 m **25.** 3,300 cm^2; 260 cm

MIXED REVIEW **29.** obtuse **31.** acute **33.** $\frac{17}{20}$ **35.** $1\frac{2}{5}$ **37.** $\frac{1}{10}$

Lesson 8-4 — pages 349–353

ON YOUR OWN **1.** 44 cm **3.** 28 m **5.** 53 mm **7.** 1,963 cm^2 **9.** 5,027 $in.^2$ **11.** 6 cm; 3 cm^2 **13.** 36 in.; 108 $in.^2$ **15a.** 98.52 m^2 **b.** 98.47 m^2 **c.** 99 m^2 **17.** 88 ft; 616 ft^2 **19.** 22 yd; $38\frac{1}{2}$ yd^2 **21.** $69\frac{1}{7}$ mm; $380\frac{2}{7}$ mm^2 **23.** 6.5 ft **25.** 14.8 mm

27a. About 6.3 m; the differences are the same. **b.** About 6.3 m forward; the outer lane is 6.3 m longer. **29.** 7.6 cm^2

MIXED REVIEW **31.** 12.5% **33.** −2 **35.** 5

CHECKPOINT **1.** ft^2 **2.** 126 m^2; 54 m **3.** 96 ft^2; 44 ft **4.** 28 cm^2; 25.6 cm **5.** 84 $in.^2$; 44 in. **6.** 471 cm; 17,671 cm^2

Lesson 8-5 — pages 354–357

ON YOUR OWN **1.** 64 **3.** 225 **5.** 8,100 **7.** 196 **9.** 289 **11.** 8 **13.** 9 **15.** 12 **17.** 10 **19.** 4 **21.** 16 **23.** 70 **27.** 11 km **29.** 13 ft **31.** 30 in. **33.** 20 cm **35.** 90 ft **37a.** $\frac{1}{4}$ **b.** $\frac{1}{2}$ **c.** $\frac{2}{3}$ **39.** 7 and 8 **41.** 11 and 12 **43.** 6 and 7 **45.** 14 and 15 **47.** 19 and 20 **49.** 52 ft

MIXED REVIEW **51.** 15.75 **53.** 3.2 **55.** 51°

Problem Solving Practice — page 358

1. B **3.** B **5.** A **7.** A **9.** D

Lesson 8-6 — pages 359–363

ON YOUR OWN **1.** 12 ft **3.** 15 in. **5.** 12 ft **7.** 10 ft **9a.**

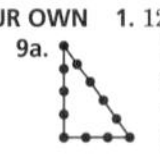

b. The lengths of the sides are 3, 4, and 5, and $3^2 + 4^2 = 5^2$. So the sides must form a right triangle. **11.** no; $8^2 + 9^2 \neq 12^2$ **13.** no; $15^2 + 18^2 \neq 24^2$ **15.** yes; $28^2 + 45^2 = 53^2$ **17.** yes; $16^2 + 30^2 = 34^2$ **19.** 12 ft

MIXED REVIEW **23.** Elicia

Lesson 8-7 — pages 364–367

ON YOUR OWN **1.** 19.7 cm **3.** 13.2 cm **5.** 6.8 cm **7.** 13.6 m **9.** 24.5 in. **11.** 23.3 ft **13a.** 20 units; 20 square units **b.** rhombus **15.** 65m **17.** 10.7 cm, 16.6 cm **19.** about 15 ft **21a.** about 85 ft **b.** about 127 ft **c.** about 95 ft **d.** 150 ft **23.** 20.1 $in.^2$

MIXED REVIEW **25.** $2^2 \cdot 7$ **27.** $2^3 \cdot 3^2$ **29.** $2^2 \cdot 3 \cdot 13$ **31.** > **33.** > **35.** 14 ft × 16 ft

Lesson 8-8 — pages 368–371

ON YOUR OWN **1.** rectangular prism **3.** triangular prism **5.** cone **7.** pentagonal pyramid **9.** $\overline{AD}$, $\overline{AE}$, $\overline{BC}$, $\overline{BF}$ **11.** $\overline{CG}$, $\overline{DH}$, $\overline{EH}$, $\overline{FG}$ **13.** cone and cylinder **15.** cylinders and rectangular prisms

17.

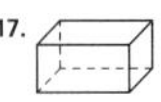

19.

25. False; pyramids have only one base and prisms have two.

MIXED REVIEW **27.** 13 **29.** −2 **31.** $\frac{43}{81}$, $\frac{5}{9}$, $\frac{7}{12}$ **33.** $\frac{10}{18}$, $\frac{4}{6}$, $\frac{18}{24}$ **35.** 5.55 in. by 9.25 in.

Toolbox — page 372

1.

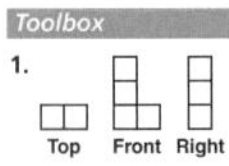

3.

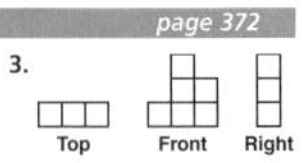

5.

Lesson 8-9 — pages 373–376

ON YOUR OWN **1.** B **9.** 848 m^2 **11.** 121 ft^2 **13.** doubling the radius

MIXED REVIEW **15.** m^2

Lesson 8-10 — pages 377–380

ON YOUR OWN **1.** 24 cm^3 **3.** $37\frac{13}{16}$ ft^3 **5.** 330 ft^3 **9.** about 1,900.7 ft^3 **11.** about 50 cm^3 **13.** 120 $in.^3$ **15a.** 24 $in.^3$; 12 $in.^3$ **b.** The area of the triangular base is 6 $in.^2$. The height is 2 in. So, 6 $in.^2$ × 2 in. = 12 $in.^3$.

MIXED REVIEW **17.** \$4.00 for 1 CD **19.** $1\frac{1}{3}$ c per loaf **21.** $\frac{43}{20{,}000}$ **23.** $\frac{429}{1{,}000}$ **25.** $\frac{3}{1{,}000}$

CHECKPOINT **1.** 15 **2.** 24.5 cm **3.** 8.5 in. **4.** 280 ft^2; 300 ft^3 **5.** 1,406.72 m^2; 4,019.2 m^3 **6.** C

Lesson 8-11 — pages 381–383

ON YOUR OWN **1.** 7, 21 **3.** 6.25, 12.5 **5.** 16¢ **7.** 1,080 cartons **9.** 1 in. by 12 in.; 3 in. by 4 in.

MIXED REVIEW **13.** 9 and 10 **15.** 7 and 8 **17.** 8 and 9 **19.** 9 in.

Toolbox — page 384

1a. 8 unit cubes **b.** 24 unit cube sides **5a.** 1,000 unit cubes **b.** 2,197 cubes; 1,014 cubes;

156 cubes; 8 cubes **c.** 14 unit cubes

Wrap Up pages 386–387

1. ft^2 **2.** 44 ft; 96 ft^2 **3.** 144 in.; 864 $in.^2$ **4.** 84 m; 315 m^2 **5.** 140 m; 900 m^2 **6.** 38 cm; 113 cm^2 **7.** 50 in.; 201 $in.^2$ **8.** 126 ft; 1,257 ft^2 **9.** 57 mm; 254 mm^2 **10.** 121 **11.** 49 **12.** 4 **13.** 8 **14.** 12 **15.** 20 **16.** 9 and 10 **17.** B **18.** 9 mm **19.** 1.4 m **20.** 11.5 in. **21a.**

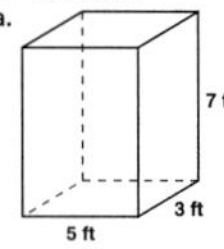

b. 105 ft^3 **c.**

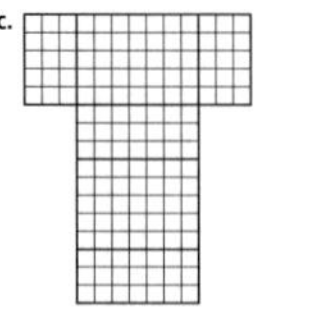

d. 142 ft^2

22a.

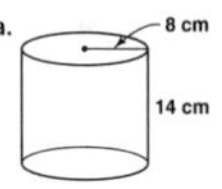

b. 2,814.9 cm^3

c.

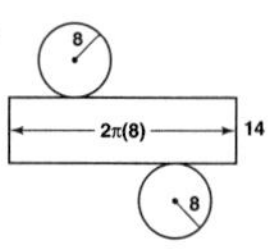

d. 1,105.8 cm^2 **23.** 2 m, 3 m, 4 m

Cumulative Review page 389

1. A 3. B 5. A 7. B 9. A 11. B

CHAPTER 9

Lesson 9-1 pages 392–396

ON YOUR OWN **1.** $\frac{4}{13}$ **3.** $\frac{3}{26}$ **5.** 0 **7.** 12% **9.** 20% **11.** 72% **13a.** 13.$\overline{3}$% **c.** 2,081 wrenches **15a.** $\frac{1}{2}$ or 50% **b.** 6 free throws **c.** No; probability cannot predict exact outcomes. **17.** A **19.** B **21.** B

MIXED REVIEW **25.** 429 cm^2 **27.** 120 ft^2 **29.** 16 **31.** 6 **33.** −69

Toolbox page 397

1. $\frac{1}{5}$ or 20%

Lesson 9-2 pages 398–400

ON YOUR OWN **3.** \$6,594 **7.** No; the discount is 30% of a greater amount than the mark up.

MIXED REVIEW **9.** 25.13 in.; 50.27 $in.^2$ **11.** 56.55 ft; 254.47 ft^2 **13.** 70 words/min **15.** \$8.50/h

Lesson 9-3 pages 401–405

ON YOUR OWN **1.** theoretical probability **3.** experimental probability **5.** $\frac{1}{6}$ **7.** $\frac{1}{3}$ **9.** 1 **11.** $\frac{1}{10}$; 0.1; 10% **13.** 1; 1; 100% **15.** $\frac{2}{5}$; 0.4; 40% **17.** 1% **19.** 11% **21.** 50% **23.** 6% **25.** 35% **27.** $\frac{3}{4}$ **31a.** $\frac{2}{7}$ **b.** $\frac{5}{7}$ **c.** 1 **d.** 1 **33a.** $\frac{6}{13}$ **b.** "red or blue" **35.** 0.3 **37.** 0.8 **39.** 1 **43.** D

MIXED REVIEW **45.** 54° **47.** 34.2° **49.** 176.4° **51.** 0.48 **53.** 0.61 **55.** 0.063

Toolbox page 406

1. 19 to 1 **3.** 1 to 25; 25 to 1 **5a.** 1 to 199 **b.** $\frac{1}{200}$ or 0.5%

Lesson 9-4 pages 407–411

ON YOUR OWN **1.** H1, H2, H3, H4, T1, T2, T3, T4 **3.** s1p1, s1p2, s1p3, s2p1, s2p2, s2p3 **5.** 12 outcomes **7.** 32 **9.** 84 **11.** 24 **13.** 60 **15.** S punch, M punch, L punch, J punch, S lemonade, M lemonade, L lemonade, J lemonade **17.** 24 orders **19.** $\frac{1}{72}$ **21a.** 7 people **b.** 6 people; 5 people **c.** 210 ways

MIXED REVIEW **23.** 90 **25.** 17 **27.** 14 **29.** obtuse **31a.** 54 million cans **b.** about 1.7 million lb

CHECKPOINT **1.** $\frac{4}{5}$; 0.8; 80% **2.** $\frac{2}{5}$; 0.4; 40% **3.** $\frac{3}{5}$; 0.6; 60% **4.** 0; 0; 0% **5.** $\frac{1}{5}$; 0.2; 20% **6.** 1; 1; 100% **7.** D

8a.

	A	B	C	D
1	1A	1B	1C	1D
2	2A	2B	2C	2D
3	3A	3B	3C	3D
4	4A	4B	4C	4D
5	5A	5B	5C	5D
6	6A	6B	6C	6D

b. 24 seats; yes

Lesson 9-5 pages 412–415

ON YOUR OWN **1.** $\frac{1}{12}$ **3.** $\frac{1}{4}$ **5.** $\frac{1}{36}$ **7.** $\frac{1}{64}$ **9.** $\frac{5}{64}$ **11.** $\frac{3}{64}$ **13.** No; the probability does not double. The probability is $\frac{1}{8} \cdot \frac{1}{8} = \frac{1}{64}$. **15.** $\frac{3}{28}$ **17a.** $\frac{7}{22}$ **b.** $\frac{5}{33}$ **c.** No; each girl has $\frac{1}{5}$ chance of being selected. Each boy has $\frac{1}{7}$ chance of being selected. **19.** independent **21.** dependent **23.** $\frac{1}{400}$ **25.** $\frac{1}{380}$ **27c.** $\frac{1}{9}$

MIXED REVIEW **29.** 28.3 yd **31.** 9.4 cm **33.** 28 **35.** $1\frac{2}{7}$ **37.** $\frac{1}{16}$

Lesson 9-6 pages 416–418

ON YOUR OWN **1.** 120 permutations **3.** 720 permutations **5.** 12 permutations **7.** 30 permuatations **9.** 840 permutations **11.** 360 permutations **13.** 800 area codes **15a.** 6, 10, 45; 6, 45, 10; 10, 6, 45; 10, 45, 6; 45, 6, 10; 45, 10, 6 **b.** 6 arrangements **17b.** 4 words; PETS, PEST, SEPT, STEP **c.** $\frac{1}{6}$

MIXED REVIEW **19.** triangle; no **21.** quadrilateral; yes **23.** $12\frac{1}{6}$ **25.** $\frac{17}{30}$ **27.** $27\frac{11}{60}$

Lesson 9-7 pages 419–422

ON YOUR OWN **1.** 3 **3.** 15 **5.** BPR, BPW, BRW, PRW **7.** BE, BO, PE, PO, RE, RO, WE, WO **9.** BEOPW, BEOPR, BEORW, BEPRW, BOPRW, EOPRW **11.** 24 combinations **13.** 18 combinations **15.** 66 ways **19.** Combination; the order in the set is not important. **21.** Permutation; the order in the photograph is important.

MIXED REVIEW **23.** 6 **25.** 14 **27.** 135 **29.** 130

CHECKPOINT **1.** $\frac{16}{121}$ **2.** $\frac{2}{55}$ **3.** $\frac{6}{55}$ **4.** 6; 3 **5.** 6; 1 **6.** 2; 1 **7.** 24; 1 **8.** 30; 15 **9.** 360; 15 **10.** 720 ways **11.** 362,880 ways

Problem Solving Practice page 423

1. A **3.** B **5.** D **7.** E

Lesson 9-8 pages 424–426

ON YOUR OWN **1.** about 1,823 deer **3.** about 2,273 deer **5.** about 2,110 deer **7.** about 1,822 deer **9.** about 2,345 deer **11.** 0.644, 0.506, 0.533, 0.833, 0.764, 0.627, 0.778, 0.773, 0.627 **13.** 357 squirrels

MIXED REVIEW **15.** $\frac{12}{125}$ **17.** $\frac{13}{50}$ **19.** $8\frac{1}{2}$ **21.** $\frac{9}{50}$ **23.** 70%

Wrap Up pages 428–429

1. $\frac{1}{7}$ **2.** $\frac{2}{7}$ **3.** $\frac{6}{7}$ **4.** $\frac{5}{7}$ **5.** $\frac{6}{7}$ **6.** $\frac{2}{7}$ **7a.** $\frac{3}{10}$; $\frac{2}{5}$; $\frac{1}{10}$; $\frac{1}{5}$ **b.** 18 blue, 24 red, 6 yellow, and 12 green marbles

8a.

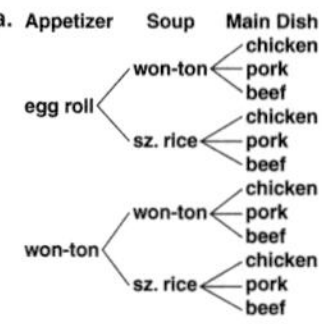

b. 12 dinners **9.** 1,320 ways **10.** dependent **11.** independent **12.** B **13.** 5 teams **14.** 24 ways **16.** about 94 lions

Cumulative Review page 431

1. B **3.** C **5.** C **7.** B **9.** C **11.** D

CHAPTER 10

Lesson10-1 pages 434–437

ON YOUR OWN **1.** Start with 5 and add 5 repeatedly; 25, 30, 35. **3.** Start with 34 and add −5 repeatedly; 14, 9, 4. **5.** Start with 63 and add −9 repeatedly; 27, 18, 9. **7a.** 17 red tiles **b.** 16 yellow tiles **9.** 46 parts **11.** Start with 1 and multiply by 2 repeatedly; 16, 32, 64. **13.** Start with 600 and multiply by $\frac{1}{2}$ repeatedly;

$37\frac{1}{2}$, $18\frac{3}{4}$, $9\frac{3}{8}$. **15.** Start with $\frac{1}{4}$ and multiply by $\frac{1}{3}$ repeatedly; $\frac{1}{324}$, $\frac{1}{972}$, $\frac{1}{2,916}$. **17a.** 256 $units^2$ **b.** 128 $units^2$ **c.** 64 $units^2$ **d.** 8 $units^2$ **19.** neither; 37, 50, 65 **21.** neither; 36, 49, 64 **23.** neither; 16, 22, 29 **25b.** 1, 4, 9, 16, 25, 36, 49 **c.** The sum of the numbers in each row is the square of the row number. **d.** 400 **27a.** 2; 3; 5; 8; 13; 21; 34 **b.** neither

MIXED REVIEW **29.** −10 **31.** 8 **33.** obtuse **35.** acute **37a.** \$0.0115 per plate, \$0.0588 per cup; \$0.0099 per plate, about \$0.048 per cup **b.** The supermarket has a better buy on each item.

Lesson10-2 pages 438–440

ON YOUR OWN **1.** 7.5×10^3 **3.** 1.25×10^2 **5.** 1.02×10^5 **7.** 4.9×10^{11} **9.** 3.5×10^5 **11.** 5.88×10^{15} **13.** Count the number of digits. Then subtract 1. **15.** The second factor must be a power of 10. **17.** The first factor must be greater than or equal to 1 but less than 10. **19.** 500,000,000,000 **21.** 830,000 **23.** 9,300,000 **25.** 667.8 **27.** 20,000,000,000,000 cells **29.** 600,000,000 bytes

MIXED REVIEW **31.** 12 permutations; 6 combinations **33.** 6 permutations; 3 combinations **35.** 100% increase **37.** about 2% increase

Toolbox page 441

1. 8×10^{-4} **3.** 6.91×10^{-6} **5.** 5.006×10^{-3} **7.** 0.0049

Lesson10-3 pages 442–445

ON YOUR OWN **1.** 31 games **3.** 636 digits **5.** 90°, 30°, 60° **7.** 11 amounts

MIXED REVIEW **9.** $13\frac{7}{8}$ **11.** $2\frac{1}{5}$ **13.** $9\frac{19}{30}$ **15.** 54 ft^3 **17.** 3 combinations

CHECKPOINT **1.** Arithmetic; start with 3 and add 3 repeatedly; 15, 18, 21. **2.** Arithmetic; start with 53 and add 128 repeatedly; 21, 13, 5. **3.** Geometric; start with 3 and multiply by 2 repeatedly; 48, 96, 192. **4.** Arithmetic; start with 4 and add 7 repeatedly; 39, 46, 53. **5.** Neither; start with 87 and subtract 10, then subtract 11, then subtract 12 and continue the subtraction pattern; 41, 27, 12. **6.** Geometric; start with 0.5 and multiply by 3 repeatedly; 40.5, 121.5, 364.5.

7. 7.38×10^8 **8.** 2.9×10^4 **9.** 7.86×10^6 **10.** 1.807×10^6 **11.** 806,000 **12.** 1,740 **13.** 8,300,000,000 **14.** 10,080,000 **15.** D **16a.** 4 **b.** 145

Lesson10-4 pages 446–449

ON YOUR OWN **1.** \$60 **3.** \$847 **5.** \$855 **7.** \$590 **9.** \$562.43 **11.** \$2,316.99 **13.** \$1,781.94 **15.** B

MIXED REVIEW **19.** 127 **21.** 1264 **23.** yes **25.** no **27.** no **29.** 8 cm long and 4 cm wide

Lesson10-5 pages 450–453

ON YOUR OWN **1.** $s = 6.5h$ **3.** $h = 2w + 1$

5a.

Input	Output
−5	22
−4	14
−3	8
−2	4
−1	2
0	2
1	4
2	8
3	14
4	22
5	32

b. −5 and 4

7.

Input	Output
1	4
2	5
3	6
4	7
5	8

9.

Input	Output
1	0.5
2	1
3	1.5
4	2
5	2.5

11a. 40 mi/h **b.** 3 **c.**

Input	Output
1	40
2	80
3	120
4	160

d. $d = 40t$ **13.** A

15a.

Input p	Output c
\$.50	\$4.50
\$1.00	\$4.00
\$1.50	\$3.50
\$2.00	\$3.00
\$2.50	\$2.50
\$3.00	\$2.00
\$3.50	\$1.50
\$4.00	\$1.00
\$4.50	\$.50
\$5.00	\$.00

b.

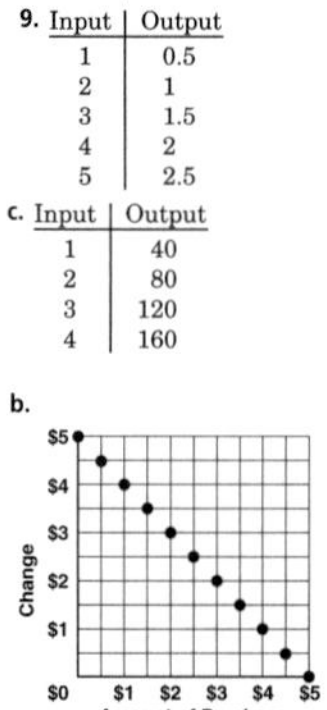

c. $c = 5 - p$ **17a.** \$21

b.

Input t	Output d
1	\$3.50
2	\$7.00
3	\$10.50
4	\$14.00
5	\$17.50

c.

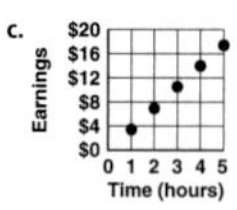

MIXED REVIEW **19.** 10,478.6 **21.** 0.497 **23.** 3.2605 **25.** > **27.** = **29.** January 8, 15, 22, 29

Lesson10-6 pages 454–457

ON YOUR OWN 1. 13 **3.** 5 **5.** 8

7.

n	$f(n)$
0	2
1	3
2	4
3	5

9.

n	$f(n)$
0	0
1	4
2	8
3	12

11.

n	$f(n)$
0	9
1	8
2	7
3	6

13.

n	$f(n)$
0	1
1	3
2	5
3	7

15a.

n	$f(n)$
1	3
2	4
3	5
4	6

b. $f(n) = n + 2$ **17.** $f(n) = 5n$ **19.** $f(n) = n - 6$ **21.** $f(n) = -8n$ **23.** $f(n) = 4n + 5$

MIXED REVIEW **27.** 45.5% **29.** 925% **31.** 650% **33.** 11.0 ft; 9.6 ft^2 **35.** 9.4 m; 7.1 m^2 **37.** 6.3 in.; 3.1 $in.^2$

CHECKPOINT **1.**

n	$f(n)$
0	0
1	3
2	6
3	9

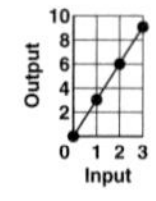

2.

n	$f(n)$
0	−4
1	−2
2	0
3	2

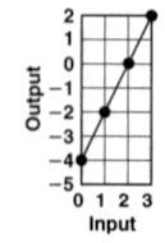

5. $f(n) = -12n$ **6.** $f(n) = 4 - n$ **7.** $f(n) = 3n + 1$ **8.** $f(n) = 7n$

Toolbox page 458

1.

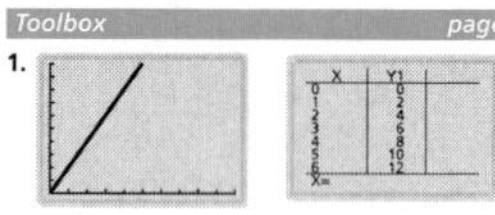

3.

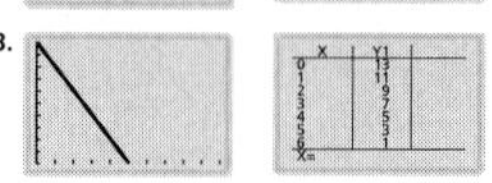

Lesson10-7 pages 459–463

ON YOUR OWN **1.** C **3.** B

5.

7.

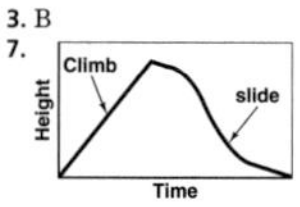

9. A; B; graph A shows speed because it shows a quantity that is not changing with time. The quantity in graph B increases at a constant rate. **11b.** about 1800 **13.** Carmen's graph

MIXED REVIEW **17.** 4 **19.** 144

21.
2 0
3 3 4 4
4 4 5 6 8 8
5 0 3
5 | 0 means 50

23. 29 h

Problem Solving Practice page 464

1. C **3.** D **5.** B **7.** D **9.** D

Wrap Up pages 466–467

1. arithmetic; 23, 27, 31 **2.** geometric; 3, $\frac{3}{2}$, $\frac{3}{4}$ **3.** geometric; 243; 729; 2,187 **4.** neither; −2, −10, −19 **5.** Start with 7 and add 4 repeatedly; start with 48 and multiply by $\frac{1}{2}$ repeatedly; start with 3 and multiply by 3 repeatedly. **6.** A **7.** 1.52×10^9 **8.** 2.5×10^5 **9.** 3.83×10^8 **10.** 8.76×10^4 **11.** 249,000,000 **12.** 110 triangles **13.** \$450 **14.** \$720 **15.** \$1,914.42 **16a.** $f(n) = 2n + 2$

b. 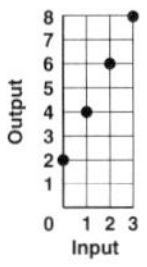

17a.

Input n	Output $f(n)$
0	3
2	4
4	5
6	6

b. $f(n) = \frac{1}{2}n + 3$ **18.** 3; 5; 7; 9

Cumulative Review page 469

1. D **3.** B **5.** D **7.** D **9.** A

CHAPTER 11

Lesson 11-1 pages 472–476

ON YOUR OWN **1.** C **3.** F **5.** A **7.** $(-3, -2)$ **9.** $(5, -4)$ **11.** $(2, 6)$ **13a.** 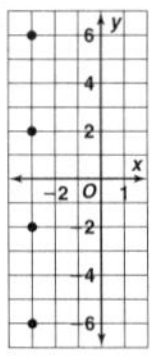 **b.** All the points lie on a vertical line.

15. Starting from the origin, move 5 units right. Then move 1 unit down. **17.** B **19.** I **21.** III **23.** II **25.** I **31.** I: (+ , +); II: (− , +); III: (− , −); IV: (+ , −)

MIXED REVIEW **33.** $270 **35.** $756

Lesson 11-2 pages 477–481

ON YOUR OWN **7.** yes; $24 = (12) + 12$ **9.** yes; $0 = (-12) + 12$ **11.** C **13.** B, C **15.** none **17.** If you substitute −1 for x and −5 for y, the equality is not true. **19.** line q

21a.

x	$x - 7$	y	(x,y)
0	$0 - 7$	−7	(0, −7)
−3	$-3 - 7$	−10	(−3, −10)
10	$10 - 7$	3	(10, 3)

b. 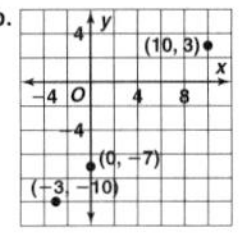

c. Yes; the solutions lie on one line. **23.** C **25.** $(-1, 2)$ **27.** 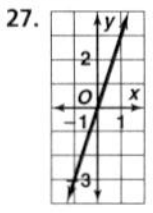

29. 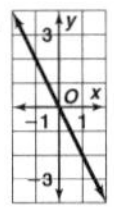

35. The third point serves as a check that you graphed the first two points correctly.

37a. 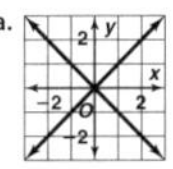

b. (0, 0) **c.** perpendicular

MIXED REVIEW **39.** $f(x) = 25x + 35$ **41.** no **43.** yes **45.** 10 onions

Lesson 11-3 pages 482–484

ON YOUR OWN **1.** $\frac{1}{2}$ **3.** $-\frac{1}{3}$ **5.** 1 **7.** −8 **9.** Kelton; Kenji thought the rise was positive. **11a.** $12,000 **b.** −1 **c.** The car loses $1,000 in value each year.

MIXED REVIEW **13.** arithmetic; 24, 29, 34 **15.** arithmetic; 34, 41, 48 **17.** II **19.** I **21.** II **23.** 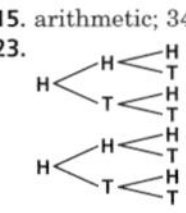

Toolbox page 485

1a. $-\frac{3}{5}$ **b.** The value that multiplies x has the same value as the slope.
3a. 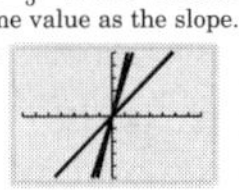
b. $y = 4x$; $y = x$ **c.** For lines with positive slopes, the greater the value of the slope, the steeper the graph of the line.
d. closer to the y-axis

7a. 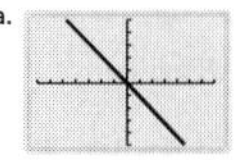 **b.** II and IV **c.** yes

Lesson 11-4 pages 486–489

ON YOUR OWN
1. 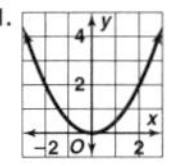 **3.** 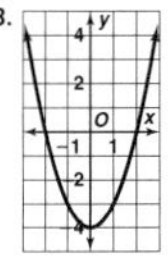 **9.** parabola **11.** V-shape **13a.** 16 ft; 64 ft; 144 ft **b.** about 6.4 s

15b. 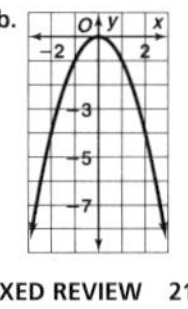 **c.** The graph of $y = -x^2$ is a reflection of the graph of $y = x^2$ in the x-axis. **17.** A **19.** F

MIXED REVIEW **21.** $\frac{1}{600}$ **23.** $\frac{156}{600}$ or $\frac{13}{50}$ **25.** yes; $5 = 2(4) - 3$ **27.** no; $-5 \neq 2(0) - 3$ **29.** no; $9 \neq 2(3) - 3$

CHECKPOINT **1.** B **2.** D **3.** G **4.** $(4, -1)$ **5.** $(-2, -3)$ **6.** $(2, 3)$ **7.** $(4, 0)$ **8.** C

9b. 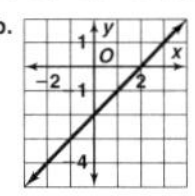 **c.** 1 **10b.** 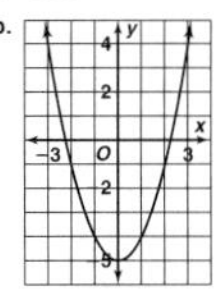

Lesson 11-5 pages 490–492

ON YOUR OWN **1.** $42.9 = 5 + 2x$; $18.95 **3.** $17 = 5D - 3$; 4 mystery novels **5.** $2.8 + 0.25n = 4.3$; 6 quarters **7.** $30\frac{1}{3}$ yr; 35 yr **9.** $\frac{1}{8}$

MIXED REVIEW **11.** $\frac{548}{1,000}$ or $\frac{137}{250}$; $\frac{452}{1,000}$, or $\frac{113}{250}$ **13.** $4,180 **15.** $4,885.79 **17.** 11 ft

Toolbox page 493

1. turn **3.** flip

Lesson 11-6 pages 494–498

ON YOUR OWN **1.** $(2, 1)$ **3.** 5 units left; 7 units down
5. 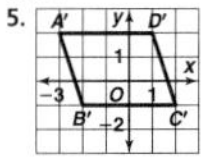 $A'(-3, 2)$, $B'(-2, -1)$, $C'(2, -1)$, $D'(1, 2)$

7a–b. 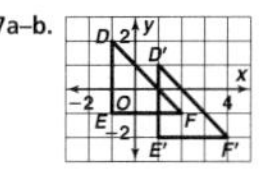 **c.** $D'(1, 1)$, $E'(1, -2)$, $F'(4, -2)$ **9.** $S'(4, -1)$, $T'(0, -3)$ **11.** right 3 units, up 1 unit **13.** right 2 units, down 3 units **15.** 2; 1

17. $(x, y) \longrightarrow (x + 5, y + 4)$ **19.** $(x, y) \longrightarrow (x + 4, y + 2)$ **21.** $(x, y) \longrightarrow (x + 5, y - 2)$ **23.** $(x, y) \longrightarrow (x - 3, y - 4)$

MIXED REVIEW **25.** 431,000 **27.** 8,596

29a.

x	−2	−1	0	1	2
y	8	2	0	2	8

b. 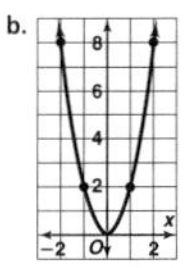

Lesson 11-7 pages 499–503

ON YOUR OWN
1. 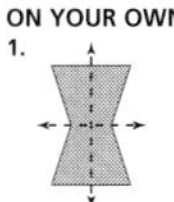 **3.** none **5.** 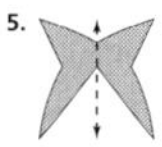

7. Three lines of symmetry, one down the center of each petal. **11.** A, B **13.** It is not the same

distance from the x-axis. **15.** (5, 7) **17.** (1, 1) **19.** (5, −2) **21.** The image of a translation has the same orientation as the original figure, and the distance between any point and its image is the same. The image of a reflection faces in the opposite direction, and the farther away a point is from the line of reflection, the greater the distance between the point and its image. **23.** translation; $(x, y) \longrightarrow (x + 5, y + 3)$ **25.** reflection; x-axis

27a. 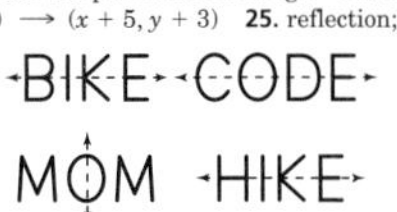

MIXED REVIEW 29.

x	0	1	2	3
$f(x)$	32	35	38	41

31.

x	0	1	2	3
$f(x)$	6	5	4	3

33. always **35.** 2,000 black bears

CHECKPOINT
1. 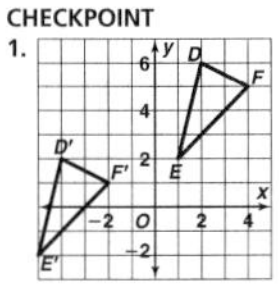 **2.** 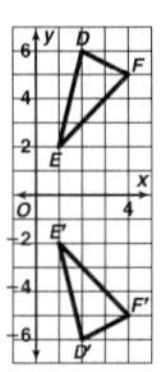

3. Yes; the rise and run do not change when you translate a line, so the slope does not change. **5a.** $y = 2p - 10$ **b.** 40 pizzas

Problem Solving Practice page 504

1. D **3.** C **5.** B **7.** C **9.** C

Lesson 11-8 pages 505–508

ON YOUR OWN **1.** No; you cannot rotate the figure 180° or less so that the image fits on top of the original figure. **3.** Yes; the image after 180° or 90° rotation fits exactly on top of the original figure. **5.** No; you cannot rotate the figure 180° or less so that the image fits on top of the original figure. **7.** Yes; the image after 72° rotation fits exactly on top of the original figure.
9. 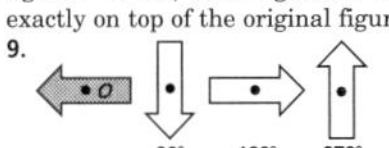

11. 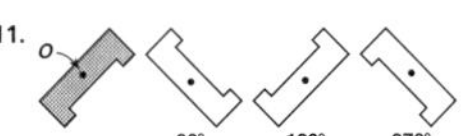

13. The figures in exercises 10 and 12 have rotational symmetry because each can be fit exactly on top of itself after a rotation of 180° or less. **15.** reflection **17.** rotation **19.** rotation

MIXED REVIEW **21.** 64 yd **23.** 34 mm

Wrap Up pages 510-511

1a. A **b.** G **c.** F **2a.** (0, 2) **b.** (−3, −2) **c.** (−1, 0) **3a.** yes; $(10) = 3(5) - 5$ **b.** no; $(-1) \neq 3(-2) - 5$ **c.** yes; $(-2) = 3(1) - 5$
4b. 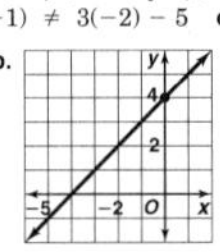 **5.** B

6. 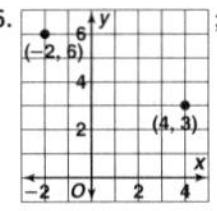; $2\frac{1}{2}$ **7.** 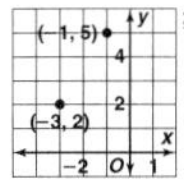; $\frac{3}{2}$

10a. 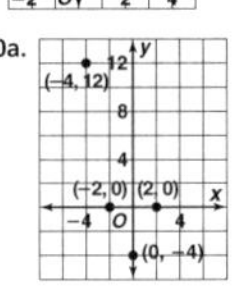

b. $y = x^2 - 4$; all four points lie on its graph. **11.** I; II **12.** $3.25

13. 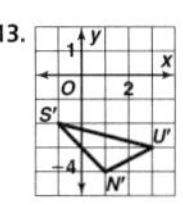 **15.** translation **16.** reflection **17.** reflection **18.** rotation

Cumulative Review page 513

1. D **3.** A **5.** B **7.** B **9.** B **11.** C

EXTRA PRACTICE

CHAPTER 1 **3.** 11 **5.** D **7.** 18 **9.** 61.33; 60; 60

CHAPTER 2 **1.** 0.092, 0.095, 0.099, 0.102 **3.** 0.505, 0.52, 0.55, 0.56 **5.** 0.699, 0.7, 0.708, 0.712 **7.** > **9.** = **11.** > **13.** < **15.** 2 **17.** $27 **19.** $60 **21.** 8.28 **23.** 9.107 **25.** 0.82 **27.** 4.02 **29.** 4.93 **31.** 16.032 **33.** 7.917 **35.** 29.607 **37.** $2.\overline{6}$ **39.** $3.1\overline{3}$ **41.** 6.3 **43.** $3.\overline{3}$ **45.** 7 **47.** 30.144 **49.** 10.92 **51.** 4

CHAPTER 3 **1.** $x - 3$ **3.** $2x - 5$ **5.** 12; 14; −14; −9; −7; 7 **7.** T **9.** T **11.** −11, −1, 3, $|-8|$, $|10|$ **13.** 6 **15.** 0 **17.** −100 **19.** −6 **21.** 18 **23.** 28 **25.** −7 **27.** −75 **29.** −3 **31.** 2 **33.** $51 = 3x$, $x = 17$ **35.** 42 **37.** −4

CHAPTER 4 **1.** $\frac{4}{8}$ or $\frac{1}{2}$ **3.** $\frac{4}{12}$ or $\frac{1}{3}$ **5.** $\frac{7}{8}$ **7.** $\frac{2}{3}$ **9.** $\frac{1}{3}$ **11.** $\frac{1}{5}$ **13.** $\frac{22}{45}$ **15.** $\frac{1}{7}$ **17.** > **19.** = **21.** < **23.** 125 **25.** 225 **27.** 64 **29.** 1 **31.** 17 **33.** 10 **35.** $\frac{26}{7}$ **37.** $\frac{22}{5}$ **39.** $\frac{12}{5}$ **41.** $4\frac{4}{5}$ **43.** $7\frac{1}{4}$ **45.** $6\frac{2}{9}$ **47.** $\frac{73}{200}$ **49.** $\frac{21}{50}$ **51.** $\frac{7}{10}$ **53.** $11.\overline{3}$ **55.** 3.25 **57.** $16.\overline{6}$

CHAPTER 5 **1.** 1 **3.** $\frac{1}{2}$ **5.** 4 **7.** 78 **9.** 2 **11.** $\frac{4}{3}$ **13.** $\frac{11}{15}$ **15.** $\frac{1}{2}$ **17.** $\frac{7}{24}$ **19.** $\frac{21}{20}$ **21.** 7 **23.** $5\frac{11}{12}$ **25.** $5\frac{5}{8}$ **27.** $7\frac{7}{8}$ **29.** $6\frac{1}{6}$ **31.** $\frac{3}{20}$ **33.** $\frac{1}{4}$ **35.** 25 **37.** $4\frac{1}{8}$ **39.** $16\frac{1}{8}$ **41.** 3 **43.** 1 **45.** $2\frac{2}{9}$ **47.** $1\frac{9}{10}$ **49.** $1\frac{7}{15}$ **51.** 12 **53.** 660 **55.** 12,250 **57.** $2\frac{1}{4}$ **59.** $\frac{3}{8}$ **61.** $\frac{11}{14}$ **63.** 152 **65.** 11

CHAPTER 6 **1.** 2 : 3, 2 to 3 **3.** 4 : 7, $\frac{4}{7}$ **5.** 25 : 50, 25 to 50 **7.** 48 oz **9.** 10 lb **11.** 3 **13.** 20 **15.** 25 **17.** 24 **19.** $\frac{1}{2}$ or 0.5 **21.** $x = \frac{5}{3}$ **23.** 83% **25.** 220% **27.** $\frac{16}{25}$, 0.64 **29.** 2,730% **31.** 0.0975% **33.** 10% **35.** 135 **37.** 60% **39.** 32.5 **41.** 60% increase **43.** about 2% increase **45.** 40% decrease

CHAPTER 7 **1.**  **3.** d **5.** b **7.** 90° **9a.** T **b.** F **c.** T **d.** T **e.** F **11.** regular pentagon **13.** rectangle **15.** 61.92°

CHAPTER 8 **1.** 180 ft, 1,400 ft^2 **3.** 40 m^2, 30 m **5.** 6.875 cm^2, 13 cm **7.** 900 mm^2, 146 mm **9.** 1 **11.** 7 **13.** 30 **15.** 8 m **17.** 8 cm **19.** triangular prism, 36 $in.^2$ **21.** rectangular prism, 202 ft^2

CHAPTER 9 **1a.** $\frac{15}{300}$ **b.** 70 **3.** $\frac{5}{6}$ **5.** $\frac{1}{6}$ **7b.** $\frac{1}{12}$, $\frac{3}{12}$ or $\frac{1}{4}$ **9.** $\frac{5}{36}$ **11.** $\frac{3}{16}$ **13.** $\frac{2}{16}$ **15.** combination; 10 ways **17.** 658

CHAPTER 10 **1.** arithmetic; 19, 22, 25 **3.** neither; 46, 23, 44 **5.** arithmetic; 15.7, 15.1, 14.5 **7.** 7×10^4 **9.** 6.1×10^5 **11.** 2.2×10^3 **13.** 70,300 **15.** 25,600,000 **17.** 8,290.1 **19.** $1,120.72 **21.** $f(n) = 6n$ **23.** $f(n) = 3n + 1$
25. 5, 6, 7, 8 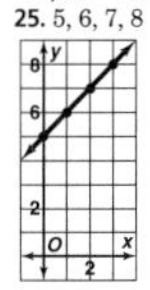 **27.** 8, 7, 6, 5 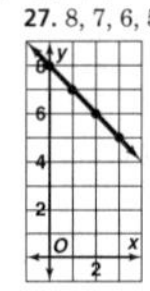

CHAPTER 11 **1.** G **3.** L **5.** (4, −1) **7.** (−6, 1) **9.** (3, 4) **11.** $\frac{2}{3}$ **13.** yes; $2 + 18 = 20$ **15.** no; $36 + 18 \neq -18$

17.

x	y
−2	7
−1	4
0	3
1	4
2	7

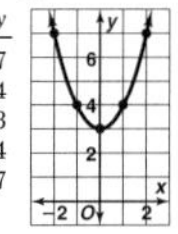

19.

x	y
−2	4
−1	2
0	0
1	2
2	4

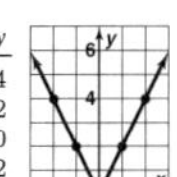

23a–b. 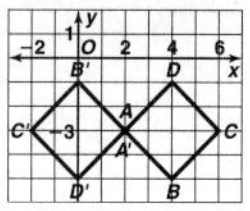

c. (2, −3), (0, −1), (−2, −3), (0, −5)

SKILLS HANDBOOK

PAGE 528 **1.** > **3.** > **5.** < **7.** < **9.** > **11.** 3,347; 3,474; 3,734; 3,747; 3,774 **13.** 30,256,403; 30,265,403; 32,056,403; 302,056,403

PAGE 529 **1.** 40 **3.** 670 **5.** 7,030 **7.** 6,000 **9.** 44,000 **11.** 1,000 **13.** 6,000 **15.** 82,000 **17.** 35,000 **19.** 68,900 **21.** 3,407,000 **23.** 71,230,000 **25.** 400,000 **27.** 3,680 **29.** 69,000 **31.** 566,000 **33.** 1,400,000

PAGE 530 **1.** 444 **3.** 371 **5.** 392 **7.** 1,536 **9.** 1,350 **11.** 5,712 **13.** 2,520 **15.** 1,862 **17.** 9,214 **19.** 492 **21.** 729 **23.** 2,208 **25.** 884 **27.** 4,056 **29.** 2,478 **31.** 1,440 **33.** 5,467

PAGE 531 **1.** 15 R1 **3.** 12 R6 **5.** 13 R3 **7.** 217 R2 **9.** 25 R6 **11.** 7 R41 **13.** 7 R27 **15.** 3 R36 **17.** 5 R21 **19.** 3 R7 **21.** 14 R52 **23.** 37 R12 **25.** 21 R30 **27.** 7 R3 **29.** 11 R3 **31.** 64 R3 **33.** 50 R4 **35.** 103 R1 **37.** 26 R8 **39.** 7 R32 **41.** 5 R22 **43.** 6 R21 **45.** 3 R52 **47.** 15 R3 **49.** 22 R12

PAGE 532 **1.** tens **3.** ones **5.** ten-thousandths **7.** 3 tens **9.** 6 ones **11.** 1 ten-thousandths **13.** 6 hundredths **15.** 6 tenths **17.** 6 tens **19.** 6 thousands **21.** 6 tenths **23.** 6 hundredths **25.** 6 ten-thousandths **27.** 6 hundred-thousandths **29.** 3 hundredths **31.** 8 tenths

PAGE 533 **1.** 0.03 **3.** 6.02 **5.** 2.05 **7.** 0.000007 **9.** 0.011 **11.** 0.304 **13.** three million and nine hundredths **15.** nine hundred and two hundredths **17.** fifteen hundred-thousandths

PAGE 534 **1.** 2.8 **3.** 19.7 **5.** 499.5 **7.** 4.7 **9.** 400.0 **11.** 96.4 **13.** 31.72 **15.** 1.79 **17.** 736.94 **19.** 0.70 **21.** 12.10 **23.** 0.92 **25.** 0.439 **27.** 3.495 **29.** 0.601 **31.** 4 **33.** 80 **35.** 431

PAGE 535 **1.** 2.4 **3.** 0.28 **5.** 0.155 **7.** 18.6 **9.** 1.35 **11.** 249.6 **13.** 12.05 **15.** 12.15 **17.** 0.1 **19.** 0.302 **21.** 1.757 **23.** 18.012 **25.** 28.452 **27.** 535.5 **29.** 250.8 **31.** 24.96

PAGE 536 **1.** 0.06 **3.** 0.003 **5.** 0.014 **7.** 0.027 **9.** 0.004 **11.** 0.0025 **13.** 0.032 **15.** 0.0009 **17.** 0.04 **19.** 0.0007 **21.** 0.0074 **23.** 0.076 **25.** 0.085 **27.** 0.007 **29.** 0.027 **31.** 0.0102 **33.** 0.0603 **35.** 0.081 **37.** 0.0066

PAGE 537 **1.** 7.14 **3.** 0.776 **5.** 8.79 **7.** 0.11 **9.** 0.184 **11.** 7.4 **13.** 0.93 **15.** 8.76 **17.** 2.07 **19.** 0.0036 **21.** 0.0147 **23.** 6.123 **25.** 3.98 **27.** 0.561 **29.** 0.868

PAGE 538 **1.** 0.032 **3.** 0.07 **5.** 9 **7.** 52 **9.** 5 **11.** 1.803 **13.** 823 **15.** 502 **17.** 2,367 **19.** 0.0009 **21.** 426 **23.** 0.47 **25.** 0.032 **27.** 26 **29.** 0.0008 **31.** 15

PAGE 539 **1.** 0.0025 **3.** 0.0081 **5.** 0.065 **7.** 0.075 **9.** 0.085 **11.** 0.0157 **13.** 1.05 **15.** 0.065 **17.** 0.68 **19.** 1.125 **21.** 0.006 **23.** 0.009 **25.** 0.0085 **27.** 0.0035 **29.** 0.033 **31.** 0.0921 **33.** 0.043 **35.** 2.92 **37.** 7.96 **39.** 25

PAGE 540 **1.** $\frac{4}{5}$ **3.** $\frac{4}{7}$ **5.** $4\frac{4}{7}$ **7.** $\frac{1}{2}$ **9.** $\frac{3}{8}$ **11.** $\frac{3}{5}$ **13.** $\frac{3}{5}$ **15.** $5\frac{2}{5}$ **17.** $11\frac{3}{5}$ **19.** $6\frac{1}{2}$ **21.** $11\frac{1}{2}$

PAGE 541 **1.** 0.1 **3.** 0.001 **5.** 0.000012 **7.** 30,000 **9.** 3,300 **11.** 0.72 **13.** 1,300,000 **15.** 4.9 **17.** 1.06 **19.** 1.2

PAGE 542 **1.** 1,000 **3.** 1,000 **5.** 0.2 **7.** 30,000 **9.** 0.18 **11.** 0.0006 **13.** 72,000,000 **15.** 0.45 **17.** 0.2 **19.** 4,200 **21.** 28,000,000 **23.** 4,000,000

PAGE 543 **1.** 0.001 **3.** 0.000001 **5.** 1,000 **7.** 0.008 **9.** 200 **11.** 5,200,000 **13.** 3,700 **15.** 0.37 **17.** 900,000 **19.** 0.12 **21.** 1.006 **23.** 0.0002 **25.** 800,000 **27.** 6,200,000

Additional Answers

CHAPTER 1

LESSON 1-1

pages 4–5 Think and Discuss

3c.

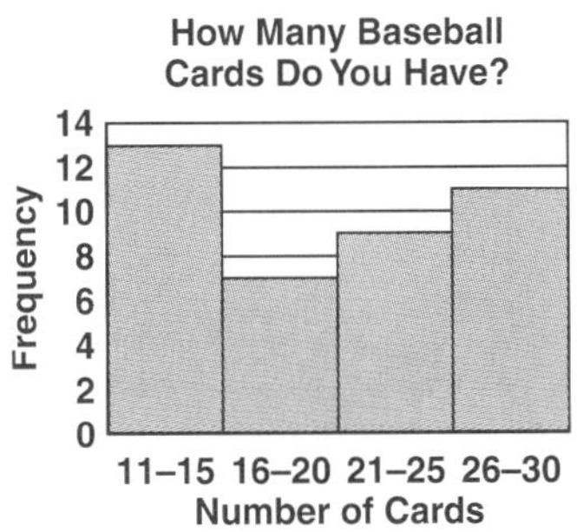

pages 6–7 On Your Own

3. Number of TVs per Households

TVs	Frequency
1	6
2	6
3	5
4	1

4. Miles to Shopping Center

Miles	Frequency
1	1
2	1
3	2
4	3
5	3
6	2
7	1
8	1
9	1
10	2

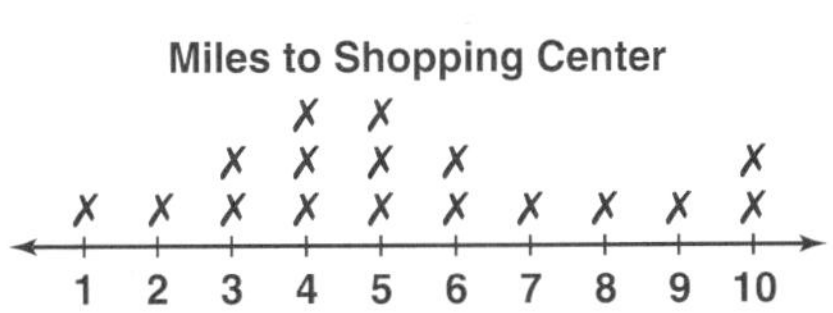

11.

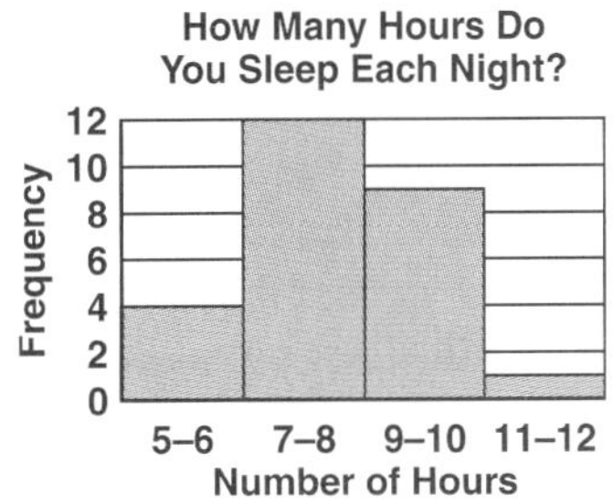

12.

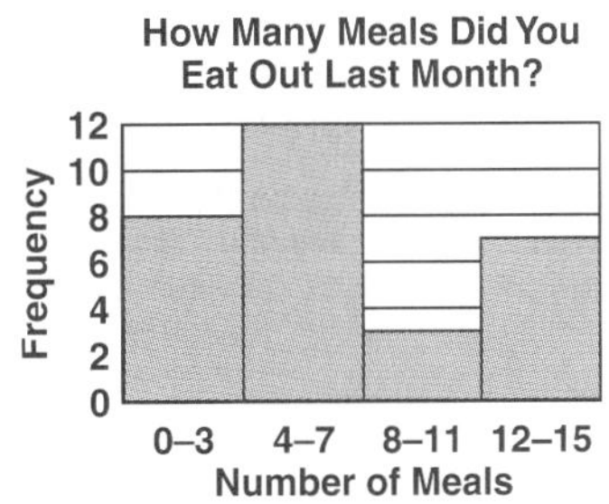

13a. What Time Do You Get Up?

Time	Frequency
5:30–5:59	2
6:00–6:29	5
6:30–6:59	1
7:00–7:29	3
7:30–7:59	3
8:00–8:29	2

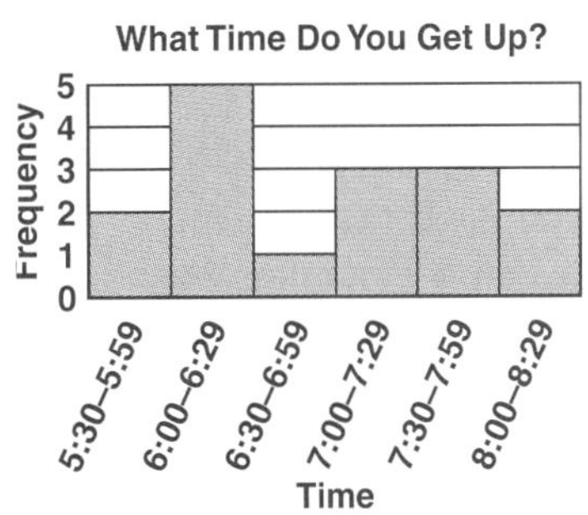

LESSON 1-3

pages 14–15 On Your Own

9.

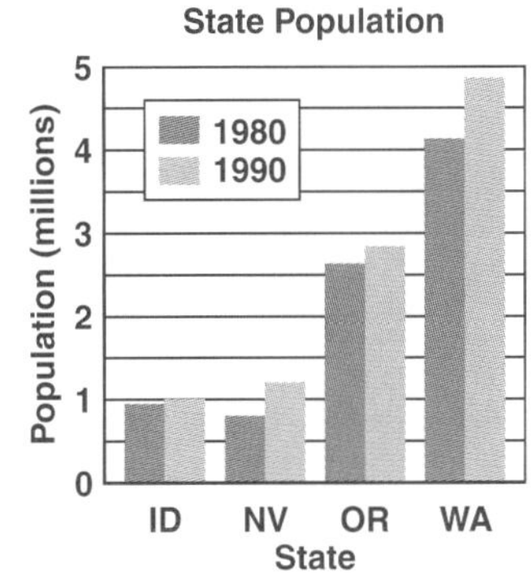

10.

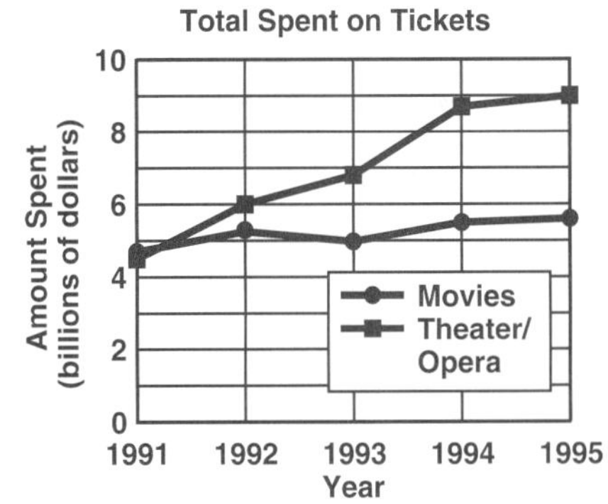

page 15 Mixed Review

12.

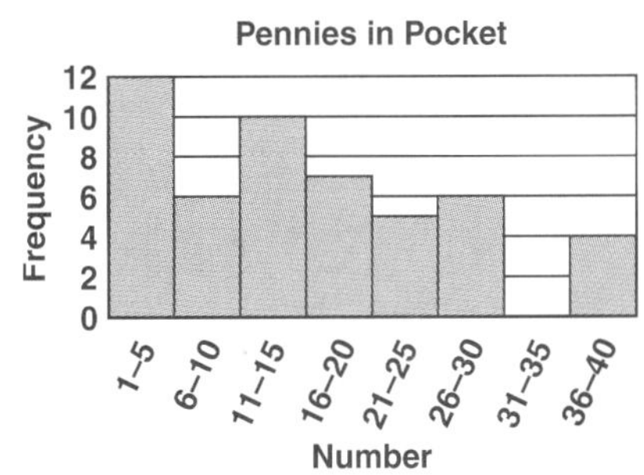

LESSON 1-7

page 30 Work Together

1. Answers may vary. Sample: People who owned telephones were more likely to vote for Dewey.

Additional Answers

LESSON 1-8

pages 36–37 On Your Own

3.

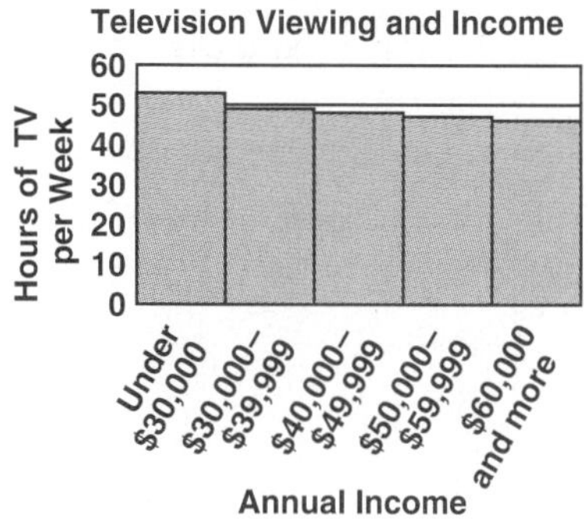

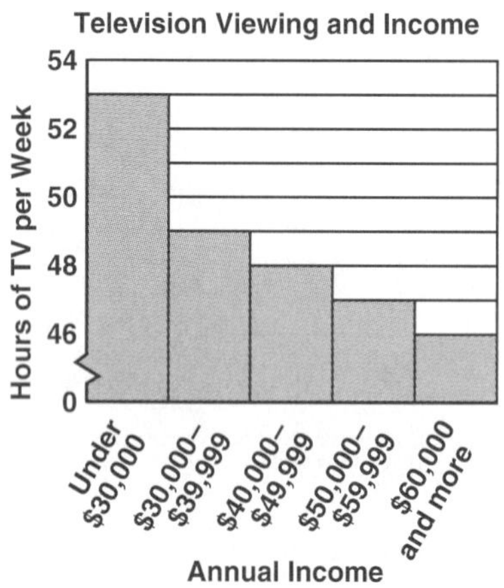

6b.

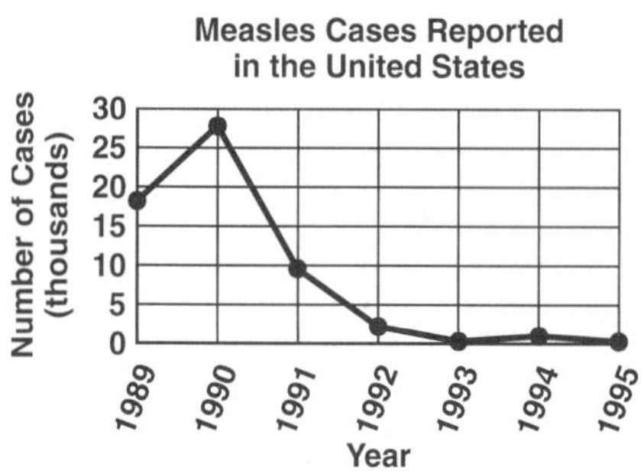

LESSON 1-9

pages 39–40 Think and Discuss

2. About 14 lb; if you draw a line to show the trend, it will cross the vertical line for 10 books at about 14 lb.

page 41 Work Together

4.

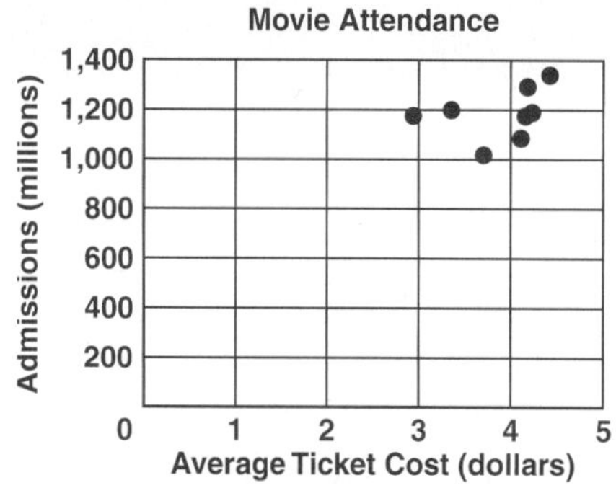

pages 41–42 On Your Own

1. The moose population is generally increasing; there does not seem to be a pattern in the wolf population.

2a.

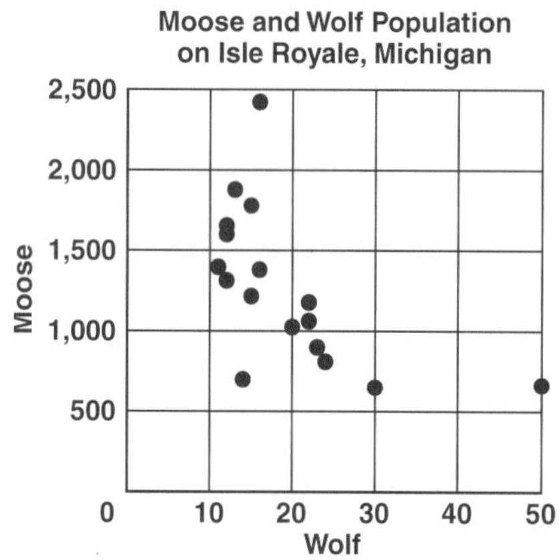

b. Answers may vary. Sample: Yes; there seems to be a negative trend, because the greater the wolf population is, the smaller the moose population seems to be.

3. None; there is no relationship between the number of children and the number of pets in a family.

4. Negative; if you spend more time watching television, you are likely to spend less time studying.

5. None; the number of governors a state has had depends on the age of the state, not its area.

page 42 Mixed Review

9.
```
1 | 5 9 9
2 | 2 4 5 7 7 9 9
3 | 0 4
```
1 | 5 means 15 students

pages 44–45 Wrap Up

1.

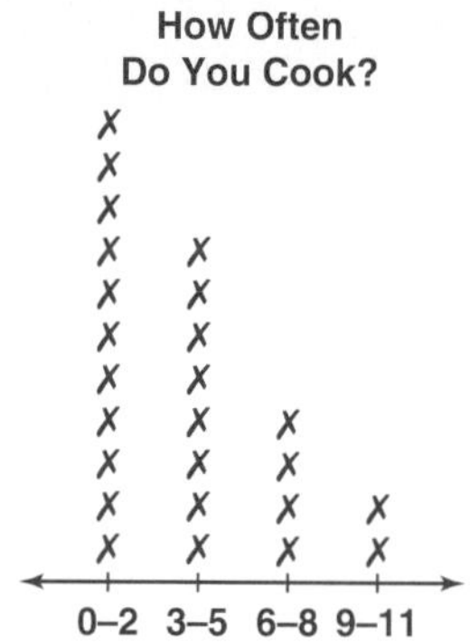

3a.

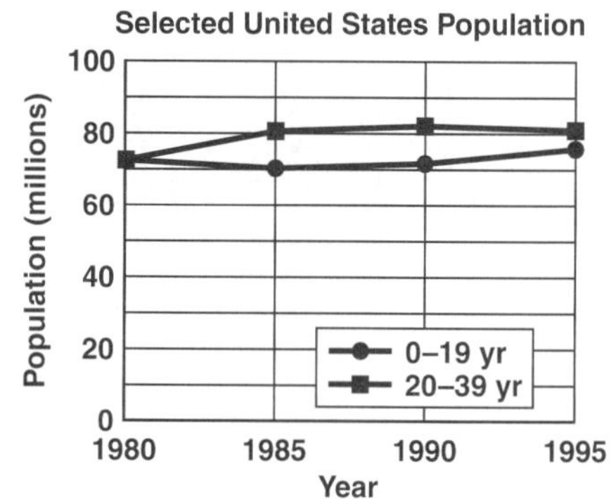

5.
```
0 | 0
1 | 0 5 5 5
2 | 0 5 5
3 | 0 5
4 | 0 0 0
5 |
6 |
7 | 5
```
4 | 0 means 40 min

9a.

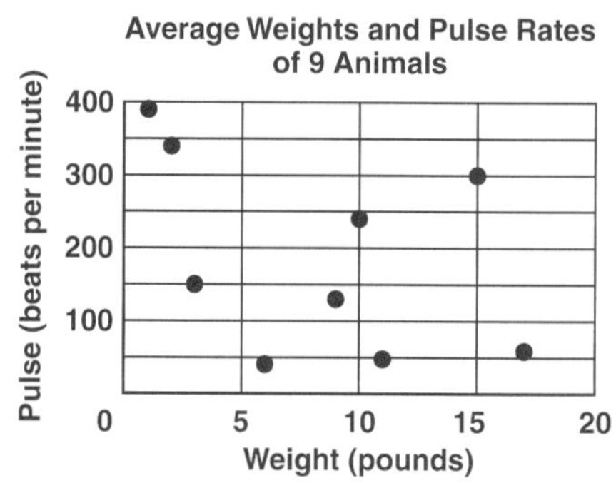

page 46 Assessment

1a.

Min	Frequency	Min	Frequency
0	1	35	2
10	2	40	1
15	1	45	2
20	1	50	2
25	2	60	2
30	3	90	1

b. Answers may vary. Sample: Use 15 min intervals: 0–14, 15–29, 30–44, 45–59, 60–74, 75–89, 90–104

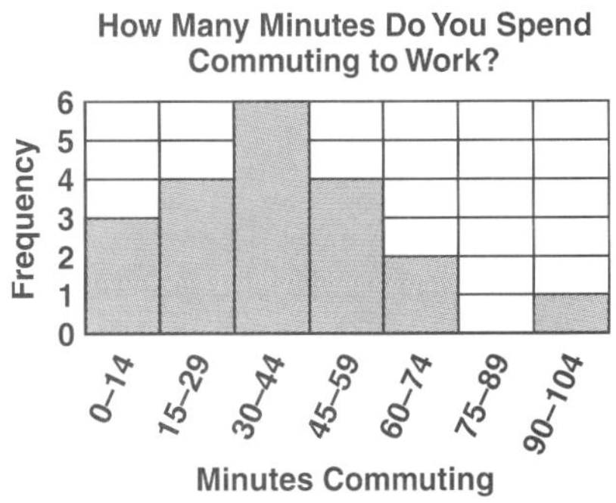

3.

6.

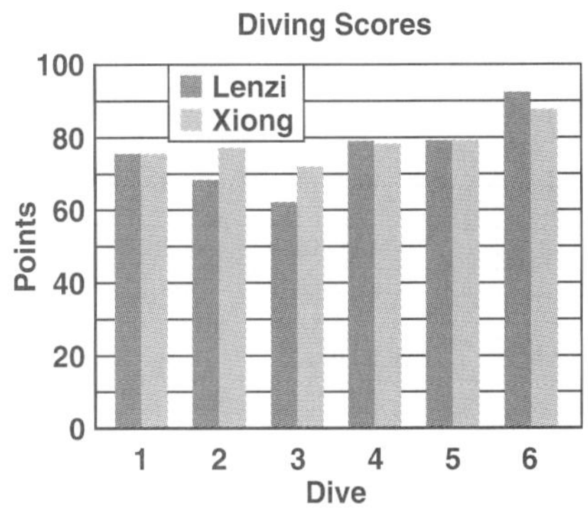

9.

2	1
3	4 8
4	1 5
5	5 6 6
6	6
7	8

2 | 1 means 21

11. Answers may vary. Sample: A graph can have a scale that is too large or too small to show meaningful differences. A bar graph can have a break in the scale which makes the differences in the data appear much larger than they really are.

CHAPTER 2

LESSON 2-4

pages 64–55 Think and Discuss

6. the sizes of pitchers, cups, and cans of lemonade, the selling price of prepared lemonade, how much lemonade can be made from 1 can; the number of pitchers; the number of cups in a package

page 66 Mixed Review

12.

2	7 9
3	7
4	0 6 8

4 | 0 means 40

13.

1	3 3 4 7
2	2

2 | 2 means 2.2

14.

1	6 6 8 9
2	1 3

1 | 6 means 16

LESSON 2-5

page 67 Work Together

1.

CHAPTER 3

LESSON 3-3

pages 102–104 Think and Discuss

6a.

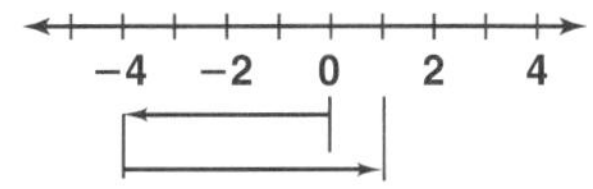

$-4 + 5 = 1$

b.

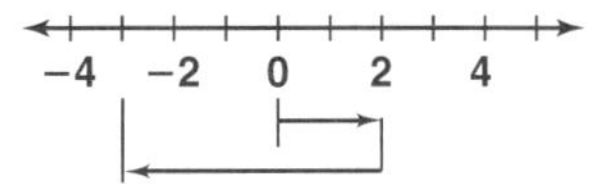

$2 + (-5) = -3$

c.

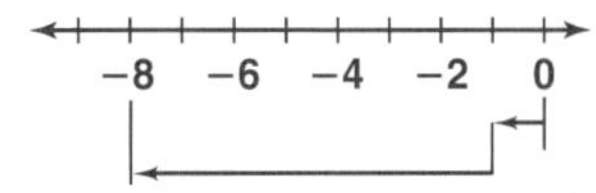

$-1 + (-7) = -8$

pages 104–105 On Your Own

20.

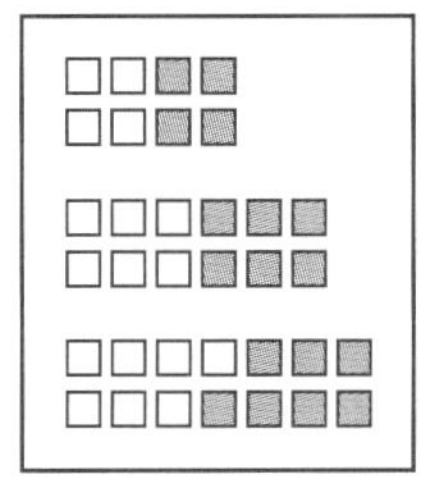

21.

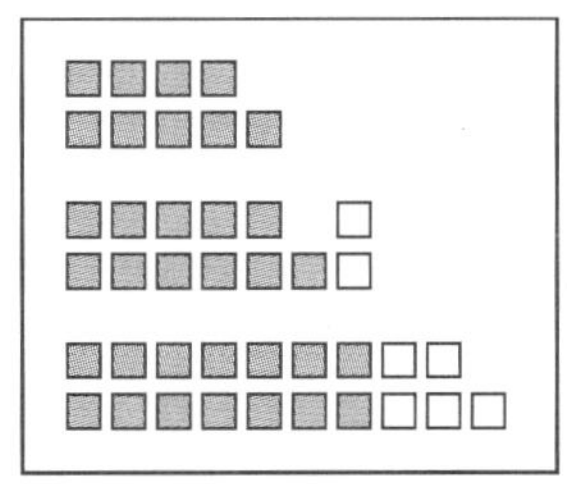

24. Find absolute value of each integer. Find the difference between the absolute values. Choose the sign of the integer with the greater absolute value.

pages 138–139 Wrap Up

33. Find the absolute values of −5 and 8. The number with the greater absolute value has the same sign as the sum. The sum's absolute value is the difference of the absolute values of the numbers. The product is negative because the numbers have different signs.

page 140 Assessment

2a. 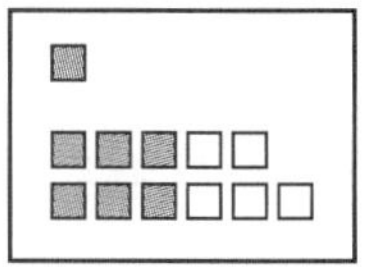

b. 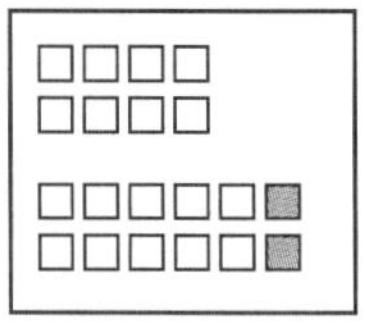

c. 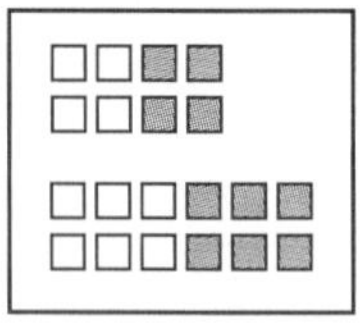

d. 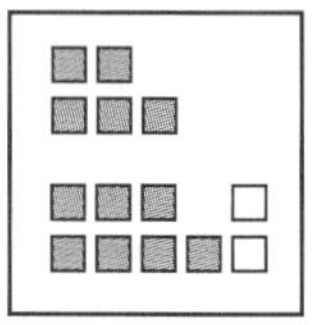

CHAPTER 4

LESSON 4-3

pages 153–154 On Your Own

28. $\frac{3}{6}, \frac{9}{16}, \frac{5}{8}$
29. $\frac{3}{15}, \frac{3}{10}, \frac{3}{5}$
30. $\frac{5}{8}, \frac{3}{4}, \frac{7}{9}$
31. $\frac{1}{2}, \frac{3}{5}, \frac{2}{3}$

page 184 Assessment

2. Answers may vary.
   Sample:

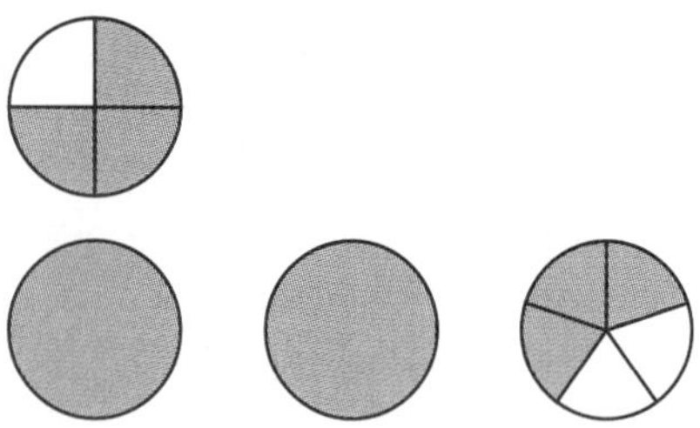

CHAPTER 5

LESSON 5-3

pages 198–199 On Your Own

12. Estimate $3\frac{2}{3} + 4\frac{1}{2} < 4 + 5 = 9$; the LCD is 6, so $3\frac{2}{3} + 4\frac{1}{2} = 3\frac{4}{6} + 4\frac{3}{6}$; add whole numbers $3 + 4 = 7$ and fractions $\frac{4}{6} + \frac{3}{6} = \frac{7}{6} = 1\frac{1}{6}$; combine the sums $7 + 1\frac{1}{6} = 8\frac{1}{6}$, which is close to the estimate of 9.

LESSON 5-7

pages 214–215 Think and Discuss

3.

Event	Time	Time Allowed
Leave home	4:45 P.M.	
Start dinner	6:30 P.M.	$\frac{3}{4}$h
Arrive at theater	7:45 P.M.	$1\frac{1}{4}$h
Concert starts	8:00 P.M.	$\frac{1}{4}$h

pages 215–216 On Your Own

5b. Compute the area of each rectangle outlines with tiles. To find the number of black tiles, add the areas of black outline rectangles and subtract the areas of white outline rectangles. Then subtract the number of black tiles from the area of the floor to find the number of white tiles.

LESSON 5-9

pages 223–224 On Your Own

5b. You divide the number to the right by the number to the left; you divide 24 by 4 to solve the first equation and 4 by 24 to solve the second equation.

CHAPTER 6

LESSON 6-6

pages 256–257 Think and Discuss

3. 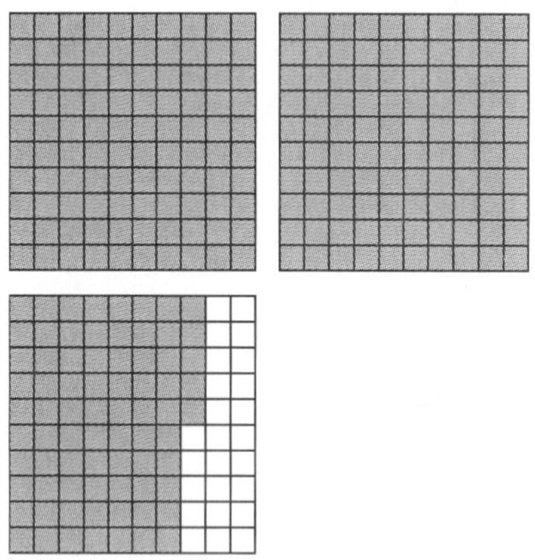

pages 258–259 On Your Own

21. 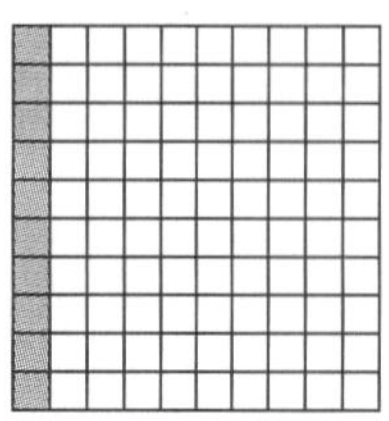

22. 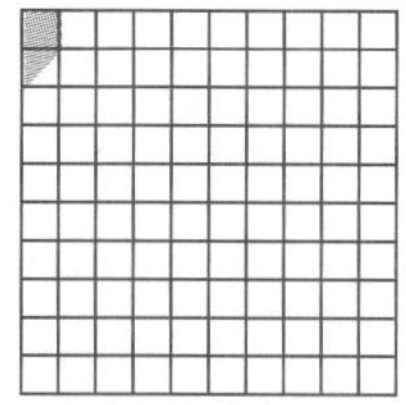

23. 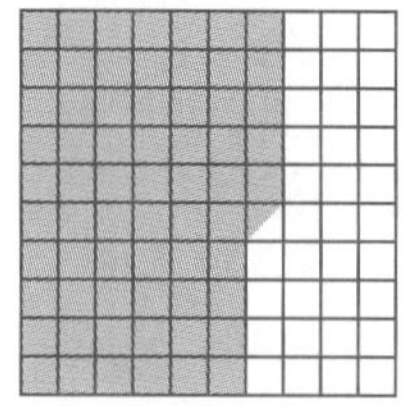

pages 258–259 On Your Own

24. 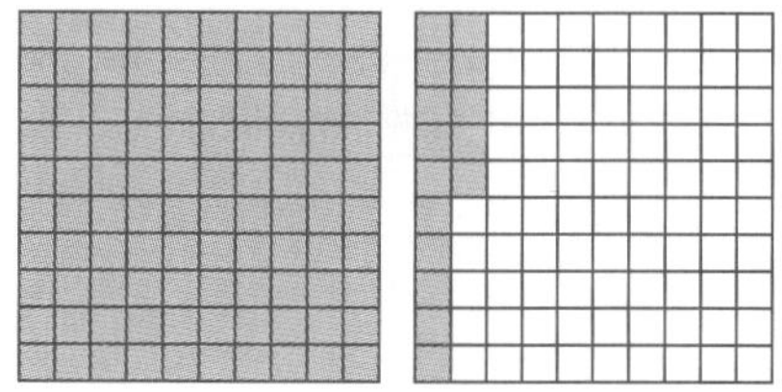

25. 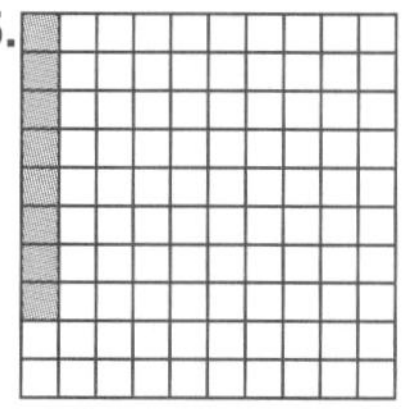

26. 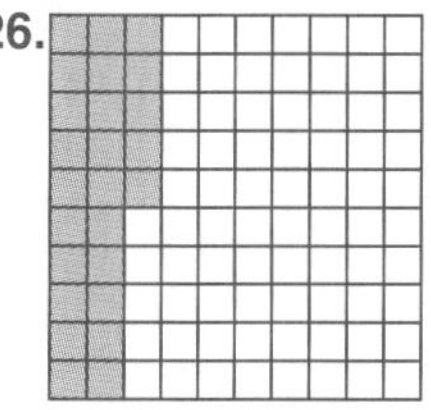

27. 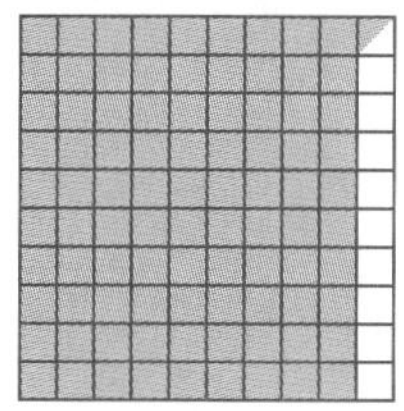

pages 284 Assessment

10a. 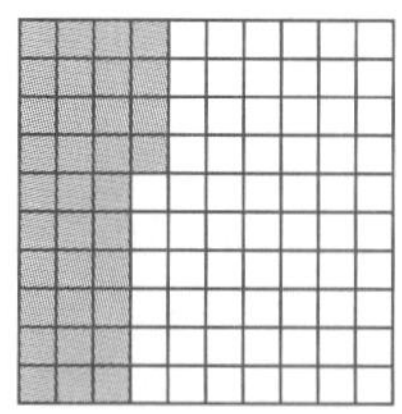

b. 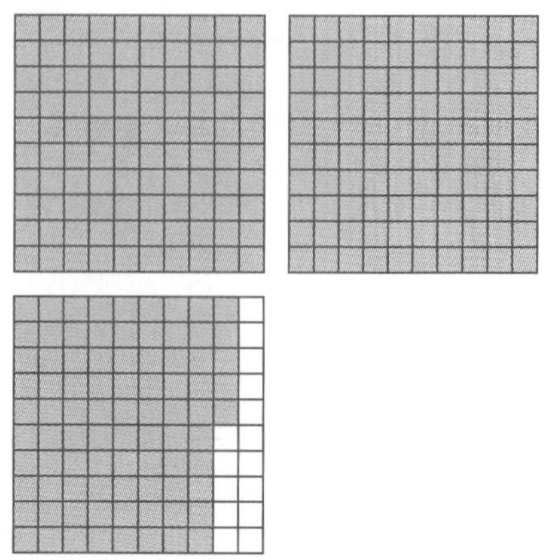

c. 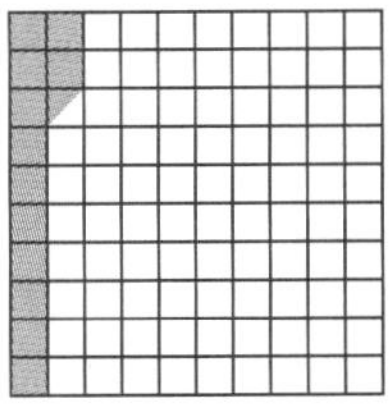

12. 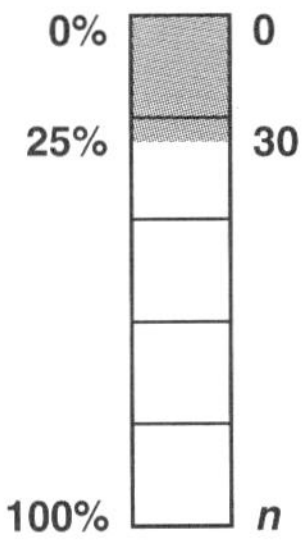

13. Answers may vary. Sample: Find the amount of change by subtracting the new price from the original price. Then divide the amount of change by the original price. Multiply by 100 to find the percent of change.

CHAPTER 7

LESSON 7-1

page 288 Work Together

1a. 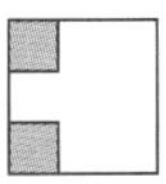

b. Answers may vary. Sample:

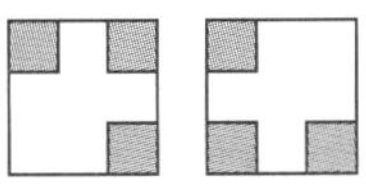

Yes; the two top squares could stay stationary.

2a. 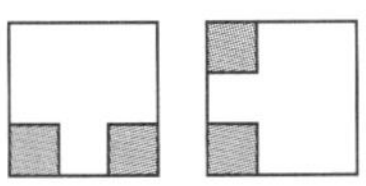

b. 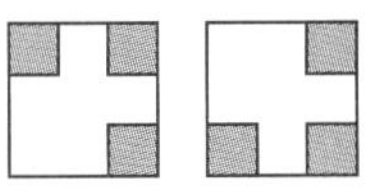

pages 289–290 On Your Own

4. 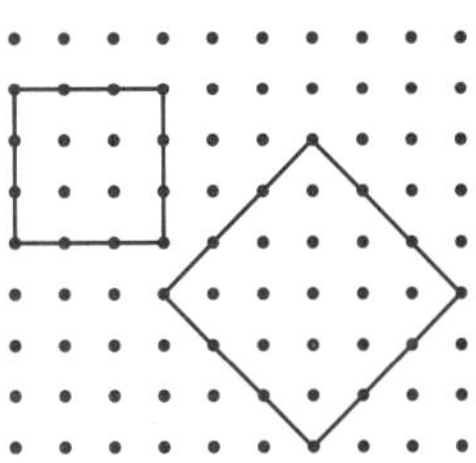

pages 330–331 Wrap Up

21. 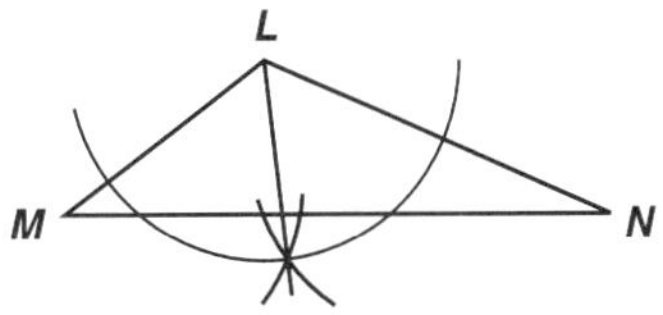

22. 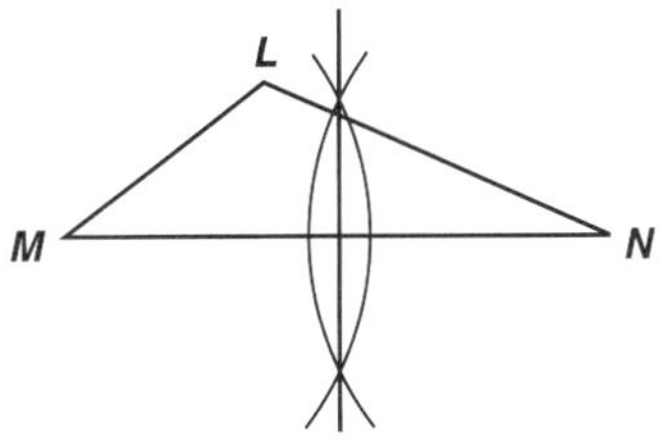

page 332 Assessment

1. 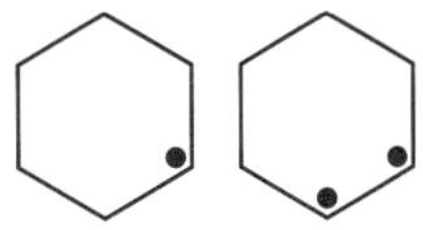

6. 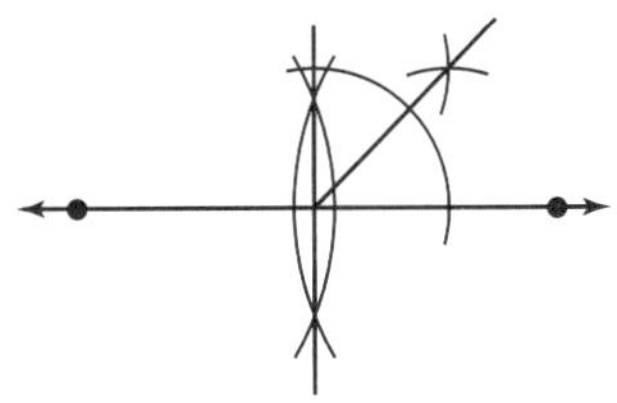

10. $m\angle DBE = 31°$, $m\angle ABC = 31°$, $m\angle CAB = 59°$, $AB \approx 5.83$, $EB \approx 5.83$, $ED = 3$, $BD = 5$

12. 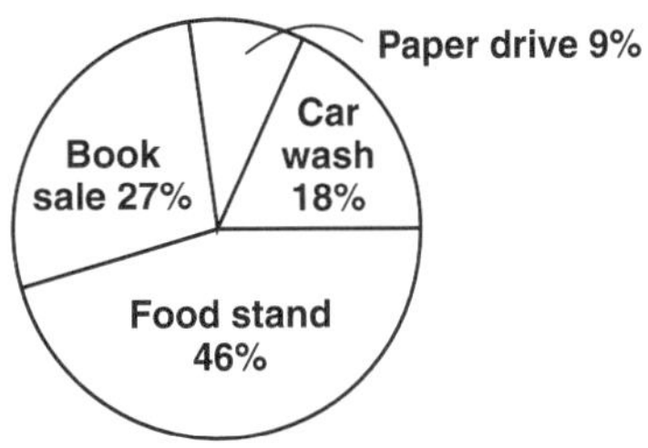

CHAPTER 8

LESSON 8–9

pages 375–376 On Your Own

6. 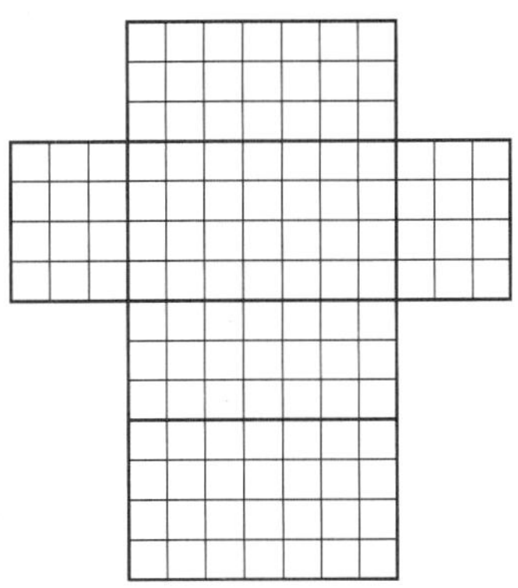

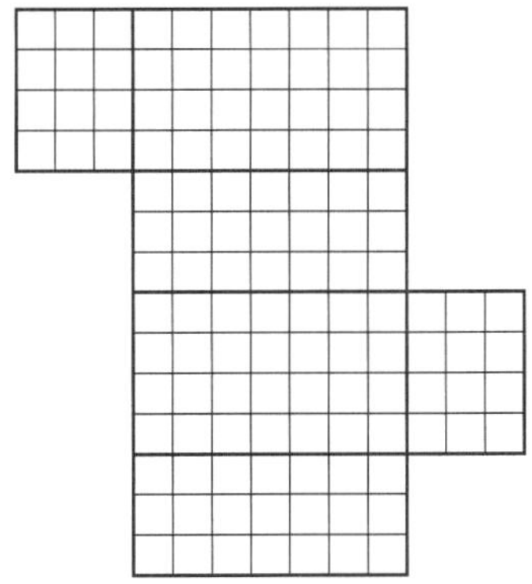

9. 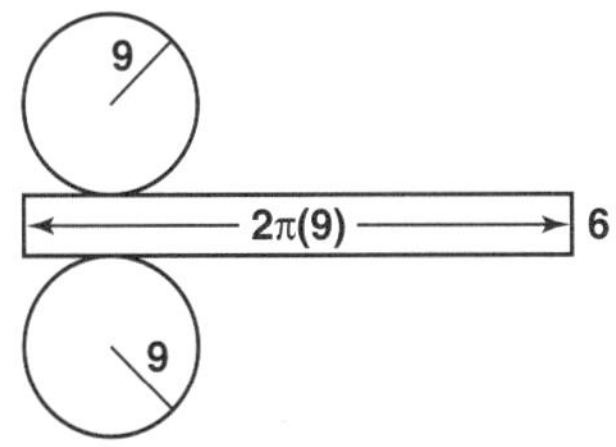

10. 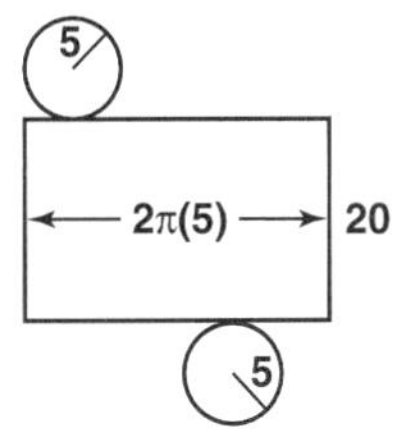

11. 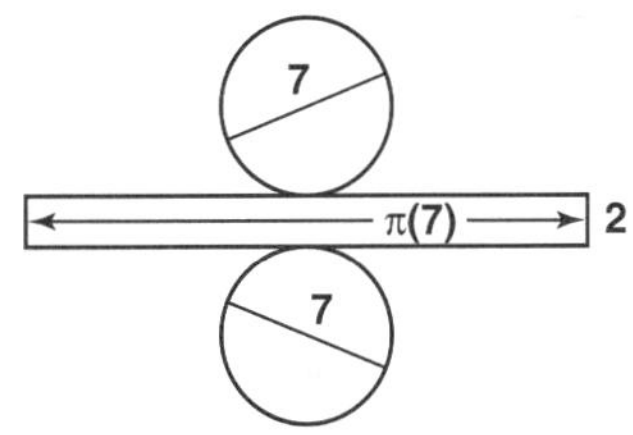

13. Doubling the radius; doubling the radius doubles the area of the curved surface and multiplies the area of the bases by 4. Doubling the height only doubles the area of the curved surface. For a cylinder whose height and radius are each 1 unit, the surface area is 4π units^2. If its radius is doubled, the surface area is 12π units^2. If only its height is doubled, the surface area is 6π units^2.

page 386–387 Wrap Up

21a. 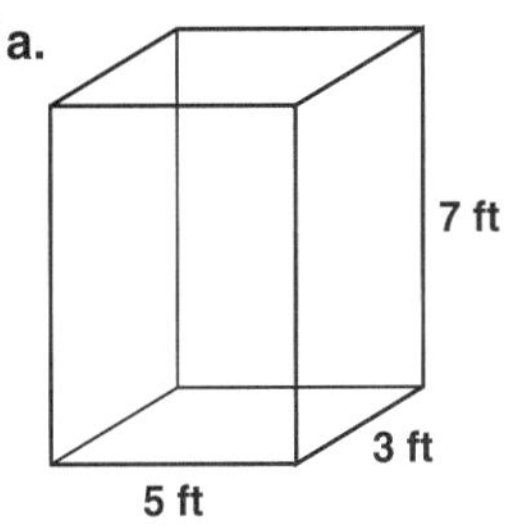

c.

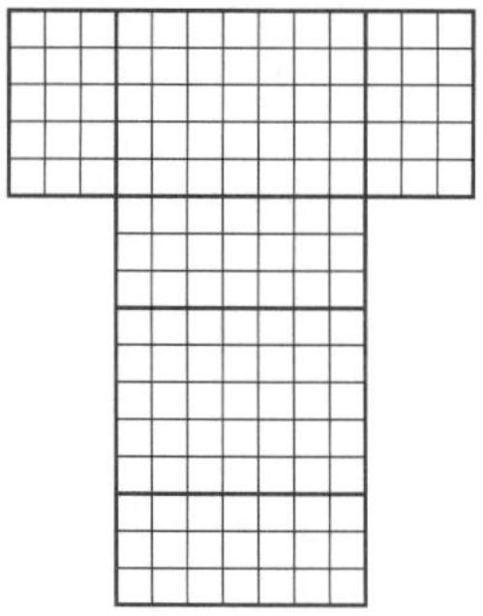

CHAPTER 9

LESSON 9-6

pages 416–417 Think and Disucss

4a.

STO STP SPT SPO SOT SOP
TSP TSO TPS TPO TOS TOP
PST PSO PTS PTO POS POT
OST OSP OTS OTP OPS OPT

b. The numbers are the same; there is only 1 possible choice for the 4th item after you choose the first 3, and any number multiplied by 1 is that number.

pages 417–418 On Your Own

17a.

PETS, PEST, PTES, PTSE, PSET, PSTE,
EPTS, EPST, ETPS, ETSP, ESPT, ESTP,
TPES, TPSE, TEPS, TESP, TSPE, TSEP,
SPET, SPTE, SEPT, SETP, STPE, STEP

18a.

DEFG, DEGF, DFEG, DFGE, DGEF, DGFE,
EDFG, EDGF, EFDG, EFGD, EGDF, EGFD,
FDEG, FDGE, FEDG, FEGD, FGDE, FGED,
GDEF, GDFE, GEDF, GEFD, GFDE, GFED

LESSON 9-7

pages 419–420 Think and Discuss

1. List all the combinations with a blue sweater, in order. Then list the remaining combinations with a yellow sweater, in order, and so on.

pages 428–429 Wrap Up

8a.

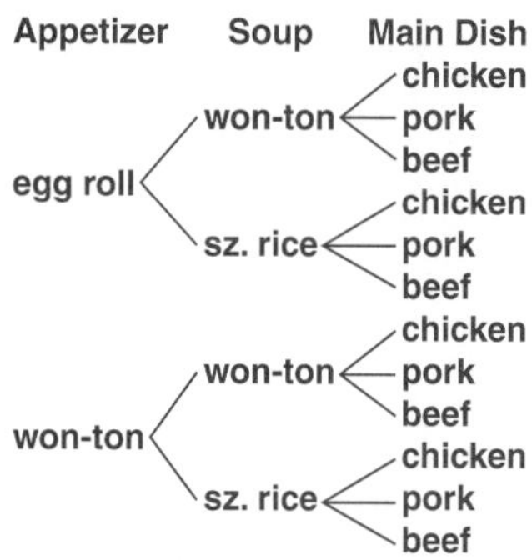

CHAPTER 10

LESSON 10-1

page 434 Work Together

1a.

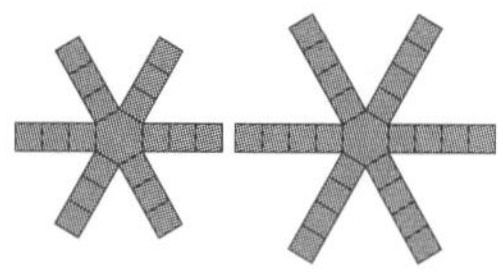

pages 436–437 On Your Own

27a.

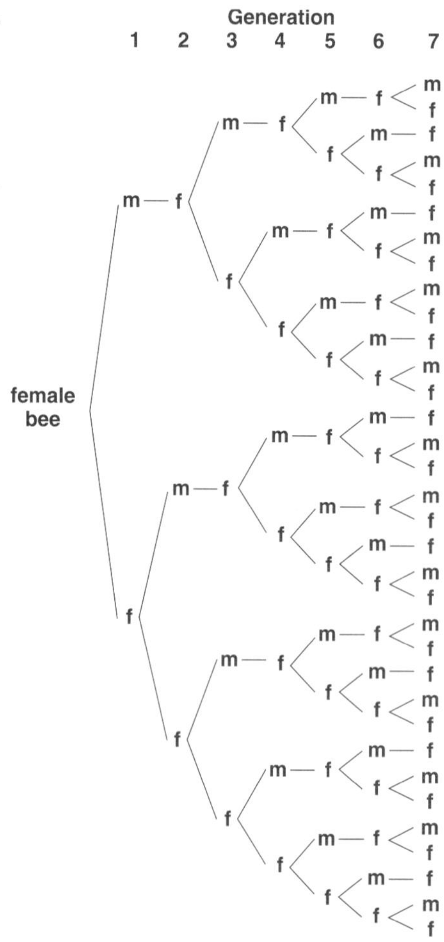

LESSON 10-3

pages 442–443 Think and Discuss

7.

	1	2	3	4	5	6	7	8	9	10
1	O	O	O	O	O	O	O	O	O	O
2	O	C	O	C	O	C	O	C	O	C
3	O	C	C	C	O	O	O	C	C	C
4	O	C	C	O	O	O	O	O	C	C
5	O	C	C	O	C	O	O	O	C	O
6	O	C	C	O	C	C	O	O	C	O
7	O	C	C	O	C	C	C	O	C	O
8	O	C	C	O	C	C	C	C	C	O
9	O	C	C	O	C	C	C	C	O	O
10	O	C	C	O	C	C	C	C	O	C
11	O	C	C	O	C	C	C	C	O	C
12	O	C	C	O	C	C	C	C	O	C
13	O	C	C	O	C	C	C	C	O	C
14	O	C	C	O	C	C	C	C	O	C
15	O	C	C	O	C	C	C	C	O	C
16	O	C	C	O	C	C	C	C	O	C
17	O	C	C	O	C	C	C	C	O	C
18	O	C	C	O	C	C	C	C	O	C
19	O	C	C	O	C	C	C	C	O	C
20	O	C	C	O	C	C	C	C	O	C

	11	12	13	14	15	16	17	18	19	20
1	O	O	O	O	O	O	O	O	O	O
2	O	C	O	C	O	C	O	C	O	C
3	O	O	O	C	C	C	O	O	O	C
4	O	C	O	C	C	O	O	O	O	O
5	O	C	O	C	O	O	O	O	O	C
6	O	O	O	C	O	O	O	C	O	C
7	O	O	O	O	O	O	O	C	O	C
8	O	O	O	O	O	C	O	C	O	C
9	O	O	O	O	O	C	O	O	O	C
10	O	O	O	O	O	C	O	O	O	O
11	C	O	O	O	O	C	O	O	O	O
12	C	C	O	O	O	C	O	O	O	O
13	C	C	C	O	O	C	O	O	O	O
14	C	C	C	C	O	C	O	O	O	O
15	C	C	C	C	C	C	O	O	O	O
16	C	C	C	C	C	O	O	O	O	O
17	C	C	C	C	C	O	C	O	O	O
18	C	C	C	C	C	O	C	C	O	O
19	C	C	C	C	C	O	C	C	C	O
20	C	C	C	C	C	O	C	C	C	C

LESSON 10-5

pages 450–451 Think and Discuss

8.

Input	Output
0	0
1	3
2	6
3	9
4	12
5	15
6	18
7	21
8	24

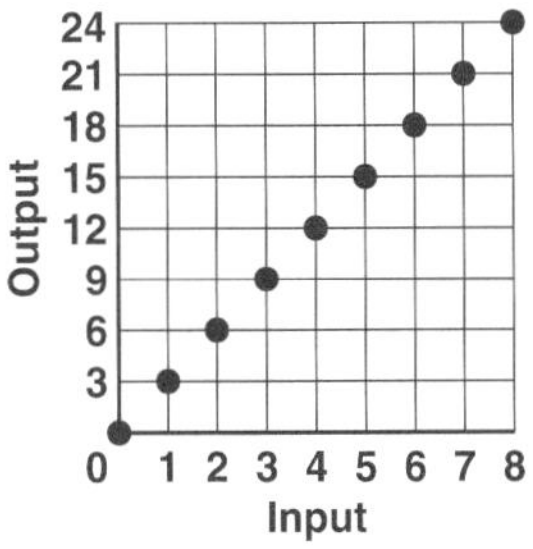

pages 452–453 On Your Own

15a.

Input p	Output c
$.50	$4.50
$1.00	$4.00
$1.50	$3.50
$2.00	$3.00
$2.50	$2.50
$3.00	$2.00
$3.50	$1.50
$4.00	$1.00
$4.50	$.50
$5.00	$.00

b.

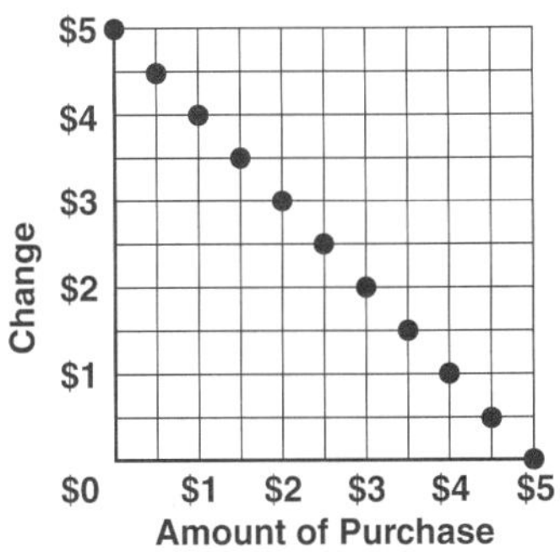

17b.

Input t	Output d
1	$3.50
2	$7.00
3	$10.50
4	$14.00
5	$17.50

c.

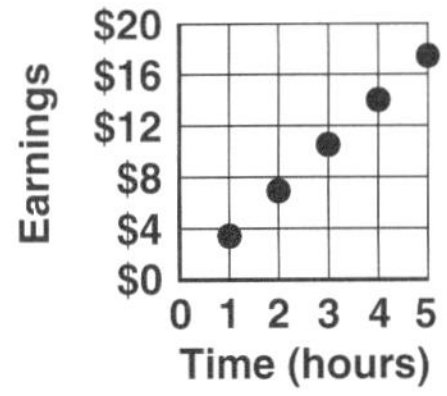

LESSON 10-6

page 457 Checkpoint 2

1.

n	$f(n)$
0	0
1	3
2	6
3	9

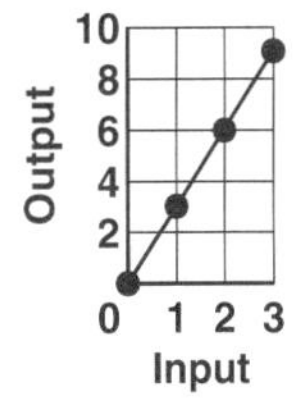

2.

n	$f(n)$
0	−4
1	−2
2	0
3	2

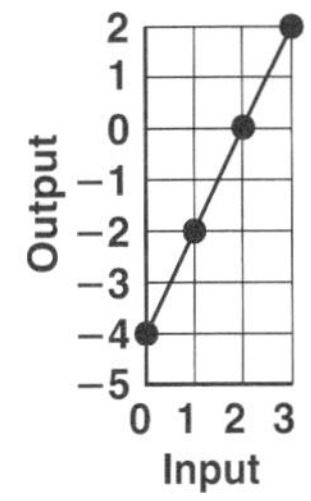

3.

n	$f(n)$
0	8
1	7
2	6
3	5

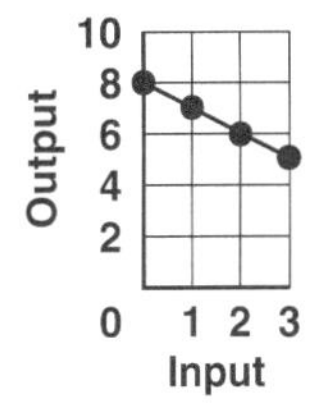

4.

n	$f(n)$
0	7
1	8
2	9
3	10

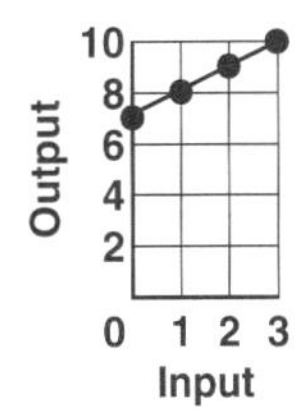

page 458 Math Toolbox

4.

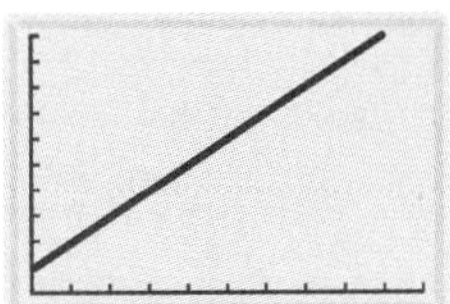

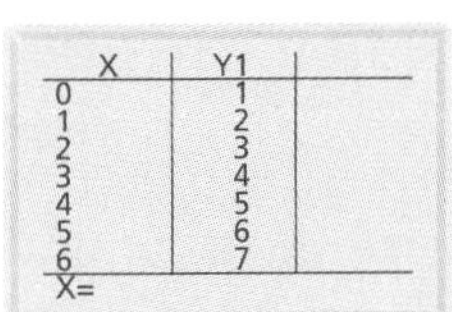

X	Y1
0	1
1	2
2	3
3	4
4	5
5	6
6	7

X=

5.

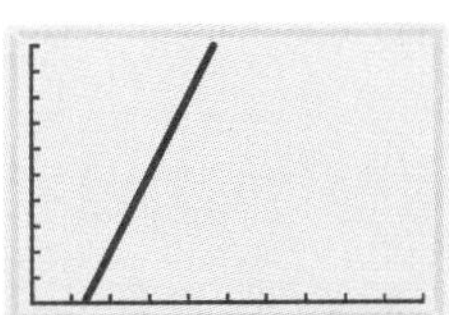

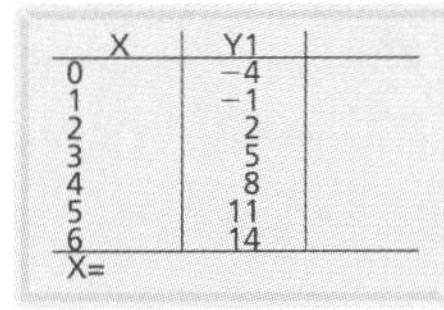

X	Y1
0	−4
1	−1
2	2
3	5
4	8
5	11
6	14

X=

6.

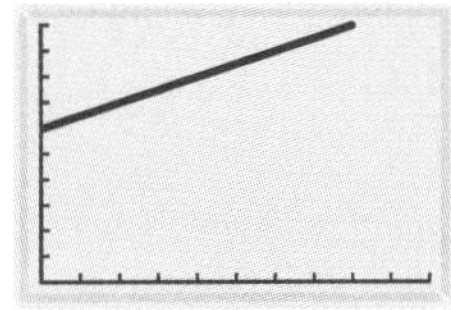

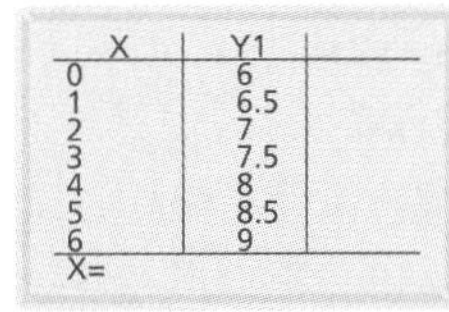

X	Y1
0	6
1	6.5
2	7
3	7.5
4	8
5	8.5
6	9

X=

7.

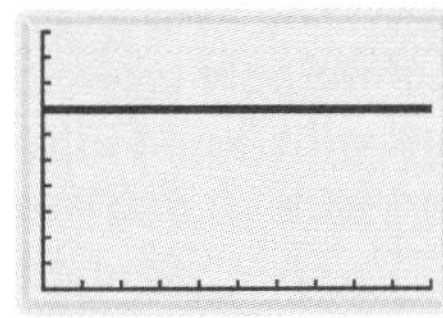

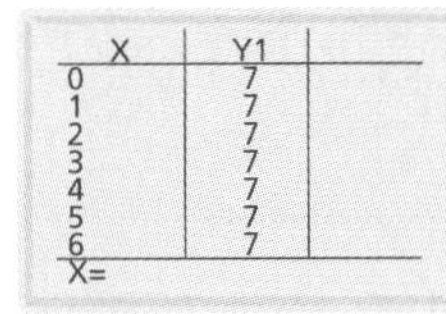

X	Y1
0	7
1	7
2	7
3	7
4	7
5	7
6	7

X=

8.

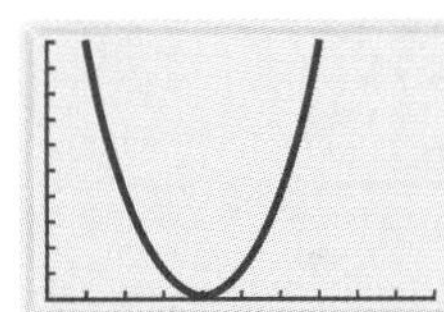

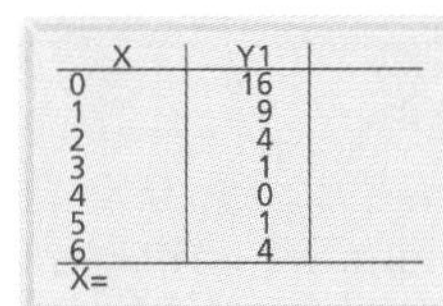

X	Y1
0	16
1	9
2	4
3	1
4	0
5	1
6	4

X=

pages 466–467 Wrap Up

16b.

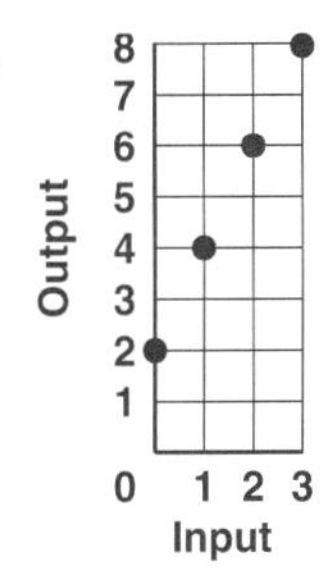

17a.

Input n	Output $f(n)$
0	3
2	4
4	5
6	6

Additional Answers

20.

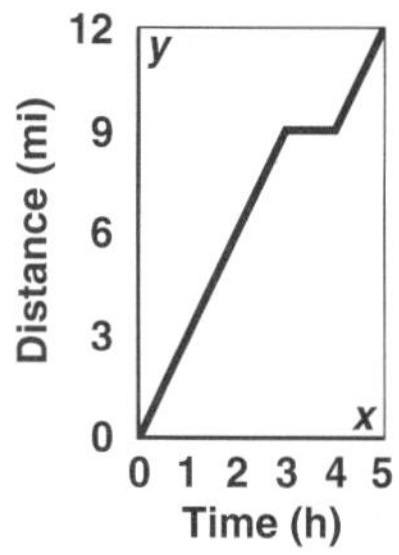

page 468 Assessment

1a. geometric; 81, 243, 729

b. arithmetic; 24, 29, 34

c. neither; 13, 18, 24

d. arithmetic; 2, 0, −2

e. arithmetic; 15, 19, 23

f. geometric; 24, 48, 96

2. Start with 1 and multiply by 3 repeatedly; start with 4 and add 5 repeatedly; start with 10 and add −2 repeatedly; start with −1 and add 4 repeatedly; start with 1.5 and multiply by 2 repeatedly.

8a.

Input n	Output c
1	\$2.95
2	\$5.90
3	\$8.85
4	\$11.80
5	\$14.75

b.

Input s	Output p
5 in.	20 in.
6 in.	24 in.
7 in.	28 in.
8 in.	32 in.
9 in.	36 in.

11. She can use the function $e = 4.5t$ where t is the number of hours she works and e is her earnings in dollars.

13a.

Input e	Output s
\$10	\$2
\$20	\$4
\$30	\$6
\$40	\$8

14.

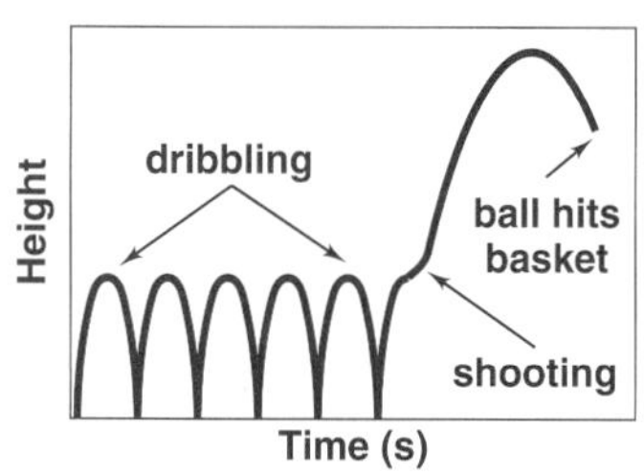

CHAPTER 11

LESSON 11-3

pages 483–484 On Your Own

10. Answers may vary. Sample: Find the coordinate pairs of 2 points on the line. Find the difference between the *y*-coordinates (rise). Then find the difference between the *x*-coordinates in the same order (run). Write the slope as the ratio $\frac{\text{rise}}{\text{run}}$.

12a–b.

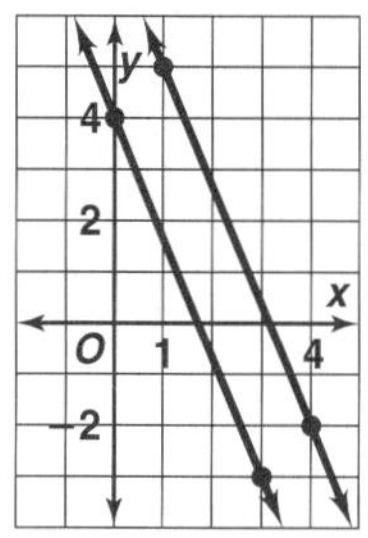

LESSON 11-4

pages 486–487 Think and Discuss

1b.

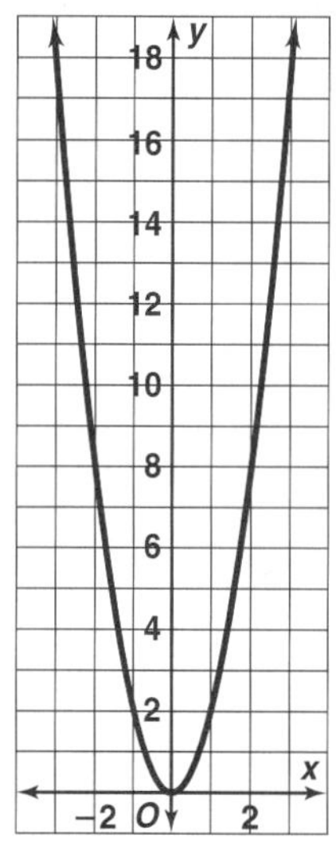

pages 487–489 On Your Own

1–8. Tables may vary. Samples are given.

1.

x	−3	−2	−1	0	1	2	3
y	4.5	2	0.5	0	0.5	2	4.5

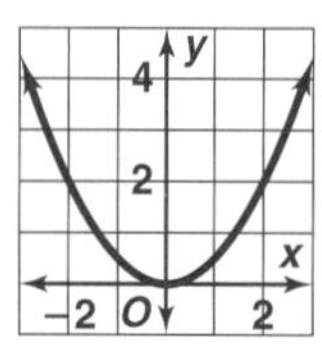

2.

x	−2	−1	−0.5	0	0.5	1	2
y	12	3	0.75	0	0.75	3	12

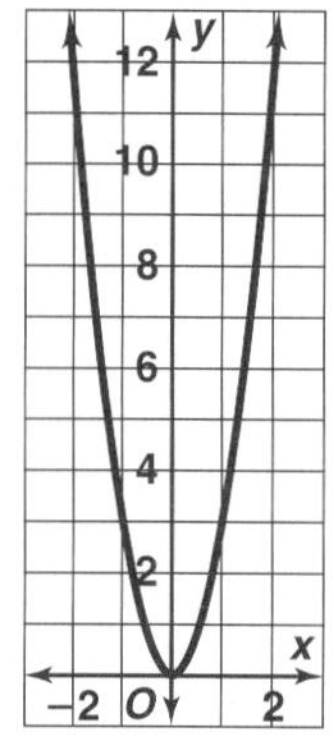

3.

x	−3	−2	−1	0	1	2	3
y	5	0	−3	−4	−3	0	5

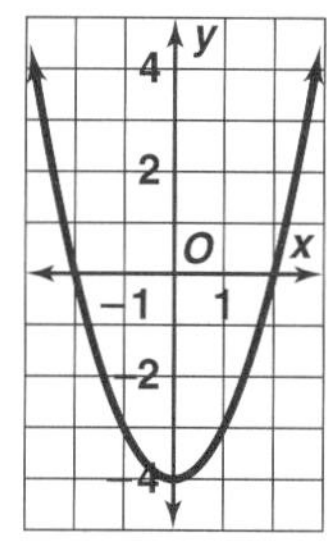

4.

x	−3	−2	−1	0	1	2	3
y	13	8	5	4	5	8	13

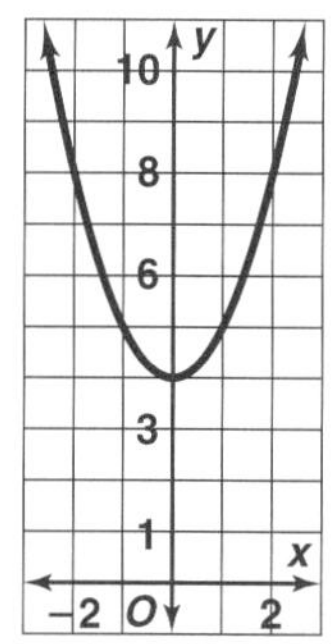

5.

x	−2	−1	0	1	2
y	6	3	0	3	6

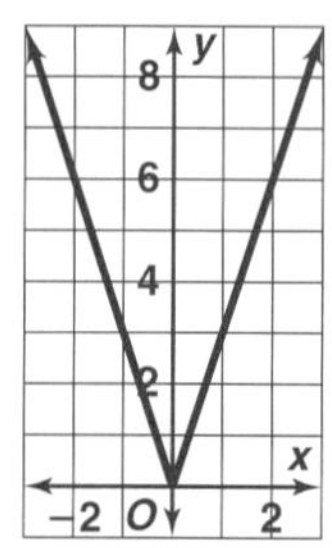

6.

x	−4	−2	−1	0	1	2	4
y	2	1	0.5	0	0.5	1	2

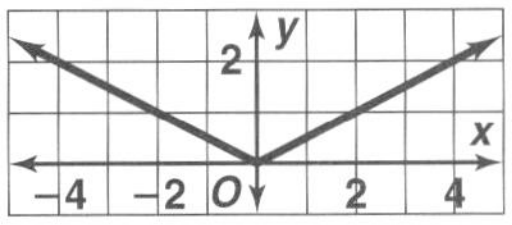

7.

x	−3	−2	−1	0	1	2	3
y	4	3	2	1	2	3	4

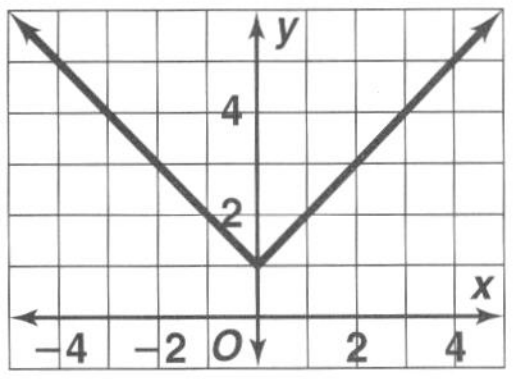

8.

x	−3	−2	−1	0	1	2	3
y	2	1	0	−1	0	1	2

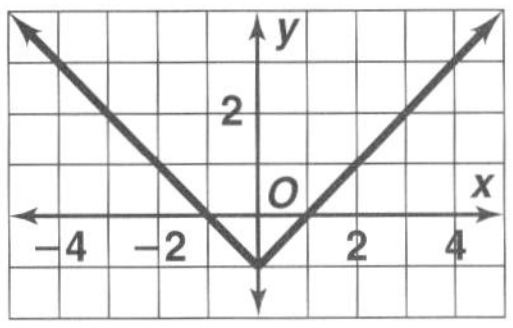

20a.

x	−3	−2	−1	0	1	2	3
y	−3	−2	−1	0	−1	−2	−3

b. 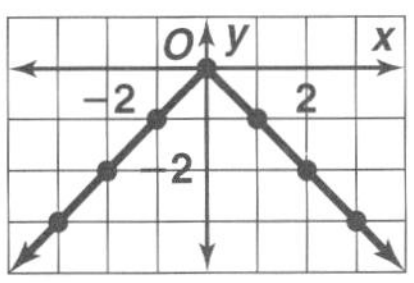

page 489 Checkpoint 1

10b. 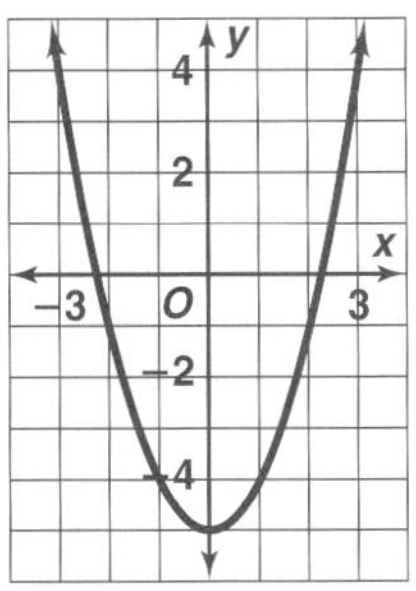

LESSON 11-7

page 502 Checkpoint 2

2. 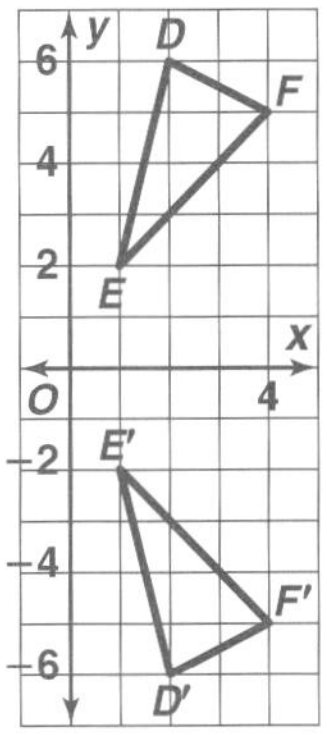

LESSON 11-8

pages 507–508 On Your Own

9. 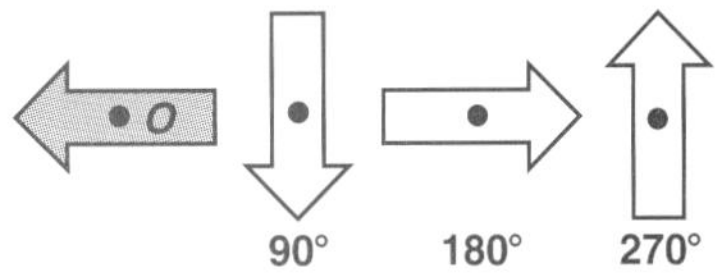

10. 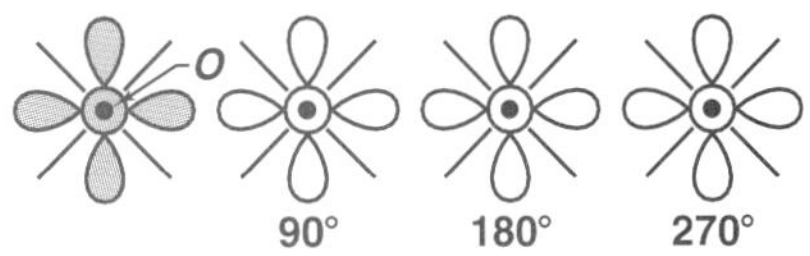

11. 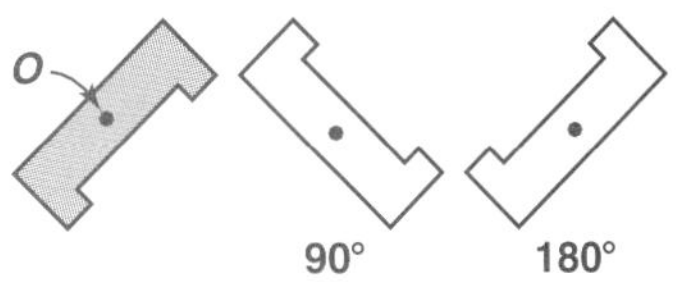

12. 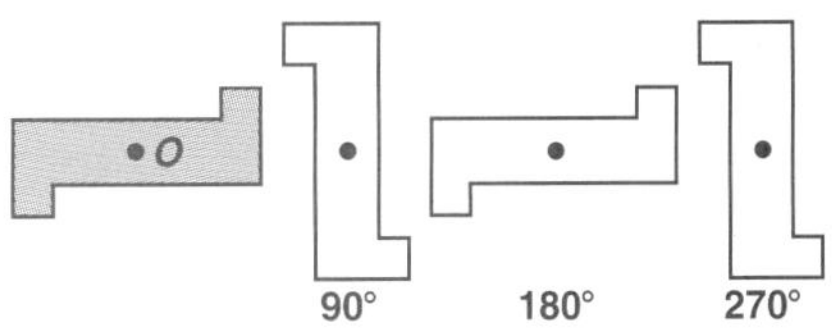

pages 510–511 Wrap Up

4b. 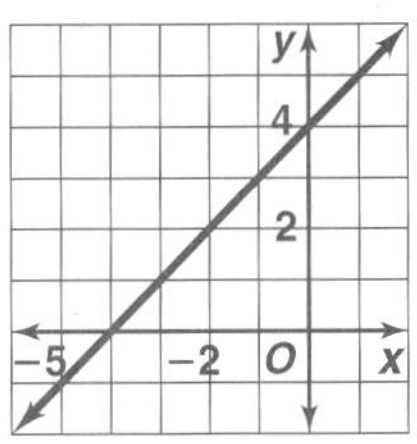

6. 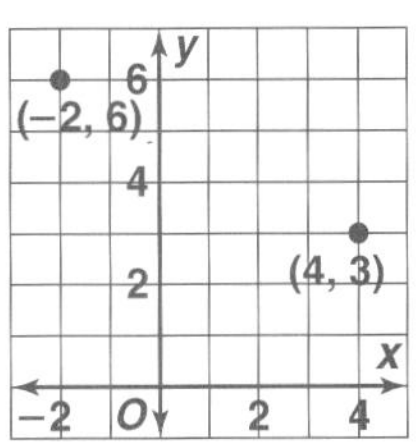

7. 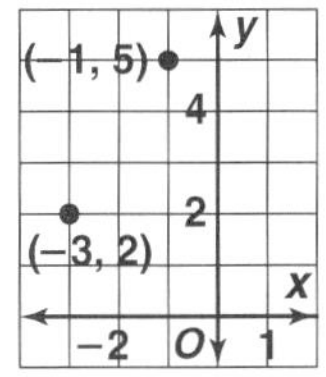

8. 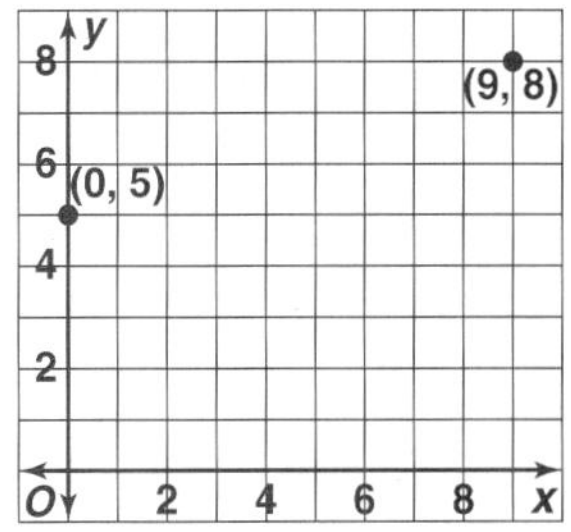

9. 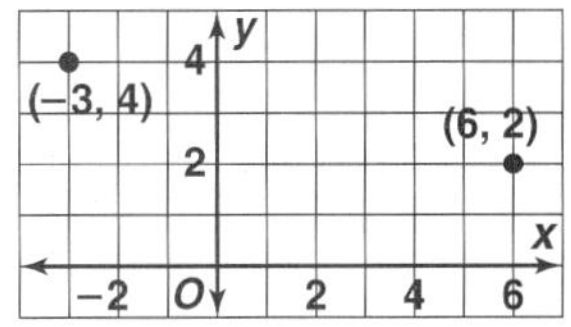

10a. 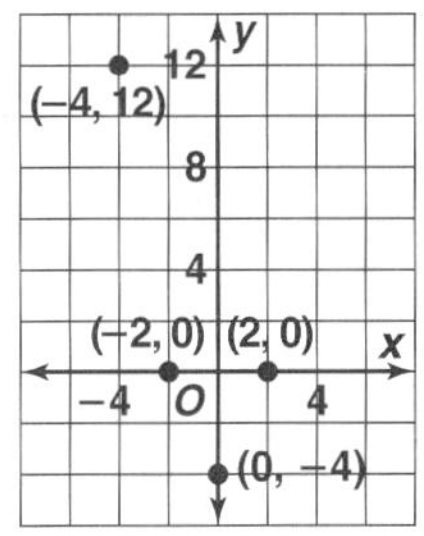

page 512 Assessment

8a–b. 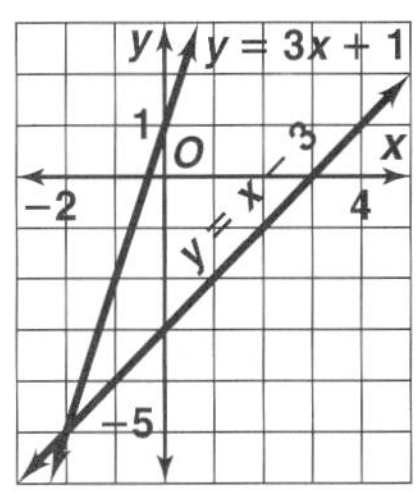

9a. 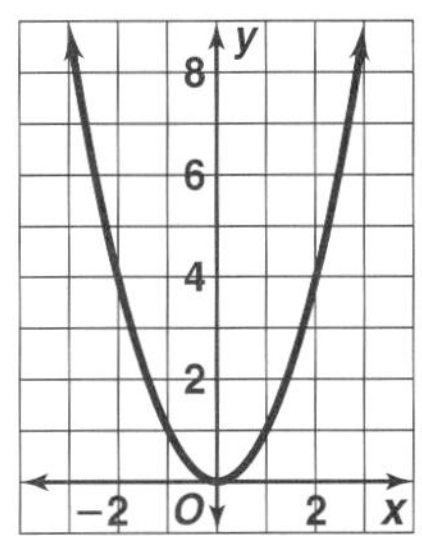

b. 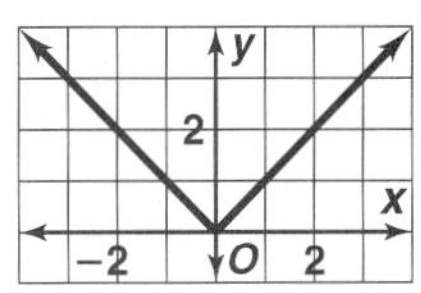

10a–c.

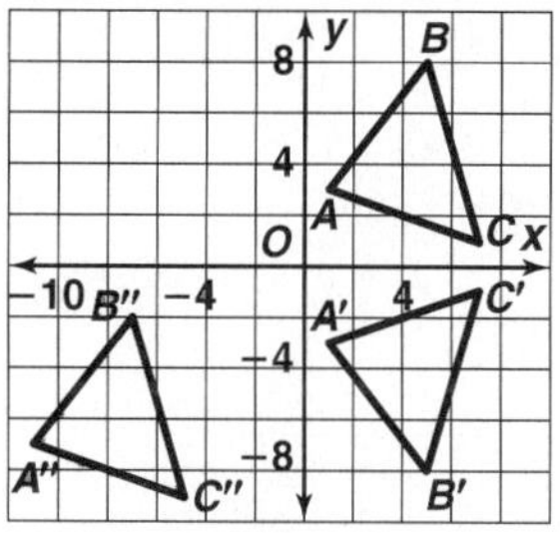

11.

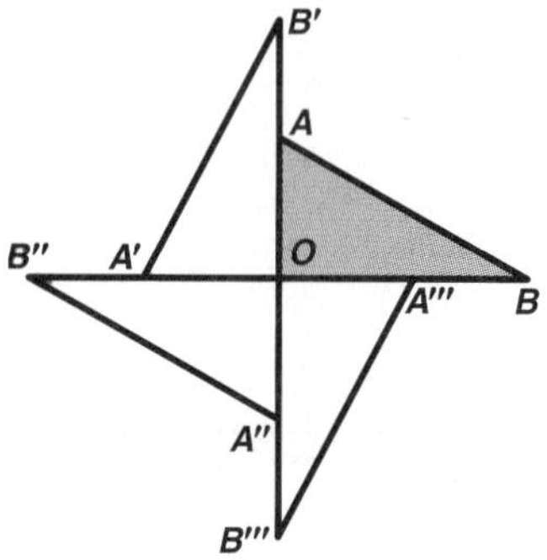

12.

x	−3	−2	−1	0	1	2	3
y	$2\frac{1}{2}$	3	$3\frac{1}{2}$	4	$4\frac{1}{2}$	5	$5\frac{1}{2}$

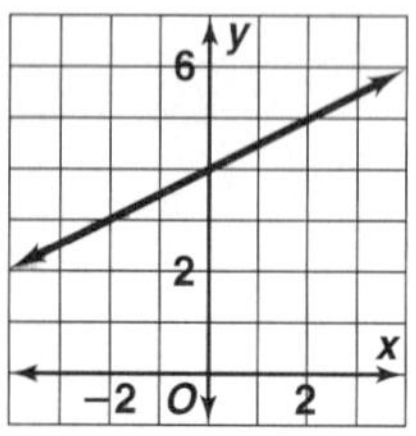

Index

Teacher's Edition entries appear in blue type.

Index

T

U

V

Acknowledgments

Cover Design

Bruce Bond; Martucci Studio

Cover Photos

Martucci Studio

Book Design

Olena Serbyn; Brown Publishing Network

Page Design and Design Management

Brown Publishing Network

Illustration

Annie Bissett: 199, 203, 392, 395, 401, 460, 484, 491
Dan Brawner: 35, 410, 437
Daniel Collins: 151, 308, 450, 452, 453
Andrea Golden: 34, 146, 153, 244, 494
Tom Klare: xxviii, 28, 64, 168, 409, 448, 486, 490
Tom Lochray: 39, 249, 277
Karen Minot: 69, 97, 134, 164, 208, 220, 239, 251, 321, 345, 420, 444, 472, 496
Michael Moran: 236
Outlook/ANCO: 57, 66, 156, 178, 242, 248, 300, 337, 378
Steve Pica: 14, 382
Matthew Pippin: 315
Gary Torrisi: 303
Camille Venti: 54, 172, 214, 216, 219, 262, 263, 268, 269, 398
Rose Zgodzinski: 51, 115, 121, 169, 196, 254, 267, 318, 414

Photography

Photo Research: Brown Publishing Network

Front Matter: vii, David Young-Wolff/Photo Edit; **viii,** Superstock; **ix,** M. Siluk/The Image Works; **x,** AP/Wide World; **xi,** Superstock; **xii,** David Young-Wolff/Photo Edit; **xiv,** Thomas Craig/FPG; **xv,** David Young-Wolff/Tony Stone Images; **xvi,** Chris Marona/Photo Researchers; **xvii,** The Image Bank; **xviii,** Lawrence Migdale; **xix t,** Bob Daemmrich/The Image Works; **xix c,** Prentice Hall photo by Irene Perlman; **xx,** Alan & Linda Detrick/Photo Researchers; **xxiii,** Uniphoto; **xxiv,** Kindra Clineff/The Picture Cube; **xxvi,** Prentice Hall photo by Ken O'Donoghue

Chapter 1: 2–3, Superstock; **5t,** David Young-Wolff/Photo Edit; **5b,** Al Tielemans/Duomo; **6,** David Young-Wolff/Photo Edit; **8,** Superstock; **13,** Archive Photos; **18,** Lee Snyder/Photo Researchers; **20,** AP/Wide World; **23,** Tom Stack & Assoc.; **25,** Jose Pelaez/Stock Market; **30,** Corbis-Bettman; **32,** AP/Wide World; **34,** Grant Heilman; **36,** Steve Sutton/Duomo; **39,** Tom Stewart/Stock Market; **41,** Gary Milburn/Tom Stack & Assoc.

Chapter 2: 48–49, Domainede Bellevue/Stock Boston; **50,** Brock Peter/Gamma Liaison; **53,** Brian Kenney/Natural Selection; **57,** Superstock; **58,** Frank Siteman/Monkmeyer; **61,** Prentice Hall photo by Ken O'Donoghue; **59,** Photo Image Tech.; **65,** Prentice Hall photo by Ken O'Donoghue; **66,** Superstock; **72,** David Young-Wolff/Photo Edit; **83,** Jim Amos/ Photo Researchers

Chapter 3: 90–91, Jeffrey W. Meters/Uniphoto; **92 all,** Prentice Hall photo by Ken O'Donoghue; **93 all,** Prentice Hall photo by Russ Lappa; **98,** Skjold/Image Works; **99,** Agence France Presse/Corbis-Bettmann; **107,** Superstock; **113,** Michael K. Nichols/National Geographic Society; **116,** Gupton/Uniphoto; **118 all,** Prentice Hall photo by Ken O'Donoghue; **119,** Prentice Hall photo by Tracy Wheeler; **123,** Prentice Hall photo by Ken O'Donoghue; **126,** Superstock; **128,** Sky and Telescope; **131,** UPI/Corbis-Bettmann; **133,** M. Siluk/Image Works; **135 all,** Prentice Hall photo by Russ Lappa; **136,** Animals, Animals

Chapter 4: 142–143, Dennis O'Clair/Tony Stone Images; **144 all,** Prentice Hall photo by Russ Lappa; **151,** Michelle Bridwell/Photo Edit; **147,** Laima Druskis/Stock Boston; **153,** Grace Davies; **156,** Prentice Hall photo by Russ Lappa; **156,** Hans Wolf/Image Bank; **160,** Prentice Hall photo by Tracy Wheeler; **165 all,** AP/Wide World; **166,** Will & Deni McIntyre/Photo Researchers; **170,** Bob Daemmrich/Stock Boston; **176,** Athletic Dept., University of Georgia; **178,** Bob Daemmrich

Chapter 5: 186–187, Prentice Hall photo by Ken O'Donoghue; **188,** L. Rorke/Image Works; **190,** Tom Bross/Stock Boston; **194,** Addison Geary; **197,** Superstock; **201,** David Wilbeck/Picture Cube; **204,** Paul Conklin/Monkmeyer; **206,** Robert Tyrell; **206,** Anthony Mercieco/Photo Researchers; **211,** Steven Peters/Tony Stone Images; **212,** Superstock; **222,** Eric Poggenpohl/Folio

Chapter 6: 230–231, Courtesy of Paramount Parks; **232,** Bob Daemmrich/Stock Boston; **233,** Peter Beck/ Uniphoto; **234,** Alan Nelson/ Animals, Animals; **238,** Vandystadt; **242,** Eric Schnakenberg/FPG; **243,** UPI/Corbis-Bettmann; **248,** Francis Lepine/ Animals, Animals, Earth Scenes; **253,** NASA; **254,** Cindy Charles/Photo Edit; **257,** Leo Keeler/Animals, Animals; **261,** Animals, Animals; **265,** John Neubauer/Photo Edit; **265,** Bob Daemmrich/Stock Boston; **271,** David Young-Wolff/Photo Edit; **276,** Uniphoto

Chapter 7: 286–287, Lewellyn/Uniphoto; **288,** Eastcott/Momatiuk/Image Works; **290,** Superstock; **293,** Prentice Hall photo by Ken O'Donoghue; **295t,** E.R. Degginger/Earth Scenes; **295bl,** National Fish and Wildlife Forensics Lab; **295br,** National Fish and Wildlife Forensics Lab; **298,** William S. Helsel/Tony Stone Images; **300,** Prentice Hall photo by Ken O'Donoghue; **305,** Prentice Hall photo by Ken O'Donoghue; **308,** Superstock; **311t,** Animals, Animals; **311b,** Joyce Photographics/Photo Researchers; **316,** Prentice Hall photo; **324,** Courtesy of Wellesley College Library, Special Collections. Photo by George McLean

Chapter 8: 334–335, Winston Fraser; **337,** S. J. Krasemann/DRK Photo; **339,** Matsumoto/Explorer/Photo Researchers; **341,** Bob Daemmrich/Stock Boston; **348,** David Frazier; **350,** Mike Peters/FPG; **353,** D & I MacDonald/Picture Cube; **354,** Deborah Davies/Photo Edit; **357,** Bob Daemmrich/Stock Boston; **359,** Terry Qing/FPG; **362,** Prentice Hall photo by Russ Lappa; **364,** M. Antman/Image Works; **366,** Joe Cornish/Tony Stone Images; **367,** Prentice Hall photo by Russ Lappa; **368r,** Derek Berwin/ Image Bank; **368l,** Chuck Zsymanski/International Stock; **369,** Thomas Craig/FPG; **371l,** John Gerlach/DRK; **371c,** Cathlyn Melloan/Tony Stone Images; **371r,** Will & Deni McIntyre/Photo Researchers; **375,** Greig Cranna/Stock Boston; **378,** Peter Gridley/FPG

Chapter 9: 390–391, Prentice Hall photo by Ken O'Donoghue; **393l,** Michael Newman/Photo Edit; **393r,** J. Gerard Smith/ Monkmeyer; **402,** Bill Bachmann/Photo Researchers; **408,** Superstock; **413,** Prentice Hall photo by Tracy Wheeler; **417,** Corbis- Bettmann; **419,** Superstock; **422,** David Young-Wolff/Tony Stone Images; **424,** Phil Dotson/ Photo Researchers; **425,** Ralph Reinhold/Animals, Animals

Chapter 10: 432–433, Mark Reinstein/Uniphoto; **435,** Superstock; **435i,** Peter G. Aitken/Photo Researchers; **438,** Superstock; **440,** Corbis-Bettmann; **445,** Chris Marona Photo Researchers; **446,** Rhoda Sidney/Stock Boston; **451,** Dennis O'Clair/Tony Stone Images; **455,** Stephen Gerard/Photo Researchers; **461,** Lowe Art Museum, University of Miami/Superstock

Chapter 11: 470–471, Courtesy MSNBC; **472,** Corbis Bettmann; **476,** John Madere/The Stock Market; **477,** David Young-Wolff/Photo Edit; **480,** Annie Hunter; **488,** Bob Daemmrich; **493 all,** Prentice Hall photo by Russ Lappa; **499t,** A & F Michler; **499bl,** Charles Kennard/Stock Boston; **499br,** Jerome Wexler/Photo Researchers; **500 all,** Roy Morsch/The Stock Market; **501l,** Corel; **501r,** Jeff Lepore/Photo Researchers; **501c,** Don & Pat Valenti/DRK; **505t,** Foto World/The Image Bank; **505b,** Rod Planck/Tom Stack; **507m,** Alfred Pasieka/SPL/Photo Researchers; **507r,** Prentice Hall photo; **507l,** Image Bank

Teacher's Edition

Editorial Services: Publishers Resource Group, Inc.

Design Coordination: Susan Gerould/Perspectives